THE QUATERNARY OF THE UNITED STATES

THE QUATERNARY OF THE

UNITED STATES

A REVIEW VOLUME FOR THE VII CONGRESS

OF THE INTERNATIONAL ASSOCIATION

FOR QUATERNARY RESEARCH

H. E. WRIGHT, JR. AND DAVID G. FREY, EDITORS

PRINCETON, NEW JERSEY

PRINCETON UNIVERSITY PRESS

1965

VII INQUA CONGRESS

Boulder, Colorado, 1965

SPONSORED BY THE NATIONAL ACADEMY OF SCIENCES
NATIONAL RESEARCH COUNCIL

HONORARY OFFICERS

PRESIDENT:
  Richard F. Flint

VICE PRESIDENTS:
  Reid A. Bryson—Climatology
  William S. Cooper—Terrestrial Ecology
  David B. Ericson—Oceanography
  Lawrence M. Gould—Geomorphology and Geography
  Frederick Johnson—Archaeology and Anthropology
  Morris M. Leighton—Geology
  Alfred C. Redfield—Aquatic Ecology
  James H. Thorp—Soil Science

ORGANIZING COMMITTEE

SECRETARY GENERAL:
  Gerald M. Richmond

CHAIRMEN LOCAL COMMITTEE:
  William C. Bradley, Geological Society of America
  William S. Osburn, Ecological Society of America

CHAIRMAN FINANCE COMMITTEE:
  Terah L. Smiley, American Association for the Advancement of Science

CHAIRMEN FIELD CONFERENCES:
  C. Bertrand Schultz, Society of Vertebrate Paleontology
  H. T. U. Smith, Geological Society of America

EDITORS:
  H. E. Wright, Jr., Geological Society of America
  David G. Frey, American Society for Limnology and Oceanography

CHAIRMAN LECTURE PROGRAM:
  Edward S. Deevey, Jr., Ecological Society of America

CHAIRMAN PROGRAM COMMITTEE:
  John F. Lance, Society of Vertebrate Paleontology

MEMBERS:
  Edwin L. Hamilton, American Geophysical Union, Section on Oceanography
  Bruce C. Heezen, American Geophysical Union, Section on Oceanography
  Frances D. Hole, Soil Science Society of America
  J. Charles Kelley, American Anthropological Association
  Fritz F. Koczy, American Society for Limnology and Oceanography
  J. Murray Mitchell, Jr., American Meteorological Society
  Howard A. Powers, American Geophysical Union, Section on Volcanology
  William E. Powers, Association of American Geographers
  Erik K. Reed, Society for American Archaeology
  Horace G. Richards, The Paleontological Society
  Stanley A. Schumm, American Geophysical Union, Section on Hydrology

PREFACE

The Quaternary Period of geologic time encompasses the last ice age proper (Pleistocene Epoch) and subsequent time (Holocene or Recent Epoch). The Quaternary is unique among the geologic periods for the relative perfection of its stratigraphic record—and thus for the unmatched opportunity it affords to decipher historical details with an accuracy impossible for earlier periods. The framework of the continents even in early-Quaternary time resembled that of the present so closely that major relations of land and sea and their effects on the general circulation of the atmosphere were probably very like those of the present, except perhaps when world-wide lowering of sea level exposed continental shelves or created significant land bridges between continents and arctic islands. Reconstructions of past conditions therefore may be controlled by a geographic framework relatively easy to visualize.

The dominating circumstance during the Quaternary in many parts of the world was climatic change. It resulted not only in the expansion and recession of glaciers, desert lakes, and coastal seas, but it also affected the composition and distribution of plant and animal communities, creating conditions potentially favorable for gene flow, extinctions, disjunctions, and other biogeographic processes. Thus not only the physical but also the biological events are complicated, and all have left undeciphered records which challenge the perspicacity and ingenuity of scientists in diverse fields. Investigators are repeatedly faced with the need to trade ideas and techniques in order to understand the larger environmental aspects of their particular problems. Not a few Quaternary scientists claim competence in at least two major disciplines, such as geomorphology and prehistory, glacial geology and pollen analysis, zoology and stratigraphic paleontology, geochemistry and paleolimnology, climatology and tree-ring analysis. Major advances in any one field are bound to be important in others because they modify disciplinary interpretations and lead to a progressively more satisfactory synergistic understanding of the entire period. Our knowledge of the Quaternary is advancing so rapidly that this book, even with the exciting findings it details, is scarcely more than a stocktaking or a progress report, although it should prove of great value in consolidating the field and in indicating critical areas for interdisciplinary attack.

Quaternary studies are best approached through the principle of uniformitarianism—that the present is the key to the past. This principle can guide the reconstruction of past conditions within the framework of physical, chemical, and biological laws, which seem constant. It can be studied in operation at the present time in many situations throughout the world, but difficulties of interpretation arise regarding Pleistocene conditions that have no analogues anywhere in the world today, such as the regime of a large ice sheet in temperate latitudes or the vegetation on a large, newly deglaciated area in a temperate region far from sources of seeds of the major forest trees.

The interplay between the present and the immediate past provides continuing fascination. A great many scientists who study modern natural processes are challenged by the opportunity to extrapolate their findings by applying them to a bit of history. At the same time, those concerned with historical sequences are always in quest of new and sharper methods for reconstructing past events. Thus the Quaternary provides a focus of cooperation among not only those with different competencies but also those with different approaches.

An example may be found in the field of oceanography, in which the recent development of deep-sea coring devices and of isotope analysis has provided the materials and techniques for the study of what may be the only continuous sediment record for the entire Quaternary. The geochemical, sedimentological, and paleontological variations in these sediments have implications for paleoclimatology. Concern for these implications has stimulated oceanographers to learn about the more diversified terrestrial record of Quaternary paleoclimates for the purpose of correlation. In the exchange of ideas, the horizons of the land-oriented Quaternary scientists have been enlarged, and overall understanding of the Quaternary has been increased.

Quaternary time saw the evolution of modern man and the development of human cultures. Interest in the chronology of these events and in the environmental conditions that accompanied and may have influenced them has led to an increasing number of joint projects in which biological, geological, and geochemical techniques are applied to archaeological problems. The most spectacular of these is radiocarbon dating, but detailed studies of the paleontology, sedimentology, and geochemistry of archaeological sites are also productive in elucidating the paleoecology of Early Man.

The present volume is an attempt to review the status of investigations into many facets of the Quaternary of the United States—a large area with diverse geographic regions and diverse Quaternary histories. In a certain sense Quaternary studies are of two major types. First are descriptive analyses of the morphology and stratigraphy of geologic or archaeologic materials, *e.g.* the mapping of moraines or terraces or caves and the study of the physical and paleontologic stratigraphy of the related deposits. These studies form the backbone of Quaternary work by providing the necessary maps and materials from which the environments can be reconstructed or the sequence of events worked out. Then there are investigations of current natural processes that have some known or potential historical implications or applications. Here lie a great group of studies ranging from glaciology and tererstrial magnetism to floristic phytogeography.

After an introductory chapter on early American studies,

the book is organized in four principal sections: geology, biogeography, archaeology, and miscellany. The geologic chapters are arranged on a geographic basis; they are largely inventories of the present knowledge of the Quaternary history and geological processes, first in the area of continental glaciation, then in the unglaciated areas east of the Rocky Mountains, and finally in the western part of the country. They show the diverse methods of investigating the complex problems presented by the morphology, lithology, and stratigraphy of surficial sediments: field mapping, subsurface exploration, followed by detailed laboratory studies ranging from clay-mineral analysis to micropaleontology and isotope dating.

The chapters under the heading of biogeography (in its broad sense) include six on regional phytogeography and pollen analysis. Because these chiefly involve only the flowering plants, a separate chapter deals with the mosses. Another concerns the special problem of polyploidy as it relates to climatic history. The zoogeographic chapters are arranged on a taxonomic rather than a geographic basis, ranging from mammals to invertebrates. A special chapter treats recent adjustments in animal ranges. In a concluding essay, E. S. Deevey reflects on the nature of Quaternary biogeography.

Archaeology is treated principally in five regional chapters. These reviews emphasize the paleoecology rather than the typology of the cultures, or they deal with archaeological features that have some geological context. Most are concerned with the earlier phases of human activity in this country rather than with those of the last few millennia.

The miscellaneous chapters that conclude the volume concern diverse subjects that have new or interesting applications to Quaternary history. Although many Quaternary scientists are occupied with studying the record of geologic or biogeographic changes that record climatic fluctuations, processes other than climatic change left important records in Quaternary rocks and landforms. Thus various manifestations of crustal activity are described in chapters on tectonics, volcanic-ash deposits, and paleomagnetism. Other chapters in this section are concerned with processes whose historical implications have only recently been appreciated —isotope geochemistry, limnology, pedology, oceanography —and still others with familiar subjects in which newly developed knowledge encourages fresh approaches, such as theoretical paleoclimatology, glaciology, paleohydrology, and tree-ring analysis.

Many gaps remain in this coverage of the Quaternary of the United States, either because suitable authors were not available or because of limitations on the size of the book. Some authors found it convenient to include consideration of Canada and Mexico, but generally the coverage is limited to the continental United States (and its continental shelves). In any case, the diversity of authors and subject matter provides a broad sample of American scientists and disciplines involved in the study of the Quaternary in all of its manifestations.

Publication of this volume has been made possible by a grant from the National Science Foundation, made available for this purpose through the good offices of the National Academy of Sciences. The editors are grateful on behalf of the Organizing Committee of the 7th INQUA Congress for these contributions of assistance.

March 3, 1965   H. E. WRIGHT, JR.
                                 DAVID G. FREY
                                 EDITORS

CONTENTS

PREFACE   vii

INTRODUCTION: HISTORICAL PERSPECTIVES Richard Foster Flint   3

PART I: GEOLOGY

GLACIATED AREAS EAST OF THE ROCKY MOUNTAINS

QUATERNARY GEOLOGY OF NORTHERN GREAT PLAINS R. W. Lemke, W. M. Laird, M. J. Tipton,
R. M. Lindvall   15

GLACIATION OF MINNESOTA AND IOWA H. E. Wright, Jr., R. V. Ruhe   29

OUTLINE OF GLACIAL GEOLOGY OF ILLINOIS AND WISCONSIN John C. Frye, H. B. Willman,
Robert F. Black   43

PLEISTOCENE GEOLOGY OF INDIANA AND MICHIGAN William J. Wayne, James H. Zumberge   63

PLEISTOCENE DEPOSITS OF THE ERIE LOBE Richard P. Goldthwait, Aleksis Dreimanis, Jane L. Forsyth,
Paul F. Karrow, George W. White   85

QUATERNARY GEOLOGY OF NEW YORK Ernest H. Muller   99

THE QUATERNARY OF NEW ENGLAND J. P. Schafer, J. H. Hartshorn   113

UNGLACIATED EASTERN AND CENTRAL UNITED STATES

THE ATLANTIC COASTAL PLAIN AND THE APPALACHIAN HIGHLANDS IN THE QUATERNARY Horace G. Richards,
Sheldon Judson   129

RÉSUMÉ OF THE QUATERNARY GEOLOGY OF THE NORTHWESTERN GULF OF MEXICO PROVINCE
Hugh A. Bernard, Rufus J. LeBlanc   137

THE PLEISTOCENE IN NEBRASKA AND NORTHERN KANSAS E. C. Reed, V. H. Dreeszen, C. K. Bayne,
C. B. Schultz   187

QUATERNARY OF THE SOUTHERN GREAT PLAINS John C. Frye, A. Bryon Leonard   203

WESTERN UNITED STATES

GLACIATION OF THE ROCKY MOUNTAINS Gerald M. Richmond   217

THE CORDILLERAN ICE SHEET OF THE NORTHERN ROCKY MOUNTAINS AND RELATED QUATERNARY HISTORY
OF THE COLUMBIA PLATEAU Gerald M. Richmond, Roald Fryxell, George E. Neff, Paul L. Weis   231

NONGLACIAL QUATERNARY GEOLOGY OF THE SOUTHERN AND MIDDLE ROCKY MOUNTAINS Glenn R. Scott   243

SNAKE RIVER PLAIN Harold E. Malde   255

QUATERNARY GEOLOGY OF THE GREAT BASIN Roger B. Morrison   265

QUATERNARY GEOLOGY OF THE SOUTHWEST Frank E. Kottlowski, Maurice E. Cooley, Robert V. Ruhe   287

THE QUATERNARY OF THE PACIFIC MOUNTAIN SYSTEM IN CALIFORNIA Clyde Wahrhaftig, J. H. Birman   299

THE GLACIAL HISTORY OF WESTERN WASHINGTON AND OREGON Dwight R. Crandell   341

THE QUATERNARY GEOLOGY AND ARCHAEOLOGY OF ALASKA Troy L. Péwé, David M. Hopkins, J. L. Giddings   355

PART II: BIOGEOGRAPHY

PHYTOGEOGRAPHY AND PALYNOLOGY

PHYTOGEOGRAPHY AND PALYNOLOGY OF NORTHEASTERN UNITED STATES Margaret B. Davis   377

PROBLEMS IN THE QUATERNARY PHYTOGEOGRAPHY OF THE GREAT LAKES REGION Edward J. Cushing   403

PALYNOLOGY AND PLEISTOCENE PHYTOGEOGRAPHY OF UNGLACIATED EASTERN NORTH AMERICA
Donald R. Whitehead   417

PLEISTOCENE POLLEN ANALYSIS AND BIOGEOGRAPHY OF THE SOUTHWEST Paul S. Martin,
Peter J. Mehringer, Jr.   433

PLANT GEOGRAPHY IN THE SOUTHERN ROCKY MOUNTAINS W. A. Weber   453

A PLEISTOCENE PHYTOGEOGRAPHICAL SKETCH OF THE PACIFIC NORTHWEST AND ALASKA Calvin J. Heusser   469

THE BOREAL BRYOPHYTE FLORA AS AFFECTED BY QUATERNARY GLACIATION William C. Steere   485

POLYPLOIDY, DISTRIBUTION, AND ENVIRONMENT Albert W. Johnson, John G. Packer, Gerd Reese   497

ZOOGEOGRAPHY AND EVOLUTION

QUATERNARY MAMMALS OF NORTH AMERICA C. W. Hibbard, D. E. Ray, D. E. Savage,
D. W. Taylor, J. E. Guilday   509

AVIAN SPECIATION IN THE QUATERNARY Robert K. Selander — 527

AMPHIBIAN SPECIATION W. Frank Blair — 543

REPTILES IN THE QUATERNARY OF NORTH AMERICA Walter Auffenberg, William W. Milstead — 557

QUATERNARY FRESHWATER FISHES OF NORTH AMERICA Robert Rush Miller — 569

PLEISTOCENE EVENTS AND INSECTS Herbert H. Ross — 583

THE STUDY OF PLEISTOCENE NONMARINE MOLLUSKS IN NORTH AMERICA D. W. Taylor — 597

OTHER INVERTEBRATES—AN ESSAY IN BIOGEOGRAPHY David G. Frey — 613

RECENT ADJUSTMENTS IN ANIMAL RANGES Philip W. Smith — 633

GENERAL

PLEISTOCENE NONMARINE ENVIRONMENTS Edward S. Deevey, Jr. — 643

PART III: ARCHAEOLOGY

LATE QUATERNARY PREHISTORY IN THE NORTHEASTERN WOODLANDS James B. Griffin — 655

AN OUTLINE OF SOUTHEASTERN UNITED STATES PREHISTORY WITH PARTICULAR EMPHASIS ON THE
  PALEO-INDIAN ERA Stephen Williams, James B. Stoltman — 669

QUATERNARY HUMAN OCCUPATION OF THE PLAINS Robert L. Stephenson — 685

POSTGLACIAL CLIMATE AND ARCHAEOLOGY IN THE DESERT WEST Martin A. Baumhoff, Robert F. Heizer — 697

PACIFIC COAST ARCHAEOLOGY Clement W. Meighan — 709

PART IV: MISCELLANEOUS STUDIES

LATE QUATERNARY HISTORY, CONTINENTAL SHELVES OF THE UNITED STATES Joseph R. Curray — 723

ISOTOPE GEOCHEMISTRY AND THE PLEISTOCENE CLIMATIC RECORD Wallace S. Broecker — 737

QUATERNARY PALEOPEDOLOGY Robert V. Ruhe — 755

GEOCHEMISTRY OF SOME QUATERNARY LAKE SEDIMENTS OF NORTH AMERICA F. M. Swain — 765

QUATERNARY PALEOHYDROLOGY S. A. Schumm — 783

GLACIERS AND CLIMATE Mark F. Meier — 795

VOLCANIC-ASH CHRONOLOGY Ray E. Wilcox — 807

QUATERNARY PALEOMAGNETIC STRATIGRAPHY Allan Cox, Richard R. Doell, G. Brent Dalrymple — 817

TECTONICS OF QUATERNARY TIME IN MIDDLE NORTH AMERICA Philip B. King — 831

DENDROCHRONOLOGY Harold C. Fritts — 871

THEORETICAL PALEOCLIMATOLOGY J. Murray Mitchell, Jr. — 881

INDEX OF AUTHORS CITED — 903

SUBJECT INDEX — 913

THE QUATERNARY OF THE UNITED STATES

INTRODUCTION: HISTORICAL PERSPECTIVES

RICHARD FOSTER FLINT[1]

WE HAVE before us a volume, the first of its kind ever to be published, in which the very considerable knowledge of the post-Tertiary geology of the United States has been condensed and interpreted, by regions, by a group of specialists. It is clearly the latest word on the subject, constituting a reference book that will be used widely and continuously. Eventually it will be superseded by a newer symposium of the same sort, which will distill the additions that are made each year to the description and interpretation of the multitude of stratigraphic units and other features that together constitute the Quaternary geology of the subcontinent.

The acceleration in the growth of knowledge since about 1945 has produced so much information about this geology that the literature has become bulky and in some respects poorly accessible. Hence this volume is timely. Probably something of its kind would have been put together under other auspices during the present decade, had not the VII INQUA Congress furnished the stimulus for a compendium in 1965.

Although the volume is a distillation of what is known today, it is interesting to examine it with reference to the history of thought about the surficial geology of the United States, and to realize when and by whom the major concepts inherent in the American Quaternary were put forth. This is the reason for beginning the volume with this introduction. It tells us nothing new, but it lends some perspective to modern research in the Quaternary System.

ORIGIN OF GLACIAL DRIFT

Although the Quaternary strata include sediments of many kinds, the kind that occupied by far the greatest attention during the 19th century, and that possibly still attracts major attention today, is glacial drift. The story of early interpretation of the origin of drift is mainly a European story. However, in the early 19th century, America too had its advocates of catastrophic floods, ocean currents, waves, winds, and other far-fetched agencies as explanations for the deposition of that mantle of diverse surficial sediment and included erratic boulders, which at first was known only in the eastern part of the country.

One of the earliest published statements about the drift in America is characteristic of its author, Benjamin Silliman (1821, p. 49), in being sturdy, objective, and cautious:

"The almost universal existence of rolled pebbles, and boulders of rock, not only on the margin of the oceans, seas, lakes, and rivers; but their existence, often in enormous quantities, in situations quite removed from large waters; inland,—in high banks, imbedded in strata, or scattered, occasionally, in profusion, on the face of almost every region, and sometimes on the tops and declivities of mountains, as well as in the vallies between them; their entire difference, in many cases, from the rocks in the country where they lie —rounded masses and pebbles of primitive rocks being deposited in secondary and alluvial regions, and vice versa; these and a multitude of similar facts have ever struck us as being among the most interesting of geological occurrences, and as being very inadequately accounted for by existing theories."

Undoubtedly much of the sediment described was glacial drift. Like nearly everyone else at that time, Silliman believed in the Deluge, but he did not attribute this sediment to the Deluge, as others did.

A long step forward is represented by the observation of Peter Dobson (1826, p. 217-218) of Vernon, Connecticut:

"I have had occasion to dig up a great number of bowlders, of red sandstone, and of the conglomerate kind, in erecting a cotton manufactory; and it was not uncommon to find them worn smooth on the under side, as if done by their having been dragged over rocks and gravelly earth, in one steady position. On examination, they exihibit scratches and furrows on the abraded part; and if among the minerals composing the rock, there happened to be pebbles of feldspar, or quartz, (which was not uncommon) they usually appeared not to be worn so much as the rest of the stone, preserving their more tender parts in a ridge, extending some inches. When several of these pebbles happen to be in one block, the preserved ridges were on the same side of the pebbles, so that it is easy to determine which part of the stone moved forward, in the act of wearing. . . .[2]

"These bowlders are found, not only on the surface, but I have discovered them a number of feet deep, in the earth, in the hard compound of clay, sand, and gravel. . . .

"I think we cannot account for these appearances, unless we call in the aid of ice along with water, and that they have been worn by being suspended and carried in ice, over rocks and earth, under water."

Although the material described is probably till, the description is accurate and the inference quite logical in view of the state of knowledge then existing.

The theory of continental glaciation originated in Europe, and its greatest exponent was Louis Agassiz. In 1837 Agassiz

---

[1] Department of Geology, Yale University, New Haven, Connecticut.

[2] Such features were described independently and correctly interpreted by Chamberlin (1877, p. 200).

read his epoch-making paper before the Helvetic Society in Luzern. Although the paper, entitled *Études sur les Glaciers* (Agassiz, 1840), was not published until three years later, the news spread to America sooner than that, for in 1839 we find Timothy Conrad, the paleontologist, writing in the *American Journal of Science* (Conrad, 1839, p. 241-242):

"M. Agassiz attributes the polished surfaces of the rocks in Switzerland to the agency of ice, and the 'diluvial scratches,' as they have been termed, to sand and pebbles which moving bodies of ice carried in their resistless course. In the same manner I would account for the polished surface of the rocks in Western New York. . . ."

After the publication of *Études sur les Glaciers*, Edward Hitchcock (1841, p. 247-258) likewise accepted the theory in principle and showed lucidly how it explained the observed characteristics and distribution of the American drift. Conrad's statement and Hitchcock's paper therefore mark the establishment, in America, of the concept of the origin of the drift through the agency of glacier ice. Notwithstanding, the following decades witnessed active debate, in which it was apparent that many people were still unconvinced. Agassiz himself arrived in America in 1846, and although his authoritative voice was added to those of Conrad and Hitchcock, the controversy went on and did not die out entirely until the end of the 19th century, a few years earlier than its disappearance in Europe.

PHYSICAL FEATURES OF DRIFT

Although "moraines" began to be spoken of by Americans soon after Agassiz' book was published, apparently the term was not clearly applied to a single well-described feature until 1871, when G. K. Gilbert (1871, p. 340-342) then geologist on the Ohio Geological Survey, wrote:

". . . the ridge which determines the courses of the St. Joseph and St. Marys rivers is a buried terminal moraine of the glacier that moved southwestward through the Maumee valley. . . . Its irregularly curved outline accords intimately with the configuration of the valley, and with the direction of the ice markings; its concavity is turned toward the source of motion. . . at every stage of its [the ice sheet's] existence—its margin must have been variously notched and lobed in conformity with the contour of the country, the higher lands being first laid bare by the encroaching secular summer."

This succinct and thoughtful description apparently refers to the Wabash and Fort Wayne Moraines of current nomenclature.

Six years later T. C. Chamberlin (1877, p. 204-215) published a description and true interpretation of an end moraine of a different kind. The moraine, then known as the Potash Kettle Range or Pots and Kettles Range, was a conspicuous ridge of lobate form in eastern Wisconsin. Characterized by an abundance of stratified drift and by kames, kettles, ice-channel fillings and other ice-contact features, it was accurately described by Chamberlin, who concluded: "The Kettle Range is evidently a gigantic moraine." It consists essentially of the Johnstown and Interlobate Moraines of current terminology. In his interpretation Chamberlin made use of the recognition by Whittlesey (1859) that glacial kettles are of ice-block origin. Whittlesey's interpretation was based on analogy with the termini of glaciers in the Alps, where ice masses mixed with drift had been reported.

Chamberlin recognized the moraine as compound, and correctly visualized the variations of glacial regimen that could create a nested sequence of end-moraine ridges.

It is noteworthy that at that early date Chamberlin suggested the piping of silt and fine sand as a possible origin for some of the small basins in the Kettle Range. The piping process, commonly related to loess, did not become widely recognized in surficial geology until the middle of the 20th century.

In this publication also, Chamberlin (1877, p. 218) first used the term *till*, taking it from the British literature. The term rapidly spread into general use in America.

In connection with the origin of kettles, we note that although their origin (as ice-contact features) was explained correctly in 1867, not until several years later did a correct explanation of the origin of kames appear. In 1873 N. H. Winchell (1873, p. 62) published a clear account of how such features were made, as a result of observations in Minnesota in the previous year, although he did not use the word kame. Similar interpretations were published in Sweden by Hummel (1874) and by Upham (1877) in New England, both apparently independently. Earlier, a common opinion had been that kames were of marine origin, at least in part (*cf.* Geikie, 1874, p. 246-252).

In his early treatise on glacial drift in New Hampshire, Hitchcock (1878, p. 181-215) gave an excellent description and interpretation of striations and other glacial marks on bedrock encountered in his survey. This anticipated by a decade the more detailed and comprehensive treatise by T. C. Chamberlin, mentioned on a later page.

By 1883 Chamberlin (1883, p. 295-309) had systematized and defined the chief kinds of glacial deposits and sediments of related origin. In this respect he was influenced, no doubt, by the publications on glacial geology by James Geikie in Britain. From this time onward the two scientists kept in touch with each other, as is evident from the mutual references and quotations in the publications of the two men.

MAPPING THE DRIFT BORDER

The decades of the 1860's and 1870's saw the launching of several systematic geological surveys, mostly under State authorities of various kinds, although some surveys began even earlier. Most of them dealt with the glacial drift in reconnaissance, and some dealt with it in detail. Some of them identified a border of the glacial drift and described its character and position. With these early studies the names of many men prominent in American geology were associated. Among them were G. H. Cook in New Jersey, W. W. Mather and Lardner Vanuxem in New York, G. F. Wright and H. C. Lewis in Pennsylvania, J. S. Newberry, Edward Orton, G. K. Gilbert, and Charles Whittlesey in

Ohio, John Collett in Indiana, L. C. Wooster and Alexander Winchell in Michigan, C. A. White in Iowa, T. C. Chamberlin in Wisconsin, Warren Upham in Minnesota, and J. E. Todd in South Dakota. As a compilation, the map published by Newberry (1874, p. 76) is outstanding. It shows a generalized drift border extending from New Jersey to Kansas and many striations in New England, east-central United States, and Canada. The accompanying text is informative and well reasoned.

In 1878 a compiled map with more extensive data was published by C. H. Hitchcock (1878, p. 323). In it the drift border is shown extending westward into Montana and eastward from Cape Cod along the continental shelf as far as Newfoundland. Hitchcock therefore understood that glaciation affected a region, now submerged, east of the Atlantic Coast. The text accompanying the map speaks of centers of glacial dispersion in Greenland, Labrador, and the Rocky Mountains.

Chamberlin, who had been appointed to the U.S. Geological Survey in 1881 and had spent much time in glacial studies, made a broader synthesis of a prominent drift border, extending from Cape Cod on the east to North Dakota on the west (Chamberlin, 1883, esp. Pl. 28). He had published a preliminary version of the map five years earlier (Chamberlin, 1878, p. 209). He called the border "a moraine" and identified it with a "Second Glacial Epoch" because in many sectors other drift lay south of it. Much though by no means all of Chamberlin's "moraine" coincides with the outer limit of the drift of Wisconsin age as we understand it today. The border of the region covered by older drift was later defined gradually, over a long period.

A few years later Chamberlin (1888, Pl. 8) published a compilation of glacial striations observed by many geologists at some 2,500 localities between the Atlantic Coast and Dakota Territory, and had extended the map of glacial-drift borders through the Cordilleran region right to the Pacific Coast. The map distinguishes between "Earlier Drift" and "Later Drift" more or less along the line separating the Wisconsin drift from pre-Wisconsin drifts of today's nomenclature. This publication, incidentally, was accompanied by an elegant treatise on striations and other glacially caused markings on bedrock.

Refinement of the outer limit of glaciation has continued up to the present time, but the 1888 map, for one of its small scale, is a good representation of the major glaciated areas of the United States.

Repeated Glaciation and Stratigraphic Subdivision

As early as 1874, J. S. Newberry (1874, p. 3) had identified in Ohio a "forest bed," a layer of plant matter, overlying glacial drift. Similar material was soon found to be widespread throughout the Middle West, where in places it lay between two sheets of till. McGee (1878, p. 341) correctly viewed this relationship as implying that the forest bed "must be of interglacial age," possibly in analogy with interglacial layers earlier recognized in Europe. At about the same time Chamberlin was recognizing the existence of two drift sheets differentiated by weathering of different degrees of intensity. Probably these observations constitute the beginnings of the concept of multiple glaciation in North America.

By the end of the 1880's many geologists were at work on the areal glacial geology and stratigraphy of a wide sector of northern United States. Among them were G. H. Stone (eskers of Maine), W. M. Davis (drumlins of southern New England), N. S. Shaler (Mt. Desert, Nantucket, and Martha's Vineyard Islands), G. F. Wright (drift border in Ohio, Indiana, and Illinois), J. C. Branner (areal studies in Ohio and Indiana), Frank Leverett (northeastern Illinois), R. D. Salisbury (Driftless Area), I. M. Buell (boulder trains in Wisconsin), and J. E. Todd (areal studies in the Dakotas, Nebraska, and Iowa). Chamberlin acted as official and unofficial coordinator and synthesizer of much of this work, as is reflected in his publications dating from around that time.

Shortly afterward the practice of applying geographic names to drift sheets was introduced in America. The Third Edition of Geikie's *Great Ice Age* (Geikie, 1894) contains two chapters on the glacial features of North America contributed by Chamberlin; in them the Kansan, East-Iowan, and East-Wisconsin stages of glaciation, separated by unnamed intervals of deglaciation, were introduced for the first time. The name Kansan was applied to the drift subsequently called Nebraskan, and the names East-Iowan and East-Wisconsin were soon shortened to Iowan and Wisconsin as used in subsequent literature. The general scheme, begun by Chamberlin, of classifying the American Pleistocene into glacial and interglacial stages endured for many decades without modification and still, with some changes, constitutes an important element in the classification generally favored today.

It is interesting to contrast the stratigraphic classification that developed in New England and adjacent regions with that which evolved in the Middle West. The two are different, and the differences are based on fundamental differences between the physical-geologic conditions in the two regions. As J. D. Dana (1873, p. 210) remarked, "No distinct terminal moraines . . . have been observed in New England." All the earlier New England reports emphasize (1) the presence of large quantities of stratified drift with diverse morphology, (2) a post-drift marine overlap in extensive coastal areas, and (3) the widespread existence of terraces in stream valleys. Two or more glacial sequences in stratigraphic superposition were not found in the region before the 20th century.

In contrast, the earlier Middle Western reports emphasize end moraines, till sheets in superposition, interglacial layers with fossil plants and mammals, loess, and sediments and shorelines of the glacial Great Lakes, altogether a more complex and more nearly complete sequence.

The evolution of the sequence in New England is well illustrated in the classifications shown in three editions of Dana's *Manual of Geology*, a standard textbook, between 1863 and 1895 (Table 1). Although stratigraphic names of Middle-Western origin have long since been introduced into the New England sequence, the names Champlain and Recent are still used, although with some differences of meaning.

TABLE 1

Stratigraphic Sequences Shown in Three Editions of the *Manual of Geology* by J. D. Dana

Dana, 1863, p. 535-586.	Dana, 1875, p. 527ff.	Dana, 1895, p. 940ff.
Age of Man, with deposits of modern origin: alluvium, deltas, beaches, sand dunes.		
Post-Tertiary { Recent or Terrace epoch, marked by upwarping, trenching, and terrace cutting by streams. Champlain epoch, with alluvial, lacustrine, and marine sediments, the latter representing marine invasion of coastal regions. Glacial epoch, marked by drift and modified drift, mostly glacial but in part deposited by icebergs.	*Quaternary* { Recent or Terrace Period Champlain Period (The earlier part was the era of melting of the great glacier.) Glacial Period b. Alluvian epoch a. Diluvian epoch	*Quaternary era or Era of Man* { Recent Period Champlain Period Glacial Period c. Final retreat b. First retreat a. Early advance } = Pleistocene of Lyell

No comparable sequence of publications exists for the Middle-Western region, but the history of the major stratigraphic names used in that region can be extracted from the literature (see Table 2).

ORIGIN OF LOESS

Loess had been recognized in Europe for decades. Beginning with Lyell and his contemporaries, it had been thought by many to be of lacustrine or alluvial origin. It was the classic discussion by Richthofen (1877, p. 74-84) of loess in China that first clearly argued the case for deposition by wind. Pumpelly, who had earlier studied the Chinese loess and had subscribed to the widespread lacustrine hypothesis, and who had subsequently worked on loess in Missouri, rejected his own earlier explanation and adopted the eolian hypothesis for central North America, but with the added significant opinion that most of the American loess was derived from outwash sediments rather than from the products of rock weathering (Pumpelly, 1879, p. 135). There was much debate about the matter; apparently not until 1893 did Chamberlin accept the eolian origin for even a part of the loess, and even then he still thought that the bulk of the sediment had been deposited in water.

PLUVIAL LAKES

The concept of the expansion of lakes through lowered temperature during glacial ages originated in Europe (Jamieson, 1863). However, only two years later, and apparently independently, this concept was applied to the Basin-and-Range region by I. D. Whitney (1865, p. 452). Whitney suggested the probable connection between expanded lakes and former glaciers. A quarter century later the probability of this concept was established in America through the field demonstration of a close relationship between high strandlines of pluvial lakes and drift deposited by local glaciers.

In 1889, J. C. Russell (1889, p. 369) showed through the geologic relation of strandlines to end moraines that the lake in the Mono basin, on the east flank of the Sierra Nevada, was approximately contemporaneous with local glaciation. Almost at the same time Gilbert (1890, p. 318) demonstrated a similar time relation between pluvial Lake Bonneville and former glaciers in the Wasatch Mountains.

Apart from the specific relation between glaciers and lakes in the Basin-and-Range region, an important contribution to the climatic significance of the former lakes was made by Meinzer (1922). He plotted the distribution of existing lakes and former lakes then known, and he con-

TABLE 2

Origin of Names of Major Stratigraphic Units Currently Used in Middle-Western United States

Stage	Named by	Original reference	Source of name	Remarks
Wisconsin	T. C. Chamberlin	Geikie, 1894, p. 763 (named *East-Wisconsin*)	State of Wisconsin	Name shortened to *Wisconsin* (Chamberlin, 1895, p. 270).
Sangamon	Frank Leverett	Leverett, 1898a, p. 176	Sangamon County, Illinois	
Illinoian	Frank Leverett	Chamberlin, 1896, p. 874 (named *Illinois*)	State of Illinois	Name changed to *Illinoian* (Leverett, 1898a, p. 171).
Yarmouth	Frank Leverett	Leverett, 1898b, p. 239	Spoil of dug well, Yarmouth, Iowa	
Kansan	T. C. Chamberlin	Geikie, 1894, p. 755 (named *Kansan formation*)	Northeastern Kansas	The name was first applied to the drift now called Nebraskan, but was shifted to apply to post-Aftonian drift in Iowa (Chamberlin, 1896, p. 873).
Aftonian	T. C. Chamberlin	Chamberlin, 1895, p. 272	Peat exposed near Afton Junction, Iowa	Peat ("forest bed") described by W J McGee (1891, p. 486-496).
Nebraskan	Bohumil Shimek	Shimek, 1909, p. 408	State of Nebraska	Had earlier been called *sub-Aftonian* and *pre-Kansan*.

sidered that the least-dry parts of the region today are comparable with the parts that were driest during the last glacial age. On a basis of the difference of latitude between the two parts, he attempted to derive a value for the inferred change in mean annual temperature since glacial time. This was one of the earliest attempts at quantification of differences between pluvial and existing climatic parameters.

Although widespread usage now labels as *pluvial* the former expanded lakes in regions that are dry today, the label was not applied to the lakes at the time when they were first recognized, nor indeed was it originally applied to dry regions at all. Both the concept of greatly increased precipitation at times during the Pleistocene and the term *pluvial period* originated with Alfred Tylor, a British manufacturer and active amateur geologist. Tylor (1868) propounded the belief that there had been a time in the Quaternary when rainfall values reached many times their present values, and proposed for it the term *pluvial period*. Contrary to widespread present belief, the term was not originally applied to the dry regions or the tropical regions with which it is associated today. It was applied specifically to bodies of valley gravel, occurring as fills, terraces and mantles of outwash, coarse alluvium, and colluvium in England and northern France. Large runoff and hence heavy rainfall were inferred from the coarse grain size and topographic position of the gravel bodies. In other words the term *pluvial period* was first invoked to explain climatic conditions inferred from sediments in high-middle latitudes and nothing else. Only later (*cf.* Hull, 1885, p. 182) was the term transferred to dry regions and to lower latitudes.

Ice Sheets and Isostasy

The general concept of uplift of the crust by postglacial rebound, following isostatic depression under the weight of ice sheets, was first proposed in Europe as a theory (Jamieson, 1865, p. 178), but it was soon taken up in America. N. S. Shaler (1874, p. 338) applied it to explain observations of postglacial emergence on the coast of Maine. McGee (1881) deduced the existence of a time lag (since approximated by measurement) between the withdrawal of an ice sheet and crustal recovery. During his classic study of pluvial Lake Bonneville, Gilbert (1890, p. 362-383) tested the principle by measuring strandlines. He found that they are warped, and he attributed their domelike deformation to isostatic compensation following removal of the very considerable weight of the water when the lake disappeared.

Subsequently many American geologists, among them F. B. Taylor, J. W. Goldthwait, G. K. Gilbert, and Frank Leverett, contributed largely to the complex of measurements of altitude and observations of stratigraphic relations, by which the outline of the history and deformation of the Great Lakes was basically established. That complex is equalled in importance only by the data developed by Scandinavian and Finnish scientists on the similar features of the Baltic region.

Glacial Control of Sea Level

Although the first correct deduction of the relation between the building of the Pleistocene ice sheets and fluctuation of the level of the sea is a European contribution dating back to Charles Maclaren (1841), one of the early discussions of the problem is American, the work of Charles Whittlesey (1868). That discussion includes an admirably lucid statement of the hydrologic cycle, emphasizing the exchange among liquid, gaseous, and solid water-substance. Whittlesey deduced that lowered secular temperature would result in lowering the snowline. Also he calculated that, on assumptions as to the extent and thickness of former ice sheets, glacial-age sea level might have been lowered by as much as 350 to 400 ft.

Another theoretical discussion, by N. S. Shaler (1875), appeared shortly afterward. Shaler's calculation led him to believe that glacial-age sea level might have been lower by as much as 1,200 ft. A third discussion, by Warren Upham (*in* C. H. Hitchcock, 1878, p. 18, 329-333), appeared a few years later.

However, little information from direct field observation in America was brought to bear on the problem until near the end of the 19th century. Thereafter, study of the Pleistocene sediments and morphology of the Atlantic Coastal Plain led to the appearance of a series of publications through several decades. The early contributions, based on field studies in Virginia or the Chesapeake Bay region, were the work of McGee (1888a, 1888b), Shaler (1890), and Darton (1902). These workers recognized, in both the morphology of the terrain and the internal character of the surficial sediments, evidence of Pleistocene marine submergence of the outer part of the Coastal Plain. These publications were followed by a number of others, treating of various segments of the Coastal Plain from Maryland to Florida, and relying heavily on morphology with little attempt at detailed stratigraphic study. Typical of this group is a paper (Shattuck, 1901) setting forth the concept of several successive "terraces" at various altitudes, each covered with a thin blanket of marine sediments and each terminating landward in a wave-cut cliff. Most or all of the "terraces" were thought to be of Pleistocene age. The succession of benchlike forms was thought by some to have resulted from crustal movements, and by others to reflect eustatic movements of sea level. Although these views prevailed for several decades, it is now realized that they were rigid and unrealistic.

Direct field observation of coral reefs and morphology of islands in the tropical Pacific led R. A. Daly (1910) to propose what he later (Daly, 1915) called the glacial-control hypothesis of submergence of coral reefs, as an alternative to the hypothesis of crustal subsidence advocated earlier by Darwin and Dana. Today both subsidence and glacial control are recognized as having contributed in varying degrees to the submergence of Pacific islands.

Paleontology

The earliest large American contribution to the theory of distribution of organisms seems to have been that of Asa Gray (1878). Comparing the large collections of plants brought back from Japan by the voyages of Perry and Rogers with those from temperate latitudes elsewhere, Gray perceived strong resemblances between eastern North America and eastern Asia, and he inferred that the floras reflected a circumpolar dispersion of plants in Tertiary time. Based on the inferences of Oswald Heer and others in Europe in the 1860's, the sequence of events suggested by Gray was that the appearance of cold glacial-age climates pushed the widespread late-Tertiary floras toward the equator and introduced arctic plants into middle latitudes, around the margins of the ice sheets. Then, during nonglacial times, the arctic kinds returned toward the pole. Basically this concept has stood the test of nearly a hundred years of subsequent research.

Comparable results on shifts of populations among animals were reached much more slowly because of the scarcity and fragmentary nature of the fossil evidence. Although extinct mammals had been found as fossils early in the 19th century, their sporadic occurrence was insufficient as a basis for a sound theory. It was not until 1914 that O. P. Hay (1914) published a systematic account of the Pleistocene mammals of a large area, in the form of a monograph on Iowa. But even this did not include biogeographic inferences. The publication was followed, at long intervals, by systematic catalogs, by regions and localities, of Pleistocene mammals right across North America (Hay, 1923-1927). These works included maps and discussions of biogeography, stratigraphic ranges, extinctions, and post-Tertiary evolution. Since the appearance of this work, opinion has changed as to the stratigraphic positions of many of the occurrences, but the contribution remains basic.

At about the same time there appeared a comparable monograph on the life of the Pleistocene Period. The work of F. C. Baker (1920), this publication emphasized freshwater mollusks, but nevertheless dealt with other invertebrates and with vertebrates and plants as well. Although far less detailed than Hay's work as regards vertebrates, Baker's monograph discussed biogeography at greater length. These two monographs together mark the first long step toward cataloguing and synthesizing Pleistocene faunas and floras in North America.

DATING OF PLEISTOCENE EVENTS

Apparently the earliest attempt in America to date an event in Pleistocene time was based on measurement made in 1789 by Andrew Ellicott, the first American surveyor to measure the Niagara Gorge and Falls. Ellicott told of his measurements to his friend William Maclay, Senator from Pennsylvania, who wrote in his journal on February 1, 1790, as follows (Maclay, 1927, p. 185):

"Mr. Ellicott's accounts of Niagara Falls are amazing indeed. I communicated to him my scheme of an attempt to account for the age of the world, or at least to fix the period when the water began to cut the ledge of rock over which it falls. The distance from the present pitch to where the falls originally were, is now seven miles. For this space a tremendous channel is cut in a solid limestone rock, in all parts one hundred and fifty feet deep, but near two hundred and fifty at the mouth or part where the attrition began. People who have known the place since Sir William Johnson took possession of it, about thirty years ago, give out that there is an attrition of twenty feet in that time.

Now, if 20 feet = 30 years = 7 miles, or 36,960 feet; answer, 55,440 years."

Several later estimates were made, mostly during the 19th century; not until 1928, when it was shown by the Canadian geologist W. A. Johnston (1928) that geologic relations in the gorge invalidate any attempt at extrapolation on existing rates of retreat of the Falls, did this kind of estimate cease to be made. Attempts to date the retreat of the St. Anthony Falls of the Mississippi River encountered analogous difficulties.

Efforts to extrapolate into the past the estimated rates of activity of existing processes have been made repeatedly. An early attempt to use the rate of recession of wave-cut cliffs of Lake Michigan to date the Glenwood phase of glacial Lake Chicago, made by Edmund Andrews (1870), yielded a value too small by comparison with estimates from modern radiocarbon dates. An estimate of the time elapsed since deglaciation of the escarpment south of Lake Erie, based on rates of stream dissection (Wright, 1911, p. 565) proved later to be not far from C^{14} dates of contemporaneous events.

Various estimates have been based on the progress of processes of weathering, although similar attempts were made earlier in Europe. Notable among American efforts are the attempt by François Matthes (1930, p. 70-72) to measure the time elapsed since the El Portal glaciation in the Sierra Nevada, and calculations on the dates of Pleistocene soils (including "gumbotils") made in Iowa by G. F. Kay (1931) and in Bermuda by R. W. Sayles (1931). All these calculations involved assumptions recognized by their authors; perhaps their most useful result was the stimulation of thought about Pleistocene chronology.

At least two attempts have been made to date postglacial time by means of rates of accumulation of peat. In 1881, G. F. Wright (1881) measured the thickness of peat in a kettle near Andover, Massachusetts, as the equivalent of 8 ft. Applying a rate of accumulation of 1 in. per century from a measurement of post-Roman peat in northern France, he derived a value of approximately 10,000 years for the time elapsed since the kettle was formed during deglaciation. An interesting sidelight on this calculation is Wright's view of the bearing of this value on the then fashionable Croll hypothesis of climatic change. After deducing that under Croll's hypothesis the last glaciation should have ended, not 10,000 but about 80,000 years ago, Wright remarked: "These considerations have led me to look with increasing distrust upon the astronomical calculations which are made concerning the Glacial period. . . ." Some geologists today would express similar doubts about the more elaborate astronomical theory put forth by Milankovitch.

Another attempt at dating by means of peat accumulation was made in Alaska (Capps, 1915), using an ingenious combination of measurement of peat thickness and counting of the annual rings in related tree stumps.

Two other calculations, based on quite different processes, are worth mention. One was a calculation by H. S. Gale (1915, p. 260-264) of the "age" of Owens Lake, California.

The quantities of chlorine and sodium in solution in the lake in the year 1912 were divided by the respective annual inflow of these elements estimated from sampling water from Owens River. By "age" Gale meant the time since Owens Lake ceased to overflow and began to accumulate these elements. Like most such calculations this one involved assumptions that could not be proved, at least at that time. However, this was possibly the first use of this geochemical method to arrive at a date of a Pleistocene event.

The other calculation was made by A. C. Swinnerton (1925), who attempted to date the deglaciation of a locality in Ohio. He derived the volume of existing travertine at a large spring by the measured rate of accumulation, making a number of assumptions as to constancy of local climatic and geologic conditions that could actually well have been variable.

The foregoing examples are cited as an indication of the ingenuity that has been displayed by American scientists in trying to solve the problem of absolute ages in places where some means, however imperfect, seemed to present itself. The various methods used are seen to be second-class by comparison with direct radiometry.

An early application, in American science, of radiometry to a Pleistocene event was the attempt by Schlundt and Moore (1909, p. 33) to date the radium-bearing travertine of Terrace Mountain in Yellowstone National Park. The travertine underlies, and is older than, the latest glacial drift in the area and contains far less radium than does the travertine now being deposited. On the assumptions that (1) the older travertine had a comparable concentration of radium when first deposited and (2) no radium has been lost by leaching of the older deposit, and with correction of the half-life value for radium, the calculated age of the older travertine is 11,200 years. The actual age is now thought to be greater, perhaps because of errors in the assumptions.

The rapid advances in radiometry through the use of radiocarbon and potassium/argon constitute a part of modern science and are not properly history. The dimensions of Quaternary time are now seen in much better perspective, thanks to radiometry, than in the view that was available a bare quarter-century ago.

GENERAL RETROSPECT

To look through the literature of Quaternary geology, particularly the literature of the 19th century, is to perceive that advances in knowledge in that field in the United States proceeded almost step by step with advances in European countries. To some extent this was the result of intercommunication through the medium of scientific journals; citations and quotations show that such intercommunication took place in both directions. But this is not the whole explanation. From the dates of publications it is evident that scientists on both sides of the Atlantic Ocean often were thinking about the same problems at the same times, and not infrequently the same idea seems to have been put forward independently by people in two different countries. Whether this was stimulated by communication via newspapers or via private correspondence, or whether certain problems were strongly "in the air" at certain times could probably not be shown without very extensive and intensive search of the record.

Certainly the publication of syntheses must have helped. The most noteworthy 19th-century synthesis of the Quaternary was James Geikie's *The Great Ice Age* (1874, 1894). The subtitle, *Its Relation to the Antiquity of Man*, shows that the work was probably conceived originally during the scientific ferment that followed the publication of Darwin's *The Origin of Species* in 1859. That this was the case is borne out by the trend of Geikie's preface to the book, although he made no open statement of the fact. The book was intended not only for scientists but for general readers, and the demand among the latter group must have been great. During the period 1874 to 1894 the growth of knowledge about the Quaternary, in both Britain and America, was very rapid, as is apparent from comparison of the two editions of Geikie's work.

A somewhat similar American work was G. F. Wright's *The Ice Age in North America* (1890). It was surely patterned in part after Geikie's book, and indeed it carried a closely similar subtitle, reflecting the continued wide public interest in prehistoric man. Like its predecessor, it too appeared two decades later (in 1911) in a new edition with substantial improvements over the original.

The rate of increase in the output of American literature on the Quaternary seems to have been accelerated rather steadily throughout the century and a quarter of output. Probably this is a general reflection of the gradual increase in the number of American scientists interested in Quaternary problems. The rate of increase seems to have been less, however, in the early part of the 20th century than it was in the latter part of the 19th. The change coincides with T. C. Chamberlin's shift of attention from glacial geology to cosmogony and related problems. After 1899 Chamberlin published only two original titles (apart from a textbook) that had to do with glacial geology. Chamberlin (1843-1928) had been so dynamic and productive a leader in the field during the preceding 25 years and had influenced so many geologists who had worked under his direction, that his shift of interest could easily have caused a falling-off of output apart from his own, which ran to nearly 60 titles in glacial geology alone.

Probably the most noteworthy of Chamberlin's juniors was Frank Leverett (1859-1943), who unlike Chamberlin devoted his entire professional life to glacial geology. Leverett was single-minded from the very beginning. After graduating at Ames, Iowa, in 1885, he was advised by W J McGee to apply for a job to Chamberlin, who was then President of the University of Wisconsin and in charge of glacial investigations for the U.S. Geological Survey. Leverett walked the 250 miles from Ames to Madison, was employed, and remained a member of the Survey for 43 years. He mapped systematically the glacial or Pleistocene geology of parts or all of many States, including Illinois, Indiana, Iowa, Kentucky, Michigan, Minnesota, Ohio, Pennsylvania, and Florida. His bulky Professional Papers of the Geological Survey are classics. Much of Leverett's field work was done entirely on foot. After he retired he estimated that he had walked an aggregate of about 100,000 miles in the field.

Other students of Chamberlin were R. D. Salisbury (1858-1922) and W. C. Alden (1871-1959). Both contributed extensively to the literature of glacial geology, Salisbury in New Jersey and in the New York City area, and Alden in many areas from New England to Montana. Salisbury is probably best known for his collaboration with Chamberlin in textbooks of geology, which strongly stressed Pleistocene geology.

J. D. Dana (1813-1895) antedates Chamberlin by a full generation. His contributions to glacial geology were less numerous than those of Chamberlin because his research interest was spread over a wider spectrum of geology. His first publication with a bearing on glaciation was the first edition of his classic *Manual of Geology* (Dana, 1863), which, together with his textbook, went through eight editions. Thereafter he began to publish papers on Quaternary geology (mostly in New England), and his bibliography lists twenty-nine, out of a remarkable total of 201 titles.

Another strong contributor was R. S. Tarr (1864-1912), who published 38 titles in glacial geology and glaciology. Although both Chamberlin and Salisbury had visited and examined glaciers in Greenland, Tarr spent considerable time in the study of glaciers and glacial features in Alaska, and he applied his experience to the interpretation of glacial features in New York State, about which many of his publications were written.

The names mentioned by no means exhaust the list of workers who made significant contributions to American Quaternary during the 19th century and the early part of the 20th. No attempt has been made to present a complete list. The aim has been only to point out a few milestones in research in this field. There have been many significant contributions of much later date, and some milestones as well; but this discussion has been confined to earlier generations of scientists who are no longer living. There will be time enough in the future to pick up the thread of this brief narrative and review the many things that scientists now living have accomplished.

REFERENCES

Agassiz, Louis, 1840, Études sur les glaciers: Neuchâtel, privately published, 346 p.

Andrews, Edmund, 1870, The North American lakes considered as chronometers of post-glacial time: Chicago Acad. Sci. Trans., v. 2, 1870, p. 1-23

Baker, F. C., 1920, The life of the Pleistocene or glacial period as recorded in the deposits laid down by the great ice sheets: Univ. Illinois Bull., v. 17, no. 41, 476 p.

Capps, S. R., 1915, An estimate of the age of the last great glaciation in Alaska: Washington Acad. Sci. J., v. 5, p. 108-115

Chamberlin, T. C., 1877, Geology of eastern Wisconsin, *in* Geology of Wisconsin, survey of 1873-1877, v. 2: Madison, Commissioners of Public Printing, p. 97-246

—— 1878, on the extent and significance of the Wisconsin kettle moraine: Wisconsin Acad. Sci., Arts Lett. Trans., v. 4 (1876-77), p. 201-234

—— 1883, Terminal moraine of the second glacial epoch: U.S. Geol. Surv. Ann. Rep. 3, p. 291-402

—— 1888, The rock-scorings of the great ice invasions: U.S. Geol. Surv., Ann. Rep. 7, p. 147-248

—— 1895, The classification of American glacial deposits: J. Geol., v. 3, p. 270-277

—— 1896, Nomenclature of glacial formations: J. Geol., v. 4, p. 872-876

Conrad, T. A., 1839, Notes on American geology: Amer. J. Sci., v. 35, p. 237-251

Daly, R. A., 1910, Pleistocene glaciation and the coral reef problem: Amer. J. Sci., v. 30, p. 297-308

—— 1915, The glacial-control theory of coral reefs: Amer. Acad. Arts Sci. Proc., v. 51, p. 157-251

Dana, J. D., 1863, Manual of geology: Philadelphia, Theodore Bliss & Co., 1st ed., 798 p.

—— 1873, On the Glacial and Champlain eras in New England: Amer. J. Sci., v. 5, p. 198-211

—— 1875, Manual of geology: New York, Ivison, Blakeman, Taylor & Co., 2d. ed., 828 p.

—— 1895, Manual of geology: New York, American Book Co., 4th ed., 1087 p.

Darton, N. H., 1902, Description of the Norfolk quadrangle: U.S. Geol. Surv. Geol. Atlas, Folio 80, 4 p.

Dobson, Peter, 1826, Remarks on bowlders: Amer. J. Sci., v. 10, p. 217-218

Gale, H. S., 1914, Salines in the Owens, Searles, and Panamint basins, southeastern California: U.S. Geol. Surv. Bull. 580, p. 251-323

Geikie, James, 1874, The great ice age and its relation to the antiquity of man: London, W. Isbister, 575 p.

—— 1894, The great ice age and its relation to the antiquity of man: London, Stanford, 3d. ed., 850 p.

Gilbert, G. K., 1871, On certain glacial and post-glacial phenomena of the Maumee Valley: Amer. J. Sci., v. 1, p. 339-345

—— 1890, Lake Bonneville: U.S. Geol. Surv. Monogr. 1, 438 p.

Gray, Asa, 1878, Forest geography and archaeology: Amer. J. Sci., v. 16, p. 85-94, 183-196

Hay, O. P., 1914, The Pleistocene mammals of Iowa: Iowa Geol. Surv., v. 42, Ann. Rep. for 1912, p. 1-662

—— 1923, 1924, 1927, The Pleistocene of North America and its vertebrated animals . . . : Carnegie Instn. Publ. 322, 322A, 322B (3 v.)

Hitchcock, C. H., 1878, Surface geology, *in* The geology of New Hampshire: Concord, v. 3, pt. 3, 340 p.

Hitchcock, Edward, 1841, First anniversary address before the Association of American Geologists . . . : Amer. J. Sci., v. 41, p. 232-275

Hull, Edward, 1885, Mount Seir, Sinai, and western Palestine: London, R. Bentley, 227 p.

Hummel, D., 1874, Om rullstenbildningar: K. Svenska Vetenskapsakad., Bihang til Handl., v. 2, no. 11, 36 p.

Jamieson, T. F., 1863, On the parallel roads of Glen Roy, and their place in the history of the glacial period: Geol. Soc. London Quart. J., v. 19, p. 235-259

—— 1865, On the history of the last geological changes in Scotland: Geol. Soc. London Quart. J., v. 21, p. 178

Johnston, W. A., 1928, The age of the upper great gorge of Niagara River: Roy. Soc. Can. Trans., Sec. 4, v. 22, p. 13-29

Kay, G. F., 1931, Classification and duration of the Pleistocene period: Geol. Soc. Amer. Bull., v. 43, p. 425-466

Leverett, Frank, 1898a, The weathered zone (Sangamon) between the Iowan loess and Illinoian till sheet: J. Geol., v. 6, p. 171-181

—— 1898b, The weathered zone (Yarmouth) between the Illinoian and Kansan till sheets: J. Geol., v. 6, p. 238-243

Maclaren, Charles, 1841, The glacial theory of Professor Agassiz of Neuchatel: Edinburgh, The Scotsman Office, 62 p.

Maclay, William, 1927, The journal of William Maclay, United States Senator from Pennsylvania, 1789-1791: New York, C. A. Boni, 429 p.

Matthes, F. E., 1930, Geologic history of the Yosemite Valley: U.S. Geol. Surv. Prof. Pap. 160, 137 p.

McGee, W J, 1878, On the relative positions of the Forest Bed and associated drift formations in northeastern Iowa: Amer. J. Sci., v. 15, p. 339-341

—— 1881, On local subsidence produced by an ice-sheet: Amer. J. Sci., v. 22, p. 368-369

—— 1888a, Three formations of the middle Atlantic slope: Amer. J. Sci., v. 35, p. 120-143, 328-330, 367-388, 448-466

—— 1888b, The geology of the head of Chesapeake Bay: U.S. Geol. Surv. Ann. Rep. 7, p. 537-646

—— 1891, The Pleistocene history of northeastern Iowa: U.S. Geol. Surv. Ann. Rep. 11, pt. 1, p. 189-577

Meinzer, O. E., 1922, Map of Pleistocene lakes of the Basin-and-Range province and its significance: Geol. Soc. Amer. Bull., v. 33, p. 541-552

Newberry, J. S., 1874, Geology of Ohio—surface geology: Ohio Geol. Surv. Rep. 2, p. 1-80

Pumpelly, Raphael, 1879, The relation of secular rock-disintegration to loess, glacial drift and rock basins: Amer. J. Sci., v. 17, p. 133-144

Richthofen, Ferdinand von, 1877, China: Berlin, D. Reimer, v. 1, 758 p.

Russell, I. C., 1889, Quaternary history of Mono Valley, California: U.S. Geol. Surv. Ann. Rep. 8, p. 261-394

Sayles, R. W., 1931, Bermuda during the Ice Age: Amer. Acad. Arts Sci. Proc., v. 66, p. 381-468

Schlundt, Herman, and Moore, R. B., 1909, Radioactivity of the thermal waters of Yellowstone National Park: U.S. Geol. Surv. Bull. 395, 35 p.

Shaler, N. S., 1874, Preliminary report on the recent changes of level on the coast of Maine. . . : Boston Soc. Nat. Hist. Mem. 2, p. 320-340

—— 1875, Notes on some of the phenomena of elevation and subsidence of the continents: Boston Soc. Nat. Hist. Proc., v. 17, p. 288-292

—— 1890, General account of the fresh-water morasses of the United States, with a description of the Dismal Swamp district of Virginia and North Carolina: U.S. Geol. Surv., Ann. Rep. 10, p. 255-339

Shattuck, G. B., 1901, The Pleistocene problem of the North Atlantic coastal plain: Johns Hopkins Univ. Circ. 20, p. 69-75

Shimek, Bohumil, 1909, Aftonian sands and gravels in western Iowa: Geol. Soc. Amer. Bull., v. 20, p. 399-408

Silliman, Benjamin, 1821, Notice of "Geological essays . . .": Amer. J. Sci., v. 3, p. 47-57

Swinnerton, A. C., 1925, A method of estimating postglacial time: Science, v. 62, p. 566

Tylor, Alfred, 1868, On the Amiens gravel: Geol. Soc. London Quart. J., v. 24, p. 103-125

Upham, Warren, 1877, On the origin of kames or eskers in New Hampshire: Amer. Assoc. Adv. Sci. Proc., v. 25, p. 216-225

Whitney, J. D., 1865, Geological Survey of California: Geology, v. 1: Philadelphia, Sherman & Co., 498 p.

Whittlesey, Charles, 1860, On the drift cavities, or "potash kettles" of Wisconsin: Amer. Assoc. Adv. Sci. Proc., v. 13, p. 297-301

—— 1868, Depression of the ocean during the ice period: Amer. Assoc. Adv. Sci. Proc., v. 16, p. 92-97

Winchell, N. H., 1873, The geological and natural history survey of Minnesota: First Ann. Rep. (1872): 168 p.

Wright, G. F., 1881, An attempt to calculate approximately the date of the glacial era in eastern North America . . . : Amer. J. Sci., v. 21, p. 120-123

—— 1889, The ice age in North America: New York, Appleton, 622 p.

—— 1911, The ice age in North America and its bearings upon the antiquity of man: Oberlin, Ohio, Bibliotheca Sacra Co., 5th ed., 763 p.

PART I: GEOLOGY

GLACIATED AREA EAST OF THE ROCKY MOUNTAINS

QUATERNARY GEOLOGY OF NORTHERN GREAT PLAINS

GLACIATION OF MINNESOTA AND IOWA

OUTLINE OF GLACIAL GEOLOGY OF ILLINOIS AND WISCONSIN

PLEISTOCENE GEOLOGY OF INDIANA AND MICHIGAN

PLEISTOCENE DEPOSITS OF THE ERIE LOBE

QUATERNARY GEOLOGY OF NEW YORK

THE QUATERNARY OF NEW ENGLAND

UNGLACIATED EASTERN AND CENTRAL UNITED STATES

THE ATLANTIC COASTAL PLAIN AND THE APPALACHIAN HIGHLANDS IN THE QUATERNARY

RÉSUMÉ OF THE QUATERNARY GEOLOGY OF THE NORTHWESTERN GULF OF MEXICO PROVINCE

THE PLEISTOCENE IN NEBRASKA AND NORTHERN KANSAS

QUATERNARY OF THE SOUTHERN GREAT PLAINS

WESTERN UNITED STATES

GLACIATION OF THE ROCKY MOUNTAINS

THE CORDILLERAN ICE SHEET OF THE NORTHERN ROCKY MOUNTAINS AND RELATED QUATERNARY HISTORY OF THE COLUMBIA PLATEAU

NONGLACIAL QUATERNARY GEOLOGY OF THE SOUTHERN AND MIDDLE ROCKY MOUNTAINS

SNAKE RIVER PLAIN

QUATERNARY GEOLOGY OF THE GREAT BASIN

QUATERNARY GEOLOGY OF THE SOUTHWEST

THE QUATERNARY OF THE PACIFIC MOUNTAIN SYSTEM IN CALIFORNIA

THE GLACIAL HISTORY OF WESTERN WASHINGTON AND OREGON

THE QUATERNARY GEOLOGY AND ARCHAEOLOGY OF ALASKA

QUATERNARY GEOLOGY OF NORTHERN GREAT PLAINS *

R. W. LEMKE,[1] W. M. LAIRD,[2] M. J. TIPTON,[3] R. M. LINDVALL[1]

THIS PAPER outlines the Quaternary geology of South Dakota, North Dakota, and the part of Montana that lies east of the Rocky Mountains (Fig. 1). This area, which comprises about 580,000 km² (225,000 sq miles) lies chiefly in the northern Great Plains physiographic province. The eastern parts of North Dakota and South Dakota, however, are in the Central Lowland province.

Most of the discussion concerns the area that was covered by continental glaciers (Fig. 1). Alpine glaciation along the east flanks of the Rocky Mountains in Montana is discussed briefly for purposes of correlation with the continental glaciations.

The glacial map of the United States east of the Rocky Mountains (Flint, 1959) at a scale of 1:1,750,000 depicts the overall area. The most recent State maps of glacial deposits (scale 1:500,000) are those of South Dakota by Flint (1955), of North Dakota by Colton *et al.* (1963), and of Montana east of the Rocky Mountains by Colton *et al.* (1961).

PREGLACIAL SETTING AND DRAINAGE

The bedrock underlying the continental glacial drift is chiefly poorly consolidated and easily eroded shales, siltstones, and sandstones of Cretaceous and Tertiary age, but in southeastern North Dakota and northeastern South Dakota rocks of Paleozoic and of Precambrian age directly underlie the drift. The preglacial land surface was more dissected and relief was greater than that of the present drift surface; it probably resembled the present unglaciated areas of these states.

The pattern and direction of the surface drainage also was different from that following glaciation. Figure 2 shows the known and inferred courses of this ancestral drainage. In preglacial time the Cheyenne River in South Dakota

and all streams north of it in the report area drained into Hudson Bay in Canada (Alden, 1932, Pl. 1; Flint, 1949, p. 68; Benson, 1953, p. 165; Lemke, 1960, p. 108). Flint (1955, Pl. 7) indicated that all streams south of the Cheyenne River drained into the Gulf of Mexico. However, recent investigations by F. V. Steece and L. W. Howells and by L. S. Hedges (reports in preparation) in the central part of the James River Lowland indicate that the ancestral Bad River and possibly the ancestral White River also drained northward into the ancestral Cheyenne River instead of flowing south as shown on Figure 2. Thus, in preglacial time the present course of the Missouri River in South Dakota, North Dakota, and eastern Montana had not yet been established.

DESCRIPTION OF GLACIATED REGION

GREAT PLAINS AREA

Most of the drift surface of the northern Great Plains is gently rolling and slopes eastward from an altitude of about 1,200 m in Montana to approximately 300 m in eastern North and South Dakota. Drainage is into the Gulf of Mexico by way of the Missouri River, its tributaries, and the Mississippi River. Stream valleys together with a few mountain outliers and morainal hills and ridges break monotonous expanses of subdued topography. Much of the Missouri River valley is 2-3 km wide, having steep, locally dissected bedrock walls 100 to more than 200 m high. The floor of the valley is nearly flat and in most places is underlain by alluvium exceeding 30 m in thickness.

The Coteau du Missouri, the easternmost subdivision of the Great Plains province, is a topographically high belt of hummocky dead-ice morainal material and includes end moraines of several different ice advances. This feature, which is 30-120 km wide, extends from northeastern Montana to south-central South Dakota. It attains a maximum altitude of approximately 750 m in northwestern North Dakota. Its northeast-facing escarpment (Fig. 1), which forms the approximate boundary between the Great Plains province to the west and the Central Lowland province to the east, commonly is 60-90 m high in North Dakota but is generally somewhat less prominent in many parts of South Dakota. This escarpment acted as a buttress to advancing ice sheets and played an important role in deter-

* The authors have drawn freely upon many published and unpublished sources for information; all are gratefully acknowledged. We appreciate critical reading and suggestions by D. R. Crandell, J. T. McGill, R. D. Miller, R. Van Horn, F. V. Steece, S. J. Tuthill, and D. J. Varnes. However, the responsibility for the conclusions and interpretations drawn here rests with the authors.

[1] U.S. Geological Survey, Federal Center, Denver, Colorado.
[2] State Geological Survey, University of North Dakota, Grand Forks, North Dakota.
[3] South Dakota Geological Survey, Vermillion, South Dakota.

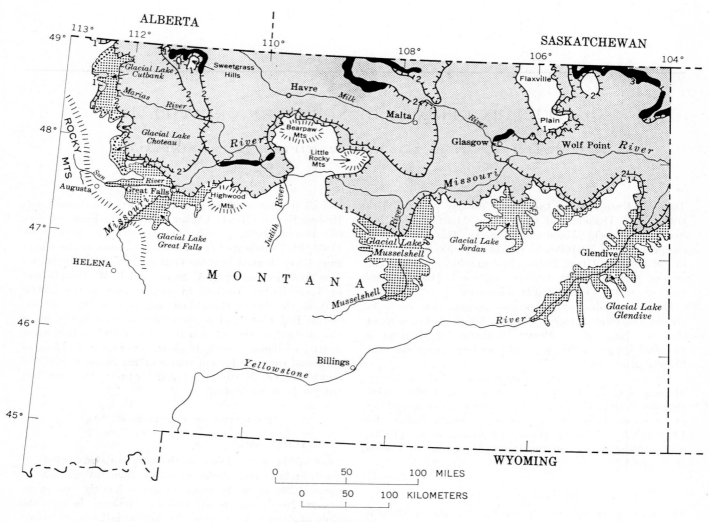

EXPLANATION

Drift of Wisconsin age

Drift of Illinoian age

Unglaciated areas

EDINBURG

Prominent end moraine

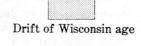

Approximate outer limit of significant glacial advance or readvance of Wisconsin age, not necessarily of stade rank.   Numbered from oldest to youngest. Dotted where covered by glacial lakes

Area of glacial lake

⌐ ⌐ ⌐ ⌐ ⌐ ⌐ ⌐ ⌐ ⌐ ⌐

Northeast-facing escarpment of Coteau du Missouri. (Marks the division between northern Great Plains and Central Lowlands Provinces)

Mountains and highlands

▲ ⑤ 10.0

Dated Carbon 14 locality
Circled number is coded to table in text.   The other number is the age of the sample to nearest thousand years before present

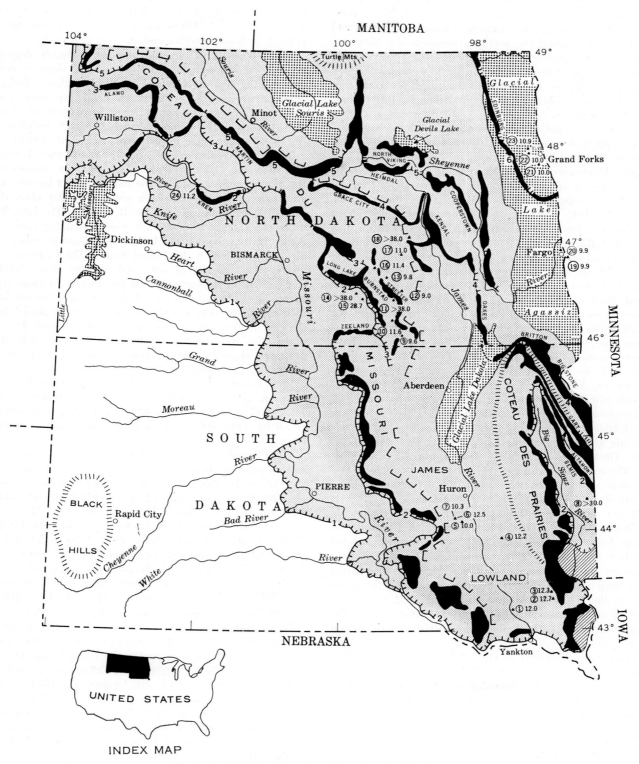

Figure 1. Map showing glaciated and unglaciated areas.

mining directions of ice advances and the positions of end moraines and other glacial features.

Drift on the Coteau du Missouri was formerly known as the Altamont moraine when it was believed that it represented a single large terminal moraine. Later, as the complex origin of the drift became better known, Townsend and Jenke (1951) named the northwest segment the Max moraine. In some places the highest and steepest parts of the Coteau du Missouri are underlain by topographically high bedrock, mostly of Tertiary age. These high areas are separated by several broad low sags underlain by Pierre Shale of Cretaceous age.

Several mountain outliers and other high areas are drift-free in the otherwise glaciated portion of Montana. These include the Sweetgrass Hills, Bearpaw, Highwood, and Little Rocky Mountains, and the Flaxville Plain (Fig. 1). Drift was deposited to an altitude of approximately 1,485 m (4,950 ft) along the north flank of West Butte in the Sweetgrass Hills at a time when glacier ice probably ranged in thickness from 300 to 500 m. Drift extends to an altitude of 1,275 m (4,250 ft) on the north side of the Bearpaw Mountains, indicating a minimum ice thickness of about 500 m on the surrounding plains. The continental glacier reached an altitude of 1,170 m (3,900 ft) along the north flank of the Highwood Mountains. If it is assumed that the ice sheet reached its maximum height against the north flanks of these three high areas at approximately the same time, the ice surface between these points must have sloped southward at less than 0.1%. Two areas of the Flaxville Plain in northeast Montana also were not covered by glacier ice. Ice reached a maximum altitude of approximately 870 m (2,900 ft) along the edges of this plain.

Proglacial lakes in the northern Great Plains formed in north-trending valleys when drainage was blocked by advancing glacier ice include Glacial Lakes Cut Bank, Choteau, Great Falls, Musselshell, Jordan, and Glendive (Fig. 1). The first three probably were dammed by at least two separate ice advances, resulting in the deposition of laminated silt and clay as much as 22 m thick.

Water reached a maximum altitude of approximately 1,170 m (3,900 ft) in Glacial Lakes Cut Bank, Choteau, and Great Falls, and these lakes were probably interconnected at their maximum heights. Glacial Lake Great Falls was partially lowered from its maximum height by the cutting of a deep spillway channel, Shonkin Sag, along the north side of the Highwood Mountains (Alden, 1932, p. 88). In part of the area covered by Glacial Lake Great Falls, lacustrine deposits both overlie and underlie a thick section of till.

The ephemeral nature of Glacial Lakes Musselshell, Jordan, and Glendive is suggested by the near absence of lacustrine deposits. The boundaries and existence of these lakes are based in large part upon the distribution of ice-rafted erratics, altitudes of supposed spillways, and topography.

CENTRAL LOWLAND AREA

In North Dakota the Central Lowland surface slopes northeastward from an altitude of about 570 m (1,900 ft) near the Coteau du Missouri to about 240 m (800 ft) on the floor of Glacial Lake Agassiz in the northeast corner of the State. Drainage is northward into Hudson Bay by way of the Souris and Red Rivers. The Turtle Mountains, which rise 90-120 m above the surrounding terrain, are a mesa-like high of Tertiary bedrock capped by dead-ice morainal material. Approximately half the Turtle Mountains lie in North Dakota and the rest in Canada.

Thick deposits of ground moraine, outwash deposits, well-defined end moraines, and glacial-lake deposits cover most of the Central Lowland in North Dakota. Bedrock outcrops are mostly confined to small exposures along stream valleys. In the Souris River loop north of Minot, drift (mostly till) commonly ranges from 30 to 75 m in thickness, and in some buried channels exceeds 150 m.

Three glacial lakes covered part of the Central Lowland area of North Dakota. Of these, Glacial Lake Agassiz was the most extensive and had the most complex history. The area covered by this lake is a remarkably flat plain that slopes imperceptibly toward the Red River. The lake floor in North Dakota is 50-75 km wide, extending from the South Dakota border northward into Canada, where its area exceeds that in the United States. The lacustrine deposits, which consist of silt, sand, and in places bedded clays, range in thickness from a few meters to more than 20 m. These deposits lie on till in some areas but on bedrock in others. Glacial Lake Souris was a proglacial lake that enlarged northward as the ice front receded. Its bed is very flat, local relief generally being less than 3 m. The associated deposits, which range in thickness from zero to at least 22 m, consist chiefly of sand with lesser quantities of fine gravel, silt, and clay. Deposits of Glacial Devils Lake are thin and patchy in most places (Aronow et al., 1963, p. 67); boulders and cobbles, derived from reworking of till by wave action, are scattered over the former lake floor.

The Central Lowland in South Dakota extends over the eastern third of the State. The most conspicuous feature is the Coteau des Prairies, a widespread highland area reaching altitudes of over 630 m (2,100 ft), which extends southeastward from the North Dakota border into Minnesota and northwest Iowa. It is bounded on the east by the Minnesota–Red River Lowland (Flint, 1955, p. 5) and on the west by the James River Lowland. Unlike the Coteau du Missouri, its height of 180-240 m is mainly due to a thick accumulation of glacial drift rather than to bedrock. Test holes on this plateau penetrated as much as 210 m of drift before reaching the underlying Pierre Shale.

The broad, arcuate James River lowland lies mostly at altitudes ranging from 390 to 420 m (1,300 to 1,400 ft). In the center of its northern part is the Glacial Lake Dakota Plain, which is 145 km long in South Dakota and extends an additional 25-30 km into North Dakota. The plain is generally 40-50 km wide; local relief rarely exceeds 3 m and in most places is less than 1 m. Lake sediments, which consist mostly of silt with some fine sand and clay, have an average thickness of about 12 m and a maximum thickness of about 30 m.

The Minnesota–Red River Lowland is a broad, low depression drained to the southeast by the Minnesota River and to the north by the Red River. The extreme northeast

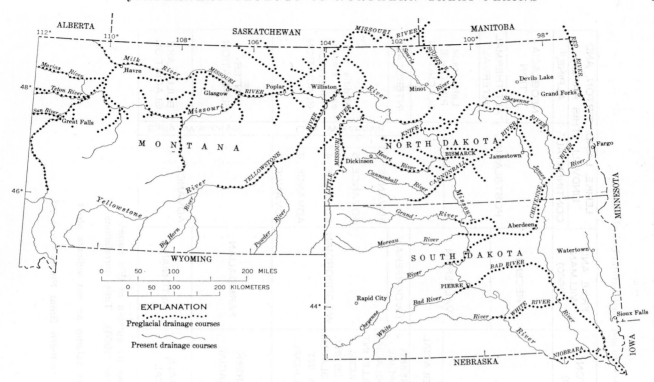

Figure 2. Map showing major preglacial drainage courses.

corner of South Dakota was occupied by the south end of Glacial Lake Agassiz, which was drained by a steep-sided trench, mostly 1-3 km wide and about 30 m deep. This trench now contains Lake Traverse and Big Stone Lake. The ridge between these lakes forms the present Continental Divide (altitude about 295 m or 980 ft) between northward drainage into Hudson Bay via the Red River and southward drainage into the Gulf of Mexico via the Minnesota and Mississippi Rivers.

PRE-WISCONSIN GLACIATIONS

Four glaciations have been recognized in the midwestern United States. These are, from oldest to youngest, the Nebraskan, Kansan, Illinoian, and Wisconsin, which are separated by the Aftonian, Yarmouth, and Sangamon Interglaciations, respectively. In the area of this report, Wisconsin glacial deposits predominate; therefore, the three older glaciations are discussed together.

Continental drift of pre-Wisconsin age has not been definitely recognized in either Montana or North Dakota but has been identified in a number of places in South Dakota (Flint, 1955, p. 30-41; Simpson, 1960, p. 74-77; Steece *et al.*, 1960).

The Nebraskan glacier probably covered most of South Dakota east of the Coteau du Missouri. Drift of Nebraskan age has been identified near Hartford 15 miles west of Sioux Falls (Steece *et al.*, 1960).

The Kansan glacier likewise probably covered all of South Dakota east of the Coteau du Missouri. Drift of Kansan age and sediments of the Yarmouth Interglaciation have been identified near Hartford (Steece *et al.*, 1960)

and at a number of other exposures in the vicinity of Sioux Falls.

Illinoian drift, unlike drift of previous glaciations, is exposed in southeastern South Dakota (Fig. 1), according to Steece (1959) and Tipton (1959, 1960). The identification of Illinoian drift in northeastern Nebraska (Flint *et al.*, 1959; E. C. Reed, oral communication, 1959) supports this belief. Flint (1955, p. 30) suggested possible glaciation during the Illinoian in South Dakota on the basis of a few outcrops of till, the widespread presence of Loveland Loess in nearby states, and drainage relations. Warren (1952) believed that the part of the Missouri River near Chamberlain (about 100 km southeast of Pierre) was formed during the Illinoian. However, White (1964) has suggested that the Missouri River was formed during early Wisconsin time.

From the distribution of till of pre-Wisconsin age in South Dakota, it is evident that glaciers advanced southward chiefly via the James River and Red River lowlands. Whether the glaciers topped the Coteau du Missouri and extended farther westward is unknown.

Till older than Wisconsin age has not been definitely identified in North Dakota. Clayton (1962, p. 55) described a till found in several exposures about 90 km southeast of Bismarck that may be older than Wisconsin. This till, which is overlain by 0.3 m of gravel stained with iron oxide and about 6 m of younger till, is well consolidated. Unlike tills in the area that are believed by Clayton to be of Wisconsin age, it has numerous widely spaced joints as much as 3 m long. The joint surfaces are coated with iron and manganese oxide. No carbonate leaching was observed in this till, but in all other respects it differs little from tills

TABLE 1

Classification and Correlation of the Wisconsin Glaciations in Midwestern and North-Central United States[a]

YEARS[b]	LEIGHTON (1933)	THWAITES (1943, 1946)	FLINT (1955)	LEIGHTON (1956, 1957)	LEIGHTON (1960)	FRYE AND WILLMAN (1960)	LEMKE, LAIRD, TIPTON, AND LINDVALL (THIS PAPER) CONTINENTAL[c]	ALPINE[d]
0			RECENT			RECENT	POSTGLACIAL	NEOGLACIATION
5000								"ALTITHERMAL INTERVAL"
10,000	MANKATO	5th-MANKATO (or VALDERS) 4th VALDERS	MANKATO	VALDERS	VALDERS GLACIAL	VALDERAN		Late stage, PINEDALE GLACIATION
		TWO CREEKS	INTERVAL	TWO CREEKS	TWO CREEKS INTERGLACIAL	TWOCREEKAN	ADVANCE 6	INTERSTADE
	INTERSTADIAL			MANKATO	MANKATO GLACIAL		ADVANCE 5	
15,000	CARY	3d-CARY	CARY	CARY	BOWMANVILLE INT. / CARY GLACIAL / ST. CHARLES INT.	WOODFORDIAN	ADVANCE 4	Middle and early stages, PINEDALE GLACIATION
	INTERSTADIAL		INTERVAL	INTERSTADIAL			ADVANCE 3	
	TAZEWELL	2d-TAZEWELL	TAZEWELL	TAZEWELL	TAZEWELL GLACIAL / GARDENA INT.		ADVANCE 2	
20,000	INTERSTADIAL		INTERVAL	INTERSTADIAL	IOWAN GLACIAL			
	IOWAN (OF ILL.)	1st IOWAN	IOWAN	IOWAN (OF ILL.)				
25,000					FARM CREEK INTERGLACIAL	FARMDALIAN		INTER-GLACIATION
30,000					FARMDALE GLACIAL	ALTONIAN	ADVANCE 1	BULL LAKE GLACIATION
70,000								

(Time scale notes: ------- 40,000 yrs. ------- Type Iowan drift of Iowa in this age or older.)

(Late Wisconsin / Early Wisconsin divisions marked in CONTINENTAL[c] column.)

[a] From Wright (1957) and Frye and Willman (1963); modifications and additions by authors of this paper.

[b] Time scale in radiocarbon years before present; taken from Frye and Willman (1963). Time correlations of equivalent units of other classifications are approximate.

[c] Units used here restricted to discussion in this paper. Position of units in column do not indicate strict time correlation or necessarily direct correlation with other classifications.

[d] Tentative correlation based upon tracing of continental drift sheets across northern Great Plains--work of G. M. Richmond (this volume), and R. W. Lemke (this paper).

of Wisconsin age. Compact jointed till that has a manganese coating along joint surfaces underlies an upper Wisconsin till north of Minot (Lemke and Kaye, 1958, p. 93-98). Invertebrate fossils assigned to the Yarmouth Interglaciation have been found in terrace deposits in southwestern North Dakota (Tuthill *et al.*, in press).

Continental till of pre-Wisconsin age has not been positively identified in Montana. A till possibly older than Wisconsin has been reported in northeastern Montana along Smoke Creek (Howard, 1960, p. 23; Witkind, 1959, p. 18, 27). As discussed by Howard, the material in question may actually not be a till; however, it underlies a till of Wisconsin age.

The belief that glaciers of pre-Wisconsin age reached southward at least to a point about 90 km north of the northern boundary of Montana is supported by exposures of drift of pre-Wisconsin age along Oldman River in the vicinity of Lethbridge, Alberta. Stalker (1963) described measured sections in this area where, on the basis of stratigraphic relations and C14 dates, continental drifts of Nebraskan, Kansan, and Illinoian ages may be present.

WISCONSIN GLACIATIONS

Six distinct and separate glacial advances during Wisconsin time are postulated to have taken place in the area (Fig. 1). The lithological similarity of the tills, the near absence of loess sheets and fossil soils between the drift sheets, and irregularities in some of the C14 dates have precluded distinguishing drift sheets by the more conventional method of superposition. Therefore, it has been necessary to differentiate drift sheets chiefly by such features as the presence of prominent end moraines and ice-marginal channels, the trends of moraines, drumlins, and eskers, the relative development and modification of drainage systems, the relations of valley trains and gravel terraces, and the variations and ruggedness of the topography.

The tills of all the ice advances are very similar. Laboratory analyses and field observations indicate that they consist typically of nearly equal parts of clay, silt, and sand (Lemke, 1960, p. 46; Winters, 1963, p. 28). Gravel-sized materials generally constitute less than 5%, and cobbles and boulders less than 1%. The unoxidized tills are generally dark olive gray to bluish gray. Oxidation of iron results in a buff or drab yellow color, which commonly extends to depths of 10-15 m and which generally is the only discernible weathering effect. Partial cementation by caliche 0.5-1.5 m below the surface is common.

NOMENCLATURE PROBLEMS

Opinion differs as to the age and correlations of continental drift sheets of Wisconsin age in the United States. Moreover, recent changes in stratigraphic nomenclature and shifts in the stratigraphic position of certain glacial deposits have added to the problems (Table 1). Because of these problems and the long distances to type localities or dated localities, we have merely numbered the different ice advances. Each ice advance (numbered from oldest to youngest) will be described separately, together with a tentative correlation with the stratigraphic sequence of other workers. It should be emphasized that a particular advance may or may not be of stadial rank. In some instances it may represent an advance of only a few kilometers beyond a former glacier terminus, and thus it may have little regional significance.

ADVANCE 1

The outer margin of advance 1, as shown on Figure 1, marks the maximum extent of glaciation during Wisconsin time. Its position is based upon the outer limit of glacial erratics, except that in the southeastern part of South Dakota, where erratics are scarce, it is marked by end-moraine remnants. The position of this margin in South Dakota is based largely on the work of Flint (1955, Pl. 1), as modified in the southeastern part of the State by Tipton (1959, 1960), Steece (1959), and Steece *et al.* (1960). In North Dakota the position of the margin is based chiefly on the work of Benson (1953, p. 184-194) and Howard (1960, Pl. 1). Laird (this paper) believes that the limits of glaciation near the southern boundary of the State should be several kilometers west of the position as now shown; however, accurate determination of this line must await more detailed investigation. In Montana the limits are based on the work of Colton *et al.* (1961, map) and an unpublished map by Richmond and Lemke.

In North and South Dakota the drift sheet of advance 1 forms a northwest-trending belt, 90-160 km wide, west of the Coteau du Missouri. It also occurs in the Big Sioux River valley of eastern South Dakota. The till is thin or missing in most places owing to erosion or non-deposition. The advance of ice over much of these two states, especially west of the Missouri River, is revealed only by erratic boulders and a few stratified ice-contact deposits. East of the Missouri River, in areas where the till is thicker and more continuous, surface drainage generally is well integrated. In Montana the belt of exposed drift is generally narrower than in the other two States but otherwise is similar.

Present evidence based on three radiocarbon dates (Table 2) suggests that advance 1 occurred during the latter part of early Wisconsin time. One sample (W-990) gave a date of more than 38,000 years B.P. (before the present), one (W-1045) of 28,700 ± 800 years B.P. in southern North Dakota, and one (W-115) of more than 30,000 years B.P. in South Dakota. The drift of this advance is correlated with the "Altonian substage" of Frye and William (1963, p. 503) and the "Farmdale glacial substage" of Leighton (1960).

Richmond and Lemke on their unpublished map have correlated the continental drifts in Montana with alpine drift units in the adjacent Rocky Mountains. The drift of advance 1 correlates with that of the late stage of the Bull Lake Glaciation in the Glacier National Park area, Montana. Richmond (1960, p. 223) also believes that this drift correlates with the Iowan Till of Iowa, which has been dated as >29,000 years B.P. (Ruhe and Scholtes, 1959).

ADVANCE 2

The limits of advance 2 are not known with certainty and are particularly difficult to distinguish from the limits of advance 3, in both South Dakota and southern North Dakota and also in Montana, where individual lobes advanced into the State from Canada. In South Dakota the

TABLE 2

Radiocarbon Dates[a]

Map No.[b]	Sample No.[c]	Location	Material dated	Lithology of enclosing material	Depth below surface (meters)	Collector	Date (years B.P.)
1	W-1189	NW¼ sec. 29, T. 97 N., R. 57 W., Hutchinson County, S.D.	Wood fragments	Till above and gravel below	57.6	R. A. Schoon 1961	12,050 ± 400
2	Y-595	SW¼ sec. 15, T. 98 N., R. 53 W., Turner County, S.D.	*Picea* or *Larix*	Outwash	9.6	G. A. Avery	12,760 ± 120
3	Y-452	Parker, S.D. NW¼ sec. 28, T. 99 N., R. 53 W., Turner County, S.D.	Spruce wood	Till	7.8	H. A. Mateer; G. A. Avery	12,330 ± 180
4	W-801	NW¼ sec. 36, T. 106 N., R. 58 W., Miner County, S.D.	Wood fragments	Silt lens in till	3.6	M. J. Tipton 1958	12,200 ± 400
5	W-1033	SE¼ sec. 3, T. 107 N., R. 62 W., Sanborn, S.D.	Mollusk shells	Lake sediments in outwash	0.6	F. V. Steece 1959	10,060 ± 300
6	W-987	NE¼ sec. 26, T. 108 N., R. 63 W., Jerauld County, S.D.	Wood fragments	60-cm soil(?) between two tills	12.3	Wayne McDaniel 1951	12,530 ± 350
7	W-983	NE¼ sec. 26, T. 108 N., R. 63 W., Jerauld County, S.D. (Same well as sample W-987)	Wood fragments	Soil(?) horizon between upper unoxidized till and lower oxidized till	12.3	L. W. Howells 1960	10,350 ± 300
8	W-115	Sec. 26, T. 110 N., R. 48 W., Brookings County, S.D.	Spruce wood	"Drift"	41.4	G. A. Avery	>30,000
9	W-1149	SE¼ sec. 36, T. 130 N., R. 68 W., McIntosh County, N.D.	Shells	Sand	3+	S. J. Tuthill; Lee Clayton	9,620 ± 350
10	W-974	NW¼ sec. 20, T. 132 N., R. 68 W., McIntosh County, N.D.	Shells-molluscan	Perched lake silts	0.6-2.4	John Bonneville	11,650 ± 310
11	W-1021	SE¼ sec. 9, T. 134 N., R. 68 W., Logan County, N.D.	Peat	Pitted outwash gravel	13.5	Lee Clayton	>38,000
12	W-1019	NW¼ sec. 20, T. 135 N., R. 67 W., Logan County, N.D.	Clam shells *in situ*	Sand and silt of stagnation drift	0.52	Lee Clayton	9,000 ± 300
13	W-954	SE¼ sec. 29, T. 137 N., R. 69 W., Stutsman County, N.D.	Clam shells	In clay with till at base	0.3	Charles Huxel; H. C. Winters	9,870 ± 290
14	W-990	SW¼ sec. 32, T. 135 N., R. 72 W., Logan County, N.D.	Black peat	Outwash sand and gravel	1.5+	Lee Clayton	>38,000
15	W-1045	NW¼ sec. 24, T. 134 N., R. 72 W., Logan County, N.D.	Peat underlying iron-cemented till	Gravels	1.5-3.3	John Bonneville	28,700 ± 800
16	W-542	SW¼ sec. 25, T. 138 N., R. 71 W., Kidder County, N.D.	Wood	Sand overlying till	3.6-4.5	R. W. Lemke	11,480 ± 300
17	W-956	SE¼ sec. 17, T. 139 N., R. 67 W., Stutsman County, N.D.	Clam shells	Stagnation moraine outwash	Near surface	Charles Huxel; H. C. Winters	11,070 ± 300
18	W-1020	NE¼ sec. 21, T. 141 N., R. 66 W., Stutsman County, N.D.	Wood	Outwash under till	15	R. W. Schmidt	>38,000
19	W-388	Moorhead, Clay County, Minn.	Wood	Lake clay	?	W. F. Libby	9,930 ± 280
20	W-993	C sec. 20, T. 140 N., R. 48 W., Cass County, N.D.	Wood	Silt and clay	8.4	John Brophy	9,900 ± 400
21	W-1005	SW¼ sec. 14, T. 150 N., R. 51 W., N.D.	Wood	Beach gravel	2.1	F. D. Holland; W. M. Laird	10,050 ± 300
22	W-900	NW¼ sec. 31, T. 152 N., R. 52 W.; 15 miles west of Grand Forks, N.D.	Wood	Lacustrine sand over till	3	R. W. Lemke	10,080 ± 280
23	W-723	NE¼ sec. 25, T. 152 N., R. 53 W.; 15 miles west of Grand Forks, N.D.	Wood	Lacustrine sand	3	R. W. Lemke	10,960 ± 300
24	W-402	SE¼ sec. 30, T. 146 N., R. 89 W., Mercer County, N.D.	Gastropods	Marl lens in till	?	W. E. Benson	11,220 ± 300

[a] Tenuous nature of stratigraphic information on glacial deposits makes correlation of radiocarbon-dated localities with numbered ice advances impractical at present.

[b] Keyed to Figure 1.

[c] W = U.S. Geological Survey
Y = Yale University

placement of the limits of advance 2 is based largely on the work of Flint (1955). The outer margin of the Bemis moraine marks the maximum advance in the eastern part of the State, but in North Dakota the limit of the advance is not well defined. The Long Lake and Zeeland end moraines of Clayton (1962, p. 26-30) probably mark the distal edge in southern North Dakota; farther north, the limit is tentatively placed at the outer margin of the Krem moraine.

Three separate ice lobes moved into Montana during

advance 2. The easternmost lobe advanced southwestward around the east side of the Flaxville Plain. A second lobe advanced around the east side of the Sweetgrass Hills and was split into two sublobes by the Bearpaw and Little Rocky Mountains. The direction of advance of one sublobe east of the Bearpaw Mountains is well marked by a southeast-trending boulder train, 90 km long, heading at an isolated intrusive rock mass known as Snake Butte (Knechtel, 1942). The southeast direction of advance of this sublobe is further indicated by the presence of elongate southeast-trending drumlins. In contrast, similar drumlins formed by the other sublobe trend southwestward (Colton *et al.*, 1961). The third major lobe advanced south and southeastward around the west side of the Sweetgrass Hills, but left no well-defined terminal moraine.

Surface drainage on this drift is considerably less well integrated than that on the drift of advance 1. The ground moraine surface is characterized by numerous undrained depressions, most of which are shallow and have gently sloping sides. Local relief on some end moraines is as much as 15 m. The till in most places is 6-15 m thick, but locally it is considerably thicker.

The age of the drift is uncertain. In Iowa, Ruhe and Scholtes (1959) assigned the Bemis and Altamont moraines to the Cary Stade. On this basis, at least the outer belt of drift of advance 2 as outlined in part by the Bemis moraine in South Dakota (Fig. 1) would be Cary in age. In the Big Sioux Valley of South Dakota, Tipton (1958a, 1958b) and Steece (1958a, 1958b, 1958c) were unable to locate the break between drifts of Iowan and Tazewell age shown by Flint (1955, Pl. 1) in front of the Bemis moraine. They therefore assigned the glacial deposits in front of the Bemis moraine to the Iowan Stade.

The drift of advance 2 correlates with the early stade of the Pinedale Glaciation (Richmond, 1960) in the area just east of the Rocky Mountains in Montana. This is roughly correlative with the early part of the "Woodfordian stage" of Frye and Willman (1963).

ADVANCE 3

In North Dakota advance 3 is more conspicuously represented than any other glacial advance; its drift covers the entire Coteau du Missouri. The prominent Burnstad moraine (Fig. 1), which overlaps part of the Long Lake moraine of advance 2, is the terminal moraine in southern North Dakota, and the Alamo moraine marks the outer margin of the advance in the northwestern part of the State. The conspicuous Streeter moraine is interpreted as a recessional moraine of this advance.

Much of the prominence of the drift of this advance in northwestern North Dakota and northeastern Montana results from buried bedrock hills. In the southern part of North Dakota, however, this prominence reflects thick accumulations of drift (Clayton, 1962, p. 27).

Larger moraines, such as the Burnstad, commonly are made up of several sub-parallel, steep-sided ridges having a local relief of about 6 m. The Streeter moraine, a steep-sided ridge on which are superimposed small, looping, parallel ridges, is as much as 90 m high. Dead-ice moraine, also called stagnation moraine (Colton *et al.*, 1963; Clay-

ton, 1962, p. 34) forms the topography characteristic of much of the Coteau du Missouri. Here, drainage is almost entirely unintegrated, local relief is sharp, and kettles and other undrained depressions are innumerable. Ice-contact faces locally give the surface a terraced appearance (Clayton, 1962). This type of drift surface, we believe, resulted from large-scale glacial stagnation, in which superglacial till has collapsed into depressions left by isolated melting ice blocks.

The outer margin of the advance in South Dakota has not been determined. It seems likely, however, that an ice lobe moved southward into the James River lowland during this advance. Tentative correlations by Flint (1955, p. 118) suggest that either the Altamont moraine or the Gary moraine marks the terminus of advance 3 in northeastern South Dakota.

Radiocarbon dates confound attempts to date the drift sheet formed by advance 3. Material from two samples (W-1020 and W-1021) give dates greater than 38,000 years. These samples may have been contaminated by old carbon, possibly detrital lignite fragments of Tertiary age. The remainder of the dates fall largely between 10,000 and 12,000 years. Almost all of those about 10,000 years were obtained from organic matter in outwash overlying till and therefore are minimum ages. Also, several samples were obtained from areas of dead-ice moraine and may represent outwash from isolated, partially or wholly buried blocks of ice that survived melting through a considerable period of time—possibly well into the Two Creeks Interstade.

If the Altamont or Gary moraines mark the outer limits of advance 3, then the drift sheet should be assigned to the Cary Stade on the basis of work by Wright and Ruhe (this volume) and would correlate with the "Woodfordian stage" of Frye and Willman (1963).

ADVANCE 4

The terminus of advance 4 is marked by the Big Stone moraine in South Dakota and by the Britton, Oakes, Kensal, and Grace City moraines in North Dakota. The drift of this advance is exposed in a belt mostly 25 to 65 km wide. The orientation of drumlins, washboard moraines, and end moraines indicates that the ice advanced and retreated in two lobes, one from the northwest and the other from the northeast. A narrow interlobate area between the Grace City moraine and the Kensal moraine marks the junction of these lobes.

Leighton (1957, p. 1037-1038) suggested that the Big Stone moraine marks the maximum advance of ice of Valders age. If true, all the drift of advance 4 would belong to the Valders Stade. Elson (1957, p. 999-1002), however, believed that Valders ice did not reach northwestern Minnesota or North Dakota, an interpretation in accord with work done in Minnesota by Wright and Ruhe (this volume). Studies in Saskatchewan by several workers, as summarized by H. A. Roed (written communication), indicate that an ice lobe, which a radiocarbon date suggests may have been Valders ice, did not reach into North Dakota. W. M. Laird, however, believes that all drift sheets younger than that of advance 3 are recessional moraines from this main advance. Resolution of this problem must await additional regional studies and radiocarbon dates.

ADVANCE 5

Moraines of advance 5 sharply truncate the moraines and other drift of advance 4. The glacier of advance 5 moved into North Dakota as two distinct lobes split by the Turtle Mountains, although the mountains were probably at least partly overridden during the maximum stand of the ice. West of the Turtle Mountains, the Souris River lobe (Lemke, 1960, p. 111) advanced southeastward and formed the Martin terminal moraine. East of the Turtle Mountains, the Leeds lobe advanced south and southwestward and formed the Heimdal and Cooperstown terminal moraines. We believe that the North Viking moraine is a recessional moraine of this lobe. The trends of parallel linear drumlins (Lemke, 1958), some of which are several kilometers long, and of arcuate washboard moraines provide a good record of the direction of advance and retreat of the two lobes.

Drainage on drift of advance 5 is almost completely unintegrated. Kettle holes are sharply defined, and many have steep walls. All the till is calcareous to the surface and consists in most places of about 25% clay, 40% silt, 30% sand, and 5% gravel (Lemke, 1960, p. 48). Erratic boulders, commonly as much as 1 m long, are mostly of granite or limestone from Canada. The till of the Souris River lobe contains abundant lignite chips, whereas the till of the Leeds lobe generally does not.

During glacier recession, Glacial Lake Souris and Glacial Devils Lake came into existence. Drainage of Glacial Devils Lake was for a short time down the James River; later drainage was into Glacial Lake Agassiz via spillways and the Sheyenne River (Aronow, 1963). Glacial Lake Souris expanded northward into Saskatchewan as the ice front receded into Canada. Early drainage was down the Sheyenne River into the southern part of Glacial Lake Agassiz. Later, when the area north of the Turtle Mountains became ice-free, Glacial Lake Souris drained northward into Manitoba and entered Glacial Lake Agassiz at the northern border of North Dakota.

If Valders ice did not extend into North Dakota, the drift of advance 5 must have been deposited during late Mankato time. Although this drift represents a distinct advance, the glacier may have retreated only a few kilometers or tens of kilometers between advances 4 and 5.

ADVANCE 6

The discontinuous, looping Edinburg moraine in northeastern North Dakota defines the outer margin of the last glacier to occupy the State. The fact that the generally north-south trending moraine definitely truncates a series of northeast-southwest trending arcuate washboard moraines, which indicate ice recession toward the northwest, suggests that the Edinburg moraine does not represent merely a halt in the recession of the glacier of advance 5. The Holt moraine in Minnesota (Leverett, 1932, p. 117) and the Darlingford moraine in Manitoba seem to be continuations of the Edinburg moraine.

The Edinburg moraine is poorly defined because much of it is thinly veneered by lacustrine deposits of Glacial Lake Agassiz II of Elson (1938), who believed this stand of the lake was formed by melt waters draining from Valders ice in Manitoba. If so, advance 6 is probably of Mankato age.

This implies that advances 3 to 6 occurred during a relatively short time interval and that succeeding advances probably were separated by a glacier recession of only a few kilometer or tens of kilometers. If, on the other hand, drift of advances 4 through 6 was deposited during all of post-Cary time, then deposition of drift during these ice advances might have occurred over a considerably longer period of time.

POSTGLACIAL HISTORY OF GLACIATED AREA

The topography in the area covered by the last five glacial advances has been little modified since deglaciation. Nearly all glacial features are well preserved, and there has been little or no downcutting by present-day streams. Sand dunes have formed on some of the glacial-lake floors and outwash plains in North and South Dakota, but most of these probably formed soon after deglaciation of the respective area.

Periglacial features are nearly all confined to the drift sheet of advance 1 and adjacent nonglaciated areas. Frost-induced involutions in gravels and frost wedges in weathered bedrock form an irregular polygonal pattern in some areas in central Montana (Schafer, 1949). Similar features are sparingly present in drift of advance 1 in the same area but are lacking in drift of the younger advances.

Isolated remnants of two postglacial ash falls, described by Powers and Wilcox (1964), are preserved in the western part of the report area of Montana (see Wilcox, this volume). The older of these, derived from Glacier Peak volcano in Washington, is found on Pinedale drift (M. R. Mudge, oral communication) near Augusta, Montana. The younger ash, which came from the Mount Mazama (Crater Lake) eruption in Oregon about 6,600 years ago (W-858) is present at Galata, Montana (Horberg and Robie, 1955; Powers and Wilcox, 1964). In a roadcut 32 km southwest of Great Falls, Montana, Lemke discovered a well-developed paleosol that directly underlies the Mazama ash and in turn is underlain by alluvial deposits. This paleosol is believed to be of pre-Altithermal age. The pre-ash alluvium, as well as a post-ash alluvium, is widespread in the Great Falls area. These alluvial deposits once partially filled many minor tributaries incised into the older drifts but are now actively being removed by headward erosion.

UNGLACIATED AREAS

Several mountain outliers and parts of the high plains in the glaciated area of Montana were too high to be covered by continental ice sheets. The mountain outliers, which reach altitudes of 1,800 to 2,250 m (6,000 to 7,500 ft), consist chiefly of volcanic and sedimentary rocks. The Flaxville Plain, a driftless area in northeastern Montana, is surfaced by the Flaxville Gravel of Miocene or Pliocene age underlain by strata of early Tertiary age.

Areas beyond the limits of glaciation in the three States include approximately the western half of South Dakota, the southwestern corner of North Dakota, and approximately the southern half of Montana (Fig. 1).

The unglaciated area in South Dakota lies west of the Missouri River and ranges in altitude from about 600 m (2,000 ft) in the east to 900 m (3,000 ft) in the west. Isolated to closely spaced hills and buttes rise to altitudes of more than 1,080 m (3,600 ft). Nearly all the streams have cut canyons 60 m or more in depth. Extensive badland topography has developed, particularly along the Cheyenne and White Rivers; the most spectacular exposures are east of the Black Hills in the Badlands National Monument. Three to four sets of discontinuous, nonglacial fluvial terraces, which range in age from middle Tertiary to Pleistocene, flank most of the main streams. The terraces are underlain by gravels derived in part from the Black Hills, which rise to an altitude of 2,172 m (7,241 ft) and consist of sedimentary and crystalline rocks.

Sand dunes derived from underlying sandy bedrock abound in the extreme south-central part of South Dakota, where they form an undulating surface of low relief. Springs flow from their northern margin.

The unglaciated upland of North Dakota is a continuation of the upland in South Dakota. It slopes gently eastward at altitudes mostly between 840 and 750 m (2,800 and 2,500 ft). Isolated erosion remnants, which reach a maximum altitude of 1,060 m (3,530 ft), surmount the upland. The gently rolling upland surface appears to be in a stage of late maturity. Drainage patterns are well developed, but at present there is relatively little surface runoff because of the semiarid climate. Extensive badlands have formed in many places adjacent to the Missouri and Little Missouri Rivers. The upland is modified by a number of wide, southeast-trending valleys, some of which, now devoid of streams, were glacial melt-water diversion channels utilized by the Missouri, Yellowstone, and Little Missouri Rivers and other streams. Some valleys were probably pre-Pleistocene stream courses, inasmuch as they contain extensive terrace gravels of lithology different from the gravels of glacial origin. These gravels may have been derived from the Black Hills or from outcrops of conglomerate in the Tertiary bedrock.

The unglaciated eastern part of Montana is much the same as the unglaciated parts of North Dakota and South Dakota. The Yellowstone River and its tributaries have cut trenches 1.5-6.5 km wide and a few hundred meters deep. Episodes of cutting and filling have produced several terraces. Broad troughs through the divides between adjacent streams were utilized by water draining from proglacial lakes.

Gravel deposits of several ages from stream terraces along the Yellowstone River in southeastern Montana. Gravel deposits occur in isolated patches along the western side of the lower reaches of the Yellowstone valley, 200 to 240 m above the present valley bottom (Howard, 1960, p. 10). These gravels form the No. 1 bench of Alden (1932, map), who showed remnants of these gravels extending up the Yellowstone valley past Billings nearly to the southern border of Montana. They are now regarded as being equivalent to the Miocene or Pliocene Flaxville Gravel of northeastern Montana. Younger gravels of similar lithology occur in terraces at a lower level along the Yellowstone valley and some of its tributaries. These gravels, which form the No. 2 bench of Alden (1932, p. 44), also extend along the Yellowstone valley nearly to the southern border of the State. In the lower reaches of the Yellowstone valley they

are called the Cartwright Gravel by Howard (1960, p. 19-21). Although adequate evidence of the age is lacking, they probably are of Pleistocene age and were derived from the southwest in pre-Wisconsin time. Still lower and younger terrace gravels in the Yellowstone valley, mapped as bench No. 3 by Alden, have been named the Crane Creek Gravel of Pleistocene age in the lower reaches of the Yellowstone by Howard. The Crane Creek Gravel, whose surface is about 7 m above the present floodplain of the Yellowstone, is superficially similar to the other nonglacial or largely nonglacial gravels of the region and does not contain glacial pebbles south of the glacial limit. Correlative gravel terraces along the Missouri River east of Glasgow are overlain by till that probably was deposited by glacial advance 2.

Mountain outliers in the northern Great Plains of westcentral Montana include the Highwood, the Bearpaw, and the Little Rocky Mountains (Fig. 1) as well as the Judith, North and South Moccasin, and Big Snowy Mountains (not shown on map) which lie in the nonglaciated High Plains area to the south. Three well-developed pediments of different ages flank the mountain outliers in places and merge with alluvial fans and terraces in the adjacent plains. These pediments correspond to benches No. 1, 2, and 3 of Alden (1932, Pl. 1). We believe bench No. 1 is equivalent to the Flaxville Plain and benches No. 2 and 3 are Pleistocene in age.

Alden (1932) has correlated a terrace along the Sun River between Great Falls and Augusta with his bench No. 3. This terrace was deposited by melt-water from alpine ice during the Bull Lake Glaciation (M. R. Mudge, oral communication). Immediately west of Augusta the terrace is overlain by till deposited by alpine ice of the early stade of Pinedale Glaciation. The gravels of this terrace were traced by Mudge and Lemke down the Sun River valley and were found to overlie and partly interfinger with lacustrine deposits laid down in Glacial Lake Great Falls during the time of advance 1. If these correlations are correct, the Sun River terrace (Alden's bench No. 3) is correlative with the Iowan till of Ruhe and Scholtes (1959) in Iowa.

REFERENCES

Alden, W. C., 1932, Physiography and glacial geology of eastern Montana and adjacent areas: U.S. Geol. Surv. Prof. Pap. 174, 133 p.

Aronow, Saul, 1963, Late Pleistocene glacial drainage in the Devils Lake region, North Dakota: Geol. Soc. Amer. Bull., v. 74, p. 859-873

Aronow, Saul, Dennis, P. E., and Akin, P. D., 1953, Geology and ground-water resources of the Minnewuakan area, Benson County, North Dakota: North Dakota Geol. Surv. Ground-Water Stud. 19, 125 p.

Benson, W. E., 1953, Geology of the Knife River area, North Dakota: U.S. Geol. Surv. Open-File Rep., 323 p.; also Yale Univ., Ph.D. thesis

Clayton, Lee, 1962, Glacial geology of Logan and McIntosh Counties, North Dakota: North Dakota Geol. Surv. Bull. 37, 84 p.

Colton, R. B., Lemke, R. W., and Lindvall, R. M., 1961,

Glacial map of Montana east of the Rocky Mountains: U.S. Geol. Surv. Misc. Geol. Inv. Map I-327

—— 1963, Preliminary glacial map of North Dakota: U.S. Geol. Surv. Misc. Geol. Inv. Map I-331

Elson, J. A., 1957, Lake Agassiz and the Mankato-Valders problem: Science, v. 126, p. 999-1002

—— 1958, Pleistocene history of southwestern Manitoba, *in* Guidebook 9th Ann. Field Conf., Midwestern Friends of the Pleistocene: North Dakota Geol. Surv. Misc. Ser. 10, p. 62-73

Flint, R. F., 1949, Pleistocene drainage diversions in South Dakota: Geogr. Annaler, v. 31, p. 56-74

—— 1955, Pleistocene geology of eastern South Dakota: U.S. Geol. Surv. Prof. Pap. 262, 173 p.

Flint, R. F., *et al.*, 1959, Glacial map of the United States east of the Rocky Mountains [scale 1:1,750,000]: Geol. Soc. America

Frye, J. C., and Willman, H. B., 1960, Classification of the Wisconsinan Stage in the Lake Michigan glacial lobe: Illinois State Geol. Surv. Circ. 285, 16 p.

—— 1963, Development of Wisconsinan classification in Illinois related to radiocarbon chronology: Geol. Soc. Amer. Bull., v. 74, p. 501-505

Hedges, L. S., in preparation, Pleistocene geology of Beadle County, South Dakota: South Dakota Geol. Surv. Rep. Inv.

Horberg, C. L., and Robie, R. A., 1955, Postglacial volcanic ash in the Rocky Mountain piedmont, Montana and Alberta: Geol. Soc. Amer. Bull., v. 66, p. 949-955

Howard, A. D., 1960, Cenozoic history of northeastern Montana and northwestern North Dakota with emphasis on the Pleistocene: U.S. Geol. Surv. Prof. Pap. 326, 107 p.

Knechtel, M. M., 1942, Snake Butte boulder train and related glacial phenomena, north-central Montana: Geol. Soc. Amer. Bull., v. 53, p. 917-935

Leighton, M. M., 1933, The naming of the subdivisions of the Wisconsin glacial age: Science, v. 77, p. 168

—— 1956, Radiocarbon dates and Pleistocene chronological problems in the Mississippi Valley region; a reply: J. Geol., v. 64, p. 193-194

—— 1957, Radiocarbon dates of Mankato drift in Minnesota: Science, v. 125, p. 1037-1039

—— 1960, The classification of the Wisconsin glacial stage of north-central United States: J. Geol., v. 68, p. 529-552

Lemke, R. W., 1958, Narrow linear drumlins near Velva, North Dakota: Amer. J. Sci., v. 256, p. 270-283

—— 1960, Geology of the Souris River area, North Dakota: U.S. Geol. Surv. Prof. Pap. 325, p. 138

Lemke, R. W., and Kaye, C. A., 1958, Two tills in the Donnybrook area, North Dakota, *in* Guidebook 9th Ann. Field Conf., Midwestern Friends of the Pleistocene: North Dakota Geol. Surv. Misc. Ser. 10, p. 93-98

Leverett, Frank, 1932, Quaternary geology of Minnesota and parts of adjacent states: U.S. Geol. Surv. Prof. Pap. 161, 149 p.

Powers, H. A., and Wilcox, R. E., 1964, Volcanic ash from Mount Mazama (Crater Lake) and from Glacier Peak: Science, v. 144, p. 1334-1336

Richmond, G. M., 1960, Correlation of alpine and continental glacial deposits of Glacier National Park and adjacent High Plains, Montana: U.S. Geol. Surv. Prof. Pap. 400-B, p. 223-224

——, this volume, Glaciation of the Northern Rocky Mountains

Ruhe, R. V., and Scholtes, W. H., 1959, Important elements in the classification of the Wisconsin glacial stage—a discussion: J. Geol., v. 67, p. 585-598

Schafer, J. P., 1949, Some periglacial features in central Montana: J. Geol., v. 57, p. 154-174

Simpson, H. E., 1960, Geology of the Yankton area, South Dakota and Nebraska: U.S. Geol. Surv. Prof. Pap. 328, 124 p.

Stalker, A. MacS., 1963, Quaternary stratigraphy in southern Alberta: Geol. Surv. Canada, Pap. 62-34, p. 1-52

Steece, F. V., 1958a, Geology of the Watertown quadrangle, South Dakota: South Dakota Geol. Surv., map and text

—— 1958b, Geology of the Hayti quadrangle, South Dakota: South Dakota Geol. Surv., map and text

—— 1958c, Geology of the Estelline quadrangle, South Dakota: South Dakota Geol. Surv., map and text

Steece, F. V., 1959, Geology of the Sioux Falls quadrangle, South Dakota: South Dakota Geol. Surv., map and text

Steece, F. V., and Howells, L. W., in preparation, Geology and ground water supplies in Sanborn County, South Dakota: South Dakota Geol. Surv. Bull. 17

Steece, F. V., Tipton, M. J., and Agnew, A. F., 1960, Glacial geology of the Coteau des Prairies, South Dakota: Guidebook 11th Ann. Field Conf. Midwestern Friends of the Pleistocene, South Dakota, 21 p.

Thwaites, F. T., 1943, Pleistocene of part of northeastern Wisconsin: Geol. Soc. Amer. Bull., v. 54, p. 87-144

—— 1946, Outlines of glacial geology: Ann Arbor, Mich., Edwards Bros., Inc., 119 p.

Tipton, M. J., 1958a, Geology of the Still Lake quadrangle, South Dakota: South Dakota Geol. Surv., map and text

—— 1958b, Geology of the South Shore quadrangle, South Dakota: South Dakota Geol. Surv., map and text

—— 1960, A new glacial drift sheet in South Dakota?: South Dakota Acad. Sci. Proc., v. 38, p. 45-48

—— 1959, Geology of Dell Rapids quadrangle, South Dakota: South Dakota Geol. Surv., map and text

Townsend, R. C., and Jenke, A. L., 1951, The problem of the origin of the Max moraine of North Dakota and Canada: Amer. J. Sci., v. 249, p. 842-858

Tuthill, S. J., Laird, W. M., and Frye, C. I., in press, Fossil molluscan fauna from the upper terrace of the Cannonball River, Grant County, North Dakota: North Dakota Acad. Sci. Proc., v. 18

Warren, C. R., 1952, Probable Illinoian age of part of the Missouri River, South Dakota: Geol. Soc. Amer. Bull., v. 63, p. 1143-1155

White, E. M., 1964, Post-Illinoian age for Missouri River in South Dakota proposed from relationship to a White River terrace: Amer. J. Sci., v. 262, p. 494-496

Wilcox, R. E., this volume, Volcanic-ash chronology

Witkind, I. J., 1959, Quaternary geology of the Smoke Creek-Medicine Lake-Grenora area, Montana and North Dakota: U.S. Geol. Surv. Bull. 1073, 80 p.

Winters, H. A., 1963, Geology and ground water resources of Stutsman County, North Dakota; Pt. ɪ, Geology: North Dakota Geol. Surv. Bull. 41, 84 p.

Wright, H. E., Jr., 1957, Radiocarbon dates of Mankato drift in Minnesota: Science, v. 125, p. 1038-1039

Wright, H. E., Jr., and Ruhe, R. V., this volume, Glaciation of Minnesota and Iowa

Zumberge, J. H., and Wright, H. E., Jr., 1956, The Cary-Mankato-Valders problem: Geol. Soc. Amer. Guidebook Ser., Field Trip 3, Glacial geology, eastern Minnesota, p. 65-81

Summary

The area discussed includes about 580,000 km² (225,000 sq. miles) of South Dakota, North Dakota, and Montana in the Central Lowland and northern Great Plains physiographic provinces of the United States. Most of the discussion concerns the area covered predominantly by Wisconsin continental glacial deposits. The drift surface is mostly gently rolling, and it slopes eastward from an altitude of about 1,200 m in northwestern Montana to about 300 m in eastern North and South Dakota. Present drainage is into the Gulf of Mexico by way of the Missouri River, its tributaries, and the Mississippi River. In preglacial times, however, all streams north of the Bad River in South Dakota drained northward into Hudson Bay. Bedrock consists chiefly of shales, siltstones, and sandstones of Cretaceous and Tertiary ages.

Six distinct advances of continental glaciers are believed to have occurred in the region during Wisconsin time. Because all the drift deposited is very similar in appearance and lithology, and because only a few radiocarbon age dates are available, the correlation of these advances with the Pleistocene stratigraphic sequence of the midwestern United States is uncertain. The advances are numbered arbitrarily from oldest to youngest and are so described and designated in this report. Many glacial lakes existed in the area during Pleistocene time, including Devils Lake and Lakes Agassiz, Souris, Dakota, Glendive, Jordan, Musselshell, Great Falls, Choteau, and Cut Bank. Pleistocene stream terraces, pediments, and deposits of windblown sand and silt occur in many places in the unglaciated portion of the report area.

GLACIATION OF MINNESOTA AND IOWA

H. E. WRIGHT, JR.,[1] R. V. RUHE[2]

MULTIPLE GLACIATION has dominated the development of the landscape of Minnesota and Iowa, leaving an almost continuous cover of till and such related sediments as glaciofluvial gravels, glacial-lake deposits, and upland loess. Bedrock is extensively exposed only in northeasternmost Minnesota near Lake Superior and the Canadian border, although the drift has been stripped from the deep postglacial valleys of the Mississippi and Missouri Rivers and their tributaries in Iowa and southern Minnesota.

Glacial features of Wisconsin age form the surface of most of Minnesota and northern Iowa, and their relations reveal a complex history of ice advance and retreat. In southern Iowa, on the other hand, all of the major pre-Wisconsin glacial and interglacial episodes are represented by glacial drifts, loesses, interglacial paleosols, and buried erosion surfaces. Together the two states thus record practically the entire range of activity of the main Pleistocene continental ice sheet.

The pioneer glacial studies in Minnesota were made by Winchell and Upham (Winchell, 1884, 1888) and in Iowa by McGee (1891) and Bain (1897). These men delineated the major moraines and ice lobes and demonstrated multiple glaciation. Among the early studies of special interest was the work on Glacial Lake Agassiz in northwestern Minnesota by Upham (1896) and on the retreat of St. Anthony Falls on the Mississippi River near Minneapolis by Winchell (1888, p. 313-341).

In the next generation, Leverett mapped the entire state of Minnesota (1929, 1932) with assistance locally of F. W. Sardeson. In Iowa the leading workers were Alden and Leighton (1917), Carman (1931), and Kay (Kay and Apfel, 1929; Kay and Graham, 1943). In the last two decades the glacial studies in Minnesota have been supported largely by the Minnesota Geological Survey, those in Iowa by the Soil Conservation Service and the Iowa Geological Survey.

PRE-WISCONSIN GLACIATIONS

In Minnesota, drifts presumably of pre-Wisconsin age are exposed in iron-ore pits and deep river cuts, but they cannot be traced with continuity or correlated easily with pre-Wisconsin drifts elsewhere. In Iowa, however, the older drifts are well exposed on ridge crests, hill slopes, river banks, and roadcuts in the southern part of the state (Fig. 1), and they have provided the basis for several of the major subdivisions of the Pleistocene sequence. Standard sections of the Nebraskan and Kansan glacial stages and

[1] School of Earth Sciences, University of Minnesota, Minneapolis, Minnesota.
[2] Soil Conservation Service, Iowa State University, Ames, Iowa.

the type locality of the Aftonian interglacial stage are all located near Afton Junction in southern Iowa. The type locality of the Yarmouth interglacial stage is at Yarmouth in southeastern Iowa.

NEBRASKAN

Nebraskan till nowhere forms the upland surface in Iowa and Minnesota, being covered by Kansan drift or younger drifts and loesses. It is a loam to clay-loam till with 45% carbonate rocks, 3% other sedimentary rocks, and 52% igneous and metamorphic rocks brought from Minnesota and Canada. It has been studied mainly in the southern half of Iowa, where its average thickness is estimated as 30-50 m (Kay and Apfel, 1929, p. 181).

AFTONIAN

In the gravel pits of the Afton-Thayer area, Union County (Kay and Apfel, 1929, p. 185), the gravels between the Kansan and Nebraskan tills were called Aftonian interglacial gravels for many years. They are now known to contain both Nebraskan and Kansan glacial gravels, but in the vicinity the Aftonian paleosol ("Nebraskan Gumbotil") separates the two tills. The Aftonian paleosol is either the B-horizon of a Planosol or Gray-Brown Podzolic soil or the A3- and B-horizons of a Humic-Gley soil or Grumosol (Ruhe, this volume). This "gumbotil" grades downward through yellowish-brown non-calcareous till ("oxidized and leached zone" of Kay and Apfel, 1929) to yellowish-brown calcareous till ("oxidized and unleached zone") and thus to the dark-gray calcareous parent material ("unoxidized and unleached zone").

Associated with the Aftonian paleosol at many localities is peat and muck. Lake clays occur above the paleosol and under Kansan till (Ruhe, 1954b). At other localities erosion surfaces separating the Nebraskan and Kansan tills represent the Aftonian interglacial age (Ruhe, 1954b).

KANSAN

Kansan till is indistinguishable lithologically from Nebraskan. Its average thickness has been estimated as 20 m (Kay and Apfel, 1929, p. 256). In south-central Iowa it is covered by thin Wisconsin loess on flat divides, but the till is exposed on valley-flanking pediments that were eroded in at least two post-Kansan cycles along dissecting streams (Ruhe, 1956).

YARMOUTH

The "Kansan gumbotil" is a Yarmouth paleosol with average thickness of 3.3 m where buried by Illinoian drift in southeasternmost Iowa (Kay and Apfel, 1929, p. 259). In

Shelby County, southwestern Iowa, a similar paleosol, which is overlain by Loveland loess of Illinoian age, has an average thickness of 1.7 m (R. V. Ruhe, unpublished). Of the 50 major cuts along the new route of the Rock Island Railroad in southwestern Iowa, Yarmouth paleosol is found on Kansan till in 5 cuts and on lake clay in 17 cuts (Ruhe, 1954b), and Yarmouth interglacial deposits crop out in 13 cuts. In other cuts, lake clay occurs on top of Yarmouth paleosol at elevations between 1,266 and 1,279 ft above sea level (384 and 388 m) and is overlain by Loveland loess—apparently a late-Yarmouth lake on the Kansan till plain. Loveland loess is also found in the area at elevations below the lake clay, so the late Yarmouth was also a time of erosion, and the major drainage net of southeastern Iowa dates from this time. Similar pre-Illinoian erosion is known from southeastern Iowa (Kay and Apfel, 1929, p. 268).

ILLINOIAN

Illinoian till occurs only in a narrow belt close to the Mississippi River in southeastern Iowa (Kay and Graham, 1943, p. 15-44). It is similar in composition to the Kansan and Nebraskan tills, even though its eastward continuity into Illinois implies that it was deposited by ice from the Lake Michigan basin rather than by ice from western Minnesota. This ice from the northeast displaced the Mississippi River westward into the Goose Lake and Leverett Channels in Clinton and Lee Counties, Iowa, and dammed the Iowa and Cedar Rivers to form Glacial Lake Calvin (Schoewe, 1920). After ice retreat the Mississippi River shifted its course to the east.

Illinoian drift of the Superior lobe is reported from southeastern Minnesota (Leverett, 1932; Ruhe and Gould, 1954), but its correlation is not certain. In adjacent Wisconsin this

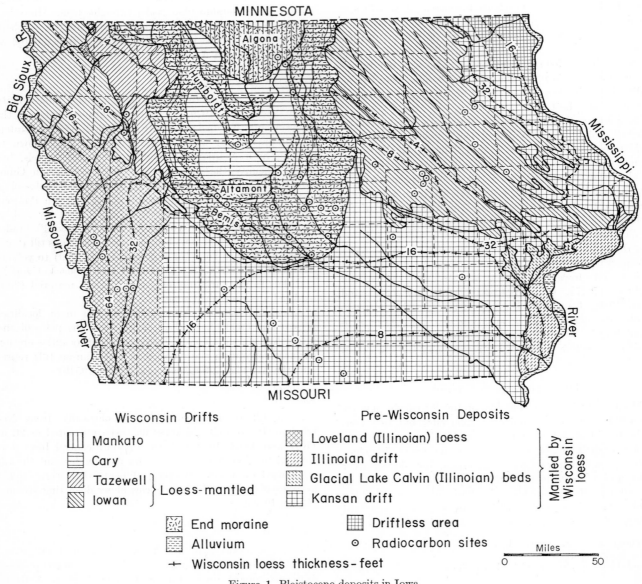

Figure 1. Pleistocene deposits in Iowa.

drift is correlated as Rockian (=Altonian = early Wisconsin) (Frye *et al.*, this volume).

Loveland loess, which is also a record of the Illinoian Glacial Age, has its type locality in southwestern Iowa. It was originally considered to be aqueous (Shimek, 1909), but it has since been demonstrated to be eolian (Kay, 1928). Along the new cuts of the Rock Island Railroad in southwestern Iowa, the Loveland loess decreases eastward in thickness (Fig. 2) and in coarse-silt content in the same manner as the overlying Wisconsin loess (Ruhe, 1954a, p. 665). Both sediments were deposited in many topographic positions through wide elevations.

The Loveland loess in Iowa is restricted to a band 50-125 km broad east of the Missouri River, but it extends southward along the river through Missouri to the Mississippi River, where it correlates with the pro-Illinoian loess of Illinois (Leighton and Willman, 1950, p. 601). It does not extend directly across Iowa to the area of Illinoian till, as believed by Kay and Graham (1943, p. 65), who erroneously interpreted the basal increment of the widespread Wisconsin loess as Loveland.

SANGAMON

Gumbotil and underlying weathering horizons on Illinoian till in southeastern Iowa are overlain by Wisconsin loess and thus record the Sangamon Interglacial Age. The Sangamon paleosol on Loveland loess exposed along the Rock Island Railroad cuts in southwestern Iowa increases in intensity of development as the loess thins from 8 to 5 m over a distance of 27 km (Ruhe, this volume). Comparable degree in intensification is developed in the soils on Wisconsin loess only with a thinning from 12 to 2.4 m over a distance of 203 km.

As the blanket of Loveland loess on the Yarmouth paleosol thins eastward across Iowa, its surficial Sangamon paleosol merges laterally with the emerging Yarmouth paleosol, which is formed on Kansan till. Thus in the large area of south-central Iowa between the Illinoian deposits on the west (Loveland loess) and on the east (till), the gumbotil on Kansan drift and under Wisconsin loess is actually a compound Yarmouth-Sangamon paleosol (Ruhe, 1956, p. 445).

This Yarmouth-Sangamon paleosol and the subjacent Kansan till in southern Iowa is cut by a widespread erosion surface in the form of valley-flanking pediments. The surface commonly has a stone-line and overlying pedi-sediment, which in turn has a paleosol that may extend through the stone-line and into the subjacent till. In southwestern Iowa this erosion surface bevels Loveland loess and its surficial Sangamon paleosol, which in turn is buried by basal Wisconsin loess. The widespread pediment is therefore late Sangamon in age. At places it descends to valley-slope fans and alluvial plains that stand well above present valley floors (Ruhe, 1960, p. 167). Elements of this late-Sangamon surface and its associated paleosols have been identified beneath younger Wisconsin drifts in northern Iowa.

THE IOWAN PROBLEM

The Iowan Stage or Substage has had a harried history. First described by McGee (1891) from a type locality at

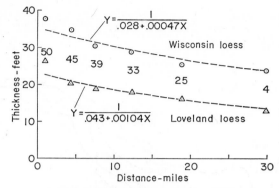

Figure 2. Thicknesses of Wisconsin and Loveland loesses from west (cut 50) to east (cut 4) along Rock Island Railroad, Pottawattamie County, southwest Iowa.

Doris Station in northeastern Iowa, it was considered for many years a separate stage of the Pleistocene (Leverett, 1926; Kay and Apfel, 1929, p. 17), being represented by till in eastern (Calvin, 1911; Alden and Leighton, 1917) and western (Carman, 1931) Iowa and by loess in Iowa and also in Illinois.

Another view, that the Iowan was the first substage of the Wisconsin, was championed by Leighton (1933), who thereupon introduced geographical names (Tazewell, Cary, Mankato) for Wisconsin subdivisions that had previously been termed Early, Middle, and Late Wisconsin. Leverett (1939), in one of his last publications, grudgingly yielded to the new classification, and for many years the Iowan stood as the earliest Wisconsin substage, although Leighton himself (Leighton and Willman, 1950, p. 602) later inserted the Farmdale substage beneath the Iowan on the basis of loess stratigraphy in Illinois.

Radiocarbon dates of coniferous wood extracted from presumed Iowan till in northeastern Iowa proved to be >29,000 to >37,000 years old, leading Ruhe and Scholtes (1959, p. 592) to suggest that the so-called Iowan till was pre-Wisconsin or at least that it was older than the Farmdale, which in its type area is 22,000-29,000 years old (Frye *et al.*, this volume). Current detailed geomorphic and stratigraphic studies, supported by drilling, by Ruhe and associates in the type area of Iowan till indicate that the landscape for the Iowan drift is a multi-leveled sequence of erosion surfaces and that many of these levels cut into Kansan and Nebraskan till. Thus the radiocarbon dates mentioned may refer to pre-Iowan rather than Iowan drift.

Drill holes on the summits of hills in areas of Kansan inliers and paha in the Iowan area (Scholtes, 1955) penetrate Wisconsin loess, Yarmouth-Sangamon paleosols, Kansan till, Aftonian paleosols, and Nebraskan till successively downward. In traverses drilled down the sloping flanks of the hills and paha, the same stratigraphic sequence occurs. On the adjacent, lower-lying so-called "typical Iowan drift plain" that surround the inliers and paha, the same deposits and horizons are identified in drill cores along traverses as long as 30 km. Such studies in Tama County and adjacent parts of Grundy and Blackhawk Counties fail to show the

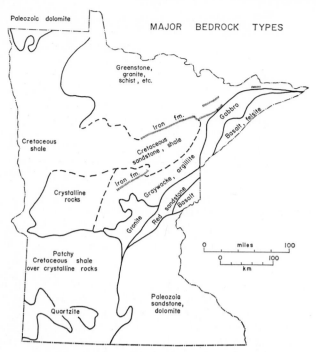

Figure 3. Generalized map of the bedrock of Minnesota.

presence of Iowan drift around the inliers and pahas. The paleosol and till cores of these features are not pre-Iowan topographic highs around which Iowan ice advanced but did not override, as previously proposed (Scholtes, 1955, p. 196-198). Instead the cores of inliers and pahas are erosion remnants on interstream divides (T. E. Fenton and R. V. Ruhe, unpublished).

The problem of the Iowan drift can only be resolved by detailed geomorphic and stratigraphic studies, the latter mainly in the subsurface. In the current work in the type area in northeastern Iowa, Iowan drift has yet to be identified.

The loess that continuously covers the Iowan till was formerly termed Peorian loess (Kay and Graham, 1943, p. 156) but is now called simply Wisconsin loess (Ruhe, 1954a). Its thickness decreases systematically eastward from its source areas (Fig. 2; Hutton, 1947). Parameters of particle size also change systematically with long distance of travel, although over short distances the changes are more complex (Ruhe, 1954a, p. 666). Radiocarbon dates from the basal part of the loess, which contains an A-C soil profile, indicate correlation with the Farmdale in many areas: coniferous wood from the A-horizon provides dates of 24,500 ± 880 (W-141) and 21,360 ± 850 (I-1023) in southwestern Iowa, 25,000 ± 2,500 (I-1267) and 29,000 ± 3,500 (I-1269) in northeastern Iowa, and 20,290 ± 1000 (I-1022) in southeastern Iowa.

Loess deposition was apparently interrupted in northwestern Iowa by advance of the ice. The till in this area that Carman (1931) had mapped as Iowan (Kay and Graham, 1943) contains wood at the base with a date of 20,000 ± 880 years (O-1325). This date confirms Ruhe's (1950, 1952) reclassification of much of this till to Taze-

well, for the Tazewell (Shelbyville) till of Illinois is 19,200 ± 700 years old (W-187), and pre-Shelbyville loess in Illinois has dates of 20,340 ± 750 (W-349) and 20,300 ± 400 years (W-870). The reclassification in Iowa was based on the relatively abrupt decrease in thickness of the loess mantle at the outer limit of Tazewell drift, presumably because the late-Iowan, pre-Tazewell component of the loess was overridden. From this boundary eastward the loess thins systematically from 200 cm to 100-125 cm at the margin of the younger Wisconsin drift, which buries the entire loess and its weak paleosol and which has no continuous loess cover of its own. The Tazewell drift as thus identified has few undrained depressions; its topographic and stratigraphic contrast with the younger Wisconsin drifts (see below) is pronounced (Ruhe, 1952).

Wood dates from within the loess in central Iowa are 17,030 ± 500 (I-1020), 16,720 ± 500 (W-126), 16,100 ± 1,000 (I-1270), and 16,100 ± 500 (I-1024). Dates from wood from the top of the loess, where it is buried by younger Wisconsin till in central Iowa, are about 14,000 years (see below). As no paleosols occur within the loess, except for the basal A-C paleosol, loess deposition must have been continuous from the time of the Farmdale, 29,000 years ago, through the Tazewell until the invasion of the ice into central Iowa 14,000 years ago.

WISCONSIN

INTRODUCTION

Wisconsin glacial drift covers most of Minnesota and northern Iowa, and Wisconsin loess blankets much of the rest of the area. Whereas the pre-Wisconsin drifts in Iowa all have essentially the same lithology, implying a common source, the Wisconsin drifts in Minnesota have a highly varied lithology and complex stratigraphy, which reflect the configuration of the several lobes that protruded from the ice-sheet margin during various intervals of advance and retreat. This lobation of the ice margin was controlled by the major bedrock topography of the area over which the ice moved. An understanding of the relations therefore requires knowledge of both the lithology and topography of the bedrock.

Precambrian basic igneous rocks form the highlands north of Lake Superior (Fig. 3). Red sandstone occurs in a belt extending south from the head of Lake Superior. Paleozoic dolomite and sandstone are found in southeastern Minnesota and adjacent Iowa and also in the northwestern corner of Minnesota and adjacent Manitoba. Cretaceous shale occurs primarily in western Minnesota. The north-central part of Minnesota and adjacent Ontario are underlain by undiagnostic granitic and metamorphic rocks.

The bedrock topography (Fig. 4) is marked by (1) a deep lowland now occupied by Lake Superior, (2) a shallower lowland, here called the Minneapolis lowland, extending northeast through Minneapolis *en echelon* with the Superior lowland, (3) a long lowland in three segments now occupied by the Red, Minnesota, and Des Moines Rivers, and (4) a shallow lowland centering in the Red Lakes area in northwestern Minnesota. This topography probably dates in part from Cretaceous time, for Upper Cretaceous marine ·

sediments are found in both the Red Lakes lowland and the Red-Minnesota lowland (Sloan, 1964).

Four major ice lobes are recognized for the glaciation of Minnesota and Iowa. On the east the Superior Lobe followed the Superior and Minneapolis lowlands, bringing generally red sandy till with pebbles of red sandstone and slate. Immediately to the northwest in northern Minnesota was the Rainy Lobe, which produced drift of variable color and composition according to the dominant rock types that it traversed. On the gabbro highland northwest of the Lake Superior basin the Rainy Lobe drift is gray or blue gray. Farther west the drift is light gray to light brown because of the abundance of granitic rocks from the terrane north of the Mesabi iron range. In central Minnesota the drift is brown because it is dominated by fragments of initially gray metamorphic rocks that apparently have oxidized readily in the fine fraction to a uniform brown color.

Leverett (1932) considered the Rainy and Superior Lobes as one, referring them to the Patrician ice center of Ontario 200 miles north of Minnesota. He did recognize, however, that during the late Wisconsin the Superior Lobe from the "Labradorian ice center" to the northeast moved quite separately into the area.

In western Minnesota the Des Moines Lobe followed the major lowland to central Iowa and sent sublobes eastward across northern Minnesota (St. Louis Sublobe) and across southern Minnesota (Grantsburg Sublobe), bringing gray (buff where oxidized) calcareous silty till with fragments of Cretaceous shale. Not so far west was the Wadena Lobe, which brought gray to buff sandy calcareous till to the Red Lakes lowland from the carbonate terrane of Manitoba that lies north of the limits of Cretaceous shale. The Des Moines and Wadena Lobes were not differentiated by Leverett (1932), who referred all the calcareous drift to the Keewatin ice center northwest of Hudson Bay.

TERMINOLOGY

The following description of the glacial geology of the Wisconsin Glacial Stage in Minnesota and Iowa is organized as a geologic history. Because of the uncertainties of correlation of the glacial events in this area with those in other parts of the Great Lakes region, the history is recounted as phases of ice advance of individual lobes; correlations between the phases of different ice lobes, as indicated by stratigraphic or drainage relations, are made where possible (Table 1). Phases are informal units of geologic time that are identified or defined on the basis of either morphologic or stratigraphic features and are given local geographic names. They thus are not necessarily bound by the stratigraphic strictures of the rock-stratigraphic, time-stratigraphic, or geologic-climate units of the Stratigraphic Code (American Commission of Stratigraphic Nomenclature, 1961) or even by those of the morphostratigraphic units of Frye and Willman (1960; see Wright, 1964).

HEWITT PHASE OF WADENA LOBE

The Hewitt phase (Fig. 5) is here named from till exposed in a Wadena Lobe drumlin on U.S. Highway 210 one mile east of Hewitt, Todd County (Wright, 1962, Table 2, Pl. 1). The Wadena Drumlin Field as exposed is about 110 km

long and 65 km broad; it is overlapped on all sides by younger drift. It consists of about 1,200 drumlins formed by ice advancing toward the southwest and fanning to the west and south. The till of the drumlins is buff, sandy, calcareous, and without Cretaceous shale, implying a source in southeastern Manitoba north of the area of Cretaceous bedrock. The Wadena Lobe apparently entered the shallow Red Lakes lowland of northwestern Minnesota from the northwest but was blocked in its eastward progress by the contemporaneous Rainy Lobe advancing from the northeast. The Wadena Lobe was diverted thereby to the southwest to form the drumlin field. In the process of diversion it became contaminated by Rainy Lobe drift so that portions of the Wadena Lobe drift contain many indicator stones from the northeast (Wright, 1962).

The eastern extent of the Wadena Lobe in the Hewitt phase is not known because its drift is buried by younger drift of eastern source. On the south and west the Wadena Lobe is believed to have terminated in the Alexandria moraine complex, which forms a long arc of lake-dotted moraine bounding the drumlin field. This moraine, however, as well as the fringe of the drumlin field itself, was buried by later advance of the Des Moines Lobe from the west and southwest. On the north the drumlin field is buried by outwash leading from the Itasca Moraine, which was formed during the following phase of the Wadena Lobe.

The other ice lobes in Minnesota were probably active at the same time as the Hewitt phase of the Wadena Lobe but had not attained their maximum positions. Synchronous presence of the Rainy Lobe has already been postulated to explain the diversion of the Wadena Lobe from a south-

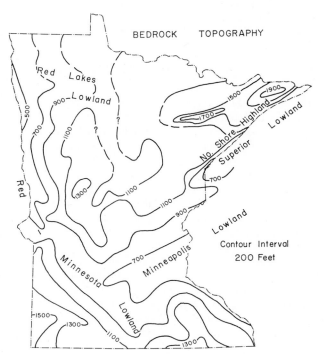

Figure 4. Generalized topographic map of the bedrock surface in Minnesota (compiled from well records by W. Vollendorf, 1950).

TABLE 1

Phases of Wisconsin Glaciation in Minnesota
(Figures indicate radiocarbon dates before the present. Read upward from bottom.)

DES MOINES LOBE			WADENA LOBE (Red Lakes lowland)	RAINY LOBE (Upland)	SUPERIOR LOBE (Superior lowland; Minneapolis lowland in St. Croix phase)
MAIN (Red–Minnesota–Des Moines valleys)	GRANTSBURG SUBLOBE (Minneapolis lowland)	ST. LOUIS SUBLOBE (Red Lakes lowland)			
9,200-7,000 L. Agassiz II 11,000-10,000 L. Agassiz I 11,740		L. Aitkin IIb Aitkin soil 11,635 L. Aitkin IIa and L. Upham II ALBORN PHASE		?	L. Duluth L. Nemadji NICKERSON PHASE Nickerson Mor.
MANKATO PHASE Algona Mor. 13,000	12,700-11,800 Anoka Sandplain PINE CITY PHASE L. Grantsburg Pine City Mor.	Advancing			11,500 SPLIT ROCK PHASE Hinckley Sandpl. Split Rock Dr.
BEMIS PHASE Bemis Mor. 14,000	?	Advancing?		VERMILION PHASE Vermilion Mor.	L. Aitkin I & L. Upham I AUTOMBA PHASE Highland-Mille Lacs Mor., Automba Dr.
?			ITASCA PHASE Itasca Mor.	ST. CROIX PHASE St. Croix Moraine 13,270 Brainerd Dr. Pierz Dr. Toimi Dr.	
?			>40,000 HEWITT PHASE Wadena Drumlins	Advancing	?

easterly to a southwesterly heading. The Des Moines Lobe must have occupied the Red River lowland at this time because this area is topographically lower than the shallow Red Lakes lowland of northwestern Minnesota into which the Wadena Lobe advanced; the Wadena Lobe must therefore have been an offshoot of the Des Moines Lobe but from a source farther north than its later counterpart (St. Louis Sublobe).

ITASCA PHASE OF WADENA LOBE, ST. CROIX PHASE
OF SUPERIOR AND RAINY LOBES

The Wadena Lobe retreated to the Itasca Moraine, and the Superior and Rainy Lobes reached a common terminus at the St. Croix Moraine, which may be traced in a great loop from western Wisconsin on the St. Croix River southwestward to Minneapolis and thence to the northwest and north to a place where it becomes interlobate with the Itasca Moraine of the Wadena Lobe (Fig. 6). These two moraines give their names to the correlative phases of the respective ice lobes. The eastern and southern parts of the St. Croix Moraine are made of red sandy drift, diagnostic of the Superior Lobe. The northwestern part, however, is made of brown sandy till, characteristic of both the Pierz and Brainerd Sublobes of the Rainy Lobe. Here the drift rests on the Hewitt Till of the Wadena Lobe, with interlamination at the contact. These stratigraphic relations were interpreted by Schneider (1961) and Wright (1956) as indicating at least partial synchroneity of the Wadena and Pierz Lobes. As a result of the studies of two other Minnesota drifts by Cushing (1963), however, a more probable explanation is that erosion of Hewitt Till, perhaps still with dead ice, by active Pierz Lobe ice of the St. Croix phase, was followed by its deformation into a foliate structure.

Not only is the St. Croix Moraine west of the Mississippi River continuous as a topographic feature despite changing composition, but the fan-shaped Pierz Drumlin Field east of the moraine is also a continuous feature with generally gradational composition from red on the south to brown on the north. Although such gradations might imply that a single ice lobe was involved, perhaps in the sense of the Patrician lobe of Leverett (1932), it is possible to consider that two separate ice streams, one centered in the Superior basin and the other on the upland to the northwest, merged together in central Minnesota and fanned to the southwest and northwest to form a single Pierz Drumlin Field and the single St. Croix Moraine, in the same sense that two tributary valley glaciers from different sources may join in the main valley and then spread on the piedmont as a single ice mass. Lateral shifting of the two streams is implied by the occurrence of both red and brown till in superposition as major stratigraphic units in both the drumlin field and the moraine.

The relation of the Superior to the Rainy Lobe in the St. Croix phase is not completely clear, however, partly because their drifts were buried by younger ice advances in an area 130 km broad northeast of the Pierz Drumlin Field. North of the area of burial are Rainy Lobe drumlins with distinct southwest trend—a group called the Toimi Drumlin Field in St. Louis and Lake Counties (Wright, 1956), and a smaller group west of Hibbing on the western Mesabi iron range (Cotter et al., 1964). As the history of glacier fluctuation is reconstructed for the Hewitt and St. Croix phases of the sequence, the broad Rainy Lobe moved slowly southwestward across the upland. On its right margin it blocked and diverted the Wadena Lobe, which was moving more rapidly into the Red Lakes lowland of northwestern Minnesota, as already recounted. The Wadena Lobe thereupon reached its maximum in the Hewitt phase and retreated. Meanwhile the Rainy Lobe pushed onward over part of the area just vacated. On its left flank it was confluent with the Superior Lobe, which was a thicker ice stream moving more rapidly in the deep Superior basin. This ice, advancing southwestward out of the basin, carried with it on its right flank, so to speak, the left portion of the Rainy Lobe, here called its Pierz Sublobe, and together they formed the Pierz Drumlin Field of red and brown drift.

The rest or western part of the Rainy Lobe, here called the Brainerd Sublobe, moved forward separately. Its drift is indistinguishable in lithology from that of the Pierz Sublobe, so the sequence must be reconstructed from the geomorphic relations. According to Schneider (1961), the Brainerd Drumlin Field, with southwest trend, crosscuts the northern edge of the Pierz field south of Brainerd. The Brainerd ice reached its terminus at the northernmost segment of the St. Croix Moraine, where it met at an angle the Wadena Lobe at the Itasca Moraine. Outwash from these two moraines formed the Park Rapids Outwash Plain and other extensive outwash fans and plains that partially bury the northeast portion of the Wadena Drumlin Field (Wright, 1962). Some of the outwash from the Brainerd Sublobe drained southward along the inner (eastern) margin of that segment of the St. Croix Moraine from which the Pierz Sublobe had already withdrawn (Schneider, 1961).

Wastage of the Superior and Rainy Lobes of the St. Croix phase from the St. Croix Moraine left a remarkable record of tunnel valleys and eskers, currently under study by E. J. Cushing. The tunnel valleys form a system trending southwest, parallel to the axis of the Superior Lobe, with only a slight tendency to fan to the west in the St. Cloud area and to the south near Minneapolis. The downstream ends of many of the tunnel valleys have been buried by younger drifts so are partially obscured. The tunnel valleys were formed in the ablation zone of the glacier when the ice was still thick enough to permit the development of closed, water-filled drainage tunnels at the base under enough hydrostatic pressure to provide the water velocity necessary to erode sizable gorges in the substratum. The sub-parallel pattern of tunnel valleys cuts obliquely across the Pierz Drumlin Field. It must reflect the surface contour in the ablation zone of the ice lobe and thus the hydrostatic gradient; it does not reflect the subglacier topography, which in fact in this area has a general southeastward slope into the Minneapolis lowland, at right angles to the southwesterly trend of the tunnel valleys.

Many of the tunnel valleys penetrate the St. Croix Moraine and must have been formed when the ice stood at its maximum. In fact the dissection of the moraine by tunnel valleys in the area northwest of Minneapolis may have been great enough to create gaps that later eased the eastward penetration of the Grantsburg Sublobe. As the ice thinned and stagnated during wastage, the hydrostatic pressure was reduced or lost by air intake through crevasses or other openings, and the streams changed from erosional to depositional, forming eskers in or beside the previously eroded channels. The system worked headward during ice wastage and extended for 130 km from the St. Croix Moraine to the low divide between the Minneapolis and Superior lowlands, beyond which it is buried or modified

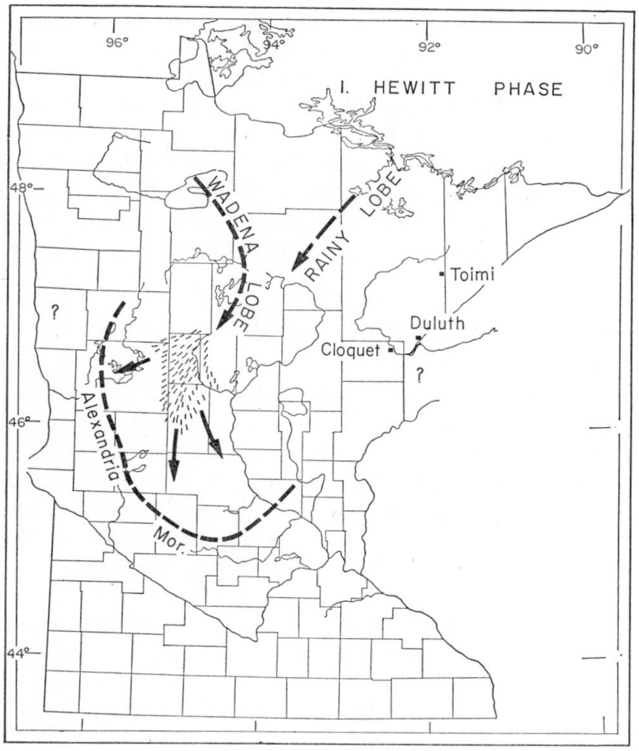

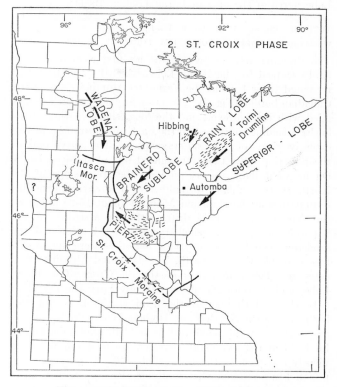

Figure 5. Hewitt phase of Wisconsin glaciation in Minnesota.

Figure 6. St. Croix phase of Wisconsin glaciation in Minnesota.

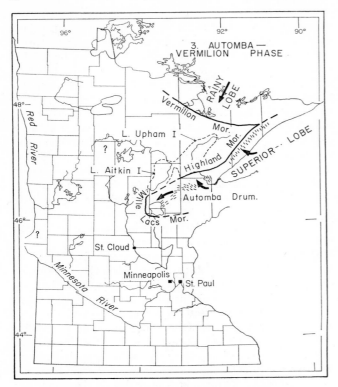

Figure 7. Automba-Vermilion phase of Wisconsin glaciation in Minnesota.

by younger drift. Similar tunnel valleys and eskers are found farther north in the Toimi Drumlins of the Rainy Lobe north of the area of burial (Baker, 1964).

AUTOMBA PHASE OF SUPERIOR LOBE,
VERMILION PHASE OF THE RAINY LOBE

The thinning and wastage of the ice first cleared the upland occupied by the Rainy Lobe, which by this time had retreated to or beyond the Vermilion Moraine close to the Canadian border (Fig. 7). The Deep Superior basin was still filled with ice, however, and the long, shallow Minneapolis lowland leading southwest to the St. Croix Moraine still had extensive areas of thin and stagnant ice. The active part of the Superior Lobe then readvanced out of its deep basin. On its right flank the ice rose up the steep slope of the North Shore Highland to build a strip of narrow drumlins terminating in the Highland Moraine about 15-25 km from the North Shore. This drift, although assigned to the Superior Lobe, lacks the characteristic red color and red sandstone pebbles because these materials were apparently less available this far north. The Highland Moraine truncates the Toimi Drumlins of the St. Croix-phase Rainy Lobe, and its outwash plains partially bury the drumlins.

In the Duluth area at the head of the Lake Superior basin, where the North Shore Highland ends, the ice fanned out to the west and northwest to build the Automba Drumlin Field of red sandy till, covering much of the area previously occupied by the Rainy Lobe. The ice probably terminated in a moraine that continues the southwest trend of the Highland Moraine to the Mille Lacs Moraine on the west side of Lake Mille Lacs in central Minnesota. The

path of this lobe seems anomalous in the respect that the ice apparently did not follow southwestward down the axis of the Minneapolis lowland, although it had enough thickness to do this, but rather climbed out of the lowland and flowed westward to the Mille Lacs area. One possible but not completely satisfactory explanation is that the Minneapolis lowland was still plugged with stagnant ice remaining from the St. Croix phase. The stagnant ice was so drift-laden as a result of long wastage that it was not appreciably reactivated by the ice advance of the Automba phase. This active ice lobe thus was blocked from a southwesterly course and spilled instead westward onto the upland and around the northern margin of the dead-ice area, as recorded by the curving pattern of the Automba Drumlin Field. The ice left no recognizable moraine on its left flank, and it may have been dispersed as a thin overburden on the dead ice against which it impinged.

The Superior Lobe in this re-expanded position must have blocked the drainage of the St. Louis River, which could then have formed a large proglacial lake (Lake Upham I) north of the ice front, extending north to the Mesabi iron range. It may have formed a similar Glacial Lake Aitkin I farther to the west in the present Mississippi drainage. The two lakes were probably confluent and drained into the Mississippi system. They are believed to have received red lake clay and silt from the Superior Lobe meltwater. Lake Aitkin I must in addition have received brown lake sediments from ice to the northwest or north. These lake sediments were to be overridden in the next phase by ice from the west to produce red and brown clay tills.

The positions of the Wadena and Des Moines Lobes during the Automba phase are unknown. The former must have wasted completely at some time after its earlier stand at the Itasca Moraine because the Red Lakes lowland that it had occupied became filled subsequently with the St. Louis Sublobe of the Des Moines Lobe. Presumably this clearance coincided with the deep retreat of the Rainy Lobe and the broad stagnation of the Superior Lobe at the end of the St. Croix phase. Perhaps the St. Louis Sublobe then started its advance and contributed brown clay to Lake Aitkin I.

SPLIT ROCK PHASE OF SUPERIOR LOBE, PINE CITY PHASE
OF GRANTSBURG SUBLOBE

By the end of the Automba phase the active Superior Lobe had retreated across the low bedrock divide between the Minneapolis and Superior lowlands, although much stagnant ice was left in its wake. Red clay must have been deposited in one or more proglacial lakes of unknown dimensions, because when the ice readvanced southwestward in a narrow tongue as far as the bedrock divide it discontinuously covered eskers, tunnel valleys, and other older features with a veneer of red clay till (Fig. 8). In some cases the cap of clay till on eskers is underlain or replaced by a cap of sandy till. The sandy till can be interpreted as a product of Automba-phase till or till-laden dead ice redeposited or reactivated by the overriding ice of the Split Rock phase (E. J. Cushing, in preparation). Alternatively, it may have been deposited earlier in a separate movement by active ice of the Automba phase itself on top of the wastage features of the St. Croix phase.

A small bulge of ice extended westward over the edge of the Automba Drumlins to an elevation of 1,250 ft (380 m) up the basin of the Split Rock River, constructing a small field of drumlins of different form, here called the Split Rock Drumlins, from which the phase takes its name.

Elsewhere the right (northwest) side of this thin lobe formed two well-marked successive frontal outwash plains at 1,300 and 1,280 ft with ice-contact slopes and esker sources. Some of the western drainage continued into Lake Upham I. The rest of the western drainage and all the southern drainage from this narrow lobe moved southeastward toward the St. Croix River, but it was intercepted along the north edge of the Grantsburg Sublobe of the Des Moines Lobe by Lake Grantsburg and here formed the Hinckley Sundplain.

The Grantsburg Sublobe at its maximum built the Pine City Moraine (Leverett, 1932, p. 79), thus defining the Pine City phase. The ice had protruded northeastward up the Minneapolis lowland, which had previously been filled by the Superior Lobe in the St. Croix phase. It broke across the western arm of the St. Croix Moraine and buried the tunnel valleys, eskers, and other wastage features of the Superior Lobe. In the process it picked up red drift or drift-laden dead ice to produce the intricate interlaminated red and buff structures that mark the contact between the two drifts (Cushing, 1963). As the ice wasted, the Anoka Sandplain developed in its place. It received, as had Lake Grantsburg, the drainage of the Mississippi River as well as of the Superior Lobe, but its development was principally influenced by the pattern of local ice wastage (Cooper, 1935; E. J. Cushing, in preparation).

ALBORN PHASE OF ST. LOUIS SUBLOBE, NICKERSON PHASE OF SUPERIOR LOBE

The St. Louis Sublobe branched from the Des Moines Lobe far enough to the south to pick up Cretaceous shale, in contrast to the earlier Wadena Lobe, which reached the Red Lakes lowland from the non-shaly, carbonate terrane of the Lake Winnipeg area in Manitoba (Fig. 9). The St. Louis Sublobe was not blocked by the Rainy Lobe in its eastward advance into the Red Lake lowland as the Wadena Lobe had been. In fact on its left-hand side in northernmost Minnesota it buried the Vermilion Moraine of the Rainy Lobe. It crossed the low western end of the Mesabi iron range and overrode the red and brown clays of Glacial Lakes Aitkin I and Upham I, redepositing them in a complex of red or brown clay till interlaminated or intermixed with the light-brown shale-bearing silty till that is more characteristic of the up-glacier, uncontaminated portion of the St. Louis Sublobe drift. The ice advanced to an elevation of 1,550 ft (470 m) on the south flank of the Mesabi-range area, and eastward it buried the edge of the Toimi Drumlin Field and the dissecting tunnel valleys of the Rainy Lobe. It covered portions of the Highland Moraine and other Automba-phase features of the Superior Lobe and locally built its own morainic topography. This phase takes its name from the Alborn Till near its terminus in southwestern St. Louis County (Baker, 1964).

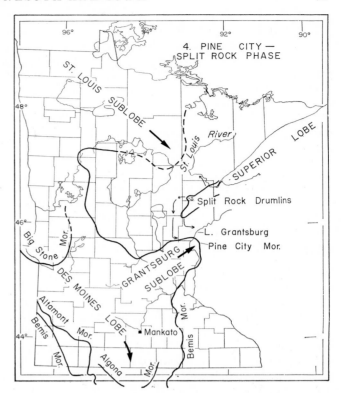

Figure 8. Pine City–Split Rock phase of Wisconsin glaciation in Minnesota.

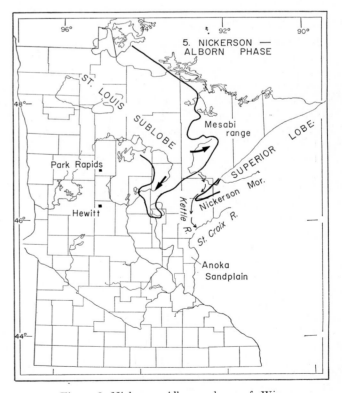

Figure 9. Nickerson-Alborn phase of Wisconsin glaciation in Minnesota.

Outwash from the St. Louis Sublobe extended in part eastward from the newly formed St. Louis River to Cloquet, whence it was diverted by the Superior Lobe southward across the Split Rock Drumlins and into the Kettle River, a tributary of the St. Croix. By this time the Grantsburg Sublobe had wasted almost completely and no longer diverted the Mississippi River.

The Superior Lobe had withdrawn from its Split Rock-phase position to the Nickerson Moraine, which is a striking feature of strong local relief in red clay till near the west end of the Superior lowland. During the waning portion of the phase the St. Louis Sublobe retreated. Glacial Lakes Upham II and Aitkin II formed at its front and supplied increasing amounts of water to the St. Louis River, which then flowed southward down the diversion channel around the Superior Lobe to the Kettle River. Progressive withdrawal of the blocking ice mass permitted the development of drainage channels at about 1,200, 1,170, 1,130, and 1,100 ft near the point of the Nickerson Moraine, until finally the Superior Lobe withdrew far enough into the basin to form Glacial Lake Nemadji, which had an outlet at 1,050 ft to the Kettle River. The clear outlet waters cut a gorge along the Kettle and St. Croix Rivers through the deposits of the Anoka Sandplain and Lake Grantsburg and into the bedrock. The dissection may have been speeded by the drop in base level induced by contemporaneous dissection of the Mississippi River, to which the St. Croix is tributary, by the outlet waters of Glacial Lake Agassiz (see below). This would imply complete wastage of the Des Moines Lobe to open at least the Minnesota portion

of the Lake Agassiz basin while the Superior Lobe was still blocking the St. Louis River. This river in turn was still the outlet of Lake Upham II, which may still have been supplied by melt-water from the wasting St. Louis Sublobe. Glacial Lake Duluth, which drained directly to the St. Croix River in northwestern Wisconsin rather than first into the Kettle River, formed immediately after, and the St. Croix River gorge was further deepened.

The relations of the St. Louis and Superior Sublobes as here recounted represent a revision in which several persons have had a part, notably Thomas (1959) and Baker (1964), as well as E. J. Cushing and John E. Foss in the course of their incidental field work in the area. The earlier interpretation, which had difficulties from its inception (Wright, 1955), is thereby discarded: it had assumed that the red clay till around much of the basins of Glacial Lakes Upham and Aitkin was deposited by the Superior Lobe climbing west and north out of the head of the Lake Superior basin. The revision was facilitated by the availability of new topographic maps, which now can be used to demonstrate the close control of elevation on the ice margins as well as on the drainage courses. Additional study revealed a persistent 25-km gap in the distribution of red clay till in the area west of the head of Lake Superior. This gap, previously discounted as an instance of non-deposition of the part of the Superior Lobe, is now considered to represent ground covered by neither the St. Louis Lobe nor Superior Lobe during their clay-till phases.

BEMIS AND MANKATO PHASES OF THE DES MOINES LOBE

The drift of the St. Louis Sublobe, as traced westward along its southern border, covers that of the Wadena Lobe north of the Itasca Moraine—the two gray calcareous drifts may be distinguished by the generally siltier texture and the shale content of the St. Louis Sublobe drift. The border of the younger drift may be traced thence southward to mark the east edge of the main Des Moines Lobe (Fig. 8). It buried the western and southern edges of the Wadena Drumlin Field. It forms the surface drift in the big Alexandria moraine complex, which, however, may have a buried core of Hewitt-phase Wadena Lobe moraine. The drift border thence may be traced eastward as the left-hand edge of the Grantsburg Sublobe.

The Des Moines Lobe proper at this time was extended southward to Mankato in southern Minnesota and onward to central Iowa. The attainment of its terminus at the Bemis Moraine is here called the Bemis phase. During retreat the ice formed the Altamont Moraine and then the broad Algona Moraine in northern Iowa (Kay and Graham, 1943, p. 239; Ruhe *et al.*, 1957; Ruhe and Scholtes, 1959). The Algona Moraine may be considered to mark the Mankato phase, for the ice soon retreated past the townsite of Mankato in southern Minnesota and thence northwest to the divide between the Minnesota and Red River valleys. Here at the Big Stone Moraine it dispatched great floods of outwash which coursed irregularly across the till plain to the south and eventually became channeled into the Minnesota River valley. Further retreat opened the basin of Glacial Lake Agassiz north of the Big Stone Moraine (Fig. 10), and as the lake expanded into Canada the spillway

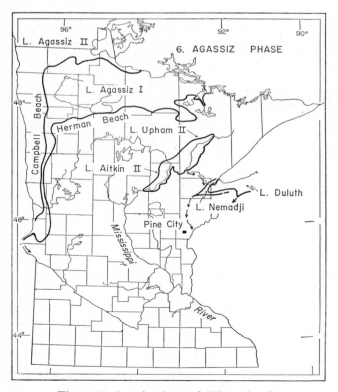

Figure 10. Agassiz phase of Wisconsin glaciation in Minnesota.

waters (Glacial River Warren) cut the outlet gorge as much as 100 m deep through late-Mankato outwash for hundreds of miles to the Mississippi River at Minneapolis and beyond to Illinois (Zumberge, 1952). As the outlet was eroded, successive beaches were formed at elevations ranging in the outlet region from 1,060 (Herman) to 980 ft (Campbell). The beaches may be traced northward into Canada, where the elevations are higher because of postglacial tilting (Upham, 1896; Leverett, 1932; Elson, 1957).

CHRONOLOGY AND CORRELATION OF WISCONSIN DRIFTS

The Hewitt Till of the Wadena Lobe is marked by undrained depressions, and the soils are no better developed than the soils on other Wisconsin drifts in Minnesota (Fig. 5). The drumlins were considered to be Iowan in correlation by Leverett (1932) but early Cary by Wright (1962). A radiocarbon date on wood from silts above this drift and beneath the Des Moines Lobe drift of the Bemis or Mankato phase is >40,000 years (W-1232). On the basis of the topographic expression and shallow weathering profile, however, the Hewitt phase should be younger than is implied by the date, so confirmation is desirable.

The St. Croix Moraine (Fig. 6) was correlated by Leverett (1932) with the Middle Wisconsin (Cary) of Illinois, and this correlation is retained by Black (Frye *et al.*, this volume). The only radiocarbon date available on the St. Croix Moraine is from the basal organic sediment at Kirchner Marsh south of Minneapolis: 13,270 ± 200 (Y-1326; Wright *et al.*, 1963). Recession of active ice from the moraine may have occurred at an earlier date, so the correlation of the St. Croix Moraine either with the Cary or with earlier moraines of Illinois and Indiana, which are at least 14,000 years old, is possible. No C^{14} dates are available for the Automba-Vermilion phases (Fig. 7).

The Split Rock phase of the Superior Lobe (Fig. 8) has a minimum date on a kettle-bottom sample in its outwash west of Cloquet of 11,500 (W-1059, Farnham *et al.*, 1964), implying that this phase is older than the Two Creeks interval. The Pine City phase of the Grantsburg Sublobe, whose maximum stand and early wastage is contemporaneous with the Split Rock and Nickerson phases of the Superior Lobe, fits this age assignment, for kettles in its outwash have bottom dates of 12,700-11,800 years old (Wright and Rubin, 1956).

The Alborn phase of the St. Louis Sublobe (Fig. 9) is older than 11,635 years (W-502 and W-1141, Farnham *et al.*, 1964), according to dates on a soil formed during a dry interval of Glacial Lake Aitkin II. An anomalous pair of dates on Alborn-phase till on the Mesabi iron range, however, implies a post-Two Creeks rather than pre-Two Creeks age for the Alborn phase: 11,330 (W-827) and 11,100 (W-1140) (Farnham *et al.*, 1964).

The Bemis and Mankato phases of the main Des Moines Lobe (Fig. 8) are also older than the Two Creeks interval. The ice reached its terminus at the Bemis Moraine in central Iowa at the time of the Cary phase of the Lake Michigan lobe, as is suggested by the well-controlled 14,000-year dates on wood (including rooted trees) buried by drift of the Bemis phase: 13,820 ± 400 (W-513), 13,910 ± 400 (W-517), 14,470 ± 400 (W-512), and 14,700 ± 400 (W-153)

(Ruhe *et al.*, 1957). The next moraine to the north, the Altamont, was previously included in the Mankato phase (Ruhe, 1952b). However, better chronological control is available at the broad Algona Moraine still farther north, whose outwash buried trees and peat dated as 12,970 (W-626) and 13,030 (W-625) (Ruhe and Scholtes, 1959), and this moraine is now taken to mark the climax of the Mankato phase, equivalent in time to the Port Huron phase of the Lake Michigan Lobe (Wright, 1964). The retreating Mankato ice uncovered the area near Mankato itself before 12,650 years ago (W-824, Jelgersma, 1962).

The drift peripheral to the Bemis Moraine in eastern Iowa is the problematical Iowan till, deposited by an earlier Des Moines Lobe. In western Iowa, however, a portion of it is correlated with the Tazewell phase, a proper subdivision of the Wisconsin glaciation of the Lake Michigan Lobe in Illinois (see the above discussion of the Iowan problem).

The exact chronological relations between the main Des Moines Lobe and its two sublobes are not yet clear, for carbon dates on the sublobes all measure the times of wastage and furthermore are minimal dates. The two sublobes did not reach their maxima at exactly the same time, as shown by drainage relations with the Split Rock and Nickerson phases of the Superior Lobe. The maximum stand of the main lobe at the Bemis Moraine, 14,000 years ago, may have occurred either at about the same time as the sublobe maxima or before. The evidence indicates, however, that all these advances, as well as the associated red-clay-till advances of the Superior Lobe, predate the Two Creeks interval. The Valders phase of the Lake Michigan Lobe accordingly is not recorded in Minnesota.

Lake Agassiz was first formed in the Red River lowland about 12,000 years ago when the Des Moines Lobe retreated at the end of the Mankato phase, and it rapidly expanded into the Red Lakes lowland, into which the highest major beach (Herman) may be traced (Fig. 10). This level was abandoned by 11,740 years ago (Y-1327, Shay, 1965) as the southern outlet was eroded. Continued retreat of the ice permitted drainage of the lake to the east through some course in Ontario, as yet unidentified, and the lake dropped to low levels about 11,000-10,000 years ago (Johnston, 1946; Elson, 1957; Shay, 1965).

Readvance of the ice from the northeast (and/or crustal tilting) closed the eastern outlet and raised the lake again to the lowest level of southern outlet (Campbell Beach), forming Lake Agassiz II. Zoltai (1961) indicates that the ice (the Rainy Lobe of Minnesota) may at this time have been as far south as the Rainy Lake Moraine at the Minnesota border. North of the Rainy Lake Moraine are three younger moraines recording retreatal positions of the Rainy Lobe. The middle one of the three (Hartman Moraine) may extend eastward to the Dog Lake Moraine, which is interlobate with the red-clay-till Marks Moriane of a sublobe from the Superior basin (Zoltai, 1963). A proglacial lake in front of the Marks Moraine carried red clay westward to the Lake Agassiz basin, where it was deposited in the uppermost sediments of Lake Agassiz in the area between the Hartman Moraine on the north and the Minnesota border on the south. If these are the sediments of Lake Agassiz II, as is implied by Elson (1957, Fig. 2), then a means is available for correlating the Agassiz events with those of the Lake Superior basin in the following way:

Lake Agassiz II withdrew from the Campbell Beach 9,200 years ago (W-1057), as low outlets to the east were uncovered, presumably by retreat of the ice from the Hartman–Dog Lake–Marks Moraines. The red clay and the Marks Moraine are therefore not much older than 9,200 years. Zoltai (1963) indicates that Lake Duluth then was formed, but this Ontario portion of Lake Duluth (if it be a portion) must therefore be much younger than Lake Nemadji and its immediate successor Lake Duluth in the type area at the western end of Lake Superior, where it was first formed at the close of the Nickerson phase, perhaps 11,500 years ago. The Ontario lake may rather be compared with a similar ice-marginal lake on the south side of the Superior Lobe in northern Michigan—Lake Ontonagon, whose red lake clay bears wood dated at 10,220 years ago (M-359).

If Elson's (1957) projection of the Campbell beach to the Hartman Moraine is incorrect, then the red-clay band may refer to Lake Agassiz I (pre-Campbell) instead of II, and the Hartman Moraine could correlate with the Valders phase or even with the Nickerson phase of the Minnesota sequence. Such a correlation is supported by a recent C^{14} date of 9,380 years ago (GSC-287) from a Lake Superior beach much lower than Lake Duluth and associated with an ice front 120 miles northeast of the Hartman Moraine and separated from it by two more moraines, providing one considers that at least 2,000 years is necessary for 120 miles of ice retreat and moraine formation (S. C. Zoltai, written communication).

References

Alden, W. C., and Leighton, M. M., 1917, The Iowan drift, a review of the evidence of the Iowan stage of glaciation: Iowa Geol. Surv., v. 26, p. 49-212

American Commission on Stratigraphic Nomenclature, 1961, Code of stratigraphic nomenclature: Amer. Assoc. Petroleum Geologists Bull., v. 45, p. 645-665

Bain, H. F., 1897, Relations of the Wisconsin and Kansan drift sheets in central Iowa and related phenomena: Iowa Geol. Surv., v. 7, p. 433-487

Baker, R. G., 1964, Late-Wisconsin glacial geology and vegetation history of the Alborn area, St. Louis County, Minnesota: Univ. Minnesota M.S. thesis, 44 p.

Calvin, Samuel, 1911, The Iowan drift: J. Geol., v. 19, p. 577-602

Carman, J. E., 1931, Further studies on the Pleistocene geology of northwestern Iowa: Iowa Geol. Surv., v. 35, p. 15-194

Cooper, W. S., 1935, The history of the upper Mississippi River in late Wisconsin and postglacial time: Minnesota Geol. Surv. Bull. 26, 116 p.

Cotter, R. D., Young, H. L., and Winter, T. C., 1964, Preliminary surficial geologic map of the Mesabi-Vermilion iron range area, northeastern Minnesota: U.S. Geol. Surv. Misc. Geol. Inv. Map 1-403

Cushing, E. J., 1963, Origin of pseudostratification and interlayering in glacial tills (abst.): Geol. Soc. Amer. Spec. Pap. 76, p. 58

Elson, J. A., 1957, Lake Agassiz and the Mankato-Valders problem: Science, v. 126, p. 999-1002

Farnham, R. S., McAndrews, J. H., and Wright, H. E., Jr., 1964, A late-Wisconsin buried soil near Aitkin, Minnesota, and its paleobotanical setting: Amer. J. Sci., v. 262, p. 393-412

Frye, J. C., and Willman, H. B., 1960, Classification of the Wisconsinan Stage in the Lake Michigan glacial lobe: Illinois State Geol. Surv. Circ. 285, 16 p.

Frye, J. C., William, H. B., and Black, R. F., this volume, Outline of glacial geology of Illinois and Wisconsin

Hutton, C. E., 1947, Studies of loess-derived soils in southwestern Iowa: Soil. Sci. Soc. Amer. Proc., v. 12, p. 424-431

Jelgersma, Saskia, 1962, A late-glacial pollen diagram from Madelia, southcentral Minnesota: Amer. J. Sci., v. 260, p. 522-529

Johnston, W. A., 1946, Glacial Lake Agassiz, with special reference to the mode of deformation of the beaches: Geol. Surv. Canada Bull. 7, 29 p.

Kay, G. F., 1928, Loveland loess, post-Illinoian, pre-Iowan in age: Science, v. 68, p. 482-483

Kay, G. F., and Apfel, E. T., 1929, The pre-Illinoian Pleistocene geology of Iowa: Iowa Geol. Surv., v. 34, 304 p.

Kay, G. F., and Graham, J. B., 1943, The Illinoian and post-Illinoian Pleistocene geology of Iowa: Iowa Geol. Surv., v. 38, p. 1-262

Leighton, M. M., 1933, The naming of the subdivisions of the Wisconsin glacial age: Science, v. 77, p. 168

Leighton, M. M., and Willman, H. B., 1950, Loess formations of the Mississippi Valley: J. Geol., v. 58, p. 599-623

Leverett, Frank, 1926, The Pleistocene glacial stages: were there more than four? Amer. Philos. Soc. Proc., v. 45, p. 105-118

—— 1929, Moraines and shorelines of the Lake Superior region: U.S. Geol. Surv. Prof. Pap. 154-A, 72 p.

—— 1932, Quarternary geology of Minnesota and parts of adjacent states: U.S. Geol. Surv. Prof. Pap. 161, 149 p.

—— 1939, The place of the Iowan drift: J. Geol., v. 47, p. 398-407

McGee, W J, 1891, The Pleistocene history of northeastern Iowa: U.S. Geol. Surv. Ann. Rep. 11, p. 189-577

Rubin, M., and Alexander, C., 1960, U.S. Geological Survey radiocarbon dates v: Amer. J. Sci. Radiocarbon Suppl., v. 2, p. 129-185

Ruhe, R. V., 1950, Graphic analysis of drift topographies: Amer. J. Sci., v. 248, p. 435-443

—— 1952, Topographic discontinuities of the Des Moines lobe: Amer. J. Sci., v. 250, p. 46-56

—— 1954a, Relations of the properties of Wisconsin loess to topography in western Iowa: Amer. J. Sci., v. 252, p. 663-672

—— 1954b, Pleistocene soils along the Rock Island relocation in southwestern Iowa: Amer. Railway Engr. Assoc. Bull. 514, p. 639-645

—— 1956, Geomorphic surfaces and the nature of soils: Soil Sci., v. 82, 441-455

—— 1960, Elements of the soil landscape: 7th Intern. Congr. Soil Sci. Trans., v. 4, p. 165-170

Ruhe, R. V., this volume, Quaternary paleopedology

Ruhe, R. V., and Gould, L. M., 1954, Glacial geology of the Dakota County area, Minnesota: Geol. Soc. Amer. Bull., v. 65, p. 769-792

Ruhe, R. V., Rubin, Meyer, and Scholtes, W. H., 1957, Late Pleistocene radiocarbon chronology in Iowa: Amer. J. Sci., v. 255, p. 671-689

Ruhe, R. V., and Scholtes, W. H., 1959, Important elements in the classification of the Wisconsin glacial stage: a discussion: J. Geol., v. 67, p. 585-593

Schneider, A. F., 1961, Pleistocene geology of the Randall region, central Minnesota: Minnesota Geol. Surv. Bull. 40, 151 p.

Scholtes, W. H., 1955, Properties and classification of the paha loess-derived soils in northeastern Iowa: Iowa State Univ. J. Sci., v. 30, p. 163-209

Schoewe, W. H., 1920, the origin and history of extinct Lake Calvin: Iowa Geol. Surv., v. 29, p. 49-222

Shay, C. T., 1965, Postglacial vegetation development in northwestern Minnesota, and its implications for prehistoric man: Univ. Minnesota M.S. thesis

Shimek, Bohumil, 1909, Aftonian sand and gravels in western Iowa: Geol. Soc. Amer. Bull., v. 20, p. 399-408

Sloan, R. S., 1964, The Cretaceous System in Minnesota: Minnesota Geol. Surv. Rep. Inv. 5, 64 p.

Thomas, J. A., 1959, Geology of the Cloquet area, northeastern Minnesota: Univ. Minnesota M.S. thesis, 67 p.

Upham, Warren, 1896, The glacial Lake Agassiz: U.S. Geol. Survey Monogr. 25, 685 p.

Winchell, N. H., 1884, 1888, Geology of Minnesota: Minnesota Geol. Nat. Hist. Surv., Final Rep., v. 1, 697 p., v. 2, 695 p.

Wright, H. E., Jr., 1955, Valders drift in Minnesota: J. Geol., v. 63, p. 403-411

—— 1956, Sequence of glaciation in eastern Minnesota. Geol. Soc. Amer. Guidebook, Minneapolis Meeting, pt. 3, p. 1-24

—— 1962, Role of the Wadena lobe in the Wisconsin glaciation of Minnesota: Geol. Soc. Amer. Bull., v. 73, p. 73-100

—— 1964, Classification of the Wisconsin glacial stage: J. Geol., v. 72, p. 628-637

Wright, H. E., Jr., and Rubin, Meyer, 1956, Radiocarbon dates of Mankato drift in Minnesota: Science, v. 124, p. 625-626; Discussion: 1957, Science, v. 125, p. 1037-1039

Wright, H. E., Jr., Winter, T. C., and Patten, H. L., 1963, Two pollen diagrams from southeastern Minnesota: problems in the regional late-glacial and postglacial vegetational history: Geol. Soc. Amer. Bull., v. 74, p. 1371-1396

Zoltai, S. C., 1961, Glacial history of part of northwestern Ontario: Geol. Assoc. Canada Proc., v. 13, p. 61-83

—— 1963, Glacial features of the Canadian Lakehead area: Can. Geographer, v. 7, p. 101-115

Zumberge, J. H., 1952, Lakes of Minnesota—their origin and classification: Minnesota Geol. Surv. Bull. 35, 99 p.

SUMMARY

Drifts of all four major glacial and interglacial stages of the Pleistocene occur in the area. Nebraskan drift and Aftonian paleosols and sediments are found buried by Kansan drift in southern Iowa. Kansan drift and Yarmouth paleosol and sediments are common under younger loess in south-central Iowa. Illinoian till is found only close to the Mississippi River in southeastern Iowa, but its correlative Loveland loess is widespread near the Missouri River in western Iowa, with well-developed Sangamon paleosol on top. Much of the so-called Iowan till may actually be older till from which the top has been eroded, as implied by C^{14} dates, but the Iowan problem is not completely solved. Loess was extensively deposited in Iowa during the period 29,000 to 20,000 years ago, when it was interrupted by the ice advance of the Tazewell phase of Wisconsin glaciation. Loess deposition continued in Iowa until about 14,000 years ago.

Wisconsin glaciation in Minnesota involved the interactions of four major ice lobes, from west to east the Des Moines, Wadena, Rainy, and Superior, localized by bedrock lowlands and characterized by distinctive rock types that reflect the bedrock geology of northern Minnesota and adjacent Canada. Only the Des Moines Lobe affected Iowa, reaching a maximum there about 14,000 years ago (=Cary). The Wisconsin glacial history in Minnesota is described in five phases of ice advance, correlated by C^{14} dates with the Cary (possibly Tazewell) to Port Huron advances of the Lake Michigan Lobe. Interactions of ice lobes are recorded by erosion and redeposition of drifts, stratigraphic superposition, overriding of moraines, drumlins, tunnel valleys, eskers, and other landforms, formation of ice-bordered lakes, and blocking of outwash valley trains and lake-outlet stream channels. Glacial Lakes Duluth, Upham, Aitkin, and Agassiz record late stages in ice recession. The active ice was apparently wasted completely from Minnesota by the time of the Two Creeks interval, and it did not re-enter the area during the Valders phase.

OUTLINE OF GLACIAL GEOLOGY OF ILLINOIS AND WISCONSIN

JOHN C. FRYE,[1] H. B. WILLMAN,[1] ROBERT F. BLACK[2]

THE GEOGRAPHIC position of Illinois and Wisconsin makes them unique in the glacial history of North America, because glacial lobes from both east and west of Hudson Bay, Canada, extensively invaded them and attained the southernmost limit of continental glaciation in the northern hemisphere (Fig. 1). Perhaps also because of their geographic setting these two states contain deposits (Fig. 2) from the greatest number of glacial advances so far documented for any region in the United States (Fig. 3).

The presently used North American standard classification of Pleistocene glacial deposits was developed during the last three-quarters of a century in the upper Mississippi Valley region, and type localities for the Illinoian, Sangamonian, and Wisconsinan occur within Illinois and Wisconsin. Type sequences for the Illinoian and Wisconsinan are drawn from deposits made by the Lake Michigan lobe, whereas type sequences for the Nebraskan and Kansan, west of the Mississippi River, are drawn from deposits made by the western (Keewatin) glacial advance. The stratigraphic relation of the younger Pleistocene deposits to the Kansan is based on their overlapping relations in the Mississippi Valley, particularly in western Illinois.

The early descriptions of the surficial drift did not recognize their glacial origin (Worthen, 1866). However, shortly thereafter the drift was acknowledged to be the product of continental glaciers. Chamberlin (1878, 1880) seems to have been the first to use topographic form to interpret glacial movements and weathering of the drift to infer age. Later the presence of prominent and widespread buried soils served as the primary criterion for establishment of major episodes of glaciation (Leverett, 1889, 1909). Erosion of bedrock valleys and differences of stream-terrace levels added support to the concept of great time intervals between glaciations (Chamberlin, 1890; Hershey, 1893). Salisbury (1893) detailed 12 criteria for the recognition of distinct glacial epochs. This was followed by the first attempt to give geographic names to drifts of different ages (Chamberlin, in Geikie, 1894). Minor subdivisions and units for mapping purposes continued to be based largely on topographic expression (Leverett, 1899; Leighton, 1917; Alden, 1909, 1918; Thwaites, 1928a; Leighton and Powers, 1934). The single classification that developed in this manner was a mixture of units based on different kinds of criteria.

The present policy utilizes multiple schemes of stratigraphic classification (Willman, Swann, and Frye, 1958; A.C.S.N., 1961), as described for use in the Pleistocene

(Frye and Leonard, 1952; this volume; Frye and Willman, 1960). The major time-stratigraphic units (stages) are recognized throughout the Midwest, and subdivisions of these units (substages) are recognized in these two states for the Illinoian and Wisconsinan. The deposits are objectively classed as rock-stratigraphic units of local extent and morphostratigraphic units, which may be even more local

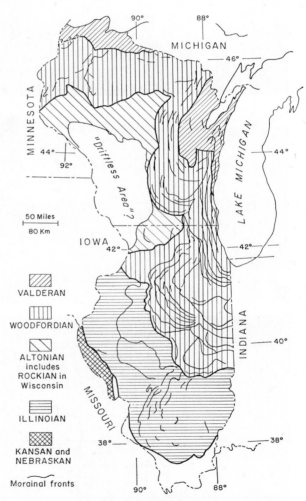

Figure 1. Map of Illinois and Wisconsin showing the distribution of surficial glacial deposits. The "Driftless Area" may have been partly or wholly covered by glacial ice during the Pleistocene. Modified from Thwaites (1956), Ekblaw (1960), and Flint et al. (1959).

[1] Illinois State Geological Survey, Urbana, Illinois.
[2] Department of Geology, University of Wisconsin, Madison 6, Wisconsin.

Figure 2. Pleistocene stratigraphy and surface features in Illinois and Wisconsin.

in extent. The development of these classifications is in a preliminary state. Soils are recognized as units in a separate stratigraphic classification.

Traditional methods of correlation are still of value in studying and correlating glacial deposits in the Illinois-Wisconsin area—intercalated buried soils, peat zones, gravel, and loess; fossils; general lithology; and topographic expression of end moraines, recessional moraines, and terraces. However, in recent years two relatively new techniques have greatly increased the precision and detail of correlation in this area. These are the extensive use of radiocarbon dates in the Wisconsinan (approximately 100 dates have been determined from the two states; Figure 5), and extensive studies of the mineral compositions of the fine sand, silt, and clay fractions of tills, loesses, and outwash by X-ray diffraction and optical-microscope analysis. This latter technique has been particularly useful in Illinois because of the diversity in source areas of the Pleistocene deposits, but it is applicable to all ages of Pleistocene deposits.

The rocks below the glacial deposits in the area range from Precambrian in northern Wisconsin upward through each system of Paleozoic rocks, including the Pennsylvanian (Weller *et al.*, 1945; Bean, 1939). Rocks of Cretaceous age occur to the northwest of these states and in small areas in extreme western Illinois (Frye, Willman, and Glass, 1964) and southwestern Wisconsin (Andrews, 1958). In general, however, the age of the bedrock becomes progressively younger southward through the region, and more than half of the glaciated area of Illinois is underlain by Pennsylvanian rocks.

Key to Figure 2:

A. Pro-Kansan silts (calcareous and sparsely fossiliferous) on Afton Soil developed on Nebraskan outwash. Zion Church geologic section, SE¼, SE¼, SW¼, sec. 9, T. 3 S., R. 8 W., Adams County, Illinois.

B. Peoria Loess (Woodfordian) and Roxana Loess (Altonian), on Sangamon Soil in Mendon till (Liman), on Yarmouth Soil in Kansan till. Rushville (4.5 W.) geologic section, NW¼, SW¼, SW¼, sec. 5, T. 1 N., R. 1 W., Schuyler County, Illinois.

C. Peoria Loess (Woodfordian) and Roxana Loess (Altonian) on Sangamon Soil in Buffalo Hart till (Illinoian). Hipple School North geologic section, NW¼, SW¼, SW¼, sec. 8, T. 7 N., R. 3 E., Fulton County, Illinois.

D. Richland Loess, on thick Shelbyville till, on Morton Loess (Woodfordian), on Farmdale Silt (Farmdalian), on accretion-gley of the Sangamon Soil on Buffalo Hart till (Illinoian). Farm Creek railroad-cut geologic section, cent. sec. 31, T. 26 N., R. 3 W., Tazewell County, Illinois.

E. Monument of St. Peter Sandstone (Ordovician) 5 km southeast of Monticello, Green County, Wisconsin (NW¼, SW¼, sec. 28, T. 3 N., R. 8 E.). The outcrop is at least 5 km inside the area covered by ice of late Altonian age.

F. Ice-wedge cast of clean yellow-brown sand in red-brown gravelly sand and sandy gravel of late Altonian (Rockian) age, River Falls, Wisconsin (SW¼, SW¼, sec. 36, T. 28 N., R. 19 W.).

G. Two Creeks paleosol on silts, overlain by Valders till, at depth of 365 cm, SW¼, SE¼, sec. 19, T. 23 N., R. 19 E., Outagamie County, Wisconsin.

H. Terminal moraine and outwash plain of the Chippewa lobe of middle Woodfordian "Cary" age in Chippewa County, Wisconsin. View northeast from a point 7 km north of Chippewa Falls, on highway 53.

The topography of Illinois and Wisconsin when the first continental glaciers advanced possessed significantly less relief than the present topography of the bedrock surface (Trowbridge, 1921; Frye, 1963). A plains topography may have existed at the position of the present uplands, and the major Nebraskan valleys were well above the present flood plains, which in turn are 150 to 250 ft (50 to 75 m) above the bedrock floors of the deeply filled valleys. Present data from Illinois indicate that the deep valleys were trenched in post-Nebraskan time, perhaps reaching their deepest incision during the Kansan, and that the maximum topographic relief of the Kansan has not been attained since then. Thwaites (1960) doubts that any erosional surfaces that formed before major valley incision have survived in southwestern Wisconsin.

Essential to a description of the glacial stratigraphy of these states is an understanding of the lobate configuration of the glaciers that advanced out of Canada into the region. The maximum extension of the several glacial lobes into Illinois is shown in Figure 4, and the arrows show, in a general way, the axial position of the several lobes. As these lobes crossed different parts of the Canadian Shield, they eroded different crystalline rocks and so are characterized by recognizable differences in their heavy-mineral suites. Because they crossed different belts of Paleozoic and Mesozoic rocks they are also characterized by differences in their assemblages of clay and carbonate minerals (Willman *et al.*, 1963). Distinctive rock types also characterize the pebbles and coarser materials found in the drift of some lobes (Anderson, 1957). The contrasting mineral compositions are shown by the averages for the several tills and loesses in Illinois given in Tables 1 and 2.

Five distinct glacial lobes advanced into the region, and one was complex within itself. Glaciers that entered Illinois and Wisconsin from the northwest dispersed from centers west of Hudson Bay that may be grouped as the Keewatin center. As glaciers from this dispersal center advanced on a broad front, the composition of the tills gradationally change across the area. In Illinois (Frye *et al.*, 1962; Willman *et al.*, 1963) the tills and loesses derived from this source are relatively rich in montmorillonite among the clay minerals and in hornblende and epidote among the heavy minerals, and they contain markedly more calcite than dolomite. In the tills of western Wisconsin, illite and montmorillonite prevail (Akers, 1961), and among the heavy minerals hornblende, epidote, pyroxene, magnetite, and garnet may dominate.

Lake Michigan and Green Bay define the position of two nearly parallel lobes that were particularly significant during the Illinoian and Wisconsinan. The dispersal center for glaciers in these lobes was in Ontario, slightly north-northeast of these two basins. Ice from Lake Superior also entered Green Bay. Tills from the Lake Michigan lobe are rich in illite among the clay minerals and in hornblende, garnet, and epidote among the transparent heavy minerals; they contain more dolomite than calcite. Tills from Green Bay are similar but contain less garnet and illite and more vermiculite and epidote. Precambrian pebbles are distinct between part of the Green Bay lobe and the Lake Michigan lobe (Anderson, 1957). Tills deposited by the

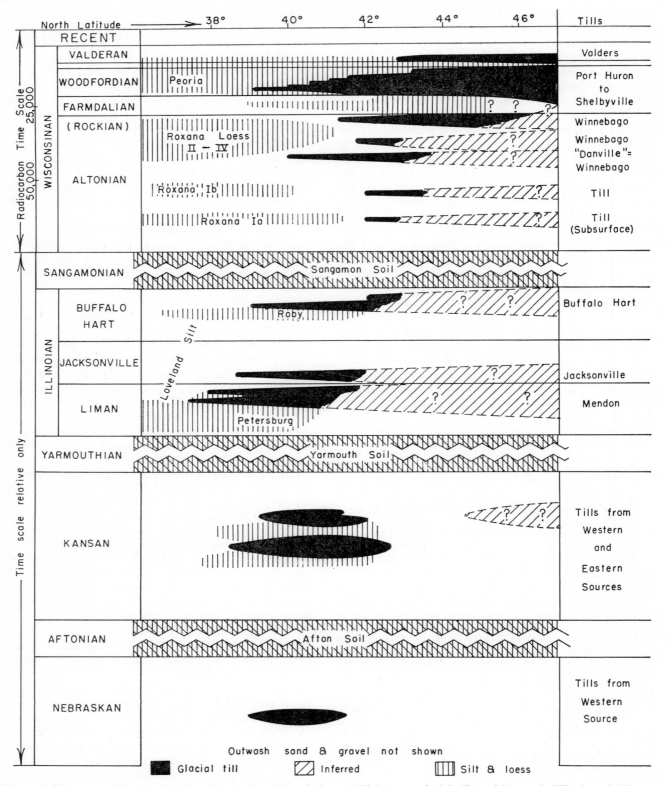

Figure 3. Time-space diagram showing the stratigraphic relations of Pleistocene glacial tills and loesses in Illinois and Wisconsin. The southernmost extent of each glacial advance is plotted without regard to east-west position within the states. Kansan and Nebraskan glaciers that invaded Illinois from the northeast or northwest did not reach into extreme northern Illinois or southern Wisconsin.

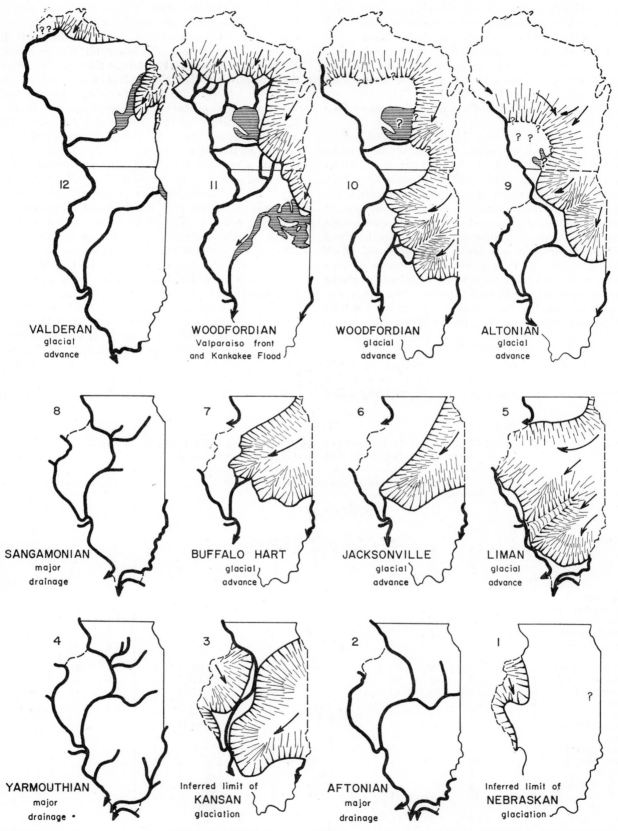

Figure 4. Sketch maps showing the glacial history of Illinois and Wisconsin. For scale, the Illinois-Wisconsin boundary is 150 miles (240 km) long.

glaciers moving from Saginaw Bay (Zumberge, 1960) across Michigan and into Illinois are also similar to those from Lake Michigan but have a somewhat higher garnet content among the heavy minerals. The easternmost source area is represented by tills in east-central and southern Illinois that were produced by the glacial lobe advancing southwestward from the Lake Erie basin. These tills are distinguished by their high content of calcite, garnet, and illite.

The following outline leaves blank much of the early Pleistocene history of Wisconsin. Although glacial deposits in western (Chamberlin, R. T., 1910; Flint *et al.*, 1959) and central (Weidman, 1907, 1913) Wisconsin have been correlated with each major stage of the Pleistocene, the oldest drift in central Wisconsin is clearly Wisconsinan according to depth of leaching and weathering of constituents (Hole, 1943). As its correlative drift to the west has been dated by radiocarbon as only about 30,000 years old, Black (1959a) interprets the drift of western Wisconsin as Wisconsinan. Isolated deposits most easily explained by glacial action are found in the classical "Driftless Area" of southwestern Wisconsin, but unfortunately no way has yet been found to date them. Some may be pre-Wisconsinan.

NEBRASKAN STAGE

The first recorded Pleistocene glacial advance in North America was named Nebraskan because of its extension into the state of Nebraska. This stage was originally called Kansan (Chamberlin, 1894, p. 753-764), but after Bain (1897, p. 464) traced the overlying till from the original type locality in Union County, Iowa, into the surficial till of northeastern Kansas the lower till was renamed the Nebraskan (Shimek, 1909), and the till above was renamed the Kansan. Nebraskan glaciers from a Keewatin center are known to have invaded this area only in western Illinois. Exposures of till of this age are exceedingly rare east of the Mississippi River, but its presence at a few places (Wanless, 1957) demonstrates that the glacier crossed the present position of the river (Fig. 4). Upland deposits in Calhoun County, Illinois (Rubey, 1952), formerly supposed to have been unglaciated, may be Nebraskan till (Willman and Frye, 1958). Erratic boulders in the "Driftless Area" of northwestern Illinois may also represent Nebraskan glaciation, and outwash deposits at several places in western Illinois are demonstrably of Nebraskan age (Frye *et al.*, 1964). From southern Illinois southward in the Mississippi Valley, chert gravels generally considered of Tertiary age (Leighton and Willman, 1950) have been correlated by Fisk (1944) with stages of the Pleistocene.

It has been suggested that Nebraskan till from an eastern glacial lobe may occur in extreme east-central Illinois (Eveland, 1952), but evidence to establish this relationship is not conclusive (Ekblaw and Willman, 1957). Although several localities of outwash and a few of till of this age are known, so far no Nebraskan loess is recognized in the area.

It seems probable that the Nebraskan glacier largely

TABLE 1

Heavy and Light Minerals in the Sand Fraction of Glacial and Related Deposits in Illinois
(From Frye *et al.*, 1962; Willman *et al.*, 1963; Frye *et al.*, 1964)

Stratigraphic unit	Transparent heavy minerals (average percent)										Light minerals (average)			
	Tourmaline	Zircon	Garnet	Epidote	Rutile	Sillimanite	Kyanite	Staurolite	Hornblende	Others	Quartz	K Feldspar	Na-Ca Feldspar	Others
Wisconsinan														
Woodfordian till	1	2	12	14	tr.	—	tr.	—	64	7	70	19	8	3
Peoria Loess	2	9	8	22	—	—	—	tr.	51	8	72	15	9	4
Winnebago till	2	1	12	17	tr.	—	—	tr.	62	6	72	17	8	3
Roxana Loess	2	11	11	24	—	—	—	tr.	46	6	72	16	9	3
Illinoian														
Buffalo Hart till	3	3	12	11	tr.	—	tr.	—	66	5	73	13	8	6
Jacksonville till	2	2	16	16	—	—	—	—	57	7	70	18	7	5
Mendon till	3	2	16	15	tr.	—	tr.	—	55	9	73	13	9	5
Kansan														
Eastern till	1	1	21	5	—	—	—	—	58	14	76	10	10	4
Western till	4	4	10	23	1	—	tr.	2	49	7	76	12	8	4
Tertiary														
Grover gravel	19	60	2	5	2	—	2	5	1	4				
"Lafayette" gravel	11	36	3	2	2	6	16	32	—	1				
Cretaceous														
McNairy Fm.	11	8	tr.	1	6	8	45	15	—	6				
Baylis Fm.	31	45	1	1	3	—	3	14	1	1				
Pennsylvanian														
in western Ill.	22	60	3	tr.	11	1	—	—	—	3				

tr. = trace
Fm. = formation

TABLE 2

Clay and Carbonate Minerals in Glacial Deposits in Illinois: by Stratigraphic Unit
(Analyses by H. D. Glass in Frye *et al.*, 1962; Willman *et al.*, 1963; Frye *et al.*, 1964)

Stratigraphic unit	Clay minerals (average percent)			Carbonate minerals
	Montmoril-lonite	Illite	Kaolinite and chlorite	(Ca = calcite; Do = dolomite)
Wisconsinan				
Woodfordian till	4	79	17	Do > Ca
Peoria Loess	65	24	11	Do > Ca
Winnebago till	25	59	16	Do > Ca
Roxana Loess	63	17	20	Do > Ca
Illinoian				
Buffalo Hart till	5	69	26	Do > Ca
Jacksonville till	21	68	11	Do > Ca
Mendon till	36	45	19	Do > Ca
Petersburg Silt	66	19	15	Do > Ca
Kansan				
Western till (west of about 90°30′ W. Long.)	66	13	21	Do < Ca
Western till (east of about 90°30′ W. Long.)	43	35	22	Do = Ca
Eastern till	8	65	27	Do < Ca

determined the position of the Ancient Mississippi River throughout its course above the mouth of the Missouri River and, less directly, the position of the river southward to the head of the Embayment region.

AFTONIAN STAGE

The Aftonian Stage, defined from water-laid sediments at Afton Junction, Iowa (Chamberlin, 1894), is known with certainty in Illinois only as the Afton Soil, which is exposed at a few localities. The Afton Soil has recently been described in Adams County (Frye *et al.*, 1964), where it occurs in Nebraskan outwash gravels (Fig. 2A) overlain by calcareous pro-Kansan silts and Kansan till. In the same part of western Illinois, peaty deposits formerly classed as Aftonian or older (Horberg, 1956) are now judged to be early Kansan in age, but compact, greenish gray, noncalcareous silt present locally beneath the Kansan till may be Aftonian or older. At several places in western Illinois, weathering profiles below known Kansan deposits and on bedrock, Cretaceous sand, or lag gravel from Nebraskan deposits could represent an Afton Soil, if it is assumed that Nebraskan glaciers eroded the preglacial soil.

KANSAN STAGE

The Kansan Stage, redefined from deposits in Union County, Iowa, is named from a type area in northeastern Kansas (Frye and Leonard, 1952). Type Kansan is based on till deposited by the Keewatin (western) glacier that invaded western Illinois from Iowa and Missouri (Fig. 4). A till in eastern Illinois (MacClintock, 1929) that was deposited by an eastern (Erie) glacial lobe is correlated with the Kansan of western Illinois, because they have the same relation to the overlying Illinoian till and because their associated water-laid deposits contain a similar fauna of fossil mollusks, but the physical stratigraphic relations of these

tills from eastern and western sources have not been as yet firmly established (Fig. 4).

Although Kansan till of eastern source occurs nowhere in Illinois as the surface till, western (Keewatin) Kansan till in an area in Adams and Pike Counties (Frye *et al.*, 1964) is the uppermost glacial deposit (Figs. 1 and 4). Also, at several places west of the Illinois River Valley Kansan till is well exposed below Illinoian till (Willman *et al.*, 1963), which overrode it from the northeast (Fig. 2B). Water-laid silt, sand, and gravel within the western Kansan drift may in the future serve as a basis for subdivision of Kansan drift.

Till and associated glacial-fluvial deposits on high terraces of the Wisconsin River have been correlated with the Kansan Stage (MacClintock, 1922). They were partly derived from the northwest and may temporarily have reversed the river. Thwaites (1928b) disagreed and traced some other possibly equivalent terraces of the "Driftless Area" to the drifts in central Wisconsin that are now considered Wisconsinan (Hole, 1943).

In both eastern and western Illinois, water-laid and loess-like silts are associated with the lower part of the Kansan till or occur conformably below it. Such silts are generally calcareous and at several places have yielded fossil snail faunas. At no place has evidence of weathering been observed between such silts and the overlying till, but at several places these calcareous Kansan silts rest on an Afton Soil. Water-laid or loessial deposits of Kansan age have not been observed resting on Kansan till. The upper surface of the Kansan till, except where dissected by subsequent erosion, generally is deeply weathered.

Deposits of Kansan age have not as yet been identified in the subsurface of northernmost Illinois or in eastern Wisconsin, but Kansan drift in north-central Illinois has a mineral composition more like the Illinoian of the Lake Michigan lobe than the eastern Kansan of the Erie lobe and may indicate the existence of a Lake Michigan glacial lobe during Kansan time (Johnson, 1964).

YARMOUTHIAN STAGE

The name Yarmouth was proposed by Leverett (1898a) to apply to the soil that separates the tills of Kansan and Illinoian age in east-central Iowa. In extreme western Illinois the Yarmouth Soil is overlain by Illinoian Loveland Silt. Along the Illinois River Valley (Fig. 2B) and farther east in central Illinois it is overlain by tills of Illinoian age. The soil commonly shows a poorly to moderately well-drained profile, developed *in situ*, but at several places it consists of accretion-gley deposits as much as 5 to 6 feet thick. In southern Illinois the Yarmouth Soil has been developed in Paleozoic rocks and is directly overlain by Illinoian till and by Loveland Silt (Frye *et al.*, 1962), but this soil has not as yet been identified in extreme northern Illinois or in Wisconsin.

Great lake trout and other fossils in northern Wisconsin, formerly correlated (Hussakof, 1916) with the Yarmouthian Stage, are now considered Wisconsinan.

ILLINOIAN STAGE

The name Illinois till sheet was first proposed by Leverett (*in* Chamberlin, 1896), and shortly thereafter he (Leverett, 1899) documented the extent of Illinoian glaciation in central and southern Illinois. The stage was defined as the deposits lying above the Yarmouth Soil and below the Sangamon Soil (Fig. 2B, C) in western, central, and southern Illinois. Much of the area within North America in which deposits of this age constitute the surficial glacial deposits lies in the state of Illinois (Fig. 1), and it is here that its stratigraphic position above Kansan tills and below Wisconsinan tills has been demonstrated. The drift formerly called Illinoian in northern Illinois and southern Wisconsin (Alden, 1918; Leighton and Brophy, 1961) is here considered Wisconsinan, as shown by Shaffer (1956).

Glacial lobes in the position of the Lake Michigan Basin have not been identified for the Nebraskan nor with certainty for the Kansan, but in Illinoian time a lobe in this position attained particular prominence (Fig. 4). Whereas western (Keewatin) glaciers had invaded the western part of Illinois during the two previous advances, Illinoian glaciers did not reach Illinois from the west. A glacial advance from the northeast (Saginaw or Erie lobe), however, extended into southeastern Illinois, deflecting the Lake Michigan lobe glacier to the west, and attained the southernmost extent of any Pleistocene continental glacier in the northern hemisphere.

Three substages (time-stratigraphic units) are recognized within the Illinoian of Illinois (Fig. 3). The oldest (lowest) of these, formerly called Payson, has recently been re-described and renamed Liman (Frye *et al.*, 1964), the second is called Jacksonville, and the youngest Buffalo Hart.

Beyond the limit of Illinoian glaciation, Illinoian loess and water-laid silts and sands are commonly deeply weathered and have the Sangamon Soil in their uppermost part; these silts are in turn overlain by Wisconsinan loesses. Because of the correlation of these deposits with loess and sandy loess called Loveland in western Iowa and the Great Plains region (Frye and Leonard, 1951), they are classed as Loveland Silt in Illinois (Leighton and Willman, 1950). As the largest and most extensive Illinoian silt unit is the Petersburg Silt of early Illinoian age, it is presumed that a major part of the Loveland is of the same age. However, the Loveland includes silt and sand deposits representing the entire Illinoian. At some places in western Illinois at least one minor soil occurs within the Loveland Silt.

LIMAN SUBSTAGE

The Liman Substage was defined from the Pryor School section in Lima Township, Adams County, Illinois (Frye *et al.*, 1964). At this locality, and generally throughout western and south-central Illinois, it includes two rock-stratigraphic units—the Petersburg Silt at the base and the Mendon and equivalent tills above.

The Petersburg contains both loess and water-laid silts and fine sands, it attains a maximum thickness of more than 30 ft (9 m), and locally it contains an abundant fauna of fossil snails. At many places it rests on a well-developed Yarmouth Soil developed in Kansan till or in bedrock, but a weathered zone separating it from the overlying till has nowhere been observed. The Petersburg is interpreted as loess, outwash, and lacustrine sediments deposited during the period of advance of the earliest Illinoian glacier. The mineralogy of this unit in the Illinois and Mississippi Valley area shows a striking change from bottom to top, reflecting the composition of the underlying western Kansan till in the base and the Illinoian till of the advancing Lake Michigan lobe in its upper part.

Whereas tills of Liman age in western and central Illinois were deposited by the glacial lobe that advanced through the basin of Lake Michigan, tills of this age in southern and east-central Illinois were deposited by a glacial lobe from the northeast, probably the Saginaw lobe (Figs. 1, 4). The two areas are separated by an interlobate belt of ridged drift. These earliest Illinoian tills are distinguishable, on the basis of their mineral composition (Tables 1, 2), from each other and from the Kansan tills below (Willman *et al.*, 1963). In southwestern Illinois a thin zone of silt, locally containing sparse fossil snail shells, occurs within the tills of Liman age.

The most striking characteristic of Liman deposits is the vast expanse of essentially featureless till plain in south-central and west-central Illinois. In no other area of North America is found a region underlain by glacial till that so completely lacks both topographic features of glacial deposition and erosional dissection. In fact, it resembles the topography of the High Plains except for the sharp ridges and hillocks that locally demonstrate the glacial origin of the topography. Although many of these ridges have been ascribed to crevasse fillings in stagnant ice (Leighton and Brophy, 1961; Leighton, 1959), their preponderant composition of glacial till and their topographic shape and large size prompt us to interpret them as interlobate ridges rising above a till plain that has been smoothed by local erosion and deposition, as indicated by abundant accretion gleys.

Glaciers of Liman age overrode the Ancient Mississippi

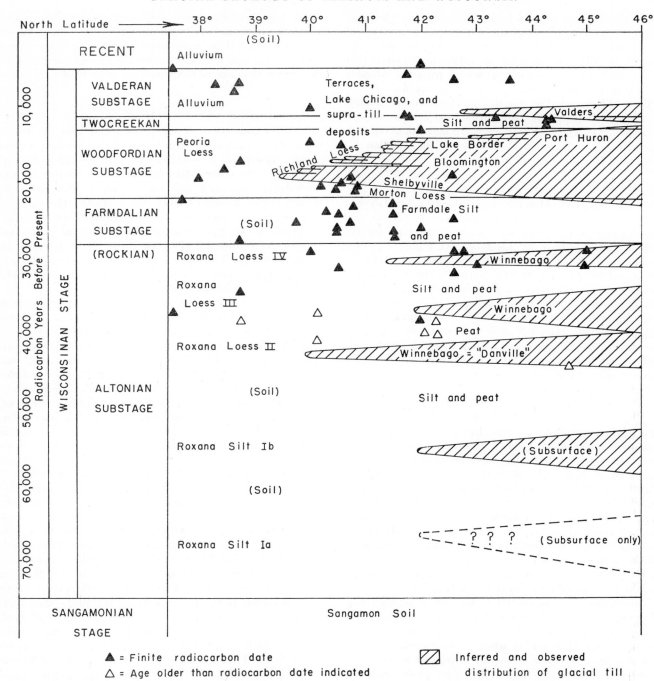

Figure 5. Time-space diagram showing the relation of available radiocarbon dates to the Wisconsinan glaciers in Illinois and Wisconsin. The southernmost extent of each glacial advance is plotted without regard to east-west position within the states. Each radiocarbon date symbol indicates a single determination except for the Two Creeks locality in Wisconsin where the symbols represent averages of many dates. The majority of the dates shown were determined by the U.S. Geological Survey in the Washington Laboratory (W), but some dates are included from Chicago (C), Isotopes, Inc. (I), Lamont (L), and Yale (Y).

Valley and forced the river into a position across eastern Iowa (Schoewe, 1920). When the Illinoian glacier retreated, the river returned to the position of the major valley through Illinois (Fig. 4), from which it was later permanently deflected by the early Woodfordian glacier (Shaffer, 1954).

JACKSONVILLE SUBSTAGE

The name Jacksonville was first applied by Ball (1937) to a moraine that occurs just west of Jacksonville, Illinois, and the till of this area was later used as the type for the substage (Leighton and Willman, 1950). The substage includes the till and outwash that occur stratigraphically above the Mendon till and below the Roby Silt (Johnson, 1964). As neither a soil profile nor extensive deposits of fossiliferous silts have been observed separating the Jacksonville till from the Mendon till below, it is judged that this glacial advance was not separated from the Mendon by a long interval of time.

West of Illinois Valley, the Buffalo Hart glacier extended beyond the limits of the Jacksonville, and in this area the Jacksonville is represented by extensive deposits of outwash gravel, sand, and varved clays between the Mendon till below and Buffalo Hart till above.

BUFFALO HART SUBSTAGE

The Buffalo Hart Moraine was described by Leverett (1899) from northeastern Sangamon County, Illinois, and the deposits of that area were used as the type for the Buffalo Hart Substage by Leighton and Willman (1950). As now used, the substage includes the Roby Silt (Johnson, 1964) and the overlying Buffalo Hart till. This till, which is recognized in a relatively small area in central Illinois, is distinguished from the earlier Illinoian by its surface topography and by its position above the fossiliferous Roby Silt. The Buffalo Hart till plain topographically resembles the early Woodfordian more than it does the earlier Illinoian, but it is sharply distinguished from the overlying younger tills and loesses by the presence of the Sangamon Soil in its top.

SANGAMONIAN STAGE

The Sangamon Soil, first named by Worthen (1873) from exposures in Sangamon County, Illinois, was used by Leverett (1898b) as a basis for an interglacial interval; the Sangamonian Stage is based on the Sangamon Soil. Tills of both Buffalo Hart and Jacksonville age occur in Sangamon County, but the name Sangamon Soil, as a soil-stratigraphic unit, is applied to the soil where developed on Liman, Kansan, or older deposits. The stage is named from the Sangamon Soil as developed in Buffalo Hart till, and therefore it encompasses only the span of time from the retreat of the youngest Illinoian glacier to the deposition of the earliest Roxana (Wisconsinan) Loess (Fig. 3).

Throughout most of central Illinois the Sangamon Soil, where formed on Illinoian till (Fig. 2B, C), is generally a poorly drained profile with a gray-brown to dark gray-brown B-zone. However, in western and extreme southern Illinois where the soil is commonly developed on silt, sand, or bedrock, it has a relatively well-drained profile with red-brown to dark red B-zones. The Sangamon Soil has been identified in southwestern Wisconsin (Hogan and Beatty, 1963).

At many places in Illinois the Sangamon Soil (Fig. 2D) is not a profile formed *in situ* but consists of a deposit called accretion-gley (Frye, Shaffer, *et al.*, 1960; Frye, Willman, and Glass, 1960; Frye and Willman, 1963b). This material (formerly called gumbotil: Leighton and MacClintock, 1930, 1962) accumulated slowly in the initial shallow swales on the till-plain surface as a result of sheet wash from the slightly higher parts of the till-plain and perhaps the minor addition of eolian silt. Such deposits show less mineral decomposition than the B-zones of the profiles formed *in situ* and are gray in color and rich in montmorillonite. At

places they contain organic zones and streaks, and locally they are inconspicuously bedded. Deposits of Sangamon accretion-gley attain a maximum thickness of more than 6 ft (2 m), and they are essentially the only deposits in the region that can be demonstrated to be of Sangamonian age.

WISCONSINAN STAGE

In 1894 Chamberlin proposed the name East Wisconsin Stage of Glaciation to include the glacial deposits extensively exposed in the southeastern part of that state and extending into central Illinois, where the relation to the underlying Sangamon Soil and Illinoian drift could be demonstrated. In 1895 Chamberlin shortened the name to Wisconsin, and since then this region has been generally accepted as the type area for the youngest of the major episodes of continental glaciation in the United States. In conformance with modern stratigraphic practice, the adjectival form, Wisconsinan, is now widely used to apply to the time-stratigraphic unit.

Wisconsinan glaciers covered most if not all of Wisconsin and most of north and east-central Illinois (Fig. 4). Loess deposits of Wisconsinan age form a surficial mantle over much of the area (Fig. 6). Black believes that Wisconsinan glaciers covered the "Driftless Area" of Wisconsin, but Frye and Willman consider the scattered erratic cobbles in the Illinois part of the "Driftless Area" as more likely to be remnants of an old glaciation, probably Nebraskan.

As early as 1878, Chamberlin recognized differences in the Wisconsinan drifts, and he postulated a two-fold glacial advance (Chamberlin, 1883a, b). The major framework of Wisconsinan classification was established by Leverett in 1899 when he recognized an Early Wisconsin with four substages and a Late Wisconsin with three substages, distinguished mainly by topography and direction of ice flow. Naming and correlation of the various substages was largely developed on the basis of topographic expression of moraines with only partial agreement (Leighton, 1960; Flint, 1963; Frye and Willman, 1963a). The subdivision followed here is based primarily on the stratigraphy of the till sheets and related loess sequences and on radiocarbon dates (Frye and Willman, 1960, 1963b; Frye *et al.*, 1962) with some supporting data from paleontology (Leonard and Frye, 1960) and from subsurface studies (Kempton, 1963; Kempton and Hackett, 1964). It uses the sequence of deposits related to the Lake Michigan lobe in Wisconsin and Illinois as a type section, and it recognizes the widely traced and radiocarbon-dated zones of weathering and peat accumulation as being better time planes for differentiation of time-stratigraphic substages than the morainal fronts. Subdivisions based on morainal fronts are useful for local but not for interlobe correlation, which reduces such units to subdivisions of substages.

Sub-substages are currently not recognized as formal units in time-stratigraphic classification, but for comparison with older literature the following informal subdivisions are used:

Early Woodfordian "Tazewell" refers to the deposits previously called Iowan (of Illinois), all of the Tazewell, and the earliest Cary moraines as far as the morainal front represented by the Valparaiso and West Chicago moraines in Illinois and the Johnstown and correlative moraines in Wisconsin.

Middle Woodfordian "Cary" refers to the deposits related to the Valparaiso, West Chicago, and Johnstown moraines as far as the front of the unnamed moraine at Sheboygan, Wisconsin (Thwaites and Bertrand, 1957, Fig. 1), correlated with the Port Huron moraine in Michigan but omits the youngest moraines that were generally included in the Cary before 1957.

Late Woodfordian "Mankato" refers to the deposits related to the unnamed moraine at Sheboygan, Wisconsin, and the younger deposits older than Two Creeks. Before 1957 these deposits were included in the Cary but were renamed Mankato when type Mankato was found to be older than the Two Creeks deposits. In the pre-1957 literature, the term Mankato refers generally to the deposits younger than the Two Creeks deposits; they are called Valderan in this report.

The relation of tills and loess deposits to radiocarbon dates and to the present system of classification is shown in Figure 5. Radiocarbon ages older than those shown in Figure 5 are inferred by extrapolation from older finite dates of deposits in Ontario and Ohio. Five substages (Altonian, Farmdalian, Woodfordian, Twocreekan, and Valderan) are now recognized within the Wisconsinan Stage, and of these the earliest, the Altonian, includes approximately half of the time span of the stage (Fig. 5). Topographic expression, or the form of the glacial deposits, is still used and was formalized by the recognition of morphostratigraphic units as a basis for local mapping, particularly within the Woodfordian of Illinois, as shown in Figure 7 (Ekblaw, 1960; Flint *et al.*, 1959).

ALTONIAN SUBSTAGE

The Altonian Substage is named from Alton, Illinois (Frye and Willman, 1960) and is based on the succession of silts and loesses called the Roxana Silt. Many of the deposits formerly called Late Sangamon Loess (Leverett, 1899; Leighton, 1926; Smith, 1942; Wascher *et al.*, 1948) and Farmdale Loess (Leighton and Willman, 1950; Wanless, 1957; Leighton, 1960) are now assigned to the Roxana.

The Roxana Silt, which is extensively exposed along the Illinois and Mississippi Valleys of central and southern Illinois, was largely deposited as loess derived from the outwash valley trains of the Ancient Mississippi and Ancient Iowa Rivers (Frye *et al.*, 1962). It commonly rests on Sangamon Soil, and five zones have been recognized within it (Fig. 5). Zone Ia at the base consists of silt and sand and locally contains small pebbles; it is strongly weathered and at many places is colluvium. Zone Ib is loess, sandy loess, or sand; it is locally calcareous, and a few snail shells have been found within it, but it commonly is weathered in at least the upper part and locally contains a humic zone at the top. Zone II is calcareous and fossiliferous in the thick sections along the valley bluffs; shells from the top of this zone gave radiocarbon dates $35,200 \pm 1,000$ (W-729) and $37,000 \pm 1,500$ (W-869) from localities nearly 200 miles apart. These dates indicate that this zone is contemporaneous with silts between Winnebago tills in northern Illinois

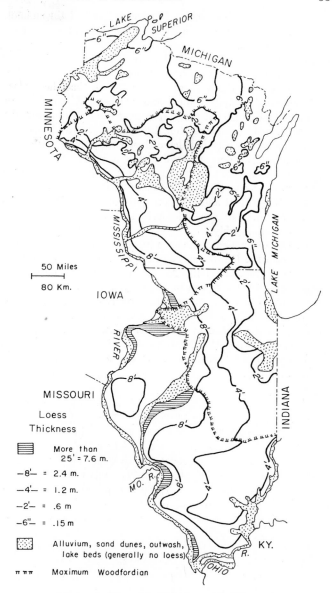

Figure 6. Map of Illinois and Wisconsin showing the generalized thickness of loess. Beyond the limit of Wisconsinan glaciation the thickness includes Roxana (Altonian) and Peoria (Woodfordian and younger) Loesses, in the area of Altonian tills it consists of Peoria Loess, and inside the Woodfordian maximum it consists of Richland Loess (middle to late Woodfordian and younger). Modified and generalized from Smith (1942), Leighton and Willman (1950), and Hole (1950).

dated $38,000 \pm 3,000$ (I-847). Zone III also is calcareous and fossiliferous in the thick sequences but is distinguishable from Zones II and IV by its color—gray in contrast to the pink below and above. Zone IV is generally leached of carbonates, at least in its upper part. Away from the valley bluffs (Frye *et al.*, 1963; Frye *et al.*, 1962; Smith,

1942) the Roxana becomes thin and is leached throughout, but the zonation is distinguishable by degree of weathering, texture, and color.

Tills now classed as Altonian were recognized below the surface drifts of northeastern Illinois (Horberg, 1953), but it was not until the work of Shaffer (1956) that the surface tills of northwestern Illinois and southern Wisconsin were demonstrated to be of early Wisconsinan age. Subsequently, subsurface studies (Kempton, 1963; Kempton and Hackett, 1964) in northern Illinois have shown the complexity of the Altonian glacial deposits, and it now appears (Fig. 5) that glacial advances in northern Illinois were approximately contemporaneous with each of the five zones of the Roxana Silt of the central and southern part of the state. The surface drift of southern Wisconsin seems equivalent to the latest Altonian only.

In Wisconsin, simultaneous advances of ice, one southeastward from the Des Moines and Superior lobes and the other westward from the Lake Michigan and Green Bay lobes, took place about 29,000 to 32,000 years ago, according to radiocarbon dates of spruce logs overrun or incorporated in the drift. The lobes overrode a residual soil rich in illite and chert and joined in the center of the state. This latest Altonian advance (locally termed Rockian) covered much if not all of the "Driftless Area" but did little work there (Black, 1962).

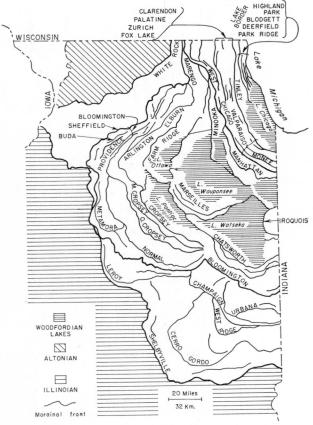

Figure 7. Woodfordian moraines and lakes in Illinois. Modified from Ekblaw (1960), Flint *et al.* (1959), and other sources.

Positive evidence of glaciation in the "Driftless Area" of Wisconsin comes from abundant fragments of Precambrian igneous rocks and Paleozoic chert and sandstone that rest on younger formations. Erratics of sedimentary rocks are especially abundant in the central and northern parts of the area. Sparse igneous erratics occur in isolated kame-like deposits south of Taylor in the northern part of the area and in fresh gravel on the upland beneath thick loess at Hazel Green. Igneous erratics are also found on bedrock terraces along the Wisconsin River near Muscoda. Large angular to subangular blocks of dolomite occur in sand and gravel in foreset beds that indicate a flow of the Wisconsin River reverse to the present. This gravel of apparently western source contains unusual concentrations of agates similar to deposits of Rockian age in west-central Wisconsin. The dolomitic gravel is covered with chert-rich gravel, sand, and silt that contains 1-2% fresh igneous rocks and also blocks of Baraboo quartzite up to 1.5 m, indicating a north-easterly source.

Rubble deposits on the uplands of the Wisconsin "Driftless Area" are mostly angular chert and sandstone, but locally they contain well-rounded and polished pebbles thought to be derived from the Windrow Formation of Tertiary or Cretaceous age. These deposits commonly have anomalous clay-mineral suites (Akers, 1961); they also contain fresh glauconite topographically above known sources. The stratification and form of the deposits suggest kames.

Direction of ice flow may be inferred from boulder trains. For example, southeast of a sandstone pinnacle near Boss-town in the central part dozens of angular blocks of sand-stone up to 5 m in length extend about 200 m obliquely across a gentle slope underlain by dolomite with clay re-siduum. A few fresh blocks have accumulated at the base of the pinnacle on the west, north, and east sides, but the disparity in concentration is so striking that it suggests glaciation. Overturned folds in residuum in several places on flat uplands also suggest a southeastward ice movement.

The absence of preserved loess older than 30,000 years in the area, the paucity of clay and chert residuum on flat uplands or in all valleys but one (South Fork of Baraboo River at Hillsboro), and lack of weathering of exposed igneous rocks suggest ice cover of much if not all the Wisconsin "Driftless Area" as recently as Rockian time. The Rockian drift in places resembles the younger Woodfordian and Valderan drifts in texture and in content of clay minerals, heavy minerals, and pebble types (Akers, 1961; Ellsworth, 1932; Oakes, 1960). A pre-Wisconsinan age for some of it can neither be confirmed nor denied.

Rock monuments and pinnacles have been widely interrupted to indicate lack of glaciation (Martin, 1932, p. 91) or antiquity of glaciation (Leighton and Brophy, 1961, p. 29) in the "Driftless Area" of Wisconsin, or they have been ignored where striae on outcrops of easily weathered basic-igneous rocks and other evidence attest to the recency of glaciation (Martin, 1932, Pl. 28). It is clear that equally large monuments were produced in northwest Wisconsin after definite glaciation during Woodfordian times. Most monuments in the "Driftless Area" are locally cemented sandstone (Fig. 2E) in the very friable St. Peter Formation, and most are at the ends of spurs or on the southeast sides of large high knobs. In general only minimal amounts of loose sand need to be removed from cliffs to isolate the cemented zones. For example, Footville monument in southern Wisconsin (Leighton and Brophy, 1961, p. 29), which is 19 ft (5.7 m) high, was exposed about 30,000 years ago. The loose sand needs to be washed or blown off the surface only at a maximum rate of 0.2 mm per year to round the cliff and isolate the monument. Abundant ice-wedge casts in southwest Wisconsin (Fig. 2F; Black, 1964) indicate permafrost conditions some time during the period from about 28,000 to 12,500 years ago. Strong mass movements, the inferred absence of trees, and presence of ventifacts suggest that rapid erosion under strong periglacial conditions was commonplace.

FARMDALIAN SUBSTAGE

The Farmdale Substage was defined by Leighton and Willman (1950) from the Farmdale silt and peat as it was exposed along Farm Creek, east of Peoria, Illinois. The name Farmdale Substage was used to encompass all Wisconsinan deposits occurring below the Morton (then called Iowan) Loess and above the Sangamon Soil (Fig. 2D). With the discovery of a complex sequence of loesses and tills stratigraphically below the type Farmdale but above Sangamon Soil, Frye and Willman (1960) redefined the Farmdalian Substage as including only the span of time represented by the Farmdale silt and peat in its type area, a zone that has been widely dated by radiocarbon throughout the Midwest; it comprises those deposits between the Roxana Loess and the Morton Loess (Fig. 5) with a radiocarbon age of about 22,000 B.P. to 28,000 B.P. (before the present) or perhaps slightly more.

The Farmdale Silt is known primarily from central and north-central Illinois where it contains eolian, colluvial, and lacustrine deposits, peat, and organic silts. Although found largely in the areas where the peat was buried by younger tills, Farmdale peaty silt is known at a few places capping terrace remnants in the Illinois Valley. Isolated small remnants of paleosols in southwestern Wisconsin may be Farmdalian (Hogan and Beatty, 1963). The Farmdalian Substage is an interval of major glacial withdrawal, but, as the sediments and fauna indicate cool moist conditions, it is judged that continental deglaciation did not occur. In Wisconsin, permafrost and buried glacial ice survived through the substage.

WOODFORDIAN SUBSTAGE

The Woodfordian Substage was named (Frye and Willman, 1960) from Woodford County, Illinois, and defined as representing the span of time from the base of the Morton Loess (top of the Farmdale Silt) upward through the overlying succession of tills to the base of the Two Creeks deposits of Wisconsin. Within this type succession are included the original types for the Tazewell and Cary Substages of former usage (Leighton, 1933), the Iowan loess of Illinois (Morton Loess), and the redefined Mankato (Leighton, 1957). An exceptionally large number of radiocarbon dates from the Woodfordian and from the beds immediately above and below it (Fig. 6) serve to establish its age as from about 22,000 radiocarbon years B.P. to about 12,500 radiocarbon years B.P.

The maximum spread of ice during Wisconsinan glaciation came in the Woodfordian Substage (Fig. 4), when ice from the Lake Michigan and Erie lobes advanced as far south as central Illinois (Fig. 1). Locally, cryoturbations formed beyond the limit of the ice (Frye and Willman, 1958). The ice appears to have advanced persistently through an interval of 2,000 to 3,000 years and reached its maximum between 19,000 and 20,000 years ago (Fig. 5).

The two major lobes met in eastern Illinois in a major re-entrant along which the moraines diverge at a sharp angle. The Erie drift is more bouldery and contains more limestone, and its heavy minerals contain more garnet than Lake Michigan drift, whereas the latter is richer in dolomite, black shale, and epidote. Erie drift lacks the pink color found in some of the Lake Michigan drifts.

In Illinois, Woodfordian tills are dominantly pebbly clayey silts or silty clays. Boulders and cobbles are generally scarce, but the youngest drifts are more bouldery. The tills of the Lake Michigan lobe can be separated into major units on the basis of gross differences in lithology. Although there are lateral variations, the Shelbyville-Champaign till is commonly gray and sandy, the Bloomington-Normal till is largely pink and very sandy, the Cropsey-Farm Ridge till is largely yellow-gray and very silty, the Marseilles-Minooka till is largely greenish gray and very clayey with an abundance of small pebbles, the Valparaiso till is largely gray, sandy, and commonly gravelly, and the Tinley-Lake Border till is gray and clayey and contains much black shale. Variations in the drift are reflected in the soils (Wascher *et al.*, 1960).

In Wisconsin, the Woodfordian tills are mostly sandy and bouldery, but these generally represent the middle Woodfordian "Cary" portion. The oldest and youngest tills tend to be finer textured. At any one locality drifts laid down by ice of different ages but traversing the same route are similar.

In Illinois a sequence of more than 30 end moraines (Fig. 7) was deposited during the retreating stage, an interval of less than 8,000 years. To accomplish this, the ice must have been continuously active, and stagnation features are rare. Nearly all the end moraines show evidence of readvance before deposition, although some probably readvanced only a few miles. The changes in realignment of the ice front, overridden moraines, differences in composition of the successive drift sheets, interbedded water-laid deposits, and many exposures showing superposition of several till sheets all suggest that some of the Woodfordian readvances covered as much as 50 to 100 miles (80 to 160 km) (Willman and Payne, 1942). The high rate of ice-front fluctuation required to form the sequence of moraines is consistent with the absence of leaching of carbonates between the till sheets and the absence of breaks within the loess deposited during the interval of moraine building.

The moraines are remarkably uniform in size, many about 50 feet (15 m) high and 1 to 2 miles (1.5 to 3 km) wide, suggesting a roughly rhythmic fluctuation of the ice front. Many of the larger moraines show evidence of a complex structure and have closely spaced, parallel crests that suggest superposition of several episodes of moraine building. Many moraines show thickening and widening to the apex of minor lobes, probably resulting from greater debris transport along the axis of most rapid movement.

Lakes are common in the younger drift but rare in the drift older than about 14,000 years. The older drift contains peat and marl deposits laid down in lakes, but the difference in abundance of lakes is perhaps due to more than age, because the older drift is more gently undulating and generally lacks the sharp hummocky surface that distinguishes the areas with abundant lakes. The change to the very youthful-appearing drift occurs at the Valparaiso-West Chicago front.

When the advancing Woodfordian ice reached the headwaters of the valleys draining to the Mississippi and Illinois Rivers, aggradation and widespread silting of the valleys resulted in initiation of the greatest episode of loess deposition on the continent. Advancing over the initial loess deposits, which are called Morton Loess (Frye and Willman, 1960), the ice reached the big bend in the Ancient Mississippi Valley in north-central Illinois about 21,000 years ago, as shown by a change in mineral composition in the Morton Loess (Glass et al., 1964).

When the ice retreated from its maximum spread, loess continued to be deposited, and the name Richland Loess is applied to the loess overlying the Woodfordian drift. Outside the area covered by the Woodfordian glaciers and their outwash, the Morton and Richland Loesses are not differentiated and are combined in the Peoria Loess, defined from exposures near Peoria, Illinois. Beyond the limit of Woodfordian glaciation, the Peoria Loess mantles earlier Pleistocene deposits and bedrock and, with the single exception of the Sangamon Soil, is the most widely traceable Pleistocene unit in the interior United States. It has been identified from eastern Colorado to Ohio and from Wisconsin to Mississippi.

Outwash from the Woodfordian ice aggraded the major valleys 50 ft (15 m) and locally more. The outwash is largely sand and sandy gravel except near the ice border, where the deposits grade sharply into bouldery gravel. In most valleys these deposits form the most extensive terraces; the older terraces commonly have a cover of loess and sand dunes on unweathered outwash, but the younger have little loess. Along the Mississippi Valley these deposits have been almost entirely swept away by later floods. Remnants are found along the tributary valleys where the up-valley slope of the terrace surfaces attests the rapidity of aggradation of the major valleys.

When the ice built the Valparaiso and West Chicago end moraines, it discharged large volumes of meltwater into the Rock, Fox, DuPage, Des Plaines, and Kankakee Valleys. Drainage from the Lake Michigan, Saginaw, and Erie lobes was concentrated into the Kankakee Valley and formed the Kankakee Flood (Ekblaw and Athy, 1925). At its maximum the flood spread over the uplands between the end moraines, forming Lakes Watseka, Wauponsee, Pontiac, and Ottawa (Fig. 7), all short-lived lakes that produced few shoreline features except where discharges were concentrated through the moraines. Bars of angular boulder rubble show the violence of the discharge in the Kankakee

region. Laminated silt and sand deposits locally show periglacial involutions (Sharp, 1942). Passage of the flood down the valley resulted in deep erosion of earlier valley-train deposits, and high-water stages were perhaps 50 ft (15 m) above normal flood stages. Sand, silt, and clay deposited on the bluffs are locally preserved within the Peoria Loess. In southern Illinois the high water is believed to be responsible for diversion of the Mississippi River across the headwaters of a tributary valley into the Ohio Valley and permanent establishment of the river through the Thebes Gorge (Leighton and Willman, 1950).

When ice withdrew from the massive Valparaiso Moraine, Lake Chicago formed between the ice and the moraine (Bretz, 1955, 1959). Earlier stages of a lake in the Michigan basin probably had an outlet to the Des Plaines Valley at Joliet along the buried Hadley Valley, which is more deeply entrenched in bedrock than the present valley (Horberg, 1950). Valparaiso and older drift completely buried Hadley Valley, and, with retreat of the ice from the Valparaiso Moraine, drainage was established at the position of the present Des Plaines Valley, several miles north of the old channel.

Early stages of the post-Valparaiso Lake Chicago were controlled by a buried ridge of Niagaran dolomite that crossed the outlet river at Lemont at an elevation of 640 ft (195 m). By the time the ice advanced to the backslope of the Valparaiso end moraine and deposited the Tinley end moraine, the outlet had been lowered to 620 ft (189 m) or lower, and the 640-ft (195-m) levels attained by the first major stages of Lake Chicago probably result from the large volume and depth of water passing through the outlet. The three major shorelines of Lake Chicago truncate the Tinley drift, but the earliest stages occurred during the stand of the ice at the Lake Border Moraines. The shorelines at levels of 640 ft (195 m) (Glenwood), 620 ft (189 m) (Calumet), and 605 ft (184 m) (Toleston), were all reoccupied several times, and the history of the lake is complex and controversial (Bretz, 1955; Hough, 1958). The low-level lake stage represented by the Two Creeks deposits, which mark the end of Woodfordian time, has been variously related to the Calumet and Glenwood lake stages.

Discharge from the Calumet lake stage required deepening of the outlet to about 600 ft (183 m), and this process required a great volume of water, which apparently came from the discharge of eastern lakes to Lake Chicago through the Grand River across Michigan. The outlet channel was deepened into dolomite for about 25 miles (37 km), and below the area where the bedrock was swept clean the channel was filled with gravel consisting of well-rounded cobbles of dolomite. Cobbles as large as 6 in. (15 cm) are abundant in the gravel near Ottawa, 40 miles (65 km) down the valley from the parent dolomite ledges (Willman and Payne, 1942), and a well-defined low terrace of gravel, grading to pebbly sand, marks the level of the Lake Chicago discharge down the valley until it passes below floodplain level near Beardstown.

In Wisconsin, an early Woodfordian "Tazewell" moraine was deposited beyond the limit reached by ice of middle Woodfordian time in only a few places. The middle Woodfordian "Cary" moraines are multiple yet form a distinct front or end moraine (including the Kettle inter-lobate moraine) (Alden, 1918) that is traceable with only minor breaks across the state from Illinois to Minnesota. It is the most striking glacial discontinuity in the state (Chamberlin, 1878). Outwash aprons of gravel and sand up to 500 ft (150 m) thick occur along portions of the front (Fig. 2H). Weidman (1907) called attention to the paucity of outwash from the front in central Wisconsin, and it now seems clear that early Woodfordian and Altonian outwash have been overridden for many kilometers in southern Wisconsin (Oakes, 1960). Only a small fraction of the outwash can definitely be attributed to middle and late Woodfordian times.

Following the establishment of the prominent end moraine of middle Woodfordian "Cary" time, ice stagnation occurred throughout Wisconsin. The famous drumlin field of southeastern Wisconsin (Alden, 1918) displays typical kames and associated glaciofluvial deposits, many of which have been incorrectly mapped as recessional end moraines. Such features are particularly well developed and widespread in the lake country of northern Wisconsin. Pitted outwash (Thwaites, 1926) is especially abundant in the Woodfordian drift. Latest Woodfordian end moraines bordering southern Lake Michigan reflect the resurgence of clay- and silt-rich ice from the basin.

Many lakes came into existence in central Wisconsin with the retreat of the Woodfordian ice (Trowbridge, 1917; Bretz, 1950). Glacial Lake Wisconsin (Alden, 1918; Martin, 1932) probably formed at least twice. Early Lake Oshkosh (Thwaites and Bertrand, 1957) appeared in the Green Bay–Fox River lowland. Drainage of Glacial Lake Keweenaw (Hough, 1958) and later Lake Duluth (Leverett, 1929, 1932) and other waters associated with retreat of Woodfordian and Valderan ice from the Lake Superior basin cut the large gorge and giant potholes of the St. Croix Dalles (Chamberlin, 1905). The famous Wisconsin River Dells (Martin, 1932) also were cut at the close of the Woodfordian Substage.

Loess up to 20 ft (6 m) thick in southwestern Wisconsin (Fig. 6) shows no marked irregularities of physical and chemical pedogenic properties that might reflect multiple deposition (Hogan and Beatty, 1963; Glenn et al., 1900). The entire sequence is correlated with the Peoria Loess of Illinois.

The Late Woodfordian and Valderan varved clays of Wisconsin are more uniform in their gross composition than in their heavy minerals, which cannot be used for correlation even within the same lake (Ellsworth, 1932).

TWOCREEKAN SUBSTAGE

The Twocreekan Substage (Frye and Willman, 1960) is based on the Two Creeks Forest Bed and associated silt deposits of eastern Wisconsin, which were discovered by Goldthwait (1907) and most recently described by Thwaites and Bertrand (1957). The oldest tree found had 142 years of growth (Wilson, 1936). The initial phase is characterized by aquatic and semiaquatic mollusks on early Lake Chicago clays (Wilson, 1932). Fossils of woodland mosses, sedges, mollusks, mites, wood-boring beetles, fungi, and trees such as spruce, birch, and jackpine are found in the overlying

organic sediments. Pollen analyses imply that the forest was dominated by *Picea* (West, 1961). These are the first records of trees in Wisconsin in deposits younger than latest Altonian (Rockian) (Black, 1962). Later, aquatic mosses and mollusks came in along with sediment from the advancing Valders ice. Although Antevs (1962) believes the substage was about 19,000 years B.P., radiocarbon dates of the wood average 11,850 years (Broecker and Farrand, 1963).

At many places in the Green Bay–Fox River lowland, pieces of Two Creeks wood occur in the overlying Valders till, but organic deposits formed in place are scarce (Fig. 2G). However, weakly developed buried soils interpreted as Twocreekan are relatively common in the same area. In the Duck Creek Ridges southwest of Green Bay, red clayey till above the dated organic sediments cannot be distinguished lithologically or texturally from that below (Piette, 1963).

During Twocreekan time Lake Chicago was at a low level, and discharge of the major rivers was reduced as the ice generally retreated beyond their headwaters.

A zone of caliche nodules locally recognized in the upper part of the Peoria Loess may indicate an interruption in loess deposition and partial solution of carbonates. At other places dark organic streaks may likewise indicate a slowdown in loess deposition. With the migration of the forests into Wisconsin during this substage came ancient man (Black, 1959b; Black and Wittry, 1959) and many animals, including bison, mammoth, and mastodon (Parmalee, 1959; Potzger, 1951).

VALDERAN SUBSTAGE

The Valderan Substage, which draws its name from the Valders Till of eastern Wisconsin (Thwaites, 1943; Thwaites and Bertrand, 1957), is defined (Frye and Willman, 1960) as including that till and subsequent glacial and alluvial deposits that accumulated before the dissipation of the continental glacier and the return of sea level to approximately its present position at about 5,000 years B.P. Presently available radiocarbon dates suggest that the upper 50 ft (15 m) of alluvial fill of the Mississippi Valley in southwestern Illinois was deposited subsequent to 7,000 radiocarbon years B.P. The upper 23 ft (7 m) of fill of the Wisconsin River Valley near Portage was deposited rapidly about 6,000 radiocarbon years B.P.

During Valderan time, ice of the Lake Michigan lobe readvanced to the vicinity of Milwaukee, Wisconsin, but did not reach Illinois. Ice entered the Green Bay lowland (Thwaites, 1943). It may have come out of the Lake Superior lowland onto the highlands of northern Wisconsin (Leverett, 1929), although recent field work by Black suggests that it did not reach the highlands. The location of the ice terminus is mapped with difficulty, as the ice is commonly ended in proglacial lakes, and the lithology of the drift is not diagnostic. Although the drift was defined as red clay till, it is texturally more complicated (Lee et al., 1962). All such drift is not necessarily Valderan, and other kinds of drift may be Valderan. Murray (1953) showed that texturally-unlike Valders and "Cary" (middle Woodfordian) tills contained the same heavy minerals. Other criteria must be used in mapping the distribution of the

Valders till. Prominent moraines, kames, eskers, and other features are now considered characteristic of the Valders drift (Suttner, 1963).

Lake Chicago and associated Later Lake Oshkosh (Thwaites and Bertrand, 1957) re-established the Des Plaines outlet when the water level rose to the Calumet beach (Bretz, 1959). At a lower lake stage, the prominent Toleston beach was constructed. By the end of Valderan time the lake level was at an unusually low stage (Chippewa), about 350 ft (107 m) below the present lake of 580 ft (177 m) (Hough, 1958).

The *Picea* forest that came into Wisconsin during Two-creekan time was overrun by Valderan ice. At the edge of the ice a *Picea* woodland with openings existed. On retreat of the ice, the *Picea* forest reoccupied the region outside the limits of the front, and a *Picea* woodland with openings invaded the areas vacated by the ice (West, 1961).

A widely traceable valley train of Valderan or latest Woodfordian age is represented in the lowest major terrace of Mississippi Valley. The material in this terrace is generally distinguishable from that of older valley trains because the ice front was largely north of the margin of Paleozoic limestone and dolomite formations, so that much of the material is noncalcareous, even though not weathered.

Some loess was probably added to the Peoria Loess during this interval, but no large body of loess comparable to the Bignell of the Missouri Valley appears to have been deposited in the Mississippi Valley. The terraces of this age have little loess and are almost without sand dunes.

Recent Stage

The Recent Stage as used in Illinois and Wisconsin (Frye and Willman, 1960) lacks the basis for definition in stratigraphy that has been used for all previous stages and substages. This time-stratigraphic unit is arbitrarily defined as starting at 5,000 radiocarbon years B.P., since it is judged that at about that point in time sea level had risen to about its present position, and all direct influence of continental glaciers had ceased. Great Lakes drainage, in response to isostatic movements, may have continued through the Des Plaines outlet as recently as about 3,000 years ago (Hough, 1958). Deposits generally classified as Recent include much older deposits and, in general, represent alluvium, dune sands, colluvium, and lacustrine sediments that were deposited after the last recognizable influence of glaciers. The regimen of the Mississippi and Illinois Rivers and the morphology of their floodplains have been described in detail in western Illinois by Rubey (1952).

Undated but presumably post-Valderan pollen sequences from bogs associated with the Wisconsin River (Hansen, 1939) and with the last remnant of Glacial Lake Wisconsin (Hansen, 1937) show typical changes from spruce to pine and finally to hardwood forests with some prairie (West, 1961).

References

Akers, R. H., 1961, Clay minerals of glacial deposits of west-central Wisconsin: Univ. Wisconsin M.S. thesis, 82 p.

Alden, W. C., 1909, Concerning certain criteria for discrimination of the age of glacial drift sheets as modified by topographic situation and drainage relations: J. Geol., v. 17, p. 694-709

—— 1918, Quaternary geology of southeastern Wisconsin: U.S. Geol. Surv. Prof. Pap. 106, 356 p.

American Commission on Stratigraphic Nomenclature, 1961, Code of stratigraphic nomenclature: Amer. Assoc. Petroleum Geologists, v. 45, p. 645-665

Anderson, R. C., 1957, Pebble and sand lithology of the major Wisconsin glacial lobes of the central lowland: Geol. Soc. Amer. Bull., v. 68, p. 1415-1449

Andrews, G. W., 1958, Windrow Formation of the upper Mississippi Valley region—A sedimentary and stratigraphic study: J. Geol., v. 66, p. 597-624

Antevs, Ernst, 1962, Transatlantic climatic agreement versus C14 dates: J. Geol., v. 70, p. 194-205

Bain, H. F., 1897, Relations of the Wisconsin and Kansan drift sheets in central Iowa, and related phenomena: Iowa Geol. Surv., v. 6, p. 429-476

Ball, J. R., 1937, The physiography and surficial geology of the Carlinville quadrangle, Illinois: Illinois State Acad. Sci. Trans., v. 30, p. 219-223

Bean, E. F., 1939, Geologic map of Wisconsin: Madison, Univ. of Wisconsin, Wisconsin Geol. Nat. Hist. Surv.

Black, R. F., 1959a, Friends of the Pleistocene: Science, v. 130, p. 172-173

—— 1959b, Geology of Raddatz rockshelter, Sk5, Wisconsin: Wisconsin Arch., v. 40, p. 69-82

—— 1962, Pleistocene chronology of Wisconsin (abst.): Geol. Soc. Amer. Spec. Pap. 68, p. 137

—— 1964, Periglacial phenomena of Wisconsin, north-central United States: Biuletyn Peryglacjalny (in press)

Black, R. F., and Wittry, W. L., 1959, Pleistocene man in south-central Wisconsin (abst.): Geol. Soc. Amer. Bull., v. 70, p. 1570-1571

Bretz, J H., 1950, Glacial Lake Merrimac: Illinois State Acad. Sci. Trans., v. 43, p. 132-136

—— 1955, Geology of the Chicago region. Part II. The Pleistocene: Illinois Geol. Surv. Bull. 65, 132 p.

—— 1959, The double Calumet stage of Lake Chicago: J. Geol., v. 67, p. 675-684

Broecker, W. S., and Farrand, W. R., 1963, Radiocarbon age of the Two Creeks forest bed, Wisconsin: Geol. Soc. Amer. Bull., v. 74, p. 795-802

Chamberlin, R. T., 1905, The glacial features of the St. Croix Dalles region: J. Geol., v. 13, p. 238-256

—— 1910, Older drifts in the St. Croix region: J. Geol., v. 18, p. 542-548

Chamberlin, T. C., 1878, On the extent and significance of the Wisconsin kettle moraine: Wisconsin Acad. Sci. Trans., v. 4, p. 201-234

—— 1880, Le Kettle moraine et les mouvements glaciaires qui lui ont donne naissance: Intern. Geol. Congr. Paris Compt. Rend., p. 254-268

—— 1883a, Geology of Wisconsin: Wisconsin Geol. Nat. Hist. Surv., v. 1, p. 1-300

—— 1883b, Terminal moraine of the second glacial epoch: U.S. Geol. Surv. Ann. Rep. 3, p. 291-402

—— 1890, Some additional evidences bearing on the interval between the glacial epochs: Geol. Soc. Amer. Bull., v. 1, p. 469-480

—— 1894, Glacial phenomena of North America, in James Geikie, The great ice age: New York, D. Appleton & Co., 3d ed., p. 724-774

—— 1895, The classification of American glacial deposits: J. Geol., v. 3, p. 270-277

—— 1896, Editorial: J. Geol., v. 4, p. 872-876

Ekblaw, G. E., 1960, Map—Glacial geology of northeastern Illinois: Illinois Geol. Surv.

Ekblaw, G. E., and Athy, L. F., 1925, Glacial Kankakee Torrent in northeastern Illinois: Geol. Soc. Amer. Bull., v. 36, p. 417-428

Ekblaw, G. E., and Willman, H. B., 1957, Farmdale drift near Danville, Illinois: Illinois State Acad. Sci. Trans., v. 47, p. 129-138

Ellsworth, E. W., 1932, Varved clays of Wisconsin: Wisconsin Acad. Sci. Trans., v. 27, p. 47-58

Eveland, H. E., 1952, Pleistocene geology of the Danville region: Illinois Geol. Surv. Rep. Inv. 159, 32 p.

Fisk, H. N., 1944, Geological investigation of the alluvial valley of the lower Mississippi River: Mississippi River Comm., War Dept., Corps of Engineers, U.S. Army, 63 p.

Flint, R. F., 1963, Status of the Pleistocene Wisconsin Stage in Central North America: Science, v. 139, p. 402-404

Flint, R. F., Colton, R. B., Golthwait, R. P., and Willman, H. B., 1959, Glacial map of the United States east of the Rocky Mountains: Geol. Soc. Amer.

Frye, J. C., 1963, Problems of interpreting the bedrock surface of Illinois: Illinois State Acad. Sci. Trans., v. 56, p. 3-11

Frye, J. C., Glass, H. D., Leonard, A. B., and Willman, H.B., 1963, Late Pleistocene loesses of Midwestern United States of America: Biuletyn Peryglacjalny, Nr. 12, p. 111-118

Frye, J. C., Glass, H. D., and Willman, H. B., 1962, Stratigraphy and mineralogy of the Wisconsinan loesses of Illinois: Illinois Geol. Surv. Circ. 334, 55 p.

Frye, J. C., and Leonard, A. B., 1951, Stratigraphy of the late Pleistocene loesses of Kansas: J. Geol., v. 59, p. 287-305

—— 1952, Pleistocene geology of Kansas: Kansas Geol. Surv. Bull. 99, 230 p.

Frye, J. C., Shaffer, P. R., Willman, H. B., and Ekblaw, G. E., 1960, Accretion-gley and the gumbotil dilemma: Amer. J. Sci., v. 258, p. 185-190

Frye, J. C., and Willman, H. B., 1958, Permafrost features near the Wisconsin glacial margin in Illinois: Amer. J. Sci., v. 256, p. 518-524

—— 1960, Classification of the Wisconsinan Stage in the Lake Michigan glacial lobe: Illinois Geol. Surv. Circ. 285, 16 p.

—— 1963a, Development of Wisconsinan classification in Illinois related to radiocarbon chronology: Geol. Soc. Amer. Bull., v. 74, p. 501-506

—— 1963b, Loess stratigraphy, Wisconsinan classification and accretion-gleys in central-western Illinois: Illinois Geol. Surv. Guidebook series no. 5, 37 p.

Frye, J. C., Willman, H. B., and Glass, H. D., 1960, Gum-

botil, accretion-gley, and the weathering profile: Illinois Geol. Surv. Circ. 295, 39 p.

—— 1964, Cretaceous deposits and the Illinoian glacial boundary in western Illinois: Illinois Geol. Surv. Circ. 364, p. 28

Glass, H. D., Frye, J. C., and Willman, H. B., 1964, Record of Mississippi River diversion in the Morton Loess of Illinois: Illinois State Acad. Sci. Trans., v. 57, p. 24-27

Glenn, R. C., Jackson, M. L., Hole, F. D., and Lee, G. B., 1960, Chemical weathering of layer silicate clays in loess-derived Tama silt loam of southwestern Wisconsin: Eighth Natl. Conf. on Clays and Clay Minerals, Intern. Earth Sci. Ser. Monogr. 9, New York, Pergamon Press, p. 68-83

Goldthwait, J. W., 1907, The abandoned shore lines of eastern Wisconsin: Wisconsin Geol. Surv. Bull. 17, 134 p.

Hansen, H. P., 1937, Pollen analysis of two Wisconsin bogs of different age: Ecology, v. 18, p. 136-148

—— 1939, Postglacial vegetation of the Driftless Area of Wisconsin: Amer. Midl. Nat., v. 21, p. 752-762

Hershey, O. H., 1893, The Pleistocene rock gorges of northwestern Illinois: Amer. Geol., v. 12, p. 314-323

Hogan, J. D., and Beatty, M. T., 1963, Age and properties of Peorian loess and buried paleosols in southwestern Wisconsin: Soil Sci. Soc. Amer. Proc., v. 27, p. 345-350

Hole, F. D., 1943, Correlation of the glacial border drift of north central Wisconsin: Amer. J. Sci., v. 241, p. 498-516

—— 1950, Areas having aeolian silt and sand deposits in Wisconsin: Map. Soils Div., Wisconsin Geol. Nat. Hist. Surv.

Horberg, Leland, 1950, Bedrock topography of Illinois: Illinois Geol. Surv. Bull. 73, 111 p.

—— 1953, Pleistocene deposits below the Wisconsin drift in northeastern Illinois: Illinois Geol. Surv. Rep. Inv. 165, 61 p.

—— 1956, Pleistocene deposits along the Mississippi Valley in central-western Illinois: Illinois Geol. Surv. Rep. Inv. 192, 39 p.

Hough, J. L., 1958, Geology of the Great Lakes: Urbana, Univ. of Illinois Press, 313 p.

Hussakof, Louis, 1916, Discovery of the great lake trout, Cristivomer namaycush, in the Pleistocene of Wisconsin: J. Geol., v. 24, p. 685-689

Johnson, W. H., 1964, Stratigraphy and petrography of Illinoian and Kansan drift in central Illinois: Illinois Geol. Surv. Circ. 378

Kempton, J. P., 1963, Subsurface stratigraphy of the Pleistocene deposits of central-northern Illinois: Illinois Geol. Surv. Circ. 356, 43 p.

Kempton, J. P., and Hackett, J. E., 1964, Radiocarbon dates from the pre-Woodfordian Wisconsinan of northern Illinois (abst.): Geol. Soc. Amer. Spec. Pap. 76, Abstracts for 1963, p. 91

Lee, G. B., Janke, W. E., and Beaver, A. J., 1962, Particle-size analysis of Valders drift in eastern Wisconsin: Science, v. 138, p. 154-155

Leighton, M. M., 1917, The Iowan glaciation and the so-called Iowan loess deposits: Iowa Acad. Sci. Proc., v. 24, p. 87-92

—— 1926, A notable type Pleistocene section: the Farm

Creek exposure near Peoria, Illinois: J. Geol., v. 34, p. 167-174

—— 1933, The naming of the subdivisions of the Wisconsin glacial age: Science, v. 77, p. 168

—— 1957, The Cary-Mankato-Valders problem: J. Geol., v. 65, p. 108-111

—— 1959, Stagnancy of the Illinoian glacial lobe east of the Illinois and Mississippi Rivers: J. Geol., v. 67, p. 337-344

—— 1960, The classification of the Wisconsin glacial stage of North Central United States: J. Geol., v. 68, p. 529-552

Leighton, M. M., and Brophy, J. A., 1961, Illinoian glaciation in Illinois: J. Geol., v. 69, p. 1-31

Leighton, M. M., and MacClintock, Paul, 1930, Weathered zones of the drift sheets of Illinois: J. Geol., v. 38, p. 28-53

—— 1962, The weathered mantle of glacial tills beneath original surface in north-central United States: J. Geol., v. 70, p. 267-293

Leighton, M. M., and Powers, W. E., 1934, Evaluation of boundaries in the mapping of glaciated areas: J. Geol., v. 42, p. 77-87

Leighton, M. M., and Willman, H. B., 1950, Loess formations of the Mississippi Valley: J. Geol., v. 58, p. 599-623

Leonard, A. B., and Frye, J. C., 1960, Wisconsinan molluscan faunas of the Illinois Valley region: Illinois Geol. Surv. Circ. 304, 32 p.

Leverett, Frank, 1889, On the occurrence of the "forest bed" beneath intramorainic drift: Amer. Assoc. Adv. Sci. Proc. v. 37, p. 183-184

—— 1898a, The weathered zone (Yarmouth) between the Illinoian and Kansan till sheets: J. Geol., v. 6, 238-243

—— 1898b, The weathered zone (Sangamon), between the Iowan loess and the Illinoian till sheet: J. Geol., v. 6, p. 171-181

—— 1899, The Illinois glacial lobe: U.S. Geol. Surv. Monogr. 38, 817 p.

—— 1909, Weathering and erosion as time measures: Amer. J. Sci., v. 27, p. 349-368

—— 1929, Moraines and shore lines of the Lake Superior region: U.S. Geol. Surv. Prof. Pap. 154, 72 p.

—— 1932, Quaternary geology of Minnesota and parts of adjacent states: U.S. Geol. Surv. Prof. Pap. 161, 149 p.

MacClintock, Paul, 1922, The Pleistocene history of the lower Wisconsin River: J. Geol., v. 30, p. 673-689

—— 1929, Recent discoveries of pre-Illinoian drift in southern Illinois: Illinois State Geol. Surv. Rep. Inv. 19, p. 26-57

Martin, Lawrence, 1932, The physical geography of Wisconsin: Wisconsin Geol. Surv. Bull. 36, 609 p.

Murray, R. C., 1953, The petrology of the Cary and Valders tills of northeastern Wisconsin: Amer. J. Sci., v. 251, p. 140-155

Oakes, E. L., 1960, The Woodfordian moraines of Rock County, Wisconsin: Univ. Wisconsin M.S. thesis, 61 p.

Parmalee, P. W., 1959, Animal remains from the Raddatz rockshelter, Sk5, Wisconsin: Wisconsin Arch., v. 40, p. 83-90

Piette, C. R., 1963, Geology of Duck Creek Ridges, east-central Wisconsin: Univ. Wisconsin M.S. thesis, 86 p.

Potzger, J. E., 1951, The fossil record near the glacial border: Ohio J. Sci., v. 51, p. 126-133

Rubey, W. W., 1952, Geology and mineral resources of the Hardin and Brussels Quadrangles (in Illinois): U.S. Geol. Surv. Prof. Pap. 218, 179 p.

Salisbury, R. D., 1893, Distinct glacial epochs and the criteria for their recognition: J. Geol., v. 1, p. 61-84

Schoewe, W. H., 1920, The origin and history of extinct Lake Calvin: Iowa Geol. Surv., v. 29, p. 49-22

Shaffer, P. R., 1954, Extension of Tazewell glacial substage of western Illinois into eastern Iowa: Geol. Soc. Amer. Bull. 65, p. 443-456

—— 1956, Farmdale drift into northwestern Illinois: Illinois Geol. Surv. Rep. Inv. 198, 25 p.

Sharp, R. P., 1942, Periglacial involutions in northeastern Illinois: J. Geol., v. 50, p. 113-133

Shimek, Bohumil, 1909, Aftonian sands and gravel in western Iowa: Geol. Soc. Amer. Bull., v. 20, p. 399-408

Smith, G. D., 1942, Illinois loess—variations in its properties and distribution: A pedologic interpretation: Univ. Illinois Agr. Exp. Stat. Bull. 490, p. 139-184.

Suttner, L. J., 1963, Geology of Brillion Ridge, east-central Wisconsin: Univ. Wisconsin M.S. thesis, 99 p.

Thwaites, F. T., 1926, The origin and significance of pitted outwash: J. Geol., v. 34, p. 308-319

—— 1928a, The development of the theory of multiple glaciation in North America: Wisconsin Acad. Sci. Trans., v. 23, p. 41-164

—— 1928b, Pre-Wisconsin terraces of the Driftless Area of Wisconsin: Geol. Soc. Amer. Bull., v. 39, p. 621-641

—— 1943, Pleistocene of part of northeastern Wisconsin: Geol. Soc. Amer. Bull., v. 54, p. 87-144

—— 1956, Wisconsin glacial deposits—Map: Wisconsin Geol. Nat. Hist. Surv.

—— 1960, Evidences of dissected erosion surfaces in the Driftless Area: Wisconsin Acad. Sci. Trans., v. 49, p. 17-49

Thwaites, F. T., and Bertrand, Kenneth, 1957, Pleistocene geology of the Door Peninsula, Wisconsin: Geol. Soc. Amer. Bull., v. 68, p. 831-879

Trowbridge, A. C., 1917, The history of Devil's Lake, Wisconsin: J. Geol., v. 25, p. 344-372

—— 1921, The erosional history of the Driftless Area: Univ. Iowa Stud. Nat. Hist., v. 9, 127 p.

Wanless, H. R., 1957, Geology and mineral resources of the Beardstown, Glasford, Havana, and Vermont Quadrangles: Illinois Geol. Surv. Bull. 82, 233 p.

Wascher, H. L., Alexander, J. D., Ray, B. W., Beavers, A. H., and Odell, R. T., 1960, Characteristics of soils associated with glacial tills in northeastern Illinois: Univ. Illinois Agr. Exp. Stat. Bull. 665, 155 p.

Wascher, H. L., Humbert, R. P., and Cady, J. G., 1948, Loess in the southern Mississippi Valley—Identification and distribution of the loess sheets: Soil Sci. Soc. Amer. Proc. 1947, v. 12, p. 389-399

Weidman, Samuel, 1907, The geology of north-central Wisconsin: Wisconsin Geol. Surv. Bull. 16, 697 p.

—— 1913, The Pleistocene succession in Wisconsin: Science, v. 37, p. 456-457

Weller, J. M., *et al.,* 1945, Geologic map of Illinois: Illinois Geol. Surv.

West, R. G., 1961, Late and postglacial vegetational history in Wisconsin, particularly changes associated with the Valders readvance: Amer. J. Sci., v. 259, p. 766-783

Willman, H. B., and Frye, J. C., 1958, Problems of Pleistocene geology in the greater St. Louis area: *in* Geol. Soc. Amer. Guidebook, St. Louis Meetings, p. 9-19

Willman, H. B., Glass, H. D., and Frye, J. C., 1963, Mineralogy of glacial tills and their weathering profiles in Illinois. Part I, Glacial tills: Illinois Geol. Surv. Circ. 347, 55 p.

Willman, H. B., and Payne, J. N., 1942, Geology and mineral resources of the Marseilles, Ottawa, and Streator Quadrangles: Illinois Geol. Surv. Bull. 66, 388 p.

Willman, H. B., Swann, D. H., and Frye, J. C., 1958, Stratigraphic policy of the Illinois State Geological Survey: Illinois State Geol. Surv. Circ. 249, 14 p.

Wilson, L. R., 1932, The Two Creeks forest bed, Manitowoc County, Wisconsin: Wisconsin Acad. Sci. Trans., v. 27, p. 31-46

—— 1936, Further fossil studies of the Two Creeks forest bed, Manitowoc County, Wisconsin: Torrey Bot. Club Bull., v. 63, p. 317-325

Worthen, A. H., 1866, Physical features, general principles, and surface geology, *in* Geology of Illinois: Geol. Surv. Illinois, v. 1, p. 1-39

—— 1873, Geology of Sangamon County: Illinois Geol. Surv., v. 5, p. 306-319

Zumberge, J. H., 1960, Correlation of Wisconsin drifts in Illinois, Indiana, Michigan, and Ohio: Geol. Soc. Amer. Bull. 71, p. 1177-1188

ACKNOWLEDGMENT: Field studies and report preparation by R. F. Black were supported in part by funds from the National Science Foundation, the Wisconsin State Highway Commission, and the Wisconsin Alumni Research Foundation through the Graduate School of the University of Wisconsin.

SUMMARY

Deposits of each of the four glacial stages occur in Illinois and Wisconsin, as do soils formed during each of the three major interglacial stages. Wisconsin and northeastern Illinois is the type region for the Wisconsinan Stage, and central Illinois is the type region for the Illinoian Stage. The Sangamonian Stage is named for buried soil in the Sangamon River basin in Sangamon County, Illinois, and the substages used here for the Wisconsinan and Illinoian are based on type sequences in these two states.

The geographic position of Illinois in the area of overlap of tills deposited by glaciers from both eastern and western centers of dispersal makes it the only region in North America where the physical relations of the pre-Illinoian tills from these two principal centers can be examined. It also is a focal point of drainage diversions produced by the several glacial advances. These drainage diversions resulted in changes in mineral composition of outwash and loess as the tills from different sources have recognizably different compositions.

The stratigraphic succession from Nebraskan to Recent as it occurs in these two states is briefly outlined and methods of correlation are described. Recent work on the mineralogy of Pleistocene deposits, the subdivision and classification of the Illinoian and Wisconsinan Stages, and the evidence for glaciation of the "Driftless Area" is summarized.

PLEISTOCENE GEOLOGY OF INDIANA AND MICHIGAN *

WILLIAM J. WAYNE,[1] JAMES H. ZUMBERGE[2]

THE FIRST comprehensive studies of the Pleistocene geology of Indiana and Michigan were those of Leverett (1899, 1902; Leverett and Taylor, 1915), although earlier workers had mapped the drift in many areas (Hubbard, 1840; Thompson, 1886, 1889; Dryer, 1894). Subsequent statewide treatment has been provided in Indiana by Malott (1922), Thornbury (1958), and Wayne (1956b, 1963). In addition, considerably more detailed knowledge has come from the work of Gooding (1957, 1963), Harrison (1959, 1960, 1963), Kapp and Gooding (1964b), Thornbury (1937), Wayne (1958a, 1959), and Zumberge (1960). Surficial geologic maps have been prepared for Michigan by Martin (1955, 1957) and for both Indiana and Michigan by Flint *et al.* (1959).

About 80% of Indiana was covered with ice during one or more Pleistocene glaciations (Leverett and Taylor, 1915, Pl. 6; Wayne, 1958b; Flint *et al.*, 1959). In the two-thirds of the state that lies north of the Wisconsin glacial boundary, most of the landscape was formed by glacial construction (Fig. 1). Between the Wisconsin boundary and the maximum extent of the earlier glaciations, glacially formed features are interspersed with topography that was clearly developed on the underlying bedrock. South of the limit reached by glacial ice, valleys partly filled with outwash and lacustrine sediments dominate the topography.

The physiography of southern Indiana is characterized by southward-trending areas of alternating uplands and lowlands (Fig. 1; Malott, 1922; Wayne, 1956b). The broad Wabash Lowland on the west side of the state, underlain by Pennsylvanian shales and coals, and the Scottsburg Lowland in the southeastern part of Indiana, underlain by Devonian and lower Mississippian shales, provided avenues between adjacent uplands along which the lobes of the earlier glaciers extended nearly to the 38th parallel. Resistant Mississippian and lower Pennsylvanian rocks formed an upland barrier between these two lobes that was too high for the ice to cover (Fig. 1).

Michigan consists of two tracts of land called the Northern and Southern Peninsulas. The surface is dominated by a youthful topography developed on glacial drift of Wisconsin age. The surface drainage lines are poorly developed, and inland lakes form an important part of the landscape throughout most of Michigan and northern Indiana (Scott, 1921).

Michigan and Indiana are bordered by more than 2,300 miles of shoreline of the Great Lakes of Superior, Michigan, Huron, and Erie. The shorelines vary in character from long stretches of sandy beaches along Lake Michigan to the steep sandstone cliffs of Lake Superior. The coasts are attacked by wave erosion during periods of high water levels, such as occurred in 1952 when considerable damage to property and loss of shore installations were sustained. During low-water phases, such as in 1934 and 1964, considerable dredging in harbors and connecting channels is required (St. Clair River, Detroit River).

The levels of the Great Lakes follow a pattern of highs in the summer and lows in the winter. Seasonal fluctuations are normally about 30 cm on Lake Superior, 30 to 45 cm on Lakes Michigan and Huron, and 45 to 60 cm on Lakes Erie and Ontario. Table 1 gives some information on the morphometry of the lakes.

The bedrock geology of Michigan consists of two distinct provinces. The Michigan Basin, containing Cambrian to Pennsylvanian shales, sandstones, carbonate rocks, and evaporites, occupies all the Southern Peninsula and the eastern half of the Northern Peninsula. The Precambrian shield, which occupies the western half of the Northern Peninsula, contains chiefly Proterozoic metamorphosed lava flows, Huronian iron formations, Killarney granite intrusives, and Keweenawan lava flows, conglomerates, and sandstones.

The glacial deposits of Indiana, Michigan, and adjacent states and the history of their deposition have been the subject of several schemes of classification by the various workers who have studied them during the past 75 years. The early classifications of Leverett and Malott and of Leighton (1933) were reviewed and compared by Thornbury (1937) and by Wayne (1963). Thornbury (1937) introduced into Indiana the substage terminology that Leighton (1933) had recently developed for the classification of the Wisconsin Stage in Illinois. This classification has undergone many changes in recent years, but the use of stages and substages remains the primary basis of time-stratigraphic classification of the Pleistocene Series.

Correlation problems inherent in this time-rock classification system, when it is used alone, have been a major factor in encouraging the development of a rock-stratigraphic classification for glacial sediments in Indiana (Wayne, 1963). Both sets of terminology have been used in this summary (Fig. 2).

All surficial deposits in Michigan are products of glaciation during the Wisconsin Age. Their classification is based on morphologic features of various drift sheets rather than on stratigraphic type sections. The Wisconsin drift sheets

* Indiana part of this report is published by permission of the State Geologist, Indiana Department of Conservation, Geological Survey.
[1] Indiana Geological Survey, Indiana University, Bloomington, Indiana.
[2] Grand Valley State College, Allendale, Michigan.

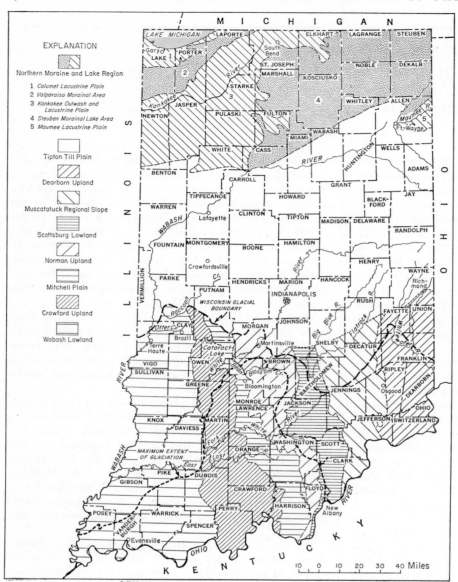

Figure 1. Map of Indiana showing physiographic units and glacial boundaries.

and their associated moraines in Michigan have been assigned to the Cary, Port Huron (Mankato), and Valders Substages. This system is built on the original classification of Leverett and Taylor (1915), Leverett (1929b), and Leighton (1933) and on important modifications by Bretz (1951a), Melhorn (1954), Zumberge *et al.* (1956), Hough (1958, p. 94), Leighton (1960), and Zumberge (1960).

In addition to the three Wisconsin drift sheets and their associated end moraines, the late-Pleistocene chronology of Michigan and parts of northern Indiana is built around the phases of proglacial lakes that began to develop during the retreat of the Cary ice from the basins of Lake Michigan, Lake Huron, and Lake Erie.

LATE-TERTIARY GEOMORPHIC HISTORY AND PRE-PLEISTOCENE TOPOGRAPHY

Except for deposition of alluvial and colluvial deposits, nearly all of Indiana and Michigan probably was eroded continuously from the time that late Paleozoic sedimenta-

tion ceased until the area was covered by Pleistocene glaciers. Direct evidence of Mesozoic physiographic history is lost, but the Ohio River Formation in southern Indiana probably represents a depositional record from the early part of the Tertiary Period (Wayne, 1960, p. 29). Evidently, thick residual soils existed at the time that unit was deposited; the basal part of the Ohio River Formation is in many places a thick cherty clay, now compacted and altered by burial, but otherwise similar to the surficial soils on the adjacent limestone plain.

In the other parts of Indiana and Michigan, subaerial erosion and weathering continued throughout Tertiary and early Quaternary time. Reddish-brown cherty clay soils 12 m or more thick are preserved in broad areas of the Mitchell Plain (Fig. 1), where development of karst has reduced the amount of water available to erode the surface.

Scattered deposits of siliceous gravels at high levels, called the Lafayette Gravel (Malott, 1922, p. 132), are the residue of old stream deposits and are considered to be middle to

TABLE 1

Morphometry of the Great Lakes
(From U.S. Lake Survey)

	Superior	Michigan	Huron	Erie	Ontario	Total[a]
Area (sq. miles)						
Drainage basin[b]	80,000	67,860	72,620	32,490	34,800	295,200
Water surface	31,820	22,400	23,010	9,930	7,520	95,170
Shoreline (miles)						
United States	1,427	1,661	769	490	331	5,506
Canada	1,549	0	2,416	366	395	5,471
Total	2,976	1,661	3,185	856	726	10,977
Depth (ft)						
Average	487	276	195	58	264	
Maximum	1,333	923	750	210	778	
Mean surface elevation						
(ft above sea level)	602	580	580	573	246	

[a] Includes Lake St. Clair and its drainage basin.
[b] Including lake area.

late Tertiary in age. They probably represent deposits of more than one episode of deposition and degradation during and shortly following a late-Tertiary erosion cycle, during which an erosion surface known as the Lexington Peneplain was formed. Uplift of this surface is now generally considered to have begun during the Miocene or Pliocene Epoch (Thornbury, 1958, p. 454). Remnants of this peneplain are preserved on the dissected uplands of the unglaciated part of Indiana (Malott, 1922) and on the buried uplands (Wayne, 1956b). The buried bedrock physiography of Indiana was developed on flat-lying limestones, shales, and sandstones and is the northward continuation of the physiographic units recognized in the unglaciated part of the state. Bedrock physiography of Michigan is still not well known, but studies to date (Mozola, 1962) indicate that similar features underlie the thick drift cover of that state.

Most of Indiana was drained during Tertiary time by the Teays River and its tributaries. The Teays (Tight, 1903) headed in the Appalachian Mountains and flowed northwestward through West Virginia, Ohio, Indiana, and Illinois, where it joined the ancestral Mississippi (Horberg, 1950; Wayne, 1952). Before the earliest glaciers reached Indiana, the Teays had eroded a gorge as much as 75 m below the adjacent limestone plains in north-central Indiana. Major tributary streams had cut their valleys to accordance. Glacial erosion was slight, so that details of the buried topographic features remain essentially those of erosion by running water. Differences of interpretation place the time of deep valley erosion of the Teays as preglacial (Horberg, 1950; Wayne, 1956b) or interglacial (Stout et al., 1943; Stout, 1953).

The drainage history of the Teays Valley has been inferred from studies of the sediments that partly fill its abandoned strath in southern Ohio and West Virginia, from the physiographic details of that region, and from bedrock topographic studies in western Ohio, Indiana, and Illinois. Most students of the Teays have considered it to have been deranged by an early glacier (Stout and Shaaf, 1931; Stout et al., 1943). Conclusions reached from a recent study of the sediments in West Virginia (Rhodehamel and

Carlston, 1963, p. 271) do not agree with this interpretation. These authors believed that the Teays was diverted before glacial ice reached it as a result of nonglacial processes of stream capture. Although their data and arguments seem reasonable, they are not altogether convincing, and it is difficult to see how their hypothesis could be applied to the creation of the Ohio River. Each abandoned segment of a major valley would have to be regarded as a separate situation of normal stream capture. Glacial diver-

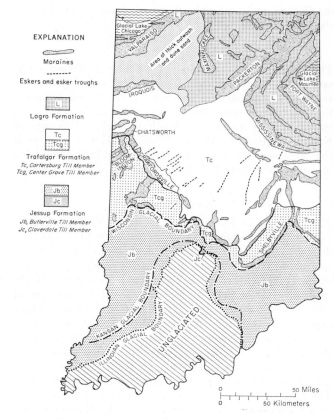

Figure 2. Map of Indiana showing extent of glacial sediments and moraines.

sion during the Nebraskan and Kansan Ages probably was the cause of derangement of the Teays and the creation of the Ohio River (Wayne, 1956b, p. 46).

Recognizable former floodplain sediments can be found on straths that stand only a few meters above the modern drainage levels outside the limits of glaciation. These sediments, included by Wayne (1963, p. 38) in the Prospect Formation, are particularly noticeable along streams that have been diverted to subsurface routes, such as Lost River. Age of the Prospect Formation may be as great as late Pliocene in some drainage basins and as young as early to middle Pleistocene in others.

NEBRASKAN STAGE

Deposits referable to the Nebraskan glaciers have not been recognized in either Indiana or Michigan. Thwaites (1946, Pl. 3) suggested that the scattered erratics of northern Kentucky (Leverett, 1929a, p. 34) might be Nebraskan in age, and Eveland (1952) interpreted an exposure at Danville, Illinois, as gumbotil of Nebraskan and Aftonian age embedded in till of Kansan age. Reinterpretation of the Danville exposures (Ekblaw and Willman, 1955, p. 134; Thornbury, 1958, p. 455) suggests that no deposits referable to Nebraskan glaciation exist there.

The most likely places for a record of Nebraskan glaciation to have remained in northern Indiana and southern Michigan are over the bedrock lowlands and in the Teays Valley and its tributaries. Unfortunately, glacial deposits there are very thick, and few logs of wells are sufficiently detailed to make possible the recognition of pre-Kansan sediments.

AFTONIAN STAGE

The lack of deposits definitely identifiable as Nebraskan in age makes it difficult to interpret any sediments in the two states as Aftonian in age. Some of the Prospect Formation in Indiana may be Aftonian in age, however, and buried alluvial materials beneath lacustrine sediments of Kansan age undoubtedly are Aftonian. There is little positive evidence about the nature of such buried deposits, because few of them have been found.

KANSAN STAGE

The presence in Indiana of deposits of Kansan age was suspected by Thornbury (1937, p. 100), but none had been demonstrated until 1954 when a new cut for an emergency spillway at Cataract Lake in Putnam County (Fig. 1) was examined. Discovery of well-preserved Kansan till in the cut provided an impetus for the careful examination of other areas for exposures of drift of Kansan age. Many exposures were found (Wayne, 1958a, Fig. 1), and a limit of the extent of Kansan ice into Indiana was inferred from the distribution of the exposures. Recent mapping (Wier and Gray, 1961) indicates that in a few places the Kansan glacial boundary may extend beyond the Illinoian ice limit. The long-known, scattered, large erratics in northern Kentucky (Leverett, 1929a) are more likely Kansan in age (Wayne, 1956b, p. 48; Thornbury, 1958, p. 456) than Nebraskan, as was suggested by Thwaites (1946). Ray (1963)

reported Kansan till in Kentucky and probable Kansan loess along the Ohio River east of Evansville, Indiana. Kansan drift has not been recognized in Michigan.

Till of Kansan age, which makes up the bulk of the Cloverdale Till Member of the Jessup Formation of Wayne (1963, p. 52), is generally pebbly, sandy, and silty and is very compact. Its lithologic features, the distinctive paleosol that caps it, and its position in an exposure generally make identification of Cloverdale till reasonably certain.

One exposure of fossiliferous proglacial loess of Kansan age has been found in Indiana; it is at the Cataract Lake spillway. This silt contains wood fragments and 20 species of snails (Wayne, 1958a, p. 15; 1963, Table 2) that suggest an ice-marginal climate and a forest cover similar to that in central Ontario today.

The Kansan glaciation of central Indiana consisted of at least two pulsations of the ice separated by a brief ice-free time (Fig. 2). A thin bed of fossiliferous silt has been found intercalated between two tills of the Cloverdale member in western Indiana (Wayne 1963, Table 2). Three exposures of this bed are known, all in the same area; its fauna of 16 snail species gives the only record so far of the land mollusks that lived around the Kansan ice margin during deglaciation.

Valley-fill sediments deposited in Indiana during the Kansan glaciation were never wholly removed during the Yarmouth Age and later erosional episodes. Cloverdale till was recognized in an auger boring west of Brazil, Indiana, where, at a depth of 12 m below the floodplain of Otter Creek, a paleosol on compact till was found. Where no identifying paleosols occur, till units are difficult to distinguish in subsurface studies. Gravel of Kansan age fills the valley of Raccoon Creek, where it can be recognized beneath a thick accumulation of younger drift. The lowest gravels, sands, and silts that fill major pre-Kansan valleys, such as the lower Wabash, White, and Ohio, probably are also of Kansan age. These glaciofluvial sediments, along with similar younger sediments, make up the Atherton Formation (Wayne, 1963, p. 31).

YARMOUTH STAGE

After the Kansan glacier had melted from Indiana, it left over most of the state a relatively thin cover of drift that probably did not greatly obscure the major features of the pre-Kansan bedrock topography. Stream erosion soon cleaned out the main valleys to a new base level, this time not so deep as the bottom of the partly filled bedrock valleys.

Floodplain sediments of Yarmouth age have been observed in several of the valleys of central Indiana. Along Raccoon Creek in Parke County, exposures of peat and old floodplain deposits can be traced for several miles along the edge of the valley and indicate that the Yarmouth floodplain was slightly lower than the modern floodplain of the same stream. The same is true of the lower part of Bean Blossom Creek, a tributary of White River (Wayne, 1958a, p. 13); farther upstream the top of the Yarmouth floodplain sediment is 3 to 4 m higher than the modern floodplain. West of Brazil in Otter Creek, Yarmouth sediments lie 12 m below the modern floodplain.

The soil profile developed during Yarmouth time on till of Kansan age is well displayed in exposures in western Indiana and has been observed in the eastern part of the state. This soil and associated interglacial sediments mark the top of the Cloverdale Till Member of the Jessup Formation. In the type section of the Cloverdale till, carbonates have been removed to a depth of 3.7 m. Bhattacharya (1962, p. 1016) found kaolinite in each of the Yarmouth paleosols he examined but not in Sangamon paleosols and Recent soils. He related this fact to a longer period of weathering.

Even though many exposures of Yarmouth sediments have been discovered, fossils other than wood fragments are scarce. Englehardt (1962) studied the pollen in the upper parts of three buried Yarmouth alluvial deposits. Two of these, near Osgood in Ripley County and on Bean Blossom Creek in Monroe County, probably were Illinoian proglacial accumulations on a Yarmouth surface; the pollen in both, though sparse, was dominated by *Picea* and *Pinus* (Englehardt, 1962, p. 92, 103). The third, a buried alluvial sediment that contains layers of compressed peat, shows a strong dominance of *Pinus* and *Picea* but also contains a small percentage of *Quercus* pollen. All mollusks recovered from Yarmouth sediments suggest a cool climate (Wayne, 1963, p. 56). Inasmuch as most floodplain sediments probably are reworked every few thousand years, absence of any but very late Yarmouth deposits is not surprising.

ILLINOIAN STAGE

Only a few exposures of pre-Wisconsin drift are known in Michigan. These were assigned to the Illinoian Stage by Leverett because of their occurrence immediately below drifts of Wisconsin age. The position of the Illinoian glacial boundary, the southernmost of the three in Indiana (see Fig. 3), is well known from the mapping by several workers (Leverett, 1899, 1902; Leverett and Taylor, 1915; Malott, 1922; Thornbury, 1937).

At least three advances of Illinoian ice reached into southwestern Indiana (Wayne, 1963, p. 53) and left tills that are separated by thin beds of fossiliferous silt. Two such tills and fossiliferous silt were reported in the Whitewater basin of southeastern Indiana by Gooding (1963, p. 669), who named the ice advances and retreats they represent the Centerville Stade, the Abington Interstade, and the Richmond Stade, respectively, from oldest to youngest (Fig. 2).

The Butlerville Till Member of the Jessup Formation of Wayne (1963, p. 14) includes all the tills of Illinoian age. The unit lies between the top of the paleosol on the Cloverdale and the top of the paleosol on the Butlerville. Deposition of the till was accompanied by outwash and loess deposition, but the loess did not escape subsequent erosion in many places. Outwash gravels, lacustrine sands, silts, and clays, and loessal silts of Illinoian age are included as part of the Atherton Formation.

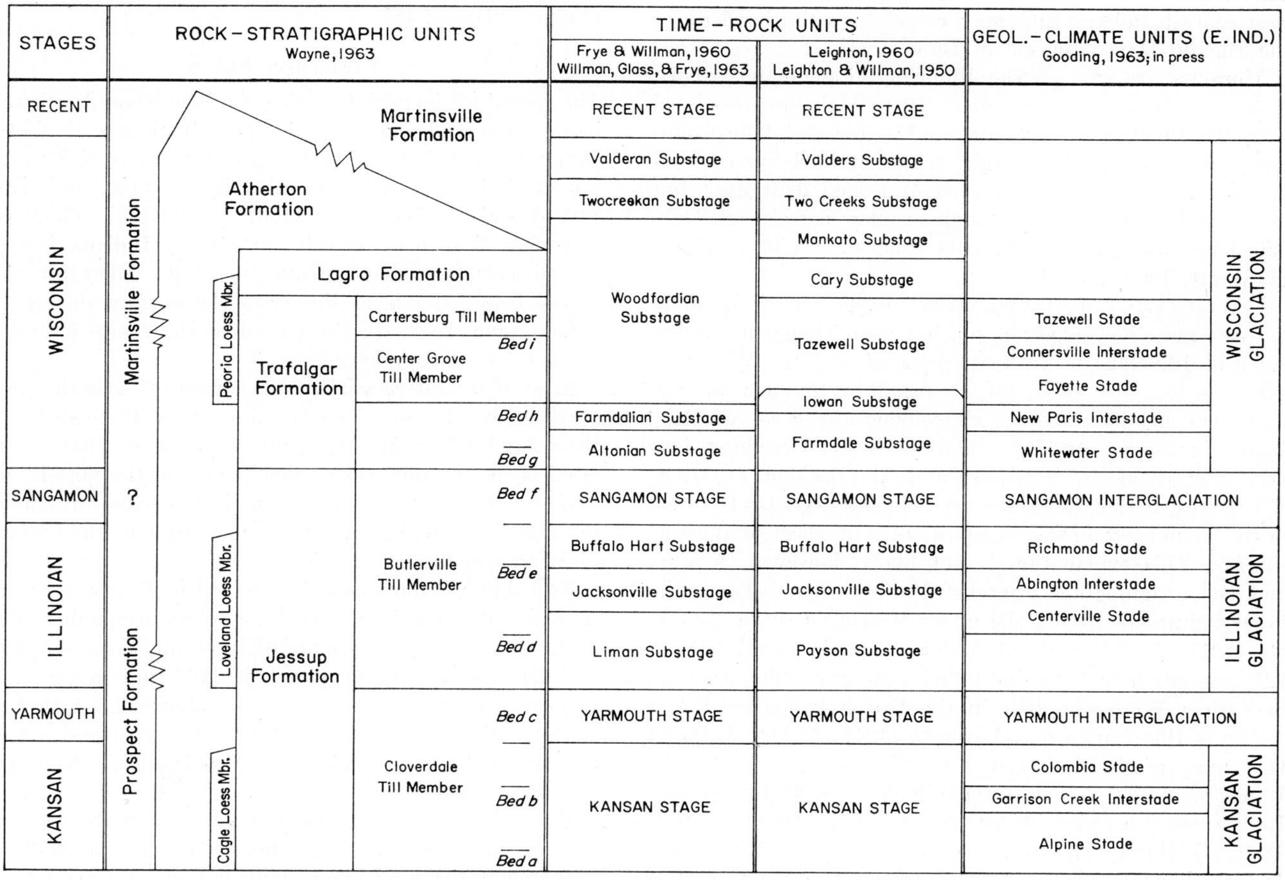

STAGES	ROCK–STRATIGRAPHIC UNITS Wayne, 1963				TIME–ROCK UNITS		GEOL.–CLIMATE UNITS (E. IND.) Gooding, 1963; in press	
					Frye & Willman, 1960 Willman, Glass, & Frye, 1963	Leighton, 1960 Leighton & Willman, 1950		
RECENT			Martinsville Formation		RECENT STAGE	RECENT STAGE		
WISCONSIN	Martinsville Formation		Atherton Formation		Valderan Substage	Valders Substage		WISCONSIN GLACIATION
					Twocreekan Substage	Two Creeks Substage		
			Lagro Formation		Woodfordian Substage	Mankato Substage		
						Cary Substage		
		Peoria Loess Mbr.	Trafalgar Formation	Cartersburg Till Member		Tazewell Substage	Tazewell Stade	
				Center Grove Till Member / Bed i			Connersville Interstade	
							Fayette Stade	
				Bed h	Farmdalian Substage	Iowan Substage	New Paris Interstade	
				Bed g	Altonian Substage	Farmdale Substage	Whitewater Stade	
SANGAMON	?		Jessup Formation	Bed f	SANGAMON STAGE	SANGAMON STAGE	SANGAMON INTERGLACIATION	
ILLINOIAN	Prospect Formation	Loveland Loess Mbr.		Butlerville Till Member / Bed e	Buffalo Hart Substage	Buffalo Hart Substage	Richmond Stade	ILLINOIAN GLACIATION
					Jacksonville Substage	Jacksonville Substage	Abington Interstade	
							Centerville Stade	
				Bed d	Liman Substage	Payson Substage		
YARMOUTH				Bed c	YARMOUTH STAGE	YARMOUTH STAGE	YARMOUTH INTERGLACIATION	
KANSAN		Cagle Loess Mbr.	Cloverdale Till Member	Bed b	KANSAN STAGE	KANSAN STAGE	Colombia Stade	KANSAN GLACIATION
							Garrison Creek Interstade	
				Bed a			Alpine Stade	

Figure 3. Correlation chart of Pleistocene stratigraphic terms and geologic-climate units used in Indiana.

Only two exposures of the lowest till of the Butlerville are known, both in Parke County. The till has a distinctive grayish-brown color not found in other tills of the Butlerville member. The overlying fossiliferous silt contains only species of very small snails.

The second advance of Illinoian ice evidently extended farther south in western Indiana than any other glacier; its deposits probably correlate with the Liman (Frye *et al.*, 1964) and Jacksonville Substages of Illinois (Fig. 2). The ice blocked nearly all westward-flowing streams, creating extensive ice-marginal lakes (Thornbury, 1950, p. 4-8). Sedimentation in many of the lakes was extensive, and some of the broader lacustrine plains, such as those of glacial Lakes Flatwoods, Quincy, and Patoka, remain essentially undissected.

The middle till of the Butlerville member is separated from a younger till in west-central Indiana by a thin fossiliferous silt bed. Exposures of the silt bed have been found in Vigo and Parke Counties (Wayne, 1963, p. 53), and a bed reported by Harrison (1963, Fig. 6) in Marion County may be the same unit. The bed has not been traced across the state, but on the basis of position and similarity of lithology and fauna it might be referable to the Abington Interstade of eastern Indiana described by Gooding (1963, p. 672). The snail fauna from this bed is dominated by small, cool-climate species, particularly such forms as *Catinella gelida* and *Columella alticola*. The till that overlies it is almost coextensive with the Wisconsin glacial boundary in west-central Indiana and may correlate with the drift of the Buffalo Hart Moraine of Illinois.

Moraines are rare on the Illinoian till plain in Indiana. A few ridges of till as much as 10 m high are associated with the Illinoian drift border in Daviess and Pike Counties, but generally the margin is not marked by a recognizable moraine. Other segments of ridged drift exist but have not been traced far enough to allow correlation. Only one, Chestnut Ridge in Jackson County, has been named (Leverett, 1902, p. 255).

Leverett (1917, p. 114) asserted that some of the more massive morainic ridges in southeastern Michigan contain cores of Illinoian till with a veneer of younger Wisconsin drift on top. An older till, presumably Illinoian in age, crops out in the wave-cut cliffs along the coast of Lake Huron between Port Huron and the head of Saginaw Bay (the Thumb area). Bergquist and MacLachlan (1951, p. 15) suggested that the blue-gray tills described by Leverett in the Thumb are unoxidized parts of a till sheet of Wisconsin age. This explanation is not likely, however, if peats and soils of undoubted interglacial origin occur between the lower indurated till and the upper Wisconsin till, as Leverett (1917, p. 113) claimed. Leverett and Taylor (1915, p. 72) suggested that an indurated blue-gray till occurring beneath a Wisconsin drift in the Huron valley near Ann Arbor is Illinoian in age. Leverett (1917, p. 114) believed that most of the Southern Peninsula was covered by the Illinoian ice, as indeed it must have been if Illinois and Indiana were invaded by ice from the northeast (Leverett, 1899; Leighton and Brophy, 1961), but D. F. Eschman (personal communication) is of the opinion that no Illinoian till crops out in eastern Michigan.

Leighton (1959) interpreted the lack of moraines and the abundance of kames in Illinois as indicating that the Illinoian glaciers became stagnant ice masses. Only a few kames have been noted in the Illinoian drift in Indiana, but several extensive outwash plains have been mapped. This evidence suggests that the main advance of Illinoian ice probably did not disappear from Indiana by stagnation.

Broad outwash plains in Indiana were laid down by meltwater from the Illinoian glacier, particularly in Morgan, Owen, Greene, and Daviess Counties. Valley-train outwash has been largely destroyed by later erosion and obscured by sedimentation, but remnants of it can be found along those valleys that never carried melt-water from the Wisconsin ice sheet as well as along most of the major valleys. These coarse sediments and the finer-grained deposits associated with them are included in the Atherton Formation of Wayne (1963, p. 31).

Loess was blown from the outwash deposits along the Wabash and Ohio Valleys and deposited as a thin blanket over the adjacent uplands. The volume of the loess (Loveland Loess Member) seems not to have been great, and it has been observed below the Butlerville Till Member only near the edges of valleys that served as major sluiceways during the Illinoian Age.

Lakes were ponded not only in the valleys blocked by the Illinoian ice sheet but also in valleys tributary to the major sluiceways. Most of these lacustrine sediments of Illinoian age are now buried beneath younger materials (Fidlar, 1948, p. 18).

SANGAMON STAGE

The record of deposition during the Sangamon Age is much better preserved and exposed for study than is that of the earlier Yarmouth Age. Many exposures of buried Sangamon soils and deposits were recorded by Leverett and Taylor (1915) and by Thornbury (1937, p. 100-123). Thinness of overlying Wisconsin deposits in central Indiana has permitted post-Wisconsin streams to erode valleys in many places below the level that was the surface during Sangamon time. Even so, the record of the entire interglacial age is far from complete.

Most of the interglacial record consists of soils that developed on the glacially derived sediments of Illinoian age and the colluvial, alluvial, and paludal sediments that accumulated in depressions and on floodplains on the post-Illinoian surface. By far the greatest number of exposures display materials that had accumulated just prior to the onslaught of Wisconsin ice.

Probably the most complete record of Sangamon vegetation in Indiana is in a buried floodplain accumulation near Richmond. The pollen studies of Kapp and Gooding (1964b, p. 312) and Englehardt (1962, p. 126) show a progression of vegetation from coniferous to deciduous forest that took place at the close of the Illinoian glaciation and a return to coniferous forest dominance that heralded the advance of Wisconsin ice.

One other fossiliferous deposit dates from the early part of the Sangamon; near Martinsville, Indiana, a small creek has trenched a marl-filled depression in an outwash plain of Illinoian age. The upper part of the accumulation has been destroyed by weathering, but the lower part contains a record of the cool-climate, aquatic snails and clams that lived in a small early post-Illinoian lake.

The main part of the Sangamon Age is poorly represented except by the products of weathering. The soil profile on the Butlerville member, where it is not buried beneath a thick layer of younger sediments, is 3 to 4 m thick, but the upper part (half a meter or more) is a veneer of loessial silt. Where the Sangamon soil has been protected from further weathering by overlying Wisconsin drift, the thickness of till that has been leached of carbonates is generally less than 2 m (Thornbury, 1937, 1940), but gravels, sands, and silts are noncalcareous to depths of 3 m or more. The soil profile seems to have been developed under conditions at least as warm as those of the present, perhaps slightly warmer. Fossil records of the warm part of Sangamon time are scarce, but the pollen records from deposits near Richmond cited earlier (Kapp and Gooding, 1964b, p. 312) represent the full vegetational record of the Sangamon and include a period warmer and drier than the present. In an exposure of Sangamon alluvium in Johnson County, Indiana, Englehardt (1962, p. 120) found a decrease of *Quercus* and a corresponding increase in conifer pollen from base to top of the section, which he interpreted as indicating the approach of Wisconsin ice.

Most of the exposures of sediments that lie directly beneath Wisconsin deposits in Indiana contain almost wholly conifer wood, pollen, and mollusks characteristic of cool climates; they have yielded radiocarbon dates of 21,000 to 23,000 years B.P. (before the present), well within the time span of the Wisconsin Age (Wayne, 1963, p. 80).

The shallow depth of oxidation of till in the Sangamon weathering profile contrasted with the much greater depth of oxidation during post-Wisconsin time suggests that ground-water levels may have been higher than at present. Local base levels of erosion may have differed, too, although the top of a late Sangamon floodplain sediment exposed along the Ohio River at Owensboro, Kentucky (L. L. Ray, 1955, oral communication), and dated as 23,150 years B.P. (W-270) is almost identical in elevation to the modern floodplain surface. Sangamon floodplain sediments buried beneath stratified silts in tributary valleys of the Whitewater and Wabash also are similar in elevation to the modern floodplains in those valleys.

Buried peats and soils in southeastern Michigan are cited by Leverett and Taylor (1915, p. 72) and Leverett (1917, p. 113) as evidence of an interglacial stage of pre-Wisconsin and post-Illinoian age. Because none of these occurrences has been studied in detail in recent times, it is impossible to evaluate Leverett's interpretation of their age. This is a problem in Michigan that still awaits elucidation.

WISCONSIN STAGE

At its greatest extent, Wisconsin ice spread over all of Michigan and about two-thirds of Indiana (Figs. 2, 5). The southern limit of Wisconsin drift was mapped by Leverett and Taylor (1915, Pl. 4) and later in greater detail by Thornbury (1937, p. 40). More detailed mapping has provided further refinements during the past decade

(Wayne, 1956b, Pl. 1; Gooding, 1957, Pl. 1; Flint *et al.*, 1959; Wier and Gray, 1961).

Since about 1950 the stratigraphy of the Wisconsin Stage has been extensively re-examined. A more critical study of available streambank exposures and many new roadcuts has provided the basis for major alterations in some existing concepts. Dreimanis' (1958, 1960) work in southern Ontario laid much of the groundwork for recognizing that sediments of Wisconsin age considerably older than those of the recognized morainal sequences in Illinois might in fact exist in North America.

Classifications of the Wisconsin Stage have been reviewed recently by Leighton (1958a, 1958b, 1959, 1960), by Frye and Willman (1960), and by Wright (1964). These and recent studies in Indiana by Wayne (1963) and Gooding (1963) are summarized in Figure 2.

TAZEWELL SUBSTAGE AND OLDER WISCONSIN DEPOSITS

In most parts of central Indiana where streams have eroded through the deposits of Wisconsin age, both physical stratigraphy and radiocarbon dates indicate little material of glacial origin that is greater than 20,000 to 23,000 years old. In the Whitewater basin, however, Gooding (1961, p. 102; 1963, p. 674) found sediments that he interpreted as indicating an extension of glacial ice into southeastern Indiana during the Wisconsin Age prior to deposition of the bulk of Wisconsin drift in the state.

Gooding (1963, p. 674) gave names to the several advances and retreats of the Wisconsin glacier represented by the sediments he had examined in the Whitewater valley (Fig. 2). The Whitewater Stade is named for a glacial advance that left a basal till containing inclusions of reddish-brown till that directly overlies Sangamon sediments and soil. Deposits representing the Whitewater Stade are overlain by fossiliferous silt left during a brief glacial retreat, which Gooding named the New Paris Interstade. Possibly these two intervals correspond in time with the Altonian and Farmdalian Substages of Frye and Willman (1960, p. 4), although a discrepancy seems to exist in the radiocarbon dates available, and the degree of weathering seems inconsistent with this interpretation. Frye and Willman placed the Altonian Subage between 50,000 and 28,000 years B.P.; all dates on the Whitewater Stade indicate an age greater than 40,000 years B.P. In spite of the long time evidently involved between the time of the Whitewater Stade and the next younger glacial advance, which Gooding called the Fayette Stade, the sediments from which the Whitewater Stade is inferred are reported to show little effect of weathering.

Gooding's Fayette Stade probably is the glacial advance that left the Center Grove Till Member of the Trafalgar Formation of Wayne (1963, p. 45). The Center Grove, like the till representing the Fayette Stade, can be observed in many exposures directly overlying a Sangamon soil profile. Both are separated from the next younger till by a fossiliferous silt bed about 30 cm thick and dated at about 20,000 years B.P. Wayne referred to the fossiliferous unit as the *Vertigo alpestris oughtoni* bed; Gooding named the deglaciation it represents the Connersville Interstade.

This silt bed has been observed in many exposures in a

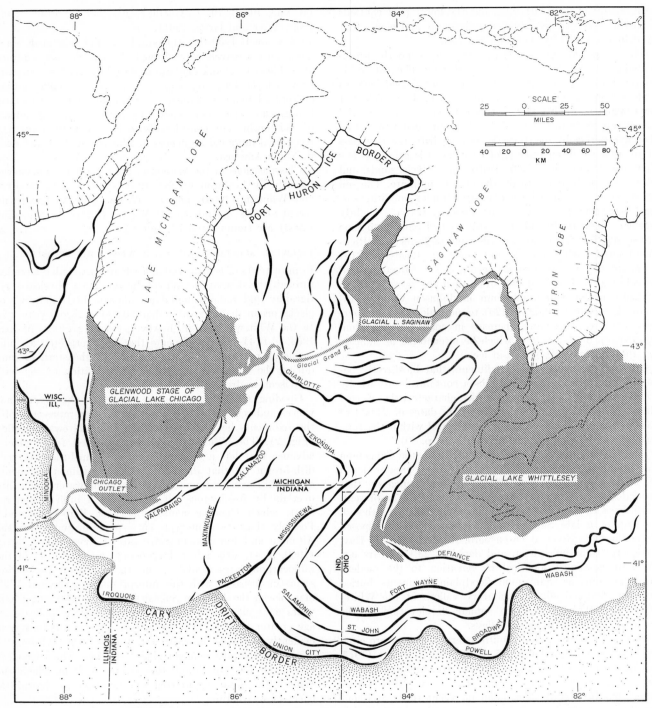

Figure 4. Paleogeographic map of the upper Great Lakes region during the Port Huron (Mankato) maximum *ca.* **13,000** B.P. Heavy black lines show trends of Cary recessional moraines. The glacial Grand River carried the overflow of glacial Lakes Whittlesey and Saginaw to Lake Chicago, where the Allendale delta was constructed. Morainic trends based on Flint *et al.* (1959); Cary drift border after Zumberge (1960). (Outline of modern Great Lakes is shown by a dashed line.)

band about 30 km wide between Crawfordsville and Richmond. It represents a brief but distinct ice-free phase during the Wisconsin Age when a subarctic fauna and flora began to repopulate the newly deglaciated land surface. Extensive outwash plains in Fountain, Montgomery, Mar-

ion, Shelby, and Wayne Counties and buried outwash gravels elsewhere in central Indiana were deposited during the next glacial advance and probably were the sources of loessial silts that preserved the fossil material. Till overlying the fossil bed was named the Cartersburg Till Member of the Trafalgar Formation by Wayne (1963, p. 48), and the glacial advance was referred to the Tazewell Stade by Gooding (1963, p. 678). Retreat of the ice margin probably did not exceed 100 to 200 km between deposition of the Center Grove and the Cartersburg members.

Recent mapping in west-central Indiana indicates that the outer limit of the Cartersburg till overlaps the deposits related to the Bloomington Moraine of the Lake Michigan Lobe and is in turn overlapped by a younger drift, perhaps that associated with the Chatsworth Moraine (Fig. 3). If this interpretation is valid, the Center Grove till would be the central-Indiana correlative of the drift sheets in Illinois related to the Shelbyville, Champaign, and Bloomington Moraines, and the Cartersburg would correlate with the Chatsworth and younger moraines. The segmented moraine along the edge of the Cartersburg till has been named the Crawfordsville Moraine (Wayne, in preparation).

Thickness of the ice sheet that deposited the Cartersburg member in central Indiana was determined by Harrison (1958) by means of preconsolidation studies of the underlying silt bed. He found that the ice sheet thickened abruptly from the margin and was 510 m thick 44 km from the edge.

Harrison's studies (1959, p. 19; 1963, p. 31) of the petrographic characteristics of the tills in Marion County, Indiana, showed that all the units he included in the Wisconsin drift, some of which conceivably could be Illinoian in age, were so nearly identical that he could not separate them statistically on petrographically defined parameters. Reconstitution of the major rock fractions in the till permitted Harrison (1960, Fig. 3) to determine the probable path taken by the ice from southeastern Canada through the Lake Erie basin to central Indiana.

During the Wisconsin Age melt-water poured down the valleys of the Wabash, both forks of White River, the Whitewater, the Ohio, and many lesser sluiceways. Gravel and sand accumulated in the sluiceways, slack-water lakes were created in all their tributaries, and loess was blown onto the adjacent uplands (Thornbury, 1950). These sediments are environmental facies of a single depositional unit, the Atherton Formation (Wayne, 1963).

The Peoria Loess Member of the Atherton Formation is fossiliferous in many localities along the Wabash and Ohio Rivers, and the vertical sequence of fossil snails can be used to determine climatic changes as the ice approached. At the ice margin the loess splits into two tongues, one of which underlies and the other overlies the Center Grove till. Fossils from the two tongues are distinctive (Wayne, 1963, Table 2) and have been studied extensively from exposures in Hendricks and Johnson Counties.

The surface of the Cartersburg till in central Indiana indicates deglaciation by stagnation. Few moraines are present, but eskers, kames, and esker troughs are abundant (Fig. 3). These features in central Indiana, together with the pattern produced by streams and by very shallow, nearly parallel flutings on the till plain just south of the Wabash River in west-central Indiana (Schneider *et al.*, 1963, p. 172), outline well the direction of ice movement in all parts of the White River Sublobe (Horberg and Anderson, 1956, p. 105).

CARY SUBSTAGE

The glaciation of Michigan and northern Indiana during the Cary Subage was accomplished by the nearly simultaneous advance of the Lake Michigan Lobe, Saginaw Lobe, and Erie Lobe. The lobate pattern of ice retreat is inferred from the festooned morainic pattern (Fig. 4; Martin, 1955; Flint *et al.*, 1959). Interpretation of the history of deposition of the complex intermingling of tills, outwash sediments, and lake deposits in the northern part of Indiana and in southern Michigan posed problems for Leverett, which have not been worked out adequately to this day. Typical tills from the three lobes can be distinguished without difficulty, but in the interlobate areas where they intertongue with each other, their identification becomes increasingly difficult. Because of this, Wayne (1963, p. 43) grouped all of them together into the Lagro Formation but suggested means to separate the tills into members wherever they could be distinguished. Tills of the Lake Michigan and Erie Lobes typically are very clayey and silty; till of the Saginaw Lobe is sandy and bouldery by contrast.

Two nearly parallel morainic ridges that lie in western Indiana have provided a basis for two fundamentally opposing interpretations regarding the maximum advance of ice during the Cary Subage. Leverett (1899, p. 258, Pl. 6) first considered the Nebo-Gilboa ridge in northern Benton County as part of the Iroquois Moraine (Figs. 3, 4), which nearly parallels it in Newton and Jasper Counties. Later he (Leverett and Taylor, 1915, p. 124) altered this interpretation and treated the two as separate moraines. Many of the field relationships observable in Indiana, including the sharp south margin of the Iroquois Moraine and the pattern of outwash deposition in it, seem to support the interpretation that ice from the north deposited both moraines, but some evidence (Zumberge, 1960, p. 1180), indicates that ice from the east may have extended in an elongated tongue and deposited these ridges and the intervening till. Zumberge (1960) started with the Minooka Moraine in Illinois, which was deposited by the Lake Michigan Lobe, and which was defined by Leighton (1960, p. 547) as the outermost moraine of Cary age. Zumberge's resultant Cary maximum advance of the three lobes is shown in Figure 4. According to his interpretation the Iroquois and Packerton Moraines of the Saginaw Lobe and the Union City Moraine of the Erie Lobe are equivalent in age and define the maximum Cary advance of the three lobes. This also is the interpretation currently accepted in Illinois. (See Horberg, 1955, Fig. 1; Frye *et al.*, this volume).

Recent mapping along the west end of the Packerton Moraine (Wayne *et al.*, in preparation) and along the Maxinkuckee Moraine (Schneider and Keller, in preparation) indicates that these moraines are not exactly as they have long been mapped. Rather than a long protruding tip at the Wabash River, the drift sheet probably had a much more rounded margin. Intensely pitted outwash plains and kames form the margin of the Maxinkuckee toward the north; later trenching of the outwash has removed much of the direct physiographic evidence that would allow a better correlation of deposits of the Saginaw Lobe on the east with the Lake Michigan Lobe on the west. That the two were nearly contemporaneous is certain.

During the retreatal phases of the Cary Subage, the Saginaw Lobe dissipated more rapidly than either the Lake Michigan or Erie Lobes. The Erie Lobe had extended into Indiana from the east during the Cary Subage, depositing the clay-rich New Holland Till Member of the Lagro Formation (Wayne, 1963, p. 44), while some ice, perhaps stagnant masses only, from the Saginaw Lobe still covered the area northwest of it. Outwash sand and gravel from the Erie Lobe occur in the area previously occupied by the Saginaw Lobe in northeastern Indiana and south-central Michigan. Additional support for this interpretation is to be found 45 km southwest of Ann Arbor, Michigan, and in Steuben and DeKalb Counties, Indiana, where till of the Erie Lobe overlies till of the Saginaw Lobe (Zumberge, 1960, p. 1185; Wayne and Thornbury, 1955, p. 9). The west edge of the clay-rich till can be traced fairly readily, but it becomes less recognizable to the northeast where kames and pitted outwash plains form the interlobate zone. Channels carried melt-water from the ice through the Mississinewa Moraine of the Erie Lobe and westward across the jumbled mass of moraines, till plains, and outwash plains left by the Saginaw Lobe.

One of the major features of the post-Cary deglaciation in Michigan was the coalescence of several melt-water channels in south-central Michigan and northeastern Indiana to produce the large discharge of the so-called Kankakee Torrent (Ekblaw and Athy, 1925), which drained southwestward across the northwest corner of Indiana to Illinois. The heads of these channels start at the Tekonsha Moraine of the Lake Michigan and Saginaw Lobes and the Mississinewa Moraine of the Erie Lobe (Fig. 4) and thus provide a basis for correlating these moraines (Zumberge, 1960, p. 1181).

Much of the correlation problem exists because, during the withdrawal of ice from northern Indiana and southern Michigan, a large amount of outwash was deposited in the Kankakee valley. Wind whipped the sand from this outwash and from the aprons of outwash south of the Valparaiso Moraine and west of the Maxinkuckee Moraine into dunes that have obscured physiographic relationships of glacial landforms. The ubiquitous sand blanket has reduced the likelihood that exposures of stratigraphic significance will be found.

During the retreat of the Cary ice, proglacial lakes formed along the south margins of all three lobes. The history of these lakes is based on identifiable changes in level recorded in abandoned shorelines that exist peripheral to the modern Great Lakes and in the character of sediments as determined from cores. A résumé of the history of these ancestral lakes is in a later section of this paper.

PORT HURON (MANKATO) SUBSTAGE

The Cary ice retreated an unknown distance to the north, possibly north of the Straits of Mackinac and then readvanced to the position of the Port Huron Moraine (Fig. 4). This feature was described by Taylor (Leverett and Taylor 1915, p. 293) as ". . . one of the best developed and most clearly defined moraines in the Great Lakes region." The *Glacial Map of the United States East of the Rocky Mountains* (Flint *et al.*, 1959) shows the Port Huron Moraine as the outer limit of a significant glacial advance,

a status that has been accorded to it by every glacial geologist who has worked in Michigan since the time of Leverett. The Port Huron Moraine was dated by Hough (1958, p. 278) at 13,000 years ago.

Bretz (1951a), Melhorn (1954, p. 31), and Zumberge *et al.* (1956) believed that the Port Huron advance was an event of late Cary time, but Leighton (1957, p. 109) argued that if the Port Huron Moraine recorded an ice advance of substage rank, it could not naturally be part of another substage. Zumberge (1960) yielded to this viewpoint but retained the name Port Huron for this substage rather than the term Mankato, which Leighton (1960, p. 547) continues to use.

The Port Huron till is generally gray blue and in places is quite sandy, characteristics that distinguish it from the red Valders till, which overlies parts of the Port Huron Moraine in Otsego and Montmorency Counties, Michigan.

TWO CREEKS SUBSTAGE

The retreat of the Port Huron ice was of sufficient magnitude to allow the draining of a proglacial lake that occupied the Lake Michigan basin. These newly exposed lacustrine deposits eventually supported a forest, which was then drowned and overridden by the readvance of the Valders ice. The buried forest near the village of Two Creeks, Wisconsin, was first described by Goldthwait (1907, p. 61) and later by Wilson (1932), but its significance was placed in fuller perspective by Thwaites (1943) and others, notably Bretz (1951a).

Recent redating of the Two Creeks forest bed has increased its age from 11,400 (Thwaites and Bertrand, 1957) to 11,850 years B.P. (Broecker and Farrand, 1963, p. 796). A buried organic layer on the eastern shore of Lake Michigan near South Haven was correlated by Zumberge and Potzger (1956, p. 277) with the Two Creeks bed in Wisconsin, but its date (10,860 years B.P., W-167) may be too young. If so, then the Two Creeks stratigraphic horizon in Michigan is represented only by a disconformity between Valders and Port Huron tills in the northern part of the Southern Peninsula of Michigan (Melhorn, 1954).

VALDERS SUBSTAGE

The ice that readvanced over the forest at Two Creeks, Wisconsin, was first recognized in Wisconsin as a separate glacial advance of substage rank by Thwaites (1943). Melhorn (1954) showed that the red Valders till was restricted to the proximal slope of the Port Huron Moraine in the northern part of the Southern Peninsula of Michigan, and Bretz (1951a) found it overlapping the Port Huron Moraine along the Lake Michigan coast between Muskegon and Grand Traverse Bay.

The most distinguishing feature of the Valders drift in both Wisconsin and Michigan is its red or pink color, which contrasts strongly with the gray-blue (unoxidized) or brown (oxidized) till of the Port Huron Substage. The color intensity of the Valders till increases with the percentage of clay in the till matrix.

No end moraine was built by the Valders ice, but a swarm of drumlins on Valders ground moraine near the southwest end of Grand Traverse Bay of Lake Michigan trends northwestward—an indication of a radial flow from the central Lake Superior region. The Port Huron ice advance, in contrast, came from the northeast, a fact that accounts for the different lithology of the two drifts.

A reddish till forming the surface drift of the Northern Peninsula of Michigan was mapped by Bergquist (1933). This drift is undoubtedly of Valders age and indicates that the Valders ice invasion was the last glacial event in the Pleistocene history of Michigan. Broecker and Farrand (1963, p. 800) concluded that all of Michigan was free of Valders ice 10,000 years ago.

RECENT STAGE

Deposition of nonglacial sediments began as soon as the ice had melted from the area. Except for their fossil content, the earliest postglacial sediments in Indiana and Michigan are indistinguishable from those now being laid down in streams and lakes. Nevertheless, for mapping purposes these sediments generally are regarded as Recent in age even though the lower parts of basin-fill deposits were laid down before the Wisconsin Age came to a close.

Sediments of the Recent Stage include alluvial deposits along streams, colluvial accumulations along the bases of steep slopes, swamp and lake sediments, such as peat and marl, and sand-dune accumulations around the edge of Lake Michigan. Alluvial, paludal, and colluvial sediments in Indiana were treated by Wayne (1963, p. 28) as environmental facies of the Martinsville Formation; the modern dunes are mapped as dune-sand facies of the Atherton Formation.

Floodplain sediments, which make up the greatest volume and area of Recent deposits, have been under continuous deposition, erosion, and redeposition since retreat of glacial ice from the individual valleys. Radiocarbon dates available (W-59, W-254, W-666, W-832, LJ-290) of wood at the base of the Martinsville indicate that few of these alluvial sediments probably exceed 7,000 to 8,000 years in age. Downstream migration of meanders in most streams of any size is a process that brings about regular reworking of older floodplain deposits; it seems likely that few floodplain deposits escape being eroded in 5,000 to 7,000 years. Although the most common kind of fossil in Indiana alluvial sediments is woody debris, mollusk shells have been found, and some vertebrate remains probably exist in the sediments, even though they are not often reported.

Paludal and lacustrine sediments, composed dominantly of fine-grained materials and deposited in quiet water, are primarily peat and marl. Thickness of sediments in some of the filled basins in central Indiana exceeds 12 m; similar thicknesses exist in the lakes and bogs of northern Indiana and throughout Michigan, but most of the deposits are much thinner.

Paleobotanists have long searched for evidence of postglacial tundra in Indiana (Dillon, 1956, p. 174), but so far data from pollen profiles of bogs have shown a forest cover of spruce when the oldest sediments accumulated (Potzger and Wilson, 1941; Prettyman, 1937; Otto, 1938; Swickard, 1941; Guennel, 1950). In recent studies of Indiana bogs (Frey, 1959; Englehardt, 1960; Kapp and Gooding, 1964a) a Two Creeks equivalent has been interpreted,

and although the cores penetrated inorganic sediments below the peat, no zone was found that indicated a postglacial tundra vegetation in Indiana.

Pollen and mollusks from intertill silt beds indicate that a narrow zone around the ice margin had tundra-like vegetation (Dillon, 1956, p. 174), but it probably never existed as a climax cover in the state (Wayne, 1956a, p. 164; Martin, 1958, p. 384). Features ascribable to intensive frost action likewise are scarce, although polygonal features have been noted near some ice marginal positions (Wayne, 1964, p. 179) in west-central Indiana.

Many filled and partly filled depressions in central and northern Indiana and Michigan contain marl, a soft fine-grained lime mud. Cores through some of the marl beds show that few are more than 5 to 7 m thick. The basal marl beds in many of the deposits are very fine-grained and medium to dark gray; the molluscan fauna consists dominantly of species of *Gyraulus*, *Valvata*, *Physa*, small lymnaeids, and *Pisidium*. The upper parts of the deposits commonly are light gray to yellowish white and contain a much larger molluscan fauna, particularly species of *Helisoma*, *Amnicola*, *Physa*, *Campeloma*, and a few of the large lymnaeids, as well as *Valvata* and *Gyraulus*. No correlation has yet been made on these depositional and faunal changes, but they may reflect post-Wisconsin climatic changes. The marl lakes are in ice-block depressions, and the lower beds may have accumulated while an ice block still existed below the basin. Nearly all the remains of extinct fossil vertebrates that have been found in Indiana and Michigan have come from the lower parts of the paludal sediments.

GEOLOGIC HISTORY OF THE GREAT LAKES

PHYSIOGRAPHY OF THE LAKE BASINS

The area of the five Great Lakes and their drainage basins is 445,000 km², of which 144,000 km² is accounted for by the lakes themselves. Lake Superior is the largest and deepest, Lake Ontario is the smallest, and Lake Erie is the shallowest. Important facts about the morphometry of the lakes are given in Table 1. General details of the bathymetry of the lakes can be found in Hough (1958), which is the latest and most detailed work in a single volume; large-scale charts of all segments of the lakes, their harbors, and connecting waterways are available from the Lake Survey Division of the U.S. Corps of Engineers, Detroit, Michigan.

The basins of the Great Lakes all lie in bedrock, and their shorelines are more or less parallel to the regional strike of the bedrock formations surrounding them. Paleozoic sediments surround most of the four lower lakes, but Precambrian rocks bound the north shore of Georgian Bay of Lake Huron and all of Lake Superior except the south shore between Marquette, Michigan, and Sault Sainte Marie, Canada. The shorelines of the lakes, except for Lake Superior, which is mostly rockbound, are developed mainly in glacial drift.

ORIGIN OF THE BASINS OF THE GREAT LAKES

The geologic processes that can produce large depressions on the earth's crust are few. Yet geomorphologists and geologists who have studied the Great Lakes do not agree completely on the origin of their basins. Paucity of information on the geology of the lake basins has been one of the main reasons for disagreement. A reasonably accurate hydrographic chart of the eastern basin of Lake Superior was not available until early in this decade (Zumberge and Gast, 1961), and almost nothing is known of the configuration of the bedrock surface beneath the lake bottoms. Thwaites (1949), Webb and Smith (1961), and Cuancara and Melik (1961) attempted a correlation of bedrock features across the basins of Lakes Michigan and Huron by using hydrographic charts, and Thwaites (1935) produced a tectonic map of the Lake Superior bottom, but these efforts will remain highly speculative until direct supporting evidence is made available.

During the last 75 years, geologists have proposed four processes to account for the origin of the basins of the Great Lakes: (1) stream erosion during the Tertiary Period, (2) glacial erosion during the Pleistocene Epoch, (3) damming by glacial drift, and (4) subsidence or warping of the earth's crust.

Newberry (1874, 1882) argued that the basins of the Great Lakes were originally stream valleys but that glacial erosion was of prime importance in the final shaping of the basins. Spencer (1891) believed that glacial modification of the ancient stream valleys ". . . could have been only slight, and does not appear to have been more than the sweeping of loose geological dust into the valleys, or on to the highlands to the south" (Spencer, 1896, p. 163). Leverett and Taylor (1915, p. 319) asserted that all the basins except that of Lake Superior had distinct characteristics of stream-eroded valleys and that all the changes produced by successive glacial invasions did not destroy these characteristics to any great extent. Martin (1916, p. 407) claimed that the Lake Superior basin ". . . owes a notable part of its exhumation, and all, or nearly all, of its present depth below lake level to erosion by the Superior lobe . . ." Shepard (1937) and Thwaites (1949) joined Martin in support of the glacial-erosion hypothesis. Schwartz (1949, p. 82) suggested faulting as a factor in the origin of the Lake Superior basin but dismissed it because of lack of supporting evidence and concluded that glacial erosion was the most important agent in the making of the basin.

Horberg and Anderson (1956, p. 103) believed that the preglacial topography of the Great Lakes region was extensively modified by glacial scour in the uplands and ". . . by profound deepening of preglacial lowlands along the axes of the Great Lakes." Hough (1958, p. 113) believed that both preglacial stream erosion and glacial scour were important in the origins of the lake basins, and he dismissed diastrophic action as a primary agent in their origin. Laidly (1961, p. 282) suggested that narrow north-south submerged troughs in eastern Lake Superior were produced by glacial erosion concentrated along pre-existing fracture zones.

The most definite statement regarding the origin of these lake basins is that they are glacially modified river valleys. The glacial modification may have been in the form of glacial erosion or glacial deposition. Zumberge and Gast

(1961) and Zumberge (1962a) showed that at least 670 ft of glacial till lies below the bottom of western Lake Superior near the Minnesota shore in 938 ft of water, and Hough (1955) reported glacial till at a depth of 35 ft below the bottom of Lake Michigan in its deepest part (923 ft). In addition to glacial deposits in the lake basins, tens of feet of lacustrine materials have accumulated in various parts since the withdrawal of glacier ice.

The most important information necessary to formulate an hypothesis on the origin of the Great Lakes basins—details of the configuration of the bedrock floors of the lakes—is lacking. Hydrographic charts do not reveal the character or shape of the bedrock floors and thus are insufficient. Modern geophysical methods, such as seismic profiling (Hersey, 1963) and shipboard drilling techniques (Zumberge, 1962b), are expensive, but until more information of this kind is forthcoming, substantial glacial erosion in any of the basins of the Great Lakes cannot be proved beyond a reasonable doubt.

EVIDENCE AND CAUSES OF FORMER LAKE STAGES

Whatever the origin of the basins of the Great Lakes, there is abundant evidence that in the past they all contained greater or lesser volumes of water than they do today. Evidence for higher water planes exists in the form of ancient shoreline features and associated lake deposits. Strandlines and wave-cut cliffs have been traced for many miles in areas peripheral to the modern lakes. In addition, the outlet channels of some of the ancestral lakes have been discovered, and deltas of former river mouths have been mapped.

Water planes below the present levels of the lakes are known from the presence of shallow-water sediments in places where normal deep-water sediments are now accumulating (Hough, 1955). A submerged river channel beneath the Straits of Mackinac led Stanley (1938) to the discovery of low-water stages in the Lake Michigan and Lake Huron basins, which were connected by the submerged valley.

The pronounced changes in the level of water planes were caused by (1) advance and retreat of the ice margin, making the proglacial lakes rise and fall, (2) erosion of lake outlets, resulting in falling water levels, and (3) warping of the crust in response to glacial unloading, causing submergence of the coastal region in some areas and emergence in others.

CRUSTAL WARPING DETERMINED BY NONHORIZONTAL STRANDLINES

The strandlines of many of the ancient lakes rise in elevation toward the north, a fact that, circumstantially, is related to late-glacial and postglacial isostatic adjustment of the earth's crust following glacial unloading. The mapping of elevations on abandoned beaches permits the drawing of isobases on a given water plane. The zero isobase for any water plane defines the hinge line, north of which the strandlines rise in elevation and south of which they have a horizontal attitude.

The hinge lines of the Great Lakes region (Fig. 5), when plotted on a map, form a family of nearly parallel lines trending in a northwesterly direction; the hinge lines defined by the oldest beaches are farthest south, and the

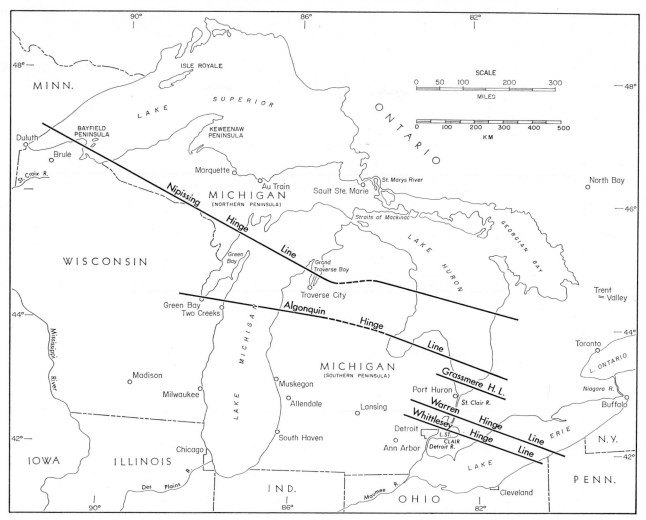

Figure 5. Index map of the upper Great Lakes region showing hinge lines (zero isobases) based on the elevations of the beaches of some of the ancestral stages of the Great Lakes. (Data for hinge lines from Leverett and Taylor, 1915, p. 505, and Hough, 1958, p. 136.)

youngest are farthest north (Leverett and Taylor, 1915, p. 505; Flint, 1957, p. 251; Gutenberg, 1941, p. 743; Hough, 1955, p. 136).

Gutenberg (1933) agreed with Leverett and Taylor (1915) that the cause of crustal uplift in the Great Lakes region was the isostatic rebound that accompanied deglaciation. Moore (1948) concluded from a study of apparent changes in the elevation of gauging stations on the shores of the present Great Lakes that the upwarping was related to earlier tectonic movement rather than isostatic adjustment of the crust during and after the disappearance of glacial ice, but MacLean (1963) showed that Moore's interpretation may have been in error because of a failure to take into account the influence of wind on the pairs of gauges used in his analysis.

Farrand (1962) showed that a uniform pattern of strongly decreasing rate of uplift from the time of deglaciation to the present must be causally related to glacial unloading of the crust.

ANCESTRAL GREAT LAKES

Lake Superior basin. The most recent study of the ancestral stages of Lake Superior is Farrand's (1960), which is here summarized. Earlier work was by Leverett (1929b), Stanley (1932), and Sharp (1953).

The Superior basin was filled by Valders ice about 11,500 years B.P. Murray (1953) postulated a proglacial Lake Keweenaw in at least part of the Lake Superior basin during Two Creeks time (Port Huron–Valders interval), but all shorelines of this water body were destroyed by the advance of the Valders ice (Fig. 6).

As the Valders ice began its withdrawal from the western part of the basin a group of small proglacial lakes formed marginal to the ice border. These lakes, known as glacial Lakes Nemadji, Brule, Ashland, and Ontonagon, formed along the southern border of the retreating ice and discharged westward to the St. Croix River along the Wisconsin-Minnesota border to the Mississippi River. Farrand (1960) referred to these lakes collectively as the epi-Duluth stage, which had original elevations of more than 1,100 ft A.T. (above sea level).

Further retreat of the Valders ice permitted the lakes of the epi-Duluth stage to merge into a single water body peripheral to the ice border, Lake Duluth, the trend of which was from the midpoint of the Minnesota shore southeastward across the lake to the base of the Keweenaw Peninsula in Michigan. Lake Duluth stood at 1,085 ft A.T. before the

region was uplifted; it drained westward, first through an outlet at Duluth and later through the Brule–St. Croix River outlet in Wisconsin. The erosion of the latter outlet allowed the water surface of Lake Duluth to fall to three lower stages at 1,070 ft, 1,060 ft, and 1,035 ft A.T. Glacial Lake Duluth terminated a little more than 10,000 years ago when further retreat of the Valders ice opened a lower outlet across the Huron Mountains northwest of Marquette,

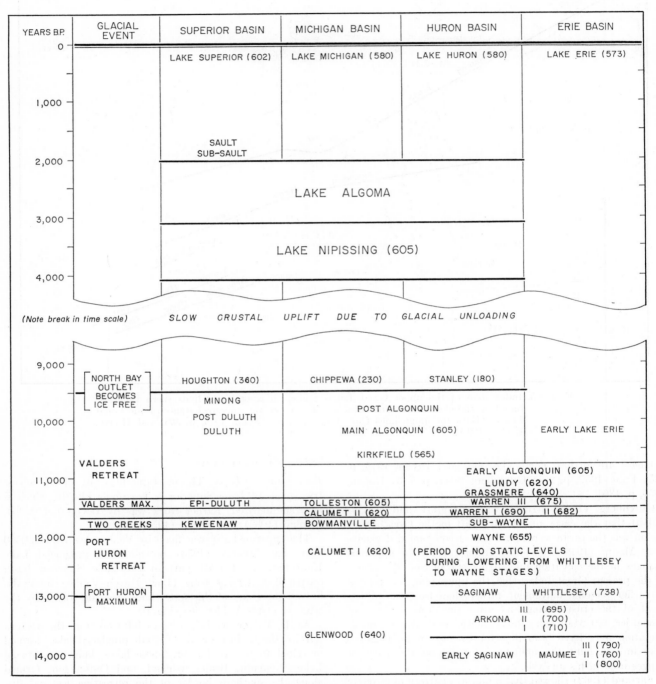

Figure 6. Correlation chart of ancestral lakes of the upper Great Lakes basins. Solid horizontal lines indicate reasonably well-established correlative events. Elevations (in feet) of lake stages from Hough (1958). Correlations based in part on Bretz (1959), Broecker and Farrand (1963), Farrand (1960), Hough (1958), and Leverett and Taylor (1915).

Michigan, and thereby initiated a series of lower lake levels of the post-Duluth stages.

Six post-Duluth glacial lakes, ranging from 1,007 ft A.T. (sub-Duluth stage) to 650 ft A.T. (Beaver Bay stage), discharged southward across the Northern Peninsula of Michigan to one of the ancestral lakes in the Lake Michigan basin. The Valders ice, which was retreating rapidly northeastward along its axis, formed a part of the shore of each of the post-Duluth lakes.

When the edge of the Valders ice finally reached the present north shore of Lake Superior in Canada, Lake Minong at 470 ft A.T. came into existence. It was the first of the lakes in the Superior basin to be free of an ice border along any part of its shoreline. Lake Minong shared a common water plane with one of the ancestral lakes in the Lake Michigan basin, Lake Sheguiandah of the post-Algonquin group. The two water bodies were connected by straits across the Northern Peninsula at Au Train and the St. Marys River, the modern outlet of Lake Superior. Lake Minong ended about 9,500 years ago.

When the ice border had retreated to North Bay, Ontario, a very low outlet to the east was opened for the discharge of the ancestral lakes in the Lake Michigan and Lake Huron basins, into which Lake Minong drained through the St. Marys River. Lake Houghton, whose water level stood at 360 ft A.T., had the lowest stage of any of the ancestral lakes in the Lake Superior basin; it is correlated with the extreme low-water stages of Lakes Chippewa and Stanley in the Lake Michigan and Lake Huron basins, respectively. The Houghton shoreline is now above the present level of Lake Superior (602 ft A.T.) on the Canadian shore because of crustal uplift, but its south shore in Wisconsin and Michigan is submerged. Farrand (1962, p. 187) puts the date of Lake Houghton at 9,600 B.P. Although no part of the Houghton shoreline was bordered by glacier ice, melt-waters were discharging into Lake Houghton (Farrand, 1960, p. 121). Outwash terraces in southward-trending valleys of the Lake Superior watershed in Ontario are graded to the Houghton level.

Lake Michigan basin. Glacial Lake Chicago was formed at the southern extremity of the Lake Michigan Lobe when the latter began its retreat from the Tinley Moraine of Cary age (Fig. 4). Three stages of Lake Chicago are represented by shore features above the modern lake: the Glenwood stage (oldest), 60 ft above Lake Michigan; the Calumet stage, 40 ft; and the Toleston stage, 20 ft (Fig. 6). Leverett (1897) assumed that the three stages of Lake Chicago were caused by successive abrupt lowerings of the water level caused by the erosion of the outlet at Chicago. Wright (1918) proposed that the three stages were not sequential in descending order, the Toleston following the Glenwood and succeeded by the Calumet.

The Glenwood stage of Lake Chicago came into being about 14,000 years B.P. (Bretz, 1959; Hough, 1958). Bretz (1959, p. 680) believed that it ended with the increase in discharge from the glacial Grand River fed by glacial lakes in the Huron and Erie basins; this increased the outflow at Chicago so that a boulder pavement in the drift dam was destroyed by erosion. Ice retreat from the Port Huron maximum opened an eastern outlet that replaced the Chicago outlet, but not until the latter had been deepened by 20 ft of erosion to 620 ft. By Two Creeks time a low-water stage in the Michigan, Huron, and Erie basins prevailed. These levels were below the head of the Grand River outlet.

Readvance of the Valders ice closed the eastern outlet and raised the water level in the Lake Michigan basin to the 620-ft level. This was the Calumet stage. It was not a static level, however, because the glacial Grand River was again swollen by discharge from the Huron and Erie basins (Lake Warren), which caused deepening of the Chicago outlet another 15 ft to the bedrock surface. This bedrock still maintained the level of the Toleston stage at 605 ft A.T., until subsequent events caused it to merge with early Lake Algonquin in the Huron basin (Bretz, 1959).

Hough (1958, p. 166) believed that the Glenwood stage persisted well into the retreatal phase of the Valders ice about 10,000 years B.P. If so, the Glenwood beaches should have been developed on the Valders till near Lake Michigan, but none has been discovered (Bretz, 1959).

Lake Huron and Lake Erie basins. The ancestral water bodies of Lakes Huron and Erie are so intimately related that they must be considered together for a coherent picture. When the Erie and Saginaw Lobes advanced, separate proglacial lakes were formed in front of them; when the lobes retreated, their glacial lakes merged to form a single continuous lake, generally at a lower level. The details of the sequence synthesized here are based on the work of Taylor (Leverett and Taylor, 1915) with modifications by Bretz (1951b, 1953, 1959, 1964) and Hough (1958).

The earliest water body in the Erie basin was glacial Lake Maumee, which was formed perhaps 14,000 years B.P. (W-198) when ice of the Erie Lobe retreated from the Fort Wayne Moraine, and whose outlet at first (highest Maumee or Maumee I) was through the Wabash Valley to the Ohio and Mississippi River systems (Figs. 6 and 7). The lowest level of Lake Maumee (Maumee II) used a lower outlet to the north along the edge of the Saginaw Lobe to the Grand River, which flowed westward across Michigan to Lake Chicago. A subsequent ice advance closed the northern outlet and caused the waters of Lake Maumee to rise to a level somewhat below that of Maumee I. This rise in level initiated Maumee III, the outlet of which was also the Wabash River. The erosion surface along the Wabash Valley planed by the overflow waters of the two high phases of Lake Maumee stands 16 to 22 ft above the modern floodplain and is called the Maumee Terrace (Fidlar, 1948).

About the time of glacial Lake Maumee, a proglacial lake in front of the Saginaw Lobe came into existence. It too discharged to Lake Chicago via the trans-Michigan Grand River valley. Further retreat of the Saginaw Lobe, which was really a sublobe of the Huron Lobe, caused the waters of glacial Lake Saginaw and glacial Lake Maumee to merge into a single water body, Lake Arkona. This lake had three stages, I, II, and III, each of which was lower than the lowest of the three Maumee levels; its outlet was the glacial Grand River. Lake Arkona covered all but the extreme east end of what is now Lake Erie as well as a major part of the Saginaw lowland.

Advance of the ice border separated Lake Arkona into

two separate parts at different elevations. That part representing the Saginaw Lobe remained at the Arkona level, but the waters of the Erie basin rose above the Arkona level to a new position intermediate in elevation between the Maumee and Arkona levels. This lake is known as Lake Whittlesey and is particularly important in the sequence because it is correlated with the Port Huron Moraine, the feature on which the Port Huron (Mankato) Substage is defined (Fig. 5).

Subsequent to the Port Huron maximum, the glacial border retreated. The retreat exposed an eastern spillway lower than the head of the Grand River valley and thereby caused the water surface to drop to the level of those in the Saginaw Bay area. This level is known as Warren I (or highest Lake Warren). A less well developed Warren beach, Warren II, at 682 ft A.T., was caused by further retreat. Ice withdrawal continued until the waters in the combined Huron and Erie basins dropped to 655 ft A.T., the Lake Wayne level, and probably lower to a sub-Wayne stage. This event is correlated with the Two Creeks interval (Bretz, 1959, p. 682; Hough, 1958, p. 150). The Grand River valley carried no discharge at this time. Hough (1963, Fig. 7) later correlated the Two Creeks interval with the Kirkfield stage of Lake Algonquin (see the section on the Ontario basin in this paper).

The readvance of the ice to the Valders maximum raised the waters in the Huron and Erie basins from the Wayne stage at 655 ft A.T. to 675 ft A.T., Lake Warren III (lowest Lake Warren); the readvance also closed the eastern outlet and reactivated the Grand River spillway. Bretz (1959, p. 681) believed that the Calumet stage of Lake Chicago occurred between the times of Lake Whittlesey and Lake Warren and that Lake Warren discharged via Grand River to the Toleston stage of Lake Chicago, but Hough (1958, p. 151) argued that Lake Warren was contemporaneous with a third Glenwood stage of Lake Chicago.

The last two stages in the Huron and Erie basins were glacial Lakes Grassmere (640 ft A.T.) and Lundy (620 ft A.T.). Hough (1958, p. 154) thought that Grassmere waters were merged with Glenwood waters of the Lake Michigan basin (both water planes had the same elevation) across the northern part of the Southern Peninsula of Michigan, but Bretz (1959, p. 682) believed that both Grassmere and Lundy discharged eastward near Syracuse, New York, and were never connected with any lake stages in the Lake Michigan basin.

Lake Ontario basin. According to Spencer (1890), Fairchild (1909), and Leverett and Taylor (1915), the retreat of the ice (later identified as of Port Huron age by Mason, 1960, and Karrow *et al.*, 1961) from the Ontario basin was accompanied by the development of ice-marginal lakes around the western and southern borders of the ice (Fig. 7). Lake waters along the western margin were merged with waters in the Erie basin from the time of the Warren stage to the Lundy stage. The opening of the Rome, New York, outlet, which discharged via the Mohawk Valley to the Hudson River, brought an end to the Lundy stage and initiated Lake Iroquois. Lake Lundy was thus reduced to a lake in the Erie basin (Early Lake Erie) which spilled

over the Niagara Escarpment to Lake Iroquois. The cutting of the present gorge of the Niagara River began at that time.

Lake Iroquois was 330 ft A.T., according to Hough (1958, p. 202). This figure was derived from an estimate of postglacial uplift, because there are no horizontal Lake Iroquois strands. Glacial retreat from the St. Lawrence lowland brought Lake Iroquois to an end. Leverett and Taylor (1915, p. 445) postulated a short-lived lake stage, glacial Lake Frontenac, following Lake Iroquois; Karrow *et al.* (1961, p. 666) stressed the very short duration of such a stage, because no strong shore features have been found below the Iroquois beaches.

As the St. Lawrence Valley became free of glacier ice, it was invaded by marine waters. Fairchild (1907) believed that this marine embayment extended into the Ontario basin and gave it the name Gilbert Gulf. Mather (1917, p. 542) called it the Champlain Sea, and Hough (1958, p. 203) referred to it as the St. Lawrence Sea. On the basis of stratigraphic sections at Hamilton, Ontario, Karrow *et al.* (1961, p. 665) deduced that marine waters never extended into the Ontario basin, although the early phase of Lake Ontario may have been very close to sea level. Postglacial uplift raised Lake Ontario to its present level.

The correlation of events in the Ontario basin with the late-Pleistocene chronology of the upper Great Lakes poses a serious problem. Hough (1958, Table 22) considered Lake Iroquois to have endured from about 9,300 years to 8,600 years ago and to have been related to the retreat of Valders ice. Mason (1960), however, argued for an older date of Lake Iroquois, making it a correlative of the waning Port Huron (Mankato) ice. Karrow *et al.* (1961, p. 665) presented radiocarbon evidence from the Hamilton, Ontario, sediments that brackets Lake Iroquois from 12,500 to 10,500 years ago, a date that supports Mason's interpretation. Dreimanis (1964, p. 248) pointed out that the acceptance of the Karrow *et al.* dates placed all lake stages from lowest Lake Warren to Lake Lundy (Fig. 7) in pre-Two Creeks time because they are all older than Lake Iroquois. Hough (1963, Fig. 7) attempted to reconcile the Karrow *et al.* dates by correlating the Kirkfield stage of Lake Algonquin with the Two Creeks interval, thereby allowing less than a thousand years for Lakes Whittlesey, Warren, Wayne, Grassmere, and Lundy. Acceptance of this revised correlation conflicts with the thesis held by Bretz (1964, p. 625) that the lowest Warren stage (Warren III at 675 ft A.T.) in the Huron and Erie basins is correlative with the Toleston stage in the Lake Michigan basin, an event that he believed was caused by the advance of the Valders ice after Two Creeks time. In order for the Warren through Lundy stages to have persisted above 600 ft A.T., ice had to block the Ontario basin.

Figure 7 shows the sequence of lake stages in the Ontario basin according to Karrow *et al.* (1961) and Dreimanis (1964) and a possible correlation with the Huron and Erie basin chronology (Hough, 1963, Fig. 7). Comparison of Figures 6 and 7 reveals the incompatibility of the two chronologies between the time of Lake Whittlesey and the Early Algonquin stage.

The lowering of Lake Lundy to Early Lake Erie caused

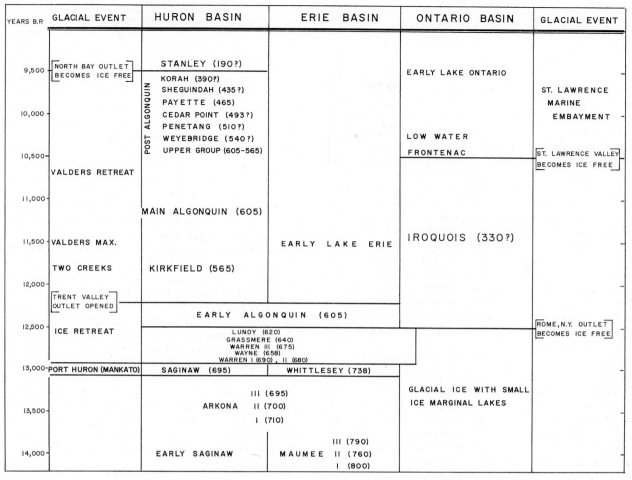

Figure 7. Correlation chart of lake stages in the Ontario, Erie, and Huron basins, based on Hough (1963), Dreimanis (1964), and Karrow *et al.* (1961).

the isolation of the waters in the Huron basin at the 605-ft A.T. level; this lake is called Early Lake Algonquin. It discharged through the newly formed St. Clair and Detroit River systems to Lake Erie and eventually merged with the waters of the Lake Michigan basin to form Lake Algonquin. The Chicago outlet, which had functioned for the Toleston stage, continued to function after the merger with Early Lake Algonquin in the Huron basin, and it gave Lake Algonquin a second outlet.

Lake Algonquin. At its highest level Lake Algonquin covered all the Lake Michigan basin and all the Huron basin except the north shore of Georgian Bay in Ontario, where a post-Valders glacial border stood. Leverett (1929b) believed that Lake Algonquin covered part of the Superior basin, but Hough (1958) and Farrand (1960) showed that the eastern part of the Superior basin was still ice-blocked. Farrand (1960, p. 114) correlated Lake Algonquin with Lake Duluth, believing that the former ". . . might be somewhat older than 10,500 B.P." (Broecker and Farrand, 1963, p. 800).

Actually, the history of Lake Algonquin is quite complex. An early Algonquin stage was restricted to the Huron basin

at a time when glacial Lake Chicago stood at the Toleston stage of 605 ft A.T. Merger of these two bodies of water culminated in the Kirkfield stage of Lake Algonquin, 40 to 60 ft lower than the main Algonquin level. The Chicago and St. Clair outlets were abandoned at this time in favor of the lower Trent valley outlet (east of Georgian Bay), which debauched to Lake Iroquois in the Ontario basin. The main Algonquin stage, which followed the Kirkfield stage, was caused either by uplift of the Trent valley or by a readvance of the glacial border. After the main Algonquin level the water level was progressively lowered to levels recorded by an upper group of beaches on Mackinac Island (Stanley, 1938) and elsewhere in Ontario north of the Algonquin hinge line. Below these beaches are four prominent strandlines studied by Stanley (1936, 1937) in the Georgian Bay area. Stanley named these the Wyebridge, Penetang, Cedar Point, and Payette stages. They all used eastern outlets, the most important one of which was at North Bay, Ontario. The original elevation of the last of these low stages, the Payette, was 465 ft A.T., as compared to 605 ft A.T. of the main Lake Algonquin.

Hough (1958, p. 234) suggested two stages below the Payette stage—the Sheguiandah and Korah. During these and previous stages below the main Algonquin level, the Chicago and St. Clair outlets were inoperative.

EXTREME LOW-WATER STAGES IN THE HURON AND MICHIGAN BASINS

Lake Algonquin waters were lowered through successive stages as lower eastern outlets were opened by ice retreat (Chapman, 1954) and eroded by outlet waters. The lowering finally culminated in low-water lakes in the Huron and Michigan basins. Stanley (1936, p. 1958; 1937, p. 1681) inferred the existence of these stages from the submerged channel through the Straits of Mackinac, and Hough (1955) added evidence from cores taken from the bottom of Lake Michigan. Hough gave the names Lake Chippewa and Lake Stanley to the two low-level lakes in the Michigan and Huron basins, respectively. Lake Chippewa was at 235 ft A.T., or about 350 ft below the present level of Lake Michigan, and Lake Stanley stood at 180 ft A.T. Zumberge and Potzger (1956) placed the date of Lakes Chippewa and Stanley at about 5,000 B.P., Hough (1958, p. 282) placed it at 6,000 years B.P., and Farrand (1960, p. 114) put it at 8,500 years B.P. According to Terasmae and Hughes (1960) the North Bay outlet was deglaciated prior to 9,500 years B.P., an event that initiated the Chippewa and Stanley stages. Hough (1963, p. 106) used this date in a later interpretation of the chronology of the Lake Huron basin.

Nipissing Great Lakes. A period of crustal uplift between 9,500 B.P. and 4,000 B.P. raised the North Bay outlet enough to cause the waters in the Michigan and Huron basins to rise until they once again spilled through the Chicago and St. Clair outlets. For a while, all three outlets were in use. Waters in the Lake Superior basin merged with the rising waters of the two lower basins so that the Nipissing Great Lakes encompassed the area of all three basins, Superior, Huron, and Michigan, and were the largest of all postglacial Great Lakes. The ice had retreated far to the north by this time to a position beyond the watersheds of any of the present Great Lakes.

The shoreline features of the Nipissing stage are among the strongest of any found in the Great Lakes region. The mouths of many stream valleys that had been graded to the Chippewa and Stanley levels were drowned by the rising Nipissing waters, and some were cut off from the main lake by construction of bay-mouth bars and spits. Eolian activity along the Michigan coast of Lake Michigan was reestablished during the later part of the rise from the Chippewa to the Nipissing level (Zumberge and Potzger, 1956, p. 279).

The Nipissing Great Lakes endured for 1,000 years between 4,000 and 3,000 B.P. The end of the Nipissing stage came when the St. Clair River at Port Huron was eroded to a lower level. The Chicago outlet had been abandoned earlier because it was floored in bedrock, and downcutting could not keep pace with the St. Clair outlet, which was floored in till.

Algoma stage. The Algoma stage is represented by shoreline features on Lakes Superior, Michigan, and Huron that occur about 10 ft below the Nipissing beaches south of the Nipissing zero isobase (Fig. 5). Before Hough (1953) recognized that the Nipissing water plane in the southern parts

of the Michigan and Huron basins was coincident with the main Algonquin stage at 605 ft A.T., the beaches now assigned to the Algoma stage had been considered Nipissing-stage features by earlier workers. The Algoma stage ended about 2,000 years ago when continued downcutting of the outlet at Port Huron brought the levels of Lakes Huron and Michigan to the present elevation of 580 ft A.T.

Lake Superior remained at a higher level, because its outlet, the St. Marys River, is floored in bedrock. Farrand (1960, p. 59) confirmed an earlier suspicion of Taylor (1895, p. 312) that at least one intermediate level between the Algoma stage and the modern Lake Superior water plane existed. This is known as the Sault stage; it is represented by beaches on the north shore of Lake Superior that have been preserved by the crustal uplift still in progress. Elsewhere around the Superior basin the Sault beaches are submerged (Farrand, 1960, p. 61).

The absolute chronology and correlations (Fig. 6) differ from previous ones in that they allow a period of 5,000 years for the transition from Lakes Chippewa and Stanley to the Nipissing Great Lakes. Hough (1958, Table 22) referred to this period as a transition phase and allowed less than 2,000 years for it. Zumberge's interpretation (Zumberge and Potzger, 1956, p. 277), which was followed by Flint (1957, p. 347), did not include any transition period, a view that is not acceptable in light of the radiocarbon date for the deglaciation of the North Bay outlet (Terasmae and Hughes, 1960) and the age of Lake Algonquin given by Broecker and Farrand (1963, p. 800). The time scale presented in Figure 6 therefore is more in accord with the facts than previous absolute chronologies, and concurs with Hough's (1963, p. 106) most recent interpretation.

REFERENCES

Bergquist, S. G., 1933, The Pleistocene history of the Tahquamenon and Manistique drainage region of the Northern Peninsula of Michigan: Michigan Dept. Conserv., Geol. Surv. Div. Publ. 40, Geol. Ser. 34, Pt. I, 148 p.

Bergquist, S. G., and MacLachlan, D. C., 1951, Pleistocene features of the Huron-Saginaw ice lobes in Michigan: Geol. Soc. Amer. Guidebook, Detroit meeting, Glacial field trip, 36 p.

Bhattacharya, Nityananda, 1962, Weathering of glacial tills in Indiana. I, Clay minerals: Geol. Soc. Amer. Bull., v. 73, p. 1007-1020

Bretz, J H., 1951a, The stages of Lake Chicago, their causes and correlations: Amer. J. Sci., v. 249, p. 401-429

—— 1951b, Causes of the glacial lake stages in Saginaw basin, Michigan: J. Geol., v. 59, p. 244-258

—— 1953, Glacial Grand River, Michigan: Michigan Acad. Sci. Pap., v. 38, p. 359-382

—— 1959, The double Calumet stage of Lake Chicago: J. Geol., v. 67, p. 675-684

—— 1964, Correlation of glacial lake stages in the Huron-Erie and Michigan basins: J. Geol., v. 72, p. 618-627

Broecker, W. S., and Farrand, W. R., 1963, Radiocarbon age of the Two Creeks forest bed, Wisconsin: Geol. Soc. Amer. Bull., v. 74, p. 795-802

Chapman, L. J., 1954, An outlet of Lake Algonquin at Fossmill, Ontario: Geol. Assoc. Canada Proc., v. 6, p. 61-68

Cuancara, A. M., and Melik, J. C., 1961, Bedrock geology of Lake Huron: Univ. Michigan, Great Lakes Res. Div., Fourth Conf. Great Lakes Res. Proc., Publ. 7, p. 116-125

Dillon, L. S., 1956, Wisconsin climate and life zones in North America: Science, v. 123, p. 167-176

Dreimanis, Aleksis, 1958, Wisconsin stratigraphy at Port Talbot on the north shore of Lake Erie, Ontario: Ohio J. Sci., v. 58, p. 65-84

—— 1960, Pre-classical Wisconsin in the eastern portion of the Great Lakes region, North America: Intern. Geol. Congr., 21st Session, Pt. 4, p. 108-119

—— 1964, Lake Warren and the Two Creeks interval: J. Geol., v. 72, p. 247-250

Dryer, C. R., 1894, The drift of the Wabash-Erie region—a summary of results: Indiana Dept. Geol. Nat. Resources Ann. Rep. 18, p. 38-90

Ekblaw, G. E., and Athy, L. F., 1925, Glacial Kankakee Torrent in northeastern Illinois: Geol. Soc. Amer. Bull., v. 36, p. 417-428

Ekblaw, G. E., and Willman, H. B., 1955, Farmdale drift near Danville, Illinois: Illinois Acad. Sci. Trans., v. 47, p. 129-138

Englehardt, D. W., 1960, A comparative pollen study of two early Wisconsin bogs in Indiana: Indiana Acad. Sci. Proc., v. 69, p. 110-118

—— 1962, A palynological study of post-glacial and interglacial deposits in Indiana: Indiana Univ. Ph.D. thesis, 148 p.

Eveland, H. E., 1952, Pleistocene geology of the Danville region: Illinois State Geol. Surv. Rep. Inv. 159, 32 p.

Fairchild, H. L., 1907, Gilbert Gulf (marine waters in the Ontario basin): Geol. Soc. Amer. Bull., v. 17, p. 112

—— 1909, Glacial waters in central New York: New York State Mus. Bull. 127, p. 5-66

Farrand, W. R., 1960, Former shorelines in western and northern Lake Superior basin: Univ. Michigan Ph.D. thesis, 226 p.

—— 1962, Postglacial uplift in North America: Amer. J. Sci., v. 260, p. 181-199

Fidlar, M. M., 1948, Physiography of the lower Wabash Valley: Indiana Div. Geol. Bull. 2, 112 p.

Flint, R. F., 1957, Glacial and Pleistocene geology: New York, John Wiley & Sons, Inc., 553 p.

Flint, R. F., Colton, R. B., Goldthwait, R. P., and Willman, H. B., 1959, Glacial map of the United States east of the Rocky Mountains (Scale 1/750,000): Geol. Soc. Amer.

Frey, D. G., 1959, The Two Creeks Interval in Indiana pollen diagrams: Inv. Indiana Lakes and Streams, v. 5, p. 131-139

Frye, J. C., and Willman, H. B., 1960, Classification of the Wisconsinan Stage in the Lake Michigan glacial lobe: Illinois State Geol. Surv. Circ. 285, 16 p.

Frye, J. C., Willman, H. B., and Glass, H. D., 1964, Cretaceous deposits and the Illinoian glacial boundary in western Illinois: Illinois State Geol. Surv. Circ. 364, 28 p.

Frye, J. C., Willman, H. B., and Black, R. F., this volume, Outline of glacial geology of Illinois and Wisconsin

Goldthwait, J. W., 1907, The abandoned shore-lines of eastern Wisconsin: Wisconsin Geol. Nat. Hist. Surv. Bull. 17, 134 p.

Gooding, Ansel, 1957, Pleistocene terraces in the upper Whitewater drainage basin, southeastern Indiana: Earlham Coll. Sci. Bull. 2, 65 p.

—— 1961, Illinoian and Wisconsin history in southeastern Indiana: Geol. Soc. Amer. Guidebook, Cincinnati meeting, p. 99-106

—— 1963, Illinoian and Wisconsin glaciations in the Whitewater basin, southeastern Indiana, and adjacent areas: J. Geol., v. 71, p. 665-682

—— in press, The Kansan glaciation in southeastern Indiana: Ohio J. Sci.

Guennel, G. K., 1950, History of forests in the Lake Chicago area: Butler Univ. Bot. Stud., v. 9, p. 140-158

Gutenberg, Beno, 1933, Tilting due to glacial melting: J. Geol., v. 41, p. 449-467

—— 1941, Changes in sea level, postglacial uplift, and mobility of the earth's interior: Geol. Soc. Amer. Bull., v. 52, p. 721-772

Harrison, Wyman, 1958, Marginal zones of vanished glaciers reconstructed from the preconsolidation pressures of overridden silts: J. Geol., v. 66, p. 72-95

—— 1959, Petrographic similarity of Wisconsin tills in Marion County, Indiana: Indiana Geol. Surv. Rep. Prog. 15, 39 p.

—— 1960, Original bedrock composition of Wisconsin till in central Indiana: J. Sed. Petrology, v. 30, p. 432-446

—— 1963, Geology of Marion County, Indiana: Indiana Geol. Surv. Bull. 28, 78 p.

Hersey, J. B., 1963, Continuous reflection profiling, *in* Hill, M. N., (ed.), The sea: New York, Interscience Publishers, v. 3, p. 47-72

Horberg, Leland, 1950, Bedrock topography of Illinois: Illinois State Geol. Surv. Bull. 73, 111 p.

—— 1955, Radiocarbon dates and Pleistocene chronological problems in the Mississippi Valley region: J. Geol., v. 63, p. 278-286

Horberg, Leland, and Anderson, R. C., 1956, Bedrock topography and Pleistocene glacial lobes in central United States: J. Geol., v. 64, p. 101-116

Hough, J. L., 1953, Revision of the Nipissing stage of the Great Lakes: Illinois State Acad. Sci. Trans., v. 46, p. 133-141

—— 1955, Lake Chippewa, a low stage of Lake Michigan indicated by bottom sediments: Geol. Soc. Amer. Bull., v. 66, p. 957-968

—— 1958, Geology of the Great Lakes: Urbana, Univ. Illinois Press, 313 p.

—— 1963, The prehistoric Great Lakes of North America: Amer. Scientist, v. 51, p. 84-109

Hubbard, Bela, 1840, Report on Lenawee, Hillsdale, Branch, St. Joseph, Cass, Berrien, Washtenaw, Oakland, and Livingston Counties, with notes on lake ridges and Great Lakes: Michigan State Geol. Surv. Ann. Rep., v. 3, p. 77-111

Kapp, Ronald, and Gooding, Ansel, 1964a, A radiocarbon dated pollen profile from Sunbeam Prairie bog, Darke County, Ohio: Amer. J. Sci., v. 262, p. 259-266

—— 1964b, Pleistocene vegetational studies in the Whitewater basin, southeastern Indiana: J. Geol., v. 72, p. 307-326

Karrow, P. F., Clarke, J. R., and Terasmae, Jaan, 1961, The age of Lake Iroquois and Lake Ontario: J. Geol., v. 69, p. 659-667

Laidly, W. T., 1961, Submarine valleys in Lake Superior: Geogr. Rev., v. 51, p. 277-283

Leighton, M. M., 1933, The naming of the subdivisions of the Wisconsin glacial age: Science, v. 77, p. 168

—— 1957, The Cary-Mankato-Valders problem: J. Geol., v. 65, p. 108-111

—— 1958a, Important elements in the classification of the Wisconsin glacial stage: J. Geol., v. 66, p. 288-309

—— 1958b, Principles and viewpoints in formulating the stratigraphic classifications of the Pleistocene: J. Geol., v. 66, p. 700-709

—— 1959, Important elements in the classification of the Wisconsin glacial stage; a reply: J. Geol., v. 67, p. 594-598

—— 1960, The classification of the Wisconsin glacial stage of north central United States: J. Geol., v. 68, p. 529-552

Leighton, M. M., and Brophy, J. A., 1961, Illinoian glaciation in Illinois: J. Geol., v. 69, p. 1-31

Leighton, M. M., and Willman, H. B., 1950, Loess formations of the Mississippi Valley: J. Geol., v. 58, p. 599-623

Leverett, Frank, 1897, The Pleistocene features and deposits of the Chicago area: Chicago Acad. Sci. Bull., v. 2, 86 p.

—— 1899, The Illinois glacial lobe: U.S. Geol. Surv. Monogr. 38, 817 p.

—— 1902, Glacial formations and drainage features of the Erie and Ohio basins: U.S. Geol. Surv. Monogr. 41, 802 p.

—— 1917, Surface geology of Michigan: Michigan Geol. Biol. Surv. Publ. 25, Geol. Ser. 21, 223 p.

—— 1929a, Pleistocene of northern Kentucky: Kentucky Geol. Surv., Ser. 6, v. 31, p. 1-80

—— 1929b, Moraines and shorelines of the Lake Superior region: U.S. Geol. Surv. Prof. Pap. 154-A, 72 p.

Leverett, Frank, and Taylor, F. B., 1915, Pleistocene of Indiana and Michigan and the history of the Great Lakes: U.S. Geol. Surv. Monogr. 53, 529 p.

MacLean, W. F., 1963, Modern pseudo-upwarping around Lake Erie: Univ. Michigan, Great Lakes Res. Div., Sixth Conf. Great Lakes Res. Proc., Publ. 10, p. 158-168

Malott, C. A., 1922, Physiography of Indiana, *in* Logan, W. N., Handbook of Indiana Geology: Indiana Dept. Conserv. Publ. 21, Pt. 2, p. 59-256

Martin, H. M., 1955, Map of the surface formations of the Southern Peninsula of Michigan, Scale 1/500,000: Michigan Dept. Conserv., Geol. Surv. Div. Publ. 49

—— 1957, Map of the surface formations of the Northern Peninsula of Michigan, Scale 1/500,000: Michigan Dept. Conserv., Geol. Surv. Div. Publ. 49

Martin, L. M., 1916, The physical geology of Wisconsin: Wisconsin Geol. Nat. Hist. Surv. Bull. 36, 547 p.

Martin, P. S., 1958, Pleistocene ecology and biogeography of North America, *in* Hubbs, C. L. (ed.), Zoogeography: Amer. Assoc. Adv. Sci. Publ. 51, p. 375-420

Mason, R. J., 1960, Early Man and the age of the Champlain Sea: J. Geol., v. 68, p. 366-376

Mather, K. F., 1917, The Champlain Sea in the Ontario basin: J. Geol., v. 25, p. 542-554

Melhorn, W. N., 1954, Valders glaciation of the Southern

Peninsula of Michigan: Univ. Michigan Ph. D. thesis, 174 p.

Moore, Sherman, 1948, Crustal movement in the Great Lakes area: Geol. Soc. Amer. Bull., v. 59, p. 697-710

Mozola, A. J., 1962, The bedrock topography of Wayne County, Michigan: Michigan Acad. Sci. Arts Lett., v. 47, p. 19-27

Murray, R. C., 1953, The petrology of the Cary and Valders tills of northeastern Wisconsin: Amer. J. Sci., v. 251, p. 140-155

Newberry, J. S., 1874, On the structure and origin of the Great Lakes: New York Lyceum Nat. Hist. Proc., v. 2, p. 136-138

—— 1882, On the origin and drainage of the basins of the Great Lakes: Amer. Philos. Soc., v. 20, p. 91-95

Otto, J. H., 1938, Forest succession of the southern limits of early Wisconsin glaciation as indicated by a pollen spectrum for Bacon's Swamp, Marion County, Indiana: Butler Univ. Bot. Stud., v. 4, p. 93-116

Potzger, J. E., and Wilson, I. T., 1941, Post-Pleistocene forest migration as indicated by sediments from three deep inland lakes: Amer. Midl. Nat., v. 25, p. 270-289

Prettyman, R. L., 1937, Fossil pollen analysis of Fox Prairie bog, Hamilton County, Indiana: Butler Univ. Bot. Stud., v. 4, p. 33-42

Ray, L. L., 1963, Quaternary events along the unglaciated lower Ohio River valley: U.S. Geol. Surv. Prof. Pap. 475-B, p. 125-128

Rhodehamel, E. C., and Carlston, C. W., 1963, Geologic history of the Teays Valley in West Virginia: Geol. Soc. Amer. Bull., v. 74, p. 251-274

Schneider, A. F., and Keller, Stanley, in preparation, Geologic map of the 1° × 2° Chicago Quadrangle, Indiana, Illinois, and Michigan: Indiana Geol. Surv. Regional Geol. Map, Chicago Sheet

Schneider, A. F., Johnson, G. H., and Wayne, W. J., 1963, Some linear glacial features in west-central Indiana (abst.): Indiana Acad. Sci. Proc., v. 72, p. 172-173

Schwartz, G. M., 1949, Geology of the Duluth metropolitan area: Minnesota Geol. Surv. Bull. 33, 136 p.

Scott, I. D., 1921, Inland lakes of Michigan: Michigan Geol. Biol. Surv. Publ. 30, Geol. ser. 25, 383 p.

Sharp, R. P., 1953, Shorelines of the glacial Great Lakes in Cook County, Minnesota: Amer. J. Sci., v. 251, p. 109-139

Shepard, F. P., 1937, Origin of the Great Lakes basins: J. Geol., v. 45, p. 76-88

Spencer, J. W., 1890, The deformation of Iroquois beach and birth of Lake Ontario: Amer. J. Sci., 3rd ser., v. 40, p. 443-451

—— 1891, Origin of the basins of the Great Lakes of America: Amer. Geologist, v. 7, p. 86-97

—— 1896, How the Great Lakes were built: Popular Sci. Monthly, v. 49, p. 157-172

Stanley, G. M., 1932, Abandoned strands of Isle Royale and northeastern Lake Superior: Univ. Michigan Ph.D. thesis, 158 p.

—— 1936, Lower Algonquin beaches of Penetanguishene Peninsula: Geol. Soc. Amer. Bull., v. 47, p. 1933-1960

—— 1937, Lower Algonquin beaches of Cape Rich, Georgian Bay: Geol. Soc. Amer. Bull., v. 48, p. 1665-1686

—— 1938, The submerged valley through Mackinac Straits: J. Geol., v. 46, p. 966-974

—— 1945, Pre-historic Mackinac Island: Michigan Dept. Conserv. Geol. Surv. Div. Publ. 43, Geol. Ser. 36, 74 p.

Stout, Wilbur, 1953, Age of the fringe drift in eastern Ohio: Ohio J. Sci., v. 53, p. 183-189

Stout, Wilbur, and Shaaf, Downs, 1931, Minford silts of southern Ohio: Geol. Soc. Amer. Bull., v. 42, p. 663-672

Stout, Wilbur, VerSteeg, Karl, and Lamb, G. F., 1943, Geology of water in Ohio: Ohio Geol. Surv., 4th ser., Bull. 44, 694 p.

Swickard, D. A., 1941, Comparison of pollen spectra from bogs of early and late Wisconsin glaciation in Indiana: Butler Univ. Bot. Stud., v. 5, p. 67-84

Taylor, F. B., 1895, The Nipissing beach on the north Superior shore: Amer. Geologist, v. 7, p. 86-97

Terasmae, Jaan, and Hughes, O. L., 1960, Glacial retreat in the North Bay area, Ontario: Science, v. 131, p. 1444-1446

Thompson, Maurice, 1886, Glacial deposits of Indiana: Indiana Dept. Geol. Nat. Hist. Ann. Rep. 15, p. 44-56

—— 1889, The drift beds of Indiana: Indiana Dept. Geol. Nat. Hist. Ann. Rep. 16, p. 20-40

Thornbury, W. D., 1937, Glacial geology of southern and south-central Indiana: Indiana Div. Geol., 138 p.

—— 1940, Weathered zones and glacial chronology in southern Indiana: J. Geol., v. 48, p. 449-475

—— 1950, Glacial sluiceways and lacustrine plains of southern Indiana: Indiana Div. Geol. Bull. 4, 21 p.

—— 1958, The geomorphic history of the upper Wabash Valley: Amer. J. Sci., v. 256, p. 449-469

Thwaites, F. T., 1935, Sublacustrine topographic map of the bottom of Lake Superior: Kansas Geol. Soc. Guidebook, Ninth Ann. Field Conf., p. 226-228

—— 1943, Pleistocene of part of northeastern Wisconsin: Geol. Soc. Amer. Bull., v. 54, p. 87-144

—— 1946, Outline of glacial geology: Ann Arbor, Michigan, Edwards Bros., Inc., 129 p.

—— 1949, Geomorphology of the basin of Lake Michigan: Michigan Acad. Sci. Arts Lett., v. 33, p. 243-251

Thwaites, F. T., and Bertrand, Kenneth, 1957, Pleistocene geology of the Door Peninsula, Wisconsin: Geol. Soc. Amer. Bull., v. 68, p. 831-880

Tight, W. G., 1903, Drainage modifications in southeastern Ohio and adjacent parts of West Virginia and Kentucky: U.S. Geol. Surv. Prof. Pap. 13, 111 p.

Wayne, W. J., 1952, Pleistocene evolution of the Ohio and Wabash Valleys: J. Geol., v. 60, p. 575-585

—— 1956a, Pleistocene periglacial environment in Indiana (abst.): Indiana Acad. Sci. Proc., v. 65, p. 164

—— 1956b, Thickness of drift and bedrock physiography of Indiana north of the Wisconsin glacial boundary: Indiana Geol. Surv. Rep. Prog. 7, 70 p.

—— 1958a, Early Pleistocene sediments in Indiana: J. Geol., v. 66, p. 8-15

—— 1958b, Glacial geology of Indiana: Indiana Geol. Surv. Atlas Mineral Resources of Indiana Map. 10

—— 1959, Stratigraphic distribution of Pleistocene land snails in Indiana: Sterkiana, v. 1, p. 9-12

—— 1960, Stratigraphy of the Ohio River Formation: Indiana Geol. Surv. Bull. 21, 44 p.

—— 1963, Pleistocene formations of Indiana: Indiana Geol. Surv. Bull. 25, 85 p.

—— 1964, Pleistocene patterned ground and periglacial temperatures in Indiana (abst.): Geol. Soc. Amer. Spec. Pap. 76, p. 176-177

—— in preparation, The Crawfordsville and Knightstown Moraines in Indiana: Indiana Geol. Surv. Rep. Prog.

Wayne, W. J., and Thornbury, W. D., 1955, Wisconsin stratigraphy of northern and eastern Indiana: Indiana and Ohio Geol. Surveys, 5th Biennial Pleistocene Field Conf. Guidebook, p. 1-34

Wayne, W. J., Johnson, G. H., and Keller, Stanley (in preparation) Geologic map of the 1° × 2° Danville Quadrangle, Indiana and Illinois: Indiana Geol. Surv. Regional Geol. Map, Danville Sheet

Webb, W. M., and Smith, R., 1961, The bedrock geology of Lake Michigan (abst.): Univ. Michigan, Great Lakes Res. Div., Fourth Conf. Great Lakes Res. Proc., Publ. 7, p. 146

Wier, C. E., and Gray, H. H., 1961, Geologic map of the Indianapolis 1° × 2° Quadrangle, Indiana and Illinois: Indiana Geol. Surv. Regional Geol. Map, Indianapolis Sheet

Willman, H. B., Glass, H. D., and Frye, J. C., 1963, Mineralogy of glacial tills and their weathering profiles in Illinois: Illinois Geol. Surv. Circ. 347, 55 p.

Wilson, L. R., 1932, The Two Creeks forest bed, Manitowoc Co., Wisconsin: Wisconsin Acad. Sci. Trans., v. 27, p. 31-46

Wright, G. F., 1918, Explanation of the abandoned beaches about the south end of Lake Michigan: Geol. Soc. Amer. Bull., v. 29, p. 235-244

Wright, H. E., Jr., 1964, The classification of the Wisconsin glacial stage: J. Geol., v. 72, p. 628-637

Zumberge, J. H., 1960, Correlation of Wisconsin drifts in Illinois, Indiana, Michigan, and Ohio: Geol. Soc. Amer. Bull., v. 71, p. 1177-1188

—— 1962a, Problems on the origin of Lake Superior: Metropolitan Detroit Sci. Rev., v. 23, p. 57-59

—— 1962b, A new shipboard coring technique: J. Geophys. Res., v. 67, p. 2529-2536

Zumberge, J. H., and Gast, Paul, 1961, Geological investigations in Lake Superior: Geotimes, v. 6, p. 10-13

Zumberge, J. H., and Potzger, J. E., 1956, Late Wisconsin chronology of the Lake Michigan basin correlated with pollen studies: Geol. Soc. Amer. Bull., v. 67, p. 271-288

Zumberge, J. H., Spurr, S. H., and Melhorn, W. H., 1956, The northwestern part of the Southern Peninsula of Michigan: Univ. Michigan Dept. Geology, Friends of the Pleistocene, Midwest Section, Guidebook, 36 p.

Summary

Deposits representing the Kansan, Illinoian, and Wisconsin glacial stages have been recorded in Indiana. These Pleistocene sediments, which consist of till, outwash deposits, loess, alluvium, colluvium, marl, and peat, are more than 150 m thick in some places over buried valleys and bedrock lowlands in northern Indiana. Modern drainage lines in the northern half of the state bear little relationship to the buried Tertiary valley systems.

The Pleistocene glaciers eroded only slightly in their marginal zones but left a detailed depositional record. The stratigraphic classification of Quaternary deposits in Indiana depends primarily on recognizing sedimentary units in superposition. Criteria used to identify and trace units are lithic characteristics of tills, key beds (such as paleosols and fossiliferous intertill silts), molluscan faunas, radiocarbon dates, surface soil profiles, and geomorphology. The classification used includes both stage (time-stratigraphic) and formation (rock-stratigraphic) terminology.

Most of the ice that covered Indiana evidently came from the northeast, but several glacial advances entered the state from the Lake Michigan lowland as well. Fossiliferous intertill silts record two major pulsations of the ice margin during the Kansan Age, three during the Illinoian Age, and perhaps four during the Wisconsin Age. Additional oscillations of the ice margin during each major pulsation produced moraines and multiple till beds.

True warm-climate interglacial sediments are rare in Indiana, but nonglacial beds intercalated between tills are traceable into both Yarmouth and Sangamon paleosols in many exposures in central Indiana. Most of the fossil plant remains and mollusks from these beds indicate that the climate had become cool before they were buried beneath advancing ice.

The surface geology of Michigan is dominated by glacial drift of three Wisconsin substages: Cary, Port Huron (Mankato), and Valders. The terminal moraines of the Lake Michigan, Saginaw, and Erie Lobes define the Cary drift border in northern Indiana. The Port Huron (Mankato) Substage is represented by the Port Huron Moraine and associated glacial drift. A red or pinkish drift sheet, which occurs north of the Port Huron Moraine in part of the Southern Peninsula and most of the Northern Peninsula, represents the Valders Substage. No interstadial deposits of the Cary–Port Huron interval or Port Huron–Valders (Two Creeks) interval have been positively identified in Michigan.

The basins containing the Great Lakes originated as stream valleys during the Tertiary Period and were modified by glacial erosion and deposition during the Pleistocene Epoch. The magnitude of glacial modification cannot be determined with much certainty until more direct evidence on the nature and configuration of the bedrock surface beneath the lakes themselves is available.

Field studies and radiocarbon age determinations provide a basis for an absolute chronology of the ice retreat in the Great Lakes region. The first phase of this chronology began about 14,000 B.P. with the development of proglacial lakes marginal to each of the three lobes. The water levels of these early lakes were well above the modern water surfaces and discharged toward the Mississippi River. By 9,500 B.P. Michigan was ice-free, and the four lake basins surrounding the State contained lakes with levels well below the modern water planes. This low-water system drained eastward to the Atlantic Ocean.

From 9,500 B.P. to 4,000 B.P. there ensued a period of slow crustal uplift due to glacial unloading. This uplift caused the eastern outlets to be abandoned in favor of a reactivation of the southern outlets. It culminated in the merging of waters in the Superior, Huron, and Michigan basins. This single, three-basin lake was differentiated into the modern upper Great Lakes about 2,000 B.P.

PLEISTOCENE DEPOSITS OF THE ERIE LOBE

RICHARD P. GOLDTHWAIT,[1] ALEKSIS DREIMANIS,[2] JANE L. FORSYTH,[3]

PAUL F. KARROW,[4] GEORGE W. WHITE[5]

THE ERIE LOBE was fed by ice flow from north of Lake Ontario, if we are to believe the evidence of the striae made by the latest ice advances and the heavy minerals found in its drift (Dreimanis, 1960, 1961). The Ontario and Erie basins had been made earlier by river erosion and glaciation on weak Devonian and Ordovician shales, but they neatly directed the main ice westward past the tougher Mississippian-Pennsylvanian sandstones of the escarpment of low Appalachian Plateaus. Nevertheless, sublobes pressed southward from this mainstream into the sandstone hills of the eroded plateau, forming short lobes over northwest Pennsylvania and northeast Ohio. Near the western end of the Erie Basin the ice lobe spread far southwest into Indiana and south over central Ohio, over horizontal Silurian-Devonian calcareous rocks, where the surface was fairly low and flat. But it split around the bedrock hills to form the Miami and Scioto Lobes (Fig. 1). The bedrock hills were ultimately also covered by ice. The Illinoian ice earlier had a very similar pattern with slightly different re-entrants, but Kansan (?) ice may have come in from the northwest. Kansan drift is evident only in extreme southwestern Ohio and northern Kentucky.

The principal ice limits of all stages and the main Wisconsin moraines were first fully worked out by Leverett (1902). His approach was wholly from topography and morphology. Since 1945 there has been a rebirth of studies, based on stratigraphy. In each part of the area the successful method of approach has been different in detail, so results have differed: (1) at the edge in western Indiana, Ansel Gooding uses analysis of soils, sediments, and fossils of at least seven separate drifts, with loess a prominent feature; (2) at the southern limit, Richard Durrell works chiefly by morphology and weathering analysis on three stages of drift; (3) in central and western Ohio, Jane Forsyth and Richard Goldthwait use soils, sediments, and radiocarbon dating, and moraines are important; (4) in northeastern Ohio and adjacent Pennsylvania, George White and V. C. Shepps find that analysis of sediments and weathering are useful in differentiating five to seven till sheets in each lobe, and that moraines mean little; and (5) in southern Ontario, Aleksis Dreimanis, Paul Karrow, and Jaan Terasmae use lithologic, fabric, and fossil analysis along with carbon-14 dating.

[1] Department of Geology, Ohio State University, Columbus, Ohio.

[2] Department of Geology, University of Western Ontario, London, Ontario.

[3] Ohio Geological Survey, Columbus, Ohio.

[4] Ontario Department of Mines, Toronto, Ontario.

[5] Department of Geology, University of Illinois, Urbana, Illinois.

CENTRAL AND WESTERN OHIO

Drifts of three different glaciations, Kansan(?), Illinoian, and Wisconsin, cover central and western Ohio. Western Ohio is underlain by early Paleozoic limestone and dolomite and is generally flat in contrast to the mature hills of eastern Ohio, which are composed of late Paleozoic sandstone and shale. Because of this topographic difference, the ice extended much farther south in western Ohio; as a result of the differences in bedrock, the glacial drift in western Ohio has a much higher content of calcium carbonate and a different set of soils. Soils have been one of the most valuable tools for the glacial geologist in Ohio, being used both in the recognition of different ages of drift and in the identification of subtle but apparently significant differences in the composition of the deposits.

KANSAN(?)

Oldest are the deposits considered to be Kansan, which occur in the southwestern corner of Ohio and the northern tip of Kentucky (Durrell, 1961). Most of the till near the Ohio River is Illinoian, characterized by strongly weathered soils 2-3 m deep and occurring both on the uplands and in the valleys. In the critical area west and south of Cincinnati, however, till restricted to uplands bears soils very strongly weathered to depths of 4-6 m. Because this till is not present in the valleys, major dissection is believed to have taken place following its deposition and before deposition of the Illinoian till. This relation matches the stratigraphy of Illinoian over Kansan drifts in adjacent Indiana (Wayne, 1958).

Some have speculated that this drift may be Nebraskan (?). If the pre-Illinoian drift in Indiana and Illinois is correctly identified as Kansan age—and paleosols support this correlation—then the drift in question in Ohio is also Kansan. Even more speculative in origin are the large crystalline boulders (granite, quartzite) on or near hilltops of sedimentary rock far above known river terraces in north-central and western Kentucky (see Goldthwait et al., 1961). One hypothesis at least would make these the only remaining erratics of a still earlier, more extensive glaciation: the Nebraskan(?).

ILLINOIAN DRIFT

Deposits of the Illinoian glacier form a continuous belt beyond the boundary of the Wisconsin drift. It reaches the Ohio River east of Cincinnati and extends northeast to the major re-entrant in central Ohio. Almost everywhere in western Ohio these deposits form very flat ground moraine (till plain) on horizontal bedrock surface. The till is gen-

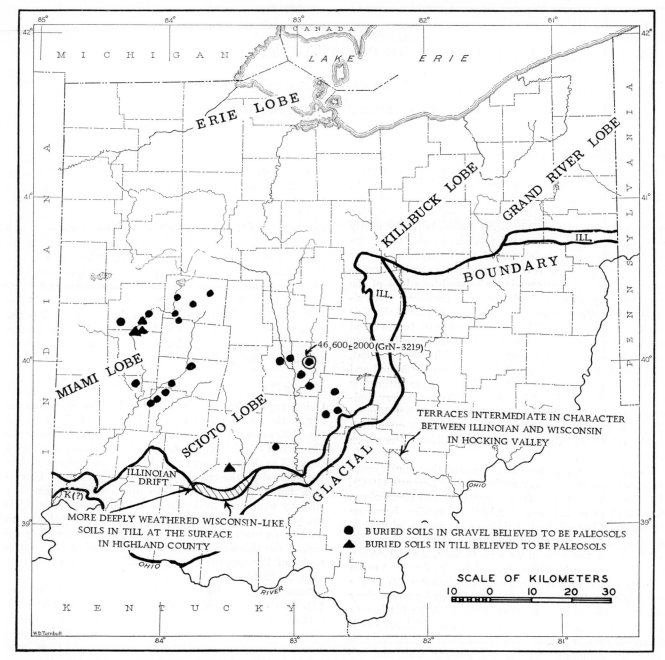

Figure 1. Map of Ohio showing location of major ice lobes and the sites providing critical "Early" Wisconsin data. The site of the single finite "Early" Wisconsin radiocarbon date is shown by the double circle.

erally covered by several feet of loess, believed by many to be mostly of Wisconsin age. In central Ohio, however, where the drift extends up onto the western margin of the Appalachian Low Plateaus, the ground moraine has marked relief because of the irregular surface of the partially buried bedrock hills. Illinoian kames and outwash terraces occur near and beyond the glacial boundary in most major southward- and eastward-flowing river valleys, especially in these hills (Kempton and Goldthwait, 1959; Jones, 1959; Forsyth, 1961c, 1962). Although wood has been found in this drift, no finite radiocarbon date is possible.

"EARLY" OR "MID" WISCONSIN DRIFT

Following the Illinoian glaciation came the controversial "Early" Wisconsin, believed to correlate with the early Altonian of Frye and Willman (1960) in Illinois, early Würm of Austria (Flint and Brandtner, 1961), and possibly the Iowan of Iowa (Ruhe *et al.*, 1957).

In Ohio, "Early" Wisconsin is represented (1) by a narrow band of till along the Wisconsin boundary in southern Ohio characterized by unusually deep Russell soils (Forsyth, 1957; Forsyth and Bowman, 1963; Forsyth, 1963), (2) by an outwash terrace intermediate in elevation and soil characteristics between Wisconsin and Illinoian in the Hocking Valley of southeastern Ohio (Kempton and Goldthwait, 1959), and (3) by a number of widely scattered buried soils, shown in Figure 1, some of which are surely paleosols (Forsyth, 1957). Most of these buried soils are developed in gravel where it directly underlies calcareous till. In a few spots, notably near Sidney in western Ohio (Miami Lobe), the soil is in an underlying till (LaRocque and Forsyth, 1957; Forsyth and LaRocque, 1956). At one of these localities between till and a paleosol is peat indicating cool interstadial conditions, the Sidney Soil Interval. Dissenters

(Gooding *et al.*, 1959) have argued that the buried soils in gravel are contemporaneous with the modern soil at the surface, as indeed they must be in some observed situations; but in other, critical cases, the overlying cover of till is too thick, too massive, and insufficiently weathered to permit such an interpretation (Goldthwait, 1959b). No finite radiocarbon dates are known directly from the underlying till, though infinite dates (greater than 32,000 years) are available from several localities. The one finite date (46,600 ± 2,000, GrN 3219; Fig. 1) comes from material underneath "Late" Wisconsin till and bits of possible "Sidney" paleosol

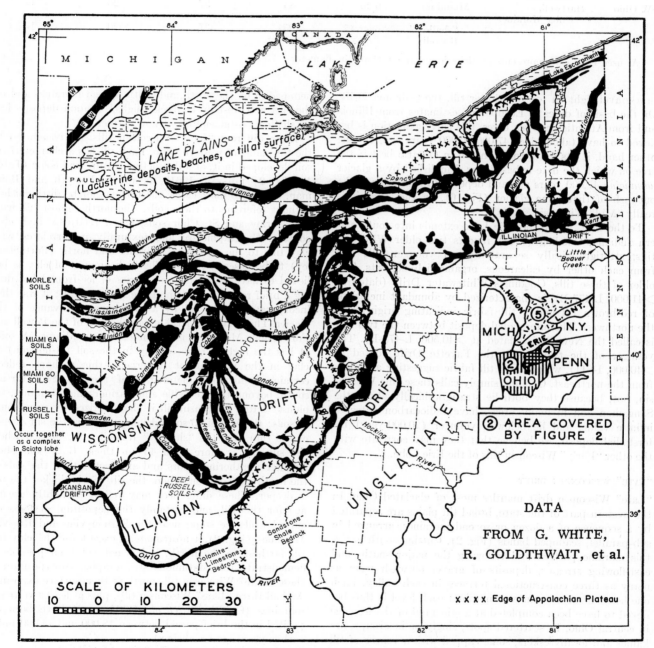

Figure 2. Map of Ohio showing named end moraines, till soils, and edge of Appalachian Plateau (where sandy soils are present). Extensive late-Wisconsin lake deposits in northern Ohio are dashed; uppermost limits of beaches are shown by a uniform solid line.

TABLE 1

"Late" Wisconsin Tills of Western Ohio, Their Soils and Diagnostic Characteristics

				Average soil characteristics			
				B-horizon			
Area	Southern boundary	Associated soil group	Depth of silt cap (cm)	Thickness (cm)	Clay[a] content (%)	Clay[a] in till (%)	Ratio of clay in B to clay in till[a]
NW Ohio	Union City, Powell Moraines	Morley (St. Clair)	none	68	45	30	1.5
W Ohio	Farmersville, Reesville Moraines	Miami 6A	none	55	45	20	2.2
SW Ohio	Hartwell, Cuba Moraines	Miami 60	0-45	83	37	20	1.8
		"shallow" Russell	over 45	125	37	20	1.8

[a] As used here, clay represents particles less than 0.002 mm in diameter

in a gravel right on top of a lower till, the Gahanna Drift. On the basis of dates in Europe and estimates from Illinois and from Atlantic deep-sea cores, this early glaciation is believed to have taken place 47,000-70,000 years ago. On the other hand, it fits dates to the north in Ontario best if the tree on which the date is based was demolished by a glacier *advancing* 47,000 years ago and deposited much later in the outwash of that same glacier (Fig. 6). In this case, it is really "Mid" Wisconsin.

To the west, where the Erie Lobe extends into southeastern Indiana, Gooding (1963) reports two older Wisconsin tills, stratigraphically separated from younger tills and from each other by calcareous, organic-rich deposits. The older of these tills, Gooding's Whitewater Drift (dated at >41,000, L-477-B), is characterized by abundant inclusions of red-brown till and a till fabric indicating origin from the northwest. The interstadial deposit between the two tills is called the New Paris (dated at >40,500, L-478-B). The younger of the two tills is the Fayette Drift (dated at >40,000, I-611), which has a till fabric suggesting an origin from the northeast. Gooding simply calls these tills Wisconsin, but, because they both lie stratigraphically above the Sangamon Soil in many areas, have radiocarbon dates of infinite value, and lie below a younger (20,000-year) interstadial deposit, we believe that they may correlate with the other "Early" Wisconsin tills of the Erie Lobe.

"LATE" WISCONSIN DRIFT

"Late" Wisconsin drift mantles most of glaciated Ohio. In the western part of the state, broad till plains are separated by a sequence of a dozen or so end moraines, arranged in sub-parallel, scalloped bands (Fig. 2). Cutting south across this moraine pattern and following the major south- and east-flowing streams, deposits of gravel outwash form as many as three constructional terraces in each valley. Each one heads at or near an end moraine; each level is thus believed to have been completed at a stillstand of the ice edge in central Ohio. In scattered spots, singly or in groups, are kames and locally eskers, some capped with a veneer of till and some not. These ice-contact features are most abundant in the interlobate areas and hills, as though the ice had wasted away more irregularly there. A few low areas,

hemmed in on the north and south by end moraines and on the east and west by bedrock "highs," contain deposits left by shallow postglacial lakes, now extinct.

Three different "Late" Wisconsin tills are recognized in the till plains of western Ohio. Each till has a characteristic soil developed in it, of a distinctive texture and color (Table 1; Fig. 2; Forsyth, 1961b, in press; Forsyth and Bowman, 1963); in most cases, the tills cannot be distinguished without reference to these soils. The northernmost till, with the Morley and St. Clair soils, has a relatively high clay content. Geographically and texturally it correlates with clay tills to the northeast (Hiram) and north (Port Stanley) to be described later. The high amount of clay is believed to have originated in a series of ice-front lakes during a brief retreat called the Lake Erie interval; it was then incorporated in the till by a subsequent readvance of the glacier. The next earlier till, exposed south of the Powell and Fort Union Moraines, is characterized by Miami 6A soils. It has the highest ratio of clay in the soil (B-horizon) to clay in the till (parent material); this perhaps reflects certain chemical characteristics of the till. Still farther south, beyond the Reesville and Farmersville Moraines, the oldest "Late" Wisconsin till is characterized by two groups of soils: the Miami 60 soils, developed where the silt (loess) cap is thin, and the "shallow" Russell soils, formed where the silt cap is more than 45 cm thick. Both soils show brighter weathering colors and are deeper than the soils to the north; in addition, where the silt cap is thicker the soil is deeper. These differences may reflect a slightly greater age for this till, and certainly the deposition of loess occurred while ice stood near the Farmersville and Reesville Moraines (Fig. 2). Unfortunately, except for the clay-rich till farthest to the north, it has not yet been possible to demonstrate the continuous stratigraphic superposition of these "Late" Wisconsin tills north of their surface exposures. And all three "Late" Wisconsin tills, plus at least twelve end moraines (Goldthwait *et al.*, 1961), must have been deposited in the brief period between 18,000 and 14,000 radiocarbon years ago (see below).

The advance of this "Late" Wisconsin glacier is recorded by radiocarbon dates from wood (mostly spruce, *Picea*) buried in the till deposited by the ice. Many such dates (Fig.

3) are now available for western Ohio, all internally consistent, and they tell the story of an advancing ice front that entered Ohio more than 25,000 years ago and reached its southernmost position 20,000 years ago in the Miami Lobe and 18,000 years ago in the Scioto Lobe (Goldthwait, 1958; Forsyth, 1961a). With these dates (Fig. 3), overall rates of advance for the ice can be calculated. In the north the ice front advanced 105 m per year; in the south it advanced 15 m per year in the Scioto Lobe and 32 m per year in the Miami Lobe (Goldthwait, 1959a). The oldest post-till dates on trees submerged by the rising water of Lake Whittlesey

in the early Erie basin are 13,000-14,000 years ago (14,300 ± 450, W-198, in northwest Ohio; 13,600 ± 500, W-33, at Cleveland; 12,920 ± 400, W-430, south of Sandusky). Postglacial wood in a depression on the Wabash Moraine in eastern Indiana gave a date of 14,300 ± 450 (W-198).

LATE-GLACIAL LAKES

As the ice front retreated out of Ohio, it occupied several successive positions within the Lake Erie basin, where it acted as a temporary dam and formed several different lake levels, the highest of which stood more than 67 m above

Figure 3. Location of significant radiocarbon dates marking the advance of the "Late" Wisconsin glacier. Others at 25,000 to 28,000 years old lie north of Lake Erie in Ontario.

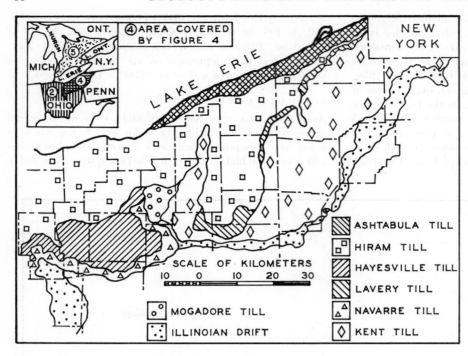

Figure 4. Map of Illinoian drift and Wisconsin rock-stratigraphic units of Killbuck Lobe in north-central Ohio and Grand River Lobe in northeast Ohio and northwest Pennsylvania.

present Lake Erie. The ancient shorelines, which have not been tilted in Ohio, are marked by beach ridges composed of sand and some gravel. Shallow lake-botton silts and clays have a discontinuous distribution among the lower beach ridges (Fig. 2). Major lake levels were Glacial Lakes Maumee, Whittlesey, and Warren, which have been related traditionally to ice advances at Defiance Moraine, Port Huron Moraine, and Valders Moraine in Michigan (Hough, 1963). Radiocarbon dates from Ontario now make these all earlier than Two Creeks Time—11,800 years B.P. (before the present). Drainage from these lakes escaped to the west during these higher, earlier lake stages and then to the east during the lower, later lake stages, beginning with Lake Wayne (pre-Warren) at least 11,800 years ago. Once the ice had retreated north out of the Erie basin, drainage over the escarpment at Niagara Falls was initiated, and Lake Erie became the first of all the Great Lakes to reach its present strandline. It was lower at first because of isostatic depression of its outlet, as shown by beach materials 15 m to 18 m below the present lake level.

Northeastern Ohio and Northwestern Pennsylvania

Ice in the Erie Lobe and in lobes dependent from it advanced several times into the hills of northeastern Ohio, northwestern Pennsylvania, and southwestern New York. Drift of the Grand River Lobe (White, 1951) extends from southwestern New York across northwestern Pennsylvania into northeastern Ohio (Fig. 4). The Killbuck Lobe, entirely in Ohio, extends westward for about 120 km to its junction with the Scioto Lobe. The higher land of the Appalachian Plateau impeded the southward advance of all the ice sheets.

The ice advances were at various times synchronous in the Grand River and Killbuck Lobes; however, the earlier tills

of each lobe are actually distinct, and the deposits of each lobe must be considered as separate rock-stratigraphic units, although correlation can be made from lobe to lobe (Shepps *et al.*, 1959; Totten, 1962; White, 1960, 1961, 1964). Only the tills of the latest advances can be traced directly from one lobe to another. The ice of each advance deposited till of more or less distinct textural, mineralogic, and petrologic character. These differences are reflected in the weathering characteristics and soil types of the tills.

ILLINOIAN DRIFT

It has long been known that drift with typical post-Illinoian weathering is not exposed in the Killbuck Lobe. However, at the outer edge of the Grand River Lobe, and remarkably parallel to Wisconsin drift limits, is deeply weathered sandy drift in a belt, up to 19 km wide, from just south of Canton, Ohio, through northwestern Pennsylvania nearly to New York. It is now possible to divide this drift into an "inner phase" and an "outer phase" of Illinoian drift. These tills, especially the olive-brown "inner phase," have now been identified to the north and northwest under Wisconsin tills, and from studies now in progress it appears that these may be traced in the subsurface through the lobe.

Other kinds of materials underlying Wisconsin tills belong to Illinoian or early Wisconsin glaciation. Kame terraces are common along the sides of the valleys in the plateau. Some very large pits in these terraces are a major source of sand and gravel for highway and other construction purposes. The gravel of the terraces is overlain by one to three till sheets of later age. The episode of gravel deposition and terrace formation was therefore very early Wisconsin or Illinoian. A buried gravel terrace in the southeastern part of Cleveland (Maple Heights) is known to be Illinoian in age because of the Sangamon soil (White, 1953a, 1953b) on its buried surface.

"EARLY" OR "MID" WISCONSIN DRIFT

Evidence of "Early" Wisconsin ice advance is not clearly identified in northeastern Ohio. There are no carbon-dated "Early" Wisconsin drifts. The most likely candidate is Mogadore Till, which is olive to yellow-brown, sandy till exposed in a "window" around Akron and surrounded by younger, less weathered drifts. Weathered Illinoian till lies under it in places, but since it is also stained to 2-m depth with strongly developed surface soils, and since it underlies other Wisconsin till in adjacent areas, it is at least as old as "Early" Wisconsin. Also under Wisconsin till near Cleveland is a lower loess containing fossils (Leonard, 1953) that suggest correlation with Farmdale loess of Illinois. In the recent classification of Frye and Willman (1960), this corresponds to the short interval between Altonian ("Early" Wisconsin) and Woodfordian ("Late" Wisconsin), about 26,000 years ago.

"LATE" WISCONSIN DRIFT

Those Wisconsin tills that can be traced on the surface and in the subsurface throughout each lobe and can be correlated from one lobe to the other have been named as rock-stratigraphic units, as shown in Table 2. The earlier tills are more discontinuous and are less well known.

Some correlation is possible, because the Hiram Till limit has recently been traced (Totten, 1962) to the outer margin of Miami 6B clay soils in central and western Ohio (Powell Moraine), and both are rich in clay. If the sequence of ice advances and drifts in the Killbuck Lobe was the same as in the Scioto Lobe, it would follow that Hayesville Till should be the same as the surface drift of the Miami 6A soil region as far south as the Reesville Moraine, and Navarre Till would be the same as the Miami 60 soil region as far south as the Cuba Moraine. Unlike western Ohio, no bogs yet found in the outer moraine confirm or deny the 18,000-20,000-year age of this outermost Wisconsin drift. On the basis of one dated bog on top, the drift is at least 14,000 years old. The lowest Wisconsin till over loess and gravels near Cleveland is dated 24,600 ± 800 (W-17; White, 1953a); this might date the advance of ice which delivered the Navarre and Kent Tills.

The end moraines in the plateau are more irregular and diffuse than in the Till Plains to the west (Fig. 3). They are composed of superimposed tills of several ages and hence do not necessarily provide markers for delimiting drift margins or determining the history and extent of ice advances (White, 1962). The history of ice advances must be based upon the outer limit of the till sheets and not on end moraines.

In addition to the till deposits, other glacial deposits are outwash gravel and sand in the form of kames, crevasse fillings, and kame terraces. These ice-contact forms are particularly abundant in this hilly country and are demonstrations of the irregular down-wastage of the ice (White, 1964). Melt-water streams in the south-sloping valleys in the Appalachian Plateau deposited valley trains. Lake sediments were deposited in north-sloping valleys, mainly in the northern part of the region. The largest of the lakes was in the Grand River lowland in extreme northeastern Ohio. As this was dammed by the ice depositing the last Ashtabula Drift, it probably coincided also with one of the earliest high lake levels (Maumee or Whittlesey) of the Erie Basin.

SOUTHERN ONTARIO

Pleistocene glacial deposits of the southern fringe of Ontario, adjoining Lake Erie and Lake Ontario, have been deposited principally by the Ontario-Erie glacial lobe. Other glacial flows from the north also entered this area during the maximum glacial advances, and the Huron Lobe competed with the Erie Lobe at the western end of Lake Erie. Stratigraphy is worked out principally from the nonglacial flora and from radiocarbon dates. Most Pleistocene deposits of this region are of Wisconsin age.

TABLE 2

Glacial Deposits of Northeastern Ohio and Northwestern Pennsylvania

Stage	Killbuck Lobe Unit	Grand River Lobe Unit	Material
"Late" Wisconsin	Ashtabula Till	Ashtabula Till	Brown silty-clay till
	Hiram Till	Hiram Till	Brown clay till
	Hayesville Till	Lavery Till	Brown silty-clay till
	Navarre Till	Kent Till	Yellow-brown silty-sandy till
Sidney? Interval	Weathered zone	Weathered zone	Weathered till and discontinuous thin paleosol
"Early"? Wisconsin	Millbrook Till	Mogadore Till	Yellow-brown to olive-brown sandy till
Sangamon?	Weathered zone		Deeply rusted, red-yellow gravels
Illinoian	Unnamed till	"Inner phase" till (of Pennsylvania)	Yellow to olive-brown sandy till with many gravel kames
	Unnamed till	"Outer phase" till (of Pennsylvania)	Discontinuous deeply weathered till and scattered erratics
Pre-Illinoian	Unnamed tills	Unnamed tills	Generally sandy and coarse-sandy tills

ILLINOIAN AND SANGAMON DRIFT

The thin layer of the clayey York Till, resting on Ordovician bedrock and underlying the Don beds at Toronto, is commonly considered to be of Illinoian age.

A considerable portion of the Sangamon interglacial is represented by the Don beds at Toronto. These are deltaic sediments, deposited in a lake that was 18 m higher than the present Lake Ontario. The top of the Don beds is leached of carbonate because of lowering of the lake at the end of the interglacial. More than 70 species of trees and herbs, 20 of diatoms, and 6 of mammals have been identified among the fossil remains. These suggest that the maximum mean annual temperature was at least 3° C warmer than at present (Coleman, 1941; Terasmae, 1960). The radiocarbon age (L-409) is more than 46,000 years B.P.

"EARLY" WISCONSIN

The Scarborough beds, exposed extensively in the Toronto area, consist of up to 100 ft of lacustrine clay and silt overlain by up to 50 ft of deltaic sands with plant remains (Karrow, 1962). They were deposited at a considerably higher lake level than the Don beds. The Scarborough beds began to form during one of the first Wisconsin glacial advances from Labrador; this advance blocked the St. Lawrence outlet and deposited the Becanour Till in the St. Lawrence Lowland but did not reach the Toronto area. The flora (more than 50 species identified) suggest cool boreal climate, with the mean annual temperature about 5° C lower than at present (Terasmae, 1960). Wood found in Scarborough sands has been dated as more than 52,000 years (Gro-2555) and more than 40,000 B.P. (L-522B).

Apparently this very early Wisconsin ice retreated temporarily to open the St. Lawrence outlet during the St. Pierre interstadial interval more than $67,000 \pm 1,000$ years ago (Gro-1711, the older of the two preliminary dates from the St. Pierre interstadial beds in the St. Lawrence Lowlands). This caused a great lowering of the lake level in the Ontario basin, and deep gullies were cut through the Scarborough and the Don beds, later to be filled with till (Karrow, 1962).

Then came the major "Early" Wisconsin glacial advance from Labrador, which deposited the clayey to silty Sunnybrook Till in the Toronto area, the correlative (?) clayey Canning Till at Paris, and the silty Bradtville Till, found on Devonian bedrock in borings at Port Talbot, Ontario (Dreimanis, 1963). Presumably these should correlate with the first Wisconsin invasion southward into Ohio (Mogadore Till and Gahanna Drift), but as was shown earlier a dated gravel in Gahanna Drift suggests that glaciation ended there only 47,000 years ago.

"MID" WISCONSIN

In the Toronto area, sediments containing pollen of boreal plants and a paleosol (Watt, 1954) are covered by at least two tills. Wood from the Woodbridge section is more than 49,700 years old (CSC-203) and may belong to the early half of the "Mid" Wisconsin interstadial or to the "Early" Wisconsin.

Along the north shore of Lake Erie are several excellent exposures of peat and gytta between till layers. Certainly at Port Talbot the glacial retreat, after deposition of the Bradtville Till, left the Erie basin and probably also the Ontario basin free of ice during a long, cool interstadial interval: the Port Talbot (Dreimanis, 1958, 1960, 1961). Boreal forests of pine, spruce, and larch covered southwest Ontario. The buried St. David's gorge in the Niagara peninsula may have formed during this interstadial. Larger and probably older buried gorges are present farther west in the Niagara peninsula. However, a glacial advance (Dunwich Till) seems to divide the Port Talbot interstadial in two parts. This glacier advanced from the north, reached the north shore of Lake Erie, and deposited the sandy till and associated glacio-lacustrine sediments, rich in dolomite. Radiocarbon dates from the upper portion of the peat are (Fig. 5): $47,000 \pm 2,500$, Gro-2570; $47,500 \pm 250$, Gro-2597 and 2601; $44,900 \pm 1,000$ years B.P., Gro-2619 (DeVries and Dreimanis, 1960). The Port Talbot interstadial is therefore not dated. The overlying Southwold Till contains wood dated at $44,200 \pm 1,500$ years ago (Gro-2580).

Is it possible that the wood in "Early" Wisconsin Gahanna Drift, far south in Ohio, represents a tree ploughed up by the ice at the beginning of a glacial episode and not just a log buried by outwash at the end? If so, Gahanna Drift correlates with Southwold Till, rather than with Dunwich Till (Fig. 6).

Another possibility is that the Southwold Till that underlies the lithologically similar Catfish Creek Drift at Port Talbot is the basal layer of the latter. If this interpretation is correct, then a second wood sample from the Catfish Creek Till dates not from the Plum Point interval (see Figure 6 and the C[14] dates below) but from the latest episode in a very long Port Talbot interstadial interval. This interstadial then terminated only 27,000 or 25,000 years ago; radiocarbon dates at the base of the overlying Catfish Creek Till at Plum Point are $27,250 \pm 150$, Gro-2625; $27,500 \pm 1,200$, W-177; $28,200 \pm 1,500$, L-185B; $24,600 \pm 1,600$ years B.P., L-217B (Fig. 5).

"LATE" WISCONSIN

Southern Ontario was covered by an ice sheet beginning with the burial of logs in Catfish Creek Till 25,000 to 28,000 years ago (Fig. 6). The sandy, silty Catfish Creek Till is texturally similar to the Mogadore Till in northeastern Ohio, but both G. W. White and A. Dreimanis now think, on the basis of weathering and stratigraphy, that it is equivalent to Kent and Navarre Tills (Fig. 6). During the 11,000 years of this glaciation the ice advanced into southern Ohio as far as did any Wisconsin ice. Presumably this single till in Ontario is the equivalent of at least two series of tills and moraines in southwestern Ohio and southeastern Indiana (Cuba and Reesville Moraines, Hartwell and Farmersville Moraines, or Shelbyville and Bloomington Drift of Gooding, 1963).

The first major glacial retreat into southern Ontario, probably as far as the eastern portion of Lake Erie, occurred during the Lake Erie interval (Dreimanis, 1958). The high ground northeast of London, Ontario, became ice-free first, and the first high lake of the Erie Basin encroached between the retreating Erie and Huron Lobes as far as London. Its beach gravels, buried underneath till in

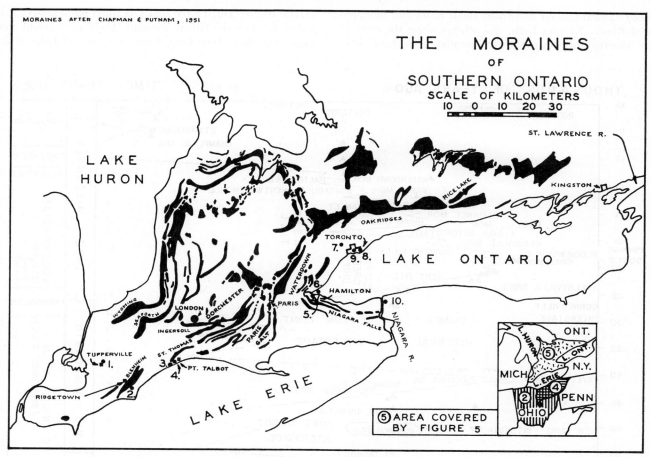

Figure 5. Map of end moraines of southern Ontario, after Chapman and Putnam (1951), showing sites (numbered) from which radiocarbon dates have been obtained. Dates marked by stars represent values younger than the latest glacial deposits in the area.

1. 11,860 ± 170 (GSC-211)*
   12,000 ± 200 (S-172)*

2. 12,660 ± 440 (S-25)*

3. 24,600 ± 1,600 (L-2178)
   27,250 ± 150 (Gro-2625)
   27,500 ± 1,200 (W-177)
   28,200 ± 1,500 (L-185-B)

4. 44,200 ± 1,500 (Gro-2580)
   44,900 ± 1,000 (Gro-2619)
   47,000 ± 2,500 (Gro-2570)
   47,500 ± 2,500 (Gro-2601)

5. 11,510 ± 240 (Y-691)*

6. 10,150 ± 450 (TB-50)*

7. > 49,700 (GSC-203)

8. > 40,000 (L-522-B)
   > 52,000 (Gro-2555)

9. > 46,000 (L-409)

10. 12,080 ± 300 (W-883)*
    12,660 ± 400 (W-861)*

Note: Gro is earlier symbol for GrN.

this area, are found at elevations so low (285 m) as to suggest temporary opening of an outlet across Michigan. Several small end moraines were formed by the retreating Erie Lobe east of London; for instance, the Dorchester Moraine is built of silty Catfish Creek Till.

The Erie Lobe readvanced the last time more than 100 km, meeting the advancing Huron Lobe in the area southwest of London. Overriding of the clays and silts of the pre-existing lake phase resulted in formation of a silty clay till, the Port Stanley Till, which forms the top of the Lake Erie bluffs. This uppermost till is rich in clay, so it correlates well with Hiram Till in Ohio. As now traced in Ohio, the ice spread 110 km south to Powell Moraine.

Further retreat of the Erie Lobe produced many end moraines (Fig. 6) of Port Stanley Till, most notably Ingersoll and Blenheim Moraines, St. Thomas Moraine (which was contemporaneous with the lowest Lake Maumee shore at 275-280 m), and Tillsonburg Moraine (Chapman and Putnam, 1951).

After a pronounced retreat of the Erie Lobe, a glacial readvance built the Paris and Galt Moraines (Karrow, 1963). They contain the sandy Wentworth Till, except where finer-grained lacustrine sediments have been incorporated. In part these could correspond to the very youngest (Ashtabula) till, which is also more sandy and occurs only along the lake shore in Ohio. The Wentworth Till can be traced eastward as far as various small water-laid moraines (Waterdown, Niagara Falls, and others) along the crest of the Niagara escarpment; these moraines consist of silty-

clayey Halton Till. To the east this till is more sandy; it is called the Leaside Till at Toronto. These escarpment moraines may have been built during the time of Lake Whit-

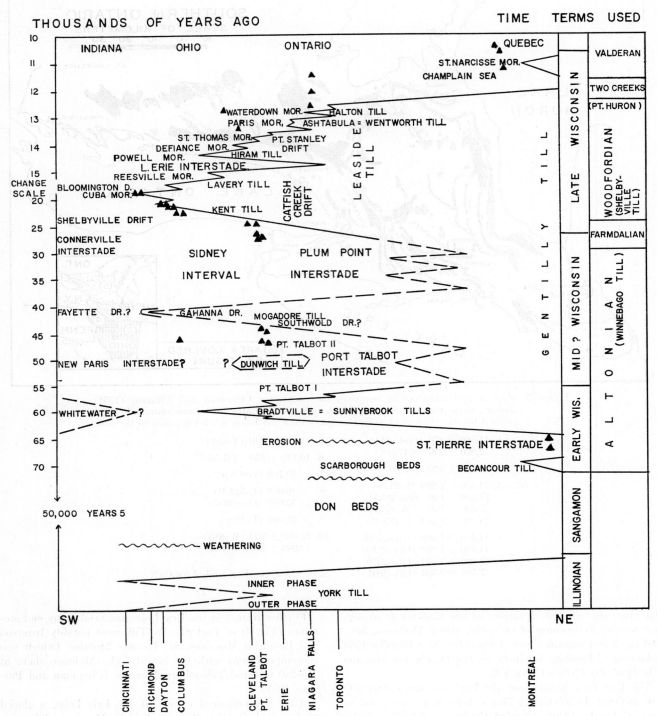

Figure 6. Diagrammatic stratigraphy of Pleistocene deposits in the Ontario and Erie Basins. The horizontal scale represents a southwest-northeast line from the Ohio-Indiana line (left) to the St. Lawrence Valley (right). The vertical scale represents time, from Illinoian (bottom) to Recent (top), and the jagged line represents the coming and going of the ice edge, which originates to the right (northeast). Radiocarbon dates are plotted as triangles. Figure 5 gives detail of dates and their locations in southern Ontario.

tlesey 13,000 years ago, since Whittlesey beaches are found along drumlins that are in front of them, with wood dated as 12,660 ± 440 years B.P. (S-25).

LATE-GLACIAL LAKES

Unlike the horizontal strandlines of Ohio, the beaches north of the lakes are tilted; the hinge lines run through Lake Erie. The Whittlesey beaches are tilted from 270 m above sea level west of London to more than 300 m west of Hamilton, Ontario, a distance of 120 km. The Lake Arkona and Lake Whittlesey beaches are sporadic in southwestern Ontario, as stagnant ice still prevailed in many areas during their formation.

During the retreat from the Niagara escarpment, a lower outlet westward formed Lake Warren in the Erie, Huron, and probably also western Ontario basins. Old shores are tilted from 221 m to 290 m. Organic beach sediments at Tupperville, slightly younger than the Lake Warren clays, are dated as 12,000 ± 200 (S-172) and 11,860 ± 170 (CSC-211) years old (Dreimanis, 1964). Further retreat of the Ontario Lobe opened the Mohawk outlet to Hudson River, causing gradual lowering of lake level to below the Niagara escarpment and initiating the formation of Niagara Gorge and Lake Iroquois in the Ontario basin. Glacial ice still blocked drainage east toward the St. Lawrence Valley (Karrow *et al.*, 1961). Several radiocarbon dates averaging 12,000 years B.P. are available from the Lake Iroquois beach (at Hamilton, Ontario, and at Lewiston, New York, 12,660 ± 400, W-861; 12,080 ± 300, W-883; 11,510 ± 240, Y-691, years B.P.).

Further ice retreat opened the St. Lawrence Valley, and Lake Iroquois was drained about 11,000 years ago. Because of isostatic depression of land in the St. Lawrence Valley, water level in the Ontario basin dropped to 70 m or more below the present level of Lake Ontario (10,150 ± 450 years B.P., TB-50). Whether the lake level was above the sea level of that time is still uncertain. Gradual postglacial uplift of the outlet near Kingston, Ontario, has dammed Lake Ontario up to its present elevation (80 m).

REFERENCES

Chapman, L. J., and Putnam, D. F., 1951, The physiography of southern Ontario: Toronto, Univ. Toronto Press, 284 p.

Coleman, A. P., 1941, The last million years: Toronto, Univ. Toronto Press, 216 p.

Delong, R. M., and White, G. W., 1963, Glacial geology of Stark County: Ohio Geol. Surv. Bull. 61, 209 p.

DeVries, Hessel, and Dreimanis, Aleksis, 1960, Finite radiocarbon dates of the Port Talbot interstadial deposits in southern Ontario: Science, v. 131, p. 1738-1739

Dreimanis, Aleksis, 1958, Wisconsin stratigraphy at Port Talbot on the north shore of Lake Erie, Ontario: Ohio J. Sci., v. 58, p. 65-84

—— 1960, Pre-classical Wisconsin in the eastern portion of the Great Lakes region, North America: Intern. Geol. Congr., 21st sess. Norden, 1960, Rep., Pt. 4, p. 108-119

—— 1961, Tills of southern Ontario, *in* Soils in Canada: Roy. Soc. Can. Spec. Publ. 3, p. 80-96

—— 1963, New test drillings in lower Wisconsin deposits at Port Talbot, Ontario. Geol. Soc. Amer. Spec. Pap. 76, p. 51

—— 1964, Lake Warren and the Two Creeks interval: J. Geol., v. 72, p. 247-250

Durrell, R. H., 1961, The Pleistocene Geology of the Cincinnati area: Geol. Soc. Amer. Guidebook, Cincinnati Meetings, p. 47-57

Flint, R. F., and Brandtner, Friedrich, 1961, Climatic changes since the last interglacial: Amer. J. Sci., v. 259, p. 321-328

Forsyth, Jane L., 1957, "Early" Wisconsin drift in Ohio (abst.): Geol. Soc. Amer. Bull., v. 68, p. 1728

—— 1961a, Dating Ohio's glaciers: Ohio Div. Geol. Surv. Inf. Circ. 30, 9 p.

—— 1961b, Wisconsin glacial deposits: Geol. Soc. Amer. Guidebook, Cincinnati Meetings, p. 58-61

—— 1961c, Pleistocene geology, *in* Root, S. I., Rodriquez, Joaquin, and Forsyth, J. L., Geology of Knox County: Ohio Div. Geol. Surv. Bull. 59, p. 107-138

—— 1962, Glacial geology, *in* Wolfe, E. W., Forsyth, J. L., and Dove, G. D., Geology of Fairfield County: Ohio Div. Geol. Surv. Bull. 60, p. 116-149

—— 1963, A brief summary of Ohio's Pleistocene glacial geology, *in* Stratigraphy of the Silurian rocks in western Ohio: Michigan Basin Geol. Soc. Ann. Field Excursion Guidebook, p. 68-71

—— in press, Contribution of soils to the mapping and interpretation of Wisconsin tills in western Ohio: Ohio J. Sci.

Forsyth, Jane L., and LaRocque, J. A. A., 1956, Age of the buried soil at Sidney, Ohio (abst.): Geol. Soc. Amer. Bull., v. 67, p. 1696

Forsyth, Jane L., and Bowman, R. S., 1963, Geology of the Highland-Adams County area: Ohio Acad. Sci. Field Guide, 30 p.

Frye, J. C., and Willman, H. B., 1960, Classification of the Wisconsinan stage in the Lake Michigan glacial lobe: Illinois Geol. Surv. Circ. 285, 16 p.

Goldthwait, R. P., 1958, Wisconsin age forests in western Ohio. I, Age and glacial events: Ohio J. Sci., v. 58, p. 209-219

—— 1959a, Scenes in Ohio during the last Ice Age: Ohio J. Sci., v. 59, p. 193-216

—— 1959b, Leached, clay-enriched zones in post-Sangamonian drift in southwestern Ohio and southeastern Indiana; a reply: Geol. Soc. Amer. Bull. 70, p. 927-928

Goldthwait, R. P., White, G. W., and Forsyth, Jane L., 1961, Glacial map of Ohio: U.S. Geol. Surv. Misc. Geol. Inv. Map I-316

Goldthwait, R. P., and Forsyth, Jane L., 1962, unpublished field guide for the Midwestern Friends of the Pleistocene

Gooding, A. M., 1963, Illinoian and Wisconsin glaciation in the Whitewater drainage basin, southeastern Indiana, and adjacent areas: J. Geol., v. 71, p. 665-682

Gooding, A. M., Thorp, James, and Gamble, Erling, 1959, Leached, clay-enriched zones in post-Sangamonian drift in southwestern Ohio and southeastern Indiana: Geol. Soc. Amer. Bull., v. 70, p. 921-925

Hough, J. L., 1963, The prehistoric Great Lakes of North America: Amer. Scientist, v. 51, p. 84-109

Jones, R. L., 1959, Outwash terraces along Licking River, Ohio: Ohio State Univ. M.Sc. thesis, 94 p.

Karrow, P. F., 1962, Preliminary report on the Pleistocene geology of the Scarborough area: Ontario Dept. Mines Prel. Rep. 1962-1, 7 p.

—— 1963, Pleistocene geology of the Hamilton-Galt area: Ontario Dept. Mines Geol. Rep. 16, 68 p.

Karrow, P. F., Clarke, J. R., and Terasmae, Jaan, 1961, The age of Lake Iroquois and Lake Ontario: J. Geol., v. 69, p. 659-667

Kempton, J. P., and Goldthwait, R. P., 1959, Glacial outwash terraces of the Hocking and Scioto River Valleys, Ohio: Ohio J. Sci., v. 59, p. 135-151

LaRocque, J. A. A., and Forsyth, Jane L., 1957, Pleistocene molluscan faunules of the Sidney cut, Shelby County, Ohio: Ohio J. Sci., v. 57, p. 81-89

Leonard, A. B., 1953, Molluscan faunules in Wisconsinan loess at Cleveland, Ohio: Amer. J. Sci., v. 251, p. 369-376

Leverett, Frank, 1902, Glacial formations and drainage features of the Erie and Ohio basins: U.S. Geol. Surv. Monogr. 41, 802 p.

Ruhe, R. V., Rubin, Meyer, and Scholtes, W. H., 1957, Late Pleistocene radiocarbon chronology in Iowa: Amer. J. Sci., v. 255, p. 671-689

Shepps, V. C., White, G. W., Droste, J. E., and Sitler, R. F., 1959, Glacial geology of northwestern Pennsylvania: Pennsylvania Geol. Surv. Bull. G-32, 59 p.

Terasmae, Jaan, 1960, A palynological study of Pleistocene interglacial beds at Toronto, Ontario: Geol. Surv. Canada Bull. 56, p. 23-41

Totten, S. M., 1962, Glacial geology of Richland County, Ohio: Univ. Illinois Ph.D. thesis, 136 p.

Watt, A. K., 1954, Correlation of the Pleistocene geology as seen in the subway (Toronto) with that of the Toronto region, Canada: Geol. Assoc. Canada Proc. 1953, v. 6, p. 69-81

Wayne, W. J., 1958, Early Pleistocene sediments in Indiana: J. Geol., v. 66, p. 8-15

White, G. W., 1951, Illinoian and Wisconsin drift of the southern part of the Grand River lobe in eastern Ohio: Geol. Soc. Amer. Bull., v. 62, p. 967-977

—— 1953a, Sangamon soil and early Wisconsin loesses at Cleveland, Ohio: Amer. J. Sci., v. 251, p. 362-368

—— 1953b, Geology and water-bearing characteristics of the unconsolidated deposits of Cuyahoga County, *in* Winslow, J. D., White, G. W., and Webber, E. E., The water resources of Cuyahoga County, Ohio: Ohio Dept. Nat. Resources Div. Water Bull. 26, p. 36-41

—— 1960, Classification of Wisconsin glacial deposits in northeastern Ohio: U.S. Geol. Surv. Bull. 1121-A, 12 p.

—— 1961, Classification of glacial deposits in the Killbuck Lobe, northeast-central Ohio: U.S. Geol. Surv. Prof. Pap. 424-C, p. 71-73

—— 1962, Multiple tills of end moraines: U.S. Geol. Surv. Prof. Pap. 450-C, p. 96-98

Summary

Pre-Illinoian drift occurs at the surface only in southwestern Ohio and northern Kentucky, where very deeply weathered till, believed to be Kansan, is restricted to uplands. Less deeply weathered Illinoian till, together with associated gravel deposits (kames, eskers, and crevasse fillings) is present on uplands and in valleys in a wide belt along most of the glacial boundary throughout Ohio and western Pennsylvania.

"Early" Wisconsin drift is recognized in all areas. In southwestern Ohio, it is identified by a narrow belt of till characterized by significantly deeper soils, a terrace intermediate in elevation and in soil development between "Late" Wisconsin and Illinoian, and a wide distribution of buried soils. In southeastern Indiana, two post-Sangamon tills with infinite dates appear to be of this age. In northeastern Ohio, an older more sandy till is thought to be "Early" Wisconsin. In southern Ontario, two tills, known by radiocarbon dates to antedate "Late" Wisconsin, are recognized.

"Late" Wisconsin drift mantles most of the area. Some local areas of ice-contact gravel (kames, eskers) occur. Extensive terraces of both Wisconsin and Illinoian age are locally present, both within and beyond the glacial boundary; several different levels are distinguished by both elevation and soils.

Southwestern Ohio	*Northeastern Ohio*	*Southern Ontario*
12,000		12,000
	Ashtabula Till	Wentworth Till
till with Morley soil	Hiram Till	Port Stanley Till
till with Miami 6A soil	Hayesville-Lavery Tills	Catfish Creek Till
till with Miami 60–Russell soils	Navarre–Kent Tills	Catfish Creek Till
18-23,000	25,000	27,000
major retreat	major retreat	major retreat
		Southwold Till—44,000
46,000		47,000
Gahanna Drift	Millbrook–Mogadore Tills	Dunwich Till
		major retreat
		Bradtville Till

Most of the Wisconsin drift, however, is till. Subdivisions of the till are based on soils and moraines in western Ohio; physical characteristics, stratigraphy, and soils in northeastern Ohio; and physical characteristics, stratigraphy, and radiocarbon dates in southern Ontario. The main units represented, both "Early" and "Late" Wisconsin, are listed (p. 96), with generalized radiocarbon dates, according to a very tentative intraregional correlation.

Subsequent retreat of the glacier produced, in the basins of Lake Erie and Ontario, a series of lake levels, recorded by beaches, with varying directions of overflow. These beaches are horizontal in Ohio but are tilted farther northeast, mainly as a result of late Pleistocene upwarping.

QUATERNARY GEOLOGY OF NEW YORK*

ERNEST H. MULLER[1]

GEOGRAPHICALLY AND historically New York plays a focal role in investigations of the Quaternary of glaciated eastern United States.

Geographically, New York occupies a central position for the correlation of fragmental interpretations in disjunct areas of New England with the well-formulated glacial chronology of the mid-continent. On the western border, New York's moraine and proglacial-lake successions are closely tied to those of adjacent Pennsylvania and Ohio. On Long Island, the glacial sequence is like that of coastal Rhode Island, Massachusetts, and the offshore islands. Western New England and northeastern New York share the moderate to high topographic relief that has frustrated establishment of a continuous glacial chronology. Problems of correlation between these dissimilar areas focus in New York where glaciated plateau, coastal plain, and rugged upland occur in close proximity.

Historically, New York glacial deposits and topographic features have stimulated speculation and scientific interest since early colonial days. When the first sparks of the new Glacial Theory struck in North America in 1843, district geologists of New York survey adhered initially to the accepted theory of iceberg-rafting in explanation of surficial deposits and features. As early as 1843, however, Chester Dewey, principal of the Collegiate Institute of Rochester (later the University of Rochester) interpreted polished and scratched rock of the Lockport cuesta near Rochester (Fig. 1) as having been produced by glacial scour.

More than a thousand published papers and graduate theses deal with problems of the New York Quaternary geology (Muller, in press). A large proportion of the published papers are descriptive; many deal with minutiae, and some of the more comprehensive studies are now outdated. Nevertheless, New York Quaternary investigations have been influential in the conflict of opposing viewpoints by which important concepts of glacial geology have developed. New York's contribution to glacial geology has been primarily determined by its geomorphology and subordinately by vogues in physiographic research. Lake basins early provided a measure of the effectiveness of glacial erosion. Viewpoints ranged from those of the "sandpaperers" to those of the "gougers," who considered the basins of the Great Lakes to be products primarily of glacial scour. When skirmishing in this continuing debate shifted to the origin of the Finger Lake basins, the effectiveness of channeled glacial scour was quickly demonstrated (Lincoln, 1892,

1894; Tarr, 1894, 1904, 1906). Similarly, other features well exemplified within the state led to investigations that contributed to concepts of drumlin formation, isostatic adjustment, ice-sheet stagnation, physiographic analysis of multiple erosion surfaces, and growth of local centers of Alpine glaciation after ice-sheet recession.

PHYSIOGRAPHY

A brief consideration of physiographic relationships provides a frame of reference for the discussion of Quaternary geology to follow. Boundaries between physiographic provinces as proposed by various authorities are basically similar (Lobeck, 1921; Fenneman, 1930; Cressey, 1941), but the specific nomenclature used herein is that of Cressey as employed in the recently published "Geologic Map of New York" (Broughton et al., 1962).

Most of New York is characterized by topography developed on essentially undeformed sediments of Ordovician, Silurian, and Devonian age. With regional dip generally less than a degree, the strata occupy a broad, gently synclinal basin, sloping southward from neighboring crystalline terranes of the Canadian Shield and the Adirondack dome, and westward from the belt of folded Paleozoic rocks in eastern New York. Progressively older strata are exposed toward the borders of this basin. Dissimilar erosional resistance of these beds accounts for crudely cuesta-form topography of the northern margin of the plateau (Lobeck, 1927; Hanefeld, 1960; von Engeln, 1961). Physiographic units of this undeformed platform are the Appalachian and Tug Hill Uplands and the Erie-Ontario Lowland.

The Appalachian Upland includes all of the southern half of New York except for the eastern strip that is structurally more complex. Principal drainage lines in the southern part of the Appalachian Upland trend dominantly southwestward and flow into the Delaware, Susquehanna, and Allegheny systems, from southeast to southwest respectively. The northern portion of the plateau lies in the drainage basin of the St. Lawrence River, with much of its southern drainage divide determined by the Valley Heads Moraine (Fairchild, 1932b). Southward penetration into the plateau by headwaters of the northward-draining obsequent streams is limited. Most such streams are short with steep gradients and small drainage basins, but the Genesee River and Cattaraugus Creek drain significant areas south of the Valley Heads Moraine. Clayton (in press) has recently suggested that southward-decreasing intensity of effects of glaciation provides a basis for physiographic subdivision of this part of the Appalachian Upland. Glacial modification of the dissected plateau is most intense along its north margin and seems focused near the northern ends of Cayuga and

* Published by permission of the Assistant Commissioner, New York State Museum and Science Service.

[1] Department of Geology, Syracuse University, Syracuse, New York.

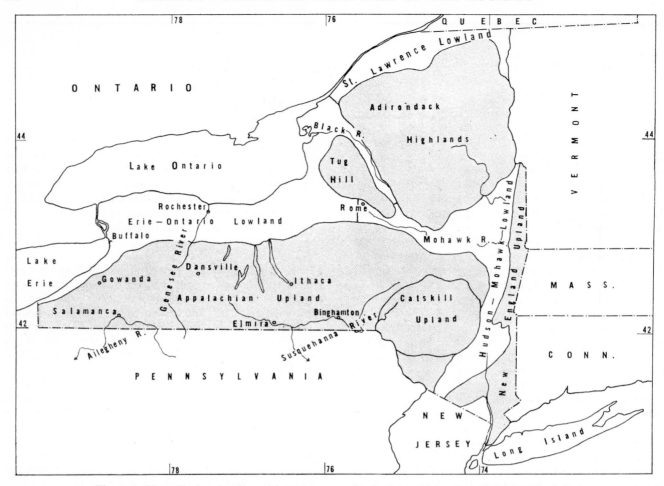

Figure 1. New York, showing cities, rivers, and physiographic units. Uplands stippled; lowlands plain.

Seneca Lakes and in the Genesee basin. Southward the intensity of glaciation decreases toward the state line, though scoured uplands and a network of troughs ("through valleys") distinguish the glaciated from the unglaciated parts of the plateau. In spite of glacial erosion, summits in southwestern New York show marked accordance, widely lying in the range of elevations between 550 and 750 m above sea level.

A semicircular area of the Appalachian Upland south of the Allegheny River in southwestern New York bears no evidence of glaciation. This area otherwise continuous with and similar to the adjacent upland to the north, is the Salamanca re-entrant, the northernmost unglaciated area in the region between the Mississippi River and the Atlantic Ocean.

Coarse clastic sedimentary rocks of Devonian age, partly terrestrial, comprise the complex "Catskill delta" in the eastern third of the Appalachian Upland. The massive nature and erosional resistance of these rocks account for the topographic relief of the Catskills, culminating in the 1,281-m summit of Slide Mountain. As the product of dissection of uplifted but undeformed strata, this area is properly characterized as plateau. Nevertheless, accordant summit remnants are widely spaced, and the eastern front of

the upland is so bold and striking that in the popular mind, at least, the summits are not plateau remnants but the Catskill Mountains.

The Tug Hill Upland is a plateau remnant isolated from the closely related Appalachian Upland by the Mohawk Lowlands, and from the adjacent Adirondack Highlands by the Black River Valley. With strata dipping regionally southwest from the Adirondack massif, Tug Hill owes its prominence primarily to erosional resistance of the Ordovician Oswego sandstone. Lacking significant through valleys, this upland contains some of the most extensive wilderness areas in New York. Summit accordance at 550 to 600 m has been correlated with physiographic history of the Appalachian Upland (Newell, 1940), but the cuesta-form character of the Tug Hill, as stressed recently by Hanefeld (1960), lays such correlation open to question.

The Erie-Ontario Lowland differs from the previously discussed uplands only because of the erosional susceptibility of its underlying bedrock. Developed largely on carbonate and fine clastic sediments, this area is almost entirely below 250 m above sea level. Its cuesta-form nature is particularly evident in the west, where the Niagara and Onondaga scarps are separated by broad lowlands developed on Salina shales. Glacial modification of the lowland has been intense.

As a consequence the topography is strongly drumlinized. A southerly projection at the northeastern end of this belt is the Black River Valley, which separates Tug Hill from the Adirondack Highlands.

The Hudson-Mohawk Lowlands owe their existence to the erosional susceptibility of a thick section of Ordovician shale. The east-trending limb of this physiographic unit is developed on southward-dipping strata bordering the Adirondack dome to the north. Although relatively unfolded, this section has been involved in marginal Adirondack faulting transverse to the lowland. The south-trending limb, occupied by the Hudson River, is more complex in structure, being developed in the intensively folded zone between the Catskills and the New England Uplands.

The lowland rim that flanks the Adirondacks extends north from the Hudson Lowlands along the New York–Vermont border. North and northeast of the Adirondacks it is the St. Lawrence–Champlain Lowland, developed on Cambrian and Ordovician sandstone and carbonate strata that dip generally away from the massif. Summits are generally below 300 m, and areas nearest to the levels of the St. Lawrence River and Lake Champlain contain marine sediments recording the late-glacial invasion by the Champlain Sea.

The Adirondack Highlands comprise a belt of structurally complex crystalline rocks. Initially mapped as dominantly igneous, they are now recognized as exposing limited areas of plutonic and basement rocks unroofed in the cores of complexly deformed metasedimentary structures. The highest point in New York, Mt. Marcy, with summit elevation of 1,630 m, is in an area of erosionally resistant anorthosite in the east-central Adirondacks. Glacial drift, coarse and crudely stratified, partly fills most valleys, accounting for numerous lakes, swamps, and deranged drainage. The Adirondack Highlands served as a cleaver that split the waning continental ice sheet into flanking lobes while the highest peaks generated local glaciers and supported persistent ice fields.

The New England Upland includes an elongate belt along the eastern border of the state; it is characterized by complex folding, faulting, and metamorphism. The Taconic Mountains in the northern part of this border zone possess marked north-south grain, representing the trend of alternate schist ridges and marble valleys. Southward the province splits into two limbs. Rocks of the New York City Group underlie low rounded knobs and ridges in a belt that extends south to Manhattan. The more westerly limb, composing the Hudson Highlands, trends obliquely across the Hudson River and into northwestern New Jersey. At the Hudson Gorge, local relief on the bedrock surface is about 750 m, ranging from 250 m below to 500 m above sea level.

Two small physiographic units are limited to the southeastern part of the state. One of these, the Triassic Lowland, occupies a down-faulted basin between the Hudson Highlands and the area of exposure of the New York City Group. Rocks of this area are dominantly red sandstone and shale, but the topographically conspicuous units are diabase sills. One such injected body comprises the scenic Palisades of the Hudson. The second small physiographic unit in southeastern New York is the Atlantic Coastal Lowland, which includes Long Island and part of Staten Island. Consisting largely of glacial and fluvioglacial deposits associated with the Harbor Hill and Ronkonkoma Moraines, this province nevertheless owes its existence to a low and largely concealed swell of coastal-plain sediments.

PREGLACIAL CONDITIONS

Pliocene physiographic relationships presumably differed little from those of today. Physiographic boundaries were unchanged by glaciation. Present uplands were dissected plateaus at the onset of glaciation; the lowlands of today were lowland provinces in the Pliocene, and the Adirondack Highlands have been dominant and persistent positive features throughout much of geologic time.

In details of present landscapes, however, the imprint of glaciation is dominant. In the Salamanca re-entrant, and in the glaciated southern counties, glacial processes failed to efface the record of preglacial landforms. In those areas, a measure of total change during the Pleistocene may be assayed, and the character of pre-Pleistocene landscapes may be inferred. Northward, however, the mark of glaciation is all-masking. The nature of the pre-Pleistocene landscape, as well as the measure of Pleistocene erosion, becomes conjectural and controversial in the Erie-Ontario Lowland.

EROSION LEVELS

The Appalachian Plateaus have been a classic area for the interpretation of erosion surfaces ever since Davis (1889) first assumed Cretaceous base-leveling and Tertiary and Quaternary erosion cycles in explanation of accordance of summits at several levels (Bryan *et al.*, 1933).

Tarr (1902) referred upland summit accordance in southern New York to the Cretaceous peneplain previously recognized by Davis (1891). In the first detailed physiographic analysis of the New York and Pennsylvania plateau, Campbell (1903) generalized contours on summits related to an intermediate erosion surface. Correlating them with the Harrisburg peneplain of early Tertiary age, he recognized a dome centered on the western border of Potter County, Pennsylvania, near the New York border. He attributed this to domal upwarping, an hypothesis not supported by subsequent investigators. Campbell concluded that because glaciation had not altered the erosion surface "in its essential characteristics . . . we may safely compare the surface features here shown with those of other regions."

Subsequent investigators concurred in distinguishing multiple erosion surfaces and relating them to successive cycles of uplift and erosion, while differing as to details of correlation (Glenn, 1903; Fuller and Alden, 1903a, b; Butts, 1910; Fridley, 1929; Ver Steeg, 1930). Commencing in northeastern Ohio and adjacent Pennsylvania, Cole (1934, 1935, 1937, 1938, 1941) employed projected profiles in quadrangle-by-quadrangle correlation of summit levels into New York. He recognized the Upland peneplain (Table 1) and the Allegheny erosion surface as being represented by accordant summits, with straths at lower elevations. He recognized the tendency of the surface of summit accordance to slope toward ancestral trunk streams. Although Cole noted the relationship of structure to elevation of the summit surface, he failed to acknowledge the measure of

TABLE 1

Equivalence of Erosion Surfaces in New York. After Cole, 1938

Campbell, 1903	Fridley, 1929	Ver Steeg, 1930	Cole, 1938
Schooley	Kittatinny	Schooley (Kittatinny)	Upland
Harrisburg	Schooley	Harrisburg	Allegheny

denudation implied. He tacitly inferred that summit erosion had taken place by normal processes, and his only reference to glaciation was as a suggested basis for dating incipient erosion surfaces identified in glacially scoured lowlands. Later studies applied similar interpretations in correlation of summit accordance in the Tug Hill Plateau (Newell, 1940) and to recognition of erosion surfaces in the Adirondacks (Crowl, 1950).

In adjacent Pennsylvania, Ashley (1935) concluded that although the present surface of summit accordance may indeed reflect a former peneplain, it has been reduced in level by varying amounts according to erosional resistance of the rocks involved. He further assaulted the practice then current of identifying multiple summit levels with multiple erosion cycles by stressing the youthfulness and changeableness of even such stable landscape features as accordant summits. In similar tenor, Denny (1956a) concluded that, although this part of the Appalachian Plateau may have been peneplaned one or more times, the existing plateau tops are not the remnants of such ancient surfaces but have been reduced in elevation. In the Finger Lakes region, von Engeln (1961) cites the synclinal nature of Connecticut Hill southwest of Ithaca as confirmatory evidence of the peneplain origin of summit accordance. Connecticut Hill, at 639 m the highest point in the vicinity, is one of several ridges on the axis of this open syncline. The ridges average 30 to 60 m higher than adjacent summits. Such subtle reverse correspondence of topography of the upland surface to structure is suggestive of an advanced stage in the responsible cycle of erosion.

Correlation of erosion levels from unglaciated to glaciated parts of the Appalachian Plateau is justified only if the imprint of glaciation in summit reduction is light. Cole's projected profiles and generalized summit contours show both the validity of such conclusion in southern New York and its decreasing appropriateness northward. The difference between actual summit elevations and those of the extrapolated hypothetical upland surface affords a measure of summit reduction ascribable to glaciation (Muller, 1963b). Although intensity of summit reduction increases northward, differences in exposure to major glacier flow account for marked variation in erosive effectiveness at any given distance north of the drift border. Summits as far as 80 km north of the limit of glaciation in certain cases can have been reduced by no more than 50 m. At the same time, summits within a few kilometers of the drift border have been measurably affected by glacial scour. Summits near the center of an upland area experienced less reduction than those at the margin of such an area. Summits in line of flow, as at the bend or end of a trunk trough, were subject to particularly intensive reduction and modification,

DRAINAGE

The pattern and distribution of present major streams reflects a dominating inheritance from drainage systems developed prior to glaciation. Pre-Pleistocene trunk streams, like those of today, drained the axes of the major lowland provinces. Elements of the preglacial drainage pattern that no longer exist as such are suggested by drift-filled trunk valleys, barbed tributaries, valleys that narrow downstream, and valley reaches that bear anomalous relationship to the streams that occupy them.

Hypothetical reconstruction of preglacial drainage patterns have been proposed by Chamberlin and Leverett (1894), Spencer (1881), Grabau (1908), Fairchild (1925), and Broughton *et al.* (1962). All concur in inferring the existence of trunk streams in present major lowlands, with ancestral Erigan and Ontarian Rivers flowing along the axes of the Erie and Ontario basins, respectively. A consensus among these studies suggests westward drainage from the Precambrian Frontenac and Little Falls Arches, which served as divides between eastward- and westward-draining basins. The evidence, however, is by no means conclusive, nor is the opinion unanimous. Although the drift-filled Dundas Valley, west of Hamilton, Ontario, has been suggested as a relic of outflow from the Ontario basin, its gradient is presently eastward. From 120 m below sea level at the inlet to Hamilton Harbor, it rises westward toward the Niagara escarpment, with the aspect of a drift-filled preglacial or interglacial outlet of the eastward-discharging Grand River (Karrow, 1963). Inasmuch as glacial scour is particularly effective in erosion of lowlands aligned parallel to major ice flow, and the Erie and Ontario basins owe their breadth and depth largely to glacial erosion, it is unlikely that recognizable remnants of the hypothesized valley of the Ontarian River still exist. Its course of outflow from the present Ontario Basin must remain undetermined. Indeed, the low altitude of the northeastward threshold across the Frontenac Arch in the St. Lawrence Valley is far less impressive than the continuous barrier of the Niagara escarpment on the west.

South-bank tributaries of the Ancestral Erigan and Ontarian Rivers penetrated the north margin of the Appalachian Upland, enlarging their basins by progressive piracy. Major changes in location of the divide between northward and southward drainage occurred as a result of Pleistocene glaciation. In southwestern New York, for instance, streams now tributary to the Ohio by way of the Allegheny River, prior to glaciation drained north through the Conewango trough into the Erie Basin (Carll, 1880; Leverett, 1902; Muller, 1963a). The course of this Ancestral Allegheny River is marked by progressive decrease in elevation of the bedrock floor from about 300 m near Salamanca to about 75 m above sea level at Gowanda (Muller, 1960). The preglacial valley is sharply incised at the north margin of the plateau near Gowanda, but 10 km southwest of Gowanda the valley is filled with more than 300 m of drift, the greatest depth to bedrock yet reported in New York west of the Finger Lakes. Virtually the entire drainage basin of the Ancestral Allegheny River, comparable in size to that of the present Genesee River, was diverted from northward to southward escape as a result of glaciation, and the present Allegheny River was pieced together by the linking of several disjunct valley reaches into a single stream peripheral to the ice sheet.

In central New York the Genesee River, the only stream that presently flows from Pennsylvania north across New York, underwent less extensive derangement from the trunk troughs that presumably represent its ancestral course. A major east-bank tributary of the Ancestral Genesee has been inferred by Fairchild (1926) to have flowed southwest from the trough of present Canandaigua Lake, curving west past Dansville, thence northwest to the Genesee.

The marked alignment of Seneca trough and the Chemung River led Fairchild (1925, 1934) to hypothesize the existence of a preglacial "Susqueseneca" River, which carried the drainage of all New York portions of the present Susquehanna basin north to Lake Ontario. Valley fill more than 365 m thick near Watkins Glen (Fairchild, 1934) indicates that the bedrock profile slopes northward toward Seneca Lake, but it does not in itself substantiate existence of the hypothesized "Susqueseneca" River. The rock floors of Seneca, Cayuga, and Onondaga troughs (Kantrowitz, 1964) have been eroded below sea level. By the same token, the northward gradient from the Susquehanna to the Seneca basin may be controlled by intensive scour by ice flowing out of the Seneca trough. In opposition to Fairchild's hypothesis, von Engeln (1961) cites the divergence of valley walls and opposed angles of juncture of tributary valleys north and south of a line a few kilometers from the southern end of Seneca Lake as evidence that the preglacial divide corresponded closely to that of the present. In similar vein, Durham (1958) argued that the preglacial divide in Onondaga Valley south of Syracuse controlled the location of the Valley Heads Moraine, which comprises the present watershed boundary. Durham suggests, but does not demonstrate, that such relationship of Valley Heads Moraine to preglacial divide may also be present in other through troughs of central New York.

The angular relationship between components of the Delaware and Susquehanna drainage systems in the western Catskills has tempted yet frustrated satisfactory explanation (Coates, 1963). Whereas Ruedemann (1932) visualized the Delaware as aggressively capturing headwaters of the Susquehanna, Mackin (1933) deemed the Susquehanna the aggressor in progressive piracy of Delaware headwaters. Neither author cites glacial derangement as a possible cause of such changes, apparently considering them to have taken place in Tertiary time.

Although a trunk stream is assumed to have drained the Hudson trench and parts of the Mohawk and Champlain troughs, only in the lower course of the Hudson can remnants of preglacial channels be established. The gorge through the Highlands at West Point is such a remnant, subjected to intensive modification where ice-flow was channeled between opposing ridges. Test-drilling for the Catskill Aqueduct showed the bedrock trough to be more than 230 m deep and fiord-like in its characteristics (Edwards, 1892; Berkey, 1911, 1933; Berkey and Rice, 1921; Kemp, 1912). Seismic and bore-hole data for construction of the New York Thruway crossing of Tappan Zee about

24 km south of the Highlands shows maximum depth to bedrock to be 225 m (Worzel and Drake, 1959), though seaward the bedrock profile rises as the intensity of former glacial scour diminishes (Berkey, 1948). The Hackensack Meadows, west of New York City in New Jersey, are underlain by a bedrock basin conjectured to have originated as the valley of the preglacial Hudson River. If such was its origin, glacial derangement may have shifted the Hudson to its present structurally controlled course along the contact between Triassic and Precambrian rocks.

PALEOSOL

Glacial scour and periglacial slope processes were such that virtually all New York soils are of late Wisconsin or more recent derivation. Only in narrow transverse valleys cut deeply enough to escape intense glacial scour might preglacial paleosol be preserved. One such location is presently exposed midway between Lake George and Warrensburg in the southeastern Adirondacks. Roadcuts expose 9 m of saprolith developed in Grenville gneiss beneath two fluvioglacial boulder-gravel units, each of which is likewise marked by distinct weathering profile. The preglacial saprolith is loose enough to be crumbled between one's fingers in the upper part of the profile. The base of the exposed section consists of relatively coherent joint-block cores exposed in limonitic rotten rock. Although the biotite gneiss in which this paleosol is developed may be subject to rapid disintegration (Minard, 1959) under suitable groundwater conditions, and although inferred fault control of the transverse valley may have favored such a groundwater environment, the juxtaposition of unweathered pre-Wisconsin boulder gravel over such thick saprolith strongly indicates its origin as Tertiary paleosol.

LIMIT OF GLACIATION

The southern limit of glaciation enters New York in two areas. The one extends the length of Long Island and crosses Staten Island. The other borders the Salamanca reentrant on the Pennsylvania State Line in western New York.

LONG ISLAND

Long Island owes its physiographic character to deposition of glacial drift on an eroded core of coastal-plain sediments. Maximum elevation on the island is about 125 m where a belt of moraine topography crosses West Hill, but the glacial deposits comprise only the top 20 to 30 m, superposed on an eroded, drift-concealed Cretaceous rise.

Stratigraphic relationships of the nonglacial deposits with units of the unglaciated coastal belt are considered elsewhere in this volume in the chapter on the Atlantic Coastal Plain. The following brief discussion relates primarily to the stratigraphic record of multiple glaciation and the principal topographic features of Wisconsin glaciation.

The sequence of glaciation of Long Island was inferred by Fuller (1914) to commence with deposition of the Manetto Gravel (Table 2), which he interpreted as being of fluvioglacial origin because of its content of relatively abundant granite pebbles and occasional boulders as much as 0.6 m in maximum dimension. The overlying Jameco

TABLE 2

Correlation of Pleistocene Formations of Long Island (after Donner, 1964)

Stage	Fuller, 1914	Fleming, 1935	MacClintock and Richards, 1936	Donner, 1964
Wisconsin	Harbor Hill Moraine Ronkonkoma Moraine	Harbor Hill Moraine Ronkonkoma Moraine	Harbor Hill Moraine Ronkonkoma Moraine	Harbor Hill Moraine Ronkonkoma Moraine
		Hempstead Gravel	Manhasset Formation	Manhasset Fm. { Hempstead Gravel Montauk Till Herod Gravel
		Montauk Till		
		Herod Gravel		
Sangamon	Vineyard erosion surface		Jacob Sand Gardiners Clay	Gardiners Fm. { Jacob Sand Gardiners Clay
Illinoian	Hempstead Gravel } Manhasset Montauk Till } Fm. Herod Gravel }			
Yarmouth	Jacob Sand Gardiners Clay	Jacob Sand Gardiners Clay	Gardiners Clay (in part)	
Kansan	Jameco Gravel			
Pre-Kansan	Manetto Gravel			

Gravel he likewise considered to be of early Pleistocene fluvioglacial origin, bounded both beneath and above by erosional unconformity. The Manhasset Formation, including both fluvioglacial (Herod and Hempstead Gravels) and glacial (Montauk Till) units, Fuller considered to be of pre-Wisconsin age on the basis of an inferred erosion interval. The magnitude of this hiatus has subsequently been questioned. Fuller (1914, p. 134) described "contemporaneous erosion" such that the Montauk Till showed an unconformable upper contact even though the normal stratigraphic sequence was not interrupted. Fleming (1935) discounted the interval of weathering between the Montauk and younger tills. MacClintock and Richards (1936) similarly questioned the validity of distinguishing the Montauk Till as a unit separate from the younger tills. Donner (1964) follows MacClintock and Richards in assigning the Gardiners Clay to the Sangamon Interglacial, but he affirms Fuller's (1937) differentiation of Montauk from younger tills (Table 2). Age greater than 38,000 years is indicated by radiocarbon analyses of dated materials included in or lying beneath the Manhasset Formation (Rubin and Alexander, 1960).

Two clearly defined moraines are the most conspicuous features of Long Island physiography. The Ronkonkoma Moraine extends from Lake Success in the west, where it emerges from beneath the later Harbor Hill Moraine, to the South Fluke at the east end of whale-shaped Long Island. In places the moraine is topographically prominent, but elsewhere, particularly in the middle of the island, the moraine consists of depressed, irregular topography bordered by southward-sloping outwash plain. The extensive fluvioglacial deposits south of the moraine obscure underlying materials, making it impossible precisely to define the limit of glaciation.

The Harbor Hill Moraine, which lies close along the north coast of Long Island, is more bouldery and consists of a series of coalescing kame or outwash fans. The two till sheets are not generally exposed in the same bluff. West of Lake Success, the Harbor Hill Moraine overrides and conceals the Ronkonkoma Moraine, whereas eastward the two diverge slightly. It is as though the minor climatic change that initiated the waning hemicycle of the main Wisconsin glaciation produced dissimilar response in maritime and continental portions of the ice margin.

SALAMANCA RE-ENTRANT

In southwestern New York the drift margin is marked by a major northward re-entrant bordered approximately by the course of the Allegheny River where it flows northwest to Salamanca, thence recurves southwest toward Warren, Pennsylvania. This triangular area of New York escaped glaciation partly because of its elevation, with summit accordance approaching 730 m above sea level. The unglaciated re-entrant owes its existence partly to its location between glacier lobes from the Ontario and Erie basins. Known from the work of Lewis (1884), Chamberlin (1883), and Leverett (1902, 1934), the drift border has more recently been studied in detail by MacClintock and Apfel (1944) and Bryant (1955).

Although no direct evidence of pre-Illinoian glaciation is recognized in the Salamanca re-entrant, its existence may be inferred from relationships of subsequent deposits. Prior to glaciation, the Ancestral Allegheny flowed northwest to the Erie Basin, its headwater divides being essentially at the level of accordant summits. Pre-Illinoian and early Illinoian ice extended far enough south across New York to impound the Ancestral Allegheny, diverting its flow southward across the lowest available cols. The col at Kinzua southwest of

Salamanca was thus reduced by about 215 m, essentially to its present level, before deposition of the earliest preserved glacial materials in the Salamanca re-entrant.

MacClintock and Apfel (1944) mapped terrace remnants at 35 to 55 m above the Allegheny River as Illinoian. Although poorly exposed, these terraces appear to include outwash, kame terrace, and deltaic and perhaps morainal materials. The alignment of meltwater-drainage notches and the distribution of terrace remnants indicate that ice tongues extended across the Allegheny River both southwest of Salamanca and west of Olean (Bryant, 1955; Muller, 1960). Attenuated drift found locally beyond the Wisconsin end moraine may in some cases relate to pre-Wisconsin glaciation (Shepps *et al.*, 1959; Muller, 1963a).

EARLY WISCONSIN

The possibility that drift-border features of the Salamanca re-entrant may relate not to the Illinoian Stage but to a pre-Farmdale Wisconsin glaciation is suggested by stratigraphic evidence exposed by the South Branch of Cattaraugus Creek near Otto, 22.5 km north-northwest of Salamanca. Drab gravels composed dominantly of local sandstone crop out beneath a thick and badly slumped section of glacial and lacustrine sediments (Table 3). Near the base of the bluff are interbedded gravel, sand, and organic zones that were initially interpreted as representing the Sangamon Stage (MacClintock and Apfel, 1944). Recent review of paleobotanical and glacial evidence (Muller, 1964a) suggests that the organic horizons relate to an intraglacial rather than to a major interglacial interval. A finite age of 63,900 ± 1,700 years (GRN-3213) for the main organic unit justifies tentative correlation with peat and wood of the St. Pierre and Pierreville exposures in Quebec (Terasmae, 1958; Gadd, 1960; Flint, 1963), dated respectively at 65,300 ± 1,400 years (GRN-1799) and 67,000 ± 1,000 years (GRO-1711) (J. C. Vogel, personal communication). The Otto organic zone is thus older than strata exposed in the Plum Point and Port Talbot sections in Ontario (Dreimanis, 1958, 1960, 1964), but may correspond with interglacial sediments in the subsurface at these Ontario exposures and with beds exposed in banks of Clear Creek near Gowanda (Muller, 1960). At Gowanda, as at all other sites in central New York for which radiocarbon analysis has been made on plant remains below the youngest till, the indicated age is beyond 38,000 years, the approximate range of routine radiocarbon dating.

WISCONSIN GLACIATION

CRITERIA FOR CORRELATION

Consistent stratigraphic relationships and continuous tracing of moraines are the most widely reliable criteria for correlation of glacial deposits. Both are particularly difficult to apply in areas of moderate to high relief such as the Appalachian Uplands. Glacial deposits of the Erie-Ontario Lowland were laid down in proglacial lakes, resulting in subdued topographic expression of moraines that might otherwise be readily followed. These factors have frustrated effective tracing of moraines and correlation from one valley to the next.

Textural criteria for distinguishing till sheets, effectively applied by Shepps (1953, 1958) in adjacent Ohio and Pennsylvania, have been used with variable success in New York. In westernmost New York, Muller (1956, 1963a) distinguished isolated patches of clay till in stratigraphic position comparable to that of the texturally similar Hiram till of northeastern Ohio (White, 1960). Shumaker (1957), relying on textural criteria, mapped the assimilation of interglacial sediments from a transverse valley into basal load of the ice sheet as reflected in the resulting lodgment till. Street (1963) recognized a gradual rise in silt with increase in crystalline and carbonate erratic grains in a traverse at right angles away from the Genesee Valley. Moss and Ritter (1962) found little overlap of fields occupied by Valley Heads and Olean drift as plotted on a sand-silt-clay triangular diagram. They (p. 100) recognized the Valley Heads till to be locally higher in clay content where the ice was

TABLE 3

Composite Section Exposed in Streambank,
South Branch of Cattaraugus Creek near Otto

Unit	(Top of section)	Approximate thickness in meters
10	Stratified sand, silt and clay	0.9 m
9b	Till, calcareous, gray-brown with silty-clay matrix; pebbly with "bright" lithology; silt streaks; unleached but oxidized	6.1 m
9a	Till, as above, but unoxidized	3.0 m
8	Stratified sand, silt and clay; sparsely pebbly	0.9 m
7	Till, calcareous, gray with sandy-silt matrix; sparsely to moderately pebbly; includes pockets and streaks of washed drift	12.2 m
6	Pebble gravel, calcareous, decreasingly coarse at base	1.5 m
5	Rhythmically laminated silt and clay, calcareous, deformed	1.5 m
4	Gravel, coarse with angular to sub-rounded pebbles and cobbles of sandstone and siltstone; essentially noncalcareous. Contains fine sand 0.2 m thick about 2.5 m below top. This marker grades northeast into organic silt dated at more than 52,000 years (GRO-2565)[a]	6.1 m
3	Sand, silt, pebbly silt, muck, and peat, interbedded. Includes boulder-gravel lens near north end of exposure. Contains several organic zones. Top of main zone is dated at 63,900 ± 1,700 years (GRN-3213)[a]	2.1 m
2	Gravel, cobble-size with lag concentration of boulders 0.5 m across just above contact with underlying bedrock. May thicken northwest where base is concealed	1.1 m
1	"Till, blue-gray, weathered, rich in igneous stones" (MacClintock and Apfel, 1944). This unit is no longer exposed as such	1.1 m
0	Bedrock: blue-gray siltstone of Machias Formation	

[a] Groningen Laboratory dates are identified by GRN where ages have been corrected for the Suess effect; earlier analyses are identified by GRO preceding the serial number of the analysis.

inferred to have advanced over lake sediments. The Olean till south of Binghamton was found to be abnormally sandy as a result of uptake of alluvial material from the Susquehanna valley. Because similar terrane traversed by the ice in widely separated areas may account for textural similarity, this alone is not an adequate criterion for correlation. Nor is the validity of a correlation based on textural criteria to be strengthened by reference to pedologic or other similarities that are themselves texturally controlled.

Compositional criteria are more specific in relating till components to source terrane than are textural criteria. Pebble counts and heavy-mineral analyses are two types of compositional study commonly employed. Pebble counts are convenient, easily made, and record a parameter that responds sensitively to change in subglacial terrane. Preliminary investigation suggests that increased consistency of data obtained by using volume or weight percentages rather than simple numerical count commonly does not justify the extra effort involved. Pebble counts have been variously made by grab sampling in fluvioglacial gravel and by individually digging out every pebble and cobble within a specified band or area of exposure (Denny and Postel, 1964). Such counts have been used to substantiate dissimilarity of contrasting drifts (MacClintock and Apfel, 1944), to measure drift dispersion, attrition, and progressive change in till constitution (Holmes, 1952; Moss and Ritter, 1962; Denny and Lyford, 1963), and to infer the extension of unmapped contacts or unknown flow lines (Kaiser, 1962). The east-west disposition of sedimentary contacts normal to the flow of ice into the Appalachian Uplands is more favorable for studying variation patterns of drift constituents than for distinguishing dissimilar tills.

Heavy-mineral analyses by contrast to pebble studies are more time-consuming, but they measure parameters that are commonly more representative. Heavy minerals in New York tills are almost entirely exotic, being derived from outside of the sedimentary terrane. Quantities of heavy minerals in the Paleozoic sediments of the Appalachian Upland are too small to affect total heavy-mineral content significantly. Furthermore, they are of mineral species that are uncommon in the tills (Connally, 1964). Recent heavy-mineral studies have provided data for interpreting broadly dissimilar ice-flow directions and distinguishing between the resulting tills (Dreimanis, 1960; Lewis, 1960; Connally, 1964) and for inferences as to direction of ice-flow (Wingard, 1962) and age of moraines (Connally, 1960). Further work is necessary before the pattern of heavy-mineral distribution will be adequately defined to permit unequivocal interpretation.

Criteria indicative of ice-flow direction, but independent of source terrane, are occasionally useful in mapping in New York. Continuity of flow lines suggested by long axes of streamline ridges in Chautauqua County indicates little change in flow direction during recession from the terminal moraine to the plateau margin (Muller, 1963a). A minor contrast in orientation of long axes of ridges in Allegany and Cattaraugus Counties characterizes the tentatively inferred Kent border. In the St. Lawrence Lowlands particular stress has been laid on directional criteria in distinguishing between Malone till deposited by ice flowing from the northeast and Fort Covington till deposited from the northwest (MacClintock, 1954b, 1958; MacClintock and Stewart, 1963). MacClintock and Dreimanis (1964) describe evidence indicating that reorientation of till fabric may take place as much as 10.5 m beneath the sole of an overriding ice sheet.

Pedologic differences between soils developed under similar conditions of climate, vegetation, exposure, and parent material may commonly be ascribed to difference in age. Unfortunately the range of ages among soils in New York is inadequate for significant profile differences attributable to age differences alone. Development of the deeper weathering profile takes place more rapidly than solum development. As a result, depth of leaching has been proposed as a more sensitive age-dependent criterion for distinguishing between drifts. First applied in distinguishing between drifts bordering the Salamanca re-entrant (MacClintock and Apfel, 1944), this criterion was subsequently used in reconnaissance eastward across the state (MacClintock, 1954a). Pedologists questioned whether factors other than age difference were adequately taken into account. Merritt and Muller (1959) in the Finger Lake region found depth of leaching to be a function primarily of original carbonate content rather than of age difference.

Perceptive interpretation of combinations of textural, compositional, directional, pedologic, and geomorphic criteria, as derived from detailed quadrangle-by-quadrangle mapping, should ultimately make possible the correlation of stratigraphic units and the tracing of moraines from one valley to the next. For the present, the reconnaissance nature of most mapping in New York and the lack of objectivity in relying on one or another type of criterion alone have resulted in such differences of interpretation as are candidly illustrated by Denny (1956b, p. 84).

OLEAN SUBSTAGE

MacClintock and Apfel (1944) recognized two drifts bordering the Salamanca re-entrant. They distinguished drift with low lime content, deep leaching of carbonates, and modified constructional topography from drift with relatively high lime content, shallower leaching of carbonates, and unmodified constructional topography. The former drift they mapped at the Wisconsin terminal moraine from Little Valley eastward, naming it the Olean drift for its major development where an ice tongue extended south across the Allegheny Valley near the city of Olean.

Although the terminal moraine is commonly inconspicuous, the limit of glaciation can be confidently delineated on the basis of the presence or absence of occasional erratic cobbles. Valley-marginal kames and loop moraines are subdued and modified by frost-abetted slope processes. Stone nets, block streams, and rock cities are developed in many places, but no features that require the former existence of permafrost have been reported. Uplands are mantled with such thin drift and such sparse erratic material that they appear at first glance to have escaped glaciation. In extensive areas the weathering profile penetrates the drift mantle and into the underlying rubbly plateau rock. Calcareous material is virtually absent except in valley-bottom deposits.

The Olean Moraine is considered approximately correlative with the Ronkonkoma and Harbor Hill Moraines of Long Island. Present mapping is inadequate to demonstrate exact relationships by continuous tracing; nor has radiocarbon dating served yet to define the time equivalence of the Olean with either the Ronkonkoma or Harbor Hill Moraines. The Olean drift has been variously correlated with the Iowan or Tazewell substage of the Wisconsin (MacClintock and Apfel, 1944), the Iowan-Tazewell complex (Flint, 1953), the Tazewell (MacClintock, 1954a) and the "pre-Bradyan Wisconsin" (Denny, 1956a). Although all agree on pre-Cary Wisconsin age, existing data are not such as to rule out the possibility of pre-Farmdale age for part of the Olean drift (Dreimanis, 1960; Denny and Lyford, 1963).

KENT (BINGHAMTON) SUBSTAGE

At the Wisconsin terminal moraine west of the Salamanca re-entrant, MacClintock and Apfel (1944) mapped a drift younger than the Olean. East of Little Valley this moraine lies well north of the drift border. In eastward reconnaissance they spotted locations that defined a border between deeply leached Olean drift to the south and kame gravels characterized by "head-high" leaching, significant proportions of carbonate and crystalline pebbles, and relatively unmodified constructional topography on the north. In this manner they tentatively related the drift west of the Salamanca re-entrant to kame gravels near Binghamton, assigning them the name Binghamton drift. The equivalence of the Binghamton Moraine of MacClintock and Apfel to the Kent Moraine of White (1960) has been confirmed by continuous tracing (Shepps et al., 1959; Muller, 1960, 1963a). Eastward as far as the Genesee Valley, an ice-margin alignment has been traced, primarily on the basis of topographic features and moraine deposits. This border corresponds roughly with the lithologically determined boundary recognized by MacClintock and Apfel. In the Genesee Valley little basis exists for choosing between several associations of ice-marginal features that comprise a series of moraine fragments without clear evidence of major break between any adjoining pair.

Denny (1956b) and Denny and Lyford (1963) deny the existence of Binghamton till in the Elmira area, thereby casting doubt on the validity of the correlation of tills on opposite sides of the Elmira area that were supposedly related to each other by continuous tracing. They suggest that the Binghamton border may be overridden and masked by younger deposits north of Elmira. Connally (1961) traces a drift border from the massive kames near Almond and Alfred eastward toward the Valley Heads Moraine near Bath. This moraine he calls the Almond Moraine, recognizing it as a probable equivalent of the Kent Moraine in western New York.

The "Binghamton problem" thus arises from differences of interpretation of a lithologic change as evidence of an event during glacier recession. In the contrast between drift characteristics northeast and northwest of the Salamanca re-entrant, respectively, MacClintock and Apfel (1944, p. 1162) recognized evidence of a "notable withdrawal, rearrangement and readvance of ice lobes" sufficient to "constitute an important demarcation within the Wisconsin".

To subsequent investigators the lithologic changes have generally appeared transitional except where locally telescoped as a result of topographic controls (Holmes, 1952; Denny and Lyford, 1963). Upland drift of "Olean lithology" is closely associated with and even surrounded by valley-filling drift of "Binghamton lithology" south of the Valley Heads border in central New York (Williams et al., 1909; Merritt and Muller, 1959; Moss and Ritter, 1962) in a manner that makes it impossible to draw a dynamically creditable glacier border between the two.

Several factors independent of glacier fluctuation and minor variation in ice-flow direction help to account for the contrast between drab, rubbly, lime-deficient upland till and adjacent lowland till rich in exotic constituents derived from through valleys that open at the north margin of the plateau. Because regional dip is gently southward, outcrop belts swing abruptly toward the plateau where they cross major through valleys. The result is significantly shorter transport for exotic constituents derived from through-valley exposures than for those from exposures at the north margin of adjacent upland. Channeling of basal ice-flow by underlying topography presumably served to intensify southward transport in through valleys, whereas ice overriding the uplands was both relieved of exotic load by shearing over stagnant basal ice and given fresh debris derived from scour of exposed upland surfaces. Denny (1956b) suggested uptake of previously deposited fluvioglacial material as one source of enrichment of exotic constituents in lowland till. Moss and Ritter (1962) contrasted the bright, carbonate-rich gravels of through valleys with the drab, lime-deficient gravel of valleys that originate against upland divides. Where erosion and continued uptake cease, the coarse component of basal load of a glacier undergoes progressive enrichment in the rock types most resistant to attrition. Such enrichment takes place whether transportation occurs in a single episode, in multiple episodes of glaciation, or in alternate episodes of glacial and fluvioglacial transportation. Thus southward penetration by resistant crystalline and quartzitic cobbles and by tough though softer carbonate cobbles is at a maximum in valleys and at a minimum over uplands.

Lithologic implications now inseparable from the name Binghamton drift, together with the uncertainty of correlation of till near Binghamton with that west of Elmira, make it undesirable to retain the name Binghamton in a morphostratigraphic or time-stratigraphic sense. Accordingly, the names Kent Till, Kent Moraine, and Kent Glaciation have recently been adopted from adjacent Ohio and Pennsylvania for use in New York (Muller, 1963a). East of the Genesee River the Almond Moraine is tentatively considered to be correlative. Among locally recognized recessional moraines are the Clymer and Findley Moraines in Chautauqua County and the Arkport Moraine (Connally, 1961) in northwestern Steuben County. It must remain for future mapping northwest of the Catskills to establish whether the extensive kame areas in valleys tributary to the Susquehanna are related to Kent Glaciation.

Internally consistent dates on marl and basal peat from the Corry bog in Pennsylvania near the southwestern corner of New York indicate that the ice sheet had abandoned the Kent terminal moraine more than 14,000 years ago (Droste *et al.*, 1959). This dating is in accord with accepted correlation of the Kent with early Cary (Shepps *et al.*, 1959) and the Binghamton with Cary age (Flint, 1953; MacClintock, 1954a).

VALLEY HEADS SUBSTAGE

Across much of western New York, a single moraine forms the divide between drainage northward into the St. Lawrence River and southward into the Allegheny, Susquehanna, and Delaware Rivers. Briefly described by Chamberlin (1883) and mapped in local detail south of the Seneca and Cayuga basins by Tarr (1905), this moraine was without formal name until Fairchild's (1932b) introduction of the term Valley Heads Moraine. In western New York, Leverett first applied the name Dayton Moraine to one element of the moraine complex where the north margin of the Appalachian Plateau faces the Erie lake plain. Subsequently recognizing the complexity of this moraine belt, he supplanted the name Dayton Moraine with the more inclusive term Lake Escarpment Moraines. Westward divergence of the moraines into Pennsylvania and Ohio made possible the distinguishing of Euclid, Painesville, Ashtabula, and Girard Moraines, as members of the morainic system that are too tightly grouped to allow for separate mapping in New York. Shepps *et al.* (1959) and White (1960) use the name Ashtabula Moraine in a sense synonymous with Leverett's Lake Escarpment Moraines, rather than as a single member of this complex. The long-assumed equivalence of Lake Escarpment and Valley Heads Moraines is confirmed by recent mapping.

In Chautauqua County, as well as in adjacent Pennsylvania (Muller, 1963a; Shepps *et al.*, 1959), minor moraine ridges lie essentially parallel to but south of the Lake Escarpment Moraines. Shepps (1955) applied the name Lavery Moraine to the outermost of these. Characterized by light-gray moderately pebbly silty till, it is leached to average depth of about 1.2 m and comprises a narrow but rather continuous belt of low ridges and swells.

In several troughs in Chautauqua County, isolated tongues of sparsely pebbly calcareous gray clay till to silty clay till extend south from beneath the massive Lake Escarpment Moraine. While tentatively correlating the isolated patches of clay till in Chautauqua County with till of similar character mapped in Ohio as Hiram till and closely bordered by the Defiance Moraine (White, 1960), Muller (1963a) noted that the related properties are texturally controlled. Such till properties may well be produced by assimilation of either abundant shale or lacustrine clay into the basal load of different ice sheets at very different times and places. To the extent that the properties are derived from assimilation of proglacial lake sediments, such clay till is more apt to characterize a moraine of glacial advance than one of the waning glacial hemicycle.

Shepps *et al.* (1959) interpreted the Lavery Moraine as being of Middle Cary age and the Defiance Moraine as distinct from the Lake Escarpment complex of moraines. Present evidence in western New York suggests that all three may be closely associated in age. Close parallelism of the three moraines and the existence of kettle lakes in Lake Escarpment outwash suggest that retreat from one position may have been closely followed by development of the succeeding moraine without major time lapse between any two members of the series. In central and western New York south of the Ontario basin, a similar rhythm of glacier oscillation is suggested by the Valley Heads array. In many valleys, as notably the Tully Valley south of Syracuse, the moraine succession from south to north includes one or more relatively inconspicuous ice-border positions followed by the massive divide-forming ridge and several minor ridges so closely related as to be best mapped at the present time merely as an end-moraine complex. Causes of the massive nature of the main valley-blocking loops were investigated by von Engeln (1938). Although the Valley Heads Moraine has been commonly assumed to mark a significant readvance, the magnitudes of the preceding recession and advance to the Valley Heads position have not been demonstrated.

The Adirondack Mountains, which had been earlier overtopped by the continental ice sheet, were by this time probably sources of local glaciers (Kemp, 1898; Ogilvie, 1902; Johnson, 1917; Alling, 1921). The continental ice sheet was divided and deflected around the Adirondacks, initially coalescing south of the mountains. During Valley Heads time, however, the Oneida-Black River lobe on the west became separated from the Mohawk-Champlain lobe on the east, impounding Lake Herkimer between them (Fairchild, 1912). It is perhaps in this area of sensitive response of the ice border that the measure of pre-Valley Heads recession and advance can best be sought.

Radiocarbon dates on organic material from sediments deposited after Valley Heads recession (Table 4) indicate that more than 12,000 years ago the ice sheet had already begun its withdrawal from the massive Valley Heads Moraine. The particular dates listed are considered to postdate the Valley Heads maximum closely and are consistent with correlation of the Valley Heads with the Port Huron Substage. C. D. Holmes (personal communication) has recently suggested that some of the unexpectedly young dates for basal material in postglacial bog profiles may be

TABLE 4

Radiocarbon Dates Relating to Valley Heads Recession

Spec.	Location	Material	Date
W-507	Cherry Tavern, Erie County	Wood over outwash	$12,020 \pm 300$
W-861	Lewiston, Niagara County	Wood in lake silt	$12,600 \pm 400$
W-883	Lewiston, Niagara County	Same as W-861	$12,080 \pm 300$
Y-460	King Ferry, Cayuga County	Wood in shallow kettle	$11,410 \pm 410$

accounted for by persistence of snowfields and stagnant ice in sheltered depressions long after glacier recession had taken place. This is, however, only one of several possible explanations and is not yet supported by independent evidence.

Recession from the Valley Heads border is marked in western New York by a series of marginal positions, the Gowanda, Hamburg, Marilla, and Alden Moraines of Leverett (1902), which record minor oscillations during a time of general recession. In the Erie Basin, shore features of Lakes Whittlesey and Warren are well developed and provide a basis for correlation with moraines in western Ontario and Michigan (Leverett and Taylor, 1915; Leverett, 1939; Taylor, 1939).

In each northward-opening valley south of the Ontario basin, withdrawal of the ice margin resulted in ponding of proglacial meltwaters, the "primitive lakes" of Fairchild's writings. Progressive uncovering of lower outlets resulted in a succession of lake levels, joining the separate troughs (Fairchild, 1932a; Hough, 1958, 1963). Southward outflow from Lake Newberry gave way in turn to westward drainage of Lake Warren and later eastward drainage by way of the Mohawk and Hudson Valleys. Hanging deltas such as those splendidly displayed in the Cayuga trough are the clearest demonstration of such former lake levels. Strand features such as those identified by Chisnell (1951) near Ithaca are very weakly developed in plateau basins. The absence of more obvious record of the former lake history in the form of extensive bottom deposits and well-marked strand features undoubtedly results in part from the unsuitability of slopes for development and preservation of such features, the protection from dominant winds afforded by the depth and orientation of the major troughs, and the brevity of each lake stage. Analogies between ice-bordered lakes of central New York and recently studied self-draining lakes of Alaska are suggested by Sissons' (1960) identification of subglacial as well as marginal drainage channels along the north-facing scarp of the plateau between Syracuse and Rome. Increasing evidence supports the conclusion that the larger channels, such as those south of Syracuse, are products of several episodes of meltwater erosion, recording multiple glacial advances and the oscillatory nature of the ice border (Muller, 1964b).

Lake Iroquois came into existence upon recession of ice from the divide between the Oneida and Mohawk basins. Well-marked strand features of Lake Iroquois, followed for many miles by "Ridge Road," U.S. Highway 104, afford excellent demonstration of postglacial isostatic rebound as they rise eastward from about 115 m at the Niagara River to about 137 m above sea level near Rome, and more steeply northward where the strand was developed along the receding ice border. With uncovering of Covey Hill on the northward salient of the Adirondack Mountains across the International Boundary (MacClintock and Terasmae, 1960), the Rome outlet of Lake Iroquois was abandoned.

Present knowledge of events that followed in the late-glacial history of New York is intimately tied to information developing in current investigations in adjacent Quebec. At the 1963 field conference of the Eastern Friends of the Pleistocene near Riviere-du-Loup, 195 km northeast of

Quebec, H. A. Lee demonstrated relationships of the St. Antonin Moraine to invading marine waters of the Champlain Sea (Lee, 1962a, b). Subsequent investigations by Gadd (1964) led to tracing of the St. Antonin Moraine southwestward as the "Highland Front Morainic System" to the vicinity of Granby in 1963. Work in progress by Gadd and MacDonald at the time of this writing may establish the relationships of the "Highland Front Morainic System" to features under study by C. S. Denny in the northeastern part of the Adirondacks, and to the Malone and Fort Covington Moraines of MacClintock and Stewart (1963) with their presumed equivalents in Vermont. Gadd (1964) now considers that the age of the "Highland Front Morainic System" is strongly established as more than 11,500 years on the basis of Champlain Sea dates. If so, recession from the Highland Front in Quebec and from the Adirondack flanks and the Appalachian Upland in western New York may have occurred within a brief interval, and withdrawal from all three was complete before the end of the Two Creeks Interstadial.

REFERENCES

Alling, H. L., 1921, Glacial geology of the Mt. Marcy Quadrangle, N.Y.: New York State Mus. Bull. 229-230, p. 62-84

Antevs, Ernst, 1928, The last glaciation, with special reference to the ice retreat in northeastern North America: Amer. Geol. Soc. Res. Ser. 17, 292 p.

Ashley, G. H., 1935, Studies in Appalachian Mountain sculpture: Geol. Soc. Amer. Bull., v. 46, p. 1395-1436

Berkey, C. P., 1911, Geology of the New York City Aqueduct: New York State Mus. Bull. 146, 283 p.

—— 1933, New York City and vicinity: 16th Intern. Geol. Congr., Guidebook 9, p. 77-122

—— 1948, Engineering geology in and near New York: Geol. Soc. Amer., 61st Ann. Meeting, Guidebook of Excursions, p. 51-66

Berkey, C. P., and Rice, Marion, 1921, Geology of the West Point Quadrangle, N.Y.: New York State Mus. Bull. 225-226, 152 p.

Broughton, J. G., Fisher, D. W., Isachsen, Y. W., Rickard, L. V., and Offield, T. W., 1962, Geologic map of New York: New York State Mus. Map and Chart Ser. No. 5

Bryan, Kirk, Cleaves, A. B., and Smith, H. T. U., 1933, The present status of the Appalachian problem: Z. Geomorph., v. 7, p. 312-320

Bryant, J. C., 1955, A refinement of the upland glacial drift border in southern Cattaraugus County, New York: Cornell Univ. M.S. thesis, 127 p.

Butts, Charles, 1910, Warren Folio: U.S. Geol. Surv. Geol. Atlas, Folio 172, 11 p.

Campbell, M. R., 1903, Geographic development of northern Pennsylvania and southern New York: Geol. Soc. Amer. Bull., v. 14, p. 277-296

Carll, J. F., 1880, A discussion of the pre-glacial and post-glacial drainage in northwestern Pennsylvania and southwestern New York: 2d Geol. Surv. Pennsylvania, Rep. 3, p. 1-10, 330-397

Chamberlin, T. C., 1883, Terminal moraine of the second glacial epoch: U.S. Geol. Surv., Ann. Rep. 3, p. 291-402

Chamberlin, T. C., and Leverett, Frank, 1894, Further studies of the drainage features of the upper Ohio basin: Amer. J. Sci., v. 47, p. 247-283

Chisnell, T. C., 1951, Recognition and interpretation of pro-glacial strand lines in the Cayuga basin, Cornell Univ. Ph.D. thesis, 64 p.

Clayton, Keith, in press, Glacial erosion in the Finger Lake region: Z. Geomorph. (submitted for publ.)

Coates, D. R., 1963, General geology of south-central New York: New York State Geol. Assoc., 35th Ann. Meeting, Guidebook, Harpur College, p. 19-49

Cole, W. S., 1934, Identification of erosion surfaces in eastern and southern Ohio: J. Geol., v. 42, p. 285-294

—— 1935, Rock resistance and peneplain expression: J. Geol., v. 43, p. 1049-1062

—— 1937, Development and structural control of erosion surfaces: J. Geol., v. 45, p. 141-157

—— 1938, Erosion surfaces of western and central New York: J. Geol., v. 46, p. 191-206

—— 1941, Nomenclature and correlation of Appalachian erosion surfaces: J. Geol., v. 49, p. 129-148

Connally, G. G., 1960, Heavy minerals in the glacial drift of western New York: Rochester Acad. Sci. Proc., v. 10, p. 241-278

—— 1961, The glacial geology of the western Finger Lakes region, New York. New York State Mus. Prog. Rep. 2, 35 p.

—— 1964, Garnet ratios and provenance in the glacial drift of western New York: Science, v. 144, p. 1452-1453

Cressey, G. B., 1941, Land-form regions of New York State (abst.): Geol. Soc. Amer. Bull., v. 52, p. 1893-1894

Crowl, G. H., 1950, Erosion surfaces of the Adirondacks (abst.): Geol. Soc. Amer. Bull., v. 61, p. 1565

Davis, W. M., 1889, The rivers and valleys of Pennsylvania: Natl. Geog. Soc. Mag., v. 1, p. 183-253

—— 1891, The geological dates of origin of certain topographic forms on the Atlantic slope of the United States: Geol. Soc. Amer. Bull., v. 2, p. 545-586

Denny, C. S., 1956a, Surficial geology and geomorphology of Potter County, Pennsylvania: U.S. Geol. Surv. Prof. Pap. 288, 72 p.

—— 1956b, Wisconsin drifts in the Elmira region, New York, and their possible equivalents in New England: Amer. J. Sci., v. 254, p. 82-95

Denny, C. S., and Lyford, W. H., 1963, Surficial geology and soils of the Elmira-Williamsport region, New York and Pennsylvania: U.S. Geol. Surv. Prof. Pap. 379, 60 p.

Denny, C. S., and Postel, A. W., 1964, Rapid method of estimating lithology of glacial drift of the Adirondack Mountains, New York: U.S. Geol. Surv. Prof. Pap. 501, p. 143-145

Dewey, Chester, 1843a, On the polished rocks of Rochester, N.Y.: Assoc. Amer. Geol. Nat. Rep., p. 264-266

—— 1843b, Striae and furrows of the polished rocks of western New York: Amer. J. Sci., v. 44, p. 146-150

Donner, Joakim, 1964, Pleistocene geology of eastern Long Island, New York: Amer. J. Sci., v. 262, p. 355-376

Dreimanis, Aleksis, 1958, Wisconsin stratigraphy at Port Talbot on the north shore of Lake Erie, Ontario: Ohio J. Sci., v. 58, p. 65-84

—— 1960, Pre-classical Wisconsin in the eastern portion of the Great Lakes region, North America: Intern. Geol. Congr., 21st Ses., Copenhagen, Rep. 4, p. 108-119

—— 1964, Notes on the Pleistocene time-scale in Canada, *in* Osborne, F. F. (ed.), Geochronology in Canada: Toronto, Univ. Toronto Press, p. 139-156

Droste, J. B., Rubin, Meyer, and White, G. W., 1959, Age of marginal Wisconsin drift at Corry, northeastern Pennsylvania: Science, v. 130, p. 1760

Durham, Forrest, 1958, Location of the Valley Heads Moraine near Tully Center, New York, determined by preglacial divide: Geol. Soc. Amer. Bull., v. 69, p. 1319-1321

Edwards, A. M., 1892, Hudson River "fiord": Amer. J. Sci., v. 43, p. 182-183

Engeln, O. D. von, 1938, Large, sharply defined terminal moraine ridges: Intern. Geogr. Union Congr., Amsterdam, 1938, Compt. Rend., v. 2, p. 211-213

—— 1961, The Finger Lakes region: its origin and nature: Ithaca, N.Y., Cornell Univ. Press, 147 p.

Fairchild, H. L., 1912, The glacial waters in the Black and Mohawk valleys: New York State Mus. Bull. 160, 47 p.

—— 1925, The Susquehanna River in New York and evolution of western New York drainage: New York State Mus. Bull. 256, 99 p.

—— 1926, The Dansville Valley and drainage history of western New York: Rochester Acad. Sci. Proc., v. 6, p. 217-242

—— 1932a, Closing stage of New York glacial history: Geol. Soc. Amer. Bull., v. 43, p. 603-626

—— 1932b, New York moraines: Geol. Soc. Amer. Bull., v. 43, p. 627-662

—— 1934, Seneca Valley physiographic and glacial history: Geol. Soc. Amer. Bull., v. 45, p. 1073-1110

Fenneman, N. M. (ed.), 1930, Physical divisions of the United States: U.S. Geol. Surv. map

Fleming, W. L. S., 1935, Glacial geology of central Long Island: Amer. J. Sci., v. 30, p. 216-238

Flint, R. F., 1953, Probable Wisconsin substages and late-Wisconsin events in northeastern United States and southeastern Canada: Geol. Soc. Amer. Bull., v. 64, p. 897-919

—— 1963, Status of the Pleistocene Wisconsin Stage in central North America: Science, v. 139, p. 402-404

Fridley, H. M., 1929, Identification of erosion surfaces in south-central New York: J. Geol., v. 37, p. 113-134

Fuller, M. L., 1914, The geology of Long Island, N.Y.: U.S. Geol. Surv. Prof. Pap. 82, 231 p.

—— 1937, Comment on MacClintock, Paul, and Richards, H. G., 1936, Correlation of late Pleistocene marine and glacial deposits of New Jersey and New York: Geol. Soc. Amer. Bull., v. 47, p. 1982-1994

Fuller, M. L., and Alden, W. C., 1903a, Gaines Folio, Pennsylvania: U.S. Geol. Surv., Geol. Atlas, Folio 92, 9 p.

—— 1903b, Elkland and Tioga Folio, Pennsylvania: U.S. Geol. Surv. Geol. Atlas, Folio 93, 9 p.

Gadd, N. R., 1960, Surficial geology of the Becancour Map-area, Quebec: Geol. Surv. Canada, Pap. 59-8, 34 p.

—— 1964, Moraines in the Appalachian region of Quebec. Geol. Soc. Amer. Bull., v. 75, p. 1249-1254

Glenn, L. C., 1903, Devonic and Carbonic formations of

southwestern New York: New York State Mus. Bull., v. 69, p. 967-989

Grabau, A. W., 1908, Preglacial drainage in central-western New York: Science, n.s., v. 28, p. 527-534

Hanefeld, Horst, 1960, Die Glaziale Umgestaltung der Schichtstufenlandschaft am Nordrand der Alleghenies: Univ. Kiel, Geogr. Inst. Schrift., v. 19, p. 1-183

Holmes, C. D., 1952, Drift dispersion in west-central New York: Geol. Soc. Amer. Bull., v. 63, p. 993-1010

—— 1959, Late glacial ice-margin alignments in western New York (abst.): Geol. Soc. Amer. Bull., v. 70, p. 1619

Hough, J. L., 1958, Geology of the Great Lakes: Urbana, Illinois, Univ. Illinois Press, 313 p.

—— 1963, The prehistoric Great Lakes of North America: Amer. Scientist, v. 51, p. 84-109

Johnson, D. W., 1917, Date of local glaciation in the White, Adirondack and Catskill Mountains: Geol. Soc. Amer. Bull., v. 28, p. 543-553

Kaiser, R. F., 1962, Composition and origin of glacial till, Mexico and Kasoag quadrangles, New York: J. Sed. Petrology, v. 32, p. 502-513

Kantrowitz, I. H., 1964, Bedrock topography in the Oneida Lake area, New York: New York State Geol. Assoc., 36th Ann. Meeting, Guidebook, Syracuse Univ., p. 39-41

Karrow, Paul, 1963, Pleistocene geology of the Hamilton-Galt area: Ontario Dept. Mines Geol. Rep. 16, 68 p.

Kemp, J. F., 1898, Geology of the Lake Placid region: New York State Mus. Bull. 21, p. 49-67

—— 1912, The Storm King crossing of the Hudson River, by the new Catskill Aqueduct of New York City: Amer. J. Sci., v. 34, p. 1-11

Lee, H. A., 1962a, Pleistocene glacial-marine relations, Trois Pistoles, Quebec (abst.): Geol. Soc. Amer. Spec. Pap. 73, p. 195

—— 1962b, Surficial geology of the Riviere-du-Loup–Trois Pistoles area, Quebec: Geol. Surv. Canada Pap. 61-32, 2 p.

Leverett, Frank, 1895, On the correlation of New York moraines with raised beaches of Lake Erie: Amer. J. Sci., v. 50, p. 1-20

—— 1902, Glacial formations and drainage features of the Erie and Ohio basins: U.S. Geol. Surv. Monogr. 41, 802 p.

—— 1934, Glacial deposits outside the Wisconsin terminal moraine in Pennsylvania: Pennsylvania Geol. Surv., 4th ser., Bull. G-7, 123 p.

—— 1939, Correlation of beaches with moraines in the Huron and Erie basins: Amer. J. Sci., v. 237, p. 456-475

Leverett, Frank, and Taylor, F. B., 1915, The Pleistocene of Indiana and Michigan and the history of the Great Lakes: U.S. Geol. Surv. Monogr. 53, 529 p.

Lewis, Douglas, 1960, Heavy mineral content of tills in western New York: Compass, v. 37, p. 163-173

Lewis, H. C., 1884, Report on the terminal moraine in Pennsylvania and western New York: Pennsylvania Geol. Surv., 2nd ser., Bull. Z, 299 p.

Lincoln, D. F., 1892, Glaciation in the Finger Lake region of New York: Amer. J. Sci., v. 44, p. 290-301

—— 1894, The amount of glacial erosion in the Finger Lake region of New York: Amer. J. Sci., v. 47, p. 105-113

Lobeck, A. K., 1921, A physiographic diagram of the United States: Chicago, A. J. Nystrom & Co.

—— 1927, A popular guide to the geology and physiography of Allegany State Park: New York State Mus. Handbook 1, 288 p.

MacClintock, Paul, 1954a, Leaching of Wisconsin glacial gravels in eastern North America: Geol. Soc. Amer. Bull., v. 65, p. 369-383

—— 1954b, Pleistocene geology of the St. Lawrence Lowland—a report of progress: New York State Mus. Sci. Serv. Rep. Inv. 10, 20 p.

—— 1958, Glacial geology of the St. Lawrence seaway and power projects; New York State Mus. Sci. Serv. Rep. Inv., 26 p.

MacClintock, Paul, and Apfel, E. T., 1944, Correlation of the drifts of the Salamanca re-entrant, New York: Geol. Soc. Amer. Bull., v. 55, p. 1143-1164

MacClintock, Paul, and Dreimanis, Aleksis, 1964, Re-orientation of till fabric by overriding glacier in the St. Lawrence Valley: Amer. J. Sci., v. 262, p. 133-142

MacClintock, Paul, and Richards, H. G., 1936, Correlation of late Pleistocene marine and glacial deposits of New Jersey and New York: Geol. Soc. Amer. Bull., v. 47, p. 289-338

MacClintock, Paul, and Stewart, D. P., 1963, Glacial geology of the St. Lawrence Lowlands: New York State Mus. Bull. 394, 152 p.

MacClintock, Paul, and Terasmae, Jaan, 1960, Glacial history of Covey Hill: J. Geol., v. 68, p. 232-241

Mackin, J. H., 1933, The evolution of the Hudson-Delaware-Susquehanna drainage: Amer. J. Sci., v. 26, p. 319-331

Merritt, R. S., and Muller, E. H., 1959, Depth of leaching in relation to carbonate content of till in central New York State: Amer. J. Sci., v. 257, p. 465-480

Minard, J. P., 1959, Recent saprolite: Science, v. 129, p. 1206-1209

Moss, J. H., and Ritter, D. F., 1962, New evidence regarding the Binghamton Substage in the region between the Finger Lakes and Catskills, New York: Amer. J. Sci., v. 260, p. 81-106

Muller, E. H., 1956. Texture as a basis for correlation of till sheets in Chautauqua County, western New York (abst.): Geol. Soc. Amer. Bull., v. 67, p. 1819

—— 1960, Glacial geology of Cattaraugus County, New York: Friends of Pleistocene Geol., 23rd Ann. Meeting, Guidebook, Syracuse Univ., 33 p.

—— 1963a, Geology of Chautauqua County, New York. Part II, Pleistocene Geology: New York State Mus. Bull. 392, 60 p.

—— 1963b, Reduction of periglacial erosion surfaces as a measure of the effectiveness of glacial erosion: Intern. Quat. Assoc. Congr., 6th, Warsaw, Rep., v. 3, p. 233-242

—— 1964a, Quaternary section at Otto, New York: Amer. J. Sci., v. 262, p. 461-478

—— 1964b, Surficial geology of the Syracuse field area: New York State Geol. Assoc., 36th Ann. Meeting Guidebook, Syracuse Univ., p. 25-35

—— in press, Bibliography of New York Quaternary geology: New York State Mus. Bull.

Newell, J. G., 1940, The geomorphic development of the Tug Hill Plateau: Syracuse Univ. M.S. thesis, 104 p.

Ogilvie, Ida H., 1902, Glacial phenomena in the Adirondacks and Champlain Valley: J. Geol., v. 10, p. 397-412

Rubin, Meyer, and Alexander, Corinne, 1960, U.S. Geological Survey radiocarbon dates v: Amer. J. Sci., Radiocarbon Supply., v. 2, p. 129-185

Ruedemann, Rudolf, 1932, Development of drainage of Catskills: Amer. J. Sci., v. 23, p. 337-349

Shepps, V. C., 1953, Correlation of the tills of northeastern Ohio by size analysis: J. Sed. Petrology, v. 23, p. 34-48

—— 1955, The glacial geology of a part of northwestern Pennsylvania: Univ. Illinois Ph.D. thesis, Univ. Microfilms No. 13563, 117 p.

Shepps, V. C., White, G. W., Droste, J. B., and Sitler, R. F., 1959, Glacial geology of northwestern Pennsylvania: Pennsylvania Geol. Surv., 4th ser., Bull. G-32, 59 p.

Shumaker, R. C., 1957, Till texture variation and Pleistocene deposits of the Union Springs and Scipio quadrangles, Cayuga County, New York: Cornell Univ. M.S. thesis, 44 p.

Sissons, J. B., 1960, Subglacial, marginal and other glacial drainage in the Syracuse-Oneida area, New York. Geol. Soc. Amer. Bull., v. 71, p. 1575-1588

Spencer, J. W. W., 1881, Discovery of the pre-glacial outlet of the basin of Lake Erie into that of Lake Ontario: Pennsylvania Geol. Surv., 2nd ser., Rep. Q-4, p. 357-406

Street, J. S., 1963, Significance of variations in till constitution in the Rush Creek area, New York: Syracuse Univ. M.S. thesis, 68 p.

Tarr, R. S., 1894, Lake Cayuga, a rock basin: Amer. Geologist, v. 14, p. 194-195

—— 1902, The physical geography of New York State: New York, Macmillan Co., 397 p.

—— 1904, Hanging valleys in the Finger Lake region of central New York: Amer. Geologist, v. 33, p. 271-291

—— 1905, Moraines of the Seneca and Cayuga Lake valleys: Geol. Soc. Amer. Bull., v. 16, p. 215-228

—— 1906, Glacial erosion in the Finger Lake region of central New York: J. Geol., v. 14, p. 18-21

Taylor, F. B., 1939, Correlatives of the Port Huron morainic system of Michigan in Ontario and western New York: Amer. J. Sci., v. 237, p. 375-388

Terasmae, Jaan, 1958, Non-glacial deposits in the St. Lawrence Lowlands, Quebec: Geol. Surv. Canada Bull., v. 46, p. 13-28

Ver Steeg, Karl, 1930, Some features of Appalachian peneplanes. Erosion surfaces of Appalachian plateaus: Pan-Amer. Geologist, v. 53, p. 359-364; v. 54, p. 17-28

Vries, Hessel de, and Dreimanis, Aleksis, 1960, Finite radiocarbon dates of the Port Talbot interstadial deposits in southern Ontario: Science, v. 131, p. 1738-1739

White, G. W., 1960, Classification of Wisconsin glacial deposits in northeastern Ohio: U.S. Geol. Surv. Bull. 1121-A, 12 p.

Williams, H. S., Tarr, R. S., and Kindle, E. M., 1909, Watkins Glen–Catatonk Folio, New York: U.S. Geol. Surv., Geol. Atlas, Folio 169, 33 p.

Wingard, N. E., 1962, A heavy mineral investigation of glacial tills in western New York: Michigan State Univ. M.S. thesis, 64 p.

Worzel, J. L., and Drake, C. L., 1959, Structure section across the Hudson River at Nyack, N.Y. from seismic observations: New York Acad. Sci. Ann., v. 80, p. 1092-1105

Summary

New York was totally glaciated except for two small areas, the south shore of Long Island and the Salamanca re-entrant, south of the Allegheny River. Unconsolidated materials on Long Island record five glaciations, and by their stratigraphic relationships they afford basis for correlation with strata of the unglaciated Coastal Plain to the south. Comparison of the level of summit accordance in the Salamanca re-entrant with elevations of scoured summits provides a measure of the northward increase in intensity of glaciation. Interaction of the upland surface of moderate relief and the overriding ice sheet are well displayed in the rounded summits, the through-valley network and finger-lake troughs, and the glens, waterfalls, and abandoned meltwater channels that characterize New York glacial landscapes.

Stratigraphic relationships, tracing of moraines and associated glacio-marginal features, and analyses of textural, lithologic, heavy-mineral, and flow-direction data have been used in correlating New York glacial deposits. Pre-Farmdale Wisconsin glaciation is recorded at Otto and in other drift-filled valleys transverse to principal glacier flow. Surface deposits that record the main Wisconsin glaciation include the Olean, Kent, and Valley Head Substages. Deglaciation was accompanied by ponding of proglacial lakes, the last of which may have been drained during the Two Creeks interval.

THE QUATERNARY OF NEW ENGLAND *

J. P. SCHAFER,[1] J. H. HARTSHORN[1]

THE QUATERNARY history of New England is mostly glacial history. Several ice advances, including the last main Wisconsin advance, extended completely across New England to or beyond the present south coast. Little evidence of interglacial events remains except in a few coastal stratigraphic sections, and postglacial processes have changed the landscape little except along shorelines and large streams.

GEOGRAPHIC AND GEOLOGIC SETTING

Almost all New England is hilly or mountainous. Topographic relief ranges from less than 50 m in some coastal areas to more than 900 m in the central White Mountains. Mount Washington (1,917 m), in the Presidential Range of the White Mountains, is the highest point.

PHYSIOGRAPHIC DIVISIONS

The major physiographic divisions of New England were defined by Fenneman (1938, p. 13, 216, 343, and Pl. I). The New England province, comprising almost all New England, is divided into five sections, of which the most extensive is the New England Upland section. The Seaboard Lowland section is the sloping east margin of the upland; the smoother surface and lower relief of this coastal strip results partly from its extensive cover of glacial drift. The other three sections are mountainous areas that stand above the upland. The White Mountain section extends from the White Mountains of New Hampshire northeast through an area of scattered mountains and mountain groups to Mount Katahdin. The Green Mountain and Taconic sections form a mountainous belt in western New England. The lowland along Lake Champlain in western-

most Vermont is in the Champlain section of the St. Lawrence Valley province. Low-lying Cape Cod and the adjoining islands are in the north part of the Coastal Plain province.

INFLUENCE OF BEDROCK ON TOPOGRAPHY

Many of the topographic features of New England are related to bedrock structure and lithology. The dominant rocks are metamorphosed Paleozoic sedimentary and volcanic rocks, mostly schists, gneisses, and phyllites. Their topography shows in many places a good adjustment to strata of different erodibility. The metamorphic rocks are cut by many large and small bodies of early Paleozoic to early Mesozoic plutonic rocks, mostly felsic. These rocks vary greatly in topographic expression; some underlie lowlands, others show little or no differential erosion, and still others form outstanding residual mountains and mountain groups. Within areas of plutonic rocks, details of topography are commonly determined by one or more sets of fractures.

At several places, relatively nonmetamorphosed sedimentary rocks produce broad lowlands: the Triassic rocks of the Connecticut Valley in central Connecticut and Massachusetts, the Pennsylvania rocks of the Narragansett basin in eastern Rhode Island and adjacent Massachusetts, the late Paleozoic rocks of the Boston basin, and the early Paleozoic rocks of the Lake Champlain lowland.

Cape Cod and the islands off southern New England constitute the northeast end of the Atlantic Coastal Plain. Farther northeast, the Mesozoic and Cenozoic sedimentary rocks that underlie the Coastal Plain and continental shelf are entirely submerged. The edge of the continental shelf lies about 130 km south of the islands, at a depth of about 125 m. Submarine and subsurface data (reviewed by Zeigler et al., 1964, p. 706) indicate the extensive presence of Coastal Plain strata, perhaps both Cretaceous and Tertiary, beneath and around outer Cape Cod. The Cretaceous and Tertiary outcrops of Martha's Vineyard and Block Island show severe ice-thrust deformation and probably have been shoved from original positions below present sea level.

THE PRE-PLEISTOCENE LANDSCAPE

The extensive older literature on the pre-Pleistocene geomorphic history of New England is well summarized by Fenneman (1938, p. 348). Much of this literature is based on now abandoned assumptions and on data derived from views in the field and from small-scale topographic maps. Therefore, the dissected peneplains and terraces inferred in these works cannot now be accepted without detailed restudy (Flint, 1963b).

* Publication authorized by the Director, U.S. Geological Survey. We owe a great debt of gratitude to the many geologists with whom we have discussed problems of the New England Pleistocene over the years, in the office and in the field, and whose published and unpublished ideas we have extensively used, not always with citations. We are particularly grateful to our colleagues on the U.S. Geological Survey, Clifford A. Kaye, Fred Pessl, Jr., and Carl Koteff, for many improvements in the manuscript. Of course, they are in no way responsible for any errors or infelicities that remain.

We have made no attempt at a systematic survey of the extensive literature on our subject. Very few older works are cited; in most topics, only examples are referred to even among recent papers. Secondary summaries often are cited rather than original sources. However, the references that we have included will lead the interested reader to many other papers.

We wish to emphasize that the correlations within New England and with the Midwest are various orders of guesses, based on all too little evidence. Some probably are obsolete before this manuscript reaches the printer. *Caveat emptor!*

[1] U.S. Geological Survey, Boston, Massachusetts.

Figure 1. Outline map of New England. Numbered localities are described in text. Ticked lines are drift margins: A, margin of Burlington till, derived from northwest (Stewart and MacClintock, 1964, Fig. 1); B, border of Mankato (*i.e.*, Valders) drift (Flint, 1953, Pl. 2); C, margin of Fort Covington drift (MacClintock and Terasmae, 1960, Fig. 1). Moraines of southeastern New England are shown on Figure 2.

The bedrock valleys of New England were cut to substantially their present depths before Wisconsin time, and probably before the beginning of the Pleistocene, except for local deepening of floors of major valleys by glacial erosion. The unique Brandon lignite (Barghoorn and Spackman, 1949), which contains a flora of early or mid-Tertiary age, lies low on a valley side near Brandon, Vermont (locality 1, Fig. 1), at the west foot of the Green Mountains; the topographic position of this deposit indicates that dissection down nearly to the present level had taken place by early or middle Teritary time.

The bedrock topography of today is still fundamentally the stream-carved landscape of pre-Pleistocene time; glacial erosion has generally modified it only in detail. The topography of high-relief areas, such as western Massachusetts, shows little evidence of glacial modification. Areas of lower relief, such as much of eastern Massachusetts, commonly show conspicuous drainage changes, largely because of obstruction of bedrock valleys by glacial deposits (Han-

sen, 1953). In some coastal areas, the bedrock topography is almost entirely covered by drift. Some major valleys have bedrock floors 30-130 m below sea level near the coast (Upson and Spencer, 1964).

The very large majority of bedrock outcrops in New England show little or no weathering. However, weathered rock underlying unweathered drift occurs at many places (*e.g.*, Goldthwait and Kruger, 1938), both on hills and in valleys, and is locally nearly continuous (as in substantial areas of western Rhode Island). This material, which is as much as 8 m thick, is probably the lower part of a once continuous weathered mantle, comparable to that on similar rocks in the Appalachian Piedmont south of the glacial limit, where it is commonly 20-30 m thick. The weathering may be partly interglacial, but it is believed to be largely pre-Pleistocene (*cf.* Borns and Allen, 1963). The existence of the weathered material is an indication of the weakness of glacial erosion and the persistence of the pre-glacial landscape.

GLACIAL EROSION AND DEPOSITION

The principal indication of the amount of glacial erosion is the amount of drift. The average thickness of drift in New England is most likely less than 10 m, and perhaps close to 5 m. Flint (1930, p. 47) estimated 1.5-3 m for Connecticut; Goldthwait and Kruger (1938, p. 1196) estimated 3-5 m for New Hampshire. The Goldthwaits (1951, p. 22) give a figure of 9.7 m for the average thickness of drift in about 1,600 drilled wells in New Hampshire, but areas of thin drift are most likely under-represented in that sample. Our guess is that at least a comparable amount of drift derived from the land area, and perhaps several times as much, lies offshore below present sea level, and that the average amount of glacial erosion indicated by the drift is 20 m or more. As the lowest bedrock relief in the Coastal Lowland section is about 30 m, and the relief of most of New England is much greater, glacial erosion cannot generally have changed the positions of valleys and divides. Similar conclusions were reached by Shaler (1893, p. 212), Flint (1963b, p. 695), and others. However, differential erosion of considerably greater depth has occurred locally. Glacial overdeepening produced a rock basin more than 30 m deep in the Triassic sedimentary rocks of the Connecticut Valley in Connecticut (Cushman, 1964, p. 19 and Pl. 2), and the Massachusetts part of that valley has another rock basin. Concentrated ice scour in preglacial passes cut the U-shaped notches of the White Mountains (Goldthwait, 1940, p. 26).

Many details of glacial erosion are controlled by the jointing of the rocks. Two detailed studies of this relationship are by Jahns (1943) and by Chapman and Rioux (1958). The spacing of joints generally also controls the size of boulders. The largest known glacial boulder in New England is the Madison Boulder in east-central New Hampshire, 25 by 11 by 7 m, transported about 3 km from its source.

The directions of selected glacial striations and grooves are shown in relation to surrounding areas on the glacial maps of North America and of the United States (Flint *et al.*, 1945, 1959). They trend generally between south and east; regional and local variations are mostly related to topography (Flint, 1957, p. 59), but some probably were produced by different glaciations. These glacial maps also show indicator fans (Flint, 1957, p. 126) and drumlins (Alden, 1924, Pl. 13). As discussed below, most of the drumlins are likely older than the last glaciation.

The tills of New England show a wide variety of types determined by bedrock lithology. Most tills are light to dark gray depending on the amount of mafic minerals in the rocks from which they are derived. Others are red (derived from Triassic or Pennsylvanian sedimentary rocks), black (Pennsylvanian phyllite), nearly white (very light granite), or rusty (pyritic schist). The abundance and degree of rounding of rock fragments in tills also vary. The finer sizes are mostly sand and silt. Clay-size material is less than 10% in most tills, but as much as 25% in some drumlin tills; little of it consists of clay minerals.

Glacial sand and gravel are abundant in most valleys of low-relief areas but occur only as scattered small masses in most upland or mountainous areas. In coastal Maine and New Hampshire, glacial sand and gravel bodies are generally covered by emerged marine silt and clay.

PRE-WISCONSIN STRATIGRAPHY

At least one older till is widespread beneath the drift of the last or Wisconsin ice sheet in New England. Stratigraphic sections that include pre-Wisconsin deposits other than this till are almost entirely restricted to southeastern coastal areas. The Wisconsin drift shows little modification by weathering or erosion, and in the large majority of exposures it lies directly on bedrock. The older drifts are of patchy distribution and are more or less deeply weathered and eroded. The probability is considered here that some of the drifts called pre-Wisconsin are actually of post-Sangamon age (Table 3). Therefore, throughout this discussion, the term Wisconsin means "classical" Wisconsin (in the sense of Flint, 1963a), and the term pre-Wisconsin refers to older drifts. This unsatisfactory state of the classification of the late Pleistocene will presumably be changed by introduction of new terms. However, we do not now wish either to present new local terms or to adopt terms from elsewhere for formal local use. We cite Midwestern time terms (*cf.* Frye and Willman, 1963) for comparison, but with no implication that glacier fluctuations there were necessarily contemporaneous with fluctuations in New England.

MARTHA'S VINEYARD

The most comprehensive Pleistocene stratigraphic section in New England is that compiled from several sea cliffs of the western part of the island of Martha's Vineyard. This section was first described in detail by Woodworth and Wigglesworth (1934, p. 162-195), who based their interpretation of the stratigraphy upon Fuller's (1914) Long Island section. Martha's Vineyard has recently been carefully restudied by Kaye (1964a, b). He substantially confirms the earlier conclusions of the number of drifts present; however, because of some differences in relative positions of the units he does not use the earlier stratigraphic names.

The section (Table 1) includes six drifts and the periglacial effects of a nearby seventh glaciation, the deposits of an interglaciation, and the weathering and erosional effects of two other interglaciations. The units are discontinuous and some are texturally variable; moreover, they are almost everywhere much deformed by ice thrust. The Gay Head cliff at the west end of the island, with its imbricated thrust plates of Pleistocene, Tertiary, and varicolored Cretaceous beds, is an example of glacial tectonics to compare with Møns Klint in Denmark.

The interglacial deposits include the fossiliferous Aquinnah Conglomerate, which Woodworth and Wigglesworth placed at the base of their Pleistocene section; however, Kaye has found a till (Drift 1) beneath beds that he correlates with the Aquinnah. Drifts 1 and 2 have a much smaller content of crystalline rock material than do the younger drifts, and probably were derived largely from the Coastal Plain sediments. Kaye supports the correlation by earlier workers of the distinctive thick till of Drift 3 with

TABLE 1

Pleistocene Stratigraphic Section of Martha's Vineyard
(Kaye, 1964a)

Deposit	Description	Suggested correlation (Kaye)
Drift 7	Thin till at one locality; overlies sand with C[14] date 15,300 yrs B.P.	Late Wisconsin (Port Huron)
Drift 6	Buzzards Bay moraine; ice did not reach Martha's Vineyard	Middle Wisconsin
Drift 5	Till overlying proglacial sand and clay; moraine and outwash plain of east part of island	Early Wisconsin
	Weathering and erosion	Sangamon
Drift 4	Till; extensive ice-thrust imbrication of older deposits	Late Illinoian
Drift 3	Stratified, slightly pinkish till, overlying proglacial gravel, sand, and clay	Early Illinoian
	Weathering	Yarmouth
Drift 2	Gray till	Kansan
Interglacial deposits	Greensand, gravel, and clay; Aquinnah Conglomerate; weathering	Aftonian
Drift 1	Clayey gray till	Nebraskan

Note: No correlation is intended between numbered drifts of Table 1 and Table 2. The numerals of Table 1 are Kaye's manuscript designations, not used in the published reference, but added here at his suggestion.

the Montauk Till of the Manhasset Formation of Long Island. However, the clays correlated by earlier workers with the probably interglacial Gardiners Clay of Long Island are believed by Kaye to be proglacial deposits. The major ice-thrust deformation was accomplished at the time of deposition of Drift 4, building the hilly uplands along the northwest side of the island. Kaye (1964b) concludes that Drifts 3 and 4 are terminal moraines of their respective ice sheets (Fig. 2).

BLOCK ISLAND, NANTUCKET, AND CAPE COD

At various localities in these districts, some elements of the Long Island–Martha's Vineyard stratigraphy were identified by Fuller (1914) and by Woodworth and Wigglesworth (1934). Most of these correlations were based on lithologic and textural comparison of fragmentary sections and cannot now be accepted without careful restudy.

The cliffs of Block Island expose thick, probably pre-Wisconsin drift beneath relatively thin Wisconsin till (Woodworth and Wigglesworth, 1934, p. 217; also unpublished data from Kaye). The thick, stratified till of the south cliff may reasonably be correlated with the similar till of Drift 3 of Martha's Vineyard and with the Montauk Till of Long Island.

Nantucket and Cape Cod are composed mainly of moraine and outwash of Wisconsin age. The pre-Wisconsin deposits of Nantucket include the shell-bearing Sankaty Sand of uncertain age (Woodworth and Wigglesworth, 1934, p. 94-98).

The best-known supposed pre-Wisconsin section on Cape Cod is that at Highland Light (or Cape Cod Light; 2, Fig. 1). Silt-clay lenses, correlated with the Gardiners Clay,

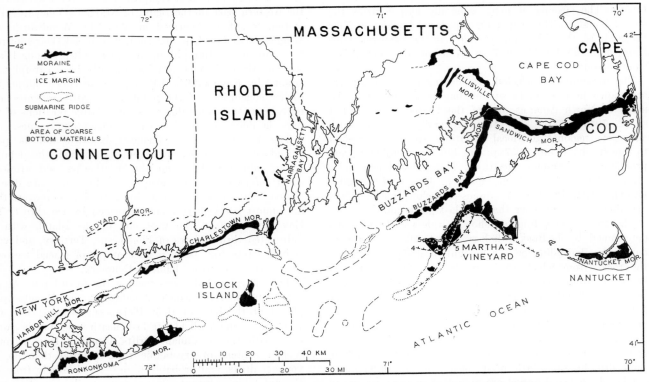

Figure 2. End moraines of southeastern New England. Ice-marginal lines of Martha's Vineyard after Kaye (1964b, Fig. 1); numbers are those of Kaye's drifts (Table 1). Other sources of information are given in text and by Schafer (1961).

are interbedded with coarser beds, which were given other names from the Long Island stratigraphy (Woodworth and Wigglesworth, 1934, p. 252). However, recent restudy by Zeigler *et al.* (1964) has led to the conclusion that these beds are part of a continuous section of drift, deposited during the retreat of Wisconsin ice. The cliff at Indian Hill on the west side of Cape Cod Bay was thought to expose Gardiners Clay, but this section also is probably of Wisconsin age.

BOSTON BASIN

Observations on the Pleistocene stratigraphy of the Boston area have been made since well back in the last century. The two most recent summaries, by Judson (1949) and Kaye (1961), are based in large part on information from excavations and borings. Judson named Boston and Lexington substages of the Wisconsin glaciation; his Boston drift includes the till of the drumlins (containing at two places inclusions of pre-Boston till), and the overlapping marine clay, commonly called the Boston blue clay. However, Kaye believes that the deep oxidation (to a maximum of 20 m) of his Drift III, the drumlin till, took place before the deposition of his Clay III, the Boston blue clay (Table 2). This degree of weathering of the drumlin till shows that it is pre-Wisconsin in the sense of this discussion. Beneath the drumlin till, Kaye finds two drifts and two clays; Clay II is probably a proglacial clay related to Drift III, and Clay I is perhaps similarly related to Drift II. Data from new excavations (Kaye, oral communication, 1964) indicate that the basin section may be even more complicated than shown here and that the sediments locally are very much deformed by ice thrust.

THE TWO-TILL PROBLEM

Evidence of two tills, believed to be of different ages, occurs at many localities in eastern Massachusetts, particularly north and northwest of Boston. They are discussed briefly, mostly with reference to the Boston basin, by the authors cited in the preceding paragraph. Other brief references are in recent descriptions of specific map areas, but there is no extensive general discussion. For some years the two tills have been referred to informally as "new till" and "old till."

The older till is generally more compact, contains more silt and clay, is platy or foliated, and is locally stratified. It makes up drumlins, and it also occurs as non-streamlined till covering bedrock. It is oxidized to depths of commonly 4-9 m (extreme range from about 2 m, perhaps partly eroded, to a maximum of 20 m). The carbonate of transported marine shells, which occur in drumlin till of part of the Boston basin, has generally been leached from at least part of the weathered zone, but rock fragments show little decomposition in the zone. The till is light gray beneath the yellowish-brown weathered zone.

The younger till, part of the Wisconsin drift sheet, is generally less compact, sandier, and without platy or foliated structure, but similar in lithologic composition to nearby older till. In some places it laps onto the weathered older till, but nowhere is it known to constitute the main mass of drumlins. During the time of deposition of the younger till, the drumlins seem mostly to have been sites of erosion or non-deposition. The younger till is almost unweathered, and in few places does it show more than 0.5 m or at most 1 m of weathered zone beneath the late-glacial windblown material and the humus zone. The light-gray A′ soil horizons that occur on some oxidized older tills as a part of fragipan development (Walter Lyford, written communication, 1963) are easily confused with superimposed younger till.

A similar two-till relationship continues westward into the drumlin field of central Massachusetts, where Paxton soils are mapped on drumlin till and Gloucester soils on the younger till. Two tills, probably of different ages, are described from northeastern Connecticut by White (1947) and have also been seen in the southeast corner of the state. Flint (1961) describes, from Lake Chamberlain (3, Fig. 1) in south-central Connecticut, two tills distinguished by lithology, fabric, striation directions, and other characteristics, but not separated by a weathering zone. He names the lower the Lake Chamberlain Till, and the upper (Wisconsin) the Hamden Till.

An organic deposit between two tills (Caldwell, 1959) at New Sharon, Maine (4, Fig. 1), has been dated at >38,000 B.P. (W-910). Thus the lower of these tills is certainly older than the last glaciation. Wood in the base of a complex drift section near Wallingford, Connecticut (5, Fig. 1), has been dated at >40,000 B.P. (Y-451 *bis*). Peat overlain by till 18 m thick (probably the older till of the above discussion) and underlain by sand and silt about 3 m thick, near Worcester, Massachusetts (6, Fig. 1), has been dated at >38,000 B.P. (W-647, L-380); microfossils indicate an interglacial climate.

Not all examples of two superposed or adjacent tills, in eastern Massachusetts or elsewhere, have been interpreted as deposited during different ice advances. Some authors (*e.g.*, Denny, 1958, p. 76) describe pairs of tills as subglacial and supraglacial-englacial tills deposited by the same ice sheet. Local differences in tills have been attributed to lithologic control either of texture (*e.g.*, Han-

TABLE 2

Pleistocene Stratigraphic Section of Boston Basin
(Kaye, 1961)

Deposit	Description	Suggested correlation (Kaye)
Drift IV	Mostly outwash in basin, till and outwash in uplands; ice flow S. 10°-30° E.	Late Wisconsin (Cary) (Lexington substage)
	Oxidation of Clay III	
Clay III	Marine; preconsolidated; C¹⁴ dates 14,250 B.P. and 13,800 B.P.	Middle Wisconsin (Tazewell)
	Deep oxidation of Drift III	
Drift III	The drumlin till; ice flow S. 60°-80° E.	Early Wisconsin (Iowan)
Clay II	Probably marine	Early Iowan (?), Sangamon
	Deep oxidation of Drift II	Sangamon
Drift II	Mostly outwash, some till	Illinoian
Clay I	Probably marine	Early Illinoian (?), Yarmouth (?)
Drift I	Very compact till	Kansan or Nebraskan

ley, 1959), or of depth of weathering (as in the area of the pyritic Brimfield Schist of central Massachusetts).

TENTATIVE CORRELATIONS

The age of the Gardiners Clay and accompanying Jacob Sand is one of the most important check-points in the pre-Wisconsin stratigraphy of southern New England. Fuller (1914, p. 92), in his detailed description of the formation on Long Island and adjacent islands, concluded on the basis of fossils that the clay was of Yarmouth interglacial age. He recognized (p. 94) the problem of source of material; other clays in New England are generally regarded as fed by glacial melt-waters. Fuller's expansion of the Long Island section to include all four glacials and three interglacials of the Midwestern sequence later came into doubt; the Gardiners Clay was moved from Yarmouth to Sangamon, and the Manhasset Formation from Illinoian to early Wisconsin (Flint, 1947, p. 269). Hyyppä (1955) studied the microfossils, not of the original Gardiners Clay of Long Island, but of the clays of Martha's Vineyard and the Cape Cod area that had been correlated with the Gardiners almost entirely on the basis of appearance. He concluded that the Gardiners was a glaciomarine deposit formed in a "cool coniferous" climate, and he placed it in the Iowan-Tazewell Interstade. On this basis, Flint (1957, p. 356) tentatively placed the Gardiners between "classical"

Wisconsin and the newly recognized glacial time that precedes the "classical" Wisconsin but follows the Sangamon, thus moving the Manhasset Formation upward into the "classical" Wisconsin. However, a study of Foraminifera in the clay on Long Island led Weiss (1954, p. 157) to confirm the interglacial character of the clay there and to suggest its deposition in shallow, probably brackish water such as the present protected bays on the south shore of Long Island. A pollen study has led Donner (1964, p. 366) also to believe in the interglacial age of the clay and to restore it to a Sangamon position, correlative with the Cape May Formation of the Coastal Plain of New Jersey. This is the position given it in Table 3. The clays formerly called Gardiners on Martha's Vineyard and in the Cape Cod area are evidently not correlative with the type Gardiners on and near Long Island, according to their micropaleontology and also their geology as described above. If the Gardiners is Sangamon, then the overlying Manhasset, which Fuller (1914, p. 208) believed was separated from the time of deposition of the Wisconsin end moraines by an interval of great erosion, may plausibly be attributed to a post-Sangamon ice advance substantially older than the last glaciation.

Kaye has provisionally correlated his Martha's Vineyard and Boston basin sections with the Midwest sequence, mostly by working back from the last drifts and matching weathering zones with interglacial intervals. In the

TABLE 3

Tentative Correlation Chart of Pleistocene of Southern New England

Time units	Long Island and Connecticut	Rhode Island	Martha's Vineyard, Nantucket, and Cape Cod	Boston basin and vicinity	General
(Only a few main references are cited)	Fuller, 1914; Flint, 1953	Kaye, 1960; Schafer, 1961	Woodworth and Wigglesworth, 1934; Mather *et al.*, 1942; Kaye, 1964a	Judson, 1949; Kaye, 1961	
Wisconsin ("classical") (= Woodfordian)	Connecticut Valley lake sediments			Marine sediments north of Boston basin	
	Drift of Middletown readvance			Drift IV; Cambridge readvance (Lexington drift)	
				Weathering Clay III (marine)	
	Clays at Middletown and Berlin Clay at New Haven	Clay at Barrington		Clays at Taunton and Bridgewater	Wisconsin drift; "new till" of eastern Massachusetts and elsewhere
	Ledyard and other minor moraines	Minor moraines	Ellisville and other minor moraines; sand and clay of outer Cape Cod		
	Harbor Hill moraine	Charlestown moraine	Drift 6; Buzzards Bay and Sandwich moraines of Cape Cod		
	Ronkonkoma moraine	Surface drift of Block Island	Drift 5; Nantucket moraine		
(= Farmdalian?)	Erosion		Weathering and erosion	Weathering	Weathering
(= Altonian?)	Manhasset Formation, including Montauk Till Member	Montauk Till of Block Island	Drift 3 and Drift 4	Drift III (drumlin till, Boston Till) Clay II	"Old till" of eastern Massachusetts and elsewhere
Sangamon	Jacob Sand (marine) Gardiners Clay (marine)		Weathering	Weathering Unexposed source beds of many of marine shells in drumlin till	
Pre-Sangamon	Jameco Gravel Erosion Mannetto Gravel		Drift 2 Weathering; interglacial deposits Drift 1	Drift II Clay I Drift I	

Martha's Vineyard section (Table 1), his early Wisconsin Drift 5 is the southernmost part of the latest or Wisconsin drift sheet; the next preceding Drifts 3 and 4 (between which there is no evidence of interglacial conditions) he calls Illinoian. On the basis of the similarity of the till in Drift 3 to the Montauk Till of Long Island and Block Island (Kaye, 1964a, b), Drifts 3 and 4 are correlated with the Manhasset Formation in Table 3. The submarine features that seem to constitute a lobate ice-marginal connection from western Martha's Vineyard to Block Island and thence to the east tip of Long Island were suggested by Schafer (1961) to be the terminal Wisconsin moraine. However, Kaye believes that this is the terminal moraine of the Montauk Till–Drift 3 complex, which is much thicker than the Wisconsin drift at the three connected localities.

In the Boston basin (Table 2), Kaye's middle Wisconsin Clay III is likely of the age of the last glaciation. The deep oxidation of Drift III (the drumlin till), which he calls early Wisconsin (Iowan), indicates that it predates the "classical" Wisconsin. The drumlin till was correlated with the Montauk Till by Fuller (1914, p. 221), as by Upham 34 years earlier. The correlation is based mainly upon the position of these thick, somewhat similar drifts unconformably beneath the Wisconsin drift sheet, and is still plausible, though not certain. Also plausible but not proved is the correlation with these tills of Flint's Lake Chamberlain Till of Connecticut, and Caldwell's older till at New Sharon, Maine. Only one pre-Wisconsin till is known except at a few localities, but there is no necessity that all single old tills be correlative, or that all drumlins be made of the same till.

If a glaciation occurred relatively early in post-Sangamon time (Flint, 1963a), a period of as much as several tens of thousands of years may have been available for erosion and weathering. Such a glacial interval and the succeeding interstadial interval presumably would be at least partly equivalent to the Altonian and Farmdalian of Frye and Willman (1963).

Beneath the level here interpreted as Sangamon, there are two drifts each on Long Island, on Martha's Vineyard, and in the Boston basin. However, we have even less basis for correlations among these than for correlations among the younger deposits, so the older units are grouped as pre-Sangamon.

THE LAST GLACIATION

THE LAST ICE SHEET IN SOUTHERN NEW ENGLAND

The coastal moraines. The Laurentide Ice Sheet of Wisconsin age grew from the highlands of eastern Canada (Flint, 1957, p. 313) southward to Long Island and the islands of southeastern New England. It covered all New England except small areas of Martha's Vineyard and Nantucket. The terminal position of the ice margin is marked by the moraines of Nantucket and Martha's Vineyard (Kaye's Drift 5) and by the Ronkonkoma moraine of Long Island (Fig. 2). The uplands of western Martha's Vineyard were mapped as part of this moraine system by Woodworth and Wigglesworth (1934); however, according to Kaye (1964b), these uplands were built by the next earlier ice

advance (Drift 4) and were only locally overridden by the last ice sheet. Kaye (1964a, p. 137) has identified proglacial marine deposits whose position above present sea level he attributes to ice thrust. The outwash plains of these islands certainly were built to a sea level no higher than the present. Older drift is thinly mantled by Wisconsin drift on Block Island, and the last ice sheet probably extended at least slightly south of the island. This moraine system includes one re-entrant angle on Martha's Vineyard and probably another near Block Island.

Possible thicknesses and surface slopes of the ice sheet at its time of maximum extent were discussed by Antevs (1928, p. 59). However, aside from comparisons with existing glaciers, one can only say that all mountains of New England and adjoining areas are believed to have been overridden. Mount Washington (1,917 m) stands 1,500 m or more above nearby lowlands, so that is a minimum thickness of the ice there.

A second line of moraines lies 8-50 km behind the terminal line. These moraines include the Sandwich and Buzzards Bay moraines of Cape Cod, the Charlestown of Rhode Island, and the Harbor Hill of Long Island. Their submarine connections are shown by bottom topography and deposits (Schafer, 1961). This moraine line includes two re-entrant angles, the successors of the two angles of the outer line. These angles define two lobes, one in eastern Rhode Island and adjoining Massachusetts, and one on Cape Cod; a third lobe lay east of Cape Cod. The relationships at the angles indicate that the change from a stable to a negative regime attacked the ice sheet progressively from west to east.

The Charlestown moraine (Kaye, 1960) consists of a complex of collapse landforms with an irregular polygonal pattern, built of ablation moraine. It evidently was formed by accumulation of supraglacial drift on the margin of the ice sheet, followed by development of the distinctive topography and materials during differential melting of the stagnant buried ice. The Buzzards Bay moraine has similar dead-ice topography. However, the Sandwich moraine (Mather *et al.*, 1942) contains many small ridges parallel to the general trend of the moraine; it was formed by local readvance of the ice onto the head of a large outwash plain.

Age of the glacial maximum. Radiocarbon dates from several sources bear on the problem of the time of the last glaciation of southern New England:

1. Materials earlier than the last advance, redeposited in the drift. Horn core of extinct bison, near Harvard, Massachusetts (7, Fig. 1); 21,200 ± 1,000 B.P. (W-544). Marine shells from stratified drift on outer Cape Cod (2, Fig. 1); 26,900 ± 700 B.P. and 20,700 ± 2,000 B.P. (Zeigler *et al.*, 1964, p. 710).

2. Plant material (tundra flora) in clay, Zacks Cliff, west end of Martha's Vineyard; 15,300 ± 800 B.P. (W-1187; Kaye, 1964a, p. 138). Dated material is underlain by weathered Drift 5, and overlain by sand that nearby is overlain by another till (Drift 7, Table 1).

3. Basal parts of deposits overlying last drift in southern Connecticut. Rogers Lake, Lyme (8, Fig. 1); 14,240 ± 240 B.P. (Y-950/51). Totoket Bog, near New Haven (9, Fig. 1);

$13,550 \pm 460$ B.P. (Y-285). At both localities, these are the lowest and oldest of a consistent series of dates (Davis, this volume).

4. Basal parts of deposits overlying drift in eastern Massachusetts. Squibnocket, west end of Martha's Vineyard; $12,700 \pm 300$ B.P. (W-710). Dates from several other localities are slightly younger (Kaye, 1962; Kaye and Barghoorn, 1964).

If the dates of group 1 are taken at face value, they indicate an ice advance about 20,000 years ago. Unfortunately, these dates are from somewhat unreliable materials. In the well-dated Midwestern sequence, the post-Farmdale readvance approached its maximum extent about 20,000-22,000 years ago (Flint, 1963a; Frye and Willman, 1963). Until more dates are available, we may tentatively consider that the advance of the last ice sheet took place in New England at about the same time as in the Midwest.

A readvance from north of Boston to Martha's Vineyard in the period about 13,800 to 12,500 years ago has been suggested by Kaye (Kaye and Barghoorn, 1964, p. 77; Kaye, 1964a, p. 138). In the Boston area, this is the Cambridge readvance, which overrode the 14,000-year-old Clay III. Kaye extends this readvance to Martha's Vineyard on the basis of the upper till at Zacks Cliff, the Squibnocket date (which he believes very closely followed deglaciation nearby), and other evidence. However, this seems to be in conflict with the dates from southern Connecticut (group 3), where deglaciation must have been later than on Martha's Vineyard. One may suggest as an alternative that the 15,300-year-old deposit at Zacks Cliff was formed very near the ice margin and was overridden by a local readvance near or a little before 15,000 B.P.; that the ice retreated from southernmost Connecticut before 14,240 B.P. and from the Boston basin before about 14,000 B.P.; and that the Cambridge readvance did not extend far south of the Boston basin.

No single hypothesis seems to fit these data satisfactorily at present. More detailed local study and more information on the interpretation of radiocarbon dates are needed. However, the last glaciation in southern New England most likely included much of Woodfordian time (Frye and Willman, 1963; Flint, 1963a). The coastal moraines were correlated with the Olean drift (the outermost Wisconsin drift) of northern Pennsylvania and southern New York by Flint (1953) and by MacClintock (1954), but with the somewhat younger Valley Heads and Binghamton drifts of southern and central New York by Denny (1956).

Minor recessional moraines. The general absence of recessional moraines north of the coastal moraines has been extensively discussed in relation to the mode of deglaciation. Minor moraines do occur within a belt less than 30 km wide, north of the Charlestown–Cape Cod moraines (Fig. 2), but very rarely beyond that distance. Short moraine segments northwest of the Cape Cod interlobate angle (Mather, 1952) define two or three positions of the angle as it retreated. Moraines in similar positions occur north of the interlobate angle in southern Rhode Island (Kaye, 1960, p. 381; Schafer, 1961).

Goldsmith (1960, 1964) has described two lines of small discontinuous moraines in southeastern Connecticut, about 13 and 20 km north of the Charlestown–Harbor Hill moraine line and nearly parallel to it. Unpublished maps and reconnaissance by Schafer and others show that these moraines extend far beyond the area mapped by Goldsmith. The southern line probably extends 77 km from the Rhode Island interlobate angle to the place where the moraine disappears into Long Island Sound. Goldsmith has named the northern line the Ledyard moraine; the southern line, which is double in places, has not been named.

Stagnation-zone retreat. The mode of retreat of the last ice sheet in New England, as revealed by its deposits, has been a subject of discussion for nearly a hundred years. Marginal stagnation of the ice was suggested in the last century, as was the use of glaciofluvial deposits as indications of episodes of ice retreat (*e.g.*, Woodworth, 1897). Successive positions of an active ice margin in central Massachusetts were inferred by Alden (1924), who mapped as terminal moraines some deposits that would now be called ice-contact stratified drift. The subject of stagnation was reopened by Flint (1930 and other papers), followed by other authors (*e.g.*, Goldthwait, 1938; Rich, 1943). Detailed mapping, mostly by the U.S. Geological Survey, has emphasized stagnation-zone retreat (Currier, 1941), in which the ice-marginal stratified drift is deposited within and beyond a marginal zone of stagnant or dead ice, commonly a few kilometers wide. This hypothesis is based on the distinctive characteristics of the ice-contact deposits (Flint, 1957, p. 146-159). In suitable areas, the arrangement of the deposits makes it possible to identify successive episodes (sequences) of deposition, and thus the position of the irregular margin and separated bodies of dead ice (White, 1947; Jahns, 1953). Other maps and reports of the U.S. Geological Survey in the last fifteen years exemplify these ideas in various forms and in different topographic situations. The amount of time available for ice retreat makes it clear that these episodes of deposition can have occupied no more than a few tens of years each.

The minor recessional moraines of southeastern Connecticut and adjacent Rhode Island lie in areas whose stratified drift seems to demonstrate stagnation-zone retreat. It is possible that these moraines were built mostly at the contact (presumably a shear zone) between the active ice and marginal dead ice.

These ideas of marginal stagnation were resisted throughout his life by Lougee, who insisted on the retreat of the ice sheet with an active margin (Lougee, 1940). His interpretation of stratified drift permitted him to identify extensive marine or lacustrine water planes (*e.g.*, Lougee and Vander Pyl, 1951), where others find only the deposits of glacial streams or small lakes. This led him to a complicated chronology of uplift and steep tilting (Lougee, 1953), and to other conclusions that failed to win wide acceptance.

Glacial lakes. The many lakes dammed by drift or by ice during glacial retreat (Alden, 1924) ranged in size from small ponds to the great lake in the Connecticut Valley (discussed in a separate section). The deposits of some lakes include large bodies of varved clay; the deposits of some others consist only of coarse deltas that filled small basins.

Table 3 includes the deposits of only a few of these that are of particular interest; the clays listed above the level of the minor moraines are not exactly correlative, but they fall at about the same level by coincidence. The large literature on glacial lakes includes descriptions of some that, according to recent work, do not exist. In contrast, recent remapping (Koteff, 1963) near Concord, Massachusetts, just west of Boston, extends an earlier description of a series of lake stages and indicates a postglacial tilt of about 1 m/km (5-6 ft/mile).

A problem of sea level and climate has been raised by work by Hyyppä (1955) on clays at Taunton and Bridgewater, Massachusetts (10, Fig. 1), and correlated nonfossiliferous clay at Barrington in eastern Rhode Island. From marine diatoms he concludes that the clays represent a marine invasion at least 20 m above present sea level; from pollen profiles he concludes that they were deposited at a time of "warm deciduous" climate. However, detailed mapping (Hartshorn, 1960) confirms the previous interpretation that the Taunton-Bridgewater clays, which are varved in part, were deposited in a lake at the ice margin. This contradiction is explained by the discovery that some or perhaps all of the microfossils are rebedded from older deposits (Davis, 1961, p. 215).

Marine clay at Boston. The main body of clay at Boston was included by Judson (1949, p. 12-23) with the underlying drumlin till in the drift of his Boston substage of the Wisconsin. However, Kaye (1961) believes that a period of deep weathering separates the two intervals of deposition. Therefore, the clay (Kaye's Clay III) is presumably of ("classical") Wisconsin age. The clay occurs to an altitude of 14 m, and the fauna indicates that sea level may have been 18 m or more above that of the present. Radiocarbon dates of barnacle plates from the clay at the north edge of the Boston basin are 14,250 ± 250 B.P. and 13,800 ± 300 B.P. (W-735 and L-598A; Kaye and Barghoorn, 1964, p. 75). The clay was eroded and weathered at a time of sea level probably more than 10 m below that of the present, and then covered in some places by the succeeding Drift IV. It is oxidized to a depth of about 1 m beneath Drift IV, and to a maximum depth of 3 m where it is exposed at the present surface.

The submergence shown by this clay is the southernmost proof of a sea level above that of the present in New England, later than the time of deposition of the drumlin till. The marine limit passes below sea level shortly south of Boston. One uncertainty about the position of Clay III is that the Boston basin section does not seem to contain a till or outwash correlative with the main Wisconsin advance to the coastal moraines. Another uncertainty concerns the relationship of Clay III with the emerged marine clay and other deposits, described below, that extend from Salem, about 5 km north of the Boston basin, northeastward along the coast into Canada. The geographic and stratigraphic evidence and radiocarbon dates support a suggestion that these clays are separated in time by Drift IV (Table 3). That separation requires a rise of sea level in the Boston basin following the deposition of Drift IV. The clay in the northwest part of the basin, inferred by Chute (1959, p.

202) to be younger than the main body of clay, has been suggested by Oldale (1961) to be evidence of that rise of sea level; however, such evidence is lacking elsewhere in the basin.

The Middletown-Cambridge readvance. The retreat of the last ice sheet in the Connecticut Valley in Connecticut was interrupted by a readvance of more than 26 km (Flint, 1953, p. 899), to Middletown (11, Fig. 1). This readvance is shown by till and stratified drift overlying varved lake sediments at Middletown, Berlin, and elsewhere. Radiocarbon dates imply that the readvance occurred "before, but probably not long before, about 13,000 yr ago" (Flint, 1956, p. 275), or in Port Huron time (Deevy, 1958, p. 34).

Another readvance occurred in the northwest part of the Boston basin (Chute, 1959, p. 197; Kaye, 1961). An ice lobe advanced, probably at least 5 km, to build a short ice-marginal ridge in Cambridge called the Fresh Pond moraine. The moraine and its outwash plain (Drift IV) generally are underlain by the 14,000-year-old Boston marine clay (Clay III); the till is very clayey because of ice erosion of the clay. Judson (1949, p. 23) correlated this event with the deposition of the ordinary sandy till in Lexington (more than 3 km northwest of Cambridge) under the name of the Lexington substage of the Wisconsin. However, we believe that the till in Lexington cannot be separated from the generalized Wisconsin drift sheet (the "new till"), of which the deposits of this readvance are but a local phase. Therefore, we suggest the name Cambridge readvance as more appropriate. The presence of the "General" column at the right of Table 3 emphasizes this point.

The preconsolidation of Clay III in front of the Fresh Pond moraine in the Boston basin is interpreted by Kaye (1961; 1964a, p. 138; Kaye and Barghoorn, 1964, p. 77) as evidence that this readvance extended beyond the moraine. He further correlates Drift IV of the basin with Drift 7 of Martha's Vineyard as (Kaye and Barghoorn, 1964, p. 78) "a thin, short-lived readvance following the retreat of a much more important ice sheet" (*i.e.* the ice sheet of Drifts 5 and 6). The readvance is tentatively dated at 13,800 B.P. to 12,500 B.P., or Port Huron in age. An alternative interpretation, suggested above in connection with the age of the maximum of the last glaciation, is that the Cambridge readvance was a local event less than 14,000 years ago, and that the last retreat from Martha's Vineyard occurred close to 15,000 years ago. On that basis, the correlation (Flint, 1953, p. 901) of the Middletown and Cambridge readvances seems probable, although no similar ice-marginal features are known between the two localities. If, as others believe, a readvance of Port Huron age is represented in northern Vermont, the Middletown-Cambridge readvance is presumably of Cary (perhaps late Cary) age.

DEGLACIATION OF NORTHERN NEW ENGLAND

The Connecticut Valley lakes. As the ice sheet retreated from the maximum extent (11, Fig. 1) of the Middletown readvance in Connecticut, it built a great body of stratified drift whose ice-contact head was near Rocky Hill, 13 km north of Middletown. This valley fill became the dam of a glacial lake that expanded northward as the ice retreated

(Flint, 1953, p. 899). The lake spillway in New Britain, shortly west of the dam, is now at an altitude of about 20 m, but it may have been deepened as much as 10 m by escaping lake water.

Varved clay and silt extend from Rocky Hill to St. Johnsbury, Vermont (12, Fig. 1) and beyond. The lake at its greatest size was a continuous water body (Lake Hitchcock of Lougee, 1939) through the broad Triassic lowland to the north border of Massachusetts, and northward into the narrower valley along the New Hampshire–Vermont border. Lake beaches are common in Connecticut and generally are southwestward-curving spits and bars at the south ends of hills (Colton and Cushman, 1962). Major tributary streams formed deltas, some of which have ice-contact heads. The altitudes of beaches and deltas increase to the north, because of postglacial tilt. Altitudes of deltas in Massachusetts (Jahns and Willard, 1942, p. 274) indicate a postglacial tilt of 0.8 m/km (4.2 ft/mile). Other figures are of the same order of magnitude. At some places in Connecticut, beach elevations indicate more than one lake level.

The varved bottom deposits of the lake were studied in great detail by Antevs (1922). The distance of 298 km from near the dam to St. Johnsbury was covered by a continuous series of overlapping varve sections, except for a gap (estimated at 200 to 300 years) at Claremont in southwestern New Hampshire. The time occupied by the recession of the ice was determined as about 4,100 years; the average rate of retreat was 14 yr/km, or 73 m/yr; the range between districts was from 31 m/yr to 1100 m/yr, generally faster northward (Antevs, 1922, p. 74). Later work (Lougee, 1939; the Goldthwaits, 1951, p. 44) revealed that when the retreating ice margin reached Lyme, New Hampshire (13, Fig. 1), the water level abruptly dropped 27 m. This change probably records the draining of Lake Hitchcock by failure of the dam in Connecticut. The succeeding Lake Upham extended about 70 km south of Lyme, and it grew north beyond St. Johnsbury as the ice retreated.

Several radiocarbon dates bear on the age of the lakes: the Middletown readvance, which just precedes Lake Hitchcock, is described above as not long before 13,000 years ago; the final draining of the south end of the lake was between 10,710 B.P. and 10,650 B.P. (Y-253 and Y-251; Flint, 1956, p. 276); and the period of stability or readvance that terminated the varve series at St. Johnsbury cannot be younger than Valders (more than 11,000 years ago). Therefore, the radiocarbon chronology does not contain enough time for the 4,100-year varve series. However, Antevs (1962) retains his conviction that the radiocarbon chronology of northeastern North America is faulty, that it is much too short, and that it has resulted in an erroneous correlation with the Scandinavian chronology.

Deglaciation of New Hampshire and Vermont. Ice retreat in the Connecticut Valley lakes may have been marked by a calving cliff of active ice. Elsewhere, the character of the stratified drift indicates retreat with a terminal zone of dead ice (Goldthwait, 1938; Denny, 1958, p. 87; Stewart, 1961), and with the formation of many small ice-marginal lakes. A readvance near Claremont in southwestern New Hamp-

shire was inferred from the varve series by Antevs (1922, p. 81) and correlated with features extending about 80 km eastward; but this was discarded by Goldthwait (1938, p. 350). Another readvance, near St. Johnsbury, Vermont (12, Fig. 1), is believed to have occupied about 280 years (Antevs, 1922, p. 83); it is supported by similar evidence nearby on the Connecticut River, but correlated "moraines" have again been discarded (Goldthwait, 1938, p. 349).

An exposure at Shelburne in northwestern Vermont (Stewart, 1961, p. 102) shows Burlington till of northwest derivation overlying Shelburne till of northeast derivation. Stewart and MacClintock (1964) have recently mapped a short section of the eastern border of the Burlington till (A, Fig. 1). The tills are distinguished by directions of fabric and striations and by lithology. At the Stannard Brook area (14, Fig. 1), just in front of the border, the till of northeast derivation overlies two still older tills of northwest derivation, interbedded with lake sediments. The area of the St. Johnsbury readvance lies shortly to the east, in the area of till of northeast derivation. The Burlington till is correlated by Stewart and MacClintock (1964) with the Fort Covington drift (C, Fig. 1) that wraps around the north side of the Adirondack Mountains in northeastern New York (MacClintock and Terasmae, 1960); they correlate the Fort Covington drift with the Port Huron readvance, partly on the basis of a Two Creeks age of the succeeding Champlain Sea. However, according to Broecker and Farrand (1963, p. 799), the dates of the Champlain Sea (11,300 to 10,500 B.P.) fall well after the Valders maximum (slightly younger than 11,850 B.P.). Of course, the Burlington till and the Middletown-Cambridge readvance cannot both be of Port Huron age.

The St. Johnsbury readvance was correlated by Flint (1953, p. 907) with a readvance at Glens Falls (15, Fig. 1) in east-central New York; the inferred drift border (B, Fig. 1) was extended northeast across Maine on the evidence of pollen studies in northern Maine. This drift border Flint suggested to be of Mankato age, in the former sense of equivalence to Valders rather than to Port Huron. On the evidence cited in the preceding paragraph, one may raise the possibility that the Fort Covington–Burlington drift (possibly including the readvance at Glens Falls?) represents a more important event than the St. Johnsbury readvance, which may be only a brief, local oscillation during the retreat of the ice of northeast origin. Present information does not give an adequate basis for considering possible correlations between the Fort Covington–Burlington drift and the moraines known in adjacent Quebec, except to indicate that the Valders ice margin most likely lies in Quebec and that any ice borders in northern Vermont and New Hampshire are therefore of pre-Two Creeks age.

Evidence of striations and erratics, principally in southernmost Quebec, indicates that small ice caps may have persisted in northern New Hampshire and adjacent Maine, and perhaps also in northernmost Vermont, after retreat of the ice sheet (Flint, 1951, p. 26; 1953, Pl. 2). However, unpublished information contradicts some of that evidence (Flint, written communication, 1965).

Water bodies in the Champlain lowland. When the tongue of ice that occupied the Champlain-Hudson lowland retreated from the position at Glens Falls, New York (Flint, 1953, p. 907), it progressively opened the northward-draining basin that now contains Lake Champlain. This basin was occupied first by an ice-dammed lake called Lake Vermont, and later by the Champlain Sea (Chapman, 1937). Lake Vermont included an earlier, higher Coveville stage and a Fort Ann stage. All the lake and marine water planes are tilted; the plane based on the beaches and shore terraces of the Fort Ann stage rises north-northwestward about 1 m/km (5 ft/mile). There is some difficulty in distinguishing shore features of major lake stages from the deposits of local ice-marginal lakes. The disputed history of the Champlain Sea is indicated in some of the references in the last section.

Coastal marine submergence. Along the coast north of Boston, marine submergence accompanied or closely followed deglaciation. Outwash commonly grades into deltas, or extends over marine sediments. The finer-grained part of the load of melt-water streams was spread widely as marine fine sand, silt, and clay, named the Presumpscot Formation in southwestern Maine (Bloom, 1960, p. 55). Locally abundant fossils, including pelecypods, gastropods, and other organisms, indicate cold-water conditions. In southwestern Maine, the fauna of the sediments reflects a water temperature comparable to that now about 7-8 degrees latitude to the north (Bloom, 1960, p. 78). Radiocarbon dates of shells from marine sediments in Maine range from 11,800 ± 240 B.P. (W-737) to 12,800 ± 450 B.P. (W-1011) (Bloom, 1963, p. 866; Borns, 1963).

Many of the features once identified as parts of marine strandlines are now thought to be of glacial origin (Goldthwait, 1938, p. 363), and very few strand features are now accepted. Near Salem, Massachusetts, just north of the Boston basin, the marine limit is about 15 m (Oldale, 1961); the relationship of the sediments there to the 14,000-year-old Clay III of the Boston basin is discussed above. In southwestern Maine, the marine limit rises northward from about 60 m to 90 m in altitude and is believed to be an isochronal line (Bloom, 1960, p. 105). The amount and direction of maximum tilt are uncertain, but probably it is more than 0.4 m/km (2 ft/mile) upward to the north-northwest. Farther north in Maine the marine limit rises to about 120 m; the problem of distinguishing lacustrine and marine sediments in narrow valleys is discussed by Caldwell (1959). The generalized isobases of uplift mapped by Flint (1957, p. 251) are evidently based on Clay III as well as on the marine features to the north, but it makes little difference at that scale.

Deglaciation of Maine. The stratified drift deposited during deglaciation of Maine is evidence that here as elsewhere in New England the disappearance of the ice sheet was generally marked by development of a marginal zone of dead ice. The great eskers of central and eastern Maine (Leavitt and Perkins, 1935, p. 59), the largest in the United States, include branching systems as much as 150 km long. Clearly they were formed in tunnels (and perhaps partly in open channels) in dead ice. It is not certain what portion of an esker was being deposited at one time; some eskers evidently were built as series of segments.

The so-called Newington moraine, once described as extending from southwestern Maine to the northeastern corner of Massachusetts, is no longer accepted as a moraine (Goldthwait, 1938, p. 357; Bloom, 1960, p. 24). Other possible morainic features near the cost in easternmost Maine (Leavitt and Perkins, 1935, p. 46) deserve restudy. Bloom (1960, p. 28) has identified areas of closely spaced, small washboard moraines in southwestern Maine.

Evidence that ice locally overrode and deformed the emerged marine sediments has led Bloom (1960, p. 68, 128) to describe the Kennebunk glacial advance, named for an exposure near Kennebunk (16, Fig. 1). This advance occurred during the time of marine submergence; its effects have been seen along a line at least 19 km and perhaps 43 km long, parallel to and about 3-8 km inland from the present shoreline. The advance is associated with an area of northwest-trending striations, in contrast with more northerly striations beyond the presumed limit of the advance. Bloom (1963, p. 873) suggests that this glaciation originated from an independent ice cap of Valders age, centered over the White Mountains.

Borns (1963) suggests a Mankato (Port Huron) age for an ice margin that stood in the late-glacial sea near Bangor (17, Fig. 1). Unpublished studies by Borns (written communication, 1964) in the upper Kennebec valley of western Maine (vicinity of 18, Fig. 1) reveal that valleys cut in the emerged marine sediments and overlying outwash contain a gravel fill. This fill is believed to be a younger glaciofluvial sediment, derived from ice in the headwaters of the Kennebec River; Borns suggests that it is of Valders age, correlative with Bloom's Kennebunk advance.

MOUNTAIN GLACIERS OF NORTHERN NEW ENGLAND

Cirques and troughs hollowed out by small mountain glaciers have long been known on Mount Washington and other parts of the Presidential Range of the White Mountains, and on Mount Katahdin. The largest of these glaciers, in the Great Gulf trough of the Presidential Range, was about 4 km long and was fed from three cirques. The main problem in the literature on these cirques (summarized by Flint, 1951, p. 24) is that of the times of their excavation and last occupation by local glaciers. Most likely the excavation of cirques mainly preceded the covering of the mountains by the last ice sheet. On Mount Katahdin, the ice sheet was succeeded by cirque glaciers that sharpened the erosional topography and built distinct moraines (Antevs, 1932, p. 15). On the Presidential Range, the evidence is not so clear. Antevs (1932, p. 11) suggests that local glaciers succeeded the last ice sheet in at least some cirques; R. P. Goldthwait (1940, p. 20) believes that the ice sheet followed all significant mountain glaciation; Thompson (1960-1961, p. 458) urges that cirque glaciers were latest. This problem of the contrast between Mount Katahdin and the Presidential Range would be solved if, as suggested by Borns (written communication, 1964), the last cirque glaciers existed on Mount Katahdin at a time when the

White Mountains were still covered by a local ice cap. Cirques and cirque-like valley heads occur at a number of other places in the high mountains of New Hampshire, Maine, and Vermont, but most of them are deeply trenched by V-shaped ravines, and they show no signs of reoccupation by cirque glaciers after the retreat of the last ice sheet.

LATE-GLACIAL WIND AND FROST ACTION

Pollen diagrams have been the principal source of information on late-glacial and postglacial climate in New England; the problems of interpretation are discussed by Davis (this volume). Fossil frost and wind phenomena (summarized by Smith, 1962, p. 327) give information on former climates. Some features that may not be strictly late-glacial are also discussed here.

PERIGLACIAL FEATURES IN SOUTHERN NEW ENGLAND

The most widespread periglacial phenomenon is the late-glacial, wind-deposited mixture of sand and silt. It was derived mostly from areas of stratified drift during deglaciation, before the surface was covered by vegetation, and it does not indicate aridity of climate. This mantle of eolian material is nearly ubiquitous in much of southeastern New England, where stratified drift is most extensive. It is commonly 1-1.5 m thick and is very important in soil genesis. In most places it is too sandy to be called loess, as Smith and Fraser (1935) had done. In areas of higher relief and less extensive stratified drift, the eolian material is less extensive and thinner, and where present it may lose its identity by mixing with underlying drift and by soil-forming processes.

Ventifacts of a wide variety of rock types commonly are contained in this eolian material, especially where it is relatively extensive and thick. The ventifacts are variably polished, pitted, and fluted, but very few are faceted. They range in size from boulders more than 3 m long to grains 2 mm or less in diameter. Ventifacts are best developed in the southeastern coastal area, as on Cape Cod (Mather *et al.*, 1942, p. 1163); they occur at several stratigraphic levels on Martha's Vineyard (Kaye, 1964a).

Wind-abraded bedrock outcrops (Hartshorn, 1962) show dominant late-glacial wind directions by flutes or other directional features. Eight such outcrops in eastern Massachusetts, Rhode Island, and eastern Connecticut were cut by winds from the north or north-northeast; only two were cut by winds from the northwest or west, the directions that would be expected at present.

Periglacial frost structures are exposed mostly as deformations of the contact between the eolian material and the underlying drift. The most common frost structures are involutions, presumably formed in the active zone of annual freeze and thaw. Ice-wedge structures are known from about fifteen localities; they generally are isolated structures, but they occur as polygonally intersecting groups near Thompson in the northeastern corner of Connecticut. The wedge structures commonly are 3 m deep and 0.3 m wide and seem more likely to have developed in perennially than in annually frozen ground; however, the permafrost may have lasted but a short time. Rare phenomena include solifluction deposits, clastic dikes, and frost-wedged bedrock.

At Cambridge, Massachusetts, in the Boston basin, a thin solifluction deposit (sandy silt and sand) contains pollen of high non-arboreal content and macrofossils of arctic-alpine tundra plants (Argus and Davis, 1962). Periglacial frost action in southern New England, except for the older and more intense frost action reported from Martha's Vineyard by Kaye (1964a, p. 138), seems to have been comparable to that in northern Poland or southernmost Sweden. Mean annual temperatures now are about 8-10°C in most of southern New England.

SAND DUNES IN THE CONNECTICUT VALLEY

The most extensive inland dunes in New England are within the area of glacial Lake Hitchcock; the largest are on the east side of the Connecticut River in southern Massachusetts. Some dunes lie directly on lake-bottom deposits. At Chicopee, dunes on a large lake delta are mostly U-shaped or parabolic; dune shape and direction of dip of beds indicate that they were formed by winds from the northwest.

At Longmeadow, dunes lie on a river terrace that was cut in lake-bottom deposits after the lake was drained. The large dunes are 30-200 m wide, as much as 15 m high, and range in length from small elliptical dunes to compound transverse dunes more than 2 km long. The beds consistently dip gently south, and the dunes evidently were formed by winds from the north.

The surface on which the Chicopee dunes lie was available for dune-building earlier (late-glacial or very early postglacial time) than was the Longmeadow area. However, the likely directions of change of winds (considering the wind-abraded bedrock outcrops mentioned above) indicate that the Longmeadow dunes may be the older. The main dissection of the lake deposits by the Connecticut River and its tributaries probably took place quickly after the lake was drained. The subsequent covering with vegetation and decrease in stream activity must have ended any important dune-building, so that the dunes are probably no later than early postglacial in age.

FROST ACTION ABOVE TIMBERLINE

Timberline—the upper limit of continuous scrub forest—is at altitudes of about 1,465-1,585 m on Mount Washington and other parts of the Presidential Range (Antevs, 1932, p. 71). Most of the surface above this line is covered by coarse frost-riven and frost-moved rubble, which appears also on Mount Katahdin and a few other mountains. Antevs (1932, p. 34) first described the patterns of distribution of this rubble; he distinguished large inactive stone nets, stone stripes, and other features from small, presently active features. For example, nets with lichen-covered stones and turf-covered centers 1-3 m in diameter are contrasted with nets that are nearly free of vegetation and have a mesh diameter of 0.3-0.45 m. Antevs (1932, p. 39) believed that most of the frost-shattering and movement of rubble had occurred immediately after the mountain tops became free of the last ice sheet and that modern frost action was relatively insignificant. R. P. Goldthwait (1940, p. 30) supports this distinction with additional evidence. However, Thompson (1960-1961) believes that all the rubble is now active and moving. Permafrost now exists above timberline because of the very severe climate; the mean annual temperature at the summit of Mount Washington (1917 m) is −2.8°C. Patterned ground and other phenomena of mass movement at lower elevations present a similar problem of age (Denny, 1958, p. 92).

Postglacial Changes

Most of the New England landscape now seems to be very much as it was at the time of deglaciation, except that it is covered by vegetation, and that many of the depressions are partly filled with bog and swamp sediments. The principal postglacial changes have been those along shorelines and rivers.

The present position of the shoreline is the result of the interaction of postglacial eustatic change and crustal movement. In general, an initial submergence, presumably caused by rapid eustatic rise of sea level as the ice sheet melted, is followed by an emergence caused by rapid crustal uplift, and finally by another submergence. The maximum level of the initial submergence rises northward, as is shown by the late-glacial or early postglacial marine deposits, and it is below present sea level south of the Boston area. The shoreline of the subsequent emergence is well below present sea level (probably at least 40 m below in southeastern Connecticut, but less to the north), and valleys cut at the time of emergence were partly filled with estuarine deposits during the final submergence (Upson and Spencer, 1964, p. 38).

Graphs of these changes of level, controlled by radiocarbon dates, have been constructed for several parts of New England, such as Cape Cod (Redfield and Rubin, 1962), coastal Connecticut (Bloom and Stuiver, 1963), southwestern Maine (Bloom, 1963), and the Boston area (Kaye and Barghoorn, 1964). In the last two of these studies, particular effort has been made to separate the effects of eustatic and crustal changes. Most authors have indicated that the final submergence consisted of an earlier part in which submergence was relatively rapid, and a later part, occupying about the last 3,000 years, in which submergence at a less rapid rate of about 0.1 m per century has continued to the present. However, this view has been challenged by the interpretation that sea level has been essentially stable for the last 3,000 years, with minor fluctuations (Kaye and Barghoorn, 1964, p. 76; Kaye 1964c).

The present shoreline and its erosional and depositional features were described in detail by Johnson (1925). An example of modern studies is that on beach changes on outer Cape Cod by Zeigler and Tuttle (1961). The exceptional shoreline changes produced by a hurricane of subtropical origin are described by Nichols and Marston (1939). Submarine sediments, forms, and processes are the subjects of very active study at present.

Stream processes have been little studied in New England. Jahns (1947) described the fluvial features of the Connecticut Valley in Massachusetts, in relation to the glacial history and to modern floods. Unprecedented floods in 1955 (Bogart, 1960), caused by subtropical air masses, locally produced unprecedented erosional effects.

Slope processes also have been given little attention.

Mass movement on a somewhat surprising scale on moderate slopes in central Massachusetts is indicated by careful studies of soils and vegetation (Lyford *et al.*, 1963). The most conspicuous kind of mass movement in New England consists of the well-known debris avalanches on steep slopes in the White Mountains (Flaccus, 1958).

Present wind action is almost entirely coastal, and large dune masses occur on Cape Cod and elsewhere. Inland areas of active dune sand generally are the effect of agricultural disturbance of once continuous vegetation. Wind abrasion of stones is taking place locally along coasts, and in a few places such as large sand pits inland.

Because most of New England has undergone little geological change in postglacial time, very few archaeological sites can be fitted into a geological stratigraphy or sequence of events. The principal exceptions are coastal sites that have been involved in postglacial changes of level (*e.g.* Johnson, 1949). However, artifacts of different cultural levels at many places show a consistent stratification within the uppermost meter or less of surface materials. An example is the Bull Brook site at Ipswich in northeastern Massachusetts, where radiocarbon dates of disseminated fine charcoal associated with a lower level characterized by fluted points indicate an age of about 9,000 years, the oldest dated site in New England (Byers, 1959). The persistence of this kind of near-surface archaeological stratigraphy indicates that at such places the intensity of postglacial disturbance by roots and by wind-toppled trees must be less than that inferred by Denny (1958, p. 90).

References

Alden, W. C., 1924, The physical features of central Massachusetts: U.S. Geol. Surv. Bull. 760-B, p. 13-105

Antevs, Ernst, 1922, The recession of the last ice sheet in New England: Amer. Geogr. Soc. Res. Ser. No. 11, 120 p.

—— 1928, The last glaciation: Amer. Geogr. Soc. Res. Ser. No. 17, 292 p.

—— 1932, Alpine zone of Mt. Washington Range: Auburn, Maine, Merrill & Webber, 118 p.

—— 1962, Transatlantic climatic agreement versus C14 dates: J. Geol., v. 70, p. 194-205

Argus, G. W., and Davis, M. B., 1962, Macrofossils from a late-glacial deposit at Cambridge, Massachusetts: Amer. Midl. Nat., v. 67, p. 106-117

Barghoorn, E. S., Jr., and Spackman, W., Jr., 1949, A preliminary study of the flora of the Brandon lignite: Amer. J. Sci., v. 247, p. 33-39

Bloom, A. L., 1960, Late Pleistocene changes of sea level in southwestern Maine: Maine Geol. Surv., 143 p.

—— 1963, Late-Pleistocene fluctuations of sea level and postglacial crustal rebound in coastal Maine: Amer. J. Sci., v. 261, p. 862-879

Bloom, A. L., and Stuiver, Minze, 1963, Submergence of the Connecticut coast: Science, v. 139, p. 332-334

Bogart, D. B., 1960, Floods of August-October 1955, New England to North Carolina: U.S. Geol. Surv. Water-Supply Pap. 1420, 854 p.

Borns, H. W., Jr., 1963, Preliminary report on the age and distribution of the late Pleistocene ice in north central Maine: Amer. J. Sci., v. 261, p. 738-740

Borns, H. W., Jr., and Allen, H. W., 1963, Pre-glacial residual soil in Thomaston, Maine: J. Sed. Petrology, v. 33, p. 675-679

Broecker, W. S., and Farrand, W. R., 1963, Radiocarbon age of the Two Creeks forest bed, Wisconsin: Geol. Soc. Amer. Bull., v. 74, p. 795-802

Byers, D. S., 1959, Radiocarbon dates for the Bull Brook site, Massachusetts: Amer. Antiq., v. 24, p. 427-429

Caldwell, D. W., 1959, Glacial lake and glacial marine clays of the Farmington area, Maine: Maine Geol. Surv. Spec. Geol. Stud. 3, 48 p.

Chapman, C. A., and Rioux, R. L., 1958, Statistical study of topography, sheeting, and jointing in granite, Acadia National Park, Maine: Amer. J. Sci., v. 256, p. 111-127

Chapman, D. H., 1937, Late-glacial and postglacial history of the Champlain Valley: Amer. J. Sci., v. 34 (5th ser.), p. 89-124

Chute, N. E., 1959, Glacial geology of the Mystic Lakes–Fresh Pond area, Massachusetts: U.S. Geol. Surv. Bull. 1061-F, p. 187-216

Colton, R. B., and Cushman, R. V., 1962, Lacustrine features in north-central Connecticut (abst.): Geol. Soc. Amer. Spec. Pap. 68, p. 155

Currier, L. W., 1941, Disappearance of the last ice sheet in Massachusetts by stagnation zone retreat (abst.): Geol. Soc. Amer. Bull., v. 52, p. 1895

Cushman, R. V., 1964, Ground-water resources of north-central Connecticut: U.S. Geol. Surv. Water-Supply Pap. 1752, 96 p.

Davis, M. B., 1961, The problem of rebedded pollen in late-glacial sediments at Taunton, Massachusetts: Amer. J. Sci., v. 259, p. 211-222

Deevey, E. S., 1958, Radiocarbon-dated pollen sequences in eastern North America: Geobot. Inst. Rübel Veröff., Heft 34, p. 30-37

Denny, C. S., 1956, Wisconsin drifts in the Elmira region, New York, and their possible equivalents in New England: Amer. J. Sci., v. 254, p. 82-95

——— 1958, Surficial geology of the Canaan area, New Hampshire: U.S. Geol. Surv. Bull. 1061-C, p. 73-101

Donner, J. J., 1964, Pleistocene geology of eastern Long Island, New York: Amer. J. Sci., v. 262, p. 355-376

Fenneman, N. M., 1938, Physiography of eastern United States: New York, McGraw-Hill, 714 p.

Flaccus, Edward, 1958, White Mountain landslides: Appalachia, No. 127, p. 175-191

Flint, R. F., 1930, The glacial geology of Connecticut: Connecticut State Geol. Nat. Hist. Surv. Bull. 47, 294 p.

——— 1947, Glacial geology and the Pleistocene Epoch: New York, John Wiley & Sons, 589 p.

——— 1951, Highland centers of former glacial outflow in northeastern North America: Geol. Soc. Amer. Bull., v. 62, p. 21-37

——— 1953, Probable Wisconsin substages and late Wisconsin events in northeastern United States and southeastern Canada: Geol. Soc. Amer. Bull., v. 64, p. 897-919

——— 1956, New radiocarbon dates and late-Pleistocene stratigraphy: Amer. J. Sci., v. 254, p. 265-287

——— 1957, Glacial and Pleistocene geology: New York, John Wiley & Sons, 553 p.

——— 1961, Two tills in southern Connecticut: Geol. Soc. Amer. Bull., v. 72, p. 1687-1692

——— 1963a, Status of the Pleistocene Wisconsin stage in central North America: Science, v. 139, p. 402-404

——— 1963b, Altitude, lithology, and the Fall Zone in Connecticut: J. Geol., v. 71, p. 683-697

Flint, R. F., *et al.*, 1945, Glacial map of North America: Geol. Soc. Amer. Spec. Pap. 60

Flint, R. F., *et al.*, 1959, Glacial map of the United States east of the Rocky Mountains: Geol. Soc. Amer.

Frye, J. C., and Willman, H. B., 1963, Development of Wisconsinan classification in Illinois related to radiocarbon chronology: Geol. Soc. Amer. Bull., v. 74, p. 501-506

Fuller, M. L., 1914, The geology of Long Island, New York: U.S. Geol. Surv. Prof. Pap. 82, 231 p.

Goldsmith, Richard, 1960, A post-Harbor Hill–Charlestown moraine in southeastern Connecticut: Amer. J. Sci., v. 258, p. 740-743

——— 1964, Surficial geology of the Niantic quadrangle, Connecticut: U.S. Geol. Surv. Geol. Quad. Map GQ-329

Goldthwait, J. W., 1938, The uncovering of New Hampshire by the last ice sheet: Amer. J. Sci., v. 36, 5th ser., p. 345-372

Goldthwait, J. W., Goldthwait, Lawrence, and Goldthwait, R. P., 1951, The geology of New Hampshire. Part I, Surficial geology: New Hampshire State Planning and Development Comm., 81 p.

Goldthwait, J. W., and Kruger, F. C., 1938, Weathered rock in and under the drift in New Hampshire: Geol. Soc. Amer. Bull., v. 49, p. 1183-1198

Goldthwait, R. P., 1940, Geology of the Presidential Range: New Hampshire Acad. Sci. Bull. No. 1, 43 p.

Hanley, J. B., 1959, Surficial geology of the Poland quadrangle, Maine: U.S. Geol. Surv. Geol. Quad. Map GQ-120

Hansen, W. R., 1953, Late Tertiary and Pleistocene drainage changes in the Hudson and Maynard quadrangles, Massachusetts: J. Geol., v. 61, p. 353-362

Hartshorn, J. H., 1960, Geology of the Bridgewater quadrangle, Massachusetts: U.S. Geol. Surv. Geol. Quad. Map GQ-127

——— 1962, Late-glacial eolian activity in Massachusetts (abst.): Geol. Soc. Amer. Spec. Pap. 68, p. 194

Hyyppä, Esa, 1955, On the Pleistocene geology of southeastern New England: Bull. Comm. Geol. Finlande, No. 167, p. 155-225

Jahns, R. H., 1943, Sheet structure in granites; its origin and use as a measure of glacial erosion in New England: J. Geol., v. 51, p. 71-98

——— 1947, Geologic features of the Connecticut Valley, Massachusetts, as related to recent floods: U.S. Geol. Surv. Water-Supply Pap. 996, 158 p.

——— 1953, Surficial geology of the Ayer quadrangle, Massachusetts: U.S. Geol. Surv. Geol. Quad. Map GQ-21

Jahns, R. H., and Willard, M. E., 1942, Late Pleistocene and recent deposits in the Connecticut Valley, Massachusetts: Amer. J. Sci., v. 240, p. 161-191, 265-287

Johnson, D. W., 1925, The New England–Acadian shoreline: New York, John Wiley & Sons, 608 p.

Johnson, Frederick (ed.), 1949, The Boylston Street Fishweir II: Peabody Fdn. Archaeology Pap., v. 4, No. 1, 133 p.

Judson, S. S., Jr., 1949, The Pleistocene stratigraphy of Boston, Massachusetts, and its relation to the Boylston Street Fishweir, p. 7-48 in Johnson, Frederick (ed.), The Boylston Street Fishweir II: Peabody Fdn. Archaeology Pap., v. 4, No. 1, 133 p.

Kaye, C. A., 1960, Surficial geology of the Kingston quadrangle, Rhode Island: U.S. Geol. Surv. Bull. 1071-I, p. 341-396

—— 1961, Pleistocene stratigraphy of Boston, Massachusetts: U.S. Geol. Surv. Prof. Pap. 424-B, p. 73-76

—— 1962, Early postglacial beavers in southeastern New England: Science, v. 132, p. 906-907

—— 1964a, Outline of Pleistocene geology of Martha's Vineyard, Massachusetts: U.S. Geol. Surv. Prof. Pap. 501-C, p. 134-139

—— 1964b, Illinoian and Early Wisconsin moraines of Martha's Vineyard, Massachusetts: U.S. Geol. Surv. Prof. Pap. 501-C, p. 140-143

—— 1964c, The upper limit of barnacles as an index of sea-level change on the New England coast during the past 100 years: J. Geol., v. 72, p. 580-600

Kaye, C. A., and Barghoorn, E. S., 1964, Late Quaternary sea-level change and crustal rise at Boston, Massachusetts, with notes on the autocompaction of peat: Geol. Soc. Amer. Bull., v. 75, p. 63-80

Koteff, Carl, 1963, Glacial lakes near Concord, Massachusetts: U.S. Geol. Surv. Prof. Pap. 475-C, p. 142-144

Leavitt, H. W., and Perkins, E. H., 1935, Glacial geology of Maine: Maine Technol. Exper. Stat. Bull. 30, v. 2, 232 p.

Lougee, R. J., 1939, Geology of the Connecticut watershed: New Hampshire Fish and Game Dept., Biological Survey of the Connecticut watershed, Survey Rep. 4, p. 131-149

—— 1940, Deglaciation of New England: J. Geomorph., v. 3, p. 189-217

—— 1953, A chronology of postglacial time in eastern North America: Sci. Monthly, v. 76, p. 259-276

Lougee, R. J., and Vander Pyl, A. W., 1951, Glacial water levels in the Thames-Willimantic River Valley: Sci. Monthly, v. 73, p. 275-283

Lyford, W. H., Goodlett, J. C., and Coates, W. H., 1963, Landforms, soils with fragipans, and forest on a slope in the Harvard Forest: Harvard Univ. Harvard For. Bull. 30, 68 p.

MacClintock, Paul, 1954, Leaching of Wisconsin glacial gravels in eastern North America: Geol. Soc. Amer. Bull., v. 65, p. 369-384

MacClintock, Paul, and Terasmae, Jaan, 1960, Glacial history of Covey Hill: J. Geology, v. 68, p. 232-241

Mather, K. F., 1952, Glacial geology in the Buzzards Bay region and western Cape Cod: Geol. Soc. Amer. Guidebook for field trips in New England, p. 119-142

Mather, K. F., Goldthwait, R. P., and Thiesmeyer, L. R., 1942, Pleistocene geology of western Cape Cod, Massachusetts: Geol. Soc. Amer. Bull., v. 53, p. 1127-1174

Nichols, R. L., and Marston, A. W., 1939, Shoreline changes in Rhode Island produced by hurricane of September 21, 1938: Geol. Soc. Amer. Bull., v. 50, p. 1357-1370

Oldale, R. N., 1961, Late-glacial marine deposits in the Salem quadrangle, Massachusetts: U.S. Geol. Surv. Prof. Pap. 424C, p. 59-60

Redfield, A. C., and Rubin, Meyer, 1962, The age of salt marsh peat and its relation to recent changes in sea level at Barnstable, Massachusetts: Natl. Acad. Sci. Proc., v. 48, p. 1728-1735

Rich, J. L., 1943, Buried stagnant ice as a normal product of a progressively retreating glacier in a hilly region: Amer. J. Sci., v. 241, p. 95-100

Schafer, J. P., 1961, Correlation of end moraines in southern Rhode Island: U.S. Geol. Survey Prof. Pap. 424-D, p. 68-70

Shaler, N. S., 1893, The conditions of erosion beneath deep glaciers, based upon a study of the boulder train from Iron Hill, Cumberland, R.I.: Harvard Coll. Mus. Comp. Zool. Bull. 16, p. 185-225

Smith, H. T. U., 1962, Periglacial frost features and related phenomena in the United States: Biul. Peryglacjalny, Nr. 11, p. 326-342

Smith, H. T. U., and Fraser, H. J., 1935, Loess in the vicinity of Boston, Massachusetts: Amer. J. Sci., v. 30, 5th ser., p. 16-32

Stewart, D. P., 1961, The glacial geology of Vermont: Vermont Geol. Surv. Bull. 19, 124 p.

Stewart, D. P., and MacClintock, Paul, 1964, The Wisconsin stratigraphy of northern Vermont: Amer. J. Sci., v. 262, p. 1089-1097

Thompson, W. F., 1960-1961, The shape of New England mountains: Appalachia, v. 33, p. 145-159, 316-335, 458-478

Upson, J. E., and Spencer, C. W., 1964, Bedrock valleys of the New England coast as related to fluctuations of sea level: U.S. Geol. Surv. Prof. Pap. 454-M, p. 1-44

Weiss, Lawrence, 1954, Foraminifera and origin of the Gardiners Clay (Pleistocene), eastern Long Island, New York: U.S. Geol. Surv. Prof. Pap. 254-G, p. 143-163

White, S. E., 1947, Two tills and the development of glacial drainage in the vicinity of Stafford Springs, Connecticut: Amer. J. Sci., v. 245, p. 754-778

Woodworth, J. B., 1898, Some glacial wash plains of southern New England: Essex Inst. Bull., v. 29, p. 71-119

Woodworth, J. B., and Wigglesworth, Edward, et al., 1934, Geography and geology of the region including Cape Cod, the Elizabeth Islands, Nantucket, Marthas Vineyard, No Mans Land and Block Island: Harvard Coll. Mus. Comp. Zool. Mem., v. 52, 338 p.

Zeigler, J. M., and Tuttle, S. D., 1961, Beach changes based on daily measurements of four Cape Cod beaches: J. Geol., v. 69, p. 583-599

Zeigler, J. M., Tuttle, S. D., Tasha, H. J., and Giese, G. S., 1964, Pleistocene geology of outer Cape Cod, Massachusetts: Geol. Soc. Amer. Bull., v. 75, p. 705-714

Summary

Several ice advances crossed New England to or beyond the present south coast. The most comprehensive stratigraphic sections are those of Martha's Vinyard, with seven drifts, and the Boston basin, with four drifts. At least some of the older drifts are of pre-Sangamon age. A widespread penultimate glaciation may be of post-Sangamon, pre-classical Wisconsin age.

The maximum advance of the last ice sheet, which built the southern coastal moraines, was probably in Tazewell (early Woodfordian) time. Its disappearance was mostly by stagnation-zone retreat. Large glacial lakes are inferred from lacustrine deposits in the Connecticut Valley and Champlain lowland. Late-glacial marine submergence occurred in the Champlain lowland and along the coast north from Boston; marine deposits rise to a maximum elevation of 120 m in Maine. Readvances in southern New England (Middletown-Cambridge), northern Vermont, and southwestern Maine are not well dated, but they may be approximately of Cary, Port Huron, and perhaps Valders age. The last ice masses in New England were a possible local ice cap on the White Mountains and in western Maine, and cirque glaciers on Mount Katahdin.

Frost and eolian features record late-glacial (and perhaps early postglacial) climatic and other conditions different from those of the present. Postglacial changes have been minor in comparison with the effects of glaciation, except for changes of level. Altitudes of glaciolacustrine and marine deposits indicate postglacial tilt upward to the north. The marine limit intersects present sea level near Boston.

THE ATLANTIC COASTAL PLAIN AND
THE APPALACHIAN HIGHLANDS IN THE QUATERNARY *

HORACE G. RICHARDS,[1] SHELDON JUDSON[2]

GENERAL STATEMENT

In eastern United States south of the glacial boundary, much information exists on the stratigraphy of the Coastal Plain. In contrast, data on the Pleistocene history of the neighboring Appalachian Highlands are scanty. More space is therefore devoted to Richards' discussion on the stratigraphy of the Coastal Plain than to Judson's observations on geomorphic processes recorded in the Highlands and the Coastal Plain.

PLEISTOCENE STRATIGRAPHY OF THE ATLANTIC COASTAL PLAIN

HORACE G. RICHARDS

ON THE Atlantic Seaboard south of the terminal moraine of the Wisconsin glaciation Pleistocene formations are composed of gravel, sand, silt, and clay, ranging in thickness from a few feet to a score or more. They lie unconformably on the unconsolidated sediments of the Coastal Plain. At some places they form terraces, with what is considered by some to be low wave-cut bluffs or beach ridges at their landward margin.

Cooke has attributed terrace remnants ranging from 25 to 270 ft (7.5 to 81 m) in elevation to interglacial high stands of sea level (Table 1). The lowest terrace (Pamlico, 25 ft, 7.5 m) forms a fairly continuous broad stretch of flat terrain. Its origin is easily demonstrated by the abundance of marine fossils (Fig. 1). The higher terraces are largely discontinuous and patchy, and their marine origin has been questioned by numerous writers, notably Flint (1940), Hack (1955), and Richards (1962). It has recently been shown that the formations underlying the terraces may not necessarily be of the same age as the terraces themselves (Moore, 1956), but in the present review it will generally be assumed that the terraces and formations are coextensive.

Most earlier writers have regarded the east coast of the United States south of the Wisconsin drift border as having been relatively stable during and since the Pleistocene.

* Much of this chapter has been adapted from portions of Richards' "Studies on the marine Pleistocene" (1962) with the permission of the American Philosophical Society. Dr. Wallace Broecker of the Lamont Geological Observatory kindly permitted the use of certain radiocarbon dates of shells submitted by Richards.

[1] Academy of Natural Sciences, Philadelphia, Pennsylvania.

[2] Department of Geology, Princeton University, Princeton, New Jersey.

TABLE 1

Correlation of Pleistocene Terraces
(Adapted from various papers by C. W. Cooke)

Altitude of shore line		Name of terrace	Age
(ft)	(m)		
?	?	—	Nebraskan
215	65.2	Coharie	Aftonian
170	51.5	Sunderland	
?	?	—	Kansan
140	42.4	Okefenokee	
100	30.0	Wicomico	
70	21.2	Penholloway	Yarmouth
42	12.7	Talbot	
?	?	(Horry Clay)	Illinoian
25	7.5	Pamlico	Sangamon
?	?	—	Wisconsin

This concept has been questioned by some recent workers (Harrison, 1965), and the possibility of at least local warping must be given serious consideration.

LONG ISLAND

While the Pleistocene geology of Long Island is more fully discussed by Muller (this volume), it is desirable to summarize briefly certain aspects of the geology of the island in view of its probable correlation with the deposits of the Coastal Plain of New Jersey.

The most extensive report on the Pleistocene of Long Island is that of Fuller (1914), who recognized four glacial and three interglacial stages. This interpretation was questioned by MacClintock and Richards (1936), who proposed a somewhat less complicated interpretation that was

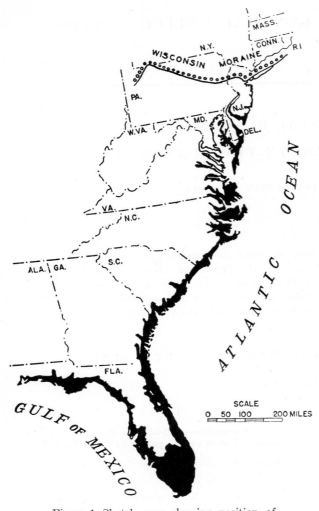

Figure 1. Sketch map showing position of Sangamon (Pamlico) shoreline along the Atlantic Coastal Plain.

The Cape May Formation was originally regarded as largely alluvial and contemporary with Wisconsin outwash (Salisbury and Knapp, 1917). The presence of a warm-climate marine fauna, especially from Cape May County, favored an interglacial dating (Richards, 1933; MacClintock and Richards, 1936) and correlation with the Pamlico terrace formation farther south.

Excavations for the Cape May Canal have shown that the Cape May Formation is complex (Richards, 1944). The sands and clays of the marine phase are overlain by sands and gravels of non-marine origin. The fauna from the spoil banks consists of two assemblages: (1) a warm fauna thought to be of Sangamon age, and (2) a cold fauna, especially characterized by *Neptunea stonei,* thought to be of Wisconsin age. Some shells from the spoil bank of the Canal were dated at Lamont as older than 35,000 radiocarbon years B.P. (before the present).

The marine phase of the Cape May Formation can be seen above sea level at only two places. One is along the banks of the Cape May Canal at the bridge on the Seashore Road, where casts of *Mactra* and *Mercenaria* can be seen up to 5 ft (1.5 m) above low tide in a silt overlain by cross-bedded sand. The other locality is along Maurice River at Port Elizabeth, Cumberland County, where abundant deposits of oyster shells can be seen up to 10 ft (3 m) above low tide. These have been dated at Lamont as greater than 35,000 B.P.

New Jersey

Three nonglacial Pleistocene formations have been described from New Jersey—the non-marine Bridgeton and Pensauken and the partly marine Cape May. An older formation, the Beacon Hill, is generally regarded as Pliocene, but the inclusion of large boulders near Woodmansie suggests that it may be early Pleistocene.

The Bridgeton and Pensauken formations are very difficult to distinguish and are generally separated on the basis of elevations. They were originally described as alluvial (Salisbury and Knapp, 1917), although a few writers have suggested that they represent shorelines dating from the first two interglacial ages. However, no conclusive evidence of a marine origin has been demonstrated, and the lithology of the formations—largely sand and gravel—strongly suggests an alluvial origin. MacClintock and Richards (1936) give evidence for alluvial origin and state: "It seems legitimate to consider the older gravels either as one formation with many and complex parts, or a series of many formations." Thus, the Bridgeton-Pensauken complex might represent a fairly long interval of time covering much of the early and middle Pleistocene. The presence of ice-rafted boulders, for example in the Pensauken formation near Jamesburg, N.J., as well as products of local solifluction, suggest a glacial age, while warm-climate fossil plants in Middlesex County, N.J. (Berry and Hawkins, 1935), suggest an interglacial dating.

The non-marine phase of the Cape May Formation can be traced up the Delaware River, where it apparently merges with the Wisconsin outwash somewhere between Camden and Trenton. Swamp deposits under Philadelphia, Pa., presumably in the Cape May Formation, have yielded

in line with the glacial-control theory for sea-level change and that could be better correlated with the sequence in New Jersey.

The principal nonglacial Pleistocene formations on Long Island are the fossiliferous Gardiners Clay and the overlying Jacob Sand. These are especially well exposed on Gardiners Island, where they have been greatly deformed by the overriding ice. Fuller regarded the Gardiners and Jacob as of Yarmouth age, with the Sangamon being represented by the Vineyard erosion interval. MacClintock and Richards (1936) found no evidence for this interval of erosion. On the basis of temperature-sensitive molluscan faunas, they prefer to regard the Gardiners clay as Sangamon, or possibly in part of Yarmouth age, and the Jacob Sand as late Sangamon or early Wisconsin. A Sangamon age of the Gardiners Clay has recently been favored by Donner (1964) on the basis of pollen studies.

The Gardiners Clay occurs in the subsurface of western Long Island and has been correlated with the Cape May Formation of New Jersey (MacClintock and Richards, 1936).

well-preserved remains of cypress (*Taxodium distichum*), which have been dated as older than 42,000 B.P. (P-304) (Richards, 1960).

Measurements with sub-bottom depth-recording instruments have indicated a prominent reflecting horizon at about 80 fath (146 m) off the coast of New Jersey. This is interpreted as a wave-cut feature (Ewing *et al.*, 1960). Fossils from cores in this area indicate cold, shallow water, probably representing a glacial stage (Richards and Werner, 1964).

DELAWARE

Until recently very little work has been done on the Pleistocene deposits of Delaware, and the formation names applied are usually those of New Jersey or Maryland. The localities yielding marine fossils are mostly from shallow excavations or well borings and contain few species of significance.

Jordan (1962) suggests the revival of the term Columbia for the entire section of Pleistocene sediments that overlies the Tertiary on the Coastal Plain of Delaware, a use first proposed by McGee (1888). In 1964 Jordan described these sediments as follows:

"The Columbia deposits of Delaware form a sheet of sand with a maximum thickness of approximately 150 feet which covers most of the Coastal Plain portion of the State. The dispersal pattern, deduced from foreset dip directions of cross-bedding, indicates that the sediment entered the study area from the northeast, *i.e.*, from the direction of the valley of the Delaware River between Wilmington and Trenton, and spread south and southeast over Delaware. . . .

"The Columbia sediment is essentially medium sand but coarser admixtures are typical in the northern, and finer admixtures in the southern parts of the area. . . .

"The sands represent deposits of a major stream system, the distal portion of which has been reworked by a transgressing and regressing sea which at one time covered at least the south half of Sussex County. The systematic variation of the properties studied suggests only a single cycle of deposition. It is postulated that the stream which deposited the Columbia sands derived its great volume of water (and sediment) in part from the melt-water of a continental glacier. Channel cutting and filling are attributed to the distributary portion of this stream system operating on the Coastal Plain during a time of glacial advance and lowered sea level. A later stand of the sea several tens of feet above the present level is required by the marine features of southern Delaware."

MARYLAND

Shattuck (1906) recognized the Talbot, Wicomico, and Sunderland formations. Only the lowest, Talbot, contained marine fossils, mostly from two localities in St. Mary's County—Wailes Bluff and Langley's Bluff. These localities are now referred to the Pamlico terrace formation as redefined by Cooke (1931).

The best known locality is Wailes Bluff at Cornfield Harbor near the mouth of the Potomac River, where about 78 species of invertebrates have been recorded. The fossils occur up to an elevation 10 ft (3 m) above sea level. In general the fauna suggests a slightly warmer climate than that of today, and the formation has been correlated as Sangamon (Richards, 1936).

It is noted that, as at Cape May, N.J., the marine phase is overlain by non-fossiliferous sand and gravel, suggesting a shoaling sea at the beginning of Wisconsin time. Blake (1953), on the other hand, regarded the age as Aftonian.

While no marine fossils have been found in the higher gravels, Cooke (1958) believes that later dissection has obscured the shoreline features. On the other hand Hack (1955), on the basis of mapping in Prince Georges and Charles Counties, believes that the higher gravels are non-marine and that no evidence of Pleistocene marine transgression exists higher than 100 ft (30 m). Actual marine fossils do not occur above about 10 ft.

VIRGINIA

Clark and Miller (1912) extended Shattuck's formations of Maryland into Virginia. They regarded the Talbot formation as largely of marine origin, although they realized that the presence of fossil plants at various localities indicated that at least part of the formation was non-marine.

Wentworth (1930) divided the Talbot of Virginia into three parts as follows: (1) Princess Anne terrace and formation of marine origin. Occurs from 10 to 15 ft elevation (3 to 4.5 m). (2) Dismal Swamp terrace and formation, largely of marine origin. Upper surface of marine part ranges from 15 to 25 ft elevation (4.5 to 7.6 m). (3) Chowan terrace, mostly fluvial, from 25 ft near the coast to 80-90 ft (7.6 to 24-27.3 m) near the Fall Belt.

Cooke (1931) reintroduced the term Pamlico, originally used by Stephenson (1912) for the Dismal Swamp, pointing out its priority. He also used the term Talbot in a restricted sense for the Chowan. Later Cooke (1935) doubted the regional extent of the Princess Anne terrace.

Flint (1940, 1942) objected to the correlations of Cooke and presented evidence to show that the higher terraces are of fluvial origin and that only two definite shorelines can be demonstrated in Virginia and the Carolinas. He did not correlate either of these shorelines with any of the terrace names. He used the name "Suffolk Scarp" as proposed by Wentworth (1930) for a line approximately equivalent to the inner edge of the Pamlico terrace. Its toe is between 20 and 30 ft (6 to 9 m) in elevation. The higher shoreline of Wentworth (Surry Scarp) has an elevation at its toe of 90 ft (27.3 m). The marine origin of the higher scarp is mainly based on physiographic evidence, although, as stated later, some paleontological evidence exists in South Carolina.

A detailed study of the Pleistocene of southeastern Virginia has recently been undertaken by Oaks and Coch (1963). Their preliminary study has revealed various formations below the level of the Suffolk Scarp, instead of the one (Pamlico) previously assigned to most of these deposits.

It is possible, as suggested by Oaks and Coch, that these various formations may represent a large part of Pleistocene time and thus indicate at least two interglacial high stands of the sea. On the other hand, they may represent various minor units within the Sangamon. The fact that the marine faunas of the various localities (as studied by the present writer) are very similar, except for ecological variations, gives a slight preference to the latter view. At any rate, no paleontological evidence for a sea higher than 33 ft (10 m) has been obtained. Undoubtedly many of the problems of the Virginia Pleistocene will be resolved when the final report by Oaks and Coch is published.

NORTH CAROLINA

Johnson (1907) recognized a series of five well-preserved terraces as well as remnants of two higher terraces in North Carolina. Stephenson (1912) subdivided the Talbot of Shattuck into two well-marked terraces—the Chowan (60 ft, 18 m) and the Pamlico (20 ft, 6 m). According to Stephenson (1912, p. 282), "the eastern boundary is marked by a well defined sea-facing escarpment which separates the Chowan terrace from the lower-lying Pamlico terrace plain." Cooke extended this subdivision northward into Maryland and Virginia and southward into South Carolina. He substituted the term Talbot for Chowan.

In North Carolina marine fossils have been found only in the Pamlico Formation. The fauna suggests a climate slightly warmer than that of today in the same latitude; it has been correlated with the Sangamon interglacial (Richards, 1936, 1950). While many of the fossil localities are close to or below sea level, in a few places along the Neuse River the fossils occur up to 25 ft (8 m) elevation and are overlain by non-fossiliferous sands probably equivalent to the upper member at Cape May, N.J., and Cornfield Harbor, Md.

Along the Neuse River 16 km below New Bern, N.C., the marine Pamlico overlies truncated cypress stumps, 2-2.5 m in diameter, which are embedded in dark carbonaceous clay. This has been referred to the Horry clay, thought to have been deposited during a time of low sea level in pre-Sangamon time (Cooke, 1937).

In the swamp country of eastern Virginia and North Carolina, the Pamlico Formation is overlain by more than 10 ft (3 m) of peat and plant remains. Dachnowski-Stokes and Wells (1929) have traced the late-Pleistocene history of parts of Carteret County, N.C., and show that after the deposition of the Pamlico shells sea level was lowered, during which time the peat was deposited. This peat is probably of Wisconsin and Recent age.

The higher "terraces" or "shorelines" contain no evidence of marine origin and are probably fluvial.

DuBar and Solliday (1963) suggest dropping the term "Pamlico" as a lithologic unit but retaining it for the relatively flat seaward-sloping terrace-plain that lies below an elevation of 25 ft (7.5 m). The late-Pleistocene deposits of the Lower Neuse Estuary (formerly referred to the Pamlico) are referred to a new unit that he calls the Flanner Beach Formation.

SOUTH CAROLINA

The first work on the marine Pleistocene of South Carolina was that of Holmes (1860), who described the rich fauna at Simmons Bluff on Yonges Island. This fauna was later studied in some detail by Pugh (1905). The first mapping of the Pleistocene terraces in the state was the work of Cooke (1936). As in North Carolina, all localities con-

taining marine fossils were referred to the Pamlico terrace formation (Richards, 1936).

Excavations for the Santee-Cooper Canal in 1941 revealed a bed of shells at elevation 65 ft (20 m), lying above the Eocene limestone. The fauna was a mixture of Pliocene and Pleistocene species and may represent an early-Pleistocene deposit possibly equivalent to the Penhalloway terrace deposit (Richards, 1943); on the other hand, it may represent a very late Pliocene deposit not recognized elsewhere along the East Coast. If it is Pleistocene, as seems likely, it represents the highest elevation along the East Coast where marine fossils have been found.

Doering (1960) favors the view that an early-Pleistocene sea invaded the southern Atlantic Coastal Plain.

Evidence of marine Pleistocene at higher elevations than Cooke's Pamlico is given by Malde (1959), who described the new Ladson Formation, which includes portions of both the Talbot and Penholloway terraces of Cooke. More recently Colquhoun (1962) has reported traces of a 95-ft (30-m) shoreline (Penholloway) that he regards as marine. Cooke (1937) described the Horry Clay from a section of the Intra-Coastal Canal 2.5 miles northwest of Myrtle Beach, Horry County, S.C. As near New Bern, N.C., this clay contains cypress stumps. According to Cooke, "the presence of rooted tree stumps beneath a thick marine deposit that eventually accumulated in quiet water gives conclusive evidence that the sea stood lower on the land when they grew than in the immediately succeeding epoch."

GEORGIA

Veatch and Stephenson (1911) recognized two Pleistocene terraces in Georgia, the Satilla (to 40 ft, 12 m elevation) and the Okefenokee (to 125 ft, 38 m elevation). Later work of Cooke (1943) revealed other terraces, including the Pamlico, to which all marine fossil localities have been referred.

On the other hand, MacNeil (1950) recognized on physiographic evidence four marine shorelines in Georgia and Florida as follows:

Okefenokee (Sunderland)	150 ft, 45.5 m,	Yarmouth
Wicomico	100 ft, 30 m,	Sangamon
Pamlico	25-30 ft, 7.5-9 m,	mid-Wisconsin
Silver Bluff	8-10 ft, 2.5-3 m,	post-Wisconsin

MacNeil's mid-Wisconsin dating of the Pamlico is questioned by the present writer because there is little evidence of sufficient deglaciation to raise the sea level 25 ft (7.5 m) during any of the Wisconsin interstadials. Also the dead radiocarbon dates from shells from the Pamlico Formation in the Carolinas and farther north do not support a mid-Wisconsin date. The Silver Bluff shoreline may be post-Wisconsin but more likely is late interglacial, representing a falling sea. This correlation is discussed further under Florida. No paleontologic evidence exists for the Wicomico or Okefenokee shorelines in Georgia.

FLORIDA

Considerable work has been done on the Pleistocene of Florida, including that of Matson and Sanford (1913),

Cooke and Mossom (1929), Richards (1938), and Cooke (1945).

The present author still holds in general to the correlation of the Anastasia Formation (mostly coquina), the Miami Oolite, the Key Largo Limestone, and at least most of the Fort Thompson Formation with the Pamlico Formation farther north; they thus date from the Sangamon interglacial (Richards, 1938).

On the other hand, Parker and Cooke (1944), recognizing that the Fort Thompson in southern Florida consists of alternating freshwater and marine limestone, have suggested that the formation represents the various glacial and interglacial stages of the entire Pleistocene. The bands are very thin (only 10 to 20 ft for the entire formation) and the fossils of the various marine and freshwater beds are repeated. Therefore it seems better to the present author to regard the Fort Thompson as representing a single interglacial—probably the last. In any case, no marine fossils higher than 30 ft above present sea level have been observed in Florida. This opinion has also been expressed by DuBar (1958).

DuBar (1958) has reinterpreted as Pleistocene the Caloosahatchee Formation, long regarded as Pliocene on the basis of its extensive marine molluscan fauna. This change was partly based upon the study of some vertebrate fossils, especially *Equus leidyi*. The present writer believes that the evidence of the invertebrates far outweighs that of the vertebrates and prefers to regard the Caloosahatchee as Pliocene.

A series of marine terraces has been recognized in Florida. These are thought to represent "land-marginal marine sediments deposited during cycles of eustatic adjustment in sea level associated with maxima and minima developments of ice in the Pleistocene" (Puri and Vernon, 1959, p. 239). Five surfaces have been recognized and correlated with high stands of the sea (Table 2). This correlation differs somewhat from earlier correlations proposed by Cooke (1945) and MacNeil (1950). However, in view of the lack of fossils at higher elevations and the difficulty of correlating terraces in Florida with the glacial sequence, the dating of the older Pleistocene of Florida must be regarded as uncertain.

TABLE 2

Correlation of Pleistocene of Florida
(Puri and Vernon, 1959)

Late Wisconsin Interglacial	Silver Bluff, 8 ft
Late Wisconsin Glacial	Erosion
Peorian Interglacial	Pamlico, 30 ft
Early Wisconsin Glacial	Erosion
Sangamon Interglacial	Wicomico, 100 ft
Illinoian Glacial	Erosion
Yarmouth Interglacial	Okefenokee, 150 ft
Kansan Glacial	Erosion
Aftonian Interglacial	Coharie, 220 ft
Nebraskan Glacial	Erosion. High-level alluvium

It is possible that the Silver Bluff shoreline, well exposed just south of the city of Miami, may be intra-Wisconsin or even date from the post-Wisconsin Climatic Optimum, as has been suggested. However, the degree of oxidation of the heavy minerals in the Silver Bluff soil suggests a Pleistocene age and an origin by the retreating Pamlico sea (Price, 1956). Furthermore, there is no convincing evidence that sea level was as high as the Silver Bluff shoreline (8-10 ft, 2.5-3 m) during or since Wisconsin time.

SUMMARY AND CORRELATION

No completely satisfactory correlation between the marine Pleistocene deposits of the Atlantic Coastal Plain and the glacial chronology has been made. There is good evidence that the lowest deposits (less than 7.5 m in elevation) date from the last interglacial stage (Sangamon). These deposits are probably equivalent, at least in part, to the Gardiners Clay of Long Island. All of these formations contain invertebrate fossils, suggesting a climate at least as warm as that of today. The Jacobs sand of Long Island probably represents late-Sangamon or very early Wisconsin time. Deposits of glacial age are not to be expected along the Coastal Plain from New Jersey southward because sea level was low during those stages. The Horry clay of North and South Carolina probably represents the low sea level of Wisconsin time.

The age of the higher level Pleistocene deposits of the Coastal Plain must be regarded as unproved.

QUATERNARY PROCESSES IN THE ATLANTIC COASTAL PLAIN AND APPALACHIAN HIGHLANDS

SHELDON JUDSON

INTENSIVE FROST ACTION

Several workers have ascribed various features to the effect of periglacial conditions south of the glacial border. The observations are scattered, however, and the origin of some features is still uncertain.

Boulder fields and block streams in the Appalachian Highlands are known from inside the Wisconsin border southward into Virginia. Smith and Smith (1945) and Peltier (1945) suggest that these are periglacial in origin. Peltier (1949) and Smith (1953) expand this idea. In later studies Hack and Goodlett (1960) show that these features

can originate under present climatic conditions. A genesis in a modern climate does not prove that these features cannot originate under periglacial conditions, but it does demonstrate that they are not diagnostic of such a climate.

South of the glacial border the Coastal Plain is pocked by shallow depressions from New Jersey to Florida. Prouty (1952) estimates that they may number half a million. These include the famous and controversial "Carolina Bays" that have been assigned both a meteoritic and terrestrial origin. In New Jersey, where the basins are irregular in shape, not more than 6 m in depth, and at the largest

Figure 2. Shattered shale of the Brunswick formation (Triassic) near Princeton, N.J. Bedrock here dips 10 degrees to the north. Note fan-like orientation of the shale fragments, an arrangement attributed to periglacial frost action. Scale is one meter in height.

2.5 km² in area, Wolfe (1953) suggests origin by freeze-thaw activity in permanently frozen ground of the periglacial zone, as implied by the presence within the basins of involutions. Rasmussen (1953) suggests that they have an origin in common with the more southerly undrained depressions of the Coastal Plain and that the frost features related to the New Jersey basins are later modifications.

There seems no question that many surficial deposits bear the mark of rigorous frost action. Just outside the Wisconsin border in the Appalachian Plateaus, Denny (1956) has described structures in soils that appear indubitably related to periglacial climates of Wisconsin ice. These include convoluted paleosols, boulder stripes, block fields, and boulder rings. Similar features are described in the unglaciated portion of the Susquehanna River drainage by Peltier (1949).

Farther east and south in central New Jersey, soils affected by periglacial climates are not uncommon (Fig. 2; Wolfe, 1953; Tedrow and MacClintock, 1953). The farthest south that such soils have been seen by this writer is Burlington, N.J., about 65 km south of the margin of the Wisconsin ice.

Still farther south in the Coastal Plain of southern Maryland, Nikiforoff (1955) has described hardpans from soils of the Beltsville series. These hardpans have aquired coherence not by cementation but by compaction. Nikiforoff suggests that the compaction occurred during periglacial climates of the Wisconsin. In Maryland these soils are about 200 km south of the Wisconsin ice border in New Jersey. In addition Nikiforoff suggests that hardpan found in the Grenada soils of Kentucky and neighboring states may have the same origins.

WIND ACTION

The results of wind action are reflected in deposits of loess and sand (Thorp and Smith, 1952). Ventifacts are also present.

Extensive deposits of loess are associated with three river systems leading from the glaciated terrain. These are the Delaware River, the Susquehanna River, and the Allegheny-Beaver-Monongahela system of westernmost Pennsylvania. The deposits are discontinuous and thin (generally less than 1 m). In New Jersey, Tedrow and MacClintock (1953) assign the loess to the early Wisconsin and an overlying zone of frost-derived deposits to the late Wisconsin.

Wind-worked deposits of sand are more widespread than loess and are present along the Coastal Plain southward from New Jersey to Florida. Some deposits are dune-shaped, and others are sheets of sand. Some are related to sandy formations underlying the Coastal Plain and areas associated with shorelines of the late Pleistocene. Ventifacts are known from the loess and sand deposits of New Jersey (Wolfe, 1953) and Pennsylvania.

GEOMORPHOLOGY

The most common interpretation of the geomorphic history of the Appalachian Highlands follows W. M. Davis' work, which began to appear in 1889. The work of Davis and his many followers suggests that elements of the present landscape are inherited from the Mesozoic and Tertiary. Some workers early questioned this view, but it still dominates the thinking on landscape development of the Appalachians. More recent studies suggest that at least some of the landscape features of the Appalachians can be explained in other ways.

The summits of the Appalachian Plateaus in north-central Pennsylvania have long been assigned to remnants of uplifted and dissected peneplains. In contrast, Denny (1956) shows that in Potter County, Pa., these upland surfaces "are structurally controlled surfaces held up by the sandstone and conglomerate beds in the Pottsville and Pocono formations." He concludes that the plateau tops may have been lowered as much as 60 m during the Pleistocene "and that if this portion of the Appalachian Plateaus was ever reduced to a peneplain, such a hypothetical surface must have lain many hundreds of feet above the uplands of the present day."

Gravel deposits in the Shenandoah valley of Virginia generally have been interpreted as covering the uplifted and dissected remnants of the Harrisburg Peneplain of late Tertiary age. King (1950) suggests that these gravels are Pleistocene. Hack (1960) believes that they were probably laid down by processes still going on and that the varying elevations and dissection of the gravel bodies can best be explained by differential erosion and stream capture independently of a regional change in base level.

Campbell (1903) named the Harrisburg peneplain on the basis of observations in the Lebanon Valley near Harrisburg, Pa. Meisler (1962) concludes that the peneplain hypothesis does not adequately account for the landforms of the Lebanon Valley. He postulates that stream capture and normal erosion of differing rock types have produced the present features in relatively recent times and that this was accomplished without appreciable change of regional base level.

The meanders of the North Fork of the Shenandoah Valley were originally interpreted (Butts, 1940) as inherited from alluvial meanders formed on a peneplain and preserved as the river was rejuvenated by uplift. Hack and Young (1959) show that rejuvenation and a former surface of low relief were not factors in the creation of these intrenched meanders. Rather they are the response of normal erosion to the lithology, structure, and arrangement of rocks and to the action of hydraulic factors.

REFERENCES

Berry, E. W., and Hawkins, A. C., 1935, Flora of the Pensauken Formation in New Jersey: Geol. Soc. Amer. Bull., v. 46, p. 245-252

Blake, S. F., 1953, The Pleistocene fauna of Wailes Bluff and Langley's Bluff, Maryland: Smithson. Instn. Misc. Coll., v. 121, p. 1-32

Butts, Charles, 1940, Geology of the Appalachian Valley in Virginia. Part I, Geologic text and illustrations: Virginia Geol. Surv. Bull. 52, 568 p.

Campbell, M. B., 1903, Geographic development of northern Pennsylvania and southern New York: Geol. Soc. Amer. Bull., v. 14, p. 277-296

Clark, W. B., and Miller, B. L., 1912, Physiography and geology of the Coastal Plain Province of Virginia: Virginia Geol. Surv. Bull. 4, p. 13-122

Colquhoun, D. J., 1962, Wicomico shoreline in Orangeburg, Dorchester, and Berkeley Counties, South Carolina: South Carolina State Develop. Board, Geol. Notes, v. 5, p. 43-50

Cooke, C. W., 1931, Seven coastal terraces in the southeastern states: Washington Acad. Sci. J., v. 21, p. 503-513

—— 1935, Tentative ages of Pleistocene shore lines: Washington Acad. Sci. J., v. 25, p. 331-333

—— 1936, Geology of the Coastal Plain of South Carolina: U.S. Geol. Surv. Bull. 867, 196 p.

—— 1937, The Pleistocene Horry clay and Pamlico formation near Myrtle Beach, S.C.: Washington Acad. Sci. J., v. 27, p. 1-5

—— 1943, Geology of the coastal plain of Georgia: U.S. Geol. Surv. Bull. 941, 121 p.

—— 1945, Geology of Florida: Florida Geol. Surv. Bull. 29, 339 p.

—— 1958, Pleistocene shore lines in Maryland: Geol. Soc. Amer. Bull., v. 69, p. 1187-1190

Cooke, C. W., and Mossom, D. S., 1929, Geology of Florida: Florida Geol. Surv. 20th Rep., p. 29-227

Dachnowski-Stokes, A. P., and Wells, B. W., 1929, The vegetation, age and stratigraphy of the "Open Land" peat area in Carteret County, North Carolina: Washington Acad. Sci. J., v. 19, p. 1-11

Davis, W. M., 1889, The rivers and valleys of Pennsylvania: Natl. Geogr. Mag., v. 1, p. 183-253

Denny, C. S., 1956, Surficial geology and geomorphology of Potter County, Pennsylvania: U.S. Geol. Surv. Prof. Pap. 288, 72 p.

Doering, John, 1960, Quarternary surface formations of southern part of Atlantic Coastal Plain: J. Geol., v. 68, p. 182-202

Donner, J. J., 1964, Pleistocene geology of eastern Long Island, New York: Amer. J. Sci., v. 262, p. 355-376

DuBar, Jules, 1958, Stratigraphy and paleontology of the late Neogene strata of the Caloosahatchee River area of southern Florida: Florida Geol. Surv. Bull. 40, 267 p.

DuBar, Jules, and Solliday, J. R., 1963, Stratigraphy of the Neogene deposits, Lower Neuse estuary, North Carolina: Southeastern Geol., v. 4, p. 213-233

Ewing, John, Ewing, Maurice, and Fray, Charles, 1960, Buried erosional terrace on the edge of the continental shelf east of New Jersey (abst.): Geol. Soc. Amer. Bull., v. 71, p. 1860

Flint, R. F., 1940, Pleistocene features of the Atlantic Coastal Plain: Amer. J. Sci., v. 238, p. 757-787

—— 1942, Atlantic Coastal "terraces": Washington Acad. Sci. J., v. 32, p. 235-237

Fuller, M. L., 1914, The geology of Long Island, New York: U.S. Geol. Surv. Prof. Pap. 82, 231 p.

Hack, J. T., 1955, Geology of the Brandywine area and origin of the upland of southern Maryland: U.S. Geol. Surv. Prof. Pap. 267-A, 42 p.

—— 1960, Interpretation of erosional topography in humid temperate regions: Amer. J. Sci., v. 258-A (Bradley vol.), p. 80-97

Hack, J. T. and Goodlett, J. C., 1960, Geomorophology and forest ecology of a mountain region in the Central Appalachians: U.S. Geol. Surv. Prof. Pap. 347, 66 p.

Hack, J. T., and Young, R. S., 1959, Intrenched meanders of the North Fork of the Shenandoah River, Virginia: U.S. Geol. Surv. Prof. Pap. 354-A, p. 1-10

Harrison, Wyman, 1965, Possible Late Pleistocene uplift, Chesapeake Bay entrance: J. Geol. (in press)

Holmes, F. S., 1860, Post-Pliocene fossils of South Carolina: Charleston, S.C., Russell and Jones, 122 p.

Johnson, B. L., 1907, Pleistocene terracing in the North Carolina Coastal Plain: Science, v. 26, p. 640-642

Jordan, R. R., 1962, Stratigraphy of the sedimentary rocks of Delaware: Delaware Geol. Surv. Bull. 9, 51 p.

—— 1964, Columbia (Pleistocene) sediments of Delaware: Delaware Geol. Surv. Bull. 12, 69 p.

King, P. B., 1950, Geology of the Elkton Area, Virginia: U.S. Geol. Surv. Prof. Pap. 230, 82 p.

MacClintock, Paul, and Richards, H. G., 1936, Correlation of late Pleistocene marine and glacial geology of New Jersey and New York: Geol. Soc. Amer. Bull., v. 47, p. 289-338

MacNeil, F. S., 1950, Pleistocene shore lines in Florida and Georgia: U.S. Geol. Surv. Prof. Pap. 221-F, p. 95-107

Malde, H. E., 1959, Geology of the Charleston phosphate area, South Carolina: U.S. Geol. Surv. Bull. 1079, 105 p.

Matson, G. C., and Sanford, Samuel, 1913, Geology and ground waters of Florida: U.S. Geol. Surv. Water-Supply Pap. 319, 445 p.

McGee, W. J., 1888, Three formations of the Middle Atlantic Slope: Amer. J. Sci., 3rd ser., v. 35, p. 120-143, 328-330, 367-388, 448-466

Meisler, Harold, 1962, Origin of erosional surfaces in the Lebanon Valley, Pennsylvania: Geol. Soc. Amer. Bull., v. 73, p. 1071-1082

Moore, Wayne E., 1956, Stratigraphy of Pleistocene terrace

deposits in Virginia (abst.): Geol. Soc. Amer. Bull., v. 67, p. 1755

Muller, E. A., this volume, Quaternary geology of New York

Nikiforoff, C. C., 1955, Hardpan soils of the Coastal Plain of southern Maryland: U.S. Geol. Surv. Prof. Pap. 267-B, p. 45-63

Oaks, R. Q., and Coch, N. K., 1963, Pleistocene sea levels, southeastern Virginia: Science, v. 140, p. 979-983

Parker, G. G., and Cooke, C. W., 1944, Late Cenozoic geology of southern Florida, with a discussion of the groundwater: Florida Geol. Surv. Bull. 27, 119 p.

Peltier, L. C., 1945, Block fields in Pennsylvania (abst.): Geol. Soc. Amer. Bull. v. 56, p. 1190

—— 1949, Pleistocene terraces of the Susquehanna River, Pennsylvania: Pennsylvania Geol. Surv., 4th ser., Bull. G-23, 158 p.

Price, W. A., 1956, Environment and history in identification of shoreline types: Quaternaria, v. 3, p. 155-166

Prouty, W. V., 1952, Carolina bays and their origin: Geol. Soc. Amer. Bull., v. 63, p. 167-224

Pugh, G. T., 1905, Pleistocene deposits of South Carolina: Vanderbilt Univ. M.S. thesis, 74 p.

Puri, Harbans, and Vernon, R. O., 1959, Summary of the geology of Florida and a guidebook to the classic exposures: Florida Geol. Surv. Spec. Publ. 5, 255 p.

Rasmussen, W. C., 1953, Periglacial frost-thaw basin in New Jersey: a discussion: J. Geol., v. 61, p. 473-474

Richards, H. G., 1933, Marine fossils from New Jersey indicating a mild interglacial stage: Amer. Philos. Soc. Proc., v. 72, p. 181-214

—— 1936, Fauna of the Pleistocene Pamlico Formation of the southern Atlantic Coastal Plain: Geol. Soc. Amer. Bull., v. 47, p. 1611-1656

—— 1938, Marine Pleistocene of Florida: Geol. Soc. Amer. Bull., v. 49, p. 1267-1295

—— 1943, Pliocene and Pleistocene mollusks from the Santee-Cooper area, South Carolina: Acad. Nat. Sci. Philadelphia Notula Naturae 118, 7 p.

—— 1944, Notes on the geology and paleontology of the Cape May Canal, New Jersey: Acad. Nat. Sci. Philadelphia Notula Naturae 134, 12 p.

—— 1950, Geology of the Coastal Plain of North Carolina: Amer. Philos. Soc. Trans., v. 40, p. 1-83

—— 1960, The dating of the "Subway Tree" of Philadelphia: Pennsylvania Acad. Sci. Proc., v. 34, p. 107-108

—— 1962, Studies on the Marine Pleistocene: Amer. Philos. Soc. Trans., v. 52, p. 1-141

Richards, H. G., and Werner, Eberhart, 1964, Invertebrate fossils from cores from the continental shelf off New Jersey: Acad. Nat. Sci. Philadelphia Notula Naturae 372. 7 p.

Salisbury, R. D., and Knapp, G. N., 1917, The Quaternary formations of southern New Jersey: New Jersey Geol. Surv., v. 8, Final Report of the State Geologist, 218 p.

Shattuck, G. B., 1906, The Pliocene and Pleistocene deposits of Maryland, in Pliocene and Pleistocene: Maryland Geol. Surv., p. 21-137

Smith, H. T. U., 1953, The Hickory Run boulder field, Carbon County, Pennsylvania: Amer. J. Sci., v. 251, p. 625-642

Smith, H. T. U., and Smith, Althea P., 1945, Periglacial rock streams in the Blue Ridge Area (abst.): Geol. Soc. Amer. Bull., v. 56, p. 1198

Stephenson, L. W., 1912, The coastal plain of North Carolina; the Cretaceous, Lafayette and Quaternary formations: North Carolina Geol. Surv. Bull. 3, p. 73-171, 258-290

Tedrow, J. C. F., and MacClintock, Paul, 1953, Loess in New Jersey soil materials: Soil Sci., v. 75, p. 19-29

Thorp, James, and Smith, H. T. U., 1952, Pleistocene eolian deposits of the United States and parts of Canada: Geol. Soc. Amer. Map scale 1:2,500,000.

Veatch, Otto, and Stephenson, L. W., 1911, Preliminary report on the geology of the Coastal Plain of Georgia: Georgia Geol. Surv. Bull. 26, 466 p.

Wentworth, C. K., 1930, Sand and gravel resources of the Coastal Plain of Virginia: Virginia Geol. Surv. Bull. 32, 146 p.

Wolfe, P. E., 1953, Periglacial frost-thaw basins in New Jersey: J. Geol., v. 61, p. 133-141

Summary

The principal nonglacial Pleistocene deposit on Long Island, New York, is the Gardiners Clay, which is regarded as at least in part of Sangamon age. It is overlain by the Jacob Sand; both the Gardiners and Jacobs contain marine fossils. On the Coastal Plain from New Jersey to Florida there is a series of terrace-like deposits. These have been regarded by some as having been formed during high interglacial stands of the sea. Only the lowest terrace deposit, however, the Cape May-Pamlico, contains marine fossils, and this is regarded as of Sangamon age.

Evidence of periglacial activity is preserved in surficial deposits south of the Wisconsin ice margin and possibly as far south as Maryland and Kentucky.

Davis' concept of the cycle of erosion, as developed largely in the Appalachian Mountains, is being re-evaluated in the same area.

RÉSUMÉ OF THE QUATERNARY GEOLOGY OF THE NORTHWESTERN GULF OF MEXICO PROVINCE*

HUGH A. BERNARD,[1] RUFUS J. LEBLANC[2]

THE QUATERNARY GULF COASTAL plains are depositional in origin. Their occurrences and associated deposits as related to the Gulf of Mexico basin and older outcrops are shown in Figures 1-2. In the northwestern or clastic portion of the Gulf basin, the plains form a belt varying in width from a few miles to more than 250 miles and are transected by nine major river systems.

The youngest Quaternary plain comprises the Recent (postglacial) depositional surface and occurs principally along the coast. This surface lies only a few feet above sea level and is composed of deltaic and coastal interdeltaic plains (Figs. 2-7), the latter consisting principally of barrier islands, beach ridges, tidal deltas, bay, lagoons, very shallow neritic zone offshore, bay and coastal mudflats and marshes. As shown in Figure 2, the Recent coastwise plain merges with narrow alluvial floodplains of the river systems. These floodplains extend inland and occupy relatively narrow valleys of the rivers. They rise gradually in elevation, at rates of less than 1 ft to 1.4 ft per statute mile, and are the topographically lowest portions of the Quaternary plains.

Seaward the youngest plain merges with the continental shelf, which extends to the 600-ft bottom contour and varies in width from approximately 120 nautical miles off the Louisiana-Texas boundary to 10 miles off the active mouths of the Mississippi River, where this river has recently constructed a deltaic platform across the shelf.

Shelf slopes are generally gradual to the 300-ft contour and become steeper between the 300- and 600-ft contour (Figs. 1 and 3-6). Slopes of approximately 3.3 ft per nautical mile from the shore to the 300-ft contour occur off the Louisiana-Texas boundary which includes the area of the Late Pleistocene (interglacial) Mississippi Delta. Off the recently submerged parts of the Recent Mississippi subaerial deltaic plain (less than 3,000 years old), slopes are 1 ft or less per mile. Steeper slopes to the 300-ft contour

occur off the south Texas coast—approximately 6 ft per nautical mile off the shores of the Brazos and Rio Grande deltas and 10 ft per mile off the coastal interdeltaic plains between the Colorado and Rio Grande Rivers. Slopes from the 300-ft contour to the edge of the shelf vary from 60 ft per mile off the modern birdfoot delta of the Mississippi River to 30 ft per mile off the Louisiana-Texas boundary.

The continental slope of the Gulf Basin varies considerably in width and topography (Gealy, 1955). The greatest width and most rugged topography of the shelf occur within the clastic province of the northwest Gulf of Mexico (Figs. 1 and 8). Gealy (1955) contoured this area and concluded that:

"the configuration of the slope and the nature of its sediments suggest a genetic interpretation for its varied topography and high relief. A hummocky zone on the upper part of the slope shows features resembling landslide scars and deposits, sediment flow scars, and surface expression of faults. These features indicate that the upper part of the slope is underlain by a mass of relatively unstable sediments, probably deposited when sea level was near the present 75 fathom curve. Steep slopes and lack of hummocks on the lower part of the slope indicate that the underlying sediments are relatively stable."

Gealy called attention to the Sigsbee Scarp (340 miles long and as high as 4,000 ft), which occurs at the base of the lower slope, and presented various explanations as to the origin of the topography of the lower slope.

All of the continental slopes are steep scarps in the southeast part of the Gulf, which includes the carbonate province (Figs. 1 and 8). These scarps have been interpreted to be fault scarps, erosional scarps, carbonate buildups, or a combination of one or more of these features. Ewing *et al.* (1955) and Fisk and McFarlan (1955) pointed out that a continental rise occurs at the base of the Sigsbee Scarp in the northwestern Gulf and grades near the 1,500- and 2,000-fathom contours into the abyssal plain and Mississippi fan or cone off the Mississippi trench (Figs. 1 and 8).

The Pleistocene coastal plains occur between the Recent plain and the youngest Tertiary outcrops inland. These plains consist of the following four, progressively older, depositional surfaces representing interglacial stages: Prairie (in Louisiana and Texas) or Beaumont (in Texas), Montgomery (Louisiana and Texas) or Upper Lissie of Deussen (1914) (in Texas), Bentley (Louisiana and Texas) or Lower Lissie of Deussen (1914) (in Texas), and Williana (Louisiana) or Willis (Texas) (Fig. 9). Each plain has equivalent

*EPR Publication No. 400. The authors are grateful to Shell Development Company and Shell Oil Company for permission to publish this resume. Space is not available to acknowledge the large number of associates who have given much of their time, assistance, and advice.

The authors wish to dedicate this resume to the memory of the late Dr. Harold N. Fisk, their former professor, employer, associate, and very close friend. This resume is in large part the result of the impact of his contributions, teachings, and inspiration on the authors and many other associates in the field of Quaternary Geology of the Gulf Coastal Province.

[1] Shell Development Company, Exploration and Production Division, Houston, Texas.

[2] Shell Oil Company, Houston, Texas.

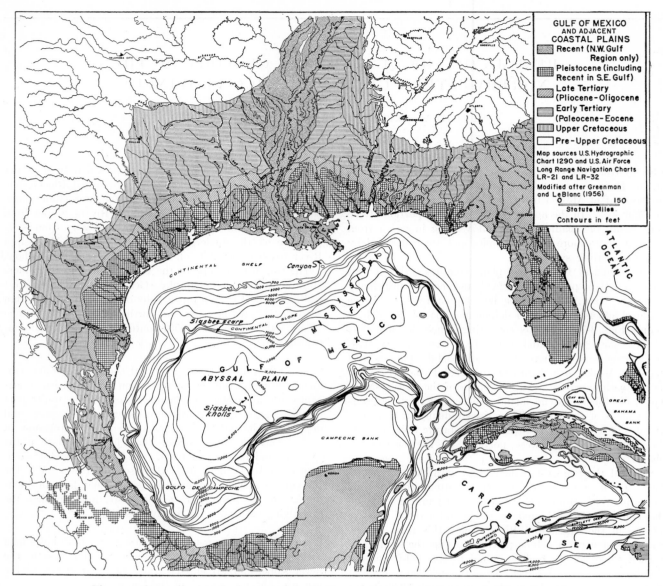

Figure 1. Generalized geologic map of the Gulf coastal plains and the principal hydrographic
features of the Gulf of Mexico. Modified after Greenman and LeBlanc (1956) and
Ewing, Ericson, and Heezen (1958).

paired river terraces underlain by alluvial deposits, which
extend inland with the stream valleys (Figs. 2, 10, and 11).

Each Quaternary surface is underlain by similar depositional sequences, which consist of alluvial, deltaic, coastal
interdeltaic, and marine sections. Within the entrenched
valleys inland and near the coast, the sections consist of
basal alluvial sand and gravel grading upward into deltaic
or coastal interdeltaic finer sand, silt, and clay (Figs. 5-7).
Near the coast and especially in the nearshore areas of the
broad stream divides, sedimentary sequences grade upward
from basal marine sand, silt, and clay into deltaic or
coastal interdeltaic deposits. However, near- and offshore
entrenched valley fills consisting of alluvial and deltaic deposits may grade upward into marine and/or deltaic or
coastal interdeltaic deposits (Figs. 4-6).

In the onshore and shallow offshore areas each sedi-

mentary sequence rests unconformably upon an eroded
and/or weathered surface. Five Quaternary depositional
and four erosional surfaces are correlated with the major
interglacial and glacial stages (Fig. 9). Thus, the Quaternary coastwise plains of Texas and Louisiana represent a
series of coalescing alluvial, deltaic, and coastal interdeltaic
plains developed principally by the major river systems and
coastal processes during the high-standing-sea-level substages of each interglacial stage. The erosional surfaces were
developed during the lower-sea-level substages of each
glacial stage and the rising-sea-level substage of each early
interglacial substage.

In the distant offshore areas where deposition (fast or
slow), nondeposition, or erosion (below sea level) occurred
during both glacial and interglacial stages, little is known
about the sedimentary record except for what has been

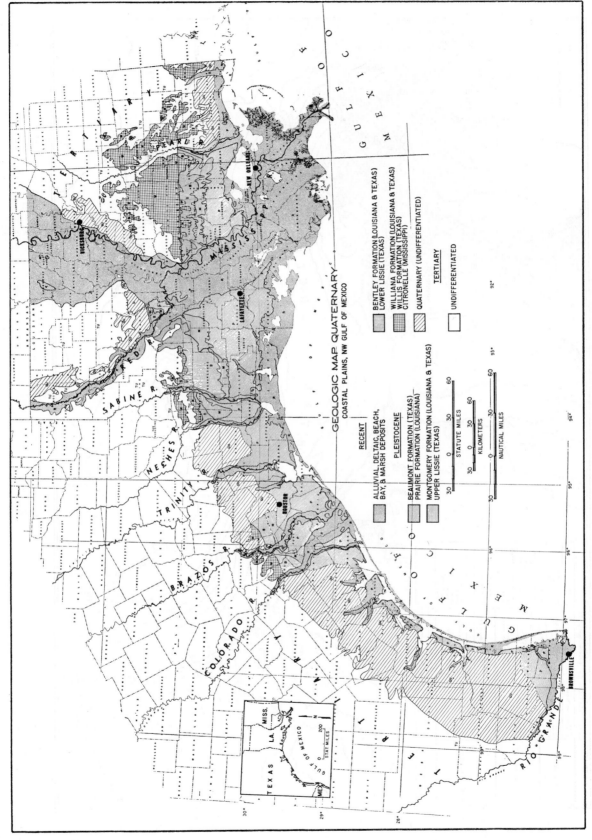

Figure 2. Geologic map of the Quaternary coastal plains adjacent to the northwestern part of the Gulf of Mexico.

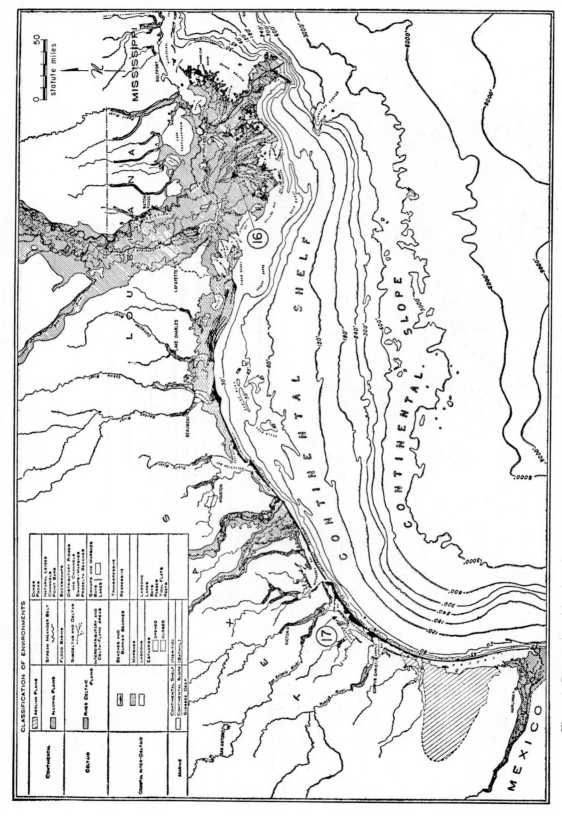

Figure 3. Recent depositional environments of the coastal plains of Louisiana and Texas. Circled numbers indicate locations of figures that follow. After LeBlanc and Bernard (1954).

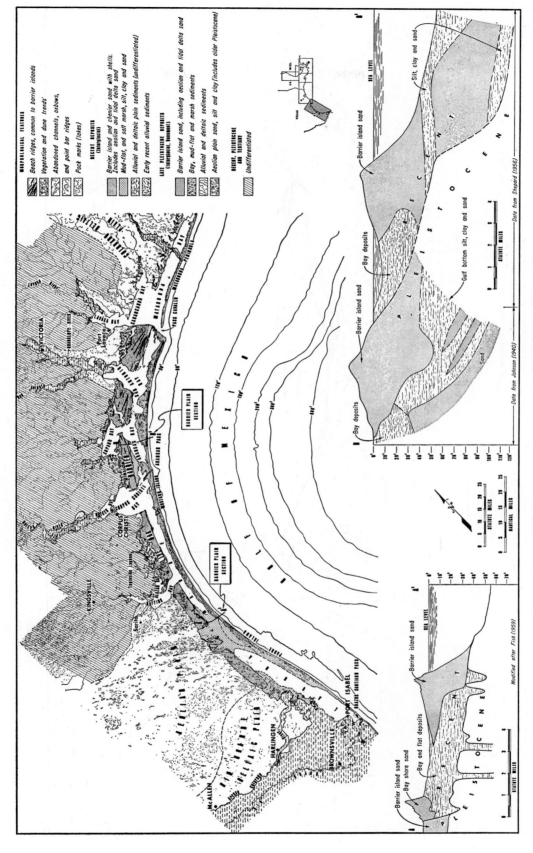

Figure 4. Late Quaternary geologic and geomorphic map of sout'1 Texas.

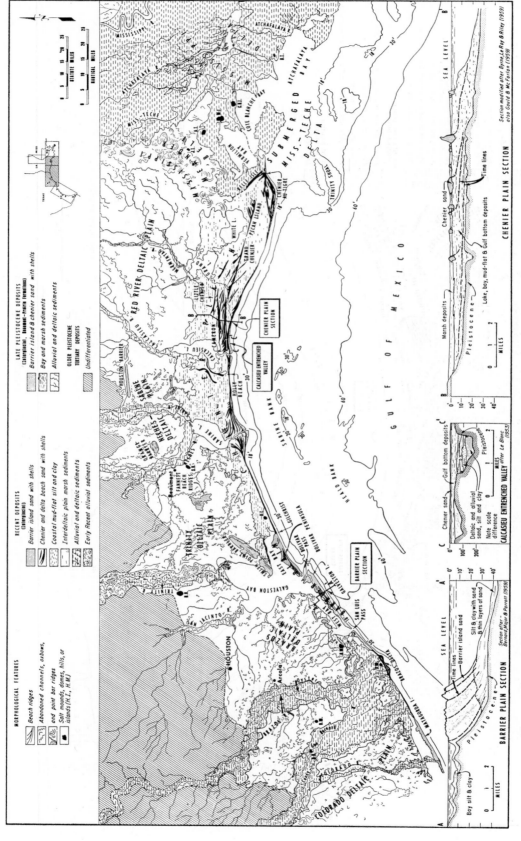

Figure 5. Late Quaternary geologic and geomorphic map of southeast Texas and southwest Louisiana. After Bernard, LeBlanc, and Major (1962).

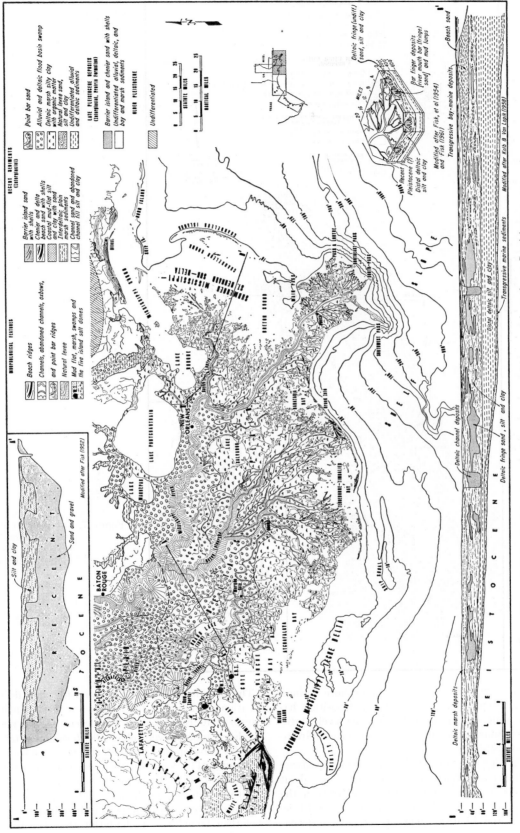

Figure 6. Late Quaternary geologic and geomorphic map of southeast Louisiana.

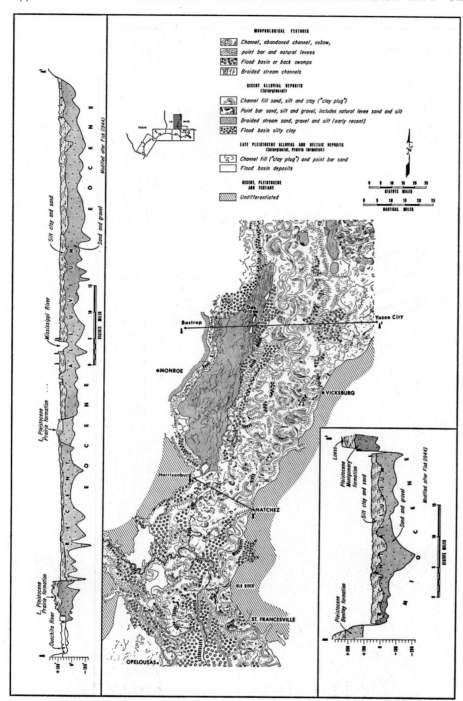

Figure 7. Late Quaternary geologic and geomorphic map of northeast Louisiana and parts of adjacent states.

interpreted from short punch cores or deep offshore borings. However, in the deep-water areas offshore, deposition has been relatively slow during high-standing-sea-level stages and relatively fast during the lower-sea-level stages (Greenman and LeBlanc, 1956).

The highest and most inland of the Pleistocene coastwise plains, the Williana and Willis, lies at elevations of about 200 to almost 600 ft and within a wide belt between the Late Tertiary outcrops and the Bentley or Lower Lissie. The elevation of the Bentley plain ranges from approximately 100 ft to over 200 ft. The Montgomery or Upper Lissie ranges in elevation from about 70 ft to over 125 ft.

The Beaumont and Prairie coastwise plain decreases in elevation from 70 and 100 ft to a few feet or inches above sea level at its contact with the Recent coastal plain.

Each progressively older Pleistocene coastal plain passes under the deposits forming the next younger plain (Figs. 10 and 11). Some of the adjacent coastwise plains are separated by steep erosional scarps near the major streams, but in most areas of the wide, flat-topped stream divides the plains merge almost imperceptibly into each other. Many of their boundaries in the latter areas can be detected only by the differences in the slopes of the adjacent plains.

Each successively younger and seaward Pleistocene plain

slopes seaward at progressively smaller rates. These rates vary in different areas along the coast because of different initial depositional slopes and differential coastal warping or rates of seaward tilting caused by tectonics and differential compaction. The average rate of seaward tilting in south-east Texas since the development of the Beaumont plain is estimated to have been 1 ft per 100,000 years. In south Texas little is known about the relative rates of slope for these surfaces. The following seaward gradients (in feet per mile) have been measured:

Central Texas		*Southeast Texas*		*Central Louisiana*	
Near Brazos River (Bernard, LeBlanc, and Major, 1962)		Between Neches and Sabine Rivers, (Bernard, 1950)		(Fisk, 1939a, 1944)	
Willis	10	Williana	10.5-14.0	Williana	9.2->10
Bentley	3.5	Bentley	5.0	Bentley	4.3- 8
Montgomery	2.5	Montgomery	2.4- 3.4	Montgomery	2.9- 5
Beaumont	2	Prairie	1.1- 1.2	Prairie	1.2- 2.4
		Deweyville	1.1- 1.2	High-level flood plain	0.02->1.0
Recent	1.2-1.4	Recent	0.01-1.4	Recent	0.01- 1.0

The slope relationships between these depositional surfaces reflect a net inland uplift and coastal subsidence during the Quaternary. Coastal sedimentation and subsidence have been relatively continuous in the Gulf Coastal region since the early Tertiary (Fig. 12).

QUATERNARY COASTAL PLAINS

The Late Quaternary of Texas and Louisiana, including the offshore neritic, bathyal, and abyssal zones, provides the geologist with a laboratory containing many natural-scale, interrelated models of depositional environments in which clastic sediments have been and are being deposited. Sediment sources, geologic processes (depositional, erosional, and structural) can be related to the nature and genesis of these deposits, for both large- and small-scale models. These sediments are representative of much of the geologic sec-tion, and what is especially important, they provide us with a record of the entire Quaternary Period.

The coastwise environments contain many different model sand bodies and interrelated silt and clay facies that are representative of alluvial, deltaic, and coastal interdeltaic processes. A knowledge of the geologic history, processes, nature and influx of sediments, setting (framework), genesis, lithologic character, faunal and floral content, sequence, directional features, shape, and trend of the Late Quaternary sand bodies and related facies is of great value in understanding and predicting the complex interrelationships of similar older rock facies.

PREVIOUS WORK

More than 350 papers concerned primarily with the Quaternary of the Atlantic and Gulf coastal areas have been pub-

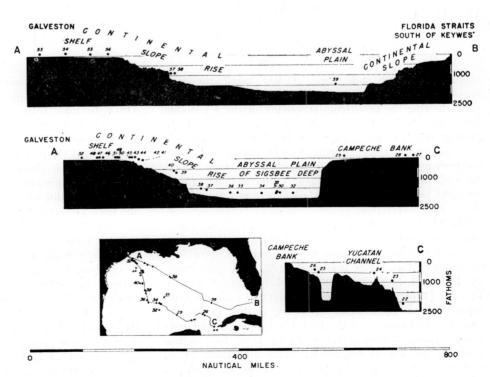

Figure 8. Topographic profiles across the Gulf of Mexico. After Ewing, Worzel and Heezen (1955).

Hays and Kennedy (1903)	Deussen (1914 and 1924)	Doering (1935)	Doering (1956)	Bernard (1950) (East Texas)	Fisk (1938, '40, '44) (Louisiana)	This Paper 1965
Beaumont*	Beaumont	Beaumont	Eunice*	Prairie	Prairie*	Prairie, or Beaumont
			Oberlin*			
Columbia	Lissie*	Lissie	Lissie	Montgomery	Montgomery*	Montgomery, or Upper Lissie
				Bentley	Bentley*	Bentley, or Lower Lissie
Lafayette	Reynosa	Willis*	Citronelle	Williana	Williana*	Williana, or Willis

(a)

* Denotes original definition

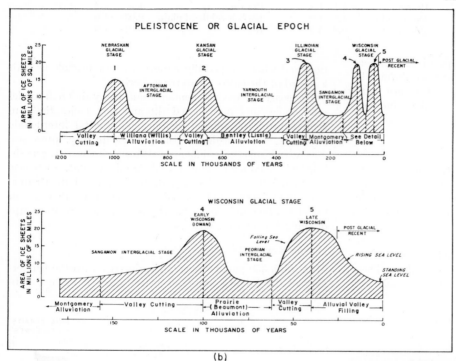

(b)

Figure 9a and b. Correlation of Pleistocene formations of Texas and Louisiana (a) and Pleistocene events (b). Modified after Fisk (1944).

lished. Woodward and Gueno (1941) listed the most important papers published up to 1940 and presented a table showing the geochronic synonymy of the Pleistocene formations and terraces in these areas. Bernard (1950) brought this list and synonymy up to date, including publications up to 1949. Murray (1961) presented a very comprehensive summary of the Quaternary geology of both the Gulf and Atlantic coastal plains, and included a most complete bibliography of published papers and unpublished theses and dissertations.

The Quaternary history, as related to sea-level movements, tectonics, compaction, and also the development of the Gulf Coastal plains and related sediments have been described by Fisk (1939, 1944, 1947, 1952, 1955, 1959, 1960), by Fisk and McFarlan (1955), and by Russell (1940). Deussen (1914 and 1924) presented the first comprehensive reports on the Quaternary of Texas. Barton (1930a, b) described and recognized the Late Pleistocene (interglacial) coastal plain (Beaumont) of southeast Texas as a deltaic plain. Howe and Moresi (1931, 1933) and Howe et al. (1935) described the two youngest plains in southwest

Louisiana as deltaic and chenier and marsh plains. Russell (1936) described the physiography of the Lower Mississippi Delta. In 1935, 1956, and 1958 Doering described and reviewed the Quaternary surface formations of the Gulf Coast region. Doering (1935) introduced the concept that the plains of the post-Fleming are depositional surfaces that had an original slope comparable to that of the present streams and were afterward tilted coastward because of the transfer of sediments from the eroded landward block to the loaded seaward block.

Price (1930, 1933a, 1933b, 1934, 1936, 1938, 1951a) contributed largely to the Quaternary geology of south Texas.

Welch (1942), Holland (1943), and Varvaro (1957) described and mapped in detail the older coastal plains and deposits in southwest Louisiana. Bernard (1950) described and mapped in detail the Quaternary of southeast Texas. Bernard, LeBlanc, and Major (1962) reviewed and mapped the coastal plains and deposits of southeast Texas and especially those along the Brazos River.

Gould and McFarlan (1959) and Byrne et al. (1959) described in detail the history and stratigraphy of the Chenier Plain in southwestern Louisiana. Bernard, Major, and Parrott (1959) described in detail the history and stratigraphy of the Barrier Islands of southeast Texas. LeBlanc and Hodgson (1959) reviewed the origin and development of the Texas shoreline.

Gould and Morgan (1962) reviewed and mapped the Late Quaternary plains in coastal Louisiana.

LeBlanc and Bernard (1954) summarized the Early and Late Recent history and development of the Gulf coastal plains and compared this history with that of the Dutch

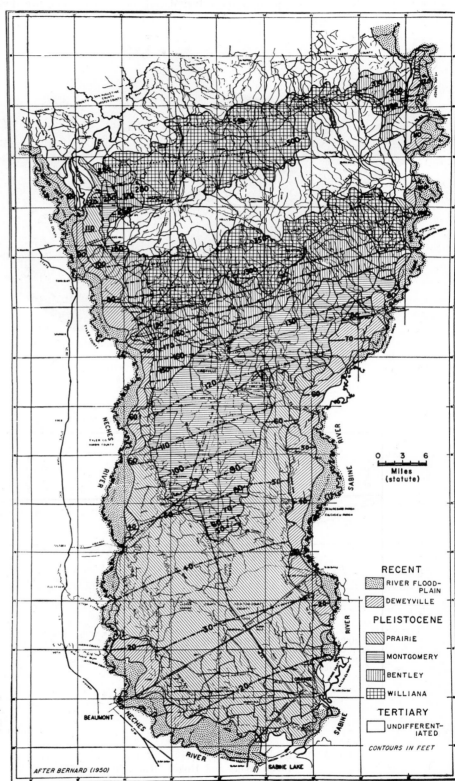

Figure 10. Generalized structure of the Quaternary depositional surfaces of southeast Texas. After Bernard (1950).

Coast. Recently Bernard, Major, and Parrott (1959), Bernard, LeBlanc, and Major (1962), Curray (1960), Gould and McFarlan (1959), Gould and Morgan (1962), McFarlan (1961), and Shepard (1960c) interpreted the Late Quaternary sea-level positions and movements in the northwest Gulf of Mexico by means of radiocarbon dating of

shells, wood, and peat from numerous known depositional environments.

QUATERNARY SUBDIVISIONS

The Quaternary events, as recorded in the Gulf coastal sediments, are divided logically into stages resulting from

Figure 11. Generalized block diagram illustrating the relationships between the Quaternary alluvial terraces and contemporaneous coastal plain surfaces and their related deposits. The Lissie is synonymous with the Bentley plain and the "Unnamed" Surface is synonymous with the Montgomery plain.

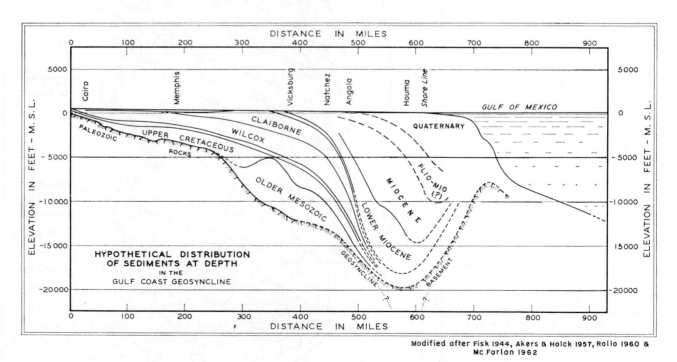

Modified after Fisk 1944, Akers & Holck 1957, Rollo 1960 & McFarlan 1962

Figure 12. Generalized cross section of the Gulf Coast Geosyncline, modified after Fisk (1944), Akers and Holck (1957), Rollo (1960), and McFarlan (1962). See Figure 40 for source of McFarlan's data.

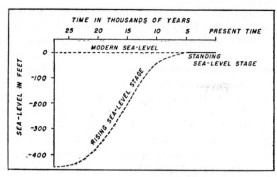

Figure 13. Graphic representation of Fisk's conclusions regarding the history of sea-level changes since the last ice age. After LeBlanc and Bernard (1954).

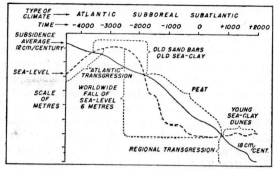

Figure 14. Graphic representation of the supposed movements of sea level and subsidence of the bottom in The Netherlands. After Umbgrove (1950) and reprinted from LeBlanc and Bernard (1954).

sea-level movements and are correlated with the glacial and interglacial stages (Figs. 9 and 13). A "glacial" stage includes a net lowering and low-sea-level substages. An "interglacial" stage includes net rising and high-standing-sea-level substages.

LATE QUATERNARY HISTORY

Recent history began more than 25,000 years ago with the beginning of the last rising-sea-level substage (Early Recent), which ended between 3,000 and 5,000 years ago, and includes the present high-standing-sea-level substage (Late Recent). Pleistocene history includes previous glacial and interglacial stages. Evidence for a continuous relative rise of sea level or a relative fluctuating sea level during the past 3,000 or 5,000 years as interpreted by Umbgrove (1950) and many others, does not exist along more than 1,000 miles of coastal plains in Louisiana, Texas, and Mexico (Figs. 13 and 14) (LeBlanc and Bernard, 1954).

Sufficient space is not available in this brief resume to point out in detail why many interpretations of relative sea-level movements based on radiocarbon dates are believed by the authors to be erroneous.

The recognition of local subsidence rates due to compaction, depth of water in which organisms lived, range of water depths in which peat forms; recognition of marsh or swamp peats; recognition of reworked marsh or swamp peats; and ability to determine subsequent exchange with atmospheric CO_2 since death of animals or plants remains must all be taken into consideration when making interpretations of sea-level movements.

LATE PLEISTOCENE (LAST GLACIAL) LOWERING- AND LOW-SEA-LEVEL SUBSTAGES

Along the coast the lowering- and low-sea-level substages are represented by relatively mature soil profiles and entrenched valleys that were developed and cut as stream base levels were lowered (Figs. 4-6, 9, 11, and 13). Because of a lowering of sea level of at least 300 ft (Ludwick and Walton, 1957) and possibly 450 ft (Fisk, 1944, 1947; Fisk and McFarlan, 1955), most of the sediment was deposited on the outer edge of the present shelf, on the upper slope,

and within the abyssal plain. However, little is known of the stratigraphic record representing this time. Fisk (1944) estimated that more than 1,280 cubic miles of sediment were excavated from the Mississippi entrenched valley; these sediments and possibly much more were carried through the entrenched valley and deposited in the deeper parts of the Gulf during this time. It is possible that the Mississippi subaqueous cone formed off the Mississippi trench at the base of the continental shelf and within the abyssal plain during this time (Fisk and McFarlan, 1955). Certainly some of the sands and gravel deposited within the base of the stream trenches cut on land and on the shelf represent this part of this record.

RECENT RISING- AND HIGH-STANDING-SEA-LEVEL SUBSTAGES

The rising- and standing-sea-level substages are recorded at many nearshore and offshore localities by very thin marine sands, silts, and clays commonly containing abundant shells (Fig. 6, Section B-B'). Thicker sections of predominantly alluvial and deltaic sand, silt, and clay representing these substages occur within the entrenched valleys of the larger streams, on both the coastal plain and the shallow parts of the continental shelf. Basal deposits of the low- and rising-sea-level substages within the entrenched valleys are predominantly coarser than those of the standing-sea-level substage because river gradients and the capacity of the streams to transport material were greater (Figs. 5-7, Calcasieu and Mississippi entrenched valley deposits).

Low river terraces (Deweyville Terrace, Bernard, 1950), characterized by very large, river-meander scars (Barton, 1930b), are common to many of the smaller streams such as the Trinity, Neches, and Sabine (Figs. 5 and 10); radiocarbon dates of wood fragments from these deposits range from 17,000 to over 30,000 years. Within the Mississippi alluvial plain, the high-level floodplain characterized by abandoned braided stream channels (Fisk, 1944) probably correlates with the low terraces of the smaller rivers mentioned above (Fig. 7). No coastwise plain equivalent in age to this surface has been found in the Northwestern Gulf. Therefore, it is believed that these surfaces were formed during the last rising-sea-level substage. Their related sediments have not yet been recognized in offshore punch cores or borings.

The greatest volume of sediment representing the standing-sea-level substage in the Gulf has been deposited in the coastal region of Texas and Louisiana (Greenman and LeBlanc, 1956). As erosional and depositional processes became adjusted to the standing base level, sediments have prograded seaward, caused a net regression of the shore, and formed an offlap or regressive sequence of sediments; examine Figures 4-6 and 11 for this evidence. Other processes, such as lateral shifting sites of maximum deltaic sedimentation, local changes in sediment supply, waves, and currents, have caused local and temporary transgressive sequences during the stillstand (Figs. 5 and 6) (Fisk, 1944; Greenman and LeBlanc, 1956; Bernard, Major, and Parrott, 1959, 1961; Gould and McFarlan, 1959).

RECENT AND PLEISTOCENE UNCONFORMITY

The Recent and Pleistocene (interglacial) sediments in coastal Texas and Louisiana are separated by a prominent unconformity. As a result of exposure to weathering during lower sea levels, the Pleistocene sediments at the contact generally contain comparatively little water, are relatively stiff and mottled, oxidized, and/or leached. Lime nodules, caliche, and ferruginous concretions frequently occur in the Pleistocene. In the coastal area and offshore, the Pleistocene at the contact contains numerous borings and burrows filled with Recent sediments. The overlying Recent sediments have a relatively greater moisture content; are soft; consist of silt, sand, and clay; and contain abundant organic remains. The Recent clay and silt are commonly olive grey in color. The Recent-Pleistocene unconformity is easily recognized at many locations. Below the oxidized zone the Pleistocene is very similar to the Recent and cannot be differentiated lithologically or paleontologically. At and near the base of the entrenched valleys, both seaward and inland of the coast line, the Recent deposits usually consist of coarse, nonfossiliferous alluvial sand and/or gravel that lie upon eroded late Pleistocene or older sediments.

CONTROL OF SEDIMENTATION BY TECTONICS,
COMPACTION, AND SEA LEVEL

Relative to present sea level, regional subsidence offshore and uplift inland, or gradual seaward tilting, continued during the Quaternary. This differential vertical movement has resulted from isostatic adjustment caused by sedimentary loading (Doering, 1935; Fisk, 1944) and to a large measure by greater compaction rates in the offshore areas where predominantly finer grained sediments (clay and silt) have been deposited (Figs. 10-12). The Late Quaternary hinge lines or zones between subsidence and uplift coincide approximately with the initial mainland shorelines of the Recent and Late Pleistocene (Interglacial, Prairie, or Beaumont) high-standing-sea-level substages in South Texas, northeastern Mexico, and along the northern and eastern Gulf Coast, a distance of over 1,500 statute miles. Along most of the Mexican and Texas coasts the position of the hinge has shifted only a few miles seaward since the last Pleistocene interglacial (Prairie or Beaumont) high-standing sea level (Figs. 4 and 5), but east of Galveston Bay

and toward the area of maximum sedimentation (Mississippi deltaic) the hinge has shifted seaward a distance of over 30 miles. Evidence of differential coastal plain warping or rates of seaward advance of the hinge lines may be gained by an examination of Figure 5, which shows a pronounced divergence of these initial strand lines. Eastward from Galveston Bay, elevations of the Pleistocene strand deposits become progressively greater. At the Houston Barrier (north of Calcasieu Lake) the elevations of the strand deposits are more than 20 ft higher than the contemporary strand deposits of the Smith Point Barrier near Galveston Bay (Fig. 5). To the east of the site of maximum Mississippi deltaic sedimentation and subsidence (Fisk and McFarlan, 1955), the last Pleistocene (Prairie) high-standing-sea-level strand deposits near Biloxi, Mississippi, are only a few feet above those of the modern strand deposits, *e.g.* those of Ship, Horn, and other islands further eastward (Fig. 6). Northeast (near the east-west boundary between Louisiana and Mississippi) of the area of maximum Pleistocene deltaic sedimentation (H. V. Howe, personal communication, 1936; Fisk, 1939) and northwest of this area between the Sabine and Neches River in Texas (Bernard, 1950) the highest elevations (nearly 600 ft) of the older Pleistocene interglacial (Williana) deposits have been recorded. Farther west and east of this area, elevations of these deposits decline to a maximum of nearly 400 ft above sea level.

Seaward of the different Quaternary hinge lines, deltaic, coastal interdeltaic, and marine sedimentation predominated over alluvial sedimentation and erosion. In these areas alluvial sedimentation and erosion occurred only during lower-sea-level substages, but inland from these hinge lines, alluvial sedimentation predominated over deltaic, coastal interdeltaic, and normal marine sedimentation.

The initial shoreline of the Late Recent standing-sea-level substage was seaward of that of the Late Pleistocene. Although the zone of coastal sedimentation shifts with the movement of the hinge, the level of the sea, and seaward prograding sedimentation during stillstands of the sea, there has been a net seaward movement of this zone during the Quaternary and Tertiary periods (Figs. 1 and 12). However, the rates of seaward movement of this zone have been slower along those sections of the Gulf basin where coastal interdeltaic sedimentation has predominated over deltaic sedimentation.

In the northwest Gulf coastal area, the present hinge line is determined by the seaward slope of the Late Pleistocene (Interglacial, Prairie, or Beaumont formations) depositional plain and the present sea-level stand. This controlled the regional depositional strike between the Recent and Pleistocene deposits. Its position controls the boundary between the alluvial and deltaic environments of the largest streams, such as the Mississippi, Brazos, Colorado, and Rio Grande.

Inland from the hinge and within the stream valleys depositional slopes are relatively steeper due primarily to gradual and progressive uplift, but seaward the slopes are relatively small and are determined principally by the progradation of coastal interdeltaic and deltaic sediments of the larger rivers into a relatively still standing body of water. At the break in slope, these streams, constantly seeking shorter sea routes and steeper gradients, periodically bifurcate, or form a delta.

Because of this change in gradients of the larger streams near the hinge line between the alluvial and deltaic environments, a distinct change in grain size occurs. The average median grain size of the bed load within the deltaic distributaries is fine sand, while that of the stream deposits within the alluvial plains inland from the hinge is considerably greater and ranges from fine sand to gravel. It is important to call the reader's attention at this point to the fact that the average median grain size of the terrigenous shoreline deposits (with few exceptions) between the Mississippi River and Rio Grande is fine to very fine due to the preponderance of river-borne deltaic sediment over that derived by coastal erosion of unindurated sediments or older deposits of nondeltaic origin. Because of the predominant wind and wave directions, a net westward transport of sediment occurs along the Louisiana and east Texas coasts and a net northward movement occurs along the northeast Mexican and south Texas coasts.

Coastal sedimentation by the smaller streams such as the Trinity, Neches, and Sabine (Fig. 5) did not keep pace with the last rising sea level and, consequently, their entrenched valleys were drowned for considerable distances inland from the hinge at the beginning of the standing-sea-level substage. Therefore the boundaries between the alluvial and deltaic environments, for these streams, are at the bay heads and inland from the hinge line.

LATE QUATERNARY COASTAL PLAINS

Two high-standing-sea-level stages are well represented in Mississippi, Louisiana, Texas, and the northeastern coast of Mexico by the Late Pleistocene (Interglacial, Prairie, or Beaumont formations) and the Late Recent alluvial, deltaic, and interdeltaic plains (Figs. 2-7). The elevation of the Late Pleistocene standing sea level was approximately the same as the present one, and the deposits forming each plain prograded seaward during each substage. The geological processes, sediment sources, transportation, and deposition resulting in the formation of these two plains were very similar. These plains differ only in geologic age and stages of maturity; the Prairie or Beaumont plain has reached maturity, but the Late Recent plains are still in a youthful stage of development. For a comparison of maturity, note the size of the Late Recent Trinity Delta, which is about three miles wide at the head of Galveston Bay, and the size of the Late Pleistocene Trinity Delta to the east, which covers an area of about three Texas counties (Fig. 5). Note also that the Late Pleistocene (Interglacial) deltas of the Trinity, Neches, Sabine, Red, and Mississippi Rivers prograded considerable distances seaward (more than 25 nautical miles) beyond the initial strand line, indicated by the line of coastal barriers and beaches including Smith Point, Fannett, Orange, and Houston Bayou (Figs. 5-6). Available data from borings show that the Mississippi Delta prograded its shore over 100 nautical miles seaward of these initial strand deposits (Fig. 5) and near the present 90-ft depth contour (Fisk and McFarlan, 1956). The southernmost subaerial sediments of the Mississippi Delta have subsided more than 100 ft since they were deposited. For comparison, the very late Recent Mississippi Delta has prograded its subaerial plain an average of 70 miles seaward of the present hinge line and across a large part of the continental shelf in the past 2,000 years. Thus much of the present continental shelf off Louisiana and southeast Texas was occupied by coalescing deltas of the Mississippi during the Late Pleistocene Interglacial stage.

Given sufficient time, approximately 20,000-25,000 years, and a constant stand of the sea, the future events along this part of the coast should be similar to those of the Last Pleistocene Interglacial stage. The rivers, if not controlled by man, should prograde their deltas far seaward of the present strand. The Mississippi deltaic plain should eventually cover most of the present shelf off the Louisiana coast and possibly part of southeast Texas coast before the cycle is terminated by the next falling-sea-level substage.

TOPOGRAPHIC AND STRATIGRAPHIC RELATIONSHIPS BETWEEN THE LATE QUATERNARY PLAINS AND RELATED DEPOSITS

All evidence suggests that the initial depositional slopes of the late Pleistocene surfaces were similar to those of the Recent (Doering, 1935; Fisk, 1939, 1944; Bernard, 1950). Because of continued coastal subsidence and landward uplift the slopes of the older Pleistocene depositional plains are greater than those of the Recent.[3]

Seaward of the hinge line the deposits of the Recent rising-sea-level substage onlap (transgress) the Pleistocene, and deposits of the Recent standing-sea-level substage offlap (regress) the rising-sea-level and/or Pleistocene sediments. The offlapping sequences consist of normal marine, deltaic, and coastal interdeltaic deposits. Inland from the hinge line most Recent sediments are alluvial in origin and fill the entrenched valleys cut into the previous Pleistocene or older deposits. The Recent alluvial plains inland from the hinge are bounded by valley scarps. These scarps are the uppermost parts of entrenched valley walls, and in places they have been modified by lateral erosion of the late Recent streams. The scarps decrease in height seaward and disappear at the hinge line. Recent alluviation within these entrenched valleys has not and, providing there is no rise in base level, should not reach the height of the uplifted Pleistocene plains.

LATE QUATERNARY GEOMORPHIC FEATURES

The physiographic features of the Louisiana and Texas Late Quaternary plains have been grouped into three types: those resulting from depositional processes, from erosional processes, and from tectonics. The great majority of the geomorphic features are depositional in origin. Comparatively few forms are of erosional or tectonic origin.

[3] South of Houston (Figs. 5 and 11) the seaward slope of the Late Pleistocene (Beaumont) deltaic plain of the Brazos River is approximately 2.0 ft per statute mile and the slopes of the Recent alluvial and deltaic plains of the Brazos are approximately 1.4 and 1.2 ft per mile. Slopes of the progressively older Pleistocene (interglacial) plains are progressively greater.

DEPOSITIONAL ENVIRONMENTS AND RELATED SEDIMENTS

Geomorphic features of depositional origin provide a basis for classifying the sedimentary environments in the Gulf coastal area. The texture, fabric, sedimentary features, geometry, and trends of the sediments associated with various depositional forms are controlled by the nature of the geological processes and the availability and influx of different sediment types. The surface morphology of these features controls the floral and faunal distributions and also affects the nature of the secondary geological processes.

Because of limited space available for detailed descriptions and illustrations, only the most common geomorphic forms are classified below; following this classification, the important forms and related sediments, geometry, sequence, processes, genesis, etc. are described and discussed in alphabetical order.

CONTINENTAL (13)[4]
  Aeolian plain (1)
    Sand dunes of all types (1)
    Blow-out basin and/or intermittent lake (1)
    Clay-silt dune (1)
  Alluvial or fluvial floodplain (3)
    Meandering stream floodplain (25)
      Meander belt (24)
        Point bar (29), including ridges and swales (30)
        Natural levee (27)
        Abandoned channel, includes oxbow lake (2), pock mark (28)
      Flood basin (20)
        Semiarid or non-vegetated (20)
        Swamp (20)
        Marsh (20)
        Lake (20)
        Gathering stream (20)
    Braided stream (9)
      Channel (9)
        Dispersal channel (9)
        Gathering channel (9)
      Interchannel flat, vegetated and non-vegetated (9)
      Sand dunes of all types (9)
TRANSITIONAL (34)
  Delta (14) (Note: includes several different delta types. Delta plains may be subdivided into *upper and lower deltaic plains* (16), both of which include the following deltaic plain environments.)
    Deltaic plain (16) (Principal subdivisions similar to those of meandering stream plain).
      Abandoned straight distributary channel (2), pock mark (28), and natural levee (27)
      Meander belt (24) (subdivisions are similar to those of the Alluvial Plain.)
      Flood basin (20)
        Swamp (back swamp) (20)
        Marsh (20)
        Lake (20)
        Bay (20) (transitional with interdistributary bay within deltaic fringe)
        Gathering channel (20)
        Tidal channel (20)
        Dune, sand, and/or clay dune (1)
    Prodeltaic environment (31) (subaqueous part of delta also called fluviomarine environment).
    Deltaic fringe (15) (shallow subaqueous prodeltaic en-

vironment also called proximal or delta front or platform.)
      Distributary mouth bar (19)
      Bar finger (4)
      Coalescing distributary mouth bars (19)
      (Delta front or platform)
      Interdistributary bay (21)
      Mudflat (26)
      Barrier island and spit (5)
      Chenier or beach (8, 10, and 11)
      Tidal flat, delta, and channel (33)
    Distal prodelta (called prodelta by Fisk and others) (17)
  Coastal interdeltaic plain (12) (Note: includes coastal fresh to hypersaline bays or lakes and littoral and/or very shallow neritic zone)
    Chenier plain (11)
      Chenier (beach ridge or abandoned beach ridge) (8, 10, 11)
        Transgressive (onlap) (8, 10, 11)
        Regressive (offlap) (8, 10, 11)
      Mudflat (26) (major regressive or offlap deposits)
      Marsh (23)
      Lake, and/or bay (11)
      Tidal pass, channel, and delta (33)
    Barrier island plain (6)
      Coastal barrier, barrier island, and associated barrier spit (5)
        Beach ridge (8)
        Swale (5) and pock mark (28)
        Sand dune (5, 8)
        Shore face (5a, 32)
        Tidal channel, delta, and flat (5, 33)
      Bay and/or lagoon (5, 7)
        Tidal channel, delta, and flat (33)
        Mudflat (26)
NORMAL MARINE (22)
  Shelf or neritic (22) (transitional with or includes subaqueous seaward parts of deltaic and coastal interdeltaic environments, less than 500- or 600-ft water depths)
    Inner (22) (less than 120-ft water depths, includes subaqueous shoals, flats, bars, ridges, and mounds or rises)
    Middle (22) (120-300-ft water depths, includes mounds or rises and canyons)
    Outer (22) (300-600-ft water depths, include mounds or rises and canyons)
    Slope or bathyal (22)
      Upper slope (22) includes mounds, canyons, silled basins, and scarps
      Lower slope or continental rise includes scarf (22)
    Deep or abyssal (22)
      Plain (22)
      Fan or cone (22)
      Sea mount or knoll (22)

Aeolian plain (*1*). The Quaternary aeolian plain of south Texas (Figs. 3-4) covers the Pleistocene deltaic plains, abandoned lagoons, mudflats, barriers, and beaches and includes active and stabilized sand dunes of all types, blow-out basins (intermittent lakes or pock marks) and silt-clay dunes. The latter dunes (Huffman and Price, 1949) consist of accumulation of wind-blown, mud-cracked flakes of silt-clay laminae derived from intermittent lakes, or lagoonal mudflats. These particles become stabilized by vegetation and adhesion processes when wetted-down during rainfalls. The "clay" dunes are parallel to and occur usually on the northwest sides of the intermittent lakes or basins or mudflats. Vegetation within the plains consists of scrub oaks and semiarid vegetation common to south Texas.

---

[4] Numerical position assigned to environment or feature, discussed below. Most of these are presented in alphabetical order.

Abandoned river channels and oxbows (2). Abandoned channels within both the alluvial and deltaic plains appear on the surface as low, arcuate, sinuous, or relatively straight low swales and/or oxbow lakes flanked by natural levees (Figs. 4-6 and 15-16). Depending upon the degree of maturity (stage of filling) and natural and artificial drainage and rainfall, these swales may or may not be filled with water. They usually contain a soil and natural flora distinctly different from that of the surrounding areas.

The nature and sequence of the associated sediments are determined largely by the manner and rapidity of channel abandonment. Slowly abandoned channels are commonly filled with a coarser downward sequence consisting of clay and silt (occasionally organically rich and commonly laminated), with thin layers of silt and sand grading downward to sand and rarely gravel. Rapidly abandoned channels such as some oxbow lakes are filled mainly with clay and silt and very little sand; these fine grained channel fillings are called "clay plugs," and they commonly overlie basal point bar or channel sands with gravel.

Alluvial or fluvial plains (3). Alluvial or fluvial plains are flood basins of meandering and braided streams. These plains are confined within stream valleys, and their slopes

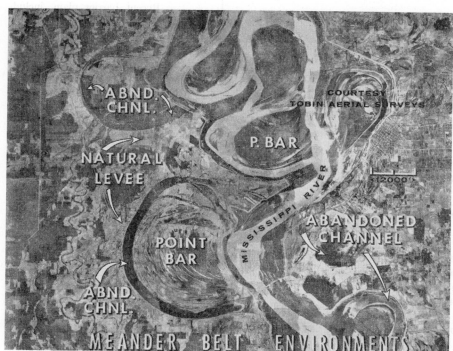

Figure 15. Meander belt environments of deposition. After Bernard and Major (1963). Photograph courtesy of Edgar Tobin Aerial Surveys.

Figure 16. Aerial mosaic of abandoned distributary channels, natural levees, and flood basin marshes of the Mississippi-Teche delta and the Mississippi-LaFourche subdelta. See Figure 3 for location. After LeBlanc and Bernard (1954). Photograph courtesy of Edgar Tobin Aerial Surveys.

Figure 17. Aerial photograph of the Late Pleistocene (Beaumont) deltaic plains, lagoon, and associated barrier island, and the Recent barrier plain, including the barrier islands with abandoned beach ridges, washover fans, and sand dunes and the associated bays or lagoons. See Figure 3 for location of this area. After Le-Blanc and Bernard (1954). Photograph courtesy Edgar Tobin Aerial Surveys.

are steeper than those of the deltaic plains with which they merge in a seaward direction (Figs. 3, 6, and 11).

Bar fingers (4). Bar fingers are thick, elongate, finger-like deposits of river-mouth bar "sands" that underlie the main distributaries of the Mississippi delta and prograde into deep water offshore (Fisk *et al.,* 1954; Fisk, 1961). These deposits have no surface expression, except the present bars off the distributary mouths. Their great thicknesses have resulted from very rapid penecontemporaneous subsidence or "downward-buildup" and progradation of the river-mouth bar "sands" deposited by fluvial and marine processes. The deposits offlap, subside into, and both laterally and vertically displace, the distal prodelta silty clay sediments deposited in deeper water and at greater distances off the river-mouth bars. Their thicknesses, geometry, and occurrences are shown in Figure 6. Flowage of the very soft, hydroplastic, prodelta silty-clay caused by subsidence of denser bar sands results in shale diapirism and formation of mud lumps (Morgan, 1951; Morgan *et al.,* 1963; Fisk *et al.,* 1954; Fisk, 1961), (Fig. 6).

Barrier islands and associated barrier spits (5). Coastal barriers, barrier islands, and/or spits are low, elongate, onshore or offshore islands, also called barrier bars, or outer banks, that are usually parallel or subparallel to the mainland shore. Spits such as Bolivar Peninsula are connected to the mainland and restrict the entrances of the drowned bays or the entrenched valleys of the smaller streams. In the flat-topped, broad stream-divide areas, the barriers separate the elongate, narrow lagoons from the open Gulf. Chains of barrier islands are most common in the coastal interdeltaic environments. Barrier islands also occur on delta margins; examples are the Chandeleur Islands and Grand Isle (Fig. 6). See Barrier Island Plain (6).

(a) *Morphologic features and depositional environments.* The characteristic topographic features of mature barrier islands (Fig. 5) are low, parallel ridges, shallow swales be-

tween the ridges, tidal deltas, and wash-over fans and spits (Figs. 4-5, 17-18, and 20). Sand dunes of all types are the most characteristic depositional forms of many barriers along the south Texas coast. The bay sides of most mature barrier islands are characterized by large numbers of abandoned tidal channels or "guts," which trend at right angles to the long axis of the barriers (Figs. 17-18 and 20). Many "guts" are former swale areas between hooked beach-spit accretions formed at the ends of the islands or within migrating tidal channels crossing an island. Tidal processes and storm-generated over-wash currents keep most "guts" open for long periods of time.

The shoreface subenvironment extends from the low-tide shoreline seaward to the 30- or 50-ft depth contour. Its profile is concave upwards. It may be subdivided into three depositional zones: an upper shoreface or breaker zone with its characteristic breaker or longshore bars, a middle zone, and a lower shoreface zone, which is the seaward toe of the island and the base of the concave upward profile (Fig. 20).

(b) *Chains of barrier island sand.* The Bolivar-Galveston barrier (Fig. 5) consists of approximately 0.5 cubic mile of clean, well-sorted fine sand with shells. This barrier comprises the easternmost part of a chain of barriers, which continue, with few interruptions by river deltas, south along the Texas and Mexican coast for approximately 600 miles. Similar Pleistocene barrier chains, such as Live Oak, Smith Point, Orange and Houston Bayou barriers formed during the last Pleistocene high-sea-level stand and during temporary stands of both the rising- and falling-sea-level stages (Figs. 4 and 5).

(c) *Geological processes.* Principal processes affecting the sediment supply and development of these barriers are the prevailing winds, waves, and currents directed from the southeast and northeast quadrants. Wave heights average 2 ft in 10-ft water depths and 4 ft in 50-ft water depths off Galveston. Ten- to twenty-foot waves occur during hurricanes. The combined effect of winds, surface currents, and

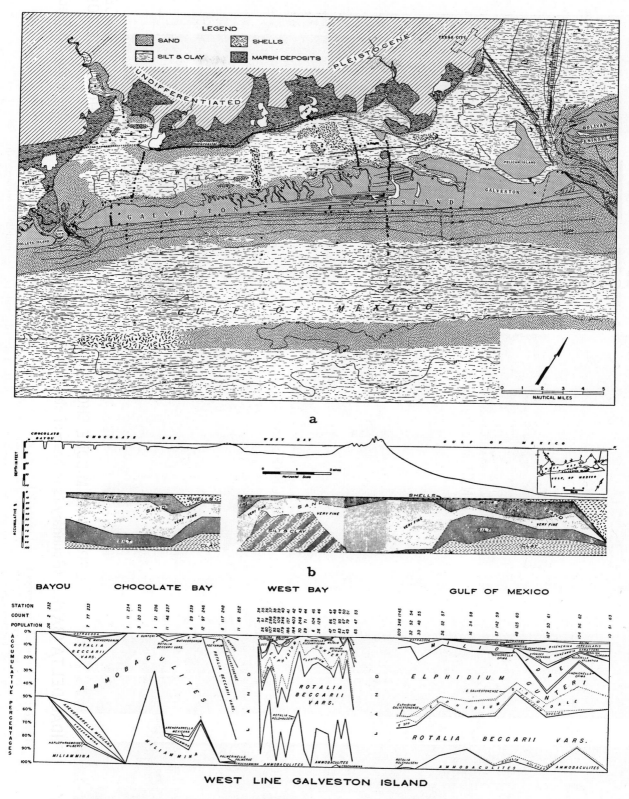

Figure 18. Distribution of bottom sediments and associated microfaunas in the Galveston barrier island area. After Bernard, LeBlanc, and Major (1962).

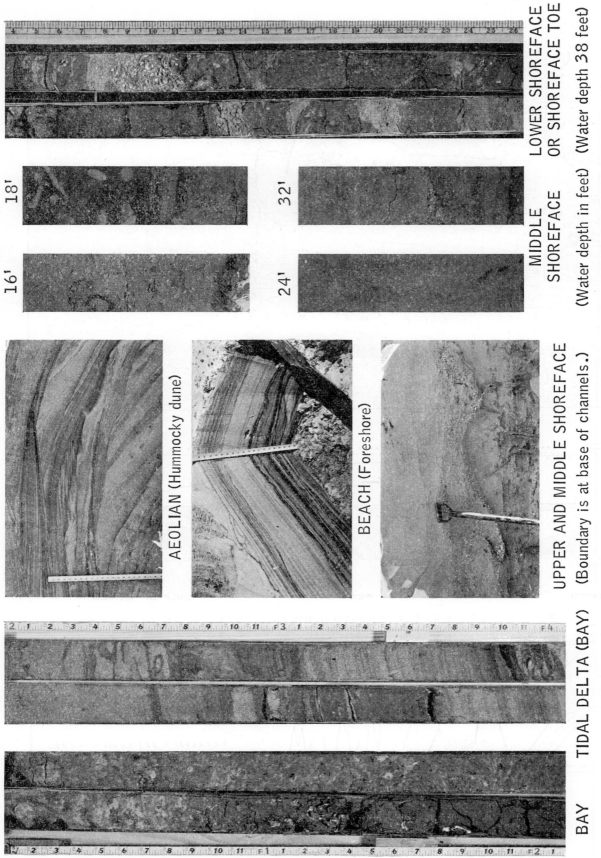

Figure 19. Sedimentary structures typical of the lithofacies common to the Galveston barrier island and associated environments. The light areas represent very fine sand and shells. The dark areas represent silt and clay, except for the dark heavy mineral laminae in the aeolian and beach sands and the dark, reduced sand in the middle shoreface core (18 ft). After Bernard, LeBlanc, and Major (1962).

waves refracting shoreward produce westward longshore currents along the Louisiana and southeast Texas coasts and northward along the south Texas coast.

Tides are semi-diurnal and diurnal and range in height from less than 1 to 2.5 ft. Tidal currents in channels vary from less than 1 to a maximum of 3.5 knots during flood and 4.3 knots during ebb tides. The direction of force and duration of the wind has a considerable effect on the waves, tides, and currents. Fifteen-foot tides and very large waves occur during major hurricanes, and very low tides accompany strong northerly winds of long duration.

Surface water temperatures average less than 90° F, and range between 80° and 100° F during the summer. During the winter the average is less than 60° F, and the range is between 32° and 80° F. Shallow parts of the bays freeze over during the very rare severe winters. Salinity varies with the runoff, from almost fresh during winter and spring to approximately 30 parts per thousand during long, dry, summer and fall seasons.

(d) *Sediment sources.* Most of the sand forming the barriers off the Louisiana and southeast Texas coast was derived from easterly sources as far away as the westernmost parts of the Mississippi Delta and from southerly sources along the south Texas coast by waves and currents reworking Late Pleistocene and Recent deltaic and coastal interdeltaic deposits in the near-shore zone (approximately 0-50-ft water depths). Although some very fine grained sediments may be derived from deeper sources offshore, most of this very fine material deposited in the coastal interdeltaic environments is supplied by the rivers and reworking of the Late Quaternary deposits along the shore.

(e) *Occurrences of bottom facies.* The occurrences and distribution of the different lithofacies and foraminiferal facies in the Galveston area are shown in Figures 18 and 19. Details of the lithofacies and megainvertebrate facies have been presented by Bernard, LeBlanc, and Major (1962).

(f) *Genesis of barrier islands and spits.* During the initial standing-sea-level substage, the Galveston barrier began as a small bar about four miles offshore in five to eight feet of water. The island emerged and grew principally seaward by beach and shoreface accretion and southwestward along the shore by beach, spit, tidal channel, and tidal delta accretion. The offlapping development of the island sand mass during the stillstand is revealed by the sequence of the facies in numerous continuous cores, by the relationships of beach ridges and swales, and by radiocarbon dates and other data (Figs. 4-5, 18-20). Barriers such as those on the south Texas coast generally continue to grow upwards by the deposition of dune sand.

Fisk (1959) and Shepard (1956) present data supporting the hypothesis that some of the coastal barriers began to form and build up with a decrease in rate of sea-level rise during the end of the rising-sea-level stage.

Barrier island plain (6). The barrier island plain along the Texas coast (Figs. 4 and 5) consists of barrier islands and spits including tidal channels and deltas, bay-head river deltas, and the shallow bays behind the islands. The plain merges with the very shallow littoral or neritic zone offshore.

The offshore deposits related to the barrier extend to the convex upward break in slope near the 30-50-ft contours. The larger bays having their long axes approximately perpendicular to the coast are drowned vestiges of the entrenched valleys since modified by shore erosion (LeBlanc and Hodgson, 1959). Elongate, narrow bays of lagoons occur between the barriers and the mainland shore or the strike of the flat-topped stream divides, or the original depositional surfaces of the previous high-standing sea level. See Barrier Islands (5).

Bays and/or lagoons (7). See Barrier Plain, Chenier Plain (11), and Barrier Islands (5).

Beach ridges (8). A beach ridge is a low, narrow, elongate ridge, parallel to the shore, usually with a steep seaward side (foreshore) and a gentle landward slope (backshore). In general, the profile across a ridge is much like that of a natural levee. The sediments consist of fine, well-sorted sand, usually with abundant shells and fragments. The ridges are commonly recurved inland near tidal passes, separating and/or crossing barrier islands, and near the major tidal passes within the chenier plain. The maximum height of Gulf Coast beach ridges is approximately 12 ft above mean sea level. Sand dunes principally of the hummocky types may occur on the ridges. In south Texas dunes are over 40 ft above sea level and generally mask the beach ridges (Fig. 17). Beach ridges are very common on barrier islands. In southwest Louisiana abandoned beach ridges are called cheniers (Fig. 21). Many of these ridges, including many along the northwestern shores of the Gulf of California, western North America, consist principally of shells and shell fragments (Douglas Inman, personal communication, 1963). Cheniers are common to many deltas and occur most frequently near the mouths of the river distributaries (Figs. 5-6, 17 and 20).

Beach ridges or cheniers are of two types, transgressive and regressive. See Chenier Plain (11) for explanation of their genesis.

Braided stream floodplain (9). Braided stream floodplains include braided channels (dispersal and gathering), interchannel flats (vegetated or non-vegetated), and sand dunes. In the Gulf Coast these plains are more common and widespread in the upper Mississippi Valley (Fisk, 1944) and are of Early Recent age (Fig. 7).

Chenier (10). See Beach Ridge (8) and Chenier Plain (11).

Chenier plain (11). The chenier plain of southwest Louisiana is characterized by abandoned beach ridges called cheniers, extensive marshes, numerous lakes (many of which are vestiges of drowned river valleys), and coastal mudflats. The word chenier, meaning oak covered, has been derived from the French word, *le chêne,* meaning oak tree. Most of these abandoned beach ridges or islands, surrounded by marsh terrain, are covered with a dense growth of majestic live oak trees beautifully draped with Spanish moss. These islands and oak trees, to which the natives strap themselves, offer the only protection during severe hurricane tides and waves. The ridges are on the average 15-20 miles long, 500-1,000 ft wide, and 5-15 ft thick (Figs. 5 and 21).

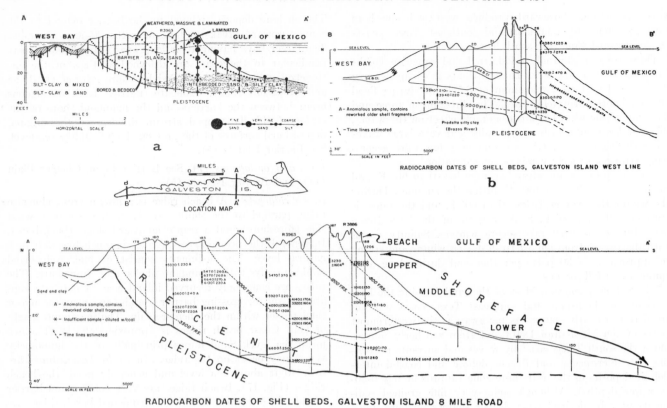

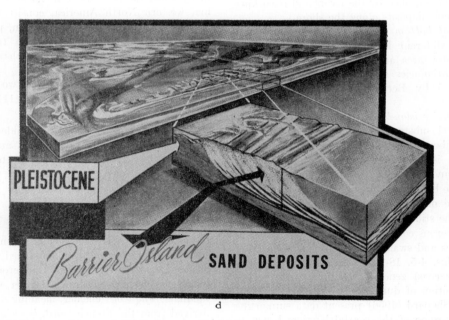

Figure 20a, b, c, and d. Cross sections and block diagram illustrating the offlap sequence of the lithofacies (a), radiocarbon dated time lines (b and c), and the generalized geometry and offlap sqeuence of the barrier island facies (d). Inasmuch as shells are frequently reworked and deposited before final burial, only the youngest shells occurring in groups and in sequence were used to establish dates. The time lines conform with the offshore profile of equilibrium, the profile of the Recent-Pleistocene contact, and the offlap sequence of beach ridges on the surface of the island. After Bernard, LeBlanc, and Major (1962).

a

b

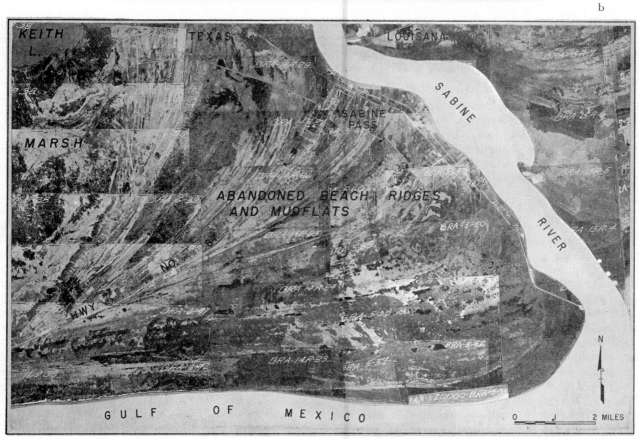

Figure 21a and b. Aerial oblique photograph (a) showing the relationships of abandoned beach ridges (cheniers), marsh, and intertidal and subaqueous shallow mudflats along the coast of south Louisiana at Chenier au Tigre (see Fig. 5 for location). The white line indicates the position of the last beach and shore line about 35 years ago. Since then extensive mudflats have accreted to this part of the coast because of the large recent influx of silt and clay contributed to this part of the coast by the Mississippi-Atachafalaya course. (b) is an aerial photomosaic of abandoned beach ridges and marsh-covered mudflats near Sabine Lake (see Fig. 5 for location). After LeBlanc and Hodgson (1959). Photograph courtesy of Edgar Tobin Aerial Surveys.

The influx of silt and clay, contributed to the coastal waters by rivers and by coastal erosion in excess of the capacity of the waves and currents to transport the sediment, results in the formation of widespread, offlapping (regressive) sequence of mudflat deposits along the coast. The buildup of mudflats dissipates wave energy at greater distances offshore and thereby increases the rate of deposition nearer the shore. As the mudflats become emergent, marsh vegetation takes root, traps additional sediment, and reduces coastal erosion of the flats.

When the rate of sediment supply is reduced by either an eastward shift of the Mississippi distributaries, long drought periods, or a local decrease in coastal erosion, the waves and longshore currents have the capacity to steepen the offshore profile, erode and straighten the shoreline, and form an onlap (transgressive) sequence of beach deposits. The deposits transgress either marsh or non-vegetated, subaerial or very shallow, subaqueous mudflat deposits. However, some sequences (Fig. 5, Section B-B') of chenier deposits, especially those near some migrating tidal passes (such as Mermentau Pass) transporting relatively small amounts of silt and clay, result from spit accretion within the pass and seaward along the shore. These cheniers are similar to barrier islands and spits in the barrier plain.

Mudflats prograde a much greater distance seaward, from 1 to 2 miles or more within a 50-year period, than cheniers form and/or transgress landward, seldom more than 200 ft in a comparative period; consequently a net offlap sequence of deposits has resulted in the development of the chenier plain.

Coastal interdeltaic plain (12). The coastal interdeltaic plain includes the relatively narrow depositional surface and related environments, which extend parallel to the coast and between the deltas of the largest streams, the Mississippi, Brazos, Colorado, and Rio Grande. This plain includes the chenier and barrier plains (Figs. 3-5).

Continental plains (13). The continental environments include the alluvial and aeolian plains.

Deltas, types and development (14). Deltas and deltaic sediments forming a large part of the coastal plains have been produced by the rapid deposition of stream-borne materials into the relatively still-standing Gulf of Mexico and connected water bodies. Notwithstanding the effects of subsidence and sea-level movements, most deltaic sediments are deposited within the subaqueous prodeltaic (31) area, off the shore of the subaerial deltaic plain. As these materials build upward to the level of the sea, the remainder of the deltaic sediments are deposited within the subaerial deltaic plain (16).

Nearly 2,500 years ago Herodotus, using the Nile as an example, stated that the land area reclaimed from the sea by the deposition of river sediments is generally deltoid in shape. The buildup and progradation of deltaic sediments produce a distinct change in stream gradient from the fluvial or alluvial plain to the deltaic plain. Near the point of gradient change, the channels generally begin to bifurcate and form subaerial deltaic plains. The boundaries of the subaerial plain of an individual delta are the lateral-

most distributaries and the general trend of the coast line. Successively smaller distributaries form subdeltas of progressively smaller magnitudes. See Figures 3-6, 16, and 22. The boundaries between the subaqueous part of the delta and other environments are transitional.

The subdivisions and terminologies assigned by various authors to the different deltaic environments are outlined above and the principal ones are described below.

(a) *Classification of deltas.* Deltas may be classified on the basis of the nature of the associated water bodies, *e.g.* lake, bay, inland sea, and marine delta. Other classifications may be based on the depth of the water bodies into which they prograde, basin structure, or configuration.

A large number of delta types have previously been described. Most of these have been related to the vicissitudes of the sedimentary processes by which the deltas form. Names were derived largely from the shapes of the delta shorelines and the subaerial gradients of the deposits. The configuration of the delta shores and many other depositional forms expressed by the different deltaic facies appear to be directly influenced by the relative relationships of the amount or rate of sediment influx to the nature and energy of the coastal processes. The more common and better understood delta types, listed in order of relative decreasing sediment influx and increasing energy of the coastal processes (waves, currents, and tides) are: birdfoot, lobate, cuspate, arcuate, and estuarine. The subdeltas of the Colorado River illustrate this relationship. During the first part of this century, the Colorado River, transporting approximately the same yearly sediment load, built a birdfoot-lobate type of delta across Matagorda Bay, a low-energy water body, and recently began to form a cuspate delta in the Gulf of Mexico, a water body of comparatively higher energy.

The Brazos River, which is similar in size to the Colorado, has constructed several cuspate-type deltas in the Gulf of Mexico (Fig. 5). The bay-head deltas of the Guadalupe and Trinity Rivers are compounded birdfoot-lobate types (Figs. 4 and 5). The Rio Grande delta is a modified arcuate-cuspate type; however, many of its subdeltas within the lagoons or bays are of the birdfoot or lobate types. The Nueces and San Jacinto (bay-head deltas), Figures 4 and 5, are probably of the estuarine type. Most river deltas are compounded; their deltas or subdeltas are generally representative of two or more types of delta. The Mississippi delta can be described as a compounded birdfoot-lobate-cuspate type. However, one type formed by a river generally predominates.

The classic delta type, commonly described in textbooks, located very near major scarps is classified as the Gilbert type, which is similar to an alluvial fan. This type does not occur along the Gulf Coast. The present Colorado River of the western United States is a mature compounded Gilbert-estuarine type.

(b) *Mississippi delta.* As shown in Figure 42, the Mississippi has developed three deltas, including three prominent major subdeltas, during the standing-sea-level stage. The associated deposits consist of an offlapping wedge of deltaic sediments over a thick-to-very-thin wedge of onlapping alluvial, deltaic, bay, and shallow-to-deep neritic sediments deposited during both the rising- and standing-sea-level stages (Figs. 22 and 23). The seaward advance of the delta's shoreline during the past 3,000-5,000 years has averaged over 70 statute miles seaward of the hinge line or Pleistocene-Recent contact. The buildup of these sediments has occurred in water depths ranging from 0 to approximately 350 ft.

As the delta prograded seaward, especially in shallow waters generally less than 200 ft, a normal delta sequence (Fig. 6) built upward from distal prodelta, deltaic fringe, flood basin (marsh, swamp, lake, or bay), and natural levee deposits. As the deltaic plain became emergent very large to very small river distributary channels and tidal channels cut through all or parts of the sequence and were backfilled with an upward sequence of sand, silt, and clay and marsh or swamp deposits. Figures 6 and 22-26, illustrate the nature, geometry, development, and interrelationships of the different deltaic facies. As the delta advances into deep water, subsidence of river-mouth bar sands into distal, hydroplastic silty clay results in the development of bar fingers, diapirs, and mudlump islands.

Following delta or subdelta abandonment, slow subsidence

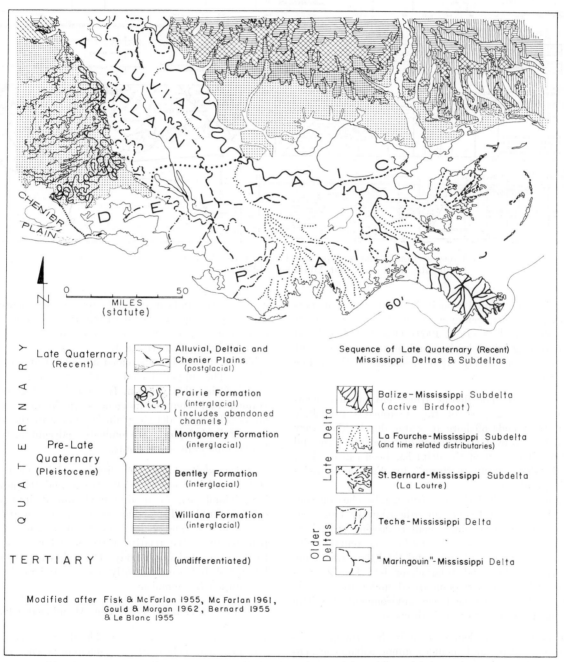

Figure 22. Generalized map illustrating the development of the Late Recent Mississippi deltas. Modified after Fisk and McFarlan (1955), Bernard (1955), LeBlanc (1955), McFarlan (1961), and Gould and Morgan (1962).

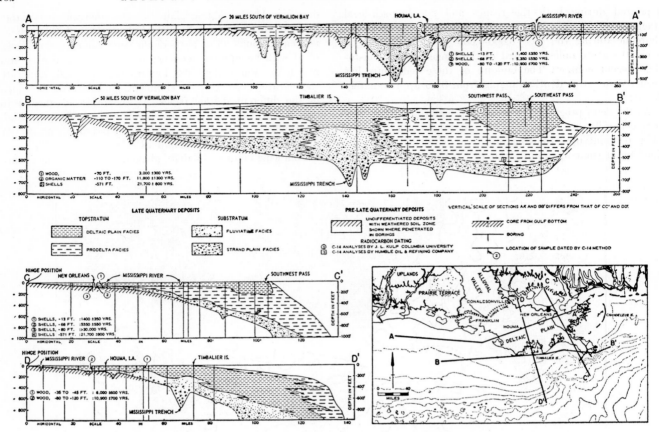

Figure 23. Cross sectional relationships and facies of the Late Quaternary deltaic mass of
sediments. After Fisk and McFarlan (1955).

of the deltaic plain caused principally by compaction permits contemporaneous accumulation of thick peat and organically rich silty clays (Fisk, 1960) (Fig. 26). Local and widespread transgressions by bay and marine waters result from continued or relatively rapid subsidence of the deltaic plain (Fig. 6).

Deltaic fringe (15). The deltaic fringe environment comprises the shallowest part of the subaqueous prodeltaic plain area. It extends offshore to water depths that vary from a few feet to over 50 ft depending upon the size and type of delta. This part of the delta has been called "delta front" and "delta front platform" by Fisk and "delta proximal" by others.

The deltaic fringe includes the fringing beaches or cheniers, distributary mouth bars, interdistributary bays, undifferentiated fringe (including small coalescing river bars and sand swept by waves and longshore currents), delta margin coastal barriers and spits, and tidal flats (including mudflats, tidal deltas, and tidal channels). The deposits vary considerably and are summarized under items listed above. See outline of deltaic fringe environments for item numbers under which each unit is discussed.

Deltaic plain (16). The deltaic plain is the principal subaerial part of a delta and includes minor subaqueous environments such as channels and lakes. The plain is generally deltoid in shape and is bounded by the principal

distributaries and the general trend of the shoreline. The deltaic plain comprises distributary and tidal channels, natural levees, and flood basins (swamps, marshes, lakes, bays, and gathering streams).

The plain may be subdivided into upper and lower deltaic plains. The upper includes subenvironments similar to those of the alluvial plain. Its deposits are generally finer grained and contain indigenous freshwater faunas and floras. The lower deltaic plain is similar to the upper, but finer grained deposits predominate and contain brackish to hypersaline faunas and floras.

Distal prodelta (17). The distal prodelta environment is transitional between the delta fringe and the normal lake, bay, inland sea, or marine environment into which the delta progrades. The sediments are very fine grained, silty clay, and clay and generally contain a sparce fauna (depending upon the relative rates of sedimentation) native to the associated water body. The sediments are commonly laminated, but are frequently massive and rarely burrowed or churned by organisms.

Distributary channel (18). See Abandoned Channel (2).

Distributary mouth bar (19). The distributary mouth bar, the principal deltaic fringe subenvironment, is the very shallow, symmetrically to asymmetrically crescent-shaped mass of sand, silt, and clay deposited rapidly off the bell-

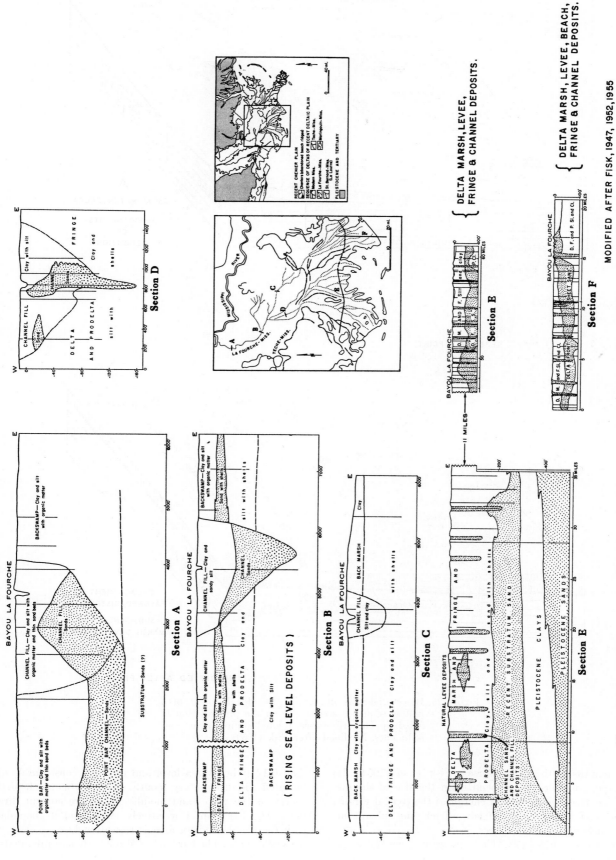

Figure 24. Cross sections of the Mississippi-Teche delta and the Mississippi-LaFourche subdelta. Modified after Fisk (1947, 1952, 1955) and Fisk *et al.* (1953).

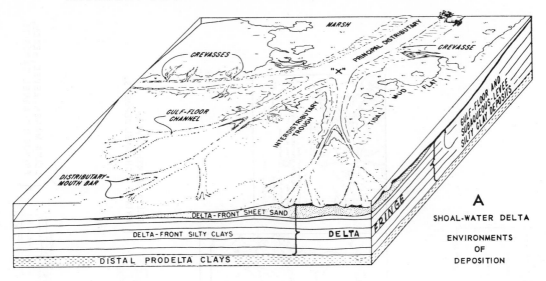

"X" – REFERENCE POINT

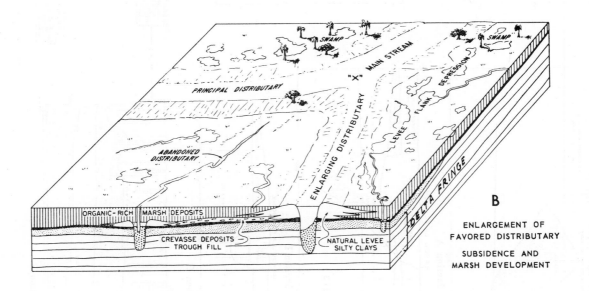

MODIFIED AFTER FISK, 1960

Figure 25. Block diagrams illustrating the development of a
deltaic sequence resulting from the progradation of
Mississippi distributaries, related environments and
sediments. Modified after Fisk (1960).

shaped mouths of the river courses (Fisk, *et al.*, 1954). Its size, shape, and thickness depend upon the size of the distributaries, river currents, and energy of the coastal waters. The bar consists of a crest, a front, a back, and subaqueous bar channels and natural levees.

(a) *Bar crest and front.* The bar crest is generally less

than 6-12 ft below sea level and lies at a considerable distance off the distributary mouth. It dissipates much of the energy of the waves and modifies longshore current directions. The bar front is relatively steep, and its boundary with the distal prodelta area is transitional.

(b) *Bar back.* The bar back is also less than approximately

6-12 ft below sea level and lies between the river mouth and the bar crest. It is more or less protected from severe wave action and longshore currents. River currents aided by tidal currents are capable of cutting and backfilling numerous deep (less than 25 ft) to very shallow bar channels across the bar back and crest. Subaqueous natural levees flank each channel, and the levees of the main bar channel are the seaward continuations of the subaerial natural levee flanking the distributary channel.

(c) *Middle ground*. Emergent parts of the bar that form along its central axis are called middle grounds and generally mark the position of the next channel bifurcation.

(d) *Coalescing distributary mouth bars*. Coalescing distributary mouth bars of smaller, adjacent distributaries develop blanket-like zones containing delta fringe sands, called "delta front sheet sands" by Fisk (1955).

(e) *Bar finger and mudlump*. Rapid subsidence of bar sands of the major distributaries prograding in deep water results in the development of bar fingers, mud diapirs, and mudlumps; see Bar Fingers (4) for details.

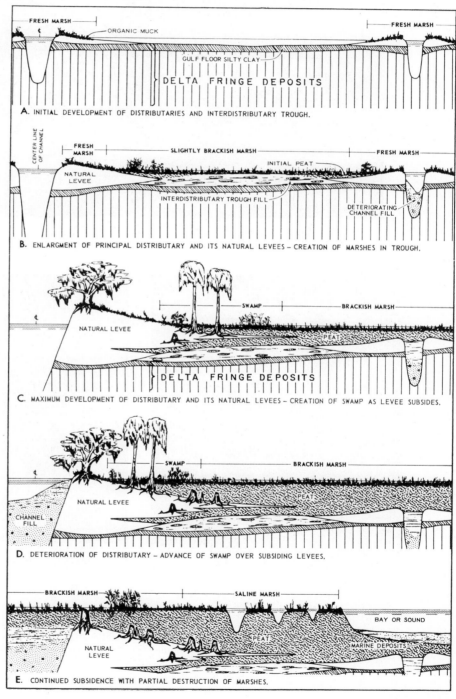

Figure 26. Progressive stages in the development of Mississippi deltaic channel, natural levee, and marsh; also related environments and sediments. Modified after Fisk (1960).

MODIFIED AFTER FISK, 1960

Figure 27a, b, c, and d. Late Pleistocene (Beaumont) flood basin deposits of the Brazos River in southwest Houston, Texas. Note immature soil zones, mammoth tusks, calcareous and ferrugineous nodules. The calcareous nodules commonly contain ferrugineous nodules (c). The immature soil zones contain very common calcareous root tubules. After Bernard, LeBlanc, and Major (1962).

Flood basin (20). Flood basins are low, flat, relatively featureless and poorly drained areas within the alluvial and deltaic plains (Figs. 6 and 7). They lie adjacent to and between the slightly higher stream meander belts or natural levees flanking straight distributaries in the deltaic plains. These plains are or were subject to flooding during overbank flood stages. The flood basins include swamps (back swamps), fresh and brackish water marshes, numerous lakes, and gathering streams. In south Texas the flood basins contain a semiarid vegetation and are barren during long drought periods. Many of the lakes and playas are associated with silt-clay dunes. For an explanation of the origin of "clay" dunes, see Aeolian Plain (1).

Flood basins of abandoned deltas continue to subside because of compaction and permit the accumulation of thick sections of peat and organically rich silt and clay (Figs. 25 and 26). Lakes become larger and rounded, and bays form as subsidence continues. Tidal streams that connect these lakes and bays meander. Large subsiding flood-basin areas, formerly covered with marsh or swamps, lying between subdeltas and major distributaries, have been called "delta-flank depressions" by Russell (1936).

Flood-basin sediments are very fine grained and usually consist of silts and clays (Fig. 27). The swamp and marsh deposits are disturbed by roots, are mottled, and commonly contain calcareous and ferruginous nodules, root tubules, and abundant organic material, which is more common in the deltaic flood basins than in the alluvial flood basins. Because of intermittent, rapid buildup of flood-basin deposits during rising-sea-level stages, most of the soil zones buried within these buildups are immature. Lake deposits are commonly laminated. Flood-basin deposits, especially those in semiarid regions of south Texas, are commonly algal-laminated and contain calcareous nodules and gypsum crystals.

Soils of flood-basin deposits are usually dark in color, but those of some rivers of Recent age commonly retain the color of the source material.

Late Pleistocene deltaic and alluvial flood basins are cultivated, usually for rice crops, or they contain a natural flora consisting of grasses and shrubs.

Interdistributary bays (21). Interdistributary bays lie between the larger distributaries of the deltaic plain and are included within the deltaic fringe environment. Examples are Barataria Bay and East Bay, which lies between South and Southwest Passes (Fig. 6). Most bays, such as the former Garden Island Bay lying between Southeast and South Passes, are eventually filled with deltaic sequences (Russell, 1936) formed by the smaller coalescing distributary mouth bars (Fig. 6).

Marine environments (22). The marine environments of the northwestern Gulf of Mexico consist of the shelf (neritic zone), the slope (bathyal zone), and the deep (abyssal plain) (LeBlanc and Greenman, 1953; Greenman and Le-Blanc, 1956) (Figs. 1 and 8). The normal marine shelf is transitional between, or includes, the subaqueous seaward parts of the deltaic and coastal interdeltaic environments. The topographic features of the shelf, slope, and deep have been described by Daly (1934, 1942), Shepard (1937),

Carsey (1950), Mattison (1948), LeBlanc and Greenman (1953), Fisk and McFarlan (1955), Gealy (1955), Ewing *et al.* (1955), Greenman and LeBlanc (1956), and Ewing, Ericson, and Heezen (1958).

The inner (less than 120 ft), middle (120-300 ft), and outer neritic (300-600 ft) shelfs contain many flats, shoals, bars or ridges, and mounds or rises. Most of the flats and large shoals are remnants of transgressed Pleistocene and Recent deltas (Figs. 3 and 5-6). The shoals, bars, and ridges are interpreted to be Early Recent and Pleistocene strandline deposits. The mounds or rises are believed to be topographic expressions of salt domes.

The topography and genesis of the slope, described by Gealy (1955), LeBlanc and Greenman (1956), and Ewing, Ericson, and Heezen (1958), have been discussed in the introduction. The development of the Mississippi Canyon and its associated abyssal fan and also the continental rise and abyssal plain (Fisk and McFarlan, 1955; Ewing, Ericson, and Heezen, 1958) have been interpreted to be the products of slides and turbidity currents (Figs. 1 and 8). However, much of the fan or cone off the Mississippi Canyon was probably built up also by pelagic sediments derived principally from the Mississippi and other major streams during the last Pleistocene glacial stage when sea level was near the present 300-450-ft contours. Plums of fresh water containing very fine sand, silt, clay, and macerated organic material (pelagic sediment) overriding denser sea water and extending more than 65 miles off the Mississippi mouths have been observed (Scrutton and Moore, 1953).

The Recent sediments and uppermost Pleistocene deposits in the northwestern Gulf of Mexico have been described by Stetson (1953), Trask (1953), Greenman and LeBlanc (1956), and Ewing, Ericson, and Heezen (1958); see Figures 28 and 29. The Recent continental shelf facies consist of sand, silty clay, clay, and shells. The rises or mounds on the shelf and upper slope are covered with coarse-textured facies of sandy and silty glauconitic deposits, foraminiferal ooze, and calcareous biostronal deposits, including coral. The upper slope, from 600 to 8,000 ft, consists of green-gray to brown-gray homogeneous clay facies. The western and central slope and deep from 3,000 to 12,000 ft contain a light yellow-brown mottled clay facies. The eastern deep contains a foraminiferal ooze. Phleger and Parker (1951) found a gradual depth zonation of benthonic foraminiferal fauna and increasing pelagic-benthonic foraminiferal ratios in all the shelf, slope, and deep sediments. Most samples contained abundant Foraminifera.

The underlying Pleistocene sediments consist principally of gray, laminated-to-thin-bedded silt and clay with a very few thin layers of very fine sand. Ewing, Ericson, and Heezen (1958) reported that only one core over 30 ft long penetrated the entire section. Foraminifera are relatively rare in these sediments and contain both deep-water and reworked, shallow-water benthonic Foraminifera (Phleger and Parker, 1951). One core in the western part of the deep contained about three feet of very fine sand with inner neritic benthonic Foraminifera.

Because Ewing, Ericson, and Heezen (1958) found no

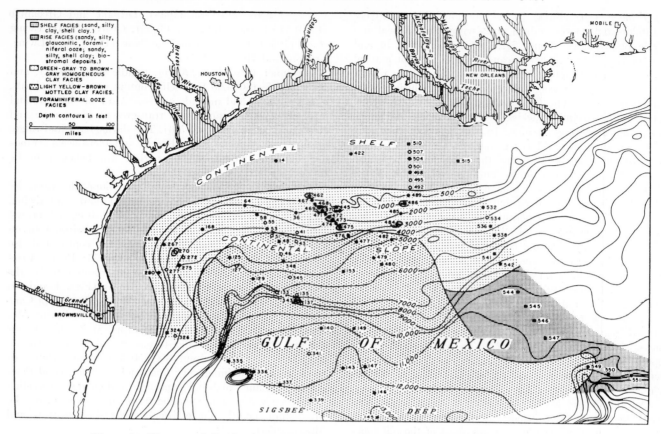

Figure 28. Nature and distribution of the Recent continental shelf, slope, and deep sedimentary facies in the northwestern Gulf of Mexico. After Greenman and LeBlanc (1956).

gray lithologic types, similar to the Pleistocene sediments described above, on three knolls in the central part of the Sigsbee deep, they believe that all the sediments described above were deposited by turbidity (bottom) currents.

LeBlanc and Greenman (1953) and Greenman and Le-Blanc (1956) reported that the thicknesses of both early and late Recent sediments occurring in the Gulf of Mexico are thickest (over 450 ft) within the entrenched valleys and near the present deltas, from a few feet to a maximum of 50 ft along the coast in the coastal interdeltaic areas (not including entrenched valley fill), from a few feet to about 30 ft on the shelf off the coastal interdeltaic plain, from less than 1 to 8 ft on the slope, and less than 1 to 6 ft within the deep.

Marshes (23). The Recent coastal marshes are very similar to those of the flood basins, and comprise the most widespread features of the chenier plain (Figs. 5-6 and 21). They contain many rounded lakes and meandering tidal channels, are very poorly drained, and are inundated during very high tides. Soils of Late Pleistocene marshes normally support a vegetation consisting of salt grass, rather than the types of grass and reed common to the Recent marshes.

Meander belts (24). Meander belts are the areas within which streams meander (Figs. 6-7 and 15). The widths of meander belts are generally 18-20 times the width of the

stream and are determined by the radius of curvature of the meanders. Mature meander belts of the Brazos and Rio Grande are between 1 and 2 miles wide, and those of the Mississippi are between 10 and 15 miles wide (Figs. 4-7 and 15).

Meander belts have a greater relief and higher elevations than those of the flood basins; the maximum for the Brazos is about 5 ft and for the Mississippi about 15 ft. Meander belt subenvironments are point bars, abandoned channels, and natural levees. Soils are silty and sandy, except those of abandoned channels. They are cultivated for row crops or support a dense growth of trees.

Meandering-stream floodplain (25). The meandering-stream floodplain consists of stream meander belts and flood basins (Figs. 6-7).

Mudflats (26). Mudflats consist of widespread accumulations of silt and clay and are common along the Gulf shores in the Mississippi Delta, in southwestern Louisiana, and in the lagoons of south Texas (Figs. 4, 5, and 21).

(a) *Coastal mudflats.* The exposed parts of the coastal mudflats are only a few feet above sea level and are flooded during high tides (Fig. 21). A salt-marsh flora rapidly establishes itself on the exposed flats and traps and binds additional sediment. The presence of subaqueous coastal mudflats that are not exposed at very low tides are usually

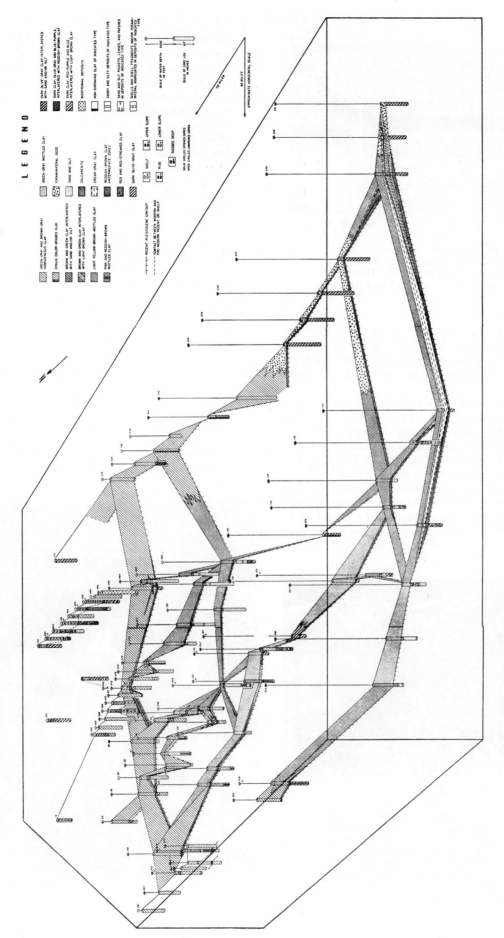

Figure 29. Cored Recent and Pleistocene sediments and their stratigraphic relations in the northwestern Gulf of Mexico. After Greenman and LeBlanc (1956).

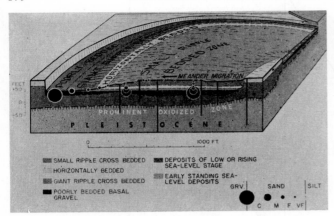

Figure 30. Development and sequence of point-bar deposits of the Brazos River northwest of Houston, Texas. After Bernard and Major (1963).

water or rain water running off the flats. Blue-green algae flourish on most parts of the flats. Mud cracks, gas-formed mounds, and algal ridges are common on the surfaces of the flats. Sparce shells, pumice fragments, and abundant eel grass are deposited on the flats by storm tides and by the strong southeast winds.

The uppermost parts of the mudflat sequence are algal-laminated and interbedded with thin layers of calcareous silt, clay, and grass mats; they grade downward to dark, reduced mud that often contains H_2S and very high counts of reducing bacteria (Fisk, 1959). Gas vesicles and animal burrows are common in these muds. Sand and silt transported by wind and storm tides from the offshore barrier islands and mainland commonly form thin layers in the mudflat deposits. Few species of Foraminifera and small mollusks, which tolerate extreme variations in temperature and salinity, are common in these deposits.

On the uppermost parts of the flats, microscopic crystals of halite and gypsum precipitate from the wind-driven lagoonal water (Fisk, 1939) and also from runoff water of the Rio Grande. Gypsum is precipitated in the pore spaces of sandy substrata, cementing sand grains and forming sand-gypsum crystals. These crystals increase in size with depth. Some gypsum or sand-gypsum crystals near the surface of the flats that are about 3 ft above sea level are more than 1 in. long, and at a depth of 12 ft below sea level, are more than 1 ft long (Fisk, 1959).

During long dry periods, pellets of mud-cracked silt laminae that form on the flats are transported by the wind to the leeward edges of the mudflats, where they form "clay" dunes; see Aeolian Plain (1).

indicated by larger waves breaking at great distances off shore. Resultant waves on the shallow flats are small in height and length. The origin and development of these coastal mudflats are discussed in greater detail under Chenier Plain (11).

The deposits consist of laminated, bedded, or massive and occasionally burrowed silty clay with very fine sand and few-to-many thin layers of sand, silt, and shells.

(b) *Lagoonal mudflats.* The lagoonal mudflats are most common in Laguna Madre (Fisk, 1959; Lohse, 1958). Edges of these flats are generally marked by very low beach ridges of shell, sand, and grass, principally eel grass and some turtle grass. Some ridges contain the calcareous algae, *Acetabularia*, which have been found to be abundant in parts of Laguna Madre. Gullies are common along some edges of the flats, and these were cut by very high tidal

a

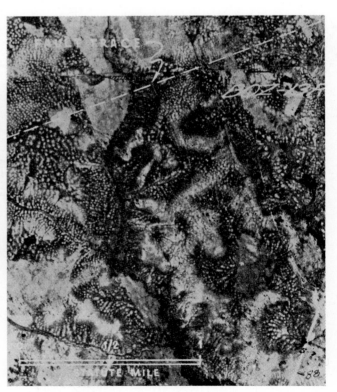

b

Figure 31a and b. Pimple mounds on the Montgomery coastwise plain in southeast Texas. Note trace of fault scarp in (b). After Bernard (1950). Aerial mosaic index (b) courtesy U.S. Dept. of Agriculture.

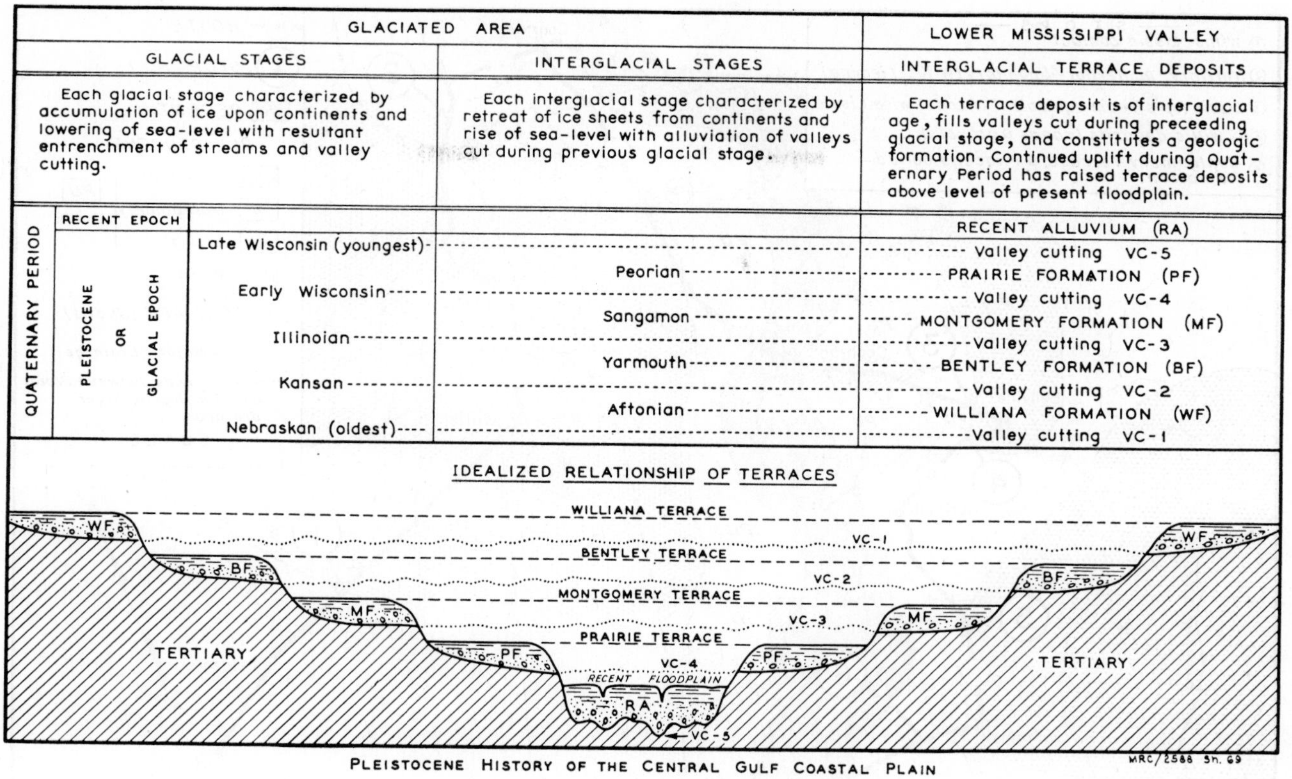
GLACIATED AREA
LOWER MISSISSIPPI VALLEY
GLACIAL STAGES
INTERGLACIAL STAGES
INTERGLACIAL TERRACE DEPOSITS
Each glacial stage characterized by accumulation of ice upon continents and lowering of sea-level with resultant entrenchment of streams and valley cutting.
Each interglacial stage characterized by retreat of ice sheets from continents and rise of sea-level with alluviation of valleys cut during previous glacial stage.
Each terrace deposit is of interglacial age, fills valleys cut during preceeding glacial stage, and constitutes a geologic formation. Continued uplift during Quaternary Period has raised terrace deposits above level of present floodplain.
QUATERNARY PERIOD
RECENT EPOCH
RECENT ALLUVIUM (RA)
PLEISTOCENE OR GLACIAL EPOCH
Late Wisconsin (youngest)
Valley cutting VC-5
Peorian
PRAIRIE FORMATION (PF)
Early Wisconsin
Valley cutting VC-4
Sangamon
MONTGOMERY FORMATION (MF)
Illinoian
Valley cutting VC-3
Yarmouth
BENTLEY FORMATION (BF)
Kansan
Valley cutting VC-2
Aftonian
WILLIANA FORMATION (WF)
Nebraskan (oldest)
Valley cutting VC-1
IDEALIZED RELATIONSHIP OF TERRACES
WILLIANA TERRACE
BENTLEY TERRACE
MONTGOMERY TERRACE
PRAIRIE TERRACE
RECENT FLOODPLAIN
WF
BF
MF
PF
RA
VC-1
VC-2
VC-3
VC-4
VC-5
TERTIARY
TERTIARY
PLEISTOCENE HISTORY OF THE CENTRAL GULF COASTAL PLAIN
MRC/2588 Sh. 69

Figure 32. Pleistocene history of the central Gulf Coastal Plain. After Fisk (1944).

Natural levee (*27*). A natural levee is a very low, subdued ridge having its crest near a river channel or an abandoned channel (Figs. 6, 15, and 16). The slope toward the river is very steep, and the slope away from the river is very gentle. These natural levees build up during overbank river stages. Most of the sediment, including the coarser materials, fine sand, and silt, is deposited near the edge of the bank, where it is commonly trapped by vegetation. The finer grained materials are deposited on the back slopes and merge or interfinger with the flood-basin deposits. The levees at the distributary mouths merge with the subaqueous natural levees flanking the bar channels. See Distributary Mouth Bar (19).

The dimensions of the levees vary with the size of the stream and their degree of maturity. Those of the Brazos, Colorado, and Rio Grande vary from a few inches to 5 ft in height and a few feet to 500 or 1,000 ft in width. Those of the Mississippi vary from less than a foot in height and a few feet in width to 15 ft in height and 1 to 2 miles in width. These deposits of sand, silt, and clays are laminated and crossbedded on a small scale, mottled, and disturbed by weathering, roots, and animal burrows. The soils are generally light colored and support a dense growth of timber or are cultivated in rows.

Pock marks (*28*). Pock marks are very small, circular-shaped depressions or intermittent lakes. Their rounded margins are the result of erosion and deposition. Very small, low ridges occur on the flank of many depressions. Most pock marks in Texas and Louisiana are incompletely filled parts of abandoned river channels and swales between point bars and beach ridges and swales. Some pock marks are deflated, "blow-out" depressions within the aeolian plain. Most pock marks have been wallowing ponds for animals.

Point bar (*29*). A point bar (Fisk, 1944) is the principal depositional environment within a stream's meander belt. Its characteristic topography is a system of parallel ridges and swales (Figs. 6-7 and 15). Point-bar deposits within alluvial valleys consist of a downward-grading sequence of silty clay, silt, and fine-to-coarse sand and gravel (Fig. 30). The maximum grain size of the deposits transported by the river and deposited on point bars within the deltaic plain is fine to medium sand.

A typical point-bar section for an average-sized river such as the Brazos may be subdivided into four zones, each characterized by a particular class of sedimentary structures: (1) small ripple (or small-scale) crossbedding, (2) horizontal lamination, (3) giant ripple (medium-scale) crossbedding, and (4) poor or massive bedding. Mississippi point-bar sequences generally lack the horizontally laminated zone and contain more clay interbeds in the upper part of the section (Bernard and Major, 1963). The uppermost point-bar deposits cannot be readily distinguished from natural levee deposits into which they grade upwards.

The section is an offlap sequence deposited within the channel or on the depositional (convex) bank as the stream migrated toward and eroded the caving (concave) bank. The average thickness of the sequence for a stream such

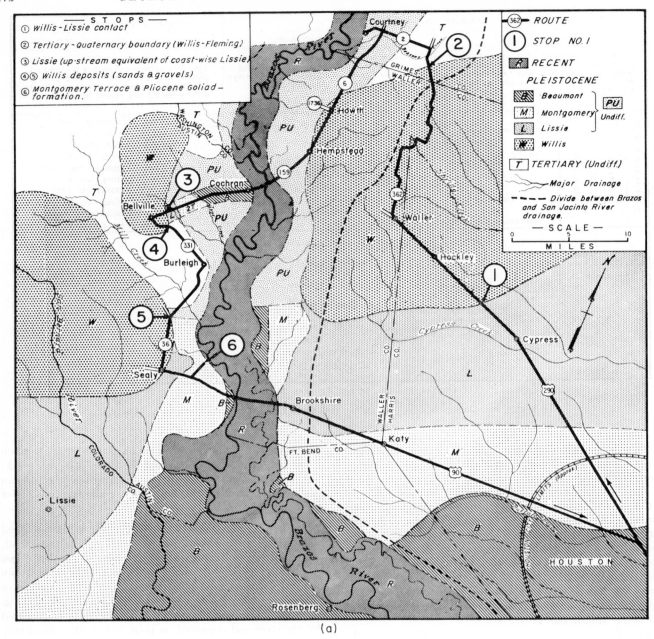

(a)

as the Brazos is 55 ft, which is equal to the average maximum depth of the river during flood stages. The aerial dimension of an individual point-bar deposit is primarily controlled by the radius of curvature of the river meander, which for the Brazos ranges between 600 and 2,400 ft.

The soils are sandy and support a dense natural growth of timber, or they are cultivated for row crops.

Point bar ridges and swales (30). The characteristic topography of a point bar consists of an arcuate system of alternating low ridges and swales aligned parallel to the depositional or convex bank of a point bar. The highest point-bar ridges are incipient or immature natural levees that do not reach maturity because of the relatively rapid migration of the meander towards the eroding bank.

Prodeltaic environment (31). The prodeltaic environment is the subaqueous part of the delta and it includes the Deltaic Fringe (15) and Distal Prodeltaic (17) environments. It has been called the "fluviomarine environment" by other authors.

Shoreface (32). See Barrier Island (5a).

Tidal deltas, channels, and wash-over fans (33). Tidal deltas occur on both the seaward and bayward sides of large tidal channels or passes crossing or separating barrier islands and barrier spits and connecting inland water bodies with the Gulf. The tidal deltas on the seaward sides of the barriers are generally crescent-shaped bars transected by subaqueous channels. They are somewhat similar to river-mouth bars. The tidal deltas within the bays are more

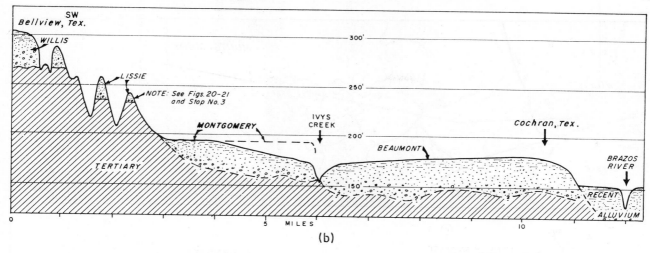

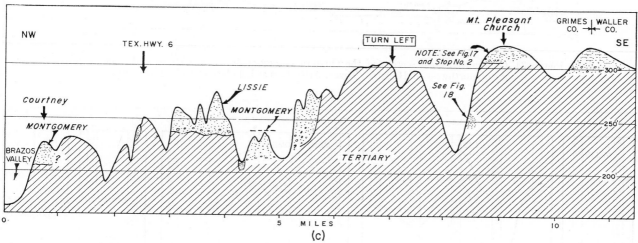

Figure 33a, b, and c. Generalized geologic map and cross sections of the Quaternary and Late Tertiary formations northwest of Houston, Texas. After Bernard, LeBlanc, and Major (1962).

extensive than their counterparts on the seaward side of the barriers.

Minor features within these tidal deltas are tidal channels, flood and ebb tidal bars, subaqueous dunes, giant ripples, tidal flats consisting of sand or mud, and tidal marshes.

The position of the tidal deltas on the seaward side of barriers is indicated by large waves breaking at great distances offshore. The position of bay tidal deltas in the more protected waters is seldom indicated by breakers.

Following the closure of tidal passes on the Gulf side by the deposition of beach, shoreface, and abandoned channel sand fill, the tidal deltas on the seaward side are usually destroyed by marine erosion. Tidal deltas in the bay may continue to grow intermittently by deposition of sediment transported by storm-generated wash-over currents that temporarily reopen the tidal passes. At this stage of development much of the area of the "delta" is emergent and is called a wash-over fan, *e.g.* those forming in Aransas and San Antonio Bays (Fig. 4).

Transitional (34). The transitional environments include the Deltaic (16) and Coastal interdeltaic (12) environments.

EROSIONAL FEATURES

Recent-Pleistocene valley scarps. Inland from the coastal hinge line between the Recent and the Pleistocene, the Recent alluvial valleys or plains of the larger streams are separated from the higher Pleistocene plains by conspicuous scarps, ranging in height from a few feet to 25 ft. These scarps disappear at the hinge line but become progressively higher inland. Trees are common in the valleys and on or near the scarps. Most of the Pleistocene uplands are either grass-covered, or cultivated. The presence of a Recent-Pleistocene scarp in coastal areas may be detected by the difference in soil character between the Recent and Pleistocene sediments.

Youthful valleys. The Pleistocene plains are very young depositional surfaces of low elevation and gentle slope, and

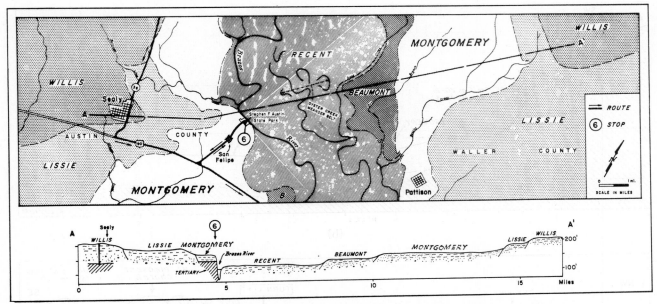

Figure 34. Generalized cross section of the Quaternary across the Brazos River and adjacent
areas, northwest of Houston, Texas. After Bernard, LeBlanc, and Major (1962).

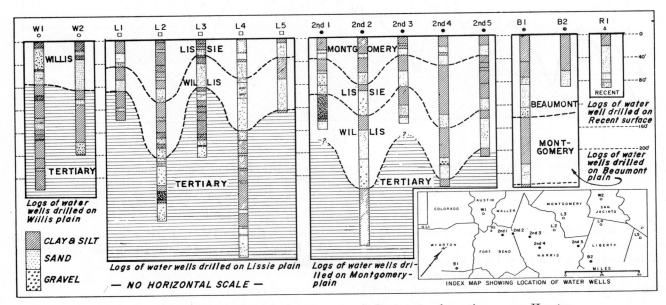

Figure 35. Generalized lithology and sequences of Quaternary formations near Houston,
Texas. After Bernard, LeBlanc and Major (1962).

the drainage is consequent to the seaward slope of the plain
and the depositional morphology of the sediments. The
small streams or creeks are in an early youthful stage of
development, and most of their valleys are V-shaped and
contain a dense growth of brush and trees.

FEATURES OF VARIABLE AND UNKNOWN ORIGIN

Pimple mounds. Pimple mounds are very low (6 in. to over
5 ft high), circular-shaped (occasionally oblong) mounds
varying in diameter from a few feet to over 200 ft (Fig.
31). In southeast Texas and in coastal southwest Louisiana

they occur only on silty or sandy terrain having very gentle
slopes. Mounds are rare on most Recent surfaces but are
very common on the Pleistocene plains. Mounds of Recent
age are forming in the very shallow intertidal zone of the
Colorado-Matagorda Delta, on tidal flats in Aransas Bay,
and on the back side of St. Joseph Island, the western end
of Galveston Island, near the mouth of the Brazos River,
etc.

The mounds occur singularly, but may be compounded
and consist of double, triple, or quadruple mounds. The
single mounds are commonly in alignment with the long

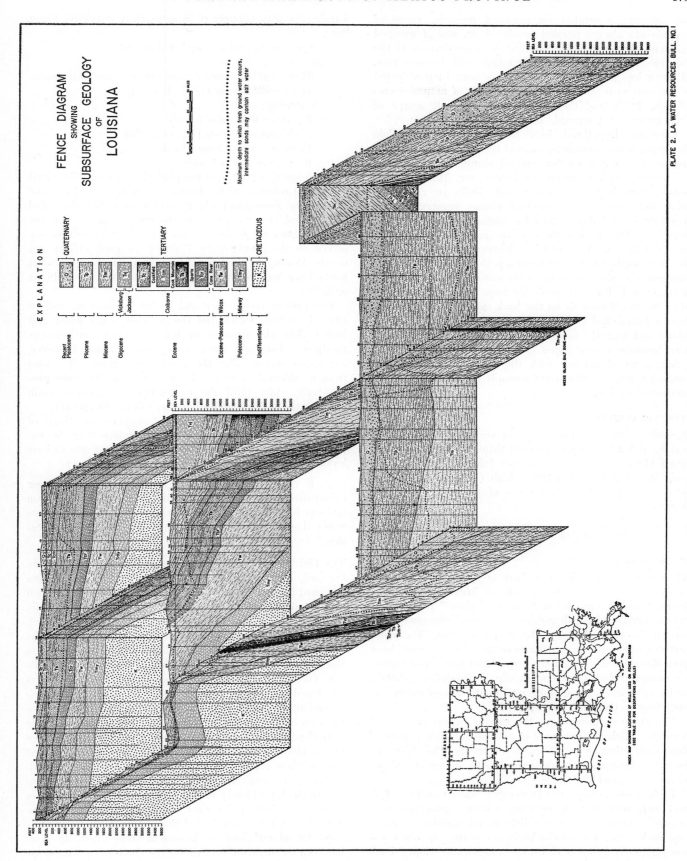

Figure 36. Fence diagram showing the subsurface geology of Louisiana. After Rollo (1960).

axes of the associated compounded mounds. Lines of mounds are always parallel to the slope, and if mapped in detail, they will follow subdued drainage divides. If the drainage is dendritic, the alignments will be dendritic. More or less parallel lines of mounds have been observed to conform with the back slope directions of natural levees (Welch, 1942) and the slope of eroded fault scarps of Quaternary age (Bernard, 1950) (Fig. 31).

Numerous hypotheses have been advanced to explain the origin of these mounds, some of the more common being erosion, differential erosion around clumps of vegetation, ant mound, gopher mound, sand dune, etc. Many mounds occurring in the Colorado-Matagorda Delta are caused by tidal and wave erosion around clump vegetation. The rounding is probably caused by variable wind and wave directions. This is also the case for mounds occurring on the tidal flats in Aransas Bay; however, sand is supplied to the mounds by aeolian processes during long, dry seasons and low tides, and some of the mounds in the Colorado-Matagorda Delta have probably been formed by colonies of crabs. Small mounds on the back side of the Recent St. Joseph Island and those on the western end of Galveston Island and near the mouth of the Brazos River are stabilized hummocky sand dunes.

Alignment of mounds with the drainage in Texas and Louisiana suggests that most mounds in this area are the product of erosion.

TECTONIC FEATURES

Tectonic features in this area are very low, eroded fault scarps, with a maximum observed throw of 15 ft (Bernard, 1950) (Fig. 31) and "salt" mounds (also hills and islands) from less than 1 to over 200 ft high (Figs. 5 and 6). The latter are topographic expressions of piercement-type salt domes.

SUMMARY OF QUATERNARY GEOLOGY

QUATERNARY SURFACES

There are six depositional surfaces of Quaternary interglacial age in the northwestern Gulf of Mexico region. The terms "alluvial terraces" or "coastwise plains" refer to uplifted, seaward-tilted, depositional surfaces subsequently or repeatedly entrenched by the major streams. The older terraces, especially those parts near the major streams, have been dissected more than the younger surfaces. The youngest surface includes the modern alluvial floodplains, deltaic, and coastal interdeltaic plains and their seaward extensions including the Gulf shelf, slope, and deep.

The other surfaces along the stream valleys are paired terraces, which are remnants of alluvial surfaces, separated from each other by prominent escarpments. The older surfaces have progressively higher elevations and greater slopes (Figs. 10, 11, and 32-34).

Each terrace, except the Deweyville (shown on Figs. 4, 5, and 10), merges with contemporaneous, progradational, coastwise terraces or plains of deltaic and interdeltaic origin, and each younger coastwise plain lies nearer the coast and has progressively lower elevations and seaward slopes. Each progressively older coastwise plain passes under the deposits forming the next younger plain along their respective hinge lines.

The Quaternary surfaces are listed below:

Recent
  Modern alluvial, deltaic and coastal interdeltaic plains
  Deweyville terrace (Early Recent)
Pleistocene
  Prairie or Beaumont terrace
  Montgomery terrace (Upper Lissie)
  Bentley terrace (Lower Lissie)
  Williana or Willis terrace

The original depositional morphological features described above and common to the Recent and youngest Pleistocene (Prairie or Beaumont) plains have been either destroyed or obscured by subsequent weathering and erosion on the older terraces or plains. Stream meanders have been observed on the Montgomery Plain by Bernard (1950) and on the Bentley by Welch (1942). No original depositional forms have been reported on the oldest plain, the Williana or Willis.

The progressively older and higher terraces or former alluvial surfaces within the stream valleys are wider and higher than the younger or lower terraces and present floodplain along any given valley cross-profile. However, any given terrace, like the floodplain surfaces, if traced from its alluvial to its coastwise equivalent, becomes progressively wider until the contemporary coastwise plain occupies the entire stream-divide area (Figs. 10 and 11).

Evidence in Texas and Louisiana supports the thesis of Vernon (1942) that the above relationships may be explained by the progressive seaward extension of stream base levels. His explanation follows:

". . . if the factors controlling stream base levels occur progressively downgradient, and if every stream flood plain narrows headward, then each stream terrace would be narrower than the older ones along any given valley cross-section."

The Pleistocene deltaic plains have advanced progressively seaward, interrupted only by eustatic fluctuations of sea level and local advances and retreats of the shore line, which are caused by continued coastal subsidence and lateral shifting sites of deltaic sedimentation. Doering (1935), Fisk (1939), and Bernard (1950) have pointed out that the initial slopes of the older floodplains were very similar to the modern ones and have since been tilted seaward. Deussen (1914) recognized that the southeast Texas rivers developed on Tertiary rocks and were subsequently extended across the Quaternary plains formed by these rivers. Deussen (1914, 1924) pointed out that streams of the coastal plains of Texas are bordered by terraces that range in age from Pleistocene to Recent. He further stated that some of these terraces could be correlated with the seaward-facing plains and, like the terraces, record successive uplifts in the later history of the coastal plains. Other terraces appear to be local and are not related to crustal movements. Stricklin (1953) demonstrated that many of the stream terraces far inland along the Brazos in areas where the river has been downcutting throughout the Quaternary Period are unpaired degradational surfaces.

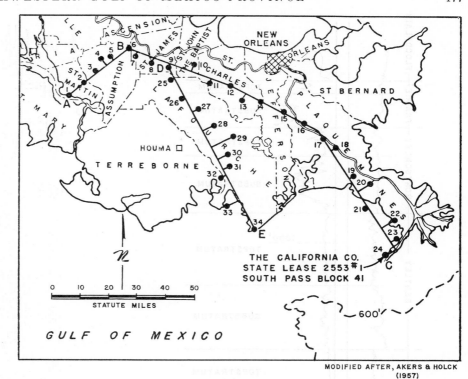

Figure 37. Sketch map of southeast Louisiana showing locations of cross sections of the Quaternary by Akers and Holck; see Figure 39. Modified after Akers and Holck (1957).

MODIFIED AFTER, AKERS & HOLCK (1957)

BASE OF THE PLEISTOCENE

The Williana and Willis have been considered to be Late Pliocene by Doering (1935, 1956) and many other authors. The concept held by some, that the Pliocene Goliad Formation is equivalent to the Willis, is rejected. The Goliad is definitely older than the Willis and is of Pliocene age (Quinn, 1955).

Matson (1916) placed his high-level Citronelle (Williana, Bentley, and Montgomery) sands and gravel in the Pliocene because he was influenced by previous authors and because he found Pliocene leaves, identified by Berry (1916), in deposits at Lambert's Station, located a few miles south of the type locality of the Citronelle Formation. However, Fisk (1938a) and Roy (1939) called attention to the fact that the leaf-bearing deposits at Lambert's Station were brought to the surface by a fault and are unconformably overlain by the so-called Citronelle.

The base of the Williana or Willis represents the base of the Pleistocene. In the outcrops, near Sealy, Texas (Fig. 33), the youngest Tertiary beds underlying the Willis are white, calcareous clays with interbeds of sand and gravel of the Pliocene Goliad Formation. This formation contains large quantities of poorly sorted, coarse materials, including reworked Cretaceous fossils and chert gravel, which have a different composition than those of the Willis. It appears that the Late Tertiary gravels were derived largely from the Cretaceous rocks west of Austin, Texas. The composition of the Willis gravels indicates that they were derived from sources farther removed from the Gulf Coast. Thus recognition of the base of the Pleistocene in the subsurface on the basis of gravel composition might be possible in this area.

The base of the Pleistocene has been determined at the outcrops and in the shallow subsurface by the general lithology. Numerous wells drilled in the region north of Houston, Texas, and south of the Tertiary outcrops were logged in considerable detail (Bernard, LeBlanc, and Major, 1962). The contacts between the basal red Willis and the underlying white calcareous clays and interbedded sands and gravels of the Pliocene Goliad Formation were determined. Thus the Pliocene-Pleistocene boundary has been traced seaward in the subsurface for approximately 40 miles from the outcrop. Sand and gravel sections that occur in the vicinity of Houston below depths of 500 ft are Pliocene in age. Graveliferous deposits older than Pleistocene in age have been recognized in south Louisiana by H. V. Howe (personal communication).

QUATERNARY FORMATIONS,
THEIR STRATIGRAPHIC AND STRUCTURAL RELATIONSHIPS

The Prairie (Beaumont), Montgomery (Upper Lissie), Bentley (Lower Lissie), and Williana (Willis) river terraces and their equivalent coastal plains of the northwestern Gulf represent relict depositional surfaces of sedimentary formations. Fisk (1938a) described these deposits as members of the Pleistocene series of Grant and La Salle parishes, Louisiana. Following R. J. Russell's suggestion, Fisk (1940) elevated the deposits associated with each plain to the rank of formations: Prairie, Montgomery, Bentley, and Williana.

Fisk (1939) recognized that the river terraces and related coastwise surfaces were contemporaneous in origin. He demonstrated that the greater slopes and elevations are associated with the progressively older surfaces. He explained that eustatic lowering- and rising-sea-level stages caused cyclical entrenchment, and alluvial drowning or filling by streams resulted in the development of the principal

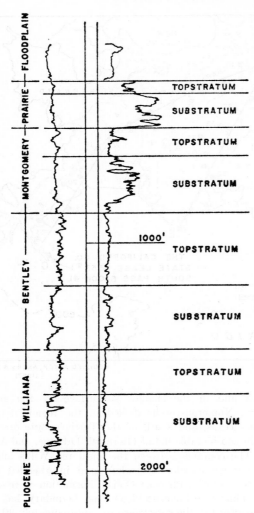

Figure 38. Typical electrical log of subsurface Quaternary alluvial deposits in southeast Louisiana. After Akers and Holck (1957).

depositional surfaces and the buildup of the related formations (Fig. 9). Continued structural movements, epeirogenic uplift, and seaward tilting caused the fluvial surfaces and deposits to be preserved as terraced remnants along the principal stream valleys (Figs. 32-34). Seaward tilting and subsidence due to compaction and isostatic downdrag adjacent to the area of geosynclinal subsidence have been responsible for coastward plunging of the older coastwise deltaic and coastal interdeltaic plains under the deposits of younger age (Figs. 10 and 11).

Available logs of borings and outcrops of these formations in Louisiana and southeast Texas support the observations of Fisk and others that each Quaternary depositional surface is underlain by a separate stratigraphic unit grading frequently from graveliferous basal sands upwards into finer sands, silts, and clays (Bernard, 1950; Bernard, LeBlanc, and Major, 1962, Fig. 35; John Wesselman, U.S. Geol. Surv., Groundwater Branch, personal communication). Howe *et al.* (1935) first showed that it was possible to map the oxidized soil zone marking top of the Late Pleistocene Prairie Formation in Cameron and Vermilion parishes, Louisiana. A map

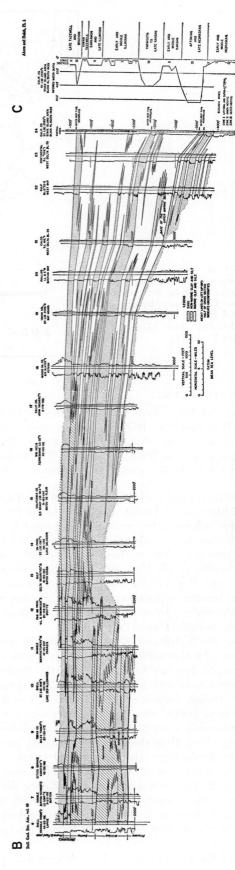

Figure 39. Cross section of the Quaternary deposits (section B-C, Fig. 37) in southeast Louisiana. After Akers and Holck (1957).

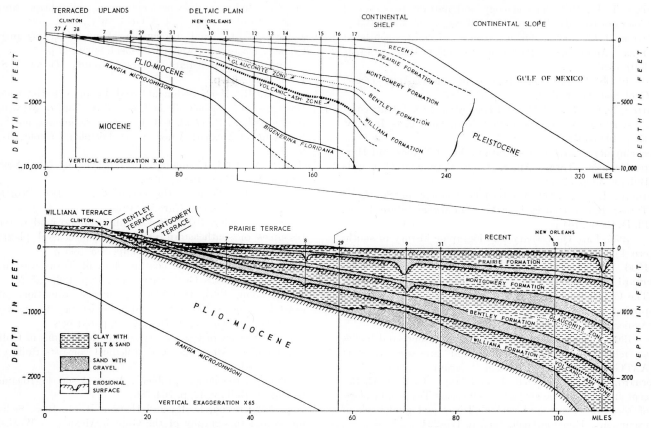

Figure 40. Generalized cross sections of the Quaternary deposits in southeast Louisiana and part of the adjacent continental shelf. After McFarlan (1962), reprinted from Murray (1961).

contoured by Fisk (1949a) on the top of the Prairie Formation displayed a typical branch-work of buried dendritic streams. Frink (1941) demonstrated that it was possible to trace the basal graveliferous deposits of the outcrops of each formation into the subsurface for considerable distances. Hecker (1949) traced the Quaternary formations into the subsurface in eastern Louisiana using the oxidized zones as the top and the basal graveliferous deposits as the base of each formation.

Wells drilled on the Willis surface, together with numerous outcrops, show that the Willis consists basically of a downward fine-to-coarse sequence, which lies unconformably upon Tertiary sands or gravels (Bernard, LeBlanc, and Major, 1962). Wells drilled on the Bentley (Lower Lissie) surface penetrated a similar sequence, which lies unconformably over a similar Williana or Willis sequence before reaching the Tertiary. Wells drilled on the Montgomery (Upper Lissie) penetrated three similar sequences overlying Tertiary clays (Fig. 35). Logs of wells show similar sequences as far south as the Nueces River in south Texas near Corpus Christi.

Akers and Holck (1957), Rollo (1960), and McFarlan (1962) have demonstrated that similar sequences can be traced in the subsurface of coastal Louisiana and offshore almost to the edge of the continental shelf, where they grade into progressively thickening deltaic and interfingering, thickening wedges of marine sediments (Figs. 36-40).

Most of these deposits at the outer edge of the shelf probably represent both glacial and interglacial stages. These thick sections may account in part for the large volumes of sediment excavated from the entrenched valleys, as much as 1,280 cubic miles during the last glacially low-sea-level stage (Fisk, 1944), and additional material, which passed through the valleys during the low-sea-level stages. If the base of the Pleistocene indicated by McFarlan is projected seaward, the Pleistocene near the outer edge of the continental shelf must be approximately 10,000 ft thick (Fig. 40).

Although the Gulf Coastal area was not glaciated during the Pleistocene Epoch, glaciation and deglaciation have had a profound influence on the geology of this region. Additional studies of the Gulf Pleistocene deposits will undoubtedly contribute much to further our knowledge and understanding of Quaternary history.

REFERENCES

Akers, W. H., and Holck, A. J. J., 1957, Pleistocene beds near the edge of the continental shelf, southeastern Louisiana: Geol. Soc. Amer. Bull., v. 68, p. 983-992

Anderson, H. V., and Murray, G. E., 1953, Shallow Pleistocene fossils in St. Tammany Parish, Louisiana: J. Paleont., v. 27, p. 845-846

Antevs, Ernst, 1929, Quaternary marine terraces in non-glaciated regions and changes of level of sea and land: Amer. J. Sci., 5th ser., v. 17, p. 33-49

Bailey, T. L., 1923, The geology and natural resources of Colorado County, Texas: Univ. Texas Bull. 2333, 163 p.

Barton, D. C., 1930a, Surface geology of coastal southeast Texas: Amer. Assoc. Petroleum Geologists Bull., v. 14, p. 1301-1320

—— 1930b, Deltaic coastal plain of southeastern Texas: Geol. Soc. Amer. Bull., v. 41, p. 359-382

Barton, D. C., Ritz, C. H., and Hickey, M., 1933, Gulf coast geosyncline: Amer. Assoc. Petroleum Geologists Bull., v. 17, p. 1446-1458

Beckelhymer, R. L., 1946, Stratigraphy of Waller and Harris Counties, Texas: Amer. Assoc. Petroleum Geologists Bull., v. 30, p. 52-62

Bernard, H. A., 1950, Quaternary geology of Southeast Texas: Baton Rouge, Louisiana, Louisiana State Univ., Ph.D. thesis, 164 p.

—— 1955, Late Quaternary physiographic history of southern Louisiana (abst.): Geol. Soc. Amer. Bull., v. 66, p. 1530

Bernard, H. A., Major, C. F., Jr., and Parrott, B. S., 1959, The Galveston barrier island and environs; a model for predicting reservoir occurrence and trend: Gulf Coast Assoc. Geol. Soc. Trans., v. 9, p. 221-224

—— 1961, Genesis of barrier island and chenier sand bodies as related to sediment influx and processes (abst.): AAPG—SEPM—RMS Annual Program

Bernard, H. A., LeBlanc, R. J., and Major, C. F., 1962, Recent and Pleistocene geology of southeast Texas *in* Geology of the Gulf Coast and central Texas and guidebook of excursions: Houston Geol. Soc., p. 175-224

Berry, E. W., 1916, The flora of the Citronelle formation: U.S. Geol. Surv. Prof. Pap. 98, p. 193-208

Bridges, R. C., 1939, Shallow Pleistocene marine shell stratum in Livingston Parish, Louisiana: J. Paleont., v. 13, p. 615-616

Brooks, H. K., 1964, Submarine scarps of the Bahama Banks (abst.): GSA and Assoc. Soc. Joint Meeting (Miami Beach) Program, p. 20-21

Brown, C. A., 1937, The flora of Pleistocene deposits in the western Florida Parishes, West Feliciana and East Baton Rouge Parishes, Louisiana: Louisiana: Louisiana Dept. Conserv. Geol. Bull., v. 12, p. 59-96

Byrne, J. V., Le Roy, D. O., and Riley, C. M., 1959, The chenier plain and its stratigraphy, southwestern Louisiana: Gulf Coast Assoc. Geol. Soc. Trans., v. 9, p. 237-260

Carsey, J. B., 1950, Geology of Gulf coastal area and continental shelf: Amer. Assoc. Petroleum Geologists Bull., v. 34, p. 361-385

Cassell, D. E., 1958, Geology of the Coldspring area and petrology of the Fleming formation, San Jacinto County, Texas: Austin, Texas, Univ. of Texas, unpublished master's thesis, p. 1-24, 84-90, 96-112

Coleman, J. M., and Webb, J. E., 1964, Minor sedimentary structures in a prograding distributary: Marine Geol. Bull., v. 1, p. 240-258

Cox, C. L., Jr., 1950, Pleistocene terraces of the Lower Brazos River, Texas: Baton Rouge, Louisiana, Louisiana State Univ., unpublished master's thesis, 53 p.

Cromack, G. H., 1942, Records of wells, drillers' logs, water analyses, and map showing locations of wells, Jasper and Newton Counties, Texas: U.S. Geol. Surv., 49 p.

Cromack, G. H., and Livingston, Penn, 1942, Orange County, Texas water wells: U.S. Geol. Surv., 42 p.

—— 1942, Water well data, Jefferson County, Texas: U.S. Geol. Surv., 64 p.

Curray, J. R., 1960, Sediments and history of Holocene transgression, continental shelf, northwest Gulf of Mexico, *in* Shepard, F. P., *et al.* (eds.), Recent sediments, northwest Gulf of Mexico: Amer. Assoc. Petroleum Geologists, p. 221-226

Daly, R. A., 1934, Changing world of the ice age, New Haven, Yale Univ. Press, 46 p.

—— 1942, The floor of the ocean, Chapel Hill, North Carolina, Univ. North Carolina Press

Deussen, Alexander, 1914, Geology and underground water resources of southeastern part of Texas coastal plain: U.S. Geol. Surv. Water-Supply Pap. 335, 365 p.

—— 1924, Geology of the coastal plain of Texas west of Brazos River: U.S. Geol. Surv. Prof. Pap. 126, 145 p.

Doering, John, 1935, Post-Fleming surface formations of coastal southeast Texas and south Louisiana: Amer. Assoc. Petroleum Geologists Bull., v. 19, p. 651-688

—— 1956, Review of Quaternary surface formations of Gulf Coast region: Amer. Assoc. Petroleum Geologists Bull., v. 40, p. 1816-1862

—— 1958, Citronelle age problem: Amer. Assoc. Petroleum Geologists Bull., v. 42, p. 764-786

Ewing, M., Ericson, D. B., and Heezen, B. C., 1958, Sediments and topography of the Gulf of Mexico, *in* Weeks, L. G. (ed.), Habitat of oil: Amer. Assoc. Petroleum Geologists, p. 995-1053

Ewing, M., Worzel, J. L., Ericson, D. B., and Heezen, B. C., 1955, Geophysical and geological investigations in the Gulf of Mexico, Part I: Geophysics, v. 20, p. 1-18

Fisk, H. N., 1938a, Geology of Grant and LaSalle Parishes, Louisiana: Louisiana Dept. Conserv. Geol. Bull., v. 10, 246 p.

—— 1938b, Pleistocene exposures in western Florida Parishes of Louisiana: Louisiana Dept. Conserv. Geol. Bull., v. 12, p. 3-25

—— 1939, Depositional terrace slopes in Louisiana: J. Geomorph., v. 2, p. 181-200

—— 1940, Geology of Avoyelles and Rapides Parishes, Louisiana: Louisiana Dept. Conserv. Geol. Bull., v. 18, p. 3-240

—— 1944, Geological investigation of the alluvial valley of the lower Mississippi River: Vicksburg, Mississippi River Comm., 78 p.

—— 1947, Fine-grained alluvial deposits and their effects on Mississippi River activity: Vicksburg, Miss., U.S. Army Corps Engineers, Miss. River Comm., p. 82

—— 1948, Geological investigation of the lower Mermentau river basin and adjacent areas in coastal Louisiana: Vicksburg, Miss. River Comm., 41 p., mimeo.

—— 1952, Geological investigation of the Atchafalaya basin and the problems of Mississippi River diversion: Vicksburg, Miss. River Comm., 145 p.

Fisk, H. N., *et al.*, 1954, Sedimentary framework of the

modern Mississippi delta: J. Sed. Petrology, v. 24, p. 76-99

—— 1955, Sand facies of Recent Mississippi Delta deposits: 4th World Petroleum Congr. (Rome) Proc., Sec. 1c, p. 377-398

—— 1959, Padre Island and Laguna Madre mud flats, south coastal Texas: Baton Rouge, Louisiana State Univ., Coastal Studies Inst., 2nd Coastal Geogr. Conf., p. 103-151

—— 1960, Recent Mississippi River sedimentation and peat accumulation: 4th Intern. Congr. Carboniferous Stratigraphy and Geology (Heerlen, Holland 1958), Compt. Rend., p. 187-199

—— 1961, Bar-finger sands of the Mississippi delta, in Geometry of sandstone bodies: Tulsa, Oklahoma, Amer. Assoc. Petroleum Geologists, p. 29-52

Fisk, H. N., and McFarlan, E., Jr., 1955, Late Quaternary deltaic deposits of the Mississippi River: Geol. Soc. Amer. Spec. Pap. 62, p. 279-302

Flint, R. F., 1947, Glacial geology and the Pleistocene Epoch: New York, John Wiley and Sons, Inc., 575 p.

Frink, J. W., 1941, Subsurface Pleistocene of Louisiana: Louisiana Dept. Conserv. Geol. Bull., v. 19, p. 367-419

Frye, J. C., and Leonard, A. B., 1953, Definition of time line separating a glacial and interglacial age in the Pleistocene: Amer. Assoc. Petroleum Geologists Bull., v. 37, p. 2581-2586

Gealy, B. L., 1955, Topography of the continental slope in northwest Gulf of Mexico: Geol. Soc. Amer. Bull., v. 66, p. 203-228

Geyer, R. A., 1951, Bibliography of oceanography, marine biology, geology, geophysics, and meteorology of the Gulf of Mexico: Texas J. Sci., v. 2, No. 1, p. 44-92

Goldstein, A., Jr., 1942, Sedimentary petrologic provinces of the northern Gulf of Mexico: J. Sed. Petrology, v. 12, No. 2, p. 77-84

Gould, H. R., 1964, The Mississippi delta complex (abst.): Program Annual AAPG-SEPM 1965 Meeting, New Orleans, Louisiana

Gould, H. R., and McFarlan, Edward, Jr., 1959, Geologic history of the chenier plain, southwestern Louisiana: Gulf Coast Assoc. Geol. Soc. Trans., v. 9, p. 261-270

Gould, H. R., and Morgan, J. P., 1962, Coastal Louisiana swamps and marshlands, in Geology of the Gulf Coast and central Texas and guidebook of excursions: Houston, Texas, Houston Geol. Soc., p. 287-341

Greenman, N. N., and LeBlanc, R. J., 1956, Recent marine sediments and environments of northwest Gulf of Mexico: Amer. Assoc. Petroleum Geologists Bull., v. 40, p. 813-847

Griffin, G. M., and Parrott, B. S., 1964, Development of clay mineral zones during delta migration: Amer. Assoc. Petroleum Geologists Bull., v. 48, p. 57-69

Gulf Coast Association of Geological Societies, 1958, sedimentology of South Texas: Field Trip Guidebook, p. 114

Hardin, G. C., Jr., 1961, Subsurface geology in Geology of Texas and vicinity: Houston Geol. Soc., Spec. Publ., p. 21-26

Harris, G. D., 1904, Underground waters of southern Louisiana: U.S. Geol. Surv. Water-Supply Pap. 101, 98 p.

Hayes, G. W., and Kennedy, W., 1903, Oil fields of the Texas-Louisiana Gulf coastal plain: U.S. Geol. Surv. Bull. 212, 174 p.

Hecker, E. N., 1949, Subsurface correlation of Pleistocene deposits, East Baton Rouge Parish: Louisiana State Univ., unpublished master's thesis, 28 p.

Henry, V. J., 1956, Investigation of shoreline-like features in the Galveston Bay region, Texas, in Oceanographic survey of Gulf of Mexico: Texas A & M Res. Fdn., A & M Project 24, Ref. 56-12T, April 1956, p. 76

Hilgard, E. W., 1866, On the Quaternary formations of the state of Mississippi: Amer. J. Sci., 2nd ser., v. 42, p. 311-325

Holland, W. C., 1943, Physiography of Beauregard and Allen Parishes: Louisiana State Univ. Ph.D thesis

Howe, H. V., 1933, Review of the Tertiary stratigraphy of Louisiana: Amer. Assoc. Petroleum Geologists Bull., v. 17, p. 613-655

—— 1936, Louisiana petroleum stratigraphy: Oil and Gas J., v. 34, p. 98-111, 124-128

Howe, H. V., and Moresi, C. K., 1931, Geology of Iberia Parish, Louisiana: Louisiana Dept. Conserv. Geol. Bull., v. 1, 187 p.

—— 1933, Geology of Lafayette and St. Martin Parishes, Louisiana: Louisiana Dept. Conserv. Geol. Bull., v. 3, 238 p.

Howe, H. V., Russell, R. J., and McGuirt, J. H., 1935, Geology of Cameron and Vermilion Parishes, Louisiana: Louisiana Dept. Conserv. Geol. Bull., v. 6, p. 1-72

Huffman, G. G., and Price, W. A., 1949, Clay dune formation near Corpus Christi, Texas: J. Sed. Petrology, v. 19, No. 3, p. 118-127

Hsu, J. K., 1960, Texture and mineralogy of the Recent sands of the Gulf Coast: J. Sed. Petrology, v. 30, p. 380-403

Johnson, D. W., 1919, Shore processes and shoreline development: New York, John Wiley and Sons

Kelsey, L. O., 1935, The Marsalis terrace; a high level terrace of the Trinity River, Dallas, Texas: Field and Lab., v. 3, p. 54-56

Kennedy, William, 1892, A section from Terrell, Kaufman County, to Sabine Pass on the Gulf of Mexico: Texas Geol. Surv., 3rd Ann. Rep., p. 45, 62-64, 119

Krinitzsky, E. L., 1949, Origin of pimple mounds: Amer. J. Sci., 5th ser., v. 47, p. 706-714

Lang, J. W., Winslow, A. G., and White, W. N., 1950, Geology and groundwater resources of the Houston district Texas: Texas States Board Water Engineers Bull. 5001, p. 55

LeBlanc, R. J., 1955, Quaternary geology of the central Gulf coastal plain (abst.): Geol. Soc. Amer. Bull., v. 66, p. 1589

LeBlanc, R. J., and Bernard, H. A., 1954, Résumé of late Recent geologic history of the Gulf Coast: Geologie en Mijnbouw, n.s., v. 16c, No. 6, p. 185-194

LeBlanc, R. J., and Hodgson, W. D., 1959, Origin and development of the Texas shoreline: Louisiana State Univ., Coastal Studies Inst., 2nd Coastal Geogr. Conf., p. 57-101

LeBlanc, R. J., and Greenman, N. N., 1953, Recent geology

of the nothern Gulf of Mexico region (abst): Houston, Texas, AAPG-SEPM-SE Ann. Mtg., p. 14

Lohse, E. A., 1955, Dynamic geology of the modern coastal region, northwest Gulf of Mexico, *in* Finding ancient shorelines: Soc. Econ. Paleon. Mineral. Spec. Publ. No. 3, p. 99-103

—— 1958, Mouth of Rio Grande, *in* Sedimentology of south Texas: Gulf Coast Assoc. Geol. Soc. Field Trip Guidebook, p. 55-56

—— 1958, Buena Vista mudflat, *in* Sedimentology of south Texas: Gulf Coast Assoc. Geol. Soc. Field Trip Guidebook, p. 58-60

Lowman, S. W., 1949, Sedimentary facies in Gulf Coast: Amer. Assoc. Petroleum Geologists Bull., v. 33, p. 1939-1997

Ludwick, John C., and Walton, William R., 1957, Shelf-edge, calcareous prominences in northeastern Gulf of Mexico: Amer. Assoc. Petroleum Geologists Bull., v. 41, p. 2054-2101

Lynch, S. A., 1954, Geology of the Gulf of Mexico, *in* Gulf of Mexico; its origin, waters, and marine life: U.S. Dept. Interior, Fish and Wildlife Service, Fishery Bull. 89, v. 55, p. 67-86

MacGee, W. J., 1890b, The Lafayette formation: U.S. Geol. Surv. 12th Ann. Rep., p. 347-521

Marmer, H. A., 1954, Tides and sea level in the Gulf of Mexico, *in* Gulf of Mexico; its origin, waters, and marine life: U.S. Dept. Interior, Fish and Wildlife Service, Fishery Bull. 89, v. 55, p. 101-118

Matson, G. C., 1916, The Pliocene Citronelle formation of the Gulf coastal plain; U.S. Geol. Surv. Prof. Pap. 98 L, p. 167-192

Mattison, G. C., 1948, Bottom configuration in the Gulf of Mexico: J. Coast and Geod. Surv., v. 1, p. 76-81

McFarlan, E., Jr., 1955, Radiocarbon dating of the late Quaternary in southern Louisiana (abst.): Geol. Soc. Amer. Bull., v. 55, p. 1594-1595

—— 1961, Radiocarbon dating of late Quaternary deposits, south Louisiana: Geol. Soc. Amer. Bull., v. 72, p. 129-158

Metcalf, R. J., 1940, Deposition of Lissie and Beaumont formations of Gulf Coast of Texas: Amer. Assoc. Petroleum Geologists Bull., v. 24, p. 693-700

Meyer, W. G., 1939, Stratigraphy and historical geology of Gulf coastal plains in vicinity of Harris County, Texas: Amer. Assoc. Petroleum Geologists Bull., v. 23, p. 145-211

Mississippi River Commission, 1949a, Geological investigation of gravel deposits in the lower Mississppi valley and adjacent uplands: Vicksburg, Miss. River Comm., 58 p.

—— 1949b, The entrenched valley of the lower Red River: Vicksburg, Miss. River Comm., 49 p.

Morgan, J. P., 1951, Mudlumps at the mouth of the Mississippi River, Louisiana State Univ. Ph.D. thesis

Morgan, J. P., and Larimore, P. B., 1957, Changes in the Louisiana shoreline: Gulf Coast Assoc. Geol. Soc. Trans., v. 7, p. 303-310

Morgan, J. P., Van Lopik, J. R., and Nichols, G. G., 1953, The occurrence and development of mudflats along the western Louisiana coast: Louisiana State Univ., Coastal Studies Inst. Tech. Rep. 2, p. 34

Morgan, J. P., Coleman, J. M., and Gagliano, S. M., 1963, Mudlumps at the mouth of South Pass, Mississippi River; sedimentology, origin and relation to deltaic processes: Coastal Studies Series No. 10, Baton Rouge, Louisiana State Univ. Press., p. 190

Murray, G. E., 1947, Cenozoic deposits of the Gulf coastal plain: Amer. Assoc. Petroleum Geologists Bull., v. 31, p. 1825-1850

—— 1948, Geology of Desoto and Red River Parishes, Louisiana: Louisiana Dept. Conserv. Bull., v. 25, 312 p.

—— 1961, Geology of the Atlantic and Gulf coastal province of North America: New York, Harper and Brothers, 692 p.

Parker, R. H., 1960, Ecology and distributional patterns of marine macro-invertebrates, Northern Gulf of Mexico, *in* Shepard, F. P., *et al.* (eds.), Recent sediments, northwest Gulf of Mexico: Amer. Assoc. Petroleum Geologists, p. 302-338

Petitt, B. M., Jr., and Winslow, A G., 1957, Geology and ground-water resources of Galveston County, Texas: U.S. Geol. Surv. Water-Supply Pap. 1416, p. 157

Phleger, F. B., 1951, Displaced Foraminifera faunas, *in* Turbidity currents and the transportation of coarse sediments to deep water: Soc. Econ. Paleont. Min. Spec. Publ. No. 2, pp. 66-75

Phleger, F. B., and Parker, F. L., 1951, Ecology of Foraminifera, northwest Gulf of Mexico: Geol. Soc. Amer. Mem. 46, 152 p.

—— 1960, Sedimentary patterns of microfaunas in northern Gulf of Mexico, *in* Shepard, F. P., *et al.* (eds.), Recent sediments, northwest Gulf of Mexico: Amer. Assoc. Petroleum Geologists, p. 267-301

Price, W. A., 1930, Physiography of Corpus Christi area, Texas (abst.): Pan-Am. Geol., v. 53, p. 216

—— 1933a, Reynosa problem of south Texas and the origin of caliche: Amer. Assoc. Petroleum Geologists Bull., v. 17, p. 488-522

—— 1933b, Role of diastrophism in topography of Corpus Christi area, Texas: Amer. Assoc. Petroleum Geologists Bull., v. 17, p. 907-962

—— 1936, Role of diastrophism in topography of Corpus Christi area, South Texas; Gulf Coast oil fields: Amer. Assoc. Petroleum Geologists Bull., p. 205-250

—— 1938, Geology of the Rio Grande delta, Texas and Mexico, interpreted by geomorphology and soils (abst.): Oil and Gas J., v. 36, p. 71

—— 1947, Equilibrium of form and forces in tidal basins of coast of Texas and Louisiana: Amer. Assoc. Petroleum Geologists Bull., v. 31, p. 1619-1663

—— 1951a, Barrier island, not "offshore bar": Science, v. 113, p. 487-488

—— 1951b, Building of Gulf of Mexico; secondary events in a regionally concordant basin: Gulf Coast Assoc. Geol. Soc. Trans., v. 1, p. 7-39

—— 1954a, Dynamic environments; reconnaissance mapping, geologic and geomorphic, of continental shelf of Gulf of Mexico: Gulf Coast Assoc. Geol. Soc. Trans., v. 4, p. 75-107

—— 1954b, Shorelines and coasts of the Gulf of Mexico, *in*

Gulf of Mexico; its origin, waters, and marine life: U.S. Dept. Interior, Fish and Wildlife Service, Fishery Bull. 89, v. 55, p. 39-86

—— 1958, Sedimentology and Quaternary geomorphology of South Texas: Gulf Coast Assoc. Geol. Soc. Trans., v. 8, 41 p.

Quinn, J. H., 1955, Miocene Equidae of the Texas Gulf coastal plain: Univ. of Texas Publ. 5516, p. 102

—— 1957, Paired-river terraces and Pleistocene glaciation: J. Geol., v. 65, p. 149-166

—— 1957, Pleistocene Equidae of Texas: Texas Univ., Bur. Econ. Geol. Rep. Inv. 33, p. 51

Richards, H. G., 1938, Marine Pleistocene of the Gulf coastal plain of Alabama, Mississippi and Louisiana: Geol. Soc. Amer. Bull., v. 50, p. 297-315

—— 1939, Marine Pleistocene of Texas: Geol. Soc. Amer. Bull., v. 50, p. 1885-1896

Rollo, J. R., 1960, Ground water in Louisiana: Louisiana Geol. Surv. Bull. (in cooperation with U.S. Geol. Surv.), No. 2

Rose, N. A., 1943, Ground water and relation of geology to its occurrence in Houston district, Texas: Amer. Assoc. Petroleum Geologists Bull., v. 27, p. 1081-1101

Roy, C. J., 1939, The type locality of Citronelle formation, Citronelle, Alabama: Amer. Assoc. Petroleum Geologists Bull., v. 23, p. 1553-1559

Rusnak, G. A., 1960, Sediments of Laguna Madre, Texas, *in* Shepard, F. P., *et al.* (eds.), Recent sediments, northwest Gulf of Mexico: Amer. Assoc. Petroleum Geologists, p. 153-196

Russell, R. J., 1936, Physiography of the Lower Mississippi delta: Louisiana Dept. Conserv. Geol. Bull., v. 8, p. 3-199

—— 1938a, Geology of Iberville and Ascension Parishes, Louisiana: Louisiana Dept. Conserv. Geol. Bull., v. 13, p. 1-86

—— 1938b, Quaternary surfaces in Louisiana: Congr. Intern. Geogr. (Amsterdam) Compt. Rend., v. 2, p. 406-412

—— 1940, Quaternary history of Louisiana: Geol. Soc. Amer. Bull., v. 51, p. 1199-1234

—— (ed.), 1961, Louisiana coastal marsh ecology: Louisiana State Univ., Coastal Studies Inst. Tech. Rep. 14, p. 273

Russell, R. J., and Fisk, H. N., 1942, Isostatic effects of Mississippi River delta sedimentation: Washington, D.C., Amer. Geophy. Union, p. 56-59

Scruton, P. C., 1960, Delta building and the deltaic sequence, *in* Shepard, F. P., *et al.* (eds.), Recent sediments of northwest Gulf of Mexico: Amer. Assoc. Petrol. Geol. Bull., Spec. Publ., p. 82-102

Scruton, P. C., and Moore, D. G., 1953, Distribution of turbidity off the Mississippi Delta: Amer. Assoc. Petroleum Geologists Bull., v. 37, p. 1067-1074

Shattuck, G. B., 1901, The Pliocene and Pleistocene deposits of Maryland: Maryland Geol. Surv., 137 p.

Shepard, F. P., 1937, Salt domes related to Mississippi submarine trough: Geol. Soc. Amer. Bull., v. 48, p. 1349-1362

—— 1952, Revised nomenclature for depositional coastal features: Amer. Assoc. Petroleum Geologists Bull., v. 36, p. 1902-1912

—— 1953, Sediment zones bordering the barrier islands of central Texas coast, *in* Finding ancient shorelines: Soc. Econ. Paleont. Min. Spec. Publ. No. 3, p. 78-96

—— 1956, Late Pleistocene and Recent history of the central Texas coast: J. Geol., v. 64, p. 56-69

—— 1960a, Mississippi Delta; marginal environments, sediments and growth, *in* Shepard, F. P., *et al.* (eds.), Recent sediments, northwest Gulf of Mexico: Amer. Assoc. Petroleum Geologists, p. 56-81

—— 1960b, Gulf coast barriers, *in* Shepard, F. P., *et al.* (eds.), Recent sediments, northwest Gulf of Mexico: Amer. Assoc. Petroleum Geologists, p. 197-220

—— 1960c, Rise of sea level along northwest Gulf of Mexico, *in* Shepard, F. P., *et al.* (eds.), Recent sediments, northwest Gulf of Mexico: Amer. Assoc. Petroleum Geologists, p. 338-344

Shepard, F. P., and Moore, D. G., 1955, Central Texas coast sedimentation: characteristics of sedimentary environment, Recent history and diagenesis: Amer. Assoc. Petrol. Geol. Bull., v. 39, p. 1463-1593

—— 1960, Bays of central Texas coast, *in* Shepard, F. P., *et al.* (eds.), Recent sediments, northwest Gulf of Mexico: Amer. Assoc. Petroleum Geologists, p. 117-152

Shuler, E. W., 1935, Terraces of the Trinity River, Dallas County, Texas: Field and Lab., v. 3, p. 44-53

Stanley, T. B., Jr., and Maher, J. C., 1944, Ground-water resources of Jefferson Davis and Acadia Parishes, Louisiana: Louisiana Dept. of Public Works, 93 p.

Stetson, H. C., 1953, The sediments of the western Gulf of Mexico. Part I, The continental terrace of the western Gulf of Mexico; its surface sediments, origin, and development: M.I.T. and Woods Hole Oceanog. Inst., Papers in Phys. Oceanog. and Meteorol., v. 12, No. 4, p. 45

Stricklin, F. L., Jr., 1953, River terraces on the Brazos River, Texas: Louisiana State University, Department of Geology Ph.D. thesis

—— 1961, Degradational stream deposits of the Brazos River, central Texas: Geol. Soc. Amer. Bull., v. 72, p. 19-36

Trask, P. D., Phleger, F. B., Jr., and Stetson, H. C., 1947, Recent changes in sedimentation in the Gulf of Mexico: Science, v. 106, p. 460-461

—— 1953, The sediments of the western Gulf of Mexico. Part II, Chemical Studies, sediments of the western Gulf of Mexico: M.I.T. and Woods Hole Oceanog. Inst., Papers in Phys. Oceanog. and Meteorol., v. 12, No. 4

Treadwell, T. K., 1949, Submarine topography of continental slope of northwest Gulf of Mexico: Univ. California, Scripps Inst. Oceanog., Submarine Geol. Rept. No. 7, 7 p.

Trowbridge, A. C., 1923, A geological reconnaissance of the Gulf Coastal Plain of Texas near the Rio Grande: U.S. Geol. Surv. Prof. Pap. 131, pp. 85-107

—— 1930, Building of the Mississippi Delta, Amer. Assoc. Petroleum Geologists Bull., v. 14, p. 867-901

—— 1954, Mississippi River and Gulf Coast terraces and sediments as related to Pleistocene history—a problem: Geol. Soc. Amer. Bull., v. 65, p. 793-812

Van Andel, T. H., 1960, Sources and dispersion of Holocene sediments, northern Gulf of Mexico, *in* Shepard, F. P., *et al.* (eds.), Recent sediments, northwest Gulf of Mexico: Amer. Assoc. Petroleum Geologists, Spec. Publ., p. 34-55

Van Lopik, J. R., 1955, Recent geology and geomorphic history of central coastal Louisiana: Louisiana State Univ., Coastal Studies Inst. Tech. Rep. 7, 88 p.

Varvaro, Gasper G., 1957, Geology of Evangeline and St. Landry Parishes, Louisiana: Louisiana Dept. Conserv. Geol. Bull. 31, 295 p.

Vernon, R. O., 1942, Geology of Holmes and Washington Counties, Florida: Florida Geol. Surv. Bull., v. 21, 161 p.

Weaver, Paul, 1950, Variations in history of continental shelves: Amer. Assoc. Petroleum Geologists Bull., v. 34, p. 351-360

Weeks, A. W., 1933, Lissie, Reynosa, and Upland terrace deposits of coastal plains of Texas between Brazos River and Rio Grande: Amer. Assoc. Petroleum Geologists Bull., v. 17, p. 453-487

—— 1945a, Quaternary deposits of the Texas coastal plain between Brazos River and Rio Grande, Amer. Assoc. Petroleum Geologists Bull., v. 29, p. 1693-1720

—— 1945b, Oakville, Cuero and Goliad formations of Texas coastal plain between Brazos River and Rio Grande, Amer. Assoc. Petroleum Geologists Bull., v. 29, p. 1721-1732

Welch, R. N., 1942, Geology of Vernon Parish, Louisiana: Louisiana Dept. Conserv. Geol. Bull., v. 22, 90 p.

Wilson, J. A., 1956, Miocene formations and vertebrate biostratigraphic units, Texas coastal plain: Amer. Assoc. Petroleum Geologists Bull., v. 40, p. 2233-2246

—— 1962, Tertiary formations between Austin and Houston, with special emphasis on the Miocene and Pliocene, *in* Geology of the Gulf Coast and central Texas and guidebook of excursions: Houston Geol. Soc., p. 342-353

Woodward, T. P., and Gueno, Albert, 1941, The sand and gravel deposits of Louisiana: Louisiana Dept. Conserv. Geol. Bull., v. 19, 365 p.

SUMMARY

Deposits of Quaternary age occur over very extensive areas in the clastic province of the northwestern Gulf of Mexico region. The Quaternary coastal plain of Louisiana and Texas, which is largely depositional in origin, forms a belt 10 to 250 miles wide, parallel to the coast line. Quaternary deposits also extend seaward in the Gulf of Mexico beneath the continental shelf and slope.

The Quaternary coastal plain consists of four Pleistocene surfaces and related formations and a Recent surface and associated deposits. The Recent coastwise plain lies adjacent to the coast, only a few feet above sea level, and is underlain mainly by deltaic and coastal interdeltaic deposits. This coastwise Recent surface merges with narrow alluvial valleys inland. Seaward it merges with the continental shelf, which is 10 to 120 miles wide.

The Pleistocene coastal plain occurs between the Recent formations near the coast and the Tertiary formations inland. The four surfaces, from youngest to oldest, are as follows: the Prairie (Louisiana) or Beaumont (Texas); the Montgomery (Louisiana) or Upper Lissie (Texas); the Bentley (Louisiana) or Lower Lissie (Texas); and the Williana (Louisiana) or the Willis (Texas). Each Pleistocene surface is underlain by sequences of sediments that are similar to those of the Recent, consisting mainly of continental beds, updip, grading seaward into deltaic and coastal interdeltaic, and finally marine in extreme downdip portions. On shore and near shore each sedimentary sequence rests unconformably upon an eroded surface. The five sedimentary sequences are correlated with the interglacial stages. The eroded surfaces or periods of erosion are correlated with low-sea-level substages of the glacial stages. Far offshore in the deeper parts of the Gulf, sedimentation was continuous during both glacial and interglacial stages.

The highest and most inland coastwise plain is the Williana or Willis, and it lies at elevations of 600 to 200 ft. The elevation of the Bentley or Lower Lissie plain ranges from 200 to 100 ft, the Montgomery or Upper Lissie from 125 to 70 ft, and the Prairie or Beaumont from about 100 ft to a few feet above sea level.

Evidence indicates that the initial depositional slopes of each Pleistocene plain were similar to that of the Recent. As a result of continued coastal subsidence and landward uplift the gradient of each successively older Pleistocene surface is progressively greater. These gradients vary along the coast because of different initial depositional slopes of the dissimilar environments and warping caused by tectonics and varying rates of compaction. The rate of seaward gradient of the Williana is about 10 ft per mile, the Bentley 3.5 to 8, the Montgomery 2.5 to 5, and the Prairie 1.1 to 2.4 ft. In contrast the seaward gradient of the Recent surface ranges from 0.01 to as much as 1.4 ft per mile.

Late Quaternary deposits are classified on the basis of their environments of deposition, which consist of three main groups: continental, transitional, and marine. The continental environments consist mainly of alluvial floodplains, which include meander belts and flood basins, and aeolian plains. The transitional group of environments includes deltaic and the coastal interdeltaic, which is characterized by barrier islands, lagoons, and chenier plains. The marine environments include the shelf and slope; much of the innershelf environments are transitional with and can be included with those occurring along shore, deltaic, or coastal interdeltaic environments. Descriptions of the principal depositional forms and related sediments in each type of environment are summarized.

Deposits of Quaternary age vary considerably in thickness. The thickness of each Pleistocene unit in the coastal plain area of Texas varies from less than 10 ft to a maximum of about 150 to 200 ft within the entrenched alluvial valleys and from a few to 50 ft in interdeltaic or stream divide areas. A maximum of at least 600 ft occurs within the Mississippi delta region of Louisiana. The total thickness of Quaternary beds in the Louisiana-Texas offshore is probably in excess of 10,000 ft.

THE PLEISTOCENE IN NEBRASKA AND NORTHERN KANSAS

E. C. REED,[1] V. H. DREESZEN,[1] C. K. BAYNE,[2] C. B. SCHULTZ[3]

INTRODUCTION

AREA COVERED

The area covered in this discussion (Fig. 1) contains about 259,000 km². Elevations range from about 230 m in the southeast corner to more than 1340 m in the west-central part. The Missouri River forms the eastern boundary of the area. The eastern sixth of the area is glaciated, and periglacial deposits occur in the central and western parts.

TECHNIQUES OF CORRELATION

The classification and correlation of the Pleistocene deposits of this region are based on stratigraphic, geomorphologic, pedologic, paleontologic, and petrographic investigations. Special techniques include studies of systematic collections of vertebrate and invertebrate fossils of the deposits, petrographic studies of the volcanic-ash deposits, pedologic studies of the paleosols, extensive subsurface investigations based on systematic test-drilling by the Kansas and Ne-

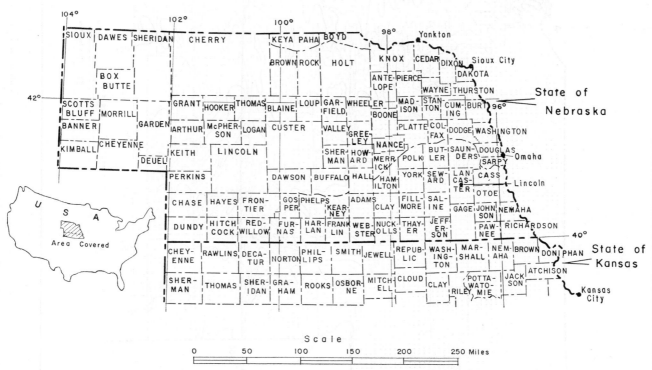

Figure 1. Location map of Nebraska and northern Kansas region showing county names and localities referred to in the text.

The region is ideally located for the study of the periglacial stratigraphy of the Pleistocene because of the fine preservation of the Pleistocene sequence and because the eastern part includes areas that were glaciated during parts of the four major ages of continental glaciation. Thus it is possible to trace most of the periglacial sequence into the glacial sequence.

braska Geological Surveys in cooperation with the Ground Water Branch of the U.S. Geological Survey, and sedimentation studies of periglacial deposits influenced by climatic and sea-level changes related to glaciation.

PRE-QUATERNARY GEOLOGY

The systematic test-drilling programs of the state surveys in the region provide accurate data on the configuration and nature of the bedrock surface that underlies the Pleistocene deposits (Fig. 2). The Pleistocene rests on Pennsyl-

[1] Nebraska Geological Survey, Lincoln, Nebraska.
[2] Kansas Geological Survey, Lawrence, Nebraska.
[3] University of Nebraska State Museum, Lincoln, Nebraska.

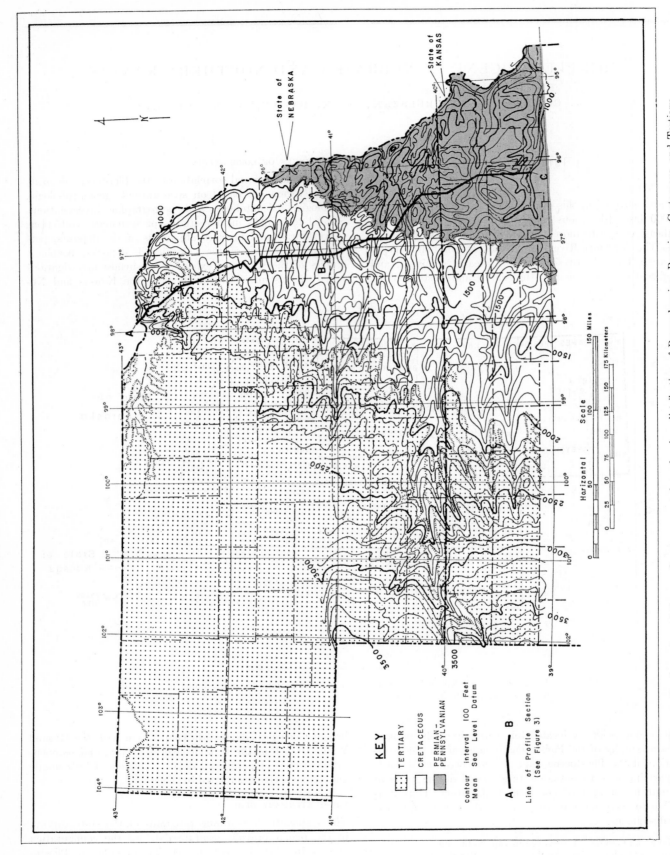

Figure 2. Configuration of the pre-Quaternary surface showing distribution of Pennsylvanian, Permian, Cretaceous, and Tertiary bedrock and location of schematic profile section (Fig. 5).

TABLE 1

Classification of the Pleistocene System in Kansas

	Stages	Formations
Upper Pleistocene	Late (post-Bradyan) Wisconsinan	Bignell formation and Late Wisconsinan terrace deposits
	Bradyan[a] and Early (pre-Bradyan) Wisconsinan	Brady Soil
		Peoria formation and Early Wisconsinan terrace deposits
	Sangamonian[a] and Illinoian	Sangamon soil
		Loveland formation and Crete formation
Lower Pleistocene	Yarmouthian[a] and Kansan	Yarmouth soil
		Sappa formation including Pearlette ash bed Grand Island formation Kansas till Atchison formation
		Afton soil
	Aftonian[a] and Nebraskan	Fullerton formation Holdrege formation Nebraska till David City formation

[a] Interglacial and interstadial units not limited to soil development

vanian and Permian limestones and shales in the southeastern corner of the region at elevations generally below 365 m. The relative induration of the Pennsylvanian and Permian limestones and shales resulted in the development of narrow, rock-defended valleys separated by rock benches developed on the thicker limestone sequences. A northeast-trending band of Cretaceous bedrock, averaging about 40 km in width and ranging in elevation from about 325 to more than 650 m above sea level, occurs below the Pleistocene in the east-central part of the region, immediately west and northwest of the Pennsylvanian and Permian bedrock terrane. The Cretaceous rocks consist of shale, chalk, sandstone, and minor thicknesses of limestone; they have a regional dip to the west-northwest. Broader valleys are typical of this region, except where they traverse the limestones and more indurated sandstone terrane, where "water gaps" and "dip slopes" are common. The bedrock of the western and northwestern parts of the region is Tertiary in age (Oligocene to Pliocene) and continental in origin, consisting of sandstones of variable induration, siltstones, and interlayered beds of relatively unconsolidated sand and gravel. The Tertiary sediments were deposited on a surface that sloped east-southeast. The variable induration of the Tertiary bedrock has influenced the width of the Pleistocene valleys eroded into them, and the westernmost part of the region is typically a Tertiary bedrock surface, in part mantled with late-Pleistocene eolian deposits.

The configuration of the bedrock surface is the result of multiple erosion in early Pleistocene and later time and does not have a simple drainage pattern. Extensive major erosion in early Nebraskan, early Kansan, early Illinoian, early

Wisconsinan, and Recent time has materially altered the pre-existing surfaces.

CLASSIFICATION

The classification of the Pleistocene deposits of this region is that of the state geological surveys. The Kansas classification (Table 1) is essentially that of Jewett et al. (1959) with minor adjustments for easier comparison with the Nebraska classification. Each glacial stage and succeeding interglacial stage is grouped together to avoid differences of opinion concerning the assignment of deposits to glacial or interglacial stages. The Kansas classification is less complicated than the Nebraska classification because a less nearly complete sequence of deposits is generally represented in Kansas, and a simpler classification meets most requirements. The most recent and complete summary of Pleistocene stratigraphy in Kansas is that of Frye and Leonard (1952).

The Nebraska classification (Table 2) recognizes a two-fold Nebraskan stage and three-fold Kansan, Illinoian, and Wisconsinan stages (Reed and Dreeszen, 1964). Deposits are referred to glacial stages that are separated from each other by interglacial soils. Interstadial intervals are recognized within the glacial stages and permit a further separation of the deposits of each glacial stage.

Common unit names are used in the Kansas and Nebraska classifications, and these units are believed to be essentially equivalent. Additional unit names have been added in the Nebraska classification to permit a closer correlation of the glacial and periglacial sequences.

TABLE 2

Classification of Pleistocene Deposits in Nebraska

Time-stratigraphic units			Rock stratigraphic units	
			Glacial deposits	Periglacial deposits
		12		
Wisconsinan	Late		No till	Bignell loess and alluvium (T2)
		11		
	Medial		Hartington till	Peoria loess and silt and dunesand (T3)
				Todd Valley sand and dunesand (T3)
		10		
	Early		No till	Gilman Canyon loess and alluvium
		9		
Illinoian	Late		No till	Loveland loess and silt (T4)
				Crete sand and gravel (T4)
		8		
	Medial		No till	Beaver Creek loess and alluvium (T4)
		7		
	Early		Santee till	Grafton loess and alluvium (T4)
			pro-Santee sand and gravel	
		6		
Kansan	Late		Clarkson till	Sappa loess and silt (Pearlette volc. ash) (T5)
				Grand Island sand and gravel (T5)
		5		
	Medial		Cedar Bluffs till	Walnut Creek loess and alluvium (T5)
		4		
	Early		Nickerson till	Red Cloud alluvium (T5)
			Atchison sand and gravel	
		3		
Nebraskan	Late		Iowa Point till	Fullerton loess and silt (T6)
				Holdrege sand and gravel (T6)
		2		
	Early		Elk Creek till	Seward silt and loess (T6)
			David City sand and gravel	David City sand and gravel (T6)
		1		

T2 and T6 refer deposits to numbered terrace-fills.

Significant interglacial and interstadial events at numbered intervals:
1. Development of Tertiary climax soil; major proglacial erosion of Pennsylvanian, Permian, Cretaceous and Tertiary bedrock.
2. Development of interstadial soil; erosion.
3. Development of Afton interglacial soil; major proglacial erosion.
4. Development of Fontanelle interstadial soil; minor erosion.
5. Development of interstadial soil; minor erosion.
6. Development of Yarmouth interglacial soil; major proglacial erosion.
7. Development of interstadial soil; minor erosion.
8. Development of interstadial soil; minor erosion.
9. Development of Sangamon interglacial soil; major proglacial erosion.
10. Development of Farmdale soil; minor erosion.
11. Development of Brady soil; minor erosion.
12. Soil development; Recent erosion and deposition (Terrace 0 and 1 Deposits).

GEOMORPHOLOGY AND DRAINAGE-PATTERN DEVELOPMENT

The drainage pattern of eastern Nebraska and northeastern Kansas is generally developed on loess-mantled pre-Sangamonian Pleistocene till. The variable thickness of loess mantle and the erosion of the till at several times during the Pleistocene obscure the geomorphic relationships of the glacial moraines. However, apparently many of the present drainage patterns began to develop in middle to late Kansan time, and some drainage divides have been recognized as loess-mantled moraines (Bayne and Fent, 1963; Reed and Dreeszen, 1964).

Nebraskan moraines are unidentifiable because they were in part eroded and were overridden by the Kansan ice. The first advance of the Kansan ice, resulting in the deposition of the Nickerson till (Table 2), was the most extensive; it probably extended farther west than the west edge of York

County in Nebraska (Fig. 1), where outliers of Nickerson till occur under a loess-mantled Illinoian terrace (Figs. 3 and 4). The moraine of the Nickerson till probably determined the drainage divide between the Big Blue and Little Blue River systems near the Kansas-Nebraska line, but this moraine was later extensively eroded, and terrace deposits generally mantle erosion remnants of the Nickerson till.

The second advance of the Kansan ice, which deposited the Cedar Bluffs till (Table 2), resulted in the pronounced moraine that forms the divide between the Big Blue River system and drainages tributary to the present Missouri River above Kansas City (Fig. 3). This divide forms an almost continuous feature across the southern part of eastern Nebraska and northeastern Kansas; it is breached by the Platte River valley in Nebraska and by the Missouri River above Kansas City and probably extends northeast-

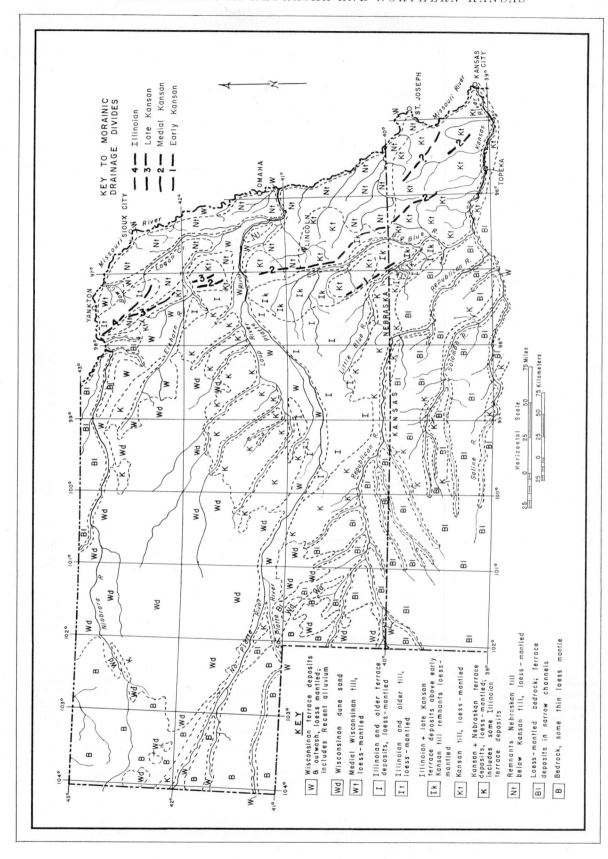

Figure 3. Areal map of Quaternary deposits showing generalized drainage and location of moraine-controlled drainage divides.

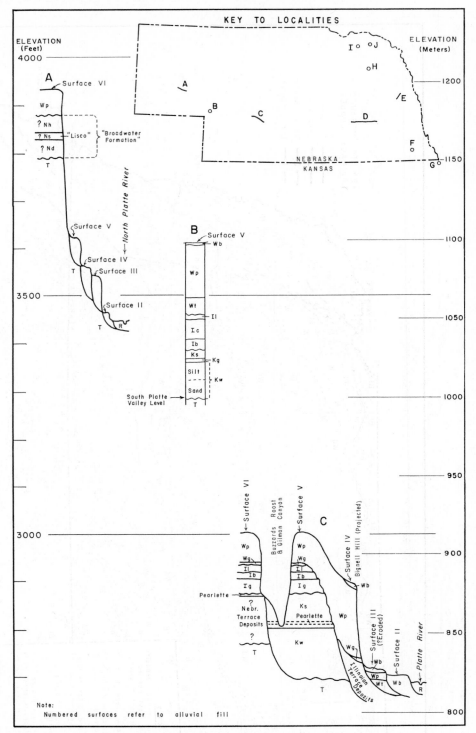

Figure 4. Correlation chart of Pleistocene sequences at significant localities in Nebraska and northeastern Kansas.

A. Nebraskan terrace deposits at Broadwater-Lisco localities in southeastern Morrill County, Nebraska.
B. Kansan terrace deposits in western Keith County, Nebraska (test-hole record).
C. Nebraskan, Kansan, Illinoian, and Wisconsinan terrace deposits near Bignell and Brady and at Gilman Canyon—Buzzards Roost locality in southeastern Lincoln County, Nebraska.
D. Illinoian terrace deposits above Kansan and Nebraskan terrace deposits in deeper part of periglacial basin, central to western Seward County, Nebraska.
E. Relation of Nickerson and Cedar Bluffs tills to older and younger deposits in Fremont-Fontanelle localities, northeastern Saunders to southwestern Dodge counties, Nebraska.

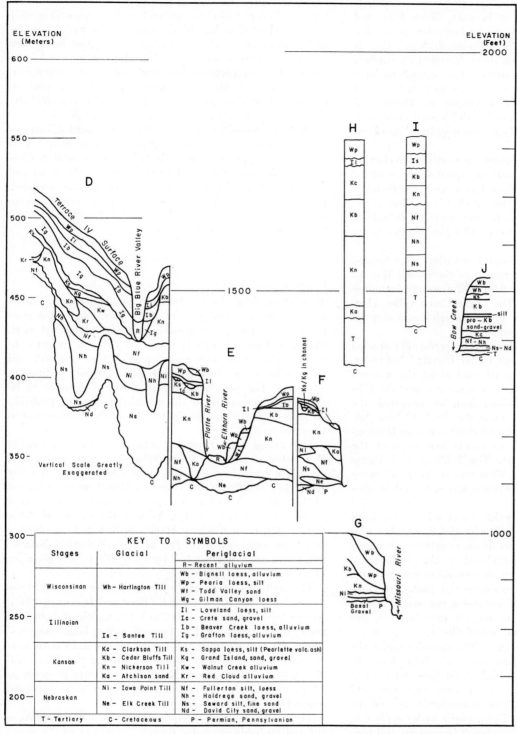

ELEVATION
(Meters)

ELEVATION
(Feet)

KEY TO SYMBOLS

Stages	Glacial	Periglacial
		R – Recent alluvium
Wisconsinan	Wh – Hartington Till	Wb – Bignell loess, alluvium Wp – Peoria loess, silt Wt – Todd Valley sand Wg – Gilman Canyon loess
Illinoian	Is – Santee Till	Il – Loveland loess, silt Ic – Crete sand, gravel Ib – Beaver Creek loess, alluvium Ig – Grafton loess, alluvium
Kansan	Kc – Clarkson Till Kb – Cedar Bluffs Till Kn – Nickerson Till Ka – Atchison sand	Ks – Sappa loess, silt (Pearlette volc. ash) Kg – Grand Island, sand, gravel Kw – Walnut Creek alluvium Kr – Red Cloud alluvium
Nebraskan	Ni – Iowa Point Till Ne – Elk Creek Till	Nf – Fullerton silt, loess Nh – Holdrege sand, gravel Ns – Seward silt, fine sand Nd – David City sand, gravel
T – Tertiary	C – Cretaceous	P – Permian, Pennsylvanian

F. Relation of Elk Creek till to older and younger deposits at Elk Creek type
locality, northeastern Pawnee County, Nebraska.

G. Relation of Iowa Point till to older and younger deposits at Iowa Point type
locality, northern Doniphan County, Kansas.

H. Relation of Clarkson till to older and younger deposits in late-Kansan moraine
drainage divide, northwestern Stanton County, Nebraska (test-hole record).

I. Relation of Santee till to older and younger deposits in early-Illinoian moraine
drainage divide, eastern Knox County, Nebraska (test-hole record).

J. Relation of Hartington till to older and younger deposits at Hartington type
locality, central Cedar County, Nebraska (outcrop and test-hole record).

ward across northwestern Missouri and into southwestern Iowa. The Missouri River between Sioux City and Kansas City trends down the ground-moraine depression of the Kansan glaciation. The interior drainage that is tributary to the Missouri River above Kansas City exhibits many southeastward-curving trends that appear to have been controlled by minor recessional moraines formed during the retreat of the second Kansan ice. Differential headward erosion of some valleys has deflected divide areas, resulting in a more sinuous divide than may have existed at the time of ice retreat.

North of the Platte River valley in northeast Nebraska a pronounced drainage divide may be traced across Stanton, southwestern Wayne, northeastern Pierce, and eastern Knox counties (Figs. 1 and 3), but this divide is complicated because it is formed by a third Kansan moraine (Clarkson till) in its southern part and by an Illinoian moraine in its northern part.

Some broad south-southeast-trending valleys were formed in eastern Nebraska after the retreat of the second Kansan ice sheet and were filled with Sappa silts, locally including the Pearlette ash (Table 2). The Logan Creek valley (Fig. 3) probably originated at this time, although it was also the outlet for medial-Wisconsinan outwash.

A medial-Wisconsinan ice sheet (Hartington till) crossed the Missouri River in northern Cedar County, Nebraska, and temporarily diverted it southward along the western margin of the Illinoian and Kansan moraines into the Elkhorn valley. As the medial-Wisconsinan ice retreated, the Missouri valley was reopened along the South Dakota–Nebraska line. The moraine of the medial-Wisconsinan Hartington till controlled the drainage divide and outlined the Bow Creek drainage (Fig. 3). The Elkhorn and Platte Rivers were formed in medial-Wisconsinan time, and many of the present valleys were deepened and narrowed in late-Wisconsinan time.

The geomorphology of the periglacial area is distinct from that of the glaciated area of Nebraska and Kansas but also reflects the glacial sequence. Six distinct surfaces are recognized. Each surface can be correlated by the stratigraphy of the deposits involved and by the general elevation above the present valley floors. These surfaces or plains are numbered from 1 to 6 in order of increasing age and generally of increasing height. They are not all true terraces, because they usually represent valley-fills that are loess-mantled or eroded to some degree. The deposits under the oldest level, number 6, are correlated with Nebraskan tills (Fig. 4A); they occur at the highest relative elevation in the western part; they are progressively lower eastward and can be traced into the lowest level immediately west of the till border (Figs. 3 and 4D). The deposits under surface 5, correlated with the Kansan tills, occur in western and central Nebraska at the next-to-highest level and can be traced eastward into the next-to-lowest level immediately west of the till border, resting on an eroded surface-6 level (Fig. 4A, B, C, D). The deposits of surface 4, correlated with the Illinoian till, are lower than surface 5 in western and central Nebraska and rest on the eroded top of surface 5 west of the till border (Fig. 4C, D). The deposits under surface 3 (Fig. 4E) occur at lower levels than surface 4 throughout the

region and are correlated with medial Wisconsinan. Surface 2 is at a lower level than surface 3 in the region (Fig. 4E) and is correlated as late Wisconsinan on the basis of radiocarbon dates as much as $10,493 \pm 1,500$ years before the present (C-470) from charcoal in the lower part of the terrace deposits (Schultz, Lueninghoener and Frankforter, 1951). Surface 1, the lowest level, is dated as Recent on the basis of a radiocarbon date of $2,147 \pm 150$ years (C-469) from charcoal in the middle part of the deposits.

The deposits under many of the loess-mantled surfaces represent more than a single depositional sequence. Two depositional sequences are indicated in the surface-6 (Nebraskan) deposits, three each in the surface-5 (Kansan) and surface-4 (Illinoian) deposits, and two in the surface-2 (late-Wisconsinan) deposits. The deposits of surface 3 seem to represent a single alluviation correlated with the medial Wisconsinan (Reed and Dreeszen, 1964).

PLEISTOCENE STRATIGRAPHY

NEBRASKAN DEPOSITS

Two advances of the ice during Nebraskan time are indicated in the glaciated part of the region, and two depositional sequences are represented in the periglacial part. Reed and Dreeszen (1964) point out that the earlier continental glaciations were more complex than realized, and there seems to be good evidence for a two-fold Nebraskan glaciation. The periglacial deposits are not assumed to be exact time equivalents of the glacial deposits but probably are more closely related to the retreats of the separate glaciations involved.

The *David City formation* (Lugn, 1935), the earliest Pleistocene deposit, is a pro-Nebraskan sand and gravel grading upward into silts and clays and overlain by early Nebraskan till. Reed and Dreeszen (1964) restrict the use of the name in Nebraska to deposits related to the advance of the early-Nebraskan ice, as was the intent of Lugn (1935). The name has been applied in Kansas to similar deposits generally related to the advance of the late-Nebraskan ice in areas not reached by the earliest Nebraskan ice (Frye and Leonard, 1949).

The earliest advance of the Nebraskan ice resulted in the deposition of the *Elk Creek till* (Reed and Dreeszen, 1964). At the type locality the Elk Creek till, which is about 3 m thick, rests upon eroded Pennsylvanian limestones and shales. Its top is eroded and buried by about 18 m of late-Nebraskan silts, with an Afton soil on the top (Fig. 4F). Test-holes in southeastern Nebraska penetrate as much as 15 m of Elk Creek till below late-Nebraskan silts and above David City sands and gravels.

The periglacial deposits equivalent to the early-Nebraskan till and probably deposited during the retreat of the early-Nebraskan ice are included in the *Seward formation* (Condra *et al.*, 1950). This is a succession of silts and fine sands, locally including a basal gravel, that rests upon eroded Cretaceous bedrock in the deeper parts of the periglacial basins west of the till border in Nebraska (Fig. 4D). Condra *et al.* (1950) classified these sediments as questionably Tertiary or early Pleistocene, but Reed and Dreeszen (1964) refer them to the early Nebraskan. The Seward formation unconformably underlies the Holdrege sand and gravel and Fullerton silts of late-Nebraskan age and can be traced into the glaciated area, where it occurs below a late-Nebraskan till.

The early-Nebraskan deposits were significantly eroded before they were covered by the late-Nebraskan deposits, developing a greater relief than is typical of the interstadial contacts of the later glaciations. Locally all the early-Nebraskan deposits were removed before the beginning of sedimentation related to late-Nebraskan glaciation.

The *Iowa Point till* (Reed and Dreeszen, 1964) is believed to be late Nebraskan in age and is the till classified by Frye and Leonard (1949) as "Nebraska till." The Afton soil is developed in the upper part of the Iowa Point till at the type locality in northeastern Kansas, with no evidence of any discontinuity between the till and the Afton soil. A proglacial gravel underlies the till at the type locality and rests on the relatively high, eroded Pennsylvanian limestone and shale bedrock (Fig. 4G). This basal gravel was correlated as David City by Frye and Leonard (1949), but Reed and Dreeszen (1964) believe that it may be related to the readvance of the Nebraska ice and therefore not the David City of restricted usage. Although only about 2 m of Iowa Point till is exposed at the type locality, as much as 15 m has been drilled in southeastern Nebraska (Fig. 5), where it overlies the Seward formation of early-Nebraskan age and is overlain by deposits of Kansan age.

The periglacial deposits of late Nebraskan age are the *Holdrege sand and gravel* and the *Fullerton silts* (Lugn, 1935), which form a coarse- to fine-textured sequence. The Afton soil is developed in the upper part of the Fullerton. The Holdrege-Fullerton rests upon eroded Seward silts in the deepest parts of the periglacial basins (Fig. 4D) and can be traced into the glaciated area, where it was deposited on the eroded surface of the Elk Creek till (Fig. 5). This depositional sequence is interpreted by Reed and Dreeszen (1964) as related to late-Nebraskan glaciation and probably represents accumulation during the retreat of the late-Nebraskan (Iowa Point) ice. It is widely represented in the entire region, and its equivalent has been identified in the Southern High Plains on the basis of the Afton soil horizon at its top.

Nebraskan deposits are recognized in restricted channels in westernmost Nebraska, where they have been referred to the "Broadwater formation" by Schultz and Stout (1948) and represent the alluvial fill under the highest Pleistocene terrace (Fig. 4A). An early Pleistocene vertebrate fauna from the "Broadwater" is closely related to the vertebrate fauna studied by Frankforter (1950) in the Elkhorn River valley region from deposits below till of Kansan age. The "Broadwater formation" consists of lower and upper units of sands and gravels separated by the "Lisco silt member," which Lugn (1935) regarded as correlative with the Fullerton. Reed and Dreeszen (1964) believe that the "Lisco" is probably older than the Fullerton because of the absence of a strongly developed soil at its top. They suggest that the "Broadwater" of Schultz and Stout may represent a two-fold Nebraskan depositional sequence related to early- and late-Nebraskan glaciations. Deposits of Kansan age, including the Pearlette volcanic ash, occur under lower

surfaces in western and central Nebraska (Fig. 4A, B), and an unconformity of major erosion separates the deposits under the two surfaces (surfaces 6 and 5).

AFTONIAN INTERGLACIAL STAGE

The separation of Pleistocene deposits into glacial and interglacial stages depends upon individual viewpoints and considerations. Controversy cannot be avoided, but classification can be simplified by restricting the interglacial stages to the periods when extensive soils developed under comparatively warm climates. This restriction of interglacial time is followed in this discussion although it is not the preference of all of the authors.

The *Afton soil* is one of the most important key beds of the Pleistocene in this region, because it can be traced from the glaciated area into the periglacial region. In the glaciated area it is developed on the Iowa Point till or on the Fullerton silts where the Iowa Point till is not represented. It is a dark gray to black carbonaceous horizon in the eastern part of the region, where it was developed under comparatively poor drainage. It becomes progressively better drained westward. It has a strong brown color throughout the periglacial region and has a thick zone of clay enrichment in its lower part. Large calcareous concretions are common in the Fullerton silts below the Afton soil, some of them occurring in bands, and large ferruginous concretions are common in the silts of the more poorly drained areas.

KANSAN DEPOSITS

The Nebraskan deposits of the region were extensively eroded after the development of the Afton soil and were completely removed in many places (Fig. 5). Reed and Dreeszen (1964) relate this period of major erosion to progressively lower sea levels as the early-Kansan ice sheet developed and moved into the region from the north and northeast. The Kansan was the period of maximum glaciation in the northern mid-continental part of the United States, as evidenced by the fact that it reached farther south and southwest than any other glaciation (Flint *et al.*, 1959). Recent studies in Nebraska (Reed and Dreeszen, 1964) demonstrate that the Kansan was a multiple and not a single glaciation. Two tills of Kansan age are represented in northeastern Kansas (Frye and Walters, 1950) and southeastern Nebraska, and a third Kansan till is differentiated in northeastern Nebraska (Fig. 5). Three post-Aftonian, pre-Yarmouthian depositional sequences are recorded in the deeper parts of the periglacial basin area of Nebraska (Fig. 4D), although only the youngest of these sequences has been preserved in much of northern Kansas (Frye and Leonard, 1952) and central to western Nebraska.

The *Atchison formation* (Frye and Leonard, 1952) is the oldest deposit of Kansan age in the region and is a proglacial sand or sand and gravel grading upward to silts and clays that underlie early-Kansan till. It is very widespread in the glaciated part of the region as a valley fill in channels eroded into the Nebraskan deposits (Fig. 5), and the absence of leaching in the upper silts and clays indicates a close depositional relationship to the overlying early-Kansan till. It is more than 30 m thick in places but is

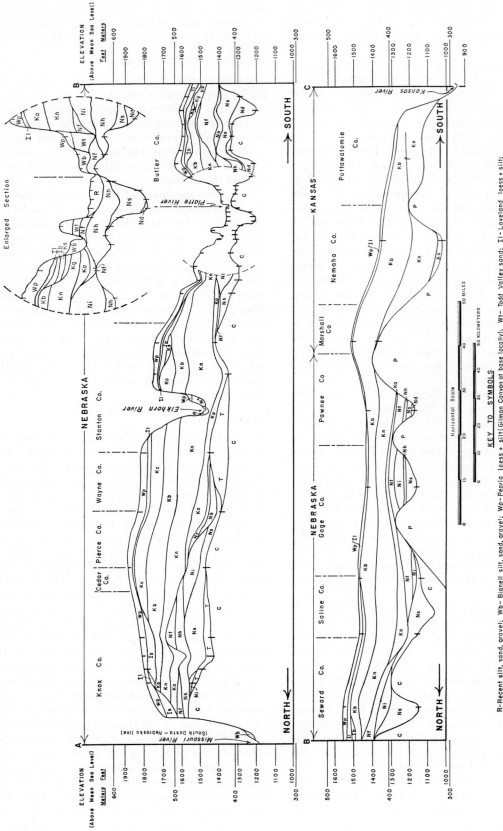

KEY TO SYMBOLS

R-Recent silt, sand, gravel; Wb-Bignell silt, sand, gravel; Wp-Peoria loess + silt (Gilman Canyon at base locally); Wt-Todd Valley sand; Il-Loveland loess + silt;
Ib - Beaver Creek loess, silt, sand; Is-Santee till; Kc-Clarkson till; Ks-Sappa loess + silt (includes Pearlette); Kg-Grand Island sand, gravel; Kb-Cedar Bluffs till; Kn-Nickerson
till; Ka-Atchison sand; Nf-Fullerton silt; Ni-Iowa Point till; Nh-Holdrege sand + gravel; Ns-Seward silt, fine sand; Nd-David City sand + gravel; T-Tertiary silts +
sandstones; C-Cretaceous shale, chalk, limestone, sandstone; P-Permian + Pennsylvanian limestone, shale. Location of test holes indicated by vertical lines.

(For location of Profile Section, see Figure 2)

Figure 5. North-south schematic geologic-profile section based on test drilling of the Kansas and Nebraska Geological Surveys.

generally much thinner and locally is very thin or missing. The coarse-textured part of the formation tends to be a fine- to medium-grained sand in most occurrences, with some gravel in its lower part, although locally it is coarse-textured. The associated upper silts and clays are more local in their occurrence and are generally not more than a meter in thickness. Schultz, Reed, and Lugn (1951) suggest that the Red Cloud sand and gravel was a periglacial equivalent to the Atchison formation according to the similarities of the vertebrate faunas. However, Reed and Dreeszen (1964) suggest that the Red Cloud may be related to the retreat of the Nickerson ice.

The *Nickerson till* (Reed and Dreeszen, 1964) is the oldest Kansan till in the region and is the most extensive of all tills in the glaciated area (Fig. 3), as it can be traced westward into the deeper parts of the periglacial basin region of Nebraska below later Kansan and Illinoian terrace deposits (Fig. 4D) and can be traced southward to, and in places beyond, the Kansas River valley in northeastern Kansas (Fig. 5). Thicknesses of more than 45 m of Nickerson till have been drilled in the glaciated region (Fig. 5), although it is generally thinner. The top of the Nickerson till, where uneroded, is marked by the *Fontanelle interstadial soil* (Reed and Dreeszen, 1964). This soil was interpreted by Lugn (1935) as the Afton interglacial soil. The Fontanelle interstadial soil, a leached zone, usually not more than a half-meter thick, resting on a meter or so of oxidized Nickerson till, provides a sharp contact between the early- and medial-Kansan tills where exposed in eastern Nebraska. In some subsurface occurrences, the top of the Nickerson till is marked by a meter of silts that may be proglacial deposits of the medial Kansan; in other places it is evidenced by the contact between unoxidized till above and a comparatively thin zone of oxidized till below; and in still other places the uppermost oxidized zone of the Nickerson till has been removed, and unoxidized medial-Kansan till rests on the eroded surface of the Nickerson till. Differentiation in the last case is difficult.

The *Red Cloud formation* is believed to be the periglacial equivalent of the Nickerson till (Reed and Dreeszen, 1964), as it is the oldest and lowest of three post-Aftonian, pre-Yarmouthian depositional sequences in the deeper parts of the periglacial basin in Nebraska (Fig. 4) and was probably deposited during the retreat of the Nickerson ice. It is not recognized outside of Nebraska and is assumed to have been removed or not deposited elsewhere. The Red Cloud formation consists of sands and gravels deposited above the Fullerton silts or in channels cut into the Fullerton, and it becomes progressively finer-textured upward, grading into silts in some places. The thickness ranges from a few meters to 15 m or more. It occurs below the depositional sequence correlated with the medial-Kansan till with minor unconformable relationships.

The *Cedar Bluffs till* (Reed and Dreeszen, 1964), correlated as medial Kansan, rests on the Nickerson till in the glaciated area, and its occurrence is somewhat less extensive than the Nickerson till (Figs. 3 and 5). Its loess-mantled moraine generally forms the drainage divide between the Big Blue River and the Missouri River drainage in south-

eastern Nebraska and northeastern Kansas. The Cedar Bluffs till varies from 12 m or less to about 30 m in thickness, and its upper part is generally deeply oxidized. The top of the Cedar Bluffs till, where it occurs below the late-Kansan till, is marked by a change from oxidized till below to unoxidized till above in most places, but locally a proglacial silt or clay, up to 1.5 m in thickness, marks its top. Locally the Sappa loess, including the Pearlette volcanic ash bed, rests upon eroded Cedar Bluffs till, and the Yarmouth soil is developed at the top of the Cedar Bluffs till outside (southwest) of the reach of the late-Kansan ice. Maximum thicknesses of both the Nickerson and Cedar Bluffs till occur in or near their moraines, and these tills, especially the Cedar Bluffs, thin progressively eastward toward the Missouri River valley.

The *Walnut Creek formation* (Reed and Dreeszen, 1964) is the medial depositional sequence of the Kansan terrace deposits in the deeper parts of the periglacial basin area of Nebraska (Fig. 4C, D); it has been traced into central Nebraska but is not recognized in Kansas. It consists of sand and some gravel and occurs above and channeled into the Red Cloud formation; it grades upward into silts that are locally snail-bearing. It is comparatively thin at its type locality but more than 15 m thick in some test-holes. Its top is marked by a carbonaceous soil horizon with a weak subsoil that is correlated with the interstadial horizon separating the Cedar Bluffs and the late-Kansan till in the glaciated region (Reed and Dreeszen, 1964). The Walnut Creek formation is believed to have been deposited at the time of Cedar Bluffs ice retreat.

The *Clarkson till* (Reed and Dreeszen, 1964) is limited in its occurrence to northeastern Nebraska, north of the Platte River valley (Figs. 4H and 5). Its loess-mantled moraine parallels the Cedar Bluffs moraine across Stanton County, Nebraska, where it is located a few miles east of the Cedar Bluffs moraine (Fig. 3). The Clarkson till rests on the Cedar Bluffs till or on an interstadial soil developed on the Cedar Bluffs till; it has a maximum thickness of about 15 m. East of the Clarkson moraine the Clarkson till has not been recognized, probably because it was removed by post-Yarmouthian, pre-Illinoian erosion. The Yarmouth soil is developed at the top of the Clarkson till.

The *Grand Island sand and gravel* (Lugn, 1935) and *Sappa silt* (Condra *et al.*, 1950), including the *Pearlette volcanic ash* bed, make up a coarse- to fine-textured depositional sequence that is correlated by Reed and Dreeszen (1964) as late Kansan and believed to be the periglacial equivalent of the Clarkson till, deposited during the retreat of the Clarkson ice. The Grand Island–Sappa depositional sequence is the most widespread Kansan deposit of the periglacial region and is traceable throughout Nebraska, across Kansas, and into the southern Great Plains. The petrographically distinct (Swineford, 1949) Pearlette volcanic ash, represented throughout Nebraska and Kansas, southeastern South Dakota, northwestern Iowa, the Southern Great Plains, and parts of Colorado, presents the most precise key horizon of the entire periglacial sequence.

Lugn (1935) included the Pearlette volcanic ash in the Loveland formation; Condra *et al.* (1950) placed the

Pearlette volcanic ash in the pre-Loveland Sappa formation of pre-Yarmouthian age, and this correlation was confirmed by Frye *et al.* (1948).

The Pearlette volcanic ash forms a readily recognized horizon in the lower part of the Sappa formation in both the fluviatile and loessic phases in the periglacial area and is locally preserved above the Cedar Bluffs till. The more nearly complete, uneroded occurrences of the Sappa silts include a Yarmouth soil in the upper part. Thus the stratigraphic position of the Pearlette volcanic ash above the Cedar Bluffs till and below the Yarmouth soil is well established. The distinctive molluscan fauna has contributed to the identification of the Sappa formation at many localities where the volcanic ash is missing (Leonard, 1950).

YARMOUTHIAN INTERGLACIAL STAGE

The Yarmouthian interglacial age is herein restricted to the period of soil development under warm conditions and stabilized sea level, although some authors refer part of the deposits described above to the Yarmouthian. The *Yarmouth soil* is developed in the upper part of the Cedar Bluffs till where the late-Kansan Clarkson till is absent, in the upper part of the Clarkson till, and in the upper part of the Sappa silt. It is a strongly developed soil, generally formed under well-drained conditions and often with a thick zone of secondary lime accumulation in the lower part of the profile. In some occurrences, where the lime-accumulation zone is thick, the overlying Illinoian deposits are thin, and there the lime accumulation may represent translocation of lime in Sangamonian as well as Yarmouthian time.

ILLINOIAN DEPOSITS

The Kansan and older deposits of the region were extensively eroded in early Illinoian time. A three-fold subdivision is inferred for the Illinoian deposits of the periglacial region. At least one till of post-Yarmouthian, pre-Sangamonian age occurs in northeastern Nebraska (Reed and Dreeszen, 1964).

The *Santee till* (Table 2, Fig. 5) is exposed in Knox County, Nebraska, where it rests upon eroded Kansan till, on the Sappa formation, on the late-Nebraskan Fullerton silts (Reed and Dreeszen, 1964), and locally on a pre-Illinoian sand and gravel. It is generally darker in color than the Kansan tills, with less depth of oxidation, and it has a maximum thickness of about 15 m. Although its top is extensively eroded and commonly mantled with medial-Wisconsinan loess, some localities show the Sangamon soil preserved in the upper part of the till. The Santee till is believed to be early Illinoian in age.

The *Grafton formation* (Reed and Dreeszen, 1964) is believed to be the periglacial equivalent of the Santee till, as it is the oldest periglacial depositional sequence of post-Kansan age. It rests upon the eroded top of the Sappa and older Kansan periglacial deposits. It consists of sands and gravels grading upward into silts. It is extensive under the loess-mantled Illinoian terraces but is not differentiated in Kansas. A loessic equivalent, the *Grafton loess*, occurs in a similar stratigraphic position in central Nebraska (Fig. 4C), where it is separated from younger Illinoian materials by

an interstadial soil and rests upon Sappa silts that contain the Pearlette ash.

The periglacial equivalent of the medial-Illinoian till of Illinois is believed to be the *Beaver Creek formation* (Reed and Dreeszen, 1964), a sequence of sand with some gravel grading upward to silts. It is channeled into the upper part of the Grafton formation. Its top is marked by an interstadial soil, and it has a thickness of about 10 m at its type locality. In central Nebraska the Beaver Creek loess occurs above the Grafton loess (Fig. 4C) and is separated from the late-Illinoian loess by an interstadial soil.

No late-Illinoian till is identified in the region, but the *Crete sand and gravel* (Condra *et al.*, 1950) occurs below the *Loveland silt*. This coarse- to fine-textured depositional sequence (Crete plus Loveland) is widely distributed throughout the region. It fills channels in the Beaver Creek formation in the loess-mantled Illinoian terrace deposits (Fig. 3), and it is more closely related to present valley systems than the earlier Illinoian deposits. The Crete and Loveland occur throughout the region, and the top of the Loveland is marked by the Sangamon soil.

SANGAMONIAN INTERGLACIAL STAGE

The *Sangamon soil* is one of the most widely recognized horizons of the Pleistocene in this region (Thorp *et al.*, 1950). It is a strongly developed soil with marked depth of leaching and oxidation, with a zone of clay enrichment in its lower part. It is developed on the Loveland silt and directly on the Kansan and Illinoian tills where these tills are not mantled by younger pre-Sangamonian deposits. A thick zone of carbonaceous silt that commonly occurs above the Sangamon soil was formerly considered to be the A-horizon of the Sangamon soil. However, Reed and Dreeszen (1964) believe that this zone represents an early-Wisconsinan accumulation.

WISCONSINAN DEPOSITS

The Wisconsinan of the region is divided into early, medial, and late Wisconsinan by Reed and Dreeszen (1964). No till of early or late Wisconsinan is recognized, but the Hartington till (Table 2, Fig. 4J) is correlated with the medial-Wisconsinan till of southeastern South Dakota. In the periglacial part of the region the early Wisconsinan is represented by thin deposits, the medial Wisconsinan is comparatively thick, and the late Wisconsinan is largely differentiated near present valleys.

The *Gilman Canyon formation* (Reed and Dreeszen, 1964) is classified as early Wisconsinan. It consists of a basal carbonaceous silt (formerly classified as the A-horizon of the Sangamon soil) overlain by about one meter of leached loess below the calcareous loess of the Peoria formation. It is separated from the medial-Wisconsinan deposits by an interstadial soil.

The *Hartington till* is the only Wisconsinan till in the region. It is represented only in the northern part of Cedar County, Nebraska, where the medial-Wisconsinan ice crossed the Missouri River (Fig. 3). The medial-Wisconsinan till in adjoining parts of South Dakota was studied extensively by Flint (1955) and Simpson (1960). It is comparatively thin (about 3 m thick) and rests on deeply eroded pre-Wisconsinan deposits, including the late-Kansan Sappa silts. Early-Wisconsinan time was probably largely represented by extensive erosion, as all of the Illinoian deposits were removed from the area before the invasion of the Hartington ice. The Hartington ice diverted the Missouri River southward into the Elkhorn River valley, and outwash from the Hartington ice was carried down the Logan valley until the Missouri River valley was reopened late in medial-Wisconsinan time (Reed and Dreeszen, 1964).

The *Todd Valley sand* and the *Peoria silt* (Lugn, 1935) form a depositional sequence in the periglacial region that is the equivalent of the Hartington till (Reed and Dreeszen, 1964). Upland occurrences of this interval classified as *Peoria loess* extensively mantle the uplands of the region. The Todd Valley–Peoria depositional sequence is well represented in the terrace deposits related to surface 3 of the terrace sequence (Fig. 5).

Late-Wisconsinan time was a period of valley deepening in the region, along with the deposition of the *Bignell sands and gravels and silts* under the terrace-2 surfaces and the *Bignell loess* (Schultz and Stout, 1945) in the uplands. The Bignell loess thickens toward present-day valleys and is separated from the Peoria loess and silt by the Brady interstadial soil (Schultz and Stout, 1945). Carbon separated from the A-horizon of the Brady soil at the Bignell type locality gave a radiocarbon date of $9,160 \pm 250$ years before the present (W-234). However, snails collected by A. B. Leonard from the Bignell loess above the Brady soil in Doniphan County, northeastern Kansas, resulted in radiocarbon dates ranging from $12,550 \pm 400$ to $12,700 \pm 300$ years (W-231 and W-233). If it may be assumed that the snail-shell dates of Leonard are somewhat older than they should be because of ingested, older radioactive carbon and that the Brady soil dates of the Bignell type locality are the result of some contamination from younger plant roots, then it may be concluded that the Brady soil is close to the age of the Two Creeks forest bed which separates the medial- and late-Wisconsinan deposits in Wisconsin. Carbon collected from the lower part of the Bignell terrace deposits has given radiocarbon dates ranging from $8,274 \pm 500$ years (C-108a) to $9,880 \pm 670$ years (C-471) (Schultz, Lueninghoener, and Frankforter, 1951).

RECENT DEPOSITS

A comparatively low terrace level occurs below terrace-surface 2 and above the present flood plains along many of the streams. This has been designated as terrace-surface 1 (Schultz, Lueninghoener, and Frankforter, 1951) and is believed to be Recent on the basis of tree-ring dating of a few thousand years from wood included in the fill.

THE SAND HILLS OF NEBRASKA

An area of more than 52,000 km² of stabilized sand hills is an unusual feature of north-central Nebraska, with smaller areas to the west and southwest (Fig. 3). Lugn (1935) included the dune sand in his "Sand Hills Formation" and differentiated an older dune sand, which he correlated with the Peoria loess, and a younger dune sand. Reed and Dreeszen (1964) applied the names *Peoria*

dunesand and *Bignell dunesand* to the earlier and later eolian deposits of the region.

Smith (1951; Thorp and Smith, 1952) reported some occurrences of longitudinal dunes superimposed upon transverse dunes, suggesting two periods of dune formation. He also recorded the presence of a buried soil within the dune-sand complex. Reed and Dreeszen (1964) correlate the buried soil between the older and younger dune sand with the Brady interstadial soil, which occurs between the Peoria and Bignell loesses in the areas of loess accumulation. The older Pleistocene history of the region is poorly understood because the area has not been test-drilled extensively to date. The bedrock of the sand-hills area is the Ogallala formation of Pliocene age, and these late-Tertiary continental deposits were probably the original source of the sand.

Fluviatile Pleistocene deposits are known to occur below the dune sand at a number of localities. Reed and Dreeszen (1964) suggest that the Ogallala bedrock of the region was probably eroded at a number of times during the early and middle Pleistocene, and fluviatile deposits accumulated in channels cut into the bedrock. This alluvium was subject to wind action during medial-Wisconsinan time, when the Peoria dune sand accumulated, with the finer materials being blown out of the area southeastward to form the thick deposits of Peoria loess in south-central Nebraska (Thorp and Smith, 1952). It is apparent that the Peoria loess was in part derived from the sand-hills area (Lugn, 1962) and in part derived from Wisconsinian outwash plains in the eastern part of Nebraska and northern Kansas.

The dune-sand deposits obliterated the earlier Pleistocene drainage pattern in the sand hills, resulting in the formation of many closed basins and water-table lakes.

THE PLEISTOCENE MAMMALS OF NEBRASKA

Fossil remains of Pleistocene mammals are found in inter-till deposits of the glaciated area as well as in the terrace deposits of the periglacial area. Their stratigraphic relations have been investigated by Lugn (1935), Schultz (1934), Barbour and Schultz (1937), Schultz and Stout (1945, 1948), Schultz and Frankforter (1946, 1948), Schultz, Lueninghoener, and Frankforter (1948, 1951), Condra et al. (1950), Frankforter (1950), Schultz, Reed, and Lugn (1951), and Schultz and Tanner (1957).

Vertebrate fossils have been found in abundance in the fills of all six Pleistocene terraces. The Pleistocene faunas of the Central Great Plains can be considered under three distinct divisions: Early (Nebraskan to early Kansan), Medial (late Kansan to medial Illinoian), and Late Pleistocene (late Illinoian to Wisconsinan). A fourth faunal assemblage, that of the Recent, does not differ greatly from the typical late-Wisconsinan fauna. The Recent fauna dates back about 6,000 to 7,000 years.

The larger mammals have proved to be good indicators of regional changes in climate and migrations during the Pleistocene. The distribution of certain Recent rodents and other small mammals indicates that some of these forms have persisted in suitable local micro-habitats since regional climates changed. Small mammals may have survived in cool, moist localities in ravines or near springs for long periods involving changing climatic conditions, but the larger mammals may better reflect the regional climate.

Geologic evidence in the field has proved to be of utmost importance in the proper interpretation of paleoecologic and climatic evidence. Too often habitat differences in contemporary faunas are considered to be distinctions caused by regional climatic controls (Schultz and Stout, 1948, p. 562), but actually they may reflect edaphic differentiation.

EARLY PLEISTOCENE FAUNAS

The Early Pleistocene faunas of the terrace-6 deposits of western Nebraska, which are considered to be equivalent in age to the Villafranchian of Europe (Schultz and Stout, 1948, p. 560) are typified by the following large mammals:

> *Paramylodon* sp.
> *Megalonyx* sp.
> *Procastoroides sweeti*
> *Castoroides?* sp.
> *Canis* sp.
> *Borophagus* sp.
> *Satherium priscinaria middleswarti*
> *Mephitis* sp.
> *Smilodon* sp.
> *Stegomastodon mirificus*
> *Mammut (Pleiomastodon)* sp.
> *Equus (Plesippus) simplicidens*
> *Nannippus?* sp.
> *Platygonus* sp.
> *Camelops* sp.
> *Tanupolama* sp.
> *Gigantocamelus fricki*
> *Capromeryx arizonensis schultzi*

MEDIAL PLEISTOCENE FAUNAS

The Medial Pleistocene faunas of Nebraska are best known from the terrace-5 deposits of Sheridan County. The larger mammals include the following:

> *Paramylodon nebraskensis*
> *Megalonyx leidyi*
> *Castoroides? nebraskensis*
> *Canis* sp.
> *Canis dirus nebrascensis*
> *Arctodus simus nebraskensis*
> *Mustela* sp.
> *Smilodon nebrascensis*
> *Mammuthus (Archidiskodon) imperator*
> *Equus excelsus*
> *Equus niobrarensis*
> *Equus calobatus nebrascensis*
> *Platygonus vatus*
> *Camelops kansanus*
> *Tanupolama americanus*
> *Odocroileus sheridanus*
> *Capromeryx furcifer*
> *Hayocaros falkenbachi*

Illinoian terrace deposits at localities along the North Fork of the Middle Loup River in Cherry County (Jakway, 1963) contain a Medial Pleistocene fauna that is later than the Sheridan County fauna. This Illinoian fauna includes:

> *Mammut americanus*
> *Symbos cavifrons*
> *Bison alleni*

Tapirus sp. and *Panthera onca augusta* are known from the same area but may occur at a slightly different stratigraphic level.

A large number of Asian mammals migrated to North America in Medial Pleistocene time and probably reached Nebraska during an interstadial interval of the Kansan glaciation, because a few specimens of mammoth and other Medial Pleistocene mammals have been found in northeastern Nebraska. The till overlying the vertebrate-bearing deposits is believed, by the Nebraska Geological Survey, to be late Kansan in age. The following Asiatic mammals made their first appearance in the Central Great Plains during the Medial Pleistocene:

> *Arctodus simus*
> *Ursus* sp.
> *Pantheria augusta*
> *Mammuthus (Archidiskodon) imperator*
> *Bison latifrons*
> *Symbos cavifrons*
> *Ovobus moschatus*
> *Bootherium* sp.
> *Euceratherium* sp.
> *Platycarabos dodsoni*
> *Cervalces scotti*
> *Alces* sp.
> *Odocoileus sheridanus*
> *Sangamona* sp.
> *Cervus* sp.
> *Rangifer* sp.
> *Ovis* sp.

The horses and camels, which had been natives to the Central Great Plains since early Oligocene times, were the most common ungulates during the Early Pleistocene, prior to the migration of the Asiatic mammals to the region. Once the Asiatic forms appeared in large numbers in the Plains area, the horses and camels began to diminish in numbers, and by Late Pleistocene time the horses and camels were well on their way to extinction. Final extinction in southwestern United States took place about 7,000 to 8,000 years ago.

Although rhinoceroses are well known from the Pleistocene of Europe and Asia, no remains of these important mammals have been found in Pleistocene deposits of North America. Fossil rhinoceros bones, however, are commonly encountered in the uppermost Pliocene deposits of the Central Great Plains.

LATE PLEISTOCENE FAUNAS

The Gilman Canyon and Bignell loesses and valley sediments of equivalent ages are the chief sources of Late Pleistocene mammals. Among the typical mammals reported from the Late Pleistocene of the Central Great Plains are the following:

Megalonyx sp.
Castoroides? sp.
Mustela sp.
Canis sp.
Vulpes sp.
Procyon sp.
Taxidea sp.
Mammut americanus
Mammuthus (Archidiskodon) maibeni
Mammuthus (Parelephas) columbi
Mammuthus primigenius
Equus excelsus
Platygonus compressus
Camelops sp.
Sangamona sp.
Odocoileus sp.
Rangifer sp.
Cervalces roosevelti
Cervus canadensis
Antilocapra cf. *americana*
Symbos cavifrons
Botherium sp.
Bison antiquus antiquus
B. antiquus barbouri
B. occidentalis

The earliest known remains of bison in the Central Great Plains are from late-Kansan or early-Yarmouthian deposits (Medial Pleistocene), and these (*Bison latifrons*) were truly giants, with horn-spreads of almost three meters from tip to tip of the horn-sheaths. The size of the skulls and horns, as well as of the other skeletal parts, diminished gradually, and by Sangamon interglacial time the horn-spread was only about half as great. Today a large living bison, *B. bison bison*, rarely has a horn-spread of more than 60 cm. Fossil bison remains make splendid index fossils, since the morphologic changes took place rather rapidly during the Pleistocene.

The mammoths also developed at a fairly rapid rate, but the mammoth skeletons increased in size from late-Kansan to Sangamonian times, then decreased somewhat during the Late Pleistocene. The enamel on the molars of the Medial Pleistocene mammoths was much thicker, and the enamel folds were less complicated than in the late Pleistocene forms. There also were fewer plates in the Medial Pleistocene molars. The mammoth remains also are fair indicators of the geologic age of the deposits in which they are found.

Pleistocene faunas are referred to as Blancan, Irvingtonian, and Rancholabrean by some vertebrate paleontologists, but that classification is not used here because the Nebraska faunas are not exact equivalents and because the Blancan, Irvingtonian, and Rancholabrean faunas are geographically isolated from glaciated areas and thus less satisfactorily related to the glacial sequence.

References

Barbour, E. H., and Schultz, C. B., 1937, An early Pleistocene fauna from Nebraska: Amer. Mus. Novitates, No. 942, p. 1-10

Bayne, C. K., and Fent, O. S., 1963, The drainage history of the upper Kansas River basin: Kansas Acad. Sci. Trans., v. 66, p. 363-373

Condra, G. E., Reed, E. C., and Gordon, E. D., 1950, Correlation of the Pleistocene deposits of Nebraska: Nebraska Geol. Surv. Bull. 15A, 74 p.

Flint, R. F., 1955, Pleistocene geology of eastern South Dakota: U.S. Geol. Surv. Prof. Pap. 262, 173 p.

Flint, R. F., *et al.*, 1959, Glacial map of the United States east of the Rocky Mountains (scale 1:750,000): Geol. Soc. Amer.

Frankforter, W. D., 1950, The Pleistocene geology of the middle portion of the Elkhorn River valley: Univ. Nebraska Stud., No. 5, 46 p.

Frye, J. C., and Leonard, A. B., 1949, Pleistocene stratigraphic sequence in northeastern Kansas: Amer. J. Sci., v. 247, p. 883-899

—— 1952, Pleistocene geology of Kansas: Kansas Geol. Surv. Bull. 99, 230 p.

Frye, J. C., Swineford, Ada, and Leonard, A. B., 1948, Correlation of Pleistocene deposits of the central Great Plains with the glacial section: J. Geol., v. 56, p. 501-525

Frye, J. C., and Walters, K. L., 1950, Subsurface reconnaissance of glacial deposits in Kansas: Kansas Geol. Surv. Bull. 86, p. 141-158

Jakway, George, 1963, The Pleistocene faunal assemblages of the Middle Loup River terrace-fills of Nebraska: Univ. Nebraska Ph.D. thesis, 143 p.

Jewett, J. M., *et al.*, 1959, Graphic column and classification of rocks in Kansas: Kansas Geol. Surv., published chart

Leonard, A. B., 1950, A Yarmouthian molluscan fauna in the mid-continent region of the United States: Univ. Kansas Paleont. Contr., Mollusca, art. 3, p. 1-48

Lugn, A. L., 1935, The Pleistocene geology of Nebraska: Nebraska Geol. Surv. Bull. 10, 213 p.

—— 1962, The origin and sources of loess: Univ. Nebraska Studies, New ser., No. 26, 105 p.

Reed, E. C., and Dreeszen, V. H., 1964, Revision of the classification of the Pleistocene deposits of Nebraska: Nebraska Geol. Surv. Pap. 18, 65 p.

Schultz, C. B., 1934, The Pleistocene mammals of Nebraska: Univ. Nebraska State Mus. Bull. 1, No. 41, p. 357-393

Schultz, C. B., and Frankforter, W. D., 1946, The geologic history of the bison in the Great Plains (Preliminary Report): Univ. Nebraska State Mus. Bull., v. 3, No. 1, 10 p.

—— 1948, Preliminary report on the Lime Creek sites (New evidence of early man in southwestern Nebraska): Univ. Nebraska State Mus. Bull. 3, No. 4, p. 32-42

Schultz, C. B., Lueninghoener, G. C., and Frankforter, W. D., 1948, Preliminary geomorphological studies of the Lime Creek area: Univ. Nebraska State Mus. Bull. 3, No. 4, p. 32-42

—— 1951, A graphic résumé of the Pleistocene of Nebraska with notes on the fossil mammalian remains: Univ. Nebraska State Mus., Contr. Div. Vert. Paleont., 41 p.

Schultz, C. B., Reed, E. C., and Lugn, A. L., 1951, The Red Cloud formation in Nebraska: Science, v. 114, p. 547-549

Schultz, C. B., and Stout, T. M., 1945, Pleistocene loess deposits of Nebraska: Amer. J. Sci., v. 243, p. 231-244

—— 1948, Pleistocene mammals and terraces in the Great Plains: Geol. Soc. Amer. Bull., v. 59, p. 553-591

Schultz, C. B., and Tanner, L. G., 1957, Medial Pleistocene fossil vertebrate localities in Nebraska: Univ. Nebraska State Mus. Bull., v. 4, p. 59-81

Simpson, H. E., 1960, Geology of the Yankton area, South Dakota: U.S. Geol. Surv. Prof. Pap. 328, 124 p.

Smith, H. T. U., 1951, Photo interpretation studies in the sand hills of western Nebraska: unpublished report

Swineford, Ada, 1949, Source area of Great Plains volcanic ash: J. Geol., v. 57, p. 307-311

Thorp, James, Johnson, W. M., and Reed, E. C., 1950, Some post-Pliocene buried soils of central United States: J. Soil Sci., v. 2, p. 1-19

Thorp, James, Smith, H. T. U., *et al.*, 1952, Pleistocene eolian deposits of the United States, Alaska, and parts of Canada (map, scale 1:2,500,000): Geol. Soc. Amer.

Summary

The Pleistocene deposits in this region rest upon the eroded surface of Pennsylvanian, Permian, and Cretaceous sedimentary rocks in the east and Tertiary in the west. The eastern sixth of the region was glaciated during Nebraskan, Kansan, Illinoian, and Wisconsinan times, resulting in rolling, loess-mantled moraines that determine the drainage divides. Southeastward-sloping plains typify the central part of the region, where extensive periglacial deposits of Pleistocene age occur that are related to loess-mantled terraces. An area of over 52,000 km^2 of stabilized sand dunes of Wisconsinan age occurs in north-central Nebraska. The westernmost part of the area slopes to the southeast and east; it is underlain by Tertiary bedrock, generally loess-mantled, with some Pleistocene terrace deposits in narrow channels.

The Pleistocene periglacial deposits are well represented in the terrace and basin sequences and can be traced into the glaciated region by means of interglacial soil horizons and test-hole records. Two separate glacial drifts of Nebraskan age, separated by an interstadial soil and an erosion surface, are identified in the eastern glaciated region and are correlated with two depositional sequences in the periglacial region. Three separate Kansan drifts, separated by interstadial soils and minor erosion surfaces, are represented in the glaciated region, and three depositional sequences, correlated with the Kansan glaciations, are present in the periglacial region. The Pearlette volcanic ash occurs within the upper depositional sequence of the Kansan in the periglacial region and rests upon sediments of the second Kansan glaciation in the glaciated region. A till believed to be of early Illinoian age occurs in the northern part of the glaciated area. Three depositional sequences, correlated with a tripartite Illinoian, are differentiated in the periglacial region. One till of medial-Wisconsinan age is represented in the northernmost part of the glaciated region, and three depositional sequences of early-, medial-, and late-Wisconsinan age are recognized in the periglacial region. The Afton, Yarmouth, and Sangamon interglacial soils and surfaces of major erosion in turn separate the drifts of the four major glacial ages. The periglacial deposits are fluviatile and eolian, and the glacial deposits are tills locally resting upon proglacial sands and gravels of fluviatile origin.

The classification in the state of Nebraska is more complex than that in Kansas because of more nearly complete preservation of Pleistocene deposits. Rock-stratigraphic names are applied to recognizable depositional units that can be identified and correlated. The molluscan faunas are useful in correlation. The vertebrate fossils permit subdivision of the Pleistocene deposits into Early (Nebraskan and pro-Kansan), Medial (middle- and late-Kansan to early-Illinoian), and Late Pleistocene (late-Illinoian and Wisconsinan) deposits.

QUATERNARY OF THE SOUTHERN GREAT PLAINS

JOHN C. FRYE,[1] A. BYRON LEONARD[2]

INTRODUCTION

PHYSIOGRAPHY

THE PART of the Great Plains (Fenneman, 1931) discussed in this report (Fig. 1) extends from central-western Kansas and the eastern edge of Colorado (39° N. Latitude) southward to the area in southwestern Texas where the High Plains grade into the Edwards Plateau (32° N. Latitude). It is a region dominated by the relatively flat but eastward-sloping surface of a plateau called the High Plains and "Llano Estacado" (Fig. 2A, B), but it also includes the dissected eastern and western margins of this plateau (Fig. 2C, D). In elevation the surface of the High Plains ranges from more than 5,000 to less than 2,500 ft above sea level.

Strong local relief occurs only along the escarpments that mark the eastern and western limits of the High Plains and along the canyons that notch the area. It is, therefore, primarily along these escarpments and canyons that the deposits are adequately exposed for study.

West of the High Plains, a belt of erosional topography occurs between the plateau surface and the eastern front of the Rocky Mountains—the Colorado Piedmont, Raton Section, and Pecos Valley. This belt is crossed by only the Arkansas and Canadian Rivers.

East of the High Plains occurs a belt of dissected topography, ranging from the wide zone called the Plains Border in northern Kansas (Adams, 1903; Fenneman, 1931), through the 15- to 30-mile-wide strip of "Red Hills" in southern Kansas (Frye and Leonard, 1952) and the related topography in western Oklahoma and northern Texas, to a sharply defined, east-facing escarpment in central western Texas (Frye and Leonard, 1957b). In the areas where this zone of transitional topography is narrow, it has been called the Break of the Plains.

East of this bounding strip lies the Osage Plains, or Osage Hills, Section of the Central Lowland Province. The High Plains surface is dominated by an almost continuous capping of late Tertiary deposits (Baker, 1915; Darton, 1905; Frye, 1946), and remnants of these deposits occur on the higher elements of the dissected border (Frye and Leonard, 1964), but in the Osage Plains late Tertiary deposits are largely absent. Only in the Flint Hills of central and southern Kansas (Frye and Leonard, 1952), where cherty limestones of Permian age form a group of prominent cuestas, and in north-central Texas, where resistant Cre-

taceous limestones also produce high cuestas (Frye and Leonard, 1963), are remnants of Tertiary stream gravels found.

At their southern extremity in southwestern Texas, the limits of the High Plains are much more difficult to establish (Frye and Leonard, 1964). The Pecos Valley, with the Mescalero pediment on its eastern flank, serves to limit clearly the High Plains in eastern New Mexico. However, as this valley enters Texas (Leonard and Frye, 1962) it swings toward the east, and, where it again flows generally southward to its junction with the Rio Grande, it enters deep canyons sharply cut into the Cretaceous limestones that characterize the Edwards Plateau. Also, the upland

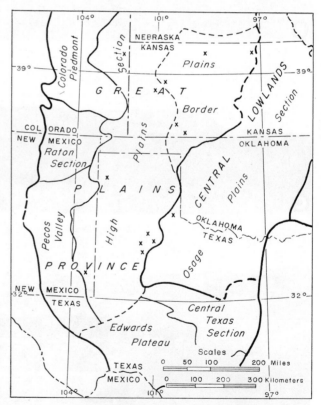

Figure 1. Location of the southern Great Plains and the several physiographic sections referred to in this report (adapted from Fenneman, 1931). Photographs in Figures 2 and 4 were taken at locations marked ✕.

[1] Illinois State Geological Survey, Urbana, Illinois.
[2] Department of Zoology, University of Kansas, Lawrence, Kansas.

Figure 2. Topography and early Pleistocene deposits in the southern Great Plains.

surface of the High Plains merges almost imperceptibly into the surface of the Edwards Plateau. The blanket of late Tertiary sediment thins and becomes discontinuous southward, and it disappears on the eroded surface of the limestones that cap the Plateau.

Although the southern Great Plains region is externally drained, a significant part of the upland surface is undrained (Evans and Meade, 1945; Frye, 1950). Shallow depressions are developed largely in late Tertiary and Pleistocene deposits, although some in the southern plains in Texas are in Cretaceous rocks. They have complex origins, including differential filling of erosional valleys and of solution-collapse basins, differential compaction, silt infiltration (Frye, 1950) in alluvial sediments, wind deflation, solution of caliche zones, and perhaps even animal action. In some areas on the High Plains surface these shallow depressions are so numerous that the area is dotted with intermittent lakes after the infrequent heavy rains.

The climate of the southern Great Plains is subhumid to semiarid. The average annual rainfall ranges from approximately 25 in. in the southeastern to less than 15 in. in the northwestern part of the area described.

The region was, before the agricultural exploitation by European man, essentially a treeless prairie, having stands of trees and woody shrubs mainly along water courses. The original prairie contained a wide variety of surviving short-stemmed grasses (*Andropogon, Bouteloa, Sporobolus, Stipa,* and others) and other herbaceous plants (*Allium, Ambrosia, Ipomoea, Lupinus, Cirsium,* large numbers of Compositae and many less common plants; *Opuntia* and *Yucca* are most prominent in the southwestern portion of the region). The buffalo grass (*Buchloe dactyloides*) has become even more conspicuous, since European settlement, on ranches where certain management is practiced; this grass is famous for having been the source material for the sod houses of the early settlers.

Woody shrubs along stream courses comprise coral berry (*Symphoricarpos*), dogwood (*Cornus*), sand plum (*Prunus*), several kinds of sumac (*Rhus*), and others in the northern part of the region considered here, but toward the southwest xerophytic shrubs, such as mesquite (*Prosopis*), creosote bush (*Larrea*), greasewood (*Forsellia*), and the shrub live oak (*Quercus turbinella*), become more conspicuous. *Tamarix* and *Artemisia* are widely distributed, as are species of sensitive plant (*Mimosa*). Among common trees are the cottonwood (*Populus deltoides*) and willow (*Salix*) and a small assemblage of less common kinds, such as the walnut (*Juglans*) and various kinds of oak (*Quercus*). The hackberry (*Celtis*) is also widespread and in many places is found as the sole tree on well-drained erosional slopes, where it is often associated with the aromatic sumac (*Rhus aromatica*).

The large herbivorous animals, such as bison (*Bison*), deer (*Odocoileus*), antelope (*Antilocapra*), and the less common elk (*Cervus*), have long since disappeared from the Great Plains, along with their large predators: the bear (*Ursus*), great wolf (*Canis lupis*), and puma (*Felis concolor*). However, many of the smaller vertebrates from the original fauna are still common: rabbit (*Sylvilagus*), American hare (*Lepus*), varieties of skunks (*Mephitis*), several insectivores, and numerous small rodents. The racoon (*Procyon*), the small plains wolf or coyote (*Canis latrons*), and the only North American marsupial (*Didelphys,* the opossum) have thrived under agriculture and are undoubtedly more numerous than they were in pre-Columbian time.

The molluscan fauna of the Great Plains is sparse in species, although large populations of one or more species may exist locally. All the aquatic gastropods are pulmonates, *Physa* and *Helisoma* predominating, although *Lymnaea, Gyraulus,* and a few others are widespread (Frye and Leonard, 1957a). Unionid mussels are not common and are erratically distributed, apparently because most streams on the Great Plains have unsuitable bottom environments, but the sphaeriid mussels (*Sphaerium* and *Pisidium*) are widespread and often occur in large numbers in ephemeral ponds in the undrained depressions mentioned earlier.

Terrestrial gastropods on the southern Great Plains include *Pupoides, Gastrocopta, Hawaiia, Vertigo, Succinea,* and a few others. In the southern part of the region, *Bulimulus, Succinea,* and occasionally other kinds adapted to endure low humidity and extremely high temperatures become conspicuous elements of the fauna. Most terrestrial gastropods in the southern Great Plains are found in woodland borders and brushy areas along stream courses, but a few species, such as *Gastrocopta armifera, Hawaiia minuscula,* and *Pupoides albilabris,* occur also in grassland habitats.

PRE-QUATERNARY GEOLOGY

The southern Great Plains are underlain at various depths by relatively flat late Paleozoic rocks (Moore *et al.,* 1951; Sellards *et al.,* 1932). Permian rocks are exposed along the

---

Key to Figure 2:

A. High Plains surface in Yuma County, Colorado. Surface is Wisconsinan Loess over Ogallala Formation (Pliocene).

B. High Plains surface south of McDonald, Lea County, New Mexico. Surface on caliche of the Ogallala climax soil; very thin surface soil exposes fragments of indurated caliche at surface.

C. East-facing escarpment of High Plains, southwest of Post, Garza County, Texas. The Ash Hollow Floral Zone of the Ogallala Formation (Pliocene) is the "caprock" of the escarpment. Illinoian "cover sands" and thin Wisconsinan silts mantle the High Plains back of the escarpment, and the Tule Formation (Kansan) occurs as fill in the reentrant valleys.

D. Dissected High Plains, Scott County, Kansas. Ash Hollow Member of the Ogallala Formation (Pliocene) crops out in two ledges in the valley sides; the High Plains surface is mantled with Crete and Loveland deposits (Illinoian) containing the Sangamon Soil, and with Wisconsinan loesses; Kansan and younger alluvial deposits occur in the valley fill.

E. Type locality of the Blanco Formation (Nebraskan), Crosby County, Texas, with bedded sand, silt, and some clay, about 40 ft thick.

F. Meade Formation (Kansan), consisting of the Sappa Member (with thin white Pearlette Volcanic Ash) overlying the Grand Island Member. Dark gray Carlile Shale (Cretaceous) is in the lower part of the exposure. Gove County, Kansas.

G. Tule Formation (Kansan), Spring Creek Canyon, Garza County, Texas.

TIME-STRATIGRAPHIC CLASSIFICATION in the MID-WEST		KANSAS Rock-stratigraphic units used here	TEXAS Rock-stratigraphic and Morphostratigraphic units used here
RECENT		(Alluvium, dune sand)	(Alluvium, dune sand)
PLEISTOCENE · WISCONSINAN	VALDERAN	Bignell Loess	Cooke Alluvial Terrace
	TWOCREEKAN	Brady Soil	Ambrose Alluvial Terrace
	WOODFORDIAN	Peoria Loess	Tahoka Fm. Lake Lomax deposits
	FARMDALIAN	"Basal zone of Peoria"	
	ALTONIAN	*(Deposits of several terraces, dune sands, basin fills)*	*(Terraces, loess, dune sands, basin fills)*
PLEISTOCENE	SANGAMONIAN	Sangamon Soil	Sangamon Soil
	ILLINOIAN	Loveland Silt; Crete Sand and Gravel *(Terrace deposits)*	"Cover sands", terrace deposits, dune sands
	YARMOUTHIAN	Yarmouth Soil	Yarmouth Soil
	KANSAN	Meade Fm. { Sappa Mem. / Grand Isl. M. } Kansas Glacial Till, Atchison Formation	Hardeman Alluv. Terr. Tule Formation (Terrace deposits, basin fills)
	AFTONIAN	Afton Soil	Afton Soil
	NEBRASKAN	Blanco Fm. { Fullerton M. / Holdrege M. } Nebraska Glacial Till, David City Formation	Blanco Formation (Terrace deposits, basin fills)
PLIOCENE		"Ogallala climax soil"	"Ogallala climax soil"
		Ogallala Formation { Kimball Mem. / Ash Hollow Mem. / Valentine Mem. }	Ogallala Formation

Figure 3. Time-stratigraphic subdivisions for the upper Mississippi Valley region of the Midwest, and rock-stratigraphic units used in this report for Kansas and Texas. Named morphostratigraphic units in Texas also are shown, but biostratigraphic units and locally used names are omitted.

eastern margin of the High Plains in southern Kansas, western Oklahoma, and northwestern Texas. In much of the region, however, Cretaceous rocks constitute the surface upon which the late Tertiary sediments were deposited, with Triassic rocks locally occupying this position. These rocks below the late Tertiary are predominantly weakly resistant to erosion and consist largely of siltstones, shales, fine-grained sandstones, and some chalks and chalky shales, but in the southern extremities of the High Plains resistant limestones of Cretaceous age occur and exert a controlling influence on the topography.

From the end of the Cretaceous Period to early or middle Miocene this region was subjected to erosion. Although the total volume of rock removed from the region during this period was exceedingly large, the topography probably remained that of a dissected plain with mesas capped by resistant Cretaceous limestones forming the most precipitous and prominent elements of the topography. It was upon such a dissected plain, crossed by major east-trending valleys, that deposition was initiated during middle to late Miocene time.

It has been suggested (Sellards et al., 1932) that the late Tertiary alluvial blanket of the central and southern Great Plains originated as a sequence of coalescing alluvial fans spreading out eastward from the Rocky Mountains. How-

ever, the stratigraphy of the Ogallala Formation opposes this hypothesis (Frye and Leonard, 1959). In the building of large alluvial fans the deposits progressively overlap the older surface away from the area of initial deposition. If they were fan deposits, the sediments under the High Plains would become younger eastward as well as upward through the thickest part of the fan, and, in a much more compressed relationship, they would overlap westward onto the mountain front and laterally toward their points of contact with adjacent fans. When the stratigraphy of the Ogallala is examined in detail (Frye et al., 1956; Frye and Leonard, 1959), it is evident that such a relationship does not obtain. Rather, the oldest unit, the Valentine Member (or Floral Zone), occurs in the lowest part of the erosional valleys cut into the pre-Tertiary bedrock and is thus arranged in west-to-east (or northwest-to-southeast) belts across the Plains. It has been impossible to trace physically the Valentine Member from north to south through the southern Plains because it is discontinuous in this direction, but correlation of the unit from one filled valley to the next has readily been made by paleontological means.

The middle and volumetrically largest unit of the Ogallala, the Ash Hollow Member (or Floral Zone), everywhere overlaps the Valentine. In much of the region it filled the pre-existing valleys virtually to the level of the bedrock divides, and in some places Ash Hollow sediments coalesced across the tops of the former divides.

The uppermost unit of the Ogallala, the Kimball Member (or Floral Zone), reflects the product of a truly integrated floodplain-channel complex that completely buried all elements of the former topography from northwestern Kansas to as far south as Howard County, Texas. In Howard County and southward, Cretaceous limestones stand prominently above this alluvial plain; the Ogallala is discontinuous and locally occurs as a high terrace deposit.

In the southern Great Plains the Ogallala Formation is intimately related to the Quaternary deposits, both in geographic position and as a prime sediment source. The Ogallala, named from a type locality near Ogallala, Nebraska (Darton, 1905), has been correlated southward through the Great Plains (Frye and Leonard, 1959) and includes the entire body of late Tertiary clastic sediments. It has generally been assigned a Pliocene age, but the lower part of the formation may locally include deposits of late Miocene age. At widely scattered localities, large and significant faunas of fossil vertebrates have been described from the Ogallala (e.g., Clarendon and Hemphill in Texas, and Long Island and Rhino Hill in Kansas), but in the field the abundant and almost ever-present fossil seeds of herbs and grasses furnish a basis for detailed regional correlation. In the central part of the Great Plains, fossil mollusks also have proved to be of value for correlation in some areas.

The lowest subdivision of the Ogallala is based on a type area in Cherry County, Nebraska. In Kansas it is called the Valentine Member (Fig. 3), but it is recognized in Texas only as the biostratigraphic unit called the Valentine Floral Zone. The Valentine occurs in the lowest parts of the pre-Ogallala erosional valleys, and its deposits reflect a local source, particularly in the smaller bedrock valleys where sediments from the mountains to the west either were lacking or were strongly diluted by more locally derived material.

The second (middle) unit of the Ogallala is based on a type section near Lewellen, Nebraska, and is called the Ash Hollow Member in Kansas and a floral zone in Texas. The Ash Hollow is more uniform throughout the southern Great Plains than is the Valentine and largely reflects a western source. It consists of a complex of floodplain sediments with intercalated channel gravels and local lentils of volcanic ash and marl. With the exception of the channel gravels, the deposits are predominantly fine sand and silt. The upper part of the unit contains several buried soils. In Kansas the Valentine and lower part of the Ash Hollow are gray to gray-tan, with red-brown and tan becoming prominent in the upper part; in southern Texas both units are tan to red-brown throughout. Calcium carbonate occurs in the unit not only as a caliche zone associated with the buried soils but also as a soft cement in medium to fine sands.

The uppermost unit of the Ogallala Formation (Kimball Member) is the thinnest and most widespread. At a few places in its lower part channel gravels occur, but it consists predominantly of silt with some clay and sand. The Kimball is generally marked at the top by a prominent zone of relatively dense calcium carbonate that has been called "algal" limestone because of small spheroidal structures formerly thought to be fossil algae; more recently it has been referred to as pisolitic limestone (Swineford *et al.*, 1958). It commonly is the resistant layer capping the High Plains escarpment and locally has been called the "caprock." The upper part of the Kimball contains up to 60% calcium carbonate, with sand, silt, and sparse granules. The entire mass of the "caprock" commonly has been brecciated and secondarily recemented with laminated overgrowths. It is judged to have formed as the caliche zone of the "Ogallala climax soil," modified by the effects of climatic cycles during the Pleistocene—brecciation by desiccation during periods of aridity, alternating with solution and secondary deposition of carbonate.

TECHNIQUES OF CORRELATION

In the southern Great Plains region, a wide range of techniques has been used for correlation of Quaternary deposits. Stratigraphic sequence and lithology are generally less useful in this region than in some others because of the similarity of sources for all Quaternary deposits. The Ogallala Formation is the most widespread source, augmented by some contributions from the local pre-Ogallala rocks and from the mountains to the west. However, the occurrence of some distinctive rock types within the Ogallala and the presence as clastic fragments of Ogallala rocks in the younger deposits permit differentiation of Pleistocene from Pliocene sediments.

Paleontology is widely useful for correlation. Fossil vertebrates occur in distinctive assemblages at a significant number of localities, and fossil mollusks occur abundantly and widely in all major stratigraphic units (Leonard, 1950, 1952; Taylor, 1960).

Physiographic sequences of terraces and continuity of individual terraces have proved to be useful criteria for correlation within a drainage system but are not diagnostic for correlation among isolated drainage systems.

Buried soils are one of the most useful of the physical criteria for regional correlation (Frye, 1949). They occur in the alluvial sequences and also in the succession of loesses that mantle some of the uplands. They therefore can be used for physical tracing between drainage basins. The ranges in morphology of the buried soils clearly reflect the ranges in climate during the interval of their formation and therefore serve also as a clue to paleoecology. In general the characters of the three major soils (Afton, Yarmouth, and Sangamon) are sufficiently similar that they are difficult to distinguish from each other in any one area on the basis of morphology alone. However, their morphology clearly distinguishes them from the many minor soils, including the Brady Soil, and from the strongly developed Ogallala climax soil at the top of the Ogallala Formation.

In some favorable situations, for example the Red River Basin of northern Texas (Frye and Leonard, 1963), the morphology of surface soils may serve as a clue to the age of deposits.

Petrographically distinctive volcanic ash deposits (Frye *et al.*, 1948) have been used extensively for correlation throughout the central and southern Great Plains. The Pearlette Volcanic Ash, originally described by Cragin (1896) from southwestern Kansas, has been used widely as a marker for late Kansan deposits.

Radiocarbon dates have had limited use in the Wisconsinan of the southern Great Plains because only a few age determinations have been made by this method. The measurement of the slow degradation of residual insoluble protein-nitrogen contained in fossil shells is a new method of estimating relative age of Quaternary deposits. This method has been used successfully in studies of Great Plains chronology (Ho, 1964).

STRATIGRAPHIC CLASSIFICATION

Current practices and policies of stratigraphic classification and nomenclature followed by many workers have recently been summarized by the American Commission on Stratigraphic Nomenclature (1961). The fundamental basis of the present code is the provision for multiple systems of classification. Multiple systems have long been used by stratigraphers in many segments of the rock sequence as a scheme for classifying on the basis of various characteristics. Rock-stratigraphic units based on gross lithology, bio-stratigraphic units based on the occurrence of assemblages of organic remains, and time-stratigraphic units based on the span of time represented by the deposition of one or more rock layers have become generally accepted for nearly all parts of the geologic column.

The code also provides for two categories of classification that have particular applicability in the late Cenozoic, namely, soil-stratigraphic units and geologic-climate units. The latter unit is defined as follows (A.C.S.N., 1961, p. 660): "A geologic-climate unit is an inferred widespread climatic episode defined from a subdivision of Quaternary rocks." Recently (Frye and Willman, 1960) a category of morphostratigraphic units has been proposed, primarily for use in the Pleistocene. This unit was defined as "comprising a body of rock that is identified primarily from the surface form it displays; it may or may not be distinctive lithologically from contiguous units; it may or may not transgress time throughout its extent."

In the southern Great Plains all of the above listed categories of stratigraphic units, with the single exception of the geologic-climate unit, are currently in use for late Cenozoic deposits. Names of time-stratigraphic units (system, series, stage, substage) are written in adjectival form in order to distinguish them from other categories (Fig. 3). This practice makes for clarity, because some place names are used for both time-stratigraphic and rock-stratigraphic units that encompass different sequences. For example, the term Kansas Till (a rock-stratigraphic unit) has been used in Kansas (Frye and Leonard, 1952) to apply only to the unit of glacially deposited till and intercalated glacio-fluvial materials, whereas the term Kansan Stage (a time-stratigraphic unit) designates the interval of time represented by the deposition of the Atchison Formation, the Kansas Till, and the Meade Formation (Fig. 3). Furthermore, the term Kansas Till is used only as far as the distinctive lithologic characteristics of the strata permit identification of the essentially continuous body of rocks, whereas the Kansan Stage refers to any rocks that can be shown to have been deposited during the time span represented by the type sequence. Such usage is in accord with the rules suggested in the Stratigraphic Code for use throughout the entire geologic column.

For those stages that are considered to be interglacial intervals (Aftonian, Yarmouthian, Sangamonian) the time-stratigraphic unit is defined in a manner not practiced in the pre-Quaternary part of the geologic column. These units are based on soil-stratigraphic units (Afton Soil, Yarmouth Soil, Sangamon Soil), and therefore the span of time, rather than being that in which a sequence of rocks was deposited, is that during which pre-existing deposits were altered to form the soil profile.

Although the primary categories of stratigraphic classification used in the southern Great Plains region are time-stratigraphic, rock-stratigraphic, and soil-stratigraphic (Fig. 3), biostratigraphic units of several types, based on fossil vertebrates, fossil mollusks, and fossil plant materials, have been extensively used in the region. Morphostratigraphic units have been formally proposed for use only in the Red River Basin of northern Texas (Frye and Leonard, 1963).

NEBRASKAN STAGE

The oldest Quaternary deposits recognized in the southern Great Plains are assigned to the Nebraskan Stage. The stage is based on a sequence of deposits in eastern Nebraska, northeast of the region discussed here; Nebraskan glaciers reached into the northeastern corner of Kansas but did not reach the region under discussion. In the type region, the Nebraskan Stage (time-stratigraphic unit) includes four rock-stratigraphic units—the David City Formation, consisting of proglacial sand and gravel, the Nebraska Till, and the retreatal glaciofluvial deposits of the Holdrege and Fullerton Formations. The stage encompasses the time of the formation, advance, and retreat of the first Pleistocene continental glacier.

A significant episode of weathering followed by erosion affected the Great Plains region after the culmination of deposition of the Ogallala Formation (middle to late Pliocene) and prior to initial Nebraskan deposition. During this hiatus, streams notched the surface of the late Tertiary alluvial plain and the peripheral plains topography that had been cut on older rocks, but they left large areas of the High Plains surface undissected. No deposits of latest Pliocene or earliest Nebraskan age are known with certainty in the southern Great Plains, but it is possible that very minor quantities occur in structural traps such as the Meade Basin of southwestern Kansas.

In the southern Great Plains the Nebraskan Stage consists entirely of water-laid sediments of three genetic types: (1) outwash sediments derived, at least in part, from the advancing and retreating continental glaciers to the north and northeast and from mountain or piedmont glaciers to the northwest; (2) alluvium deposited by through-flowing streams from the west that were responding to influences of climatic change, and perhaps to structural movements, but were not directly affected by glaciers; and (3) sediments derived from within the Great Plains themselves and deposited within erosional valleys or structural or solution-subsidence basins.

In Texas the deposits now classed as Nebraskan first attracted scientific attention because they contained vertebrate fossils. Cummins (1891) applied the name Blanco beds to strata that included the presently accepted type section of the Blanco Formation (Fig. 2E), but he also included in his description strata that are now assigned to the Ogallala Formation. For many years the Blanco Formation was considered Pliocene in age, but Evans and Meade (1945) and Meade (1945) assigned it to the Nebraskan on the basis of its stratigraphic relations (unconformably younger than the Ogallala) and a restudy of its vertebrate fauna. This age assignment within the glacial sequence to the northeast was confirmed (Frye *et al.*, 1948) by stratigraphic tracing, petrographic studies, and studies of molluscan faunas.

In western Texas the Blanco Formation is not extensively exposed. However, the type area in Blanco Canyon, Crosby County, the exposures west of Channing in Hartley County, and exposures in Palo Duro Canyon in Randall County have yielded an abundant vertebrate fauna. At these High Plains localities the formation consists largely of fine to coarse sand, silt, and clay, thin bedded to laminated and gray to gray-tan (Evans and Meade, 1945; Frye and Leonard, 1957b; Reeves, 1963). In Crosby County the Blanco Formation includes some clays and thin limestones. Topographically, the Blanco beds are unconformably younger than the Ogallala and never overlie its uneroded top. East of the High Plains escarpment in Hall County, the Blanco Formation appears as a high terrace of the Red River Valley and includes coarse gravels in its base (Frye and Leonard, 1963).

In southwestern Kansas, deposits of Nebraskan age have been studied in the Meade Basin area (Hibbard, 1944; Leonard, 1948; Frye and Leonard, 1952). Elsewhere in western Kansas, deposits of Nebraskan age occur as remnants of terraces and abandoned valley segments in the central Smoky Hill Valley region and as poorly exposed upland alluvial deposits in Sedgwick, McPherson, Barber, Pratt, and other counties. They are known from subsurface data to occupy the lower parts of abandoned valley fillings in the Great Bend region.

More than a third of the molluscan species known to occur in Nebraskan deposits in the southern Great Plains are not known from older or younger deposits of the region. The most striking attribute of Nebraskan faunas is that which reflects the climatic reversal following the extremely adverse environments that obtained during and immediately following the late phases of Ogallala deposition. Data concerning Nebraskan molluscan faunas are drawn from the northern half of the region here under discussion. These data show that branchiate mollusks, entirely absent in the immediately underlying sediments, reappeared in this region in significant numbers (Frye and Leonard, 1952).

AFTONIAN STAGE

The Aftonian Stage encompasses the span of time during which the Afton Soil was developed. Present knowledge of Quaternary stratigraphy in the southern Great Plains indicates that the Aftonian was an interval of regional stability and soil formation and that alluvial deposits of this age are exceedingly sparse.

The Afton Soil has been described (Frye and Leonard, 1952) in northeastern Kansas, where it has a deep Prairie to Humic-gley profile developed in glacial till. In the southern Great Plains, however, it invariably displays a strongly developed caliche zone that locally is more than 2 ft thick, with a B-horizon that becomes progressively redder toward the south. At some places in central-western Texas (Frye and Leonard, 1957b), the caliche of the Afton Soil has been mistakenly correlated with the Ogallala climax soil. The three major buried soils in the Great Plains Pleistocene are progressively better preserved and more widely exposed with decreasing age. Whereas the Sangamon Soil has been studied almost continuously throughout the region, interpretation of the Afton Soil is necessarily based on widely scattered and inadequate exposures.

KANSAN STAGE

In the southern Great Plains the deposits of the Kansan Stage are second only to those of the Wisconsinan Stage in volume of deposits, geographic distribution, diversity of lithology, abundance of fauna, and precision of correlation. The Kansan Stage takes its name from deposits in northeastern Kansas (Frye and Leonard, 1952), northeast of the region under discussion, and by several lines of evidence its correlation is extended into the southern Great Plains. In the type region the Kansan Stage (time-stratigraphic unit) is defined by three rock-stratigraphic units in Atchison and Doniphan Counties, Kansas (Frye and Leonard, 1952) (Fig. 3)—the Atchison Formation (pro-Kansan glacial outwash), the Kansas Till, and the Meade Formation (Grand Island and Sappa Members).

In Texas the Tule Formation (Fig. 2G) and the Hardeman Alluvial Terrace of the Red River Basin (Fig. 4A) are of Kansan age. In the fine-textured upper part of the Kansan deposits throughout the Great Plains region, discontinuous lenticular deposits of the petrographically dis-

tinctive Pearlette Volcanic Ash (Fig. 2F; Fig. 4B) (Frye *et al.*, 1948; Frye and Leonard, 1957b) serve as a time plane for the correlation of deposits of late Kansan age.

In the northern part of the southern Great Plains, middle to late Kansan deposits occur as relatively high alluvial terraces of the Smoky Hill River Valley (Fig. 2F). The deposits have coarse gravels and sands at the base and grade upward into sandy silts that locally contain lentils of Pearlette Volcanic Ash. In central western Kansas, deposits of Kansan age also fill abandoned valleys (*e.g.*, the valley across Scott County, and Wilson Valley in Ellsworth and Lincoln Counties). In the Great Bend lowland south of the Arkansas River, Kansan deposits occupy abandoned channels of the river and are now generally covered by dune sands. The Kansan Stage is represented generally by alluvial deposits of the typically graded series displayed along the Smoky Hill River Valley. Outwash deposits from mountain glaciers may have been introduced into the region by the Arkansas River, but the Kansan sediments were largely derived from the Ogallala Formation within the Great Plains region. Therefore these deposits reflect the rock types of the Rocky Mountains with minor additions from the older bedrock.

South of the Arkansas River, particularly in Meade County, are extensive and relatively thick deposits of Kansan age that were formed in structural depressions. The Meade Basin (Frye and Hibbard, 1941), controlled by a series of faults *en echelon* along its eastern edge, was the largest and most persistent of these structural traps, but other areas produced by solution-subsidence and perhaps also by faulting occur in the region. The deposits contain more sand and silt and present a more complex stratigraphy than the normal alluvium. They have proved to be particularly rich in both vertebrate (Hibbard, 1944) and invertebrate (Leonard, 1950) faunas and, partly for this reason, have been studied intensively.

In the panhandle region of Texas and extreme western Oklahoma, deposits of Kansan age are not abundant, but a few deposits of Pearlette Volcanic Ash and associated snail faunas have been described, particularly from along tributaries to the Canadian and Red Rivers. Southward in Texas, however, deposits of this age are more abundant and form the prominent Hardeman Alluvial Terrace (Frye and Leonard, 1963) of the Red River Valley. The deposits here have some similarity to the alluvial terrace sequences of western Kansas, but they differ in having less coarse gravel (perhaps because the Ogallala Formation in this region also contains less coarse gravel), in having more fragments derived from the local pre-Ogallala bedrock, in being more strongly red and brown, and in clearly containing no glacial outwash from the west. The type locality of the Tule Formation occurs near the Briscoe-Swisher county line in Tule Canyon, tributary to the Red River from the southwest.

Locally, deposits of sand and silt with volcanic ash occur as fills in relatively small depressions in the High Plains of central-western Texas. The Tule Formation is well developed along major canyons at the eastern margin of the High Plains (Frye and Leonard, 1957b; Reeves, 1963). In Blanco and Yellowhouse Canyons, Tule deposits form a prominent terrace (Fig. 4C). In Spring Creek Canyon (Fig.

Figure 4. Pleistocene deposits and buried soils in the southern Great Plains.

2G) Tule deposits are exposed as the dissected fill of a broad valley or shallow basin, and fossiliferous Kansan deposits related to minor valleys from the High Plains scarp have been studied at several places (*e.g.*, west of Post, Garza County). Near the southern limit of the High Plains, a terrace deposit of Kansan age containing Pearlette Volcanic Ash and a distinctive snail fauna has been studied along Beals Branch in southeastern Howard County (Frye and Leonard, 1957b, 1964). Throughout western Texas the sediments of the Tule Formation reflect a relatively local source; where they are deposited in valleys, they demonstrate post-Blanco erosion followed by Kansan alluviation insufficient to raise them to the level of the Nebraskan valley flats. The Tule sediments and their faunas indicate higher precipitation than now obtains in the region.

Molluscan and vertebrate faunas clearly indicate that ecological conditions in the Great Plains reached their Quaternary optimum during the Kansan Stage. The trend toward greater precipitation and lower average annual temperatures that began in the Nebraskan culminated in the Kansan. These climatic trends may be deduced from the occurrence of populous and richly varied molluscan faunas characteristic of mesophytic environments. Although some elements of the molluscan fauna, and many of the vertebrates, indicate an increase in the forest element of the flora, none of the molluscan elements from the forested parts of the lower Missouri Valley is known to have reached the Great Plains. The diagnostic molluscan faunas in late Kansan deposits (Leonard, 1950), particularly in their association with the Pearlette Volcanic Ash, have served as a basis for correlation of the glacial sequence of northeastern Kansas

and adjacent areas with the nonglacial sequence of the southern Great Plains (Frye *et al.*, 1948).

YARMOUTHIAN STAGE

The Yarmouthian Stage encompasses the span of time during which the Yarmouth Soil was developed. Present knowledge of Quaternary stratigraphy in the southern Great Plains indicates that the Yarmouthian, like the Aftonian, was an interval of regional stability and soil formation and that alluvial deposits of this age are exceedingly scarce.

The Yarmouth Soil was named by Frank Leverett from a well section at Yarmouth, Des Moines County, Iowa, and has been described in northeastern (Frye and Leonard, 1952) and north-central Kansas (Fig. 4E). To the north and east of the region considered here, this soil has been observed as a Prairie, Chernozem, and Humic-gley soil, but in the southern Great Plains it ranges from Chernozem and Brown soils to profiles resembling a deeply developed Reddish Brown or Red Desert soil. In central-western Texas it is difficult indeed to distinguish the Yarmouth from the Afton Soil on the basis of morphology alone. On the terraces of the Red River Valley (Frye and Leonard, 1963) where the Yarmouth surface has not been covered by younger deposits, this profile has a depth and degree of development that distinguish it from the younger profiles of the same area.

ILLINOIAN STAGE

In the type region of Illinois, glaciers of the Illinoian Stage reached farther south than any other continental glacier in the northern hemisphere. However, in the southern Great Plains region the Illinoian is the least conspicuous of the glacial stages.

The Illinoian Stage is defined from the succession of glacial tills, moraines, and eolian and alluvial deposits in central and southern Illinois. In the type area it is characterized (Willman *et al.*, 1963) by three distinctly separate glacial tills, preceded and separated by silts and sands of both eolian and fluvial origin.

In the Kansas part of the southern Great Plains the Illinoian Stage consists of stream-deposited gravel, sand, and silt along major valleys and eolian deposits on the upland divide areas (Loveland) and locally on older terraces (Frye and Leonard, 1952). Terraces of Illinoian deposits are particularly well developed along southern tributaries of the Republican River (Prairie Dog Creek, Sappa Creek) and in the valleys of the Solomon and Smoky Hill Rivers. In these valleys the deposits contain gravel and sand at the base (Crete) and grade upward into sandy silt and silt (Loveland). Along the Arkansas River Valley across the High Plains and in the Great Bend Lowland, the Crete-Loveland deposits are not a distinct terrace but form part of the complex underlying the valley flat and the sand-hills tract of the Great Bend region. They locally form the upper part of fills of abandoned valleys, but in some places they merge with the deposits of existing floodplains.

South of the Arkansas Valley, the Meade Basin, the Ashland-Englewood Basin, and smaller basin areas also are in contrast to the regions to the north and south. In the major basins, Illinoian deposits overlie the Kansan with only minor

Key to Figure 4:
A. High terrace of the Red River (Hardeman Alluvial Terrace) underlain by Kansan alluvial deposits, Hall County, Texas.
B. Pearlette Volcanic Ash, serving as local "caprock" in Tule Formation (Kansan) that contains abundant molluscan fauna; at this locality, west of Channing, Hartley County, Texas, the Tule Formation overlies fossiliferous deposits of Nebraskan age.
C. Tule Formation (Kansan), containing abundant molluscan fauna, that underlies surface of extensive terrace. Note channel fill of Illinoian alluvium unconformable on Tule Formation at right side of photo. East of Crosbyton, Crosby County, Texas.
D. Wisconsinan dune sand over interdune fill of clayey silt (Wisconsinan), near Fowler, Meade County, Kansas.
E. Yarmouth Soil, near Kirwin, Phillips County, Kansas. Caliche zone is below head of pick. At this locality the Yarmouth Soil is overlain by Crete-Loveland deposits containing the Sangamon Soil in the top, which in turn is overlain by Peoria Loess (Wisconsinan).
F. Sangamon Soil at the surface, developed in "cover sands," Crosby County, Texas. Note sharply defined and strongly developed caliche zone at bottom.
G. Sangamon Soil developed in Loveland Loess (Illinoian), overlain by Peoria Loess (Wisconsinan), in roadcut, Republic County, Kansas.
H. Brady Soil developed in fossiliferous Wisconsinan alluvium, overlain by alluvium of latest Wisconsinan and Recent age that contains a weakly developed soil; note sharp but irregular top of caliche zone of the Brady Soil. Clark County, Kansas.

erosional unconformity, and in some of the solution-subsidence basins Illinoian deposits rest directly on Permian bedrock. As in the Kansan, the normal alluvial sequence of gravels grading upward through sands to silts does not obtain, but finer textured, basin-type deposits are prevalent. In the basin areas, tan and gray deposits are interspersed with red and brown in contrast to the gray-tan and tan that characterize the alluvial sequence.

In western Texas, alluvial deposits of Illinoian age are minor in comparison with those of the Kansan and Wisconsinan. Illinoian deposits occur as relatively minor terrace fills along the major valleys and canyons, but as the preceding cycle of erosion had not been adequate to cut entirely through the earlier Kansan sediments the Illinoian forms unconformable lenses set into the older Kansan (Fig. 4C). East of the High Plains the Illinoian is developed as a recognizable terrace (Frye and Leonard, 1963), but even there it is minor compared to the terraces of the older and younger stages.

In the southern part of the High Plains of Texas the Illinoian Stage has its most conspicuous development as a blanket of sediment, called "cover sands," across the upland divide areas (Frye and Leonard, 1957b). No formal rock-stratigraphic unit has been proposed for these deposits, which are in part eolian, in part sheet-wash, and perhaps also in part the filling of basins. They are consistently red, red-brown, or tan-brown and are sandy and thin. They are so barren of fossils that only a few snail shells have been found in them, and they are commonly poorly sorted and reflect a local source. Although quite thin compared to other Pleistocene units, "cover sands" are widespread in the southern Great Plains. The color, distribution, fabric, and meager and limited fauna of the sediments, indicate that the Illinoian was a relatively arid interval in the southwest.

The early Pleistocene climatic trend toward moist and cool conditions, which reversed the progressive desiccation of latest Tertiary time, was not maintained during the Illinoian in the southern Great Plains. Branchiate snails and other elements of the molluscan fauna not adapted to ephemeral bodies of water permanently disappeared from the region after the Kansan, and less than half the total number of molluscan species known from the Kansan have been discovered in Illinoian sediments. Climatically, Illinoian time in the southern Great Plains is anomalous because elsewhere the Illinoian was a time of major glacial advances, suggesting precipitation rates as high as those during the Kansan. It may be speculated that the Illinoian climate of this region was influenced by accentuated pre-Illinoian uplift of the mountains to the west.

Sangamonian Stage

The Sangamonian Stage encompasses the span of time during which the Sangamon Soil was developed. Like the two preceding interglacial stages, it was an interval of regional stability and soil formation; alluvial deposits of this age are exceedingly sparse.

The name Sangamon Soil was proposed for a soil developed in Illinoian drift and overlain by loess in Sangamon County, Illinois. It is the most widespread and continuously traceable stratigraphic marker bed in the southern Great Plains region. In Kansas it occurs widely as a buried soil developed in Loveland Loess of the uplands (Fig. 4G) and in Crete-Loveland sediments in the valley fills (Frye and Leonard, 1952). Southward into central-western Texas, beyond the region of Wisconsinan loesses and dune sands, it becomes the surface soil (Fig. 4F). As a stratigraphic datum it rivals the late-Kansan Pearlette Volcanic Ash in its distinctive character but surpasses it in abundance of exposures and geographic extent. This soil has been identified and traced from Ohio through the type area of Illinois to southwestern Texas, a distance approaching 2,000 miles.

In northeastern Kansas the Sangamon Soil is a Reddish Prairie to reddish Chernozem soil, and carbonates are leached to a maximum depth of 22 ft. In this area it has a minor accumulation of caliche at the base of the leached zone, and the caliche increases toward the southwest. In the northeast the B-horizon is clayey, has a maximum thickness of more than 2 ft, and is well structured.

As this soil is traced westward and then southward, it passes through deeply developed phases of Chestnut, Reddish Chestnut, and Reddish Brown soils and may be classed as a deeply developed Red Desert soil in places in southwestern Texas. Throughout this region it retains a clayey, well-structured B-horizon at least 1 ft thick, and the caliche zone attains a maximum development of 2½ to 3 ft thick. In areas where the degree of development of the several buried soils can be directly compared, the Sangamon is at least as strongly developed as the Yarmouth and approaches the Afton, but it falls far short of the "Ogallala climax soil." It is much more strongly developed than the Brady or post-Brady soils in the same region.

An unusual feature of the Sangamon Soil, displayed in northern Kansas but not readily observed in the Texas region, is its multiple character. At several places (Frye and Leonard, 1954) a succession of minor soils occurs below the Sangamon in the late Illinoian deposits. These minor soils are not Sangamon, because they occur below it, but as they have not been formally named they are mentioned here. In the areas observed they are of the same soil type as the Sangamon above but are much less strongly developed. As they have not been correlated regionally, their primary importance is to indicate that there were relatively brief intervals of stability and soil formation, followed by alluviation in the central Great Plains, during middle to late Illinoian time.

The Sangamon Soil indicates a relatively long interval of erosional stability under a climate that was at least as rigorous as that obtaining in the region today. However, the fact that significant precipitation occurred is demonstrated by the well-developed B-horizon and the great depth to the caliche zone.

Wisconsinan Stage

Deposits of the Wisconsinan Stage are the most widespread of the surficial deposits in the southern Great Plains. They consist of gravelly to silty alluvium, sandy to clayey basin deposits, dune sand, and loess. In the northern part of the region they occur as valley fillings, low and intermediate level terraces, dissected and undissected fillings of structural, collapse, and deflation basins, and loess and dune sands; in the southern part sheet sands and dune sands are dominant.

The Wisconsinan Stage is defined from glacial deposits in the type region of eastern Wisconsin and northeastern Illinois. The original definition was presumed to include only the Shelbyville till and younger deposits, but recent re-evaluation of the deposits in the type region (Frye and Willman, 1960; Willman *et al.*, 1963) has demonstrated that a complex sequence of pre-Shelbyville tills, silts, and alluvium occurs stratigraphically above the Sangamon Soil. As now defined by these authors, the stage embraces a time span from approximately 70,000 radiocarbon years B.P. to approximately 5,000 radiocarbon years B.P. In Illinois, substages defined within the Wisconsinan are based on the stratigraphic succession of loesses, silts, and glacial tills related to the Lake Michigan Lobe and are supported by faunal zones and radiocarbon dates. The substages include the Altonian Substage (70,000± B.P. to 28,000 B.P.) at the base, the Farmdalian Substage (28,000 B.P. to 22,000 B.P.), the Woodfordian Substage (22,000 B.P. to 12,500 B.P.), the Twocreekan Substage (12,500 B.P. to 11,000 B.P.), and the Valderan Substage (11,000 B.P. to 5,000 B.P.) (Fig. 3).

In the southern Great Plains region the Altonian, Farmdalian, and Woodfordian Substages are generally not differentiated but are referred to collectively as pre-Bradyan (early Wisconsinan of some literature), and the Valderan Substage is commonly referred to as post-Bradyan (late Wisconsinan). The Bradyan interval, named from the Brady Soil, probably started sometime during the late Woodfordian, but for practical purposes it may be considered as approximately contemporaneous with the Twocreekan Substage.

PRE-BRADYAN WISCONSINAN DEPOSITS

In the southern Great Plains the bulk of all Wisconsinan deposits is pre-Bradyan in age. The time span covered by these deposits, if our correlation with Illinois and Wisconsin is correct, is from perhaps as early as 70,000 radiocarbon years B.P. to approximately 12,500 radiocarbon years B.P. Some other workers restrict the Wisconsinan in the southern Great Plains to these early deposits and class the materials here included within the post-Bradyan (late Wisconsinan) as part of the Recent .

In Kansas (Frye and Leonard, 1952) north of the Arkansas River, the pre-Bradyan alluvial deposits appear as a persistent terrace above the limit of most floods in all major and many minor valleys. In Prairie Dog Creek Valley this terrace has been named Almena, in the Solomon River Valley it is called the Kirwin terrace, in the Smoky Hill River Valley it is the Schoenchen terrace, and in the Kansas River Valley the Newman terrace. The alluvial deposits underlying these terrace surfaces are up to 80 ft thick and invariably consist of sands and gravels in the lower part (known only from bore holes) and grade upward through sands to sandy silts at the top. In some places relatively thin loess deposits overlie a soil developed in the top of the alluvial materials. These terrace surfaces are commonly 30 to 35 ft above the level of the adjacent river channels but in some places range from less than 20 to more than 45 ft above channel level. Along much of the Arkansas River

Valley of this region there is a comparable terrace, but its surface is generally at an elevation only slightly above the active floodplain and in some areas is barely distinguishable from it; locally it is masked by younger sand dunes. Although these early Wisconsinan terrace deposits are poorly exposed and therefore have yielded few fossils, their age is established by the physiographic position of the terrace between fossiliferous terraces at a higher position and the floodplain below, by the absence on their surfaces of the widespread Peoria Loess of equivalent age, and by the degree of development of the surface soils.

South of the Arkansas River, pre-Bradyan water-laid deposits occur extensively as basin fills, particularly in the Meade Basin, the Ashland-Englewood Basin of Kansas and Oklahoma, and in Harper and Barber Counties, Kansas. These deposits consist largely of sand, with some silt and clay, are gray, tan, brown, and red, are commonly well bedded, and are locally richly fossiliferous (Frye and Hibbard, 1941; Hibbard, 1944; Leonard, 1952). Broad, sloping pediment veneers of this age occur along the Cimarron Valley of southwestern Kansas.

In Texas, from the northern limit southward to Borden County, virtually all valleys emerging from the High Plains contain an early Wisconsinan terrace. This terrace in the Red River Valley has been named the Ambrose Alluvial Terrace (Frye and Leonard, 1963). In addition to widespread valley alluviation, slackwater deposits of early Wisconsinan age occur extensively in Texas as the fillings of basins of various sizes. It is from such a deposit that Evans and Meade (1945) named the Tahoka Formation, and deposits that are probably of this age occur in a still larger lake basin in Howard, Martin, and Glasscock Counties, which was named Lake Lomax by Frye and Leonard (1964). These accumulations of sediment in relatively large basins are dominantly fine to medium sand and silt, locally strongly impregnated with gypsum, but clays and fresh-water limestones also occur in some basins. The deposits are commonly light gray to light tan and are well-bedded to thin-bedded. Locally some red zones, presumably derived from adjacent Permian and Triassic rocks, have been observed. Literally hundreds of shallow depressions on the High Plains surface that range in size from a few to more than 100 acres contain from 2 to 12 ft of pre-Bradyan Wisconsinan silt, clay, and sand. These shallow depression fills are generally gray and, where thick, commonly contain fossil snails.

Wisconsinan sediments occur most extensively in the southern Great Plains region as eolian deposits on the broad upland flats and the high terrace surfaces. In the northern part of this region these surfaces are invariably mantled with Peoria Loess, which gives way to dune sands along the Arkansas River, in the Great Bend Lowland, and in local basin areas (Fig. 4D) and pinches out southward in the panhandle region of Texas. Although much of the High Plains surface in extreme west-central Texas and east-central New Mexico is free of eolian cover, in the southeastern part of the High Plains province in Texas and in southeastern New Mexico, sheet sands and dune sands are again a common upper veneer.

The stratigraphy, paleontology, and petrography of the Peoria Loess has been studied in detail in Kansas (Frye and

Leonard, 1951; Swineford and Frye, 1951). In the northern part of the region here under discussion it has maximum thickness on the upland flats of 20 to 30 ft, consists of coarse silt, and is light yellow-tan, friable, massive, fossiliferous, and calcareous except in the soil at the top and in the basal zone. It becomes progressively thinner and finer southward but is sandy where it grades into eolian sand immediately adjacent to the Arkansas River Valley. In the Texas panhandle adjacent to the Canadian River Valley it again becomes a medium to coarse silt, but it pinches out entirely south of the panhandle. The Peoria Loess has been zoned (Leonard, 1951) on the basis of its fossil snails only near the Nebraska line, and southward in this region it contains an internally homogeneous fauna.

The most significant stratigraphic subdivision of the Peoria Loess of the southern Great Plains is the "Basal Zone." This zone is leached of its carbonate and fossil shells, is organically stained, and has the appearance of a super-attenuated A-horizon above the Sangamon Soil. As it attains a thickness of 2 to 4 ft and is not so altered as the true A-horizon of the Sangamon Soil on which it rests, it clearly represents a slow accumulation of loess on the older soil surface. The sediment was deposited so slowly that it was altered to A-horizon material before it was buried. In Nebraska this zone has been called the upper part of the "Citellus Zone," and in Kansas it was correlated with the Farmdale of Illinois, because the Farmdale was then considered the earliest Wisconsinan. As the Farmdale is now known to have been preceded by significant Wisconsinan events, it may be advisable to consider this basal zone as the time equivalent of both the Altonian and Farmdalian Substages of Illinois (Fig. 3).

The distinctive molluscan assemblages in the pre-Bradyan Wisconsinan deposits are exceeded in numbers and variety within this region only by those in pre-Yarmouthian deposits. However, Wisconsinan faunal assemblages differ from the Kansan in the complete absence of branchiate gastropods and in the predominance of terrestrial pulmonates.

BRADYAN INTERVAL

The Bradyan interval takes its identity from the Brady Soil. The Brady Soil was named from a type locality in the Platte River Valley in western Nebraska where it occurs as a buried soil in the alluvial sequence of the valley. On the uplands it occurs in the top of the Peoria Loess; it is overlain by the post-Bradyan Wisconsinan Bignell Loess. It has been examined in much of western Kansas, where it commonly occurs in the loess sequence, but it also has been studied in an alluvial sequence (Fig. 4H). The Brady Soil of the southern Great Plains is marked nearly everywhere by a well-developed caliche zone (C_{ca}-horizon). It includes representatives of Chernozem, Chestnut, and Brown soils and is readily distinguishable from the older Sangamon Soil by its much shallower depth of development and general lack of red color. Southward into Texas it is rarely observed as a buried soil, but its development is included within the surface soil that has been described on the Ambrose Alluvial Terrace in the Red River Valley. The surface soil on the Lake Lomax deposits in the southernmost High Plains is probably a corollary to the Brady, but it has some of the characters of a Sierozem.

Pre-Bradyan alluviation of valleys was intermittent, and valleys were alternately filled and eroded, but this sequence of events was obscured by the major episode of alluviation, faunally correlated (Frye and Leonard, 1951) with the Shelbyville and younger glacial advances in Illinois, that obliterated any evidence of earlier Wisconsinan terraces. The Bradyan interval is conspicuous because the valleys were subsequently incised far below the level of pre-Bradyan alluviation and because post-Bradyan episodes of deposition have been inadequate to approach again this level. This alluvial history indicates that the Bradyan was an interval of strong and relatively sudden climatic change. This conclusion is substantiated by the striking contrast in molluscan faunal assemblages that inhabited the southern Great Plains immediately before and after the Bradyan interval. Post-Bradyan molluscan assemblages represent only a small fraction of the species occurring in immediately pre-Bradyan deposits and were even more depauperate than the sparse faunas occurring today in the southern Great Plains. Any intervals of relief from the generally rigorous post-Bradyan climate were not of sufficient duration to permit re-entry into the region of any significant number of species.

POST-BRADYAN WISCONSINAN DEPOSITS

Deposits of post-Bradyan Wisconsinan age have been clearly recognized and differentiated within the sequence of loesses on the uplands in the northern part of the region of this report. The Bignell Loess, named from a type locality in western Nebraska, has been widely recognized in western Kansas. It is gray-tan to yellow-tan massive silt, calcareous below the surface soil and sparsely fossiliferous. Shells from the lower part of the Bignell Loess in Doniphan County, Kansas, were dated $12,500 \pm 400$ (W-231) and $12,700 \pm 300$ (W-233). The Bignell rests on the Brady Soil and is commonly less than 10 ft thick. Unlike the Peoria Loess it is not a continuous blanket but occurs as discontinuous patches, at many places in slight topographic sags, over the upland surface. Although minor pulses of loess deposition subsequently may have affected the southern Great Plains region, post-Bignell loesses, if indeed they exist, are so incorporated into the surface soil as to be indistinguishable.

From southern Kansas southward across western Texas, the Bignell Loess has not been recognized, but its stratigraphic position is locally occupied by eolian sands and by thin deposits of silts and fine sands in many shallow High Plains depressions.

Within the alluvial fills of the valleys, the post-Bradyan Wisconsinan deposits in northern and west-central Kansas generally do not form a distinctive terrace but appear to be part of the floodplain complex, being distinguished from the more recent pulses of alluviation by minor buried soils. These young buried soils have B-horizons that are weakly developed or absent. The physiographic relations and weak soils have led to the common practice of mapping the late Wisconsinan as part of the Recent alluvium.

From southern Kansas southward across Texas, however, the late Wisconsinan deposits commonly underlie distinctive low terraces that stand as much as 15 to 20 ft above the levels of the adjacent channels and therefore can more clearly be differentiated from the Recent alluvium underlying the floodplains (although it should be pointed out that these low terraces in many cases are within the reach of major floods). In the Red River Valley, such a terrace has been named the Cooke Alluvial Terrace. In nearly every one of the latest Wisconsinan terraces the deposits consist of sands and silts and lack the basal gravels that typify the deposits of all the older Pleistocene terrace sequences.

In the largest of the present and former lake basins (*e.g.*, Lakes Lomax and Tahoka) dissection or deflation has breached the earlier fills, and late Wisconsinan lacustrine deposits form low terraces along the existing drainageways.

In the southern part of the region the surfaces of these young terraces display a weakly developed soil (locally even lacking a recognizable B-horizon) that is clearly distinguishable from the Brady Soil. The deposits are locally meagerly fossiliferous and at one place an Indian hearth has been found within them.

The boundary between the Wisconsinan and Recent Stages that is used in this report is much less distinctive, both stratigraphically and physiographically, than the boundaries used between all other stages within the Pleistocene. In the southern Great Plains, remote from the direct influences of both continental glaciers and sea-level fluctuations, only the effects of climatic changes are recorded. The boundary can be defined with any feeling of confidence only in the alluvial fills and some basins.

RECENT STAGE

Subdivision of the deposits of the Recent Stage has not been given the critical attention in the southern Great Plains that it has received in Nebraska to the north. It may be stated in general that the Recent (approximately the last 5,000 radiocarbon years) of the southern Great Plains has been characterized by brief minor pulses of erosion alternating with minor episodes of alluviation, and by eolian activity that has caused minor deflation, accumulation and migration of dune sands, and, since the appearance of extensive stock raising and agriculture, regional shallow deflation accompanied by highly localized deposition of fine sands and silts around both natural and artificial obstructions. During this time gully erosion has locally been accentuated and the intermittent pools of the minor valleys, previously retained by grass sod, have largely disappeared.

One or locally two minor soils have been observed in the Recent alluvium of minor valleys, but these have not been correlated widely enough in the region to serve as a basis for a chronology. In the sand-dune tracts (Smith, 1940) recurrent cycles of activity and stabilization have been described, but here again they have not been correlated widely in the region.

On the upland and terrace surfaces where eolian activity has not been effective, soil-forming processes have continued through the Recent. However, the soil profiles, the sediments, and the faunas all suggest that the Recent is a time of relatively adverse climatic conditions that started during

the Bradyan interval and was interrupted only briefly when the episode of late Wisconsinan alluviation and loess deposition occurred.

REFERENCES

Adams, G. I., 1903, Physiographic divisions of Kansas: Kansas Acad. Sci. Trans., v. 18, p. 109-123

American Commission on Stratigraphic Nomenclature, 1961, Code of stratigraphic nomenclature: Amer. Assoc. Petroleum Geologists, v. 45, p. 645-665

Baker, C. L., 1915, Geology and underground waters of the northern Llano Estacado: Univ. Texas Bull. 57, 225 p.

Cragin, F. W., 1896, Preliminary notice of three late Neocene terranes of Kansas: Colorado Coll. Stud., v. 6, p. 53-54

Cummins, W. F., 1891, Report on the geology of northwestern Texas: pt. 1, Stratigraphic geology: Texas Geol. Surv. Ann. Rep. 2, 1890, p. 259-435

Darton, N. H., 1905, Preliminary report on the geology and underground water resources of the central Great Plains: U.S. Geol. Surv. Prof. Pap. 32, 433 p.

Evans, G. L., and Meade, G. E., 1945, Quaternary of the Texas High Plains: Univ. Texas Publ. 4401, p. 485-507

Fenneman, N. M., 1931, Physiography of western United States: New York, McGraw Hill, 534 p.

Frye, J. C., 1946, The High Plains surface in Kansas: Kansas Acad. Sci. Trans., v. 49, p. 71-86

—— 1949, Use of fossil soils in Kansas Pleistocene stratigraphy: Kansas Acad. Sci. Trans., v. 52, p. 478-482

—— 1950, Origin of Kansas Great Plains depressions: Kansas Geol. Surv. Bull. 86, pt. 1, p. 1-20

Frye, J. C., and Hibbard, C. W., 1941, Pliocene and Pleistocene stratigraphy and paleontology of the Meade Basin, southwestern Kansas: Kansas Geol. Surv. Bull. 38, pt. 13, p. 389-424

Frye, J. C., and Leonard, A. B., 1951, Stratigraphy of the late Pleistocene loesses of Kansas: J. Geol., v. 59, p. 287-305

—— 1952, Pleistocene geology of Kansas: Kansas Geol. Surv. Bull. 99, 230 p.

—— 1954, Significant new exposures of Pleistocene deposits at Kirwin, Phillips County, Kansas: Kansas Geol. Surv. Bull. 109, pt. 3, p. 33-48

—— 1957a, Ecological interpretations of Pliocene and Pleistocene stratigraphy in the Great Plains region: Amer. J. Sci., v. 255, p. 1-11 (also, Univ. Texas Bur. Econ. Geol. Rep. Inv. 29)

—— 1957b, Studies of Cenozoic geology along the eastern margin of Texas High Plains, Armstrong to Howard Counties: Univ. Texas Bur. Econ. Geol. Rep. Inv. 32, 62 p.

—— 1959, Correlation of the Ogallala Formation (Neogene) in western Texas with type localities in Nebraska: Univ. Texas Bur. Econ. Geol. Rep. Inv. 39, 46 p.

—— 1963, Pleistocene geology of the Red River Basin in Texas: Univ. Texas Bur. Econ. Geol. Rep. Inv. 49, 48 p.

—— 1964, Relation of Ogallala Formation to the southern High Plains in Texas: Univ. Texas Bur. Econ. Geol. Rep. Inv. 51, 25 p.

Frye, J. C., Leonard, A. B., and Swineford, Ada, 1956,

Stratigraphy of the Ogallala Formation (Neogene) of northern Kansas: Kansas Geol. Surv. Bull. 118, 92 p.

Frye, J. C., Swineford, Ada, and Leonard, A. B., 1948, Correlation of Pleistocene deposits of the central Great Plains with the glacial section: J. Geol., v. 56, p. 501-525

Frye, J. C., and Willman, H. B., 1960, Classification of the Wisconsinan Stage in the Lake Michigan Glacial Lobe: Illinois State Geol. Surv. Circ. 285, 16 p.

Hibbard, C. W., 1944, Stratigraphy and vertebrate paleontology of Pleistocene deposits of southwestern Kansas: Geol. Soc. Amer. Bull., v. 55, p. 707-754

Ho, Tong-yun, 1964, Protein-nitrogen content in fossil shells as a new stratigraphic and paleoecologic indicator: Univ. Kansas Ph.D. thesis, 46 p.

Leonard, A. B., 1948, Invertebrates of the Blancan: Geol. Soc. Amer. Bull., v. 59, p. 589-591

—— 1950, A Yarmouthian molluscan fauna in the mid-continent region of the United States: Univ. Kansas Paleont. Contr., Mollusca Art. 3, 48 p.

—— 1951, Stratigraphic zonation of the Peoria Loess in Kansas: J. Geol., v. 59, p. 323-332

—— 1952, Illinoian and Wisconsinan molluscan faunas in Kansas: Univ. Kansas Paleont. Contr., Mollusca Art. 4, 38 p.

Leonard, A. B., and Frye, J. C., 1962, Pleistocene molluscan faunas and physiographic history of Pecos Valley in Texas: Univ. Texas Bur. Econ. Geol. Rep. Inv. 45, 42 p.

Meade, G .E., 1945, The Blanco fauna: Univ. Texas Pub. 4401, p. 309-556

Moore, R. C., *et al.*, 1951, The Kansas rock column: Kansas Geol. Surv. Bull. 89, 132 p.

Reeves, C. C., Jr., 1963, Origin of Spring Creek beds, Garza and Lynn Counties, Texas: Texas J. Sci., v. 15, p. 322-338

Sellards, E. H., Adkins, W. S., and Plummer, F. B., 1932, The geology of Texas: Univ. Texas Bull. 3232, v. 1, Stratigraphy, 1007 p.

Smith, H. T. U., 1940, Geologic studies in southwestern Kansas: Kansas Geol. Surv. Bull. 34, 212 p.

Swineford, Ada, and Frye, J. C., 1951, Petrography of the Peoria Loess in Kansas: J. Geol., v. 59, p. 306-322

Swineford, Ada, Leonard, A. B., and Frye, J. C., 1958, Petrology of the Pliocene pisolitic limestone in the Great Plains: Kansas Geol. Surv. Bull. 130, pt. 2, p. 97-116

Taylor, D. W., 1960, Late Cenozoic molluscan faunas from the High Plains: U.S. Geol. Surv. Prof. Pap. 337, 94 p.

Willman, H. B., Glass, H. D., and Frye, J. C., 1963, Mineralogy of glacial tills and their weathering profiles in Illinois: pt. I, Glacial tills: Illinois State Geol. Surv. Circ. 347, 55 p.

SUMMARY

The part of the Great Plains discussed here includes the western half of Kansas south of Solomon River, extreme western Oklahoma, northwestern and central-western Texas, and adjacent areas in New Mexico and Colorado. This region is dominated by the High Plains, a plateau produced by late Tertiary alluvial deposits sloping eastward to southeastward and bounded on both east and west by escarpments. The southern Great Plains are underlain by late Paleozoic and Mesozoic rocks, and the late Tertiary Ogallala Formation rests on Permian, Triassic, and Cretaceous rocks in different parts of the region. The top of the Ogallala is marked by soil caliche that has undergone several cycles of brecciation and recementation to form a resistant "caprock."

Quaternary deposits occur as alluvial terrace deposits along the valleys flowing eastward through the High Plains and the dissected area to the east; as fillings of basins of several ages and origins throughout the region; and as eolian deposits of loess and sand on the surface of the upland and of the higher and older terraces. Pleistocene deposits of the southern Great Plains have been correlated with the glacial sequence of the Midwest by use of invertebrate and vertebrate fossils; by distinctive buried soils, particularly the Sangamon Soil that has been recognized almost continuously from the Mississippi Valley to central-western Texas; by comparison of the morphology of buried soils; by the tracing of terraces along valleys and matching terrace sequences from one valley to another; by use of distinctive lithologic types, particularly the petrographically distinctive Pearlette Volcanic Ash; and, to a limited extent, by use of radiocarbon dating.

The Nebraskan, Kansan, Illinoian, and Wisconsinan Stages are all represented by alluvial and basin-fill deposits, and the two youngest stages by extensive eolian deposits. Throughout the region the deposits are named and described as rock-stratigraphic units of relatively local extent; biostratigraphic and morphostratigraphic units have been described locally. The stages that include the major interglacial intervals (Aftonion, Yarmouthian, and Sangamonian) are represented in the southern Great Plains primarily by buried soils that are described as soil-stratigraphic units.

GLACIATION OF THE ROCKY MOUNTAINS *

GERALD M. RICHMOND[1]

DURING QUATERNARY glaciations, individual valley glaciers were widespread throughout the Rocky Mountains from Canada to central New Mexico, and local ice caps existed in a number of ranges. Five Pleistocene glaciations, separated by interglaciations, are recognized. The last glaciation is subdivided into at least three stades, or minor advances, separated by brief interstades. The next to the last glaciation is subdivided into two and locally three advances, separated by interstades which record disappearance of the ice throughout most of the Rocky Mountains. However, the interstades were of lesser duration than major interglaciations.

Final recession of late Pleistocene glaciers was followed by a warm and dry episode known as the Altithermal interval (Antevs, 1948). This in turn was succeeded by the Neoglaciation or "Little Ice Age" (Matthes, 1940), which consisted of two minor episodes of cirque glaciation, each with subsidiary pulsations.

The Rocky Mountains are a complex of many ranges (Fig. 1), most of which trend in a northerly direction. Their crestline constitutes the continental divide separating Pacific and Atlantic watersheds.

In western Montana and Idaho individual ranges tend to be relatively narrow, 7,000 to 9,000 ft (2,100 to 2,700 m) in altitude and separated by broad valleys. In Wyoming and northeastern Utah individual ranges are broad, 11,500 to 12,500 ft (3,400 to 3,700 m) in altitude and separated by large intermontane basins. In Colorado and New Mexico relatively narrow ranges, 12,000 to over 14,000 ft (3,600 to 4,200 m) in altitude are separated by high intermontane basins and broad valleys.

Though tectonically developed during early Tertiary time, the present altitude and relief of the Rocky Mountains results largely from uplift and local volcanism during the middle and late Tertiary and the Quaternary. By the end of middle Pliocene time the mountains were within 1,000 to 2,000 ft (300 to 600 m) of their present altitudes and local relief in the summit areas was about 1,000 to 1,500 ft (300 to 450 m). Widespread rolling hills and gently sloping pediments, the so-called Rocky Mountain erosion surface, then extended from the divides to the depositional surface of Pliocene sediments in the intermontane basins and on the High Plains east of the mountains.

---

* Publication authorized by the Director, U.S. Geological Survey.
[1] U.S. Geological Survey, Federal Center, Denver, Colorado.

The present relief of as much as 2,000 to 5,000 ft (600 to 1,500 m) is a result of uplift and erosion in late Pliocene and middle Pleistocene time, the latter mainly between the second and third major glaciations.

GLACIAL CHRONOLOGY

Evidence for an earlier and a later epoch of glaciation was recognized in several early studies of the Rocky Mountains (Gilbert, 1890; Ball, 1908; Atwood, 1909; Capps, 1909). Subsequently three glaciations were differentiated in many places: Glacier National Park (Alden and Stebinger, 1913; Alden, 1912, 1932), San Juan Mountains (Atwood and Mather, 1912, 1932), Wind River Mountains (Blackwelder, 1915), Teton Mountains (Fryxell, 1930). Most workers correlated the oldest glaciation with the Kansan, the intermediate with the Illinoian or early Wisconsin of Leverett (1939), and the youngest with the Wisconsin. Minor advances within the Wisconsin were first recognized in the Southern Rocky Mountains by Bryan and Ray (1940; Ray, 1940).

Between 1945 and 1960 many studies were made of the glacial chronology of individual valleys and ranges, and a great many local names for deposits in different ranges were proposed because of uncertainties in correlation between ranges. Possible regional correlations have been suggested by Nelson (1954), Holmes and Moss (1955), Flint (1957), Miller (1958), and Williams (1961). The deposits of successive glaciations in the Wind River Mountains, as originally defined by Blackwelder (1915) and modified by subsequent studies, have recently been proposed as a regional standard for correlation (Richmond, 1962a, 1964a).

PRE-BULL LAKE TILL

Blackwelder (1915) defined the "Buffalo glacial stage" from deposits of deeply weathered glacial drift lacking morainal topography and resting on high interstream divides in many parts of the Wind River and Teton Mountains of northwestern Wyoming. Although such deposits have been widely identified in this region (Fryxell, 1930; Horberg, 1938), those in the type area along the Buffalo Fork of the Snake River have morainal form, are not deeply weathered, and have other characteristics similar to deposits of the Bull Lake Glaciation. Elsewhere, along the east flank of the Wind River Mountains, "Buffalo Till" includes tills of three glaciations separated by deeply weathered interglacial soils (Richmond, 1964a). On the south-

Figure 1. Index map of Rocky Mountains, showing locations of areas discussed in text.

Northern Rocky Mountains	1.	Glacier National Park
	2.	Swan River Range
	3.	Salmon River Mountains
	4.	Lemhi Range
Middle Rocky Mountains	5.	Beartooth Mountains
	6.	Yellowstone National Park
	7.	Teton Mountains
	8.	Bighorn Mountains
	9.	Wind River Mountains
	10.	Uinta Mountains
	11.	Wasatch Mountains
Southern Rocky Mountains	12.	Medicine Bow Mountains
	13.	Laramie Range
	14.	Never-Summer Range
	15.	Rocky Mountain National Park
	16.	Front Range
	17.	Mosquito Range
	18.	Sawatch Mountains
	19.	White River Plateau
	20.	San Juan Mountains
	21.	Sangre de Cristo Mountains
	22.	Sierra Blanca
Colorado Plateau	23.	La Sal Mountains
	24.	Aquarius Plateau

west flank of the mountains, some deposits called "Buffalo Till" (Richmond, 1948; Moss, 1951a) are now known to be bouldery fan gravels of Pliocene age. The terms "Buffalo Till" and "Buffalo glacial stage" have therefore been abandoned.

In other parts of the Rocky Mountains certain other deposits, thought to be old tills, have proved to be of different origin. The Cerro Till (Atwood and Mather, 1932), in its type area, is known to be a landslide deposit (R. G. Dickinson and W. R. Hansen, oral communication, 1964) as are also some deposits of the Owl Mountain Till (Eschman, 1955) in the Never Summer Range, Colorado (D. M. Kinney, oral communication, 1962). The type deposit of the Prairie Divide Till (Bryan and Ray, 1940) is a bouldery facies of the Miocene and Pliocene Ogallala Formation (N. M. Denson, oral communication, 1963).

Nevertheless, deeply weathered old Pleistocene till, referred to here as pre-Bull Lake till, exists in many places in the Rocky Mountains. It commonly occurs as sheetlike deposits on interstream divides above or beyond the outer limits of Bull Lake Glaciation, and 1,000 feet (300 m) or more above canyon floors. However, some of the till also forms large, broad, smoothly sloping moraines that locally extend into the canyons.

Most pre-Bull Lake till has a flat to gently rolling surface. Boulders are commonly sparse, except on steep erosional slopes, and tend to be partly buried by younger eolian or colluvial deposits. Most are fractured, and many crystalline rocks are deeply decomposed or exfoliated. Some are fresh, however. In places only the core of a boulder projects above the surface from a larger subsurface base. Other boulders form pedestal rocks, weathered to a narrow neck at ground level. No readily soluble rock such as limestone remains on original depositional surfaces, and sandstone and volcanic rocks are commonly crumbly. Conversely, quartz, chert, and dense siliceous rocks tend to be concentrated at the surface in greater proportion than in the parent till. Striations are extremely rare on stones at the surface and tend to be preserved only on the undersides of dense rocks. Wind-fluted boulders and ventifacts are common on piedmont deposits, and partly peeled thick rinds of desert varnish may occur on some rock types, especially sandstone.

Beneath the weathered zone, the fresh till is much like younger tills, but is commonly more compact and contains more silt and clay. It may also contain a higher proportion of deeply weathered crystalline rocks and grus derived from preglacially weathered outcrops. Striations are rarely preserved but may be present on resistant rock types.

PRE-BULL LAKE SOILS

Pre-Bull Lake soils on pre-Bull Lake deposits are commonly partly or mostly stripped. However, they are locally preserved intact except for the A-horizon. The soils are everywhere very strongly developed as compared to younger soils. In pedalfer facies, the B-horizon tends to be 1.2 to 1.8 m thick, reddish (2.5 *YR* to 7.5 *YR*) in its upper part and yellowish red (7.5 *YR* to 10 *YR*) in its lower part. The material is commonly compact, plastic, completely leached, and clayey. The upper part is more clayey than the lower. Surface profiles tend to have a strongly developed columnar or prismatic structure; buried profiles are commonly structureless. Crystalline rock fragments tend to be partly or wholly decomposed to a crumbly feldspathic grus and to clay. Soluble rock fragments have been wholly or mostly leached, but may be outlined by relict insoluble residues.

In pedocal facies, a Cca-horizon, in which calcium carbonate impregnates the matrix and thickly coats the stones, occurs beneath the B-horizon from which it commonly is sharply separated. Where fully preserved it may be 1.2 to 3 m thick.

At southern latitudes the Cca-horizon may be a well-cemented soil caliche; it is friable at northern latitudes, even though thoroughly impregnated with carbonate.

The boundary between pedocal and pedalfer soils of pre-Bull Lake age is at an altitude of about 5,700 ft (1,700 m) in northern Montana, about 7,500 ft (2,250 m) in central Wyoming, about 8,200 ft (2,460 m) in central Colorado and about 9,000 ft (2,700 m) in northern New Mexico and southeastern Utah.

EVIDENCE FOR THREE PRE-BULL LAKE GLACIATIONS

The existence of more than one pre-Bull Lake glaciation in Wyoming was long suspected (Blackwelder, 1915), and possible evidence for two such glaciations was shown in Glacier National Park, Montana (Alden and Stebinger, 1913). Three superposed pre-Bull Lake tills, separated by deeply weathered interglacial soils, have recently been found in Glacier National Park (Richmond, 1957a), in the Wind River Mountains (Richmond, 1962a, 1964a), and in the La Sal Mountains of southeastern Utah (Richmond, 1957a, 1962b). Exposures at Bull Lake on the east flank of the Wind River Mountains have been designated as the type locality for three pre-Bull Lake glaciations, from oldest to youngest: Washakie Point Glaciation, Cedar

Ridge Glaciation, and Sacagawea Ridge Glaciation. Though the three tills are lithologically distinct at their type locality, they are elsewhere lithologically similar, and indistinguishable except where superposed. In places, the oldest till can be traced to a position on the oldest of three widespread Pleistocene pediments, the intermediate to a lower intermediate pediment, and the youngest to a still lower pediment or outwash terrace. Evidence for the Nebraskan, Kansan, and Illinoian ages of comparable pediments along the east base of the Front Range in Colorado is given by Scott (this volume).

WASHAKIE POINT GLACIATION

The Washakie Point Glaciation is defined from the Washakie Point Till at its type locality at Bull Lake on the east flank of the Wind River Mountains, Wyoming (Richmond, 1964a). The till rests on a Pleistocene pediment that extends basinward from the mouth of a late Pliocene canyon about 1,500 ft (500 m) deep, and outwash from the till caps a rock terrace about 760 ft (228 m) above the present major drainage. At the type locality, the till bears a strongly developed soil and is overlain directly by till of the next younger Cedar Ridge Glaciation.

The oldest of three pre-Bull Lake tills in Glacier National Park and in the La Sal Mountains of southeast Utah has similar stratigraphic relations. Though little is known about this ancient till, its general distribution and physiographic setting suggest that during Washakie Point Glaciation the ice probably occupied shallow cirques along mountain divides, and spread basinward through broad shallow valleys to the heads of canyons. In the Northern Rocky Mountains and in parts of the Middle Rocky Mountains the ice flowed through these canyons and formed piedmont lobes on early Pleistocene pediments at the mountain front. Elsewhere in the Middle Rocky Mountains, and in general throughout the Southern Rocky Mountains, the ice terminated either in the canyons or in the broad shallow valleys upstream from the canyon heads. As far as can be determined, the maximum extent of ice during the Washakie Point Glaciation was somewhat less than during all younger glaciations. When possible subsequent uplift is neglected, the average lower altitude limit of glaciers was at about 5,500 ft (1,650 m) in northern Montana, about 6,500 ft (1,950 m) in central Wyoming, and about 7,500 ft (2,250 m) in southeastern Utah.

CEDAR RIDGE GLACIATION

The Cedar Ridge Glaciation is defined from the Cedar Ridge Till at its type locality at Bull Lake on the east flank of the Wind River Mountains, Wyoming (Richmond, 1962a, 1964a). The till and associated deposits overlie the Washakie Point Till disconformably, and a deeply weathered soil on the till is overlain disconformably by the Sacagawea Ridge Till. Outwash from the Cedar Ridge Till caps a rock terrace 100 ft (33 m) below that on which outwash of Washakie Point Glaciation rests and about 650 ft (195 m) above the present major stream.

In Glacier National Park and in the La Sal Mountains, till of the Cedar Ridge Glaciation also occurs as the intermediate of three superposed pre-Bull Lake tills. It extends onto an intermediate pediment 200 to 300 ft (60 to 90 m) below that on which outwash of Washakie Point age rests. Throughout the Rocky Mountains this intermediate pediment is the most extensive of the three pre-Bull Lake pediments.

The general distribution of glaciers and their physiographic relations during Cedar Ridge time were much like those of Washakie Point Glaciation except that the Cedar Ridge glaciers were more widespread than those of any other Pleistocene glaciation. The glaciers, however, were not confined to canyons as during subsequent glaciations and were probably thinner than subsequent glaciers. The average lower limit of the ice appears to have been a few hundred feet below that of Washakie Point Glaciation.

A volcanic ash having properties like those of the Pearlette Ash Member of the Sappa Formation of late Kansan age in Nebraska is known from many localities in the Rocky Mountains (Powers *et al.*, 1958; Powers, *in* Richmond, 1962b). It commonly occurs in the upper part of gravels or fine-grained alluvium of Cedar Ridge age, but it also occurs in places on the interglacial soil developed on Cedar Ridge deposits.

SACAGAWEA RIDGE GLACIATION

The Sacagawea Ridge Glaciation is defined from the Sacagawea Ridge Till at its type locality at Dinwoody Lake on the east flank of the Wind River Mountains, Wyoming (Richmond, 1962a, 1964a). Here, it overlies the soil developed on the Cedar Ridge Till and is overlain disconformably by Bull Lake Till.

In the type area, outwash gravels of the Sacagawea Ridge Glaciation cap two rock terraces, 270 and 160 ft (80 and 50 m) below the terrace capped by outwash of the Cedar Ridge Glaciation, and 500 and 380 ft (150 and 115 m) above present major drainage. Though this suggests the possibility of two advances of the ice during Sacagawea Ridge Glaciation, no evidence for more than one advance has been recognized in the till.

The Sacagawea Ridge Till forms broad mature moraines which, though locally overlapping older deposits on interstream divides, extend into the canyons. They outline piedmont lobes on the youngest of three pre-Bull Lake pediments at the mountain fronts in the Northern Rocky Mountains and in parts of the Middle Rocky Mountains, but in the Southern Rocky Mountains they commonly terminate on remnants of old valley floors within the canyons. An example is the deeply weathered end moraine at the type locality of the Durango Till in the San Juan Mountains, Colorado (Fig. 1), which lies within a canyon on a rock bench 280 ft (85 m) above the stream (Atwood and Mather, 1932). Other such deposits are reported in the Sawatch Range, Colorado (Nelson, 1954), in the La Sal Mountains, Utah (Richmond, 1962b), and in the Sangre de Cristo Mountains, New Mexico (Richmond, 1963).

The Sacagawea Ridge Glaciation differed in its general distribution and physiographic setting from older glaciations in that the ice was in many places confined to canyons cut or extensively deepened during the Cedar Ridge–Sacagawea Ridge interglaciation. Most present major drainage courses were established by the end of this interglacia-

tion; many resulted from piracy during the canyon erosion. Confinement of the glaciers to canyons caused them to be thicker than during preceding glaciations. The ice also extended slightly farther from the cirques than during any other Pleistocene glaciation. The end moraines commonly lie a short distance downstream from those of the next younger glaciation, the Bull Lake. The average lower limit of the ice was probably about 5,000 ft (1,500 m) in northern Montana, 6,000 ft (1,800 m) in central Wyoming, 8,000 ft (2,400 m) in southern Colorado and southeastern Utah, and 10,000 ft (3,000 m) in central New Mexico.

PRE-BULL LAKE INTERGLACIATIONS

The climate of all three pre-Bull Lake interglaciations, as reflected in the character and degree of development of the soils separating the deposits of the successive glaciations, appears to have been about the same. In Glacier National Park buried red clayey pedalfer profiles, 1.8 to 2.4 m thick, occur on each of the three pre-Bull Lake tills at an altitude of 6,000 ft (1,800 m). The highest relict profiles are preserved at about 8,000 ft (2,400 m), which is above most cirque floors. Similar conditions prevail in the La Sal Mountains, Utah, where pre-Bull Lake pedalfer soils, as much as 2.5 m thick, are preserved as high as 10,500 ft (3,150 m) (Richmond, 1962b), which is also above the altitude of most cirque floors. Pre-Bull Lake cirques were therefore not only free of ice during the interglaciations, but the climate probably was warmer and wetter than today at some time during the latter half of the soil-forming maxima. The duration of these conditions must also have been sufficient for the development of red clayey soils that are 3 to 4 times thicker than the postglacial yellowish brown, slightly clayey soils on similar materials on gentle slopes at the same altitude. Pedocal soils are formed on deposits of all three pre-Bull Lake glaciations at altitudes below about 5,700 ft (1,710 m) in Glacier Park to altitudes below about 9,000 ft (2,700 m) in the La Sal Mountains. This limit is about 1,200 ft (360 m) above that of postglacial soils, and it strongly suggests that the conditions during carbonate precipitation were warmer and drier than today. The fact that the concentration of calcium carbonate in these old soils is many times greater than in postglacial soils also suggests a long interval of soil formation.

BULL LAKE GLACIATION

The Bull Lake Glaciation is defined from the Bull Lake Till, which forms a series of broad, smoothly sloping moraines at Bull Lake on the east flank of the Wind River Mountains, Wyoming (Blackwelder, 1915). At this locality the Bull Lake Till overlies the Sacagawea Ridge Till and is overlapped by rough hummocky moraines of the Pinedale Glaciation.

The Bull Lake Till commonly forms two moraines marking two stades of glaciation; in a few places three moraines have been recognized (Richmond, 1964a). These moraines are graded to separate outwash gravels that cap rock terraces 200, 100, and 80 ft (60, 30, and 25 m) above the major drainage at Bull Lake and indicate three advances of the valley glacier.

Moraines of the Bull Lake Glaciation are commonly large

and have smooth slopes. End moraines are broadly breached and do not retain lakes. Lateral moraines are deeply notched by tributary streams. Kettles are commonly filled with colluvium, locally by eolian deposits, and rarely contain water. Boulders are numerous at the surface of the moraines, especially in the Middle and Southern Rocky Mountains, but tend to be sparse in the Northern Rocky Mountains. They are, however, everywhere less abundant than on moraines of the Pinedale Glaciation. Many boulders are broken or exfoliated, and many are stained to a depth of about a centimeter. Limestone fragments tend to display evidence of solution. Wind-polished or faceted stones are locally common on piedmont moraines.

Bull Lake Till tends to be compact and to contain more silt and clay than Pinedale Till. Deeply rotted boulders are less common in the fresh till than in pre-Bull Lake tills, but they are more common than in Pinedale Till. Correlation of some locally named deposits of the Bull Lake Glaciation in various parts of the Rocky Mountains is shown in Table 1.

During Bull Lake Glaciation some individual glaciers were 50 to 90 miles (80 to 145 km) long. However, most of these resulted from special circumstances of ice accumulation or topographic setting. For example, ice flowed east from the mountains in Glacier National Park for 50 miles (80 km) because of the eastward diversion of cap ice that accumulated west of the continental divide (Richmond *et al.*, this volume). The great extent of ice in the valley of the Yellowstone River, Montana (Horberg, 1940), and in the valley of the Animas River in the San Juan Mountains, Colorado (Atwood and Mather, 1932), was due to the addition of cap ice lateral to the main valley glacier. More commonly, the maximum length of Bull Lake glaciers was 30 to 40 miles (50 to 65 km) in northern Montana, 20 to 25 miles (30 to 40 km) in western Wyoming, 10 to 15 miles (15 to 25 km) in Colorado, and 2 to 5 miles (3 to 8 km) in New Mexico and southern Utah. The average altitude of end moraines of Bull Lake glaciers is shown in Figure 2. Extensive ice caps occurred in the mountains of west-central Montana, the Salmon River Mountains, the Yellowstone-Beartooth Plateau, the Wind River Mountains, the White River Plateau, the San Juan Mountains, and the Aquarius Plateau (Fig. 1). Small caps abounded elsewhere. The average lower limit of ice caps is shown in Figure 3.

In north-central Montana, glaciers from Glacier National Park merged with the continental ice sheets at a point about 25 miles (40 km) east of the mountains, just west of longitude 113°. Here boulders of crystalline rocks, derived from the Canadian Shield, appear in continental till of Bull Lake age. During Bull Lake maxima the continental ice extended south from the Canadian boundary along the east front of the mountains at longitude 112°25'. Here it enclosed a lake, Glacial Lake Cutbank, at an altitude of 3,900 ft (1,190 m), over whose deposits it subsequently advanced. At about latitude 47°50' N. the ice margin turned eastward across the High Plains (Lemke *et al.*, this volume).

In the western part of Yellowstone National Park, a thick obsidian-rhyolite flow overlies ice-scoured surfaces and till of the late stage of Bull Lake Glaciation (Richmond, 1964c). A large plain of obsidian sand heading against the

flow, rather than conforming to existing drainage, suggests that the eruption may have taken place while Bull Lake ice still lay in the area.

The oldest C^{14} dates recorded from the Rocky Mountain region are derived from lake deposits correlative with the late stage of Bull Lake Glaciation. Peat 4 m below the top of lake beds near American Falls, Idaho, yielded an age of >42,000 years (W-292) (Trimble and Carr, 1961). The lake beds are overlain by deposits of a flood from Lake Bonneville in late Bull Lake time. These deposits in turn are cut by terrace gravels that contain mollusk shells 29,700 ± 1,000 years old (W-731). Other dates ranging from more than 25,000 to more than 37,000 years (Broecker and Kulp, 1957) have also been obtained from silt in southern Alberta, Canada, that lies beneath till of the last major glaciation and above an older till considered to be of early Wisconsin (Horberg, 1952, 1954) and late Bull Lake age (Richmond, 1960a).

BULL LAKE–PINEDALE INTERGLACIATION AND BULL LAKE
NONGLACIAL INTERVALS

A mature zonal soil is developed at the surface of deposits of the Bull Lake Glaciation and is overlain by Pinedale deposits in many places. A similar soil also occurs between the tills and outwash deposits of the first and second Bull Lake advances in Glacier National Park (Richmond, 1960a), in the Wind River Mountains (Richmond, 1964a), in the Wasatch Mountains (Richmond, 1964b), and in the La Sal Mountains (Richmond, 1962b). No soil has been found between tills or outwash of the second and third advances, but three similarly mature zonal soils are developed in and on stratigraphic successions of alluvial deposits of Bull Lake age in the San Juan Mountains, Colorado, and in loess of Bull Lake age on the Columbia Plateau (Richmond *et al.*, this volume).

The soil separating Bull Lake and Pinedale deposits has long been considered interglacial (Blackwelder, 1915). The first soil to be recognized between deposits of Bull Lake glacial advances was considered interstadial (Richmond, 1962b) because it appeared less strongly developed than that separating Bull Lake and Pinedale deposits. However, increasing knowledge of soils in Bull Lake deposits demonstrates their similarity in degree of development to the Bull Lake–Pinedale soil and indicates that the three soil-forming intervals were alike. Their mature zonal character further shows that these intervals were of greater duration than were interstades of Pinedale Glaciation. Distribution of the soils in cirques and summit areas suggests deglaciation of the Rocky Mountains, at least as far north as Glacier National Park. The Bull Lake Glaciation therefore may be subdivisible ultimately into two or possibly three glaciations separated by interglaciations of lesser duration than pre-Bull Lake interglaciations. In the absence of such redefinition, the term "nonglacial interval" is applied for purposes of this paper to intervals separating advances of Bull Lake Glaciation.

Soils that occur on and in Bull Lake deposits are characterized by reddish brown (5 YR) to brown (7.5 YR) B-horizons, 0.3 to 1.2 m thick, that contain sufficient illuviated clay to be slightly plastic. They tend to have a

TABLE 1

Correlation of Some Quaternary Glacial Deposits in the Rocky Mountains
(xxxxx = Moraine recognized by the present writer)

Locality / Reference	Washakie Point Glaciation	Cedar Ridge Glaciation	Sacagawea Ridge Glaciation	Bull Lake Glaciation (early stade)	Bull Lake Glaciation (late stade)	Pinedale Glaciation (early stade)	Pinedale Glaciation (middle stade)	Pinedale Glaciation (late stade)	Temple Lake Stade (Neoglaciation)	Gannett Peak Stade (Neoglaciation)
Wind River Mtns., Wyo. Richmond (1964a)	Washakie Point Glaciation	Cedar Ridge Glaciation	Sacagawea Ridge Glaciation	early stade	late stade	early stade	middle stade	late stade	Temple Lake Stade	Gannett Peak Stade
Glacier Natl. Park, Mont. Horberg (1954)		Kennedy drift		Early Wisconsin mountain drift		Late Wisconsin mountain drift				
Richmond (1960a)	early Pleistocene	early or middle Pleistocene	middle Pleistocene	Bull Lake Glaciation — early stade	late stade	Pinedale Glaciation — early stade	middle stade	late stade	Temple Lake advance	historic advance
Lemhi Range, Idaho Dort (1962)			Buffalo outwash	Bull Lake moraines		Pinedale moraines			Temple Lake moraine	Little Ice Age moraine
Yellowstone Plateau Richmond (1964c)	Pre-Bull Lake glaciation			Bull Lake Glaciation — early stade	late stade	Pinedale Glaciation — early stade	middle stade	late stade	Neoglaciation	
Teton Mountains, Wyo. Fryxell (1930)	Buffalo stage			Bull Lake stage — early stade	late stade	Pinedale stage — early stade	middle stade	late stade	Temple Lake Stade	Gannett Peak Stade
Uinta Mtns., Wyo. Bradley (1936)	Little Dry stage			Blacks Fork stage xxxxx	xxxxx	Smith Fork stage		xxxxx	xxxxx	xxxxx
Medicine Bow Mtns., Wyo. Ray (1940); Mears (1953)			xxxxx	Wisconsin I xxxxx		Wisconsin II xxxxx		Wisconsin III & IV xxxxx	xxxxx	xxxxx
Never Summer Range, Colo. Eschman (1955)	Owl Mountain substage		xxxxx	Gould substage xxxxx		Silver Creek substage xxxxx		American Lakes substage	Cirque moraines	
Cache la Poudre River, Colo. Ray (1940)			xxxxx	Wisconsin I (pre-Home)	Wisconsin II (Home)	Wisconsin III (Corral Creek) xxxxx		Wisconsin IV (Long Draw) xxxxx	Wisconsin V (Sprague)	xxxxx
Rocky Mtn. Natl. Park, Colo. Ives (1938)				Stillwater stage		River stage	Arapahoe stage	Monarch stage	Outer recent moraines	Inner recent moraines
Ray (1940)				Wisconsin I		Wisconsin II		Wisconsin III & IV	Wisconsin V	
Jones and Quam (1944)			Old Moraine remnants	Park Border moraines		Upper Valley moraines				

Source	Neoglaciation — Gannett Peak Stade	Neoglaciation — Temple Lake Stade	Pinedale Glaciation (Wisconsin stage) — late stade	Pinedale Glaciation — middle stade	Pinedale Glaciation — early stade	Bull Lake Glaciation (pre-Wisconsin stage) — late stade	Bull Lake Glaciation — early stade	Pre-Bull Lake glaciation
Richmond (1960b)	Neoglaciation		Pinedale Glaciation (Wisconsin stage)			Bull Lake Glaciation (pre-Wisconsin stage)		Pre-Bull Lake glaciation
Mosquito Range, Colo. Singewald (1950)	Neoglaciation		Wisconsin stage			pre-Wisconsin stage		
Sawatch Range, Colo. Ray (1940)	xxxxx / Wisconsin V	xxxxx / Wisconsin IV	Alma substage / Wisconsin IV	Briscoe substage / Wisconsin IIb and III	Fairplay substage	Bigelow substage / xxxxx / Wisconsin IIa	Thomasville substage / xxxxx / Wisconsin I	
Nelson (1954)	xxxxx	Chapman Gulch Glaciation / xxxxx	Hellgate upvalley recessional	Hellgate substage / xxxxx	Ivanhoe substage / xxxxx	Bigelow substage / xxxxx	Thomasville substage / xxxxx	Lime Creek stage
White River Plateau, Colo.	xxxxx	xxxxx	xxxxx	xxxxx	xxxxx	xxxxx	xxxxx	
San Juan Mtns., Colo. Atwood and Mather (1932)				Durango stage		other Durango moraines	Type Durango moraine / xxxxx	Cerro Till (but type deposit is landslide)
Wasatch Mtns., Utah Richmond (1964b)	xxxxx	xxxxx	Pinedale Glaciation — late stade / xxxxx	middle stade / xxxxx	early stade / xxxxx	Bull Lake Glaciation — late stade / xxxxx	early stage / xxxxx	Pre-Bull Lake glaciation
Aquarius Plateau, Utah Flint and Denny (1958)	Gannett Peak Stade	Temple Lake Stade / Rock glaciers	Blind Lake Drift	Donkey Creek Drift	Donkey Creek Drift	Carcass Creek Drift	Carcass Creek Drift	
La Sal Mtns., Utah Richmond (1962b)	Gold Basin Formation — upper member	lower member	Beaver Basin Formation — upper member		lower member	Placer Creek Formation — upper member	lower member	Harpole Mesa Formation — upper member / middle member / lower member
Sangre de Cristo Mtns. (Lake Peak), N. Mex. Ray (1940)			Wisconsin IV	Wisconsin III	Wisconsin III	Wisconsin II	Wisconsin II	Pre-Bull Lake glaciation
Richmond (1963)	Neoglaciation	Temple Lake Stade	Pinedale Glaciation — late stade	middle stade	early stade	Bull Lake Glaciation — late stade	early stade	
Sierra Blanca, N. Mex. Richmond (1963)	—	Temple Lake Stade	Pinedale Glaciation — late stade	middle stade	early stade	Bull Lake Glaciation — late stade	early stade	

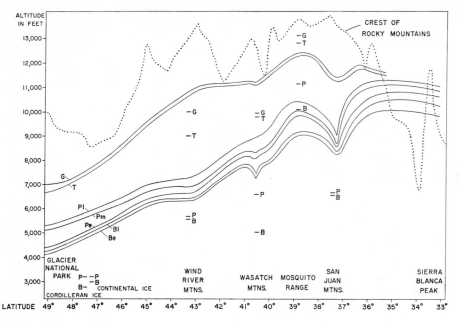

Figure 2. Average altitudes of late Pleistocene and Recent moraines in the Rocky Mountains. Be, Bl: early and late stades of Bull Lake Glaciation; Pe, Pm, Pl: early, middle, and late stades of Pinedale Glaciation; T, G: Temple Lake and Gannett Peak Stades of Neoglaciation; —B, —P, —T, —G: lowest or highest moraines at specific localities.

moderately developed, subangular blocky structure. At more northerly latitudes the color may be yellowish brown (10 *YR*). The Cca-horizon of pedocal soils ranges from 0.3 to 1.8 m thick. On similar parent materials they are thickest and contain most carbonate at southern latitudes and lower altitudes. The carbonate is commonly soft and powdery, but it may cement the matrix and have a distinct platy structure. Coatings on rock fragments are commonly ⅛ inch (3 mm) or more thick, especially on the undersides. In most areas, the soils grade from Sierozems or Brown soils at lower altitudes through Brown Forest soils or Prairie soils, to Brown Podzolic soils at higher altitudes (Thorp, 1931; Richmond, 1962b).

The average altitude of the pedalfer-pedocal boundary is at about 5,200 ft (1,560 m) in north-central Montana, about 7,000 ft (2,100 m) in west-central Wyoming, about 7,500 ft (2,250 m) in central Colorado, and 8,500 to 9,000 ft (2,550 to 2,700 m) in southeastern Utah and central New Mexico. In the southern part of the Rocky Mountains these soils are preserved over 60% to 80% of the area of Bull Lake deposits. In the northern part they are preserved over only 10% to 20% owing largely to erosion by solifluction in Pinedale time.

PINEDALE GLACIATION

The Pinedale Glaciation is defined from the Pinedale Till (Blackwelder, 1915), which forms a series of rough hummocky moraines around several glacial lakes near the town of Pinedale at the southwest base of the Wind River Mountains, Wyoming. At this locality, and also at Bull Lake, these moraines rest on, breach, or lie just upvalley from those of Bull Lake age.

Throughout the Rocky Mountains the Pinedale Till commonly forms three groups of moraines, each related to different outwash deposits. At least three stades of glaciation are therefore indicated.

Moraines of the Pinedale Glaciation are steep, irregular, and commonly but not everywhere smaller than those of the Bull Lake Glaciation. Kettles are well preserved and many contain water at least seasonally. End moraines are narrowly breached by erosion; lateral moraines are but little modified. End moraines of the early stade rarely retain a lake. Those of the middle and late stades commonly retain lakes if situated on sufficiently flat valley floors.

Boulders are very numerous on the surface of the moraines. Most are fresh, few are fractured, and some may be striated. Wind-polished or wind-grooved stones may be present locally on piedmont moraines.

The fresh till tends to be less compact and more sandy than Bull Lake Till. Deeply rotted rock fragments are less common than in Bull Lake Till.

Correlation of some locally named deposits of the Pinedale Glaciation in various parts of the Rocky Mountains is shown in Table 1.

In north-central Montana and western Wyoming moraines of the early and middle stades outline large piedmont lobes at the mountain fronts or lie at the mouths of canyons. They record glaciers from 10 to about 40 miles (15 to 70 km) long. In a few places they completely overlap moraines of Bull Lake age. In western Montana, northern Idaho, and most of Colorado the moraines lie somewhat higher in the canyons and record glaciers 5 to 20 miles (8-35 km) long. In these places they also lie just back of moraines of the Bull Lake Glaciation or form narrow tongues breaching those moraines as in Rocky Mountain National Park, Colorado (Richmond, 1960b). In New Mexico and southern Utah, Pinedale moraines lie well up in the canyons and locally are 1 to 2 miles (1.5 to 3 km) upstream from moraines of the Bull Lake Glaciation. They record glaciers less than 1 to about 5 miles (1 to 8 km) in length.

Moraines of the early and middle stades commonly lie fairly close together. Those of the late stade lie at some distance upvalley, and tend to occur just below the cirques in the Southern Rocky Mountains. The average altitudes of end moraines of Pinedale Glaciation are shown in Figure 2.

Ice caps formed during Pinedale Glaciation in the same places as during Bull Lake Glaciation, but they were of somewhat lesser extent. Their lower limits have not yet been clearly distinguished from those of Bull Lake ice caps (Fig. 3).

In north-central Montana, Pinedale glaciers from the mountains in Glacier National Park merged at the east foot of the mountains with continental ice bearing crystalline erratics from the Canadian Shield. The mountain ice was, in fact, displaced, for mountain till of the early stage of Pinedale Glaciation is overlain conformably by continental drift of early Pinedale age at several places (Alden, 1932; Horberg, 1954). The outermost end moraine formed by alpine ice grades into that of the continental ice sheet bearing crystalline erratics just west of longitude 113°10′ along the divide south of the Canadian boundary, about 10 miles (16 km) east of the mountain front. This transition occurs 15 miles (25 km) closer to the mountains than in end moraines of Bull Lake age.

The outermost continental end moraines of Pinedale age extend southward from longitude 113° at the Canadian boundary along a line somewhat farther east than during Bull Lake Glaciation. As in Bull Lake time, Pinedale ice enclosed Glacial Lake Cutbank, which was more extensive even though 175 ft (55 m) lower (3,725 ft [1,130 m] altitude) than during Bull Lake time.

At the western edge of Yellowstone National Park, moraines of early Pinedale age extend across and along the margins of thick obsidian rhyolite flows that overlie icescoured surfaces and till of the Bull Lake Glaciation (Richmond, 1964c).

Very few C^{14} dates are available from Pinedale deposits and none are from till. Dates from deposits of Lake Bonneville, considered correlative with the early and middle stages of Pinedale Glaciation, range from 25,400 to 11,300 years B.P. (Broecker and Orr, 1958; Rubin and Alexander, 1958, 1960). One lake rise to the Bonneville shoreline,

dated at 23,150 ± 1,000 years B.P. (L-363-H) (Broecker and Orr, 1958), may approximate the maximum of the early stage. The interstade separating the middle and late stages may be dated from marl and snails in kettles in early and middle Pinedale outwash and from charcoal in occupation sites of Folsom man that separate middle and late Pinedale alluvial deposits. These dates range from 11,330 ± 330 (W-914) to 8,800 ± 250 years B.P. (W-393). Deglaciation was complete at lower altitudes by about 7,280 ± 400 years B.P. (W-775) and at higher altitudes by about 6,190 ± 300 years B.P. (M-956) according to age determinations on samples from the base of postglacial peat deposits.

THE ALTITHERMAL INTERVAL AND PINEDALE INTERSTADES

An immature zonal soil is developed at the surface of deposits of the Pinedale Glaciation. The major features of this soil formed during the Altithermal interval, as is indicated by the presence of the soil on deposits of late Pinedale age beneath deposits formed during Neoglaciation. However, the slightly more strongly developed aspects of the soil on deposits of the early and middle stages reflect a longer period of weathering on these deposits, and include the effects of environment during Pinedale interstades.

Soils of Altithermal age in the Northern Rocky Mountains range in character from Chernozems or Prairie soils at lower altitudes upward through Brown soils and Brown Forest soils to Brown Podzolic soils and, locally, true Podzols at higher altitudes. In the Southern Rocky Mountains, Sierozems may be present at lower altitudes, and true Podzols are rare. The pedalfer-pedocal boundary is about 200 ft (60 m) lower than for soils formed during the Bull Lake–Pinedale interglaciation.

The soils are characterized by yellowish brown (10 *YR*) B-horizons, 0.3 to 0.6 m thick, that display very little illuviation and weak to moderate structural development. In pedocals, the carbonate does not impregnate the matrix thoroughly and forms only thin coatings on pebbles and cobbles. Cca-horizons are commonly 0.3 to 0.6 m thick.

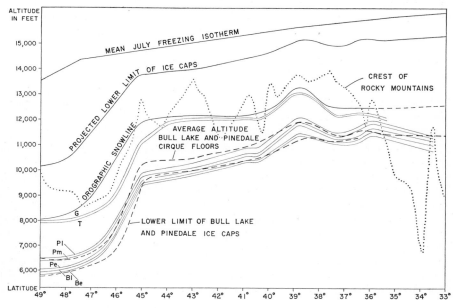

Figure 3. Modern and late Pleistocene climatic data in the Rocky Mountains. Pleistocene orographic snowlines based on average median altitude between terminal moraine and cirque headwall for individual glaciations: Be, Bl: early and late stages of Bull Lake Glaciation; Pe, Pm, Pl: early, middle, and late stages of Pinedale Glaciation; T, G: Temple Lake and Gannett Peak Stades of Neoglaciation.

Throughout western Montana lenses of volcanic ash derived from an eruption of Mount Mazama, Oregon (Wilcox, this volume), occur in or on the soil formed during the Altithermal interval. Numerous C[14] dates from organic matter above and below the ash in Oregon and Washington show its age to be about 6,600 years B.P., thus it was formed at about the beginning of the Altithermal interval.

The character of the environment during the interstade separating the early and middle stades of Pinedale Glaciation is not well known. Recession of the glaciers ranged from almost none to a few kilometers, and it appears to have been dependent more on local orographic conditions than on latitude.

In a few places, as in Glacier National Park and in the La Sal Mountains, Utah, a very weak azonal soil or layer of gray alluvial silty clay separates outwash gravels of the early and middle stades and shows that deposition of coarse outwash ceased at least for a short period of time. Elsewhere, erosion of terraces that separate outwash deposits of the early and middle stades also shows that deposition of coarse outwash ceased temporarily. The amount of erosion separating the deposits is locally as much as 60 ft (20 m).

The interstade separating deposits of the middle and late stades of Pinedale Glaciation is characterized by as much as 15 miles (25 km) of recession for larger glaciers of the Northern and Middle Rocky Mountains and from 10 miles (16 km) to less than a mile (1.5 km) for glaciers in the Southern Rocky Mountains. A weak azonal soil or slack-water alluvial deposits also separate the outwash deposits in places. The dark gray iron-stained character of the soil suggests a cool wet floodplain environment. The interval may be approximately dated from lenses of volcanic ash that occur on middle Pinedale deposits beneath deposits of late Pinedale and Neoglaciation age. The ash is derived from Glacier Peak, Washington (Powers and Wilcox, 1964), and in eastern Washington it occurs with shells having a C[14] age of 12,000 B.P. (Fryxell, 1965).

The pedalfer-pedocal boundary of Pinedale interstadial buried soils is poorly known, but its altitude appears to be somewhat lower than that of the soil of the Altithermal interval.

NEOGLACIATION

Deposits of two minor glacier advances have formed in the cirques of the Rocky Mountains since the end of the Altithermal interval (Richmond, 1962b). Together they represent the "Little Ice Age" of Matthes (1939, 1940), or the Neoglaciation (Moss, 1951a).

Temple Lake Stade. The older advance is the Temple Lake Stade, named from a moraine in the north-facing cirque of Temple Peak in the southern part of the Wind River Mountains (Hack, 1943; Moss, 1951a, b), and first considered to be a late advance of the Pinedale Glaciation. Moraines of the Temple Lake Stade occur only as far south as latitude 35°40′ in the Sangre de Cristo Mountains, New Mexico. Their average altitude is shown in Figure 2.

The moraines are 6 to 18 m high, rough, and bouldery. They support a tundra vegetation and small stands of scrub spruce. Most are 1 to 3 km from the cirque headwall. The till is fresh, sandy, and very bouldery. Striated stones are rare.

A weak azonal soil, commonly 30 to 45 cm thick, is developed on the till. Rock glaciers or protalus ramparts occur in place of moraines of the Temple Lake Stade in many parts of the Rocky Mountains. Locally, as in Rocky Mountain National Park (Richmond, 1960b), two moraines represent minor pulsations of the ice.

Alluviation during the Temple Lake Stade resulted in two depositional units separated by a minor erosional unconformity. C[14] dates from charcoal derived from Paleo-Indian hearth sites associated with a pre-pottery stone culture in the alluvium suggest deposition of the lower unit between about 3,100 (W-621) and 1,800 years B.P. (W-802) and deposition of the upper unit between about 1,800 and 1,000 years B.P. (W-616).

Gannett Peak Stade. The younger advance of Neoglaciation is called the Gannett Peak Stade from a moraine at the foot of Gannett Glacier east of Gannett Peak in the northern part of the Wind River Mountains, Wyoming (Richmond, 1957b, 1960b). Moraines of this stade are in front of existing glaciers or in recently deglaciated cirques as far south as latitude 36°30′ in the Sangre de Cristo Mountains, New Mexico. Their average altitude is shown in Figure 2. The southernmost active glaciers occur in Rocky Mountain National Park at latitude 40°15′.

Moraines of the Gannett Peak Stade are fresh, rough, and bouldery; they bear no soil, and support no vegetation except pioneer plants on their outer slopes and sparse lichen on the boulders. The moraines are in cirques upslope from those of the Temple Lake Stade. Locally, two or three are present. Historic records show that glaciers abutted these moraines as recently as about 1850. How much older some may be can only be inferred by analogy with moraines in the Canadian Rocky Mountains, the Cascade Mountains, and Alaska, where sequences of moraines dated by tree-ring analyses indicate advances in the 16th, 17th, 18th, and 19th centuries (Sigafoos and Hendricks, 1961; Mathews, 1951; Lawrence, 1948; Heusser, 1956, 1957). Of these, the advance to the 1850 moraine was in general the most extensive. It is possible that some moraines that formed during the 16th and 17th centuries may have been mapped as deposits of Temple Lake age in the Rocky Mountains.

CORRELATION

Correlation of some glacial deposits within the Rocky Mountain region is shown in Table 1. The glacial advances and recessions appear to have been nearly synchronous with the rises and falls of Lake Bonneville, the high-lake maxima shortly following the glacial maxima (Morrison, 1965). Physical correlation of the moraines and lake deposits can be made only at Little Cottonwood and Bells Canyons, near Salt Lake City, Utah (Richmond, 1964b). Here, outwash of the early and late stades of Bull Lake Glaciation interfinger with the deposits of two high stands of Lake Bonneville, the latter of which coincided with the Bonneville shoreline. The soil formed during the Bull Lake–Pinedale interglaciation is developed on these deposits. Younger deposits of at least one and possibly two high stands of the lake at the Bonneville shoreline, and the fall of the lake to the Provo shoreline, are correlated

TABLE 2

Correlation of the Glaciations of the Rocky Mountains with those of the Midcontinent Region and the Alps of Europe

Approximate age B.P.	Alps of Europe		Approximate age B.P.	ROCKY MOUNTAINS Richmond (this paper)			Approximate age B.P.	Midcontinent Region After Frye & Willman (1960)	
	Post-glacial		800 — 900 — 4,000 —	Neoglaciation	Gannett Peak Stade			RECENT	
					Interstade				
					Temple Lake Stade				
6,500 —			6,500 —	Altithermal interval			5,000 —		
	Daun Gschnitz Schlern			Pinedale	Late stade				VALDERAN SUBSTAGE
11,000 —			10,000 —		Interstade		11,000 —		
	Allerød Interval		12,000 —						TWOCREEKAN SUBSTAGE
	Main Würm	Two Recessional moraines		Glaciation	Middle stade		12,500 —		WOODFORDIAN SUBSTAGE several advances
		Interstade			Interstade				
		Outer moraine			Early stade		22,000 —		FARMDALIAN SUBSTAGE
29,000 —			25,000 —	Interglaciation			28,000 —		
34,000 —	Paudorf Interval		32,000 —						ALTONIAN SUBSTAGE
45,000 —	Early Würm		45,000 —	Bull Lake	Late stade	2nd episode			
	Göttweig Interval					Nonglacial interval			
53,000 —						1st episode	50,000 to 70,000 estimated		
	Riss	Riss II		Glaciation	Nonglacial interval				SANGAMONIAN STAGE
		Nonglacial interval							
		Riss I			Early stade				
	M/R Interglaciation			Interglaciation					
	Mindel Glaciation	II		Sacagawea Ridge Glaciation					ILLINOIAN STAGE
		I							
	G/M Interglaciation			Interglaciation					YARMOUTHIAN STAGE
	Günz Glaciation	II		xxxxxx(1) Cedar Ridge Glaciation					xxxxxx(1) KANSAN STAGE
		I							
	D/G Interglaciation			Interglaciation					AFTONIAN STAGE
	Donau Glaciation	III		Washakie Point Glaciation					NEBRASKAN STAGE
		II							
		I							

(1) Pearlette Ash Member of Sappa Formation in Midcontinent Region and petrographic equivalent in Rocky Mountains

indirectly with the early and middle stades of the Pinedale Glaciation (Richmond, 1964b).

Possible correlation of Rocky Mountain glaciations with those of the midcontinent region (Frye and Willman, 1960) are shown in Table 2. Radiocarbon dates are of assistance in relating events younger than 45,000 years, though several problems of correlation of particular units within both Bull Lake and Pinedale deposits remain. The characteristics of pre-Wisconsin soils in the midcontinent region and of pre-Bull Lake soils in the Rocky Mountains serve as physical markers for the older units. The Pearlette Ash Member of the Sappa Formation in Kansas and Nebraska and its petrographic equivalent in the Rocky Mountains are distinctive markers of late-Kansan age.

Correlation of Rocky Mountain glaciations with those of the European Alps (Table 2) is based on observations of Alpine glacial stratigraphy made by the writer during field trips with many European scientists in 1960-1961. Radiocarbon dates, geomorphology, and stratigraphy all support correlation of events of Pinedale Glaciation with those of the Main Würm.

The soil developed during the Mindel/Riss Interglaciation, which the writer believes correlative with the Krems Soil of the Austrian loess, is the best stratigraphic marker for all regions in the Alps. Its characteristics are remarkably similar to those of pedalfer facies of the youngest pre-Bull Lake soil of the Rocky Mountains. Riss moraines are morphologically like moraines of the Bull Lake Glaciation, and the soil on Riss Till is much more strongly developed than that on tills of Main Würm age. No end moraines of the Early Würm advance have been identified; but C[14] dates from deposits called Early Würm in the Alpine Foreland and in Switzerland that range in age from about 45,000 B.P. (GRO 2,593) to about 29,000 B.P. (B-20) suggest their equivalence to the youngest deposits of the Bull Lake Glaciation. Buried soils on so-called Early Würm deposits throughout the Alpine Foreland appear to this writer to be more nearly comparable to soils on Riss Till than to soils on Main Würm Till or to the Krems Soil.

PLEISTOCENE SNOWLINES

Climatic snowline as defined by European glaciologists is the average altitude of the lower limit of névé (firn) on glaciers or permanent snowbanks. In North America this is called the orographic snowline because its level is controlled by the effects of topography, wind direction, and cirque orientation on snow accumulation.

The orographic snowline shown for the Rocky Mountains (Fig. 3) is the lower limit of névé on small glaciers as far south as Rocky Mountain National Park (latitude 40°15′); from there southward into the Sangre de Cristo Mountains (latitude 36°) it is the average lower limit of permanent snowbanks.

Late Pleistocene orographic snowline is commonly inferred to be the average altitude of floors of small cirques. The average altitude of cirque floors occupied by glaciers during the Bull Lake and Pinedale Glaciations (Fig. 3) lies 800 to 1,000 ft (250 to 300 m) below the present orographic snowline in the Southern Rocky Mountains, about 1,700 ft (515 m) below it in the Middle Rocky Mountains, and as much as 2,000 ft (600 m) below it in the Northern Rocky Mountains.

Another measure of late Pleistocene orographic snowline, widely used in Europe, is the median altitude between the terminal moraine of a given glacial advance and the highest point on the cirque headwall. As an approximation, median lines between the altitudes of terminal moraines of successive stades of the Bull Lake and Pinedale Glaciations and the highest point on cirque headwalls upvalley (as determined from topographic maps) have been plotted in Figure 3. They lie 1,200 to 1,500 ft (360 to 450 m) below the present orographic snowline in the Southern Rocky Mountains and 2,000 to 2,500 ft (600 to 750 m) below it in the Northern Rocky Mountains. This difference between present and late Pleistocene orographic snowlines is similar to the 2,200 to 2,500-ft (650 to 750-m) difference found by Klute (1928), but less than the 3,000 to 4,000-ft (900 to 1,200-m) determined by Antevs (1954).

A second kind of snowline is the "regional snowline" of Matthes (1940), which is "the level above which snow accumulates from year to year to generate ice bodies over a large part or all of the land depending upon latitude, altitude and topography." This snowline is approximated by the lower limit of ice caps.

A theoretically projected approximation of the lower limit of cap ice over the Rocky Mountains (Fig. 3) has been constructed from summer-temperature data on existing cap ice at Mount Columbia in Alberta, Canada, from radiosonde data at stations in the Rocky Mountain region, and from data on ablation periods at points in the mountains. Though crude, it compares favorably with projections proposed by Klute (1928) and Antevs (1954).

The average lower limit of late Pleistocene ice caps (Fig. 3) has been drawn from data for many localities where the lower limits of Bull Lake and Pinedale cap ice are known. The resultant curve is not unlike that determined by Louis (1927). Comparison of this curve with that for theoretical present-day cap ice indicates a late Pleistocene depression of regional snowline of about 4,000 ft (1,200 m). This amount of depression is similar to, though somewhat less than, the 4,500 ft (1,350 m) postulated by Stearns (1942) from the amount of lowering of the life zone of the alpine marmot in New Mexico.

If present free-air temperature gradients are applicable, mean summer temperatures during late Pleistocene glacial maxima were about 16° F (8° C) colder than at present in the Southern Rocky Mountains, and 17.5° F (9° C) colder in the Northern Rocky Mountains. It is likely, as pointed out by Leopold (1951), that winter temperatures then were much the same as at present.

REFERENCES

Alden, W. C., 1912, Pre-Wisconsin glacial drift in the region of Glacier National Park, Montana: Geol. Soc. Amer. Bull., v. 23, p. 687-708

—— 1932, Physiography and glacial geology of eastern Montana and adjacent areas: U.S. Geol. Surv. Prof. Pap. 174, 133 p.

Alden, W. C., and Stebinger, Eugene, 1913, Pre-Wisconsin glacial drift in the region of Glacier National Park, Montana: Geol. Soc. Amer. Bull., v. 24, p. 529-572

Antevs, E. V., 1948, Climatic changes and pre-white man, *in* A symposium on the Great Basin, with emphasis on glacial and post-glacial times: Univ. Utah Bull., v. 38, p. 168-191

—— 1954, Climate of New Mexico during the last glaciopluvial: J. Geol., v. 62, p. 182-191

Atwood, W. W., 1909, Glaciation of the Uinta and Wasatch Mountains: U.S. Geol. Surv. Prof. Pap. 61, 96 p.

Atwood, W. W., and Mather, K. F., 1912, The evidence of three distinct glacial epochs in the Pleistocene history of the San Juan Mountains, Colorado: J. Geol., v. 20, p. 385-409

—— 1932, Physiography and Quaternary geology of the San Juan Mountains, Colorado: U.S. Geol. Surv. Prof. Pap. 166, 176 p.

Ball, S. M., 1908, Geology of the Georgetown quadrangle, Colorado: U.S. Geol. Surv. Prof. Pap. 63, p. 29-63

Blackwelder, Eliot, 1915, Post-Cretaceous history of the mountains of central western Wyoming: J. Geol., v. 23, p. 97-117, 193-217, 307-340

Bradley, W. H., 1936, Geomorphology of the north flank of the Uinta Mountains: U.S. Geol. Surv. Prof. Pap. 185-I, 204 p.

Broecker, W. S., and Kulp, J. L., 1957, Lamont natural radiocarbon measurements IV: Science, v. 126, p. 1324-1344

Broecker, W. S., and Orr, P. C., 1958, Radiocarbon chronology of Lake Lahontan and Lake Bonneville: Geol. Soc. Amer. Bull., v. 69, p. 1009-1032

Bryan, Kirk, and Ray, L. L., 1940, Geologic antiquity of the Lindenmeier site in Colorado: Smithson. Instn. Misc. Coll., Publ. 3554, 76 p.

Capps, S. R., 1909, Pleistocene geology of the Leadville quadrangle, Colorado: U.S. Geol. Surv. Bull. 386, 99 p.

Crane, H. R., and Griffin, J. B., 1961, University of Michigan radiocarbon dates VI: Radiocarbon, v. 3, p. 105-125

Dort, Wakefield, Jr., 1962, Multiple glaciation of southern Lemhi Mountains, Idaho; preliminary reconnaissance report: Idaho State Coll. Mus. J., v. 5, p. 2-17

Eschman, D. F., 1955, Glaciation of the Michigan River Basin, North Park, Colorado: J. Geol., v. 63, p. 197-213

Flint, R. F., 1957, Glacial geology and the Pleistocene epoch: New York, John Wiley and Sons, 553 p.

Flint, R. F., and Denny, C. S., 1958, Quaternary geology of Boulder Mountain, Aquarius Plateau, Utah: U.S. Geol. Surv. Bull. 1061-D, 103 p.

Frye, J. C., and Willman, H. B., 1960, Classification of the Wisconsinan Stage in the Lake Michigan glacial lobe: Illinois State Geol. Surv. Circ. 285, 16 p.

Fryxell, F. M., 1930, Glacial features of Jackson Hole, Wyoming: Augustana Library Publ. 13, 128 p.

Fryxell, Roald, 1965, Relative ages of the Mazama and Glacier Peak volcanic ash layers: Science, v. 1947, p. 1288-1290

Gilbert, G. K., 1890, Lake Bonneville: U.S. Geol. Surv. Monogr. 1, 438 p.

Hack, J. T., 1943, Antiquity of the Finley site: Amer. Antiq., v. 8, p. 235-245

Heusser, C. J., 1956, Post-glacial environments in the Canadian Rocky Mountains: Ecol. Monogr., v. 26, p. 263-302

—— 1957, Variations of Blue, Hoh, and White glaciers during recent centuries: Arctic, v. 10, p. 139-150

Holmes, G. W., and Moss, J. H., 1955, Pleistocene geology of the southwestern Wind River Mountains, Wyoming: Geol. Soc. Amer. Bull., v. 66, p. 629-654

Horberg, Leland, 1938, The structural geology and physiography of the Teton Pass area, Wyoming: Augustana Library Publ. 16, 86 p.

—— 1940, Geomorphic problems and glacial geology of the Yellowstone valley, Park County, Montana: J. Geol., v. 48, p. 275-303

—— 1952, Pleistocene drift sheets in the Lethbridge region, Alberta, Canada: J. Geol., v. 60, p. 303-330

—— 1954, Rocky Mountain and continental Pleistocene deposits in the Waterton region, Alberta, Canada: Geol. Soc. Amer. Bull., v. 65, p. 1093-1150

Ives, R. L., 1938, Glacial geology of the Monarch Valley, Grand County, Colorado: Geol. Soc. Amer. Bull., v. 49, p. 1045-1066

Jones, W. D., and Quam, L. O., 1944, Glacial landforms in Rocky Mountain National Park, Colorado: J. Geol., v. 52, p. 217-234

Klute, Fritz, 1928, Die Bedeutung der Depression der Schneegrenze für eiszeitliche Probleme: Z. Gletscherkunde, v. 16, p. 70-93

Lawrence, D. B., 1948, Mt. Hood's latest eruption and glacier advances: Mazama, v. 30, p. 22-29

Lemke, R. W., Laird, W. M., Tipton, M. J., and Lindvall, R. M., this volume, Quaternary geology of Northern Great Plains

Leopold, L. B., 1951, Pleistocene climate in New Mexico: Amer. J. Sci., v. 249, p. 152-168

Leverett, Frank, 1939, The place of the Iowan drift: J. Geol., v. 47, p. 398-407

Louis, Herbert, 1927, Die Verbreitung von Glazialformen im Westen der Vereinigten Staaten: Z. Geomorph., v. 2, p. 221-235

Mathews, W. H., 1951, Historic and prehistoric fluctuations of alpine glaciers in the Mount Garibaldi map area, southwestern British Columbia: J. Geol., v. 59, p. 357-380

Matthes, F. E., 1939, Report of the Committee on glaciers: Amer. Geophys. Union Trans., 20th Ann. Mtg., pt. 4, p. 518-523

—— 1940, Report of the Committee on glaciers: Amer. Geophys. Union Trans., 21st Ann. Mtg., pt. 1, p. 396-405

Mears, Brainerd, Jr., 1953, Quaternary features of the Medicine Bow Mountains, Wyoming: Wyoming Geol. Assoc. Guidebook, 8th Ann. Field Conf., p. 81-84

Miller, J. P., 1958, Problems of the Pleistocene in Cordilleran North America, as related to reconstruction of environmental changes that affected early man, *in* Climate and man in the southwest: Univ. Arizona Bull., v. 28, pt. 4, 50 p.

Morrison, R. B., 1965, Lake Bonneville; Quaternary stratigraphy of eastern Jordan Valley, south of Salt Lake City, Utah: U.S. Geol. Surv. Prof. Pap. 477, (in press)

Moss, J. H., 1951a, Early man in the Eden Valley [Wyoming]: Univ. Pennsylvania Mus. Monogr. 6, p. 9-92

—— 1951b, Late glacial advances in the southern Wind River Mountains, Wyoming: Amer. J. Sci., v. 249, p. 865-883

Nelson, R. L., 1954, Glacial geology of the Frying Pan River Drainage, Colorado: J. Geol., v. 62, p. 325-343

Powers, H. A., Young, E. J., and Barnett, P. R., 1958, Possible extension into Idaho, Nevada and Utah of the Pearlette ash of Meade County, Kansas (abst.): Geol. Soc. Amer. Bull., v. 69, p. 1631

Powers, H. A., and Wilcox, R. E., 1964, Volcanic ash from Mount Mazama (Crater Lake) and from Glacier Peak: Science, v. 144, p. 1334-1346

Ray, L. L., 1940, Glacial chronology of the southern Rocky Mountains: Geol. Soc. Amer. Bull., v. 51, p. 1851-1917

Richmond, G. M., 1948, Modification of Blackwelder's sequence of Pleistocene glaciation in the Wind River Mountains, Wyoming (abst.): Geol. Soc. Amer. Bull., v. 59, p. 1400-1401

—— 1957a, Three pre-Wisconsin glacial stages in the Rocky Mountain region: Geol. Soc. Amer. Bull., v. 68, p. 239-262

—— 1957b, Correlation of Quaternary deposits in the Rocky Mountain region, U.S.A.: V Intern. Congr. INQUA, Madrid-Barcelona, Résumées des communications, p. 157

—— 1960a, Correlation of alpine and continental glacial deposits of Glacier National Park and adjacent High Plains, Montana: U.S. Geol. Surv. Prof. Pap. 400-B, p. 223-224.

—— 1960b, Glaciation of the east slope of Rocky Mountain National Park, Colorado: Geol. Soc. Amer. Bull., v. 71, p. 1371-1382

—— 1962a, Three pre-Bull Lake tills in the Wind River Mountains, Wyoming: U.S. Geol. Surv. Prof. Pap. 450-D, p. 132-136

—— 1962b, Quaternary stratigraphy of the La Sal Mountains, Utah: U.S. Geol. Surv. Prof. Pap. 324, 135 p.

—— 1963, Correlation of some glacial deposits in New Mexico: U.S. Geol. Surv. Prof. Pap. 450-D, p. 121-125

—— 1964a, Three pre-Bull Lake tills in the Wind River Mountains, Wyoming, reinterpreted: U.S. Geol. Surv. Prof. Pap. 501-D, p. 104-109

—— 1964b, Glaciation of Little Cottonwood and Bells Canyons, Wasatch Mountains, Utah: U.S. Geol. Surv. Prof. Pap. 454-D, 41 p.

—— 1964c, Glacial geology of the West Yellowstone Basin and adjacent parts of Yellowstone National Park: U.S. Geol. Surv. Prof. Pap. 435-T, p. 223-236

Richmond, G. M., Fryxell, Roald, Neff, G. E., and Weis, P. L., this volume, The Cordilleran ice sheet of the Northern Rocky Mountains and related Quaternary history of the Columbia Plateau

Rubin, Meyer, and Alexander, Corinne, 1958, U.S. Geological Survey radiocarbon dates IV: Science, v. 127, p. 1476-1487

—— 1960, U.S. Geological Survey radiocarbon dates V: Amer. J. Sci., Radiocarbon Suppl., v. 2, p. 129-185

Rubin, Meyer, and Berthold, S. M., 1961, U.S. Geological Survey radiocarbon dates VI: Radiocarbon, v. 3, p. 86-98

Scott, G. R., this volume, Nonglacial geology of the Southern and Middle Rocky Mountains

Sigafoos, R. S., and Hendricks, E. L., 1961, Botanical evidence of the modern history of Nisqually Glacier, Washington: U.S. Geol. Surv. Prof. Pap. 387-A, 20 p.

Singewald, Q. D., 1950, Gold placers and their geological environment in northwestern Park County, Colorado: U.S. Geol. Surv. Bull. 955-D, 103 p.

Stearns, C. E., 1942, A fossil marmot from New Mexico and its climatic significance: Amer. J. Sci., v. 240, p. 867-878

Thorp, James, 1931, The effects of vegetation and climate upon northern and northwestern Wyoming: J. Soil Sci., v. 32, p. 283-301

Trimble, D. E., and Carr, W. J., 1961, The Michaud delta and Bonneville River near Pocatello, Idaho: U.S. Geol. Surv. Prof. Pap. 424-B, p. 164-166

Wilcox, R. E., this volume, Volcanic-ash chronology

Williams, P. L., 1961, Glacial geology of Stanley Basin: Idaho Bur. Mines and Geology Pamph. 123, 28 p.

SUMMARY

Glaciers were developed in most of the ranges of the Rocky Mountains as far south as latitude 33°22′ during the Pleistocene, and as far as latitude 35°40′ during the Recent. Early Pleistocene glaciers appear to have been broad shallow lobate masses, but after canyon erosion in mid-Pleistocene time, subsequent glaciers formed thick tongues in the canyons. Late Pleistocene ice caps occurred about as far south as latitude 37°.

Five distinct glaciations are recognized; from oldest to youngest they are named Washakie Point, Cedar Ridge, Sacagawea Ridge, Bull Lake, and Pinedale. Deposits of the three oldest glaciations are deeply weathered and their deposition was separated by major interglaciations. The oldest two are pre-canyon in age. Bull Lake Glaciation includes two and perhaps three glacial advances separated by intervals of deglaciation of lesser duration than preceding interglaciations. Pinedale Glaciation includes at least three stades, or minor advances, and perhaps more, separated by brief interstades. It was followed by the Altithermal interval. Neoglaciation, comprising the Temple Lake and Gannett Peak Stades, was confined to cirques.

The average altitude of end moraines of late Pleistocene glaciers rises from between 4,200 and 5,400 ft (1,260 and 1,620 m) at latitude 49° to between 10,200 and 11,400 ft (3,060 and 3,420 m) at latitude 33°20′. A depression of late Pleistocene regional snowline of about 4,000 ft (1,200 m) is indicated by the altitude of the lower limit of late Pleistocene ice caps. Summer temperatures were probably 16-17° F (8°-9° C) colder than at present.

THE CORDILLERAN ICE SHEET OF THE NORTHERN ROCKY MOUNTAINS, AND RELATED QUATERNARY HISTORY OF THE COLUMBIA PLATEAU

GERALD M. RICHMOND,[1] ROALD FRYXELL,[2] GEORGE E. NEFF,[3]
PAUL L. WEIS[4]

DURING EACH Quaternary glaciation, the Cordilleran Ice Sheet pushed southward from Canada into the conterminous United States, covering much of the Northern Rocky Mountains west of the Continental Divide and locally encroaching onto the Columbia Plateau (Fig. 1).

The Northern Rocky Mountains in western Montana and northern Idaho consist of northwest-trending ranges and valleys controlled by faults and underlain mainly by Precambrian sedimentary rocks of the Belt Series. In northeastern Washington, irregular mountain ridges are developed in Paleozoic metasedimentary rocks and Mesozoic granite batholiths.

The Columbia Plateau of eastern Washington is underlain by vast flows of Miocene and Pliocene(?) Columbia River Basalt. At the eastern margin of the plateau, these flows intertongue with lake beds of the Latah Formation and rest unconformably on deeply dissected granitic terrane. The surface of the plateau is covered extensively by intermittently accumulated Quaternary loess including that of the Palouse Formation; its western part is also covered by the older predominantly lacustrine and alluvial sediments of the Ringold Formation.

Near the maximum of each glacial advance, ice dammed the Clark Fork River at Lake Pend Oreille to form Glacial Lake Missoula, and blocked the Columbia River at Grand Coulee to form Glacial Lake Columbia. At times it also blocked the Spokane River east and west of Spokane, forming Glacial Lakes Coeur d'Alene and Spokane.

The ice dam that impounded Lake Missoula collapsed at least three times, releasing catastrophic floods of enormous magnitude, which swept through the Spokane area and southwestward across the Columbia Plateau. The last of these floods followed the early maximum of the last or Pinedale Glaciation. Two additional earlier floods from unknown sources spilled eastward across the western part of the plateau.

---

[1] U.S. Geological Survey, Federal Center, Denver, Colorado.
[2] Department of Sociology and Anthropology, Washington State University, Pullman, Washington.
[3] U.S. Bureau of Reclamation, Ephrata, Washington.
[4] U.S. Geological Survey, Washington, D.C.

CORDILLERAN ICE SHEET

NATURE AND EXTENT

The Cordilleran Ice Sheet formed through coalescence of large piedmont glaciers in the Rocky Mountains and Cascade Ranges of Canada and flowed south into the United States, where it incorporated glaciers of local origin. It lay between the Continental Divide on the east and the Cascade Range on the west and extended south to about 47°30′ Latitude (Fig. 1). Nunataks projected but a few hundred feet above it. Its surface sloped at 15 to 50 ft/mile (3-10 m/km) (Flint, 1935) from an altitude of about 7,300 ft (2,200 m) at the Canadian boundary, where the ice was 3,500 to 5,000 ft (1,000-1,500 m) thick over major valleys, to an altitude of about 2,000 ft (600 m) at its southern limit, which was outlined by ten lobes along major drainage lines (Fig. 1).

NOMENCLATURE AND CORRELATION

Early identification of three glaciations in eastern Washington was based mainly on the distribution of erratics subsequently shown to be of flood origin (Bretz, 1923, 1928). Bretz (1924) differentiated a "Spokane Glaciation" (earlier) and a Wisconsin Glaciation (later) (Table 1). Flint (1935, 1936, 1937) recognized evidence for but a single glaciation, the Wisconsin. In western Montana and northern Idaho, Alden (1953) recognized three glaciations: early pre-Wisconsin, Illinoian or Iowan, and Wisconsin. We also differentiate deposits of three glaciations. The oldest is a very deeply weathered drift correlated with pre-Bull Lake till elsewhere in the Rocky Mountains (Richmond, this volume). The intermediate includes two (locally three) tills stratigraphically separated by mature zonal soils or disconformities indicative of nonglacial conditions. These tills form large mature moraines and are correlated with the early and late stages of Bull Lake Glaciation (Richmond, this volume). The youngest deposits form fresh bouldery moraines bearing immature zonal soils and mark a maximum and one or more secondary advances correlated with the early, middle, and late stages of Pinedale Glaciation (Richmond, this volume). A suggested correlation with glaciations in the Pacific Northwest (Crandell, this volume) is shown in Table 1.

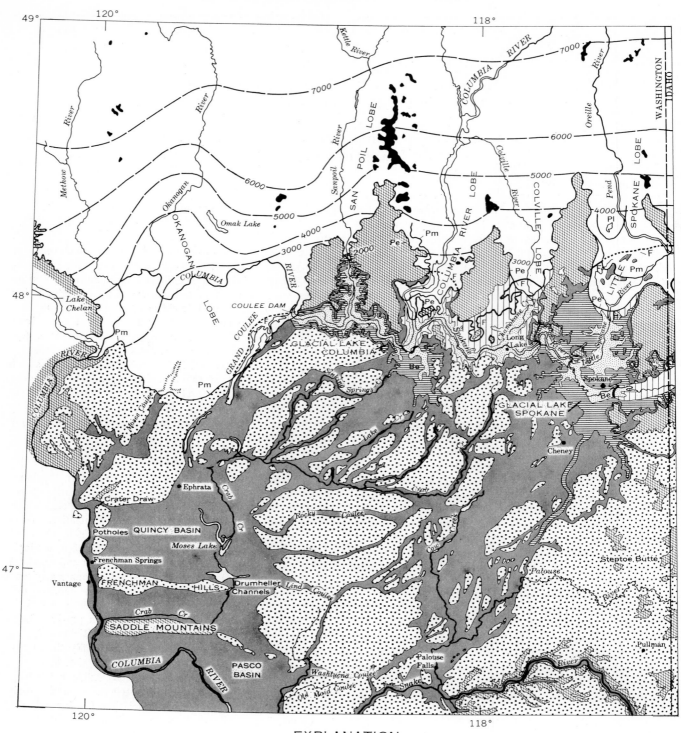

EXPLANATION

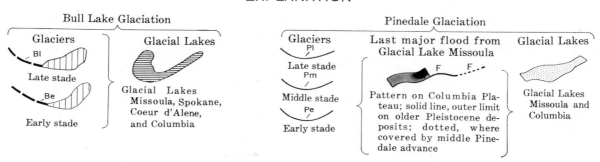

Bull Lake Glaciation

Glaciers
Bl
Late stage

Be
Early stage

Glacial Lakes

Glacial Lakes
Missoula, Spokane,
Coeur d'Alene,
and Columbia

Pinedale Glaciation

Glaciers
Pl
Late stage
Pm
Middle stage
Pe
Early stage

Last major flood from
Glacial Lake Missoula

F   F

Pattern on Columbia Pla-
teau; solid line, outer limit
on older Pleistocene de-
posits; dotted, where
covered by middle Pine-
dale advance

Glacial Lakes

Glacial Lakes
Missoula and
Columbia

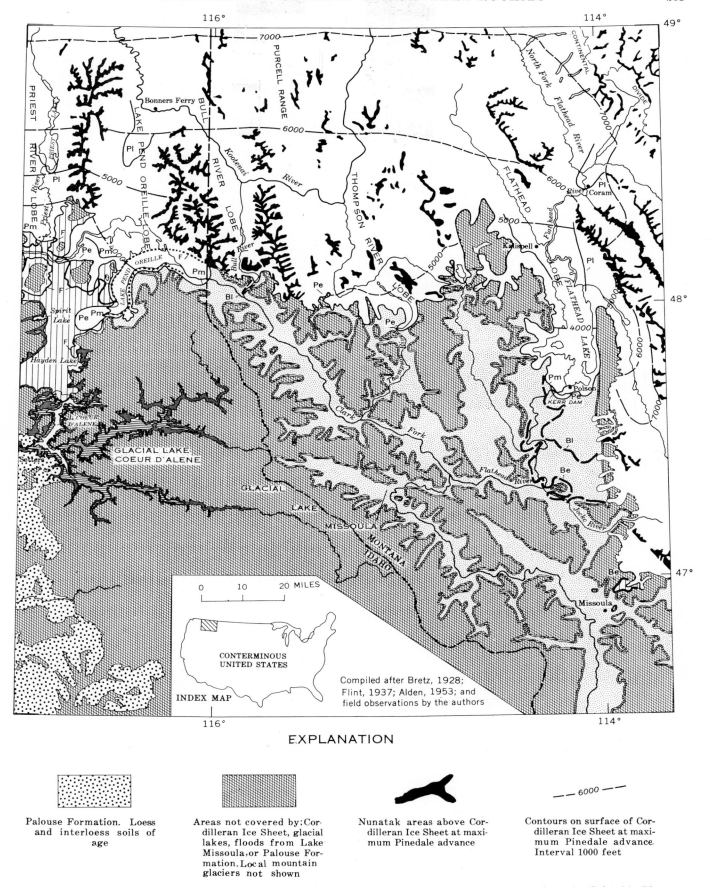

EXPLANATION

| Palouse Formation. Loess and interloess soils of age | Areas not covered by: Cordilleran Ice Sheet, glacial lakes, floods from Lake Missoula, or Palouse Formation. Local mountain glaciers not shown | Nunatak areas above Cordilleran Ice Sheet at maximum Pinedale advance | Contours on surface of Cordilleran Ice Sheet at maximum Pinedale advance. Interval 1000 feet |

Figure 1. Map of Cordilleran Ice Sheet and related features in the Northern Rocky Mountains and on the Columbia Plateau.

TABLE 1

Correlation of Deposits and Events of the Cordilleran Region and Columbia Plateau

Approx. years B.P.	ROCKY MOUNTAINS — Glacial chronology after Richmond (this volume)	CORDILLERAN GLACIATION — Eastern Washington Bretz (1923 1928) Flint (1935 1936 1937)	Western Montana Alden (1953)	Recognized in this paper	GLACIAL LAKES — Lake Missoula (Dammed by Pend Oreille ice lobe at Clark Fork)	Lake Coeur d'Alene (Dammed by Pend Oreille ice lobe at Coeur d'Alene)	Lake Spokane (Dammed by Colville ice lobe at Spokane River)	Lake Columbia (Dammed by Okanogan ice lobe at Grand Coulee)	COLUMBIA PLATEAU — Loess and soils	Catastrophic floods	PACIFIC NORTHWEST — Glacial chronology after Crandell (this volume)
	RECENT — Neoglaciation — Gannett Peak Stade			Local cirque moraines and rock glaciers					Very weak soil		Neoglaciation
— 600	Interstade								Pale loess		
— 900									Very weak soil		
— 4,000	Temple Lake Stade								Pale loess		
	Altithermal interval			Moderately developed soil	Moderately developed soil	Present level of lake (2,125 ft.) attained by gradual lowering	Moderately developed soil	Moderately developed soil	Weakly developed soil	Weakly developed soil	Hypsithermal
— 6,600	Mt. Mazama ash			Mt. Mazama ash	Mt. Mazama ash		Mt. Mazama ash	Mt. Mazama ash	Mt. Mazama ash	Mt. Mazama ash	Mt. Mazama ash
	Pinedale Glaciation — Late stade	Wisconsin Glaciation	Wisconsin — Recession	Recessional gravel	Gradual withdrawal				Pale loess		interval
			Kalispell Moraine	End moraine	Flathead Lake at 3,200 ft.						= (9,000) =
											Sumas Stade
— 10,000	Interstade		Recession	Recessional moraine	Gradual withdrawal				Weakly developed soil		= (11,000) =
— 12,000	Glacier Peak ash			Glacier Peak ash					Glacier Peak ash	Glacier Peak ash	Everson Interstade
	Middle stade		Polson Moraine	End moraines	Lake rise to +3,850 ft.	Retained by flood gravel at 2,300 ft.		Nespelem terrace 1,700 ft. Ice dam recedes	Pale loess	Final flood on Columbia River	= (13,500) =
								Lake surface 1,950 to 1,800 ft.			Vashon Stade
	Interstade			Recessional gravel	Catastrophic flood withdrawal	Catastrophic flood to 2,665+ ft.	Catastrophic flood deposits	Catastrophic flood deposits	Catastrophic flood erosion; Touchet Beds	Catastrophic flood deposits of Lake Missoula	Recession
	Early stade			End moraine	Lake rise to 4,200 ft.	Lake surface —2,400 ft.		Lake surface at 1,950 ft.	Pale loess		Evans Creek Stade
— 25,000	Interglaciation		Deep weathering	Strongly developed soil	Strongly developed soil		Disconformity	Disconformity	Strongly developed soil	Strongly developed soil	Olympia Interglaciation
— 32,000	Bull Lake Glaciation — Late stade — 2nd episode	WISCONSIN — Illinoian or Iowan — Mission Moraine	Till	Lake rise possibly to 4,400 ft.				Brown loess	Flood deposits from Lake Missoula	Flood deposits from west	Younger glacial episode
— 45,000	Nonglacial interval		Deep weathering	Disconformity	Disconformity	?	?	?	Strongly developed soil		
— 50,000	1st episode		Till	Lake rise to 4,400 ft.	Ice dammed at 2,400 ft.	Surface at 2,350–2,400 ft.	Lake surface at 2,350(?) ft.	Brown loess		?	
	Nonglacial interval	Spokane Glaciation	Earlier pre-Wisconsin — Earlier advance	Strongly developed soil	Strongly developed soil	?	?	?	Strongly developed soil		?	Nonglacial interval
	Early stade			Till proglacial gravel	Lake rise to 4,400 ft.				Brown loess			Older glacial episode
	Interglaciation			Very strongly developed soil					Very strongly developed soil (caliche)	Very strongly developed soil (caliche)	Puyallup Interglaciation
	Sacagawea Ridge Glaciation			Till					Brown loess and lake sediments	Flood deposits from Lake Missoula	Stuck Glaciation — 2nd episode
											1st episode
	Interglaciation				(Valley floor at Bull Lake ice dam 2,200 ft. alt.)	(Valley floor at Bull Lake ice dam 1,800 ft. alt.)	(Valley floor at Bull Lake ice dam 1,400 ft. alt.)	(Valley floor at Bull Lake ice dam 950 ft. alt.)	Very strongly developed soil (caliche)		Alderton Interglaciation
									Oxidized tuff		
	Cedar Ridge Glaciation								Ringold Formation (in part)		Orting Glaciation — 3rd episode
	Interglaciation										2nd episode
	Washakie Point Glaciation										1st episode

FLATHEAD LOBE

Three glaciations are recognized in deposits of the Flathead Lobe (Fig. 1). Deeply oxidized clayey drift in the lee of rock knobs south of Kalispell may represent a pre-Bull Lake glaciation. Bull Lake ice extended down the valley of the Flathead River to the Jocko River (Fig. 1), where till of the early stade bearing a mature zonal soil occurs beneath lake beds of the late stade; the Mission moraine of Alden (1953), 20 km to the northeast, is the terminus of the late stade. Exposures of three tills separated by lacustrine sediments in the bluffs below Kerr Dam suggest that three advances occurred in Bull Lake time. Each suite of lake deposits consists of a lower unit of varved clayey silt, indicative of glacial recession; a disconformity; and an upper unit of lake sand and massive silt, suggestive of glacial readvance. Recession between the early and late stades was of major proportions, for a mature brown podzolic soil, 1 m thick, separates the tills of these stades along the North Fork of the Flathead River (Fig. 1) 145 km north of the Mission moraine.

The bouldery Polson moraine of Alden (1953) south of Flathead Lake is a compound feature including moraines of both the early and middle stades of Pinedale Glaciation. The deposits formed subaerially (Nobles, 1952) but were successively covered by the rising waters of Lake Missoula. They bear an immature zonal brown soil. Moraines at Kalispell and Coram (Alden, 1953) represent two lobes of the late stade of Pinedale Glaciation, at which time separation of the local mountain glaciers from the ice sheet had begun.

THOMPSON RIVER AND BULL RIVER LOBES

The Thompson River and Bull River Lobes were formed by ice flowing down the Kootenai River east of the Purcell Range and up the Kootenai River to the west. The ice margin shown on Figure 1 is that of the maximum advance of Pinedale Glaciation. An early Pinedale end moraine on Bull River is thickly mantled with flood deposits of Lake Missoula, which form kame deposits on both sides of the valley for 3 to 5 km upstream. Till of the Bull Lake Glaciation occurs beneath lake silt at the valley mouth. Thus the Bull River Lobe may have reached Clark Fork in Bull Lake time.

LAKE PEND OREILLE LOBE

The Lake Pend Oreille Lobe entered Lake Pend Oreille from the north and, during Bull Lake Glaciation, extended southwest as far as Spokane (Fig. 1) and impounded Lake Missoula to the east. The ice border is marked east of Spirit Lake (Fig. 1) by a lateral moraine eroded by floodwaters, and at Hayden Lake it is marked by a moraine bearing a mature reddish-brown clayey soil covered by thin flood deposits. To the southwest, tributary valleys are blocked by stream-crossbedded, kame-terrace gravel, overlain disconformably by younger flood deposits. Farther southwest, below 2,370 ft (723 m) altitude and beneath flood deposits, tributaries are blocked by deltaic kame sand, indicating that the ice terminated in a lake, which has been named Glacial Lake Spokane (Anderson, 1927).

West of Spokane deposits on the Columbia Plateau, inferred by previous workers to be glacial (Bretz, 1923; Anderson, 1927; Flint, 1937), are all of flood or colluvial origin. Thus only one Bull Lake advance of this lobe has been recognized.

During the early and middle stades of Pinedale Glaciation the Lake Pend Oreille Lobe again filled Lake Pend Oreille, overflowing a short distance to the west and southwest (Fig. 1). Eastward it extended up Clark Fork to the Idaho state line, merging with local mountain glaciers and again impounding Lake Missoula (Alden, 1953). End moraines of the early stade were mostly destroyed by a catastrophic flood from Lake Missoula. Undisturbed moraines of the middle stade lie across the path of the flood. A still later stand of the ice occurred at Bonners Ferry, north of Lake Pend Oreille.

PRIEST RIVER AND LITTLE SPOKANE RIVER LOBES

The Priest River Lobe merged with the Lake Pend Oreille Lobe during Bull Lake but not during Pinedale Glaciation. The outermost Pinedale moraine on Priest River is the Wisconsin end moraine of Alden (1953). It rests on lake deposits (Walker, 1964) of early Pinedale age and is itself probably of middle Pinedale age.

The southerly limit of the Little Spokane River Lobe (Fig. 1) is determined from the northerly extent of deposits of Glacial Lake Spokane and from the position of deeply weathered unglaciated granite hills on the valley floor. No Bull Lake deposits are preserved, but in the valley of the Little Spokane River an arkosic sandy outwash plain of early Pinedale age is cut by spectacular scour channels of the last flood from Lake Missoula that are overlapped by a well-preserved end moraine of middle Pinedale age.

COLVILLE AND COLUMBIA RIVER LOBES

During the maximum of Bull Lake Glaciation both the Colville and Columbia River Lobes abutted the margin of the Columbia Plateau south of the Spokane River (Fig. 1). Below loess hills along the plateau rim, compact, arkosic granite-rich till containing but little basalt occurs in canyon heads beneath basalt-rich gravels deposited by flood-waters from Glacial Lake Missoula. The loess hills were in part above flood level. Ice did not encroach on the plateau surface, as inferred by Bretz (1923) and Flint (1935), and deposits on the plateau surface inferred by Flint (1935) to be till are flood gravels or flood-reworked loess. Loess-covered till described by Flint (1937) north of the Spokane River bears a mature zonal brown soil and is of Bull Lake age. The eastern edge of the ice in the valley of the Spokane River (Fig. 1) impounded Glacial Lake Spokane.

The outermost Pinedale end moraine of the Colville Lobe, noted by Salisbury (1901), is at Springdale. On the Columbia River, the end moraine of the early stage of Pinedale Glaciation lies just north of the Spokane River and is mantled with flood deposits to an altitude of 2,480 ft (756 m). The end moraine of the middle stade immediately to the north (Fig. 1), although lower, is not mantled with flood deposits.

SAN POIL LOBE

The San Poil Lobe (Pardee, 1918; Flint and Irwin, 1939) terminated 25 km north of the Columbia River in Pinedale time (Fig. 1), where it was stopped by a rock spur. No other advance is known.

OKANOGAN LOBE

The Okanogan Lobe was the largest lobe of the Cordilleran Ice Sheet, and it was the only lobe to advance onto the Columbia Plateau. In Pinedale time it terminated in a massive moraine 50 km south of the Columbia River (Salisbury, 1901; Waters, 1933; Flint, 1935) and spread eastward to block the Columbia River at Grand Coulee (Fig. 1). Bretz (1928) regarded the head of Moses Coulee as related to an earlier glacial spillway, and weathered sediments and till of possible Bull Lake age underlie till of Pinedale age 30 km west of Grand Coulee; the extent of this early advance is otherwise unknown.

Two glacial advances in Pinedale time are recorded at the canyon rim northeast of Grand Coulee, where two tills separated by thick outwash gravel reflect two minor pulsations of the ice (Flint and Irwin, 1939). These advances formed ice dams that impounded Glacial Lake Columbia both before and after the catastrophic flood from Glacial Lake Missoula; they are regarded here as representing the early and middle stades of Pinedale Glaciation. The altitude of the Pinedale end moraine northeast of the Columbia River at Grand Coulee, and of Pinedale kame gravel at the south rim of the canyon, fixes the minimum altitude of these dams at 1,950 ft (595 m).

Readvance of the Okanogan Lobe after the catastrophic flood passed through Grand Coulee is demonstrated by striations and local patches of drift in the upper part of the coulee (Bretz, 1932) and by ice-shove deformation of lacustrine sediments on the coulee floor.

Glacial Lake Missoula

THE LAKE AND ITS ICE DAM

Glacial Lake Missoula (Pardee, 1910) was the largest of several lakes impounded by the Cordilleran Ice Sheet. It lay in the drainage of the Clark Fork River and was dammed by the Lake Pend Oreille Lobe just east of the Montana-Idaho boundary (Fig. 1). During Bull Lake glacial maxima the lake rose at least twice to an altitude of about 4,400 ft (1,340 m), as recorded by two lake-silt units at this altitude resting on proglacial gravel. Mature zonal soils characteristic of deposits of the Bull Lake Glaciation separate and overlie the silts. These deposits are exposed along the Clark Fork River at the confluence of Little Blackfoot River 75 km upstream from the point shown at the southeast corner of Figure 1.

During the early maximum of Pinedale Glaciation, Lake Missoula stood at an altitude of 4,200 ft (1,280 m) contained more than 500 cubic miles (2,000 km³) of water, and had a surface area of about 2,900 sq. miles (7,500 km²) (Pardee, 1942). At the dam, the water was at least 2,000 ft (700 m) deep against ice at least 3,500 ft (1,070 m) thick.

Features of the lake include faint but distinct closely spaced strandlines, extending to an upper limit of 4,200 ft (1,280 m) (Pardee, 1910); buff, massive to thinly laminated, locally varved lake silt in the broader sectors of the valley; local horizontally bedded or crossbedded delta gravel in tributary canyons; and widely distributed ice-rafted cobbles and boulders (Pardee, 1910, 1942; Alden, 1953). The laminated silt is of two types: (1) thick, brown, compact, well-laminated clayey silt of Bull Lake age that forms extensive terraces along the valley sides and (2) thin, pale-brown, relatively soft, commonly massive silt of Pinedale age that mantles both the older silt terraces and the valley floor.

The outlet of the lake during its high stands was along the east edge of the glacier in Lake Pend Oreille. Here kame gravel of Pinedale age has an ice-contact margin at altitudes between 4,000 and 4,200 ft (1,220-1,280 m), indicating glacial control of the maximum lake level.

RELATION TO GLACIATION

Impounding of Glacial Lake Missoula by the Pend Oreille Lobe probably occurred during each glacial advance into the basin of Lake Pend Oreille, though but one stade of Bull Lake advance and two Pinedale advances can be demonstrated for the Lake Pend Oreille Lobe. Within the area of Glacial Lake Missoula, lake beds conformably overlie tills recording three advances of the Flathead Lobe during Bull Lake Glaciation. The two high stands of the lake at

4,400 ft (1,340 m) are correlated with the two earlier of these advances.

Moraines of the early and middle Pinedale advances of the Flathead Lobe near Polson at the south end of Flathead Lake intertongue with and are overlapped by lake deposits. Their crests are at an altitude of about 3,400 ft (1,040 m). They also have strandlines developed on them, indicating that each formed subaerially and later was covered by rising lake waters. Along Flathead River, north of its confluence with Jocko River (Fig. 1), two Pinedale lake silt units overlie proglacial-lake sand and gravel that rest on compact lake silt of Bull Lake age.

The earlier Pinedale lake is believed to have risen to 4,200 ft (1,280 m), the upper limit of strandlines on the Clark Fork drainage. The second Pinedale lake probably rose to nearly the same height, but at least to an altitude of 3,580 ft (1,090 m), as recorded by strandlines cut on flood deposits formed during catastrophic emptying of the lake following the early rise (Pardee, 1942).

Lake silt interfingering with and overlapping the moraine of the late stade of Pinedale Glaciation at Kalispell at an altitude of 3,100 ft (945 m) probably formed in an ancestral Flathead Lake retained by the moraines at Polson. Channels in these moraines are at 3,200 ft (975 m). No record of a lake in the valley of Clark Fork at this time is recognized, and no contemporary glacier advanced into the basin of Lake Pend Orielle.

EVIDENCE OF CATASTROPHIC FLOOD WITHDRAWAL

Proof of catastrophic flood withdrawal of Lake Missoula was demonstrated by Pardee (1942). He described (a) flood-scoured channels containing closed depressions along divides below maximum lake level, (b) successions of giant arcuate ripples or ridges of gravel, averaging 5 to 9 m in height and 75 m in wavelength, that rest on sloping bedrock surfaces, (c) large deltaic masses of gravel that rest in part on the ripples, (d) flood-denuded rock slopes along Clark Fork, (e) high eddy deposits of flood debris at altitudes between 2,800 and 3,900 ft (850-1,190 m) in gulches and on the downstream sides of projecting spurs along the several narrows of Clark Fork, and (f) large flood bars of boulders and coarse gravel on the wider parts of the valley floor.

Pardee pointed out also that a flood gradient would be established because the confining effects of the successive narrows would permit drainage of the lower reaches of the valley more rapidly than the upper. He estimated that the flow of water attained a maximum rate of 9.5 cubic miles (38 km³) per hour.

This catastrophic flood, according to Pardee, followed a rise of Lake Missoula to 4,200 ft (1,280 m) here correlated with the early stade of Pinedale Glaciation. It was followed by a subsequent rise, here correlated with the middle stade, from which the lake was lowered gradually.

Glacial Lake Coeur d'Alene

Modern Lake Coeur d'Alene occupies a drowned dendritic valley east of Spokane and south of Lake Pend Oreille (Fig. 1). It is about 190 ft (58 m) deep at its lower end and has a surface elevation of 2,125 ft (648 m). Erratic boulders and cobbles of granite occur on adjacent mountain slopes as high as 2,665 ft (813 m) altitude—540 ft (180 m) above the lake (Hershey, 1912; Anderson, 1927; Dort, 1962). As the valley is unglaciated, these show that the lake level was once considerably higher.

Most workers have assumed that the lake was impounded to an altitude of at least 2,575 ft (785 m) by ice of the Pend Oreille Lobe in the valley to the north (Anderson, 1927; Dort, 1960, 1962) during the Spokane Glaciation (Bretz, 1923, 1924), here correlated with the Bull Lake Glaciation (Table 1). The erratic boulders are believed to have been carried to their present positions by floating ice (Hershey, 1912; Anderson, 1927).

An outlet for such a lake occurs at an altitude of 2,575 ft (785 m) on the southwest margin of the lake basin divide at the town of Setters (Dort, 1958). However, the maximum height of moraines of the Bull Lake Glaciation immediately north of Lake Coeur d'Alene is only about 2,400 ft (730 m), at least 175 ft (53 m) below Setters and 265 ft (81 m) below the highest erratics. Furthermore, the outlet at Setters is cut in loess (Lewis and Denecke, 1923) of Bull Lake age on which a post-Bull Lake soil is developed. The outlet therefore must be younger than the Bull Lake Glaciation; and glaciers of Pinedale age did not extend to the lake.

As reinterpreted here, Glacial Lake Coeur d'Alene had a level of about 2,400 ft (730 m) altitude during Bull Lake Glaciation and at this time drained along the margin of the glacier into the valley east of Spokane (Anderson, 1927). That the erratic boulders are concentrated at and below this level is shown by a plot of their positions (Dort, 1962, Fig. 4). Subsequent rise of the lake to altitudes irregularly as high as 2,665 ft (813 m) and the overflow at Setters (Fig. 1) are believed to have occurred during the release of flood-waters from Glacial Lake Missoula in early Pinedale time. The maximum height of these flood-waters just north of the lake was about 2,600 ft (790 m).

GLACIAL LAKE SPOKANE

Glacial Lake Spokane was recognized first from deposits of lake silt southeast of Spokane (Large, 1922; Anderson, 1927) and was believed to have been impounded against hills in this area by the confluence of the Lake Pend Oreille and Little Spokane glacial lobes and their extension across the plateau to the vicinity of Cheney (Bretz, 1923; Flint, 1937). Doubt that these lobes joined, or that ice extended onto this part of the plateau, is expressed above.

The lake was inferred to have overflowed southward through spillways at an altitude of 2,450-2,500 ft (750-765 m) (Bretz, 1923; Anderson, 1927). These spillways are in part cut in loess of Bull Lake age and were last occupied by flood-waters from Glacial Lake Missoula in early Pinedale time.

Though an ice-dammed lake definitely existed in the Spokane area, the location of its dam, it surface altitude, extent, and age require re-evaluation.

When the Colville Lobe of the ice sheet blocked the Spokane River at Long Lake (Fig. 1) during Bull Lake Glaciation it impounded a lake to the east, here called Glacial Lake Spokane. The surface elevation of this lake was between 2,350 and 2,400 ft (715-730 m) in altitude as indicated by the surface of a large kame delta south of Long Lake and by numerous deposits of lake silt extending to similar altitudes east and west of Little Spokane River. Flint (1936) described some of these deposits, noting thin lenses of loose silty till in them. We believe that these till lenses were deposited from stranded icebergs derived from either the Little Spokane Lobe to the north (Fig. 1), or from the Lake Pend Oreille Lobe to the east. Deltaic kame sand recording the presence of the lake against Bull Lake ice east of Spokane extend to an altitude of 2,370 ft (720 m). All these lake deposits are overlain by flood gravels from Lake Missoula. Thus Glacial Lake Spokane had a considerably greater extent (Fig. 1) than originally inferred by Large (1922) and is of Bull Lake age. At a surface altitude of 2,370 ft (720 m) it probably overflowed across the plateau near Cheney, though proof is lacking.

GLACIAL LAKE COLUMBIA

The Okanogan Lobe blocked the Columbia River at Grand Coulee (Salisbury, 1901; Bretz, 1923, 1928; Flint, 1935) during Pinedale Glaciation and probably also during Bull Lake Glaciation. Water was impounded along the unglaciated sector of the Columbia River to the east, forming a lake, here called Glacial Lake Columbia. During Bull Lake glacial maxima, the outlet probably was along the east rim of Grand Coulee, whose general altitude of about 2,350 ft (720 m) is thought to have been essentially the level of the lake. Some overflow or seepage may also have escaped into the head of Sinking Springs Creek or Lake Creek (Fig. 1). The east end of the lake would have abutted the terminus of the Columbia River glacial lobe. As yet no deposits of Bull Lake age of this lake have been distinguished.

Glacial Lake Columbia clearly existed in Pinedale time. Kame deposits of Pinedale age on the south wall of the Columbia River at Grand Coulee and glacial erratics on the north wall indicate an ice dam at an elevation of about 1,950 ft (595 m). At the confluence of the Columbia and Spokane Rivers, lake sand 6 m thick occurs at an altitude of 1,950 ft (595 m) beneath gravels of the last flood from Glacial Lake Missoula that extend to 2,360 ft (720 m). A lake at 1,950 ft (595 m) altitude would have extended up Spokane River to the site of the city of Spokane, past the location of the ice dam that in Bull Lake time impounded Glacial Lake Spokane (Fig. 1). Pinedale lake sand mantled with flood deposits occurs in a broad, flood-modified terrace at altitudes of 1,920 to 1,950 ft (585-595 m) on the west side of the Little Spokane River north of Spokane. Farther north, above 1,950 ft (595 m) altitude, this terrace grades into a flood-modified, arkosic, sandy outwash plain of early Pinedale age.

The fact that the Okanogan Lobe crossed Grand Coulee twice in Pinedale time indicates that the lake also formed twice. This conclusion is supported by the presence of gravel deltas overlying basalt-rich flood deposits north of the Spokane River at its confluences with the Columbia River and with Chamokane Creek. Lake silt on flood deposits at 1,950 ft (595 m) altitude in the valley of the Little Spokane River shows that the second Pinedale lobe was as high as the first. Overflow again was along the ice margin at Grand Coulee.

A widespread terrace at an altitude of 1,700 ft (520 m) (Flint, 1935, 1936) and underlain by the Nespelem Silt (Pardee, 1918; Flint, 1935) represents a late stage of Lake Columbia. At first this lake extended to a rock sill on the floor of Grand Coulee; later it extended northward down the Columbia River at successively lower altitudes as the ice front receded. Waters (1933) suggested that disintegration of the ice front resulted in abrupt draining of the lake and flooding along the Columbia River downstream.

Loess Deposits on the Columbia Plateau

Eolian deposits, predominantly silt and fine sand, mantle the Columbia River Plateau. These sediments have been described variously as residual weathering products of basalt (Russell, 1897, 1901), eolian deposits (Salisbury, 1901; Calkins, 1905; Bryan, 1927; Culver, 1937; Tullis, 1944; Lewis, 1960), periglacial loess swept southward from the Cordilleran Ice Sheet (Hobbs, 1947; Campbell, 1953), and glacio-lacustrine sediments superficially reworked by wind (Treasher, 1925, 1926). The peculiar "Palouse Hills," especially along the Washington-Idaho border, have been considered (Kirkham *et al.*, 1931; Rockie, 1934; Newcomb, 1938) to be barchan-like dunes, nivation hollows, slump scars, or remnants of a dissected lacustrine plain. Within this area, the sediments attain thicknesses greater than 150 ft (45 m), and the dominant grain size is silt. We consider the deposits to be loess, locally reworked by slopewash and streams.

Four stratigraphically distinct units are recognized. Similarity in morphology and stratigraphic sequence of buried and relict soils in the loesses make correlation of these units possible throughout the region.

Pre-Bull Lake loesses are capped by very mature weathering profiles more than 3 m thick, consisting of remnants of strongly developed structural and textural B-horizons, indurated siliceous caliche, and very coarse indurated concretions of manganese dioxide. Two such weathering profiles have been recognized (Table 1). The earlier caliche usually is associated with a highly oxidized sandy tuff, which imparts to it a pinkish cast uncommon in later caliche.

Loess of Bull Lake age comprises the Palouse Formation (Treasher, 1925; Scheid, 1940; Newcomb, 1961). Together with older loesses, it has been stripped from the basalt in scabland channels and is thus older than the last catastrophic flood across the Columbia Plateau. It bears mature zonal soils having well-developed structural and textural B-horizons of lesser thickness than in soils of pre-Bull Lake age. Chalky-white Cca-horizons, less indurated than earlier caliches, characteristically occur in these soils in arid portions of the plateau. At least three such soils and three loesses of Bull Lake age can be distinguished (Table 1). A loess bearing such a soil underlies the terminal moraine of the Okanogan Lobe; another conformably overlies till of Bull Lake age near the confluence of the Columbia and Spokane Rivers.

Loess of Pinedale to Recent age overlies older loesses. That of middle Pinedale or younger age also occurs on portions of the scabland channels and is more extensive than earlier loesses. Soil profiles on loess of Pinedale age are not so strongly developed as those on loess of Bull Lake age.

They commonly have moderately developed structural and textural B-horizons, generally less than 1 m thick, and almost everywhere they lack the caliche of older soils. Soils of Recent age typically have A-C profiles of minimal development.

Greatly increased precipitation at the northeastern and eastern margins of the Columbia Plateau has caused changes in facies in all these soils; caliche and Cca-horizons are almost absent, and B-horizons display greatly increased clay accumulation and stronger structural development. Tracing of these changes from the more arid regions has demonstrated that the relative degree of development of each successive soil is similar in both areas.

Deposition of the loess by southwesterly winds from a nonglacial source is indicated (a) by the alignment of linear loess hills in south-central Washington, which closely parallels the present direction of prevailing winds (Lewis, 1960), (b) by the northeasterly orientation of the steepest slopes and the progressive northeasterly overlap of buried surfaces within the "Palouse Hills," (c) by thick deposits in the lee of bedrock ridges, over which the loess has been draped, and (d) by uniformly decreasing grain size of the loess toward the northeast. Sheetwash, streams, and local ponding played a secondary role in loess deposition. The "Palouse Hills" at the Washington-Idaho border resulted from many alternating episodes of eolian deposition and stream erosion.

Minerals common to all the loesses include quartz, feldspars, micas, and, in lesser amounts, augite, hypersthene, volcanic glass, and other heavy minerals. Some parts of the Pinedale and Recent loesses contain more than 30% volcanic glass and differ from earlier loesses in having illite rather than vermiculite as the dominant clay (Rieger and Smith, 1955; Lotspeich and Smith, 1953).

Sediments of the Ringold Formation in the western part of the plateau generally are regarded as a major source of the loess. However, other sources were also involved. Some post-scabland loess was derived from the lacustrine Touchet Beds (Flint, 1938), and probably some was derived from alluvium along the Snake and Columbia Rivers. Eolian sedimentation was most rapid after the early Pinedale catastrophic flood from Lake Missoula and during the Altithermal interval (Antevs, 1948), but locally it has continued without significant pause to the present.

The Ringold Formation and Pleistocene Deformation of the Columbia Plateau

Sediments older than the Palouse Formation and overlying the Miocene and Pliocene(?) Columbia River Basalt, in the Pasco and Quincy Basins (Fig. 1), are known as the Ringold Formation (Merriam and Buwalda, 1917). In the Pasco Basin these deposits exceed 600 ft (185 m) in thickness and are divided into three parts (Newcomb, 1958): a lower unit of "blue clays" including local sand and gravel; a middle unit of oxidized sand and gravel, locally conglomeratic, which grades basinward into sand and silt; and an upper unit of lacustrine and eolian sand, silt, and clay. A conspicuous weathering profile, consisting of a thick oxidized zone on a highly siliceous caliche, defines the upper limit of the formation (Culver, 1937). Vertebrate fossils from the middle and upper units are of Pleistocene age (Strand and Hough, 1952). The lower part may possibly be Pliocene.

Most of the Ringold Formation is believed to postdate broad folding and dissection of the Columbia Plateau in Pliocene time (Chaney, 1959; Mackin, 1961), though in the deeper parts of the basins it may contain some sediment contemporaneous with downwarping. Folding may have continued during deposition because sediments eroded from gradually rising monoclinal ridges overlap the ridges disconformably. Later deformation of the Ringold (Brown and McConiga, 1960) is indicated by local warping and faulting of the middle and upper units at Saddle Mountain and Frenchman Hills (Fig. 1) and by deep youthful erosion of a former mature topography on the anticlinal uplands. Both deformation and erosion are locally younger than caliche marking the top of the formation.

EARLY CATASTROPHIC FLOODS ON THE COLUMBIA PLATEAU

EARLY FLOODS FROM THE WEST

The oldest known catastrophic floods on the Columbia Plateau are recorded by deposits in the western part of Quincy Basin east of the Columbia River (Fig. 1). There, beneath 1.5 m of hard, white siliceous caliche of probable pre-Bull Lake age (Table 1), are deposits of boulder gravel with foreset beds dipping southeast (Bretz *et al.*, 1956). Rapid eastward gradation—from piles of unsorted boulders, indicative of chaotic deposition, to well-sorted pebbly sand, containing rock types absent to the east but abundantly exposed along the canyon of the Columbia River—shows that these deposits came from the west. A deep catastrophic flood sloping to the southeast is suggested by the southeastward decrease in altitude of these flood deposits on drainage divides. Similar deposits overlying the caliche, but eroded by the early Pinedale flood-waters from Lake Missoula, suggest that a second flood from the west probably took place in Bull Lake time. The source of these floods is not known.

EARLY FLOODS FROM GLACIAL LAKE MISSOULA

The ice dams at the mouth of the Clark Fork River, which repeatedly stored great volumes of water in Glacial Lake Missoula, were breached repeatedly by overflow from the lake, although at least one gradual withdrawal of the lake is documented (Pardee, 1942). Deposits of three major floods from Glacial Lake Missoula have been distinguished on the Columbia Plateau, and as many as seven have been suggested on the basis of physiographic evidence (Bretz *et al.*, 1956; Bretz, 1959).

Deposits thought to record a pre-Bull Lake flood lie in the upper reaches of Old Maid Coulee (Bretz *et al.*, 1956), at the mouth of Lind Coulee, and along the northwestern margin of Washtucna Coulee (Fig. 1). These deposits are either capped by thick caliche or lie beyond reach of later floods. A flood in Bull Lake time is recorded by two deposits. One deposit, at Cheney (Fig. 1), consists of characteristic flood gravel that includes boulders of loess and soft Miocene clay; it is separated from overlying flood gravel of Pinedale age by a mature zonal brown soil. The second deposit of Bull Lake age is in the canyon of the Columbia River 10 km

north of Vantage (Fig. 1). There the flood gravel contains pebbles of interbasalt diatomite from Quincy Basin to the east and is separated from overlying flood deposits of Pinedale age by a zone of soil carbonate 45 cm thick.

THE LAST CATASTROPHIC FLOOD FROM GLACIAL LAKE MISSOULA

The youngest catastrophic flood, first recognized and described by Bretz (1923), scoured moraines and other deposits of early Pinedale age. Its deposits overlie early Pinedale glacial and lake deposits and are themselves overlain by moraines and other deposits of middle Pinedale age. Transported wood in the deposits of the flood at Vantage, but probably derived from older deposits, yields a radiocarbon date of 32,700 ± 900 years (UW-9; Fryxell, 1962).

THE FLOOD PATH FROM GLACIAL LAKE MISSOULA TO SPOKANE

From the mouth of the Clark Fork River to Spokane, water released by collapse of the early Pinedale ice dam reshaped or destroyed all earlier deposits in its path. No older flood deposits have been found here, though such floods could have found no other outlet. Effects of the Pinedale flood, however, are widespread. High-level eddy deposits and erosional features record a water surface sloping 10 ft/mile (2 m/km) from an altitude of about 3,000 ft (900 m) at the south end of Lake Pend Oreille westward to 2,600 ft (795 m) near Lake Coeur d'Alene and 2,525 ft (770 m) near Spokane.

The flood surged into the basin of Lake Coeur d'Alene, spilling southwest across a divide at Setters (Fig. 1) and carrying ice-rafted boulders up tributary valleys to altitudes as high as 2,665 ft (813 m). East of Spokane, the velocity of the flood was checked sufficiently to cause most of the bedload of granitic rocks to be dropped; a short distance south on the basalt plateau, flood deposits are typically more than 90% basalt. The surface of Glacial Lake Columbia, controlled by the basalt plateau and the ice dam at Grand Coulee, was at an altitude of 1,950 ft (595 m) immediately before the flood. Flood-water raised the lake level more than 500 ft (150 m) and spilled southward through a succession of drainage divides, all above 2,450 ft (750 m), that extend from Cheney to Grand Coulee.

Discharge of flood-water through these distributaries reduced the flood surface gradient to about one foot per mile (0.2 m/km) between Spokane and the Columbia River, and the maximum flood level decreased westward to 2,480 ft (750 m) at the mouth of Spokane River (Becraft and Weis, 1963).

THE CHANNELED SCABLANDS

Flood-water traversed the Columbia Plateau along two great tracts from which the Palouse Formation was stripped, and the basalt scoured to form channels and cataracts. Drainage divides were indiscriminately crossed and recrossed, and the margins of the flood tracts were strewn with debris. When the flood subsided the coulees were left free of drainage.

The remarkable network of anastomosing channels left by the flood comprises the "channeled scablands" (Bretz, 1923). Erosional and depositional features characteristic of these tracts are wholly unlike those of normal stream valleys.

Joint-controlled plucking and quarrying of basalt (Bretz, 1924) by water of great depth and velocity eroded linear tracts as wide as 30 km in places, occupying drainage divides 300 to 400 ft (90-120 m) above adjacent valley floors. Empty bedrock basins 30 m or more deep are found on the crests of such divides, and closed depressions twice as deep occur in the floors of narrow coulees. Huge cataracts up to 5 km in width were cut in divides and across structural ridges crossed by the flood. Differential erosion of weakly resistant flows has left benches and butte-like remnants of basalt along many tracts, and stripping of loess is recorded by steep marginal scarps in loess and by streamlined loess "islands" within channels.

Debris left by the flood consists of poorly sorted bouldery gravel forming deltas below cataracts and constructional bars in mid-channels. Bars also were built along canyon walls and across the mouths of tributary canyons. Characteristically these features retain their constructional form. Exposures show torrential foreset bedding dipping downcurrent and up the mouths of tributary valleys. Boulders of loess and other poorly consolidated sediments, freshly quarried angular basalt columns, and battered cobbles showing percussion marks occur in most deposits. Giant ripple marks constructed of coarse gravel mark the surfaces of many bars.

Interpretations of this bizarre landscape have ranged from initial recognition of these features as simply being related to normal discharge from Pleistocene glaciers (Russell, 1898; Leighton, 1919) to the hypothesis of catastrophic flooding, which has been conclusively demonstrated by Bretz (1923 and many subsequent publications) over the past 30 years.

Largest of the flood-channel systems is the Cheney-Palouse scabland tract, which lay directly in the path of the flood southwest of Spokane. Within this tract, flood features are most spectacularly displayed; as in all the tracts, these features require enormous discharge and high velocity.

From a maximum altitude of 2,525 ft (770 m) at the head of the tract, the flood surface dropped to 1,300 ft (400 m) in the vicinity of Palouse Falls (Bretz, 1929). There the water swept across the drainage divide south of the Palouse River, stripping bare a swath 14 km wide (Trimble, 1954; Gard and Waldron, 1954), and poured directly into the Snake River Canyon. Twenty-five kilometers west, another branch simultaneously spilled again into the Snake, cutting a slot-like spillway 400 ft (120 m) into basalt. In the valley of the Palouse River, flood-water flowed at an altitude of about 1,250 ft (380 m) directly into Pasco Basin. When the flood subsided, the Palouse River remained entrenched in a narrow, joint-controlled passage across the old divide at Palouse Falls (Trimble, 1950), from where it now drops 196 ft (60 m) over an otherwise abandoned cataract. To the west the pre-flood canyon of the Palouse continues for more than 55 km without drainage.

West of the Cheney-Palouse tract, water that crossed a series of divides coalesced to form a second network of scabland channels (Fig. 1) that discharged into Quincy Basin.

At Coulee Dam, the flood was deflected southward by the Okanogan Ice Lobe and poured along the ice front down the east side of Grand Coulee, which had been eroded by the Columbia River during previous glacial episodes (Bretz,

1932). Beyond the coulee, the water flushed into Quincy Basin and discharged simultaneously down Drumheller Channels into Pasco Basin and over the Frenchman Springs, Potholes, and Crater Draw cataracts (Fig. 1) into the Columbia River. Huge deltas were built across the canyon of the Columbia River at the mouth of each cataract, and water filled the canyon at Vantage to depths greater than 700 ft (215 m).

Water from all tracts eventually reached the lower Columbia. The narrows at Wallula Gap (immediately south of area shown on Figure 1) caused hydraulic damming of the flood, raising the water surface to an altitude of about 1,250 ft (380 m), as recorded by the upper limit of ice-rafted erratics in Pasco Basin. Coarse gravel deposits near Vantage, in Pasco Basin, and in the canyon of the Snake River grade upward and laterally into rhythmically bedded silt, the Touchet Beds (Flint, 1938), which consist of the suspended load of this lake deposited in slack water. Below Wallula Gap, the escaping flood-water continued with renewed violence, sweeping the Columbia to depths of at least 750 ft (230 m) as far as Portland, Oregon, where it formed a massive delta (Bretz, 1925, 1928).

Readvance of the Okanogan Lobe in mid-Pinedale time, after subsidence of the flood, blocked the upper part of Grand Coulee, and no substantial drainage has passed through it since the ice withdrew.

LATE- AND POSTGLACIAL HISTORY OF THE REGION

Gradual thinning of the Cordilleran Ice Sheet resulted first in exposure of the mountain ridges and segregation of the ice into individual valley lobes; eventual stagnation is recorded by widespread kame terraces and other ice-contact features in the valleys and by kame-and-kettle topography on the Okanogan Plateau (Flint, 1935). Deposition of outwash across the surface of stagnant ice masses along the Okanogan and Columbia Rivers resulted in construction of the Great Terrace of Russell (1898) at an altitude of about 1,200 ft (365 m).

A postglacial episode of maximum warmth and drought between 8,000 and 4,000 years ago is inferred from the pollen record of peat bogs in the Pacific Northwest (Hansen, 1947). This interval of minimum effective precipitation—the Altithermal interval of Antevs (1948)—reached its peak between 6,500 and 4,500 years ago. At this time, loess was deposited and ventifacts were formed on desiccated terraces that are now beneath low water of the Columbia River; many tributary streams became intermittent and gullies were alluviated; rockfall in caves diminished; talus slopes were partially or wholly stabilized; and mudflow deposits became less abundant. Archaeological studies suggest that extinction of some Pleistocene animals and a general decrease in abundance of big game forced prehistoric men to rely more on fishing and gathering than on hunting (Cressman et al., 1940; Daugherty, 1956, 1962; Butler, 1962; Swanson, 1962). Subsequent episodes of increased moisture are thought to have been contemporaneous with pulsations of cirque glaciers during the Temple Lake and Gannett Peak Stades of Neoglaciation in the Rocky Mountains (Richmond, this volume).

Correlation of these events is aided by the regional distribution of two volcanic ash beds (Powers and Wilcox, 1964; Fryxell, 1965; Wilcox, this volume) (Table 1). The earlier of these is attributed to an eruption at Glacier Peak in the northern Cascade Mountains and occurred after recession of the Okanogan Lobe from the Columbia Plateau. A radiocarbon date of 12,000 ± 310 years B.P. (WSU-155) was obtained from peat interlayered in the ash (Fryxell, 1965). The younger ashfall, which is more widespread and more commonly exposed, has been traced to a catastrophic eruption of Mount Mazama at Crater Lake, Oregon (Powers and Wilcox, 1964). Numerous radiocarbon dates place the age of this event at about 6,600 years ago.

REFERENCES

Alden, W. C., 1953, Physiography and glacial geology of western Montana and adjacent areas: U.S. Geol. Surv. Prof. Pap. 231, 200 p.

Anderson, A. L., 1927, Some Miocene and Pleistocene drainage changes in northern Idaho: Idaho Bur. Mines Geol. Pamph. 18, 29 p.

Antevs, Ernst, 1948, The Great Basin, with emphasis on glacial and postglacial times: Climatic changes and pre-white man: Univ. Utah Bull. 33, p. 168-191

Becraft, G. E., and Weis, P. L., 1963, Geology and mineral deposits of the Turtle Lake quadrangle, Washington: U.S. Geol. Surv. Bull. 1131, 73 p.

Bretz, J H., 1923, Glacial drainage on the Columbia Plateau: Geol. Soc. Amer. Bull., v. 34, p. 573-608

—— 1924, The age of the Spokane glaciation: Amer. J. Sci., 5th ser., v. 8, p. 336-342

—— 1925, The Spokane Flood beyond the channeled scablands: J. Geol., v. 33, p. 97-115, 236-259

—— 1928, The channeled scabland of eastern Washington: Geogr. Rev., v. 18, p. 446-477

—— 1929, Valley deposits east of the channeled scablands of Washington: J. Geol., v. 37, p. 393-427, 505-541

—— 1932, The Grand Coulee: Amer. Geogr. Soc. Spec. Publ. 15, 89 p.

—— 1959, Washington's channeled scabland: Washington Div. Mines Geol. Bull. 45, 57 p.

Bretz, J H., Smith, H. T. U., and Neff, G. E., 1956, Channeled scabland of Washington: New data and interpretations: Geol. Soc. Amer. Bull., v. 67, p. 957-1049

Brown, R. E., and McConiga, M. W., 1960, Some contributions to the stratigraphy and indicated deformation of the Ringold Formation: Northwest Sci., v. 34, p. 43-54

Bryan, Kirk, 1927, The "Palouse soil" problem: U.S. Geol. Surv. Bull. 790, p. 21-45

Butler, B. R., 1962, Contributions to the Prehistory of the Columbia Plateau: Idaho State Coll., Mus. Occ. Pap. 9, 86 p.

Calkins, F. C., 1905, Geology and water resources of a portion of east-central Washington: U.S. Geol. Surv. Water-Supply Pap. 118, 96 p.

Campbell, C. D., 1953, Washington geology and resources: Washington State Coll. Resource Stud., v. 21, p. 114-153

Chaney, R. W., 1959, Miocene floras of the Columbia Plateau: Carnegie Instn. Publ. 617, 237 p.

Crandell, D. R., this volume, The glacial history of western Washington and Oregon

Cressman, L. S., Williams, Howel, and Krieger, A. D., 1940, Early Man in Oregon: Archaeological Studies in the northern Great Basin: Univ. Oregon Monogr. 3, Studies in Anthropology, p. 1-78

Culver, H. E., 1937, Extensions of the Ringold formation: Northwest Sci., v. 11, p. 57-60

Daugherty, R. D., 1956, The archaeology of the Lind Coulee Site, Washington: Amer. Philos. Soc. Proc., v. 100, p. 223-278

—— 1962, The intermontane western tradition: Amer. Antiq., v. 28, p. 144-150

Dort, Wakefield, Jr., 1958, Gold-bearing gravels near Murray, Idaho: Idaho Bur. Mines Geol. Pamph. 116, 21 p.

—— 1960, Glacial Lake Coeur d'Alene and berg-rafted boulders: Idaho Acad. Sci. J., v. 1, p. 81-92

—— 1962, Glaciation of the Coeur d'Alene district, Idaho: Geol. Soc. Amer. Bull., v. 73, p. 889-906

Flint, R. F., 1935, Glacial features of the southern Okanogan region: Geol. Soc. Amer. Bull., v. 46, p. 169-194

—— 1936, Stratified drift and deglaciation in eastern Washington: Geol. Soc. Amer. Bull., v. 47, p. 1849-1884

—— 1937, Pleistocene drift border of eastern Washington: Geol. Soc. Amer. Bull., v. 48, p. 203-232

—— 1938, Origin of the Cheney-Palouse scabland tract, Washington: Geol. Soc. Amer. Bull., v. 49, p. 461-523

Flint, R. F., and Irwin, W. H., 1939, Glacial geology of Grand Coulee dam, Washington: Geol. Soc. Amer. Bull., v. 50, p. 661-680

Fryxell, Roald, 1962, A radiocarbon limiting date for scabland flooding: Northwest Sci., v. 36, p. 113-119

—— 1965, Mazama and Glacier Peak volcanic ash layers; relative ages: Science, v. 147, p. 1288-1290

Gard, L. M., Jr., and Waldron, H. H., 1954, Geology of the Starbuck quadrangle, Washington: U.S. Geol. Surv. Geol. Quad. Map GQ-38

Hansen, H. P., 1947, Postglacial forest succession, climate and chronology in the Pacific Northwest: Amer. Philos. Soc. Trans., v. 37, p. 1-130

Hershey, O. H., 1912, Some Tertiary and Quaternary geology of western Montana, northern Idaho, and eastern Washington: Geol. Soc. Amer. Bull., v. 23, p. 517-536

Hobbs, W. H., 1947, The glacial history of the Scabland and Okanogan Lobes, Cordilleran Continental Glacier: Ann Arbor, Mich., J. W. Edwards, 36 p.

Kirkham, V. R. D., Johnson, M. M., and Holm, Donald, 1931, the origin of the Palouse Hills topography: Science, v. 73, p. 207-209

Large, Thomas, 1922, The glaciation of the Cordilleran region: Science, v. 56, p. 335-336

Leighton, M. M., 1919, The road-building sand and gravel of Washington: Washington Geol. Surv. Bull. 22, 307 p.

Lewis, H. G., and Denecke, W. A., 1923, Soil survey of Kootenai County, Idaho: U.S. Dept. Agric., Bur. Soils, 45 p.

Lewis, P. F., 1960, Linear topography in the southwestern Palouse, Washington-Oregon: Assoc. Amer. Geogr. Ann., v. 50, p. 98-111

Lotspeich, F. B., and Smith, H. W., 1953, Soils of the Palouse loess: Pt. I. The Palouse Catena *in*: Soil Sci., v. 76, p. 467-480

Mackin, J. H., 1961, A stratigraphic section in the Yakima Basalt and the Ellensburg Formation in south-central Washington: Washington Div. Mines Geol., Rep. Inv. 19, 45 p.

Merriam, J. C., and Buwalda, J. P., 1917, Age of strata referred to the Ellensburg Formation in the White Bluffs of the Columbia River: Berkeley, Univ. California Dept. Geol. Sci. Bull., v. 10, 255-266

Newcomb, R. C., 1938, Cause of the asymmetrical profiles of the typical Palouse hill: Northwest Sci., v. 12, p. 96.

—— 1958, Ringold formation of Pleistocene age in type locality, the White Bluffs, Washington: Amer. J. Sci., v. 256, p. 328-340

—— 1961, Age of the Palouse-Formation in the Walla Walla and Umatilla River Basins, Oregon and Washington: Northwest Sci., v. 35, p. 122-127

Nobles, L. H., 1952, Glacial sequence in the Mission Valley, western Montana (abst.): Geol. Soc. Amer. Bull., v. 63, p. 1286

Pardee, J. T., 1910, The glacial Lake Missoula, Montana: J. Geol., v. 8, p. 376-386

—— 1918, Geology and mineral deposits of the Colville Indian Reservation, Washington: U.S. Geol. Surv. Bull. 677, 186 p.

—— 1942, Unusual currents in glacial lake Missoula, Montana: Geol. Soc. Amer. Bull., v. 53, p. 1569-1599

Powers, H. A., and Wilcox, R. E., 1964, Volcanic ash deposits from Mount Mazama (Crater Lake) and from Glacier Peak: Science, v. 144, p. 1334-1336

Richmond, G. M., this volume, Glaciation of the Rocky Mountains

Rieger, Samuel, and Smith, H. W., 1955, Soils of the Palouse Loess, II. Development of the A_2 horizon: Soil Sci. 79, p. 301-319

Rockie, W. A., 1934, Snowdrifts and the Palouse topography: Geogr. Rev., v. 24, p. 380-385

Russell, I. C., 1897, A reconnaissance in southeastern Washington: U.S. Geol. Surv. Water-Supply Pap. 4, 96 p.

—— 1898, The great terrace of the Columbia and other topographic features in the neighborhood of Lake Chelan, Washington: Amer. Geol., v. 22, p. 362-369

—— 1901, Geology and water resources of Nez Perce County, Idaho (Part I: U.S. Geol. Surv. Water-Supply Pap. 53, p. 1-85

Salisbury, R. D., 1901, Glacial work in the western mountains in 1901: J. Geol., v. 9, p. 718-731

Scheid, V. E., 1940, Significance of a fossil horse tooth found at Moscow, Idaho: Northwest Sci., v. 14, p. 55-57

Strand, J. R., and Hough, Margaret J., 1952, Age of the Ringold formation: Northwest Sci., v. 26, p. 152-154

Swanson, Earl, 1962, The emergence of Plateau Culture: Mus. Idaho State Coll., Occ. Pap. 8, 89 p.

Treasher, R. C., 1925, Origin of the loess of the Palouse region, Washington: Science, v. 61, p. 469

—— 1926, Stratigraphic aspects of loess of Palouse region: Pan-Amer. Geologist, v. 46, p. 305-314

Trimble, D. E., 1950, Joint controlled channeling in the Columbia River basalt: Northwest Sci., v. 24, p. 84-88

—— 1954, Geology of the Haas quadrangle, Washington: U.S. Geol. Surv. Geol. Quad. Map GQ-43

Tullis, E. L., 1944, Contribution to the geology of Latah County, Idaho: Geol. Soc. Amer. Bull., v. 55, p. 131-163

Walker, G. E., 1964, Ground-water in the Sandpoint region, Bonner County, Idaho: U.S. Geol. Surv. Water-Supply Pap. 1779-I, 29 p.

Waters, A. C., 1933, Terraces and coulees along the Columbia River near Lake Chelan, Washington: Geol. Soc. Amer. Bull., v. 44, p. 783-820

Wilcox, Ray E., this volume, Volcanic-ash chronology

SUMMARY

The Cordilleran Ice Sheet covered most of the Rocky Mountains west of the Continental Divide during each major Quaternary glacial advance. It extended southward onto the Columbia Plateau only west of Grand Coulee. In western Montana, one pre-Bull Lake glaciation, two stades of Bull Lake Glaciation, three stades of Pinedale Glaciation, and two stades of cirque Neoglaciation are known. In eastern Washington, one stade of Bull Lake Glaciation, two stades of Pinedale Glaciation, and cirque Neoglaciation are recognized. Major recessions separated stades of Bull Lake Glaciation; minor recessions separated stades of Pinedale Glaciation.

The ice sheet blocked the Clark Fork River at Lake Pend Oreille at least five times, impounding Glacial Lake Missoula; and it blocked the Columbia River at Grand Coulee at least three times, impounding Glacial Lake Columbia. During Bull Lake Glaciation the ice also blocked the Spokane River—at Coeur d'Alene, impounding Glacial Lake Coeur d'Alene, and at Long Lake, impounding Glacial Lake Spokane.

The ice dam impounding Glacial Lake Missoula collapsed at least three times, releasing catastrophic floods of enormous magnitude across the Columbia Plateau: once before and once during Bull Lake Glaciation, and once just after the early Pinedale glacial maximum.

Loess accumulated on the plateau during each glaciation. At least seven different Pleistocene loesses and a Recent loess are recognized: two are of pre-Bull Lake age; at least three, which comprise the Palouse Formation, are of Bull Lake age; two or more are of Pinedale age; and one is of Recent origin.

NONGLACIAL QUATERNARY GEOLOGY OF THE SOUTHERN AND MIDDLE ROCKY MOUNTAINS[*]

GLENN R. SCOTT[1]

The region discussed in this paper includes the piedmont east of the Front Range in Colorado (Fig. 1) in addition to the principal basins within the Rocky Mountains in Colorado, Wyoming, and southwestern Montana. The basins of Utah are not discussed.

The purpose of the paper is to summarize the Quaternary geology of the Colorado Piedmont and those basins that are unglaciated parts of the region shown on Figure 1. The summary is based on many published and unpublished reports and on detailed studies of the Colorado Piedmont by the author. Previous work in most of the area is inadequate and outdated in light of new concepts and techniques in absolute dating, soil stratigraphy, and geomorphology. Specifically, detailed surficial geologic maps and reports are lacking that would give the details necessary for making local and regional correlations. Preparation of the summary revealed a need for modern detailed stratigraphic studies of surficial deposits in nearly every basin.

The general physiographic and geologic setting will be discussed first, and then the Quaternary geology of the piedmont and the individual basins. The Quaternary geology of the Denver-Julesburg basin part of the Colorado Piedmont (Fig. 1) is known better than that of any of the intermontane basins; thus, it is chosen to represent the nonglacial deposits of the Southern and Middle Rocky Mountains and is discussed in more detail than the other basins.

PHYSIOGRAPHY AND GEOLOGY

The Southern and Middle Rocky Mountains consist of broad northward-trending belts of Precambrian crystalline rocks or Tertiary igneous rocks generally flanked by steeply dipping sedimentary rocks (Fenneman, 1931). Structurally the mountains are large, deeply eroded anticlines, from which erosion has removed once continuous sedimentary strata and also much crystalline rock. The resulting detritus has accumulated in basins adjoining the mountains or has been carried entirely out of the region by through-flowing streams.

The basins are down-warped areas that occupy much more area than the bordering mountains. The basin floors lie at 5,500 to 7,500 ft (1,700-2,300 m) altitude, and their gentle relief is interrupted only by isolated ridges or peaks. The basins were formed in the Tertiary Period, and most of them contain thick fills of nonmarine Tertiary sedimentary rocks.

Quaternary deposits forming the upper parts of the basin fills are mostly fluvial, but some originated by eolian, lacustrine, and mass-wasting processes. Together they probably cover less than one-half of the total area of most basins. Fluvial deposits probably comprise more than one-half the area covered by all surficial deposits; they include outwash along major glacial streams and nonglacial alluvium deposited by local streams of all sizes on pediments and on cut terraces or in fill terraces. Nonglacial alluvium on the pediments forms a steeply sloping bouldery deposit near the mountain front, but it is a gently sloping, coarse sandy or pebbly deposit near the center of each basin. Alluvium in valley fills becomes more uniform in texture toward the center of each basin. Fills that were not later channeled by streams are called straths; remnants of fills that were channeled are called fill terraces. The terms bench, level, and surface, as adapted from the references cited, are applied to flat planes cut on bedrock by stream action or to the tops of alluvial deposits. Loess and eolian sand are most abundant on the Great Plains east of the mountains, but some small deposits lie in the basins, and one huge deposit of eolian sand is in the Great Sand Dunes National Monument in the San Luis Valley. Colluvium, landslides, and solifluction deposits are widespread in all areas but are not described because of a lack of information about their sequential development.

The surficial deposits are the result of repetitive physical processes controlled by cyclic changes in climate. The number and intensity of the climatic cycles can best be inferred from alluvial deposits because alluvium is deposited during every cycle and generally is well preserved. The sum of the physical processes of each complete climatic cycle is here called a geomorphic cycle. Interpretation of the geologic record shows that an ideal geomorphic cycle is made up of five processes, in chronologic order: (1) downward stream cutting, (2) sideward stream cutting, (3) alluviation, (4) wind erosion and deposition, and (5) soil formation. A change from one process to another can be caused by any combination of changes in temperature, precipitation, discharge, and load. The general effect of each geomorphic cycle has been to force the streams down to a lower base level that is stable until renewed climatic changes generate the next geomorphic cycle. Alluvial deposits in the Colorado Piedmont are correlated here with interglaciations, in contrast to the tendency of most authors of articles on the intermontane basins to correlate them with glaciations.

Tectonic movements were of primary importance during creation of the basins but thereafter were not a dominant

[*] Publication authorized by the Director, U.S. Geological Survey.
[1] U.S. Geological Survey, Federal Center, Denver, Colorado.

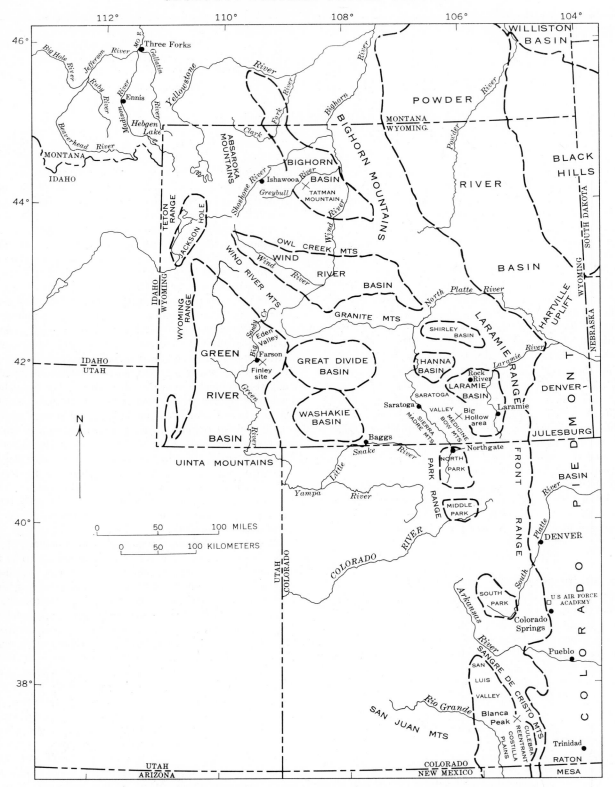

Figure 1. Principal intermontane basins and valleys in the southern and middle Rocky Mountains.

force. Faults that have disturbed Quaternary deposits are known in several of the basins. The most recently active fault is at Hebgen Lake in the headwaters of the Missouri River (Witkind, 1964, p. 37). Faults along the east side of San Luis Valley (Upson, 1939, p. 731) indicate that the valley was still sagging in relation to the mountains in Quaternary time. In eastern Colorado only three faults are known to cut deposits of the three latest pediments. Folding or tilting of the Quaternary deposits is unknown in eastern Colorado.

GEOLOGY OF THE COLORADO PIEDMONT

The Colorado Piedmont lies adjacent to the Front Range in central Colorado. At its western edge the Piedmont reaches altitudes of 5,500 to 7,500 ft (1,700-2,300 m), from which it slopes continuously and gently eastward. It is underlain by nearly horizontal sedimentary rocks of Paleozoic to Cenozoic age that turn up steeply along the mountain front. Resistant sandstone beds in this sequence make extensive hogbacks parallel to the mountain front. Easily erodible Upper Cretaceous shale and sandstone and Tertiary arkose directly underlie most of the Piedmont.

QUATERNARY DEPOSITS

Quaternary deposits of the area include nine named alluvial formations (Table 1), bog clay, landslides, and three major deposits of eolian sand and loess. Alluvium of nearly every age intertongues with contemporaneous colluvial deposits.

Most of the detailed work on the surficial deposits of the piedmont area near Denver, Colorado, has been done by Hunt (1954), Malde (1955), Scott (1960a, b, 1961, 1962, 1963a, b), Wells (1963), and others whose work is not yet published. Geologic mapping elsewhere in the Colorado Piedmont has shown alluvial sequences to be nearly identical to the sequence at Denver (Scott, 1963a, p. 53). This mapping includes work by Bryan and Ray (1940) near Greeley, by D. J. Varnes and Scott at the United States Air Force Academy near Colorado Springs, by Scott (1964) at Pueblo, and by Levings (1951) at Raton Mesa near Trinidad.

Criteria used to differentiate the deposits have been varied, and their appropriateness depends on the character of the local deposits. The order of stratigraphic succession is of foremost use in all areas, height above modern streams is second in value, and characteristics of the ancient soils is third. Less used because of scarcity or limited applicability are lithology, fossils, artifacts, marker beds such as volcanic ash, and radiocarbon dates.

Pre-Wisconsin deposits. Pre-Wisconsin surficial deposits in the Piedmont include Nussbaum Alluvium (oldest), Rocky Flats Alluvium, Verdos Alluvium, and Slocum Alluvium (youngest), all of which are gravelly veneers on pediments. The pediments are imperfect, being remnants of nearly featureless surfaces cut on bedrock across the floors of broad valleys. The deposits lie between 30 and 450 ft (9 and 135 m) above modern streams. The soils on the surficial deposits, unless buried after formation, are the product of all soil-forming times since deposition, but they are named from the time of the first formation.

The Nussbaum Alluvium (Gilbert, 1897; Scott, 1963b) of Pleistocene(?) age consists of 20 to 80 ft (6-25 m) of light-brownish-gray, poorly sorted cobble and boulder pediment gravel near the mountains and 100 ft (30 m) of well-sorted coarse sand in flat-floored valley fills far from the mountains. It lies on a broad pediment that slopes gently eastward. Near the mountain front the pediment is thinly veneered by Nussbaum Alluvium that lies about 320 to 450 ft (100-140 m) above modern streams. Close to the Kansas border, the surface of the alluvium lies 250 ft (75 m) below the Ogallala Formation, which is usually considered Pliocene in age but according to some authors may be as old as Miocene (Scott, 1963b). The Nussbaum Alluvium originally formed widespread, thin covers of gravel on pediments but locally was later augmented by valley fills that made the total deposit thicker than the possible depth of stream scour. The deposits now have been eroded to remnants preserved in isolated high mesas. A well-developed pre-Wisconsin soil has formed in the upper part of the alluvium.

The Rocky Flats Alluvium (Scott, 1960b), of Nebraskan or Aftonian age, consists of 10 to 40 ft (3-12 m) of reddish-brown, poorly sorted, well-stratified, coarse gravel to coarse sand. It covers pediments about 250 to 380 ft (75-120 m) above modern streams; it once was widespread over the area but now is restricted to a few large mesas, ridges, and knobs. Podzolic, Brown Forest, or Brown soils of Aftonian(?) age have been developed on the alluvium, depending on the type of vegetative cover.

The Verdos Alluvium (Scott, 1960b) of Kansan or Yarmouth age consists of 15 to 35 ft (5-11 m) of brown, well-stratified, coarse gravel to coarse sand. It veneers pediments that lie about 200 to 250 ft (60-75 m) above modern streams. The lower part of the Verdos Alluvium locally contains lenses of volcanic ash that has close chemical and petrographic similarities to the Pearlette Ash of Kansas (Powers *et al.*, 1958). Hibbard (1958) assigned a late Kansan age to the Pearlette Ash on the basis of vertebrate and molluscan fossils. The volcanic ash near Denver is thought to be a reliable stratigraphic marker in the Quaternary sequence and an indicator of Kansan or Yarmouth age. A Yarmouth(?) Brown soil is developed on the Verdos Alluvium.

The Slocum Alluvium (Scott, 1960b), of Illinoian or Sangamon age, ranges between 10 and 90 ft (3 and 27 m) in thickness and consists of moderate reddish-brown, well-stratified, clayey, coarse gravel or coarse sand with lenticular beds of pebbles and silt. It lies on pediments 80 to 120 ft (25-35 m) above modern streams near the mountains and in fill terraces as low as 30 ft (9 m) above modern streams far from the mountains. It contains a molluscan fauna that suggests deposition during a warmer climate than now. Because of this climatic inference the age of the Slocum and the other pediment alluviums was extended to include a part of interglacial time as well as part of glacial time. The Slocum Alluvium is the youngest fluvial deposit of recognized pre-Wisconsin age.

Loess of Sangamon age locally overlies Slocum Alluvium in sheets less than 5 ft (2 m) thick. The loess is moderate brown sandy or clayey silt. On it, and on the Slocum Alluvium where the loess is absent, a Sangamon(?) Brown soil is developed.

Wisconsin deposits. Wisconsin deposits in the piedmont area include the Louviers Alluvium and the Broadway Alluvium, valley fills which are respectively about 50 and 30 ft (15 and 9 m) above modern streams. During the interval between deposition of the two formations, loess was deposited in the piedmont area. Both alluvial deposits tentatively are as-

TABLE 1

Correlation of Glacial and Nonglacial Sequences in Rocky Mountains with Nonglacial Sequence in Nebraska
(Blank spaces indicate no record of deposit or event.)

Years before present	Standard glacial sequence		Glacial sequence, Rocky Mountains (Richmond, written communication, 1964)		Nonglacial stratigraphic sequence, Rocky Mountains–Denver area	Nonglacial stratigraphic sequence, Nebraska (Schultz et al., 1951)
800 —	Recent		Neoglaciation	Gannett Peak Stade	Loess and eolian sand Post-Piney Creek alluvium	Soil Z[1] Silt and loess
				Interstade		
1,500 — 2,000 —					Late Recent soil Piney Creek Alluvium	Soil Z Cochrane silt and loess
3,000 — 4,000 —				Temple Lake Stade		
			"Altithermal interval"		Early Recent soil Eolian sand Pre-Piney Creek alluvium	Soil Y
6,000 — 8,500 —	Pleistocene	Wisconsin	"Classical Wisconsin"	Pinedale Glaciation	Late stage	Broadway Alluvium	T2 A fill Soil YY, Bignell soil T2 B fill
10,000 —					Interstade	Wisconsin soil Younger loess	Soil X, Brady soil Silt and loess Soil W
12,000 —					Middle stage	Louviers Alluvium	Todd Valley Formation
>25,000 —					Early stage		
>32,000 —			Older Wisconsin	Bull Lake Glaciation	Interglaciation		
					Late stage		
					Interstade		
					Early stage		
		Pre-Wisconsin	Sangamon	Interglaciation		Sangamon(?) soil Older loess Slocum Alluvium	Sangamon soil Loveland Formation Crete Formation
			Illinoian	Sacagawea Ridge Glaciation			
			Yarmouth	Interglaciation		Yarmouth(?) soil Verdos Alluvium Local volcanic ash	Yarmouth soil Sappa Formation Pearlette Ash Member
			Kansan	Cedar Ridge Glaciation			Grand Island Formation Red Cloud Formation
			Aftonian	Interglaciation		Aftonian(?) soil Rocky Flats Alluvium	Aftonian soil Fullerton Formation
			Nebraskan	Washakie Point Glaciation			Holdrege Formation
	Pleistocene (?)			Deposition of high terrace gravel		Nussbaum Alluvium	

signed a "Classical Wisconsin" (equals Pinedale) age (Table 1) because of the absence of evidence that would permit placing the Louviers Alluvium in the older Wisconsin.

The absence of alluvium of recognized older Wisconsin (equals Bull Lake) age near Denver, in the other intermontane basins, and in the Central Great Plains is attributed to the possibility that this alluvium is included with pre-Wisconsin deposits because its soil is comparable to the pre-Wisconsin soils.

Louviers Alluvium (Scott, 1960b) of early Wisconsin age forms a well-developed terrace 40 to 80 ft (12-25 m) above modern streams. It consists of two facies: a reddish- or moderate-brown, well-stratified, coarse sand and gravel facies 10 to 120 ft (3-37 m) thick along large streams, which may be partly outwash; and a yellowish-brown silty facies 15 to 25 ft (5-8 m) thick along small streams, which is nonglacial. Both facies are characterized locally by graded bedding, indicating decreasing competence during deposition, and by iron and manganese oxide stains. The coarse-grained facies also contains layers of contorted clay, silt, and sand. Fossil mollusks and mammals, including mammoth, camel, and giant bison (Scott, 1963a), indicate deposition during a climatic interval colder than now.

Loess of Wisconsin age locally lies downwind (southeast) from major flood plains and eroded outcrops of soft bedrock. The loess is moderate yellowish-brown sandy silt that stands in vertical banks 5 to 15 ft (2-5 m) high. A Brown soil was developed in Wisconsin time on the Louviers Alluvium and on the loess.

Broadway Alluvium (Scott, 1960b) of late Wisconsin age forms a widespread terrace composed partly of outwash 25 to 45 ft (8-14 m) above modern streams. The alluvium consists of grayish-brown, coarse pebbly sand or cobble gravel 10 to 25 ft (3-8 m) thick. It commonly lies in a channel cut into the Louviers Alluvium. Bones and teeth of the Columbian mammoth are abundant (Scott, 1963a).

Recent deposits. Recent deposits near Denver include alluvium along modern streams and windblown sand of lesser extent than the Wisconsin loess. Three fine-grained alluvial deposits, termed pre-Piney Creek, Piney Creek, and post-Piney Creek alluvium lie in low stream terraces.

Pre-Piney Creek alluvium of early Recent age and of very limited distribution lies in fill terraces 25 ft (8 m) or more above the modern ephemeral and smaller permanent streams. It consists of as much as 40 ft (12 m) of light-brown silt and sand containing thin lenses of pebbles. Fossil mollusks indicate deposition during a climatic interval warmer than now. Artifacts of the Archaic culture were found in the alluvium with charcoal that has an age of about 5,500 years B.P. based on two radiocarbon samples (Scott, 1963a, p. 40).

Eolian sand of early Recent age forms a local thick cover downwind from major floodplains. The sand is brownish gray, slightly compacted, fine to coarse, and cross-stratified. Its maximum thickness is 40 ft (12 m). It locally contains Yuma-type artifacts, which suggest that part of it is older than the pre-Piney Creek alluvium. An early Recent Brown soil is developed on the sand, the pre-Piney Creek alluvium, and the Broadway Alluvium.

Piney Creek Alluvium (Hunt, 1954) of late Recent age forms a strath or a low fill terrace 10 to 25 ft (3-8 m) above modern streams in almost every valley. The alluvium is composed of 4 to 25 ft (1-8 m) of gray or brownish-gray humic clay, silt, sand, and some pebble beds in layers 0.5 to 10 in. (1-25 cm) thick. Bones of *Bison bison* locally are abundant (Scott, 1963a). A weakly developed, late Recent Brown soil has formed in the upper part of the alluvium.

Post-Piney Creek alluvium of late Recent age forms the lowest terrace and the floodplain of the major streams. It is composed of grayish-brown, poorly consolidated, humic, fine and medium sand and layers of black magnetite-rich sand. Its maximum thickness is about 12 ft (3.5 m) and the surface stands 0 to 12 ft (0-3.5 m) above stream level. Artifacts of the ceramic Woodland culture occur in the alluvium with charcoal that has yielded a radiocarbon age of approximately 1,500 years B.P. (Scott, 1963a, p. 46).

SUMMARY OF GEOMORPHOLOGY NEAR DENVER

A change from marine to continental conditions took place in Late Cretaceous time at the beginning of the Laramide Revolution. Continental sediments eroded from the rising mountains were deposited continuously until late Paleocene time and then intermittently into Oligocene time. By late Miocene time, erosion had stripped the mountains far below their former sedimentary cover. Sediments eroded during development of the several levels of the gently sloping subsummit Rocky Mountain surface in late Miocene to middle Pliocene time were deposited in a broad alluvial apron (Ogallala Formation) a few hundred feet thick covering the western part of the Great Plains. In late Pliocene time, streams cut down through the Ogallala Formation and the Rocky Mountain surface, owing partly to climatic change and partly to slight uplift of the mountains. V-shaped canyons were cut into the crystalline rocks in the mountains as deep as 1,500 ft (460 m) below the Rocky Mountain surface. Apparently the detritus of this downcutting was carried out of the piedmont area.

The landscape at the end of Tertiary time was marked in the mountains between 8,000 and 10,000 ft (2,400 and 3,000 m) by levels of the Rocky Mountain surface stripped of gravel and by gravel-covered levels of the same surface at 7,500 to 8,900 ft (2,300-2,700 m), both of which lay below high bedrock prominences and above stream-cut trenches 700 to 1,500 ft (210-460 m) deep. These bare or gravel-covered high surfaces probably represent several stages of planation of the Rocky Mountain surface, all productive of deposits now superposed in the composite fill of the Ogallala Formation. On the Great Plains remnants of the Ogallala Formation formed high divides 700 to 1,500 ft (210-460 m) above valley floors near the mountains and as low as 250 ft (75 m) above valley floors in eastern Colorado.

The Quaternary record consists primarily of gravel-covered pediments and fill terraces. Pediments near Denver, which range from 450 to 100 ft (140-30 m) above streams, represent four episodes of broad stream planation. Five episodes of terrace formation near Denver, when streams aggraded rather than cut sideward, left fill terraces at 5 to 60 ft (1.5-18 m) above streams.

The overall result of the surficial processes is a landscape marked by gently sloping surfaces at three general levels: (1) the high, poorly preserved, pre-Quaternary surfaces cut on Precambrian rocks of the Front Range, (2) the intermediate, well-preserved early and middle Quaternary pediments cut on sedimentary rocks at the mountain front, and (3) the low, well-preserved late Quaternary fill terraces along modern streams.

CORRELATION OF ALLUVIUM NEAR DENVER WITH ALLUVIUM IN NEBRASKA

Changes in texture and slope take place in the alluvial deposits eastward from Denver. Downstream the deposits became finer grained owing to decreased competency of the streams. In eastern Colorado the long profiles of the pre-Wisconsin deposits tend to converge with each other and with the modern stream profile (Maxwell E. Gardner, oral communication, 1964). The deposits were not traced to the point of convergence; however, Schultz et al. (1951, Figs. 1a and 2a) show the pre-Wisconsin deposits of western and central Nebraska superposed in two groups, an older group of Nebraskan and middle Kansan age and a younger group of late Kansan and Illinoian age. Lugn (1935, p. 177, Fig. 31) demonstrated that the terrace deposits not only converge but cross and are superposed. East of the point of convergence the older deposits are buried. The area along the Platte River in Nebraska where the beds converge and cross should be mapped in detail.

The close similarity of the volcanic ash in the Verdos Alluvium (Table 1) to the Pearlette Ash Member of the Sappa Formation suggests that the coarse Verdos Alluvium in Colorado is correlative with the silt and sand of the Sappa Formation (Schultz et al., 1951, p. 6) in Nebraska. The Verdos Alluvium is the only alluvium of Yarmouth or Kansan age near Denver, but in Nebraska the Sappa Formation is preceded by two other fossiliferous alluvial deposits of Kansan age, the Red Cloud and Grand Island Formations. These are correlated in turn with Kansan Glaciation by Schultz et al. (1951, Figs. 1a, 1b). During deposition of these two formations in Nebraska, streams near Denver undoubtedly were transporting equivalent sediments, which, however, were either carried through the area without being dropped or were deposited and eroded prior to formation of the Verdos Alluvium.

SURFICIAL DEPOSITS OF THE INTERMONTANE BASINS

The geology of most of the intermontane basins (Fig. 1) is similar, because degradation was the dominant process in almost all basins. In the Bighorn, for example, the alluvial deposits form a series of gravel-covered pediments and terraces clearly differentiated by altitude. In the San Luis Valley, however, where aggradation was dominant, the alluvial deposits partly fill the basin, which is now a nearly featureless plain, and the older deposits are exposed at few places.

The reports from which this summary of the intermontane basins has been taken are partly geomorphic studies and partly areal geologic studies; few are detailed enough to permit correlation between basins. The emphasis of nearly all reports is on topographic position of the alluvial deposits above modern streams rather than on stratigraphic study of the deposits. With few exceptions, correlation of alluvial deposits had not been attempted either with other deposits within a basin or between basins. The exceptions are deposits of outwash that were easier to correlate because of their association with till of known age. Because of the meager amount of information available for judging contemporaneity, only the flimsiest type of correlation is presented in Table 2. Height above modern stream level, although listed for each surface, is valid only within a local basin. It has therefore been subordinated to ancient soils, fossils, or volcanic ash beds, where they are available, as criteria for placement of the surfaces in Table 2.

Recent deposits are not discussed for all the intermontane basins, principally because younger deposits were not discussed in most of the source reports. Recent deposits in several basins are described by Leopold and Miller (1954). Because the Recent deposits of the intermontane basins are similar to those in the Colorado Piedmont, the reader is referred to that section of this article for descriptions of the Recent deposits.

UPPER BASIN OF THE MISSOURI RIVER, MONTANA

Quaternary surficial deposits in the upper basin of the Missouri River are largely fluvial and eolian. The fluvial deposits include alluvium in floodplains and terraces and on pediments. The number of related terrace and pediment surfaces preserved varies from basin to basin, and the greater number are preserved nearer the headwaters of the streams. According to Robinson (1963, p. 117) five surfaces are preserved at Three Forks in a vertical range of 1,000 ft (300 m) and six are found above Ennis along the Madison River over a range of more than 2,000 ft (600 m). These levels and the associated deposits are likely the products of climatically influenced stream processes, but the possibility of some effect from local tectonic activity cannot be overlooked. Ages have not been assigned to the terraces. The eolian deposits are light-colored silt, 5 to 15 ft (1.5-4.5 m) thick, spread on benchlands near Three Forks and probably derived from poorly consolidated Tertiary rocks or floodplains.

BIGHORN BASIN, WYOMING AND MONTANA

Surficial deposits of the Bighorn Basin include deposits of gravel on pediments, on cut terraces, and in fill terraces. Pediments on the tops and flanks of high divides lie above broad terraces along the valleys.

In the most comprehensive report on the geomorphology of the basin, Mackin (1937, p. 866-867) described five general stages of regional erosion (also see Alden, 1932). During the Tatman–Pine Ridge stage (Table 2), which Mackin thought occurred in early or middle Pliocene time, streams were flowing more than 1,200 ft (360 m) above their present floors. In the late Pliocene YU-Mesa (Polecat?) stage, streams formed gravel-capped straths 350 to 680 ft (110-210 m) above modern streams. The following Roberts-Emblem-Powell stage, as well as all subsequent stages, were thought to be of Pleistocene age; during the Roberts-Emblem-Powell stage, gravel-capped straths were formed 150 to 300 ft (45-90 m) above modern streams. Later Pleistocene deposits were laid down 75 to 210 ft (25-65 m) above modern streams in the Red Lodge–Cody stage. The

TABLE 2

Terraces and Pediments of Selected Basins of the Rocky Mountains

[Name or number of surface prefixed by letter T as used by author cited, and average elevation of top of surface in feet and meters (in parentheses) above modern streams. Blank spaces indicate that surfaces are unknown. Floodplains and lowest surfaces, which may contain both Recent and older deposits, are unlisted for most basins. Correlation lines and spaces may or may not represent time equivalence.]

Geologic climate units	Colorado Piedmont (Scott, 1963a, 1963b)	Bighorn Basin (Mackin, 1937)	Green River Basin (Holmes and Moss, 1955)	Wind River Basin (Morris et al., 1959)	Hanna Basin–Saratoga Valley (from topographic maps and from Leopold and Miller, 1954)	Laramie Basin (Harold J. Hyden, oral communication, 1964)	Powder River Basin (Kohout, 1957)	North Park Basin (Eschman, 1957)	Middle Park Basin (Glen A. Izett, oral communication, 1964)	South Park (Stark et al., 1949; Singewald, 1950)
Neoglaciation — Gannett Peak	Post-Piney Creek 0-12 (0-3.5)			T1 15-22 (4.5-7)	5-7 (1.5-2)		T1 6-12 (2-3.5)			
Neoglaciation — Temple Lake	Piney Creek 10-25 (3-8)		Parker 6 (2)	T2 28-65 (9-20)	15 (4.5)		T2 15-25 (4.5-8)	T0 <8 (2.4)		
"Altithermal interval"	Pre-Piney Creek 25 (8)									
Pinedale	Broadway 30 (9)	Greybull 10-40 (3-12)	Lower Farson 20 (6)	T3 65-118 (20-36)	20 (6)	40 (12)	T3 30-50 (9-15)	T1 20 (6)	15 (4.5)	5-20 (1.5-6)
Pinedale	Louviers 50 (15)		Upper Farson 35 (11)	T4 98-110 (30-33)	40 (12)				40 (12)	
Bull Lake			Lower Eden 60 (18)	T5 100-160 (30-50)	80 (24)	100 (30)	T4 60-80 (18-25)	T2 40 (12)	100 (30)	30-40 (9-12)
Bull Lake			Upper Eden 80 (25)	T6 140-180 (43-55)				T3 80 (24)	140 (43)	
Pre-Bull Lake	Slocum 100 (30)	Red Lodge–Cody 75-210 (25-65)	Faler or Camp 100-135 (30-40)	T7 220-240 (67-73)	100 (30)	150 (45)	T5 90-110 (27-33)	T4 100 (30)	190 (58)	80-95 (24-29)
Pre-Bull Lake	Verdos 250 (75)	Roberts-Emblem-Powell 150-300 (45-90)	Buffalo 130-195 (40-60)	T8 300-380 (90-115)	200 (60)	200 (60)	T6 120-150 (37-46)	T5 160 (50)	270 (82)	130-170 (40-52)
Pre-Bull Lake	Rocky Flats 350 (110)		Toboggan 160-300 (50-90)	T9 420-480 (130-145)	340 (100)	320 (100)	T7 215-235 (65-72)	T6 210 (65)	450 (140)	160-210 (49-64)
Pre-Bull Lake	Nussbaum 450 (140)	YU-Mesa (Polecat?) 350-680 (110-210)		T10 500-550 (150-170)		360 (110)		T7 330 (100)	570 (170)	230-310 (70-95)
Pre-Bull Lake				T11 580-620 (175-190)						330-410 (100-120)
Pre-Bull Lake				T12 680 (210)						
Pre-Bull Lake		Tatman-Pine Ridge 1,200 (360)		T13 800-825 (240-250)						

latest stage includes the Greybull terrace, 10 to 40 ft (3-12 m) above modern stream level.

On the basis of fossil pollen and physiographic position, Rohrer and Leopold (1963) considered the Tatman Mountain terrace and thus the Tatman–Pine Ridge stage to be no older than early Pleistocene.

Most of the terraces and benches probably correspond to glacial stages, according to Moss (1951, p. 67). Mackin (1937, p. 868) stated that the deeply aggraded present valley floors (post-Cody?) are associated with the last (Pinedale?) ice advance. Moss and Bonini (1961) correlated gravel in the Cody terrace with valley-train deposits that issued from a Pinedale moraine at Ishawooa, Wyoming, and the gravel is therefore in part glaciofluvial.

GREEN RIVER BASIN, WYOMING AND UTAH

Surficial deposits in the Green River Basin include Quaternary alluvium and eolian sand. The alluvial deposits in the north end of the basin have been described by Blackwelder (1950, p. 82), Richmond (1948), Moss (1951, p. 70-73), and Holmes and Moss (1955, p. 638). Eight terraces along the Green River and Big Sandy Creek range in age from early Pleistocene to Recent (Table 2).

Alluvial deposits in the southwest corner of the basin on the northwest flank of the Uinta Mountains have been examined by Bradley (1936, p. 190-193) and Hansen (1955). According to Bradley the Tipperary and the Lyman benches are capped by as much as 12 ft (3.5 m) of gravel that is cemented by caliche. Hansen described five benches ranging from 40 to 255 ft (12-80 m) above major drainage. Richmond (*in* Hansen, 1955) tentatively assigned the two older of these five benches to the Bull Lake and the three younger to the Pinedale; however, because of a great amount of caliche in the older deposits, Hansen now suggests (oral communication, 1964) that the older deposits may be pre-Wisconsin in age. These deposits probably correlate in some way with the Tipperary and Lyman benches.

Eolian sand is widespread in the east end of the basin near Farson, where dunes 20 ft (6 m) high overlie the Eden and younger terraces (Holmes and Moss, 1955, p. 644-645). At the Finley site in Eden Valley (Fig. 1), artifacts of early man (about 7,000 years B.P.?) were found in the sand by Moss (1951, p. 14).

WIND RIVER BASIN, WYOMING

Quaternary alluvial deposits in the Wind River Basin are associated with a well-formed set of pediments and fill terraces. Five broad Quaternary erosion cycles were recognized by Blackwelder (1915, p. 310), who believed them to be "largely interglacial." The oldest two cycles, the Union Pass and Black Rock, preceded Blackwelder's Buffalo (late pre-Wisconsin) Glaciation; the Circle cycle intervened between the Buffalo and Bull Lake Glaciations, the Lenore cycle between the Bull Lake and Pinedale Glaciations, and the postglacial cycle followed the Pinedale Glaciation. The Union Pass cycle was considered to be older than the oldest glacial drift.

Quaternary surficial deposits include alluvium, eolian sand, loess, and playa deposits. Coarse-grained alluvium lies along the Wind River and its larger tributaries; fine-grained alluvium lies along the small tributaries. Thirteen terraces (Table 2) have been mapped along the Wind River (Morris *et al.*, 1959, p. 27) but are not all preserved in any single small area. This is a greater number than in any other basin and some duplication is suspected. These terraces range from 15 to 825 ft (4.5-250 m) above the river and have gravel caps ranging from 2 to 25 ft (0.6-7.5 m) and averaging about 11 ft (3.3 m) in thickness. The younger are now the most extensive, but the distribution of the older suggests that they were once much more extensive. The oldest terrace, terrace 13, is equivalent to the Black Rock cycle of Blackwelder (Morris *et al.*, 1959, p. 16).

According to Morris *et al.* (1959), the terraces range in age from earliest Pleistocene to Recent, but the oldest might possibly be pre-Pleistocene. In the sequence of thirteen terraces, the oldest seven apparently are of pre-Bull Lake (pre-Wisconsin) age. Volcanic ash was found (J. D. Love, written communication, 1964) interbedded with terrace gravel along the north edge of Big Sand Mesa in secs. 4 and 5, T. 3 N., R. 4 E., Fremont County, Wyoming. Three samples of the ash were examined spectrographically and microscopically by Howard A. Powers and Ray E. Wilcox (written communication, 1964) and found to be sufficiently similar to the type Pearlette Ash Member of Kansas in minor-element content, refractive index, and phenocryst content that they strongly suggest equivalence (see Wilcox, 1965). Morris *et al.* (1959, pl. 1) assigned Big Sand Mesa to their terrace 8, which lies 360 ft (110 m) above neighboring Muddy Creek. The lower six terraces apparently are Bull Lake, Pinedale, and Recent in age.

Recent terraces described by Hadley (1960, p. 4) near the center of the basin include two at heights of 8 to 10 ft (2.4-3 m) and 18 to 20 ft (5.5-6 m) above stream level.

WASHAKIE AND GREAT DIVIDE BASINS, WYOMING

In the Washakie Basin, according to Richmond *et al.* (1958, p. 29, 174), Quaternary deposits are late Pleistocene to Recent, fine-grained, stony alluvium of local source and fine-grained material in playas. Three gravel-covered terraces of probable Pleistocene age border the Little Snake River near Baggs.

In the Great Divide Basin, Quaternary deposits include both coarse- and fine-grained alluvium, playa deposits, and eolian sand and silt. Pipiringos (1961, p. 37-38) described a single persistent but dissected Pleistocene terrace near the center of the basin composed of sand and gravel. The terrace lies 60 ft (18 m) above playas in the south end of the basin and 300 ft (90 m) above playas in the north. At the base of the gravel is a layer of red or brown silty clay similar to that in the modern playas, which suggested to Pipiringos (oral communication, 1964) an earlier time of playa formation.

The modern playas occupy a larger part of the basin than any other surficial unit. They are underlain by brown silty clay 25 to 58 ft (8-18 m) thick (Pipiringos, 1961, p. 37; Masursky, 1962, p. 21). The shallow depressions once were entirely filled by lakes but now are seasonally dry, and some are being dissected by local streams. The largest of these features, the Red Desert Flat, is about 25 miles (45 km) long and 6 miles (11 km) wide. The lakes that filled them apparently drained out of the basin to the east (Pipiringos, 1961, p. 38).

Eolian sand and silt form a well-defined, east-trending stripe of dunes across the basin. The eolian sand probably was derived from alluvium along the Green River and Sandy Creek. Many small dunes in the east end of the basin were derived from playas or other local sandy source materials (Masursky, 1962, p. 21).

HANNA BASIN AND SARATOGA VALLEY, WYOMING

Quaternary deposits in the composite Hanna Basin–Saratoga Valley include coarse- and fine-grained alluvium and dune sand. Along the North Platte River north of Saratoga, gravel deposits occur on the floodplain and in terraces 10,

30, and 50 ft (3, 9, and 15 m) above stream level (Richmond *et al.*, 1958, p. 30-31). Older, higher pediment surfaces were noted by Montagne (1957, p. 41) in the Saratoga area. New 7½-minute topographic maps for the Saratoga Valley show (Table 2) at least six surfaces at 20, 40, 80, 100, 200, and 340 ft (6, 12, 24, 30, 60, and 100 m) above modern streams near Saratoga. The upper three probably are pre-Wisconsin and the lower three Wisconsin in age.

Fine-grained, Recent alluvium borders small streams throughout the basin. Leopold and Miller (1954, p. 45) showed two levels along the North Platte River east of the Rawlins uplift, a lower silty alluvium 5 to 7 ft (1.5-2 m) above streams and an upper sandy alluvium about 15 ft (4.5 m) above streams, which is commonly overlain by dune sand.

LARAMIE BASIN, WYOMING

Quaternary deposits in the Laramie Basin include alluvium, eolian silt and sand, and playa deposits. Harold J. Hyden (oral communication, 1964) has recognized six sheets of alluvium (Table 2) in an area near Rock River. The oldest lies 360 ft (110 m) and the youngest 40 ft (12 m) above major streams; all probably are of Pleistocene age. A composite fill in the valley bottoms contains Recent and possibly older deposits.

In the Big Hollow area, Montagne (1953) mapped three gravel-covered surfaces that he named the Table Mountain, intermediate, and Centennial surfaces, lying respectively 320, 100, and 20 ft (100, 30, and 6 m) above major streams. He considered them to be early Wisconsin or pre-Wisconsin in age. In addition, two lower, gravel-covered terraces possibly of Recent age lie along the Little Laramie River (Montagne, 1954).

Modern 7½-minute topographic maps of the area south of Laramie show at least four terraces at 30, 70, 105, and 170 ft (9, 21, 32, and 52 m) above modern streams. The 170-ft (52-m) terrace contains volcanic ash (Darton *et al.*, 1910) that is tentatively correlated with the Pearlette Ash Member of the Sappa Formation. The 105-ft (31-m) terrace also is considered pre-Wisconsin in age, but the 70- and 30-ft (21- and 9-m) terraces probably are of Wisconsin age. Low Recent terraces containing fine-grained alluvium border most streams in the area.

Playas are a common feature of the Laramie Basin (Montagne, 1953, p. 80). Most are small and contain accumulations of salts. Apparently many of the playas originated as blowouts, and the wind deposited the material over a widespread area. The largest blowout, called Big Hollow, is west of Laramie and is 6 miles (11 km) long and 3 miles (5.5 km) wide. Big Hollow contains several small playas. Other smaller blowouts are common in the fine-grained bedrock west and south of Laramie.

The Shirley Basin north of the Laramie Basin contains Quaternary deposits that consist of coarse- and fine-grained alluvium. Owing to deep dissection little remains of the gravel that formerly covered part of the basin floor. According to Elbert N. Harshman (oral communication, 1963) small remnants of gravel 50 ft (15 m) thick lie 700 ft (210 m) above modern streams, and a fairly continuous 30-ft-(9-m)-high, gravel-covered terrace borders Little

Medicine Bow River in the east end of the basin. Other than these two deposits, only fine-grained Recent deposits are known along other smaller streams.

POWDER RIVER BASIN, WYOMING

Quaternary alluvium is widespread along streams in the Powder River Basin, and a large body of eolian sand lies in the southwestern corner of the basin. Quaternary alluvium was mapped in seven terraces (Table 2) and a floodplain by Kohout (1957, p. 351-354). Along the Powder River on the west side of the basin the combined width of the terraces is 3 miles (5.5 km). Each alluvial deposit is composed of silt and fine sand in the upper part and coarse sand and gravel in the lower part.

The three younger terraces have been further studied by Leopold and Miller (1954, p. 17-29). The oldest of these three terraces, the Kaycee, 5 to 20 ft (1.5-6 m) above streams, contains a composite fill locally including two formations, the Arvada Formation of late Wisconsin age, and the Ucross Formation of Recent(?) age. The Moorcroft terrace, 8 to 12 ft (2.4-3.6 m) above streams, is composed of the Recent Kaycee Formation. Colluvial facies of the Kaycee Formation also apparently locally overlie the Ucross Formation. The Lightning terrace, 4 to 7 ft (1.2-2 m) above streams, contains the Lightning Formation. Two soils are developed on these formations: one on the Ucross, or, where it is missing, on the Arvada, and the other on the Kaycee. The Arvada Formation is here tentatively correlated with the Broadway Alluvium, the Kaycee with the Piney Creek Alluvium, and the Lightning with the post-Piney Creek alluvium of the Denver area.

NORTH PARK BASIN, COLORADO

The Quaternary deposits in North Park include pediment and terrace gravel, fine-grained alluvium, and windblown sand. In the Michigan River Basin on the east side of North Park, Eschman (1957) described eight gravel-covered surfaces (Table 2). The 80-ft (24-m) terrace ends at a moraine of the Owl Mountain glacial substage of Illinoian(?) age, but it could not be definitely related to the glacial chronology. The 40- and 20-ft (12- and 6-m) terraces were traced into moraines of the Gould and Silver Lake glacial substages, respectively. In addition to the three Pleistocene terraces, one or two probable late Wisconsin or Recent terraces less than 8 ft (2.4 m) above modern streams were observed. G. M. Richmond (oral communication, 1964) correlates Eschman's Gould glacial substage [40-ft (12-m) terrace] with late Bull Lake and his Silver Creek glacial substage [20-ft (6-m) terrace] with early and middle Pinedale.

An almost identical sequence of terraces on the west side of North Park was correlated by William J. Hail, Jr. (oral communication, 1964) with glaciations of the same age as those in the Michigan River basin. According to Hail, pediments equivalent to Eschman's higher surfaces also are present in western North Park.

Dune sand covers a large part of western North Park Basin and is actively moving eastward in the North Sand Hills near the southeast corner of the Northgate district in northern North Park (Steven, 1956, p. 54).

MIDDLE PARK BASIN, COLORADO

The Quaternary deposits of Middle Park Basin consist of coarse- and fine-grained alluvium. At least nine pediments and terraces are recognized (Glen A. Izett, C. S. Venable Barclay, and Richard B. Taylor, oral communication, 1964). These lie about 15, 40, 100, 140, 190, 270, 450, and 570 ft (4.5, 12, 30, 43, 58, 82, 140, and 170 m) above modern streams. The upper four are pre-Wisconsin in age, the 140- and 100-ft (43- and 30-m) terraces possibly are correlative with Bull Lake Glaciation, and the 40- and 15-ft (12- and 4.5-m) terraces possibly are correlative with Pinedale Glaciation.

SOUTH PARK BASIN, COLORADO

The surficial deposits of South Park Basin include outwash, pediment gravel, and fine-grained alluvium. They were studied by Stark *et al.* (1949) and by Singewald (1950), all of whom tended to interpret some of the deposits as older than current usage would place them. Singewald's terraces 1 and 2, of middle(?) and late(?) Tertiary age, lie less than 160 ft (50 m) above modern streams and are here assigned to the Pleistocene.

The sequence of stream-formed surfaces mapped by Stark *et al.* (1949) and Singewald (1950) and shown by modern 7½-minute topographic maps of the basin includes a range of less than 400 ft (120 m) in altitude. The highest surface, a pediment called Badger Creek surface by Stark *et al.* (1949, p. 9), lies just outside the south end of the park and is as high as 350 ft (110 m) above Badger Creek, a tributary of the Arkansas River. Despite the late Pliocene age assigned to it by Stark *et al.* (1949, p. 147), an early Pleistocene age seems to be more reasonable because of its relation to lower pediments along Badger Creek.

All other high, stream-formed pediments of South Park were grouped under the name Como surfaces by Stark *et al.* (1949, p. 143), who observed five levels of the Como surfaces ranging from 80 to 410 ft (24-120 m) above stream level. The modern topographic maps of South Park show three surfaces, apparently of pre-Wisconsin age, at heights of 160, 120, and 80 ft (49, 37, and 24 m) above modern streams.

Terraces, probably of Wisconsin age, range from floodplain level up to about 40 ft (12 m) above modern streams. Terraces 30 to 40 ft (9-12 m) above streams, called pre-Wisconsin by Stark *et al.* (1949) and Singewald (1950), may be of Bull Lake age (Gerald M. Richmond, oral communication, 1964). Terraces 5 to 20 ft (1.5-6 m) above the streams are correlated with the Pinedale Glaciation. Fine-grained alluvium exposed in arroyos along small streams is largely Recent in age.

SAN LUIS VALLEY, COLORADO AND NEW MEXICO

The San Luis Valley is a structural basin that has been subsiding and aggrading steadily since late Miocene time and now contains a tremendous fill formed by the Santa Fe and Alamosa Formations. In the central part of the basin the influx of alluvium from the west side was so much greater than from the north that large, nearly flat alluvial fans completely dammed off south-flowing surface drainage in the northern part of the basin. Streams from the north flow along the east side of the valley into undrained basins that now are saline because of the evaporative concentration of salts. Water that does not evaporate flows underground to the south into the Rio Grande.

In two parts of the basin dissection seems to be more active than deposition; these are in the steeply sloping part of the northern end and in the area called the Culebra Re-entrant (Upson, 1939, p. 733) in the southeastern part of the valley. Terraces and pediments characterize the Culebra Re-entrant. Upson (1939, p. 734-735) describes at least four erosion surfaces cut across deformed Tertiary rocks in the Culebra Re-entrant, the highest being 450 to 500 ft (135-150 m) above modern streams. In the Costilla Plains, Upson (1939, p. 732) describes two other alluvium-covered terraces lying 50 and 100 ft (15 and 30 m) above modern streams. Atwood and Mather (1932, p. 117) describe two gravel-covered surfaces on the south flank of Blanca Peak at 35 to 40 ft (11-12 m) and at 285 to 290 ft (87-88 m) above modern streams. They correlate the gravel on the upper surface with the Florida Gravel, which at its type locality is outwash equivalent to Durango Till (Richmond *et al.*, this volume) and possibly of Illinoian age.

According to Powell (1958, p. 23), the Alamosa Formation ranges in thickness from more than 2,000 ft (600 m) near Hooper to zero around the edges of the valley. It consists of unconsolidated gravel, sand, silt, and clay. A single small collection of fresh-water mollusks suggests late Pliocene or early preglacial Pleistocene age (Siebenthal, 1910, p. 46). The upper and lower boundaries of the Alamosa are poorly defined, and by latest usage (Powell, 1958, p. 20-24) encompass deposits that probably range in age from Pliocene to Recent. The formation needs to be studied in both the surface and subsurface in order to define the kinds and ages of deposits that should be included in it in the dissected part of the valley and to redefine its boundaries in the valley fill.

The eolian sand in Great Sand Dunes National Monument occupies an area of about 40 sq. miles (1000 km²). Most of the dunes are the transverse type and reach heights of 700 ft (210 m) (Merk, 1960). Prevailing wind is from the southwest, but periodic storm winds from the northeast may offset the northeastward progression of the dunes. The dunes apparently formed by deflation of sandy sediments in San Luis Valley. Their age is probably Pleistocene and Recent.

SUMMARY OF NONGLACIAL GEOMORPHIC HISTORY OF INTERMONTANE BASINS

The nonglacial Quaternary and late Tertiary record of the Rocky Mountains is characterized by repetitive great erosion and slight deposition. Late Tertiary time was marked in the mountains by the erosion of deep canyons into subsummit pediments. On the plains deep valleys were eroded into the Ogallala and Flaxville Formations and equivalent gravel deposits that had been carried across the pediments. Uplift possibly was largely responsible for the late Tertiary erosion.

In Quaternary time a succession of pediments and terraces was formed as a result of more than 450 ft (140 m)

of erosion on the flanks of most basins. Nearly all the eroded sediments were carried out of the basins, leaving only thin veneers of gravel on pediments and terraces. The shifting of streams from one surface down to a lower surface was accomplished by downward and sideward cutting aided locally by stream captures. Probably no pediment was perfectly formed during any stage of erosion so as to form a continuous ramp along the foot of the mountains; rather each pediment is a remnant of a former broad valley floor. The greater extent of some pediments shows that in some geomorphic cycles base level was stable for a longer time. Pediments are the chief landform preserved from pre-Bull Lake time; cut or fill terraces of lesser areal extent than the pediments completely supplant the pediments in Bull Lake to Recent time. Terraces of pre-Bull Lake time were formed, but are not widely preserved; pediments were rarely formed in Bull Lake to Recent time.

REFERENCES

Alden, W. C., 1932, Physiography and glacial geology of eastern Montana and adjacent areas: U.S. Geol. Surv. Prof. Pap. 174, 133 p.

Atwood, W. W., and Mather, K. F., 1932, Physiography and Quaternary geology of the San Juan Mountains, Colorado: U.S. Geol. Surv. Prof. Pap. 166, 176 p.

Blackwelder, Eliot, 1915, Post-Cretaceous history of the mountains of central western Wyoming: J. Geol., v. 23, p. 97-117, 193-217, 307-340

—— 1950, Pleistocene geology, the Green River Basin, Wyoming: Wyoming Geol. Assoc. Guidebook, Southwest Wyoming, p. 81-85

Bradley, W. H., 1936, Geomorphology of the north flank of the Uinta Mountains [Utah]: U.S. Geol. Surv. Prof. Pap. 185-I, p. 163-199

Bryan, Kirk, and Ray, L. L., 1940, Geologic antiquity of the Lindenmeier site in Colorado: Smithson. Instn. Misc. Coll., v. 99, no. 2, publ. 3554, 76 p.

Darton, N. H., Blackwelder, Eliot, and Siebenthal, C. E., 1910, Description of the Laramie and Sherman quadrangles, Wyoming: U.S. Geol. Surv. Geol. Atlas, Laramie-Sherman Folio (173), 17 p.

Eschman, D. F., 1957, Late Cenozoic history of the Michigan River basin, North Park, Colorado: Rocky Mtn. Assoc. Geologists, Guidebook 1957, p. 32-35

Fenneman, N. M., 1931, Physiography of western United States: New York, McGraw-Hill Book Co., Inc., 534 p.

Gilbert, G. K., 1897, Description of the Pueblo quadrangle [Colorado]: U.S. Geol. Surv. Geol. Atlas, Pueblo Folio (36), 7 p.

Hadley, R. F., 1960, Recent sedimentation and erosional history of Five Mile Creek, Fremont County, Wyoming: U.S. Geol. Surv. Prof. Pap. 352-A, p. 1-16

Hansen, W. R., 1955, Geology of the Flaming Gorge quadrangle, Utah-Wyoming: U.S. Geol. Surv. Geol. Quad. Map GQ-75

Hibbard, C. W., 1958, New stratigraphic names for early Pleistocene deposits in southwestern Kansas: Amer. J. Sci., v. 256, no. 1, p. 54-59

Holmes, G. W., and Moss, J. H., 1955, Pleistocene geology of the southwestern Wind River Mountains, Wyoming: Geol. Soc. Amer. Bull., v. 66, p. 629-653

Hunt, C. B., 1954, Pleistocene and Recent deposits in the Denver area, Colorado: U.S. Geol. Surv. Bull. 996-C, p. 91-140

Kohout, F. A., 1957, Geology and ground-water resources of the Kaycee irrigation project, Johnson County, Wyoming: U.S. Geol. Surv. Water-Supply Pap. 1360-E, p. 321-374

Leopold, L. B., and Miller, J. P., 1954, A postglacial chronology for some alluvial valleys in Wyoming: U.S. Geol. Surv. Water-Supply Pap. 1261, 90 p.

Levings, W. S., 1951, Late Cenozoic erosional history of the Raton Mesa region: Colorado School Mines Quart., v. 46, no. 3, 111 p.

Lugn, A. L., 1935, The Pleistocene geology of Nebraska: Nebraska Geol. Surv. Bull. 10, 2d ser., 223 p.

Mackin, J. H., 1937, Erosional history of the Big Horn Basin, Wyoming: Geol. Soc. Amer. Bull., v. 48, p. 813-893

Malde, H. E., 1955, Surficial geology of the Louisville quadrangle, Colorado: U.S. Geol. Surv. Bull. 996-E, p. 217-259

Masursky, Harold, 1962, Uranium-bearing coal in the eastern part of the Red Desert area, Wyoming: U.S. Geol. Surv. Bull. 1099-B, 152 p.

Merk, G. P., 1960, Great Sand Dunes of Colorado, *in* Guide to the geology of Colorado: Geol. Soc. Amer., p. 127-129

Montagne, J. M. de la, 1953, Geomorphology of the Centennial–Big Hollow area, southeastern Wyoming: Wyoming Geol. Assoc. Guidebook 8th Ann. Field Conf., 1953, p. 77-80

—— 1954, Third Annual Field Trip, Medicine Bow-Laramie area, Wyoming: Friends of the Pleistocene, Rocky Mtn. Sec., 5 p.

—— 1957, Cenozoic structural and geomorphic history of northern North Park and Saratoga Valley, Colorado and Wyoming: Rocky Mtn. Assoc. Geologists, Guidebook 1957, p. 36-41

Morris, D. A., Hackett, O. M., Vanlier, K. E., and Moulder, E. A., 1959, Ground-water resources of Riverton irrigation project area, Wyoming, with a section on Chemical quality of ground water by W. H. Durum: U.S. Geol. Surv. Water-Supply Pap. 1375, 205 p.

Moss, J. H., 1951, Early Man in the Eden Valley [Wyoming]: Philadelphia, Univ. Pennsylvania Mus., 124 p.

Moss, J. H., and Bonini, W. E., 1961, Seismic evidence supporting a new interpretation of the Cody terrace near Cody, Wyoming: Geol. Soc. Amer. Bull., v. 72, p. 547-555

Pipiringos, G. N., 1961, Uranium-bearing coal in the central part of the Great Divide Basin: U.S. Geol. Surv. Bull. 1099-A, 104 p.

Powell, W. J., 1958, Ground-water resources of the San Luis Valley, Colorado: U.S. Geol. Surv. Water-Supply Pap. 1379, 284 p.

Powers, H. A., Young, E. J., and Barnett, P. R., 1958, Possible extension into Idaho, Nevada, and Utah of the Pearlette ash of Meade County, Kansas: Geol. Soc. Amer. Bull., v. 69, no. 12, pt. 2, p. 1631

Richmond, G. M., 1948, Modification of Blackwelder's sequence of Pleistocene glaciation in the Wind River Mountains, Wyoming (abst.): Geol. Soc. Amer. Bull., v. 59, p. 1400-1401

Richmond, G. M., Cattermole, J. M., Truesdell, P. E., and Foster, F. W., 1958, A reconnaissance of the sand and gravel deposits of Wyoming: U.S. Geol. Surv. Open-File Rep., 219 p.

Richmond, G. M., Fryxell, Roald, Neff, G. E., and Weis, P. L., this volume, The Cordilleran ice sheet of the Northern Rocky Mountains and related Quaternary history of the Columbia Plateau

Robinson, G. D., 1963, Geology of the Three Forks quadrangle, Montana: U.S. Geol. Surv. Prof. Pap. 370, 143 p.

Rohrer, W. L., and Leopold, Estella B., 1963, Fenton Pass Formation (Pleistocene?), Bighorn Basin, Wyoming: U.S. Geol. Surv. Prof. Pap. 475-C, p. 45-48

Schultz, C. B., Lueninghoener, G. C., and Frankforter, W. D., 1951, A graphic resume of the Pleistocene of Nebraska (with notes on the fossil mammalian remains): Nebraska State Mus. Bull., v. 3, no. 6, 41 p.

Scott, G. R., 1960a, Quaternary sequence east of the Front Range near Denver, Colorado, *in* Guide to the geology of Colorado: Geol. Soc. Amer., p. 206-211

—— 1960b, Subdivision of the Quaternary alluvium east of the Front Range near Denver, Colorado: Geol. Soc. Amer. Bull., v. 71, p. 1541-1543

—— 1961, Preliminary geologic map of the Indian Hills quadrangle, Jefferson County, Colorado: U.S. Geol. Surv. Misc. Geol. Inv. Map I-333

—— 1962, Geology of the Littleton quadrangle, Jefferson, Douglas, and Arapahoe Counties, Colorado: U.S. Geol. Surv. Bull. 1121-L, 53 p.

—— 1963a, Quaternary geology and geomorphic history of the Kassler quadrangle, Colorado: U.S. Geol. Surv. Prof. Pap. 421-A, 70 p.

—— 1963b, Nussbaum Alluvium of Pleistocene(?) age at Pueblo, Colorado: U.S. Geol. Surv. Prof. Pap. 475-C, p. 49-52

—— 1964, Geology of the northwest and northeast Pueblo quadrangles, Colorado: U.S. Geol. Surv. Misc. Geol. Inv. Map I-408

Siebenthal, C. E., 1910, Geology and water resources of the San Luis Valley, Colorado: U.S. Geol. Surv. Water-Supply Pap. 240, 128 p.

Singewald, Q. D., 1950, Gold placers and their geologic environment in northwestern Park County, Colorado: U.S. Geol. Surv. Bull. 955-D, p. 103-172

Stark, J. T., *et al.*, 1949, Geology and origin of South Park, Colorado: Geol. Soc. Amer. Mem. 33, 188 p.

Steven, T. A., 1956, Cenozoic geomorphic history of the Medicine Bow Mountains near the Northgate fluorspar district, Colorado: Colorado Sci. Soc. Proc., v. 17, **p.** 30-55

Upson, J. E., 1939, Physiographic subdivisions of the San Luis Valley, southern Colorado: J. Geol., v. 47, p. 721-736

Wells, J. D., 1963, Preliminary geologic map of the Eldorado Springs quadrangle, Boulder and Jefferson Counties, Colorado: U.S. Geol. Surv. Misc. Geol. Inv. Map I-383

Wilcox, R. E., this volume, Volcanic-ash chronology

Witkind, I. J., 1964, Reactivated faults north of Hebgen Lake, *in* The Hebgen Lake, Montana earthquake of August 17, 1959: U.S. Geol. Surv. Prof. Pap. 435, p. 37-50

Summary

Nonglacial Quaternary deposits discussed in this report are on the Colorado Piedmont along the eastern flank of the mountains and in broad basins between high mountain ranges. Alluvium on pediments and in fill terraces, higher than 450 ft (135 m) above present stream level, is the most widespread material. Windblown sand and loess are locally downwind from broad floodplains and areas of easily deflated bedrock.

The surficial material was deposited as the result of five processes, which in chronologic order are: (1) downward stream cutting, (2) sideward stream cutting, (3) alluviation, (4) wind erosion and deposition, and (5) soil formation. These processes make up a geomorphic cycle that is repeated because of the repetition of climatic cycles. Most of the alluvium in the basins is inferred to be nonglacial, but deposited during glaciations and interglaciations; only the terrace deposits along streams from glaciated areas are inferred to be partly outwash from glaciers.

The Colorado Piedmont contains 9 formations of alluvium; 4 were deposited when base level was stable long enough to permit pedimentation, and 5 were deposited as terrace fills when streams cut downward more than sideward. The pediment deposits are coarse-grained alluvium of pre-Wisconsin age, and are characterized by strongly developed soils. The terrace deposits are medium-grained alluvium of Wisconsin to Recent age, characterized by more weakly developed soils.

The intermontane basins also contain a sequence of early, gravel-covered pediments and late fill terraces. Erosion predominated over deposition in the valley floors of all except one basin.

SNAKE RIVER PLAIN *

HAROLD E. MALDE[1]

GEOGRAPHY

Curving in a great arc, 560 km long and 80-110 km wide, across the southern part of Idaho, the Snake River Plain is an incongruous physiographic feature among the rugged highlands of the northern Rocky Mountains. It is, for the most part, a lava plain, ranging in altitude from 2,000 m at the east to less than 700 m at the west. Around the perimeter are mountains and uplands composed of folded Paleozoic sedimentary rocks, granite of the Idaho batholith, and faulted Cenozoic volcanics (Fig. 1). From this envelope of surrounding highlands the Snake River gains an outlet by plunging northward through the precipitous Hells Canyon, one of the deepest gorges in North America.

At first glance, the Snake River Plain appears as a drab, monotonous lowland built of endless lava flows, dispersed from subdued eruptive centers. Closer scrutiny, however, reveals a multiplicity of Quaternary geology, not only in the clarity of volcanic processes, but also in a sedimentary record represented by thick sections of fossiliferous clastic deposits, and in erosional events expressed by ancient canyons and upland pediments. Indeed, the Quaternary features of the Snake River Plain are so enormous that their study takes on the attributes of bedrock geology—not merely the appraisal of landforms. The rocks of Quaternary age comprise a section about 1,500 m thick (although, as in other areas of continental deposits, not fully represented at any single locality), and comprehension of their origin must involve the interplay of volcanism, sedimentation, and tectonism, as well as the vagaries of erosion along a major river. The Quaternary record is especially complete in the western Snake River Plain, notably for what it tells about early and middle Pleistocene events (Malde and Powers, 1962). The eastern part is almost completely covered by late Pleistocene and Recent basalt, and exposures of older Pleistocene deposits are scanty (Stearns et al., 1938).

In geographic descriptions (Freeman et al., 1945), the Snake River Plain is commonly discussed in connection

* Publication authorized by the Director, U.S. Geological Survey. While working in the Snake River Plain, I have benefited from discussion with many geologists, paleontologists, and hydrologists who have a first-hand acquaintance with this region, especially W. J. Carr, Allan Cox, E. G. Crosthwaite, Warren Hamilton, M. J. Mundorff, H. A. Powers, D. W. Taylor, and D. E. Trimble of the U.S. Geological Survey, L. R. Kittleman, Jr., and J. A. Shotwell of the University of Oregon, C. N. Savage and R. W. Jones of the Idaho Bureau of Mines and Geology, D. H. McIntyre and G. R. Stephenson of the Agricultural Research Service, Boise, and N. R. Anderson of the University of Puget Sound. Hamilton and Trimble reviewed the manuscript.
[1] U.S. Geological Survey, Federal Center, Denver, Colorado.

with the Columbia Plateau of eastern Oregon and Washington as if (by sharing extensive tracts of basalt) it were an appendage of that province; but in fact the Snake River Plain is structurally different from the Columbia Plateau, its geologic record pertains to later events (mainly Quaternary), and its lavas are chemically distinct (Powers, 1960).

The eastern and western parts of the Snake River Plain differ in physiography and, as will be discussed later, in structure. Russell (1902, p. 61-66) described the eastern Snake River Plain as constructed by vast floods of extremely fluid basalt that poured in all directions from scores of local vents—so low in relief that they at first escape notice—thus building a broad, nearly level plain, still relatively little dissected. All these vents are believed to be Quaternary in age. They are marked on the "Tectonic Map of the United States." A few of the vents are associated with lava so fresh that they indicate Recent volcanic activity. The western Snake River Plain is much more diversified. Its controlling physiographic feature is the Snake River canyon, which begins a few miles above Twin Falls at a series of cataracts and rapidly becomes entrenched to a depth greater than 150 m. Numerous tributary canyons, absent in the eastern part, here join the Snake and thus dissect the region further. Although the first 30 km of canyon below Twin Falls is cut in basalt, the river thereafter enters a thick mass of detrital deposits, more or less protected from erosion on the north by plateaus of basalt, but intricately dissected into a wide belt of badlands on the south. Considerable parts of the badlands are carved in Quaternary deposits. A few miles from the Oregon state line, the basalt plateaus disappear, the eroded topography becomes subdued, and the Snake River flows on bottomlands of a broad valley. It then enters a mountainous stretch that leads to Hells Canyon.

TECTONIC FRAMEWORK

The Quaternary features of the Snake River Plain express the latest stages of tectonic and depositional events that began in late Tertiary time. The principal structural feature in the western Snake River Plain is a northwest-trending graben about 50 km broad, bounded on the north and south by volcanic highlands of early Pliocene age (Fig. 1). The northwesterly faults that bound the plain project into a broad zone of parallel, high-angle faults in Oregon (Hamilton, 1962) and coincide with a line of earthquake epicenters that stretches from Puget Sound to Great Salt Lake (Malde, 1959). At the bend in the central part of the plain, near the 115th meridian, conjugate northeasterly faults give shape to bordering mountain blocks on the north, and related faults seem to be expressed on the south by saw-

255

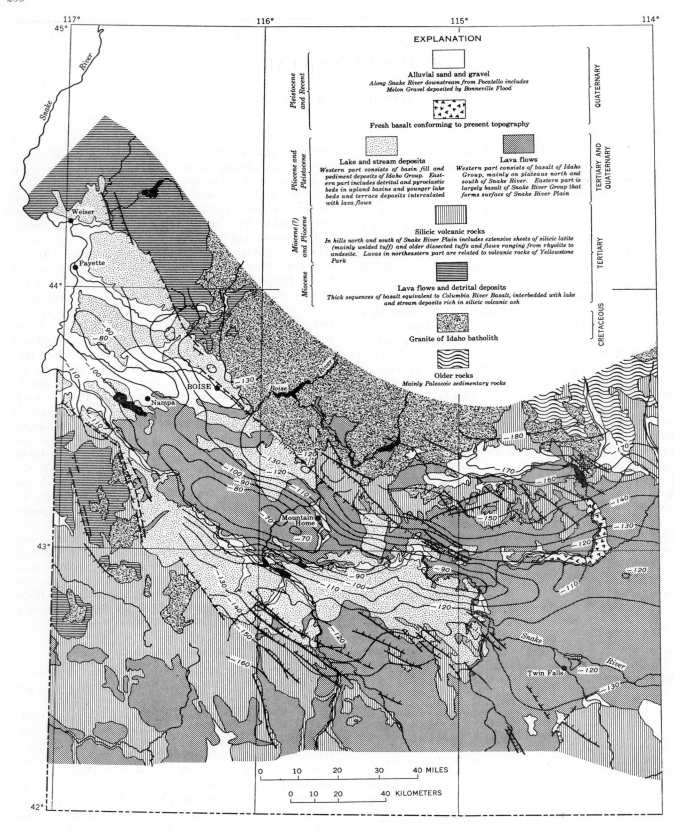

EXPLANATION

Alluvial sand and gravel
Along Snake River downstream from Pocatello includes Melon Gravel deposited by Bonneville Flood

Fresh basalt conforming to present topography

Lake and stream deposits
Western part consists of basin fill and pediment deposits of Idaho Group. Eastern part includes detrital and pyroclastic beds in upland basins and younger lake beds and terrace deposits intercalated with lava flows

Lava flows
Western part consists of basalt of Idaho Group, mainly on plateaus north and south of Snake River. Eastern part is largely basalt of Snake River Group that forms surface of Snake River Plain

Silicic volcanic rocks
In hills north and south of Snake River Plain includes extensive sheets of silicic latite (mainly welded tuff) and older dissected tuffs and flows ranging from rhyolite to andesite. Lavas in northeastern part are related to volcanic rocks of Yellowstone Park

Lava flows and detrital deposits
Thick sequences of basalt equivalent to Columbia River Basalt, interbedded with lake and stream deposits rich in silicic volcanic ash

Granite of Idaho batholith

Older rocks
Mainly Paleozoic sedimentary rocks

Pleistocene and Recent — QUATERNARY

Pliocene and Pleistocene — TERTIARY AND QUATERNARY

Miocene(?) and Pliocene — TERTIARY

Miocene — CRETACEOUS

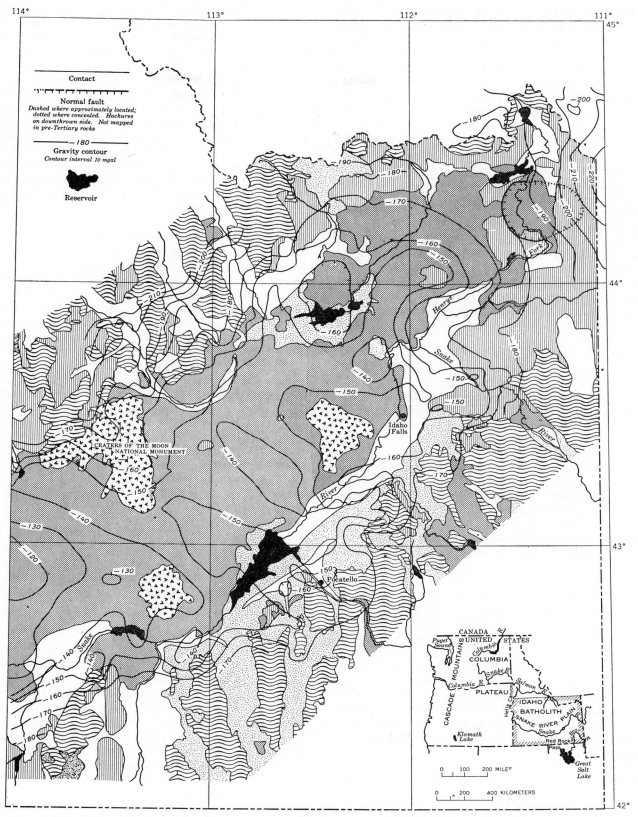

Figure 1. Generalized geologic and gravity map of Snake River Plain. Geology compiled from: Geologic Map of Idaho; Malde *et al.* (1963); and unpublished reconnaissance by Malde. Gravity contours drawn from detailed gravity surveys by Hill *et al.* (1961) and LaFehr (1962).

tooth outlines of blocks of silicic volcanics. If such north-easterly faults continue into the eastern Snake River Plain, even with small throw, they may account for the abrupt termination of mountain ranges at the borders, but inward dips of Tertiary beds at the edges of the eastern Snake River Plain suggest that it may be structurally more like a downwarp than a graben (Kirkham, 1931).

Gravity data also emphasize the structural contrast between the western and eastern Snake River Plain. In the western graben, three well-defined elongated areas of high gravity are nearly parallel to bordering faults, and the southernmost area of high gravity matches a niche formed by the faulted outline of lower Pliocene volcanic rocks. Thus the graben and the concealed heavy rocks that presumably account for the gravity highs seem to have formed concurrently, mainly before middle-Pliocene time. The areas of high gravity are plausibly explained as distended fissure fillings of material injected from the mantle (Hill, 1963), an hypothesis that implies crustal stretching, even though such fissures are not reflected in magnetic data. On the other hand, the eastern Snake River Plain, although also a broad region of high gravity, is characterized by alternating areas of subdued gravity relief that trend across the plain (LaFehr, 1962).

Within the western graben, beginning in the early Pliocene, various clastic beds and intercalated basalt flows that comprise the formations of the Idaho Group were deposited—a sequence that aggregates nearly 1,500 m in thickness. The clastics generally range in texture from sand to clay but include some gravel, siliceous volcanic ash, and diatomite. Nearly all the volcanic ash is in the lower part. The beds form light-colored sequences hundreds of meters thick that erode as badlands. Because of continued subsidence, the Tertiary and lower Quaternary formations of the group occupy successively lower positions topographically, usually in troughs bounded in part by faulted outlines of the next older unit, but the position of later Quaternary deposits was controlled by physiographic factors: pedimentation, canyon cutting, alluviation, and lava damming.

The subsidence that began in the western Snake River Plain in the Pliocene lasted into early-Pleistocene time, but (as shown by level lake beds) the middle-Pleistocene and younger rocks are not perceptibly deformed. Because of the sinking basin, continental deposits extend below sea level (Youngquist and Kiilsgaard, 1951). The eruption of voluminous lavas in the eastern Snake River Plain may also have been accompanied by subsidence as material from the mantle erupted, but the surface flows are not visibly deformed. This evident lack of deformation in later Quaternary time is puzzling, especially in the western part where unloading by late Pleistocene erosion should have caused isostatic rebound.

DETRITAL DEPOSITS OF WESTERN SNAKE RIVER PLAIN

GLENNS FERRY FORMATION

The outcrops of clastic deposits in the western Snake River Plain display an eastward enlargement of this structural

basin until Blancan time (Wood *et al.*, 1941)—an episode marked by the spread of intertonguing lake and stream deposits over the whole region. Known as the Glenns Ferry Formation (Table 1), the beds of Blancan provincial age mark an important change in the volume and extent of detrital material. The basin appears to have been extensively and deeply aggraded. Low-angle unconformities within the Glenns Ferry show that subsidence continued, although perhaps at a slower rate. Because chemically precipitated material is scarce in the Glenns Ferry, consisting only of local beds of algal limestone and oolite at the base, the lakes and streams of this period apparently were kept fresh by exterior drainage. Biogeographic considerations (Cook and Larrison, 1954; Taylor, 1960) point to an outlet in southern Oregon, probably via the Klamath-Pit River system.

Although the older clastic deposits of the western Snake River Plain contain large amounts of siliceous volcanic ash (chemically related to provincial sources), the Glenns Ferry Formation has only a few beds of ash. These include ash derived from eruptions in the Cascade Mountains of Oregon and Washington. Because the ash beds are distinctive physically and chemically, they are useful for local correlation (Powers and Malde, 1961).

The lakes and streams of the Glenns Ferry nourished an extraordinarily large and diverse molluscan fauna, comparable in variety and in degree of endemism to the fossil mollusks from the former Pontian, Dacian, and Levantine basins of southeastern Europe. Dwight W. Taylor (*in* Malde and Powers, 1962, p. 1208) reports: "Most of the mollusks from the lacustrine facies are prosobranch gastropods of the families Hydrobiidae, Pleuroceridae and Thiaridae, but *Payettia, Vorticifex*, and the peculiar *Orygoceras* are common (Dall, 1924). Nearly all these lacustrine species are extinct (94 percent)." The Glenns Ferry Formation is also notable for its fossil fish (Uyeno, 1961) and mammals (Gazin, 1936; Wilson, 1934; Hibbard, 1958).

Evernden *et al.* (1964, p. 184, samples KA 831 and KA 832) have determined potassium/argon ages of 3.3 million and 3.2 million years for two samples of volcanic ash from the Glenns Ferry Formation. Associated basalt, considered by them to be better for dating, is dated 3.5 million years (KA 1173).

TUANA GRAVEL

After Glenns Ferry time perceptible deformation ceased, and the basin deposits were broadly beveled by a layer of sand and gravel as much as 60 m thick—the Tuana Gravel. The Tuana rises gradually southward from plateau remnants near the Snake River between the 115th and 116th meridians, and most of its constituents are from hills of silicic volcanics to the south. However, the regularity of bedding and the presence of a few constituents from the north suggest that the sand and gravel were spread and sorted by the ancestral Snake River. Thus, with deposition of the Tuana Gravel, the buildup of fine-grained detritus that had characterized the Pliocene and earliest Pleistocene came to a close. The basin probably was then largely covered with coarse debris graded to marginal erosion surfaces.

BRUNEAU FORMATION

The earliest signs of canyon cutting are traced by the Bruneau Formation, a complex of lake beds and lava flows that fills a narrow trench roughly parallel to the present Snake River but lying a few kilometers south. The trench is cut in Glenns Ferry beds capped by remnants of Tuana Gravel and reaches a depth of 250 m at the mouth of the Bruneau River (116th meridian). In considerable part the sedimentary beds consist of clay, silt, and diatomite deposited in lakes impounded by lava dams, but these fine-grained materials are interbedded with several layers of beach gravel that represent temporary stages of equilibrium in lake level. The gravel was derived by reworking of the Tuana during shore erosion and rests on buried benches along the margins of the ancient canyon.

Part of the lava that impounded the lakes spilled into the ancient canyon from vents on upland erosion surfaces around Mountain Home, but dams were also erected by volcanoes along a remarkable string of vents that reaches 65 km northwestward along the Snake River from the mouth of the Bruneau River. This chain of volcanoes suggests that fractures formed by regional tectonism existed in Bruneau time. Several of these ancient volcanoes have been gutted by the modern canyon of the Snake.

In lowlands farther downstream, beyond these volcanoes, the Bruneau Formation has not been recognized, but the highest lake beds (980 m altitude) suggest that the ultimate dam may have been at the Oxbow on the Snake River (also 980 m altitude—at northwest corner of area of Figure 1). The Oxbow is the presumed site of capture of Snake River drainage by an ancestral tributary of the Salmon River that cut Hells Canyon (Wheeler and Cook, 1954). Spillover at the Oxbow in Bruneau time may have established the present connection of the Snake with the Columbia River system. If so, some other outlet of earlier age, contemporaneous with the stage of Bruneau canyon cutting, must be assumed.

The molluscan fossils from the Bruneau Formation represent almost entirely living species. Dwight W. Taylor (*in* Malde and Powers, 1962, p. 1211) reports that "only one of the species is extinct, and most of the others are living in southwestern Idaho. The abundant species of the Snake River today, such as *Gonidea angulata* (Lea), *Valvata utahensis* (Call), *Lithoglyphus fuscus* (Haldeman), and *Vorticifex effusus* (Lea), appear first in the Bruneau Formation." The vertebrate fossils, although few, represent typically Pleistocene forms. (See summary in Malde and Powers, 1962.)

On the basis of ages assigned to the mammalian and molluscan fossils, the Bruneau is dated as middle Pleistocene. A potassium/argon age of 1.4 million years (Evernden *et al.*, 1964, p. 191, sample KA 1188) for the youngest basalt suggests that the Bruneau is preglacial.

BLACK MESA GRAVEL

South of the Snake River the Bruneau Formation and older basin deposits are beveled by a pediment deposit of locally derived sand and gravel about 8 m thick that extends discontinuously about 110 km westward from the 115th meridian. Accordant remnants of this deposit, known as the Black Mesa Gravel, define a gravelly swath about 16 km wide that lies 170 m above the Snake River. This broad pediment displays no geometrical symmetry with respect to tributary canyons of the Snake and clearly antedates the modern canyon. A cap of hard caliche on its surface indicates prolonged weathering and implies that the Black Mesa is rather old, but it cannot be accurately dated. Because the Black Mesa Gravel is older than entrenchment of the present canyon, it is regarded as middle Pleistocene in age.

LAVA FLOWS OF EASTERN SNAKE RIVER PLAIN

Russell (1902), in his pioneer study of the Snake River Plain, surmised that the extensive basalt flows of the eastern plain intertongue with clastic deposits in the western basin—a conclusion confirmed by recent mapping (Malde *et al.*, 1963). Faulted Pliocene basalt that forms upland plateaus on silicic volcanic rocks intertongues with sediments near the Snake River at the 114th meridian and thickens eastward in outcrops along the canyon as far upstream as Twin Falls. Lava flows in Glenns Ferry deposits near the 115th meridian also thicken upstream. Much of the basalt of Bruneau age was erupted from sources near the Snake River within a few kilometers of the 114th meridian, where it intertongues with lake beds, although other sources are known in hills north of the Snake farther east. All of these rather ancient lava flows are more or less weathered. Fresh basalt of younger age, known as the Snake River Group, was erupted during entrenchment of the present canyon—almost entirely from sources east of the 115th meridian. Basalt of the Snake River Group came from numerous vents and covered nearly all the eastern plain. The eruption of these younger lavas apparently forced the Snake River into its course along the southern margin of the plain, from which it does not depart until reaching the head of the sedimentary basin near the 115th meridian. In places, therefore, basalt of the Snake River Group is interbedded with stream deposits (mainly gravel), but detrital material is only a minor component.

The relation of lavas of the Snake River Group to entrenchment of the present canyon is particularly well displayed near the 115th meridian. (See the stratigraphic sequence outlined in Table 1.) Here, successive lava flows fill a series of former canyons, each deeper than its predecessor, and each pursuing westward paths that lie successively farther south. This series of lavas culminates in basalt that partly fills the present canyon.

At times between lava eruptions the ancestral Snake River built terraces of gravel, which were formed at progressively lower heights as cutting continued. The oldest, the Sugar Bowl Gravel, is preserved on knobs 120 m above the river in wide places along the canyon that coincide with tributary junctions. Evidently it was deposited after the present system of tributary streams had been established. Abundant pebbles of porphyry, quartzite, and granite from glaciated mountains of central Idaho in the Sugar Bowl

TABLE 1

Sequence of Quaternary Deposition and Erosion in Western Snake River Plain (Based on Malde and Powers, 1962)

AGE			STRATIGRAPHIC UNIT	DESCRIPTION
Recent			Lava flows	Fresh basalt largely unmodified by surficial deposits.
Pleistocene	Late	Rocks equal to Snake River Group	Older alluvium	Pebble and cobble gravel on terrace 8-30 m above Snake River.
				─── TERRACE CUTTING ───
			Melon Gravel	Rounded boulders and cobbles of local basalt in matrix of basaltic sand. In Snake River canyon, forms huge bars up to 90 m high--commonly veneered with boulders ("melon patches"). Deposited 30,000 years ago by catastrophic outflow from Lake Bonneville in Utah.
				─── EROSION OF CANYON-FILLING LAVA FLOWS ───
			Lava flows	Fresh basalt and pillow lava filling or cascading into former canyon of Snake River. Upland surfaces partly mantled with eolian material.
				─── CANYON CUT TO PRESENT DEPTH ───
			Crowsnest Gravel	Mainly outwash of cobble and pebble gravel from glaciated mountains of central Idaho. Forms terrace about 60 m above Snake River.
			Thousand Springs Basalt	Succession of lava flows that filled ancient canyons and deflected Snake River toward southern margin of Snake River Plain. Smooth mantle of alluvial and eolian deposits yields cold-climate mollusks.
				─── CANYON CUTTING ───
			Sugar Bowl Gravel	Outwash of pebble gravel from glaciated mountains of central Idaho. Dissected remnants define a terrace 120 m above Snake River.
				─── TERRACE CUTTING ───
			Madson Basalt	Columnar lava filling a former canyon of Snake River 90 m deep.
				─── PARTIAL ENTRENCHMENT OF SNAKE RIVER ───
	Middle	Idaho Group (part)	Black Mesa Gravel	Gravel and sand on broad remnants of pediment widely preserved south of Snake River and 170 m higher. Hard caliche cap 2 m thick.
				─── BROAD VALLEY EROSION ───
			Bruneau Formation	Canyon fill of undeformed, unconsolidated lake beds (chiefly clay, diatomite, and beach gravel) and interbedded basalt (partly fragmental material altered locally to palagonite). Sequence interrupted by several local disconformities caused by breaching of lava dams. Fill about 250 m thick, but associated marginal deposits of fan gravel and basalt rise 90 m higher. Fossils include *Mammuthus*, *Equus*, *Gigantocamelus*, and *Paramylodon*, and a large molluscan fauna of modern character. Youngest basalt dated 1.4 million years by K-A.
				─── CANYON CUTTING ───
	Early		Tuana Gravel	Pebble and cobble gravel interbedded with sand and silt on dissected erosion surface south of Snake River and 180-250 m higher. Mainly debris from highlands farther south. Locally 60 m thick. Hard caliche cap about 2 m thick. Fossils include proboscidean remains.
				─── PLANATION OF BASIN DEPOSITS; MINOR FAULTING ───
Pliocene	Late		Glenns Ferry Formation	Basin fill of poorly consolidated detrital material and minor lava flows of basalt. Abrupt lateral changes in sedimentary facies 100-200 m thick represent adjoining environments of lakes (massive silt), river channels (thick beds of sand), and swampy flood plains (thinly bedded dark clay, olive silt, and carbonaceous shale). Bedding interrupted by numerous minor unconformities resulting from contemporaneous subsidence. About 600 m of beds exposed. Fossils include numerous vertebrates of Blancan provincial age (Wood and others, 1941), an extraordinarily large molluscan fauna consisting almost entirely of extinct forms, and abundant remains of pollen, algae, and diatoms. Basalt dated 3.5 million years by K-A.

Gravel—the earliest recognized sign of such material in the Snake River Plain—suggest that this gravel may be mainly glacial outwash. The Crowsnest Gravel, which forms a terrace about 60 m lower, is also rich in these constituents and may represent another stage of alpine glaciation. Neither the Sugar Bowl nor the Crowsnest is strongly weathered, but both have moderately well-developed calcareous soils. A still younger gravel on the canyon floor (the Melon Gravel, to be discussed later) is dated about 30,000 years old by radiocarbon. Stream deposits of probable Wisconsin age are represented by terraces of cobble and pebble gravel 8-30 m above the Snake River.

The fresh lavas near the 115th meridian that are related to entrenchment of the present canyon are only local flows in the great body of basalt that stretches 300 km northeastward. Buildup of this basalt formed a subdued crest along the axis of the plain, where most of the vents are concentrated. Although the surface flows are not deformed, alignment of vents along northeasterly and northwesterly trends suggests that eruptive centers have been structurally controlled. For example, vents at Craters of the Moon, a picturesque area of exceptionally fresh lavas and cinder cones (Stearns, 1928), lie along a southeast-trending rift that projects to an area of Recent basalt near the Snake River. Basalt at the extreme northeastern end of the plain intertongues with rhyolite tuff related to silicic volcanics of Yellowstone Park, and eruption of the rhyolite apparently coincided with a caldera collapse (Hamilton, in press), shown as a ring fault on Figure 1.

The thickness of basalt in the eastern Snake River Plain is not accurately known, but seismic data between Craters of the Moon and Idaho Falls indicate a local thickness of at least 1,300 m (Perkins *et al.*, 1947). Gravity data suggest that the basalt may fill broad troughs (areas of high gravity) that trend across the plain (Fig. 1), roughly parallel to the structure of basins and ranges to the north and south, although more widely spaced. Hence, if such basalt-filled troughs are a reality, they are probably of tectonic origin.

The great thickness of the basalt in the eastern Snake River Plain prompts questions about the age of the deeply buried part. If the lower part is Pliocene and early Pleistocene, equivalent to weathered basalt exposed west of Twin Falls, the ancestral Snake River must have crossed long stretches of basalt while transporting clastic debris to the western basin. Nevertheless, basaltic constituents are not identifiable in the basin deposits—unless a few layers of dark clay represent reworked basaltic soils. Presumably the old basalt of the western basin does not extend very far eastward, and the lavas of the eastern plains (in spite of their great thickness) are mainly younger than the basin deposits—that is, late Pleistocene.

MELON GRAVEL AND BONNEVILLE FLOOD

Gilbert (1890, p. 177) discovered that Pleistocene Lake Bonneville overflowed at Red Rock Pass (near 42°20′ N., 112° W.) and rapidly discharged a vast amount of water into the Snake River. Only recently, however, have effects of the sudden outflow been reported along the Snake River. These consist of scabland paths between Pocatello and Twin Falls and of gigantic bars of locally derived boulder gravel along the canyon downstream (Malde, 1960; Trimble and Carr, 1961; Stearns, 1962). On the Snake River Plain at Pocatello, the floodwater entered an existing Pleistocene lake and deposited coarse deltaic debris named the Michaud Gravel (Trimble and Carr, 1961). The flood debris below Twin Falls is known as the Melon Gravel, a name that evokes an image of its most conspicuous feature: broad straths strewn with melon-sized boulders.

The scabland shows that some floodwater was diverted into upland channels, which lead to marginal cataracts along the canyon rim some distance downstream. Scabland and abandoned cataracts are particularly noteworthy near American Falls (48 km downstream from Pocatello) and at Twin Falls. The bars of Melon Gravel below Twin Falls show that the canyon was flooded in places to a depth of 90 m. Relatively tranquil flow of floodwater through wide segments that occur here and there along the canyon caused flood debris to be dumped in enormous piles, and the volume of Melon Gravel thus trapped (about 2.4 billion m^3) corresponds approximately with the estimated volume of erosion at the canyon head near Twin Falls.

A constriction south of Boise in the Snake River canyon, which acted as a huge hydraulic flume, gives a basis for calculating the maximum discharge—estimated by Clifford T. Jenkins, U.S. Geological Survey, to have been 15 million ft^3/sec (0.42 million m^3/sec). At this rate the volume of water drained from Lake Bonneville would have provided floodwater for about six weeks; but discharge probably was attenuated as overflow continued, and the Bonneville flood may have lasted several months or years.

The time of the Bonneville flood is approximately dated at 30,000 years ago by radiocarbon. One date, 29,700 ± 1,000 years (Trimble and Carr, 1961, sample W-731), comes from shells in a terrace deposit southwest of Pocatello that is somewhat younger than the peak flood. Two other radiocarbon dates, 33,000 ± 1,600 years and 35,000 ± 3,000 years (Ives *et al.*, 1964, p. 54, samples W-1121 and W-1177), for organic soil baked by a lava flow in the path of the flood downstream from Red Rock Pass, are discussed by Bright (1963) in the light of his stratigraphic studies of the history of the Bear River, which indicate that diversion of the Bear River into the Bonneville basin may have caused Lake Bonneville to overflow. Furthermore, certain high levels of Lake Bonneville correspond with glacial episodes near Salt Lake City (Richmond, 1964). Thus, because of the link between the Melon Gravel and Lake Bonneville, a small part of the history of the Snake River Plain may be tied to knowledge of glacial events gained elsewhere.

REFERENCES

Bright, R. C., 1963, Pleistocene Lakes Thatcher and Bonneville, southeastern Idaho: Univ. Minnesota Ph.D. thesis, 292 p.

Cook, E. F., and Larrison, E. J., 1954, Late Pleistocene age of the Snake River diversion (abst.): Geol. Soc. Amer. Bull., v. 65, p. 1241

Dall, W. H., 1924, Discovery of a Balkan fresh-water fauna in the Idaho formation of Snake River valley, Idaho; U.S. Geol. Survey Prof. Pap. 132, p. 109-115

Evernden, J. F., Savage, D. E., Curtis, G. H., and James, G. T., 1964, Potassium-argon dates and the Cenozoic mammalian chronology of North America: Amer. J. Sci., v. 262, p. 145-198

Freeman, O. W., Forrester, J. D., and Lupher, R. L., 1945, Physiographic divisions of the Columbia intermontane province: Assoc. Amer. Geogr. Ann., v. 35, p. 53-75

Gazin, C. L., 1936, A study of the fossil horse remains from the upper Pliocene of Idaho: U.S. Natl. Mus. Proc., v. 83, p. 281-320

Gilbert, G. K., 1890, Lake Bonneville: U.S. Geol. Surv. Monogr. 1, 438 p.

Hamilton, Warren, 1962, Late Cenozoic structure of west-central Idaho: Geol. Soc. Amer. Bull., v. 73, p. 511-516

—— in press, Geology and petrogenesis of the Island Park caldera of rhyolite and basalt, eastern Idaho: U.S. Geol. Surv. Prof. Pap. 504-C

Hibbard, C. W., 1958, Summary of North American Pleistocene mammalian local faunas: Michigan Acad. Sci. Pap., v. 43, p. 3-32

Hill, D. P., 1963, Gravity and crustal structure in the western Snake River Plain: J. Geophys. Res., v. 68, p. 5807-5819

Hill, D. P., Baldwin, H. L., Jr., and Pakiser, L. C., 1961, Gravity, volcanism, and crustal deformation in the Snake River Plain, Idaho: U.S. Geol. Surv. Prof. Pap. 424-B, p. 248-250

Ives, P. C., Levin, Betsy, Robinson, R. D., and Rubin, Meyer, 1964, U.S. Geological Survey Radiocarbon dates VII: Radiocarbon, v. 6, p. 37-76

Kirkham, V. R. D., 1931, Snake River downwarp: J. Geol., v. 39, p. 456-482

LaFehr, T. L., 1962, Gravity survey in the eastern Snake River Plain, Idaho—a progress report: U.S. Geol. Surv. Repts., Open-File Ser., No. 638, 30 p.

Malde, H. E., 1959, Fault zone along northern boundary of western Snake River Plain, Idaho: Science, v. 130, p. 272

—— 1960, Evidence in the Snake River Plain, Idaho, of a catastrophic flood from Pleistocene Lake Bonneville: U.S. Geol. Surv. Prof. Pap. 400-B, p. 295-297

Malde, H. E., and Powers, H. A., 1962, Upper Cenozoic stratigraphy of western Snake River Plain, Idaho: Geol. Soc. Amer. Bull., v. 73, p. 1197-1219

Malde, H. E., Powers, H. A., and Marshall, C. H., 1963, Reconnaissance geologic map of west-central Snake River Plain, Idaho: U.S. Geol. Surv. Misc. Inv. Map I-373

Perkins, Beauregard, Jr., Gardner, D. S., Pearce, T. H.,

and Patterson, R. M., 1947, Subsurface structure of Snake River Valley, Idaho, from seismograph records of ammunition explosions (abst.): Geophysics, v. 12, p. 496

Powers, H. A., 1960, A distinctive chemical characteristic of Snake River basalts of Idaho: U.S. Geol. Surv. Prof. Pap. 400-B, p. 298

Powers, H. A., and Malde H. E., 1961, Volcanic ash beds as stratigraphic markers in basin deposits near Hagerman and Glenns Ferry, Idaho: U.S. Geol. Surv. Prof. Pap. 424-B, p. 167-170

Richmond, G. M., 1964, Glaciation of Little Cottonwood and Bells Canyon, Wasatch Mountains, Utah: U.S. Geol. Surv. Prof. Pap. 454-D, p. 1-41

Russell, I. C., 1902, Geology and water resources of the Snake River Plains of Idaho: U.S. Geol. Surv. Bull. 199, 192 p.

Stearns, H. T., 1928, Craters of the Moon National Monument, Idaho: Idaho Bur. Mines and Geol. Bull. 13, 57 p.

—— 1962, Evidence of Lake Bonneville flood along Snake River below King Hill, Idaho: Geol. Soc. Amer. Bull., v. 73, p. 385-387

Stearns, H. T., Crandall, Lynn, and Steward, W. G., 1938, Geology and ground-water resources of the Snake River plain in southeastern Idaho: U.S. Geol. Surv. Water-Supply Pap. 774, 268 p.

Taylor, D. W., 1960, Distribution of the freshwater clam *Pisidium ultramontanum;* a zoogeographic inquiry: Amer. J. Sci., v. 258-A, p. 325-334

Trimble, D. E., and Carr, W. J., 1961, Late Quaternary history of the Snake River in the American Falls region, Idaho: Geol. Soc. Amer. Bull., v. 72, p. 1739-1748

Uyeno, Teruya, 1961, Late Cenozoic cyprinid fishes from Idaho with notes on other fossil minnows in North America: Michigan Acad. Sci. Arts Ltrs. Pap., v. 46, p. 329-344

Wheeler, H. E., and Cook, E. F., 1954, Structural and stratigraphic significance of the Snake River capture, Idaho-Oregon: J. Geol., v. 62, p. 525-536

Wilson, R. W., 1934, A rodent fauna from later Cenozoic beds of southwestern Idaho: Carnegie Instn. Publ. 440, Contr. Paleont., p. 117-136

Wood, H. E., 2d, et al., 1941, Nomenclature and correlation of the North American continental Tertiary: Geol. Soc. Amer. Bull., v. 52, p. 1-48

Youngquist, W. L., and Kiilsgaard, T. H., 1951, Recent test drilling, Snake River Plains, southwestern Idaho: Amer. Assoc. Petroleum Geologists Bull., v. 35, p. 90-96

SUMMARY

The vast lowland, known as the Snake River Plain, that stretches across southern Idaho is a Pliocene structural trough filled with a complex sequence of basaltic lava and intercalated detrital deposits more than a kilometer in thickness, much of which is of Quaternary age. The trough at the western end is outlined by a northwest-trending graben 50 km broad, the site of a basin fill of lake and stream deposits rich in molluscan and vertebrate fossils. The eastern plain, on the other hand, a monotonous tract of lava diversified only by numerous subdued volcanic vents, is structurally more like a downwarp.

Canyon cutting in the western basin to a depth of 150-300 m gives excellent exposures of the Quaternary deposits and their physiographic relations. A widespread unit of Blancan provincial age at least 600 m thick, characterized by moderately faulted fine-grained sedimentary facies indicative of adjoining environments of lakes, river channels, and swampy flood plains, is beveled by undeformed lower Pleistocene sand and gravel 180-250 m above the present Snake River. A subsequent canyon 250 m deep was filled in middle Pleistocene time by lava flows and by sediments trapped in lakes behind lava dams. These deposits were then beveled by pediment gravel 170 m above the river.

Entrenchment of the present Snake River canyon, regarded as a late Pleistocene event, coincided with eruption of the surface lava flows in the eastern plain, which apparently forced the Snake River into its course along the southern margin. Two gravel terraces 120 m and 60 m above the river, which were built between lava eruptions as cutting progressed, include abundant constituents from glaciated mountains in central Idaho and possibly represent glacial outwash. Still younger gravel on the canyon floor, distinguished by enormous boulders heaped in huge bars as much as 90 m high, is attributed to catastrophic overflow of Lake Bonneville about 30,000 years ago.

QUATERNARY GEOLOGY OF THE GREAT BASIN *

ROGER B. MORRISON[1]

GEOGRAPHIC AND GEOLOGIC BACKGROUND

THE GREAT BASIN is bounded by the Colorado and Columbia Plateaus, the Sonoran Desert section of the Basin and Range Province, and the Sierra Nevada and Wasatch Range (Fig. 1). It is the largest part of the Basin and Range Province and includes most of Nevada and western Utah, with fringes extending into California, Oregon, and Idaho. It was named in 1844 by Fremont, who established the fact that from this huge area no water drained to the ocean.

BASIN AND RANGE TOPOGRAPHY AND STRUCTURE

Despite its name, the Great Basin is not a single large basin. It contains more than 150 desert basins (mostly closed) separated from each other by more than 160 discontinuous, subparallel mountain ranges, trending roughly north-south. Dutton aptly likened the pattern of ranges to that of an "army of caterpillars marching to Mexico." The distinctive "Basin and Range topography" is mainly the result of high-angle faulting; the ranges commonly are uplifted as horsts (commonly somewhat tilted), and the basins are down-dropped as grabens. The block faulting started at least as early as the Oligocene and has continued to the present. Only the younger faults, generally those of Quaternary age, are appreciably manifest in the present Basin and Range topography. The whole region also was epeirogenically uplifted as a broad arch during the Pleistocene. At the beginning of the Pleistocene the whole region lay closer to sea level, and the Sierra Nevada and Wasatch Range were considerably lower relative to the Great Basin (Axelrod, 1950, 1962; Van Houten, 1956).

Although block faulting occurred fairly continuously throughout the Quaternary (albeit only spasmodically in any given part of the region), the most intense Basin and Range deformation was in two climaxes. During the first climax, probably in very early Pleistocene time, there was strong differential uplift of the Sierra Nevada and Wasatch Range, as well as of most of the intervening mountain ranges. Axelrod (1962) and Birkeland (1963) consider that this climax was responsible for the major part of the Pliocene and Pleistocene deformation of the Sierra Nevada. It antedated the oldest recognized glaciation. The effects of the second climax, in early middle Pleistocene time, were less evenly distributed geographically. This climax was most intense along and near the eastern side of the Sierra Nevada and the western side of the Wasatch Range; also, the

youthful Basin and Range topography in the northwestern part of the Great Basin dates mainly from this climax; the north-central and southeastern parts of the Great Basin remained relatively little affected.

As most of the main faults active in Quaternary time bound mountain blocks, relief reached a maximum at the close of the second climax. Subsequently, erosion and sedimentation have been more rapid than faulting and have progressively lowered the mountains and filled the basins. However, in some areas block faulting has remained active to the present. Attesting to this are the scarps bordering many ranges in northern and central Nevada and the eastern side of the Sierra Nevada and the western side of the Wasatch Range, as well as numerous historic earthquakes in these areas, many of them resulting in surface faulting. The 1954 earthquake in Dixie Valley, Nevada, produced scarps as much as 25 ft (7.6 m) high in alluvium.

As a result of the combination of epeirogenic arching and block faulting, the whole Great Basin resembles a partly collapsed broad arch, having its highest part in eastern Nevada. For example, in northwestern Nevada and in western Utah the floors of the main basins are from 3,800 to 5,000 ft (1,158 to 1,524 m) above sea level, and in eastern Nevada from 5,300 to 6,300 ft (1,615 to 1,838 m). The region also slopes generally southward, and basin floors in the southernmost Great Basin are commonly below 2,500 ft (762 m) altitude; the lowest part of Death Valley is 280 ft (85 m) below sea level, the lowest point in the United States.

Volcanism was associated with the Quaternary block faulting in many parts of the Great Basin, but it was not so widespread; it was lacking in northeastern and southeastern Nevada and in most of western Utah. Basaltic and andesitic flows were extruded over wide areas in the northwestern Great Basin shortly before and during the first Quaternary climax of faulting. Later volcanic deposits, which are more restricted, are exemplified by prominent latite, andesite, and basalt units in the Lake Tahoe–Reno area, and the Bishop Tuff, which is widespread along the central-eastern side of the Sierra Nevada; these units were displaced locally more than 2,000 ft (610 m) by the last main climax of relative uplift of the Sierra Nevada. In late Pleistocene time only a few small volcanic centers were active—for example, at Mono and Inyo Craters, California; Pyramid Lake and Carson Desert, Nevada; and in the Sevier Desert, Utah.

Erosion and sedimentation during the Quaternary were controlled by block faulting and climatic change. Because of the intense deformation, erosion and sedimentation became so active that nearly all the present topographic fea-

* Publication authorized by the Director, U.S. Geological Survey
[1] U.S. Geological Survey, Federal Center, Denver, Colorado.

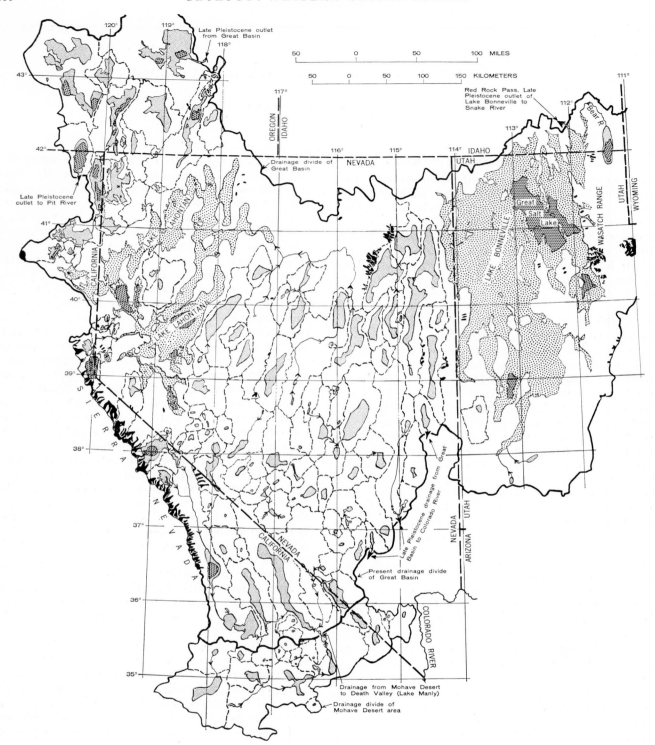

Figure 1. Map showing maximum expansion of the pluvial lakes and glaciers within the Great Basin during post-Sangamon time. Glaciers are in solid black, existing lakes in darkest stipple, and pluvial lakes in lighter stipple. Dashed lines show boundaries of drainage basins; thin solid lines (with arrows) indicate overflow connections between basins. Data on glaciers are from Atwood (1909), Blackwelder (1931, 1934), Blackwelder and Matthes (1938), Sharp (1938), and Morrison (unpublished field notes); on pluvial lakes from Miller (1946), Hubbs and Miller (1948), Crittenden (1963a), Snyder *et al.* (1964), and Morrison (unpublished compilations).

tures—from whole mountain ranges and basins to individual valleys and hills—were formed during the Pleistocene Epoch. Even the early Pleistocene landforms were so modified by erosion and deposition that their original forms are difficult to reconstruct; the late Pliocene surfaces are preserved only as local remnants, generally in mountain-summit areas.

The basins are partly filled with detritus from the adjoining mountains. The basin-fill deposits of Quaternary age range in thickness from a few feet to several thousand feet. Gently sloping alluvial surfaces that are concave basinward border the mountains. These surfaces are of two types, which frequently occur in association. Bajada, or piedmont surfaces, the first type, are formed by coalescing alluvial fans and are underlain by relatively thick accumulations of gravelly alluvium laid down by floods debouching from the mountains. Pediment surfaces, the second type, are inclined rock-cut surfaces thinly veneered with gravelly alluvium. Downslope, the pediments are overlapped by piedmont surfaces. Much of the Quaternary pedimentation took place before the last main climax of block faulting, and in places the pediments are displaced by the faults. In general, pediments are rather narrow in the northern part of the Great Basin and they become progressively wider to the south.

The floors of basins that have remained closed decrease in slope toward the basin interior until they merge into almost level alluvial plains and finally into central playas (dry lakes) in the lowest part of the basin. Progressive alluviation has raised the floors, so that dissection and exposure in depth of the basin-fill deposits are slight. Commonly the upper parts of alluvial fans are dissected because of altered stream regimen resulting from climatic change or locally from uplift by block faulting. Some basins, however, have become breached and through-going drainage to lower basins has been established, and their basin-interior deposits have been dissected by the through-flowing stream and its tributaries.

CLIMATE

The Great Basin is a semiarid to arid area lying in the rain-shadow of the Sierra Nevada, which removes much of the moisture from the generally eastward-moving air masses from the Pacific Ocean. Lesser rain-shadow effects are produced by the other mountain ranges, which are transverse to the prevailing winds. Precipitation is strongly influenced by orography—the storms tend to precipitate increasing amounts of moisture with increasing altitude. Consequently the mean annual precipitation ranges from less than 4 in. (10 cm) in the lower basins to more than 30 in. (76 cm) on the highest mountain summits; commonly a difference of more than 20 in. (51 cm) occurs in a few miles. Much of the winter precipitation is snow. Most of the summer precipitation occurs as infrequent torrential showers. Annual precipitation is extremely variable from year to year, much more so than the temperature.

Mean annual temperature for a given altitude generally differs about 11° F (6.1° C) between the southern and the northern margins of the Great Basin. January/July average temperatures are 44.5°/86° F (7°/30° C) at Las Vegas, Nevada, 32.5°/71° F (0°/21.5° C) at Reno, Nevada, 30°/77° F (−1°/25° C) at Salt Lake City, Utah, and 25°/67° F (−4°/19° C) at Burns, Oregon.

Because of the interior drainage, all loss of precipitation from the Great Basin results from evapo-transpiration. In the northern part precipitation and evapo-transpiration approximately balance, and permanent lakes exist at the terminal sumps of the largest rivers. In the southeastern part evapo-transpiration considerably exceeds the precipitation, and there are no permanent lakes.

CLIMATIC CHANGES DURING THE QUATERNARY

In the Miocene and Pliocene the climate of the Great Basin was subhumid, with 25 to 30 in. (63 to 76 cm) of estimated annual precipitation (Axelrod, 1950; Van Houten, 1956). The present desert climate of the lowlands began at the start of the Pleistocene, as determined from botanical evidence (Axelrod, 1950, p. 266). This climate developed as a result of epeirogenic uplift and of relative uplift of the Sierra Nevada and other ranges by block faulting. In contrast to earlier climates of the Cenozoic, however, the Pleistocene climate fluctuated widely, with respect to both temperature and precipitation. The cooler and wetter times generally are called pluvials. They were 8° to 15° F (4.4° to 8.3° C) cooler than now, and also appreciably less arid, as attested, for example, by markedly increased supply of coarse alluvium from the mountains and by increased mass-wasting. Runoff increased because of lower temperature and greater precipitation, tipping the balance between inflow and evaporation in the basins in favor of inflow, so that permanent lakes developed in all the terminal basins. These "lake cycles" or "lacustral intervals" were synchronous with intervals of glaciation in the higher mountains.

The general cyclic pattern of Quaternary climatic change seems to have been relatively cool-dry at the start of an interlacustral-interglacial interval, changing to warm-dry and then to warm-wet (during the weathering optimum at the end of an interlacustral-interglacial interval), then during the ensuing lacustral-glacial interval to cool-wet, to cold-wet (during the lacustral-glacial maximum) to cool-moist, and back to cool-dry. These climatic changes not only caused relatively large changes in erosional and surficial depositional processes but also caused the life zones to move hundreds of miles north- and southward and thousands of feet up and down the mountainsides.

GENERAL FEATURES OF THE QUATERNARY DEPOSITIONAL RECORD

The terminal basins of the larger rivers of the Great Basin preserve a nearly complete depositional record for the middle and late Quaternary. They have lost no sediment by exterior drainage to the ocean—in contrast to continental areas draining to the ocean, whose Quaternary successions record only part of the time they embrace. Their stratigraphic records are unusually "sensitive," because various parts of the Quaternary climatic cycles are marked by distinctive deposits. Under the generally arid to semiarid climate, the climatic changes produced proportionally much greater changes in precipitation and ground moisture-runoff conditions than in more humid regions. This resulted in similarly marked changes both in *types* and *rates* of all kinds of surficial processes, including development of vegetative cover, mass-wasting, alluviation, eolian activity,

TABLE 1

Correlation Chart

(The interglaciations in the Rocky Mountain region and Sierra Nevada *include* the times of formation of the soils that are shown immediately above the boxes designating these interglaciations; the soils are the principal record of the interglaciations.)

Approximate age, years before present	QUATERNARY SYSTEM — Pleistocene Series	MIDCONTINENT REGION TIME-STRATIGRAPHIC DIVISIONS [1]	ROCKY MOUNTAIN REGION [2] (including Wasatch Range, Utah) Geologic-climatic and soil-stratigraphic units	LAKE BONNEVILLE AREA [3] Physical stratigraphic units	RUBY-EAST HUMBOLDT RANGE, NEVADA [4] Glacial "substages" and pediment surfaces	LAKE LAHONTAN AREA [5] Physical stratigraphic units	SIERRA NEVADA [6] Geologic-climatic and soil-stratigraphic units
10,000	WISCONSINAN STAGE	Recent stage; Valderan substage; Twocreekan substage; Woodfordian substage; Farmdalian substage	Neoglaciation: Gannett Peak Stade, Temple Lake Stade (weak soil), post-Pinedale soil; Pinedale-Neoglacial interglaciation; Pinedale Glaciation — late stade (soil), middle stade, early stade	subaerial and shallow-lake sediments; early Recent soil; Recent soil; Midvale Soil; eolian sand, local alluvium; Draper Formation; Graniteville Soil; Bonneville Formation (upper member, white marl member); Promontory Soil; middle Lake Bonneville subaerial sediments (LAKE BONNEVILLE GROUP)	Angel Lake substage; interstade	Fallon Formation; Turupah Formation (upper member, lower member); Toyeh Soil, "L"-Drain Soil; Sehoo (and Indian Lakes) Formations — Sehoo Fm, upper member; Harmon School Soil; Sehoo Fm, dendritic member; weak soil; Sehoo Fm, lower member (LAHONTAN VALLEY GROUP)	Neoglaciation: Matthes Stade, Recess Peak (Frog Lake) Stade; post-Tioga soil; Hilgard Stade; post-Tioga interglaciation; Tioga Glaciation — main stade; Tenaya Stade (locally differentiated in southern S. Nevada); post-Tahoe soil
20,000		Altonian substage	post-Bull Lake soil; Bull Lake-Pinedale interglaciation (very strong soil); Bull Lake Glaciation — late stade (soil), stade, early stade	Alpine Formation; weak soil; soil; soil	Lamoille substage	Wyemaha Formation; Churchill Soil; Eetza Formation; soil	Tahoe-Tioga interglaciation; Tahoe Glaciation — late stade, interstade, early stade; pre-Tahoe soil
30,000		SANGAMONIAN STAGE	Sacagawea Ridge-Bull Lake interglaciation (very strong soil); Sacagawea Ridge Glaciation	Dimple Dell Soil; Younger pre-Lake Bonneville subaerial unit; Younger pre-Lake Bonneville lacustrine unit; pre-Dimple Dell soil	pediment surfaces 5 and (or) 6	Paiute Formation; Cocoon Soil; Younger pre-Lake Lahontan lacustrine unit; pre-Cocoon soil	Mono Basin-Tahoe interglaciation; Mono Basin (Donner Lake) Glaciation
40,000		ILLINOIAN STAGE					
50,000		YARMOUTHIAN STAGE	Cedar Ridge-Sacagawea Ridge interglaciation (very strong soil); Cedar Ridge Glaciation	Older pre-Lake Bonneville subaerial unit — Pearlette Ash Member equivalent; Older pre-Lake Bonneville lacustrine unit		Older pre-Lake Lahontan subaerial unit; Older pre-Lake Lahontan lacustrine unit	very strong soil; Sherwin-Mono Basin interglaciation
60,000		KANSAN STAGE	Washakie Point-Cedar Ridge interglaciation (very strong soil); Washakie Point Glaciation		pediment surfaces 5 and (or) 4 to 1		Sherwin (Hobart) Glaciation; McGee-Sherwin interglaciation
70,000		AFTONIAN STAGE; NEBRASKAN STAGE					McGee Glaciation

Time scale much compressed from the Wisconsinan above

[1] Wisconsinan units from Frye and Willman (1960, 1963); pre-Wisconsinan units from Leverett (1899) and Frye and Leonard (1952).

[2] From Richmond (1960, 1961, 1964a, 1964b) and Morrison (1961b, 1965a).

[3] From Hunt (1953), Bissell (1963), and Morrison (1965a, 1965b).

[4] Modified from Sharp (1938, 1940).

[5] Modified from Morrison (1964a).

[6] From Blackwelder (1931), Sharp and Birman (1963), and Birman (1964), supplemented by Putman (1949, 1950, 1960b, 1962), Birkeland (1962, 1964), Wahrhaftig (1962), and Morrison (unpublished field data). Correlations of the Hilgard and Tenaya Stades and the Mono Basin Glaciation with other areas uncertain.

weathering-profile development, etc. The change in intensity of a given surficial process typically has been exponential, between the maximum and minimum of the pertinent portions of the climatic cycle for the process. The lacustral-glacial maxima were also times of maximum alluviation and mass-wasting, whereas the interlacustral-interglacial intervals started with maximum eolian activity and minimum alluviation and mass-wasting, and they ended with intervals of stability when chemical weathering predominated over erosion and deposition.

The alluvial, colluvial, and eolian facies of the Quaternary successions are the least sensitive in recording the smaller climate-induced depositional changes. The pluvial-lake facies are the most sensitive. The early and middle Quaternary portions of the lake facies unfortunately rarely are exposed, but the late Quaternary portions commonly are well exposed. Lakes Lahontan and Bonneville provided the most sensitive and readily available record. At the latitude of these giant lakes not only the main deep-lake intervals but also the minor lacustral intervals, and even the interlacustral intervals, are well recorded by deposits and landforms. During the interlacustral intervals there was little or no surplus runoff, but generally no marked deficit even in the driest intervals. Thus even small climatic changes during the interlacustral intervals are recorded by deposits of fluctuating low-level lakes, and few depositional hiatuses exist in the lowlands of the terminal basins. South of Lakes Lahontan and Bonneville the greater aridity resulted in lakes forming only during the wettest pluvials, so that the lacustrine records are less complete.

The pluvial-lake successions, particularly of Lakes Lahontan and Bonneville, considerably surpass the glacial successions of the western Cordillera in sensitivity and clarity of their depositional records. The various lake maxima are recorded by high-shore and deep-water deposits, and the intervening lake recessions are represented by unconformities caused by subaerial erosion, by weathering profiles, by shore deposits intercalated with deep-lake sediments, and by interbedded alluvium, colluvium, eolian sand, and loess. From such criteria it is possible to determine that a certain lake recession definitely went at least as low as a certain altitude. The glacial record is much more ambiguous on the magnitude and duration of the recessions; moreover, for glaciations the record of the early, waxing cycles seems to be generally erased whereas for lacustral intervals it is fairly well preserved.

STRATIGRAPHIC CORRELATION

Inevitably problems arise in correlating deposits over so large and diverse a region as the Great Basin. An evaluation of the various techniques used for correlation of Quaternary deposits within this region is given in Morrison (1946b). The correlation chart (Table 1) is modified and expanded from the one given in Morrison (1961d) and is generalized from the chart in Morrison (1964b). Its basic framework is derived from correlating the stronger weathering profiles (soils) of similar relative development and relative age; then between these main weathering profiles, depositional cycles of similar relative age, climatic genesis, and magnitude are correlated, as are any weakly developed

weathering profiles. Radiometric dates and paleontologic data, where available, provide important controls.

EARLY AND MIDDLE QUATERNARY DEPOSITS

Pre-Wisconsin deposits are exposed at the peripheries of many intermontane basins and locally in the highlands, at places where these deposits lie above the grade of the later Quaternary streams and consequently have been dissected, rather than buried by younger alluvium. These older basin-fill deposits are exposed in few places in the interiors of the basins, however, because of the general progressive alluviation of most basin floors. Their exposures in the basin interiors are localized along rivers that have dissected deep trenches in parts of their courses above their terminal basins.

SUBAERIAL DEPOSITS AND WEATHERING PROFILES (SOILS)

In general, in the best-exposed sequences of early and middle Quaternary deposits, two major subaerial units and two very strong weathering profiles can be differentiated. The subaerial units are mainly fan gravel in the highlands and on the piedmonts and pediments. These gravels intertongue downstream with finer alluvium, and upstream locally with colluvium. The older subaerial unit is only informally named (*e.g.* the older pre-Lake Bonneville fan gravel). The younger subaerial unit has been named the Paiute Formation in the Lake Lahontan area (Morrison, 1961a, 1964a), and informally the younger pre-Lake Bonneville subaerial unit in the Lake Bonneville area (Table 1).

The two subaerial units presumably formed mainly during strong alluviation and local pedimentation in the last two main pre-Wisconsin pluvial-glacial intervals. The older gravels generally are exposed only on the higher pediments and highest parts of the piedmonts, and they generally are deeply dissected. In most cases they appear to represent a single interval of major alluviation, probably correlative with the Kansan Glaciation. In Pine Valley, near Carlin, Nevada, however, vertebrates of early Pleistocene age have been found in the lower part of such deposits, and a volcanic ash that is correlated on petrographic evidence with the Pearlette Ash Member of the Sappa Formation of late Kansan(?) age occurs in the upper part of the same depositional unit, without major stratigraphic or geomorphic break (J. F. Smith, oral communication, 1964). The younger gravels typically lie at somewhat lower elevations on the piedmonts or on lower pediments and are somewhat less dissected; they probably are correlative with the Illinoian Glaciation.

The two main weathering profiles associated with these subaerial units are very strongly developed and probably formed during the last two main pre-Wisconsin interlacustral-interglacial intervals. They are the "pre-Wisconsin paleosol" and "ancient soils" of Hunt and Sokoloff (1950, p. 114) and Hunt (1953, p. 43), who did not differentiate them. The younger soil formed on the younger subaerial unit prior to deposition of material coeval with Lakes Bonneville and Lahontan, which are of post-Sangamon (Wisconsin) age; it is correlated with the Sangamon Soil of the Midwest–Great Plains region (Morrison, 1964b). Local nomenclature and additional correlations for both soils are shown on Table 1.

The two pre-Wisconsin soils resemble each other so closely that commonly they cannot be differentiated in relict occurrences. Wherever both are buried in the same stratigraphic sequence, however, the older soil is the more strongly developed. In the desert lowlands both soils generally are maximal Chestnut or Brown soils, with deep-reddish-brown (generally hue 7.5 YR) and moderately to strongly structured textural (clayey) B-horizons 1 to 3 ft (0.3 to 0.9 m) thick, overlying a white horizon of very strong calcium carbonate concentration (Cca-horizon) and in places also considerable concentration of silica (Csi-horizon). At elevations above $5,000 \pm 200$ ft ($1,524 \pm 61$ m) the soils change facies into Western Brown Forest and Brown Podzolic soils. The Brown Podzolic soil occurs above 5,200 ft (1,585 m) and has a deep-reddish-brown textural B-horizon 4 to 6 ft (1.2 to 1.9 m) thick, moderately to strongly structured in its upper part, grading downward to lighter brown and structureless material.

Both soils have been found within about 100 ft (30 m) of the lowest elevations of the terminal basins in both the Lake Lahontan and Lake Bonneville areas.

Glacial deposits. Glacial deposits of pre-Wisconsin (pre-Tahoe) age have been identified in the Sierra Nevada and Wasatch Range but not definitely in any of the mountain ranges in the interior of the Great Basin. Blackwelder (1931) described till and probable till of two pre-Tahoe glaciations on the eastern slope of the Sierra Nevada, which he designated the McGee (older) and Sherwin "stages." He tentatively correlated these stages with the Nebraskan and Kansan "stages," respectively, in the Midwest. These older tills have lost their original morainal morphology, and therefore are part of the relative uplift by faulting and much of the canyon cutting of the Sierra Nevada. Putnam (1949) distinguished his Aeolian Buttes Till (oldest) from the Sherwin Till in an area southwest of Mono Lake; although he later (1960a, b) correlated his Aeolian Buttes with the Sherwin Till, it now seems that his first interpretation was correct. Birkeland (1962, 1964) likewise differentiated his Hobart (older) and Donner Lake Tills and outwash along the Truckee River above Reno, Nevada. Correlations of these units among various sectors of the Sierra Nevada, in some instances even between adjacent drainage systems, are still quite uncertain.

Both Blackwelder and Putnam recognized that till assigned to the Sherwin "stage" apparently records multiple glaciation, and that the younger glaciation might be equivalent to the Illinoian Glaciation in the Midwest. Sharp and Birman (1963) locally differentiated moraines intermediate in age between till of the Tahoe and Sherwin Glaciations, which they term the Mono Basin moraines, and tentatively correlated them with the Illinoian Glaciation. Birkeland (1962, p. 65) also locally recognizes till in this stratigraphic position. On the other hand, Axelrod and Ting (1960, 1961) and Axelrod (1962) suggest that the McGee and Sherwin are respectively Kansan and Illinoian, on the basis of paleobotanic, tectonic, and geomorphic relations. Putnam (1960b) also considers the McGee to be Kansan rather than Nebraskan. However, recent potassium-argon dates for basalt flows resting on various late Cenozoic erosion surfaces in the Sierra Nevada (Dalrymple, 1963) and for the Bishop Tuff suggest that some tills assigned to the McGee, Aeolian Buttes, and even to the Sherwin likely are pre-Kansan.

The tills and outwash of these glaciations bear very strongly developed weathering profiles, which, although usually deeply eroded, are comparable in degree of development to, and correlative with, those of pre-Lake Bonneville and pre-Lake Lahontan age.

At the western edge of the Wasatch Range, near the mouths of Little Cottonwood and Big Cottonwood Canyons, tiny remnants of certain or possible till of at least one and perhaps two pre-Wisconsin (pre-Bull Lake, see Table 1) glaciations have been identified (Richmond, 1964a; Morrison, 1965a). At the time these tills were deposited both canyons were broader and shallower than now and their floors were about 1,000 ft (305 m) higher at the canyon mouths.

The only area in the interior of the Great Basin where pre-Wisconsin glaciation possibly occurred is at the mouth of Lamoille Canyon, on the western side of the Ruby Mountains, Nevada. Here Blackwelder (1931, p. 910-911) reported till-like bouldery material above and obviously older than the lateral moraine of Tahoe age. Sharp (1938), however, does not believe that these and similar deposits elsewhere in the range are definitely of glacial origin. The higher interior ranges may not have risen high enough to be glaciated until the late Quaternary, in view of the evidence for their continued epeirogenic uplift and relative uplift by faulting during the Pleistocene. Hunt (1956, p. 38, 61) suggests that the general scarcity and anomalous distribution of pre-Wisconsin glacial deposits in the High Plateaus of the Colorado Plateau Province, adjoining the Great Basin, may be because these glaciations antedated much of the Pleistocene upwarp of at least 2,000 ft (610 m).

LACUSTRINE DEPOSITS

Intertonguing with the two pre-Wisconsin subaerial units in the lower part of the basins are two lacustrine units. They include gravel, sand, silt, and clay, but they generally lack algal tufa (in contrast to the late Quaternary lake deposits). In the Lake Lahontan area, the lower lacustrine unit has been recognized at only two localities—near Fallon and near Nixon, Nevada. The upper pre-Lake Lahontan lacustrine unit, probably of Illinoian age, is extensively exposed near Rye Patch Dam on the Humboldt River; here it records two deep-lake cycles separated by lake recession to below 4,100 ft (1,249 m) altitude. Small exposures of this lacustrine unit occur in two gravel pits near Fallon, and along the Truckee River near Nixon. Lacustrine gravels, bearing the Cocoon Soil, that may mark the highest shoreline of this lake unit have been identified about 80 ± 30 ft (24 ± 9 m) above the highest shoreline of Lake Lahontan, which generally lies at altitude $4,390 \pm 15$ ft ($1,338 \pm 4.5$ m), at several widely scattered localities in the Lake Lahontan area.

In the Lake Bonneville area the best exposures of both lacustrine units are in the huge gravel pits on southern Promontory Point, Utah. Here the upper and lower units are discontinuously exposed to 775 and 470 ft (236 and 143 m), respectively above the June 1951 level of Great Salt

Lake (altitude 4,200 ft; 1,250 m), but the highest exposures probably do not reach the highest shorelines of either unit. Both units commonly are intercalated with the older and younger pre-Lake Bonneville soils, and they invariably are buried beneath younger units, including deposits of Lake Bonneville. A distinctive volcanic ash bed that is petrographically identical with the Pearlette Ash Member of the Sappa Formation (H. A. Powers, oral communication, 1962) of late Kansan(?) age, locally overlies the lower unit and underlies the older pre-Lake Bonneville soil. This ash also has been identified by Powers (quoted in Richmond, 1962, p. 35) in a core from 546 ft (167 m) depth at the eastern edge of Great Salt Lake (Eardley and Gvosdetsky, 1960).

Outside the areas inundated by Lakes Bonneville and Lahontan, exposures of pre-Wisconsin lacustrine deposits are also known in a few places—as in Smith and Carson Valleys, in northwest Reno, along the middle Reese River, and in Pine Valley, Nevada—but they have not been studied in detail.

On the basis of exotic fish fauna Hubbs and Miller (1948) postulated several sites of exterior drainage from the Great Basin in early and (or) middle Pleistocene time. An especially likely site is a former connection from the Lake Lahontan area westward to the Pit River and into the Sacramento or Klamath River systems. They also postulate that the Owens Lake-to-Death Valley system discharged into the Colorado River system.

WISCONSIN DEPOSITS AND SOILS

Deposits of Wisconsin age (Wisconsinan stage of Frye and Willman, 1960; Table 1, this report) are widely distributed and generally at least fairly well exposed throughout the Great Basin. They include alluvium, colluvium, eolian sand, glacial till, outwash, several weathering profiles, and, especially, lacustrine beds that provide an unusually detailed record of climatic fluctuations of this stage.

SUBAERIAL DEPOSITS AND SOILS

Subaerial deposits and soils of Wisconsin age are widespread throughout the Great Basin. The subaerial sediments include alluvium and colluvium and locally eolian sand, loess, glacial till, and outwash.

Nonglacial deposits and soils. The alluvium comprises fan gravel on the basin piedmonts, stream-terrace gravel (including glacial outwash), and fine-grained alluvium in the basin interiors. The gravels typically were deposited on fans or terraces inset at elevations below the pre-Wisconsin gravels. Two ages of Wisconsin fan- and stream-terrace gravels commonly can be differentiated: early Wisconsin and late Wisconsin. Little or no alluviation occurred during the middle Wisconsin interlacustral-interglacial interval or during altithermal interval (of Antevs). Thus the early Wisconsin alluvium is generally correlative with the Alpine and Eetza Formations of Lakes Bonneville and Lahontan and with the Tahoe and Bull Lake Glaciations of the Sierra Nevada and Rocky Mountains; the late Wisconsin alluvium is correlative with the Bonneville-Draper sequence and the Sehoo Formation and with the Tioga and Pinedale Glaciations (see Table 1).

Subdivisions of early and late Wisconsin alluvial deposits can be differentiated locally, as in the outstanding strathterrace sequence along Little Cottonwood Creek south of Salt Lake City, Utah (Morrison, 1965a). Generally, however, only the two main units can be differentiated, because the alluvial deposits do not afford a good record of the minor climatic fluctuations.

The early Wisconsin fan and stream-terrace deposits generally are larger and coarser than the late Wisconsin ones, and typically the fans and terraces they underlie are at higher elevations and more dissected than the younger ones.

Extensive deposits of eolian sand and loess, but little or no alluvium and colluvium, characterize the earlier parts of the interlacustral-interglacial intervals. For example, in middle Lake Lahontan (Wyemaha) time, sand was deflated from sandy outwash plains of Tahoe age east of the Sierra Nevada and blown as much as 70 miles (112 km) in belts trending generally east-northeastward, across mountains and basins. In places along the main belts of sand transport the lower mountains are virtually drowned in eolian sand. In early post-Lake Lahontan and early post-Lake Bonneville time, correlative with the early part of the altithermal age of Antevs (1948, 1952, 1955), eolian activity was on a smaller, but nevertheless impressive scale. At least half a cubic mile (2.8 km³) of sediment was deflated from the southern part of the Carson Desert (Morrison, 1964a, p. 102), forming deflation basins of all sizes up to several miles across, and bounded by scraps commonly 30 ft (9 m) and locally as much as 90 ft (27 m) high. Important deflation also took place in the interiors of many other basins, as in Buena Vista Valley, Nevada (Wallace, 1961), and on the Great Salt Lake and Sevier Deserts, Utah. Likewise, extensive tracts of sand dunes were formed within and adjacent to areas of deflation. The gypsum-oolite dunes of the Great Salt Lake Desert (Jones, 1953) were constructed at this time. The widespread surficial blanket of loess throughout the Great Basin (particularly in the northern part) also derives mainly from this windy interval.

Weathering profiles (soils) formed during the later parts of most of the intervals of marked recession of the pluvial lakes during Wisconsin time. The strongly developed weathering profile that is called the Promontory Soil in the Lake Bonneville area, and called the Churchill Soil in the Lake Lahontan area (both discussed later), formed after the main eolian activity of middle Wisconsin time, and therefore it is a useful marker for differentiating early Wisconsin from late Wisconsin deposits.

The late Wisconsin deposits bear an immature weathering profile, called the Midvale Soil in the Lake Bonneville area and the Toyeh Soil in the Lake Lahontan area, which formed during the later part of the altithermal age of Antevs. According to radiocarbon and archaeologic dating this soil-forming interval is believed to have lasted from about 4,500 to 3,800 years ago. This soil ranges from a Desert or minimal Brown (and locally, a Solonetz) in the arid lowlands, changing above 4,900 ± 500 ft (1,494 ± 152 m) altitude to minimal Brown Podzolic, Gray-Brown Podzolic, minimal Planosol, and minimal Prairie (Brunizem) facies. In a given area, generally it is less than half so well developed as the middle Wisconsin soil.

The Toyeh Soil has been proposed as the logical marker for the boundary between the Pleistocene and Recent Epochs in the Great Basin region (Morrison, 1961c). This proposal is based on the fact that this soil and its correlatives form the most widely identifiable and traceable stratigraphic marker unit, and also the most nearly time-parallel unit, in all types of late Quaternary lithogenetic terranes—glacial, lacustrine, alluvial, eolian, and colluvial.

It is worthy of note that Russell, from his study of Lake Lahontan (1885), was first to find evidence of the warm-arid interval in postglacial time that has become known worldwide as the thermal maximum, postglacial climatic optimum, etc. He concluded that Pyramid, Walker, and Winnemucca Lakes dried up completely between the last deep-lake interval of Lake Lahontan and the present, because these lakes contain less salt than they should if they were merely shrunken remnants of Lake Lahontan. Supporting this conclusion are Gale's (1914) calculation for Owens Lake that the amount of salt present required about 4,000 years to accumulate, and Van Winkle's (1914) similar determination for Abert and Summer Lakes, Oregon. Antevs (1948, 1952, 1955) concluded that Lakes Lahontan and Bonneville dried up completely during this interval, which he named the altithermal age and dated as about 7,000 to 4,000 years ago.

Glacial deposits. Figure 1 shows the maximum extent of known glaciers during post-Sangamon time within the drainage area of the Great Basin. Two main glaciations during this time were recognized by Blackwelder (1931, 1934), from studies mainly in the Sierra Nevada. He designated these glaciations as the Tahoe (earlier) and Tioga glacial stages. Subsequent workers (e.g., Sharp, 1938; Putnam, 1949, 1950, 1960a, 1962; Birkeland, 1962, 1964; Sharp and Birman, 1963) accept these as the main Wisconsin glaciations, although Sharp and Birman (1963) and Birman (1964) recently recognized another glaciation, the Tenaya (formerly Graveyard), whose moraines are locally identifiable in the Sierra Nevada between those of Tahoe and Tioga ages. The Tahoe and Tioga generally are correlated respectively with the Bull Lake and Pinedale Glaciations in the Rocky Mountains. The Tenaya Glaciation probably correlates either with the late stage of the Bull Lake or more likely with the early stage of the Pinedale.

Drift of the Tahoe Glaciation has not been subdivided, although Kesseli (1941) postulated two separate advances of glaciers in Tahoe time southwest of Mono Lake on the basis of moraines. Putnam's (1949, p. 1291) possible early Tahoe moraines at Walker Creek in this area are designated by Sharp and Birman (1963) as those of their pre-Tahoe Mono Basin Glaciation, which they tentatively correlate with the Illinoian. P. W. Birkeland (written communication, 1964), however, on the basis of relative development of weathering profiles on the tills, considers that the Mono Basin likely is early Tahoe.

Likewise, drift of the Tioga Glaciation has not generally been subdivided, although in the Sierra Nevada the terminal moraines commonly are paired, and numerous recessional moraines (commonly 24 or more in the major canyons) can be identified. Birkeland (1962, p. 65) concluded that the grouping of moraines in valleys tributary to the Truckee River north of Lake Tahoe suggests at least two separate advances of ice during the Tioga Glaciation, and also a late Tioga stillstand.

Published studies of post-Sangamon glaciation of the interior ranges of the Great Basin are practically limited to reports by Blackwelder (1931, 1934), which give a few reconnaissance notes on glacial features of 17 of these ranges. The only intensive study is that by Sharp (1938) of the Ruby-East Humboldt Range, in northeastern Nevada. This range is one of the highest and longest in the north-central Great Basin. It has an average crest altitude of about 10,000 ft (3,050 m), the higher peaks rising to between 11,300 and 11,400 ft (3,445 to 3,475 m). Two glaciations ("substages") of post-Sangamon age are differentiated, the Lamoille (earlier) and the Angel Lake; they are correlated with the Tahoe and Tioga Glaciations in the Sierra Nevada respectively (Table 1). The longest glacier of the Lamoille "substage" extended about 15 miles (24 km), down to 6,100 ft (1,859 m) altitude; however, the average altitude of terminal moraines of this glaciation is 7,300 ft (2,225 m) on the west side of the range and 7,200 ft (2,195 m) on the east side. Glaciers of the Angel Lake "substage" were shorter and descended to average altitudes of 7,800 ft (2,378 m) on the west side and 7,600 ft (2,317 m) on the east side. The Wisconsin snowline apparently was at between 9,300 and 9,800 ft (2,834 and 2,987 m) altitude on the west side of the range and between 8,800 and 9,300 ft (2,682 and 2,834 m) altitude on the east side.

In the Rocky Mountains two main glaciations of post-Sangamon age are now recognized: the Bull Lake (earlier) and Pinedale Glaciations (Richmond, 1960, 1964a). Two or three stades of the Bull Lake are identified, mainly on the basis of terminal moraines, outwash-terrace levels, and local weathering profiles interbedded with the outwash deposits. The Pinedale Glaciation commonly is subdivided, on a similar basis, into three stades. The Bull Lake generally corresponds with the "earlier epoch of glaciation," and the Pinedale with the "later epoch of glaciation" of Atwood (1909), who made the first comprehensive study of Pleistocene glaciation of the Wasatch and Uinta Ranges. Richmond (1964a) and Morrison (1965a) recently studied the glacial geology of a part of the Wasatch Range and relations of the glacial deposits to those of Lake Bonneville (see below).

In the glacial record of the entire Cordilleran region there is no direct evidence of major recession and readvance of the glaciers within the Bull Lake and Pinedale Glaciations. The interpretation that important recessions (so-called interstadials) took place within each of these glaciations is postulated mainly upon unconformities and submature or immature soils that are locally preserved intercalated with the *outwash* deposits of these glaciations. Interstadial unconformities and weathering profiles have not been recognized interstratified with the tills themselves, except rarely near the outer edges of the terminal moraines. The so-called stades of the Pinedale Glaciation could be interpreted as merely temporary halts during the recession of a single glacial cycle (Richmond, 1960, 1964a). In contrast, the stratigraphic records of Lakes Lahontan and Bonneville afford direct, unambiguous evidence of important lake recessions during the lacustral intervals correlative with these glaciations, and for each lacustral-glaciation period, several more lake recessions are recognized than the controversial glacial recessions.

LACUSTRINE SUCCESSIONS

Figure 1 shows the maximum expansion of about 120 pluvial lakes of the Great Basin during post-Sangamon time. The Pleistocene pluvial lakes shown on the more detailed map of Snyder *et al.* (1964) are probably almost all of post-Sangamon age. Virtually every closed basin has ancient shore features of this age—lake terraces, spits, bars, wave-cut cliffs, gravel embankments, and deltas—at elevations well above the playas or the few permanent lakes of today. The shorelines are much better preserved than those of the pre-Wisconsin lakes. The highest shorelines generally date from Alpine and Tahoe time. Some of the lakes overflowed their basins at this time; some eroded their outlets and were completely and permanently drained, whereas others were only partly drained, so that they refilled to lower levels during subsequent pluvials.

The striking shore features of Lakes Lahontan and Bonneville, which commonly rival marine ones in their magnitude of development, prompted their investigation in one of the earliest programs of the U.S. Geological Survey, a program resulting in the classic monographs by Russell (1885) and Gilbert (1890). The earlier studies concentrated on shore morphology, which though impressive does not yield a complete, unambiguous record of the lake fluctuations. Hunt's (1953) study of Lake Bonneville in northern Utah Valley, Utah, was the first based on comprehensive stratigraphic mapping of the lacustrine and associated deposits.

Lake Bonneville. Lake Bonneville at its maximum inundated numerous coalescent intermontane basins in Utah, Idaho, and Nevada and had an area of 19,940 sq. miles (51,700 km²), almost the size of Lake Michigan, and an extreme depth of about 1,100 ft (335 m). Today the only permanent lakes within its former area are Utah, Sevier, and Great Salt Lakes; these have a widely fluctuating combined area which has ranged from about 1,000 to 2,500 sq. miles (2,600 to 6,500 km²) since 1850.

According to Gilbert (1890), Lake Bonneville was preceded by a very long dry period during which enormous alluvial fans were built. This lake rose twice to high levels, and evaporated practically to dryness between the two lake cycles. During the longer, first cycle the lake rose to nearly 1,000 ft (305 m) above the floor of Great Salt Lake but it did not overflow. During the second cycle the lake rose 90 ft (27 m) above the previous maximum and overflowed at Red Rock Pass, at the northern end of Cache Valley (in Idaho), into a tributary of the Snake River and thence to the Pacific Ocean. The outlet channel was rapidly eroded through alluvium and soft rocks until it became stabilized by a threshold of resistant bedrock about 625 ft (190 m) above Great Salt Lake (above zero datum of the Lakeshore gauge); the prominent Provo shoreline was established at this stillstand level. Subsequently, as the climate became more arid, the lake level dropped below the outlet; the most pronounced recessional stillstand was at the Stansbury shoreline, 330 ft (100 m) above present Great Salt Lake. Gilbert concluded that the desiccation between the two lake cycles lasted five times longer than post-Lake Bonneville time and was probably of interglacial magnitude. (His conclusion was based on comparative volumes of alluvial gravel deposited by a single wash, but this is far too small a sample to support so important an inference.) He therefore correlated the two lake cycles with the two glaciations of continental ice then recognized in the Midwest. Upham first (1914) correlated the desiccation with the Sangamon, later (1922) with the Aftonian. The interpretations of the fluctuations ascribed to Lake Bonneville by Gilbert and subsequent workers are given in Figure 2.

The most recent detailed studies are those in eastern Jordan Valley south of Salt Lake City (Morrison, 1961b, 1964b, 1965a); on southern Promontory Point, Utah (Goode and Eardley, 1960; Morrison, 1965b; and in the Oak City-Delta area, Utah (D. Varnes and R. Van Horn, personal communications). My present stratigraphic classification of the deposits of Lake Bonneville and interpretation of its history are outlined below and in Figure 3; they are tentative, inasmuch as studies still are in progress.

The principal stratigraphic units of Lake Bonneville age are subdivided, defined, and correlated mainly on the basis of intercalated weathering profiles (soils), for the soils generally are the best stratigraphic markers. The lacustrine sediments of this age comprise the Lake Bonneville Group (Hunt, 1953). The lowest part of this group is defined as the Alpine Formation (Hunt, 1953; Morrison, 1965b); it is correlative with the "yellow clay" of Gilbert (1890) and is intermediate in age between the Dimple Dell Soil and the Promontory Soil (Morrison, 1965b). The Alpine is much the thickest of the formations in the Lake Bonneville Group; it is 250 ft (76 m) thick in eastern Jordan Valley and more than 100 ft (30 m) thick on Promontory Point. In a few places tongues of alluvium and colluvium, locally bearing weak to moderately strong weathering profiles, project into this formation. These tongues mark diastems that obviously record lake recessions. Available evidence, still incomplete, suggests at least four main interlacustrine diastems, that separate the Alpine Formation into at least five wedges of lacustrine sediments (Fig. 3).

It should be understood that given shorelines of Lake Bonneville, particularly the older ones, range considerably in altitude from place to place because of the differential isostatic effects of loading and unloading from the various lake oscillations (Gilbert, 1890; Crittenden, 1963a, 1963b). The highest Alpine shoreline is 30 or more feet (9 m) higher than the Bonneville shoreline (defined below) in the central part of the Lake Bonneville area, but a reverse relationship holds in the outer fringes of this area. The lake maxima recorded by both of these shorelines apparently caused Lake Bonneville to overflow twice at Red Rock Pass, Idaho, into a tributary of the Snake River. The first overflow, probably during the earlier maximum, resulted in a short-lived but catastrophic flood that deposited a distinctive coarse gravel unit in the American Falls-Pocatello area, Idaho (Trimble and Carr, 1961; H. E. Malde, written communication, 1964).

Overlying the Alpine Formation and below younger units

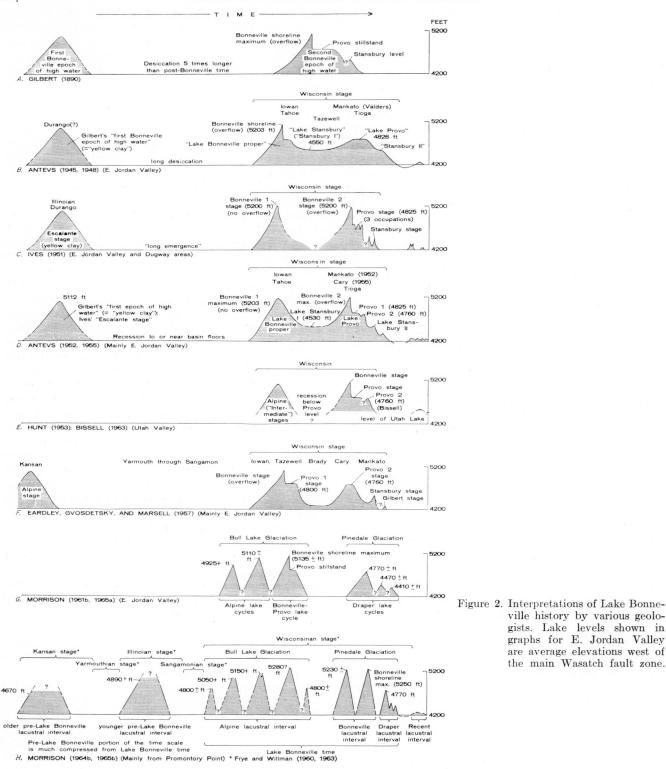

Figure 2. Interpretations of Lake Bonneville history by various geologists. Lake levels shown in graphs for E. Jordan Valley are average elevations west of the main Wasatch fault zone.

of the Lake Bonneville Group are local alluvium, colluvium, and eolian sand, and where not eroded, a strongly developed weathering profile, associated with a widespread unconformity recording subaerial exposure and erosion. At three localities these units have been identified to within 50 to 75 ft (15 to 23 m) of the present level of Great Salt Lake.

They are correlated with the Farmdalian substage of Frye and Willman (1960, 1963) (Morrison, unpublished data). The weathering profile, the Promontory Soil, generally is a Brown soil in the desert basins, but above 5,000 ± 250 ft (1,524 ± 75 m) it changes facies to a Brown Podzolic soil. The post-Alpine portion of the Lake Bonneville Group is

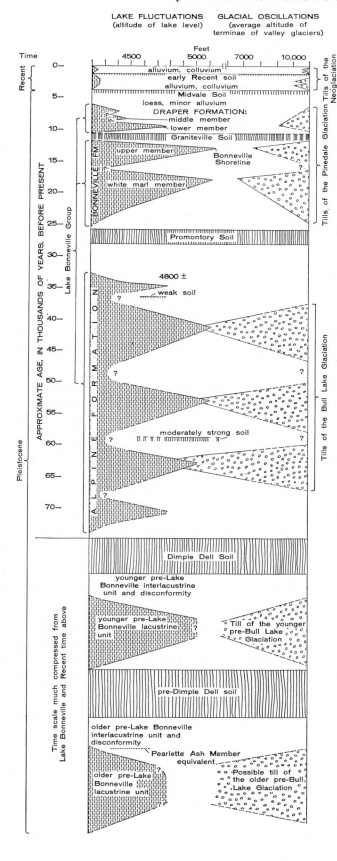

divided into the Bonneville and Draper Formations. The Bonneville Formation is known from my current studies to be intermediate in age between the Promontory and Graniteville Soils. It comprises two members, separated by a diastem that represents subaerial exposure and minor erosion and by local alluvium and colluvium but not by a soil. The white marl member, named after its distinctive offshore facies, is a prominent marker over most of the Lake Bonneville area. This member reaches elevations within 20 ft (6.1 m) below the Bonneville shoreline at two localities. The upper member can be traced to the Bonneville shoreline (Fig. 3), which refers to the highest shoreline of the *last* lake cycle that rose to the high-shore zone, and caused Lake Bonneville to overflow a second time at Red Rock Pass, Idaho. Owing to subsequent differential warping resulting from isostatic rebound the Bonneville shoreline is not always the highest shoreline at a given locality. It is the all-time highest shoreline near the outer fringes of Lake Bonneville, but is below the highest shoreline of Alpine age in the central part of the lake. It ranges in elevation from 5,085 ft (1,550 m) at Red Rock Pass, and from 5,090 to 5,200 ft, (1,551 to 1,585 m) along the Wasatch Range, to 5,300 ft (1,615 m) and higher in the innermost part of the ancient lake (Crittenden, 1963a).

Along the eastern side of Lake Bonneville a stillstand on the regression from the lake maximum represented by the Bonneville shoreline is marked by the Provo shoreline, at 4,800–4,825 ft (1,463–1,471 m) altitude. Here this shoreline is so prominent that many workers (Hunt, 1953; Williams, 1962; Bissell, 1963; Morrison, 1965a) have differentiated the deposits associated with it as a separate unit, the Provo Formation or Provo Member (of the Little Cottonwood Formation). In many other parts of Lake Bonneville, however, neither deposits nor landforms evince a marked stillstand at this level during this lake cycle; the locally prominent shore features at this general level instead are of Alpine and perhaps locally of older age.

The Graniteville Soil is intermediate in age between the Bonneville and Draper Formations. It is a Brown soil below 5,000 ± 300 ft (1,524 ± 91 m) but changes at higher altitudes to Brown Podzolic, Gray-Brown Podzolic, or Planosol facies. It is correlated with the Brady Soil of the Great Plains region and with the Twocreekan substage of Frye and Willman (1960, 1963) (Morrison, 1964b, 1965b). This moderately strong weathering profile is associated with local alluvium and colluvium and with an unconformity recording subaerial exposure and erosion, between the Bonneville and Draper Formations. The unconformity, soil, and subaerial sediments have been identified as low as 4,250 ft (1,295 m) —within 50 ft (15 m) of the 1950 level of Great Salt Lake, indicating nearly complete desiccation of Lake Bonneville.

The Draper Formation (Morrison, 1965a) comprises three

Figure 3. Fluctuations of Lake Bonneville and of Wasatch Mountain glaciers inferred from the lacustrine and glacial successions, mainly in the Little Cottonwood Canyon–Eastern Jordan Valley areas, Utah (revised interpretation, Morrison, 1964b, 1965b, and unpublished field data).

wedges of lacustrine sediments that are separated by diastems that record subaerial exposure. These wedges record the last three lake cycles of Lake Bonneville, which were relatively low and brief. The lower wedge reaches an altitude of about 4,770 ft (1,433 m), which is not quite so high as the Provo shoreline along the Wasatch Range; this maximum is locally moderately well marked by deposits and shore morphology and has been called the "Provo 2" maximum (Jones and Marsell, 1955; Eardley et al., 1957). The middle and upper wedges extend as high as 4,470 and 4,410 ft (1,362 and 1,344 m), respectively, but their maxima are only faintly marked by local shore features and deposits. The maximum of the middle wedge is at the average elevation of the Stansbury shoreline of Gilbert (1890), Antevs (1945, 1948, 1952, 1955) and Eardley et al. (1957).

At a single locality parts of the Lake Bonneville and Wasatch glacial sequences intertongue and can be directly correlated. This is a few miles south of Salt Lake City, in the famous area of faulted terminal moraines below the mouths of Little Cottonwood and Bells Canyons. As many as three successive units of till (and associated outwash) are exposed and can be correlated with the stades of the Bull Lake Glaciation in the Wasatch Range. They are underlain and separated from one another by wedges of lacustrine gravel, sand, and silt of the Alpine Formation; these record early rises of Lake Bonneville, which therefore appear to have been approximately synchronous with the tills of the Bull Lake Glaciation (Fig. 3). The uppermost till-outwash unit has at its top an unconformity recording subaerial exposure; it locally bears a strongly developed pedalfer soil which is correlated with the post-Bull Lake soil of Richmond (1961, 1964a) and with the Promontory Soil. Overlying this unconformity and soil and extending to the Bonneville shoreline are several feet to more than 25 ft (7.6 m) of lacustrine sand, pebble gravel, and local marly silt, which are correlated with the white marl and upper members of the Bonneville Formation, and which bear the typical Graniteville Soil. These relations clearly show that the Alpine Formation is of Bull Lake age and that the Bonneville Formation is post-Bull Lake.

End moraines of post-Bull Lake age are far above the Bonneville shoreline in both canyons, and the intervening remnants of outwash gravels and stream terraces are too discontinuous to permit reliable direct correlation of the younger glacial with the lacustrine sequences. These sequences can be correlated indirectly, however, by soil stratigraphy and by comparison of similar climatic-depositional cycles. On this basis, the white marl and upper members of the Bonneville Formation are correlated with early and middle stades, respectively, of the Pinedale Glaciation. Inasmuch as the second overflow ("Bonneville shoreline") of Lake Bonneville is correlated with the lake maximum recorded by the upper member of the Bonneville Formation, this overflow presumably took place during the middle Pinedale glacial maximum; it was not during the late stade of the Bull Lake Glaciation as previously inferred (Morrison, 1961b, 1965a; Richmond, 1961, 1964a). The reinterpretation of the age of the overflow agrees well with the radiocarbon chronology for Lake Bonneville, which places this lake maximum between 15,000 and 12,000 years ago (Morrison, 1965b).

Correlation of the Bonneville overflow with the middle Pinedale glacial maximum points to exceptional conditions attending this lake maximum. The middle Pinedale glacial maximum fell far short of the main glacial maxima of Bull Lake time. The earlier Bull Lake maxima not only represented stronger ice advances but also stronger pluvial maxima—yet they did not cause Lake Bonneville to overflow. Probably the anomaly of so strong a lake cycle in middle Pinedale time was because of a marked increase in inflow to Lake Bonneville. The only likely source of enough inflow is the Bear River, which contributes 43.5% of the present inflow to Great Salt Lake. This river repeatedly changed its course during Pleistocene time because of block faulting and volcanism. According to Bright's study (1963) and to radiocarbon dates from the Lake Thatcher area, Idaho (Rubin and Alexander, 1960, p. 157-158; Rubin and Berthold, 1961, p. 90), in Alpine (Bull Lake) time the Bear River flowed to the Snake River via the Portneuf River, and hence was not a tributary to Lake Bonneville. More than 34,000 years ago, probably in late- or post-Alpine, pre-Bonneville time, a lava dam diverted this river into a small basin upstream from Lake Bonneville, forming Lake Thatcher. Lake Thatcher rose to an elevation of 5,445 ft and overflowed its southern rim into the Lake Bonneville drainage, cutting a channel that completely drained the lake. This history of relatively late diversion of the Bear River into the Lake Bonneville drainage may explain the first overflow of Lake Bonneville, the anomalously high lake maxima recorded by the white marl and upper members of the Bonneville Formation, and the second overflow at the Bonneville shoreline level.

The warm climate indicated by the strongly developed Promontory and Graniteville Soils suggests that these weathering optima were interstadials marked by complete deglaciation of the Wasatch Range and almost complete drying of Lake Bonneville.

Lake Lahontan. Comparatively few geologists have studied Lake Lahontan in any detail. Their interpretations of the lake history are compared in Figure 4.

The classic study by Russell (1885) has proved generally correct. Russell observed in the river trenches two zones of clay and silt ("upper lacustral clay" and "lower lacustral clay") separated by a zone of fan alluvium and lake gravel and sand ("medial gravel"). He inferred two deep-lake periods separated by a long interval of probably complete desiccation. From detailed mapping of shore terraces and spits he reasoned that the highest level of the first lake cycle was about 30 ft (9.1 m) lower than that of the second. He determined that the lake did not overflow at any time.

J. C. Jones (1925, 1929) believed that Lake Lahontan had only a single lake cycle and inferred that all the preserved beach lines and shore deposits represent only the maximum and recessional stages of this cycle. From study of the rate of salt accumulation in Pyramid and Walker Lakes he concluded that Lake Lahontan started to form only about 2,000 years ago.

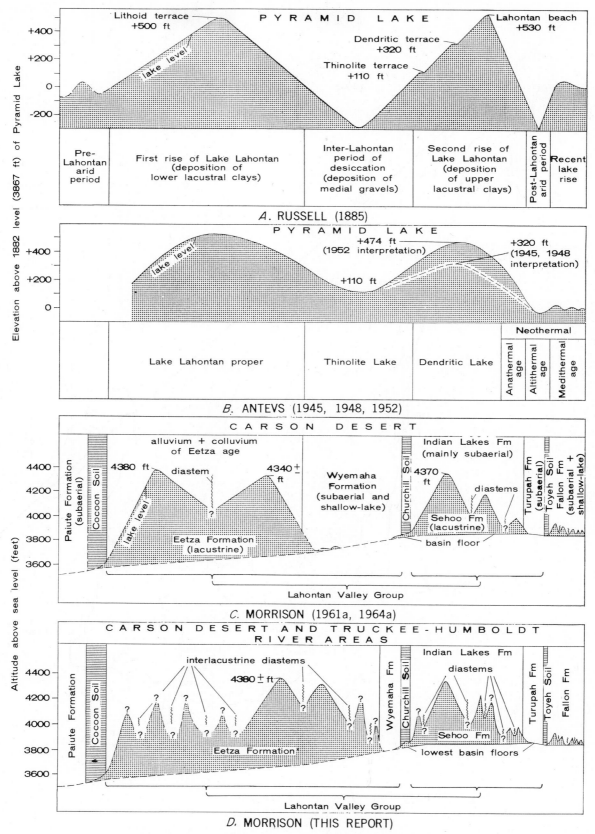

Figure 4. Interpretations of Lake Lahontan history by Russell, Antevs, and Morrison.

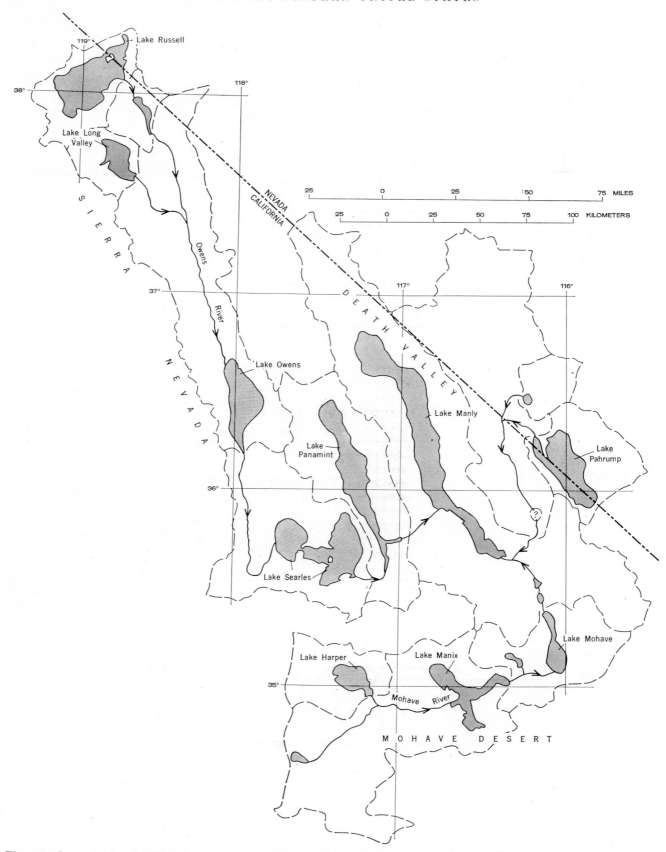

Figure 5. Owens–to–Death Valley system of pluvial lakes, showing their maximum extent during post-Sangamon time, probably
contemporaneous with the Tahoe glacial maximum. (After Gale, 1914; Blackwelder, 1933, 1941; Miller, 1946; Hubbs
and Miller, 1948; Putnam, 1949; and Synder *et al.*, 1964.)

Antevs (1945, p. 30-31; 1948, p. 171, 100-101) inferred two high-water lake cycles ("Lake Lahontan proper," correlated with the Iowan, and "Dendritic Lake," correlated with the Mankato). The first lake rose the higher. He later (1955, p. 326) correlated the second lake cycle with the Cary through Mankato and postulated a fairly regular decline from the second lake maximum, with minor recessions and six subsidiary maxima.

My first (1961a, 1964a) conclusions on Lake Lahontan (Fig. 4c), based on stratigraphic mapping in the southern Carson Desert near Fallon, Nevada, have been somewhat modified as a result of recent studies, still in progress, along the deeply entrenched lower parts of the Truckee and Humboldt Rivers. My current stratigraphic classification and interpretation of Lake Lahontan history (Fig. 4d) are as follows:

The deposits of Lake Lahontan age, both lacustrine and subaerial, but excluding soils, comprise the Lahontan Valley Group. This group is divided into five formations on the basis of intercalated weathering profiles and lithologic differences resulting from two major alternations from mainly deep-lake to subaerial and very shallow-lake conditions. The oldest formation, which is correlative with Russell's "lower lacustral clays," is the Eetza; this formation consists entirely of lacustrine sediments that record at least five lake cycles of the early deep-lake period. (In the Carson Desert study only two lake cycles of Eetza age were recognized.) The tongues of this formation that record individual lake cycles are separated from each other by unconformities and local tongues of alluvium and colluvium, which in some cases bear weakly developed soils. The lake rose to its all-time highest level during Eetza time, inundating an area of 8,665 sq. miles (22,442 km²) and attaining a maximum depth of about 700 ft (213 m) at Pyramid Lake.

The Wyemaha Formation overlies the Eetza and consists mainly of eolian sand and alluvium intertonguing with shallow-lake deposits in the lowest basin floors. It correlates with the subaerial part of Russell's "medial gravel." It bears a strongly developed Brown Soil, the Churchill Soil. The Wyemaha Formation and Churchill Soil obviously record a long interval of lake desiccation in middle Lake Lahontan time.

The late deep-lake period is recorded by the Sehoo Formation of entirely lacustrine sediments and by the intertonguing coeval Indian Lakes Formation of subaerial and very shallow-lake sediments. The Sehoo is correlative with Russell's "upper lacustral clays." Three members of the Sehoo originally were differentiated in the Carson Desert (Morrison, 1961a, 1964a), each separated from the other by a wedge of the Indian Lakes and each considered to record a single lake cycle. More recent studies (Morrison, 1964b; unpublished field data), however, show that each member actually is a doublet of two lacustrine wedges, locally separated by a wedge of the Indian Lakes Formation and/or by an interlacustrine diastem that in some cases bears a weak soil. The youngest formation in the Lahontan Valley Group, the Turupah, is entirely eolian sand, loess, and minor alluvium of post-Lake Lahontan age, deposited during the dry, windy early part of the altithermal age of Antevs (1948, 1952, 1955).

Lake Russell (ancient Mono Lake). Two deep-lake periods, separated by a desiccation interval, occurred in the basin that is now occupied by Mono Lake. Putnam (1949) named the ancient lake in honor of I. C. Russell, who first studied it intensively (1889). Russell concluded that Lake Russell did not overflow, but Putnam found evidence that an overflow channel leading to the Owens Valley–Death Valley system of channels and lakes was occupied during the maximum of the early deep-lake period. This maximum, at about 7,175 ft (2,187 m) altitude, is tentatively correlated with the Tahoe Glaciation. It is marked by a faint shoreline at a few locations. Shorelines of the second deep-lake period are so conspicuous that more than 30 levels could be identified. The highest is about 655 feet (200 m) above the 1949 surface of Mono Lake. This shoreline is correlated with the maximum of the Tioga Glaciation because it not only cuts the outer slopes of the Tahoe terminal moraines but also extends inside the former troughs occupied by the glaciers of Tahoe age. This shoreline is in contact with Tioga moraines at two localities, but there it lacks wave-cut features because deltas built by melt-water streams warded off wave attack.

Relatively complete sections of lake sediments are exposed at only a few localities, and details of lake fluctuations within the two deep-lake periods have not been worked out by stratigraphic study. Putnam (1950), however, suggested correlations between sets of lake terraces and terminal and recessional moraines of Tioga age in two main tributary creeks. He concluded that as the ice withdrew after the Tioga glacial maximum the lake level was accordingly lowered. When the ice front remained relatively stationary, the lake level remained fairly constant and broad lake terraces were cut; when ice retreat was rapid only narrow lake benches were carved.

Owens–to–Death Valley system. A remarkable chain of post-Sangamon pluvial lakes developed in the southeastern Great Basin by overflow of a series of basins (Fig. 5). In Tahoe time Lake Russell, at the head of the chain, overflowed into Owens Lake via the Owens River. Two other sizable pluvial lakes also overflowed to Owens Lake via this river. Owens Lake filled to a maximum area of 240 sq. miles (622 km²) and overflowed; then, in succession downstream, lakes in the China Lake (Indian Wells), Searles Lake, and Panamint Valleys filled and overflowed into Death Valley at the end of the chain. In Tioga time the chain was much shorter; Lake Russell did not overflow, nor did Lakes Searles and Panamint.

Lake Searles at its maximum rose about 640 ft (195 m) above present Searles Lake and had an area of 385 sq. miles (997 km²), inundating both the China Lake and Searles Lake basins and an interconnecting valley; it overflowed at the southeastern edge of the Searles Lake basin. After this early deep-lake period, Lake Searles became desiccated and then had a second deep-lake period, probably correlative with the Tioga Glaciation (Blackwelder, 1941). This lake maximum was lower than the lake maximum of Tahoe age and the lake divided into two bodies, Lake Searles and Lake China (in the China Lake basin) that were connected by a stream through an intervening valley. During this maximum Lake Searles did not overflow.

The Quaternary sediments beneath Searles Lake contain valuable deposits of trona, potash, borax, and other salts and consequently have been explored extensively by drilling to depths as great as 628 ft (191 m) (Gale, 1914). Alternating zones of mainly salts and of mainly clay and silt are encountered. Many radiocarbon dates (to 46,350 years before present) have been obtained on organic fractions from mud layers in the upper part of the succession. The major stratigraphic units from the surface downward (Flint and Gale, 1958, as modified by G. I. Smith, 1962, and oral communication, 1964) consist of the "Overburden Mud" about 30 ft (9 m) thick, of Recent age; the "Upper Salt" 40 ft (12 m) thick, of altithermal age; the "Parting Mud" about 14 ft (4 m) thick, of Tioga age; the "Lower Salt" about 18 ft (5 m) thick, of Tahoe-Tioga interglacial age; the "Bottom Mud" about 65 ft (20 m) thick, of Tahoe age; and the "Mixed Layer" below 167 ft (50 m), of possible Sangamon and Illinoian age. At present, correlations between the subsurface zones and exposed deposits and shorelines in the Searles Lake basin are uncertain.

Lake Panamint during its maximum in Tahoe time was 273 sq. miles (703 km²) in area, and over 900 ft (274 m) deep (Gale, 1914; Miller, 1946).

Lake Manly, the pluvial lake in Death Valley, was recognized by Russell (1885, 1889) and Gilbert (1890), but was first accurately mapped by Blackwelder (1933). It was fed by three separate drainage systems. The chief contributor was the Owens River-to-Death Valley system, from which Lakes Searles and Panamint successively overflowed to Lake Manly only in Tahoe time. In addition, also probably in Tahoe time, a chain of pluvial lakes successively overflowed several basins in the Mohave Desert area and drained into Lake Manly via the Mohave River. The Amargosa River, which joins the Mohave River a short distance above Death Valley, at this time and subsequently contributed drainage from overflow of three more pluvial lake basins. At its maximum, Lake Manly was about 90 miles (145 km) long, 6-11 miles (10-18 km) wide, and nearly 600 ft (183 m) deep, but it had no outlet. Blackwelder (1933, p. 470) correlated the maximum with the Tahoe Glaciation because its deposits and shore features are almost erased by erosion. Several younger, lower, short-lived lakes are reported by C. B. Hunt (U.S. Geological Survey, oral communication, 1961).

RECENT DEPOSITS

Deposits of Recent age—that is, those that are younger than the Toyeh and Midvale Soils and their correlatives—include alluvium, colluvium, eolian sand, scanty glacial deposits, and shallow-lake sediments in the pluvial lake basins. Antevs (1948, 1952, 1955) termed the interval of deposition of these deposits the medithermal age, from about 4,000 years ago to the present, and pointed out that it was characterized by climatic fluctuations not much greater than at present.

SUBAERIAL DEPOSITS

Alluvium of Recent age consists of alluvial fan, stream-terrace, and modern floodplain deposits. These deposits generally are inset somewhat below the elevations of late Wisconsin deposits of similar type. In some places, generally only along the larger streams, two ages of Recent alluvium can be differentiated. These are commonly marked by a topographic discontinuity, as between an early Recent stream terrace and a late Recent stream terrace and/or floodplain. The early Recent deposits bear a very weakly developed weathering profile that is informally termed the early Recent soil; the late Recent deposits bear no discernible weathering profile.

Eolian sand and loess of Recent age is much more limited than that of altithermal age and generally occurs in the same area.

Recent glacial deposits have been identified in the Sierra Nevada, on one of the highest mountains in eastern Nevada, and in the Wasatch Range. In the Sierra Nevada, Matthes (1941, 1942, p. 212) first recognized young moraines that postdate the climatic optimum (herein called the altithermal age) and called the interval of their development the "Little Ice Age," approximately the last 4,000 years. Sharp (1960) termed this ice readvance the Neoglaciation. Birman (1964) recognized three post-climatic optimum glacial advances, but the earliest of these, represented by Hilgard (Wahrhaftig, 1962) till, I consider more likely is pre-climatic optimum and correlative with the late stade of the Pinedale Glaciation. This opinion is based on the fact that weathering ratios for moraines of Hilgard age are as high or higher than those for moraines of Tioga age, and also on the fact that the glaciers were several miles long in the main canyons, comparable with those of the late stade of the Pinedale in the Rocky Mountains. Moraines of the Recess Peak stade (Wahrhaftig, 1962), next-younger than the Hilgard, are within or near the cirques, and have stabilized but very fresh slopes; they likely correlate with the Temple Lake Stade in the Rocky Mountains. Deposits of the Matthes stade (Wahrhaftig, 1962), the youngest, consist mainly of cliff glacierets and active rock glaciers within the higher cirque basins; they probably correlate with the Gannett Peak Stade in the Rocky Mountains. Birkeland (1962, 1964) reports a neoglacial protalus rampart in the Truckee River drainage north of Lake Tahoe and small moraines (the Frog Lake Till) in a few high cirque basins. He considers these moraines to be of late Wisconsin age, but they may be early Recent (Temple Lake Stade).

Recent glaciation is reported from only one locality in the interior ranges of the Great Basin. Kramer (1962) described a tiny rock glacier of this age on the east side of Wheeler Peak, near Ely, Nevada.

In the Wasatch Range Recent glacial deposits are restricted to those of rock glaciers on the floors of cirque basins above 9,400 ft (2,865 m) altitude. Two sets of moraines generally can be distinguished. Both sets are correlated with the Neoglaciation of Sharp (1960); the early set is correlated with the Temple Lake Stade, and the late set with the Gannett Peak Stade of this Recent glaciation (Richmond, 1964a; Morrison, 1965a). In places either or both sets of moraines have double crests, indicating intrastadial fluctuations.

LACUSTRINE DEPOSITS

Recent lacustrine history has been studied in most detail - in the southern Carson Desert, one of the chief terminal basins of the Lake Lahontan area (Morrison, 1961a, 1964a). The Recent lake fluctuations are recorded by the Fallon Formation, consisting of wedges of shallow-lake sediments intercalated with alluvium and eolian sand. Five of these lacustrine wedges have been identified; maximum lake depths of 94 to 64 ft (29 to 19 m) are represented. The first lake maximum occurred about 3,200 to 3,500 years ago, the last one about 100 years ago. After each maximum the lakes dried completely or nearly so. The longest, driest, and warmest lake recession was between the 2nd and 3rd Fallon lakes, during the 13th century A.D., when the early Recent soil (in this area named the "L" Drain Soil) formed. The time of lake maxima were marked by exceptionally heavy Indian habitation, both in open sites and in caves near the lake shores. In the Pyramid–Winnemucca Lake area, the highest Recent lake maximum, at about 3,950 ft (1,204 m) altitude, appears to correlate with the highest lake maximum at the same altitude in the Carson Desert, although at these low levels the lakes in the two basins were separate.

In the Lake Bonneville area, details of the Recent fluctuations have not been worked out, although the highest Recent lake maximum at about 4,245 to 4,260 ft (1,294 to 1,298 m) altitude (Antevs, 1948, 1955) is well recorded. This maximum appears to be the same as the "Gilbert stage" of Eardley *et al.* (1957), but it appears to be post-, not pre-altithermal as interpreted by Eardley *et al.* (1957).

EVIDENCE ON CLIMATIC CHANGES FROM THE PLUVIAL LAKES

Meinzer (1922), from consideration of all the known pluvial lakes in the Basin and Range region, concluded that during the Wisconsin pluvial maximum storm tracks were shifted southward, so that moisture conditions comparable to those in northwestern Nevada today existed in the Searles Lake–Death Valley area. There was, however, no absolute increase in amount of moisture, so that Arizona and New Mexico were about as moist during the pluvial maximum as Oregon is today. These areas differ by 8° to 10° of latitude and about 15° F (8° C) in present mean annual temperature.

Several geologists have attempted to calculate the precipitation-temperature-runoff relations needed to support a given level of a pluvial lake. Russell (1885, 1896, p. 132) and Jones (1925) estimated that if temperature remained the same as now an increase in mean annual precipitation (average for the drainage basin) to about 20 in. (51 cm) would restore Lake Lahontan to its maximum level. Antevs (1952, p. 101) estimated that during the maximum of the second deep-lake period of Lake Lahontan (which was within 10 ft of the highest maximum) the average annual precipitation was 39.4 in. (as compared to 6.3 in.—16 cm—at present) and the mean annual temperature was 4.5°-5.4° F (2.5°-3.0° C) lower than the present 50° F (10° C). Broecker and Orr (1958, p. 1030) concluded that Lake Lahontan would rise to its previous maximum level if average

precipitation over the drainage basin increased from the present 10 in. to 18 in. (25 to 46 cm), and if the mean annual temperature decreased 9° F (5° C). By somewhat more refined methods, Snyder and Langbein (1962) calculated that in Spring Valley, Nevada (which now has only a playa at about 5,535 ft (1,687 m) altitude), the late Pleistocene lake maximum, 335 sq. miles (868 km²) in area, was maintained by increased precipitation, from the present 12 to 20 in. (30 to 51 cm), and reduced evaporation, from 44 to 31 in. (112 to 79 cm). Morrison (1964b, p. 134-135, 175-178) by similar methods computed the mean annual temperature and precipitation values during the three main late Quaternary weathering optima (the Cocoon, Churchill, and Toyeh soil-forming intervals) in the Carson Desert area, Nevada.

Some geologists have theorized that the high levels of the pluvial lakes were caused largely by melting of the mountain glaciers in their drainage areas; they were not caused by increase in precipitation and/or decrease in temperature but instead by relatively sudden release of precipitation stored in the glaciers over long periods of time. From Figure 1 it is evident that most pluvial lakes in the Great Basin did not have glaciers within their drainage areas, and that for the few lake basins that contained glaciers the influence of glacial melt-water was minor. A liberal estimate of the volume of glacial ice within the Lake Lahontan drainage area at the Tahoe maximum is about 70 cubic miles[2] (292 km³), equivalent to about 64 cubic miles (267 km³) of water. At its maximum stage Lake Lahontan contained about 300 cubic miles (1,251 km³) of water. It is doubtful that even during their maximum stages of melting the glaciers contributed more than a few hundredths of the total water in the hydrologic cycle of the lake. Instead of the pluvial lakes being minor adjuncts of huge glaciers in the mountains, the pluvial lakes in the Great Basin were the chief phenomena resulting from the pluvial cycles, and the mountain glaciers were relatively incidental.

Phase data and total saline-mineral assemblages in various subsurface layers in Searles Lake, California, indicate the balance that existed between temperature, precipitation, and other climatic variables when the saline minerals were precipitated (Smith, 1959). Most of the climatic changes thus inferred are supported by pollen data.

Excellent studies of the historic fluctuations of present lakes in the Great Basin, such as Great Salt Lake, Pyramid Lake, Lake Tahoe, Eagle Lake, Mono Lake, and Walker Lake, as indicators of modern climatic changes, have been made by Harding (1935, 1942, p. 235-239), Hardman and Venstrom (1941), Antevs (1938, 1948), and Lawrence and Lawrence (1961).

EVIDENCE ON SUBCRUSTAL (ISOSTATIC) DEFORMATION CAUSED BY LAKES BONNEVILLE AND LAHONTAN

Crittenden (1963a, b) recently re-examined evidence of deformation of the Bonneville shoreline of Lake Bonneville

---

[2] Broecker and Orr's (1958, p. 1031) estimate of the ice and lake volumes seems to me far too high—1,000 and 600 cubic miles (4,170 and 2,502 km³), respectively, although they concluded that the role of glaciers in lake regimen was minor.

and confirmed Gilbert's (1890) conclusion that the uplift in the central part of the ancient lake was an isostatic response to removal of the load of lake water. The Bonneville shoreline is at least 210 ft (64 m) higher on islands in the ancient lake than at its periphery. From these data and the most recent of several chronologies of the last lake rise to the Bonneville shoreline, the subcrustal viscosity in this area is calculated as 10^{21} poises, compared with 10^{22} poises in Scandinavia—a full order of magnitude less viscous. Recent displacements on the Wasatch fault zone are opposite in direction to this uplift, and it seems that the two types of deformation are independent, the faulting occurring within the crust and the isostatic deformation mainly within the subcrust.

Eardley (1962b) considers post-Lake Bonneville isostatic adjustments in the Great Salt Lake Desert (West of Great Salt Lake) as probably causing rise of a threshold between the Desert and Great Salt Lake that was high enough by 6,000 to 5,000 years ago to act as a spillway, only occasionally overtopped by Recent rises of Great Salt Lake. These floodings of the Desert have resulted in the salt crust underlying the Bonneville Salt Flats.

The maximum amount of warping as a result of differential isostatic adjustment of the highest Lake Lahontan shoreline is only about 20 or 30 ft (6 or 9 m). This may be because this lake had less than half the area and depth of Lake Bonneville—but perhaps the subcrustal viscosity also is greater.

SEDIMENTOLOGIC STUDIES

An intensive sedimentologic study was made by Eardley and Gvosdetsky (1960) of a continuous core taken to a depth of 650 ft (183 m) from the eastern edge of Great Salt Lake, in order to determine the Pleistocene lake and climatic history. Ca and Mg carbonates, clay minerals, sand fraction, volcanic ashes, color, soils, radioactivity, oolites and fecal pellets, ostracodes, mollusks, and pollen were determined, and several radiocarbon dates were obtained from the upper portion of the core. Five strong pluvial cycles were recognized, correlated with the Wisconsin through Kansan Glaciations (but not with local shore deposits or Rocky Mountain glacial stages); ash of Pearlette age was identified at 548 ft (167 m).

A bed of Glauber's Salt (mirabilite) 9.5 miles (15.3 km) wide and more than 32 ft (10 m) in maximum thickness lies 15 to 25 ft (5 to 8 m) below the bottom of Great Salt Lake west of Promontory Point (Eardley, 1962a). Carbonate carbon from just below the top of this salt bed gave a radiocarbon age of $11,600 \pm 400$ years B.P. (Ives et al., 1964), suggesting that the salt was deposited during the desiccation interval when the Graniteville Soil formed.

The modern sediments of Great Salt Lake have been comprehensively studied by Eardley (1938), who gave important data on the origin of oolitic sands and calcareous algal bioherms, which jointly form a complete near-shore belt around the main part of the lake, west of Promontory Point and Antelope Island. Mathews (1930) studied the origin of the oolitic sands, and Carozzi (1962) the algal biostromes. Gypsum-ostracode sand dunes bordering the Great Salt Lake Desert, derived from bottom sediments of Lake Bonneville, have been studied by D. J. Jones (1953) and Eardley (1962b).

REFERENCES

Antevs, Ernst, 1938, Rainfall and tree growth in the Great Basin: Carnegie Instn. Publ. 469; Amer. Geogr. Soc. Spec. Publ. 21, 97 p.
—— 1945, Correlation of Wisconsin glacial maxima: Amer. J. Sci., v. 243-A (Daly vol.), p. 1-39
—— 1948, Climatic changes and pre-white man, in The Great Basin, with emphasis on glacial and postglacial times: Univ. Utah Bull., v. 38, p. 168-191
—— 1952, Cenozoic climates of the Great Basin: Geol. Rdsch. v. 40, p. 94-108
—— 1955, Geologic-climatic dating in the west: Amer. Antiq., v. 20, p. 317-335
Atwood, W. W., 1909, Glaciation of the Uinta and Wasatch Mountains: U.S. Geol. Surv. Prof. Pap. 61, 96 p.
Axelrod, D. I., 1950, Evolution of desert vegetation in western North America: Carnegie Instn. Publ. 590, p. 215-306
—— 1962, Post-Pliocene uplift of the Sierra Nevada, California: Geol. Soc. Amer. Bull., v. 73, p. 183-198
Axelrod, D. I., and Ting, W. S., 1960, Late Pliocene floras east of the Sierra Nevada: Berkeley, Univ. California Publ. Geol. Sci., v. 39, p. 1-118
—— 1961, Early Pleistocene floras from the Chagoopa surface, southern Sierra Nevada: Berkeley, Univ. California Publ. Geol. Sci., v. 39, p. 119-194
Birkeland, P. W., 1962, Multiple glaciation of the Truckee area, California: Geol. Soc. Sacramento and Sacramento Sect. California Assoc. Eng. Geologists, Guidebook, p. 64-67
—— 1963, Pleistocene volcanism and deformation of the Truckee area, north of Lake Tahoe, California: Geol. Soc. Amer. Bull., v. 74, p. 1453-1464
—— 1964, Pleistocene glaciation of the northern Sierra Nevada, north of Lake Tahoe, California: J. Geol., v. 72, p. 810-825
Birman, J. H., 1964, Glacial geology across the crest of the Sierra Nevada, California: Geol. Soc. Amer. Spec. Pap. 75, 80 p.
Bissell, H. J., 1963, Lake Bonneville: geology of southern Utah Valley, Utah: U.S. Geol. Surv. Prof. Pap. 257-B, p. 101-130
Blackwelder, Eliot, 1931, Pleistocene glaciation in the Sierra Nevada and Basin Ranges: Geol. Soc. Amer. Bull., v. 42, p. 865-922
—— 1933, Lake Manly, an extinct lake of Death Valley: Geogr. Rev., v. 23, p. 464-471
—— 1934, Supplementary notes on Pleistocene glaciation in the Great Basin: Wash. Acad. Sci. J., v. 24, p. 217-222
—— 1941, Lakes of two ages in Searles Basin, California (abst.): Geol. Soc. Amer. Bull., v. 52, p. 1943-1944
Blackwelder, Eliot, and Matthes, F. E., 1938, Map of distribution of the late Pleistocene (Wisconsin) glaciers in the Sierra Nevada, on (inset map) Sheet v of Geologic Map of California: California Div. Mines
Bright, R. C., 1963, Pleistocene lakes Thatcher and Bonneville, southeastern Idaho: Univ. Minnesota Ph.D. thesis, 292 p.

Broecker, W. S., and Orr, P. C., 1958, Radiocarbon chronology of Lake Lahontan and Lake Bonneville: Geol. Soc. Amer. Bull., v. 69, p. 1009-1032

Carozzi, A. V., 1962, Observations on algal biostromes in the Great Salt Lake, Utah: J. Geol., v. 70, p. 246-252

Crittenden, M. D., Jr., 1963a, New data on the isostatic deformation of Lake Bonneville: U.S. Geol. Surv. Prof. Pap. 454-F, p. 1-31

—— 1963b, Effective viscosity of the earth derived from isostatic loading of Pleistocene Lake Bonneville: J. Geophys. Res., v. 68, p. 5517-5530

Dalrymple, G. B., 1963, Potassium-argon dates of some Cenozoic rocks of the Sierra Nevada, California: Geol. Soc. Amer. Bull., v. 74, p. 379-390

Eardley, A. J., 1938, Sediments of Great Salt Lake, Utah: Amer. Assoc. Petroleum Geologists Bull., v. 22, p. 1305-1411

—— 1962a, Glauber's salt bed west of Promontory Point, Great Salt Lake: Utah Geol Mineralog. Surv. Spec. Stud. 1, 12 p.

—— 1962b, Gypsum dunes and evaporite history of the Great Salt Lake Desert: Utah Geol. Mineralog. Surv. Spec. Stud. 2, 27 p.

Eardley, A. J., and Gvosdetsky, Vasyl, 1960, Analysis of Pleistocene core from Great Salt Lake, Utah: Geol. Soc. Amer. Bull., v. 71, p. 1323-1344

Eardley, A. J., Gvosdetsky, Vasyl, and Marsell, R. E., 1957, Hydrology of Lake Bonneville and sediments and soils of its basin: Geol. Soc. Amer. Bull., v. 68, p. 1141-1202

Flint, R. F., and Gale, W. A., 1958, Stratigraphy and radiocarbon dates at Searles Lake, California: Amer. J. Sci., v. 256, p. 689-714

Frye, J. C., and Leonard, A. B., 1952, Pleistocene geology of Kansas: Kansas Geol. Surv. Bull. 99, 230 p.

Frye, J. C., and Willman, H. B., 1960, Classification of the Wisconsinan Stage in the Lake Michigan glacial lobe: Illinois Geol. Surv. Circ. 285, 16 p.

—— 1963, Development of Wisconsinan classification in Illinois related to radiocarbon chronology: Geol. Soc. Amer. Bull., v. 74, p. 501-506

Gale, H. S., 1914, Salines in the Owens, Searles, and Panamint basins, southeastern California: U.S. Geol. Surv. Bull. 580-L, p. 251-323

Gilbert, G. K., 1890, Lake Bonneville: U.S. Geol. Surv. Monogr. 1, 438 p.

Goode, H. D., and Eardley, A. J., 1960, Lake Bonneville; a preliminary report on the Quaternary deposits of Little Valley, Promontory Range, Utah (abst.): Geol. Soc. Amer. Bull., v. 71, p. 2035

Harding, S. T., 1935, Changes in lake levels in the Great Basin area: Civil Eng., v. 5, p. 87-92

—— 1942, Lakes, Ch. 6 *in* Meinzer, O. E. (ed.) Hydrology: New York, McGraw-Hill Book Co., p. 220-243

Hardman, George, and Venstrom, Cruz, 1941, A one-hundred-year record of Truckee River runoff estimated from changes in levels and volumes of Pyramid and Winnemucca Lakes: Amer. Geophys. Union Trans., v. 22, p. 71-90

Hubbs, C. L., and Miller, R. R., 1948, The zoological correlation between fish distribution and hydrographic history in the desert basins of western United States, Part II *in* The Great Basin, with emphasis on glacial and postglacial times: Univ. Utah Bull., v. 38, p. 17-166

Hunt, C. B., 1953, General geology, *in* Hunt, C. B., Varnes, H. D., and Thomas, H. E., Lake Bonneville—geology of northern Utah Valley, Utah: U.S. Geol. Surv. Prof. Pap. 257-A, p. 11-45

—— 1956, Cenozoic geology of the Colorado Plateau: U.S. Geol. Surv. Prof. Pap. 279, 99 p.

Hunt, C. B., and Sokoloff, V. P., 1950, Pre-Wisconsin soil in the Rocky Mountain region, a progress report: U.S. Geol. Surv. Prof. Pap. 221-G, p. 109-123

Ives, R. L., 1951, Pleistocene valley sediments of the Dugway area, Utah: Geol. Soc. Amer. Bull., v. 62, p. 781-797

Ives, P. C., Levin, Betsy, Robinson, R. D., and Rubin, Meyer, 1964, U.S. Geological Survey radiocarbon dates VII: Radiocarbon, v. 6, p. 37-76

Jones, D. J., 1953, Gypsum-oolite dunes, Great Salt Lake Desert, Utah: Amer. Assoc. Petroleum Geologists Bull., v. 37, p. 2530-2538

Jones, D. J., and Marsell, R. E., 1955, Pleistocene sediments of lower Jordan Valley, Utah, *in* Tertiary and Quaternary geology of eastern Bonneville Basin: Utah Geol. Soc. Guidebook No. 10, p. 85-112

Jones, J. C., 1925, The geologic history of Lake Lahontan: Carnegie Instn. Publ. 352, p. 1-50

—— 1929, Age of Lake Lahontan: Geol. Soc. Amer. Bull., v. 40, p. 533-540

Kesseli, J. E., 1941, Quaternary history of Mono Valley, California: Berkeley, Univ. California Publ. Geogr., v. 6, p. 315-362

Kramer, F. L., 1962, Rivers of stone: Pacific Discovery, v. 15, p. 11-15

Lawrence, D. B., and Lawrence, E. G., 1961, Response of enclosed lakes to current glaciopluvial climatic conditions in middle latitude western North America: New York Acad. Sci. Ann., v. 95, p. 341-356

Leverett, Frank, 1899, The Illinois glacial lobe: U.S. Geol. Surv. Monogr. 38, 817 p.

Malde, H. E., 1965, Snake River Plain, *in* VII Congr. Intern. Quaternary Assoc., Field Conference E (Northern Rocky Mountains)

Mathews, A. A. L., 1930, Origin and growth of the Great Salt Lake oolites: J. Geol., v. 38, p. 633-642

Matthes, F. E., 1941, Rebirth of the glaciers of the Sierra Nevada during late post-Pleistocene time (abst.): Geol. Soc. Amer. Bull., v. 52, p. 2030

—— 1942, Glaciers, Ch. 5 *in* Meinzer, O. E. (ed.), Hydrology; New York, McGraw-Hill Book Co., p. 149-219

Meinzer, O. E., 1922, Map of the Pleistocene lakes of the Basin-and-Range province and its significance: Geol. Soc. Amer. Bull., v. 33, p. 541-552.

Miller, R. R., 1946, Correlation between fish distribution and Pleistocene hydrography in eastern California and southwestern Nevada, with a map of the Pleistocene waters: J. Geol., v. 54, p. 43-53

Morrison, R. B., 1961a, Lake Lahontan stratigraphy and history in the Carson Desert (Fallon) area, Nevada: U.S. Geol. Surv. Prof. Pap. 424-D, p. 111-114

—— 1961b, New evidence on the history of Lake Bonneville

from an area south of Salt Lake City, Utah: U.S. Geol. Surv. Prof. Pap. 424-D, p. 125-127

—— 1961c, A suggested Pleistocene-Recent (Holocene) boundary for the Great Basin region, Nevada-Utah: U.S. Geol. Surv. Prof. Pap. 424-D, p. 115-116

—— 1961d, Correlation of the deposits of Lakes Lahontan and Bonneville and the glacial sequences of the Sierra Nevada and Wasatch Mountains, California, Nevada and Utah: U.S. Geol. Surv. Prof. Pap. 424-D, p. 122-124

—— 1964a, Lake Lahontan: Geology of southern Carson Desert, Nevada: U.S. Geol. Surv. Prof. Pap. 401, 156 p.

—— 1964b, Soil stratigraphy: Principles, applications to differentiation and correlation of Quaternary deposits and landforms, and applications to soil science: University of Nevada, Ph.D. thesis, 178 p.

—— 1965a, Lake Bonneville: Quaternary stratigraphy of eastern Jordan Valley, south of Salt Lake City, Utah: U.S. Geol. Surv. Prof. Pap. 477 (in press)

—— 1965b, New evidence on Lake Bonneville stratigraphy and history from southern Promontory Point, Utah: U.S. Geol. Surv. Prof. Pap. 525-C (in press)

Putnam, W. C., 1949, Quaternary geology of the June Lake District, California: Geol. Soc. Amer. Bull., v. 60, p. 1281-1302

—— 1950, Moraine and shoreline relationships at Mono Lake, California: Geol. Soc. Amer. Bull., v. 61, p. 115-122

—— 1960a, Origin of Rock Creek and Owens River gorges, Mono County, California: Berkeley, Univ. California Publ. Geol. Sci., v. 34, p. 221-280

—— 1960b, Faulting and Pleistocene glaciation in the east-central Sierra Nevada of California, U.S.A.: Intern. Geol. Congr., 21st sess., Copenhagen, Pt. 21, p. 270-274

—— 1962, Late Cenozoic geology of McGee Mountain, Mono County, California: Berkeley, Univ. California Publ. Geol. Sci., v. 40, p. 181-218

Richmond, G. M., 1960, Glaciations of the east slope of Rocky Mountain National Park, Colorado: Geol. Soc. Amer. Bull., v. 71, p. 1371-1382

—— 1961, New evidence of the age of Lake Bonneville from the moraines in Little Cottonwood Canyon, Utah: U.S. Geol. Surv. Prof. Pap. 424-D, p. 127-128

—— 1962, Quaternary stratigraphy of the La Sal Mountains, Utah: U.S. Geol. Surv. Prof. Pap. 324, 135 p.

—— 1964a, Glaciation of Little Cottonwood and Bells Canyons, Utah: U.S. Geol. Surv. Prof. Pap. 454-D, p. 1-41

—— 1964b, Three pre-Bull Lake tills in the Wind River Mountains, Wyoming—a reinterpretation: U.S. Geol. Surv. Prof. Pap. 501-D, p. 104-109

Rubin, Meyer, and Alexander, Corinne, 1960, U.S. Geological Survey radiocarbon dates v: Amer. J. Sci. Radiocarbon Suppl., v. 2, p. 129-185

Rubin, Meyer, and Berthold, S. M., 1961, U.S. Geological Survey radiocarbon dates vi: Radiocarbon, v. 3, p. 86-98

Russell, I. C., 1885, Geological history of Lake Lahontan, a

Quaternary lake of northwestern Nevada: U.S. Geol. Surv. Monogr. 11, 288 p.

—— 1889, Quaternary history of Mono Valley, California: U.S. Geol. Surv., 8th Ann. Rep., p. 261-394

—— 1896, Present and extinct lakes of Nevada *in* The physiography of the United States (Natl. Geogr. Soc.): New York, American Book Co., p. 101-136

Sharp, R. P., 1938, Pleistocene glaciation in the Ruby-East Humboldt Range, northeastern Nevada: J. Geomorph., v. 1, p. 296-323

—— 1940, Geomorphology of the Ruby-East Humboldt Range, Nevada: Geol. Soc. Amer. Bull., v. 51, p. 337-372

—— 1960, Pleistocene glaciation in the Trinity Alps of northern California: Amer. J. Sci., v. 258, p. 305-340

Sharp, R. P., and Birman, J. H., 1963, Additions to classical sequence of Pleistocene glaciations, Sierra Nevada, California: Geol. Soc. Amer. Bull., v. 74, p. 1079-1086

Smith, G. I., 1959, Searles Lake evaporites as an indicator of the temperature-precipitation balance in late Quaternary climates (abst.): Geol. Soc. Amer. Bull., v. 70, p. 1750

—— 1962, Subsurface stratigraphy of late Quaternary deposits, Searles Lake, California, a summary: U.S. Geol. Surv. Prof. Pap. 450-C, p. 65-69

Snyder, C. T., and Langbein, W. B., 1962, The Pleistocene lake in Spring Valley, Nevada, and its climatic implications: J. Geophys. Res., v. 67, p. 2385-2394

Snyder, C. T., Hardman, George, and Zdenek, F. F., 1964, Pleistocene lakes in the Great Basin: U.S. Geol. Surv. Misc. Geol. Inv. Map I-416

Trimble, D. E., and Carr, W. J., 1961, Late Quaternary history of the Snake River in the American Falls region, Idaho: Geol. Soc. Amer. Bull., v. 72, p. 1739-1748

Upham, Warren, 1914, The Sangamon interglacial stage in Minnesota and westward: 12th Intern. Geol. Congr. (1913), Compt. Rend., p. 455-466

—— 1922, Stages of the Ice Age: Geol. Soc. Amer. Bull., v. 33, p. 491-514

Van Houten, F. B., 1956, Reconnaissance of Cenozoic sedimentary rocks of Nevada: Amer. Assoc. Petroleum Geologists Bull., v. 40, p. 2801-2825

Van Winkle, Walton, 1914, Quality of the surface waters of Oregon: U.S. Geol. Surv. Water-Supply Pap. 363, 137 p.

Wahrhaftig, Clyde, 1962, Geomorphology of the Yosemite Valley region, California; p. 33-46, *in* Geologic guide to the Merced Canyon and Yosemite Valley, California: California Div. Mines and Geol. Bull. 182

Wallace, R. E., 1961, Deflation in Buena Vista Valley, Pershing County, Nevada: U.S. Geol. Surv. Prof. Pap. 424-D, p. 242-244

Williams, J. S., 1962, Lake Bonneville: Geology of southern Cache Valley, Utah: U.S. Geol. Surv. Prof. Pap. 257-C, p. 131-152

Summary

The Great Basin is a semiarid to arid region of interior drainage comprising about 150 mostly closed desert basins separated by more than 160 subparallel mountain ranges, largely outlined by late Cenozoic high-angle faults. The terminal basins of the larger rivers preserve a nearly complete depositional record of the middle and late Quaternary. They held lakes that fluctuated with Quaternary climatic changes, and the intertonguing lacustrine and subaerial units surpass the glacial successions of the western Cordillera as recorders of these climatic changes.

Deposits of pre-Wisconsin age include: (1) alluvium, exposed mainly in piedmont-pediment zones at basin edges; (2) lacustrine deposits, rarely exposed, of two main age units correlated with the Kansan and Illinoian Glaciations, and (3) glacial deposits, of three glaciations in the Sierra Nevada, and of possibly two in the Wasatch Range, but none definitely identified in interior ranges.

Wisconsin deposits, virtually ubiquitous, attain greatest sensitivity as climatic records in the successions of Lakes Lahontan and Bonneville. These lakes fluctuated practically in unison with glaciers in the Sierra Nevada and Wasatch Range, but the lake successions also record many minor fluctuations. Each lake had two main deep-lake periods, separated by desiccation nearly to dryness. In each deep-lake period were several lake cycles separated by lake recessions, some of them almost to dryness. For both the early and the late deep-lake periods, Lake Bonneville had five known lake cycles and Lake Lahontan had six. In altithermal time, both lakes dried completely.

Five subsequent shallow-lake cycles of Recent age have been identified in the Lake Lahontan area; only the highest Recent lake maximum is known in the Lake Bonneville area.

QUATERNARY GEOLOGY OF THE SOUTHWEST *

FRANK E. KOTTLOWSKI,[1] MAURICE E. COOLEY,[2] ROBERT V. RUHE[3]

THE REGION considered in this report (Figs. 1-3) consists of westernmost Texas, New Mexico from the Pecos Valley westward, Arizona, southeastern California, southeastern Utah, and southwestern Colorado. Physiographic sections (Fenneman, 1931) encompassed are the Pecos Valley section of Great Plains; the Sacramento, Mexican Highland, Sonoran Desert, and Salton Trough sections of the Basin and Range province; and most of the Colorado Plateau province. Geomorphic features are the mesas, high plateaus, deep canyons, and rugged escarpments of the Colorado Plateau province on the north and the isolated mountain ranges separated by desert basins of the Basin and Range province on the south.

The Quaternary geology of southern Arizona and southeastern California is described by Cooley and that of most of New Mexico by Kottlowski and Ruhe; the Colorado Plateau material is abstracted mainly from papers by Hunt (1956, 1964). Emphasis is on areas that are along or near the route of INQUA's Southwestern Arid Lands field conference.

The Southwest is a key junction of the Quaternary deposits and geomorphic surfaces of the Great Plains from the east, the semiarid Basin and Range on the west and to the northwest, the Colorado Plateau on the north, and the glaciated Rocky Mountains and their intermontane basins on the northeast. Within or bordering the region are exhibited the interrelations between Quaternary mountain glaciation, alluviation and erosion on the High Plains and along major streams that rise in the mountains and then

* Appreciation is due Charles B. Hunt, Johns Hopkins University, for allowing extensive paraphrasing from his manuscript on the Quaternary Geology of the Colorado Plateau. Editorial critique and technical advice was freely given by Kottlowski's colleagues at the New Mexico Bureau of Mines and Mineral Resources in Socorro, New Mexico, particularly Robert H. Weber and Edward C. Bingler; by Cooley's coworkers at the Tucson, Arizona, Ground-Water Branch of the U.S. Geological Survey, especially Edward S. Davidson, Franklin H. Olmsted, and J. H. Robison; Ruhe's associates of the Soil-Geomorphology Group, Soil Survey Investigations, U.S. Department of Agriculture, chiefly Fred F. Peterson, Leland H. Gile, and John W. Hawley; and by Gerald M. Richmond, Secretary General of the VII INQUA Congress, John C. Frye, Chief, Illinois Geological Survey, Charles B. Hunt, and Roger B. Morrison, U.S. Geological Survey.

Editing by Herbert E. Wright, Jr. and David G. Frey immeasurably improved the original manuscript, adding clarity and coherence, and was deeply appreciated by the writers.
[1] New Mexico Bureau of Mines and Mineral Resources, Socorro, New Mexico.
[2] U.S. Geological Survey, Federal Center, Denver, Colorado.
[3] Soil Conservation Service, Iowa State University, Ames, Iowa.

traverse semiarid grabens of the Basin and Range country, lacustrine and alluvial deposition in closed intermontane basins, and deltaic and marine sedimentation at the mouth of the Colorado River.

Except on the high mountains and high plateaus, semiaridity is the present chief characteristic of this region. The Quaternary geologic history is a record of such aridity alternating with cool wet periods and complicated by diastrophism and volcanism. Structural control of geomorphic processes is more evident for the early Quaternary, whereas climatic change was, and still is, the dominant factor during the late Quaternary.

SOUTHERN ARIZONA AND SOUTHEASTERN CALIFORNIA

The Quaternary geologic events in southern Arizona and southeastern California are controlled principally by structural upwarping and subsidence. This diastrophism maintains the Mogollon Highlands, Colorado Plateaus, Peninsular Ranges of California and Mexico, Phoenix basin, Gulf of California embayment, and the Colorado River—the master stream in the area. Quaternary events are controlled subordinately by volcanism and climate. Lava flows have dammed and diverted many drainages, and climatic shifts have affected regimes of streams and lakes.

Much of the information for the late Tertiary and Quaternary periods is summarized from reports by Lee (1905, p. 95-134), Dibblee (1954, p. 21-28), Longwell (1954, p. 53-56), Wright and Troxel (1954, p. 1-50), Heindl (1962, p. 9-24), and Cooley and Davidson (1963, p. 7-35).

REGIONAL GEOLOGIC SETTING

The main drainages were developed and the physiographic and structural features were outlined before the end of the Tertiary. The Colorado River was entrenched in the Grand Canyon and flowed uninterrupted to the Gulf of California embayment. In southern Arizona its principal tributaries, the Salt River and the reach of the Gila River west of the Pinaleno Mountains (Fig. 1), formed a partially integrated system that drained westward. The reach of the Gila River east of the Pinaleno Mountains was impounded or flowed southeastward, perhaps to the ancestral Rio Grande; this reach of the Gila River did not join the Colorado River system until middle Pleistocene time. Large-scale faulting, often referred to as basin-and-range block-faulting, continued until late Tertiary time; only minor faults have displaced Quaternary alluvium and volcanic rocks east and northeast of the Gulf of California embayment. The embayment itself, however, has subsided several thousands of feet in Quaternary time. The western

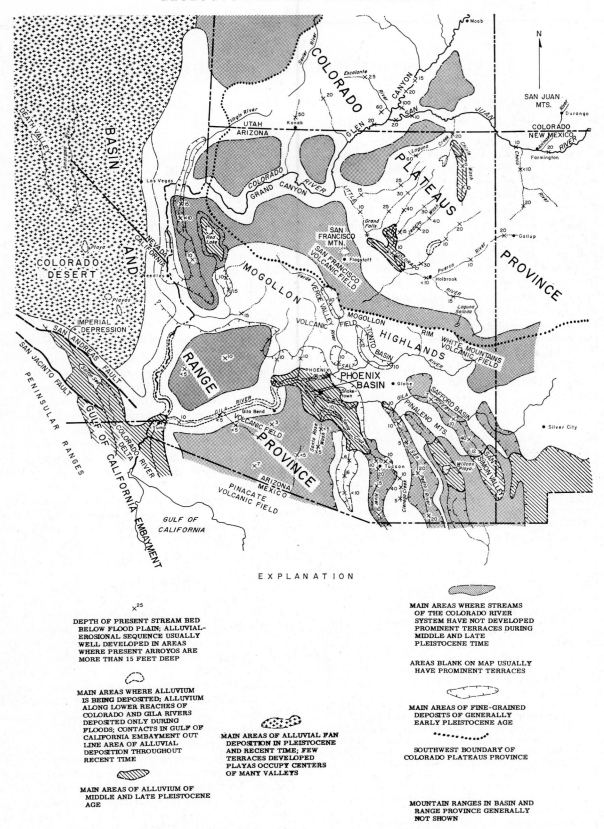

EXPLANATION

×²⁵

DEPTH OF PRESENT STREAM BED
BELOW FLOOD PLAIN; ALLUVIAL-
EROSIONAL SEQUENCE USUALLY
WELL DEVELOPED IN AREAS
WHERE PRESENT ARROYOS ARE
MORE THAN 15 FEET DEEP

MAIN AREAS WHERE ALLUVIUM
IS BEING DEPOSITED; ALLUVIUM
ALONG LOWER REACHES OF
COLORADO AND GILA RIVERS
DEPOSITED ONLY DURING
FLOODS; CONTACTS IN GULF OF
CALIFORNIA EMBAYMENT OUT
LINE AREA OF ALLUVIAL
DEPOSITION THROUGHOUT
RECENT TIME

MAIN AREAS OF ALLUVIUM OF
MIDDLE AND LATE PLEISTOCENE
AGE

MAIN AREAS OF ALLUVIAL FAN
DEPOSITION IN PLEISTOCENE
AND RECENT TIME; FEW
TERRACES DEVELOPED
PLAYAS OCCUPY CENTERS
OF MANY VALLEYS

MAIN AREAS WHERE STREAMS
OF THE COLORADO RIVER
SYSTEM HAVE NOT DEVELOPED
PROMINENT TERRACES DURING
MIDDLE AND LATE
PLEISTOCENE TIME

AREAS BLANK ON MAP USUALLY
HAVE PROMINENT TERRACES

MAIN AREAS OF FINE-GRAINED
DEPOSITS OF GENERALLY
EARLY PLEISTOCENE AGE

SOUTHWEST BOUNDARY OF
COLORADO PLATEAUS PROVINCE

MOUNTAIN RANGES IN BASIN AND
RANGE PROVINCE GENERALLY
NOT SHOWN

Figure 1. Index map showing main areas of alluvium and other Quaternary features in southern Arizona and southeastern California.

area of the Colorado Desert, Death Valley, and other valleys are subsiding, and alluvial-fan deposits and terraces are offset by Quaternary faults.

EVENTS OF EARLY PLEISTOCENE TIME

After the large-scale structural movements in Tertiary time, sedimentation was continuous in the valleys, probably from late Pliocene time to the early part of middle Pleistocene time, when it was interrupted by regional upwarping. Vertebrate fossils in the upper part of the sequence are late Pliocene to middle Pleistocene (Lance, 1960, p. 157; Philip Seff, oral communication, 1964). In this report this sequence is informally called fine-grain deposits. These deposits are mostly lenticular alluvial beds of clay and sand, often erroneously called lake beds. The sequence also includes soil zones, fresh-water limestone, and gravel. The gravel was deposited principally in the upper reaches of the main streams and at points where tributaries entered the valleys (Davidson, 1961, p. 151-153).

In the Mogollon Highlands fine-grain deposits were laid down as far upstream along the Salt River as Tonto basin. In Verde Valley more than 300 m of clay, silt, sand, and limestone, roughly correlative with the fine-grain deposits, accumulated behind a dam formed by volcanic eruptions (Jenkins, 1923, p. 65-81; Twenter and Metzger, 1963, p. 46-66). Terraced canyons and valleys were formed in the highlands.

The thickest early Pleistocene deposits, the Palm Spring and Borrego Formations (Tarbet and Holman, 1944), are in the Gulf of California embayment (Dibblee, 1954). Part of the Palm Spring Formation contains marine invertebrate fossils, which document transgressions of the seas from the south. The marine deposits intertongue with fluvial sand and gravel from the mountains to the west and north and with gravel, sand, and silt from the Colorado and Gila Rivers to the north and east. Deposits probably of the Colorado River are more than 900 m thick at the southwestern tip of Arizona, and they thin progressively but irregularly upstream (Olmsted and Robison, 1964; Metzger, 1964).

EVENTS OF MIDDLE AND LATE PLEISTOCENE TIME

Erosion and terracing were dominant along the main streams in Arizona and southeastern California during most of middle and late Pleistocene time. Sedimentation, however, was prevalent in the Phoenix basin, Gulf of California embayment, and valleys of the Colorado Desert. The general distribution of terraces, alluvial fans, and floodplain alluvium of middle and late Pleistocene time is shown on Figure 1. Generally, the alluvial fans occupying valleys of internal drainage are limited to the Colorado Desert; elsewhere drainage was mainly internal except in the Imperial Depression and part of southeastern Arizona. Some alluvium was deposited at Red Lake in northwestern Arizona, near Willcox playa (a remnant of Pleistocene Lake Cochise; Meinzer and Kelton, 1913, p. 34), in the San Simon Valley in southeastern Arizona, and in other valleys where headward cutting by tributaries of the Gila River had not established through drainage. This alluvium is post-Blanco in age and may be as young as 20,000 B.P. (before the present).

The Colorado River delta was a barrier to the northward extension of the seas in the Gulf of California embayment during most of middle and late Pleistocene time. The delta deposits intertongue to the north with the continental Brawley Formation (Dibblee, 1954) in the Imperial Depression and to the south with datable fossiliferous marine deposits. The Brawley Formation generally is fine-grained and also intertongues with the Ocotillo Conglomerate (Dibblee, 1954), which was deposited near the mountains along the flanks of the Imperial Depression.

EVENTS OF LATEST PLEISTOCENE AND EARLY RECENT TIME

Erosion was the dominant process in latest Pleistocene and early Recent time. Alluviation did take place, however, in valleys of the Colorado Desert and perhaps in the Phoenix basin; thick deposition continued on the Colorado River delta.

Recent geologic investigations generally have confirmed conclusions of earlier workers (Bryan, 1940, p. 227-232; Hack, 1942) that much of the eolian mantle of the Southwest was formed during the Altithermal period (Antevs, 1955, p. 323). Conditions were drier at this time than at present or during much of the Pleistocene Epoch (see Martin and Mehringer, this volume, for contrary view). Noticeable deflation by wind removed 6 m of deposits at Laguna Salada—an ephemeral lake southeast of Holbrook —between about 5500 and 1500 B.C.; in the Willcox playa wind erosion has been removing late Pleistocene deposits since Lake Cochise dried up near the end of Pleistocene time.

EVENTS OF LATE RECENT TIME

Late Recent time is represented by epicycles of erosion and alluviation in the canyons and valleys of the Southwest; however, the number, magnitude, and duration of the events differ from basin to basin and along reaches of the same stream. These differences are indicated indirectly by the depth of stream cutting below the floodplains and by areas of alluviation along the present drainageways (Fig. 1).

The alluvial-erosional sequence reported by Bryan (1940) and Hack (1942) is represented only along streams such as Cienega Creek, the San Pedro River, Jeddito Wash, and Laguna Creek (Tsegi area). Generally these are streams where the present cutting has been more than 5 m. The alluvial-erosional sequence along these streams may be indicative (1) of slight shifts in climate, with deposition generally taking place during moist periods between 2000 B.C. and A.D. 900-1200 and between A.D. 1300 and 1850, and erosion taking place during times of drought or of sporadic precipitation between about A.D. 1100 and 1300 and since 1850, and (2) of control of the type and amount of erosion and alluviation by such physiographic characteristics as gradient, size, shape of the watershed, and other factors (Horton, 1932, p. 350-361). All of these terraced drainageways are elongated and contain tributaries that usually join the main stem at an acute angle without a significant change in gradient.

The sequence is poorly represented along most streams in the Basin and Range province and along Chinle Wash and other washes in the Colorado Plateaus where physiographic characteristics are the main control of the type and amount of erosion and deposition and where the effects of shifts in climate are marked. The streams not showing uniform alluvial-erosional sequences similar to those reported by Bryan and Hack usually are in round or oval-shaped watersheds, and most tributaries join the main stem at nearly right angles, with a relatively sharp change in gradient.

The Colorado, San Juan, Little Colorado, Gila, and Salt Rivers apparently were aggrading during late Recent time until about the 14th or 15th centuries. For example, alluviation was the dominant process along the Gila River between A.D. 800 and 1400, when the canals that diverted water from the Gila were used by the prehistoric community of Snaketown (Haury, 1937, p. 50-58). Some time between A.D. 1250 and 1400 or slightly later these rivers excavated their channels to about the present depths.

In the Gulf of California embayment the Colorado River delta prohibited northward encroachment of the seas beyond the present limit of the Gulf of California (Fig. 1). In the Imperial Depression events of Recent time consist of alluviation, lacustrine deposition, including that in Lake Coahuila (ancestral Salton Sea) (Dibblee, 1954), and formation of lake terraces. Continued subsidence and intermittent overflow of the Colorado River into the depression probably were the main influences on erosion and sedimentation.

NEW MEXICO

Eastern New Mexico is a High Plains area drained chiefly by the Pecos and Canadian Rivers. The southern end of the glaciated Southern Rocky Mountains and their intermontane basins extend into the north-central part of the state (Fig. 2). The semiarid Basin and Range country occupies the central and southwestern areas, whereas the northwestern quarter is the southeastern part of the Colorado Plateau. A huge north-south structural depression followed by the Rio Grande splits the state into two unequal parts.

PECOS VALLEY SECTION OF GREAT PLAINS

The Pecos River rises amid the Southern Rocky Mountains in north-central New Mexico and flows southward and southeastward to join the Rio Grande in western Texas. Throughout Quaternary time, it has been dissecting and removing the thin sheet of late Tertiary alluvial sediments, the Ogallala Formation, that accumulated east of the Basin-and-Range province and that still caps the High Plains to the east along the New Mexico–Texas state line.

Between Roswell and Carlsbad, Quaternary sediments cover a broad lowland mostly west of the Pecos River. Here five surfaces and associated deposits (Fiedler and Nye, 1933; Morgan, 1938) may correlate southward and eastward with those of the Great Plains and may be related to glacial deposits in the Southern Rockies, wherein the Pecos River heads. The highest and oldest, 105-155 m above stream channels, is chiefly a rock-cut surface in the foothills of the Sacramento Mountains, but locally it has a thin cap of conglomerate. This surface may merge eastward with the High Plains surface and may correlate in the lower Pecos River area of westernmost Texas with Surface I of Leonard and Frye (1962), which is developed on the late Pliocene Ogallala Formation and is of latest Pliocene age.

The next younger surface rises 45-60 m above channels and is underlain by 2-10 m of limestone conglomerate, quartzose conglomerate, sandstone, mudstone, and clay; it includes several caliche zones and locally is as much as 60 m thick. This surface and the sediments appear to correlate downstream with Surface II (Leonard and Frye, 1962), a compound surface and a complex of several deposits probably developed in all of pre-Wisconsin Quaternary time.

Each of the three younger terraces is underlain by 5-15 m of sand, gravel, and clay and is capped by caliche. Their levels are 18-25, 5-12, and 3-10 m above stream channels. The highest terrace may be of early Wisconsin age, the middle terrace of late Wisconsin, and the lowest terrace of Recent age, according to downstream correlations (Leonard and Frye, 1962).

To the north the canyon of the Canadian River, cut into the High Plains, contains "several levels" of terrace gravels (Wanek, 1962), one being capped by a Quaternary basalt flow. The Canadian River heads along the east flank of the Sangre de Cristo Mountains, flows almost due south from Raton for 160 km, then turns abruptly to drain eastward into Texas. The river and its tributaries are cut in pre-Cenozoic rocks and locally in Ogallala Formation, Quaternary basalt flows, thin terrace gravels, and eolian sand.

BASIN AND RANGE PROVINCE IN NEW MEXICO

Quaternary deposits in central and southwestern New Mexico include glacial materials in the high mountains, alluvial and lacustrine sediments in intermontane basins,

Figure 2. Index map of New Mexico.

volcanic rocks, and fluvial deposits along the Rio Grande and Gila River and their tributaries.

Glacial deposits occur in the Sangre de Cristo Mountains (Ellis, 1935; Ray, 1940) and on Sierra Blanca (Antevs, 1935; Smith and Ray, 1941). Richmond (1963) correlated the moraines with the Bull Lake and Pinedale Glaciations (early and late Wisconsin, respectively) of the Wind River Mountains of Wyoming and identified Recent moraines in the Sangre de Cristo Mountains.

The glaciated northeastern side of Sierra Blanca is drained by tributaries of Pecos River. Two terraces along these tributaries may correlate downstream with the possible early and late Wisconsin terraces of the main river; they may thus be equivalent to the recessional stages of Bull Lake and Pinedale Glaciations on Sierra Blanca. Frye (1961) correlated recessional stages of mountain glaciation with deposition of terrace deposits along major streams far distant from the mountains.

Intermontane basin deposits. The Estancia Basin, Tularosa Basin, Plains of San Agustin, Animas Valley, and Playas Valley in New Mexico and Salt Basin in westernmost Texas have a stratigraphic history similar to that recorded on the High Plains of west Texas, where most surface deposits are of Wisconsin and Recent age. Most of these basins have been constantly filling since their formation as grabens in late Pliocene–early Pleistocene time. Consolidated gravels and pediments, believed to be of early Pleistocene age (King, 1948), occur in the margins.

Well-defined beach and lacustrine deposits in these basins mark various stages of ancient lakes. Highest shorelines suggest Lake Estancia was about 45 m in depth and 1,150 km² m area (Meinzer, 1911), Lake San Agustin 50 m and 650 km² (Powers, 1939), the lake in Salt Basin 13 m and 850 km² (King, 1948), Lake Otero in Tularosa Basin 35 m and about 1,800 km², and Lake Animas about 13 m and about 450 km² (Schwennesen, 1918). The high stage of many of these lakes is believed to be equivalent to the Tahoka Pluvial (Wendorf, 1961) of the High Plains, Cary (or Tazewell?) Glaciation (Antevs, 1954), or early Wisconsin events. Radiocarbon dates of calcareous clays deposited by Lake San Agustin (Foreman *et al.*, 1959) suggest 20,000 years B.P. as the end of lacustrine sedimentation.

Shuman (1959) identified five major surfaces and associated sediments on the west margin of Estancia Basin. He suggested the highest surface, an alluvial fan, is mid-Pleistocene in age. The lowest surface, the playa floor, is Recent in age. The intervening stepped sequence of three erosion surfaces are of Wisconsin age; they slope respectively to the highest, sixth, and lowest beaches of the twelve Lake Estancia beach lines identified by Shuman.

Some of the more spectacular Quaternary deposits of the Southwest are White Sands in the Tularosa Basin. Gypsum dissolved from Permian evaporites that crop out in the bordering fault-block mountains has been washed into and reprecipitated in the saline playas of the Tularosa Basin. Tiny gypsum crystals and cleavage flakes, picked up by the prevailing winds, have been blown into a huge mass of gypsum dunes that cover nearly 650 km² with an average thickness of about 5 m (Weber and Kottlowski, 1959). The dunes do not appear to be growing appreciably at present; much of the gypsum may have been derived from drying stages of Lake Otero, whose maximum expansion probably occurred during the Tahoka Pluvial.

Volcanism and uplift. The Southwest is spotted with accumulations of Quaternary volcanic rocks. Basalt and basaltic-andesite flows cap most of the Quaternary surfaces and intermingle with Quaternary sediments. Locally the landscapes are dotted with Quaternary volcanic necks and cinder cones. The terminal stage of Valles caldera in the Jemez Mountains northwest of Santa Fe occurred during early Pleistocene time with catastrophic eruptions of rhyolitic ash flows. Swineford (1949) believed this volcano was the source of the Pearlette Ash, lenses of which are reported in Kansan sediments from South Dakota to Texas. Identification of similar ash far west of Jemez Mountains (Richmond, 1962) suggests other western sources (Wilcox, this volume).

Large-scale earth movements were also local events. Gravity faulting and some tilting and folding are part of widespread epeirogenic uplift of mountainous regions. As noted by Richmond (1962), the downcutting during pre-Wisconsin Quaternary time was caused in part by this gradual epeirogenic uplift. These structural adjustments continue today, as indicated by fault scarps that cut recent alluvium along the fronts of such fault-block mountains as the Organ, San Andres, Sacramento, and Magdalena Mountains.

Upper Gila River. Robert H. Weber (oral communication, 1964) reports that at least part of the extensive Gila Conglomerate is of Quaternary age in west-central New Mexico, and that four alluvial surfaces occur along the Gila and San Francisco Rivers in that area. There is a high, interdivide surface underlain by river gravels, and three lower terraces are cut along the valleys at elevations of about 5, 18, and 30 m above stream channels. Weber believes than the San Francisco River once (during mid-Pleistocene time?) drained south-southeastward to join the Gila River near Cliff, and that the Gila River in turn flowed southward to join Animas Lake in Animas Valley west of Lordsburg.

Morrison (1964) mapped the Gila River Valley and adjoining areas at and near the New Mexico–Arizona state line, studying the Cenozoic rocks in detail. The upper part of the Gila Formation yielded vertebrate fossils of early Pleistocene age. Disconformably above the Gila are three types of gravel: pediment-and-terrace gravel, lake gravel, and stream-terrace gravel. The first two types are believed to be of mid-Pleistocene age, perhaps correlative with Kansan and Illinoian glaciation. They were related to a large lake in the Duncan basin fed by the ancient Gila River.

Stream gravels covering two strath terraces along the Gila River are of late Pleistocene age; unconsolidated alluvial gravel, sand, and silt underlie a still lower, younger terrace of Recent age.

Rio Grande Valley. The Rio Grande rises in the San Juan Mountains in southwestern Colorado, turns southward in

San Luis Valley, and flows south or south-southwestward to near Hatch, New Mexico, whence it turns to follow a south-southeastward course to the Big Bend country of west Texas. As noted by Bryan (1938), above the Big Bend the Rio Grande is a complex stream that flows from basin to basin, with canyons cut through interbasin constrictions made of pre-Cenozoic rocks. In the basins the river has cut terraces in an extensive, thick basin-fill of the Santa Fe Group. The lower part of this group is of late Miocene and Pliocene age, but the upper beds, which crop out along much of the Rio Grande Valley, are of Quaternary age.

The Rio Grande enters New Mexico from the north in a gorge about 60 m deep; this Rio Grande Canyon deepens southward until southwest of Taos, where the basalt-capped walls are 360 m high. Most of the basalt, basaltic-andesite, and interbedded gravels and sands of the canyon are of Quaternary age.

Rio Chama joins the Rio Grande from the northwest between Taos and Santa Fe, draining from the glaciated San Juan Mountains. The glacial sequence in the San Juans (Richmond, 1954; Atwood and Mather, 1932) consists of pre-Wisconsin tills, possibly of Kansan age: the Durango till and associated outwash deposits of early Wisconsin age, possibly equivalent to the Bull Lake till; till and outwash of late Wisconsin age, believed equivalent to Pinedale drift; deposits of two younger cirque glaciations that are correlated with the Temple Lake Stade of Neoglaciation; and a modern rock moraine formed about A.D. 1640-1860.

Muehlberger *et al.* (1960) mapped moraines and outwash deposits along the upper Chama River. They identified three terrace gravels more than 60 m above present streams and believed to be pre-Wisconsin outwash, five gravels 30-60 m above channels and correlated with early Wisconsin (Durango) outwash, and three levels of gravels within 15 m of present streams and considered to be of late Wisconsin age. Lower gravels mapped with alluvium may be of Temple Lake age and younger.

In the Sangre de Cristo Mountains northeast of Santa Fe, Richmond (1963) identified pre-Wisconsin moraines, two moraines of Bull Lake Glaciation, three moraines of Pinedale Glaciation, and the Temple Lake moraine of Neoglaciation. Rio Tesuque and Santa Fe River, tributaries to Rio Grande, head in cirques of these mountains. Downstream where the rivers leave the mountains, four terraces and outwash deposits were mapped by Kottlowski and Baldwin (Spiegel and Baldwin, 1963, Pls. 1-4).

Along Rio Tesuque, the sands of the lowest terrace, 2-3 m high, were deposited between A.D. 1250 and 1880, as dated by radiocarbon and pottery (Miller and Wendorf, 1958); the third terrace, 5 m above the channel, was dated between 2,230 B.P. and A.D. 1250 and may be related to the Temple Lake Stade. The second terrace, 27-35 m high, may be equivalent to Pinedale Glaciation, and the first terrace, 45-50 m above the streams, may correlate with Bull Lake Glaciation.

Upper beds of the Santa Fe Group near Santa Fe are in the Ancha Formation, believed to be of early Pleistocene age and unconformable on the late Miocene-Pliocene Tesuque Formation. The Ancha, 30-90 m thick, partly is over-

lain and partly intertongues westward with basalt tuff, basalt flows, and post-basalt sands, which include pumice lenses. This pumice is lithologically similar to that which underlies the Bandelier rhyolite tuff of the Jemez Mountains to the northwest and was correlated by Swineford (1949) with the Pearlette Ash of Kansan age.

Damon (1963), using the K-Ar method, dated the upper Bandelier Tuff as being 1.03 million years old. Some other pumice lenses in the Jemez Mountains are younger than the Bandelier Tuff, but they are of relatively small size. As Richmond (1962) found Pearlette-like ash in the La Sal Mountains of Utah, 400 km to the northwest, and hence windward of the Jemez volcano (prevailing winds presumably from the west), the source (or sources) of Pearlette-type ash may have been west of and younger than the Bandelier Tuff volcano (Wilcox, 1965).

Since the eruption of upper Ancha basalt and Bandelier Tuff, the Rio Grande has cut a 305-m-deep canyon through the east edge of the Jemez volcano; the terraces along Rio Tesuque are much lower and thus much younger than the surfaces cut on top of the Ancha and Bandelier formations.

Early and middle Pleistocene time appears to have been marked by uplift, volcanism, and graben-filling in central and southwestern New Mexico. The effects of climate and glaciation may have been relatively inconsequential until Wisconsin time. On the High Plains in eastern New Mexico and west Texas, pre-Wisconsin time seems to have been marked chiefly by slow erosion, with much detritus moved eastward. The thick caliche cap characteristic of the "Ogallala climax soil," probably mainly of late Pliocene age, occurs only as isolated remnants west of the High Plains. Most of the high surfaces along the Rio Grande and in the intermontane basins probably were developed in mid-Pleistocene time, with immediately underlying sediments mainly of Kansan age but with eolian sands and thin stream deposits of Illinoian age; soils probably were developed during Yarmouthian and Sangamonian times.

South of the Santa Fe area, Cenozoic deposits and geomorphic surfaces have been studied along the Rio Grande or its major tributaries by Stearns (1953), Bryan and McCann (1937), Wright (1946), Denny (1941), and Titus (1963). Typical of these terrace sequences is the one near Socorro, which includes three complexes of terrace levels and a relatively high surface, at elevations of 5-10, 30-40, 65-85, and 120-150 m above the stream channels. Uppermost silts beneath the lowest terrace are dated at A.D. 900-1200 by pottery (Robert H. Weber, oral communication, 1964).

Near Las Cruces, the Rio Grande is trenched about 130 m below La Mesa on the west and the Jornada surface on the east, and a stepped sequence of erosion surfaces rises from the floodplain to the outer valley wall. Ruhe (1962, 1964) identified three valley-border surfaces below the high La Mesa–Jornada surface—the Tortugas surface 105 m above the floodplain prior to faulting, the Picacho surface 40 m above the channel, and the Fort Selden surface complex averaging about 8 m above the floodplain. Sediments below the latter surface are dated by radiocarbon as 2,600-4,900 B.P. A similar sequence of terraces occurs near El Paso (Kottlowski, 1958).

The Quaternary sediments near Las Cruces locally are more than 100 m thick (Kottlowski, 1953). They include fluviatile sands, silts, and fossiliferous gravels, basalt flows, eolian sands, playa clays, calcrete (Gile, 1961) and caliche lenses, and various paleosols. Beneath a complex of fine-grain sediments and paleosols that underlie the high La Mesa and Jornada surfaces are gravels with well-rounded pebbles and cobbles. These gravels have yielded (Ruhe, 1962) vertebrate remains that are no older than late Kansan and no younger than Illinoian. Similar fossils at a similar stratigraphic location were found by Strain (1959) along the Rio Grande Valley southeast of El Paso.

On the Jornada surface east of Rio Grande Valley, angular gravels overlie the La Mesa paleosol complex, so the Jornada surface is younger than La Mesa surface (Ruhe, 1964). On high alluvial fans near the adjoining mountains, the high Dona Ana surface stands above the Jornada surface and may be correlative with La Mesa surface. Lower and younger surfaces and sediments occur near the mountains and near playas, and they may correlate with the younger valley-border surfaces along the Rio Grande.

The fossiliferous rounded gravels beneath La Mesa surface are widespread in south-central New Mexico; according to Ruhe (1962) they are too widespread to be river gravels of a mid-Pleistocene Rio Grande, and they may represent instead lacustrine beach gravels of Kansan (and Illinoian?) pluvials. The overlying silts, sands, paleosols, and caliche may be chiefly a combination Yarmouthian-Sangamonian soil. Frye and Leonard (1963) noted that Illinoian time on the High Plains was relatively arid, with dune and sheet sands being the major sediments deposited; La Mesa upper silts and sands may be similar deposits. The two intermediate valley-border pediments and alluvial fans, Tortugas and Picacho, and the similar low complex, Fort Selden, appear to correspond to similar features upstream, of possible middle to late Pleistocene (early Wisconsin?), late Pleistocene (late Wisconsin?), and Recent age. As noted by Ruhe (1962), the Rio Grande did not establish its valley in south-central New Mexico until after development of La Mesa surface, so its course in the Las Cruces–El Paso area is no older than mid-Pleistocene.

QUATERNARY GEOLOGIC HISTORY

Pre-Wisconsin Quaternary in central and southwestern New Mexico was characterized by uplift, volcanism, erosion, and graben-filling. Climatic changes during Wisconsin and Recent resulted in trenching and relatively minor alluviation. Four complex surfaces and associated sediments were formed during the late Quaternary along the Pecos River at the west edge of the High Plains, locally in closed intermontane basins, and along the Rio Grande and its tributaries from the Southern Rockies southward to the Big Bend country.

Thick paleosols were developed during middle Pleistocene on fossiliferous sediments deposited in late Kansan and Illinoian time. The highest Quaternary surface (such as La Mesa and Jornada) was cut on these mid-Pleistocene materials and in turn was trenched by the Rio Grande during late Quaternary (Sangamon–earliest Wisconsin?). The third highest terrace, such as Tortugas, probably devel-

oped during the time of Bull Lake Glaciation and the Tahoka Pluvial (early Wisconsin), when high-level lakes (dated at about 20,000 to 27,000 B.P.) occupied intermontane basins.

The next younger terrace, like the Picacho, probably formed during late Wisconsin time, correlative with Pinedale Glaciation. The youngest alluvial terrace complex, probably correlative with Temple Lake and Gannett Peak glaciations (Richmond, 1963), was developed mainly after 2600 B.C.

COLORADO PLATEAU

The Colorado Plateau (Fig. 3), covers about 350,000 km² between the Southern Rocky Mountains and the Basin and Range province (Hunt, 1964). Most of the Plateau has an altitude greater than 1,700 m, with some of the plateaus and many of the peaks above 3,700 m. The drainage typically is incised in deep canyons, Grand Canyon being the most spectacular. The Colorado River and its major tributaries, the Green, San Juan, and Little Colorado Rivers, drain most of the area.

The Plateau has less than 50 cm average annual precipitation. Extensive areas are bare rock; vegetation is sparse, as is the animal and human population. At one extreme are hot wind-swept deserts, whereas at the other are cool, lake-dotted, dense forests of the higher plateaus and mountains.

PHYSIOGRAPHIC SECTIONS

The Navajo section is an arid area with mesas, cuestas, rock terraces, escarpments, canyons, dry washes, and volcanic necks and buttes. The section consists of two synclinal basins, the Black Mesa Basin on the west and the deeper San Juan Basin on the east, separated by the east-dipping Defiance monocline, which trends northward in northeastern Arizona near the New Mexico state line.

Figure 3. Index map of Colorado Plateau.

The Datil section is mostly a plateau and mountain area formed chiefly of Cenozoic volcanic rocks that range from basalt to rhyolite. Along its northern edge are the Zuni Mountains, an anticlinal uplift of Precambrian and late Paleozoic rocks, and the Mount Taylor volcano, a large late-Tertiary cone. The southern part grades into the Basin and Range province of southwestern New Mexico.

The Grand Canyon section is the southwest rim of the Colorado Plateau and is structurally the highest part of the rim, but it is cut by the 1,500-m-deep canyon of the Colorado River as the river leaves the Plateau province. The Grand Canyon cuts the section in two parts; on the north, north-trending faults divide the country into high plateaus, rising step-like from west to east; on the south is the San Francisco Plateau, notched by canyons, but generally with a gently rolling surface. Near Flagstaff, several hundred volcanic cones and associated lava flows rise above the plateau, the highest being about 3,870 m in altitude, and presumably of Quaternary age.

QUATERNARY DEPOSITS

Quaternary sedimentary deposits on the Colorado Plateau (Hunt, 1956) include glacial and periglacial materials on and near the higher mountains, fanglomerate on pediments and in alluvial fans, gravel and other fluvial materials both on cut terraces and in fill terraces along streams, eolian deposits, and paleosols and caliche.

Glacial deposits. Glacial materials occur on the higher mountains and higher plateaus but are more extensive in the Southern Rockies to the east, such as the San Juan Mountains. In the La Sal Mountains, three pre-Wisconsin tills have been identified and tentatively correlated with the Nebraskan, Kansan, and Illinoian Stages (Richmond, 1962); volcanic ash amid the medial pre-Wisconsin till is petrographically similar to the Pearlette Ash, which is of Kansan age on the Great Plains. It supports the correlation with Kansan deposits and favors the theory that the Pearlette sources were not in north-central New Mexico but farther west. One pre-Wisconsin till is reported by Sharp (1942) in the San Francisco Mountains; elsewhere, even on the High Plateaus, pre-Wisconsin glaciations appear to have been lacking, or their tills were destroyed by erosion.

Both Early Wisconsin and Late Wisconsin moraines have been mapped in the La Sal Mountains (Richmond, 1962), High Plateaus (Flint and Denny, 1958; Smith *et al.*, 1963), and San Francisco Mountains (Sharp, 1942). The early Wisconsin moraines in the La Sal Mountains, correlated with Bull Lake Glaciation by Richmond (1962), are large, being as much as 45 m high. The late Wisconsin moraines, equated to Pinedale Glaciation, are smaller, about 12 m high, less extensive, less weathered, and less dissected.

The Wisconsin glacial deposits in the San Francisco Mountains (Sharp, 1942) are among the most southerly occurrences in the United States, although they are 220 km north of the latitude of glaciated Sierra Blanca in southern New Mexico. Moraines of Late Wisconsin glaciation have an average altitude of 3,150 m in the La Sal Mountains (Richmond, 1962), 2,750 m in the San Francisco Mountains

(Sharp, 1942), and 3,320 m on Sierra Blanca (Richmond, 1963).

Recent glacial materials in the Colorado Plateau area are above 3,050 m altitude and consist of small moraines and rock glaciers in the cirques. In the La Sal Mountains, the older of these Recent deposits is younger than 900 B.C., as dated by radiocarbon analysis of charcoal from pre-pottery stone-culture hearth sites, whereas the younger glacial episode may have culminated prior to A.D. 1860 (Richmond, 1962, p. 102).

Some of the high mountains and plateaus, for example the Henry Mountains, were above the snow line during the Quaternary glacial ages but were not glaciated, probably because they were in the rain shadow of higher areas and their precipitation was insufficient. These high areas, however, were affected by intensive frost action that produced widespread boulder and rubble fields. These cover a few hectares or a few hundred hectares and in most places are less than a meter thick (Richmond, 1962; Hunt, 1964). Included are patterned ground, rubble streams, and rubble sheets, either in place on flat surfaces or transported down steeper slopes.

At lower altitudes counterparts of these boulder and rubble deposits are talus cones, colluvial aprons, and debris avalanches along canyon walls and at the foot of cliffs. These deposits apparently are being eroded; Hunt *et al.* (1953) suggested they date from humid times when weathering of the cliffs was accelerated.

Fluvial deposits. The only assuredly pre-Wisconsin fill terrace along the Colorado River (Hunt, 1956, p. 38) is in a cut-off meander about halfway between the mouths of the Green and San Juan Rivers. The fill is more than 40 m thick, its base is more than 90 m above the river, and it is overlain by fanglomerate believed to be of late Pleistocene age.

Richmond (1962) identified pre-Wisconsin alluvial sands and gravels in the La Sal Mountains, and Sharp (1942) mapped pre-Wisconsin outwash materials in the San Francisco Mountains. Other outwash deposits, gravels capping pediments, and high-level gravels on some of the canyon rims and as isolated cappings on some high mesas are also of pre-Wisconsin age but have not been studied in detail.

Late Pleistocene and Recent alluvial gravels, mostly thin caps on rock-cut terraces, form terraces along the Colorado River up to about 30 m above the stream bed. At one place a gravel fill more than 30 m thick is believed to be early Wisconsin in age (Hunt, 1956, p. 38); thick lenses of spring-deposited calcium carbonate are interbedded with this alluvial fill, suggesting a much higher ground-water table during early Wisconsin time. Outwash alluvium of early and late Wisconsin ages occurs near the glaciated areas.

Hack (1942) identified three stages of alluviation, separated by periods of arroyo cutting, that are widespread in most valleys of the Colorado Plateau, particularly in the Navajo section. These three stages range from late Wisconsin in age to about A.D. 1880.

The oldest alluvium, the Jeddito Formation, has yielded

the remains of late Pleistocene vertebrates. The alluvium resembles Recent deposits (Hunt, 1956, p. 38) but tends to be thicker, contain more clay, and be more extensive and more compact. In Early Recent time, during the Altithermal interval (about 4,500-6,000 B.P. according to Malde, 1964), the Jeddito Formation was deeply eroded, and sand dunes were swept in on top of the remnants.

Overlapping the dune sand is the Tsegi alluvium (Hack, 1942, p. 62), which was deposited before pottery and bow-and-arrow weapons were introduced among the prehistoric peoples of the region. Correlative alluvium has been widely identified on the Colorado Plateau and elsewhere (Bryan, 1926, 1954; Leopold and Snyder, 1951; Bryan and Mc-Cann, 1943; Hunt, 1955; Hunt and Tanner, 1960; Richmond, 1962); it contains atlatl points as well as remains of vertebrates similar to those in modern faunas. Hearths and charcoal are abundant in the Tsegi alluvium and help to distinguish it from Jeddito alluvium and from younger alluvium. This Tsegi alluvium was deposited about the same time as the earlier of the Recent moraines and rock glaciers on the La Sal Mountains, that is, some time between 900 B.C. and A.D. 1 (Hunt, 1964). Malde and Schick (1964) suggest that alluvium correlative with the lower Tsegi is as old as 2000 B.C.

Pottery-bearing sites of the Anasazi Indians, as well as pueblo sites, irrigation systems, and pottery of the Pueblo cultures up to and including Pueblo III (A.D. 1100-1300), are found on the uppermost part of the Tsegi alluvium and have been partly removed by later arroyo cutting. About A.D. 1300 arroyos that were deeper and wider than present ones were eroded into the Tsegi alluvium.

These younger arroyos were partly filled by a still younger alluvium, the Naha Formation (Hack, 1942, p. 62), younger than Pueblo III but older than the white settlements (Hunt, 1964) and probably deposited at about the same time as the youngest rock glaciers in the La Sal Mountains.

Cutting of the present-day arroyos began about 1880. Overgrazing and other land uses that reduced the vegetation have been blamed for the arroyo-cutting (Bailey, 1935; Antevs, 1952), but Bryan (1925, 1928, 1940) concluded that overgrazing merely triggered the erosion. Earlier episodes of arroyo cutting were more severe.

Eolian deposits. Hunt (1964) reports that sand dunes on the Colorado Plateau are mostly in the Canyon Lands and Navajo sections, with two distinct deposits recognizable. The older dunes of weathered, compact, red-stained sand are of early Recent age, for they overlap the Jeddito alluvium. These stabilized dunes contain artifacts of the early Anasazi as well as remains of vegetation that at the present time grows at higher altitudes (Hunt, 1955, p. 584).

The younger dune sands overlie the Tsegi alluvium; some of these dunes have been stabilized and are overlapped by the Naha alluvium, whereas others are still active (Hunt, 1964). In the Navajo section, Hack (1941) identified three types of dune, each bearing an orderly relation to sand supply, exposure to the wind, and vegetation. Transverse dunes are located where wind and sand are considerable

and vegetation sparse, longitudinal dunes occur in intermediate areas, and parabolic dunes are found where the vegetation is moderate and the wind and sand limited.

Deeply weathered, pre-Wisconsin loess about a meter thick is extensive on the uplands at the northwest foot of the San Juan Mountains (Hunt, 1956). The soils developed on these deposits are highly productive for farming.

Lakes and lake deposits. Lake deposits are an almost insignificant part of the Quaternary sediments of the Colorado Plateau, but in this arid to semiarid country the lakes are important sources of water. San Agustin Lake was the only large natural lake, and it is about on the borderline with the Basin and Range province, actually being in graben basin more typical of that latter physiographic province.

Small lakes (Hunt, 1964) include some in depressions on lava-capped plateaus, behind landslides and end moraines, and in sinkholes and solution valleys developed on top of limestone-capped plateaus, and some waterpockets in massive sandstones, especially in the Canyon Lands section. Hunt *et al.* (1953, p. 172) noted that the latter are formed in three ways: some are plunge pools below waterfalls, others are potholes, and still others seem due to solution of cement from the sandstone and subsequent removal of the loosened sand grains.

On the flat crest of the Chuska Mountains are hundreds of small depressions, many holding lakes. Wright (1964) found the clayey lake sediments to be almost entirely of Pleistocene age. He attributes the depressions to collapse of cemented sandstone layers above vacuities produced by the piping of uncemented sand out to the steep scarp at the east side of the mountains. The piping occurred during pluvial times when water tables were high and appears to have slowed or even stopped under present conditions.

Soils, paleosols, and caliche. Soils are mostly desert types on the Colorado Plateau but are zoned by altitude (Richmond, 1962; Martin and Fletcher, 1943). Below altitudes of about 2,300 m the soils are limy (pedocals), but at higher altitudes they are acid (pedalfers) without limy subsoils.

Three ages of soils and paleosols can be distinguished. The oldest formed at various stages during pre-Wisconsin time and consists of a reddish-brown and clayey upper layer, about a meter thick, over about a meter of strongly lime-enriched subsoil containing decomposed parent rocks (Hunt and Sokoloff, 1950; Richmond, 1962). This soil is commonly associated with subdued landforms that contrast with the more rugged and more youthful landforms that have been developed under Wisconsin and Recent conditions. Chestnut soils were formed on the pre-Wisconsin loess around the west and northwest foot of the San Juan Mountains.

Soils of Wisconsin age are less clayey and less red, and stones of the parent bedrock are not decomposed. The limy subsoil is less well developed than in the older soils and is also thinner, being in most places less than 15-30 cm thick. Stones in early Wisconsin soils commonly have developed a weathering rind; in late Wisconsin soils and on late Wisconsin surfaces only a few stones show such rind.

Leaching has been slight in the Recent soils, in most places less than about 5 cm.

Thick deposits of calcium carbonate (caliche) have formed as a result of ground-water seepage. Hunt (1964) points out that these deposits are especially conspicuous on the sloping, gravel-covered pediments where ground water seeps downslope on the pediment surface at the base of the gravel sheet. In the semiarid climate, subsurface evaporation through the porous gravel causes the calcium carbonate to precipitate.

Large areas of bare rock on the Colorado Plateau are stained by desert varnish composed mainly of iron and manganese oxide. Much of this desert varnish was formed during the wet period prior to A.D. 1, more or less concurrently with deposition of the Tsegi alluvium. The stain has been developed only locally on prehistoric sites and surfaces that are of pottery and bow-and-arrow ages, but it is widespread on older sites and deposits; thus Hunt (1962, p. 194) has used the desert varnish to help identify sites and surfaces more than 2,000 years old.

QUATERNARY GEOLOGIC HISTORY

Early and middle Pleistocene history was marked chiefly by erosion on the Colorado Plateau. Few deposits record that history. The canyons along the main streams were deepened. The Grand Canyon at the beginning of Quaternary was at least two-thirds as deep as it is now and has been deepened less than 430 m during Quaternary time (Hunt, 1964). Near the La Sal Mountains, Richmond (1962) found that the Colorado River canyon was about 245 m deep before the earliest (Nebraskan?) till was deposited; it has been deepened only 60 m during the Quaternary.

Late Pleistocene history of the canyons has been an alternation of deposition of thick fill in the canyons and erosion of that fill; even in the headwater areas, cutting in bedrock has not been deep during the Late Pleistocene (Hunt, 1956, p. 85). As in pre-Wisconsin Quaternary times, glacial tills were deposited on the higher mountains and plateaus, and outwash materials were laid down adjacent to the glaciated regions. The Jeddito alluvium was deposited in areas distant from glaciated uplands and the deeply cut canyons.

During the Recent, three episodes of arroyo cutting separated by the Tsegi and Naha stages of alluviation occurred, and two dune-sand deposits were formed, all apparently reflecting climatic changes. Volcanism of earlier Quaternary time continued to form basalt flows and cinder cones, particularly in the San Francisco Mountains and in the Datil section south and southeast of the Zuni Mountains.

Since about 1880, arroyo cutting has been a dominant geomorphic process throughout most of the Colorado Plateau, reflecting increasingly dry climatic conditions; in the glaciated regions, frost action has decreased, rock glaciers are inactive, and tree lines appear to be rising (Richmond, 1962, p. 103).

REFERENCES

Antevs, Ernst, 1935, The occurrence of flints and extinct animals in pluvial deposits near Clovis, New Mexico, *in* Age of the Clovis Lake clays: Philadelphia Acad. Nat. Sci. Proc., v. 87, p. 304-312

—— 1952, Arroyo-cutting and filling: J. Geol., v. 60, p. 375-385

—— 1954, Climate of New Mexico during the last Glacio-Pluvial: J. Geol., v. 62, p. 182-191

—— 1955, Geologic-climatic dating in the West: Amer. Antiq., v. 20, p. 317-335

Atwood, W. W., and Mather, K. F., 1932, Physiography and Quaternary geology of the San Juan Mountains, Colorado: U.S. Geol. Surv. Prof. Pap. 166, 176 p.

Bailey, R. W., 1935, Epicycles of erosion in the valleys of the Colorado Plateau province: J. Geol., v. 43, p. 337-355

Bryan, Kirk, 1925, Date of channel trenching (arroyo cutting) in the arid Southwest: Science, v. 62, p. 338-344

—— 1926, Recent deposits of Chaco Canyon, New Mexico, in relation to the life of the prehistoric peoples of Pueblo Bonito (abst.): Washington Acad. Sci. J., v. 16, p. 75-76

—— 1928, Historic evidence on changes in the channel of Rio Puerco, a tributary of the Rio Grande in New Mexico: J. Geol., v. 36, p. 265-282

—— 1938, Geology and ground-water conditions of the Rio Grande depression in Colorado and New Mexico, *in* (U.S.) Natl. Res. Plan. Bd., Rio Grande Joint Invest. Upper Rio Grande basin: Washington, D.C., U.S. Govt. Print. Off., v. 1, pt. 2, p. 197-225

—— 1940, Erosion in the valleys of the Southwest: New Mexico Quart., v. 10, p. 227-232

—— 1954, The geology of Chaco Canyon, New Mexico: Smithson. Inst. Misc. Coll., v. 122, 65 p.

Bryan, Kirk, and McCann, F. T., 1937, The Ceja del Rio Puerco: a border feature of the Basin and Range province in New Mexico: J. Geol., v. 45, p. 801-828

—— 1943, Sand dunes and alluvium near Grants, New Mexico: Amer. Antiq., v. 8, p. 281-290

Cooley, M. E., and Davidson, E. S., 1963, The Mogollon Highlands—their influence on Mesozoic and Cenozoic erosion and sedimentation: Arizona Geol. Soc. Dig., v. 6, p. 7-35

Damon, P. E., 1963, Correlation and chronology of ore deposits and volcanic rocks: Res. Div., U.S. Atomic Energy Comm., Ann. Prog. Rep. No. 5, Contract AT(11-1)-689, 13 p.

Davidson, E. S., 1961, Facies distribution and hydrology of intermontane basin fill, Safford basin, Arizona: U.S. Geol. Surv. Prof. Pap. 424-C, p. 151-153

Denny, C. S., 1941, Quaternary geology of the San Acacia area, New Mexico: J. Geol., v. 49, p. 225-260

Dibblee, T. W., Jr., 1954, Geology of the Imperial Valley region, California: California Dept. Nat. Resources Div. Mines Bull. 170, p. 21-28

Ellis, R. W., 1935, Glaciation in New Mexico: Univ. New Mexico Bull., Geol. Ser., v. 5, p. 1-31

Fenneman, N. M., 1931, Physiography of western United States: New York, McGraw-Hill Book Co., 534 p.

Fiedler, A. G., and Nye, S. S., 1933, Geology and ground-water resources of the Roswell artesian basin, New Mexico: U.S. Geol. Surv. Water-Supply Pap. 639, 372 p.

Flint, R. F., and Denny, C. S., 1958, Quaternary geology

of Boulder Mountain, Aquarius Plateau, Utah: U.S. Geol. Surv. Bull. 1061-D, p. 103-164

Foreman, Fred, Clisby, Kathryn H., and Sears, P. B., 1959, Plio- Pleistocene sediments and climates of the San Agustin Plains, New Mexico: New Mexico Geol. Soc. Guidebook, West-Central New Mexico, p. 117-120

Frye, J. C., 1961, Fluvial deposition and the glacial cycle: J. Geol., v. 69, p. 600-603

Frye, J. C., and Leonard, A. B., 1963, Pleistocene geology of Red River Basin in Texas: Univ. Texas Bur. Econ. Geol. Rep. Inv. 49, 48 p.

Gile, L. H., 1961, A classification of Ca horizons in soils of a desert region, Dona Ana County, New Mexico: Soil Sci. Soc. Amer. Proc., v. 25, p. 52-61

Hack, J. T., 1941, Dunes of the western Navajo country: Geogr. Rev., v. 31, p. 240-263

—— 1942, The changing environment of the Hopi Indians of Arizona: Harvard Univ. Peabody Mus. Amer. Arch. and Ethnol. Pap., v. 35, No. 1, 85 p.

Haury, E. W., 1937, The Snaketown canal: Gila Pueblo, Globe, Ariz., Medallion Pap. 25, p. 50-58

Heindl, L. A., 1962, Cenozoic geology of Arizona—A 1960 resume: Arizona Geol. Soc. Dig., v. 5, p. 9-24

Horton, R. E., 1932, Drainage basin characteristics: Amer. Geophys. Union Trans., v. 13, p. 350-361

Hunt, Alice P., and Tanner, Dallas, 1960, Early man sites near Moab, Utah: Amer. Antiq., v. 26, p. 110-117

Hunt, C. B., 1955, Recent geology of Cane Wash, Monument Valley, Arizona: Science, v. 122, p. 583-585

—— 1956, Cenozoic geology of the Colorado Plateau: U.S. Geol. Surv. Prof. Pap. 279, 99 p.

—— 1962, Stratigraphy of desert varnish: U.S. Geol. Surv. Prof. Pap. 424-B, p. 194-195

—— 1964, Quaternary geology of the Colorado Plateau: unpubl. manuscript

Hunt, C. B., Averitt, Paul, and Miller, R. L., 1953, Geology and geography of the Henry Mountains region, Utah: U.S. Geol. Surv. Prof. Pap. 228, 234 p.

Hunt, C. B., and Sokoloff, V. P., 1950, Pre-Wisconsin soil in the Rocky Mountain region: U.S. Geol. Surv. Prof. Pap. 221-G, p. 109-123

Jenkins, O. P., 1923, Verde River lake beds near Clarksdale, Arizona: Amer. J. Sci., v. 5, p. 65-81

King, P. B., 1948, Geology of the southern Guadalupe Mountains, Texas: U.S. Geol. Surv. Prof. Pap. 215, 183 p.

Kottlowski, F. E., 1953, Tertiary-Quaternary sediments of the Rio Grande Valley in southern New Mexico: New Mexico Geol. Soc. Guidebook, Southwest. New Mex., p. 144-148

—— 1958, Geologic history of the Rio Grande near El Paso: West Texas Geol. Soc. Guidebook, Franklin and Hueco Mtns., Texas, p. 46-54

Lance, J. F., 1960, Stratigraphic and structural position of Cenozoic fossil localities in Arizona: Arizona Geol. Soc. Dig., v. 4, p. 155-160

Lee, W. T., 1905, Underground waters of Salt River Valley, Arizona: U.S. Geol. Surv. Water-Supply Pap. 136, 196 p.

Leonard, A. B., and Frye, J. C., 1962, Pleistocene molluscan faunas and physiographic history of Pecos Valley

in Texas: Univ. Texas Bur. Econ. Geol. Rep. Inv. 45, 42 p.

Leopold, L. B., and Snyder, C. T., 1951, Alluvial fills near Gallup, New Mexico: U.S. Geol. Surv. Water-Supply Pap. 1110-A, p. 1-17

Longwell, C. R., 1954, History of the lower Colorado River and the Imperial depression: California Dept. Nat. Resources Div. Mines Bull. 170, p. 53-56

Malde, H. E., 1964, Environment and man in arid America: Science, v. 145, p. 123-129

Malde, H. E., and Schick, A. P., 1964, Thorne cave, northeastern Utah—geology: Amer. Antiq., v. 30, p. 60-73

Martin, P. S., and Mehringer, P. J., Jr., this volume, Pleistocene pollen analysis and biogeography of the Southwest

Martin, W. P., and Fletcher, J. E., 1943, Vertical zonation of great soil groups on Mount Graham, Arizona, as correlated with climate, vegetation, and profile characteristics: Univ. Ariz. Agr. Exp. Stat. Tech. Bull. 99, 38 p.

Meinzer, O. E., 1911, Geology and water resources of the Estancia Valley, New Mexico: U.S. Geol. Surv. Water-Supply Pap. 275, 89 p.

Meinzer, O. E., and Kelton, F. C., 1913, Geology and water resources of Sulphur Spring Valley, Arizona: U.S. Geol. Surv. Water-supply Pap. 320, p. 9-213

Metzger, D. G., 1964, Progress report on geohydrologic investigation in the Parker-Blythe-Cibola and Needles areas, *in* Investigation of the water resources of the lower Colorado River area—progress report: U.S. Geol. Surv. Open-File Rep. 3, Tucson, Ariz., 128 p.

Miller, J. P., and Wendorf, Fred, 1958, Alluvial chronology of the Tesuque Valley, New Mexico: J. Geol., v. 66, p. 177-194

Morgan, A. M., 1938, Geology and shallow-water resources of the Roswell artesian basin, New Mexico: New Mexico State Eng. 12th and 13th Biennial Reps., p. 155-249

Morrison, R. B., 1964, Geology of the Duncan and Canador Peak quadrangles, New Mexico and Arizona: U.S. Geol. Surv. Misc. Map (in press)

Muehlberger, W. R., Adams, G. E., Longgood, T. E. Jr., and St. John, B. E., 1960, Stratigraphy of the Chama quadrangle, northern Rio Arriba County, New Mexico: New Mexico Geol. Soc. Guidebook, Rio Chama County, p. 93-102

Olmsted, F. H., and Robison, J. H., 1964, Progress report on geologic investigation of the Yuma area and the East Mesa area of Imperial Valley, *in* Investigation of the water resources of the lower Colorado River area—progress report: U.S. Geol. Surv. Open-File Rep. 3, Tucson, Ariz., 229 p.

Powers, W. E., 1939, Basin and shore features of the extinct Lake San Agustin, New Mexico: J. Geomorph., v. 2, p. 345-356

Ray, L. L., 1940, Glacial chronolgy of the southern Rocky Mountains: Geol. Soc. Amer. Bull., v. 51, p. 1851-1917

Richmond, G. M., 1954, Modification of the glacial chronology of the San Juan Mountains, Colorado: Science, v. 119, p. 614-615

—— 1962, Quaternary stratigraphy of the La Sal Mountains, Utah: U.S. Geol. Surv. Prof. Pap. 324, 135 p.

—— 1963, Correlation of some glacial deposits in New Mexico: U.S. Geol. Surv. Prof. Pap. 450-E, p. 121-125

Ruhe, R. V., 1962, Age of the Rio Grande Valley in southern New Mexico: J. Geol., v. 70, p. 151-167

—— 1964, Landscape morphology and alluvial deposits in southern New Mexico: Amer. Assoc. Geogr. Ann., v. 54, p. 147-159

Schwennesen, A. T., 1918, Ground water in the Animas, Playas, Hachita, and San Luis basins, New Mexico: U.S. Geol. Surv. Water-Supply Pap. 422, 152 p.

Sharp, R. P., 1942, Multiple Pleistocene glaciation on San Francisco Mountain, Arizona: J. Geol., v. 50, p. 481-503

Shuman, R. C., 1959, Soils and the soil landscape in Estancia Basin, New Mexico: Soil Conserv. Ser. Soil Survey Inv., unpubl. manuscript, 29 p.

Smith, H. T. U., and Ray, L. L., 1941, Southernmost glaciated peak in the United States: Science, v. 93, p. 209

Smith, J. F., Jr., Huff, L. C., Hinrichs, E. N., and Luedke, R. G., 1963, Geology of the Capitol Reef area, Wayne and Garfield Counties, Utah: U.S. Geol. Surv. Prof. Pap. 363, 102 p.

Spiegel, Zane, and Baldwin, Brewster, 1963, Geology and water resources of the Santa Fe area, New Mexico: U.S. Geol. Surv. Water-Supply Pap. 1525, 258 p.

Stearns, C. E., 1953, Tertiary geology of the Galisteo-Tonque area, New Mexico: Geol. Soc. Amer. Bull., v. 64, p. 459-507

Strain, W. S., 1959, Blancan mammalian fauna from Rio Grande Valley, Hudspeth County, Texas: Geol. Soc. Amer. Bull., v. 70, p. 375-378

Swineford, Ada, 1949, Source area of Great Plains Pleistocene volcanic ash: J. Geol., v. 57, p. 307-311

Tarbet, L. A., and Holman, W. H., 1944, Stratigraphy and micropaleontology of the west side of Imperial Valley, California (abst.): Amer. Assoc. Petroleum Geologists Bull., v. 28, p. 1781

Titus, F. B., Jr., 1963, Geology and ground-water conditions in eastern Valencia County, New Mexico: New Mexico Bur. Mines Min. Resources Ground-Water Rep. 7, 113 p.

Twenter, F. R., and Metzger, D. G., 1963, Geology and ground water in Verde Valley—the Mogollon Rim region, Arizona: U.S. Geol. Surv. Bull. 1177, 132 p.

Wanek, A. A., 1962, Reconnaissance geologic map of parts of Harding, San Miguel, and Mora Counties, New Mexico: U.S. Geol. Surv. Oil Gas Inv. Map OM-208

Weber, R. H., and Kottlowski, F. E., 1959, Gypsum resources of New Mexico: New Mexico Bur. Mines Min. Resources Bull. 68, 68 p.

Wendorf, Fred, 1961, An interpretation of Late Pleistocene environments of the Llano Estacado, *in* Paleoecology of the Llano Estacado: Santa Fe, Mus. New Mexico Press, Fort Burgwin Res. Center, Publ. 1, p. 115-133

Wilcox, R. E., this volume, Volcanic ash chronology

Wright, H. E., Jr., 1946, Tertiary and Quaternary geology of the lower Rio Puerco area, New Mexico: Geol. Soc. Amer. Bull., v. 57, p. 383-456

—— 1964, Origin of the lakes in the Chuska Mountains, northwestern New Mex.: Geol. Soc. Amer. Bull., v. 75, p. 589-598

Wright, L. A., and Troxel, B. W., 1954, Western Mojave Desert and Death Valley region: California Dept. Nat. Resources Div. Mines Bull. 170, Geol. guide 1, 50 p.

Summary

Quaternary sediments on the Colorado Plateau and in the southern Basin and Range province of the Southwest include glacial materials in high mountains and the higher plateaus, alluvial and lacustrine sediments in intermontane basins, volcanic accumulations, eolian deposits, paleosols and caliche, and fluvial materials along the Colorado River, Rio Grande, Pecos River, Gila River, and their tributaries.

Quaternary events in southern Arizona and southeastern California were controlled mainly by upwarping and subsidence and subordinately by volcanism and climate; climatic changes are recognized chiefly in deposits of late Pleistocene and Recent time. Quaternary alluvial deposits of the Colorado River grade southward into marine sediments in the Gulf of California embayment and thin upstream; however, only a third of the depth of the river's Grand Canyon has been cut during the Quaternary.

On the Colorado Plateau, early and middle Pleistocene was characterized chiefly by erosion, and higher elevations were affected by pre-Wisconsin glaciation. Uplift, volcanism, erosion, and graben-filling were the major processes in the southern Basin and Range country during pre-Wisconsin Quaternary time. The deposits of the early Pleistocene are predominantly fine-grained materials, relatively thick in local basins and folded or tilted in most localities. The thinner, mid-Pleistocene sediments are mainly stream and lacustrine gravels, with some finer grained materials; they are horizontal and tend to be more widespread, in many places capping extensive surfaces.

Glacial events of late Pleistocene and Recent on the higher peaks appear related to alternating episodes of thin alluviation and deep cutting along the Rio Grande and Pecos and Gila Rivers, the terraces and associated sediments along the river valleys probably correlating with glacial materials dated as early Wisconsin, late Wisconsin, and Recent. The Rio Grande Valley was cut in late Pleistocene time, as was the upper Gila Valley, in contrast to the lower Gila Valley and that of the Colorado River, which were established in pre-Quaternary time. High-level lakes in intermontaine basins are mainly of mid-Wisconsin age, correlative with the Tahoka Pluvial of the High Plains to the east.

THE QUATERNARY OF THE PACIFIC MOUNTAIN SYSTEM IN CALIFORNIA*

CLYDE WAHRHAFTIG,[1] J. H. BIRMAN[2]

THE QUATERNARY OF CALIFORNIA is a system of great variety and complexity. Nearly all the climatically controlled phenomena recorded in other parts of the world—glaciation, periglacial phenomena, changes of sea level, fluctuations of pluvial lakes, alluvial-terrace formation, and soil-forming processes—are present in California, which was undergoing during the Quaternary a major tectonic revolution accompanied by volcanism. The close proximity of the various kinds of Quaternary features, and their association with tectonics and volcanism, have given rise to hopes that the different kinds of climatic succession might be correlated more successfully in California than elsewhere. To date these hopes have been only partially realized, although parts of the glacial sequence have been correlated with radiometrically dated volcanic rocks.

Limitations of space and time have made it possible to cover at length Quaternary phenomena in only four provinces: the Sierra Nevada, Great Valley, Coast Ranges, and Klamath Mountains. The important marine Quaternary succession in Southern California is treated only briefly. The pluvial chronology of the desert basins in eastern California will be found in the chapter on the Quaternary Geology of the Great Basin (Morrison, this volume).

PRE-QUATERNARY GEOLOGIC HISTORY

California lies mostly in the eugeosynclinal part of the Cordilleran mobile belt. In most of the state, volcanic rocks and clastic sediments accumulated during the Paleozoic and first half of the Mesozoic, but a thick miogeosynclinal succession of carbonate rocks, quartzite, and shale accumulated along its eastern margin. In late Jurassic and early Cretaceous time (140 to 80 million years ago) the rocks of the geosyncline were intensely folded and faulted, partly metamorphosed, and intruded by enormous composite granitic batholiths, which are now exposed over most of the high mountain ranges and probably underlie much of the Great Valley. This granitic and metamorphic terrane (here called Sierran basement) constitutes one of the two major basement types whose structure and mechanical properties influenced late-Cenozoic deformation.

In Jurassic and Cretaceous time, during and after the emplacement of the batholiths, there accumulated on the sea floor immediately west of the deformed belt a great thickness of clastic sedimentary rocks. These rocks can be divided into two belts: (1) an eastern belt of relatively fossiliferous and well-bedded flysch-type sediments, 6,000-10,000 m thick along the east border of the Coast Ranges, which thins eastward and laps onto the Sierran basement; and (2) a western belt of poorly fossiliferous, irregularly bedded arkosic wacke, argillite, radiolarian chert, and greenstone, intruded by alpine-type serpentinite and ultramafic bodies. The western belt, called the Franciscan Formation, is intensely deformed and locally metamorphosed. The Franciscan Formation underlies large segments of the coastal part of California and constitutes the second of the two major basement types, which is here called Franciscan basement. Its base has never been seen (Bailey et al., 1964).

The eastern half of the state has been land continuously since the mid-Cretaceous orogeny, but the western half has at various times been partly or wholly submerged. The early Cenozoic was a time of relative quiescence. Tectonic activity increased in upper Miocene time, when several of the deep basins of Southern California were blocked out (Emery, 1960). Tectonism continued through the Pliocene, resulting in accumulations of thousands of meters of sand, silt, and gravel of marine and continental deposition in narrow basins. Near the end of the Pliocene the sea was expelled to near the present shoreline. Orogenic activity may have reached its climax in the early Quaternary, when many of the lower Pleistocene formations were folded, although the climax was reached in various parts of the state at various times within the upper Cenozoic, and some areas appear to be as tectonically active today as at any time in the past.

A system of long northwest-trending transcurrent faults, possibly dating back to the Cretaceous, has broken the coastal part of California into narrow slices and is still active. The most important fault, the San Andreas, is estimated to have a right-lateral offset of 500 km since Cretaceous time and 280 km since lower Miocene time (Hill and Dibblee, 1953; Curtis et al., 1958); geodetically measured drift of opposite sides of the fault past each other is 5 cm per year at the present time (Whitten, 1949, p. 88).

More detailed accounts of the tectonic history of California are to be found in Reed (1933), Reed and Hollister (1936), Jenkins et al. (1943), Jahns (1954), King (1958, 1959), and Bowen (1962). The papers by King are especially recommended for their comprehensive view of the place of California in the tectonic pattern and history of

* Parts of the manuscript were critically read by W. B. Bull, M. N. Christensen, M. G. Croft, Jon Galehouse, N. T. Hall, D. M. Hopkins, R. J. Janda, and P. B. King. Illustrations were drafted by John Flambert. Birman is responsible for the section on the Glacial Geology of the Sierra Nevada, Wahrhaftig for the remainder of this chapter and for all the illustrations.

[1] Department of Geology, University of California, Berkeley, California.
[2] Department of Geology, Occidental College, Los Angeles, California.

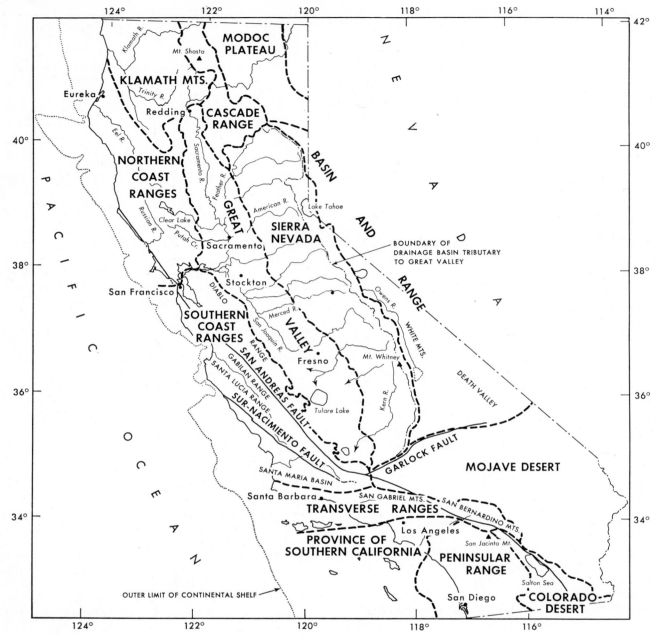

Figure 1. Physiographic provinces of California. Modified from Geomorphic Map of California by Olaf P. Jenkins, *in* Hinds, 1952, Pl. 2.

western North America. A geophysical model for central California is presented by Thompson and Talwani (1964).

PHYSIOGRAPHIC DIVISIONS

The physiographic divisions of California are shown on Figure 1. They are described in detail by Fenneman (1939) and Hinds (1952). The following brief summary is designed to acquaint the reader with the physical setting of the Quaternary deposits.

BASIN AND RANGE PROVINCE

Along its eastern margin, California includes part of the predominantly arid Basin and Range province. Narrow rugged north-trending ranges 15-18 km wide and 40-150 km long rise 900 to 3,300 m above deeply alluviated valleys 8-25 km wide. White Mountain Peak is 4,350 m above sea level, and Death Valley 90 m below. The major relief features are of fault origin, and the valleys are graben or down-dropped sides of tilted fault blocks. Fresh scarplets cutting alluvium along the range fronts indicate that faulting is still active. Drainage is almost entirely internal, and the few perennial streams that rise in the high mountains (chiefly in the Sierra Nevada west of this province) lose themselves in playas or salt lakes.

The mountains of the northern part of the province are chiefly of volcanic rocks of Pliocene and Pleistocene age, resting on a crystalline, largely granitic basement. South of the latitude of Yosemite, the mountains consist predominantly of folded and faulted miogeosynclinal Paleozoic rocks, locally intruded by granitic plutons. The playas are underlain by thick deposits of salines, including borates; similar evaporates in deformed sedimentary sequences as old as lower or middle Pliocene and possibly older (Dibblee, 1958; Drewes, 1964) indicate aridity and interior drainage well back into the Tertiary.

The southernmost part of the Basin and Range Province in California is divided into two sub-provinces: (1) the Mojave Desert, an area of low northwest-trending ranges, broad pediments, and alluviated basins, underlain chiefly by crystalline rocks; and (2) the Colorado Desert, a low-lying plain, locally below sea level, underlain by deformed Cenozoic sediments and thick alluvial fill.

MODOC PLATEAU AND CASCADE RANGE

The Modoc Plateau is an irregular basaltic plateau 1,200-1,500 m high, surmounted by numerous volcanoes that rise 300-600 m higher. It is segmented into fault blocks by numerous northwest-trending faults, whose fresh scarps are 100-500 m high. The southernmost 250 km of the Cascade Range is in California and is essentially the slightly upturned western edge of the Modoc Plateau, dominated by two great Quaternary volcanoes, Mt. Shasta, 4,300 m, on the north, which bears glaciers, and Lassen Peak, 3,200 m, on the south, which was active in 1917.

SIERRA NEVADA

The Sierra Nevada is a great westward-tilted fault block. Its eastern slope is an abrupt mountain wall rising 750 to 3,100 m at an average slope of 15%, and locally 35%, to reach crestline altitudes of 2,500-4,400 m. For long distances the eastern slope is a rugged, deeply dissected fault scarp, but in places it is a complex of faults *en echelon*, ramp structures, and monoclines. The gentle western slope descends from the crest to altitudes of 100-200 m at its foot in distances of 80 to 100 km. Streams on the west slope have cut narrow gorges 600-2,000 m deep into an upland surface that slopes gently westward in the north part and descends in a series of steps with fronts 50-750 m high in the south part.

Bedrock includes Paleozoic and Mesozoic metamorphic rocks intruded by a great complex of granitic rocks. The great Sierra Nevada batholith, a complex of many plutons, lies east of 120°00'; to the west, metamorphic rocks predominate. A superjacent cover of early Cenozoic auriferous gravels, Miocene rhyolitic ignimbrite, and Pliocene andesitic mudflows caps the upland surface of the northern Sierra Nevada. Scattered remnants of Cenozoic basalt flows, many of them Quaternary, are found in the southern part of the range. A region 55 km wide along the crest of the range was intensely glaciated.

KLAMATH MOUNTAINS

The Klamath Mountains are a very rugged mountain region in northwestern California and southwestern Oregon. Clusters of high peaks 1,800-2,700 m in altitude rise above a general level of accordant summits, which are at 900 m on

the west and 1,500-1,800 m on the east. Narrow canyon floors are less than 300-750 m above sea level even near the center of the range, giving the mountains a local relief of 900-1,500 m.

The Klamath Mountains are underlain by a central belt of ancient schist, flanked on the east by highly deformed Paleozoic sedimentary and volcanic rocks and on the west by metamorphosed Jurassic(?) rocks. Structural trends are northwest in the southern part, north at the Oregon border, and northeast in Oregon, where this terrane passes beneath the volcanics of the Cascade Mountains to reappear as an east-trending belt in northeast Oregon. Intrusive rocks include enormous ultramafic bodies and small batholiths and stocks of granitic rocks (Irwin, 1960).

NORTHERN COAST RANGES

The northern Coast Ranges are an almost continuously mountainous highland area whose summit altitudes range from 800 m in the west and south to 1,800-2,200 m in the north and east. On their east side they drop abruptly to a belt of low foothills bordering the Sacramento Valley. Bedrock is chiefly the Franciscan Formation. The eastern foothills have a valley-and-ridge topography developed on a steeply dipping homoclinal sequence of Jurassic and Cretaceous sandstone and shale. Downfaulted late-Cenozoic sediments underlie isolated basins within the mountains; they flank the southern margin of the mountains along San Francisco Bay. A large field of volcanics of Pliocene and Pleistocene age extends due south across the southern part of the range.

SOUTHERN COAST RANGES

Just north of San Francisco Bay, the northern Coast Ranges split into four or five parallel ranges separated by structural valleys. The Coast Ranges southward from San Francisco Bay are two or three parallel mountain ranges 15-50 km wide separated by structural depressions 1-15 km wide. The ranges trend slightly obliquely to the province as a whole, so that the valleys open northwestward to the sea or southeastward to the Great Valley. Except at the extreme southeast end, where several mountains reach altitudes of 2,400-2,700 m, the ranges are less than 2,000 m high, and range-crests are commonly 750-1,400 m high. Local relief is 300-600 m, but some fault scarps are 900-1,200 m high. The valleys are commonly less than 250 m above sea level. The border with the Great Valley is generally abrupt; the Santa Lucia Range has a particularly bold coastline: mountains 1,000-1,500 m high lie within 4 or 5 km of the coast.

The southern Coast Ranges are extremely complex geologically. The basement consists of granitic and metamorphic rocks of the Sierran type under a belt 40-65 km wide extending diagonally through the center of the province. This belt is flanked on both sides by basement of the Franciscan type. The San Andreas Fault bounds the Sierran terrane on the northeast, and the Sur-Naciemento zone forms its southwestern boundary. These major structural blocks are broken into many minor blocks by faults branching from the San Andreas and Sur-Naciemento Faults; the history of each block is different from that of its neighbors. Unconformities are common, with sediments alternately shed from one block to another. The major faults are probably transcurrent faults.

The northeastern part of the central granitic block (the Gabilan Range) has behaved as a single rigid structural mass, while the southwestern (Santa Lucia Range) and northwestern (Santa Cruz Range) parts have been complexly deformed, both by overthrusting and by tight folds, some with granitic cores.

The areas of Franciscan basement have been deformed by folding, and great masses of serpentine have been forced diapir-fashion through the Franciscan and upper Cretaceous sediments.

Much of the deformation of the southern Coast Ranges took place in Quaternary time, and deformed Pleistocene continental and marine sedimentary rocks are widely distributed.

GREAT VALLEY

The Great Valley is a flat alluvial plain mostly less than 300 m above sea level. It is drained by two axial streams, the south-flowing Sacramento in the north half and the northwest-flowing San Joaquin in the south half; their waters mingle in a network of channels in the delta region and enter Suisun Bay, an arm of San Francisco Bay that penetrates to the Great Valley. The connection with the Pacific Ocean is by a series of narrow straits that are the drowned canyons of a Pleistocene river. The climate of the Great Valley is semiarid and under natural conditions it was a treeless, grass-covered plain. The southern fifth of its length normally does not drain to the ocean.

TRANSVERSE RANGES

The dominantly northwesterly trends to topography and structure are abruptly broken between latitude 34° and 35° N by a narrow east-trending belt of ranges, the Transverse Ranges, whose seaward extension is apparently the Murray Fracture Zone. The western half consists of two or three ranges, 10-15 km wide and 600-1,500 m in altitude. Intervening valleys are below sea level on the west (Santa Barbara Channel) and 150-450 m high on the east. The narrow northern ranges—Santa Ynez and Topatopa Mountains—are a steep to overturned sequence of Eocene and Oligocene sandstone, shale, and conglomerate several thousands of meters thick, bounded on the north by a fault; the southern ranges—the Channel Islands and the Santa Monica Mountains—have a core of granitic rocks and slates (of Sierran basement) overlain by folded and faulted Miocene sediments and volcanics. The central trough (the Ventura Basin) has 4,000-4,500 m of marine Pliocene rocks and 1,200-1,500 m of marine Pleistocene rocks—possibly the thickest marine Pleistocene section in the world.

The eastern half of the Transverse Ranges includes two extremely rugged compact ranges, the San Gabriel and San Bernardino Mountains, each about 100 km long and 35-40 km wide, and reaching altitudes of 3,000 and 3,400 m respectively. These ranges are chiefly intrusive rocks and ancient schists, and Precambrian anorthosite is present in the San Gabriel Mountains. The ranges are horsts bounded by steep reverse faults, and the San Andreas Fault passes between them.

PENINSULAR RANGE

The Peninsular Range, south of the Transverse Ranges, is remarkably like the Sierra Nevada. It is a tilted fault block whose bedrock is a complex mid-Cretaceous granitic batholith intruding Mesozoic and Paleozoic volcanic and sedimentary rocks. Thin patches of little-deformed late-Cretaceous and early-Tertiary sedimentary rocks mantle its gentle western slope. The range extends most of the length of the peninsula of Baja California. It rises in broad, low, irregular steps from the Pacific Ocean to crest-line altitudes of 1,700-2,000 m about 55-70 km east of the coast, where it drops abruptly in a series of great desert escarpments 900-1,200 m high to the Colorado Desert.

The northern and northeastern end of the Peninsular Range is sliced diagonally by many northwest-trending strike-slip faults of the San Andreas system. Mt. San Jacinto, in the northeast corner of the province, has been uplifted a maximum height of 3,300 m, and its east face is a dissected scarp over 3,000 m high.

PROVINCE OF SOUTHERN CALIFORNIA

The northwest end of the Peninsular Range is depressed to a deep basin that has been the site of accumulation of marine and continental sediments since early-Miocene time. This triangular lowland is divided into two valleys by a transverse range of hills of folded Miocene and Pliocene sediments. The eastern valley is 150-500 m above sea level and is floored with coarse alluvium from the San Gabriel and San Bernardino Mountains. The western lowland, the Los Angeles Basin, is less than 150 m above sea level.

To the west, beneath the Pacific Ocean, is a region about 125 km wide that contains northwest-trending banks and islands separating basins 1,300-2,000 m deep. This submerged basin-and-range topography was apparently formed in Miocene time and has been slowly filling with sediment ever since—the Los Angeles Basin is merely the basin closest to shore that filled first. The islands exposed Eocene and Miocene sedimentary and volcanic rocks and a Franciscan basement.

Because this submerged region is more closely related to the continent than to the deep sea floor, above which it rises about 3,000 m, it is grouped with the Los Angeles basins and the valley to the east as the Southern California Province.

THE NON-GLACIAL QUATERNARY OF THE SIERRA NEVADA

INTRODUCTION

The study of the Quaternary of the Sierra Nevada involves three problems: (1) the amount of deformation and erosion in Quaternary time, (2) the extent of Quaternary volcanism, and (3) the number and extent of glaciations. The volcanic rocks have recently been dated by the potassium-argon method (Dalrymple, 1963, 1964a, 1964b; Evernden and Curtis, in press) and assigned to geomagnetic polarity epochs (Cox *et al.*, this volume). These dates have not only illuminated the second problem, but the first and third as well. The volcanic rocks are therefore discussed first.

The potassium-argon dates on the volcanic rocks confirm some views on the uplift and erosion of the Sierra Nevada and contradict other views. Taken by themselves, the dates might reasonably be questioned. However, the dated rocks fall into well-defined magnetic-polarity groups. The paleomagnetic data provide an independent test of the validity of the dates.

VOLCANIC ROCKS

Quaternary volcanic rocks are common on the east side of the Sierra Nevada and in the valleys immediately east of its eastern scarp. Scattered flows constitute a diffuse volcanic field extending from Truckee on the west to Virginia City on the east, lying just north of Lake Tahoe (Birkeland, 1963; Thompson and White, 1964). These flows, assigned to the Lousetown Formation, range in age in the Truckee area from 1.2 to 2.3 million years (Birkeland, 1964; Dalrymple, 1964a). They were erupted after the major topographic features had been blocked out by faulting and warping and before deposition of any of the glacial deposits to which they can be directly related. The Carson Range east of Lake Tahoe was arched in part since the earliest of these flows was erupted, and the basin of Lake Tahoe may have originated by downwarping of a segment of a graben during Lousetown time. The Sierra Nevada, however, appears to have had its present elevation above Martis Valley (in which Truckee lies) before the flows were extruded. Andesitic mudflows mantling the northern Sierra Nevada and making up much of the Carson Range, assigned to the Mehrten and Kates Peak formations (Curtis, 1954; Hudson, 1955; Thompson and White, 1960), are offset along the range fronts (through warping or faulting) by amounts comparable to the range-front scarps. Their age of 7.4 million years (Dalrymple, 1964a) establishes the major part of this deformation as post-middle Pliocene.

The region from Mono Lake on the north to Independence on the south has experienced major Quaternary volcanic activity that continued to recent times. The volcanic rocks are described by Gilbert (1938, 1941), Putnam (1949, 1960, 1962), Rinehart and Ross (1957, 1964), Bateman (1956, 1962, and in press), Knopf (1918), and Moore (1963).

Basalt flows from 2.6 to 3.2 million years old rest on surfaces of moderate relief and are now tilted and offset by faults with many meters to possibly 1,000 meters displacement (Dalrymple, 1964a; Putnam, 1960, 1962; Gilbert, 1941). A flow 2.6 million years old underlies the McGee till on McGee Mountain, the oldest till recognized in the Sierra Nevada (Blackwelder, 1931). Flows about 3 million years old form the crest of the Sierra at the head of the Middle Fork of the San Joaquin River, where they appear to fill valleys that once extended across the range from the Mono Basin into the San Joaquin drainage.

The Bishop Tuff, a rhyolitic ignimbrite that erupted from several sources within a short interval, totals 145 km³ in volume and underlies a large area east of the Sierra Nevada between Mono Lake and Bishop (Gilbert, 1938). It is about 700,000 years old (G. B. Dalrymple, oral communication, 1964; G. H. Curtis, oral communication, 1964; see also Cox *et al.*, this volume) and rests on the Sherwin Till, the second oldest of the glacial deposits recognized by Blackwelder (1931; see Putnam, 1960). The Bishop Tuff has been considerably warped and faulted since its extrusion, and the present ignimbrite sheet, 120-150 m thick, ranges in altitude from 1,100 to 2,500 m in a distance of 35 km; much of this relief is probably structural. It is confined to the valley between the Sierra Nevada and the White Mountains, and it appears to have been erupted when the range-front faults had the greater part, if not most, of their displacement. Thus it establishes that much of the faulting on the east side of the Sierra Nevada had occurred by 700,000 years ago, but that some of it was later.

Mammoth Mountain is a large quartz-latite volcano on the crest of the Sierra Nevada near the head of the Middle Fork of the San Joaquin; it is in part 370,000 years old (Dalrymple, 1964a).

Numerous basaltic cinder cones and flows lie along the base of the Sierran escarpment between Big Pine and Independence (Bateman, 1962; Moore, 1963). The flows are interbedded with outwash gravels and appear to be associated with outwash of Tahoe age. A flow in Sawmill Canyon rests on till of Sherwin(?) age and underlies Tahoe till; it has an age of 60,000-90,000 years (Dalrymple, 1964b), indicating that the Tahoe Glaciation correlates with the early Wisconsin of the mid-Continental United States.

The youngest volcanoes of the Sierra Nevada are the Mono and Inyo Craters, a line of rhyolitic-tuff rings and plug domes extending from Mono Lake to Mammoth Mountain. Two K-Ar dates on the Mono Craters (Evernden and Curtis, in press) are 56,000 years on one of the oldest sanadine-rich plugs and 5,000 years on a plug dome that erupted after the last high level of Mono Lake. More recent pumiceous ash falls mantle neoglacial moraines. Radiocarbon-dated charred wood from beneath the youngest pumice deposit from the Inyo Craters is 1,440 ± 150 years old (W-727).

Remnants of basaltic flows are widely distributed on the west side of the Sierra Nevada in the basins of the San Joaquin, Kings, and Kern Rivers. Most of these range in age from 2.9 to 3.8 million years (Dalrymple, 1962, 1964a). Several flows descend into the inner canyons of these rivers, and one, 3.5 million years old, descends to within a few hundred feet of the present canyon floor of the Kern River (Dalrymple, 1963).

A volcanic field of well-preserved cones and flows lies in upland valleys on the plateau between the Kern River and its South Fork (Webb, 1950). One of these flows descends nearly to the floor of the Kern River Canyon; several of the flows are mantled by patches of gravel thought to be glacial outwash.

DEFORMATION AND EROSION

At some time within the Cenozoic the Sierra Nevada was tilted westward, and its crest was uplifted a few thousand meters. In response to the tilting, the streams on its western slope carved deep canyons in a surface of moderate to low relief—a surface that in the northern part of the range was the constructional surface on Pliocene andesitic mudflows and in the southern part of the range was eroded on granitic and metamorphic rocks. The region east of the Sierra Nevada was depressed 1,000-3,000 m relative to the mountain crest along a series of faults and monoclinal

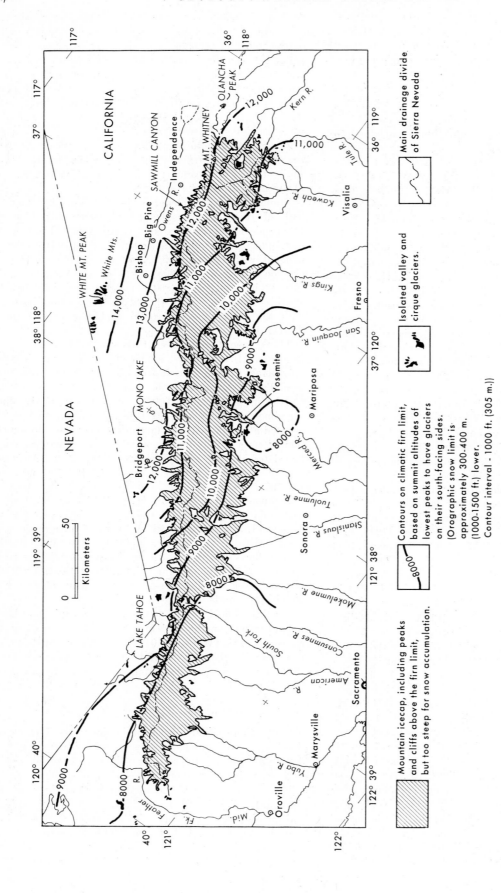

Figure 2. Wisconsin(?) glaciation and climatic firn limit in the Sierra Nevada and White Mountains. Ice limits in Truckee drainage from Birkeland (1964); in Markleeville area from Curtis (1951); on east side of Sierra Nevada between Mono Lake and Independence from Putnam (1949, 1950), Rinehart and Ross (1957, 1964), Birman (1957, 1964), Bateman (1956), Moore (1964); in Tuolumne and Merced drainages from Matthes (1930); in San Joaquin drainage from Matthes (1960) and Birman (1964). Remainder of area from study of 1:62,500 topographic maps published by the U.S. Geological Survey, supplemented in a few places by field reconnaissance and by study of distribution of morainal deposits shown on Truckee, Colfax, Pyramid Peak, and Big Trees Folios (Lindgren, 1896, 1897, 1900; Turner and Ransome, 1898).

warps. The uplift of the Sierra Nevada and the faulting along its eastern margin were not necessarily contemporaneous; potassium-argon dating of basalt flows from opposite sides of the range suggests that much of the faulting on the east side occurred after much of the tilting on the west side, as had been suspected by Matthes (1950).

Opinions as to the amount and time of uplift vary widely, as do estimates of the amount of erosion between successive phases of deformation. Lindgren (1911), Matthes (1930, 1960), and Hudson (1955, 1960) estimated uplift and tilting from restored profiles of presumably graded streams of early-Tertiary age. Lindgren and Matthes concluded that the range was tilted more or less as a block, with tilting amounting to about 13-17 m/km, and that uplift along the range crest amounted to 1,300-2,700 m. They assigned the deformation to late-Miocene and Pliocene time. Hudson concluded that the uplift since early-Tertiary time was less than 600 m in the north and less than 1,200 m near Yosemite, and that it took place after the middle Pliocene. His method of calculation led him to conclude that the range had not been tilted as a block but had deformed internally in a fairly complex manner. Recently Christensen (in press b) has evaluated the probable limits of slopes of the original graded streams, and he concluded that the uplift probably lies between 1,200 and 1,500 m in the north and 1,800 and 2,100 m in the south.

Axelrod (1957, 1962; Axelrod and Ting, 1961) has estimated the uplift of the Sierra Nevada on the basis of the climatic implications of paleofloras. In his earlier paper he estimated the uplift at the crest to be between 1,500 and 1,900 m in the Lake Tahoe region; in his later papers he argues for 1,500-2,700 m of uplift, all largely within the Pleistocene.

Matthes (1930, 1960) recognized in the central Sierra Nevada four stages of erosion: an ancient, presumably Eocene surface, almost completely destroyed; the Broad Valley stage, incised 260-500 m into the Eocene surface, and assigned to the Miocene; the Mountain Valley stage, about 180 m below the Broad Valley stage, and assigned to the Pliocene; and a stage of canyon cutting about 450 m deeper, which he placed in the early Pleistocene. Broad surfaces recognized by Lawson (1904), Knopf (1918), and Matthes (1937) in the Sequoia region are the Boreal Plateau, which is correlated with the "Eocene" surface farther north, and the Chagoopa surface, which is correlated with the Broad Valley stage. Axelrod and Ting (1961), challenging Matthes' age assignments, assign the Boreal surface to the late Pliocene and the Chagoopa surface to the early Pleistocene, with the bulk of the uplift of the Sierra Nevada occurring in mid-Pleistocene time. The evidence for this age assignment is the presence of pollen floras of strikingly modern aspect in lacustrine sediments on the remnants of the Boreal and Chagoopa surfaces.

Basalt resting on Matthes' (1960) Mountain Valley (Pliocene) valley floor of the San Joaquin River has yielded a K-Ar date of 9.5 million years (Dalrymple, 1963), which confirms Matthes' age assignment. Several flows ranging in age from 2.9 to 3.6 million years descend into canyons cut into this surface, and the 3.5-million-year flow on the Kern River shows that canyon-cutting was nearly complete by the beginning of Pleistocene time. The data of these basalt flows are not in contradiction to the paleobotanic evidence because the pollen-bearing sediments give only a minimum age for the surfaces on which they rest.

The summit flats and tributary nickpoints that were used by Matthes and others as evidence for stages of uplift and downcutting may have another origin. Wahrhaftig (1962 and in press) points out that in the granitic terrane the summit flats and valley-side benches generally do not slope westward as they should if they are remnants of westward-tilted surfaces. Furthermore, the Chagoopa surface is present only at the headwaters of the Kern River; it narrows downstream and disappears in the rugged Kern Canyon. In his view the summit flats and graded reaches between nickpoints are graded to fortuitous local base levels established by massive granitic outcrops, which are more resistant to erosion than the buried granite beneath the benches because they are dry most of the time and weather extremely slowly (*cf.* Büdel, 1957).

GLACIAL GEOLOGY OF THE SIERRA NEVADA

INTRODUCTION

The Sierra Nevada at the present time has only a few cirque glaciers on the north sides of peaks ranging in altitude from 3,400 m at 38°15′ N to 4,300 m at 37°00′ N. Climatic snow line (Flint, 1957, p. 47) is at 4,500 altitude at latitude 37° N. The climate of the Sierra Nevada, as of the rest of California, is markedly seasonal, with most of the precipitation in winter. Climate is controlled more by topography than by latitude (Dale, 1959, p. 1), and isothermal and isohyetal lines trend northwesterly, parallel to contours. The lapse rate is approximately 6° C/1,000 m (Miller, 1955, p. 14, 70). Winds throughout much of California are westerly to northwesterly, and the maritime climate along the coast gives way to more continental conditions inland.

Precipitation in the Sierra Nevada ranges from 50 to 180 cm per year, and is greater on the western slope than on the rain-shadowed eastern slope. Snowfall may amount to 11.5 m per season at some localities; maximum snowfall in the middle Sierra Nevada is at altitudes of 2,300 to 2,600 m. Snow remains for significant periods only at altitudes greater than 1,300 m, and the season's snow, which begins to fall in October, has usually disappeared except for patches at the highest altitudes by the end of July (Dale, 1959).

In the late Pleistocene a fairly continuous complex of glaciers formed along the crest of the range, with ice tongues descending both slopes. The limits of the Tahoe glaciers are best known (Fig. 2). The Tahoe and Tioga glaciers, and perhaps some of the earlier glaciers, were closely controlled by present drainage patterns and by the general topography of the range, which had already been established. Snowline was probably about 750 m lower during the glacial maxima than now. Ice was most abundant in the southern and central Sierra, between latitudes of 37° and 38° N. To the north, the lower elevation of the range resulted in smaller volume of ice; to the south, the higher temperatures kept the volume small. Because the range is asymmetrical, the larger glaciers were only 16 km long on the eastern slope and as much as 100 km long on the western slope. Ice was not a continuous cap, as the high crest of the range and many ridges and peaks were bare or at most had thin carapaces. In middle reaches of the major stream systems, large ice fields were formed where glaciers rose high enough to override divides between tributaries. Such reservoir-like masses existed in middle latitudes and middle altitudes (1,800-2,500 m). Above 2,500 m they were fed by individual glaciers; below 1,800 m they fed individual glaciers that extended several miles down main canyons. The largest of these masses were in the San Joaquin, Merced, and Tuolumne River valleys, and each had about 500 km² of surface area.

The cirques at 3,200 m on Olancha Peak (latitude 36°15′ N) are the southernmost evidence of glaciation in the Sierra (Knopf, 1918, p. 100), and the Kern River glacier reached down to 2,000 m at latitude 36°20′ (Lawson, 1904, p. 345).

In the central Sierra Nevada, main glaciers descended to altitudes of 1,300 to 2,200 m on the eastern slope (Knopf, 1918, p. 93; Blackwelder, 1931, p. 881; Putnam, 1960, p. 243; 1950, p. 116), and 600-1,200 m on the western slope (Matthes, 1930, p. 55; Birman, 1954, p. 42; 1964, p. 33). The difference is generally attributed to more abundant precipitation on the western slope.

The crest of the Sierra Nevada descends northward and is only 2,200-2,600 m high north of Lake Tahoe. Glaciers are therefore smaller to the north, and there were no great ice fields comparable to the Tuolumne ice mass from latitude 38°30′ to the north end of the range. Most glaciers in this segment did not exceed 32 km in length, and most remained above 1,500 m in altitude (Lindgren, 1896, 1900; Turner and Ransome, 1898). North of Lake Tahoe, the ice was most extensive in Truckee Valley and Bear Valley east and west of Donner Pass (Lindgren, 1907; Birkeland, 1964). Glaciers 5-8 km long formed on uplands at 2,500 m and flowed northeasterly down to 1,500 m at the headwaters of the Middle Fork of the Feather River at latitude 39°45′ N (Averill, 1937, p. 87, Pl. II; Turner, 1897). These were the northernmost large early Wisconsin glaciers in the Sierra Nevada. About 55 km farther northwest are a few small cirques with floors at 1,800 m altitude from which glaciers a few kilometers long descended to 1,600 m altitude (Turner, 1898). The northernmost evidence of Tahoe Glaciation is about 8 km north of latitude 40°, west and south of Indian Valley (McVath, 1959-1960).

HISTORY OF INVESTIGATION

Glaciation was recognized as early as 1863 by J. D. Whitney, California State Geologist, who, in a letter dated July 10, described ice polish and moraines in the Tuolumne Valley, indicating a glacier 300 m thick. In 1865, he credited Clarence King and J. T. Gardiner with recognizing abundant evidence for the existence of glacial ice in Yosemite Valley.

It was John Muir, however, who by acute observation and critical reasoning developed by 1870 an essentially modern understanding of the geomorphology of the Sierra Nevada (Colby, 1950, p. xv). In vivid writing (1872, 1874, 1880), which remains fresh and vigorous today, he em-

phasized the importance of glacial erosion in the Sierra Nevada. Believing that ice was the chief agent of erosion in Yosemite and elsewhere, he did much to direct attention to the Sierra Nevada and to the need for preservation of its wilderness. Le Conte (1873, p. 325) accepted Muir's concept of glaciation in Yosemite Valley and described glaciation at other localities in the Sierra. His was a retreat from Muir's overemphasis on glacial erosion to a concept of mere modification of existing stream valleys.

From studies between 1880 and 1883, I. C. Russell worked out the history of the Lahontan (1885a) and Mono Lake (1889) regions. He described existing glaciers in the High Sierra (1885b) and Mt. Shasta. He realized (1889, p. 326) that the present glaciers on Mt. McClure and Mt. Lyell are not shrunken remnants of the great Pleistocene glaciers but have re-formed after a period of desiccation since the last high-water stand of Lake Lahontan.

Glacial deposits were shown on the Geologic Folios of the U.S. Geological Survey (Lindgren, 1896, 1897, 1900; Turner, 1896, Turner and Ransome, 1898). Turner (1898, 1900) correctly interpreted the role of ice as modifying the stream-eroded topography of the Yosemite.

In 1904, A. C. Lawson made the first study of glaciation in the southern Sierra. He established the southernmost limits of Sierran glaciation and worked out the ice development in the upper Kern and Kaweah basins.

Between 1905 and 1907, W. D. Johnson, who had surveyed topography for Russell, recognized three definitely separable glacial advances, as indicated by two young tills and one much older till in the area between the West Walker River and Mono Lake (Blackwelder, 1931, p. 867). Johnson died before publishing the results of his reconnaissance of the eastern slope of the southern half of the Sierra Nevada.

Modern work in the Sierra began with the studies of François Matthes and Eliot Blackwelder, who worked, respectively, on the western and eastern slopes of the Sierra. Matthes was an ardent naturalist and, like Muir, was an acute and powerful observer with wide experience in recognizing past and present glacial activity. His culminating work was the *Geologic History of Yosemite Valley* (Matthes, 1930). After his Yosemite studies, in which California glacial deposits were mapped in detail for the first time, Matthes turned his attention southward to the San Joaquin and Sequoia–Kings Canyon regions. The San Joaquin studies, made in 1921, 1923, and 1927, have been published posthumously (1960); those of the Sequoia region are in press. These studies have been edited with rare skill by Fritiof Fryxell, who supplemented the observations of Matthes with his own. In all his major works Matthes recognized that Pleistocene glaciation was multiple, used the term Wisconsin, and recognized pre-Wisconsin glaciation. He first proposed the term "Little Ice Age" (1942, p. 214) for the rebirth of glaciers since the disappearance of the Wisconsin ice from the Sierra Nevada.

By 1928 Eliot Blackwelder had already recognized pre-Wisconsin glaciation on the eastern slope, and in 1929 had raised the possibility of still earlier activity. The results of his studies were presented in a series of papers from 1928 to 1932, the most important of which is his 1931 paper, in which he discussed the glacial events on the eastern slope of the Sierra and correlated them with events in the Basin Ranges and Rocky Mountains and with standard Midwestern glacial stratigraphy. He recognized the possibility of five stages (1931, p. 869) as predicted by Antevs in 1925, but his major contributions include the first use of quantitative criteria such as granite-weathering ratios and boulder-frequency counts for distinguishing separate glacial advances in California. In 1930 and 1931 he established the Tioga, Tahoe, and Sherwin glacial stages now used and applied in all modern studies. In 1932 he published the first map showing the distribution of glaciers throughout the Sierra. Blackwelder and Matthes consulted with each other but could not agree on precise correlation across the crest of the Sierra.

Later work in the Sierra Nevada was by Putnam on the eastern slope in Rock Creek (1960, 1960b), June Lake (1949), Mono Lake (1950), and McGee Mountain (1962); Sharp (1963) in the Bridgeport basin north of Mono Lake; Birman (1954, 1964) in the San Joaquin drainage on the west slope and Rock Creek on the east slope; Birkeland (1964) in the Truckee area; Thompson and White on Mt. Rose (1964); McAllister (1936) near Lake Tahoe, and Curtis (1951) near Markleeville. Work is in progress by Birkeland, by Birman in the Sequoia–Kings Canyon area, by Sharp on the east slope, and by R. J. Janda in the Middle Fork drainage of the San Joaquin River.

STRATIGRAPHY

Matthes established a threefold sequence (1930, p. 50-83):

Wisconsin (youngest)
El Portal
Glacier Point (oldest)

The Wisconsin stage was defined to include well-developed lateral moraines and closed or nearly closed recessional-moraine arcs, all of which are well preserved, bouldery, and little weathered. The El Portal stage refers to bulky lateral moraines, generally without closing arcs, recording greater extent of ice, and distinctly more weathered than the Wisconsin moraines. The Glacier Point stage refers to scattered erratic boulders on deeply weathered bedrock above the limits of the lateral moraines of the El Portal stage.

On the eastern slope of the Sierra, Eliot Blackwelder established a fourfold sequence (1931, p. 870):

Tioga (youngest)
Tahoe
Sherwin
McGee (oldest)

The Tioga and Tahoe Glaciations are assumed by most workers to represent late- and early-Wisconsin glacial activity, as they are represented by well-defined, well-preserved lateral moraines and, in the case of the Tioga, by only slightly eroded recessional-moraine arcs. This age assignment is in agreement with the potassium-argon dates reported above. Much of the original topography of the Sherwin deposits has been destroyed. The McGee Glaciation is represented by erratic boulders and weathered till perched on a mountain top high above the younger deposits.

Blackwelder and Matthes disagreed on exact correlation, and Blackwelder concluded (1931, p. 909) that: (1) the Wisconsin stage of Matthes included Tioga and Tahoe; (2) El Portal was equivalent to Sherwin; (3) the Glacier Point stage was not clearly established; and (4) there was no clear evidence for the McGee on the western slope of the range. Blackwelder correlated the Tioga and Tahoe respectively with the Pinedale and Bull Lake Glaciations of the Wind River Mountains, Wyoming, and with late Wisconsin and early Wisconsin (Iowan) of the standard Midwestern section (1931, p. 918). Sherwin and McGee were believed to represent Kansan and Nebraskan glaciations respectively, with the Illinoian not yet discovered in the Sierra. Birman (1957, 1964) and Sharp and Birman (1963) added the name Tenaya for glacial activity between Tioga and Tahoe. Birman (1957, 1964) recognized a threefold sequence, listed from oldest to youngest, Hilgard, Recess Peak, and Matthes, for post-Wisconsin events. Sharp (Sharp and Birman, 1963) introduced the term Mono Basin for a glaciation between Tahoe and Sherwin activity. The glacial sequence is summarized in Table 1.

In the Truckee area north of Lake Tahoe, Birkeland (1964) recognizes the Tioga and Tahoe Glaciations and two older, slightly more extensive glaciations, whose valley-train terraces and moraines have well-developed soils that the terraces of the Tahoe Glaciation lack. These older glaciations he calls the Donner Lake and Hobart (oldest) Glaciations. Both these glaciations are younger—probably much younger—than the Lousetown basalt flows dated at 1.3 million years.

On Mt. Rose northeast of Lake Tahoe, Thompson and White (1964) recognize Tioga and Tahoe tills. Older till they tentatively correlate with the Sherwin Glaciation.

SUMMARY OF GLACIATION

Tioga–Tenaya–Tahoe. This sequence, which is presumed to be Wisconsin, accounts for the most obvious glacial expression in the Sierra Nevada. The presumed Wisconsin age is supported by the 60,000-90,000 year K-Ar date on basalt beneath the Tahoe till in Sawmill Canyon (Dalrymple, 1964b). The probable extent of ice of this sequence is shown on Figures 2 and 3.

The deposits include well-formed and well-preserved stream-truncated lateral moraines, within which are smaller lateral moraines with complete or nearly complete recessional-moraine arcs. The younger Tioga moraines are more bouldery, less weathered, better preserved, and less eroded than the Tahoe. The Tenaya deposits are difficult to recognize without detailed mapping of the Tioga-Tahoe contact. Deposits assigned to the Tenaya have qualitative and semi-quantitative morphological and weathering characteristics intermediate between those of the Tioga and Tahoe and are not easily related to either of the latter.

In the larger canyons of the western slope, the Tahoe lateral moraines are difficult to discern because of extensive forest cover, lack of end moraines, and position of the moraine crests rather high on the valley walls. Their expression is much better in the small tributary canyons, where the Tahoe moraines are well-defined bulky ridges with few boulders on the surfaces. In general, they are the outermost and highest of the deposits that can still be recognized as having original moraine morphology.

On the Merced River, six moderately well preserved moraines at the west end of Yosemite Valley, mapped by Matthes as the Wisconsin terminals, are considered by the junior author to represent the Tenaya Glaciation. The Tioga Glaciation is represented by small but abundant and bouldery moraines on the floor of Little Yosemite Valley above Nevada Falls. At least part of the till mapped by Matthes as El Portal is believed to have been deposited during the Tahoe Glaciation.

In the San Joaquin drainage, the Tahoe glaciers extended down to about 1,100 m altitude in the main canyon. The trunk Tahoe glacier of the San Joaquin River was about 80 km long and 300 to 450 m thick; it is typical of the Tahoe glaciers in the larger canyons on the western slope of the central Sierra Nevada. Tenaya and Tioga deposits in this drainage are abundant down to altitudes of about 2,300 m. One of the best expressed of the Tenaya and Tioga complexes is in the vicinity of Lake Thomas A. Edison

Dam on Mono Creek, a tributary of the South Fork of the San Joaquin River. The moraines are small, easily identified, and very bouldery. Most of the Tenaya and Tioga glaciers were about 16 to 32 km long.

The floor of the Kings Canyon contains several rather obscure moraine arcs that are believed at this time to be Tenaya. Tioga ice was confined to the higher parts of the canyons. All three glaciations reached the Lodgepole area of Sequoia National Park in the upper drainage of the Kaweah River. The famous Giant Forest area of Sequoia National Park does not appear to have been glaciated, for it lies just outside the outer limits of Tahoe Glaciation, and in this area there is no evidence of pre-Tahoe glaciation.

Although the Tenaya and Tioga moraines are the most easily discerned on the western slope, it is the Tahoe moraines that are best expressed, especially as seen from a distance of several kilometers, on the eastern slope. Most of the canyons from the vicinity of Lone Pine at least as far north as Lake Tahoe contain well-preserved lateral and

TABLE 1

Description of Glacial Deposits, Sierra Nevada

Glaciation	Types of deposit	Age criteria
Matthes (youngest)	Cliff glacierets, perennial snowfields, rock glaciers; in headwalls of high cirques.	Slopes unstable; boulders free of lichens; interstitial ice; no soil.
Recess Peak	Recessional moraine arcs and short lateral moraines. Scattered boulders on bare bedrock, in cirques and cirque valleys.	Slopes stable, but all boulders very fresh. Lichens on boulders; a little interstitial soil. Glacial polish unusually abundant.
Hilgard	Recessional-moraine arcs and short lateral moraines. Scattered boulders on bare bedrock.	About 70% of moraine boulders are weathered. Polish on weathered materials. Virtually no modification by postglacial erosion; terminal arcs complete.
Tioga	Lateral moraines about 300 m high in larger valleys. End moraines 1.5-5 m high. Thin ground moraines. Scattered erratics on bedrock.	End moraines abundant. Dark inclusions, and aplite and pegmatite dikes protrude only slightly from bedrock or not at all. About 30% of boulders are weathered. Till surfaces very bouldery. Dissection of moraines negligible except by main streams.
Tenaya	Lateral moraines about 300 m high in larger valleys. Rare end moraines 8-15 m high. Ground moraine and glaciofluvial deposits. Scattered erratics on bedrock.	End moraines largely destroyed. Glacial polish still present on aplite and pegmatite dike surfaces and on dense fine-grained lava. Mafic inclusions and aplite and pegmatite dikes protrude slightly or not at all. About 50% of boulders are weathered. Till surfaces moderately bouldery. Moraines dissected by gullies 3-12 m deep.
Tahoe	Lateral moraines 450-600 m high in larger valleys. Ground moraine of gentle relief. Scattered erratics on bedrock.	Glacial polish found only on recently uncovered bedrock. Weathering pits and pans rare and shallow. Rock pedestals are rarely over 2 cm high. Mafic inclusions and aplite and pegmatite dikes protrude as much as 7 cm. About 70% of boulders are weathered. Till surface is not markedly bouldery. Moraines dissected by gullies 3-20 m deep.
Mono Basin	Well-formed lateral-moraine segments truncated by Tahoe moraines in Walker Creek and other canyons of the eastern slope of the Sierra Nevada. Glaciation apparently less extensive than Tahoe glaciation.	Original morphology better preserved than on Sherwin deposits, but only 5% of boulders are unweathered. Truncated by Tahoe glacial deposits. More clearly related to present drainages than Sherwin glacial deposits.
Sherwin	Bulky morainal masses with initial forms largely destroyed and obscured by surface wash. Scattered erratics on bedrock.	Bedrock weathered to 20 cm below surface. Weathering pits and pans as much as 20 cm deep. Rock pedestals as much as 1.5 m high. Mafic inclusions protrude 15-20 cm above surrounding bedrock. 85-100% boulders weathered.
McGee	Erratic boulders with little or no till matrix. Outside and above the deposits of the younger glaciations.	Extensive weathering of boulders and bedrock surfaces, absence of till matrix, and occurrence on high and rather isolated ridge crests, not related to present drainages.

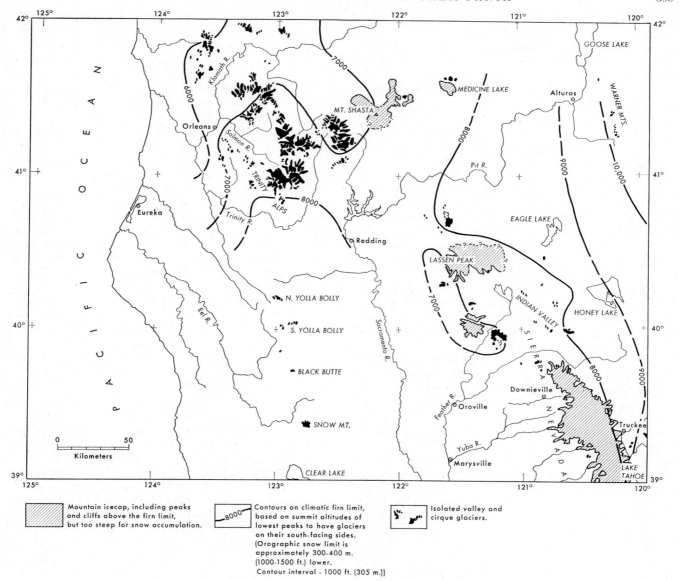

Figure 3. Wisconsin(?) glaciation and climatic firn limit in California north of latitude 39°00′. Ice limits in Truckee area are from Birkeland (1964); in Medicine Lake area from Anderson (1941); Mt. Shasta area from Williams (1949); Trinity Alps in part from Sharp (1960); northern Coast Ranges from Davis (1958). Remainder from study of 1:62,500 topographic maps published by the U.S. Geological Survey, supplemented by study of distribution of morainal deposits shown on Lassen Peak, Bidwell Bar, Downieville, and Colfax Folios (Diller, 1895; Turner, 1897 and 1898; Lindgren, 1900) and "Geologic map of Manzanita Lake Quadrangle" (MacDonald, 1963).

end moraines with associated outwash of the Tioga, Tenaya, and Tahoe Glaciations. Most of the glaciers extended beyond the mouths of the canyons and built spectacular protruding morainal embankments. The general pattern is that of large lateral moraines with truncated ends, within and against the inner sides of which are smaller lateral moraines. The innermost moraines continue across the valley as complete or nearly complete moraine arcs. The outermost and largest of the moraines are Tahoe; the innermost with nearly complete recessional arcs are Tioga.

The Tenaya moraines are mostly truncated but are distinctly more bouldery than the Tahoe and less bouldery than the Tenaya. The truncated or partially truncated curving ends of the Tenaya moraines merge upvalley into a rather distinct lateral-moraine crest intermediate between the Tioga and Tahoe crests.

Pre-Tahoe glaciation. The recent work of Sharp (Sharp and Birman, 1963) has identified the Mono Basin Glaciation in the lower part of Bloody Canyon (type locality) south of Mono Lake and in the Bridgeport Basin north of Mono Lake. In the Bloody Canyon locality the Mono Basin Glaciation is expressed by two well-preserved lateral moraines which have been cut off upcanyon by the Tahoe lateral moraines. It is possible that some of the glacial deposits mapped as Sherwin on the western slope may be Mono Basin. Moreover, at the Sherwin type locality in lower Rock Creek on the eastern slope (Blackwelder, 1931, p. 895) some of the fresher till within materials mapped as Sherwin may be of Mono Basin age.

The Sherwin deposits at their type locality on lower Rock Creek on the eastern slope of the Sierra are massive till with little original morphology. The till is hummocky but by no means as bouldery as the younger Tahoe till, and till masses cannot be easily recognized from a distance. In many exposures the boulders are sufficiently weathered to be cut as easily as the enclosing matrix. At the type locality the Sherwin till is overlain by the Bishop Tuff, which has been dated at 700,000 years (see above).

On the western slope, the Sherwin deposits are even more difficult to recognize, because of heavy forest cover. Till is difficult to distinguish from slopewash along the canyon walls and can be identified and mapped only after detailed search for distinctive foreign boulders.

The Sherwin deposits are best known from the central Sierra. They are obscure or absent from the northern and southern ends of the range. The Sherwin Glaciation does not appear to have been much more extensive than the Tahoe Glaciation. Sherwin till has not yet been clearly identified as far south as the Kaweah River. It is not yet known whether there was Sherwin ice in the southern tributaries of the Kings River.

The oldest glacial deposits recognized in California are assigned to the McGee Stage (Blackwelder, 1931, p. 902; Putnam, 1960, 1962). The McGee till consists of extensively weathered granitic materials on metamorphic bedrock and on basalt 2.6 million years old (see above). Boulders on the surface of the till at the type locality are solid, but they have been eroded by sandblasting and weathering, so that mafic inclusions stand in relief. Glacial striae are preserved on their under surfaces immediately below the ground surface. The remnant moraines lie on the tops of divides that could not be reached by glaciers in the present canyons. As Putnam (1960, p. 272) points out, the McGee till at the type locality rests on a broad upland 3,000 m in altitude; he estimates at least 1,200 m of displacement on the eastern fault system of the Sierra Nevada since the McGee Glaciation. No McGee till has yet been recognized on the western slope of the Sierra Nevada.

Post-Tioga glaciation. The Little Ice Age of Matthes (1939, p. 520; 1942, p. 190) appears to be represented in the High Sierra by at least three pulses of glacial activity since the disappearance of the Tioga glaciers. The following comments present the viewpoint of the junior author (Birman, 1954, p. 41; 1964, p. 45) and do not necessarily reflect the opinions of other workers in the Sierra Nevada.

The post-Tioga deposits are restricted to the crestal zone of the Sierra at altitudes above 2,700 m from approximately Mt. Whitney on the south to beyond Sonora Pass on the north. This area has an unusually high frequency of lakes and is characterized by extensively polished bare granitic bedrock, with little cover. All of the post-Tioga glaciations extended from cirques formed by Tioga and earlier ice activity. The oldest of the post-Tioga glaciations is referred to a rock-cut trim-line that is everywhere below and separate from the Tioga rock-cut trimline. It is possible that all of the post-Tioga glaciation is also post-Altithermal.

The oldest deposits referable to this group, assigned to the Hilgard Glaciation, consist of well-preserved moraines, at most a few miles from cirque headwalls. The Hilgard moraines contain a surprisingly high percentage of weathered boulders. The content of weathered boulders is attributed to quick removal and deposition of material weathered in post-Tioga, pre-Hilgard time. The Recess Peak ice advance, the second glaciation of this group, is represented by moraines upvalley from the Hilgard moraines, extensively polished bedrock, and at least 90% fresh boulders in the moraines. The Matthes Glaciation, the youngest, is represented by existing cliff glacierets, protalus ramparts, rock glaciers, and moraines that are still so unstable that no soil has yet accumulated in the interstices between boulders, nor are there any lichens on boulder surfaces.

THE QUATERNARY ALLUVIUM OF THE GREAT VALLEY

HISTORY OF INVESTIGATION

The Great Valley of California is one of the major agricultural and petroleum-producing regions of the United States. As there is no rain during the growing season, agricultural development of its fertile alluvial soils requires large volumes of irrigation water, much of which comes from underground reservoirs in the Quaternary alluvium. Decreasing soil fertility with increasing age of the alluvium results in striking similarities between the pattern of land use and the outcrop distribution of the alluvial formations. Petroleum and natural gas, although not of Quaternary age, accumulated in structural traps involving deformed Quaternary formations. Hence the structure and stratigraphy of the Quaternary alluvium has been investigated by the ground-water geologist, the soil scientist, and the petroleum geologist.

During the first 25 years of this century reconnaissance studies of the ground-water possibilities of the San Joaquin Valley (Mendenhall *et al.* 1914) and the Sacramento Valley (Bryan, 1923) were made; deformed Quaternary sediments along the southwest margin of the San Joaquin Valley were mapped (Arnold and Anderson, 1910; Arnold and Johnson, 1910; Anderson and Pack, 1915); and reconnaissance soil surveys established the major soil series (Holmes, Nelson *et al.*, 1915; Nelson *et al.*, 1921). Gilbert (1914, 1917) at this time conducted his classic studies of the transport of sediment by streams in order to measure the effect of hydraulic mining in the Sierra Nevada on silting of agricultural land in the Great Valley.

Subsequently, detailed studies of the ground-water geology of the Mokelumne and Turlock areas (Piper *et al.*, 1939; Davis and Hall, 1959), of the deformed alluvium along the southwest margin of the valley (Hoots, 1929, Woodring *et al.*, 1932, 1940), and of the Plio-Pleistocene deposits of the Sacramento Valley (Anderson and Russell, 1939) established many of the Quaternary formations now recognized. Toward the end of the 1930's the U.S. Bureau of Reclamation started its investigations connected with the Central Valley Water Project. The continuing work of this agency, although largely unpublished, has greatly influenced the thinking of other geologists working in the Quaternary of the Great Valley.

The present phase of investigation (1940 to the present) is related to the enormous development of surface- and ground-water resources through the Central Valley and California Water Projects, and to modern soil surveys conducted by the U.S. Department of Agriculture in cooperation with the University of California.

STRUCTURE AND GEOMORPHOLOGY

The Great Valley is an elongate basin of deposition that has been accumulating sediments since mid-Cretaceous time. These sediments are nearly flat-lying beneath the valley and wedge out eastward against the crystalline basement of the Sierra Nevada (Fig. 4); along the western margin of the valley they are bent abruptly upward in a steeply dipping homoclinal sequence as much as 12,000 m thick. The Quaternary alluvium is the uppermost 30-1,000 m of these sediments.

Five belts of distinctive geomorphology extend the length of the valley and reflect the origin and history of the alluvial sediments (Fig. 5). Along the east and west margins are two discontinuous belts of rolling hill-land, reaching altitudes of 100-300 m and local relief of 30 m, carved on older generally oxidized alluvium, which has been slightly uplifted.

Valleyward from the dissected uplands are two belts of coalescing alluvial fans. The present constructional surfaces of the alluvial fans on the east side date from the last glaciation, and the rivers that built them now cross them in flat-floored trenches 0.5-1 km wide and as much as 90 m deep. The alluvial fans on the west side are still being aggraded. Perennial streams from the northern Coast Ranges cross the fans in raised courses contained between low, flat natural levees. Abandoned stream courses radiating from the heads of the fans are marked by barely perceptible double ridges called channel ridges (Bryan, 1923, p. 28). Drainage from the southern Coast Ranges is largely ephemeral, and the alluvium has accumulated in large part as mudflow deposits; natural levees are lacking along the poorly defined stream courses. In the past 100 years the heads of many of the fans from the southern Coast Ranges have been trenched (Bull, 1964a).

The axial part of the Great Valley is a belt of riverine lands and flood basins. The axial streams that drain the valley (the Sacramento, lower Feather, and San Joaquin Rivers) flow in meandering or braided channels with natural levees 0.5-6 km wide having crests 1-5 m above the floors of flood basins on either side. These flood basins are areas of flat land 10-15 km wide, with dark gray clayey alkaline soils, formerly covered during spring floods by water held in by the natural levees of the axial streams and their tributaries.

The southern fifth of the valley does not normally drain to the sea. A chain of broad, flat lake basins, formerly covered by a few meters of water in spring and winter, lies along its axis. The water that formerly reached these

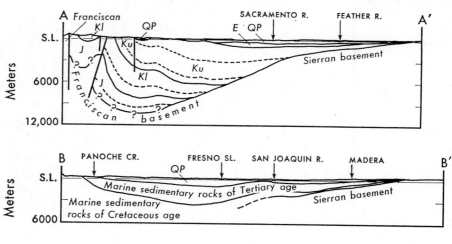

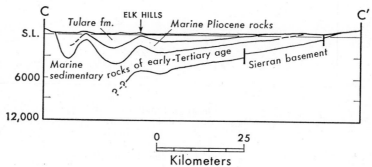

Figure 4. Three cross-sections of the Great Valley of California, showing the thickness of the pre-Quaternary and Quaternary sediments. Section A-A' from Safonov (1962, Fig. 4); Sections B-B' and C-C' from Davis *et al.* (1959, Pl. 2). For location see Figure 5.

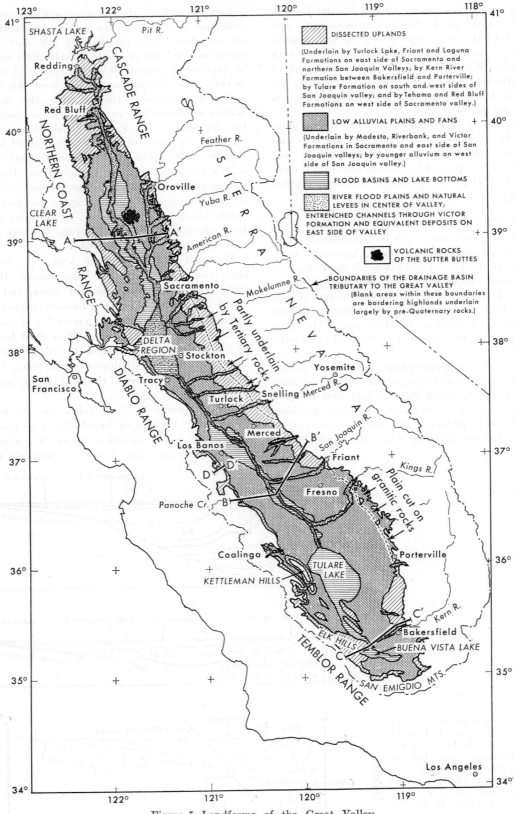

Figure 5. Landforms of the Great Valley
of California. Compiled with
slight modification from Davis
et al. (1959, Pl. 1) and Olmsted
and Davis (1961, Pl. 1).

basins is now used for irrigation throughout the southern part of the Great Valley.

Beneath the northern half of the Great Valley (the Sacramento Valley) the bulk of the sedimentary fill consists of marine Cretaceous rocks that reach a thickness of 12,000 m in the great homocline along the west side of the valley. Unconformably overlying the Cretaceous rocks, but present only in the southern half of the Sacramento Valley, are less than 2,500 m of lower Tertiary sedimentary rocks (Olmsted and Davis, 1961, p. 37; Lachenbruch, 1962; Safanov, 1962). Continental sediments of late-Pliocene and Pleistocene age, in part volcanic, rest unconformably across the truncated edges of all older rocks (Anderson and Russell, 1939; Olmsted and Davis, 1961). Thus the Sacramento Valley was above sea level during much of Cenozoic time, and it underwent erosion during at least part of the Pliocene.

The Sutter Buttes (formerly called Marysville Buttes), a cluster of fantastically eroded peaks 450-650 m high, rise from the flat center of the Sacramento Valley. The buttes are endogenous andesite domes surrounded partly by an apron of andesitic mudflows about 16 km in diameter, all of early-Pleistocene age (Williams, 1929; Johnson, 1943; Garrison, 1962). Potassium-argon dates on associated rhyolitic intrusions range from 1.5 to 1.9 million years (Evernden *et al.*, 1964).

The southern half of the Great Valley (the San Joaquin Valley) is underlain not only by Cretaceous sedimentary rocks but by a great thickness of Cenozoic rocks as well. The base of the Tertiary succession is 4,300 m below sea level in the central part of the San Joaquin Valley and nearly 5,500 m below sea level at its southern end (Cohee *et al.*, 1961). The Tertiary sequence is predominantly marine on the west side and interfingers eastward beneath the valley with non-marine sands derived from the Sierra Nevada (Church *et al.*, 1957a, b). During the Miocene and early Pliocene an archipelago lay between the San Joaquin Valley and the Pacific Ocean, and the main connection with the sea was at the southwest end of the valley (Hoots *et al.*, 1954). In late-Pliocene or early-Pleistocene time this connection was broken by the rise of the southern Coast Ranges, the sea was excluded, and drainage was redirected northward through the Golden Gate. Since this event, a total of 4,500 m of continental strata has accumulated in the south end of the valley. There is generally no break recognizable in surface or subsurface at the Plio-Pleistocene boundary.

From the vicinity of Coalinga south a series of anticlines plunge southeastward from the Coast Ranges and die out beneath the valley. Movement on these folds involved Pleistocene alluvium, and the surfaces subsequently planed across the folded alluvium have themselves been warped.

A 140-km segment of the east side of the San Joaquin Valley between Friant and Porterville lacks the dissected hill-land on old alluvium. Instead, the flat valley floor extends eastward from the edge of the alluvium for a 4-20 km as a smooth plain developed on weathered granite, and flat-floored embayments extend from this plain into the foothills of the Sierra Nevada, which rise abruptly above this plain in cliffs and bluffs several hundred meters high (Wahrhaftig, in press).

ALLUVIAL FORMATIONS OF THE NORTHEAST SAN JOAQUIN VALLEY

The alluvial sequence of Davis and Hall (1959) in the northeastern San Joaquin Valley near Turlock gives the greatest hope for correlation with the glacial sequence in the Sierra Nevada (Arkley, 1962a, b). Table 2 is a tentative correlation chart of these formations with others in the Great Valley. At the present state of knowledge, a synthesis, except on the most general terms, is premature.

In the Turlock area, the Quaternary formations along the major rivers consist of well-sorted alluvium derived primarily from granitic sources high in the Sierra Nevada. Each formation contains bodies of laminated silt composed of unweathered fragments of feldspar, biotite, hornblende, and quartz, along with bodies of medium to coarse granitic sand, locally pebbly. Each formation was dissected, and a soil developed on the dissected surface, before the deposition of the next formation. Toward the mountains the younger formations are inset into the older formations as terrace deposits lining the trenches cut by the rivers; valleyward, the terraces lap over the trench walls, and the younger formations spread out as coalescing alluvial fans, so that near the axis of the valley the formations lie in normal stratigraphic succession. In the axial part of the valley, deposition may have been continuous, and in this area it is not generally possible to identify the formations in well records. The alluvial formations along the major rivers are thought to be the finest-grained component of outwash from Pleistocene glaciers carried to the valley by melt-water from the Sierra Nevada, because of the predominance in the silts of unweathered particles of hornblende, biotite, and feldspar (R. J. Arkley, oral communication, 1962).

The three alluvial formations recognized by Davis and Hall are the Turlock Lake (oldest), Riverbank, and Modesto (youngest). The Turlock Lake is as much as 240 m thick in the center of the valley and is exposed at the surface throughout much of the dissected upland on the east border of the valley, where local relief is as much as 30 m. It characteristically has either a well-developed soil with a brown acid A-horizon 0.6-0.7 m thick overlying a 1-m-thick reddish-brown clayey B-horizon (Montpelier series) or an eroded soil with a thin A-horizon over an iron-silica hardpan B (Rocklin series). Within the Turlock Lake Formation, wells have encountered a prominent red clayey zone with iron-silica cement, probably a buried soil (Arkley, 1962a). A diatomaceous silty clay correlated with the Corcoran Clay of Frink and Kues (1954—see below) lies in the upper part of the Turlock Lake Formation, according to Arkley.

After the erosion and weathering of the Turlock Lake Formation, the Riverbank Formation was deposited in valleys cut in the older formation. The Riverbank underlies high terraces and slightly dissected alluvial-fan surfaces and has a maximum thickness of 60 m. Well-developed soils with brown or reddish-brown clayey B-horizon and a reddish-brown iron-silica hardpan 0.15-0.4 m thick (the San Joaquin and Snelling series) are developed on the Riverbank Formation.

The youngest formation, the Modesto, underlies the essentially undissected alluvial fans and has a maximum thick-

TABLE 2

Correlation of Formations in the Great Valley

	Sacramento Valley (Olmsted and Davis, 1961)		Mokelumne Area (Piper *et al.*, 1939)	Turlock Area (Davis and Hall, 1959; Arkley, 1961)	Subsurface, San Joaquin Valley (Davis *et al.*, 1959)	Southwest side, San Joaquin Valley (Various authors)
	West side	East side				
Recent	Alluvium and Fan deposits	River deposits	Alluvium	Alluvium	Alluvium and basin deposits	Alluvium
Late Pleistocene	Deeper parts of alluvial fans	Victor Formation	Victor Formation	Modesto Formation		Deformed alluvium
Early Pleistocene				Riverbank Formation	(Tulare Formation)	
Early Pleistocene	Red Bluff Formation	Arroyo Seco Gravel	Arroyo Seco Gravel	? ? Turlock Lake Formation ?	Ash at Friant Corcoran Clay Member	Tulare Formation
Pliocene? and Pleistocene?		Laguna Formation	Laguna Formation	? ? ?	Alluvial deposits	
Pliocene? and Pleistocene?	Tehama Formation	Tuscan Formation		China Hat Pediment		Lower Amnicola Zone
Pliocene? and Pleistocene?	Nomlaki Tuff Member					San Joaquin Formation
Pliocene	Neroly equivalents		Mehrten Formation	Mehrten Formation		Etchegoin Formation

ness of 30 m. The most typical soil developed on it, the Hanford series, shows only a weak humic A-horizon and no textural B-horizon. Recent alluvium mantles the floors of trenches cut into the alluvial-fan surfaces of the Modesto Formation by the rivers from the Sierra Nevada.

The Quaternary alluvial formations rests on andesitic mud-flows and volcanic conglomerate of the Mehrten Formation, which ranges in age up to late Pliocene (Hemphillian) (Piper *et al.*, 1939, p. 61; VanderHoof, 1933; Dalrymple, 1963, p. 380). Immediately south of the Merced River near Snelling, gravel consisting largely of resistant metamorphic cobbles from the foothills of the Sierra Nevada caps a high pediment, the China Hat Pediment, cut on the Mehrten Formation, that forms the flat tops of low ridges extending several miles west into the San Joaquin Valley. The gravel is above the highest remnants of the Turlock Lake Formation and slopes more steeply westward; it is therefore older than the alluvial formations (Hudson, 1960; Arkley, 1962a), and it indicates a period of extensive erosion between the deposition of the Mehrten and the Turlock Lake Formations. The gravel has a red strongly acid soil with a 45-90 cm A-horizon of gravelly loam underlain by an iron-silica hardpan 20-60 cm thick (the Redding series); more than

10 m of weathered gravel stained with iron oxide lies beneath the soil.

THE TULARE FORMATION

Along the southwestern and southern border of the San Joaquin Valley a thick series of poorly consolidated sand, silt, clay, and gravel (with a maximum exposed thickness of nearly 1,000 m) conformably overlies the youngest marine Pliocene rocks. This sequence was named the Tulare Formation by Anderson (1905) and has been traced northward from its type section in the Kettleman Hills to Tracy and southward to Tejon Pass (Anderson and Pack, 1915; Arnold and Anderson, 1910; Hoots, 1929; Woodring *et al.*, 1932; Woodring *et al.*, 1940, with summary).

The bottom 20-50 m of the type section is predominantly clay and fine sand, at the top of which is the Lower Amnicola Zone, a fossiliferous and ferruginous sandstone, with beds of water-laid tuff, containing abundant freshwater mollusks and diatoms. Overlying the Lower Amnicola Zone is as much as 900 m of poorly consolidated and poorly sorted lenticular sandstone and conglomerate interbedded with layers of silt and clay, the whole bearing a striking resemblance to the alluvial-fan deposits accumulating along the flanks of the Coast Range today. The source of these sediments was in the Coast Ranges west of the Kettleman Hills.

In the Elk Hills farther south, Woodring *et al.* (1932) assigned the uppermost 900 m of the folded sediments to the Tulare Formation. At the south end of the valley, Hoots (1930) mapped 300-1,500 m of gravel, sand, and clay resting conformably on marine Etchegoin (Pliocene), which he assigned to the Tulare. The prominent pebbles in the gravels are of granitic rocks from the core of the San Emigdio Mountains immediately to the south. The Tulare here has been overthrust by Miocene rocks from the south and is involved in folds overturned to the north; tilted younger Pleistocene alluvial-fan deposits, dipping as much as 45° N, rest on the truncated beds of the Tulare Formation, which have been overturned to dip 25° south.

Throughout the southern part of the San Joaquin Valley the Tulare appears to be conformable on the underlying marine upper Pliocene, and is folded with it in the Kettleman Hills and Elk Hills anticlines. Northward from Panoche Creek, however (Fig. 7), it rests unconformably on all older formations (Anderson and Pack, 1915, p. 101; Reiche, 1950, p. 6; Briggs, 1953, p. 48). Within the foothills, patches of nearly flat-lying Tulare rest on a surface of low relief bevelled across steeply dipping older rocks; they are folded into dome-like structures with dips of 5°-15° on their flanks and amplitudes of 300-450 m (Christensen, in press a). Along the front of the foothills, the Tulare dips eastward 30°-50° parallel to the bedding in the older formations, in a sharp monocline that flattens abruptly eastward beneath the alluvium of the Great Valley (Fig. 6). In the range-front Monocline the Tulare Formation is 180-700 m thick and includes the Corcoran Clay member, described below (Carpenter and Long, 1963).

QUATERNARY DEPOSITS BENEATH THE FLOOR OF THE SAN JOAQUIN VALLEY

The Quaternary deposits beneath the valley range in thickness from a few meters on the east edge of the valley to 700-1,500 m along the valley axis. As much as 5,000 m of alluvium is reported to overlie upper Pliocene marine sediments beneath Buena Vista Lake at the south end of the valley (Davis *et al.*, 1959, quoting De Laveaga, 1952).

The alluvium has been investigated in detail by the U.S. Bureau of Reclamation and the U.S. Geological Survey by means of electric logs, drillers' logs, and a large number of continuous rotary-drill cores of the alluvial deposits. The results of these investigations are summarized in Davis *et al.* (1959). The alluvium on the east side of the valley was deposited by rivers from the Sierra Nevada and generally consists of well-sorted clean sand and sandy gravel. Numerous layers of red sand and silt associated with iron-silica hardpans, thought to be soil zones, have been encountered in this alluvium. The alluvium grows finer westward and grades into sections of silt and clay, in which recognizable soil zones are lacking. Alluvium in the western part of the valley is mainly poorly sorted silt and silty sand and gravel derived from the Coast Ranges and deposited by ephemeral streams or as mudflows.

The Corcoran Clay Member of the Tulare Formation, a diatomaceous silty-clay layer 3-50 m thick, underlies an area of about 13,000 km² in the San Joaquin Valley, at a depth of 60-270 m beneath the surface (Frink and Kues, 1954; Davis *et al.*, 1959, p. 76). Along the east front of the Coast Ranges, the Corcoran Clay Member crops out west of Tracy (Reiche, 1953) and south of Los Banos (Long and Carpenter, 1963). At both outcrops, the Corcoran Clay Member is interbedded in alluvium of the Tulare Formation and is therefore a member of that formation.

North of the Kings River the alluvium above the Corcoran Clay Member is generally yellow or brown as a result of oxidation of some of its iron, but south of the Kings River the fine-grained alluvium beneath the center of the Valley is blue or gray, and its iron is in the ferrous state. Most of the alluvium beneath the Corcoran Clay Member throughout the valley has its iron in the ferrous state. The ferrous-iron-bearing alluvium is thought to have been deposited under marshy or lacustrine conditions, and the brown oxidized alluvium to have been deposited on the surfaces of well-drained alluvial fans (Davis *et al.*, 1959). Thus the San Joaquin Valley before Corcoran Clay Member time was predominantly marshy, and afterward marshy conditions persisted only along the valley axis and at the southern end.

The present rate of alluviation on the Arroyo Ciervo fan, about 20 km south of Panoche Creek on the west side of the San Joaquin Valley, on the basis of data of Bull (1964b, p. 36), is approximately 0.45 m per 1,000 years. The Corcoran Clay Member beneath this fan is overlain by approximately 200 m of alluvium.

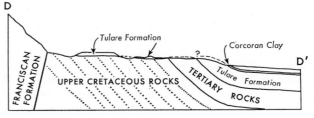

Figure 6. Diagrammatic cross-section of the eastern margin of the foothills of the Coast Ranges south of Los Banos, showing relation of Tulare Formation and Corcoran Clay to underlying rocks. Compiled from Long and Carpenter (1963) and Briggs (1953, Pl. 3). For location see Figure 5.

AGE OF THE TULARE FORMATION

The age of the Tulare Formation and the Corcoran Clay Member has been a matter of debate. Arnold and Anderson (1910, p. 153) thought that the Tulare represented a time-span from lower Pliocene to Pleistocene. Barbat and Galloway (1934) assigned the marine San Joaquin Formation beneath the Tulare to the lower Pleistocene, on the basis of the appearance of cold-water fossils in the top of the underlying Etchegoin Formation, thus placing the Tulare definitely in the Pleistocene, as it overlies the San Joaquin at its type locality. Woodring *et al.* (1940) placed the lower part of the Tulare in the Pliocene on the basis of a large number of extinct freshwater mollusks in the Lower

Amnicola Zone, and they considered the upper part of the formation to extend into the Pleistocene. K. E. Lohman (quoted by Frink and Kues, 1954, p. 2364, and by Davis *et al.*, 1959, p. 77) placed both the Corcoran Clay Member and the lower Tulare in the Pliocene because of the number of extinct diatoms that had not been reported from formations younger than Pliocene.

Durham *et al.* (1954, p. 69) report a Blancan fauna, including *Equus (Plesippus)*, *Castor*, *Odocoileus*, and *Pliomastodon*, from the San Joaquin Formation, and they point out that correlation of the Blancan with the Villefranchian places the San Joaquin in the Pleistocene according to the definition of the 1948 International Geological Congress. (However, see Hibbard *et al.*, this volume, for another view.) In 1964, Charles Hall of the U.S. Bureau of Reclamation discovered vertebrate remains in a canal excavation in the Corcoran Clay Member about 20 km south of Los Banos. According to John Mawby (oral communication, 1964) this fauna includes remains of *Equus*, a camel, and mammoth that place it in the Irvingtonian (middle Pleistocene) or Rancholabrean (upper Pleistocene), and therefore the Corcoran Clay Member is Pleistocene.

Correlatives of the alluvial formations in the Turlock area have been identified along the San Joaquin River near Fresno by R. J. Janda (oral communication, 1963). A deposit of water-laid pumiceous ash at Friant was found by Janda to lie near the top of alluvial deposits correlated by him with the Turlock Lake Formation. A potassium-argon date on this ash by G. B. Dalrymple (oral communication, 1963) of $600,000 \pm 20,000$ years establishes the lower Pleistocene age of the Turlock Lake Formation. Janda traced the ash westward along bluffs of the San Joaquin River and found it to coincide in position with an ash recognized by Frink and Kues (1954) lying directly above the Corcoran Clay Member. Thus the Corcoran is about 600,000 years old, an age in agreement with its vertebrate fossils, and in approximate agreement with current rate of accumulation of alluvium on the west side of the San Joaquin Valley.

ALLUVIAL FORMATIONS EAST OF THE DELTA REGION

The geology and ground-water resources of the area lying immediately east of the Delta region were investigated by Piper *et al.* (1939) (see Fig. 5 for location). They divided the late-Cenozoic deposits into the following formations, from youngest to oldest:

1. Alluvium beneath the present stream channels and beneath floodplains entrenched into the youngest alluvial fans, regarded as Recent in age.
2. The Victor Formation, as much as 38 m thick, consisting of sand, silt, and gravel, which underlies the youngest alluvial fans of the Mokelumne and Cosumnes Rivers.
3. The Arroyo Seco Gravel, up to 6 m thick, a pediment gravel mantling the dissected Arroyo Seco pediment along the west base of the Sierra Nevada.
4. The Laguna Formation, 120 m of poorly bedded stream-borne silt and sand with some gravel and clay, of presumed Pliocene age but possibly early Pleistocene in part, and unconformably underlying the Arroyo Seco Gravel.

5. The Mehrten Formation, andesitic conglomerate and mudflows of Pliocene and Miocene age.

Davis and Hall (1959, p. 12) correlate their Modesto and Riverbank Formations with the Victor Formation, and their Turlock Lake Formation with the Laguna. They do not find the Arroyo Seco Gravel in the region south of the Mokelumne River.

THE ALLUVIAL FORMATIONS OF THE SACRAMENTO VALLEY

Lindgren (1894) and Lindgren and Turner (1895) recognized dissected Pleistocene gravels with red hardpan soils that they correlated with glaciation in the Sierra Nevada, and undissected alluvium beneath stream channels and the central basin lands. In 1905 Diller defined the Red Bluff Formation, red-weathered and dissected alluvium that he also correlated with glacial advances in the mountains. In his ground-water study of the Sacramento Valley, Bryan (1923) traced the older alluvium around the valley and showed that it is equivalent to the Red Bluff Formation. Russell and VanderHoof (1931) showed that the lower part of Diller's Red Bluff Formation (Bryan's Older Alluvium) is actually a separate formation, on which the younger gravels, for which the name Red Bluff was retained, rest unconformably. They gave the name Tehama to the older formation.

Anderson and Russell (1939) have summarized the geology of the Tehama Formation; according to them, it consists of a 30-180-m sequence of poorly sorted massive sandy silt, sand, and silty gravel, of fluviatile origin, derived from the Coast Ranges and Klamath Mountains to the west and northwest. It rests on a smooth surface planed across steeply dipping Cretaceous rocks on the west side of the Sacramento Valley, and this surface, projected westward, intersects the high mountains of the Coast Ranges at altitudes of 750-900 m, approximately half their total altitude. This suggests that the Tehama may have been deposited as a pediment formation, although it is now locally warped and folded and has an average dip of 4° to the east.

Along the Sacramento River between Redding and Red Bluff, the Tehama Formation interfingers eastward with the Tuscan Formation, a sequence of andesitic tuffs, breccias, and volcanic sediments, locally as much as 300 m thick, which mantles the west flank of the Cascade Mountains east of northern Sacramento Valley and was apparently derived from eruptions near the site of Mt. Lassen (Diller, 1895; Anderson, 1936; Anderson and Russell, 1939). A prominent pink dacitic tuff, the Nomlaki Tuff, occurs near the base of both formations and establishes their contemporaneity.

Anderson and Russell regarded the Tehama and Tuscan as upper Pliocene on the basis of fossils collected from near the Nomlaki Tuff horizon (VanderHoof, 1933). Stirton (1936) assigns the Tehama fauna to the Blancan. Recently a potassium-argon date of 3.3 million years has been obtained from the Nomlaki Tuff near the base of the Tuscan approximately 65 km northeast of the Tehama fossil localities and on the opposite side of the Sacramento Valley (Evernden *et al.*, 1964).

Olmsted and Davis (1961) have traced the formations mapped by Piper *et al.* (1939) in the Mokelumne area northward along the east side of the Sacramento Valley and find that the Laguna Formation corresponds with Bryan's Older Alluvium, underlying the "red lands" or dissected uplands, and that the Victor Formation corresponds to Bryan's Younger Alluvium under the essentially undissected fan surfaces.

THE QUATERNARY OF THE SOUTHERN COAST RANGES

GENERAL STATEMENT

The Quaternary formations of the southern Coast Ranges record phases of a period of orogenic activity that extended from mid-Tertiary to the present. Deformed sediments exposed along the margins of structural valleys have been assigned to the upper Pliocene and lower Pleistocene. A few of these deposits along the coast are marine, but the great bulk are of continental origin and consist of poorly sorted lenticular gravel, sand, and clay, with occasional marl beds. They were derived mostly from highlands that rim the basins in which they occur. In the following pages the lithology and stratigraphic and structural relations of the formations are discussed, with the exception of the Tulare Formation, which was covered in the preceding section on the Great Valley.

The continental formations are sparsely fossiliferous; some have produced no diagnostic fossils. Many of the formations rest conformably on marine Pliocene rocks; others contain Pliocene faunas in their lower parts and Pleistocene faunas in their upper parts.

These moderately deformed Plio-Pleistocene formations are offset by major faults. Much of the present topography was developed after they were deformed. Throughout the northern and western parts of the southern Coast Ranges they rest with profound angular unconformity on tightly folded and deeply eroded older rocks. Along the border with the San Joaquin Valley, and in parts of the upper Salinas and Santa Maria basins, they are parallel to and apparently conformable upon marine Pliocene formations, and their lower contact marks the withdrawal of the sea from this part of California. The boundary between areas of conformity and unconformity is shown on Figure 7. The region of conformity is also the region of major oil-fields and has received the bulk of geologic work on the Coast Ranges. Hence the concept of a major mid-Pleistocene orogeny, more intense than any since the mid-Cretaceous, grew to dominate geologic thought about coastal California.

The youngest marine sediments are at the top of the San Joaquin Formation at the south end of the San Joaquin Valley. During the marine withdrawal that closed the San Joaquin Embayment, a major shift in drainage in the Coast Ranges took place. The strait that connected the southern end of the San Joaquin Valley to the Pacific Ocean, whose exact position is uncertain, was blocked by the rising Coast Ranges, and a new outlet to the sea for the San Joaquin Valley was established via San Francisco Bay, whose system of depressions probably came into existence about this time. According to Jon Galehouse (oral communication, 1964), the Salinas River has apparently extended itself headward along a structural valley to capture drainage of the southern Coast Ranges that formerly flowed south and east toward the southern San Joaquin Embayment.

The volume of the Plio-Pleistocene formations represents comparable volumes of erosion and presumably uplift in the mountain areas. Local angular unconformities, where rocks of Miocene or Pliocene age overlap onto the folded Cretaceous rocks, are common in the uplifted mountain areas. Within some of the basins, particularly the San Joaquin Valley, the formations are parallel, and unconformities in the Tertiary succession, if present, involve only minor amounts of tilting. The pattern of Miocene and Pliocene unconformities is repeated at the base of the deformed Plio-Pleistocene succession, with much more extensive preservation of remnants of the deformed Plio-Pleistocene sediments in the uplifted areas, probably because insufficient time has elapsed to remove them.

Generally the maximum tilting of the formations is near the borders of the ranges; on the east flank of the Diablo Range, as pointed out in the section on the Great Valley, the Tulare is tilted into a monocline on the range front, but it is nearly flat-lying both where it is preserved as remnants in the foothills and in the valley to the east (Fig. 6). The pattern of unconformities suggests repeated pulses of uplift and deformation within the mountain blocks throughout the upper Cenozoic, with deformation concentrated along their margins, and rather steady subsidence of the basins; the mountain areas may be growing at the expense of the basins.

Recent work by Christensen (in press a) has shown that the map pattern of Pleistocene deformation in the Coast Ranges is not linear but consists of a number of broad relatively flat domes centered for the most part on the areas that were already positive at the beginning of Pleistocene time. These domes bear no apparent relation to the major strike-slip faults of the region; the latter slice through domes and basins indiscriminately.

THE DEFORMED PLIO-PLEISTOCENE FORMATIONS

Fossiliferous marine sandstone and siltstone 1,500 m thick, dipping 15°-75° NE and exposed in seacliffs for 6 km south from San Francisco, have been named the Merced Formation (Lawson, 1893; see also Lawson, 1914; Ashley, 1895; Martin, 1916; Glen, 1959; Higgins, 1961). According to Glen (1959), his upper Merced Formation is Pleistocene. This view is also held by J. Wyatt Durham (oral communication, 1965), who feels that the Plio-Pleistocene boundary may even fall at some place within the upper part of Glen's lower Merced.

Deformed poorly consolidated gravels, totalling perhaps 1,500 m and dipping 5°-25° NE, are exposed along the south and west sides of Livermore Valley (Huey, 1948; Hall, 1958); they were named the Livermore Gravels by Vickery in 1925 (unpublished report quoted by Huey). They rest unconformably on tightly folded rocks as young as late Hemphillian (Evernden *et al.*, 1964, p. 164) and contain an Irvingtonian (middle-Pleistocene) fauna (Savage, 1951, p. 284).

Deformed gravels occur around the margins of the Santa Clara Valley, a structural trough whose drowned north end is San Francisco Bay. In the northeastern part of the valley these are known as the Irvington Gravels (Hall, 1958) and are the type locality for the middle-Pleistocene Irvingtonian land-mammal age (Savage, 1951). Around San

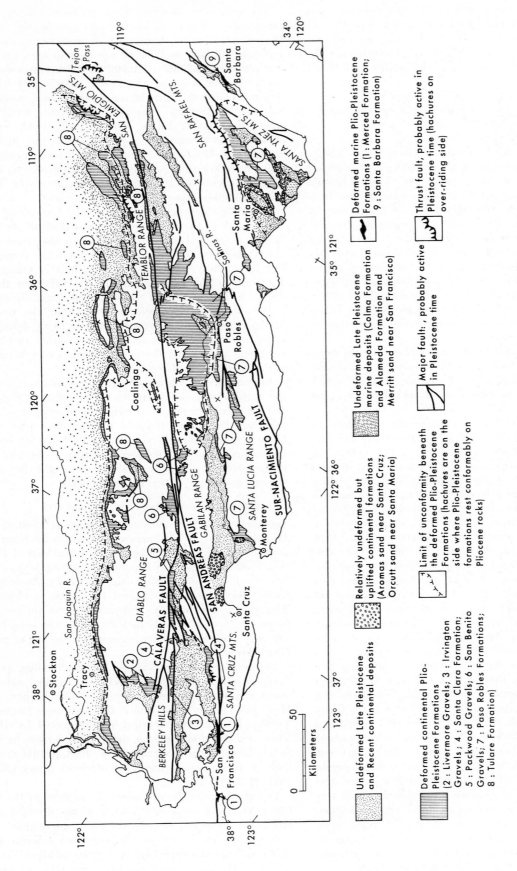

Figure 7. Map of the southern Coast Ranges showing distribution of Plio-Pleistocene and Quaternary formations, major faults, and limits of unconformity at the base of the Plio-Pleistocene formations. Compiled from Jennings (1958, 1959), Jennings and Strand (1958), Jennings and Burnett (1961), Kundert (1955), Huey (1948), Hall (1958), Anderson and Pack (1915), Crittenden (1951), Ortalda (1949), California State Water Resources Board (1955).

Jose and along the west side of Santa Clara Valley these are known as the Santa Clara Formation, which may be as much as 1,000 m thick below the center of the valley (Branner *et al.*, 1908; California State Water Resources Board, 1955; Cummings *et al.*, 1963; Crittenden, 1951). Between San Jose and Gilroy, gravels correlated with the Santa Clara Formation or slightly older, and dipping 30°-90° E or locally overturned, make up the hills along the east side of the Santa Clara Valley. These are known as the Packwood Gravels (Ortalda, 1949; Crittenden, 1951; California State Water Resources Board, 1955). They total 1,200 m in thickness and contain interbedded basalt. At the south end of Santa Clara Valley and extending southward along the San Benito River and San Andreas Fault Zone are the San Benito Gravels, 450-650 m of poorly consolidated, moderately deformed early-Quaternary and late-Pliocene conglomerate (Wilson, 1943, p. 246).

The extensive Plio-Pleistocene deposits in the upper Salinas Valley and Santa Maria Basin are known as the Paso Robles Formation (Fairbanks, 1898). The Paso Robles characteristically contains abundant pebbles of Miocene diatomaceous shale and siliceous mudstone. The Paso Robles Formation underlies an area of 4,000-5,000 km^2 in the upper Salinas Basin, where it is mainly flat-lying and 100-600 m thick (Taliaferro, 1941, 1943; Dibblee, 1962) and was probably once continuous over an area 220 km long and 45 km wide. In the Santa Maria Basin it has been mapped over a triangular area 70 km long and 40 km wide; it ranges from 100 m to 1370 m in thickness (Woodring and Bramlette, 1950; Dibblee, 1950; Upson and Thomasson, 1951; Nelson, 1925). In the center of the basins the Paso Robles Formation is conformable on the underlying marine Pliocene, and deposition was probably continuous from Pliocene time into the Pleistocene (Taliaferro, 1941, 1943; Woodring and Bramlette, 1950). Along the margins of these basins the Paso Robles rests on the underlying Pliocene with marked angular unconformity and overlaps it to rest on Miocene to Cretaceous rocks.

RELATIVELY UNDEFORMED QUATERNARY DEPOSITS
OF THE SOUTHERN COAST RANGES

The structural and erosional valleys formed during the deformation of the Plio-Pleistocene formations are underlain by relatively undeformed deposits of presumed late-Quaternary age. In the centers of the valleys these deposits may grade downward into the lower Pleistocene deposits, but around the margins they rest on them unconformably or rest directly on an irregular surface carved on much older rocks.

The late-Quaternary deposits have been studied most thoroughly in the San Francisco Bay region, where they are of importance as foundations for highways, bridges, and buildings. Seven formations have been recognized, ranging from a few meters to a few hundred meters in thickness, and in part contemporaneous (Lawson, 1915; Louderback, 1951; Trask and Rolston, 1951; Radbruch, 1957; Schlocker *et al.*, 1958). The oldest is the Alameda Formation, consisting of sand, sandy clay, clay, and fine gravel, which extends to a depth of 300 m southeast of Oakland but is generally about 60-70 m thick. It contains plant fragments, a Rancholabrean vertebrate fauna, but no marine fossils, and it is presumably terrestrial. Its upper surface is an irregular erosion surface with as much as 15 m of relief, on which a well-developed soil was formed.

Overlying the Alameda Formation are two formations, first the San Antonio, a predominantly marine dark glauconitic(?) clay with shell beds, and then the Posey, probably non-marine. They are separated by an irregular erosional surface on which a soil was formed; they may represent two periods of rising sea level, and the erosional unconformities that bound them may represent periods of falling sea level resulting from continental glaciation elsewhere. Radbruch (1957) groups these two formations with the Alameda Formation.

Overlying these are two formations that represent a third rise of sea level. Beneath San Francisco Bay and parts of Oakland and Alameda is a beach and dune sand, the Merritt Sand, which fills valleys cut in the Posey Formation and is itself dissected. It grades eastward into the Temescal Formation, which consists of alluvial-fan deposits that are in part warped and dissected. Subsequent to the deposition of these formations, sea level again fell, this last lowering probably corresponding to the Wisconsin Glaciation.

During and after the postglacial rise in sea level, as much as 30 m of bay mud with low shear strength and high porosity have accumulated on the bay floor, partially burying an irregular topography carved on the Pleistocene formations.

Deposits of flat-lying sand, silt, and clay, found around the city of San Francisco up to altitudes of 150 m, and called the Colma Formation (Schlocker *et al.*, 1958) may represent one or several high stands of sea level.

Unconsolidated alluvium beneath Santa Clara Valley southeast of San Francisco Bay extends as much as 240 m below sea level (Poland and Green, 1962), but the lower part may be in the Santa Clara Formation. According to the California State Water Resources Board (1955), the alluvium is separated from the underlying Santa Clara Formation by a prominent red oxidized zone. One horizon in the alluvium, about 90 m below the surface, contained marine mollusks. Near Gilroy toward the south end of Santa Clara Valley, freshwater mollusks and peat from fresh water tule swamps were encountered at 100 m below sea level. These younger alluvial deposits indicate that the trough of San Francisco Bay and Santa Clara Valley has subsided 210 to 300 m in late-Pleistocene time, but that sedimentation was sufficiently rapid to keep the sea out of all except its north-central portion.

At the north end of the Salinas Valley is a deposit of red cross-bedded sand, the Aromas Red Sand, of late-Pleistocene age (Allen, 1946, p. 43-45). It is as much as 225 m thick and occurs as high as 240 m above sea level. It has been uplifted, tilted slightly westward, and deeply dissected. An anomalous beheaded valley cuts across the Aromas Red Sand and leads to Elkhorn Slough, a deep meandering indentation at the head of Monterey Bay. This valley is interpreted as a tilted and abandoned course of the San Benito River. Its lower course is drowned, and it is therefore older than the last rise of sea level.

The lower part of the Salinas Valley is a structural trough underlain by alluvial deposits at least 150 m thick. At the mouth of Salinas Valley, the alluvium beneath the valley floor contains two prominent clay layers that act as aquacludes; the upper layer is about 55 m below sea level and the lower about 120 m below sea level. Each layer extends about 40 km up the valley, and the sands between them crop out on the walls of the submarine canyon at the head of Monterey Bay (Manning, 1963). The clay layers probably represent estuarine conditions in the Salinas Valley during interglacial high sea-level stands, and the intervening sands represent alluvial conditions when the sea was at or below its present level.

In the Santa Maria Basin, a slightly deformed deposit of reddish iron-cemented sand with interbedded gravel lenses, similar to the Aromas Red Sand and called the Orcutt Sand, rests unconformably on the folded and eroded Paso Robles Formation (Woodring and Bramlette, 1950, p. 51; Dibblee, 1950, p. 50; Upson and Thomasson, 1951, p. 39). It has a maximum thickness of 60 m and locally reaches altitudes of about 300 m. It is mildly deformed, with dips as high as 12°-15° on the flanks of anticlines in the Santa Maria Basin, and it appears to grade seaward into marine terrace deposits at altitudes of about 120 m.

MARINE TERRACES

The exposed coasts of the southern Coast Ranges are marked by flights of well-developed marine terraces. The most spectacular terraces are at Santa Cruz, but terraces are also well preserved in the Santa Lucia Mountains near Monterey and San Simeon and in the area west of Pismo Beach. Figure 8 is a plot of the heights of marine terraces along the southern Coast Ranges. The scale of this figure is deliberately small, as the accuracy of the determinations is not great and it is not certain from early descriptions just what parts of the terraces were measured.

As many as five or six terraces have been recognized on some favorable sites, ranging in altitude to 250 or 300 m; marine deposits and pholad borings on even the highest of these terraces confirm their marine origin. Higher terraces have been postulated on the basis of accordant level stretches of ridge crests and summit flats, but they have not been confirmed, and in consideration of the tectonic activity of the Coast Ranges it is doubtful that confirmation in the absence of marine deposits will ever be possible. Where the marine terraces are associated with the deformed Plio-Pleistocene formations, they transect these formations.

Bradley (1957) showed that the marine terraces at Santa Cruz were cut during periods of rising sea level, and that their mantle of marine terrace deposits was laid down during falling sea level. Thus each terrace represents an oscillation of sea level with respect to the adjacent land. He showed further (1956) that the lowest marine terrace at Santa Cruz (the 30-m terrace) was formed more than 39,000 years ago and is probably of Sangamon age. More recently Blanchard (1963) has dated shell material from this terrace by the Th^{230}/U^{238} method at $122,000 \pm 9,000$ years and by the Ra^{226}/U^{238} method at $110,000 \pm 9,000$ years.

Davis (1933) pointed out that the marine terraces along the California Coast slope gently seaward, as does the present wave-cut platform, and that the back parts of the marine terraces are mantled by thick deposits of colluvium and alluvium. Neither the front edge nor the back edge of the present-day topographic terrace surface can be used for correlation or for estimating uplift. The buried shoreline angle at the base of the sea-cliff, cut probably at the moment of greatest advance of the sea before withdrawal from the terrace surface, is the only suitable datum point for purposes of correlation. This shoreline angle is exposed at wide intervals in roadcuts or along stream canyons, and elsewhere it must be estimated from exposed terrace features or probed for by seismic methods or wells. It is not certain whether the terrace heights reported in the earlier of the sources for Figure 8 are for the shoreline angle or for some other part of the terrace. Failure to locate the shoreline angle may account in part for the differences in height of the same terrace reported by different observers.

The higher marine terraces are moderately deformed, and their shoreline angles rise and fall a few meters to a few tens of meters per mile, parallel to the shore. The lowest terraces are much less deformed, and for long distances their shoreline angles maintain the same altitude. The lowest terrace of the Santa Cruz Mountains is about 30 m above sea level (Bradley, 1957 and personal communication, 1964), and in the Santa Lucia Mountains the lowest terrace is about 12 m above sea level, although a 6-m terrace was recognized locally (Trask, 1926).

The continuity of the terraces is best established in the Santa Cruz Mountains, where individual terraces can be traced for distances of several kilometers. As Figure 8 shows, even the lowest terraces are considerably deformed locally, their shoreline angles rising and falling several tens of meters in a few kilometers. (The apparent sharpness of the flexure in the terraces at Capitola results from the projection of nearly east-trending shoreline angles onto the plane that trends N 27° W.) It is clear from the figure that in the Santa Cruz Mountains the terrace heights do not represent eustatic sea-level changes but probably result largely from uplift and deformation of the mountains.

Terraces on the steep coast of the Santa Lucia Mountains are rarely continuous enough for reliable correlation.

The terraces in the Point Sal and Santa Ynez River areas are cut into the sides of mountains carved from the cores of anticlines involving the deformed Paso Robles Formation and Orcutt Sand, formations of early- to middle-Pleistocene age. Thus these terraces, even the 240-m terrace, must be late Pleistocene in age. The Paso Robles Formation is continental in origin, and the Orcutt Sand is largely continental, so the terraces may represent a period of submergence after early-Pleistocene time.

There are no marine deposits in the valleys of the southern Coast Ranges or on the interior flanks of the mountains to represent the high sea-level stands of the marine terraces (Howard, 1954). In structural basins such as the Salinas and Santa Clara Valleys the alluvium is almost entirely continental. The ranges are not conspicuously asymmetric, and topography on opposite sides of the coastal divides appears to be of comparable maturity and chronologic

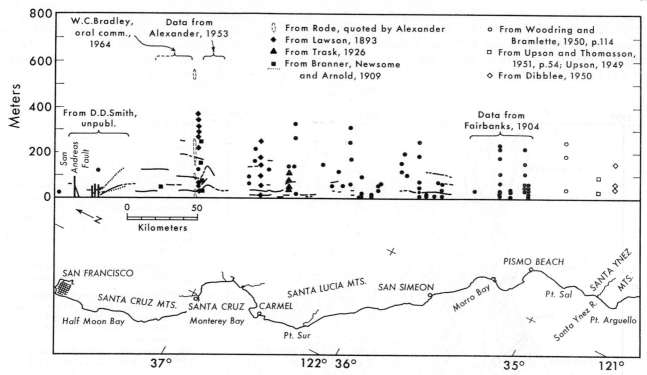

Figure 8. Marine terraces between Point Concepcion and San Francisco, projected onto a vertical plane between Lands End and Point Concepcion. Compiled from 1:24,000 topographic maps of the U.S. Geological Survey, original field surveys, and various published and unpublished sources.

age, so relative uplift of a narrow belt immediately adjacent to the shore can be ruled out as an explanation for this anomaly. At present, this contradiction between the coastal evidence for recent emergence amounting to a few hundred meters, and interior evidence of continuously continental conditions at low altitudes has no explanation.

Subsequent to the cutting of the lowest marine terrace (about 100,000-130,000 years ago; Blanchard, 1963) the sea withdrew to a level about 100 m below present sea level, as a result of ice accumulation of the Wisconsin glaciation. Large streams excavated steep-walled canyons through the flat terraces, canyons graded to lower sea level (Upson, 1949). Postglacial sea-level rise has resulted in the drowning of these valleys, which are now filled with alluvium that extends as much as 24-30 m below sea level, and the valleys, therefore, have broad, flat floors, and most streams enter the ocean via lagoons. San Francisco Bay, the largest of the valleys excavated to lowered sea level, has not yet been filled (Louderback, 1951; Trask and Rolston, 1951).

THE NORTHERN COAST RANGES AND THE KLAMATH MOUNTAINS

INTRODUCTION

The Quaternary history—in fact most of the Cenozoic history of the northern Coast Ranges and Klamath Mountains is one of erosion. Geologic mapping (much of it still reconnaissance) for the entire region has been summarized by

Irwin (1962) and is depicted on the new sheets of the Geological Map of California (Jennings and Strand, 1960; Koenig, 1963; Strand, 1962, 1963). Figure 9 shows the *gipfelfluhr* (surface generalized from summit altitudes) for northwestern California; it also shows the distribution of Plio-Pleistocene and Quaternary deposits.

A. C. Lawson (1894) and J. S. Diller (1902) were the first to study the geomorphology of the northern Coast Ranges and Klamath Mountains. They were enthusiastic proponents of the concept of the erosion cycle that had been recently developed by Davis, and they were led by the apparent accordance of summit levels throughout these mountains, when viewed from a high point, and by the numerous summit flats, to postulate a series of pauses in the supposed bodily uplift of these ranges, when partial peneplains were cut. The oldest of these was the Klamath Peneplain (Diller, 1902, Wells *et al.*, 1949; Irwin, 1960), above which the highest peaks of the Klamath Mountains were supposed to rise in isolated clusters. However, the *gipfelfluhr* shown in Figure 9 does not have that uniformity of altitude one would expect in a peneplain.

THE TERTIARY SHORELINE

Continental and marine rocks of Miocene age near Crescent City (Diller, 1902; Maxson, 1933; Cater and Wells, 1953), continental Oligocene sediments in the Weaverville area (Hinds, 1933; MacGinitie, 1937), and marine Miocene rocks near Round Valley (Clark, 1940) establish points on a Miocene shoreline that extended diagonally across the

northern Coast Ranges from Crescent City to the vicinity
of Vacaville, where the northernmost Miocene sediments on
the west side of the Sacramento Valley are found (Weaver,
1949). Land lay to the northeast of this line; to the southwest was probably an archipelago.

DEFORMED PLIO-PLEISTOCENE FORMATIONS

Within the northern Coast Ranges are many small lowlands
and plains 1-10 km broad. Although not nearly so large or
continuous as the broad structural valleys of the southern
Coast Ranges, they, also, are underlain and bordered by

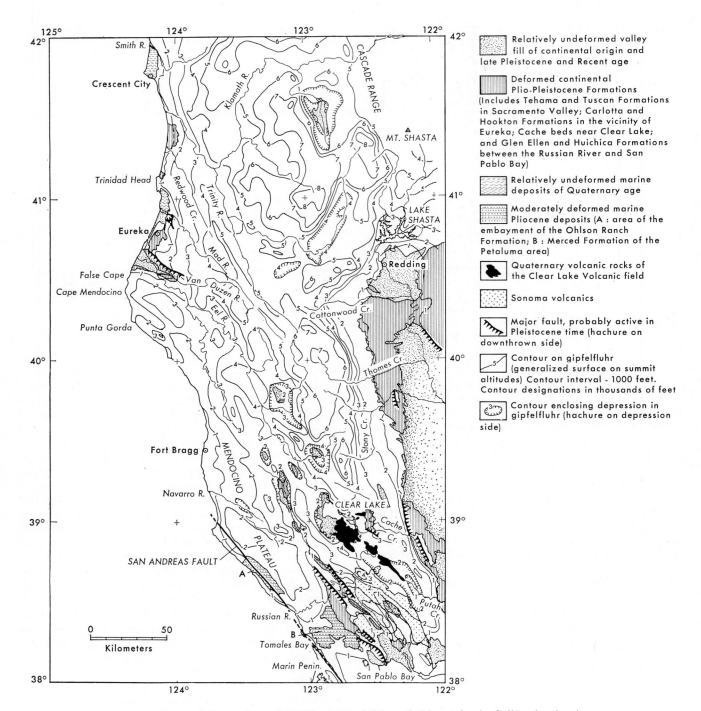

Figure 9. Map of the northern Coast Ranges and Klamath Mountains in California, showing
distribution of Plio-Pleistocene and Quaternary formations and contours on the
Gipfelfluhr (generalized surface on summit altitudes). Compiled from Strand (1962,
1963), Koenig (1963), Jennings and Strand (1960), and Army Map Service 1:250,-
000 topographic maps of Weed, Redding, Eureka, Ukiah, and Santa Rosa Quadrangles.

deformed sedimentary rocks of Pliocene and early-Pleistocene age. In some of these basins the Quaternary formations are the top of a thick succession of upper Cenozoic rocks. In most of the basins, however, the Plio-Pleistocene sediments rest with profound unconformity on Cretaceous rocks or on the Franciscan Formation. Marine formations along the coast are abundantly fossiliferous, and their stratigraphic age is known. Inland, the formations are mainly continental and have yielded fossils in only a few places. Interbedded volcanic rocks give the hope, already partly realized, of establishing absolute ages for many of these formations. These deformed rocks establish the maximum age of the latest period of folding and faulting in the northern Coast Ranges.

In the extreme northwest corner of California, the coastal flat around Crescent City is underlain by the St. George Formation, which consists of about 130 m of massive siltstone and shale with thin discontinuous sand beds, of lower Pleistocene age, dipping about 12° NE at its only exposure (Diller, 1902, p. 32; Maxson, 1933; Back, 1937, p. 20).

Deformed sediments of Miocene to Pleistocene age occupy several structural basins in a belt 15-50 km wide extending from 90 km south of Eureka to 65 km north of Eureka. They demonstrate that this belt was largely submerged during much of Pliocene time and has been considerably deformed since then. These Cenozoic sediments are in structural basins a few kilometers wide and a few tens of kilometers long that trend northwesterly. The largest includes the lower Eel River valley and the coastal lowland between the mouth of the Eel and the mouth of the Mad River. Approximately 4,200 m of sediments in this basin, named the Wildcat Group (Lawson, 1893), are predominantly marine; they have at their top 150-900 m of massive non-marine conglomerate and sandstone with some brackish and marine interbeds, of Pleistocene age, the Carlotta Formation (Ogle, 1953). The Wildcat Group is folded into a broad west-northwest-trending syncline whose flanks dip 35°-60° and are locally overturned. Cretaceous rocks overthrust the Wildcat Group on the north flank of the syncline.

Small patches of marine sediments downfaulted into the Franciscan, a few kilometers east of the Wildcat Basin along the Van Duzen River, southward on the Mattole, and southeastward on the South Fork of the Eel. (Ogle, 1953; MacGinitie; 1943; Strand, 1962), suggest that a considerable part of the northern Coast Ranges was submerged for 50 km inland from the present shore during at least some of Pliocene time. Ogle (1953) feels that parts of the intervening ridges stood as islands in the Pliocene sea.

In the southern part of the region shown in Figure 9, the coastal belt underwent mild deformation and uplift amounting locally to 450 m since late-Pliocene time, and the area east of the coastal belt was the site of late-Pliocene and Quaternary volcanism and was deformed into folds with amplitudes of several hundred to a thousand meters. The relatively slight deformation along the coast is indicated by two slightly deformed marine formations of late-Pliocene age, the Ohlson Ranch Formation (Higgins, 1960; Peck, 1960) (area A on Figure 9), and the Merced Formation (Johnson, 1943; Weaver, 1949; Travis, 1952; Gealey,

1950; Higgins, 1952) (area B on Fig. 9). These formations were deposited in coastal embayments that extended 8 to 24 km respectively eastward from the present shoreline and are now a few tens to 450 m above sea level. The Merced Formation interfingers eastward with the Sonoma Volcanics and associated continental deposits, the Glen Ellen and Huichica Formations (Weaver, 1949), which are faulted and folded. The interfingering relations help establish the pre-Quaternary paleogeography.

The Sonoma Volcanics are a pile of andesitic, basaltic, and rhyolitic tuffs and flows, with intercalated sediments, totalling 300-900 m in thickness and covering an area of 900 km² at the southern end of the northern Coast Ranges (Weaver, 1949; Travis, 1952; Cardwell, 1958; Kunkel and Upson, 1960; Koenig, 1963) (Fig. 9). Where they interfinger with the Merced Formation, both formations rest with angular unconformity on tightly folded beds of the Petaluma Formation, which Stirton (1939, 1952) and Axelrod (1944) regard as no older than middle Pliocene (see Cardwell, 1958, for a discussion). Farther east, the Sonoma Volcanics rest with angular unconformity on all older rocks.

Weaver (1949, p. 34) regarded the Merced fauna as middle Pliocene in age, but it is now regarded as upper Pliocene (Stirton, 1952). The Sonoma Volcanics have produced a flora assigned by Axelrod (1944, 1957) to the Blancan (late Pliocene or early Pleistocene), and a diatomaceous unit within the Sonoma Volcanics contains numerous species in common with the assemblage at the base of the Tulare Formation, according to Lohman (quoted by Kunkel and Upson, 1960). More recently, a potassium-argon age of 3.4 million years has been obtained on tuff from the Sonoma Volcanics (Evernden and James, 1964).

The topography of the region of the Sonoma Volcanics is partly the result of the accumulation of the volcanic rocks and their resistance to erosion, and partly of the deformation following the eruption of the volcanics. This deformation involves continental gravels that rest on the Sonoma Volcanics with angular unconformity, the early-Pleistocene Glen Ellen and Huichica Formations, which dip locally as much as 60°.

Volcanism and deformation have affected the heart of the northern Coast Ranges throughout Quaternary time. Between the Sonoma Volcanics and Clear Lake, the Clear Lake Volcanic Field (Anderson, 1938; Brice, 1958) contains eruptive deposits that range in age and state of preservation from tilted basalt flows possibly interbedded in deformed early-Quaternary sediments to undissected dacite domes, basaltic cinder cones, and basalt and obsidian flows resting on the present landscape and apparently active in late-Quaternary time. Numerous hot springs and solfataras indicate that volcanic activity is continuing. Mt. Konocti, a perfectly preserved dacitic strato-volcano rising 900 m above Clear Lake, dominates the northern part of the volcanic field.

Clear Lake, less than 15 m deep, lies along the northern side of the volcanic field in a structural depression underlain by an unknown but presumably great thickness of Quaternary alluvium, lacustrine sediments, and tuffs. The lake discharges through Cache Creek, which flows eastward through deep gorges to the Sacramento Valley.

Deformation in the Clear Lake area is best demonstrated by the Cache Beds, which are about 2,000 m of light-gray thinly bedded silt with intercalated sand and gravel, grading upward into diatomite, marl, and thin limestone beds, and tuffaceous at the top (Brice, 1953; Anderson, 1936; Upson and Kunkel, 1955). The Cache Beds dip 20°-60° W toward Clear Lake and flatten westward. They have produced few fossils, but the ramus of a lower jaw of *Elephas*, identified by V. L. VanderHoof (Anderson, 1936a, p. 369), indicates that the formation is at least in part Pleistocene. Faults with several thousand meters of displacement appear to have been active during deposition of the Cache Beds. Presumably the Cache Beds accumulated in a predecessor of the Clear Lake basin, and the eastern end of this basin was uplifted and tilted west after accumulation of 2,000 m of sediment.

Deformed unfossiliferous continental deposits similar in degree of consolidation and stratigraphic position to the Cache Beds, the Glen Ellen Formation, and the Huichica Formation underlie eight small plains in the central part of the north Coast Ranges (California Division of Water Resources, 1958). Alluvial fills in several of these valleys extend 100-200 m below the level of their bedrock lips.

Anderson Valley at the head of the Navarro River presents a special problem in that deformed alluvial deposits of Plio-Pleistocene(?) age are exposed at the west end of the valley at altitudes of 60 m, yet 9 km to the west marine sands that may be equivalent to the Ohlson Ranch Forma-

tion cap the drainage divide south of the Navarro River at 460 m altitude, and marine terraces as high as 180 m are at the mouth of the Navarro 19 km to the northwest of Anderson Valley. There is no sign in Anderson Valley of marine deposits to correspond to these high sea-level stands, and geomorphic evidence of depression of the headwaters is lacking.

The Plio-Pleistocene Tehama Formation and the Pleistocene Red Bluff Formation, described in the section on the Great Valley, contain stratigraphic evidence suggesting that north of latitude 39° 30′ N the northern Coast Ranges have been bodily uplifted since late-Pliocene time about 350-540 m with respect to the Sacramento Valley on the east, and that this uplift involved tilting of the belt underlain by the Cretaceous monocline. The same sort of stratigraphic evidence suggests that south of latitude 39° 30′ N much more intense deformation has taken place since late-Pliocene time, resulting in monoclines and normal and thrust faults of several hundred meters displacement.

South of latitude 39° 00′ N the Cretaceous monocline may have been uplifted in Pleistocene time into an arch 10-15 km wide and 300-900 m above the country on either side.

COASTAL TERRACES AND THE CONTINENTAL SHELF

Marine terraces are well preserved on long stretches of the coast and are absent from other stretches. Terrace altitudes are summarized in Figures 10 and 11. The terraces can be traced longer distances and show more regularity in altitude

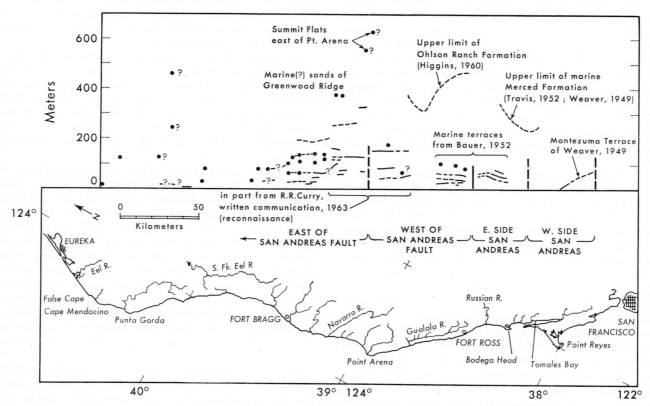

Figure 10. Marine terraces between the Golden Gate and Cape Mendocino, projected onto a vertical plane between Point Bonita and Cape Mendocino. Compiled from 1:24,-000 and 1:62,500 topographic maps of U.S. Geological Survey, original field surveys, and various published and unpublished sources.

of shoreline angle here than they do in the southern Coast Ranges. Locally, however, they are considerably warped, and areas of greatest deformation are adjacent to the San Andreas Fault (particularly on its southwest side) and around Eureka and the mouth of the Eel River. The highest marine terraces are generally a hundred meters or so below the level of the upper Pliocene marine sediments (such as the Merced and Ohlson Ranch Formations) that cap ridge crests. Assuming relatively constant rise of the coast, these terraces should be early Pleistocene in age. Terraces are as high as 270-300 m above sea level, discounting the marine features associated with the Pliocene formations. As many as four or five terraces are present along a few stretches of coast, but commonly there are only two or three. The lowest terrace extensively present along the coast has a shoreline angle of about 23-25 m above sea level, and the excellent preservation of its shoreline features suggests that it may correlate with the 30-m marine terrace at Santa Cruz and therefore probably be Sangamon in age. In a few places a terrace 6 or 12 m high can be identified below the 23-25-m terrace.

The broadest development of terraces is on the gently-sloping coast around Fort Bragg. Here flat-topped interfluves in a coastal belt about 8 km wide are benched by four to six broad marine terraces ranging from 12 to 180 m in altitude. Marine sands on these terraces range up to 15 m in thickness (California Dept. Water Resources, 1958, p. 85). This is a region of heavy winter rainfall, and it supports a forest of conifers, tan-oak, and rhododendron. The acid litter on these extremely flat, poorly drained terraces has led to strongly developed ground-water podzols (the Blacklock series) in which a chalk-white A-horizon 0.3-1 m thick consisting of pure silica silt overlies a thoroughly cemented ortstein B-horizon about 0.3-1 m thick, which rests directly on unweathered feldspathic beach sand (Gardner and Bradshaw, 1954). The vegetation, sealed off from soil nutrients by the ortstein, is now a pigmy forest, in which species normally 10-50 m tall form dense cane-like thickets less than 3 m high. The white A-horizons have given these terraces the name Mendocino White Plains.

The marine deposit covering the broad coastal flat at Crescent City has been named the Battery Formation (Maxson, 1933, p. 136; Back, 1937, p. 23). The shoreline angle of this marine terrace is about 30 m or less. According to Maxson the fauna of the Battery Formation resembles that of the Palos Verdes Sand (of presumably Sangamon age) in southern California.

Terrace deposits in the Eel River Lowland are predominantly fluvial, although they grade seaward into marine deposits. Ogle (1953) named the oldest Pleistocene terrace deposits the Hookton Formation and one of the younger the Rohnerville Formation. Both are deformed, the Hookton having dips as steep as 19° and the Rohnerville as steep as 5°. Ogle (1953) correlated the Hookton Formation with the 270 m terrace at False Cape and Cape Mendocino. This correlation requires at least 320 m of vertical deformation in the Eel River area (see Fig. 11). Inasmuch as the Carlotta Formation is early Pleistocene in age, this 320 m of deformation must have taken place in late-Pleistocene time.

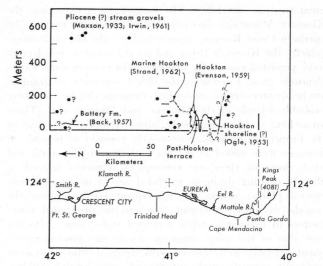

Figure 11. Marine terraces between Punta Gorda and the Oregon border, projected onto a north-south vertical plane. Compiled from topographic maps at 1:24,000 and 1:62,500 and from various sources. Height of Kings Peak is 1,244 m (4,081 ft).

The continental shelf off the northern Coast Ranges is a remarkably smooth plain that extends 8-24 km outward from the shore to the −180-m submarine contour at the top of the continental slope. Rocky bottom encountered on parts of this shelf suggests that much of it might be thinly mantled with sediment and that it might therefore be a wave-planed platform. Its remarkable smoothness contrasts strikingly with the abrupt coast, which rises 1,200 m in less than 5 km at one point a few kilometers southeast of Punta Gorda. The combination of smooth submarine platform, whose lower limit lies close to the level of Pleistocene low sea-level stands, with scattered terrace remnants along most of the coast and absence of any marine deposits younger than Pliocene inland, suggests that the shoreline has maintained a relatively constant geographic position during a steady rise of the land of as much as 300 m relative to sea level during the Quaternary, and that uplift and wave erosion have been very nearly in balance during this rise.

As elsewhere along the California coast, river-mouth estuaries and thick alluvial fill along the lower courses of large streams give ample evidence that sea level in Wisconsin time was a 100 m or more below present sea level. (Higgins, 1952, p. 240; Evenson, 1959, p. 19). Recent mineralogic studies of marine and beach sands south of the Russian River (Cherry, 1964; Minard, 1964) have shown that much of the sand on the shelf and beaches was transported southward from the mouth of the Russian River during the low sea-level stand along a shoreline several miles west of the present shore.

THE DRAINAGE PATTERN

Drainage in the Klamath Mountains and northern Coast Ranges has had the multiplicity of origins and complex history to be expected in an emergent mountain region of great tectonic instability. The longest-emergent region, the Klamath Mountains and adjacent northeastern part of the northern Coast Ranges, appears to have the oldest drainage (chiefly the Klamath River and its tributaries), which may have persisted essentially unchanged in pattern since early-Cenozoic time. Elsewhere, the oldest segments of drainage are headwater streams along high drainage divides that were probably islands in the Miocene and Pliocene seas. These areas have a drainage closely adjusted to the structure of the Franciscan bedrock. Successively younger increments of drainage were added as the sea withdrew to the south and west. Some of these are consequent segments formed as already existing drainage extended across newly emergent coastal plains; others are consequent streams along the troughs of newly emergent synclines or prograded lower courses in deltaically filled synclinal embayments. On the east side of the main drainage divide east-flowing consequent streams were incised into uplifted Plio-Pleistocene pediment gravels and superposed onto north-striking, steeply dipping sandstone and shale. Subsequent drainage changes reflect the effects of localized uplift or subsidence, or resulted from headward erosion and stream capture along belts of weak rock (for example, the north-flowing course of Stony Creek). A remarkable number of streams have been able to maintain their courses across uplifted belts and avoid defeat or capture, and other streams have not been captured although conditions seem appropriate for capture.

One of the most striking cases of supposedly imminent capture that may never occur is at the headwaters of the Mattole River and South Fork of the Eel, where the drainage divide for a distance of 27 km is between 1.5 and 3 km from the Pacific Ocean at an altitude of 330 to 800 m. In spite of the abrupt drop to the Pacific and the steepness of the ravines that score the mountain wall facing the ocean, there is relatively little evidence of eastward migration of this divide by stream capture. Most fingertip tributaries of the Mattole and Eel Rivers heading in this divide are markedly steeper than the larger streams into which they flow, and at only three or four places along the divide does an obviously underfit stream flow sluggishly eastward away from a wind gap.

The best-known example of a prograded and antecedent stream in the northern Coast Ranges is the Russian River. This stream flows southward through a linear system of structural valleys and intervening canyons for about 95 km into the north end of a plain that extends southeast toward San Pablo Bay (Fig. 9). It flows diagonally southward across this plain, and at its west side turns abruptly west to cross the southern end of the Mendocino Plateau in a narrow meandering gorge about 300 m deep. Lawson (1894, p. 269) and Weaver (1949, p. 167) thought that the Russian River originally flowed to San Pablo Bay and was deflected by crustal warping and drainage capture to a new course westward to the ocean. Higgins (1952) has effectively disproved this hypothesis and has shown that the Russian River originally emptied into the Merced embayment and prograded its course westward as the sea withdrew. According to Higgins, the plateau was uplifted after this marine withdrawal, and the river was able to maintain its course across the uplift by virtue of the volume of water and debris

it was carrying. Lesser streams to the south were deflected by the uplift of the coastal belt, and their former headwaters now flow to the Russian River or to San Pablo Bay.

Cache Creek and Putah Creek are probably antecedent to the uplift of the Vaca Mountains. The headwaters of Cache Creek subsided to allow the accumulation of the Plio-Pleistocene Cache Beds and the formation of the alluviated basin of Clear Lake. Downstream, Cache Creek crosses the Cretaceous core of the Vaca Mountains in a narrow V-shaped gorge nearly 600 m deep. At the east end of this gorge it turns south to flow for 25 km through Capay Valley, a structural depression involving the late-Pliocene Tahama Formation. The course of Cache Creek along this valley is probably the consequence of the uplift of the Rumsey Hills to the east.

Subsidence is probably still going on at the headwaters of Cache Creek, for about 8 km northeast of Clear Lake is a narrow dendritic alluvial plain, Long Valley (not shown on Fig. 9), which lies in rugged mountains of mature dendritic topography. The dendritic pattern of this plain could have come about only through erosion. Alluvium beneath the center of the plain is at least 60 m thick (Upson and Kunkel, 1955), yet the stream exiting from Long Valley, a tributary of the North Fork of Cache Creek, flows on bedrock. The deep alluviation of the valley is presumably the result of tectonic sagging across the course of Long Valley Creek.

At the headwaters of Putah Creek are several interconnecting plains of irregular pattern, about 300 m above sea level, whose surfaces are interrupted by numerous bedrock hills. The aspect here is of a mature topography that has been alluvially drowned. Some of these plains have more than 45 m of alluvium, yet drainage from them flows for many kilometers on bedrock (Upson and Kunkel, 1955). Downstream from these headwater plains, Putah Creek crosses Berryessa Valley (now Lake Berryessa), a plain 5 km wide and 20 km long underlain by an unknown thickness of alluvium. Putah Creek leaves Berryessa Valley via a narrow V-shaped gorge through the Vaca Mountains similar to the gorge of Cache Creek.

GLACIATION

The Klamath Mountains were the site of numerous small cirque and valley glaciers during the Pleistocene ice advances, as well as a few ice carapaces on sloping mountain sides (Sharp, 1960), but they did not have an extensive ice sheet, and few glaciers extended across drainage divides. In the northwestern corner of the state, mountains as low as 1,700 m had glaciers on their north sides with cirque floors as low as 1,600 m; farther east in the interior parts of the Klamath Mountains, peaks 2,000-2,100 m high had glaciers on their north sides with cirque floors as low as 1,900-2,000 ft (Davis, 1958). Contours on the climatic firn limit, approximated by the lowest mountains bearing south-facing cirques, are shown on Figure 3. In the northwest this limit was 150 m higher than the orographic firn limit, and in the southern Trinity Alps it was 450 m higher. The divergence between climatic and orographic firn limits southeastward is probably related to the decreasing cloudiness in that direction.

Pleistocene glaciers (at least those of Wisconsin age) were generally less than 15 km long. Some exceptional glaciers descended to 750-900 m altitude (Sharp, 1960); Hershey (1904) reports a patch of ancient till 680 m in altitude in the western Klamath Mountains; however, most glacial termini of Wisconsin age are more than 1,200 m above sea level (Sharp, 1960). The distribution of Pleistocene glaciers recognizable from landforms on topographic maps is shown on Figure 3. Comparison with Sharp (1960) shows that these glaciers are Wisconsin in age, and correspond to the Tahoe and Tioga glaciations of the Sierra Nevada.

At the present time ,a few glacierets have a precarious existence at altitudes of 2,500-2,600 m on the sheltered north-facing sides of peaks 2,650-2,700 m high. Thus Wisconsin glaciation in the Klamath Mountains involved a lowering of firm limits by about 600 m.

A few high peaks of the eastern summit ridge of the northern Coast Ranges, all more than 2,100 m high, had tiny cirque and valley glaciers on their north-facing slopes (Davis, 1958). Their cirque floors have altitudes of 1,700 m. Lack of south-facing cirques makes estimation of a climatic firn limit difficult, but comparison with the Yolla Bolly Mountains and Trinity Alps suggests that it is about 2,400 m in altitude. Davis correlates the latest glaciation of the northern Coast Ranges with the Tahoe Glaciation of the Sierra Nevada.

The first study of glaciers in the Klamath Mountains was by Hershey (1900). He reported (Hershey, 1903a, b) evidence for three glacial advances in the Trinity Alps: an ancient advance, most of whose deposits were destroyed; an intermediate advance, of which boulders of granitic rocks in till are completely rotted to grus, and whose till itself (consisting largely of serpentine boulders) is oxidized to depths of 4.5-6 m; and a young advance, with unweathered till and unmodified glacial landforms. He correlated the intermediate advance with the Iowan (now early Wisconsin) and the young advance with the Wisconsin. At Orleans on the Klamath River he recognized (1903b, c, 1904) a total of six terraces ranging from 14 to 250 m above present river level. The three higher terraces (140, 205, and 250 m) have deep red soils, and the boulders in their gravels are thoroughly disintegrated. The 351- and 21-m terraces have reddish-brown soils, and the 14-m terrace an immature soil. He traced the 25-m terrace into tills of the intermediate glaciation, and he correlated the ancient glaciation with one of the higher terraces.

Maxson (1933) mentioned glaciation in the extreme northwestern part of the state, and Holway (1911) described glacial deposits and landforms in the northern Coast Ranges.

Recently Sharp (1960) recognized four and possibly five distinct glacial advances in the Trinity Alps. Moraines of his Morris Meadow (late-Wisconsin) substage are fresh with well-preserved topographic form, and diorite boulders projecting from the walls of cuts into these moraines ring to the blow of a hammer. Moraines of his Rush Creek (middle-Wisconsin) substage are fairly well preserved, and diorite boulders exposed in cuts are 90% projecting; many are still fresh enough to ring to the blow of a hammer, although some boulders have disintegrated rims surrounding solid cores. Moraines of his Alpine Lake (early-Wisconsin) substage are preserved as scattered remnants only, and 90-100% of the boulders in at least the upper 4.5-6 m of cutbanks are converted to grus. Brownish-red soils with ironstone pellets occur on tills of this substage. Pre-Wisconsin till was recognized on Swift Creek, a stream draining the eastern Trinity Alps; still older till, overlain by oxidized slopewash with a deep-red soil 3 m thick and oxidized to a thickness of 20 m, was found on Canyon Creek, a tributary of the Trinity River draining the southwest part of the Trinity Alps. He found the Wisconsin tills to correlate with terraces 3, 12, and 18 m above Canyon Creek; he correlated his younger pre-Wisconsin till with a 27-m terrace and his older pre-Wisconsin till with a 90-m terrace on the same creek.

Presumably Sharp's three Wisconsin tills correspond to Hershey's younger glaciation, his late-pre-Wisconsin till to Hershey's intermediate glaciation, and his early pre-Wisconsin till to Hershey's old glaciation. Sharp does not discuss Hershey's localities, so presumably Hershey's exposures were no longer available when Sharp made his study. Sharp's description of his tills suggests that the three youngest correlate with the Tioga, Tenaya, and Tahoe Glaciations of the Sierra Nevada.

The Quaternary of Southern California

INTRODUCTION

One of the thickest marine Quaternary sections in the world is in the Ventura and Los Angeles Basins of southern California. As much as 1,500-1,850 m of fossiliferous marine lower Pleistocene sediments are moderately to intensely deformed and are overlain unconformably by marine terrace deposits on as many as 13 terraces ranging up to 450 m above sea level. The marine lower Pleistocene is the youngest part of the thick, largely terrigenous petroliferous sedimentary succession in these basins, a succession that ranges in age from Upper Cretaceous to Pleistocene and totals 15,000 m in thickness. The marine Quaternary sediments interfinger northward and eastward with continental deposits derived from the Transverse Ranges.

The remarkable deformation of the lower-Pleistocene sediments and the unconformity between them and the upper-Pleistocene terrace deposits have led many geologists (Eaton, 1928; Reed, 1933; Reed and Hollister, 1936; Bailey, 1943) to conclude that the major orogeny since mid-Cretaceous time in Southern California was in the mid-Pleistocene. However, the enormously thick terrigenous Miocene and Pliocene section in these basins and the abundance of coarse clastic rocks, particularly in the continental facies, suggest that uplift of the adjacent mountain masses must have been relatively continuous throughout much of the late Cenozoic; the deformation may appear to be more intense in the Quaternary because the locus of deformation reached the central parts of the basins then, and possibly also because the older angular unconformities, which may have been localized around the margins of the earlier basins, somewhat larger than the present basins, were destroyed during continued uplift and erosion.

Limitations of space make only a brief summary of the

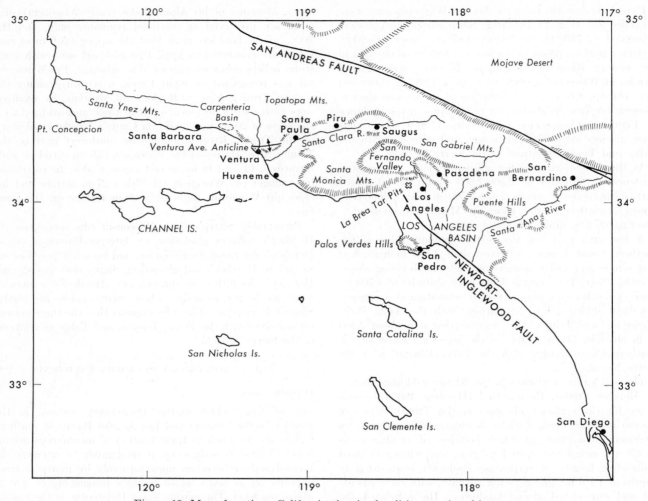

Figure 12. Map of southern California, showing localities mentioned in text.

Southern California Quaternary possible. The geologic framework of Southern California is covered in Jahns (1956), especially in Chapter 2 of that bulletin. The modern environment of marine sedimentation is treated at length in the excellent work of Emery (1960). Localities mentioned in the text are shown in Figure 12.

THE LOWER PLEISTOCENE OF THE VENTURA BASIN

The marine lower Pleistocene of the Ventura Basin is generally mapped as two formations, the Santa Barbara and the San Pedro. These rocks are exposed mainly in the western part of the basin, west of the longitude of Santa Paula, and grade eastward into the continental Saugus Formation. Locally, all formations are overlain unconformably by younger deformed continental gravels and marine terrace deposits.

The type locality of the Santa Barbara Formation is on the west side of Santa Barbara, where it is about 600 m of siltstone and fine sandstone with one conspicuous bryzoal reef bed (Upson, 1951a). It is considered by some authors (Bailey, 1935, 1943; Bailey and Jahns, 1954) to range from upper Pliocene to lower Pleistocene, and by others (Woodring *et al.*, 1940; Woodring, 1952; Upson, 1951a) to be entirely Pleistocene. In the Ventura area, the beds mapped

as Santa Barbara by Bailey (1935, 1943) consist of 650 m of silty shale and mudstone with discontinuous lenses of conglomerate and correspond to the Upper Pico as mapped by Kew (1924) and Putnam (1942). Southward toward Oxnard, the Santa Barbara thins to 60-90 m of sandstone (Thomas *et al.*, 1954).

The Santa Barbara in the Ventura area is overlain conformably by 600 m of sand and silt and 300 m of poorly consolidated gravel, correlated by Bailey (1943) with the San Pedro Formation, a usage that has been followed by Thomas *et al.* (1954) and by Page (1963). The San Pedro of Bailey corresponds to the marine Saugus of Kew (1924). It also thins southward from 900 m north of the Santa Clara River to 250 m near Hueneme.

In the Carpenteria Basin between Santa Barbara and Ventura the Santa Barbara Formation is unconformably overlain by 1,200 m of folded red continental gravel, the Casitas Formation (Upson, 1951a). At the east end of the Ventura Basin, around Saugus and at the north edge of the San Fernando Valley, the deformed continental Quaternary rocks include the Saugus Formation, 900-2,000 m of coarse conglomerate and sandstone derived from mountains to the east and north, and the Pacoima Formation, 150-300 m of extremely coarse conglomerate and breccia, which overlies the Saugus with marked angular unconformity (Winterer and Durham, 1962; Oakeshott, 1958). At its base the Saugus interfingers with marine upper Pliocene rocks and therefore corresponds to the marine Quaternary succession farther west. In the area between Ventura and Santa Paula, Bailey (1935) mapped interfingering relationships between the marine and continental formations.

The lower Pleistocene formations are folded and faulted. At its type locality the Santa Barbara Formation dips 25° SE. Farther east, at the east end of the Carpenteria Basin, it dips 59°, and the unconformably overlying Casitas Formation dips as much as 45° (Upson, 1951a). In the Ventura area, the Quaternary formations are folded along with the Pliocene into the Ventura Avenue anticline, whose flanks dip 35°-45°, and southerly dips increase eastward until in the vicinity of Santa Paula the beds are overturned. The most intense deformation is between Santa Paula and Piru, where the beds are caught in a tight syncline whose axis is the present Santa Clara River valley, overturned on both limbs, and overthrust from both north and south by older Tertiary rocks (Kew, 1924; Bailey and Jahns, 1954; Bailey, 1954; see King, this volume, Fig. 15, for a structure section). At the extreme east end of the Ventura Basin the continental formations in San Fernando Valley have been overthrust by the crystalline rocks of the San Gabriel Mountains. Structural relief here exceeds 4,500 m (Oakeshott, 1958; Winterer and Durham, 1962).

THE LOWER PLEISTOCENE OF THE LOS ANGELES BASIN

The classic area for the Southern California Quaternary is around the seaport of San Pedro and the adjacent Palos Verdes Hills. The abundant marine Pleistocene fauna was described in a classic monograph by Ralph Arnold (1903). The fossiliferous strata were later studied by Crickmay (1929), Grant and Gale (1931), and most recently by Woodring *et al.* (1946), Valentine (1961), and Valentine and Meade (1961). Woodring *et al.* divided the deposits into four formations: the Lomita Marl, Timms Point Silt, San Pedro Sand, and Palos Verdes Sand. The first three formations are all lower Pleistocene and locally dip 12°-35°; the Lomita Marl and Timms Point Silt are local facies, and grade laterally into the basal San Pedro Sand. The Palos Verdes Sand (equivalent to the Upper San Pedro of Arnold, 1903) is the marine cover on the youngest terrace, 23-45 m high, and was deposited across the bevelled edges of the older formations.

The Lomita Marl is a calcareous sand, 23-85 m thick, consisting largely of organic remains; it is present only along the eastern (lee) side of the Palos Verdes Hills. Its fossils suggest that it accumulated at a depth of 45-180 m, probably as a drifted accumulation of organic carbonate fragments, much as similar deposits accumulate today in the lee of Santa Catalina Island (Emery, 1960, p. 208-214). The Timms Point Silt is 10-33 m of brownish massive sandy silt whose contained fossils suggest accumulation in 90-180 m of water. The San Pedro Sand is 53-90 m of sand and gravel whose fossils suggest a shallow-water environment, generally less than 20 m (Woodring *et al.*, 1946). Although the presence of northern forms in the faunas from these lower Pleistocene formations led earlier workers to assign

them to one of the early-Pleistocene glacial periods, Woodring *et al.* concluded that the influence of depth on fossil assemblages makes climatic comparisons dangerous. Emiliani and Epstein (1953) likewise regarded low temperatures determined from oxygen-isotope ratios as the effect of oceanic currents and coastal upwelling as much as of world-wide climatic fluctuations.

The deformed Quaternary succession is the thin western edge of the sediments that lap against the Palos Verdes Hills, which were probably an island in the early-Quaternary sea. These sediments thicken northeastward to 900 m beneath the center of the Los Angeles Basin, where they rest conformably on marine Upper Pliocene rocks (Woodford *et al.*, 1954). Presumably the marine section in the center of the basin interfingers eastward with continental gravels exposed along the border of the Puente Hills, for example the La Habra Formation (Durham and Yerkes, 1964). North and east of the Puente Hills, 100-600 m of coarse continental gravels underlie the alluvial plain between Pasadena and San Bernardino (Dutcher and Garrett, 1963).

MARINE TERRACES AND THE LATE QUATERNARY

The marine terraces of Southern California were first described in detail by Lawson (1893b) and have been summarized by Emery (1960). Upson (1951b) found well-defined terraces at 18, 27, 38, and 60 m on the coast west of Santa Barbara and inferred sea-level stands there as high as 500 m on the basis of level ridge crests. Davis (1933) recognized three marine terraces whose height increased eastward along the coast of the Santa Monica Mountains. Ellis and Lee (1919) recognized five terraces near San Diego, at altitudes of 6, 15, 30, 75, and 150 m, and noted that the terraces are slightly deformed and increase in altitude southward across the border with Mexico.

Terraces occur on several of the Santa Barbara Islands. On Santa Rosa Island, Orr (1960) recognized seven marine terraces, of which the lowest three, 7.5, 23, and 30 m, are probably of Wisconsin age. On San Clemente Island, Lawson (1893b) and W. S. T. Smith (see Olmsted, 1958) recognized 20 marine terraces, the highest about 450 m above sea level.

Nine marine terraces were recognized by Putnam (1942) in the mountains between Ventura and the Carpenteria Basin, ranging in altitude up to 400 m. All of these, including the lowest, slope westward parallel to the coast at 20 m/km. The 60-m terrace merges with a stream terrace on the Ventura River that is upwarped 120 m within a span of 9 km by late-Pleistocene movement on the Ventura Avenue anticline. East of Ventura, fanglomerates containing an upper Pleistocene fauna dip 8°-20° south off the flank of this anticline and rest on the San Pedro Formation with angular unconformity of 25°-30° (Bailey, 1943, see King, this volume, Fig. 15, for a cross-section).

Woodring *et al.* (1946) recognized 13 marine terraces in the Palos Verdes Hills, the highest at 400 m above sea level (see King, this volume, Fig. 20, for sections). Fossiliferous marine deposits were found as high as the 12th terrace. They thought that all these terraces were cut after the lower-Pleistocene formations were folded; however, the shallow depth of accumulation of the lower-Pleistocene formations, and their distribution around the base of the hills, make it possible for some of the highest terraces to be contemporaneous with the lower-Pleistocene succession.

The Palos Verdes Sand rests on the lowest marine terrace, and both are widely distributed in the western part of the Los Angeles basin and are locally deformed. Along the northeastern margin of the Palos Verdes Hills they are warped into a monocline with about 120 m of displacement (Woodring *et al.*, 1946). Along the Newport-Inglewood fault zone the Palos Verdes Sand dips as much as 3° on the flanks of broad faulted anticlines where it has been differentially uplifted as much as 120 m (Poland, Piper *et al.*, 1956; Poland *et al.*, 1959). These structures are little eroded and are faithfully recorded in the present topography. They represent renewed or continuing movement on major oil-field anticlines in the Los Angeles Basin, on whose flanks the buried upper Pliocene beds dip 30°-45° (Driver, 1943; Grinsfelder, 1943; Stoltz, 1943; Weaver and Wilhelm, 1943).

The marine fauna of the Palos Verdes Sand and lowest marine terrace, which presumably lived during the Sangamon interglacial, has many cold-water forms of more northern distribution at present where the terrace deposits are in exposed positions; where the terrace deposits represent sheltered shallow-water embayments, warm-water forms of more southern present distribution are found. Valentine (1961; see also Valentine and Meade, 1961) interprets this to be caused by more intense upwelling than at present, which brought cold water to the surface along exposed coasts, while the shallow water of the embayments was warmed by contact with the warmer interglacial atmosphere.

As Durham (1954) points out, there are no deposits or landforms on the inner margins of the Los Angeles or Ventura Basins to correspond to the marine-terrace deposits on the exposed coastline and the offshore islands.

Little-deformed alluvial deposits around the inner margin of the Los Angeles basin may be contemporaneous with or slightly younger than the Palos Verdes Sand. In these deposits are the famous La Brea tar pits, which have produced an enormous abundance of late-Pleistocene vertebrate remains, including *Canis, Smilodon, Camelops, Bison, Equus, Mylodon, Nothrotherium, Mammut,* and *Archidiskodon* (Stock, 1930). These pits are the type locality for the upper Pleistocene Rancholabrean land-mammal age.

The Wisconsin low sea-level stand is recorded in the Los Angeles Basin by filled gorges of the Santa Ana, San Gabriel, and Los Angeles Rivers, whose floors were as much as 55 m below the present plain (Poland, Piper *et al.*, 1956; Poland *et al.*, 1959). As sea level rose these gorges were filled by a lower unit of coarse gravel and an upper unit of fine sand and silt.

GLACIATION

Evidence of seven valley glaciers on the north slope of the highest ridge of the San Bernardino Mountains has been reported by Sharp *et al.* (1959). The glaciers accumulated at altitudes of 3,100-3,400 m on the north flanks of mountains 3,200-3,500 m high and descended distances of 0.8-2.7 km to altitudes of 2,650 m or higher. Till tentatively correlated with both the Tioga and Tahoe advances of the Sierra Nevada has been recognized, but no older glacial deposits. San Jacinto Peak (3175 m) may have had a glacier on its northeast side, although the evidence is doubtful. The San Gabriel Mountains (maximum altitude 3,075 m) do not appear to have been glaciated, contrary to earlier reports.

CONCLUSIONS

The Quaternary history of California is characterized not only by climatic change, but also by widespread tectonism and volcanism. The thick Quaternary deposits are ultimately the result of tectonic activity. So impressive is the evidence for tectonism that the view has been widely held that California was affected by a mid-Pleistocene orogeny that was more intense than any since mid-Cretaceous—the Pasadenan orogeny of Stille (see King, this volume). More recent evidence does not support this view; rather, Quaternary tectonic activity in California appears to be a continuation of orogenic activity that proceeded with varying intensity since at least the middle Miocene.

The character of the deformation varies from place to place depending on (1) the character of the basement rock and (2) the physiographic province. Areas underlain by granitic batholiths and crystalline metamorphic rocks—together called Sierran basement—are characteristically broken into blocks tens of kilometers wide and hundreds of kilometers long that were tilted and displaced relative to each other but were not significantly deformed internally. Examples are the westward-tilted fault blocks of the Sierra Nevada, Peninsular Range, and Gabilan Range. Areas underlain by the thick, slightly metamorphosed eugeosynclinal succession known as the Franciscan Formation are characteristically deformed into complex folds. Examples are common in the Diablo and Santa Lucia Ranges and in the northern Coast Ranges. Sierran basement may also be intensely deformed and may appear in the cores of fairly tight folds where it is close to major strike-slip or thrust faults, as in the Santa Cruz and Santa Lucia Mountains, or overlain by a thick sedimentary succession, as in parts of the Transverse Ranges.

Geographically deformation varies from apparent crustal extension east of the Sierra Nevada to apparent crustal shortening and large right-lateral displacement near the Pacific Coast. The normal faults that produced much of the eastern front of the Sierra Nevada and are common throughout the Great Basin to the east represent crustal extension. The Sierra Nevada itself, together with the eastern two-thirds of the Great Valley, was—except at its southern end—tilted more or less as a unit. It is now 2,500-4,700 m high along its eastern crest, and the basement descends to depths greater than 6,000 m along the valley axis.

The Coast Ranges have local areas of relatively intense folding, some overthrusting along northwest-trending structures, and numerous right-lateral faults of large displacement. Current displacement on the San Andreas Fault, the largest strike-slip fault, takes place at the rate of 5 cm per year, and it supports the largest estimates of displacement along this fault since the Cretaceous or early Tertiary. The

Transverse Ranges are tightly deformed with westerly structural trends; crustal shortening seems to be involved in such structures as the Santa Clara River Valley syncline.

Quaternary volcanic rocks are widely distributed throughout California. Quaternary volcanism, like tectonic activity, is a continuation of processes that persisted throughout the later Cenozoic. Volcanism continued into the Recent; there have been two eruptions within the state in the last 150 years, radiocarbon dates indicate that several more have occurred within the last millennium, and hot springs and solfataras are common in the volcanic regions. Chief centers of Quaternary volcanic activity are the Cascade Range, Modoc Plateau, the eastern side of the Sierra Nevada—notably near Truckee, Mono Lake, Big Pine, and at the headwaters of the south fork of the Kern—the Sutter Buttes in Sacramento Valley, and the Clear Lake area in the northern Coast Ranges.

Volcanic rocks dated by the potassium-argon method show that volcanism has been persistent throughout the Quaternary. However, eruptions were particularly widespread about 3-3.5 million years ago, near the beginning of the Quaternary. The dated volcanic rocks help establish the absolute ages of the fossiliferous sediments, glacial deposits, erosion surfaces, and tectonic phenomena with which they are associated.

Sediments eroded from the Quaternary uplifts, or from mountains already in existence at the end of Pliocene time, accumulated in subsiding basins. The largest basin is the Great Valley, and the upper 700-1,500 m of the sedimentary succession in its southern half is of Quaternary age. Bordering most of the structural lowlands within the Coast Ranges and in Southern California, and buried beneath younger sediments on the floors of the structural valleys, are deformed bodies of sedimentary rocks commonly a few hundred to 1,500 m thick that range in age from uppermost Pliocene through lower and perhaps middle Pleistocene. Throughout the entire northern Coast Ranges and most of the southern Coast Ranges these deformed Plio-Pleistocene formations rest unconformably on older rocks, including tightly folded rocks of middle-Pliocene age; on the other hand, in the oil-field regions of the southern San Joaquin Valley and the basins of southern California, these beds rest conformably on the marine Pliocene, and they gave most geologists working there the impression that Cenozoic deformation prior to the middle Pleistocene had been minor. The deformed Plio-Pleistocene sediments unconformably underlie relatively undeformed alluvial, lacustrine, estuarine, and eolian deposits as much as a few hundred meters thick.

Most of the Plio-Pleistocene and late-Quaternary sediments are continental in origin and contain scattered vertebrate fossils, freshwater mollusks, and diatoms. The type Irvingtonian (middle-Pleistocene) and Rancholabrean (upper-Pleistocene) faunas of the North American land-mammal ages are from localities within California. Radiometric dates from California have shown that the late-Pliocene lower-Blancan faunas (in the sense of Hibbard *et al.*, this volume) are about 3.4 million years old and that a fauna that is either Irvingtonian or Rancholabrean is 600,000 years old.

Along the coast, marine formations contain abundant in-

vertebrate fossil assemblages. Ties with the European and Atlantic faunas have not yet been securely established, and the ages of the marine formations have been based on percentage of extinct marine forms, presence of cold-water forms, and correlation with formations having vertebrate-fossil control.

The marked climatic fluctuations during the Quaternary are represented in California by glacial deposits and landforms, marine terraces, cut-and-fill relations in alluvium, and pluvial lake cycles. (For a discussion of pluvial cycles see the article by Morrison, this volume.) During the latest glaciations the Sierra Nevada supported a mountain ice cap 450 km long and 50 km wide, mountain glaciers were common in the Cascade Range and Klamath Mountains, and a few cirque glaciers were present on high peaks of the northern Coast Ranges and of the San Bernardino Mountains in southern California. Climatic firn limit ranged from 2,000 m in the northwest corner of the state to 4,000 m near Mt. Whitney, and firn limits in general were about 600-750 m lower than at present.

The classic glacial sequence in California is in the eastern Sierra Nevada, where the following Pleistocene glaciations have been established: McGee, Sherwin, Mono Basin, Tahoe, Tenaya, Tioga. The last three are correlated with the Wisconsin of the mid-Continental United States (see Morrison, this volume). Tahoe till apparently overlies basalt dated at less than 100,000 years. The Mono Basin is younger than, and the Sherwin older than, the Bishop Tuff, dated at 700,000 years. McGee till, which is apparently older than Sherwin, rests on basalt 2.3 million years old.

Marine terraces and associated deposits are common along the California coast. As many as 20 terraces have been found in a single flight, the highest at 450 m. Terraces 400 m high transect deformed early-Pleistocene formations. The terraces are moderately deformed so that their shoreline angles slope a few tens of meters per kilometer. Locally they may be tilted a few degrees. The lowest persistent terrace is about 30 m above sea level and has been dated by the U-Th methods at about 115,000 years. In Southern California deposits on this terrace have a cold-water fauna on exposed coasts and a warm-water fauna in protected shallow embayments, suggesting that upwelling and oceanic currents may have as much of an effect on marine climate as air temperature. The type Rancholabrean fauna may be in deposits contemporaneous with or slightly younger than the lowest marine terrace. Following the cutting of the lowest marine terrace, sea level fell at least 100 m below its present level. The subsequent postglacial sea-level rise accounts for San Francisco Bay and other drowned river mouths.

The marine terraces present two problems as yet unsolved: (1) There are no deposits or landforms in the interior valleys of California to correspond with the high sea-level stand that the terraces represent. (2) The marine terraces transect continental Plio-Pleistocene formations at many places, a relationship that implies that the entire marine-terrace sequence represents a sea-level rise (relative to California) following a fairly low sea-level stand in early-Pleistocene time. Since this sequence of events has not been reported elsewhere, it may result from tectonic conditions along the California coast.

Fossiliferous sediments as well as dated volcanic rocks and marine terraces have made possible estimates of the progress of tectonic activity in various parts of California during the Quaternary. Volcanic rocks within a few hundred feet of the bottoms of gorges cut into the western slope of the Sierra Nevada indicate that the bulk of the uplift and tilting occurred more than 3.5 million years ago. On the other hand, as much as 1,000 m of displacement may have taken place on the eastern escarpment since the deposition of the McGee till, less than 2.3 million years old. Locally a few hundred meters of more of this displacement took place since the eruption of the Bishop Tuff, 700,000 years ago; moraines of Tahoe and Tioga glaciations are locally offset several meters. Inasmuch as the isotopically dated volcanics and the ancient glacial deposits indicate that the Sierra Nevada was about as high at the beginning of the Pleistocene as it is now, the Quaternary displacement along the eastern boundary escarpment may represent foundering of the Owens Valley block. The amount and time of Quaternary displacement varied greatly from place to place along the escarpment.

In the Coast Ranges a major period of uplift and erosion preceded the accumulation of the Plio-Pleistocene formations; these formations were in turn deformed, at least around the margins of the intermontane basins, once or more during the Pleistocene. Near San Francisco Bay most of this deformation seems to have taken place between Irvingtonian and Rancholabrean time. On the east side of the Diablo Range sharp monoclinal flexuring and broad folding took place less than 600,000 years ago.

Even the youngest marine terraces are locally deformed, indicating significant crustal warping in the last 100,000 years. Along the Newport-Inglewood Fault in the Los Angeles Basin, deposits of the youngest terrace dip 3° off the flanks of folds with 120 m of closure; the buried uppermost Pliocene beds in these same folds have dips of 30°-45°, suggesting that deformation has been relatively continuous throughout the Quaternary. Tectonic activity continues unabated, for California has a major earthquake about once a decade (VanderHoof, 1955; Tocher, 1959).

REFERENCES

Alexander, C. S., 1953, The marine and stream terraces of the Capitola-Watsonville area: Univ. California Publ. Geogr., v. 10, p. 1-44

Anderson, C. A., 1936a, Volcanic history of the Clear Lake area, California: Geol. Soc. Amer. Bull., v. 47, p. 629-644

—— 1936b, The Tuscan Formation of northern California, with a discussion concerning the origin of volcanic breccias: Univ. California Publ. Geol. Sci., v. 23, p. 215-275

—— 1941, Volcanoes of the Medicine Lake Highlands, California: Univ. California Publ., Dept. Geol. Sci. Bull., v. 25, p. 347-422

Anderson, C. A., and Russell, R. D., 1939, Tertiary formations of northern Sacramento Valley, California: California J. Mines Geol. (State Mineralogist's Rep.), v. 35, p. 219-253

Anderson, Robert, and Pack, R. W., 1915, Geology and oil resources of the west border of the San Joaquin Valley

north of Coalinga, California: U.S. Geol. Surv. Bull. 603, 220 p.

Arkley, R. J., 1962a, The geology, geomorphology, and soils of the San Joaquin Valley in the vicinity of the Merced River, California: California Div. Mines Geol., Bull. 182, p. 25-31

—— 1962b, Soil Survey of the Merced area, California: U.S. Dept. Agric., Soil Cons. Serv., Soil Surv., Ser. 1950, No. 7, 131 p.

Arnold, Ralph, 1903, The paleontology and stratigraphy of the marine Pliocene and Pleistocene of San Pedro, California: California Acad. Sci. Mem., v. 3, 420 p.

Arnold, Ralph, and Anderson, Robert, 1910, Geology and oil resources of the Coalinga District, California, with a report on the chemical and physical properties of the oils by Irving C. Allen: U.S. Geol. Surv. Bull. 398, 272 p.

Arnold, Ralph, and Johnson, H. R., 1910, Preliminary report on the McKittrick-Sunset oil region, Kern and San Luis Obispo Counties, California: U.S. Geol. Surv. Bull. 406, 225 p.

Ashley, G. H., 1895, The Neocene stratigraphy of the Santa Cruz Mountains of California: California Acad. Sci. Proc., 2nd ser., v. 5, pt. 1, p. 273-367

Averill, C. V., 1937, Mineral resources of Plumas County: California J. Mines Geol. (State Mineralogist's Rep.), v. 33, p. 79-143

Axelrod, D. I., 1944, Pliocene floras of California and Oregon—the Sonoma Flora: Carnegie Instn. Publ. 553, p. 162-206

—— 1957, Late Tertiary floras and the Sierra Nevadan uplift: Geol. Soc. Amer. Bull., v. 68, p. 19-46

—— 1962, Post-Pliocene uplift of the Sierra Nevada, California: Geol. Soc. Amer. Bull., v. 73, p. 183-197

Axelrod, D. I., and Ting, W. S., 1961, Early Pleistocene floras from the Chagoopa Surface, southern Sierra Nevada: Univ. California Publ. Geol. Sci., v. 39, p. 119-194

Back, William, 1957, Geology and ground-water features of the Smith River plain, Del Norte County, California: U.S. Geol. Surv. Water-Supply Pap. 1254, 76 p.

Bailey, Edgar H., Irwin, William P., and Jones, David L., 1964, Franciscan and related rocks, and their significance in the geology of western California: California Div. Mines Geol. Bull. 183, 177 p.

Bailey, T. L., 1935, Lateral change of fauna in the Lower Pleistocene: Geol. Soc. Amer. Bull., v. 46, p. 489-502

—— 1943, Late Pleistocene Coast Range orogenesis in southern California: Geol. Soc. Amer. Bull., v. 54, p. 1549-1568

—— 1954, Geology of the western Ventura Basin, Santa Barbara, Ventura, and Los Angeles Counties: in Jahns, 1954, map sheet 4

Bailey, T. L., and Jahns, R. H., 1954, Geology of the Transverse Range Province, southern California: in Jahns, 1954, Ch. 2, p. 83-106

Barbat, W. F., and Galloway, John, 1934, San Joaquin Clay, California: Amer. Assoc. Petroleum Geologists Bull., v. 18, p. 476-499

Bateman, Paul C., 1956, Economic Geology of the Bishop Tungsten District, California: California Division of Mines Special Report 47, 87 p

—— 1962, Geology, p. 100-122 *in* Schumacher, G. (ed.), Deepest valley: San Francisco, Sierra Club, 206 p.

—— in press, Geology and tungsten mineralization of the Bishop District, California: U.S. Geol. Surv. Prof. Pap. 470

Bauer, Francis H., 1952, Marine terraces between Salmon Creek and Stewart's Point, California: Berkeley, Univ. California M.A. thesis, 273 p.

Birkeland, Peter W., 1963, Pleistocene volcanism and deformation of the Truckee area, north of Lake Tahoe, California: Geol. Soc. Amer. Bull., v. 74, p. 1453-1464

—— 1964, Pleistocene glaciation of the northern Sierra Nevada north of Lake Tahoe, California: J. Geol., v. 72, p. 810-825

Birman, J. H., 1954, Pleistocene glaciation in the upper San Joaquin basin, Sierra Nevada: *in* Jahns, 1954, Ch. 5, p. 41-44

—— 1957, Glacial geology of the upper San Joaquin drainage, Sierra Nevada, California: Los Angeles, Univ. California Ph.D. thesis, 237 p.

—— 1964, Glacial geology across the crest of the Sierra Nevada: Geol. Soc. Amer. Spec. Pap. 75, 80 p.

Blackwelder, Eliot, 1931, Pleistocene glaciation in the Sierra Nevada and Basin Ranges: Geol. Soc. Amer. Bull., v. 42, p. 865-922

—— 1932, Glacial and associated stream deposits of the Sierra Nevada: Mining in California (State Mineralogist's Rep.), v. 28, p. 303-310

Blanchard, R. L., 1963, Uranium decay series disequilibrium in age determination of marine calcium carbonates: St. Louis, Washington Univ. Ph.D. thesis, 164 p.

Bowen, Oliver E., Jr. (ed.), 1962, Geologic guide to the gas and oil fields of northern California: California Div. Mines Geol. Bull. 181, 407 p.

Bradley, William C., 1956, Carbon-14 date for a marine terrace at Santa Cruz, California: Geol. Soc. Amer. Bull., v. 67, p. 675-678

—— 1957, Origin of marine-terrace deposits in the Santa Cruz Area, California: Geol. Soc. Amer. Bull., v. 68, p. 421-444

Branner, J. C., Newsom, F. S., and Arnold, Ralph, 1909, Description of the Santa Cruz area: U.S. Geol. Surv., Geol. Atlas of the United States, Folio 163

Brice, James C., 1953, Geology of Lower Lake quadrangle, California: California Div. Mines Bull. 166, 72 p.

Briggs, Louis I., 1953, Geology of the Ortigalita Peak quadrangle, California: California Div. Mines Bull. 167, 61 p.

Bryan, Kirk, 1923, Geology and ground-water resources of Sacramento Valley, California: U.S. Geol. Surv. Water-Supply Pap. 495, 285 p.

Büdel, Julius, 1957, Die "Doppelten Einebnungsflächen" in den feuchten Tropen: Z. Geomorph., v. 1, No. 2, p. 201-228

Bull, William B., 1964a, History and causes of channel trenching in western Fresno County, California: Amer. J. Sci., v. 262, p. 249-258

—— 1964b, Alluvial fans and near-surface subsidence in western Fresno County, California: U.S. Geol. Surv. Prof. Pap. 437-A, 71 p.

California Department of Water Resources, Division of Resources Planning, 1958, Recommended water well construction and sealing standards, Mendocino County: *Their* Bull. 62, 169 + 60 p.

California State Water Resources Board, 1955, Santa Clara County investigation: *Their* Bull. 7, 153 p. (see p. 99-105)

Cardwell, G. T., 1958, Geology and ground-water in the Santa Rosa and Petaluma Valley areas, Sonoma County, California: U.S. Geol. Surv. Water-Supply Pap. 1427, 273 p.

Cater, Fred W., Jr., and Wells, Francis G., 1953, Geology and mineral resources of the Gasquet quadrangle, California-Oregon: U.S. Geol. Surv. Bull. 995-C, p. 79-133

Cherry, John, 1964, Sand movement along a portion of the northern California coast: Univ. California Hydraulic Engineering Lab., Tech. Rep. HEL—4-3, 150 p.

Christensen, M. N., in press a, Late Cenozoic deformation in the Central Coast Ranges of California: Geol. Soc. Amer. Bull.

—— in press b, Late Cenozoic movements of the earth's crust—Sierra Nevada of California: Geol. Soc. Amer. Bull.

Church, H. Victor, Jr., Krammes, Kenneth, *et al.*, 1957a, Cenozoic correlation section across south San Joaquin Valley from San Andreas Fault to Sierra Nevada foothills: Amer. Assoc. Petroleum Geologists, Pacific Sect., Correlation Sect. No. 8

—— 1957b, Correlation section across central San Joaquin Valley from San Andreas Fault to Sierra Nevada foothills: Amer. Assoc. Petroleum Geologists, Pacific Sect., Correlation Sect. No. 9

Clark, Samuel G., 1940, Geology of the Covelo District, Mendocino County, California: Univ. California Publ. Dept. Geol. Sci. Bull., v. 25, p. 119-142

Cohee, George V., *et al.*, 1961, Tectonic map of the United States, exclusive of Hawaii and Alaska (1:2,500,000): U.S. Geol. Surv. and Amer. Assoc. Petroleum Geologists

Colby, W. E., 1950, John Muir's studies in the Sierra: San Francisco, The Sierra Club, 103 p.

Cox, Allan, Doell, Richard R., and Dalrymple, G. Brent, this volume, Quaternary paleomagnetic stratigraphy

Crickmay, C. H., 1929, The anomalous stratigraphy of Deadman's Island, California: J. Geol., v. 37, p. 617-638

Crittenden, Max D., Jr., 1951, Geology of the San Jose-Mount Hamilton area, California: California Div. Mines Bull. 157, 74 p.

Crowell, John C., 1962, Displacement along the San Andreas Fault, California: Geol. Soc. Amer. Spec. Pap. 71, 61 p.

Cummings, J. C., Touring, R. M., and Brabb, E. E., 1962, Geology of the northern Santa Cruz Mountains, California: *in* Bowen, 1962, p. 179-220

Curtis, Garniss H., 1951, The geology of the Topaz Lake quadrangle and the eastern half of the Ebbetts Pass quadrangle: Berkeley, Univ. California Ph.D. thesis

—— 1954, Mode of origin of pyroclastic debris in the Mehrten formation of the Sierra Nevada: Univ. California Publ. Geol. Sci., v. 29, p. 453-502

Curtis, G. H., Evernden, J. F., and Lipson, J., 1958, Age determination of some granitic rocks in California by the potassium-argon method: California Div. Mines Spec. Rep. 54, 16 p.

Dale, R. F., 1959, Climates of the states; California: U.S. Dept. Commerce, Weather Bureau, Publ. 60-4 (Climatology of the United States) 37 p.

Dalrymple, G. Brent, 1963, Potassium-argon dates of some Cenozoic volcanic rocks of the Sierra Nevada, California: Geol. Soc. Amer. Bull., v. 74, p. 379-390

—— 1964a, Cenozoic chronology of the Sierra Nevada, California: Univ. California Publ. Geol. Sci., v. 47, 41 p.

—— 1964b, Potassium-argon dates of three Pleistocene interglacial basalt flows from the Sierra Nevada, California: Geol. Soc. Amer. Bull., v. 75, p. 753-757

Davis, G. H., Green, J. H., Olmsted, F. H., and Brown, D. W., 1959, Ground-water conditions and storage capacity in the San Joaquin Valley, California: U.S. Geol. Surv. Water-Supply Pap. 1469, 287 p.

Davis, Stanley N., 1958, Glaciated peaks in the northern Coast Ranges, California: Amer. J. Sci., v. 256, p. 620-629

Davis, Stanley N., and Hall, Francis R., 1959, Water quality of eastern Stanislaus and northern Merced Counties, California: Stanford Univ. Publ. Geol. Sci., v. 6, No. 1, p. 1-112

Davis, W. M., 1933, Glacial epochs of the Santa Monica Mountains, California: Geol. Soc. Amer. Bull., v. 44, p. 1041-1133

Dibblee, T. W., Jr., 1950, Geology of southwestern Santa Barbara County, California: California Div. Mines Bull. 150, 95 p.

—— 1958, Tertiary stratigraphic units of the western Mojave Desert, California: Amer. Assoc. Petroleum Geologists Bull., v. 42, No. 1, p. 135-144

—— 1962, Displacements on the San Andreas Rift Zone and related structures in Carrizo Plain and vicinity, in Guidebook to the geology of the Carrizo Plains and San Andreas Fault: San Joaquin Geol. Soc. and Pacific Sect., Amer. Assoc. of Petroleum Geologists and Soc. Exploration Paleontologists and Mineralogists (AAPG-SEPM), p. 5-12

Diller, Joseph S., 1895, Description of the Lassen Peak sheet: U.S. Geol. Surv., Geol. Atlas of the United States, Folio No. 15

—— 1902, Topographic development of the Klamath Mountains: U.S. Geol. Surv. Bull. 196, 69 p.

—— 1906, Description of the Redding quadrangle, California: U.S. Geol. Surv., Geol. Atlas of the United States, Folio No. 138, 14 p.

Drewes, Harald, 1963, Geology of the Funeral Peak quadrangle, California, on the east flank of Death Valley: U.S. Geol. Surv. Prof. Pap. 413, 78 p.

Driver, Herschel L., 1943, Inglewood oil field, in Jenkins, 1943, p. 306-309

Durham, D. L., and Yerkes, R. F., 1964, Geology and oil resources of the eastern Puente Hills area, southern California: U.S. Geol. Surv. Prof. Pap. 420-B, 62 p.

Durham, J. Wyatt, 1954, The marine Cenozoic of southern California: in Jahns, 1954, Ch. 3, p. 23-31

Durham, J. Wyatt, Jahns, Richard H., and Savage, Donald E., 1954, Marine-nonmarine relationships in the Cenozoic section of California: in Jahns, 1954, Ch. 3, p. 59-71

Dutcher, L. C., and Garrett, A. A., 1963, Geologic and hydrologic features of the San Bernardino area, California, with special reference to underflow across the San Jacinto Fault: U.S. Geol. Surv. Water-Supply Pap. 1419, 114 p.

Eaton, J. E., 1928, Divisions and duration of the Pleistocene in southern California: Amer. Assoc. Petroleum Geologists Bull., v. 12, p. 111-141

Ellis, Arthur J., and Lee, Charles H., 1919, Geology and ground-waters of the western part of San Diego County, California: U.S. Geol. Surv. Water-Supply Pap. 446, 320 p.

Emery, K. O., 1960, The sea off southern California—a modern habitat of petroleum: New York, John Wiley and Sons, 366 p.

Emiliani, C., and Epstein, S., 1953, Temperature variations in the lower Pleistocene of southern California: J. Geol., v. 61, p. 171-181

Evenson, R. E., 1959, Geology and ground-water features of the Eureka area, Humboldt County, California: U.S. Geol. Surv. Water-Supply Pap. 1470, 80 p.

Evernden, J. F., and Curtis, G. H., in press, The potassium-argon dating of late Cenozoic rocks in East Africa and Italy: Curr. Anthrop.

Evernden, J. F., and James, G. T., 1964, Potassium-argon dates and the Tertiary floras of North America: Amer. J. Sci., v. 262, p. 945-974

Evernden, J. F., Savage, D. E., Curtis, G. H., and James, G. T., 1964, Potassium-argon dates and the Cenozoic mammalian chronology of North America: Amer. J. Sci., v. 262, p. 145-198

Fairbanks, H. W., 1898, Geology of a portion of the southern Coast Ranges: J. Geol., v. 6, p. 565-566

—— 1904, Description of the San Luis quadrangle: U.S. Geol. Surv., Geol. Atlas of the United States, Folio No. 101

Fenneman, N. M., 1931, Physiography of the western United States: New York, McGraw-Hill Book Co., 534 p.

Flint, R. F., 1957, Glacial and Pleistocene geology: New York, John Wiley and Sons, 553 p.

Frink, John W., and Kues, Harry A., 1954, Corcoran clay—a Pleistocene lacustrine deposit in San Joaquin Valley, California: Amer. Assoc. Petroleum Geologists Bull., v. 38, p. 2357-2371

Gardner, Robert A., and Bradshaw, Kenneth E., 1954, Characteristics and vegetation relationships of some Podzolic soils near the coast of northern California: Soil Sci. Soc. Amer. Proc., v. 18, p. 320-325

Garrison, Lowell E., 1962, The Marysville (Sutter) Buttes, Sutter County, California: California Div. Mines Geol. Bull. 181, p. 69-72

Gealey, William Kelso, 1951, Geology of the Healdsburg quadrangle, California: California Div. Mines Bull. 161, p. 1-50

Gilbert, Charles M., 1938, Welded tuff in eastern California: Geol. Soc. Amer. Bull., v. 49, p. 1829-1862

—— 1941, Late Tertiary geology southeast of Mono Lake, California: Geol. Soc. Amer. Bull., v. 52, p. 781-816

Gilbert, Grove Karl, 1914, The transportation of debris by running water: U.S. Geol. Surv. Prof. Pap. 86, 263 p.

—— 1917, Hydraulic-mining debris in the Sierra Nevada: U.S. Geol. Surv. Prof. Pap. 105, 154 p.

Glen, William, 1959, Pliocene and lower Pleistocene of the western part of the San Francisco Peninsula: Univ. California Publ. Geol. Sci., v. 36, No. 2, p. 147-198

Grant, U. S., IV, and Gale, Hoyt Rodney, 1931, Catalogue of the marine Pliocene and Pleistocene mollusca of California and adjacent regions: San Diego Nat. Hist. Soc. Mem., v. 1, 1036 p.

Grinsfelder, S., 1943, Dominguez oil field, *in* Jenkins, 1943, p. 318-319

Hall, Clarence A., Jr., 1958, Geology and paleontology of the Pleasanton area, Alameda and Contra Costa Counties, California: Univ. California Publ. Geol. Sci., v. 34, p. 1-90

Hershey, Oscar H., 1900, Ancient alpine glaciers of the Sierra Costa Mountains in California: J. Geol., v. 8, p. 42-56

—— 1903a, Some evidence of two glacial stages in the Klamath Mountains in California: Amer. Geologist, v. 31, p. 139-156

—— 1903b, The relation between certain river terraces and the glacial series in northwestern California: J. Geol., v. 11, p. 431-458

—— 1903c, Certain river terraces of the Klamath region, California: Amer. J. Sci., 4th ser., v. 16, p. 240-250

—— 1904, The river terraces of the Orleans Basin, California: Univ. California Publ. Dept. Geol. Bull., v. 3, p. 423-475

Hibbard, C. W., Ray, D. E., Savage, D. E., Taylor, D. W., and Guilday, J. E., this volume, Quaternary mammals of North America

Higgins, Charles G., 1952, Lower course of the Russian River, California: Univ. Cailfornia Publ. Geol Sci., v. 29, No. 5, p. 181-264

—— 1960, Ohlson Ranch Formation, Pliocene, northwestern Sonoma County, California: Univ. California Publ. Geol. Sci., v. 36, p. 199-232

—— 1961, San Andreas Fault north of San Francisco, California: Geol. Soc. Amer. Bull., v. 72, p. 51-68

Hill, Mason L., and Dibblee, T. W., Jr., 1953, San Andreas, Garlock, and Big Pine Faults, California, a study of the character, history, and tectonic significance of their displacements: Geol. Soc. Amer. Bull., v. 64, p. 443-458

Hinds, Norman E. A., 1933, Geologic formations of the Redding-Weaverville districts, northern California: California J. Mines Geol. (State Mineralogist's Rep.), v. 29, p. 77-122

—— 1952, Evolution of the California landscape: California Div. Mines Bull. 158, 240 p.

Holmes, L. C., Nelson, J. W., *et al.*, 1915, Reconnaissance soil survey of the Sacramento Valley, California: U.S. Dept. Agric., Bur. Soils, Advance Sheets, Field Operations, 1915, 148 p.

Holway, R. S., 1911, An extension of the known area of Pleistocene glaciation to the Coast Ranges of California: Amer. Geogr. Soc. Bull., v. 43, p. 161-170 (from Davis, S. N., 1958).

Hoots, H. W., 1930, Geology and oil resources along the southern border of San Joaquin Valley, California: U.S. Geol. Surv. Bull. 812, p. 243-332

Hoots, Harold W., Bear, Ted L., and Kleinpell, William D., 1954, Geological summary of the San Joaquin Valley, California: *in* Jahns, 1954, Ch. 2, p. 113-129

Howard, Arthur, 1951, Development of the landscape of the San Francisco Bay Counties: California Div. Mines Bull. 154, p. 95-106

Hudson, F. S., 1955, Measurement of the deformation of the Sierra Nevada, California, since middle Eocene: Geol. Soc. Amer. Bull., v. 66, p. 835-870

—— 1960, Post-Pliocene uplift of the Sierra Nevada, California: Geol. Soc. Amer. Bull., v. 71, p. 1547-1574

Huey, Arthur S., 1948, Geology of the Tesla quadrangle, California: California Div. Mines Bull. 140, 75 p.

Irwin, William P., 1960, Geologic reconnaissance of the northern Coast Ranges and Klamath Mountains, California, with a summary of the mineral resources: California Div. Mines Bull. 179, 80 p.

Jahns, Richard H. (ed.), 1954, Geology of southern California: California Div. Mines Bull. 170, 10 chapters, separately paged

Jenkins, Olaf P., *et al.*, 1943, Geologic formations and economic development of the oil and gas fields of California: California Div. Mines Bull. 118, 773 p.

Jennings, Charles W., 1958, San Luis Obispo sheet, geologic map of California (1:250,000), Olaf P. Jenkins edition: California Div. Mines Geol.

—— 1959, Santa Maria sheet, geologic map of California (1:250,000), Olaf P. Jenkins edition: California Div. Mines Geol.

Jennings, Charles W., and Burnett, John L., 1961, San Francisco sheet (1:250,000), geologic map of California, Olaf P. Jenkins edition: California Div. Mines Geol.

Jennings, Charles W., and Strand, Rudolph G., 1958, Santa Cruz sheet (1:250,000), geologic map of California, Olaf P. Jenkins edition: California Div. Mines Geol.

—— 1960, Ukiah sheet (1:250,000), geologic map of California, Olaf P. Jenkins edition: California Div. Mines Geol.

Johnson, F. A., 1943, Petaluma region: *in* Jenkins, 1943, p. 622-627

Johnson, Harry R., 1943, Marysville Buttes (Sutter Buttes) gas field: *in* Jenkins, 1943, p. 610-615

Kew, William S. W., 1924, Geology and oil resources of a part of Los Angeles and Ventura Counties, California: U.S. Geol. Surv. Bull. 753, 202 p.

King, Philip B., 1958, Evolution of modern surface features of western North America: *in* Hubbs, C. L. (ed.), Zoogeography: Amer. Assoc. Adv. Sci. Publ. 51, p. 3-60

—— 1959, The Evolution of North America: Princeton, N.J., Princeton Univ. Press, 190 p.

—— this volume, Tectonics of Quaternary time in middle North America

Knopf, Adolph, 1918, A geologic reconnaissance of the Inyo Range and the eastern slope of the Sierra Nevada, California, with a section on the stratigraphy of the Inyo Range by Edwin Kirk: U.S. Geol. Surv. Prof. Pap. 110, 130 p.

Koenig, James B., 1963, Santa Rosa sheet (1:250,000), geologic map of California, Olaf P. Jenkins edition: California Div. Mines Geol.

Kundert, Charles J., 1955, Bakersfield sheet, geologic map of California (1:250,000), prelim. uncolored ed.: California Div. Mines

Kunkel, Fred, and Upson, J. E., 1960, Geology and ground-water in Napa and Sonoma Valleys, Napa and Sonoma Counties, California: U.S. Geol. Surv. Water-Supply Pap. 1495, 252 p.

Lachenbruch, M. C., 1962, Geology of the west side of the Sacramento Valley, California: in Bowen, 1962, p. 53-66

Lawson, Andrew C., 1893, The post-Pliocene diastrophism of the coast of southern California: Univ. California, Dept. Geol. Bull., v. 1, p. 115-160

—— 1894, The geomorphogeny of the coast of northern California: Univ. California Dept. Geol. Bull., v. 1, p. 241-272

—— 1904, The geomorphogeny of the upper Kern Basin: Univ. California Dept. Geol. Sci. Bull., v. 3, p. 291-376

—— 1914, Description of the San Francisco District: U.S. Geol. Surv., Geol. Atlas of the United States, Folio 193 (Field edition, 1915, 180 p.)

Le Conte, Joseph, 1873, On some of the ancient glaciers of the Sierra: Amer. J. Sci., 3rd ser., v. 5, p. 325-339

Lindgren, Waldemar, 1894, Description of the Sacramento sheet: U.S. Geol. Surv., Geol. Atlas of the United States, Folio No. 5, p. 2-3

—— 1896, Description of the Pyramid Peak quadrangle: U.S. Geol. Surv., Geol. Atlas of the United States, Folio No. 31, p. 1-6

—— 1897, Description of the Truckee quadrangle: U.S. Geol. Surv., Geol. Atlas of the United States, Folio No. 37, p. 2-8

—— 1900, Description of the Colfax quadrangle: U.S. Geol. Surv., Geol. Atlas of the United States, Folio No. 66, 10 p.

—— 1911, The Tertiary gravels of the Sierra Nevada of California: U.S. Geol. Surv. Prof. Pap. 73, 226 p.

Lindgren, Waldemar, and Turner, H. W., 1895, Description of the Marysville sheet: U.S. Geol. Surv., Geol. Atlas of the United States, Folio No. 17, 2 p.

Long, Joseph S., Jr., and Carpenter, David W., 1963, Geology of the Mile 18 Pumping Plant area: Geol. Soc. Sacramento, Richter, Raymond C. (ed.), Guidebook to the annual field trip for 1963, central portion of the Great Valley of California, p. 53-56

Louderback, George D., 1951, Geologic history of San Francisco Bay: California Div. Mines Bull. 154, p. 75-94

MacDonald, Gordon A., 1963, Geology of the Manzanita Lake quadrangle, California (1:62,500): U.S. Geol. Surv. Geol. Quadrangle Map GQ 248

MacGinitie, H. D., 1937, The flora of the Weaverville beds of Trinity County, California, in Eocene flora of western America: Carnegie Instn. Contr. Paleont., Publ. 465, p. 84-151

—— 1943, Central and southern Humboldt County: in Jenkins, 1943, p. 633-635

Manning, John C., 1963, Resume of ground-water hydrology in Salinas Valley, California: Amer. Assoc. Petroleum Geologists, Soc. Exploration Mineralogists and Paleontologists, Pacific Sect. in Payne, Max B. (ed.), Guidebook to the geology of the Salinas Valley and the San Andreas Fault, annual spring field trip, May 24-25, 1963, p. 106-109

Martin, Bruce, 1916, The Pliocene of middle and northern California: Univ. California Publ., Dept. Geol. Sci. Bull., v. 9, p. 215-259

Matthes, Francois E., 1930, Geologic history of the Yosemite Valley: U.S. Geol. Surv. Prof. Pap. 160, 137 p.

—— 1938, The geologic history of Mt. Whitney: Sierra Club Bull., v. 22, p. 1-18

—— 1939, Report of the Committee on Glaciers: Amer. Geophys. Union, Trans. for 1939, pt. III, p. 518-523

—— 1942, Glaciers, in Meinzer, O. E. (ed.), Physics of the earth—hydrology: New York, McGraw-Hill Book Co., p. 149-219 (Reprinted 1949 by Dover Publications, Inc., New York)

—— 1950, The incomparable valley, a geologic interpretation of the Yosemite, edited by Fritiof Fryxell, including 24 photographs by Ansel Adams: Berkeley, Univ. California Press, 160 p.

—— 1960, Reconnaissance of the geomorphology and glacial geology of the San Joaquin Basin, Sierra Nevada, California: U.S. Geol. Surv. Prof. Pap. 329, 62 p.

Maxson, John H., 1933, Economic geology of portions of Del Norte and Siskiyou Counties, northwesternmost California: California J. Mines Geol. (State Mineralogist's Rep.), v. 29, p. 123-160

McAllister, J. F., 1936, Glacial history of an area near Lake Tahoe: Stanford University M.A. thesis

McVath, V. E., 1959-1960, Reconnaissance geology of parts of Almanor, Greenville, Kettle Rock, Chester, and Westwood quadrangles: California Division of Mines, unpublished report

Mendenhall, W. C., Dole, R. B., and Stabler, Herman, 1916, Ground water in the San Joaquin Valley, California: U.S. Geol. Surv. Water-Supply Pap. 398, 310 p.

Miller, D. H., 1955, Snow cover and climate in the Sierra Nevada, California: Univ. California Publ. Geogr., v. 11, p. 1-218

Minard, Claude R., Jr., 1964, The erosional and depositional history of the coast of northern California: Univ. California Hydraulic Engineering Lab. Tech. Rep. HEL—2-10, 63 p.

Moore, James G., 1963, Geology of the Mount Pinchot quadrangle, southern Sierra Nevada, California: U.S. Geol. Surv. Bull. 1130, 152 p.

Morrison, Roger B., this volume, Quaternary geology of the Great Basin

Muir, John, 1872, Living glaciers of California, Overland, v. 9, p. 547-549

—— 1874, Studies in the Sierra: Overland, v. 12, p. 393-403, 489-500; v. 13, p. 67-79, 174-184, 393-401, 530-540; v. 14, p. 64-73

—— 1880, Ancient glaciers of the Sierra: Californian, v. 2, p. 550-557

Nelson, J. W., Dean, Walter C., and Eckmann, E. C., 1921, Reconnaissance soil survey of the upper San Joaquin Valley, California: U.S. Dept. Agric., Bur. Soils (Advance Sheets—Field Operations) 1917

Nelson, Richard N., 1925, Geology of the hydrographic basin of the upper Santa Ynez River, California: Univ. California Publ., Dept. Geol. Sci. Bull., v. 15, p. 327-396

Oakeshott, Gordon B., 1958, Geology and mineral deposits of San Fernando quadrangle, Los Angeles County, California: California Div. Mines Bull. 172, 147 p.

Ogle, Burdette A., 1953, Geology of Eel River area, Humboldt County, California: California Div. Mines Bull. 164, 128 p.

Olmsted, F. H., 1958, Geologic reconnaissance of San Clemente Island, California: U.S. Geol. Surv. Bull. 1071-B, p. 55-68

Olmsted, F. H., and Davis, G. H., 1961, Geologic features and ground-water storage capacity of the Sacramento Valley, California: U.S. Geol. Surv. Water-Supply Pap. 1497, 241 p.

Orr, Phil C., 1960, Late Pleistocene marine terraces on Santa Rosa Island, California: Geol. Soc. Amer. Bull., v. 71, p. 1113-1120

Ortalda, Robert A., 1949, Geology of the northern part of the Morgan Hill quadrangle, California: Berkeley, Univ. California M.A. thesis, 55 p.

Page, R. W., 1963, Geology and ground-water appraisal of the Naval Air Missile Test Center Area, Point Mugu, California: U.S. Geol. Surv. Water-Supply Pap. 1619-S, 40 p.

Peck, Joseph H., Jr., 1960, Paleontology and correlation of the Ohlson Ranch Formation: Univ. California Publ. Geol. Sci., v. 36, p. 233-242

Piper, A. M., Gale, H. S., Thomas, H. E., and Robinson, T. W., 1939, Geology and ground-water hydrology of the Mokelumne area, California: U.S. Geological Surv. Water-Supply Pap. 780, 230 p.

Poland, J. F., Garrett, A. A., and Sinnott, Allen, 1959, Geology, hydrology, and chemical character of ground-waters in the Torrance–Santa Monica area, California: U.S. Geol. Surv. Water-Supply Pap. 1461, 425 p.

Poland, J. F., and Green, J. H., 1962, Subsidence in the Santa Clara Valley, California, a progress report: U.S. Geol. Surv. Water-Supply Pap. 1619-C, 16 p.

Poland, J. F., Piper, A. M., *et al.*, 1956, Ground-water geology of the Coastal Zone, Long Beach–Santa Ana area, California: U.S. Geol. Surv. Water-Supply Pap. 1109, 162 p.

Putnam, William C., 1942, Geomorphology of the Ventura region, California: Geol. Soc. Amer. Bull., v. 53, p. 691-754

—— 1949, Quaternary geology of the June Lake District, California: Geol. Soc. Amer. Bull., v. 60, p. 1281-1302

—— 1950, Moraine and shoreline relationships at Mono Lake, California: Geol. Soc. Amer. Bull., v. 61, p. 115-122

—— 1960a, Origin of Rock Creek and Owens River Gorges, Mono County, California: Univ. California Publ. Geol. Sci., v. 34, p. 221-280

—— 1960b, Faulting and Pleistocene glaciation in the east-central Sierra Nevada of California, U.S.A.: 21st Intern. Geol. Congr. Copenhagen, Rep., pt. 21, p. 270-274

—— 1962, Late Cenozoic geology of McGee Mountain, Mono County, California: Univ. California Publ. Geol. Sci., v. 40, p. 181-218

Radbruch, Dorothy H., 1957, Areal and engineering geology of the Oakland West quadrangle, California (1:24,000): U.S. Geol. Surv. Misc. Geol. Inv. Map I-239

Reed, Ralph D., 1933, Geology of California: Tulsa, Oklahoma, Amer. Assoc. Petroleum Geologists, 355 p.

Reed, Ralph D., and Hollister, J. S., 1936, Structural evolution of southern California: Tulsa, Oklahoma, Amer. Assoc. Petroleum Geologists, 157 p.

Reiche, Parry, 1950, Geology of part of the Delta-Mendota Canal, near Tracy, California: California Div. Mines Spec. Rep. No. 2, 12 p.

Rinehart, C. Dean, and Ross, Donald C., 1957, Geology of the Casa Diablo Mountain quadrangle, California (1:62,500): U.S. Geol. Surv. Geol. Quadrangle Map, No. GQ 99

—— 1964, Geology and mineral deposits of the Mount Morrison quadrangle, Sierra Nevada, California; with a section on a gravity study of Long Valley, by L. C. Pakiser: U.S. Geol. Surv. Prof. Pap. 385, 106 p.

Rubin, Meyer, and Alexander, Corrinne, 1960, U.S. Geological Survey radiocarbon dates v: Amer. J. Sci., Radiocarbon Suppl., v. 2, p. 129-185

Russell, Israel C., 1885a, Existing glaciers of the United States: U.S. Geol. Surv. 5th Ann. Rep., p. 303-355

—— 1885b, Geologic history of Lake Lahontan, a Quaternary lake of northwestern Nevada: U.S. Geol. Surv. Monogr. 11, 288 p.

—— 1889, Quaternary history of Mono Valley, California: U.S. Geol. Surv. 8th Ann. Rep., p. 251-394

Russell, R. D., and VanderHoof, V. L., 1931, A vertebrate fauna from a new Pliocene formation in northern California: Univ. California Publ., Dept. Geol. Sci. Bull., v. 20, p. 11-21

Safonov, Anatole, 1962, The challenge of the Sacramento Valley, California: *in* Bowen, 1962, p. 77-97

Savage, Donald E., 1951, Late Cenozoic vertebrates of the San Francisco Bay region: Univ. California Publ., Dept. Geol. Sci. Bull., v. 28, p. 215-314

Schlocker, J., Bonilla, M. G., and Radbruch, D. H., 1958, Geology of the San Francisco North quadrangle, California (1:24,000): U.S. Geol. Surv. Misc. Geol. Inv. Map I-272

Sharp, Robert P., 1960, Pleistocene glaciation in the Trinity Alps of northern California: Amer. J. Sci., v. 258, p. 305-340

Sharp, Robert P., Allen, Clarence R., and Meier, Mark F., 1959, Pleistocene glaciers on southern California mountains: Amer. J. Sci., v. 257, p. 81-94

Sharp, Robert P., and Birman, J. H., 1963, Addition to the classical sequence of Pleistocene glaciations, Sierra Nevada, California: Geol. Soc. Amer. Bull., v. 74, p. 1079-1086

Smith, David D., 1960, The geomorphology of part of the San Francisco Peninsula, California: Stanford University Ph.D. thesis

Stirton, R. A., 1936, Succession of North American continental Pliocene mammalian faunas: Amer. J. Sci., 5th ser. v. 32, p. 161-206

—— 1939, Cenozoic mammal remains from the San Francisco Bay region: Univ. California Publ., Dept. Geol. Sci. Bull., v. 24, p. 339-410

—— 1952, Are Petaluma horse teeth reliable in correlation?: Amer. Assoc. Petroleum Geologists Bull., v. 36, p. 2011-2025

Stock, Chester, 1930, Rancho La Brea, a record of Pleistocene life in California: Los Angeles Mus. Publ. 1, 82 p.

Stolz, Harry P., 1943, Long Beach oil field: *in* Jenkins, 1943, p. 320-324

Strand, Rudolph G., 1962, Redding sheet (1:250,000), geologic map of California, Olaf P. Jenkins edition: California Div. Mines Geol.

—— 1963, Weed sheet (1:250,000), geologic map of California, Olaf P. Jenkins edition: California Div. Mines Geol.

Taliaferro, N. L., 1941, Geologic history and structure of the central Coast Ranges of California: *in* Jenkins, 1943, p. 119-162

—— 1943, Bradley-San Miguel District: *in* Jenkins, 1943, p. 456-462

Thomas, R. G., Marliave, E. C., James, L. B., and Bean, R. T., 1954, Geology and hydrology of Ventura County: *in* Jahns, 1954, Ch. 6, p. 19-28

Thompson, George A., and Talwani, Manik, 1964, Geology of the crust and mantle, western United States: Science, v. 146, p. 1539-1549

Thompson, George A., and White, D. E., 1964, Regional geology of the Steamboat Springs area, Washoe County, Nevada: U.S. Geol. Surv. Prof. Pap. 458-A, 52 p.

Tocher, Don, 1959, Seismic history of the San Francisco region: California Div. Mines Spec. Rep. 57, p. 41-48

Trask, Parker D., 1926, Geology of Point Sur quadrangle, California: Univ. California Publ., Dept. Geol. Sci. Bull., v. 16, p. 119-186

Trask, Parker D., and Rolston, Jack W., 1951, Engineering geology of San Francisco Bay, California: Geol. Soc. Amer. Bull., v. 62, p. 1079-1110

Travis, Russell B., 1952, Geology of the Sebastopol quadrangle, California: California Div. Mines Bull. 162, 33 p.

Turner, H. W., 1897, Description of the Downieville quadrangle: U.S. Geol. Surv. Geol. Atlas of the United States, Folio No. 37, p. 3-8

—— 1898, Description of the Bidwell Bar quadrangle: U.S. Geol. Surv., Geol. Atlas of the United States, Folio No. 43, p. 3-6

—— 1900, The Pleistocene geology of the south central Sierra Nevada with especial reference to the origin of Yosemite Valley: California Acad. Sci. Proc., Ser. 3, Geol., v. 1, p. 261-321

Turner, H. W., and Ransome, F. L., 1898, Description of the Big Trees quadrangle: U.S. Geol. Surv. Geol. Atlas of the United States, Folio No. 51, p. 3-8

Upson, J. E., 1949, Late Pleistocene and Recent changes of sea level along the coast of Santa Barbara County, California: Amer. J. Sci., v. 247, p. 94-115

—— 1951a, Geology and ground-water resources of the south-coast basins of Santa Barbara County, California; with a section on surface-water resources by H. G. Thomasson, Jr.: U.S. Geol. Surv. Water-Supply Pap. 1108, 144 p.

—— 1951b, Former marine shore lines of the Gaviota quadrangle, Santa Barbara County, California: J. Geol., v. 59, p. 415-446

Upson, J. E., and Kunkel, Fred, 1955, Ground water of the Lower Lake–Middletown area, Lake County, California: U.S. Geol. Surv. Water-Supply Pap. 1297, 81 p.

Upson, J. E., and Thomasson, H. G., Jr., 1951, Geology and water resources of the Santa Ynez River Basin, Santa Barbara County, California: U.S. Geol. Surv. Water-Supply Pap. 1107, 194 p.

Valentine, James W., 1961, Paleoecologic molluscan geography of the California Pleistocene: Univ. California Publ. Geol. Sci., v. 34, p. 309-442

Valentine, James W., and Meade, Robert F., 1961, California Pleistocene paleotemperatures: Univ. California Publ. Geol. Sci., v. 40, p. 1-46

VanderHoof, V. L., 1933a, Additions to the fauna of the Tehama upper Pliocene of northern California: Amer. J. Sci., 5th ser., v. 25, p. 382-384

—— 1933b, A skull of *Pliohippus tantalus* from the later Tertiary of the Sierran foothills of California: Univ. California Publ., Dept. Geol. Sci. Bull., v. 23, p. 183-193

—— 1955, The major earthquakes of California; a historical summary: California Div. Mines Bull. 171, p. 137-141

Wahrhaftig, Clyde, 1963, Origin of stepped topography of the west-central Sierra Nevada, California (abst.): Geol. Soc. Amer. Spec. Pap. 73, p. 71

—— in press, The stepped topography of the southern Sierra Nevada, California, and its origin: Geol. Soc. Amer. Bull.

Weaver, Charles E., 1949, Geology of the north Coast Ranges immediately north of the San Francisco Bay region, California: Geol. Soc. Amer. Mem. 35, 242 p.

Weaver, D. K., and Wilhelm, V. H., 1943, Huntington Beach oil field: *in* Jenkins, 1943, p. 329-331

Webb, Robert W., 1950, Volcanic geology of Toowa Valley, southern Sierra Nevada, California: Geol. Soc. Amer. Bull., v. 61, p. 349-357

Wells, Francis G., Hotz, Preston E., and Cater, Fred W., Jr., 1949, Preliminary description of the geology of the Kerby quadrangle, Oregon: Oregon (State) Dept. Geol. Min. Ind., Bull. 40, 23 p.

Whitten, C. A., 1949, Horizontal earth movement in California: Coast and Geodetic Surv. J., April 1949, No. 2, p. 84-88

Williams, Howel, 1929, Geology of the Marysville Buttes, California: Univ. California Publ., Dept. Geol. Sci. Bull., v. 18, No. 5, p. 103-220

—— 1949, Geology of MacDoel quadrangle, California: California Div. Mines Bull. 151, p. 7-60

Wilson, Ivan F., 1943, Geology of the San Benito quadrangle, California: California J. Mines Geol. (State Mineralogist's Rep.) v. 39, No. 2, p. 183-270

Winterer, E. L., and Durham, D. L., 1962, Geology of southeastern Ventura Basin, Los Angeles County, California: U.S. Geol. Surv. Prof. Pap. 334-H, p. 275-336

Woodford, A. O., Schoellhamer, J. E., Vedder, J. G., and Yerkes, R. F., 1954, Geology of the Los Angeles Basin: *in* Jahns, 1954, Ch. 2, p. 65-81

Woodring, W. P., 1952, Plio-Pleistocene boundary in California Coast Ranges: Amer. J. Sci., v. 250, p. 401-410

Woodring, W. P., Bramlette, M. N., and Kew, W. S. W., 1946, Geology and paleontology of Palos Verdes Hills, California: U.S. Geol. Surv. Prof. Pap. 207, 145 p.

Woodring, W. P., and Bramlette, M. N., 1950, Geology and paleontology of the Santa Maria District, California: U.S. Geol. Surv. Prof. Pap. 222, 185 p.

Woodring, W. P., Roundy, P. V., and Farnsworth, H. R., 1932, Geology and oil resources of the Elk Hills, California, including Naval Petroleum Reserve No. 1: U.S. Geol. Surv. Bull. 835, 82 p.

Woodring, W. P., Stewart, Ralph, and Richards, R. W., 1940, Geology of the Kettleman Hills oil field, California: U.S. Geol. Surv. Prof. Pap. 195, 170 p.

SUMMARY

California is in the eugeosynclinal part of the Cordilleran mobile belt and has undergone orogenic activity periodically from Jurassic time; the latest major orogeny extended from mid-Tertiary to the present. Physiographic provinces include: the Sierra Nevada, a tilted fault block underlain by granitic and metamorphic rocks; the Great Valley, a sedimentary basin with thick Quaternary alluvium; the Klamath Mountains; the Coast Ranges, northwest-trending mountains of Mesozoic and Cenozoic rocks separated by structural valleys; the Transverse Ranges, an east-trending belt of mountains and structural valleys; the Peninsular Range, a tilted fault block similar to the Sierra Nevada; and the Province of Southern California, a largely submerged area of basin-and-range topography that includes several islands, the continental shelf, and a triangular lowland on the mainland. Active transcurrent faults, most important of which is the San Andreas Fault, influence the geology and topography of coastal California.

Quaternary volcanic rocks on the east side of the Sierra Nevada include basaltic flows 1.2 to 2.3 million years old north of Lake Tahoe (the Lousetown Formation); deformed basalt flows 2.6-3.2 million years old overlain unconformably by tilted and faulted ignimbrite (the Bishop Tuff) 700,000 years old, which is overlain in turn by tuff rings, obsidian domes, and a dacite volcano (the Mono Craters and Mammoth Mountains) 5,000-370,000 years old, all between Mono Lake and Bishop; and basaltic flows and cinder cones in Owens Valley. Quaternary volcanic rocks on the western slope of the Sierra Nevada include basaltic flows 2.9 to 3.8 million years old in the basins of the San Joaquin and Kern Rivers. The dated volcanic rocks established that the canyon-cutting stage on the west side of the Sierra Nevada was well advanced 3.5 million years ago and that much of the faulting on the east side took place in the last 2.6 million years.

Six glaciations have been recognized in the Sierra Nevada, not counting post-Altithermal advances. These are: the McGee, represented by ancient till on high ridge-tops resting on basalt 2.5 million years old; the Sherwin, at lesser altitudes above valley bottoms and without preserved morainal topography, overlain by the Bishop Tuff (700,000 years old) at its type locality; the Mono Basin, with well-preserved but subdued morainal topography; the Tahoe, with well-preserved morainal topography and abundant weathered granodiorite boulders; the Tenaya; and the Tioga, with fresh boulders and nearly unmodified landforms. The last three glaciations are correlated with the Wisconsin; the Tahoe rests on basalt 60,000 or 90,000 years old; the Tenaya is intermediate in post-depositional weathering between the Tahoe and the Tenaya. Three small advances subsequent to the altithermal have been recognized.

The Quaternary alluvium in the Great Valley ranges up to 1,500 m or more in thickness and is the top of a generally parallel succession of Cretaceous and Cenozoic rocks many thousands of meters thick. Alluvium on the east side of the valley is the finest component of glacial outwash from the Sierra Nevada and is separated by erosional unconformities (with soils of different degrees of development) into the Turlock Lake, Riverbank, and Modesto Formations and Recent alluvium. Alluvium on the west side of the valley was deposited by mudflows and ephemeral streams and represents an apparently continuous succession broken only by angular unconformities along the margin of the Coast Ranges. The folded and locally overturned Quaternary along the southwest margin of the valley is named the Tulare Formation. Within the Tulare and also within the Turlock Lake Formation is a diatomaceous clay, the Corcoran Clay, which underlies much of the southern half of the valley at 60-270 m below the surface; it is about 600,000 years old and contains an Irvingtonian or Rancholabrean fauna.

The structural valleys of the southern Coast Ranges are bordered in part by moderately deformed Plio-Pleistocene sediments, 300 m or more thick, derived from nearby mountains. Over much of the Coast Ranges these rest unconformably on tightly folded upper Pliocene and older rocks, indicating that the orogeny that preceded their deposition was greater than that which followed. In the southeastern Coast Ranges the Plio-Pleistocene rocks are conformable on underlying marine Pliocene and Miocene rocks and are folded with them.

Younger undeformed alluvium several hundred meters thick underlies the centers of the valleys. Marine terraces along the coast have altitudes up to 300 m and are slightly deformed. As many as five or six terraces are present locally. No sign of marine inundation inland is found to correspond with these terraces. Postglacial eustatic sea-level rise is indicated by drowned valleys and alluvium-filled gorges descending to nearly 100 m below sea level.

The northern Coast Ranges and Klamath Mountains were above sea level during most of the upper Cenozoic, and their history is largely one of erosion, uplifting and warping, and volcanism. Deformed early-Quaternary formations, in part marine, are found in a few coastal basins. Marine terraces are common along the coast, up to 300 m in altitude, and are only locally deformed. A broad continental shelf indicates that the coastline was eroded back to about its present position after each uplift.

Late-Pliocene and Quaternary volcanic fields in the southern part of the northern Coast Ranges (Sonoma Volcanics and Clear Lake Volcanic Field) are associated with continental sedimentation in local basins; they include as their youngest members well-preserved dacitic strato-volcanoes and endogenous domes and rhyolitic and basaltic flows and cinder cones. Earlier flows and sediments are considerably deformed. Small structural valleys entirely enclosed by mountains are bordered by deformed continental Plio-Pleistocene(?) deposits and are underlain by several tens to a few hundred meters of alluvium. Several streams are antecedent to Quaternary upwarps.

The Klamath Mountains had numerous valley glaciers, and a few peaks in the northern Coast Ranges were glaciated. Wisconsin firn limit ranged from 1,600 to 2,000 m.

In Southern California the marine lower Pleistocene is as much as 1,500-1,850 m thick in the Ventura Basin and as much as 900 m thick beneath the Los Angeles Basin. Included in it are the Santa Barbara Formation, the San Pedro Sand, Timms Point Silt, and Lomita Marl. It is the top of an enormously thick sedimentary succession that was continuous from the Miocene and has been folded, locally overturned, and faulted. It interfingers to the north and east with continental gravels as much as 2,000 m thick.

As many as 13 and 20 marine terraces have been recognized on some parts of the Southern California coast, ranging in altitude up to 450 m. The lowest main terrace, overlain by the Palos Verdes Sand (Upper San Pedro) is about 30 m high and corresponds to the Sangamon Interglacial. It has been locally deformed into anticlines and monoclines. The fossiliferous asphalt of Rancho La Brea, in the northern part of the Los Angeles Basin, is contemporaneous with or slightly younger than the Palos Verdes Sand. Subsequent to withdrawal of the sea from the lowest terrace, rivers in the Los Angeles Basin cut trenches through the terrace at least 55 m deep. These have subsequently been filled.

THE GLACIAL HISTORY OF WESTERN WASHINGTON AND OREGON *

DWIGHT R. CRANDELL[1]

THE QUATERNARY history of Washington and Oregon (Fig. 1) is exceedingly varied, encompassing such contrasting events as repeated advances of alpine glaciers, invasions of Washington by the Cordilleran ice sheet, flooding of broad areas in the drainage basin of the Columbia River by vast volumes of water released from glacier-dammed lakes, building of large stratovolcanoes along the Cascade Range, and formation of pluvial lakes in the closed basins of eastern Oregon. This article is limited, however, chiefly to a discussion of glaciation in the two states, although alluviation, diastrophism, and sea-level changes are briefly considered. Emphasis is placed on the stratigraphic sequence in western Washington, because it includes a record of Pleistocene glaciations and climatic changes not yet known elsewhere in the region. Glaciation and flooding in eastern Washington are discussed by Richmond *et al.* (this volume).

WASHINGTON

The part of western Washington considered in this article includes three main physiographic subdivisions: the Cascade Range, Olympic Mountains, and Puget Sound lowland (Fig. 1); the Quaternary geology of eastern Washington is discussed by Richmond and others elsewhere in this volume. The Cascade Range is 100 to 160 km wide, and altitudes generally increase toward the north. Extensive areas in the central part of the range are higher than 1,500 m, and many peaks are higher than 1,800 m; farther north, large areas are above 1,800 m, and many peaks are 2,000 to 2,800 m high.

Towering 1,000 to 2,500 m above the average crestline of the range are five large stratovolcanoes of Quaternary age. Most of these volcanoes lie west of the crest of the range and form the headwaters of about half of the fifteen major rivers that drain the western slope of the mountains.

The Puget Sound lowland is a broad structural and topographic depression between the Cascades and the Olympic Mountains. It lies mostly below an altitude of 200 m and terminates southward in the vicinity of Chehalis, although low country continues southward into the Willamette Lowland of Oregon and westward along the Chehalis River valley to the Pacific Ocean. A spur of the Cascade Range separates the Puget Sount lowland from the Fraser Lowland.

The Olympic Mountains cover an area of about 10,000 km² and form a rugged mountain mass in which many peaks rise above 2,000 m, although most of the range is below 1,500 m.

* Publication authorized by the Director, U.S. Geological Survey.
[1] U.S. Geological Survey, Federal Center, Denver, Colorado.

PUGET SOUND LOWLAND

The most extensive record of Pleistocene time recognized so far in Washington is in the southeastern part of the Puget Sound lowland, where glacial strata representing at least four major glaciations are interbedded with nonglacial deposits (Table 1). The stratigraphic record of each major glaciation includes evidence of at least two glacier fluctuations.

The source and origin of most Pleistocene sediments in the southeastern part of the lowland can be determined by their lithology. During nonglacial intervals, drainage in the lowland was northward, toward the Pacific Ocean via Admiralty Inlet and the Strait of Juan de Fuca. At these times, lithologically distinctive alluvium and mudflows that originated in the Cascade Range and at Mount Rainier volcano were deposited in the southeastern part of the lowland. During glacial maxima, however, the Cordilleran ice

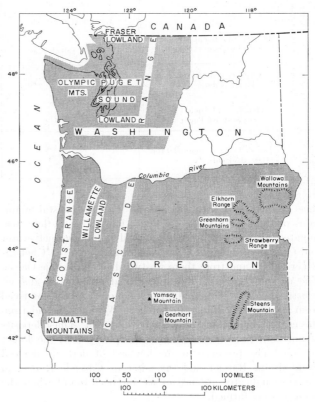

Figure 1. Index map of Washington and Oregon showing areas discussed in this paper.

341

TABLE 1

Summary of Early(?) to Middle(?) Pleistocene Events in the Southeastern Part of the Puget Sound Lowland (Prepared by D. R. Crandell and D. R. Mullineaux)

Geologic-climate unit	Event	Inferred climate
Puyallup Interglaciation	Weathering and erosion	
	Local lacustrine sedimentation in lowland	
	Fluvial and mudflow aggradation in southeastern part of lowland	Comparable to present
	Re-establishment of northwest-flowing streams	Increasing warmth
	Local lacustrine sedimentation in lowland	Cool-moist
Stuck Glaciation	Advance and retreat of Puget lobe	Glacial
	Retreat of glacier and re-establishment of northwest-flowing streams	Nonglacial
	Advance of Puget lobe	Glacial
Alderton Interglaciation	Fluvial and mudflow aggradation in southeastern part of lowland	Comparable to present
		Increasing warmth
	Re-establishment of northwest-flowing streams	Cool-moist
Orting Glaciation	Advance and retreat of Puget lobe	Glacial
	Advance and local(?) retreat of Puget lobe	
---?---	Local fluvial aggradation in lowland	Nonglacial

sheet pushed down into the lowland from the coastal mountains of Canada to form the Puget lobe. This ice lobe terminated against the Cascade foothills, forcing melt-water and Cascade drainage to flow southwesterly to the Chehalis River valley, and from there westward to the Pacific Ocean. The depositional record of the glacial episodes is characterized by drift that contains metamorphic rocks derived from the Cascade Range in northern Washington and from the coastal mountains of British Columbia. Thus deposits of northern provenance indicate the presence of the Puget ice lobe. The presence in the lowland of deposits derived from Mount Rainier and the adjacent Cascade Range, in contrast, indicates absence of ice in the lowland when the deposits were formed.

Early(?) and middle(?) Pleistocene time. Before the earliest recorded glaciation of the Puget Sound lowland, rivers locally built piedmont alluvial fans, or an alluvial plain, along

the western margin of the Cascade Range. These fluvial deposits are of early Orting age or perhaps even older than the Orting Glaciation (Table 1). They are overlain at Orting, Washington (Fig. 2), by till deposited by the Puget lobe of Orting age. In the walls of the Green River valley just west of the Cascade Range front, three tills of Orting age are separated by fluvial and lacustrine deposits, but evidence is lacking of long intervals between deposition of the tills (D. R. Mullineaux, written communication, 1961).

Orting Drift typically is oxidized throughout, but a residual soil has not been seen on it in the Puget Sound lowland. Just south of the lowland, a deeply weathered deposit of fluvial gravel, sand, and till, named the Logan Hill Formation (Snavely *et al.*, 1958), may be partly correlative with the Orting Drift. Most of the Logan Hill Formation was deposited in alluvial fans along the mountain front west of the point where the Cowlitz River valley leaves the Cascade Range. The interbedded till represents one or more advances of a piedmont glacier that originated in the Cascades.

During the Alderton Interglaciation the central part of the Puget lowland probably consisted of a drift plain broken by north-trending stream valleys. The only known depositional record of the interglaciation is exposed in the walls of the Puyallup River valley about 13 km east of Tacoma, Washington. There, interbedded fluvial sand and gravel, mudflows, and peat beds lie between glacial deposits of Orting and Stuck age. The fluvial and mudflow deposits are rich in hornblende-hypersthene andesite, and heavy minerals are dominated by hypersthene, hornblende, and magnetite. These rocks and minerals are believed to have originated at an active volcano in the headwaters of the Puyallup River, coincident with but probably predating the modern cone of Mount Rainier (Crandell, 1963b). The dominant pollen in some peat beds of Alderton age consists of Douglas fir (*Pseudotsuga menziesii* [Mirb.] Franco) and alder (probably *Alnus oregona*), both of which are common in the Puget lowland today and probably indicate that the climate of part of Alderton time was comparable to that of the present.

Drift deposited by the Puget lobe during the Stuck Glaciation is exposed in the valley walls of the Puyallup, Green, and White Rivers east of Tacoma, Washington. In the Puyallup River valley, the drift typically consists of a single sheet of till that lies between glaciofluvial deposits. Outcrops in the walls of the White and Green River valleys, however, include two widespread sheets of till that are separated by 15 to 50 m of lacustrine silt, clay, and sand and fluvial sand and gravel. Some fluvial deposits between the tills are chiefly of Mount Rainier and Cascade derivation, suggesting recession by the Puget lobe from the southeastern part of the lowland between glacial advances.

The record of the Puyallup Interglaciation is somewhat fuller than the Alderton, but deposits of Puyallup age are known only from the southeastern part of the Puget Sound lowland. These deposits consist chiefly of fluvial sand and gravel, lacustrine fine sediments, peat, and mudflows. Volcanic ash occurs in the deposits at several localities. Lithology of the sediments indicates that they were derived chiefly from Mount Rainier or an ancestor of this volcano, and

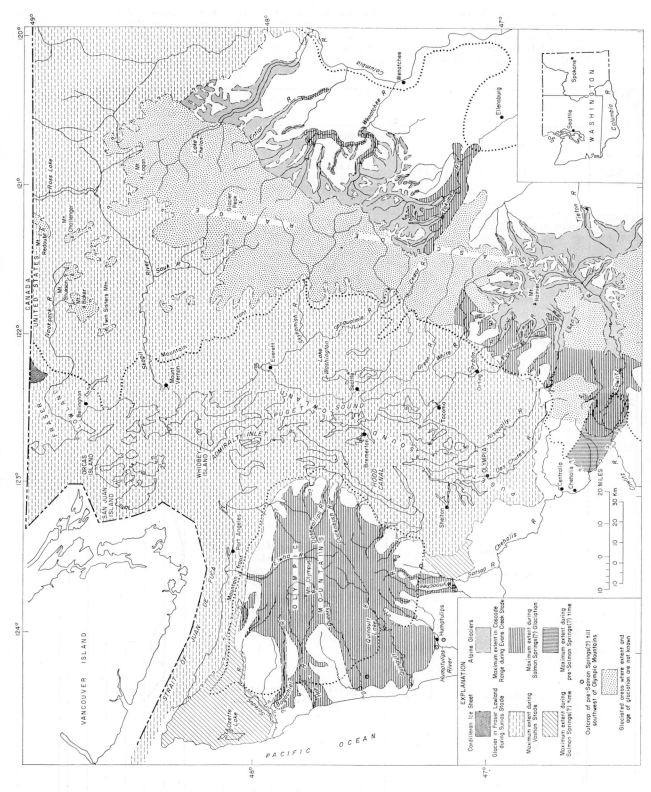

Figure 2. Inferred extent of glaciation in western Washington. Maximum extent of glacier in Yakima River valley from Stout (1964) and S. C. Porter (oral communication, 1964).

TABLE 2

Summary of Late Pleistocene Events in Western Washington (Curves showing average July temperature are from Heusser (1964) and are based on pollen profiles in a bog near Humptulips, Wash. Fossil pollen at various depths were compared with modern pollen spectra and average July temperatures at various localities along the north Pacific coast from the Columbia River northward to Alaska, and with altitudinal vegetation zones in the Olympic Mountains)

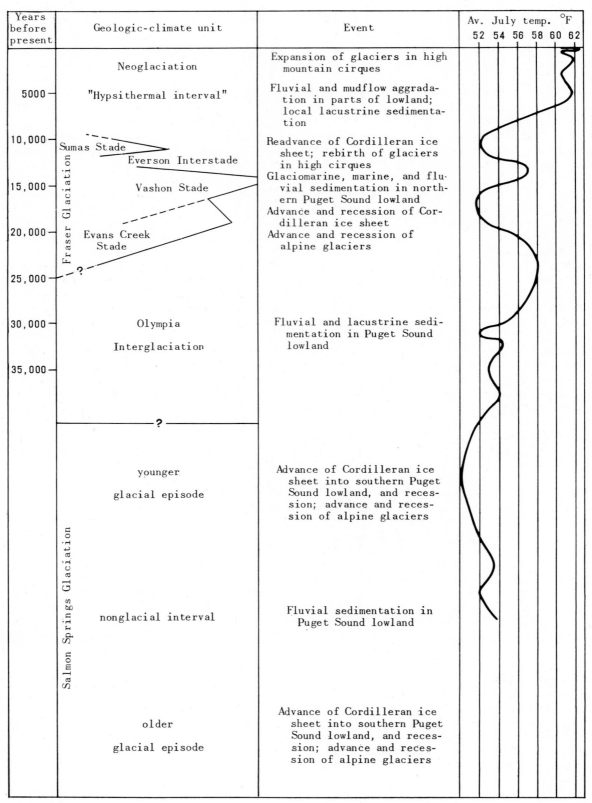

they represent virtually the same depositional environment as that of Alderton time.

Pollen in peat beds of Puyallup age indicates a climate comparable to that of today. The early phase of the interglaciation involved a more complex forest succession than did the warming of the early postglacial in the lowland. It contained more major cool phases and thus was probably more gradual and was accompanied by higher rainfall than that of the postglacial interval (Leopold and Crandell, 1957; see Heusser, this volume).

The deposits of Puyallup age probably represent only a fraction of the entire interglaciation, and their formation was followed by a long period of stream erosion and weathering before the next glaciation. During this period, clayey residual soils formed on surficial deposits both in the Puget Sound lowland and in the foothills of the Cascade Range. The Puyallup Interglaciation may be correlative with the Sangamon Interglaciation of the midwestern United States.

Late Pleistocene time. The Salmon Springs Glaciation is represented by two advances of the Puget lobe into the southern Puget Sound lowland, separated by a nonglacial interval during which the climate was cooler and moister than at the present (Table 2). Peat deposited during the nonglacial interval is more than 38,000 years old, indicating that it is older than the "classical Wisconsin" of the Great Lakes region of central North America. The Salmon Springs Glaciation may represent early to middle Wisconsin time, and it is used in this sense in the following discussion.

The maximum extent of the Puget lobe during either glacial episode in Salmon Springs time is not known, although the presence of weathered drift deposited by the Puget lobe beyond the limit of Vashon Drift at the southern and southwestern margins of the Puget Sound lowland (Fig. 2; Hansen and Mackin, 1949; Crandell, 1964) suggests that the lobe was at least as large during the Salmon Springs Glaciation as during the Vashon Stade of the Fraser Glaciation that followed.

Deposits of till-like, shell-bearing, pebbly silt and clay of late Salmon Springs(?) age occur in the lowland as far south as Seattle (Howard H. Waldron, oral communication, 1963), probably indicating that a marine embayment occupied the central part of the lowland during recession of the glacier.

A succession of deposits in the lowland north of Seattle (Hansen and Mackin, 1949) records three separate advances of the Puget lobe, the youngest of which is of Vashon age. Pollen in nonglacial deposits between the lowermost two drift sheets mostly suggests a climate cooler and moister than that of the present (see Heusser, this volume). Proboscidean bones and teeth identified by G. E. Lewis of the U.S. Geological Survey, apparently derived from the nonglacial beds but collected from beaches, are chiefly of *Mammuthus (Parelephas) columbi* (Falconer), and probably of Wisconsin age. The sketchy evidence now at hand suggests that the pre-Vashon sediments were deposited during the two glacial episodes and intervening nonglacial episode during the Salmon Springs Glaciation. It seems likely that the Puget lobe entirely disappeared from the lowland during the nonglacial episode.

During the Olympia Interglaciation, as northward drainage was re-established, nonglacial sediments were deposited in the Puget Sound lowland by streams draining the Cascade Range and Olympic Mountains. The glaciomarine drift formed in the marine embayment of late Salmon Springs time locally grades up into nonglacial lacustrine and fluvial sediments of Olympia age, indicating displacement of the embayment by aggradation. In the south-central part of the lowland, broad valleys between low hills or uplands of glacial drift were aggraded during Olympia time to altitudes 30-60 m above sea level. Peat and wood interbedded with the nonglacial deposits have yielded radiocarbon dates ranging from about 15,000 to about 35,000 years. Advance of the Cordilleran ice sheet into the Fraser Lowland of northwestern Washington terminated deposition of nonglacial sediments there some time after 22,000 years ago. Nonglacial fluvial and lacustrine deposition continued in the southern part of the lowland until about 15,000 years ago, even though long alpine glaciers were present in the adjacent mountains, and the front of the Cordilleran ice sheet had already entered northwestern Washington. Pollen from the upper part of the nonglacial deposits of Olympia age at Seattle suggest a climate cooler and more moist than at present (Mullineaux *et al.*, 1965).

The Fraser Glaciation began with the development of alpine glaciers in the mountains of western Washington and British Columbia during the Evans Creek Stade. In Washington, the alpine glaciers began to retreat before 15,000 years ago, but the Cordilleran ice sheet, which developed in the mountains of western Canada, continued to grow. It eventually expanded into the Strait of Juan de Fuca during the Vashon Stade and blocked the northern end of the Puget Sound lowland, resulting in the formation of a proglacial lake in the lowland about 15,000 years ago. As the glacier advanced southward, forming the Puget lobe, older unconsolidated glacial and nonglacial formations were deeply scoured by the glacier and redeposited by melt-water in front of the glacier. Limiting radiocarbon dates indicate that the front of the Puget lobe moved at a rate of 100-160 m per year between Seattle and its southern limit (Mullineaux *et al.*, 1965).

At its maximum extent the Puget lobe was nearly 100 km wide at the latitude of Seattle (Fig. 2). Erratics transported by the Puget lobe occur at an altitude of 1,600 m on Twin Sisters Mountain, about 35 km east of Bellingham (Easterbrook, 1963). At the western margin of the Cascade Range near the Nisqually River, 208 km south of Twin Sisters Mountain, the maximum altitude reached by the Puget lobe is about 400 m. Thus, the overall gradient of the ice surface was about 6 m/km. This is closely comparable to a north-to-south gradient of the ice surface calculated for the eastern and western margins of the lobe in the area south of Seattle.

When the lobe reached its maximum extent, it dammed valleys in the Cascade Range and Olympic Mountains that had just previously been occupied by alpine glaciers. Spillover of glacier-dammed lakes along the eastern margin of the Puget lobe caused the cutting of spectacular ice-marginal channels along the Cascade Range front. This drainage flowed southwestward to the Chehalis River valley and escaped westward to the Pacific Ocean.

The absence of a well-defined terminal moraine formed by the Puget lobe along the southern margin of the Puget Sound lowland and a lack of recessional moraines suggest that the glacier did not remain long at its maximum position. It probably melted back quickly to Admiralty Inlet, accompanied by the formation of a succession of proglacial lakes (Bretz, 1913).

Sea water entered the glacially scoured troughs along the center of the lowland shortly before 13,500 years ago, marking the beginning of the Everson Interstade. This episode was characterized by deposition of fossiliferous marine and glaciomarine sediments in front of and beneath the retreating Cordilleran glacier between about 13,500 and about 11,000 years ago (Armstrong *et al.*, in press). During this interval, the position of sea level relative to land in the Bellingham area in northwestern Washington fluctuated through a vertical interval of 180 m owing to a combination of an eustatic rise of sea level and contemporaneous isostatic rebound (Easterbrook, 1963).

During the following Sumas Stade, a lobe of the Cordilleran glacier reoccupied the Fraser River valley and advanced a short distance into the Fraser Lowland. This occurred at a late stage of the final uplift of the land following submergence during the Everson Interstade, but when the land was still 15-45 m lower with respect to sea level than at the present. This glacial advance probably occurred about 11,000 years ago; the Fraser River valley was free of ice by at least 9,000 years ago (Armstrong *et al.*, in press).

Postglacial time in the Puget Sound lowland was characterized chiefly by fluvial and mudflow aggradation. About 4,800 years ago avalanches of altered summit rocks on Mount Rainier produced mudflows that streamed down valleys on the southern and northeastern slopes of the volcano (Crandell, 1963a, b). The mudflow on the northeastern slope reached beyond the mountain front, where it spread out in a digitate lobe 32 km long and as much as 16 km wide, covering an area of at least 166 km² with thicknesses of as much as 20 m. Fluvial reworking of this deposit by the White River caused rapid alluviation in a marine trough extending from Seattle southward to Orting and aggraded it to a profile above sea level. A smaller mudflow that originated on the west flank of Mount Rainier about 500 years ago moved down the Puyallup River nearly to the mouth of the White River (Fig. 2; Crandell, 1963b).

GLACIATION IN THE CASCADE RANGE

Evidence of alpine glaciation is abundant throughout the Cascade Range of Washington. Each major valley in the range probably was glaciated during each glaciation recorded in the Puget Sound lowland, but alpine till of probable pre-Salmon Springs(?) age has been reported at only a few places. Along the west side of the Cascades, deeply weathered till and glaciofluvial deposits that contain till have been recognized in the Cowlitz River valley (Snavely *et al.*, 1958). These deposits were formed by a piedmont glacier that reached as much as 40 km beyond the mountain front. Deeply weathered till also occurs in the Nisqually River valley, but the westward extent of the pre-Salmon Springs(?) alpine glacier is obscured there by

an overlap of younger drift deposited by the Puget lobe of the Cordilleran glacier.

The piedmont glacier that formed in the drainage basin of the Cowlitz River must have been fed by very extensive ice fields and valley glaciers in the mountains, and it seems likely that comparably large glaciers formed also in the Cascade Range farther north and perhaps entered the Puget Sound lowland to merge with contemporary Cordilleran ice.

Drift probably of pre-Salmon Springs(?) age on the eastern side of the Cascade Range has so far been recognized only in the valleys of the Wenatchee (Page, 1939), Tieton, and Entiat Rivers (Long, 1951a, b).

Glaciation of the Cascade Range during Salmon Springs(?) time is well recorded in each of the valleys that head at Mount Rainier and includes two separate glacial episodes. The tills deposited during the two successive episodes are progressively more deeply oxidized with increasing age (2 m, and 3-4 m), and stones in the soil profiles of both tills have weathered rinds. Distribution of these drifts indicates that much of the central part of the Cascade Range was mantled by an ice cap or by very extensive ice fields. The glaciers extended down major valleys on the west side of the range and in some places flowed out into the adjoining lowland. Ice reached the western front of the Cascade Range along each major river valley, and a virtually continuous ice cap covered interfluves between the Puyallup and Carbon Rivers as far west as the mountain front. From the Nisqually River northward, the overlap of Vashon Drift deposited by the Puget lobe has covered the westernmost alpine till, but alpine drift probably deposited during the older glacial episode has been recognized at one place about 6 km west of the mountain front opposite the mouth of the White River valley (Crandell, 1963b). The altitude of the regional snowline in the Cascade Range northwest of Mount Rainier during the younger glacial episode probably was 900-1,100 m.

During the Evans Creek Stade of the Fraser Glaciation, the Cascade Range south of the latitude of Seattle was occupied principally by cirque and valley glaciers, although ice fields existed along the crest of the range southeast of Mount Rainier and probably at Mount Rainier itself. The regional snowline in the mountains near Mount Rainier at this time probably was at an altitude between 1,300 and 1,700 m. Farther north, the east flank of the mountains was glaciated by large valley glaciers whose limits are generally well defined by terminal moraines, but on the west side of the mountains the downvalley extent of alpine ice has been obscured by a subsequent overlap of Cordilleran ice. Nevertheless, it seems certain that each large valley north of the latitude of Seattle was occupied by a long alpine glacier. Till of Evans Creek age is generally oxidized to a maximum depth of 1 m, and stones in the soil profile are unweathered.

By the time the Puget lobe reached its maximum extent in the lowland west of the Cascade Range between 15,000 and 13,500 years ago, alpine glaciers in the Cascades had greatly decreased in size or had disappeared (Cary and Carlston, 1937; Mackin, 1941; Crandell, 1963b). This diminution of Cascade alpine glaciers apparently was contemporaneous with the retreat of glaciers in the Olympic

Mountains, which also began before 15,000 years ago (Heusser, 1964). Recession of alpine glaciers in the Cascade Range during continued expansion of the Cordilleran ice sheet could have been caused in several ways. A strong high-pressure system maintained over the ice sheet in the coastal mountains of western Canada might have deflected eastward-moving storms to the south, causing progressively greater starvation of alpine glaciers as the Cordilleran ice sheet increased in size. Moreover, storms would have lost moisture as they crossed the cold high surface of the lengthening Puget lobe. These mechanisms could have materially influenced glacier growth in the Cascade Range, but neither seems to account adequately for the early retreat of alpine glaciers on the windward flank of the Olympic Mountains. Thus it seems more likely that a climatic change of regional extent occurred prior to the maximum stand of the Puget lobe during the Vashon Stade (Mathews, 1951). This change might have been one of increased temperature, which caused alpine glaciers to become progressively smaller. At the same time a temperature increase could have resulted in greater precipitation on the ice sheet, which, owing to its size and altitude, probably maintained a local cold climate on its surface, with the result that it continued to grow.

Before the end of the Fraser Glaciation there was a temporary return of rigorous climatic conditions that permitted the rebirth of small cirque glaciers and the formation of large perennial snowbanks and rock glaciers in the Cascade Range near Mount Rainier. Deposits formed at this time are found mainly in cirques at altitudes above 1,800 m, and they are overlain by a distinctive ash layer, which is older than 8,800 years (Crandell *et al.*, 1962). This climatic episode near the end of the Fraser Glaciation is probably correlative with the Sumas Stade.

Fluctuations of glaciers in the Cascade Range during the Neoglaciation have been studied most extensively at Mount Rainier, where the oldest advance of postglacial time occurred between about 3,500 and 2,000 years ago. During a younger advance, which probably began at least as early as the 13th century, various glaciers reached their maximum extents at times ranging from the middle of the 14th century to the middle of the 19th century. An end moraine formed during the middle part of the 19th century has been recognized at six glaciers on Mount Rainier; older moraines, however, seemingly do not fall into a consistent pattern from glacier to glacier. This may be a result of insufficient data, or it may reflect different behavior patterns of the various glaciers. The glaciers have been in a state of general recession since the middle of the 18th century, interrupted by several temporary stillstands or minor readvances that continued into the early part of the 20th century (Harrison, 1956; Sigafoos and Hendricks, 1961).

Cirques at altitudes of 2,000 m and higher were reoccupied by glaciers during the Neoglaciation, suggesting a regional snowline 300 to 700 m higher than that of Evans Creek time. According to Bender and Haines (1955), the snowline at Mount Rainier moved upward from about 1,800 m in 1910 to nearly 2,300 m in 1952. During the past decade, the firn line has generally been at altitudes between 2,100 and 2,300 m (Mark F. Meier, written communication, 1963).

GLACIATION IN THE OLYMPIC MOUNTAINS

Till deposited by one or more pre-Salmon Springs(?) glaciers originating in the Olympic Mountains has been recognized in the lowland beyond the southwestern front of the mountains. The till is distinguished from the less-weathered tills of Salmon Springs(?) age by its clayey, reddish profile of weathering in which stones are wholly decomposed in the upper 2 or 3 m. Distribution of the old drift suggests that large piedmont glaciers formed on the lowland at least once in pre-Salmon Springs(?) time, fed by extensive ice fields or an ice cap in the mountains. The distribution of outcrops of the till indicates that glaciers were about the same size as the largest glaciers of Salmon Springs(?) age.

Differences in the degree of weathering of till deposited by alpine glaciers suggest that three major glaciations occurred in the Olympic Mountains in late Pleistocene time. The youngest of these is correlated with the Evans Creek Stade of the Fraser Glaciation, and the two earlier glaciations may be correlative with the Salmon Springs Glaciation. Till of Evans Creek age is characterized by oxidation to depths of about 1 m and by the absence of weathered rinds on stones in the soil profile. These features are similar to those in Vashon till in the Puget Sound lowland. The two tills of Salmon Springs(?) age have progressively deeper oxidation (1-2 m and 3-5 m) with increasing age and thicker rinds (1-2 mm and 3-6 mm) on stones in soil profiles.

Extent of glaciation on the north and east sides of the Olympic Mountains has been obscured by an overlap of Vashon Drift in the adjacent lowland and possibly by merging of alpine ice and Cordilleran ice. The south and west sides of the mountains, however, were beyond the maximum extent of Cordilleran ice, and the sequence and extent of alpine glacial advances are clearer. Distribution of alpine drifts bearing distinctive weathering profiles indicates that twice during Salmon Springs(?) time very large glaciers formed in the Olympic Mountains. During these times the central part of the range probably was virtually mantled by ice fields or an ice cap, which fed valley glaciers that spread out beyond the southwestern mountain front. During the Evans Creek Stade, valley glaciers were much shorter and generally did not extend much beyond the southwestern front of the Olympics (Crandell, 1964).

On the north flank of the mountains, alpine glaciers of probable Evans Creek age extended at least as far as the front of the range. These glaciers reached their maximum development and had already retreated before the Cordilleran ice sheet in the Strait of Juan de Fuca reached its maximum development (Brown *et al.*, 1960). At the maximum extent of the Cordilleran ice sheet, north-trending valleys were dammed to form proglacial lakes in which erratics were floated by bergs many miles upvalley from the mountain front, indicating that alpine glaciers were small at that time.

Radiocarbon analysis of peat from the bottom of a bog on a moraine of probable Evans Creek age in the Hoh River valley indicates that the Hoh valley glacier reached its maximum extent and retreated prior to about 15,000 years ago (Heusser, 1964, p. 33).

The climate of a large part of Wisconsin time has been reconstructed from pollen in a peat bog near Humptulips (Heusser, 1964; see Heusser, this volume). The bog lies on drift regarded as being of older Salmon Springs(?) age, and the vegetation sequence represented by pollen records two major glacial episodes and two nonglacial episodes in addition to postglacial time. Peat deposited during the younger of the two nonglacial episodes has a radiocarbon age of about 27,500 years, indicating that it was formed during the Olympic Interglaciation. Pollen in peat above this horizon records a glacial climate that presumably is correlative with the Fraser Glaciation. The pre-Olympia climatic episodes predate 30,000 years and probably occurred during Salmon Springs(?) time.

The climate throughout Salmon Springs(?) and Fraser time apparently was cooler than at present. The inferred average July temperature during the Fraser Glaciation and the glaciation that preceded it was 6°-7° C colder than present, and during the Olympia Interglaciation it was about 2° C colder than present (Heusser, 1964; see Heusser, this volume, Fig. 5).

Fluctuations of glaciers near Mount Olympus during the Neoglaciation were studied by Heusser (1957), who found evidence of at least one undated glacial advance that occurred before A.D. 1250 but after the Fraser Glaciation. The oldest dated advance occurred about A.D. 1650; at this time, at least one glacier extended into a forest more than seven centuries old. A subsequent advance occurred in the early 1800's. Following this advance, glaciers near Mount Olympus have been in a state of general recession, although minor oscillations or readvances occurred during the 19th century and during the early 1900's.

OREGON

The most extensive Pleistocene glaciers in western Oregon developed along the crest of the Cascade Range, although small cirque and valley glaciers also occupied parts of the Coast Range and Klamath Mountains. East of the Cascades, glaciation was restricted to mountainous areas above an altitude of about 2,400 m. The largest of these areas is in the Wallowa Mountains in the northeastern part of the State. Other areas known to have been glaciated are the Elkhorn Range, Greenhorn Mountains, Strawberry Range, Steens Mountain, Newberry volcano at the present site of Newberry Crater, and Gearhart and Yamsay Mountains (Figs. 1 and 3).

COAST RANGE AND KLAMATH MOUNTAINS

In the Coast Range of western Oregon most crestlines are at altitudes of only 300 to 1,000 m, but a few peaks and ridges are as high as 1,000 to 1,200 m. Glaciation of these mountains apparently was restricted to a few small cirque glaciers on the protected sides of the highest peaks (see Baldwin and Roberts, 1952). The Klamath Mountains in southwestern Oregon are somewhat higher than the Coast Range farther north; most summits are at altitudes between 1,000 and 1,500 m, and some peaks near the Oregon-

California boundary are as high as 2,270 m. Evidence of glaciation near Chetco Peak in the western part of the Klamath Mountains (Fig. 3) was mentioned by Wells et al. (1949). Cirque floors in the Chetco Peak area are at an altitude of 1,000 to 1,200 m, and to the east cirque lakes lie at altitudes of 1,500 to 2,000 m along the southern boundary of Oregon.

CASCADE RANGE

In Oregon the Cascade Range is subdivided into the Western Cascades and the High Cascades (Fig. 3). The Western Cascades are deeply dissected and have summit altitudes ranging from about 600 m at the western edge to about 1,800 m at the east. The High Cascades form a narrow belt of summit upland along the east side of the range, much of which is above an altitude of 1,800 m. The upland is dominated by volcanoes of Quaternary age, among which Mount Hood, Mount Jefferson and North, Middle, and South Sister reach altitudes of more than 3,000 m.

Ice covered the High Cascades at least once in late Pleistocene time from near Ollalie Butte continuously southward to Mount McLaughlin. Evidence of a summit ice cap apparently was first recognized in the headwaters of the McKenzie River by Dutton (1889), and Russell (1905) suggested that summit ice fields may have extended the entire length of the Cascades in Oregon. According to Thayer (1939), ice was 150-300 m thick on the summit upland near Ollalie Butte. Farther south, lobes from summit ice fields that extended down valleys on the east side of the range formed terminal moraines that impound many small lakes. Large areas near Crater Lake were completely mantled by ice, and long glacier tongues extended down valleys both to the east and west. Much of this ice came from the slopes of the ancient Mount Mazama volcano (Williams, 1942) at the present site of Crater Lake.

Till deposited by summit ice fields and by the valley glaciers during the last glaciation of the Cascade Range typically is oxidized to a depth of 0.5-1 m, and morainal forms are still very fresh and unmodified by erosion. These features appear to be similar to those observed in till of Fraser age in western Washington.

Glaciers in the Western Cascades consisted of two main types: tongues from the summit ice fields of the High Cascades that extended westward along major valleys, and local cirque and small valley glaciers on the higher ridges and peaks. In general, ice of the Fraser Glaciation did not extend very far into the Western Cascades, whereas older valley glaciers extended many miles farther downstream.

Evidence of multiple glaciation in the Cascade Range has been reported at only a few places. Repeated glaciation during the growth of Mount Mazama volcano is documented by layers of till interbedded with volcanic rocks in the caldera walls surrounding Crater Lake (Atwood, 1935; Williams, 1942). Thayer (1939) found drift of two glaciers in the North Santiam River valley that predated the most recent glaciation. Thayer correlated the younger of these two drifts with the Tahoe Glaciation in the Sierra Nevada and the older with the Sherwin Glaciation of the same mountains. The drift of the older glacier has a thick red soil profile.

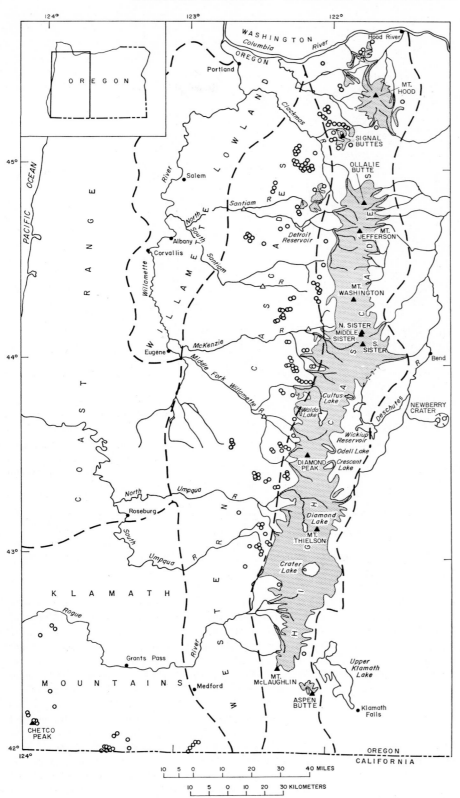

Figure 3. Extent of glaciation (shaded pattern) in the Cascade Range and Klamath Mountains in Oregon. Small circles represent glaciers too small to show at true scale. Open triangles indicate maximum known westward extent of valley glaciers in the Western Cascades. Extent of ice shown probably represents the Frazer Glaciation but may locally include areas beyond that were last glaciated in Salmon Springs(?) time. Extent of glaciation in Mount Hood–Signal Buttes area chiefly from A. C. Waters (written communication); in drainage basin of North Santiam River from Thayer (1939); in Crater Lake area from Williams (1942). Extent of glaciation at Newberry Crater is not known.

WALLOWA MOUNTAINS

The Wallowa Mountains were mantled with the most extensive glaciers in Oregon outside of the Cascade Range (Fig. 4). The mountains rise nearly 2,000 m above the surrounding plateau and reach a maximum altitude of about 3,000 m. Alpine glaciers in the central part of the mountains probably were at least 600 m thick, and ice on some divides was at least 300 m thick (Stovall, 1929). Glaciers

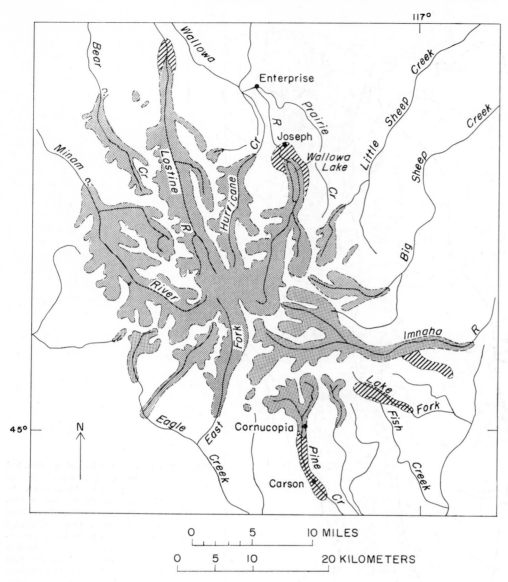

Figure 4. Inferred extent of glaciation in the Wallowa Mountains during the Fraser Glaciation. Extent of a pre-Fraser glaciation in some valleys is shown by lined pattern.

17-32 km long descended the valleys of the Lostine and Wallowa Rivers and Hurricane Creek on the north side of the mountains and the Imnaha River valley on the east side. Glaciers on the south flank generally were smaller and reached a maximum length of only about 14 km.

The largest moraines are preserved on the north margin of the range. Of these, the moraines that enclose Wallowa Lake are by far the largest and most impressive; they rise as much as 360 m above the floor of the Wallowa Lake basin. Differences in profiles of weathering and erosional modification of the moraines suggest that they represent at least three glaciations, the youngest of which probably is of Fraser age.

ALLUVIATION WEST OF THE CASCADE RANGE

Repeated episodes of fluvial and mudflow aggradation separated by intervals of fluvial erosion occurred in the area between Portland and the Cascade Range front during Pleistocene time. Reddish-brown clayey residual soils on the

oldest mudflows and alluvial deposits are as much as 6 m thick, and decomposition extends to an additional depth of 15 m. Younger deposits are decomposed to depths of 7-10 m but do not have the reddish-brown soils, and still younger deposits are weathered to depths of only about 3 m. Trimble (1963) regarded these three groups of deposits as being of early, middle, and late Pleistocene age. He attributed deposition of the oldest deposits partly to early eruptive activity of Mount Hood volcano in the Cascade Range east of Portland. There is no independent evidence as to the cause of subsequent alternations of fluvial erosion and deposition. Farther south, Allison (1936) correlated three aggradational episodes in the Willamette Lowland with glacial advances in the Cascade Range and inferred that erosion occurred during the intervening nonglacial episodes.

The youngest surficial deposit of wide extent in the Willamette Lowland is an erratic-bearing silt that was deposited when the lowland was ponded by a flood or floods in the Columbia River valley. The erratics are rock types that could only have come down the Columbia River, and Allison (1935) believed that they were transported to the Willamette Lowland by icebergs borne on flood surges when the Columbia was dammed downstream from Portland by icebergs and river ice. The flood surges were thought to have been caused by repeated failures of ice dams in the Columbia Gorge upstream from Portland. Trimble (1963) suggested that the Portland area and Willamette Lowland were inundated by a flood of catastrophic proportions that originated from the release of Glacial Lake Missoula (see Richmond *et al.*, this volume). Restricted flowage of this flood through a constriction in the Columbia River valley downstream from Portland caused ponding to an altitude of about 120 m.

COASTAL DEPOSITS OF OREGON AND WASHINGTON

Deposits of Pleistocene age along the Pacific Ocean coast of Oregon and Washington include glacial drift, marine and estuarine sediments, and dune sand. Late Pleistocene events in southern Oregon include two episodes of sea level lower than now (Baldwin, 1945). During the older episode, coastal streams cut deep valleys that were subsequently filled with estuarine sediments as sea levels rose. Subsequently sea level dropped slightly and a marine platform was cut on which marine beds were deposited. The upper surface of these beds now forms a broad coastal terrace. A second lowering of sea level, which caused at least 60 m of downcutting by coastal rivers, was followed by submergence of the coast. If the two episodes of relative emergence of the land represent eustatic lowerings of sea level, they probably occurred during the Fraser Glaciation and the glaciation preceding it.

Unconsolidated deposits of Pleistocene age that crop out in sea cliffs along the western side of the Olympic Peninsula in Washington include an older unit of till, sand, gravel, and clay and a younger unit of gravel and lignite beds capped by marine clay (Baldwin, 1939; Glover, 1940). The older unit was deformed into shallow folds, locally faulted, and eroded before the younger unit was deposited. According to Palmer (1927) and Baldwin (1939) the young marine clay is widely distributed in the coastal area up to an altitude of at least 90 m.

During the eustatic rise of sea level at the end of the Fraser Glaciation, extensive masses of dune sand accumulated along the Oregon and Washington coasts (Cooper, 1958). These dunes are chiefly of postglacial age, although Cooper found evidence of an earlier cycle of dune development that he associated with the rise of sea level at the end of the Illinoian Glaciation.

PLEISTOCENE DEFORMATION

The largest vertical movements in northwestern Washington during the Pleistocene occurred as a result of isostatic depression and rebound caused by the weight of the Cordilleran ice sheet. However, evidence bearing on the amount of rebound is complicated by a contemporaneous eustatic rise of sea level that accompanied deglaciation. In the Bellingham area, a combination of these two factors probably explains a sequence of (1) 75 m of emergence, (2) 150-210 m of submergence, and (3) 150-210 m of emergence, all of which occurred during the period between about 13,000 and

10,000 years ago (Easterbrook, 1963; see King, this volume).

Subsidence of the Puget Sound lowland during the Pleistocene is inferred by D. R. Mullineaux (written communication, 1961) from westward dips of as much as 5° in lacustrine deposits of early or middle Pleistocene age in the Green River valley southeast of Seattle. Subsidence also is suggested by the apparent absence in the central part of the lowland of deposits older than the Salmon Springs Glaciation, although these older deposits crop out at the margins of the lowland.

Pleistocene deposits in the lowland commonly are gently folded and locally are cut by faults of small displacement, some of which involve Vashon Drift. Pleistocene deformation in the Port Angeles area on the northern side of the Olympic Peninsula is represented by tilted deposits of deeply weathered drift (Brown *et al.*, 1960; see King, this volume).

Differential warping of a late Pleistocene wave-cut platform of as much as 60 m in a distance of a little less than 5 km along the southern Oregon coast has been reported by Baldwin (1945; see King, this volume). Marine terraces along this coast that occur at least as high as 450 m above sea level are believed to represent earlier Pleistocene uplift of the coastal region.

Some large vertical movements of parts of western Washington and Oregon have previously been inferred from geologic features that can now be satisfactorily explained by other means. Vertical uplift of the Portland area in late Pleistocene time was suggested by Lowry and Baldwin (1952). Their evidence was the presence of a thick deposit of gravel that extends to an altitude of 120 m. They believed that the gravel was deposited by the Columbia River during an eustatic rise of sea level, which was followed by regional uplift that raised the deposits to their present altitude. However, Trimble (1963) interpreted the gravel deposit as the product of a catastrophic flood formed by the emptying of Glacial Lake Missoula into the drainage system of the Columbia River (see Richmond *et al.*, this volume). Thus, the gravel deposit itself is no longer regarded as evidence for vertical movement of the Portland area in late Pleistocene time.

Bretz (1913) proposed that western Washington was uplifted about 300 m and then depressed an equal amount in Pleistocene time. His suggestion was based on the inferred age and origin of the deep troughs occupied by Puget Sound, and their relation to the depositional and erosional history of the lowland. Bretz thought that the deep troughs, whose floors lie as much as 263 m below sea level, are chiefly products of fluvial erosion into a flattish plain of pre-Vashon glacial drift that had been raised at least 300 m. Following the deep stream cutting, the valleys were modified by ice scour during the Vashon Stade. The region was depressed to its present altitude before or during the Vashon Stade, and after retreat of the Puget lobe the deep valleys were submerged to form Puget Sound.

Recent geologic investigations show that essentially continuous aggradation above sea level occurred in the central part of the lowland during the Olympia Interglaciation and during the early part of the Vashon Stade as well. Thus, the deep troughs were not present when the Puget lobe advanced into the lowland, and their formation is now attributed to glacial scour. Independent evidence of regional uplift and subsidence of 300 m in late Pleistocene time is lacking.

REFERENCES

Allison, I. S., 1935, Glacial erratics in Willamette Valley: Geol. Soc. Amer. Bull., v. 46, p. 615-632

—— 1936, Pleistocene alluvial stages in northwestern Oregon: Science, v. 83, p. 441-443

Armstrong, J. E., Crandell, D. R., Easterbrook, D. J., and Noble, J. B., 1965, Late Pleistocene stratigraphy and chronology in southwestern British Columbia and northwestern Washington: Geol. Soc. Amer. Bull., v. 76

Atwood, W. W., Jr., 1935, The glacial history of an extinct volcano, Crater Lake National Park: J. Geol., v. 43, p. 142-168

Baldwin, E. M., 1939, Late Cenozoic diastrophism along the Olympic coast: Washington State College MS thesis

—— 1945, Some revisions of the late Cenozoic stratigraphy of the southern Oregon coast: J. Geol., v. 53, p. 35-46

Baldwin, E. M., and Roberts, A. E., 1952, Geology of the Spirit Mountain quadrangle, Oregon: U.S. Geol. Surv. Oil and Gas Inv. Map OM-129

Bender, V. R., and Haines, A. L., 1955, Forty-two years of recession of the Nisqually Glacier on Mount Rainier: Erdkunde, v. 9, p. 275-281

Bretz, J H., 1913, Glaciation of the Puget Sound region: Washington Geol. Surv. Bull. 8, 244 p.

Brown, R. D., Jr., Gower, H. D., and Snavely, P. D., Jr., 1960, Geology of the Port Angeles–Lake Crescent area, Clallam County, Washington: U.S. Geol. Surv. Oil and Gas Inv. Map OM-203

Cary, A. S., and Carlston, C. W., 1937, Notes on Vashon stage glaciation of the South Fork of the Skyomish River valley, Washington: Northwest Sci., v. 11, p. 61-62

Cooper, W. S., 1958, Coastal sand dunes of Oregon and Washington: Geol. Soc. Amer. Mem. 72, 169 p.

Crandell, D. R., 1963a, Paradise debris flow at Mount Rainier, Washington: U.S. Geol. Surv. Prof. Pap. 475-B, p. 135-139

—— 1963b, Surficial geology and geomorphology of the Lake Tapps quadrangle, Washington: U.S. Geol. Surv. Prof. Pap. 388-A, p. 1-84

—— 1964, Pleistocene valley and piedmont glaciers of the southwestern Olympic Peninsula, Washington: U.S. Geol. Surv. Prof. Pap. 500-B, p. 135-139

Crandell, D. R., Mullineaux, D. R., Miller, R. D., and Rubin, Meyer, 1962, Pyroclastic deposits of Recent age at Mount Rainier, Washington: U.S. Geol. Surv. Prof. Pap. 450-D, p. 64-68

Dutton, C. E., 1889, Report of Capt. C. E. Dutton: U.S. Geol. Surv. Ann. Rep. 8 (1886-87), p. 156-165

Easterbrook, D. J., 1963, Late Pleistocene glacial events and relative sea-level changes in the northern Puget Lowland, Washington: Geol. Soc. Amer. Bull., v. 74, p. 1465-1484

Glover, S. L., 1940, Pleistocene deformation in the Olympic coastal region: Northwest Sci., v. 14, p. 69-71

Hansen, H. P., and Mackin, J. H., 1949, A pre-Wisconsin forest succession in the Puget Lowland, Washington: Amer. J. Sci., v. 247, p. 833-855

Harrison, A. E., 1956, Fluctuations of the Nisqually Glacier, Mount Rainier, Washington, since 1750: J. Glaciol., v. 2, p. 675-683

Heusser, C. J., 1957, Variations of Blue, Hoh, and White Glaciers during recent centuries: Arctic, v. 10, p. 139-150

—— 1964, Palynology of four bog sections from the western Olympic Peninsula, Washington: Ecology, v. 45, p. 23-40

—— this volume, A Pleistocene phytogeographical sketch of the Pacific Northwest and Alaska

King, P. B., this volume, Tectonics of Quaternary time in middle North America

Leopold, E. B., and Crandell, D. R., 1957, Pre-Wisconsin interglacial pollen spectra from Washington State, USA: Vierte Intern. Tagung der Quartarbotaniker 1957, p. 76-79

Long, W. A., 1951a, Glacial geology of the Wenatchee-Entiat area, Washington: Northwest Sci., v. 25, p. 3-16

—— 1951b, Glacial geology of the Tieton Valley, south-central Washington: Northwest Sci., v. 25, p. 142-148

Lowry, W. D., and Baldwin, E. M., 1952, Late Cenozoic geology of the lower Columbia River valley, Oregon and Washington: Geol. Soc. Amer. Bull., v. 63, p. 1-24

Mackin, J. H., 1941, Glacial geology of the Snoqualmie-Cedar area, Washington: J. Geol., v. 49, p. 449-481

Mathews, W. H., 1951, Historic and prehistoric fluctuations of alpine glaciers in the Mount Garibaldi map-area, southwestern British Columbia: J. Geol., v. 59, p. 357-380

Mullineaux, D. R., Waldron, H. H., and Rubin, Meyer, 1965, Stratigraphy and chronology of late interglacial and early Vashon glacial time in the Seattle area, Washington: U.S. Geol. Surv. Bull. 1194-O

Page, B. M., 1939, Multiple alpine glaciation in the Leavenworth area, Washington: J. Geol., v. 47, p. 785-815

Palmer, R. H., 1927, Geology and petroleum possibilities of the Olympic Peninsula, Washington: Amer. Assoc. Petroleum Geologists Bull., v. 11, p. 1321-1328

Richmond, Gerald M., Fryxell, Roald, Neff, George E., and Weis, Paul L., this volume, The Cordilleran ice sheet of the Northern Rocky Mountains and related Quaternary history of the Columbia Plateau

Russell, I. C., 1905, Preliminary report on the geology and water resources of central Oregon: U.S. Geol. Surv. Bull. 252, 138 p.

Sigafoos, R. S., and Hendricks, E. L., 1961, Botanical evidence of the modern history of Nisqually Glacier, Washington: U.S. Geol. Surv. Prof. Pap. 387-A, p. 1-20

Snavely, P. D., Jr., Brown, R. D., Jr., Roberts, A. E., and Rau, W. W., 1958, Geology and coal resources of the Centralia-Chehalis district, Washington: U.S. Geol. Surv. Bull. 1053, 159 p.

Stout, M. L., 1964, Geology of a part of the south-central Cascade Mountains, Washington: Geol. Soc. Amer. Bull., v. 75, p. 317-334

Stovall, J. C., 1929, Pleistocene geology and physiography of the Wallowa Mountains, with special reference to the Wallowa and Hurricane Canyons: Univ. of Oregon MA thesis

Thayer, T. P., 1939, Geology of the Salem Hills and the North Santiam River basin, Oregon: Oregon Dept. Geol. Min. Ind. Bull. 15, 40 p.

Trimble, D. E., 1963, The geology of Portland, Oregon, and adjacent areas: U.S. Geol. Surv. Bull. 1119, p. 1-119

Wells, F. G., Hotz, P. E., and Cater, F. W., Jr., 1949, Pre-liminary description of the geology of the Kerby quadrangle, Oregon: Oregon Dept. Geol. Min. Ind. Bull. 40, 23 p.

Williams, Howel, 1942, The geology of Crater Lake National Park, Oregon, with a reconnaissance of the Cascade Range southward to Mount Shasta: Carnegia Instn. Publ. 540, 162 p.

SUMMARY

Pleistocene glaciers in Washington and Oregon consisted of the Cordilleran ice sheet, which originated in western Canada and invaded northern Washington on both sides of the Cascade Range, and alpine glaciers in the mountain ranges of both States.

Glacial episodes of early(?) to middle(?) Pleistocene age are best known in the Puget Sound lowland of western Washington, where two major glaciations are recorded, each consisting of two or more advances of the Puget lobe of the Cordilleran glacier into the area south of Seattle, Washington. In addition, three glacial episodes occurred during late Pleistocene time, the last during the Fraser Glaciation between 25,000 and 10,000 years ago. During the earlier two glaciations of late Pleistocene time, large valley glaciers and broad piedmont glaciers were fed by vast ice fields and ice caps in the Cascade Range of both Washington and Oregon and in the Olympic Mountains of Washington. Alpine glaciers were smaller during the Fraser Glaciation, although ice fields again mantled much of the higher part of the Cascade Range in Oregon.

In the mountains of western Canada, continued growth of alpine glaciers during the Fraser Glaciation formed the Cordilleran ice sheet, which expanded into northern Washington after 22,000 years ago and which reached its maximum stand 50 miles south of Seattle between 15,000 and 13,500 years ago. Retreat of the glacier was accompanied and followed by glaciomarine conditions in the Puget Sound lowland from 13,500 to about 11,000 years ago. A readvance of the Cordilleran glacier in the Fraser Lowland of northern Washington about 11,000 years ago was followed by disappearance of the ice sheet.

Two glacial episodes in post-Altithermal time are recorded at Mount Rainier, Washington. The older episode occurred between 3,500 and 2,000 years ago, and the younger within the last thousand years.

THE QUATERNARY GEOLOGY AND ARCHAEOLOGY OF ALASKA

TROY L. PÉWÉ,[1] DAVID M. HOPKINS,[2] J. L. GIDDINGS[3]

INTRODUCTION

THE DEVELOPMENT of most of the present landscape and the coming of man in Alaska took place in the Quaternary Period. It was the time of advance and retreat of glaciers, formation and thawing of permafrost, transgression and regression of the seas, formation and erosion of sand dunes and loess deposits, and filling of basins with fluvial sediments. The spectacular effects of the geomorphic processes in regions of cold climate are well recorded here.

Alaska is the largest peninsula of North America (Fig. 1). Its area is 1,520,000 km², about 15% of the size of Europe. The main physiographic provinces are the Pacific Mountain System, the Intermontane Plateaus, the Rocky Mountain System, and the Arctic Coastal Plain (Wahrhaftig, in press).

The four major climatic zones recognized in Alaska are closely related to the physiographic provinces and are, from south to north, the maritime zone, the zone of transition from maritime to continental climate, the continental zone, and the arctic zone. The climate of Alaska is varied because of its diverse topography, the differences in the conditions of the bordering seas, and its great geographic extent. The northernmost point of Alaska lies within 18° of the North Pole, and the southernmost point is near the latitude of Copenhagen, Denmark.

PART 1: QUATERNARY GEOLOGY

T. L. PÉWÉ, D. M. HOPKINS

The earliest geologic report on an Alaskan area was largely concerned with Quaternary deposits. Kotzebue's *A Voyage of Discovery into the South Sea and Bering's Straits, for the Purpose of Exploring a Northeast Passage* (1821) contains an account of the famous bone-bearing frozen silt and of mysterious masses of buried ice at Elephant Point on Eschscholtz Bay of Kotzebue Sound, about 30 km south of the Arctic Circle. Brooks' *Geology and Geography of Alaska* contained the first comprehensive account of the Quaternary geology of Alaska.

Deposits of Quaternary age mantle virtually all of Alaska (Fig. 1). About 50% of the area is covered by glacial deposits and the rest by deposits of eolian, fluvial, lacustrine, volcanic, periglacial, and marine origin. The following brief summary of the Quaternary geology of Alaska considers the subject in three parts: (1) glacial deposits, (2) nonglacial deposits, and (3) permafrost and related phenomena. Most of the report refers to the mainland of Alaska, and little consideration is given to the Aleutian Islands or southeastern Alaska.

GLACIAL DEPOSITS

GENERAL STATEMENT

Glaciers have covered about half of Alaska at one time or another, but large areas in central and northern Alaska have never been glaciated (Fig. 2). The deposits of at least four major Pleistocene glaciations are present. In south-central Alaska, where extensive ice fields and large glaciers persist today, the glacial history seems to have begun much earlier with the deposition during late Tertiary time of marine tills and associated sediments. The extent of the late Tertiary and early Pleistocene glaciers is not known, but the extent of middle and late Pleistocene and Recent glaciers is well established (Figs. 3 and 4).

During Illinoian, Wisconsin, and Recent times, glaciers were much more extensive in southern Alaska than in northern Alaska and much more extensive on the south flanks than on the north flanks of individual mountain ranges. This indicates that the glaciers were nourished chiefly by air masses moving northward to northeastward from the northern Pacific Ocean. Glacial advances during the last 15,000 years in northern Alaska were approximately synchronous with those recorded in southern Alaska and in other parts of the northern hemisphere. These two observations provide strong evidence against the hypothesis of Ewing and Donn (1963 and earlier papers), according to which glacial advances in the far north were nourished by moist air masses moving southward from an open Arctic Ocean and therefore would be out of phase with glacial advances in more southern latitudes.

PLIOCENE GLACIATIONS

The strongly deformed Yakataga Formation and correlative sediments exposed along the north coast of the Gulf of Alaska between Cape Spencer and Cape St. Elias and on Middleton Island and in some of the Trinity Islands west of Kodiak Island contain many thick beds of conglomeratic sandy mudstone, which appear to represent glacial drift

[1] Department of Geology, University of Alaska, College, Alaska.
[2] U.S. Geological Survey, Menlo Park, California.
[3] Dr. Giddings, of the Haffenreffer Museum, Bristol, Rhode Island, died as the result of an automobile accident shortly after his part of this chapter was written.

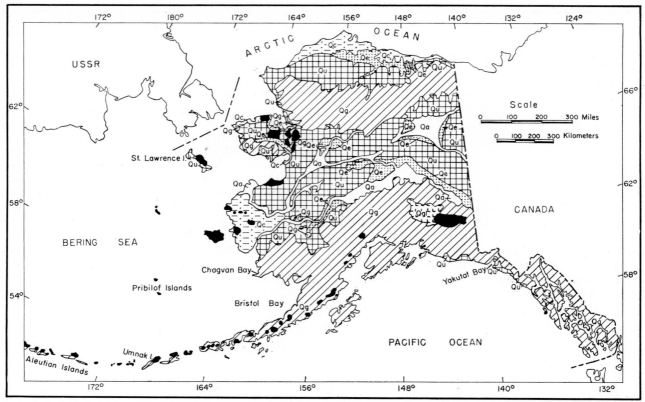

Figure 1. Sketch map of major regional groups of surficial deposits in Alaska. Qg, glacial and other deposits associated with heavily glaciated alpine mountains; Qgl, glacio-lacustrine deposits of larger Pleistocene proglacial lakes; Qu, undifferentiated deposits associated with generally unglaciated uplands and lowlands of the interior and North Slope; Qa, fluvial deposits; Qe, eolian deposits; Qc, coastal deposits of interbedded marine and terrestrial sediments. Solid black areas: deposits associated with volcanic peaks and flows of Quaternary and Tertiary age. Modified from Karlstrom (1960b, Fig. 154.1).

that accumulated either beneath an ice shelf or beneath icebergs broken from tidewater glaciers. Although the precise age of the Yakataga Formation remains uncertain, paleontologists agree that molluscan faunas collected from levels well above the lowest till-like sediments are of either late Miocene or early Pliocene age (Miller, 1957, sheet 2).

EARLY PLEISTOCENE GLACIATIONS

Local patches of drift of early Pleistocene age have been recognized in most of the glaciated areas in Alaska. Away from the Gulf of Alaska coast the early Pleistocene drift typically consists of erratic boulders or patches of till scattered over old erosion surfaces high above the present valley bottoms. Recognizable glacial landforms, such as end moraines, have been completely destroyed. The early Pleistocene glacial deposits found in most parts of Alaska cannot be further subdivided, but those found in the Nenana River Valley and in the Cook Inlet area record two early Pleistocene glaciations separated by a lengthy deglacial interval (Wahrhaftig, 1958; Karlstrom, 1964) (Table 1).

ILLINOIAN GLACIATION

Prior to 1945, geologists engaged in regional mapping commonly failed to recognize the glaciated character of terrain now known to have been overridden by glaciers during the Illinoian Glaciation. However, in a few places where abundant erratic boulders forced recognition that the area had been glaciated, the glaciation was ascribed to an ice advance of Wisconsin age. Field and photogeologic studies since 1945 have shown, however, that drift of Illinoian age is present in nearly every glaciated area in Alaska (Figs. 3, 4).

The drift most firmly identified as Illinoian in age on the basis of stratigraphic and radiometric evidence is from near Nome on the Seward Peninsula and from the shore bluffs of Kotzebue Sound and Cook Inlet (Table 1). Elsewhere the assignment of particular drift sheets to the Illinoian is based upon similarities in surface expression and similarities of position in local glacial sequences to the Illinoian drift in the Kotzebue Sound, Nome, and Cook Inlet areas.

The drift of the Nome River Glaciation at Nome and correlative drift in the Kotzebue Sound area is shown to be of Illinoian age by radiometric age determinations (Blanchard, 1963) on shells in underlying and overlying marine deposits. The Illinoian drift in the Kotzebue Sound area, described by McCulloch et al. (1965) overlies marine sediments of the Kotzebuan transgression (Hopkins, 1965), which contain shells determined by the Th^{230}/U^{238} method to be 100,000 ± 8,000 years old and by the Ra^{226}/U^{238} method to be 78,000 ± 5,000 years old.

The Illinoian Glaciation is represented in the Cook Inlet area by the drift of the Eklutna Glaciation (Karlstrom, 1957, 1960a; Miller and Dobrovolny, 1959). The Eklutna drift consists of weathered and oxidized material covered in some places by interglacial beds and then by drift of the Knik Glaciation. In the Anchorage area this is covered in turn by the Bootlegger Cove Clay (Miller and Dobrovolny, 1959; Karlstrom, 1964), which contains marine mollusks whose shells have been determined by the Th^{230}/U^{238} method to be between 33,000 and 48,000 years old (Sackett, 1958), indicating an age near the middle of the Wisconsin Glaciation, which began about 70,000 years ago (Flint, 1963). Karlstrom (1964, p. 16) concludes from a study of boulder ratios on Knik moraines that the Knik ice began to retreat 50,000 to 65,000 years ago; thus, the Knik Glaciation evidently corresponds to an early phase of the Wisconsin Glaciation. The interglacial beds that locally separate the Knik drift from the underlying Eklutna drift are of Sangamon age, and the Eklutna drift, which Karlstrom (1964,

p. 16) considers to have been deposited more than 90,000 to 110,000 years ago, evidently was deposited during the Illinoian Glaciation.

The degree of preservation of primary microrelief on the Illinoian drift varies greatly in different physiographic settings. The larger primary relief features resulting from glacial erosion and sedimentation—cirques, U-shaped valleys, major morainal ridges, and outwash terraces—remain readily recognizable, but smaller features such as minor morainal ridges, kames, eskers, and kettles have commonly been obscured or obliterated by mass wasting, deposition of colluvium from nearby slopes, and dissection by consequent gullies. In many places the addition of a mantle of late Illinoian and Wisconsin loess several meters thick has contributed further to the obliteration of minor primary surface relief.

The Illinoian moraines consist of large, smoothly rounded ridges with irregular crests and gentle slopes. They are devoid of primary microrelief features and are incised by consequent gullies at intervals of about 1 km. In the northeastern Alaska Range, slopes are consistently gentler on

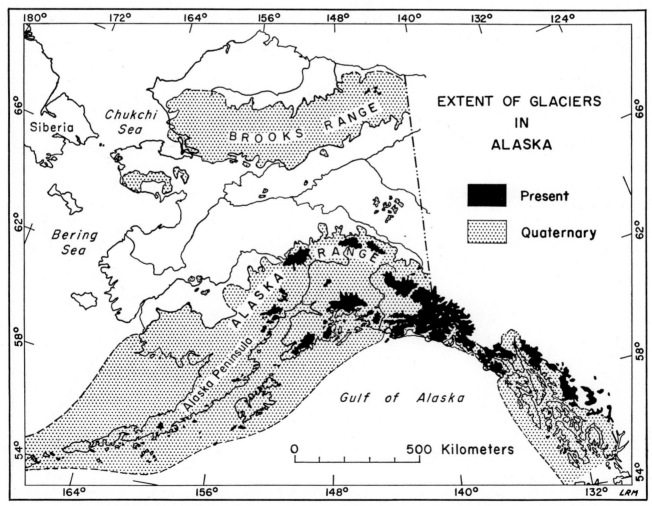

Figure 2. Extent of Quaternary glaciation in Alaska. Stipple pattern indicates areas glaciated one or more times during Quaternary time. Black pattern shows the present extent of glaciers. After Coulter *et al.* (in press).

moraines of the Delta (Illinoian) Glaciation than on moraines of the Donnelly (Wisconsin) Glaciation. Systematically sampled frontal slopes on the Delta moraine have an average steepness of 6.5%, while those of the Donnelly moraine have an average steepness of 13% (Péwé and Holmes, 1964; Holmes and Benninghoff, 1957, p. 63-69, Pl. 3A). The Delta moraine of Illinoian age contains only 1.2 kettle ponds per km², while the adjoining Donnelly moraine of Wisconsin age contains an average of 6.2 kettle ponds per km²; bogs, however, are twice as abundant on the Delta moraine as on the Donnelly moraine.

Drift of Illinoian age commonly displays a soil and weathering profile several times deeper and more intensely developed than that on Wisconsin drift in the same area. The post-Illinoian weathering profile is deeper and more intensely developed on Illinoian drift in southern than in northern Alaska.

Till, silt, sand, and gravel of the Eklutna (Illinoian) Glaciation near Anchorage are oxidized olive-tan to buff to depths of 10 m or more (Miller and Dobrovolny, 1959, p. 11). Illinoian till near Nome and on the shores of Kotzebue Sound shows oxidation colors of pale olive and dusky yellow to depths of about 3 m, and an excavation in an Illinoian esker showed a well-defined Arctic Brown soil profile more than 1.7 m thick—more than twice the thickness of Arctic Brown soils developed on an outwash of Wisconsin age in the same region (D. M. Hopkins, D. S. McCulloch, and R. J. Janda, unpublished data, 1961). Till of the Delta (Illinoian) Glaciation in the northeastern Alaska Range is oxidized to depths of 1.2 to 2 m (Péwé and Holmes, 1964; Holmes and Benninghoff, 1957, p. 79).

Some investigators (*e.g.* Péwé *et al.*, 1953; Péwé and Holmes, 1964; Holmes and Benninghoff, 1957, p. 79; Wahrhaftig, 1958, p. 32) have found a high proportion of rotten clasts, especially of granitic rocks, in near-surface zones in the Illinoian drift.

Péwé and his co-workers at the University of Alaska have undertaken a series of compilations of the former positions of snowline during Illinoian and Wisconsin time as interpreted from the altitudes of cirque floors in various parts of Alaska. The Illinoian snowline lay approximately 400-500 m below present snowline and about 170 m below Wisconsin snowline throughout much of Alaska. Snowline was highest in the dry and continental climate of east-central Alaska and lay at an altitude of about 1,250 m during Illinoian time (Péwé and Burbank, 1960). It sloped downward to near sea level on the south side of the Chugach Mountains of southern Alaska and to an altitude of about 300 m on the Seward

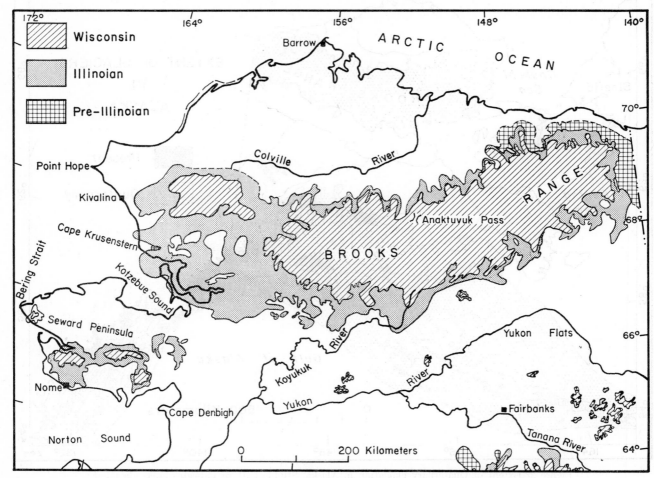

Figure 3. Extent of Quaternary glaciations in central and northern Alaska. After Coulter *et al.* (in press).

Peninsula in western Alaska. Snowline lay appreciably lower on the south sides than on the north sides of individual mountain ranges.

In western Alaska, glaciers were vastly more extensive during Illinoian time than during Wisconsin time (Fig. 3). This was evidently the result of the wide extent there of upland areas that were just high enough to support cirques and small ice caps during Illinoian time but were not high enough to project above snowline during Wisconsin time.

WISCONSIN GLACIATION

Events believed to have taken place between 70,000 and 10,000 years ago are arbitrarily assigned to the Wisconsin Glaciation. Drift of Wisconsin age is found in nearly all of the mountainous areas of Alaska. It is lacking only along the coast of the Gulf of Alaska between Cape St. Elias and Yakutat Bay (Fig. 4); the glaciers there seem to have been less extensive during Wisconsin time than during Recent time. Apparently the coastal mountains north of this part of the Gulf of Alaska coast were lower during Wisconsin time than at present and consequently supported less extensive glaciers (D. J. Milller, oral communication, 1960).

The Wisconsin Glaciation in Alaska was clearly a complex event, consisting of at least two major glacial advances and

several minor oscillations of ice fronts during the later major advance. The two major subdivisions of the Wisconsin Glaciation in the Cook Inlet area have been well established by stratigraphic investigations and radiometric dating to be approximately equivalent to the early and late Wisconsin glacial cycles in north-central United States. Easily distinguishable sets of well-preserved moraines found in other parts of Alaska have commonly been thought to represent the same two intervals. However, radiocarbon dating indicates that in the Anaktuvuk Pass area of the Brooks Range and in the Nenana Valley of the central Alaska Range the two well-preserved sets of moraines represent late Wisconsin and early Recent advances; early Wisconsin moraines are lacking (Table 1).

Drift of Wisconsin age is most firmly dated in the shore bluffs of Cook Inlet, where many stratigraphic observations and radiometrically dated organic specimens have established that the Knik Glaciation is of early Wisconsin age and that the Naptowne Glaciation is of late Wisconsin age (Miller and Dobrovolny, 1959, p. 15, 16, 57; Karlstrom, 1960a). Karlstrom (1957, 1960a) considers the Knik drift to be of "post-Illinoian, pre-Wisconsin (Sangamon)" age, and Miller and Dobrovolny (1959, p. 15) consider it to be pre-Wisconsin but not necessarily as old as Sangamon or

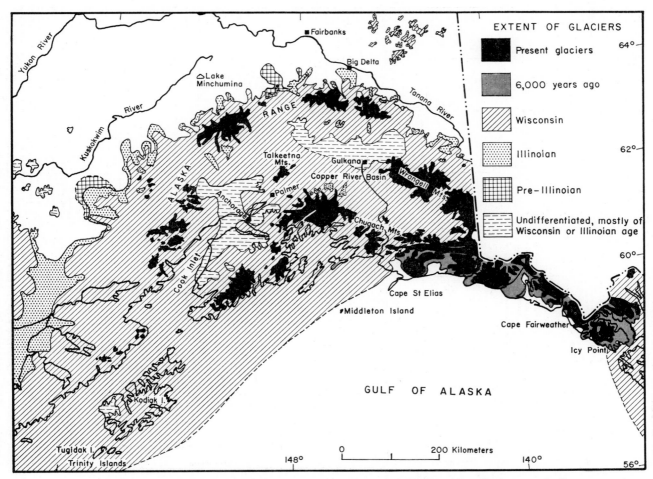

Figure 4. Extent of Quaternary glaciations in south-central Alaska. After Coulter *et al.* (in press).

TABLE 1

Correlation of Local Quaternary Glacial Sequences in Alaska

Years x 10³ before present	Epoch	Glaciation or Interglaciation	BROOKS RANGE — EASTERN (Holmes, 1959a; Holmes and Lewis, 1961)	BROOKS RANGE — CENTRAL (Porter, 1964; Detterman et al., 1958)	KOBUK VALLEY (Fernald, 1964)	SEWARD PENINSULA (Hopkins, 1963)	ALASKA PENINSULA (Muller, 1953)	COOK INLET (Karlstrom, 1957, 1960a, 1961, 1964)	FAREWELL (Fernald, 1960)	McKINLEY PARK (Reed, 1960, 1961)	NENANA RIVER (Wahrhaftig, 1958; Wahrhaftig and Cox, 1959)	BIG DELTA (Péwé, 1951b, 1952; Péwé et al., 1953; Péwé and Holmes, 1964)	JOHNSON RIVER (Holmes, 1959b)	AMPHITHEATRE MTS. (Péwé, 1961)	CHUGACH MTS. (THOMPSON PASS) (Coulter and Coulter, 1961, 1962)	MALASPINA GLACIER AREA (Plafker and Miller, 1958)	GLACIER BAY AREA (Goldthwait, 1963)
1–9	Recent	(Recent)	Glacial advance	Fan Mountain; Alapah Mountain	Glacial advance; Unealeak	Glacial advance		Tunnel Stade; Tustumena Stade (Alaskan)			Rock glaciers; Rock glaciers	Black Rapids		Glacial advance	Worthington; Marshall Pass	Glacial adv.; Glacial adv.	Little Ice Age; Glacial retreat
10	Pleistocene	Late Wisconsin	Peters	Anivik Lake Stade (equals Echooka River glaciation of Detterman et al.)	Walker Lake	Mount Osborn	Iliuk	Tanya Stade; Skilak Stade; Killey Stade; Moosehorn Stade (Naptowne)	Farewell II	Wonder Lake II	Carlo Stade of Riley Creek	Summit Lake	Glacial advance	Glacial advance (Denali II)	Glacial advance	Glacial advance	Glacial advance
	Pleistocene	Early Wisconsin	Schrader	Antler Valley Stade; Anayaknaurak Stade; Banded Mountain Stade (Itkillik)	Ambler	Salmon Lake	Brooks Lake	Knik	Farewell I	Wonder Lake I	Riley Creek	Donnelly	Donnelly	Denali I			
30	Pleistocene	Sangamon															
70	Pleistocene	Illinoian	Chamberlin	Sagavanirktok River	Kobuk	Nome River	Johnston Hill	Eklutna	Selatna	Slow Fork	Healy	Delta	Delta	Delta			
	Pleistocene	Yarmouth						Caribou Hills									
200	Pleistocene	Pre-Illinoian	Weller; Anaktuvuk River	Anaktuvuk River		Iron Creek	Mak Hill	Mount Susitna	Possible glacial advance	Dry Creek; Browne	Dry Creek; Browne	Darling Creek	Darling Creek	Darling Creek	Glacial advance	Glacial advance	Glacial advance

*Certain correlations adopted in this table differ from those used in two recently published correlation charts for local Alaskan glacial sequences (Karlstrom et al., 1964; Coulter et al., in press). The differences reflect new data that have become available between 1960, when the earlier compilations were completed, and 1964, when this paper was written, indicating that the Nome River Glaciation of Seward Peninsula and the Eklutna Glaciation of the Cook Inlet area were approximately synchronous with the Illinoian Glaciation of central United States. Local glaciations in northern Alaska previously considered to be synchronous with the Nome River Glaciation (the Chamberlin, Sagavanirktok River, and Kobuk Glaciations) are thus considered to be synchronous with one another and to be of Illinoian age as are local glaciations in southern Alaska previously considered to be synchronous with the Eklutna Glaciation (the Johnston Hill, Selatna, Slow Fork, Healy, and Delta Glaciations).

Illinoian. These differing age assignments reflect a difference in our respective concept of the duration of the Wisconsin Glaciation rather than a difference of opinion as to the absolute age and correlation of the Knik Glaciation.

In the Anaktuvuk Pass area of the central Brooks Range, Porter (1964) has shown by radiocarbon dating that the Itkillik Glaciation of Detterman *et al.* (1958) is late Wisconsin in age instead of early Wisconsin. Porter has also subdivided the Itkillik Glaciation into four stages, the Banded Mountain, Anayaknaurak, Antler Valley, and Anivik Lake Stages (Table 1), the youngest of which culminated about 6,300 to 8,300 years ago, and the second oldest of which culminated about 13,300 years ago. Radiocarbon dates suggesting minimum ages of 8,000 to 12,000 years for Wisconsin drift are available from the Delta River area (T. L. Péwé, unpublished data) and from a few other areas.

Primary depositional topography on Wisconsin drift is so sharply defined and well preserved that the glaciated character of the terrain is immediately obvious to the most casual observer.

Soils and weathering profiles on Wisconsin drift are much thinner and less conspicuous than those on Illinoian drift. The older Wisconsin moraines commonly show soil profiles about twice as thick as those on the younger Wisconsin moraines in the same area. In general, soils are thinner and less intensely developed northward or at higher elevations. In the Anchorage area, till of the early Wisconsin Knik Glaciation is oxidized to depths of 1 to 2 m where it is exposed at the surface. Holmes and Benninghoff report soil profiles only 30 to 90 cm deep (as indicated by oxidation and secondary-lime concentrations) in moraines of the Donnelly Glaciation near Big Delta, some of which are probably of early Wisconsin age (Holmes and Benninghoff, 1957, p. 84). D. M. Hopkins (unpublished data) has been unable to detect soil profiles on Wisconsin drift in the Seward Peninsula, but outwash and alluvial-fan gravel of probable Wisconsin age show Arctic Brown soil profiles 30 to 60 cm thick.

RECENT GLACIATIONS

Events that took place less than 10,000 years ago are arbitrarily assigned in this paper to the Recent Epoch. Two or possibly three glacial cycles are recorded in many parts of Alaska during this interval. The early cycle took place between 8,500 and 6,000 years ago in some areas. A later series began about 4,000 years ago and ended only a century ago, but the multiple early and late glacial advances within this later interval may have been separated by a significant deglacial interval of unknown duration centering around 1,500 to 2,000 years ago.

The Recent glacial record, as recognized throughout much of central and northern Alaska, is typified by the sequence recorded by Porter (1964) in the Anaktuvuk Pass area of the Brooks Range. Glaciers there were in an advanced position from about 8,300 years ago until about 6,300 years ago (Table 1), during his Anivik Lake Stage of the Itkillik Glaciation (equal to the Echooka River Glaciation of Detterman *et al.*, 1958). A long deglacial interval was followed by the Alapah Mountain Glaciation, which culminated about 2,800 years ago. Finally, the double moraines of the Fan Mountain Stage, which generally lie near or in the cirques

or near small remnant glaciers, are believed to have formed during the last several centuries.

A somewhat similar sequence is reported on the Kenai Peninsula of southern Alaska by Karlstrom (1964, Pl. 7 and p. 44, 56, 64). The last readvance during the Tanya Stage of the Naptowne Glaciation is thought by Karlstrom to have taken place about 6,000 years ago. Logs buried in drift indicate that some glacial advances during the Tustamena Stage of the Alaskan Glaciation took place more than 2,500 years ago, and indirect evidence leads Karlstrom to conclude that the Tustamena Stage extended from about 5,000 to 2,000 years ago. The Tunnel Stage of the Alaskan Glaciation, well-dated by radiocarbon analyses of logs buried in the older moraines and by ring counts from trees growing on young moraines, consists of several glacial advances during the last 1,500 years.

Records of early Recent glaciations are lacking along the coast of the Gulf of Alaska and in southeastern Alaska. Plafker and Miller's careful study (1958) of the moraines of the Malaspina and neighboring glaciers records a glacial advance that culminated between 1,400 and 700 years ago and that was more extensive than any Wisconsin or early Recent glacial advance. A glacial recession followed, succeeded by a readvance that began before A.D. 1700 and that ended in different places between A.D. 1791 and A.D. 1904. Studies of various parts of southeastern Alaska also suggest that glaciers advanced farther during the last few centuries than at any previous time within the last 10,000 years (Lawrence, 1958); Heusser and Marcus, 1964). The most detailed record is provided by Goldthwait's study of Glacier Bay (1963). A prolonged process of filling of the bay with outwash gravel began about 7,000 years ago. Glaciers were present in the mountains but were lacking in the fiords and lowland valleys of the Glacier Bay area; glaciers in southeastern Alaska thus were withdrawn farther than they are today. Forest beds and beds of sand apparently record a slackening of sedimentation and perhaps an accelerated or renewed glacial retreat during a few centuries after 2000 B.C., but by 1500 B.C. glaciers had begun to advance again, and during the ensuing three millennia they filled the entire bay. Finally, shortly before 1791, a glacial recession began that has continued essentially without interruption to the present day. This catastrophic retreat has resulted in recessions of the major ice tongues through distances of 75 to 100 km.

Nonglacial Deposits

EOLIAN DEPOSITS

Eolian deposits cover a large fraction of the low-lying parts of Alaska and are mostly of late Pleistocene age; only a few deposits are Recent and none is recognized as being pre-Illinoian. The deposits include large areas of loess and reworked loess (known in Alaska as "muck"), smaller areas of stabilized sand dunes, and very small areas of active dunes. Practically all the loess was derived from glacial outwash plains, and the few areas where loess is accumulating in significant quantities today adjoin the braided floodplains of streams from active glaciers. Most of the fossil sand dunes also adjoin sandy glacial outwash plains of late Pleistocene age, but a large area of stabilized dunes in the Arctic coastal plain and small areas of stabilized dunes on St. Paul Island in the Pribilof Islands and the Yukon Delta probably accumulated on the lee side of extensive sandy beaches.

The two largest areas of active dunes known in Alaska are not, however, along modern beaches but are in the Koyukuk and Kobuk Valleys. The Nogahabara active dune field in the lower valley of the Koyukuk is a small part of a Pleistocene dune field that has been reactivated. The active dune area is approximately 65 km² and consists mainly of transverse dunes 15 to 60 m in height and 90 m or more in length. The middle Kobuk valley contains another large area of Pleistocene dunes, 130 km² of which is now active (Fernald and Nichols, 1953).

Stabilized dunes, probably of Illinoian and Wisconsin age, are widespread, especially in central and northern Alaska. Only locally have they been mapped even in a reconnaissance fashion (Black, 1951; Fernald and Nichols, 1953; Collins, 1958; Weber and Péwé, 1961; Williams, 1962).

Well-formed parabolic and compound dunes cover approximately 1,150 km² on the high terrace remnants of the upper Tanana River valley. These dunes are 30 to 60 m high and are best developed in the vicinity of Northway and Tok.

North of the Tanana River in the vicinity of Big Delta, about 145 km southeast of Fairbanks, an area of about 780 km² of poor to fairly well-developed sand dunes is plastered against the bedrock hills up to an elevation of 520 m. These dunes are of parabolic and rosette types and have rather subdued to fairly fresh relief. They are thought to have originated in Illinoian time when winds from the south in the Delta River area blew sand from the widespread outwash plains and floodplains northward into the hills. They have been subsequently dissected and covered with a thick loess blanket.

The largest area of stabilized dunes in Alaska consists of several large masses south of the Tanana River that extend southward for 160 km into the drainage of the Kuskokwim River. This sand-dune area has been mapped by Florence R. Collins (unpublished data) and covers 15,500 km².

Sand dunes of both Wisconsin and pre-Wisconsin age are described by Fernald (1960) in the valley of the upper Kuskokwim River. Weber and Péwé (1961) have studied part of an area of 3,200 km² of vegetated, rather subdued fresh sand dunes on high terraces in the lower Koyukuk River valley.

Eolian sand of Pleistocene and Recent age underlies approximately 500 km² of the Yukon Flats, and eolian sand of Wisconsin or greater age covers at least 650 km² of the marginal upland (Williams, 1962). One of the largest areas in the state over which sand dunes occur is the 13,000-km² region of the northern Alaska coastal plain west of the Colville River (Black, 1951, p. 92).

Loess probably constitutes the most widespread Quaternary sediment in Alaska. It forms a blanket ranging in thickness from 1 cm to more than 60 m over almost all areas in the state that lie below altitudes of 300 to 600 m. Thick deposits of loess are most widely distributed in central and western Alaska. Most of the loess was deposited during Illinoian and Wisconsin time, but loess is still being deposited in some places.

The loess in Alaska is similar in texture and color to loess elsewhere in the world. Typically, 80% to 90% of the particles fall between 0.05 and 0.005 mm in size, but the loess coarsens toward the river floodplains that constitute the source areas (Trainer, 1961; Péwé and Holmes, 1964; Lindholm et al., 1959, p. 49). The loess is massive, cliff-forming, and locally perforated with the nesting tunnels of swallows. The thickest loess deposits known in Alaska occur on the north side of the Tanana River near Fairbanks, where a blanket 61 m thick covers the top of Gold Hill (Péwé, 1955). Greater thicknesses of silty sediments (up to 109 m) are encountered in the bottoms and on the lower slopes of small valleys in the Fairbanks area, but these represent deposits reworked from adjoining slopes. Loess is thick around the Yukon Flats (Williams, 1955, 1962) and the upper Kuskokwim Valley (Fernald, 1960, p. 247). Deposits of windblown silt and sandy silt many meters thick exist along bluffs bordering the central Copper River and near Palmer (Stump et al., 1959). Loess more than 1.5 m thick covers about three-quarters of the area of the Seward Peninsula (Hopkins, 1963, Pl. 3). The major river valleys on the Arctic Slope are flanked by loess that is generally many meters thick, but the loess blanket thins out considerably away from the river (Smith and Mertie, 1930, p. 249; Black, 1951, p. 92). Deposits a few centimeters to a few meters thick are known locally elsewhere in Alaska (Black, 1951; Muller, 1955; Karlstrom, 1955; Coonrad, 1957; Hoare and Coonrad, 1959). Isopach maps of loess thicknesses have been made in the Matanuska Valley near Palmer (Trainer, 1961) and in the lower reaches of the Delta River valley (Davidson et al., 1959; Péwé and Holmes, 1964).

Loess is still being deposited along most braided glacial streams, such as the area adjoining the Delta River near Big Delta (Fig. 4) (Péwé, 1951a), along the Knik River near Palmer (Fig. 4) (Tuck, 1938; Trainer, 1961), and near the junction of the Tanana and Yukon Rivers.

In the areas of active loess deposition, information on the rate of eolian silt accumulation can be obtained. The 7.2 m of silt measured on the top of Bodenberg Butte in the western Matanuska Valley near Palmer (Stump et al., 1959, p. 9), for example, is entirely of post-Wisconsin age. Measurements of loess thickness and radiocarbon dating of stumps and logs in the loess have given the following rates of accumulation in various places on terraces and gently sloping alluvial fans along the east side of the Delta River 32 to 80 km south of Big Delta (T. L. Péwé, unpublished data): 2.4 m of loess in 1,950 ± 150 years (L-163K); 3.8 m of loess in 4,650 ± 250 years (L-137Q); 14 m of loess in 7,000 ± 275 years (I-462); 5.2 m of loess in 5,900 ± 250 years (I-646); 3.7 m of loess in 2,300 ± 180 years (I-647). (The last figure is from the Yardang Flint Station, Reger et al., in press.) Inasmuch as loess provides an excellent medium for preservation (Péwé, 1954, p. 56), perhaps more effort should be concentrated on the search for artifacts in the Alaskan loess.

LACUSTRINE DEPOSITS

Lacustrine deposits of Quaternary age are relatively limited in Alaska, and only two large areas—the Copper River basin and the Cook Inlet area—contain widespread well-developed lake deposits.

The Copper River basin is an intermontane lowland about 14,000 km² in extent bounded by the Chugach, Wrangell, and Talkeetna Mountains and the Alaska Range. The basin is drained by canyons through the surrounding mountains, which still support large glaciers today. During Pleistocene glacial cycles, glacial ice repeatedly blocked the drainage from the basin, producing huge lakes.

The lacustrine sediments in the Copper River lowland were first reported by Mendenhall (1900, p. 33) and by Schrader and Spencer (1901, p. 74); detailed studies of the Quaternary glacial, volcanic, and lacustrine deposits were first undertaken in the 1950's by John R. Williams, Donald R. Nichols, Oscar J. Ferrians, Jr., Henry R. Schmoll, and Lynn Yehle of the U.S. Geological Survey. Only preliminary accounts of these studies have been published (Ferrians *et al.*, 1958, p. 1563; Nichols and Yehle, 1961, p. 1080-1081; Nichols, 1956, p. 11; Ferrians and Schmoll, 1957, p. 1726).

The lacustrine deposits in many places are finely laminated, rhythmically bedded sand, silt, and clay with layers of volcanic ash (Nichols, 1960, p. 353). The laminated silt and clay deposits are gray to bluish gray and dry with a blocky fracture. Many of the deposits containing ice-rafted stones grade laterally into thin-bedded, well-sorted sand and gravel. The lake sediments deposited during the last major glaciation are as much as 45 m thick in the lower parts of the basin but are very thin along the margins. More than 5,000 km² of the basin floor are underlain by these deposits.

The most recent lake episode began more than 38,000 years ago and ended about 9,400 years ago (Ferrians and Schmoll, 1957). We believe that the three major zones of lake sediments represent Wisconsin, Illinoian, and pre-Illinoian episodes, but Ferrians thinks it is more likely that they represent episodes of late and early Wisconsin and Illinoian age.

Shoreline features are found only for the latest lake, of late(?) Wisconsin age. The highest shorelines reported by Ferrians and Schmoll (1957) in the northeastern part of the lowland lie at an altitude of 750 m, but D. M. Hopkins and D. R. Nichols (unpublished data) have observed lake sediments and shoreline features up to altitudes of about 975 m in the western and northwestern parts.

Karlstrom (1964) presents evidence for the existence of a large proglacial lake, 13,000 km² in extent, in the area of upper Cook Inlet and the lower part of the Susitna Valley during the Knik and Naptowne Glaciations, which we consider to be of early and late Wisconsin age (Table 1). The lake was confined by an ice barrier in southern Cook Inlet, formed by coalescing piedmont glacial tongues from the Alaska Range to the west and the Kenai Mountains to the east. Other glaciers reached the shores of the former lake in many places.

FLUVIAL DEPOSITS

It is estimated that 25% of Alaska is covered by fluvial deposits, if the overlying loess blanket is ignored. In addition to the modern floodplains of rivers, huge glacial outwash fans flank most major mountain ranges, and many large tectonic basins (Payne, 1955), such as the valleys of the Kuskokwim and Tanana Rivers, the Yukon Flats, and

the Yukon-Koyukuk lowland, are filled with as much as a few hundred meters of fluvial sediments.

One of the most extensive areas of fluvial deposits in Alaska is in a tectonic basin termed "the Yukon Flats Cenozoic Basin" (Payne, 1955), which lies along the Yukon River south of the Brooks Range and north of the Yukon-Tanana upland. According to Williams (1962) the basin includes two physiographic units: the Yukon Flats and the marginal upland. The Yukon Flats is a broad lowland, approximately 23,000 km² in extent, which lies along the Yukon River and its tributaries and includes floodplains, terraces, alluvial fans, and small areas of sand dunes. The marginal upland, occupying an area of more than 12,000 km² at the edges of the basin, is 30 to 150 m above the alluvial lowland; it consists of a thick sequence of older alluvial deposits of the Yukon and its larger tributaries, and it includes alluvial fan deposits formed by small streams draining the adjoining highlands.

Among the many prominent lowlands with widespread fluvial sediments of middle to late Quaternary age are the upper Tanana Valley, middle Tanana Valley, Lake Minchumina area, upper Kuskokwim area (Fernald, 1960), Koyukuk Valley, and the Yukon-Koyukuk lowland (Weber and Péwé, 1961). Only a few have received even reconnaissance study. Most if not all of these areas record alternating deposition and erosion of sediments, an alternation that seems to have been synchronized with glacial and interglacial periods.

MARINE DEPOSITS

Coastal lowlands underlain by sequences of transgressive and regressive marine deposits fringe much of northern and western Alaska, from the Canadian boundary to the Kuskokwim River, and also occur along the northwest shore of the Alaska Peninsula. The southern coast adjoining the Gulf of Alaska has flights of wave-cut terraces, nearly all of Recent age, and strongly folded marine sediments of early Quaternary age. Other parts of the southern and southeastern Alaskan coasts are deeply indented by fiords and bays and, with rare exceptions, appear to have undergone net submergence during the Quaternary Period; Pleistocene and Recent marine deposits above sea level are rare in these areas.

The marine deposits of the Arctic coastal plain are grouped with the overlying nonmarine deposits in the Gubik Formation (Schrader, 1904); molluscan faunas from the Gubik Formation have been described by MacNeil (1957). The complex marine sequence at Nome has been intensively mined for placer gold. Mollusks collected in the gold-mining excavations there were described by MacNeil *et al.* (1943), and the stratigraphy has been described by Hopkins *et al.* (1960). Miller (1953) describes the deformed early Pleistocene marine sediments and the elevated Recent terraces of Middleton Island in the Gulf of Alaska and gives a list of the molluscan fossils contained in the early Quaternary sediments. These and other published studies and extensive unpublished field investigations and fossil molluscan determinations have provided the basis for the recognition of seven marine transgressions that are widely recorded along the Alaskan coasts (Hopkins, 1965; Hopkins *et al.*, 1965) (Table 2).

TABLE 2

Marine Transgressions Recorded on Alaskan Coasts (after Hopkins et al., 1965)

Transgression	Type locality	Altitude of shoreline	Climate as compared to the present	Archeological or radiometric dating	Correlation
Kruzensternian	Recent beach ridges at Cape Kruzenstern	Within 2 m. of present sea level for deposits <6,000 yr. old	Same	<6,000 yr. at Cape Kruzenstern. Up to 10,000 yr. for terraces along Gulf of Alaska Coast	Late Wisconsin and Recent
Woronzofian	Bootlegger Cove Clay near Point Woronzof, Anchorage area (Miller and Dobrovolny, 1959)	Probably a few meters below present sea level	Water: same Air: colder	<48,000 yr. >33,000 yr. (Karlstrom, 1960)	Middle Wisconsin interstade
Pelukian	"Second Beach" at Nome (Hopkins et al., 1960)	+ 7 to 10 m.	Water: warmer Air: slightly warmer	ca. 100,000 yr. (Blanchard, 1963)	Sangamon Interglaciation
Kotzebuan	Marine beds below Illinoian drift along eastern shore of Kotzebue Sound (McCulloch et al., in press)	+ 22 to 36 m.	Water: same Air: warmer	170,000 yr. 175,000 yr. (Blanchard, 1963)	Pre-Illinoian interglaciation
Unnamed	Einahnuhto Bluffs, St. Paul Is. (Merklin et al., 1964)	Higher than at present	Water: same Air: unknown	<300,000 ±100,000 yr. (G. B. Dalrymple, unpubl. data)	Middle Pleistocene interglaciation
Anvilian	"Third Beach-Intermediate Beach" at Nome (Hopkins et al., 1960)	+ 22 to 45 m.	Water: much warmer Air: warmer	Unknown	Early Pleistocene interglaciation
Beringian	"Submarine Beach" at Nome (Hopkins et al., 1960)	Higher than at present. Sea level probably lower than Anvilian sea level	Water: much warmer Air: much warmer	ca. 2,200,000 yr. on Pribilof Is. (G. B. Dalrymple, unpubl. data)	Older than first Pleistocene continental glaciation

Deposits laid down during the two early Pleistocene transgressions—the Beringian and the Anvilian transgressions—contain distinctive molluscan faunas that include appreciable numbers of extinct species as well as many species that are now limited to areas far to the south. Molluscan faunas thus far collected in deposits of an unnamed Middle Pleistocene transgression recorded at Tolstoi Point and in the Einahnuhto Bluffs of St. Paul Island are composed mostly of living species, and molluscan faunas from deposits of the Kotzebuan (pre-Illinoian), the Woronzofian (middle Wisconsin), and the Krusensternian (Recent) transgressions are composed entirely of species that are still living in nearby waters, but molluscan faunas collected in deposits of the Pelukian (Sangamon) transgression generally contain a few species that are presently limited to areas well south of their northernmost fossil occurrences.

Regressions of the sea during Pleistocene glacial maxima have repeatedly exposed most or all of the Bering-Chukchi marine platform and thus have created a broad land bridge extending from western Alaska to eastern Siberia (Hopkins, 1959). The land bridge clearly was in existence during most of the Wisconsin Glaciation (though it was probably temporarily closed during the Woronzofian transgression, about 33,000-45,000 years ago) and remained available to migrating plants, animals, and humans until it was drowned by the rising sea level about 11,000 years ago. Stratigraphic and palynologic studies in western Alaska indicate that the land bridge had tundra vegetation and a severe arctic climate (Hopkins, 1959; Colinvaux, 1963, 1964a, 1964b). During recent submarine geological studies in Chukchi Sea, traces of a subaerial stream-carved landscape have been found—a landscape that developed during the intervals when sea level was low and the Bering-Chukchi marine platform was exposed to erosion. Creager and MacManus (1961) discovered and named the Hope Sea Valley, a large, shallow, meandering channel that evidently was occupied by the large river to which the Kobuk, Noatak, Kivalina, and other large rivers in northwestern Alaska were once tributary. According to Scholl and Sainsbury (1961) several small streams have submarine extensions traceable for several miles off the present coast in the vicinity of Point Hope. Careful scrutiny of published marine charts of the Bering and Chukchi Seas suggests that there are several other major drainage courses in the bottom of Bering and Chukchi Seas, and detailed marine charts of rocky coasts in western Alaska commonly show dendritic networks of minor channels similar to those described in the Point Hope area by Scholl and Sainsbury (1961).

PERMAFROST AND PERIGLACIAL PROCESSES

PERMAFROST

Permafrost, or perennially frozen ground, is defined as soil or other surficial material, or even bedrock, that has had a temperature below freezing for two or more years. Permafrost is defined exclusively on the basis of temperature, irrespective of texture, degree of induration, water content, or lithologic character (Muller, 1945, p. 3). It has long been held that about 25% of the land area of the world is underlain by permafrost (Muller, 1945, Pl. 1; Black, 1954, p. 842).

Perennially frozen ground is present throughout most of Alaska (Fig. 5), but it is more widespread and extends to greater depths in the north than in the south. Permafrost in Alaska has been divided arbitrarily into three generalized zones—continuous, discontinuous, and sporadic zones (Black, 1950; Péwé, 1954; Hopkins, Karlstrom, *et al.*, 1955; Péwé and Paige, 1963). Inasmuch as the discontinuous and the sporadic permafrost zones are difficult to distinguish without temperature information, only two permafrost zones are considered here—the continuous and the discontinuous. Our discontinuous zone includes the discontinuous and sporadic zones of earlier classification. The recent permafrost map of Canada (Brown, 1960) outlines only these two permafrost zones.

In the continuous zone of the northern part of Alaska permafrost is present almost everywhere and extends to a depth of as much as 405 m (Brewer, 1958, p. 19). In this area, away from large bodies of water, the temperatures of permafrost at depths of 15 to 25 m are colder than $-5°$ C. The maximum depth to which appreciable annual temperature fluctuations penetrate the ground is 15-25 m. The coldest permafrost temperature recorded in Alaska is $-10.6°$ C near Barrow (Brewer, 1958, p. 22).

Southward in the discontinuous permafrost zone the thickness of permafrost decreases, and unfrozen areas are more and more common, until near the southern boundary only occasional patches of permafrost exist. The temperature of permafrost at depths of 15 to 25 m in this zone ranges from $-5°$ C in the northern part of the zone to approximately $0°$ C farther south.

The thickness of permafrost in Alaska ranges from an estimated maximum depth of 405 m near Barrow in the north to patches a few meters thick on the Alaska Peninsula in the south (Fig. 5). We have no knowledge of the distribution of permafrost in the Aleutian Islands or in southeastern Alaska. Accurate mapping of permafrost is possible only if good geothermal data are available.

Many temperature profiles of permafrost are not in equilibrium with the present climate at the sites of measurements. Lachenbruch *et al.* (in press) state, for example, that only 260 m of the 367 m of permafrost observed in a drill hole in Ogotoruk Valley, 35 km southeast of Point Hope, would exist if present surface conditions were to persist for several thousands of years. "In a sense, about 25 percent of the permafrost beneath Ogotoruk Valley is a product of an extinct climate."

The ice content is probably the most significant feature of permafrost affecting life in the north and providing evidence concerning past climates. The most conspicuous type of ice in the perennially frozen ground is the large ice wedge or mass that has a marked foliated appearance and that in contraction grows cracks in the frozen ground (Leffingwell, 1915, 1919; Lachenbruch, 1962; T. L. Péwé, unpublished data). Foliated ground-ice masses (ice wedges) are ubiquitous and actively growing in all types of unconsolidated material on the Arctic coastal plain of northern Alaska. They are common in central Alaska and the Seward Peninsula but are limited there to perennially frozen organic-rich silt (Taber, 1943; Péwé, 1957, 1958, in press, unpublished data; Hopkins, 1963). For the most part, the ice wedges in central Alaska are no longer actively growing

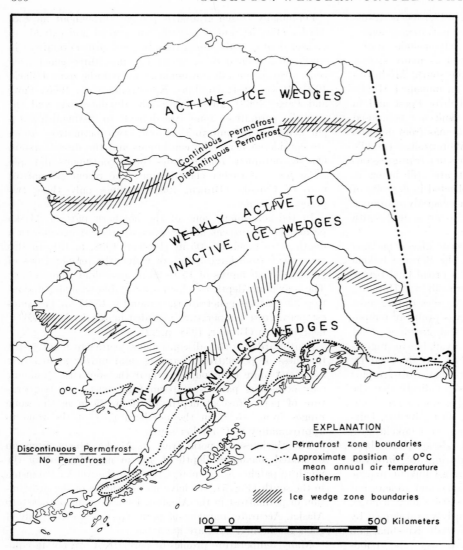

Figure 5. Distribution of ice wedges and permafrost in Alaska. Compiled by Troy L. Péwé.

(Péwé, in press) (Fig. 5). No ice wedges have been reported from the Yukon–Kuskokwim Delta or Bristol Bay area, and only one exposure is known to us in the Copper River Basin.

In places in western, central, and south-central Alaska ice wedges have melted and the void has been filled with sediments collapsing from above and the sides. In some places, several generations of "fossil" ice wedges are recognized. These "fossil" ice wedges generally indicate changes in climate (Hopkins *et al.*, 1960; Péwé, in press; Church *et al.*, in press) and are just beginning to be studied in Alaska.

PROCESSES

Throughout much of Alaska, especially the central, northern, and northwestern parts, the landscape has been and is being modified by geologic processes that are active in a periglacial region—processes of frost riving, frost stirring and sorting, solifluction, and choking of small streams with detrital material moved downslope by frost action.

Periglacial deposits may occur at various elevations in Alaska and be of various ages. Alaska provides examples of both actively forming periglacial deposits and inactive "fossil" deposits. Variations in location of the deposits and activity of the processes occur with changes in latitude and altitude. Péwé and his associates at the University of Alaska are currently analyzing past and present distribution of periglacial processes and deposits in Alaska.

Most periglacial deposits in Alaska can probably be attributed to the mass-wasting process described by the term "solifluction." Solifluction deposits are widespread in Alaska and consist of a blanket approximately 0.3 to 6 m thick of unstratified or indistinctly stratified, unsorted, heterogeneous, till-like detrital material that is similar in lithology to the material from which it was derived.

In areas of active solifluction in Alaska the terrain is characterized by relatively smoothly rounded hills and slopes, with well to poorly developed solifluction lobes or terraces. These areas lie almost entirely above or beyond the forest limit.

Examination of the widespread inactive solifluction deposits in Alaska has just begun, but it holds great promise for interpretation of Quaternary events in much of the state. Inactive solifluction deposits are reported from archeological sites on Cape Denbigh (Hopkins and Giddings, 1953, p. 18) and at Engigstciak in northwest Yukon Territory, Canada, near the Alaska-Canada boundary (Mackay *et al.*, 1961, p. 46). Inactive deposits are also widespread in the Yukon-Tanana upland.

Rock glaciers are among the most spectacular of periglacial deposits but are limited in areal extent. Active rock glaciers are abundant in the Talkeetna Mountains, Chugach Mountains, Wrangell Mountains, and in the central and southern Alaska Range (Wahrhaftig and Cox, 1959). Inactive rock glaciers can be found at lower elevations than the active ones, and no doubt they represent the lowering of snowline and changing of other climatic parameters during past glacial stages.

PART 2: ARCHAEOLOGY

J. L. GIDDINGS

The native populations of Alaska may readily be divided into four groups: (1) the Indians of the rain forests of the Pacific Coast, most of whom speak the languages of the Na-Dene stock, and the neighboring Eskimos, (2) the Aleuts, whose aberrant Eskimo sub-language and specialized culture set them apart from other Eskimos, (3) the Eskimos of the coasts of the Bering and Chukchi Seas, and (4) the Indians of the inland forests, all of whom speak closely related dialects of Athapaskan, a language of Na-Dene stock. Since recent studies indicate that none of these groups is new to its climatically distinctive area, I shall classify the archaeology of Alaska on the same regional basis.

PACIFIC COAST

Little is known of the earlier populations of southeastern Alaska. Sites a few decades or a few hundred years old in the wet Tlingit Indian areas of Angoon in central southeastern Alaska and in Yakutat Bay are poorly preserved yet show certain similarities to sites in neighboring regions, such as the presence of incised stone plaques, rock carvings, and rock paintings (de Laguna, 1960). Farther west, in Prince William Sound (Fig. 4) (de Laguna, 1956) and Cook Inlet (de Laguna, 1934), where Indian and Eskimo dialects exist side by side, the archaeology reaches back to 500 B.C. or earlier and fits roughly into the Eskimo continuity. The earliest levels had the best and most numerous chipped stone tools, though polished slate was present. Toggle harpoon heads were simple, lacking barbs, and wedges for woodworking preceded the splitting adzes of later periods. Dogs were kept, and growing middens testified to some permanence of residence. Later, design and decoration became sophisticated, and square deep houses were heated both by indoor fires and the flames of substantial pecked stone lamps. Deep accumulations of the bones of seals, deer, birds, fish, and other creatures show that the population flourished on both sea and land game.

The Eskimo middens of Kodiak Island (Heizer, 1956) were still deeper, and in them many skeletons of human beings have been found, accompanied by elaborate grave goods including lip plugs, ivory chain lengths, and carved animal figures. The earliest houses appear to have been square, and the triangular or oval lamps had pecked-out designs both on the bases and in the bowls. Many cross-ties with Eskimo sites of the Bering Sea coasts were found there at all levels. These midden mounds appear to be more recent than those of the Aleutians; nevertheless, an occasional flint found out of context in the Kodiak area encourages one to expect discoveries of earlier occupations when concerted searches are made.

ALEUTIAN ISLANDS

Following the large-scale midden explorations of Dall, Jochelson, and Hrdlička, more methodical excavations by Weyer (1929), Larsen (1953, p. 601), Laughlin and Marsh (1951, 1956), Laughlin (1958, 1963), Bank (1953), Spaulding (1962), and others have introduced precise chronology to Aleutian archaeology. As yet, however, only one monograph reporting in full on one of these later excavations has been published (Spaulding, 1962). Meanwhile, Laughlin and his colleagues have shown in preliminary reports that the midden mounds on Umnak Island began to accumulate about 4,000 years ago and that a much earlier people had lived in the vicinity (Laughlin, 1963).

The Chaluka mound, on Umnak, reveals from bottom to top a remarkable uniformity in the basic way of life. The early ways of hunting for whales and other sea mammals with boats and harpoons and of fishing with hooks have continued to the present day.

Houses were large and communal, and their floors contained lamps, root picks, wood-splitting wedges, bird spears, fishing weights, semilunar knives, and harpoon parts. Lamps illuminated the houses, and large lip plugs enhanced the person.

Despite the continuity of a single way of life, however, new genes drifted in, changing the human cranium from long to short and affecting the skull and lower skeleton in several minor ways. Along with the physical change from paleo-Aleut to neo-Aleut came style changes in artifacts, implying an influx of new people.

The older site of Anangula, off the northern shore of Umnak, has recently been shown to be a chipping place and camp site of early men who made some microblades as well as larger unifaced blades from prepared cores. Laughlin (1963) and his colleagues see in these materials, which were stratified in sands and volcanic ash, connections with the newly described late-glacial archaeological sequence of Japan. The first Aleuts may have thus arrived along the North Pacific coast when a land bridge still existed. Judging from the illustrations so far printed, however, these materials show no essential differences from postglacial artifacts in the Bering Strait area, and for the present the significance of the site rests on its radiocarbon dates of 7,660 to 8,425 years ago (Laughlin, 1963, p. 633).

No other sites comparable in age to Chaluka and Anangula have yet come to light in the Aleutians, and it looks as if the earliest people to reach Attu, at the western end of the island chain, did so less than 3,000 years ago (Spaulding, 1962, p. 42).

BERING SEA AND CHUKCHI SEA COASTS

Following early studies by Hrdlička, Jenness, Stefansson, and Rasmussen, excavations began on St. Lawrence Island and showed a long continuity of cultures in this region (Collins, 1937; Geist and Rainey, 1936; Rainey, 1941). In the deep midden mounds of this large island, which is culturally an extension of northeastern Siberia, was traced a society of walrus and seal hunters who at first, in the Okvik and Old Bering Sea periods, engraved intricate curvilinear designs on walrus ivory. From about 2,000 years ago, at least as far as the sites excavated on St. Lawrence Island are concerned, the basic economy has remained the same until the present century. In contrast to Aleutian culture, however, art styles changed periodically, and as this took place the forms of basic implements also changed. Engraved designs became stiff and formal during the Punuk period of 1,000 years ago, and accompanying this change came new methods of hunting and warring. Engraving art was rapidly lost after this period, and workmanship became strictly utilitarian like that of recent Eskimos.

While cross-ties existed between the Asian sequence of St. Lawrence Island and the sequence of the coast of the Alaskan mainland, the differences at all periods were perhaps as great as the similarities, indicating that no persistent migration took place between the already densely populated shores of the opposite sides of Bering Strait. The strongest continuity from west to east was from Punuk to Western Thule culture in Alaska to Thule culture of the whole stretch of Arctic coast between Alaska and Greenland. The whaling practices perfected early in the west apparently spread eastward in a continuous band at about the time Punuk culture was fully developed, setting the stage for the slate-polishing, lamp-using, dog-sledding cast of culture that we most readily recognize as Eskimo. For a while, in the absence of firm evidence that Old Bering Sea people had lived also on continental Alaska, it looked as though the synthesis ably presented by Collins (1937) for St. Lawrence Island and Bering Strait, with its implications of the eastward spread of the streamlined Thule culture, was all that could be said concerning the coastal archaeology of northern Alaska.

In 1939, however, a tremendous village of pit houses was found beneath the surface at Point Hope (Fig. 3), well above the Arctic Circle. More than six hundred houses, none overlapping, seemed to form a one-culture town at this site called Ipiutak. Certain absences—pottery, rubbed slate, lamps, and evidences of whaling—set the site apart from all others, while the presence of thin, delicate side blades and end blades of flinty materials give it a remarkably "Neolithic" cast. The Ipiutak hunters of walrus, seal, and caribou excelled in ivory carving in a style parallel to but distinct from that of St. Lawrence Island. They engraved freehand, curvilinear, and geometric designs on both ivory and antler, adding a few grotesque forms.

More remarkable still were the grave goods of some dozens of burials. Here, among strange "pretzel-like" objects, ornate burial trappings of a variety of kinds were found, such as nose plugs, mouth covers, and inset ivory eyes. The skeletons themselves were Eskimo-like but resembled the modern Yukaghir of northeastern Siberia almost as much as they did the long-headed, short-legged Eskimo type prevailing in eastern North America. Larsen and Rainey (1948) considered the Ipiutakers to be seasonally migratory people who spent their winters inland and inhabited their coastal houses principally when walrus hunting was most practical. They designated these Ipiutak people "paleo-Eskimos," and those of the "Arctic Whale Hunting Culture" they called "neo-Eskimos."

Although the Ipiutak and Old Bering Sea–Okvik cultures appeared to be roughly contemporaneous, there was in Ipiutak the absence of pottery, lamps, and whaling, and the mysterious presence of "Neolithic" traits such as fine diagonal flaking of bi-faced blades. This mystery was partly resolved by the discovery in 1948 of the Denbigh Flint complex at Cape Denbigh in the northern Bering Sea (Fig. 3) (Giddings, 1951, 1964; Hopkins and Giddings, 1953). In the bottom one of three cultural layers a coating of flints was found in an ancient podzol. Bones and organic artifacts had almost entirely disappeared. In this level, now dated at about 5,000 years ago, were found microblades and cores of the Old World Mesolithic style, bi-faced side blades and end blades clearly ancestral to those of Ipiutak, and abundant burins—first recognized here as an important element in New World archaeology. This basic combination at Cape Denbigh has recently been identified in five other coastal sites north around Bering Strait and Kotzebue Sound, inland in passes of the Brooks Range and neighboring wooded forests, and eastward in various combinations all the way to Pearyland in northernmost Greenland, where radiocarbon dates indicate it to have been present by 2000 B.C. (Knuth, 1958).

Dating of the Denbigh Flint complex and other cultural phases recently discovered has been facilitated by a large series of radiocarbon dates and especially by the use of two kinds of stratigraphy. Vertical stratigraphic relationships at Cape Denbigh placed a culture called Norton, which lay well above the Denbigh Flint complex, at about 500 B.C.; phases of Nukleet, a Thule-related culture, are dated at A.D. 1000 and later (Giddings, 1964). More precise and detailed, however, has been the isolation and placement of each of the previously known culture phases of continental Alaska, plus others, by a second kind of stratigraphy—horizontal—on series of beach ridges, all at about the same elevation above sea level at several points from Cape Prince of Wales on the extreme western end of Seward Peninsula around Kotzebue Sound (Giddings, 1961, 1964). In the longest series at Cape Krusenstern, 114 successive beach ridges in an area from 2.4 to 4.8 km in width and 13 km in length show the following succession and position of cultural phases:

The present outer beach (number 1) contains the leavings of recent Eskimos stretching back into at least the past century. On beaches 9 to 19 are isolated house pits, caches, and burials of the Western Thule culture. Ipiutak culture occupies beaches 29 to 35. Behind these, on beaches

36 through 50, are found hearths and tent sites of Norton culture followed by those of an earlier cultural phase discovered at Choris Peninsula on the east side of Kotzebue Sound (Giddings, 1957). In Choris culture, linear-stamped and check-stamped pottery of earliest Norton varieties occur together with many flaked spear points resembling those of much earlier "paleo-Indian" sites of the western plains. There are many signs of a break in continuity between the Denbigh and Ipiutak cultures. The Choris hunters lived in large, oval, communal houses, in contrast to the rectangular dwellings of later Eskimos.

A form of culture not yet encountered elsewhere is called Old Whaling. It is represented in a combination winter-and-summer village located on beach 53. The deep winter houses had multiple rooms, and on their floors were the bones of seals, dogs, and whales, but practically none of caribou. The bones of large whales lying outside these houses, 1.6 km from the present shore, indicate that the villagers were successful whalers at an unexpectedly early time. Their flints are large, though well made, in sharp contrast to the miniature forms of Denbigh and Ipiutak. Notched points appear here in variety—an incongruous element in the succession of coastal cultures. A large series of dates not yet published indicates that this village existed about 1800 B.C.

Between beaches 53 and 78 have been found thus far only a few tent sites, largely not culturally identifiable; but beginning with beach 78 and continuing through beach 105 are the remains of many tent sites and hearths of the Denbigh Flint complex. The beach ridges at Cape Krusenstern (Fig. 3) thus have been forming in succession for more than 5,000 years, apparently without a fluctuation in sea level of more than 1 m. This is the type locality of the Krusensternian marine transgression (Table 2).

Beyond the beach ridges and across a wide lagoon at Cape Krusenstern are the slopes of a small mountain. Near its base, on the "Lower Bench," which must have immediately overlooked the sea before beach ridges began to form, is a microblade site believed to represent the earliest aspect of Denbigh-like culture. Much higher, on another bench, where microblades and burins are lacking, are found the flints of two distinct cultural periods. The one set, Palisades II, is patinated but not chemically changed; it contains small side-notched points and other artifacts quite unlike those of the cultures on the beach ridges. The other set, Palisades I, is chemically changed throughout and includes raw flakes, choppers, and the fragment of a large bi-faced spear point.

Evidence confirming part of the beach ridge sequence comes from the Trail Creek caves, about 25 km inland from the south coast of Kotzebue Sound. Here, in the bottom levels, Larsen (1963) found a range of types of Denbigh-like flints together with arrowheads of antler into which the flints most likely had been hafted. In the middle levels came Choris-related artifacts, and, near the top, a range from Ipiutak to modern.

Quite recently a site containing notched points showing degrees of chemical change was found by R. E. Ackerman (personal communication, 1963) at Chagvan Bay (Fig. 1). Earlier reconnaissance by Larsen (1950) in the Chagvan Bay region had disclosed a range of archaeology back 2,000 years or more to a Norton-related phase of culture; and current research at the head of Bristol Bay and inland along the Brooks River by Dumond (1962) and his colleagues discloses a promising sequence reaching back to a "small tool" phase, somewhat like the Denbigh phase, about 4,000 years old.

To summarize for the coast, the earliest identified materials seem to be the chemically changed flints of the Palisades, followed by a notched-point horizon, and then by the introduction to the New World of microblades and burins, presumably about 4000 B.C. From this time forward, the record shows a continuous occupation of coastal western Alaska, although the earlier sites are so poorly preserved that they supply little cultural material other than implements of stone.

INTERIOR

The archaeology of the forested interior of Alaska is one of bits and patches. Objects excavated in one or two recently abandoned Indian villages (Rainey, 1939; de Laguna, 1947) and isolated flints picked up by workmen and observers mainly in the gold-mining projects of the Yukon River valley (Rainey, 1939; Skarland and Giddings, 1948; Johnson, 1946; Hadleigh-West, 1963) furnish most of the known collections. While some of these objects have been likened to "Early Man" flints far to the south, none has proved to be so closely similar to the prototypes as have examples from the beach ridge sequences of western Alaska, where they cannot be of great age (Giddings, 1963). Proposals of antiquity have also been made for some undated groups of artifacts found in the Anaktuvuk Pass region. There the Denbigh-related phases are identified with ease (Irving, 1953). Other undated collections from just beneath the surface, however, have been placed in a time scale making them as early as objects from distant parts of Asia showing similar flaking techniques; spear points have been placed in time to make them contemporary with early sites of the Great Plains or undated sites of the Yukon Territory of Canada (Campbell, 1963). Because most of the definitive forms and combinations of this area appear to be closely related to phases from the Kotzebue Sound–Bering Strait region, it appears doubtful that the pre-Denbigh age that is suggested for Kayuk, Naiyuk, and Kogruk collections in this region should be accepted until supported by a shorter-range dating method. The Engigstciak site (MacNeish, 1959), across the Alaskan border in northern Yukon Territory, appears to contain the cultural leavings of a long succession of peoples. Nearly all the individual forms thus far illustrated may be duplicated somewhere in the western Alaska sequence. However, the reported successions at Engigstciak appear to be mixed, and a reason for such a mixture is to be found in a recent geological report showing that solifluction has rearranged the stratigraphy in a large part of the site (Mackay et al., 1961).

A deep, evenly stratified site on the Kobuk River, the only one of its kind reported in northern North America, was partially explored in 1961 (Giddings, 1962), and again in 1963. As many as 30 cultural layers are defined from the top down through 2.5 or 3.0 m in depth. Shafts down to 6 m indicate that deeper cultural layers also exist. Cross-ties with the coastal sequence are in the following order from the surface down: Thule-related artifacts occur only to a few centimeters below the surface. Near the 0.5-m depth are four culture layers, the lower three of which are related to Norton culture and to at least one of the Anaktuvuk Pass phases. The Denbigh Flint complex lies at the 1.5-m depth, while 16 underlying culture layers contain, toward the top, materials most closely related to those of Palisades II of the coast and, deeper, larger stemmed or notched points and one or two choppers not unlike those of Palisades I. Stratigraphic indications are that these levels date 3,000 or 4,000 years earlier than the Denbigh Flint complex. The lower levels, and others interspersed with the coastal-related layers above, may prove to contain the deposits of interior, possibly Indian, tribes instead of those of the Eskimo "continuum" of the coast. Very recent surface discoveries made by archaeologists and geologists of the University of Alaska in Mount McKinley National Park, along new highways of the interior (Reger *et al.*, in press) and on hilltops near Livengood, promise new disclosures in early interior archaeology.

Conclusions

Although it is still impractical to put together the evidence from the four ecological zones, we appear to have a nearly complete post-Pleistocene sequence from the Bering Strait–Kotzebue Sound–Brooks Range region, with the possibility that Palisades I and some implements designated "British Mountain" are of late-Pleistocene age. In the Aleutian Islands, people of some undetermined continuity were present shortly after the last continental glaciation. The continuity most readily associated with Eskimo distribution and culture—that of microblades, burins, and side blades—appears to have entered the continent from Asia about 6,000 years ago. The earlier manifestations may be those of Indians, rather than Eskimos, although it will never be possible to determine this with certainty.

References

Bank, T. P., 1953, Cultural succession in the Aleutians: Amer. Antiq., v. 19, p. 40-49

Black, R. F., 1950, Permafrost, *in* Trask, P. D., Applied sedimentation: New York, John Wiley and Sons, Inc., p. 247-275

—— 1951, Eolian deposits of Alaska: Arctic, v. 4, p. 89-111

—— 1954, Permafrost—a review: Geol. Soc. Amer. Bull., v. 65, p. 839-855

Blanchard, R. A., 1963, Uranium decay series disequilibrium in age determination of marine calcium carbonates: St. Louis, Washington Univ. Ph.D. thesis, 164 p.

Brewer, M. C., 1958, Some results of geothermal investigations of permafrost in northern Alaska: Amer. Geophys. Union Trans., v. 39, p. 19-26

Brooks, A. H., 1906, The geology and geography of Alaska; a summary of existing knowledge: U.S. Geol. Surv. Prof. Pap. 45, 327 p.

Brown, R. J. E., 1960, The distribution of permafrost and its relation to air temperature in Canada and the U.S.S.R.: Arctic, v. 13, p. 163-177

Campbell, J. M., 1963, Ancient Alaska and Paleolithic Europe: Univ. Alaska, Anthrop. Pap., v. 10, p. 29-49

Church, R. E., Péwé, T. L., and Andresen, M. J., in press, Origin and environmental significance of large scale polygonal ground near Big Delta, Alaska: Cold Reg. Res. Eng. Lab., Res. Rep. 159

Colinvaux, P. A., 1963, A pollen record from Arctic Alaska reaching glacial and Bering land bridge times: Nature, v. 198, p. 609-610

—— 1964a, The environment of the Bering land bridge: Ecol. Monogr., v. 34, p. 297-329

—— 1964b, Origin of ice ages: pollen evidence from Arctic Alaska: Science, v. 145, p. 707-708

Collins, H. B., 1937, Archeology of St. Lawrence Island, Alaska: Smithson. Instn. Misc. Coll., v. 96, 431 p.

Collins, F. R., 1958, Vegetated sand dunes in central Alaska (abst.): Geol. Soc. Amer. Bull., v. 69, p. 1752

Coonrad, W. L., 1957, Geologic reconnaissance in the Yukon-Kuskokwim delta region, Alaska: U.S. Geol. Surv. Misc. Geol. Inv. Map I-223

Coulter, H. W., and Coulter, E. B., 1961, Geology of the Valdez (A-5) Quadrangle, Alaska: U.S. Geol. Surv. Geol. Quad. Map GQ-142

—— 1962, Preliminary geologic map of the Valdez-Tiekel belt, Alaska: U.S. Geol. Surv. Misc. Inv. Map I-356

Coulter, H. W., Hopkins, D. M., Karlstrom, T. N. V., Péwé, T. L., Wahrhaftig, Clyde, and Williams, J. R., in press, Extent of glaciations in Alaska: U.S. Geol. Surv. Misc. Geol. Inv. Map I-415

Creager, J. S., and MacManus, D. A., 1961, Preliminary investigations of the marine geology of the southeastern Chukchi Sea: Univ. Washington, Dept. Oceanography Tech. Rep. 68, 46 p.

Davidson, D. T., Roy, C. J., *et al.*, 1959, The geology and engineering characteristics of some Alaskan Soils: Iowa State Univ., Eng. Exp. Sta., Bull. 186, 149 p.

Detterman, R. L., Bowsher, A. L., and Dutro, J. T., Jr., 1958, Glaciation on the Arctic Slope of the Brooks Range, northern Alaska: Arctic, v. 11, p. 43-61

Dumond, D. E., 1962, Research on northwest prehistory: prehistory in the Naknek drainage, southwestern Alaska: (unpublished ms.)

Ewing, M. E., and Donn, W. L., 1963, Polar wandering and climate: Soc. Econ. Paleont. Mineralog. Spec. Publ. 10, p. 94-99

Fernald, A. T., 1960, Geomorphology of the upper Kuskokwim region, Alaska: U.S. Geol. Surv. Bull. 1071-G, p. 191-279

—— 1964, Surficial geology of the Kobuk River Valley, northwestern Alaska: U.S. Geol. Surv. Bull. 1181-K, 31 p.

Fernald, A. T., and Nichols, D. R., 1953, Active sand dunes in the Kobuk River valley, northwestern Alaska (abst.): Geol. Soc. Amer. Bull., v. 64, p. 1421-1422

Ferrians, O. J., Jr., 1963, Glaciolacustrine diamicton deposits in the Copper River Basin, Alaska: U.S. Geol. Surv. Prof. Pap. 475-C, p. 120-125

Ferrians, O. J., Jr., Nichols, D. R., and Schmoll, H. R., 1958, Pleistocene volcanic mudflow in the Copper River basin, Alaska (abst.): Geol. Soc. Amer. Bull., v. 69, p. 1563

Ferrians, O. J., Jr., and Schmoll, H. R., 1957, Extensive proglacial lake of Wisconsin age in the Copper River Basin, Alaska (abst.): Geol. Soc. Amer. Bull., v. 68, p. 1726

Flint, R. F., 1963, Status of the Pleistocene Wisconsin Stage in central North America: Science, v. 139, p. 402-404

Geist, O. W., and Rainey, F. G., 1936, Archaeological excavations at Kukulik, St. Lawrence Island, Alaska: Univ. Alaska, Misc. Publ., v. 2, 391 p.

Giddings, J. L., 1951, The Denbigh Flint complex: Amer. Antiq., v. 16, p. 193-203

—— 1957, Round houses in the western Arctic: Amer. Antiq., v. 23, p. 121-135

—— 1961, Cultural continuities of Eskimos: Amer. Antiq., v. 27, p. 155-173

—— 1962, Onion Portage and other flint sites of the Kobuk River: Arctic Anthrop., v. 1, p. 6-27

—— 1963, Some Arctic spear points and their counterparts: Univ. Alaska, Anthrop. Pap., v. 10, p. 1-12

—— 1964, The archeology of Cape Denbigh: Providence, Rhode Island, Brown Univ. Press, 331 p.

Goldthwait, R. P., 1963, Dating the Little Ice Age in Glacier Bay, Alaska: 21st Intern. Geol. Congr. Proc., Pt. 27, p. 37-46

Hadleigh-West, Frederick, 1963, Leaf-shaped points in the western Arctic: Univ. Alaska, Anthrop. Pap., v. 10, p. 51-62

Heizer, R. F., 1956, Archaeology of the Uyak Site, Kodiak Island, Alaska: Anthrop. Records, v. 17, 199 p.

Heusser, C. J., and Marcus, M. G., 1964, Historical variations of Lemon Creek Glacier, Alaska, and their relationship to the climatic record: J. Glaciol., v. 5, p. 77-86

Hoare, J. M., and Coonrad, W. L., 1959, Geology of the Russian Mission quadrangle, Alaska: U.S. Geol. Surv. Misc. Geol. Inv. Map I-292

Holmes, G. W., 1959a, Geological and hydrological investigations at Lake Peters, *in* Hartshorn, J. H., Proceedings of the First Annual Arctic planning session, Nov., 1958; Geophys. Res. Directorate Res. Notes, No. 15, U.S. Air Force, p. 2-5

—— 1959b, Glaciation in the Johnson River–Tok area, Alaska Range (abst.): Geol. Soc. Amer. Bull., v. 70, p. 1620

Holmes, G. W., and Benninghoff, W. S., 1957, Terrain study of the Army test area, Fort Greely, Alaska: U.S. Geol. Survey, Mil. Geol. Branch, 287 p.

Holmes, G. W., and Lewis, C. R., 1961, Glacial geology of the Mount Chamberlin area, Brook Range, Alaska, *in* Raasch, G. O., (ed.) Geology of the Arctic: Toronto, Univ. Toronto Press, v. 2, p. 848-864

Hopkins, D. M., 1959, Cenozoic history of the Bering land bridge: Science, v. 129, p. 1519-1528

——1963, Geology of the Imuruk Lake area, Seward Peninsula, Alaska: U.S. Geol. Surv. Bull. 1141-C, 101 p.

—— 1965, Chetvertichnye Morskie Transgressii Alyaski [Quaternary marine transgressions in Alaska]: U.S.S.R. Inst. Geol. Arctic, Trudy, in press (Russian with English summary; translation available from Amer. Geol. Inst., Washington, D.C.)

Hopkins, D. M., and Giddings, J. L., Jr., 1953, Geological background of the Iyatayet archeological site, Cape Denbigh, Alaska: Smithson. Instn. Misc. Coll., v. 121, no. 11, 33 p.

Hopkins, D. M., Karlstrom, T. N. V., *et al.*, 1955, Permafrost and ground water in Alaska: U.S. Geol. Surv. Prof. Pap. 264-F, p. 113-146

Hopkins, D. M., MacNeil, F. S., and Leopold, E. B., 1960, The coastal plain at Nome, Alaska: a late-Cenozoic type section for the Bering Strait region; 21st Intern. Geol. Congr. Proc., Copenhagen, Norden, Pt. 4, p. 46-67

Hopkins, D. M., MacNeil, F. S., Merklin, R. L., and Petrov, O. M., 1965, Quaternary correlations across Bering Strait: Science, v. 147, p. 1107-1114

Hopkins, D. M., McCulloch, D. S., and Janda, R. J., 1961, Pleistocene structure of Baldwin Peninsula, Kotzebue Sound, Alaska (abst.): Geol. Soc. Amer. Spec. Pap. 68, p. 116

Irving, W. N., 1953, Evidence of early tundra cultures in northern Alaska: Univ. Alaska, Anthrop. Pap., v. 1, p. 55-85

Johnson, Frederick, 1946, An archaeological survey along the Alaska Highway, 1944: Amer. Antiq., v. 11, p. 183-186

Karlstrom, T. N. V., 1955, Kenai Lowland, *in* Hopkins, D. M., Karlstrom, T. N. V., *et al.*, Permafrost and ground water in Alaska: U.S. Geol. Surv. Prof. Pap. 264-F, p. 133-134

—— 1957, Tentative correlation of Alaskan glacial sequences, 1956: Science, v. 125, p. 73-74

—— 1960a, The Cook Inlet, Alaska, glacial record and Quaternary classification: U.S. Geol. Surv. Prof. Pap. 400-B, p. 330-332

—— 1960b, Surficial deposits of Alaska: U.S. Geol. Surv. Prof. Pap. 400-B, p. 333-335

—— 1961, The glacial history of Alaska; its bearing on paleoclimatic theory: New York Acad. Sci. Ann., v. 95, p. 290-340

—— 1964, Quaternary geology of the Kenai lowland and glacial history of the Cook Inlet region, Alaska: U.S. Geol. Surv. Prof. Pap. 443, 69 p.

Karlstrom, T. N. V., *et al.*, 1964, Surficial geology of Alaska: U.S. Geol. Surv. Misc. Inv. Map I-357

Knuth, Eigil, 1958, Archaeology of the farthest north: 32nd Intern. Congr. Americanists, Copenhagen, 1956, Proc. p. 562-573

Kotzebue, Otto von, 1821, A voyage of discovery into the South Sea and Bering's Straits for the purpose of exploring a northeast passage: London, Longman, Hurst, Rees, Orme, & Brown, English translation in 3 v.

Lachenbruch, A. H., 1962, Mechanics of thermal contraction cracks and ice-wedge polygons in permafrost: Geol. Soc. Amer. Spec. Pap. 70, 70 p.

Lachenbruch, A. H., Green, G. W., and Marshall, B. V., in press, Permafrost and geothermal regime, *in* Wilimovsky, N. J. (ed.), Environment of the Cape Thompson area, Alaska: U.S. Atomic Energy Comm. Publ.

Laguna, Frederica de, 1934, The archaeology of Cook Inlet, Alaska: Philadelphia, Univ. Pennsylvania Press, 263 p.

—— 1947. The prehistory of northern North America as

seen from the Yukon: Amer. Arch. Soc. Mem., No. 3, 360 p.

—— 1956, Chugach prehistory, the archaeology of Prince William Sound, Alaska: Seattle, Univ. Washington Press, 289 p.

—— 1960, The story of a Tlingit community; a problem in the relationship between archaeological, ethnological, and historical methods: U.S. Bur. Amer. Ethnol. Bull. 172, 254 p.

Larsen, Helge, 1950, Archaeological investigations in southwestern Alaska: Amer. Antiq., v. 15, p. 177-186

—— 1953, Archaeological investigations in Alaska since 1939: Polar Record, v. 6, p. 593-607

—— 1963, The Trail Creek caves on Seward Peninsula, Alaska: 34th Intern. Congr. Americanists, Vienna, Proc., p. 284-291

Larsen, Helge, and Rainey, F. G., 1948, Ipiutak and the Arctic whale hunting culture: Amer. Mus. Nat. Hist., Anthrop. Pap., v. 42, 276 p.

Laughlin, W. S., 1958, Neo-Aleut and Paleo-Aleut prehistory: 32nd Intern. Congr. Americanists, Copenhagen, 1956, Proc., p. 516-530

—— 1963, Eskimos and Aleuts: their origins and evolution: Science, v. 142, p. 633-645

Laughlin, W. S., and Marsh, G. H., 1951, A new view of the history of the Aleutians: Arctic, v. 4, p. 75-88

—— 1956, Trends in Aleutian chipped stone artifacts: Univ. Alaska, Anthrop. Pap., v. 5, p. 5-21

Lawrence, D. B., 1958, Glaciers and vegetation in southeastern Alaska: Amer. Scientist, v. 46, p. 88-122

Leffingwell, E. de K., 1915, Ground-ice wedges; the dominant form of ground ice on the north coast of Alaska: J. Geol., v. 23, p. 635-654

—— 1919, The Canning River region, northern Alaska: U.S. Geol. Surv. Prof. Pap. 109, 251 p.

Lindholm, G. F., Thomas, L. A., Davidson, D. T., Handy, R. L., and Roy, J. C., 1959, Silt near Big Delta and Fairbanks, in Davidson, D. T., Roy, C. J., et al., The geology and engineering characteristics of some Alaskan soils: Iowa State Univ. Bull. 186, p. 33-70

Mackay, J. R., Mathews, W. H., and MacNeish, R. S., 1961, Geology of the Engigstciak Archaeological site, Yukon Territory: Arctic, v. 14, p. 25-52

MacNeil, F. S., 1957, Cenozoic megafossils of northern Alaska: U.S. Geol. Surv. Prof. Pap. 294-C, p. 99-126

MacNeil, F. S., Mertie, J. B., and Pilsbry, H. A., 1943, Marine invertebrate faunas of the buried beaches near Nome, Alaska: J. Paleont., v. 17, p. 69-96

MacNeish, R. S., 1959, Men out of Asia, as seen from the northwest Yukon: Univ. Alaska, Anthrop. Pap., v. 7, p. 41-70

McCulloch, D. S., Taylor, D. W., and Rubin, Meyer, 1965, Stratigraphy, nonmarine mollusks, and radiometric dates from Quaternary deposits in the Kotzebue Sound area, western Alaska: J. Geol., v. 73 (in press)

Mendenhall, W. C., 1900, A reconnaissance from Resurrection Bay to Tanana River, Alaska in 1898: U.S. Geol. Surv., Ann. Rep. 20, pt. 7, p. 265-340

Merklin, R. L., Petrov, O. M., Hopkins, D. M., and MacNeil, F. S., 1964, Popytka Korrelyatzii Pozdnekajno-

zojskikh Morskikh Osadkov Chukotki, Severo-Vostochnoj Sibiri i Zapadnoj Alyaski [An attempt of correlation to be made for the late Cenozoic deposits of Chukotka, northeastern Siberia, and western Alaska]: Acad. Sci. U.S.S.R., Izvestia, 1964g, No. 10, p. 45-57 (Russian)

Miller, D. J., 1953, Late Cenozoic marine glacial sediments and marine terraces of Middleton Island, Alaska: J. Geol. v. 61, p. 17-40

—— 1957, Geology of the southeastern part of the Robinson Mountains, Yakataga district, Alaska: U.S. Geol. Surv. Oil Gas Inv. Map. OM-187

Miller, R. D., and Dobrovolny, E., 1959, Surficial geology of Anchorage and vicinity, Alaska: U.S. Geol. Surv. Bull. 1093, 128 p.

Muller, E. H., 1953, Northern Alaska Peninsula and eastern Kilbuck Mountains, Alaska, in Péwé, T. L., et al., Multiple glaciation in Alaska: U.S. Geol. Surv. Circ. 289, p. 2-3

—— 1955, Bristol Bay Region, in Hopkins, D. M., Karlstrom, T. N. V., et al., Permafrost and ground water in Alaska: U.S. Geol. Surv. Prof. Pap. 264-F, p. 131-133

Muller, S. W., 1947, Permafrost or permanently frozen ground and related engineering problems: Ann Arbor, Edwards Bros., 231 p.

Nichols, D. R., 1956, Permafrost and groundwater conditions in the Glennallen area, Alaska: U.S. Geol. Surv. Prelim. Rep., 12 p.

—— 1960, Slump structures in Pleistocene lake sediments, Copper River Basin, Alaska: U.S. Geol. Surv. Prof. Pap. 400-B, p. 353-354

Nichols, D. R., and Yehle, L. A., 1961, Mud volcanoes in the Copper River Basin, Alaska, in Raasch, G. O., (ed.), Geology of the Arctic: Toronto, Univ. Toronto Press, v. 2, p. 1063-1087

Payne, T. G., 1955, Mesozoic and Cenozoic tectonic elements of Alaska: U.S. Geol. Surv. Misc. Geol. Inv. Map I-84

Péwé, T. L., 1951a, An observation on wind-blown silt: J. Geol., v. 59, p. 399-401

—— 1951b, Recent history of Black Rapids Glacier, Alaska (abst.): Geol. Soc. Amer. Bull., v. 62, p. 1558

—— 1952, Preliminary report of multiple glaciation in the Big Delta area, Alaska (abst.): Geol. Soc. Amer. Bull., v. 63, p. 1289

—— 1954, The geological approach to dating archaeological sites: Amer. Antiq., v. 20, p. 51-61

—— 1955, Origin of the upland silt near Fairbanks, Alaska: Geol. Soc. Amer. Bull., v. 66, p. 699-724

—— 1957, Permafrost and its effect on life in the North, in Arctic biology: Corvallis, Oregon State Coll., 18th Annual Biology Colloquium, p. 12-25

—— 1958, Geology of the Fairbanks (D-2) quadrangle, Alaska: U.S. Geol. Surv. Geol. Quad. Map GQ-110

—— 1961, Multiple glaciation in the headwaters area of the Delta River, central Alaska: U.S. Geol. Surv. Prof. Pap. 424-D, p. 200-201

—— in press, Ice wedges in Alaska—classification, distribution, and climatic significance: 1st Intern. Conf. Permafrost, Proc.

Péwé, T. L., and Burbank, L., 1960, Multiple glaciation in

the Yukon-Tanana upland, Alaska; a photogeologic interpretation (abst.): Geol. Soc. Amer. Bull., v. 71, p. 2088

Péwé, T. L., and Holmes, G. W., 1964, Geology of the Mt. Hayes (D-4) Quadrangle, Alaska: U.S. Geol. Surv. Misc. Geol. Inv. Map I-394

Péwé, T. L., and Paige, R. A., 1963, Frost heaving of piles with an example from Fairbanks, Alaska: U.S. Geol. Surv. Bull. 1111-I, p. 74

Péwé, T. L., et al., 1953, Multiple glaciation in Alaska—a progress report: U.S. Geol. Surv. Circ. 289, 13 p.

Plafker, George, and Miller, D. J., 1958, Glacial features and surficial deposits of the Malaspina district, Alaska: U.S. Geol. Surv. Misc. Geol. Inv. Map I-271

Porter, Steven, 1964, Geologic history of the Anaktuvuk Pass area, Brooks Range, Alaska: Amer. J. Sci., v. 262, p. 446-460

Rainey, F. G., 1939, Archaeology of central Alaska: Amer. Mus. Nat. Hist., Anthrop. Pap., v. 36, 426 p.

—— 1941, Eskimo prehistory; the Okvik site on the Punuk Islands: Amer. Mus. Nat. Hist., Anthrop. Pap., v. 37, 601 p.

Reed, J. C., Jr., 1960, Geology of the Mt. McKinley Quadrangle, Alaska: U.S. Geol. Surv. Open-File Rep.

—— 1961, Geology of the Mt. McKinley Quadrangle, Alaska: U.S. Geol. Surv. Bull. 1108-A, 36 p.

Reger, R. D., Péwé, T. L., Hadleigh-West, Frederick, and Skarland, Ivar, in press, Geology and archeology of the Yardang Flint Station: Univ. Alaska, Anthrop. Pap., v. 12, pt. 2, p. ——

Sackett, W. M., 1958, Ionium-radium ratios in marine-deposited calcium carbonates and related materials: St. Louis, Washington Univ. Ph.D. thesis, 50 p.

Scholl, D. W., and Sainsbury, C. L., 1961, Marine geology and bathymetry of the Chukchi Shelf off the Ogotoruk Creek area, northwest Alaska, in Raasch, G. O. (ed.), Geology of the Arctic: Toronto, Univ. Toronto Press, v. 1, p. 718-732

Schrader, F. C., 1904, A reconnaissance in northern Alaska: U.S. Geol. Surv. Prof. Pap. 20, 139 p.

Schrader, F. C., and Spencer, A. C., 1901, The geology and mineral resources of a portion of the Copper River district Alaska: U.S. Geol. Surv., 94 p.

Skarland, Ivar, and Giddings, J. L., 1948, Flint stations in central Alaska: Amer. Antiq., v. 14, p. 116-120

Smith, P. S., and Mertie, J. B., 1930, Geology and mineral resources of northwestern Alaska: U.S. Geol. Surv. Bull. 815, 351 p.

Spaulding, A. C., 1962, Archaeological investigations on Agattu, Aleutian Islands: Univ. Michigan, Anthrop. Pap., no. 18, 79 p.

Stump, R. W., Handy, R. L., Davidson, D. T., Roy, C. J., and Thomas, L. A., 1959, Silt deposits in the Matanuska Valley, in Davidson, D. T., Roy, C. J., et al., The geology and engineering characteristics of some Alaskan soils: Iowa State Univ. Bull. 186, p. 3-32

Taber, Stephen, 1943, Perennially frozen ground in Alaska; its origin and history: Geol. Soc. Amer. Bull., v. 54, p. 1433-1548

Trainer, F. W., 1961, Eolian deposits of the Matanuska Valley agricultural area, Alaska: U.S. Geol. Surv. Bull. 1121-C, 34 p.

Tuck, Ralph, 1938, The loess of the Matanuska Valley, Alaska: J. Geol., v. 46, p. 647-653

Wahrhaftig, Clyde, 1958, Quaternary geology of the Nenana River Valley and adjacent parts of the Alaska Range, in Wahrhaftig, Clyde, and Black, R. F., Quaternary and engineering geology in the central part of the Alaska Range: U.S. Geol. Surv. Prof. Pap. 293, p. 1-67

—— in press, Physiographic divisions of Alaska: U.S. Geol. Surv. Prof. Pap. 482

Wahrhaftig, Clyde, and Cox, Allan, 1959, Rock glaciers in the Alaska Range: Geol. Soc. Amer. Bull., v. 70, p. 383-436

Weber, Florence, and Péwé, T. L., 1961. Engineering geology problems in the Yukon-Koyukuk lowland, Alaska: U.S. Geol. Surv. Prof. Pap. 424-D, p. 371-373

Weyer, E. M., 1929, An Aleutian burial: Amer. Mus. Nat. Hist., Anthrop. Pap., v. 31, p. 219-238

Williams, J. R., 1955, Yukon Flats, in Hopkins, D. M., Karlstrom, T. N. V., et al., Permafrost and ground water in Alaska: U.S. Geol. Surv. Prof. Pap. 264-F, p. 124-126

—— 1962, Geologic reconnaissance of the Yukon Flats district, Alaska: U.S. Geol. Surv. Bull. 1111-H, p. 289-331

SUMMARY

Quaternary deposits mantle virtually all of Alaska. About 50% is covered by glacial deposits and the rest by deposits of eolian, fluvial, lacustrine, volcanic, periglacial, and marine origin. Local patches of early Pleistocene till are found in most of the glaciated areas. During Illinoian, Wisconsin, and Recent times glaciers were much more extensive in southern Alaska than in northern Alaska and were nourished chiefly by air mases moving north- to northeastward from the northern Pacific Ocean. The Wisconsin glaciation in Alaska was clearly a complex event, consisting of at least two major advances and including several minor oscillations during the later major advance.

Eolian deposits cover much of the low-lying parts of Alaska and are mostly of late Pleistocene age. Quaternary lacustrine deposits are relatively scarce but about 25% of the state is covered with fluvial deposits. Marine deposits are confined mostly to a coastal fringe in northern and western Alaska.

Perennially frozen ground is present throughout most of Alaska; ice wedges are widespread in northern Alaska and fairly common in central Alaska. Periglacial deposits occur throughout the state. Alaska provides examples of both actively forming and the inactive or "fossil" periglacial deposits.

The native populations of Alaska consist of the Eskimos, who occupy the coasts of the Arctic Ocean, Bering and Chukchi Seas, and the Pacific Coast west of Cordova; the Aleuts of the Aleutian Islands, who speak an aberrant Eskimo sub-language; the Athapascan-speaking Indians of the inland forests; and the Indians of the Pacific Coast east of Cordova, who speak another language of the Na-Dene stock. Numerous excavated archaeological sites provide a long and detailed record of the evolution of Eskimo and Aleut cultures, but archaeological knowledge of the pre-history of the Indian groups is scanty.

The oldest Aleut site recognized thus far is at Anangula Island, occupied as early as 8,400 years ago. The nearby Chaluka Site on Umnak Island shows continuity of a single way of life throughout the past 4,000 years, in spite of physical changes in the population and style changes in their artifacts.

The oldest well-dated Eskimo culture is represented by the Denbigh Flint Complex, characterized by microblades and cores of the Old World Mesolithic style, bi-faced side blades and end blades, and abundant burins found in deposits about 5,000 years old. Related cultural assemblages are widely distributed in western and northern Alaska and eastward across Canada to northernmost Greenland. Later cultural assemblages from the Eskimo area show greater changes with time and greater local differentiation than has been recognized thus far in Aleut sites.

A few artifact assemblages from western and northern Alaska may be of late-Pleistocene age and may represent Indian rather than Eskimo manifestations.

PART II: BIOGEOGRAPHY

PHYTOGEOGRAPHY AND PALYNOLOGY

PHYTOGEOGRAPHY AND PALYNOLOGY OF NORTHEASTERN UNITED STATES

PROBLEMS IN THE QUATERNARY PHYTOGEOGRAPHY OF THE GREAT LAKES REGION

PALYNOLOGY AND PLEISTOCENE PHYTOGEOGRAPHY OF UNGLACIATED EASTERN NORTH AMERICA

PLEISTOCENE POLLEN ANALYSIS AND BIOGRAPHY OF THE SOUTHWEST

PLANT GEOGRAPHY IN THE SOUTHERN ROCKY MOUNTAINS

A PLEISTOCENE PHYTOGEOGRAPHICAL SKETCH OF THE PACIFIC NORTHWEST AND ALASKA

THE BOREAL BRYOPHYTE FLORA AS AFFECTED BY QUATERNARY GLACIATION

POLYPLOIDY, DISTRIBUTION, AND ENVIRONMENT

ZOOGEOGRAPHY AND EVOLUTION

QUATERNARY MAMMALS OF NORTH AMERICA

AVIAN SPECIATION IN THE QUATERNARY

AMPHIBIAN SPECIATION

REPTILES IN THE QUATERNARY OF NORTH AMERICA

QUATERNARY FRESHWATER FISHES OF NORTH AMERICA

PLEISTOCENE EVENTS AND INSECTS

THE STUDY OF PLEISTOCENE NONMARINE MOLLUSKS IN NORTH AMERICA

OTHER INVERTEBRATES—AN ESSAY IN BIOGEOGRAPHY

RECENT ADJUSTMENTS IN ANIMAL RANGES

GENERAL

PLEISTOCENE NONMARINE ENVIRONMENTS

PHYTOGEOGRAPHY AND PALYNOLOGY OF
NORTHEASTERN UNITED STATES *

NORTHEASTERN UNITED STATES, including New England, New York, and the glaciated portions of Pennsylvania and New Jersey (Fig. 1), is a region of great diversity of habitat and of vegetation. The igneous and metamorphic rocks of the northern Appalachian Mountains run in a northeasterly direction through the region; to the west the landscape is underlain by the folded sedimentary rocks of the Valley and Ridge Province, while Cenozoic sediments underlie coastal New Jersey, Long Island, Cape Cod, and some of the offshore islands. This landscape was glaciated at least once during the Pleistocene; nevertheless the bedrock, particularly in regions of igneous rock, has an irregular surface of considerable relief. The maximum elevation is nearly 2,000 m in the White Mountains of New Hampshire. Postglacial marine sediments occur along the coast of Maine and in the St. Lawrence valley in northeastern New York and adjacent Canada, and in northwestern New York freshwater sediments mark the ancestral Great Lakes. In many parts of the region, however, the Pleistocene deposits are thin and irregular. Bedrock is frequently exposed, and the incomplete mantle of drift ranges in texture from clayey till to coarse gravel over very short distances. This is particularly so in regions such as New England and northern New York State, where a large proportion of the glacial debris is of glaciofluvial origin (Denny, 1956). The variations in texture and in thickness of the surficial deposits combine with the irregular topography of the bedrock to produce a variety of different local habitats for plants, allowing extensive local variation in species distribution and frequency.

The present and past vegetation of this region has been studied more intensively than in many other parts of the country. Of particular importance are the classic phytogeographic studies of Fernald, the studies in forest ecology by Raup, Goodlett, and others, and the pioneering investigations of the pollen record by Deevey and his students. In this paper I have not attempted to summarize the literature; an excellent summary has recently been provided by Ogden (1964). Instead I have tried to bring together the diverse viewpoints of phytogeographers, ecologists, and palynologists and to comment upon the way in which ideas from each of these fields have influenced or failed to influence the others.

PRESENT VEGETATION

DISTRIBUTION AND ABUNDANCE OF FOREST SPECIES

The entire northeastern United States, with the minor exceptions of salt marshes along the seacoast and alpine tundra in the high mountains, is able to support forest vegetation, as shown in the historical record. Clearing for agriculture began in the 17th and 18th centuries and reached its maximum in the early 19th century. In the Connecticut valley in New England, and in portions of New Jersey, New York and Pennsylvania (Fig. 1), where farming is economically profitable, the landscape is still almost entirely cleared. In most regions, however, the landscape is now at least half forested, and in the mountains the forest cover is almost complete. Despite the occurrence of extensive forest tracts, the geographical distribution of many important forest trees is not known in detail, and the ecological literature provides almost no quantitative descriptions on the regional scale needed for the present discussion. There are quantitative data on forest species available that have been collected by the United States Forest Service; these vary in detail from one region to another but could profitably be compared with pollen spectra. Another source of information of great potential value are the forest records made in some regions by early land surveyors. I have not made use of these sources except where they are summarized in the literature; the description of the present vegetation given here is therefore very brief; it relies heavily on unpublished quantitative surveys in New England by Goodlett and myself. I have no firsthand acquaintance with the vegetation of much of the region under consideration and therefore have not tried to describe it. Furthermore I should emphasize that

* I wish to express my appreciation to John C. Goodlett, Estella B. Leopold, Louis J. Maher, Jr., Henry I. Baldwin, and Daniel A. Livingstone for helpful comments and criticism. This work has been supported by the National Science Foundation, Project Grant G-17830. Analyses of Brownington Pond sediment were done in 1960 at the Division of Geological Sciences at Caltech and were supported by NSF Regular Postdoctoral Fellowship 40002 and Project Grant G-4802. This paper is Contribution Number 42 from the Great Lakes Research Division, University of Michigan.

[1] Great Lakes Research Division, University of Michigan, Ann Arbor, Michigan.

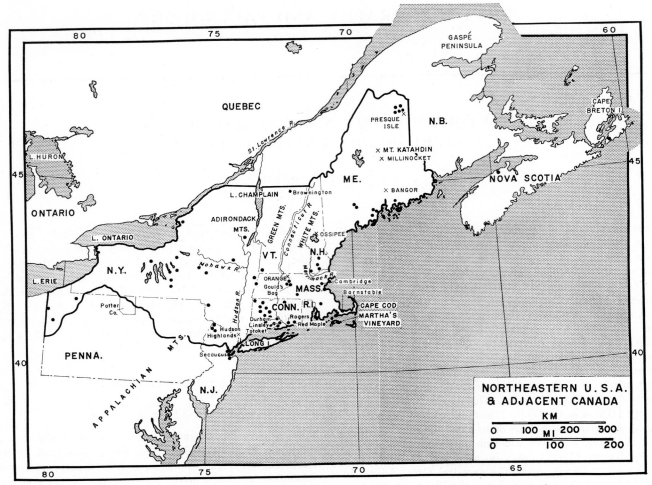

Figure 1. Outline map of glaciated northeastern United States and adjacent Canada, showing localities mentioned in text. The six states—Connecticut, Rhode Island, Massachusetts, Vermont, New Hampshire, and Maine—are referred to in the text as "New England." The region considered in this review is enclosed within the heavy black line. Its southern boundary, in New Jersey and Pennsylvania, is placed at the southern limit of Pleistocene drift. Dots indicate sites of published pollen diagrams.

the generalizations attempted here cannot be extended beyond the region outlined in Figure 1.

Primary attention will be given here to those genera that are important in the fossil record; therefore many of the 70 species now considered important forest trees (Little, 1949) will not be discussed. A key to colloquial plant names used in the text is given in Table 1. In describing species distributions, I shall in most cases mention only the portions of ranges which fall within the boundaries of glaciated northeastern United States as indicated in Figure 1. Most of the species also occur outside this area.

The number of deciduous-tree species present in the forest declines from south to north in the Northeast. A few species such as CUCUMBER tree are confined to the southwestern portion of the region we are considering. A number of other species, such as sweet GUM, HACKBERRY, SASSAFRAS, tulip-POPLAR, flowering DOGWOOD, black gum and SYCAMORE occur in northwestern New York State near Lake Ontario and also range up along the eastern coast, reaching their northeastern limit in southern Connecticut

or Massachusetts, or in central New England. Several species of OAK also reach their northern limits here, e.g. post-oak, pin-oak, and swamp-white oak, while bur-oak, which is abundant in the Midwest, reaches its eastern limit in New York State except for an outlying population in central Maine (Little, 1949; Fernald, 1950).

The various species of oak, considered together, dominate the forests locally in the southern portion of the region, specifically on well-drained sites in northern Pennsylvania (Goodlett, 1954), in the highlands of New Jersey and southern New York State (Niering, 1953; Raup, 1938), in New York State just south of Lakes Ontario and Erie (Bray, 1930), and in southern New England (Braun, 1950; Niering and Goodwin, 1962; Davis and Goodlett, unpublished data). Black, white, and scarlet oak are particularly abundant. Chestnut-oak often grows on rocky soil and bear-oak on exposed ledges. The distributions of the various species of oak in New England are now being studied in detail by John C. Goodlett, who has observed (personal communication) that several of the oak species

TABLE 1

Colloquial Names and Latin Equivalents (after Fernald, 1950)
of Plant Species and Genera Referred to in Text

Alder	*Alnus* spp.
Arbor vitae—see Cedar	
Ash, white	*Fraxinus americana*
Aspen	
large-toothed	*Populus grandidentata*
trembling	*P. tremuloides*
Aster	*Aster* spp.
Basswood	*Tilia americana*
Beech	*Fagus grandifolia*
Birch	
gray	*Betula populifolia*
paper-	*B. papyrifera*
sweet (black, cherry-)	*B. lenta*
yellow	*B. lutea*
Butternut	*Juglans cinerea*
Cedar	
Atlantic white	*Chamaecyparis thyoides*
northern white (Arbor vitae)	*Thuja occidentalis*
red	*Juniperus virginiana*
Cherry	
black	*Prunus serotina*
choke-	*P. virginiana*
pin-	*P. pensylvanica*
Chestnut	*Castanea dentata*
Cucumber	*Magnolia acuminata*
Dogwood, flowering	*Cornus florida*
Elm	
American	*Ulmus americana*
slippery	*U. rubra*
Fir, balsam-	*Abies balsamea*
Goldenrod	*Solidago* spp.
Grass	Gramineae
Gum	
black (tupelo)	*Nyssa sylvatica*
sweet	*Liquidambar styraciflua*
Hackberry	*Celtis occidentalis*
Hemlock	*Tsuga canadensis*
Hickory (shagbark, pignut, mockernut)	*Carya* spp.
Hornbeam	
hop-	*Ostrya virginiana*
American (blue beech, ironwood)	*Carpinus caroliniana*
Larch (tamarack)	*Larix laricina*
Maple	
red	*Acer rubrum*
sugar-	*A. saccharum*
Oak	
bear- (scrub-)	*Quercus ilicifolia*
black	*Q. velutina*
bur- (mossy-cup)	*Q. macrocarpa*
chestnut-	*Q. prinus*
pin-	*Q. palustris*
post-	*Q. stellata*
red	*Q. rubra*
scarlet	*Q. coccinea*
swamp-white	*Q. bicolor*
white	*Q. alba*
Pine	
jack-	*Pinus Banksiana*
pitch-	*P. rigida*
red (Norway-)	*P. resinosa*
white	*P. strobus*
Poplar	
balsam-	*Populus balsamifera*
tulip-	*Liriodendron Tulipifera*
Ragweed	*Ambrosia* spp.
Sassafras	*Sassafras albidum*
Sedge	Cyperaceae

TABLE 1 *Continued*

Spruce	
black	*Picea mariana*
red	*P. rubens*
white	*P. glauca*
Sycamore	*Platanus occidentalis*
Tree-of-heaven	*Ailanthus altissima*
Walnut, black	*Juglans nigra*
Willow	*Salix* spp.

occur only in the drier habitats near the northern limits of their ranges, whereas farther south they may grow on relatively moist sites. Red oak, for example, is confined to steep gravel slopes at the northern limit of its range in northern Vermont (Davis and Goodlett, 1960), whereas it is characteristic of relatively moist coves in southern New York and New Jersey (Niering, 1953; Raup, 1938). In northern Pennsylvania local changes from chestnut-oak to white oak to red oak coincide with changes from thin, rubbly surficial deposits to thick, non-rubbly surficial deposits (Goodlett, 1954), suggesting that chestnut-oak requires less soil moisture than white oak, and white oak less than red oak. These three species may be put into the same order in regard to their northward distribution: chestnut-oak extends continuously north to central New York and Connecticut; white oak reaches north of Lake Ontario and farther east occurs at low altitudes in central New England and north to Bangor in central Maine; red oak occurs at higher altitudes than white oak and ranges much farther north to northern Vermont and to Millinocket in central Maine (Little, 1949; Westveld *et al.*, 1956; Davis and Goodlett, 1960).

HICKORY species are abundant in the southern and southeastern part of the region, their northern limit coinciding roughly with that of white oak. BUTTERNUT has a similar distribution pattern, while black WALNUT is distributed more widely in the southwestern part of the region, extending eastward only as far as western Massachusetts (Munns, 1938; Little, 1949; Westveld *et al.*, 1956).

Several species of ASH occur in the forests. White ash is the most common, and it is probably more abundant in the southern portion of the region than in the north.

Of great importance in the northeastern forest are the MAPLES. Red maple and sugar-maple occur throughout the region and often dominate the forest. Red maple occurs in swamps and swales in the southern portion of the region, but it is also an abundant forest tree on upland soils. It is more common in central Massachusetts and in southern Connecticut than is generally appreciated: a sample from the latter region showed red maple second only to the oaks in abundance (Davis and Goodlett, unpublished data). It was similarly abundant in the old-growth forest at Stonington, Connecticut (Raup, 1941). It is the most frequent species in the region just east of Potter County, in New York and Pennsylvania (Goodlett and Lyford, 1963). At higher altitudes and latitudes, except on disturbed sites (Westveld *et al.*, 1956), red maple is less common than sugar-maple, which often is the dominant tree (Davis and Goodlett, 1960; Goodlett and Lyford, 1963).

Alpine BIRCH species occur in the high mountains, and four other species of birch, sweet birch, gray birch, paper-birch and yellow birch, are important trees in the forests of the northeast. Sweet birch reaches its northern limit in northern New York and New England (Munns, 1938; Little, 1949). Gray birch, an eastern species, ranges far north but has its western limit in central New York State and eastern Pennsylvania (Little, 1949). Paper-birch is a Boreal [2] species that ranges southward into Massachusetts, Connecticut, New York, and northern Pennsylvania (Munns, 1938; Goodlett, 1954); it is infrequent south of the Massachusetts border (Westveld et al., 1956). Yellow birch occurs throughout the northeastern and Great Lakes states and southward at higher elevations in the Appalachians (Munns, 1938; Little, 1949); it is particularly common in the deciduous forests of northern New England.

Widespread species that are more abundant in the northern forests than farther south are American ELM (slippery elm is more abundant to the west), BASSWOOD, and BEECH. Beech is of particular interest in view of the detailed taxonomic studies of the species by Camp (1950), who recognized three varieties that grow in different habitats in the Appalachians south of the drift border. He found that these types were much less distinct from one another farther north. Beech is also common in the forests bordering the Great Lakes (Braun, 1950), and occurs abundantly in Potter County in Pennsylvania (Goodlett, 1954). Additional important forest trees are the CHERRIES and POPLARS. Pin- and choke-cherry are small trees common on roadsides or other disturbed habitats, while black cherry is an abundant forest tree. It is particularly large and prominent in the forests of northern Pennsylvania (Goodlett, 1954). There are three important species of Populus: balsam-poplar is primarily Boreal in its distribution, ranging south only to central New York; trembling aspen is common in Boreal regions and occurs also south to Long Island (Fernald, 1950) and in the Appalachians south beyond our region (Munns, 1938); large-toothed aspen is more southern in its distribution, ranging throughout the Northeast but reaching a northern limit in the St. Lawrence valley.

The number of coniferous species increases toward the northern part of the Northeast. Several have their southern range limit within the region. White SPRUCE, a Boreal species, occurs in lowland forest south to Vermont and northeastern New York. It is particularly common in northeastern New England and to a lesser extent northern New York (excluding the Champlain valley) as a tree that invades grassy meadows. Red spruce is an eastern species characteristic of the Appalachians but not ranging far into the Boreal forest. It occurs together with white spruce but ranges far to the south at higher elevations in the mountains. Black spruce is characteristic of boggy sites and occurs in lowland sphagnum bogs as far south as northwestern Connecticut and western New York. Balsam-FIR is commonly found with white or red spruce.

LARCH and ARBOR VITAE are commonly found growing in otherwise grassy meadows in northern New England and in the Adirondack region of New York. They also grow in

swamps, and larch is found in sphagnum bogs at least as far south as Massachusetts. Arbor vitae is abundant in the north, particularly in limy areas (Fernald, 1950). For example, a forest sample from northern Vermont showed that arbor vitae was the second most abundant tree species (Davis and Goodlett, 1960; Westveld et al., 1956). Red CEDAR is a common tree in meadows from central New England and New York southward (Little, 1949; Raup, 1940), while the Atlantic white cedar is a swamp tree of the coastal plain that reaches its northern limit in southern New England (Little, 1949).

HEMLOCK ranges throughout northeastern United States but is rare in New Jersey, Rhode Island, southeastern New York, southern Connecticut, and eastern Massachusetts. It is more abundant in central and northern New England, and in some parts of eastern Maine hemlock is the most prominent conifer (Westveld et al., 1956; Davis and Goodlett, 1960). It is also numerous in Potter County and in the region east of Potter County in Pennsylvania (Goodlett, 1954; Goodlett and Lyford, 1963). In the adjacent counties to the west, it was one of the most abundant species in the precolonial forest, according to early land-survey notes (Lutz, 1930). Spurr (1956) studied the abundance of hemlock in central Massachusetts on a series of sites with known histories of land use but with a wide range of soil moisture. He found that local abundance was unrelated to soil moisture but depended instead on the amount of partial cutting that had been done in the forest (see below).

The most frequent of the four species of PINE is white pine. In northeastern United States, white pine rarely occurs in abundance beyond the geographical range of red oak, as was shown on a local scale in Potter County, Pennsylvania, by Goodlett (1954). It is also true on a regional scale in the sense that the regions of greatest abundance of white pine are also characterized by red oak. In other words, white pine is abundant in central New England and New York, but is less frequent in southernmost Connecticut and rare in the high mountains. It ranges to northernmost New England, but it is not a common species there. White pine grows on many types of soil, including peat bogs, but is most common on light sandy soil (Lyford et al., 1963).

Pitch-pine is more southerly in distribution. In New England and central New York it is largely confined to the sandy outwash plains (Bromley, 1935), which are extensive, for example, in the Merrimack valley in Massachusetts and New Hampshire, near Ossipee, New Hampshire, near Orange, Massachusetts, and in the Mohawk valley in New York. In southern New York and in New Jersey pitch-pine also occurs on rocky hilltops.

Red pine is a more northern species; it does not occur south of the Massachusetts boundary or south of the glacial boundary in Pennsylvania (Little, 1949; Braun, 1950). Red pine is found characteristically on coarse gravelly soil or on the sandy shores of lakes; it occurs occasionally in other kinds of habitat too, but it is not very abundant anywhere in the Northeast (H. I. Baldwin, personal communication; Dansereau, 1953). Its range does not extend into the Boreal forest region of Canada north of the St. Lawrence valley (Little, 1949; Braun, 1950).

---

[2] "Boreal" is used here in reference to the belt of coniferous forest, characterized by abundant spruce, which extends across Canada to Alaska (Braun, 1950).

The only pine species in northeastern North America that can be considered Boreal is jack-pine, and this tree is virtually absent from the region under consideration here, despite the presence of other Boreal species such as white spruce in some numbers. Jack-pine can be found in abundance only north of the St. Lawrence valley; in northeastern United States it is known only in scattered isolated stands, most of them only a few acres in area (Bell, 1897; H. I. Baldwin, 1961, personal communication).

NATURE OF DATA

An understanding of the factors that control the present distribution and abundance of the plants described above is requisite to any interpretation of changes in species distributions or frequencies in the past. Although complete understanding of controlling factors is seldom attained, the literature does provide numerous discussions of the influences of physical environment, historical factors, and human activities on the vegetation.

Most of the preceding description of species ranges is based on range maps for forest trees prepared by Little (1949) and Munns (1938). Additional information was obtained from Bell (1897). These maps are small in scale and lack detail. The frequency of disagreement among the authors indicates that the maps lack the accuracy that is desirable when one wishes to establish a correlation between species range and an environmental factor. Almost the only other source of information is Fernald's (1950) excellent manual, which tends to emphasize the greatest extent of range. It is difficult from Fernald's treatment to distinguish outlying stations for a species from the limits of the region in which the species has a continuous population. None of the sources gives estimates of abundance; the data collected by the Forest Service has not as yet been fully exploited for this purpose. Remarks on species abundances are found in the ecological literature, but they are sometimes subjective and often refer to frequency within a particular type of forest rather than to average frequency throughout a region. These descriptions can be helpful only if accompanied by information on the areal extent of the kind of forest that is being described.

Forest communities or types have been recognized within the northeastern forests by many ecologists, either by the presence or by the absence of key species (Goodlett, 1954) or on the basis of species frequencies (most other authors). In either case, the extensive local variation has made it difficult to prepare maps showing geographical distribution of forest types. In order to define types, decisions must be made concerning the size of the vegetation unit that will be recognized and named. For example, Lyford et al. (1963) have shown that several tree species on a hillslope in Massachusetts were unevenly distributed, occurring in local concentrations on certain parts of the slope. Their detailed maps, which are extremely illuminating in showing the kind of variation typical of New England forests, were compared with soils maps and records of land use. As a result, it was possible to prove that the local abundances of white pine and white ash were related to variations in soil moisture. In a case of this sort, the local stands characterized by concentrations of one or the other of these two species could be considered vegetation units related to soil units (Stout, 1952), or the forest of the entire slope could be considered a single community (cf. Goodlett, 1954).

Often the distribution of communities recognized at the second of these two map scales can also be correlated with topography and/or the nature of the surficial material (cf. examples in preceding description). On a still-smaller-scale map, a region such as New England may be divided into two (Nichols, 1935; Braun, 1950) to six (Westveld et al., 1956) forest zones or associations. Within New England there has been little agreement on the number of distinct associations that should be recognized, or on the geographical location of boundaries. This is not surprising, because the regional discontinuities in type are often less abrupt and are certainly more difficult to trace than local discontinuities. For example, Goodlett was able to define and map in detail four forest types within Potter County, Pennsylvania. These four types are as different from one another as the six forest zones into which Westveld et al. (1956) have divided New England. In other words, it was possible within this small area—one-sixtieth the size—to demonstrate two-thirds the range of variation observed in all of New England.

Palynologists have perhaps been confused when using the ecological literature because the same or similar names are often used for both description of local forest types and regional generalizations. The same names sometimes appear as names for pollen zones. For example, the term "oak-chestnut" was used as a regional name for the forests of all of southeastern New York (Braun, 1950) although local forest stands that could be termed "oak-chestnut" did not occur everywhere. In "coves," the upper reaches of small valleys where soil moisture levels are high, the forests are characterized by red oak, sugar-maple, and hemlock (Raup, 1938) and would be described as local stands of "Transition hardwoods" according to the terminology of Goodlett (1954). Again, "Transition hardwoods" has been used on a regional scale to describe the forests of all of central Massachusetts and central Maine (Westveld et al., 1956). The regional names give a misleading impression of uniformity within forest types and of sharp discontinuities between them. The verbal descriptions in the literature, on the contrary, are consistent in describing extensive local variation.

Furthermore many maps and descriptions do not show the vegetation as it is now, but instead attempt "to show the kind of forests that originally existed, or that are likely to develop" (Westveld, et al., 1956, p. 332). In other words, maps often show a climatic climax, reconstructed as the investigator imagines it would exist without human influence. Understanding of man's effect on the natural vegetation therefore becomes crucial even in the use of allegedly basic data. For this reason human disturbance is the first environmental factor I shall consider.

INFLUENCE OF MAN

Historic. Much of the Northeast has been and still is being exploited for lumber, while most of the non-mountainous portion of the region was at one time clear-cut and plowed or used as pasture. Raup and Carlson (1941) estimate that

85% of the landscape in central Massachusetts was cleared in the middle of the 19th century. At this time better farmland became available in the Midwest, and the younger members of the population began to move westward. An increasing proportion of the farmland in New England was allowed to revert to forest. The forest that grew on this land differed in species frequency from the previous forest. In central Massachusetts, white pine formed pure stands on abandoned fields; it grows now as scattered trees in a predominantly deciduous forest and apparently had a similar distribution in precolonial time. These stands were of great commercial value and were harvested after the early years of this century. They were not succeeded by pine; instead, the second-generation forest was again primarily deciduous and similar in species composition to the precolonial forest (Raup and Carlson, 1941; Goodlett, 1960; Westveld *et al.*, 1956).

The process of abandonment of what little farmland remains in New England continues, so that all stages of old-field succession may still be seen in one area or another. In southern New England red cedar is a common pioneer in old fields (Raup, 1940), being favored by continued grazing by cattle and the absence of fire (Niering and Goodwin, 1962). Gray birch and black cherry are also common old-field pioneers (Raup, 1940; Niering and Goodwin, 1962), and *Ailanthus*, a species naturalized from cultivation, occurs as well in some old fields in southernmost Connecticut. On Martha's Vineyard, red cedar and pitch-pine are characteristic of abandoned fields (Ogden, 1961). In northern New England and Nova Scotia (Westveld *et al.*, 1956; Braun, 1950), beyond the region where white pine is abundant, white spruce, balsam-fir, larch, and arbor vitae commonly invade abandoned pasture land, forming patches of almost purely coniferous forest, which stand out against the primarily deciduous forest that covers much of the landscape.

The long-range effects of logging on the forests of Potter County, Pennsylvania, were studied by Goodlett (1954), who was able to compare maps of the distributions of tree species in the present forests with maps showing the distributions of tree species in the precolonial forests. The latter were prepared from early land surveyors' records of "witness trees"—trees described to species and recorded as markers for corners of subdivisions of the land. Goodlett was also able to map the distribution of stumps of white pine and hemlock remaining from selective cutting of these species 50 years or more before, as most of the region had never been clear-cut or plowed. The data showed that the topographic distributions of species were unchanged from the precolonial forests, but the frequencies of species were very different. White pine, relatively abundant in the precolonial forest, is rare in the present forest, apparently as the result of selective cutting of this species over a long time interval and consequent removal of the seed source; hemlock, also a valuable timber tree, was probably more abundant in the precolonial forest than it is now. Chestnut, a common component in the precolonial forest, was destroyed by the chestnut blight approximately 40 years ago; only root sprouts remain, and they are usually diseased before reaching maturity.

In central Massachusetts partial cutting of forest stands has resulted in an increase of hemlock. Studies of the growth rings of trees in stands that have been logged from time to time, but which have been forested continuously, indicate that removal of canopy trees has released the shade-tolerant hemlock understory so that these trees now dominate the forest (Spurr, 1956). Cutting may also have affected the abundance of chestnut prior to the blight. Several ecologists have pointed out that because chestnut tends to sprout from stumps, the number of chestnut stems in the forest may have increased with logging, beginning in colonial times (Braun, 1950; Nichols, 1913).

Pollen evidence of the influence of agriculture on the precolonial forests is available from Martha's Vineyard. Ogden (1961) found that the species represented in the pollen rain on Martha's Vineyard at the time the colonists arrived were much the same as today but that the percentage values for beech and black gum were higher than at present.

Prehistoric. Several ecologists have hypothesized that the primeval forests found by white man upon his arrival had already been disturbed during many millennia by the activities of Indians. The idea bears an important relationship to ecological theory. In their original definitions of the climatic formation or "climax," ecologists visualized a uniform, mesophytic vegetation limited by climate alone; the effects of topographic diversity were assumed absent because the climax vegetation grew on a peneplain attained at the close of an erosion cycle (Cowles, 1911). Further, the climax forest was considered self-perpetuating, *i.e.*, to be composed of "tolerant" species, the seedlings of which can grow in the shade of the parent trees. Few ecologists now accept this definition in its entirety. Climate is not stable long enough to allow completion of vegetational succession occurring over many thousands of years, storms that disturb the vegetation are inherent in many climatic regimes (Goodlett, 1954), and the idea of an erosion cycle terminating in peneplanation, which so influenced Cowles (Drury, 1956), has itself been seriously challenged (Hack, 1960). Most ecologists applying the idea of "climatic climax" to northeastern United States use the concept loosely to embrace a vegetation with a great deal of local diversity growing on a diverse landscape. They use the term merely to indicate their conception of vegetation that would develop on upland soils in the course of several hundred years of stable climate, in the absence of human interference of any kind (*e.g.* Spurr, 1956). Unfortunately, the word climax used in this way has many connotations and lacks any precise definition. The connotations of the term have had an influence on interpretation of ecological data.

The idea, for instance, that hemlock is an important member of the climax forest of southern Connecticut appears in several papers, including the recent map of Natural Forest Vegetation Zones, which places southern Connecticut in the "Central Hardwoods–Hemlock" zone (Westveld *et al.*, 1956). The idea seems to stem from Nichols (1913), who found abundant hemlock in several old-growth forest stands in northwest Connecticut (although not in southern Connecticut) and deduced from this that the species was abundant everywhere in the virgin forest. Nichols followed strict climax theory in ignoring evidence from southern Connecticut; he considered the forests there too xerophytic in aspect to represent undisturbed vegetation. Lutz (1928) later recognized variations from site to site in southern New England in the abundance of hemlock, but followed Nichols in recognizing these as stages in an inevitable succession toward a "hardwood-hemlock" climax rather than as manifestations of the suitability or lack of suitability of the sites to hemlock. Bromley (1935) followed Nichols and Lutz in his description of the natural forests of New England, stating that "theoretically it [hemlock] is the tree best fitted to dominate the climax forest of southern New England, due to its longevity, shade tolerance, and ultimate size" (Bromley, 1935, p. 71). The viewpoint of these authors has had a curious effect, even though the predicted succession has not occurred. Ecologists who observe that hemlock is not abundant in southern Connecticut (< 0.1% in a recent sample by Davis and Goodlett, unpublished) seem forced by the theoretical argument established in the literature to justify their finding in terms other than poor fitness of the species to the environment. As a result rather elaborate explanations have been proposed for the rarity of hemlock in Connecticut. Most of these involve man as the unnatural agent reducing hemlock below its expected frequency. It is easy enough to contend that cutting of trees by European man has depleted the supply of hemlock (Niering and Goodwin, 1962), although this view contradicts evidence from Massachusetts (Spurr, 1956). Early reports, however, indicate that the tree was also rare in the precolonial forest. Niering and Goodwin (1962) follow Bromley in placing emphasis on fire as a contributing factor. They conclude from the present distribution of hemlock that the tree has survived only in ravines and other habitats where it has been protected from fire; they propose that fires set by Indians over an interval possibly as long as 9,000 years had favored fire-resistant species, reducing hemlock and other mesophytic trees to frequencies far below the levels they would otherwise have achieved. According to Niering and Goodwin's interpretation (and contrary to the views of palynologists) the postglacial deciduous forest of southern Connecticut has been controlled by man rather than by climate; if this is true, climax vegetation as visualized for this region by ecologists is not a "reconstruction," but is instead completely hypothetical.

Emphasis on fire as an ecological factor appears repeatedly in the literature. Spurr (1956) suggests that hemlock in the precolonial forest in Massachusetts was restricted to ravines where it was protected from precolonial fire. The reverse conclusion is reached for New Hampshire, where both the abundance of hemlock in virgin forest on the lower slopes and its infrequency on the upper slopes are explained by fire. In discussing this region Cline and Spurr (1942) state that hemlock has fire-resistant bark and conclude that fires had reduced the frequency of other species, thus favoring hemlock on the lower slopes. They believe, however, that on the upper slopes, where the soil was perhaps thinner, fires had reduced the abundance of hemlock by injuring its fire-sensitive roots.

Direct evidence of fires set by Indians consists of eyewitness accounts by early colonists. The conception that the resulting modification of the forests was extensive stems

from early descriptions of open, grassy meadows and of open, park-like forest through which one might easily travel on foot or on horseback (Day, 1953). Descriptions by early travelers of similar open stands farther north on the Maine coast and in the Mohawk Valley in New York indicated to Day that burning was practiced extensively even in regions where it was not actually witnessed by the colonists. On the other hand, existence of open forest in out-of-the-way places can just as easily be used to support the opposite opinion, that open forests existed without the influence of fire, *i.e.*, that they represent the "climatic and edaphic climax." Raup has espoused the latter view, arguing against "wholesale conflagrations each year" (Raup, 1937, p. 84). He believes that burning was largely confined to the vicinity of the coast and to the oak-chestnut and pine lands where the forests were dry enough to burn. Certainly he is correct in pointing out that the forests of southernmost New England, with abundant white and black oaks and hickories, are open in aspect and easily passable, even without the influence of frequent, controlled burning; this is true at the present time even though the trees there are young and therefore fairly small. A park-like aspect with trees growing some distance apart is characteristic of pine forests on sand plains such as those, for example, that presently occur in the Mohawk Valley (see photographs in Bray, 1930). The forests of northern New England, by contrast, are thicker, with denser shade, because of the difference in habit of the dominant species. A similar difference in forest aspect can be seen in Goodlett's (1954) description of Pennsylvania forests.

The controversy concerning fire and its influence on the natural forest may be solved eventually through study of the fossil record, which can document the effects of known disturbances and allow comparisons of the presettlement and modern forests (Ogden, 1961). At present it is important as an illustration of the subjectivity that can enter into studies of the present vegetation. A similar example is cited by Raup (1964) in his recent discussion of the effect of ecological theory on conservation policy. Species frequencies at present are sometimes considered, on theoretical grounds, to "take on an aspect of improbability" (McIntosh and Hurley, 1964, p. 323). Thus many maps purporting to describe the present forests do not show present species frequencies but instead show the theoretical climax considered by that particular ecologist to be well-suited to the environment.

INFLUENCE OF QUATERNARY HISTORY ON SPECIES DISTRIBUTIONS

Many phytogeographers place great emphasis on the Quaternary history of each species as a factor influencing or even controlling its present distribution (see discussion of Quaternary and Tertiary influences in Deevey, 1949). According to this view, the ranges of many species in previously glaciated territory represent migration outward from refuges where a small population survived the Ice Age. By studying numbers of similarly shaped distribution patterns, Hultén (1937) has identified the geographical locations of the refugia from which he believes entire groups of species have come. He explains the fact that some of the species now range farther from the refuge than others in terms of differences in dispersal mechanisms, or in their relative aggressiveness in colonizing different habitats. Implicit in this treatment is the idea that the range of the species is still expanding, and that it is not yet limited by climatic, edaphic, or biotic factors.

A related biogeographic concept is that disjunctions in range imply a previous continuity that has been disrupted by an environmental change of some kind. The geographic or ecologic barrier may still exist, or one may postulate that the change occurred and was reversed some time ago. In the latter instance environmental factors would no longer directly influence the distribution pattern.

These ideas have been applied to plant communities by Braun (1950) and by Raup (1938). Braun believes that the scattered distribution of forest types beyond the region where they are more or less continuous may represent the "advance guard" of an expanding distribution. She applies this idea to discontinuous distributions of southern forest types in previously glaciated regions, citing this as evidence for the continuing northward movement of deciduous forest communities into the areas from which they were eliminated by the advancing glaciers during the Ice Age. Raup invokes the scattered distribution of oak-hickory stands, which occur on hilltops, as evidence of the relic nature of this association in the Hudson Highlands of southeastern New York. He believes that a continuous distribution of the association throughout the Highlands was attained during a postglacial interval of greater warmth and dryness and that a subsequent change in climate destroyed the association except in the driest habitats where edaphic factors have delayed the eventual replacement of the association by more mesic vegetation. According to his view (Raup, 1937) the present vegetation of the region is still adjusting to a relatively recent climatic cooling. This interpretation, like Braun's implies that the distribution of communities has not achieved equilibrium with the present climatic regime.

A simpler hypothesis accounting for the distribution of oak-hickory in the Hudson Highlands is that the present environment on the tops of the hills is better suited to oaks and hickories than the environment at the base of the hills, and that for this reason these species occur in greater frequency there. Support for the mechanistic view that the vegetation is essentially stable and in equilibrium with the climate can be derived from Raup's own evidence that the distributions of species in the precolonial forests before the forests were cut were essentially the same as those in the present second-growth forests. One would expect change after disturbance if the forests had not been in equilibrium with the climate.

In my view the disjunct occurrence of a community, the individual components of which occur in other communities in the intervening area, cannot have the same biogeographic significance as the disjunct occurrence of a species. In the latter case the biological definition of a species as one or more interbreeding populations forces us to suppose that the individual plants of a species are at least descended from an interbreeding population, and that present disjunctions are due to dispersal from that population or to disruption of, or migration from, a previously continuous range. The only alternative is to invoke special creation or convergent evolution. The same is not true of a community, which in fact would not be recognized as an "association" unless it tended to arise repeatedly as a characteristic association of species in characteristic frequencies. According to ecological theory (Clements, 1904), succession in similar habitats should inevitably lead to the spontaneous generation of the same climax association, provided the appropriate species are available for colonization. This last is apparently the case in Raup's example and may also apply to the examples cited by Braun. Of course if the component species do not occur in the intervening communities, community disjunction may be synonymous with, and of the same significance as, species disjunction. A case of species disjunction used by Raup (1937) to support his thesis of recent climatic deterioration is the occurrence of bur-oak in Maine (see above). Raup believes this indicates wider distribution of this species during the postglacial climatic optimum, a recent shift to colder climate having killed bur-oak in the intervening portion of its range.

Another example of species disjunction is the scattered distribution of jack-pine in the Northeast (Baldwin, 1961). H. I. Baldwin (personal communication) believes that these stands represent remnants of a large, continuous population of this species which followed the retreating ice northward and was later all but eliminated by competition from other species.

The major work on species disjunctions in the Northeast was done by Fernald. He was interested in the floristic and physiognomic similarity of the pine-oak forests of coastal New England to the pine-barrens vegetation of nonglaciated New Jersey. He further noted the occurrence in Nova Scotia and other portions of eastern Canada of a group of species, the major portions of whose ranges were confined to the coastal plain farther south; some of the species had no known stations between New Jersey and Nova Scotia. He speculated that after glaciation these plants colonized Nova Scotia from the continental shelf, where they presumably had survived the Ice Age; subsequent submergence of the continental shelf by rising sea level cut off their potential migration route to other suitable habitats (Fernald, 1925). Raup (1941), on the other hand, has suggested that these same species have extended their ranges northward from refuges in unglaciated territory during postglacial time. He believes that their present disjunct occurrence represents the remnants of a distribution that was continuous at a time of warmer climate. Although differing from Fernald, he is in agreement at least in regard to the importance of the coastal plain and continental shelf as a migration route. Deevey (1949) also emphasizes the importance of postglacial migration northward along the coastal plain, and raises the possibility that migration occurred along this route during late-glacial time, when the continental shelf was exposed before sea level rose.

Other disjunct occurrences of interest to the biogeographer involve the arctic species now confined to alpine tundra on the summits of Mt. Marcy in New York, the White Mountains of New Hampshire (principally Mt. Washington of the Presidential Range), and Mt. Katahdin in Maine. The mountain peaks were glaciated; there has been little thought of survival of the tundra flora *in situ* during the Ice Age. The most popular theory has been that "in New England and east of the Appalachians, a 'tundra' with at least some truly arctic species not only could but most certainly did follow the retreating ice margin, finally becoming stranded there on mountain tops" (Löve, 1959). Löve goes on to suggest that this flora might have come from a coastal refugium. A similar hypothesis was proposed by Wynne–Edwards (1937, 1939) to explain the occurrence of Cordilleran (primarily western) and arctic species that are widespread in the North and West but occur in the East only in isolated localities in Nova Scotia, New Brunswick, and the Gaspé and on islands near the Gulf of St. Lawrence. Fernald (1925) used this explanation for the occurrence of disjuncts on mountain summits of New England, but he proposed an entirely different explanation for the disjunctions in the ranges of Cordilleran species occurring in the vicinity of the Gulf of St. Lawrence. He explained the latter flora in terms of survival *in situ* on non-glaciated refugia, or "nunataks," during the Ice Age. He felt no conflict in using different explanations for the two regions, as the small number of endemics in the tundra zone of the White Mountains as contrasted with the Gulf of St. Lawrence convinced him that the White Mountains flora was much younger and had had a different history. His contention that the "nunatak" localities had never been glaciated was challenged by many; but in recent years some geologists have raised the question again, suggesting that some areas of eastern Canada, while glaciated once during the Pleistocene, could have been ice-free and therefore available as refuges during at least part of the Wisconsin stage (Ives, 1963).

The plants of the alpine tundra in New England occur only as small, isolated populations confined to the highest elevations. This is easily explained by the hypothesis that the species are shade- and warmth-intolerant and therefore cannot grow in forests or occur as agricultural weeds at lower elevations. The fact that the arctic plants in the St. Lawrence Gulf region also occur as small, isolated populations has not been so easy to explain, because they are not all confined to mountain summits; some occur at or near sea level. Fernald felt that their failure to spread from the localities where he presumed they had survived the Ice Age indicated the lack of aggressiveness, or "senescence," of these species. Hultén (1937) has argued in a similar vein that the rigorous selection to which species in a refugium are exposed during a glacial age brings about a "depauperization of biotypes." Such selection, by removing all but those types best adapted to the refugium, makes difficult the recolonization of the variety of habitats available on the landscape after the ice has retreated. The effect should be expected to be most marked in the case of very small refugia. Hultén's idea of loss of variability through selection against all but the best-adapted type has received greater acceptance than Fernald's concept of senescence, or loss of a species' vitality through age. Nevertheless, Hultén's idea, like Fernald's, invokes innate factors, rather than factors in the external environment, to limit the distributions of species. Experimental studies of the plant populations themselves are therefore essential to test its validity. Cain

(1944, p. 231) has correctly warned, "Before assuming that an endemic species is of limited area because it is senescent, the question of the extent of area of suitable habitat should be investigated." Wynne–Edwards (1937, 1939) has done this and has emphasized that the endemics in the St. Lawrence region occur on patches of bedrock quite different from the surrounding rock. These environments present an ecological niche so unusual that one might expect a unique flora; the failure of that flora to expand its territory is not caused by a loss of previous variability, according to his view, but instead is simply because no favorable environment exists beyond its present range.

INFLUENCE OF CLIMATIC, EDAPHIC, AND BIOTIC FACTORS

From the preceding discussion it is clear that American ecologists have devoted much of their attention to description of plant communities and to studies of the influences of man and of Quaternary history upon them. It is ironic that although paleoecologists continually emphasize the sensitivity of vegetation to climate and use past vegetation as an indication of past climate, few investigators have even attempted to establish relationships between distributions of present species and climatic factors.

There are at least two possible explanations for the existence of northern limits for the ranges of a number of forest species within northeastern United States. One is that these species are still advancing northward from their glacial refugia and have not yet migrated beyond this point. To prove this it would be necessary to establish that the species can all exist north of their present ranges if a seed source is provided, and that they have only recently arrived at their present limits. Sears (1942a) has attempted to use the fossil pollen record to test the latter hypothesis, but from a statistical point of view the occurrence of a pollen grain in a sample can hardly be considered proof of the establishment of the corresponding plants in the vicinity (Maher, 1964).

An alternative explanation is that some climatic factor or combination of climatic factors becomes limiting at the edge of the species range, and a corollary to this is that climatic factors influence abundance of the species throughout its range (Spurr, 1953). To prove this idea it would be necessary to establish a firm correlation between the geographic distribution of the species and the geographic disposition of some climatic factor. In recent years more and more detailed climatic data have been collected throughout the United States, but during the same interval there has been a decline in interest in detailed mapping of species distributions. Until the latter have been described in detail there is little that can be done to pursue this matter.

The two ideas can be combined in the hypothesis that the species is migrating northward in response to a progressive change in a limiting climatic factor. This idea is almost untestable but is nevertheless invoked rather often by palynologists discussing late-glacial plant migrations.

Despite the lack of detailed information on species distributions, it might in some cases be possible to establish general correlations between vegetation and climate by comparing vegetation of regions with the same or with different climates. The method requires quantitative regional surveys of vegetation that are not presently available and precludes any consideration of the influence of local topography and soils or of genetic variation in the plant species involved. Nevertheless the method is widely used by paleoecologists who, in stating that similarity of vegetation indicates a climate in the past like that, for example, of eastern Canada, are not forced to pinpoint critical climatic factors. Direct comparison of fossil pollen spectra with analogous surface pollen spectra is a version of this method that may prove quite satisfactory, by-passing the need for vegetation surveys. But the method of regional comparison can only be applied to the fossil record where differences from one stratigraphic level to another in species composition or frequency are so great that differences of equivalent magnitude can be observed easily in samples of the modern vegetation or pollen rain collected in different regions. This means that even fairly drastic changes in the frequencies of very rare types are meaningless because only the most extensive sampling programs could discern equivalent geographical differences.

Changes in the frequencies of rare types could be useful, however, with detailed knowledge of the influence of the environment on each species. For example, red oak (which is well-represented by pollen in sediments) occurs only on steep gravel banks in northern Vermont, where it is at the northern limit of its range (Davis and Goodlett, 1960). This species, like many others, requires special habitats near the limit of its range. Assuming that temperature (and not migration lag) is the factor preventing the species from growing farther north, it is reasonable to suppose that if the climate became warmer in northern Vermont, red oak could tolerate sites other than well-drained gravel banks and thus could increase in frequency. On the other hand, if the climate became drier, sites other than gravel banks might be sufficiently well drained to allow the growth of red oak, so that it could increase in frequency. Thus a change in the past in the frequency of this species could be interpreted in terms of climate, although it would be difficult to distinguish between the effects of temperature and moisture. The effects of these factors on the distribution of plant species are often difficult to distinguish; as a result the same confusion exists where past distribution is used as indication of past climate.

Examples such as red oak in Vermont make clear that it is not necessary to postulate movements of great vegetation formations from north to south in response to climatic change; at the generic level almost the entire forest flora of the Northeast occurs within any given region, and many species are therefore available to expand at the expense of others as climatic change confers selective advantage (Spurr, 1953). Understanding of the nature of climatic changes might therefore be furthered by knowledge of the local factors controlling species distributions.

Local factors will not be easy to investigate without detailed geologic studies, and knowledge from one region cannot necessarily be applied to another. Northeastern United States is a region of great diversity in regard to climate, relief, bedrock, and the texture, thickness, and distribution of glacial drift. The studies of Goodlett (1954), Raup

(1951), and Stout (1952) have all emphasized the importance of soil texture (and therefore presumably the availability of moisture) in controlling some species distributions (see especially the detailed treatment by Lyford et al., 1963). Soil texture may depend on bedrock (Goodlett, 1954) or on frost action or solifluction subsequent to deposition of drift by ice (Stout, 1952; Raup, 1951; Lyford et al., 1963). Fernald (1950) often mentions the availability of lime as a factor influencing plant distributions, while Bray (1930) has emphasized the importance of local climate as affected by altitude, topography, and the proximity of lakes.

An additional difficulty, seldom admitted by paleoclimatologists, is that conditions of rapidly changing external environment are precisely those which might bring about evolutionary changes in plant and animal species. For example, many tree species have a dormancy response to a critical photoperiod and therefore have specialized photoperiod ecotypes at different latitudes. The adaptations that must take place when the climate changes or when seed is moved from one latitude to another are considered in an interesting discussion by Vaartaja (1959). One of the important aspects of photoperiod response is that a change in the response would have to be reversed again as an arctic species, for example, migrated northward in the wake of the ice. Many evolutionary changes of this kind may have occurred during the Pleistocene. Their magnitude may be judged by the variation apparent at the present time. Because of possible adaptations to different environments, fossil occurrences of several species outside their present ranges is far more convincing evidence of change in environment than the occurrence of one species. The same rule would apply to changes in frequency, although because pollen frequencies are expressed as percentages it seldom happens that we observe changes for several genera as independent events.

PAST VEGETATION

NATURE OF EVIDENCE

The fossil record of vegetation in northeastern United States since the Ice Age consists largely of pollen grains preserved in lake and bog deposits. In reviewing these data I shall consider first interglacial deposits and then proceed to the more recent evidence. The time interval since glacial retreat is divided arbitrarily into two portions: late-glacial time, from the time of ice retreat in a given area until about 10,000 years before the present; and postglacial time, from about 10,000 years B.P. until the present. Pollen evidence will be reviewed from three viewpoints: (1) stratigraphic, (2) paleobotanic, and (3) paleoclimatic.

Pollen analysis was originally developed as a stratigraphic tool, and there is no question of its value as a method for correlating sediment. The basis for correlation is the similarity of pollen spectra and the similarity in the sequence of changes in pollen composition that occur from level to level. Difficulties arise because pollen spectra are not identical in different sites. There can be large statistical errors in the determinations of percentages. These cannot be distinguished from the expected progressive changes from one

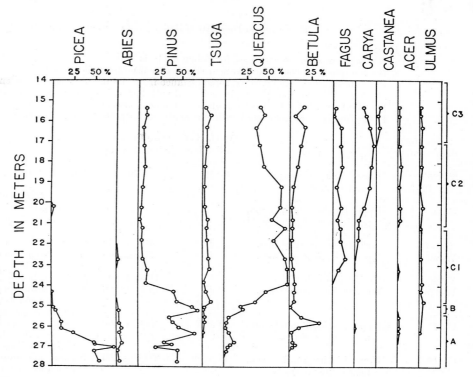

Figure 2. A pollen diagram from Linsley Pond, Connecticut, showing a type section for southern Connecticut. Vertical scale indicates depth below water surface. NAP was apparently not included in the pollen sum. Analysis by Heikki Ignatius. (From Vallentyne and Swabey, 1955)

region to another. Although correlations can often be extended from site to site for considerable distances, it can happen that because of accumulated errors the so-called equivalent strata at widely separated distances at the geographical ends of the series have completely different pollen spectra. They may in fact be different in age and in paleoecologic meaning as well. It is a thesis of this review that some of the correlations that have been made among pollen sequences in the Northeast and between the Northeast and other regions are of uncertain validity; the basis for correlation will therefore be inspected in detail. To aid in this purpose a list of radiocarbon dates from pollen deposits is presented as Table 2.

Pollen zones, the stratigraphic units of correlation, have been treated in a recent discussion by Cushing (1964). He points out that by general usage zones are defined as segments of vertical sediment profiles within which samples have similar pollen spectra. The pollen spectra within a zone differ and often change along definite trends, but they are supposed to be sufficiently different from those in adjacent parts of the profile to be distinguished from them. This may be impossible in cases where changes are continuous with depth, and there is therefore no discontinuity sufficiently sharp to be used as a zone boundary. In fact, the concept of zones is too typological to be useful in all cases, but it is nevertheless applied because of the apparent simplification it accomplishes. Generally pollen zones are recognized only if they can be seen in a characteristic sequence in a number of diagrams from nearby sites. As an example of the use of pollen zones, five major pollen zones were recognized in Connecticut 25 years ago by Deevey (1939) (Figure 2); his terminology has since been extended throughout the region and beyond and applied to pollen

zones which, although different in pollen flora and neither ecologically nor temporally equivalent, are supposed to be "stratigraphically equivalent" (Livingstone and Livingstone, 1958; Ogden, 1960). The meaning of this last term is not entirely clear, but it appears to imply that a zone resembles the type zone in *climatic* meaning relative to other zones in the sequence. In attempting to fit new pollen profiles into the accepted sequence of zones, then, investigators are continually looking for repetitions (or echoes) of the standard climatic sequences. Thus, as Cushing (1964) has emphasized, the zone names, far from being mere descriptions of the pollen spectra, have become climatic concepts influencing the interpretations given to pollen spectra. And instead of testing the notion that related climatic changes occurred simultaneously in different regions, we are in effect using this notion as an assumption basic to correlation. Cushing (1964) has therefore proposed that pollen zones be considered "Fossil Assemblage Zones," and that in naming them we follow the Code suggested by the American Commission on Stratigraphic Nomenclature (1961) and use names that are purely descriptive of the fossils, without temporal or paleoecologic connotation. I have attempted to follow this suggestion here for late-glacial diagrams; the post-glacial sequence is still not known in sufficient detail.

In choosing new names for pollen zones that would describe the dominant pollen types, I found that in many cases the new names coincided with the interpretative names used previously in correlation tables—*e.g.* "Spruce," "Pine," "Oak-Hickory," etc. This indicates that vegetational interpretations of pollen diagrams have been based almost wholly on the naïve but widely held idea that maximal pollen percentage indicates maximal vegetational abundance. It is now generally realized that (a) the degree to which

TABLE 2

Radiocarbon Dates from Pollen Sequences of Northeastern United States

Key:
A Segment of same core used for pollen analysis
B Sample from core collected near site of core used for pollen analysis
C Sample from core collected some distance from site of core used for pollen analysis
D Composite of several samples collected with boring instrument near site of core used for pollen analysis
E Wood or peat collected from open profile near samples used for pollen diagram
F Subsamples or associated sediment analyzed for pollen and correlated with pollen diagram

Laboratory date number	Site	Method of collection	Date (in years before present)	Pollen zone
Y-1261, Y-1262	Rogers Lake, Conn.; mud surface	B	770	Modern. Interpreted as measure of carbonate error in lake; deeper samples were corrected by this amount (Stuiver et al., 1963; Deevey & Stuiver, 1964)
C-36	Upper Linsley Pond, Conn., near center of pond; mud surface		876 ± 250	C-3. Interpreted as indication Ekman dredge used for collection sank below surface (Flint & Deevey, 1951)
W-677	Barnstable Marsh, Mass.	B	400 ± 100	Colonial period (Butler, 1959)
W-675	Barnstable Marsh, Mass.	B	770 ± 100	Immediately below sediment dating from colonial period (Butler, 1959)
Y-855	Guilford Marsh, Conn.	C	1180 ± 80	Post-xerothermic (Sears, 1963)
W-678	Barnstable Marsh, Mass.	B	1880 ± 100	Decline of hickory indicating time of return to cooler, more moist conditions following warm, dry period (Butler, 1959) [Apparent correlation with C2-C3 boundary]
C-37	Upper Linsley Pond, Conn., near center of pond	D & F	1800 ± 500	Hickory maximum marking "culmination" of C-2 (Flint & Deevey, 1951). Accepted as homogeneous on basis of pollen analysis of subsamples (Deevey & Potzger, 1951)
C-119	Upper Linsley Pond, Conn., near center of pond	D & F	2141 ± 250	Hickory maximum of C-2 intended, but sample rejected as probably heterogeneous on basis of pollen analysis of subsamples (Flint & Deevey, 1951; Deevey & Potzger, 1951)
C-37, C-110 (Sic)	Average of C-37 and C-119		1970 ± 360	C-3 (bottom) (Deevey, 1958)
I-510	Secaucus Marsh, N. J.	D	2025 ± 300	C-3a (Heusser, 1963)
I(NYS)-219	Crusoe Lake, N.Y.	D	3200 ± 100	Boundary between zones C-2 and C-3; the authors believe that incorporation of carbonates may explain greater age than age indicated by C-119 (Trautman & Walton, 1962)
	Crystal Lake, Pa.	D	3265 ± 210	Spruce-herb zone. Date rejected as too young; see additional date from this site (Walker & Hartman, 1960)
W-44	Durham, Conn.	[E ?]	4800 ± 400	C-1 (Leopold, 1956)
418	Boylston St. Fishweir, Boston, Mass.	E	3851 ± 390	Marine silt overlying fishweir
O-474	Boylston St. Fishweir, Boston, Mass.	E	4500 ± 130	Weir stakes (Byers, 1959)
O-475	Boylston St. Fishweir, Boston, Mass.	E	4450 ± 130	Weir stakes (Byers, 1959)
417	Boylston St. Fishweir, Boston, Mass.	E	5717 ± 500	Lower Peat underlying fishweir. Dates somewhat higher than expected for thermal maximum (Flint & Deevey, 1951)
C-38	Upper Linsley Pond, Conn., near center of pond	D & F	5159 ± 350	C1-C2 transition (Flint & Deevey, 1951); accepted as homogeneous on basis of pollen analysis of subsamples (Deevey & Potzger, 1951)
C-120	Upper Linsley Pond, Conn., near margin of pond	D & F	5305 ± 250	C1-C2 transition intended, but sample rejected as probably heterogeneous on basis of pollen analysis of subsamples (Flint & Deevey, 1951; Deevey & Potzger, 1951)
C-38, C-120	Average of C-38 and C-120		5280 ± 180	C-2 (bottom) (Deevey, 1958)
W-676	Barnstable Marsh, Mass.	B	5480 ± 100	Lower portion of pollen zone indicating warm-dry phase of climatic optimum and marked by hickory-pollen maximum (Butler, 1959) [Apparent correlation with lower portion of C2]
W-945	New Haven Harbor, Conn.	F	5900 ± 200	B or C-1 (Upson et al., 1964)
C-335	Plissey Pond, Maine	B	5962 ± 320	Uppermost zone B (Flint & Deevey, 1951); B (top) (Deevey, 1958)
I(NYS)-220	Crusoe Lake, N.Y.	D	6850 ± 150	C1-C2 boundary. Sample considered too old, possibly because of presence of carbonates (Trautman & Walton, 1962)
W-45	Durham, Conn.	[E ?]	7570 ± 250	B (Leopold, 1956) B (middle ?) (Deevey, 1958)
OWU-14	Bog near Gay Head, Martha's Vineyard, Mass.	E	8075 ± 103	B (Ogden & Hay, 1964)

TABLE 2 *Continued*

Laboratory date number	Site	Method of collection	Date (in years before present)	Pollen zone
Y-282	Durham, Conn.		8155 ± 410	B (Leopold, 1956) B (middle ?) (Deevey, 1958)
C-39	Upper Linsley Pond, Conn., near center of pond	D & F	8323 ± 400	Top of zone B (Flint & Deevey, 1951). B (middle ?) (Deevey, 1958) Accepted as homogeneous on basis of pollen analysis of subsamples (Deevey & Potzger, 1951)
OWU-27	Blaney Pond, Naushon I., Mass.	A	8108 ± 105	B (upper) (Ogden & Hay, 1964)
OWU-28	Blaney Pond, Naushon I., Mass.	A	9482 ± 319	B (lower) (Ogden & Hay, 1964)
	Crystal Lake, Pa.	A	9310 ± 150	Pine maximum (Walker & Hartman, 1960)
Y-246-1	Duartes Bog, Martha's Vineyard, Mass.	D	9910 ± 440	V-3 (Stuiver *et al.*, 1960) V-2; date rejected as too young (Ogden, 1963)
W-877	New Shoreham Bog Block Island, R.I.	D	10,500 ± 210	Base of section (Rubin & Alexander, 1960) V-4; date rejected as too young (Ogden, 1963)
Y-524	Gillis Lake, Nova Scotia	A	10,160 ± 160	A-1 (base) (Livingstone & Livingstone, 1958) L-3 (top) (Deevey, 1958) L-3 to A-1 (Deevey *et al.*, 1959)
Y-947	Rogers Lake, Conn.	A	9740 ± 160 (corr.)	A-4 (Davis & Deevey, 1964) [770 years were subtracted from age to correct for presence of ancient carbon (Stuiver *et al.*, 1963)]
Y-943	Rogers Lake, Conn.	A	9970 ± 170 (corr.)	A-4 (base) (Davis & Deevey, 1964) (see comment for Y-947)
Y-504	Totoket Bog, Conn.	B(1957)	10,440 ± 200	A-4 (Deevey *et al.*, 1959) A-4 (middle ?) (Deevey, 1958)
Y-447e	Red Maple Swamp, Conn.	A	10,480 ± 140	A-4 (Beetham & Niering, 1961) A-4 (middle ?) (Deevey, 1958)
M-413	Pleasant St. Bog, Athol, Mass.	E	10,700 ± 400	A-3 (Davis, 1958) A-3 (middle ?) (Deevey, 1958)
W-361	Duplicate to M-413		10,800 ± 250	
Y-938/39	Rogers Lake, Conn.	A	10,910 ± 180 (corr.)	A-2-3 (Davis & Deevey, 1964) (see comment for Y-947)
OWU-22	Point Judith, R.I.	E & F	10,906 ± 112	Similar stratigraphic position to Squibnocket forest bed (Ogden & Hay, 1964)
OWU-6	Squibnocket Cliff, Martha's Vineyard, Mass.	E	11,352 ± 211	See discussion of W-710 and W-647-1,2,3 (Ogden & Hay, 1964)
Y-460	Kings Ferry, N.Y.	E	11,410 ± 410	Spruce zone (Cox, 1959); spruce wood associated with mastodon bones (Deevey *et al.*, 1959)
SI-3	Duplicate to OWU-6		10,900 ± 144	See discussion of W-710 and W-647-1,2,3 (Ogden & Hay, 1964)
Y-936	Rogers Lake, Conn.	A	11,470 ± 180 (corr.)	A-2-3 (Davis & Deevey, 1964) (see comment for Y-947)
Y-503	Totoket Bog, Conn.	B(1957)	11,590 ± 200	A-2 (middle ?) (Deevey, 1958)
O-766	Squibnocket Cliff peat	E	11,650 ± 250	A-1-2 (uppermost) (Ogden, 1963)
Y-958/59	Rogers Lake, Conn.	A	11,760 ± 180 (corr.)	T (upper; transition to zone A-1 (?)) (Davis & Deevey, 1964) (see comment for Y-947)
Y-446-f	Totoket Bog, Conn.	A(1956)	12,080 ± 300	A-4 (middle). Rejected on grounds entire series systematically too old (Deevey, 1958)
W-255	Block I., R.I.		12,080 ± 200	Wood from base of postglacial kettle fill exposed in open profile
Y-505	Totoket Bog, Conn.	B(1957)	12,350 ± 400	T-3 (Deevey, 1958)
W-710	Squibnocket Cliff, Martha's Vineyard, Mass.	E	12,700 ± 300	A-1 (Ogden, 1963)
Y-647-1	Squibnocket Cliff, Martha's Vineyard, Mass.	E	12,370 ± 260	A-1 (Ogden, 1963)
Y-647-2	Squibnocket Cliff, Martha's Vineyard, Mass.	E	12,310 ± 320	A-1 (Ogden, 1963)
Y-647-3	Squibnocket Cliff, Martha's Vineyard, Mass.	E	12,350 ± 260	A-1 (Ogden, 1963)
W-46	Durham, Conn.	[E ?]	12,700 ± 280	Lower Durham Spruce Zone (Lower Zone A) (Leopold, 1956); A-2 (middle ?) (Deevey, 1958)
Y-954/55	Rogers Lake, Conn.	A	13,150 ± 150 (corr.)	T (Davis & Deevey, 1964) (See comment for Y-947)
Y-952/53	Rogers Lake, Conn.	A	13,280 ± 220 (corr.)	T (Davis & Deevey, 1964) (See comment for Y-947)
Y-502	Totoket Bog, Conn.	B(1957)	13,280 ± 420	T-2 (Deevey, 1958)
Y-447-d	Red Maple Swamp, Conn.	A	13,290 ± 120	A-1 and A-2 (Barendsen *et al.*, 1957) A-2 (middle ?) (Deevey, 1958) A-1 (Beetham & Niering, 1961)
Y-285	Totoket Bog, Conn.		13,550 ± 460	Lower Durham Spruce zone (lower zone A) (Leopold, 1956) A-2 (middle ?) (Deevey, 1958)

TABLE 2 Continued

Laboratory date number	Site	Method of collection	Date (in years before present)	Pollen zone
Y-525	Gillis Lake, Nova Scotia	A	13,450 ± 260	L-2; but date rejected as too old due to presence of redeposited carbon-bearing material (Livingstone & Livingstone, 1958; Deevey et al., 1959)
Y-446-e	Totoket Bog, Conn.	A(1956)	13,870 ± 210	A-3. Rejected on grounds entire series systematically too old (Barendsen et al., 1957; Deevey, 1958)
Y-950/51	Rogers Lake, Conn.	A	14,240 ± 240 (corr.)	T (Davis & Deevey, 1964) (See comment for Y-947)
Y-446-d	Totoket Bog, Conn.	A(1956)	14,790 ± 160	A-1 and A-2. Rejected on grounds entire series systematically too old (Barendsen et al., 1957; Deevey, 1958)
Y-446-a	Totoket Bog, Conn.	A(1956)	15,090 ± 160	T-1. Rejected on grounds entire series systematically too old (Barendsen et al., 1957; Deevey, 1958)
W-647	Millbury, near Worcester, Mass.	E & F	>38,000	Pre-Wisconsin (Lougee, 1957)

different genera are represented by pollen varies widely and (b) pollen percentages are interdependent so that an increase in one type will cause a decrease in others. Fossil spectra can therefore be interpreted only with knowledge of the way in which genera are represented by pollen in modern sediment (Martin and Gray, 1962; Davis, 1963; Ogden, 1964). Our knowledge of pollen representation in the Northeast is based on only three comparative studies, none of them very exhaustive (Potzger et al., 1956; Davis and Goodlett, 1960; Ogden, 1961), and some studies of atmospheric pollen (Hyland et al., 1953; Ogden, 1957; Ogden and Lewis, 1960). Fortunately, more extensive studies are now in progress. Because there is little opportunity to compare fossil spectra with samples of the modern pollen rain,

considerable weight is given here to the one pollen diagram in which it has been possible to correct the fossil pollen percentages for differences in pollen representation demonstrated in the local surface sediments. The numerous pitfalls that accompany the correction procedure have been discussed in another paper (Davis, 1963). At best, the corrected diagram is of value only in indicating the several most abundant and least abundant species in the vegetation.

Some light has been shed on the way in which the late-glacial pollen diagrams from southern New England reflect the ancient pollen rain by the absolute pollen diagram recently prepared from Rogers Lake, Connecticut (Davis and Deevey, 1964). By dividing the pollen number per unit volume of sediment by the time during which that sediment

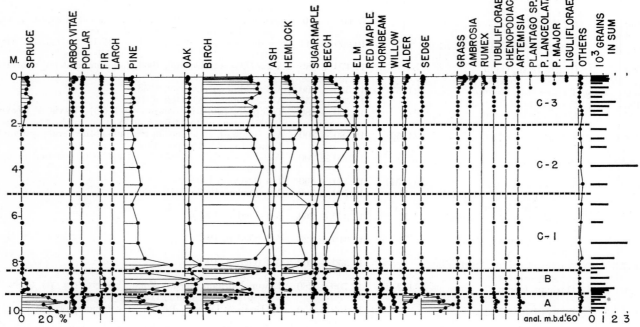

Figure 3. Percentage pollen diagram from Brownington Pond, Vermont. Percentages were calculated as percent total terrestrial plant pollen. Depth below mud surface is indicated to the left, classic pollen zone designations are shown in the right-hand portion of the diagram. The lower half of Zone A could also have been designated "Herb Pollen Zone," the upper half "Spruce Pollen Zone." The core was collected in 1958 by E. S. Deevey, G. B. Deevey, R. H. Davis, and the author. It may be incomplete at the base.

accumulated it was possible to estimate the numbers of grains deposited at the sampling point per unit surface area per unit time over a four-thousand-year interval.

The macrofossil record provides our most easily interpreted source of information. There are a few finds, most of them late-glacial, and we are fortunate that most of them have been tied in with the pollen record or dated by the radiocarbon method.

In view of the haze that surrounds our knowledge of the vegetational significance of the fossil record and our present lack of knowledge of climatic factors that might control the abundances of the plants involved, very little will be said here regarding past climates, except insofar as climatic interpretations have affected correlations.

INTERGLACIAL

Very few pre-Wisconsin Pleistocene pollen-bearing deposits are known from northeastern United States. A complete pollen sequence has recently been described from the Gardiner's clay in Long Island (Donner, 1964). The diagram shows high percentages of spruce and pine in the lowest and again in the highest samples, with an intervening maximum of oak, hickory, and beech pollen. The section is similar to postglacial pollen diagrams from the vicinity, except for the higher percentages of beech pollen. It is interpreted as the record of the warm middle part of the Sangamon interglacial, with the uppermost samples recording the inception of climatic cooling leading to the glacial climate of the Wisconsin stage. Pollen analysis indicating abundant oak and hickory pollen has also been reported from peat underlying till in a drumloidal hill in Millbury, Massachusetts (Lougee, 1957).

LATE-GLACIAL

Stratigraphy. Late-glacial pollen sequences have been studied in detail only from the vicinity of Presque Isle in northern Maine and from Massachusetts, southern Connecticut, and Martha's Vineyard. A new diagram from Vermont shows at least part of the late-glacial sequence (Fig. 3). The late-glacial levels in all the diagrams may be divided into two major pollen zones, or fossil assemblage zones: a basal Herb Pollen Zone, where herb pollen is more abundant than tree pollen, and an overlying Spruce Pollen Zone, where spruce pollen is dominant and herb pollen is less abundant than tree pollen. Generally the Herb Pollen Zone is thought to represent treeless vegetation or tundra, and the Spruce Pollen Zone a closed spruce forest. Although the pollen spectra and sequence of changes in percentages are similar at different sites, the late-glacial pollen zones are generally assumed to be of different ages in different parts of the Northeast, the boundary between the Herb Zone and the Spruce Zone representing a tundra–forest boundary that advanced northward in response to a gradually warming climate.

The interpretation of late-glacial pollen diagrams has been strongly influenced by glacial stratigraphy. It is well documented in other parts of the United States that the Wisconsin ice readvanced temporarily several times in the general course of retreat. Most investigators assume that the readvances occurred in response to short-lived episodes

of climatic cooling which interrupted the general trend toward greater warmth that marked the end of the Wisconsin glacial stage. Investigators in the Northeast have therefore expected to find evidence of vegetational response to climatic oscillations in pollen deposits dating from the time of glacial retreat.

The first diagrams that showed a basal Herb Pollen Zone and that were accepted as evidence of the late-glacial vegetation emerged from the pioneering investigations of Deevey (1951) near Presque Isle in northern Maine. Deevey recognized a detailed stratigraphy within the Herb Pollen Zone which he felt reflected a late-glacial climatic oscillation correlative with the well-known Alleröd–Younger Dryas pollen oscillation in Europe and with the Two Creeks–Valders glacial oscillation in this country. The evidence for climatic oscillation in Maine consisted of a layer of marl and increased percentages of spruce pollen in the middle layers of the Herb Pollen Zone. Deevey felt that the increased percentages might represent an increase in the abundance of spruce trees during the Two Creeks time interval, similar to the forest advance recorded in Alleröd layers in Europe. He thought the return of higher NAP (Non-Arboreal Pollen) percentages in the immediately overlying sediment might represent a temporary return to tundra vegetation, before the final establishment of postglacial forest represented by the Spruce Pollen Zone. Deevey's conclusions were presented tentatively at the time, because the diagrams did not show the zonation clearly: in each core, at least one of the three zones was represented by a single sample. Nevertheless the tripartite division of the Herb Pollen Zone has not been challenged, largely because of analogy with a pollen diagram from Cape Breton Island in Nova Scotia (Livingstone and Livingstone, 1958) which shows a tripartite division of the Herb Zone clearly, with a maximum of birch, rather than spruce pollen, in samples from the middle level. Furthermore a radiocarbon date from the Nova Scotia site confirmed in at least a general way the correlation of the sequence in Nova Scotia with the Two Creeks–Valders sequence and with the European late-glacial: mud from the base of the Spruce Pollen Zone immediately overlying the Herb Pollen Zone was dated at 10,340 ± 220 years B.P. (Y-524).

Radiocarbon dates from southern New England indicate a much greater age for the Herb Pollen Zone there. Dates from the boundary between the Herb Pollen Zone and Spruce Pollen Zone averaged about 13,000 years (Deevey, 1958). More recent dates from Rogers Lake have been corrected by subtraction of 770 years for presumed presence of older carbonate in the proportion indicated in surface samples (Stuiver *et al.*, 1963). The new corrected dates determine the age of the zone boundary at 11,500-12,000 years (Davis and Deevey, 1964). Both corrected and uncorrected dates indicate, therefore, that most or all of the Herb Pollen Zone in southern New England was deposited before the deposition of the Two Creeks Forest bed in Wisconsin.

At several sites in southernmost Connecticut and on Martha's Vineyard, samples within the Herb Pollen Zone display oscillations in the percentages of tree pollen. The changes in percentages are similar to those in the Herb Pollen Zone in Maine and are interpreted in a similar manner.

However the C[14] age of the Herb Zone in southern New England means that sequences within it represent oscillations that occurred before the Two Creeks interval and are therefore considerably older than the Herb Zone is presumed to be in Maine. For example, Leopold's diagram from Totoket, Connecticut (Leopold, 1956; Leopold and Scott, 1958), shows within the Herb Zone (T) a maximum of spruce (T-2) followed by successive maxima of birch, herb, and then birch pollen (T-3). The spruce maximum within the Herb Zone (T-2) is dated at 13,280 ± 420 years B.P. (Y-502). The herb maximum (T-3) above it has been correlated by Deevey (1958) with glacial readvance in Connecticut and with the Older Dryas phase (Zone 1C) following the Bölling oscillation in Europe. A similar interpretation was given to high herb-pollen percentages above a minor spruce-pollen maximum that occurs in the lowest samples from Red Maple Swamp, Connecticut (Beetham and Niering, 1961). Fluctuations in the percentages of herb, pine, and spruce pollen that are rather different in detail from the Totoket sequence have been described from the Herb Zone on Martha's Vineyard (Ogden, 1959, 1963).

The Herb Zone in the new Rogers Lake core in Connecticut (Davis and Deevey, 1964) is of the same age, 12,000-14,000 (corr.) years B.P., as the oldest sediment at the other sites. It shows no evidence, however, of fluctuations in tree-pollen percentages. Furthermore, at this site it was possible to use eight radiocarbon-dated levels from the Herb Zone and Spruce Zone to estimate the late-glacial rate of sediment deposition. This rate could then be used to correct the pollen number per unit volume of sediment for the number of years necessary to accumulate a unit thickness of sediment. In this way the rate of pollen accumulation per unit surface area per year could be calculated. The results indicate that at this sampling point there were no significant fluctuations in tree-pollen accumulation rates during the interval of deposition of the Herb Pollen Zone. Furthermore, the very small number of grains of all types (totaling 600-900 grains/cm²/yr) that were being deposited at Rogers Lake at this time relative to pollen deposition rates 2,000 years later (ca. 9,000/cm²/yr) suggests that changes in percentages in Herb Zone sediment could represent changes in rates of accumulation involving insignificant numbers of grains. This may explain the variation in detail of the several "Pre-Durham oscillations" described from various sites and is in accord with the observation that two diagrams from the same deposit at Cambridge, Massachusetts, show the full range of variation in percentages demonstrated in the Herb Zone at all the sites (Davis, 1961b).

A detailed stratigraphy within the Spruce Pollen Zone was recognized by Leopold (1956) at Durham, Connecticut. She believed the pollen stratigraphy there represented changes in the composition of forest vegetation in response to the relatively warm climate of the Two Creeks interval, followed by cooling associated with the advance of Valders ice. (This was in contrast to Deevey's interpretation of the Herb Zone, rather than the Spruce Zone, as representative of the Two Creeks–Valders oscillation in northern Maine.) Radiocarbon dates (Table 2) confirmed Leopold's correlation of Durham deposits with the Two Creeks horizon, then believed to be about 11,000 years old. The main features of the pollen stratigraphy at Durham were (1) a minimum in the percentage of spruce pollen (20%) and a corresponding maximum in the percentages of oak (10%) and pine (40%) pollen in the middle part of the Spruce Zone (A-3 or upper part of A-1-2-3, Spruce-Oak Pollen Subzone), and (2) an increase of spruce percentages to a sharp maximum (40%) in the upper part of the Spruce Zone (A-4, Spruce-Fir Subzone). The oak and pine maxima of A-3 were supposed to indicate a climate during the Two Creeks interval that was too warm for the growth of pure spruce forest, which had presumably migrated beyond the site to a position farther north. The overlying maximum of spruce-pollen percentages (A-4) was supposed to represent migration southward again of the hypothetical spruce forest belt in response to reversion to cooler climatic conditions (Leopold, 1956, 1958).

This interpretation, which has been followed by all subsequent investigators (Deevey, 1958; Davis, 1958, 1960, 1961b; Ogden, 1959, 1963; Beetham and Niering, 1961), relies on the idea that a maximum pollen percentage represents a maximum abundance for the corresponding genus in the vegetation. There is no clear evidence from surface samples that pollen spectra such as those from A-3 are now being deposited in regions with mixed spruce, pine, and oak forest; most surface samples that contain as much as 10% oak pollen also contain high percentages of birch pollen, as at Brownington Pond. On the other hand, the pollen spectra of Zone A-4 do resemble surface samples from Boreal forest north of 50° N latitude in Quebec and from Boreal forest on the Gaspé Peninsula (Potzger, 1953; Potzger and Courtemanche, 1956). The correspondence in percentages, although not perfect, provides support for the previous contention that Zone A-4, at least, represents Boreal forest. Leopold (1958) has compared the percentage values of spruce pollen in the two subzones with the percentages of spruce pollen in surface samples, and from this comparison she has given a paleoclimatic interpretation to the increase in spruce percentage from A-3 to A-4. A comparison of this kind, using a single pollen type, is meaningful only if the intensity of the background pollen rain is uniform at each point where the modern spruce pollen percentage is measured, and if it is equal to the intensity of the background pollen rain at the sampling points in southern New England where the spruce percentages were recorded in the past.

We now know that the intensity of the background pollen rain was not uniform in the past at one sampling point. At Rogers Lake the total pollen rain at the point where the sediment core was taken was 50% higher during the deposition of A-4 than it was during the deposition of A-2-3 (Davis and Deevey, 1964). The rates of tree-pollen deposition onto the sediment had increased markedly about 12,000 years (corr.) ago, the major increase occurring at 11,500 years (corr.) B.P., at the lower boundary (T/A-2-3) of the Spruce Pollen Zone. At this level the rate of spruce-pollen accumulation increased from <100 to 1,200 grains/cm²/yr, while pine increased from 200 to 1,500 grains/cm²/yr. This supports the earlier interpretation that an increase occurred in the number of trees on the landscape. Accumulation rates for conifer pollen continued to increase, reaching still higher values in A-4: spruce accumulation rose to 1,800/cm²/yr and pine to 3,000/cm²/yr, while fir and larch accumulation each increased from about 40 grains in A-3 to 150 grains/cm²/yr in A-4. Meanwhile, oak-pollen deposition increased from 10 to 400 grains/cm²/yr at the beginning of the Spruce Pollen Zone. The rate remained constant or decreased slightly during the deposition of Zones A-3 and A-4. In other words, the characteristic drop in oak percentage from 10% to 3% at the boundary between A-3 and A-4 does not (at Rogers Lake, at least) result from a large decrease in oak pollen but instead from an increase in conifer pollen, which depresses the percentage value for oak. These data do not support the previous idea of a reversion from mixed spruce-pine-oak forest to spruce forest, but instead they imply a steady increase in the pollen productivity of conifers, while the source of oak pollen increased and then held more or less steady during the deposition of the Spruce Pollen Zone. The data are preliminary, however, and open to several interpretations. They cannot be construed as definitive evidence before corroboration from additional sites.

Further uncertainty in the stratigraphic meaning of the Durham sequence is introduced by the new radiocarbon dates, averaging 11,800 years B.P., from the Two Creeks horizon in the Midwest (Broecker and Farrand, 1963). These authors point out that the horizon marks the end rather than the culmination of an interstadial interval. The fall of pine and deciduous tree (mainly oak) pollen percentages, and reciprocal increase of spruce, that marks the boundary between A-3 and A-4 has been C14-dated at several sites: the dates fall between 10,300 (corr.) and 10,800 years (Deevey, 1958; Davis and Deevey, 1964). The dates are too young to permit the previous correlation of this zone boundary with the end of the Two Creeks interval, although correlation with the Alleröd–Younger Dryas boundary in Europe is not unreasonable. On the other hand it is possible that the increase in tree pollen at 11,500 years (corr.) B.P. that marks the lower boundary of the Spruce Zone is not significantly different in age from the beginning of the Two Creeks interval in the Midwest.

In view of the uncertainties surrounding all the evidence of a climatic oscillation in the Northeast approximately 11,000 years ago, I am inclined to suggest that the pollen data from the Herb Pollen Zone and Spruce Pollen Zone, both in southern and northern New England, can also be interpreted merely as the record of a progressive increase in the numbers of trees on the landscape. There is no definitive proof for this viewpoint, but it should be considered as an alternative to the previous interpretations that involve climatic oscillations. I think the possibility should be kept in mind that climatic changes (if any) associated with the advance of Valders ice, and the climatic change recorded by the Younger Dryas deposits in Europe, might have failed to cause detectable changes in the vegetation of New England. In maritime regions or in regions very close to the ice margin the situation may have been very different, as indicated by the late-glacial pollen diagram from Nova Scotia.

Late-glacial climate. The long span of time indicated by the radiocarbon dates from the Herb Zone at Rogers Lake implies that the vegetation contributing this pollen assemblage persisted for several millennia; it cannot be explained simply as a successional stage, or as vegetation from which trees were lacking due to "migration lag," as I previously suggested (Davis, 1961b). It is probable that the controlling factor was climate. In an attempt to determine the paleoclimate represented by the Herb Zone, Ogden (1959; 1964) has given considerable weight to the occurrence of pollen of *Armeria* in the Herb Zone at Martha's Vineyard and at Cambridge. He believes that the present distribution of the species *A. sibirica* only to the north of the −10° C January isotherm and the 15° C July isotherm means that the presence of its pollen in the Herb Zone may, when corroborated by additional evidence, indicate a similar late-glacial climate. Although the species does occur only in regions of cold climate where trees are at least locally absent, its range limit does not follow the isotherms in question. A functional relationship of distribution to these particular temperatures has not been established, therefore, and the paleoclimatic inference to be drawn from the past distribution of the species remains imprecise. Possibly the present distribution of the species in northern coastal regions signifies dependence of *A. sibirica* on cold coastal climates. The distribution of its fossil pollen at sites near the coast is compatible with this idea.

Macrofossils give further evidence that the vegetation at this time bore a floristic resemblance to tundra (Argus and Davis, 1962). Leaves of *Salix herbacea, Vaccinium uliginosum,* and *Dryas integrifolia* have been identified in the Herb Pollen Fossil Assemblage Zone at Cambridge, Massachusetts. In the same deposits were the remains of a beetle, *Deronectes griseostriatus,* presently a Boreal species. *Salix herbacea* and *Vaccinium uliginosum* now occur in alpine tundra on the high mountains of New England; *Dryas* does not, although it is found south of Arctic America in the Gulf of St. Lawrence region, where, according to Fernald, it is confined to calcareous rocks and gravels. The three species were apparently part of the late-glacial tundra vegetation following the retreating ice northward. It is difficult to argue, then, in the face of this evidence, that the absence of *Dryas integrifolia* from the alpine flora of the New England mountains is because the species was never available for colonization. Instead, its absence may be attributed to some unfavorable aspect of the environment there (a possibility which could be tested experimentally). This conforms to Wynne-Edwards' (1937, 1939) contention that the confinement of arctic species, such as *Dryas integrifolia,* to isolated habitats in the Gulf of St. Lawrence region is caused not by historical factors but by the unique nature of the bedrock there, making habitats available that are different from those of the surrounding region. This view is further supported by pollen evidence from Michigan that *Eleagnus commutata,* now a "Cordilleran relic," was a member of the late-glacial flora there (Andersen, 1954).

The increased rate of both coniferous and deciduous tree-pollen deposition 11,500 years (corr.) ago at Rogers Lake (Davis and Deevey, 1964) and the appearance of macrofossils of trees in Spruce Zone sediment at several sites (Davis, 1958; Argus and Davis, 1962; Ogden, 1963) indicate that the vegetation had changed; apparently local conditions now favored the growth of trees. It has been assumed that the entire Spruce Pollen Zone represents closed forest, but this is not known with certainty. The question may perhaps be answered through comparison of ancient pollen accumulation rates with the intensity of modern pollen rain in regions of tundra, park-tundra, and forest. Comparison of the percentages of pollen with those in surface samples leads to speculation that Zone A-4 alone represents closed Boreal forest, and that Zone A-3 represents a kind of vegetation from which surface samples have not yet been obtained, possibly a park-tundra which does not exist today in the same geographic relationship to deciduous forest. This hypothesis should be tested with more extensive study of the modern pollen rain.

The occurrence of fairly high percentages of pollen of Temperate deciduous-tree genera, such as oak, and Temperate herbs, such as ragweed (*Ambrosia*), has led to speculation that these species grew in southern New England during late-glacial time. There is no confirmation from macrofossils of the presence of Temperate species. Their pollen is found frequently, however, and cannot be dismissed on the grounds that the pollen is rebedded from interglacial or Tertiary deposits (Davis, 1961a; Ogden, 1964). The high percentages of these pollen types can be explained, hypothetically at least, by long-distance transport. When no forest grows locally, the landscape near the sampling point acts as a "silent area" in regard to tree pollen (or "blind spot" in the terminology of Fagerlind, 1952, and Davis, 1963). Under such circumstances, the rate of deposition of tree pollen is low, and the tree pollen that does arrive at the sampling point represents trees growing at the periphery of the pollen source area. Those pollen types that are readily dispersed will arrive in greater numbers than those that are not, thus distorting the ratio in which these pollen types were produced at the source. I believe that this phenomenon accounts for the relatively high proportion of Temperate deciduous-tree pollen in the Herb Zone and perhaps also in the lower portion of the Spruce Zone (Subzones A-1, A-2, and A-3). If one follows this line of speculation, the increased deposition rates of pollen of deciduous trees in the Spruce Zone (A-2-3) at Rogers Lake could be explained as the result of movement of the source closer to the site of deposition. A similar hypothesis can be invoked to explain the high proportion of oak, ash, and hop-hornbeam pollen in the lowest levels in the late-glacial diagram from Vermont shown in Figure 3. In the next higher levels in the Vermont diagram (upper part of Zone A), the percentages of these types decrease, perhaps because windblown pollen, although arriving in the same or even in increased numbers, formed a smaller proportion of the total, the latter having increased because of the development of forest and the inception of local production of spruce pollen. In the overlying Zone B, the percentage of oak pollen again rises, again because of decreased local pollen production due in this case to the abundance of tree species that contribute exceptionally few pollen to sediments (Davis and Goodlett, 1960; Davis, 1963). The validity of this interpretation of the Vermont diagram could be tested by measurement of absolute rates

of pollen accumulation in this region during late-glacial time.

POSTGLACIAL

The postglacial sequence recognized in New England is based on the four pollen zones (B, C-1, C-2, and C-3) recognized by Deevey in Connecticut 25 years ago (Deevey, 1939). A typical diagram from the type area is shown in Figure 2. The sequence begins with the late-glacial Spruce Pollen Zone A. Overlying this is a considerable thickness of sediment with high percentages of pine pollen. Two samples displaying maximal pine-pollen percentages are demarcated Zone B in Figure 2, but other investigators have included a greater thickness of sediment in the zone, and have distinguished a lower Subzone, B-1, characterized by pollen of fir, larch, birch, alder, and jack- or red pine, and an upper Subzone B-2, with increased pollen percentages of oak and white pine (Davis, 1958, 1960; Whitehead and Bentley, 1963). The upper boundary of Zone B is generally placed where pine percentages begin to drop and hemlock percentages begin to rise.

The C-zones, extending between Zone B and the surface, are characterized by pollen of hemlock and deciduous trees; they are defined as C-1, oak and hemlock; C-2, oak and hickory; C-3, oak and chestnut.

This pollen zonation has been extended to diagrams throughout the region, even where the sequence of changes in pollen percentages is very different from Connecticut. In New Jersey, the zonation can be recognized easily (Potzger and Otto, 1943; Niering, 1953). To the north in Massachusetts, New Hampshire, and New York the maximum of hickory pollen in C-2 is less conspicuous, but there is a distinctive minimum of hemlock pollen associated with it (Krauss and Kent, 1944; Davis, 1958; Cox, 1959; McCulloch, 1939; Deevey, 1943; Whitehead and Bentley, 1963). In eastern Massachusetts, there is no rise of chestnut in C-3. The zone is recognized only by decreased percentages of hickory and oak pollen (Benninghoff, 1942; Knox, 1942; Deevey, 1948; Wilson, 1949; Butler, 1959). In western Pennsylvania and northern Maine and Vermont, where hickory pollen is almost absent, a hemlock minimum is recognizable and is defined as C-2 (Potzger and Friesner, 1948; Deevey, 1951; Walker and Hartman, 1960). In this way the classic pollen zonation has been extended to these regions. Except for the successive maxima of spruce and then pine at the bases of the profiles, however, diagrams from Maine and Vermont are different in all other respects from the Connecticut sequence. The pollen diagram from Brownington Pond, in northern Vermont (Fig. 3) may be compared with Figure 2 to illustrate this point.

The basic division of the postglacial into four zones is based on the idea that the pollen diagrams record vegetational response to climatic changes similar to those outlined in the Blytt-Sernander sequence in Europe (Sears, 1942b). The changes are supposed to have led up to a maximum of warmth and dryness, represented by the maximum of hickory in Zone C-2 in the south, and by the minimum of hemlock and corresponding maximum of pine and oak in Zone C-2 in the north; following this xerothermic interval, the vegetation responded to climatic cooling and increased moisture. The pollen changes in C-3 that are supposed to record this response, and therefore to indicate cooling and increased moisture, are an increase in chestnut pollen relative to hickory in the south, an increase of pine relative to oak and hickory in the west, and an increase of hemlock, spruce, and fir pollen relative to pine, oak, and beech in the north. These pollen changes all involve the heavy pollen producers, rather than those species, such as red maple and sugar maple, that now dominate the forest. Further, two of the genera most useful for purposes of correlation of pollen diagrams are poorly understood from the ecological point of view: chestnut is now nearly extinct and therefore inaccessible to study, and the distribution of hemlock is generally supposed to be controlled by fire or other human influences, rather than by climate (see above). The estimates of absolute age of the sequence are largely based on the similarity of pollen interpretation to climatic changes recorded elsewhere; very few radiocarbon dates have been available to test the validity of the correlation. At the present time there appears strong evidence that deposition of Zone B occurred between 7,500 and 9,500 years ago in Pennsylvania and throughout southern New England (Table 2), but a single date from Maine indicates a much younger age for this horizon there. In southern New England the age of the transition between Zones C-1 and C-2 appears established at about 5,000 years, but a greater age may be indicated for this horizon in New York. The ages of the overlying portions of the sequences are even less well known, as discussed below.

Some of the more detailed diagrams show maxima of beech pollen along the C-1/C-2 boundary and along the C-2/C-3 boundary. Deevey (1943, 1949) believes that these successive beech maxima represent successive waves of migration of beech northward from its Pleistocene refuge in the Appalachians. According to his interpretation the injection of new genetic material into an existing population brings about an increase in population size, in this case only a temporary increase each time that it occurs. The mechanism by which the change would be temporary is difficult to visualize, unless a climatic change is invoked in combination with each migration wave, in which case it really is not necessary to postulate the latter.

A further difficulty of this interpretation of the beech curve and, in fact, of the entire postglacial sequence is the assumption that a high percentage value for a pollen type in the sediment means high frequency of the plant on the landscape when the sediment was formed. The further assumption is made that an increasing percentage means an increasing vegetational frequency, and *vice versa*. Comparison of the diagram of late-glacial absolute pollen rain from Rogers Lake with the same data plotted as percentages showed that in several cases the accumulation rate of a pollen type (*e.g.* grass) was increasing at the very levels where its percentage value showed a decrease (Davis and Deevey, 1964). The same conclusion is reached on theoretical grounds when the consequences of differences in pollen productivity among species are considered algebraically (Fagerlind, 1952; Davis, 1963). For this reason it is of interest to inspect the diagram that results when the

fossil pollen spectra from Brownington Pond in northern Vermont are corrected for the differences in representation demonstrated by comparison of the surface sediment with the present forest. Figure 4 shows the reconstructed forest sequence, where it is assumed that the relationship of the ancient forest to each fossil spectrum was exactly the same as the relationship of the modern forest to pollen in the surface samples. In other words, the fossil pollen percentages have all been corrected in a manner which resulted, in the case of the surface sample, in the attainment of percentages exactly equal to those observed in a survey of the modern forest.[3]

The corrected diagram can only be interpreted in the most general terms, as statistical errors are formidable, and the other possible sources of error have not been evaluated quantitatively (Davis, 1963). Certain conclusions can be drawn from it: if there is any validity at all to the pollen-analysis method, then one must conclude that the sediments below 9 m were deposited at a time when Boreal species, particularly spruce, were relatively abundant. Balsam-fir and sugar-maple were prominent in the forest at the time Zone B was deposited; subsequently hemlock and birch and (probably) beech became more prominent. Boreal species again became abundant at the time the uppermost 2 m of sediment were deposited. At various times in the past pine and oak may have been more abundant than they are at present (Davis, 1963), but the evidence is clear that they were never so prominent as implied by the percentage diagram.

The corrected diagram implies that the minimum of hemlock pollen is a real feature, caused by a decrease in the frequency of this species to a level similar to its present abundance in the forest. Remaining unexplained—statements by palynologists notwithstanding—is the climatic significance of the change, since the enivornmental factors influencing hemlock are not understood; few ecologists have supposed that its abundance at the present time is a function of climate (see above).

Of major importance is the increase of weed pollen, particularly ragweed (*Ambrosia*), in the uppermost levels. The occurrence of *Plantago major* and *P. lanceolata* pollen is proof that these sediments date from the time of settlement by Europeans, as both these species are considered imported elements of our flora (Fernald, 1950). There seems little doubt that the increase in pollen percentages is associated with a real increase of these genera as a result of forest clearance by European settlers. The greater abundance of poplar and arbor vitae at this time, indicated by the corrected diagram, shows that these genera, now commonly found invading pastures in this region, increased in response to disturbance of the forests by European man.

[3] For each genus the ratio of pollen percentage to forest percentage as determined in a previous study (Davis and Goodlett, 1960) is termed the *R*-value (Davis, 1963). The *R*-value is a relative number, of significance only when compared to *R*-values for other genera. The pollen numbers in each sample have all been divided by the appropriate *R*-values and the results expressed as percentages. The resulting pollen diagram "corrected for differences in representation" is shown as Figure 4. Larch, basswood, and herb pollen have been excluded from the calculations, as *R*-values could not be calculated accurately.

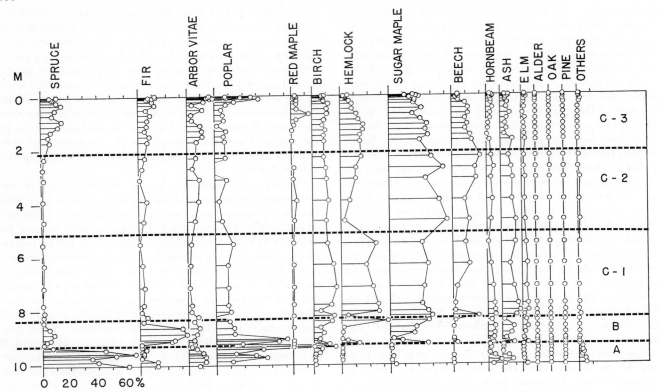

Figure 4. Forest percentages represented by the pollen percentages in Brownington Pond sediment, assuming that each genus was represented by pollen in the past in the same manner as in the surface sediment. Larch, basswood, and herb pollen are not included in the calculation; therefore the percentages refer only to the trees and shrubs exclusive of larch and basswood. The percentages resulting from correction of the surface sample are equal to those observed in a survey of the present forest in the vicinity of the pond (Davis and Goodlett, 1960).

I believe that the increase of red maple is also a response to forest disturbance, and that the increase of spruce and fir indicated in the uppermost 2 m is also related in part, if not wholly, to human influence. A similar change in pollen percentages can be seen in a diagram from Nova Scotia (Livingstone and Livingstone, 1958), also a region where conifers occur as old-field pioneer species (Braun, 1950). Increased herb pollen also occurs in the zone equivalent to C-3 in western Pennsylvania (Walker and Hartman, 1960). I believe that in most cases the increase of conifers in the upper portion of pollen profiles in the Northeast is not the result of climatic change but instead is due to forest clearance, even where the effect of European man is less visible through the investigator's failure to tabulate or identify NAP. Potzger and Friesner (1948) had previously suggested this interpretation as one possible explanation for the rise of spruce and fir percentage in the uppermost foot-level of bogs in coastal Maine.

In southern New England and New Jersey, the effect of European forest clearance is also recorded by an increase in the percentage of non-arboreal pollen, particularly ragweed. A rise of grass, *Plantago*, and Compositae pollen is dated at 400 ± 100 years B.P. at Barnstable Marsh on Cape Cod (Butler, 1959). The horizon can also be seen in Gould's Bog, Massachusetts (Davis, 1958), where it comprises all of what was previously considered C-3; high percentages of herb pollen occur in the uppermost levels in New Jersey deposits (Niering, 1953; Heusser, 1963) and are used as the distinguishing criterion of colonial age of sediments in Vermont (Whitehead and Bentley, 1963), in Connecticut (Sears, 1963), and on Martha's Vineyard (Ogden, 1961). Pollen of maize and cereals is reported by Benninghoff (1950) from the upper levels of peat from an island off the Massachusetts coast. Some of the changes in tree-pollen percentage previously considered evidence for climatic cooling are associated with the ragweed-pollen rise in southern New England, as was the case farther north; the pollen changes involve chestnut, hemlock, and pine, all species that are considered by ecologists to increase in response to European interference or to the cessation of Indian interference (Bromley, 1935; Braun, 1950; Spurr, 1956; Goodlett, 1960; *cf.* Goodlett, 1954, for exception). There is also a rise in spruce-pollen percentage at some sites; this has been interpreted by some as representing migration of spruce southward to its present limit on bogs in central New England in response to climatic change (Spurr, 1953). Alternatively, an increase in deposition rate could be due to horticultural plantings of this genus during the last hundred years. Or the pollen may be windblown from regions where spruce occurs naturally in bogs or on upper slopes, or from northern New England where it occurs on old fields. W. S. Benninghoff (personal communication) has suggested that decreased intensity of local pollen rain following forest clearance may be responsible for a rise in the percentage values of far-travelled types.

It appears, then, that some, at least, of the vegetational changes used as evidence for climatic deterioration at the end of the supposed xerothermic interval are instead the direct result of disturbance of the vegetation by European man. In the Northeast, the evidence for temperatures higher than today's had depended upon the contrast of C-2 with the "cooler" climate, extending to the present, implied by the pollen content of the overlying sediment. By discounting the latter, we weaken the case for a xerothermic or hypsithermal (Deevey and Flint, 1957) interval. Nevertheless there is still a certain amount of evidence for the idea as it applies to pollen profiles of the Northeast. There is a tendency for some of the changes associated with Zone C-3 to occur in sediments stratigraphically older than the first definitive evidence of the arrival of European man. The most convincing evidence is at Barnstable Marsh, where a decrease in hickory-pollen percentage and increase of pine in sediments is dated at $1,800 \pm 100$ years B.P. (W-678). At Brownington Pond the increase of hemlock following the hemlock minimum characteristic of C-2, as well as the first increases of spruce and fir, are found a full meter below the rise of *Ambrosia* and the first known occurrence of European weed pollen (Figs. 3 and 4). Absolute dates from sites such as Brownington Pond are essential to distinguish between the following explanations, all of which seem plausible to me, for these early increases in the frequencies of conifers: (a) European activity before the major forest clearance of the early 19th century, (b) Indian activity over a short time-interval preceding European occupation, (c) Indian influence over a long time-interval, or (d) climatic change following a xerothermic interval.

Despite the importance of the problem, the radiocarbon date from Barnstable Marsh is the only firm date available from levels correlated with the C-2/C-3 boundary (Table 2). Correlation of the $2,025 \pm 300$-year-old sample (I-510) from Secaucus Marsh with the base of Zone C-3 elsewhere is not entirely unequivocal, as the pollen sequence is not complete. Two solid-carbon dates from Connecticut average 1,970 years and are supposed to date the boundary, but one of these (C-119) was collected by multiple sampling and rejected as heterogeneous at the time of collection, while the other (C-37) was originally collected from the maximum of hickory pollen in C-2 (Flint and Deevey, 1951; Deevey and Potzger, 1951; Deevey, 1958). At this site the hickory maximum is only slightly deeper than the level of the C-2/C-3 boundary (compare Fig. 2), but the date obtained on a surface sample suggests that all the dates from this site may be too old (see Table 2). The C-2/C-3 boundary at Crusoe Lake, New York, was recently dated at $3,200 \pm 100$ years [I(NYS)-219] but this date has been rejected, in part apparently because it is older than sample C-119 from Connecticut (Trautman and Walton, 1962). I conclude that Zone C-3 is not equivalent in age at all sites where it has been described. Additional radiocarbon dates and more sophisticated methods of pollen analysis should succeed in providing a firmer basis for correlation. But the real potentiality of the pollen-analysis method can

only be realized with increased knowledge by palynologists of the distribution of species in the present forest, and with increased understanding of the changes to be expected in response to climatic change and to disturbance of the forest by aboriginal and European man.

CONCLUSIONS

The present vegetation of northeastern United States is not well known. Detailed, accurate range maps and quantitative data collected on a regional scale are needed to permit generalization about the vegetation. In the future a clear separation must be made between observation and interpretation, so that the basic data can be used in relation to hypotheses other than the one for which they are gathered. It is unfortunate that ecologists working 30 years ago did not map the vegetation as they saw it, instead of the forest vegetation they thought would develop as the result of succession. If they had, we could compare these maps with maps of the present forest and learn something about succession. As it is, the maps prepared over the years differ from one another, but tell us less of the history of the vegetation than of the history of ecological thought.

One of the major problems that must be solved is the question of the influence of aboriginal and European man on the vegetation. In my view this problem should have priority over others, not only because it is inherently interesting but because there is every reason to believe that it can be solved. Pollen deposited contemporaneously with European colonization of the New World shows changes in percentage composition; by comparing these changes with the historical record of vegetation change we have an unparalleled opportunity to observe the efficacy of pollen analysis as a record of agriculture. Having calibrated the method in this way, we are in a favored position to inspect the pollen record from prehistoric time for evidence of early human influence.

The results will help in determining the natural or "climax" vegetation, but the problem of recognizing natural vegetation will in any case become much easier with time. A smaller and smaller proportion of the land in the Northeast remains under cultivation, and, except near the large urban centers where increasing land area is being used for housing, large stretches of countryside are being allowed to return to the wild. In perusing the literature I realized that in New England, at least, the problem of recognizing the natural vegetation is far less acute now than it was thirty years ago, for example, when much of the landscape was still covered with old-field pine forest. It should be kept in mind that observations made in the 18th and 19th centuries, or in fact on old-growth forests that date from that time, are not particularly valuable as a base for reconstruction of the primeval vegetation; the New England landscape showed a far greater influence of man 150 years ago than it does now.

Information regarding the natural vegetation is basic to determination of those environmental factors that control the distribution and abundance of plants. Without this determination there can be no thought of using vegetational history to indicate climatic history. Faegri and Iversen (1964) believe that in western Europe the limiting climatic factor has been temperature, as moisture has been plentiful throughout postglacial time. In my opinion circumstances have been quite different in northeastern United States. Temperature, precipitation, storminess, and the degree of continentality all may affect present plant distributions and may also have affected the vegetation in the past. Even assuming worldwide contemporaneity of climatic changes, I should not expect to find vegetational responses in the Northeast similar to those known from Europe. For example, a vegetation limited by precipitation might not have responded at all to temperature changes recorded by vegetational changes in Europe, although it might have recorded climatic changes involving precipitation that are not recorded elsewhere.

What we have learned about past vegetation in the Northeast may be summarized as follows: Following the retreat of the Wisconsin ice, a vegetation floristically similar to subarctic vegetation developed. Boreal and Temperate trees grew within "pollen-dispersal distance" but were not present "locally," at least not in large numbers. The persistence of this kind of vegetation for over 2,000 years implies that the local absence or infrequency of trees (shown by the presence of shade-intolerant herbs, the absence of macrofossils of tree species, and the relatively low accumulation rate for tree pollen) resulted from a climate that limited tree growth to an extent similar to that at or north of the arctic tree line. Along the present coastline, the pollen rain was somewhat different from inland, perhaps reflecting the influence of a more maritime climate. About 11,500 years ago the climate apparently changed, and the development of forest vegetation began in southern New England. Boreal species were abundant at first, with spruce contributing a high proportion of the pollen rain until about 9,500 years ago; at about 8,000 B.P., Temperate deciduous trees became more abundant. A more complex sequence occurred in Nova Scotia, and there is some evidence for similar complexities in northeastern United States.

About 5,000 years ago, conditions changed in such a way that the frequency of hemlock pollen reaching the sites of deposition was reduced. This event is widespread, or at least the pollen evidence is widespread; the significance of the event is uncertain because its simultaneous occurrence everywhere is unproven and because its relationship to the actual abundance of hemlock has not been established throughout the Northeast. Furthermore there is no agreement as to what controls the distribution and abundance of hemlock now, much less in the past. A climatic interpretation is usually given to the change in pollen frequency, as most palynologists believe that hemlock is an indicator of moist climate. According to the ecological literature, however, an interpretation in terms of fire and human activity is also possible.

In recent years European man has disturbed the vegetation and changed the percentage composition of the pollen rain. The effect on the tree-pollen percentages is noticeable, and therefore the effect can be traced in diagrams where non-arboreal pollen has not been tabulated; in several cases these changes were previously attributed to climatic

cooling associated with the end of a postglacial maximum of warmth and dryness.

The superficial resemblance of the New England pollen sequence to the north European has encouraged a similar interpretation, whether or not this can be supported in terms of American vegetation. With more detailed treatment, application of modern pollen analysis, and a large number of absolute-age determinations it should be possible to unravel the stratigraphic problems touched on here and to elucidate some of the more fundamental problems of vegetational migration and response to environmental change.

REFERENCES

American Commission on Stratigraphic Nomenclature, 1961, Code of stratigraphic nomenclature: Amer. Assoc. Petroleum Geologists Bull., v. 45, p. 645-665

Andersen, S. T., 1954, A late-glacial pollen diagram from southern Michigan, U.S.A.: Geol. Survey Denmark, Ser. 2, No. 80, p. 140-155

Argus, G. W., and Davis, Margaret B., 1962, Macrofossils from a late-glacial deposit at Cambridge, Massachusetts: Amer. Midl. Nat., v. 67, p. 106-117

Baldwin, H. I., 1961, Distribution of jack pine (*Pinus banksiana* Lamb.) in New Hampshire: Fox For. Notes, v. 83, 2 p.

Barendsen, G. W., Deevey, E. S., and Gralenski, L. J., 1957, Yale natural radiocarbon measurements III: Science, v. 126, p. 908-919

Beetham, Nellie, and Niering, W. A., 1961, A pollen diagram from southeastern Connecticut: Amer. J. Sci., v. 259, p. 69-75

Bell, Richard, 1897, Geographical distribution of trees in Canada: Scot. Geogr. Mag., v. 13, p. 281-296

Benninghoff, W. S., 1942, The pollen analysis of the lower peat, *in* Johnson, F., *et al.*, The Boylston Street Fishweir: Phillips Acad., Peabody Fdn. Archaeol. Pap., v. 2, p. 96-104

—— 1950, Late Quaternary vegetation on No Man's Land Island, Massachusetts (abst.): Geol. Soc. Amer. Bull., v. 61, p. 1443-1444

Braun, E. Lucy, 1950, Deciduous forests of eastern North America: Philadelphia, Blakiston Co., 596 p.

Bray, W. L., 1930, The development of the vegetation of New York State: Syracuse Univ. Tech. Publ. Coll. For. 29, 189 p.

Broecker, W. S., and Farrand, W. R., 1963, Radiocarbon age of the Two Creeks forest bed, Wisconsin: Geol. Soc. Amer. Bull., v. 74, p. 795-802

Bromley, S. W., 1935, The original forest types of southern New England: Ecol. Monogr., v. 5, p. 61-89

Butler, Patrick, 1959, Palynological studies of the Barnstable Marsh, Cape Cod, Massachusetts: Ecology, v. 40, p. 735-737

Byers, D. S., 1959, The eastern Archaic; some problems and hypotheses: Amer. Antiq., v. 24, p. 233-256

Cain, S. A., 1944, Foundations of plant geography: New York, Harpers, 556 p.

Camp, W. H., 1950, A biogeographic and paragenetic analysis of the American beech (*Fagus*): Amer. Philos. Soc. Yearbook, p. 166-169

Clements, F. E., 1904, The development and structure of vegetation: Nebraska Stud. Veget., v. 7, p. 175

Cline, A. C., and Spurr, S. H., 1942, The virgin upland forest of central New England; a study of old growth stands in the Pisgah Mountain section of southwestern New Hampshire: Harvard Univ., Harvard For. Bull., v. 21, 58 p.

Cowles, H. C., 1911, The causes of vegetative cycles: Bot. Gaz., v. 51, p. 161-183

Cox, D. D., 1959, Some postglacial forests in central and eastern New York State as determined by the method of pollen analysis: New York State Mus. Bull. 377, 52 p.

Cushing, E. J., 1964, Application of the code of stratigraphic nomenclature to pollen stratigraphy: Minnesota Geol. Surv. manuscript.

Dansereau, Pierre, 1953, The postglacial pine period: Roy. Soc. Can. Trans. iii, sec. 5, v. 47, p. 23-38

Davis, Margaret B., 1958, Three pollen diagrams from central Massachusetts: Amer. J. Sci., v. 256, p. 540-570

—— 1960, A late-glacial pollen diagram from Taunton, Massachusetts: Torrey Bot. Club Bull., v. 87, p. 258-270

—— 1961a, The problem of rebedded pollen in late-glacial sediments at Taunton, Massachusetts: Amer. J. Sci., v. 259, p. 211-222

—— 1961b, Pollen diagrams as evidence of late-glacial climatic change in southern New England: New York Acad. Sci. Ann., v. 95, p. 623-631

—— 1963, On the theory of pollen analysis: Amer. J. Sci., v. 261, p. 897-912

Davis, Margaret B., and Deevey, E. S., Jr., 1964, Pollen accumulation rates; estimates from late-glacial sediment of Rogers Lake: Science, v. 145, p. 1293-1295

Davis, Margaret B., and Goodlett, J. C., 1960, Comparison of the present vegetation with pollen-spectra in surface samples from Brownington Pond, Vermont: Ecology, v. 41, p. 346-357

Day, G. M., 1953, The Indian as an ecological factor in the northeastern forest: Ecology, v. 34, p. 329-346

Deevey, E. S., Jr., 1939, Studies on Connecticut lake sediments. i, A postglacial climatic chronology for southern New England: Amer. J. Sci., v. 237, p. 691-724

—— 1943, Additional pollen analyses from southern New England: Amer. J. Sci., v. 241, p. 717-752

—— 1948, On the date of the last rise of sea level in southern New England, with remarks on the Grassy Island site: Amer. J. Sci., v. 246, p. 329-352

—— 1949, Biogeography of the Pleistocene. Part i, Europe and North America: Geol. Soc. Amer. Bull., v. 60, p. 1315-1416

—— 1951, Late-glacial and postglacial pollen diagrams from Maine: Amer. J. Sci., v. 249, p. 177-207

—— 1958, Radiocarbon-dated pollen sequences in eastern North America: Zurich, Geobot. Inst. Rübel Veröff., v. 34, p. 30-37

Deevey, E. S., Jr., and Flint, R. F., 1957, Postglacial hypsithermal interval: Science, v. 125, p. 182-184

Deevey, E. S., Jr., Gralenski, L. J., and Hoffren, Väinö, 1959,

Yale natural radiocarbon measurements iv: Radiocarbon, v. 1, p. 144-172

Deevey, E. S., Jr., and Potzger, J. E., 1951, Peat samples for radiocarbon analysis: Problems in pollen statistics: Amer. J. Sci., v. 249, p. 473-511

Deevey, E. S., Jr., and Stuiver, Minze, 1964, Distribution of natural isotopes of carbon in Linsley Pond and other New England lakes: Limnol. Oceanogr., v. 9, p. 1-11

Denny, C. S., 1956, Wisconsin drifts in the Elmira region, New York, and their possible equivalents in New England: Amer. J. Sci., v. 254, p. 82-95

Donner, J. J., 1964, Pleistocene geology of eastern Long Island, New York: Amer. J. Sci., v. 262, p. 355-376

Drury, W. H., Jr., 1956, Bog flats and physiographic processes in the upper Kuskokwim River region, Alaska: Harvard Univ., Gray Herb. Contr. 178, 130 p.

Faegri, Knut, and Iversen, Johs., 1964, Textbook of pollen analysis, 2nd edition: Copenhagen, Ejnar Munksgaard, 237 p.

Fagerlind, Folke, 1952, On the real signification of pollen diagrams: Bot. Notiser, v. 1952, p. 185-224

Fernald, M. L., 1925, Persistence of plants in unglaciated areas of Boreal America: Amer. Acad. Arts Sci. Mem., v. 15, p. 238-342

—— 1950, Gray's manual of botany, 8th ed.: New York, American Book Co., 1632 p.

Flint, R. F., and Deevey, E. S., Jr., 1951, Radiocarbon dating of late-Pleistocene events: Amer. J. Sci., v. 249, p. 257-300

Goodlett, J. C., 1954, Vegetation adjacent to the border of the Wisconsin drift in Potter County, Pennsylvania: Harvard Univ., Harvard For. Bull., v. 25, 93 p.

—— 1960, The development of site concepts at the Harvard Forest and their impact upon management policy: Harvard Univ., Harvard For. Bull., 28, 128 p.

Goodlett, J. C., and Lyford, W. H., 1963, Forest regions and great soil groups, *in* Denny, C. S. and Lyford, W. H., Surficial geology and soils of the Elmira-Williamsport region, New York and Pennsylvania: U.S. Geol. Surv. Prof. Pap. 379, 60 p.

Hack, J. T., 1960, Interpretation of erosional topography in humid temperate regions: Amer. J. Sci., v. 258-a, p. 80-97

Heusser, C. J., 1963, Pollen diagrams from three former cedar bogs in the Hackensack tidal marsh, northeastern New Jersey: Torrey Bot. Club Bull., v. 90, p. 16-28

Hultén, Eric, 1937, Outline of the history of arctic and boreal biota during the Quaternary period: Stockholm, Bokförlags Aktiebolaget Thule, 168 p.

Hyland, Fay, Graham, B. F., Jr., Steinmetz, F. H., and Vickers, M. A., 1953, Maine airborne pollen and fungus spore survey: Orono, Maine, University of Maine, 97 p.

Ives, J. D., 1963, Field problems in determining the maximum extent of Pleistocene glaciation along the eastern Canadian seaboard—a geographer's point of view, *in* Löve, Á. and Löve, D., North Atlantic biota and their history: Oxford, Pergamon Press, p. 337-354

Knox, A. S., 1942, The pollen analysis of the silt and the tentative dating of the deposits, *in* Johnson, F., *et al.*,

The Boylston Street Fishweir: Phillips Acad., Peabody Fdn. Archaeol. Pap., v. 2, p. 105-129

Krauss, R. W. and Kent, G. N., 1944, Analyses and correlation of four New Hampshire bogs: Ohio J. Sci., v. 44, p. 11-17

Leopold, Estella B., 1956, Two late-glacial deposits in southern Connecticut: Natl. Acad. Sci. Proc., v. 42, p. 863-867

—— 1958, Some aspects of late-glacial climate in eastern United States: Zurich, Geobot. Inst. Rübel Veröff., v. 34, p. 80-85

Leopold, Estella B., and Scott, R. A., 1958, Pollen and spores and their use in geology: Smithson. Instn. Rep., v. 1957, p. 303-323

Little, E. L., Jr., 1949, Important forest trees of the United States, in Trees. The yearbook of agriculture: U.S. Dept. Agric., Washington, p. 763-814

Livingstone, D. A., and Livingstone, Bertha G. R., 1958, Late-glacial and postglacial vegetation from Gillis Lake in Richmond County, Cape Breton Island, Nova Scotia: Amer. J. Sci., v. 256, p. 341-359

Lougee, R. J., 1957, Pre-Wisconsin peat in Millbury, Massachusetts (abst.): Geol. Soc. Amer. Bull., v. 68, p. 1896

Löve, Doris, 1959, The postglacial development of the flora of Manitoba; a discussion: Can. J. Bot., v. 37, p. 547-585

Lutz, H. J., 1928, Trends and silvicultural significance of upland forest successions in southern New England: Yale Univ. School For. Bull., No. 22, 68 p.

——1930, Original forest composition in northwestern Pennsylvania as indicated by early land survey notes: J. For., v. 28, p. 1098-1103

Lyford, W. H., Goodlett, J. C., and Coates, W. H., 1963, Landforms, soils with fragipans, and forest on a slope in the Harvard Forest: Harvard Univ., Harvard For. Bull., v. 30, 68 p.

Maher, L. J., Jr., 1964, Ephedra pollen in sediments of the Great Lakes region: Ecology, v. 45, p. 391-395

Martin, P. S., and Gray, Jane, 1962, Pollen analysis and the Cenozoic: Science, v. 137, p. 103-111

McCulloch, W. F., 1939, A postglacial forest in central New York: Ecology, v. 20, p. 264-271

McIntosh, R. P., and Hurley, R. T., 1964, The spruce-fir forests of the Catskill Mountains: Ecology, v. 45, p. 314-326

Munns, E. N., 1938, The distribution of important forest trees of the United States: U.S. Dept. Agric. Misc. Publ., No. 287, 170 p.

Nichols, G. E., 1913, The vegetation of Connecticut. II, Virgin forests: Torreya, v. 13, p. 199-215

—— 1935, The hemlock-white pine-northern harwood region of eastern North America: Ecology, v. 16, p. 403-422

Niering, W. A., 1953, The past and present vegetation of High Point State Park, New Jersey: Ecol. Monogr., v. 23, p. 127-148

Niering, W. A., and Goodwin, R. H., 1962, Ecological studies in the Connecticut Arboretum Natural Area. I, Introduction and a survey of vegetation types: Ecology, v. 43, p. 41-54

Ogden, E. C., 1957, Survey of airborne pollen and fungus spores of New York State: New York State Mus. Bull. 356, 62 p.

Ogden, E. C., and Lewis, D. M., 1960, Airborne pollen and fungus spores of New York State: New York State Mus. Bull. 378, 104 p.

Ogden, J. G., III, 1959, A late-glacial pollen sequence from Martha's Vineyard, Massachusetts: Amer. J. Sci., v. 257, p. 366-381

—— 1960, Recurrence surfaces and pollen stratigraphy of a postglacial raised bog, Kings County, Nova Scotia: Amer. J. Sci., v. 258, p. 341-353

—— 1961, Forest history of Martha's Vineyard, Massachusetts. I, Modern and pre-colonial forests: Amer. Midl. Nat., v. 66, p. 417-430

—— 1963, The Squibnocket cliff peat; radiocarbon dates and pollen stratigraphy: Amer. J. Sci., v. 261, p. 344-353

—— 1964, Pleistocene pollen records from eastern North America: Bot. Rev., in press.

Ogden, J. G., III, and Hay, Ruth J., 1964, Ohio Wesleyan University natural radiocarbon measurements I: Radiocarbon, v. 6, p. 340-348

Potzger, J. E., 1953, Nineteen bogs from southern Quebec: Can. J. Bot., v. 31, p. 383-401

Potzger, J. E., and Courtemanche, Albert, 1956, A series of bogs across Quebec from the St. Lawrence valley to James Bay: Can. J. Bot., v. 34, p. 473-500

Potzger, J. E., Courtemanche, Albert, Sylvio, Br. M., and Heuber, F. M., 1956, Pollen from moss polsters on the mat of Lac Shaw bog, Quebec, correlated with a forest survey: Butler Univ. Bot. Stud., v. 13, p. 24-35

Potzger, J. E., and Friesner, R. C., 1948, Forests of the past along the coast of southern Maine: Butler Univ. Bot. Stud., v. 8, p. 178-203

Potzger, J. E., and Otto, J. H., 1943, Post-glacial forest succession in northern New Jersey as shown by pollen records from five bogs: Amer. J. Bot., v. 30, p. 83-87

Raup, H. M., 1937, Recent changes of climate and vegetation in southern New England and adjacent New York: Harvard Univ., Arnold Arbor. J., v. 18, p. 79-117

—— 1938, Botanical studies in the Black Rock Forest: Black Rock For. Bull., No. 7, 161 p.

—— 1940, Old field forests of southeastern New England: Harvard Univ., Arnold Arbor. J., v. 21, p. 266-273

—— 1941, Botanical problems in Boreal America: Bot. Rev., v. 7, p. 147-248

—— 1941, An old forest in Stonington, Connecticut: Rhodora, v. 43, p. 67-71

—— 1951, Vegetation and cryoplanation: Ohio J. Sci., v. 51, p. 105-116

—— 1964, Some problems in ecological theory and their relation to conservation: J. Ecol., v. 52 (Suppl.), p. 19-28

Raup, H. M., and Carlson, R. E., 1941, The history of land use in the Harvard Forest: Harvard Univ., Harvard For. Bull., No. 20, 64 p.

Rubin, Meyer, and Alexander, Corrinne, 1960, United States Geological Survey radiocarbon dates V: Radiocarbon, v 2, p. 129-185

Sears, P. B., 1942a, Postglacial migration of five forest genera: Amer. J. Bot., v. 29, p. 684-691

—— 1942b, Xerothermic theory: Bot. Rev., v. 8, p. 708-736

—— 1963, Vegetation, climate and coastal submergence in Connecticut: Science, v. 140, p. 59-60

Spurr, S. H., 1953, The vegetational significance of recent temperature changes along the Atlantic seaboard: Amer. J. Sci., v. 251, p. 682-688

—— 1956, Forest associations in the Harvard Forest: Ecol. Monogr., v. 26, p. 245-262

Stout, B. B., 1952, Species distribution and soils in the Harvard Forest: Harvard Univ., Harvard For. Bull., v. 24, 29 p.

Stuiver, Minze, Deevey, E. S., and Gralenski, L. J., 1960, Yale natural radiocarbon measurements v: Radiocarbon, v. 2, p. 49-61

Stuiver, Minze, Deevey, E. S., Jr., and Rouse, Irving, 1963, Yale natural radiocarbon measurements viii: Radiocarbon, v. 5, p. 312-341

Trautman, M. A., and Walton, Alan, 1962, Isotopes, Inc. radiocarbon measurements ii: Radiocarbon, v. 4, p. 35-42

Upson, J. E., Leopold, Estella B., and Rubin, Meyer, 1964, Postglacial change of sea level in New Haven Harbor, Connecticut: Amer. J. Sci., v. 262, p. 121-132

Vaartaja, Olli, 1959, Evidence of photoperiodic ecotypes in trees: Ecol. Monogr., v. 29, p. 91-111

Vallentyne, J. R., and Swabey, Yvonne S., 1955, A reinvestigation of the history of lower Linsley Pond, Connecticut: Amer. J. Sci., v. 253, p. 313-340

Walker, P. C., and Hartman, R. T., 1960, The forest sequence of the Hartstown Bog Area in western Pennsylvania: Ecology, v. 41, p. 461-474

Westveld, Marinus, and Committee on Silviculture, New England Section, Society American Foresters, 1956, Natural forest vegetation zones of New England: J. For., v. 54, p. 332-338

Whitehead, D. R., and Bentley, D. R., 1963, A postglacial pollen diagram from southwestern Vermont: Pollen et Spores, v. 5, p. 115-127

Wilson, L. R., 1949, A microfossil analysis of the lower peat and associated sediments at the John Hancock Fishweir Site, *in* Johnson, F., ed., The Boylston Street Fishweir ii: Phillips Acad., Peabody Fdn. Archaeol. Pap., v. 4, p. 84-99

Wynne-Edwards, V. C., 1937, Isolated arctic-alpine floras in eastern North America: a discussion of their glacial and recent history: Roy. Soc. Can. Trans. iii, v. 31 (5), p. 1-26

—— 1939, Some factors in the isolation of rare alpine plants: Roy. Soc. Can. Trans. iii, v. 33 (5), p. 35-42

Summary

The present distribution of plant species in northeastern United States is often explained as the result of disturbance of the natural vegetation by clearance or partial cutting of the forest by European settlers, or by fires set by aboriginal man. Others feel that present plant distributions are determined by the locations of refuges in which the flora survived the Ice Age and by the rate of postglacial migration over available routes from these refuges.

The past distributions of plants interpreted from the fossil record are almost invariably explained as responses to past climatic changes. The increase in conifers in the most recent pollen zone, however, can more easily be correlated with forest clearance by European settlers and subsequent successional changes following farm abandonment, than with climatic change. This reinterpretation would change the estimated age of the pollen-bearing deposits, as the previous estimates were based on interpretation of cooler climate following the postglacial hypsithermal interval, and consequent correlation with post-hypsithermal deposits elsewhere.

On the other hand some present plant distributions which were previously thought the result of historical factors, for example the abundance of oak, maple, and hickory and the rarity of hemlock in southern Connecticut and southeastern New York, are more easily explained by present edaphic factors and climate. Additional studies are needed, however, to define in detail the geographical distributions of species, and to specify whenever possible those physical factors of the environment that control them. Such information is clearly requisite to accurate use of plant fossils as a record of past environment.

PROBLEMS IN THE QUATERNARY PHYTOGEOGRAPHY
OF THE GREAT LAKES REGION *

EDWARD J. CUSHING[1]

ATTEMPTS TO use the paleobotanical record to elucidate Quaternary history are essentially exercises in historical plant geography. From this viewpoint, this paper will examine some of the problems raised by the present distribution of plant taxa and vegetation types in glaciated midcontinental North America and explore the relevance of these problems to interpretation of the available Quaternary fossil record in the region.

Questions of phytogeography can generally be treated as problems either of flora—the distribution of taxa considered individually—or vegetation—the distribution of aggregates of taxa considered as units. Similarly, interpretation of the fossil record usually involves both approaches, although reconstruction of vegetation is far more difficult than enumeration of a paleoflora. In the interest of clarity, the two approaches will be dealt with separately here.

Plant nomenclature in this paper follows Fernald (1950).

PRESENT FLORA

FLORISTIC PROVINCES

The Great Lakes area may be divided into three generalized floristic provinces (Fig. 1), the Northern Conifer, Eastern Deciduous, and Grassland provinces (Gleason and Cronquist, 1964, p. 176). The boundaries between these provinces are as yet poorly defined, and subdivision into smaller floristic areas has scarcely begun. A boundary between two floristic areas is best placed in the zone of highest concentration of range limits of the species in both floristic groups (Cain, 1947). To determine the position of such a zone requires the preparation of accurate distribution maps of many species, which in turn depends on a high density of field collections or sight records and careful taxonomy. As this information for central North America is unfortunately scarce or scattered, boundaries of floristic areas have been determined in this objective way only in limited areas (Raup, 1947; Fox and Soper, 1954; Curtis, 1959).

Clearly a boundary between floristic areas may become more or less diffuse as the density of distribution limits per unit area changes. Skeptics may argue, too, that boundaries may be located almost at will by the selection of distribution maps of certain critical species to the exclusion of others. Nevertheless, the work cited above strongly sug-

gests that, when the distribution of North America species is adequately known and plotted, zones of high concentration of range limits will be recognized. The mapping of these boundary zones remains one of the great tasks of phytogeography; increased use of machine methods of data-processing (Perring, 1963; Soper, 1964) will do much to hasten its completion.

The best-known floristic boundary has been mapped in Wisconsin by Curtis (1959, p. 15); he refers to it as the tension zone that separates the Northern Hardwoods province to the north from the Prairie-Forest province to the southwest (Fig. 1). The boundary zone can be followed eastward across Michigan (Potzger, 1948) and southern Ontario (Soper, 1955) and northwestward through Minnesota into Canada, where presumably it becomes the boundary between the Northern Conifer and Grassland provinces. Other boundary zones undoubtedly occur within the area of Figure 1, but their position and intensity (*i.e.* density of range limits per unit area) are inadequately known to permit their location on a map of even such a small scale. One such zone lies near the boundary between the Northern Conifer and Eastern Deciduous provinces. Another presumably diverges south into Ohio from the zone shown in Michigan to separate the Prairie-Forest province of Curtis

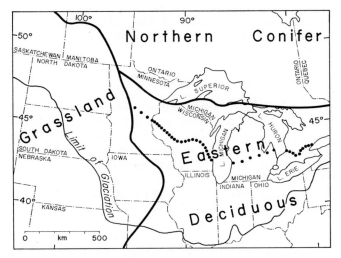

Figure 1 Major floristic provinces in the Great Lakes region, after Gleason and Cronquist (1964). Dotted line shows position of the floristic boundary of Curtis (1959) in Wisconsin and of Soper (1955) in Ontario and its extension across Minnesota and Michigan.

* For discussion and criticism, I am especially indebted to C. R. Janssen, J. H. McAndrews, J. G. Ogden, III, W. A. Watts, and H. E. Wright, Jr.

[1] Limnological Research Center and Minnesota Geological Survey, University of Minnesota, Minneapolis, Minnesota.

in Wisconsin from the Carolinian zone of Fox and Soper (1954) in southern Ontario; but this, like the boundary between the Grassland and Eastern Deciduous provinces, is likely to be less easily distinguished than the zones that are roughly latitudinal. Still another possible boundary zone in southern Ohio and Indiana is suggested by the distribution maps of Braun (1951). Because it nearly coincides with the southern limit of glaciation (Fig. 1), this possible zone especially deserves more thorough investigation.

The position of the boundaries between floristic areas is evidently the result of the reaction of the flora to regional environmental factors. In the best-known cases, these appear to be climatic rather than edaphic factors (Curtis, 1959, p. 35; Fox and Soper, 1954, p. 125), although no single climatic factor or simple combination of factors has been found whose isopleths are exactly parallel to a boundary zone throughout its length. Curtis summarizes the climatic factors that appear to be related to the boundary zone in Wisconsin; among the isopleths that are roughly correlated with the zone are those for: (1) 19.5°C average summer temperature, (2) 125 mm average evaporation in July, (3) 120 cm average annual snowfall, (4) 60 days per year with average temperature above 20°C, (5) 95 days per year with 0.25 mm of rain or more.

Besides demonstrating the presence and direction of environmental gradients to which the flora reacts, boundary zones provide significant evidence that a rough equilibrium exists between the present distribution of a large number of species and the present environment. The boundary zone in Wisconsin was mapped by superimposing range boundaries of 182 species of 12 families or orders (Curtis, 1959, p. 16), and the degree of coincidence is remarkable considering the morphological diversity of the species represented. It must be concluded that in many cases plant migration is closely adjusted to climatic change, and that a quasi-equilibrium exists between the distribution of plant species and environmental variables. This point is worth remembering when environmental interpretation of paleofloristic data is attempted.

FLORISTIC ELEMENTS

To emphasize its geographical affinities, the flora of the Great Lakes region or some part of it has often been described in terms of floristic elements. For example, Gleason (1922, p. 54) distinguished five elements in the flora of the Middle West: groups of plants "centering respectively in the southern Appalachian Mountains, in the southern Coastal Plain and the Mississippi Embayment, in the Ozark Mountains, in the plains of Kansas and Nebraska, and in Canada east of the Great Lakes." Curtis (1959, p. 8) recognized similar major groups in the flora of Wisconsin: the Alleghenian, Coastal Plain, Ozarkian, Prairie, and Boreal elements. As sometimes defined (Dansereau, 1957, p. 323; Curtis, 1959, p. 600), a floristic element is a group of species that share not only a common area of distribution but also a common origin and migratory and even evolutionary history. Conclusions about phytogeographic history based on the present distribution of elements defined in this sense may be strongly hypothetical and should be considered with

suspicion. More practical is the definition of a floristic element, advocated by Cain (1947), that is dependent only on the present distribution of species in relation to the area under consideration.

The so-called Coastal Plain element in the flora of the Great Lakes region is a much-discussed example of a group of species thought to have had a common late-glacial and postglacial history. Although there may be disagreement about just which species should be included (Fernald, 1942), the Coastal Plain element comprises species that have limited occurrence in the Great Lakes region but whose main distribution, as indicated by high density of collection stations and presumably also number of individuals, is on the Atlantic and Gulf coastal plains. Included among these species are: *Ammophila breviligulata* (beachgrass), *Panicum lucidum* (Gramineae), *Psilocarya scirpoides*, *P. nitens*, and *Fuirena pumila* (all Cyperaceae), *Cakile edentula* (searocket), *Euphorbia polygonifolia* (seaside-spurge), and others that typically occur on sandy soils and beaches. If it is assumed that these plants originated together and have a common migratory history, then it is reasonable to conclude, as Peattie (1922) and McLaughlin (1932) did, that they moved into the Great Lakes region from the Atlantic coast during late-glacial and postglacial time, perhaps along late-glacial strandlines of the Great Lakes. McLaughlin went further to explain the presence of many of the same species in the Sand Barrens of northwestern Wisconsin by postulating migration along continuous routes from the Atlantic coast available during late-glacial time. Where gaps in the present distribution of the plants exist along the supposed route, McLaughlin appealed to local eradication by postglacial physiographic changes.

The assumption basic to this reasoning may easily be questioned, however. Whether the similarities in geographical distribution of a group of species such as the Coastal Plain element have resulted from a common migratory history is a question that can ultimately be answered only by paleobotanical evidence—which in many specific cases will be impossible to obtain. On the other hand, the similarities certainly are related to similarities in the ecological preferences and tolerances of the species involved, and it is probable that some species in a given element had an entirely different distribution at times during the Quaternary when environments and the distribution of suitable habitats were different from the present. This was unquestionably true for the components of the Boreal element, which obviously had to exist somewhere other than central and eastern Canada during the glacial episodes of the Pleistocene. It was also true for at least two of the species included by McLaughlin (1932) in the Coastal Plain element in Wisconsin, for macrofossils of *Juncus balticus* and *Hemicarpha micrantha* have been found in late-glacial sediments in Minnesota or South Dakota (Baker, 1965; Watts and Wright, unpublished manuscript) far from the late-glacial migration route that McLaughlin proposed for these plants.

That Fernald (1942) rightly pointed out that these two species have a present distribution much broader than McLaughlin presumed only strengthens the argument that it is dangerous to apply to an entire floristic element (in the strict geographic sense) an hypothesis based on the peculiarities of distribution of only a few of its component species.

DISJUNCTION

The problem of the interpretation of the Coastal Plain element in the Great Lakes region is also a problem in the interpretation of discontinuous ranges for some of the species involved. It was, in fact, the disjunct distribution of some species that drew attention to the presence around the Great Lakes of other plants characteristic of the Atlantic Coast (Peattie, 1922). A spike-rush, *Eleocharis melanocarpa*, is an oft-cited example; it occurs along the Atlantic coast but inland only at the south end of Lake Michigan. Rejecting the hypothesis of long-distance dispersal to explain this and similar disjunctions, Peattie and McLaughlin (1932) instead proposed that the coastal-plain plants migrated from the Atlantic coast along a nearly continuous line of suitable habitats available in late-glacial time. Unfortunately, although such an hypothesis makes more comprehensible the migration of a disjunct like *Eleocharis melanocarpa* by reducing it to short steps, it raises a new and equally perplexing problem: how to explain the subsequent extermination of the species along the supposed migration route that bridged the present discontinuity.

A second famous example of wide discontinuities in range involves a number of species of arctic-alpine affinities in the Lake Superior region (Agassiz, 1850; Soper and Maycock, 1963). The plants occupy the rocky cliffs and shores along the exposed parts of the north shore of Lake Superior; Schuster (1958) went so far as to call this discontinuous series of extreme habitats an arctic zone, thereby emphasizing the unusual aspect of the environment and flora there.

Many of these arctic-alpine plants were cited by Fernald (1925, 1935) in support of his hypothesis of survival of these and other plants in unglaciated areas in the Great Lakes region (see reviews by Deevey, 1949, p. 1379; Butters and Abbe, 1953, p. 69). The nunatak areas in the Superior basin that Fernald favored are now known to have been glaciated, and only two hypotheses are now being seriously entertained to explain the disjunction of the arctic-alpine plants: (1) migration during postglacial time to favorable habitats in the Superior basin from the area of more continuous distribution in subarctic to arctic regions to the north, and (2) survival in favorable habitats as relicts of a wider and more continuous late-glacial distribution in the Lake Superior region. The latter hypothesis is generally favored (Butters and Abbe, 1953; Soper and Maycock, 1963) and receives support from the discovery that at least one of the disjunct species (*Dryas integrifolia*) was indeed present and perhaps widespread on the late-glacial landscape in northeastern Minnesota (Baker, 1965; Watts, unpublished data). Neither of the hypotheses necessarily demands that the species remain fixed within the specific localities where they are now found; the concept that the plants are restricted in area because of species senescence (Fernald, 1925; Cain, 1944, p. 228) is replaced by emphasis upon the peculiarities of the microclimates and habitats that they occupy, coupled with the realization that they should not be considered as "senescent or effete, but rather as successful opportunists" (Wynne-Edwards, 1939, p. 41).

Thus as new habitats become available for these pioneer plants, for example as the level of Lake Superior dropped from its early high strandlines, they were able to migrate to new sites before their earlier habitats were destroyed.

In addition to the arctic-alpine species, the rare plants of the Lake Superior region include species that are widely disjunct from the Rocky Mountains (Fernald, 1925, 1935). Prominent along these are the shrubs *Oplopanax horridus* (Araliaceae), *Rubus parviflorus* (Rosaceae), and *Ceanothus sanguineus* (Rhamnaceae). The first occurs on Isle Royale in Lake Superior and on nearby islands and shores of Ontario, but its next nearest stations are in western Montana and Alberta (Moss and Pegg, 1963); the *Rubus* is common in the Lake Superior basin, whereas the *Ceanothus* is rare, but the next nearest station for each is in the Black Hills of western South Dakota. Again, the only reasonable explanations for these disjunctions are: (1) migration by long-distance dispersal from the western areas of distribution, or (2) isolation by destruction in the intervening area of habitats that were occupied by the species in late-glacial or earlier postglacial time. There is even less reason to favor one of these explanations than in the case of the arctic-alpine disjuncts, however. Certainly, if the habitats occupied by these shrubs and the other plants of similar range listed by Fernald (1935) are as distinctive as those of the arctic-alpine species, they are much less obviously so.

Another area notorious for plants of limited or discontinuous range is the Driftless Area, defined broadly as southwestern Wisconsin and adjacent Minnesota, Iowa, and Illinois (Fassett, 1931, 1943; Rosendahl, 1947; Rosendahl and Moore, 1947). A few species are disjunct in the Driftless Area from a mainly arctic-alpine distribution; examples are *Sedum rosea* (Crassulaceae), *Chrysosplenium iowense* (Saxifragaceae), and *Rhododendron lapponicum* (Ericaceae).

A few species of the Driftless Area, notably *Dodecatheon amethystinum* (Primulaceae), have attracted attention because they occur to the east only south of the limit of glaciation. Others have scattered occurrences elsewhere close to (but not necessarily only outside) the glacial border; included here are *Lycopodium porophilum* (Lycopodiaceae), *Aconitum noveboracense* (Ranunculaceae), and *Adoxa moschatellina* (Adoxaceae). Still other taxa are either endemic to the Driftless Area or have a restricted range centered on it; these include *Talinum rugospermum* (Portulacaceae), *Sullivantia renifolia* (Saxifragaceae), *Penstemon gracilis* var. *wisconsinensis* (Scrophulariaceae), *Solidago sciaphila* (Compositae), and *Gnaphalium saxicola* (Compositae). Most of the rest of the 34 taxa listed by Curtis (1959, p. 14) have no characteristic in common; they are merely at or near the limit of their range in southwestern Wisconsin, and they may occur widely east, south, or west from there.

The Driftless Area has long been considered as an important refugium for plants during glacial intervals (Sears, 1942b; Braun, 1950, p. 523), and Curtis (1959, p. 12) calls some of the plants mentioned above "preglacial relics." Recent geological opinion (Frye *et al.*, this volume) that the Driftless Area was glaciated, perhaps as late as the Wisconsin Age, forces re-examination of this view. Regardless of when the area was last glaciated, it probably was largely available to plant colonization by late-Wisconsin time, and the arctic-alpine disjuncts mentioned above may have persisted since then in special habitats within the area. Discovery of *Rhododendron lapponicum* (seed) and *Sedum* cf. *rosea* (pollen) in late-glacial sediments in northeastern Minnesota (Baker, 1965) indicates that these plants were present in the periglacial environment, and both now occur in the Driftless Area only in isolated habitats (on sandstone or limestone cliffs) that are rare to the north. (Actually, both species occur only at the edge or just outside the Driftless Area as shown by Flint *et al.*, 1959.) The remaining unusual plants of the Driftless Area may similarly be restricted there because of the availability of a variety of unusual microclimates and habitats; this hypothesis seems as reasonable at present as the hypothesis of long geographical isolation resulting from glaciation.

The presence of endemics in the Driftless Area might be cited as evidence of long isolation of that area during the Pleistocene. It is doubtful, however, whether either the number or degree of taxonomic differentiation of the endemics mentioned above is greater than in any other area that has similar size and diversity of habitats and has been as well botanized. For example, northeastern Minnesota, which certainly was glaciated during the late Wisconsin (Wright and Ruhe, this volume), contains two known endemic species, *Poa scopulorum* (Gramineae) and *Oxytropis ixodes* (Leguminosae), both of which, like most of the Driftless Area endemics, occur on bedrock cliffs (Butters and Abbe, 1953). The systematics and genetics of the endemics is in general too poorly understood to permit more than speculation about their origin and age.

Attempts to explain patterns of disjunct distribution by historical isolation or fragmentation of range soon face arguments about the efficiency of migration of the species involved. Opinions on this matter can be resolved to two extreme positions. The first holds that for most plant species dispersal is limited, and a nearly continuous series of suitable habitats must be available to a species before it can migrate successfully. The opposing view maintains that if favorable habitats, even widely separated, are available and if sufficient time elapses, then most plants adapted to the environment of the given habitats may be expected to appear there, as the result of dispersal over unusual distances.

Application of these assumptions is well illustrated by two recent papers dealing with the North American distribution of a moss, *Tetraphis pellucida* Hedw. Steere (this volume) includes this species in a group (his "Umiat syndrome") of "temperate" bryophytes that have a pronounced disjunction from central North America to the arctic north slope of Alaska. He deprecates long-distance transport of moss spores as an explanation for disjunctions of this scale, and he concludes that the mosses in northern Alaska are relicts of a more nearly continuous distribution in interglacial or preglacial time.

On the other hand, Forman (1964) attempts to explain the present distribution of *T. pellucida* as a result of the distribution on the continent of habitats that satisfy the environmental requirements of the species. One of his reasons for choosing this moss for laboratory investigation of

its environmental tolerances was that "dispersal is not believed limiting in this species." Forman compared his laboratory data with climatic data for North America in order to map a predicted distribution for the species. Considering the paucity of climatic, especially microclimatic, data for the continent, he feels that the predicted distribution agrees reasonably well with the actual known distribution. Since the predicted area does not greatly exceed in size the actual area of distribution, Forman could argue that historical reasons (isolation or restriction and subsequent failure to reoccupy suitable habitats) were unnecessary to explain the present distribution pattern.

Of course, demonstrating that a given species within an area of concern is at present fully occupying all habitats that provide an environment lying within the tolerances of the species—*i.e.* that it is everywhere in equilibrium with the environment—is a formidable task, even if only one ecotype is involved. Moreover, such a demonstration does not test the hypothesis that the species in one part of its disjunct range is there a relict of a once wider, more nearly continuous distribution; it merely adds the information that the habitat, as well as the organism, is disjunct. It does, however, quiet the argument that the species is confined to its restricted area because of its low dispersal capability and the lapse of insufficient time to permit its spread by migration.

Since the dispersal capability of the total population of a species at some past time can never be adequately known, explanation of disjunct distribution patterns based solely on assumptions about dispersal can only remain conjectural. Disjunction is, after all, a matter of degree, for no plant occupies space continuously (Gleason and Cronquist, 1964, p. 51). At which level in the hierarchy of distribution patterns (Forman, 1964) historical factors are operative must surely vary from one species to another and, even within a single species, from one part of its range to another. Proof that a given isolated population is a relict of a once more widespread population, like proof of the parallel history of the species in a floristic element, can be attained only through paleobotanical evidence.

PRESENT VEGETATION

The vegetation of the Great Lakes region may be classified firstly by its physiognomy and secondly by its floristic composition. Three great physiognomic formations are represented: grassland, deciduous forest, and coniferous forest; and intermediates between the first and second (savanna and parkland) and second and third (mixed conifer-hardwood forest) of these are widespread (Fig. 2). The nature and origin of these intermediate vegetation types are problems that account for much of the phytosociological literature of the region.

MIXED CONIFER-HARDWOOD FOREST

The large number of dominant tree species, some of them —such as *Pinus strobus* (white pine) and *P. resinosa* (red pine)—of considerable economic importance, attracted early attention to this vegetation type. It was named the Lake Forest by Weaver and Clements (1929, p. 440), who considered it a climax formation distinct from the coniferous

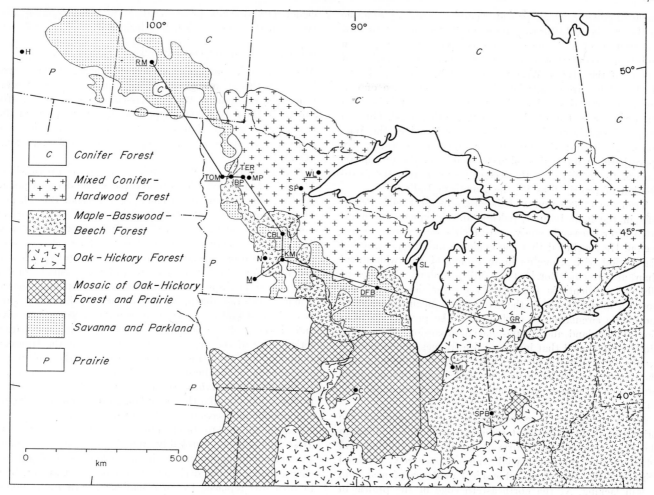

Figure 2. Major vegetation types in the Great Lakes region. Vegetation boundaries are generalized from Küchler (1964) and Rowe (1959). Paleobotanical sites mentioned in the text: BP = Bog D Pond; C, Canton site; CBL, Cedar Bog Lake; DFB, Disterhaft Farm Bog; GR, George Reserve; H, Hafichuk site; KM, Kirchner Marsh; M, Madelia; ML, Meyers Lake; MP, Martin Pond; N, Norwood; RM, Riding Mountain area; SL, Seidel Lake; SP, Spider Creek; SPB, Sunbeam Prairie Bog; TER, Terhell Pond; TOM, Thompson Pond; WL, Weber Lake. Underlined sites are included in Figure 3.

forest formation to the north and the deciduous forest formation to the south, although they postulated that coniferous species—*Pinus strobus, P. resinosa,* and *Tsuga canadensis* (hemlock)—were the climax dominants of the forest. Nichols (1935) recognized that hardwood species such as *Acer saccharum* (sugar maple), *Fagus grandifolia* (beech), *Tilia americana* (basswood), and *Betula lutea* (yellow birch) could share dominance with coniferous species in the climax forests of this transitional region, and Braun (1950) suggested that the area, which she mapped as the hemlock—white pine—northern hardwoods region, could be treated as a mosaic of coniferous, deciduous, and mixed climax forests. Much of the literature pertaining to the description and interpretation of these forests is reviewed by Maycock and Curtis (1960).

More recently, the chiefly deductive scheme propounded by Clements for vegetation classification and interpretation, with its emphasis on the uniformity of a terminal equilib-

rium state of vegetation (the climax), has been largely superseded by inductive approaches that stress the variability of vegetation, the quantitative description of that variability, and the ordination of the results into a model within which vegetation composition varies continuously in both space and time (Whittaker, 1957). Maycock and Curtis (1960) conclude that the mixed conifer-hardwood forests do indeed fit such a model and that the ecological tolerances of individual species, no two of which coincide exactly, react with environmental gradients to produce a continuous series of communities with slightly differing floristic composition. Thus no single species or group of only coniferous or deciduous species can be used to characterize the vegetation of the whole region or even a small part of it.

THE PRAIRIE PENINSULA

The origin of the great eastward extension of grassland into the area south of the Great Lakes (Fig. 2) has stimulated much discussion, which provides perhaps the best example in the region of historical arguments based on the present distribution of a distinctive, if gross, vegetation type. An ambitious reconstruction of the history of the prairie and forests of the Middle West was offered by Gleason (1922). He based his arguments largely on the occurrence of disjunct communities, which he interpreted as relics of a once greater extent of the same vegetation type. Gleason proposed two intervals of prairie expansion since the Wisconsin glaciation: the first was a result of a warm, dry (xerothermic) interval of climate soon after the disappearance of the glacier, and the second resulted from the introduction of prairie fires by the American Indian.

Transeau (1935) reviewed the origin of the Prairie Peninsula in the light both of paleobotanical evidence accumulated after Gleason's study and of climatic records for the region. He concluded that the evidence indicated a postglacial period with droughts more prolonged and widespread than at present. Borchert (1950) examined the present climatic gradients in the area in greater detail and proposed a model based on the strength of mean westerly atmospheric circulation to explain both the present distribution of grassland and its postglacial expansion to the east. He also concluded that increased fire frequency was favored by the same climatic changes that favored grassland; thus the importance of fire in pushing back and maintaining the prairie-forest border continues to be recognized (Curtis, 1959, p. 295).

Much of Gleason's reasoning about the history of the prairie in the Middle West remains untested, for although the expansion of the Prairie Peninsula into Indiana and Ohio during mid-postglacial time is scarcely doubted (Smith, 1957), direct paleobotanical evidence of grassland is still lacking. At the northeastern edge of the prairie in Minnesota, however, fluctuations in the prairie-forest border are well marked in the fossil record. This record will now be examined.

PALEOBOTANY

The paleobotanical record of the Quaternary and its interpretation in the Great Lakes region is most conveniently discussed for stratigraphic intervals of progressively older age. Sediments in the first interval yield radiocarbon ages ranging from zero to about 9,000 years before present (B.P.). The assemblages of plant fossils from this stratigraphic interval are usually compared directly with the present vegetation in the region. Fossil assemblages from sediments with radiocarbon ages greater than about 9,000 years, however, often cannot be related easily to modern plant assemblages, although the taxa identified may be modern. Of these older assemblages, those from strata with radiocarbon ages less than about 13,000 years are most numerous and may be considered together. Still older assemblages can simply be described by the name of the time-stratigraphic interval in which they occur.

The literature describing late-Quaternary plant fossils, particularly pollen, is voluminous; it has been summarized or reviewed many times, notably by Deevey (1949), Just (1959), Potzger (1946), Sears (1948), Smith (1940), and Wright (1964a). Recent developments are reviewed by Ogden (1965). Only problems that are not adequately discussed in these papers will be considered here.

PRESENT TO ABOUT 9,000 RADIOCARBON YEARS B.P.

Although the pollen stratigraphy of sediments whose ages lie within this span suggests widespread changes in vegetation and environment, the fossil assemblages are sufficiently similar to those now being deposited in various parts of the Great Lakes region that reconstruction of past vegetation can many times be based with confidence on modern analogues.

A convincing example of such an appeal is provided by McAndrews (1963, 1965), who compared the detailed pollen stratigraphy at four sites (Thompson, Terhell, Bog D, and Martin Ponds, Fig. 2) with pollen spectra from surface samples taken along a transect in northwestern Minnesota. The east-west transect, about 100 km long, crosses four major vegetation formations: mixed pine-hardwood forest, deciduous forest, oak savanna, and prairie. In this favorable area, where environmental gradients are steep and vegetational boundaries sharp, McAndrews could show that sites near the east end of the transect contained three successive and distinct pollen assemblages like those that now characterize three of the vegetational formations of the transect. Before about 4,000 radiocarbon years ago the pollen assemblage was dominated by oak (*Quercus*), composites (*Artemisia* and *Ambrosia*), and grass (Gramineae) (Bog D Pond, Fig. 3), like that now being deposited in and near the present oak savanna. Subsequent to that time the assemblage shifted to birch (*Betula*), oak, and hornbeam (*Ostrya/Carpinus*, probably mostly *Ostrya virginiana*) dominance, in agreement with the pollen assemblage now characteristic of the deciduous forest on the transect. This in turn was replaced by an assemblage, with *Pinus* pollen dominant, that is typical of the mixed pine-hardwood forest that now occupies the area surrounding the site. At the west end of the transect (Thompson Pond, Fig. 3), however, the pollen assemblages show little change through the same time interval; they suggest continuous occupation of the area by prairie.

Successions of similar magnitude are suggested by the pollen stratigraphy elsewhere in the region, but the variation among the pollen assemblages is so great, and the number of detailed diagrams still so few, that the extension of a system of pollen assemblage zones, like those defined by McAndrews (1965) for northwestern Minnesota, would be premature. The smoothed curves shown for selected sites in Figure 3, however, suggest regional changes for a few pollen types that may prove to be significant. Thus, when compared to McAndrews' transect, the stratigraphy of three cores in the Riding Mountain area (Ritchie, 1964) supports Ritchie's cautious interpretation that the vegetation changed from prairie (suggested by the comparison of Ritchie's zone II with Thompson Pond) through oak-aspen-birch forest to the mixed conifer-deciduous forest that prevails today (Fig. 3). At the same time the contrast between the Riding Mountain stratigraphy and that of Bog D Pond, localities separated by about 500 km, emphasizes the smaller tree flora and the lesser importance of oak and pine in the northern area.

Grassland, suggested by high amounts of grass and composite pollen, was also important to the southeast near the present prairie-forest border. Diagrams presented by Wright *et al.* (1963; Kirchner Marsh, Fig. 3) and Cushing (1963; Cedar Bog Lake, Fig. 3) record an interval about 6,000 years B.P. of prairie or oak savanna, as judged by McAndrews' standards, followed by the development of the present oak-dominated forest. The slight rise of *Pinus* near the top of both diagrams may be the result of a succession to pine-hardwood forest farther north, as at Bog D Pond. In contrast to the diagrams from northwestern Minnesota, however, the oak-grass-composite interval at Kirchner Marsh and Cedar Bog Lake is preceded by an assemblage rich in pollen of trees typical of more mesic conditions, especially elm (*Ulmus*). The oak savanna or prairie interval was further marked by fluctuating water levels in the two basins and the development of local herb vegetation; for Kirchner Marsh this conclusion is fully confirmed and amplified by detailed macrofossil and pollen-stratigraphic studies (Watts and Winter, 1965).

Detailed pollen diagrams farther east are rare, but in them the influence of grassland pollen types is replaced by more subtle changes in relative frequencies among tree pollen types. A diagram by West (1961) from eastern Wisconsin (Disterhaft Farm Bog, Fig. 3) shows a small increase in pollen of grasses and other herbs near the midpoint of the profile, but it is uncertain whether this is the result of an increase in grassland in the area or a change in the local vegetation surrounding the lake. Northeast, 140 km across the tension zone of Curtis (1959), another site (Seidel Lake; West, 1961) differs in the lesser importance of *Quercus* pollen and the prominence, especially in the near-surface assemblage, of pollen of trees typical of the northern hardwoods, such as *Tsuga*, *Fagus*, and *Acer*.

From still farther north in the mixed conifer-hardwood forest, a diagram by Fries (1962; Weber Lake, Fig. 3) indicates the greater importance of conifers in northeastern Minnesota than to the west at Bog D Pond or the southeast at Seidel Lake. The most prominent change in the pollen stratigraphy is a shift from a birch-spruce-fir assemblage through a pine maximum to a second birch-spruce-fir assemblage. The second spruce maximum continues to the surface and may represent the development of local bog forest. A small increase in pollen of upland composites (*Artemisia* and *Ambrosia*) just before the pine maximum may, according to Fries, mean a shorter distance to prairie vegetation during the corresponding time interval.

Most of the pollen diagrams discussed, as well as others for the region, can be fitted to a scheme of climatic change that postulates a hypsithermal (Deevey and Flint, 1957) or xerothermic (Sears, 1942a) interval followed by a decrease in temperature or increase in precipitation, or both, to the present. There is little reason, indeed, to doubt the validity of such a general scheme. The available records and radiocarbon dates suggest, however, that a subdivision of postglacial time based upon such real but vague climatic changes (Cooper, 1958) may be misleading unless it is defined by the stratigraphic record at a specified type locality. Pollen-zone boundaries that are reasonably well dated by radiocarbon (either directly or by linear interpolation or extrapolation from nearby dates in the same core) are indicated in Figure 3 by solid lines; zone boundaries not so fixed in time are shown dashed, and no judgment of their age is implied by their arbitrary position on the diagram. Even when zone boundaries are sharp, as at Bog D Pond, Cedar Bog Lake, and Kirchner Marsh, their radiocarbon ages vary as much as 1,000 years. Certainly some variation is expected because of the problems involved in dating limnic sediments (Deevey *et al.*, 1954), but equally expected is geographical variation caused by regional variation in vegetation and in the reaction of vegetation to climatic change. The number of dated pollen diagrams in the Great Lakes region are far too few at present to permit clear understanding of how even the most prominent vegetation boundary, the prairie-forest boundary, fluctuated during the past 9,000 years.

9,000 TO ABOUT 13,000 RADIOCARBON YEARS B.P.

The lower part of the sediments that began accumulating since the wasting of the Wisconsin ice sheet contains fossil assemblages that are as puzzling to interpret as they are striking in their wide geographic extent and constant composition. Certain consistent regional variations are evident, however, in the generalized diagrams of Figure 3. Nearly all diagrams agree in showing the dominance of spruce (*Picea*) pollen in the lowest pollen-bearing sediments. In the Riding Mountain area (Ritchie, 1964) the spruce-dominated assemblage is small, and the pollen of other trees, with the possible exception of *Populus*, is so sparse that it might be explained by long-distance transport. Pollen of herbs, especially *Artemisia*, is also important. The assemblage is duplicated to the west in southern Saskatchewan (H, Fig. 2), where macrofossils confirm the presence of *Picea mariana*, *Picea glauca*, *Populus tremuloides*, and *Populus balsamifera*, together with the shrubs *Shepherdia canadensis* (soapberry) and *Juniperus communis* (juniper) (Ritchie and deVries, 1964).

In northwestern and southeastern Minnesota (Thompson Pond to Kirchner Marsh, Fig. 3), the spruce-dominated pollen assemblage includes significant amounts of tamarack (*Larix*) and, particularly to the southeast, ash (*Fraxinus*, mostly *F. nigra*-type) and other deciduous trees. Pollen of *Juniperus*-type is prominent in many diagrams; although not reported by Wright *et al.* (1963), re-examination of the slides indicate that it, as well as *Populus*, is present in their zone A at Kirchner Marsh, and Watts and Winter (1965) report macrofossils of *Juniperus communis* in the same stratigraphic interval. Composite pollen (*Artemisia* and *Ambrosia*) remains important, and *Shepherdia canadensis* is present. Nearly identical pollen assemblages are found in Wisconsin (Disterhaft Farm Bog, Fig. 3) and southeastern Michigan (George Reserve).

The richness of the pollen flora of this zone, partly confirmed by macrofossil evidence especially of aquatic and damp-ground plants (Watts and Winter, 1965), has puzzled most paleoecologists who have attempted interpretation of the recent detailed pollen diagrams. Not only does the flora represent great ecological diversity—for example, the combination of forest species with heliophilous herbs such as *Artemisia* and *Ambrosia*—but it is a mixture of floristic elements

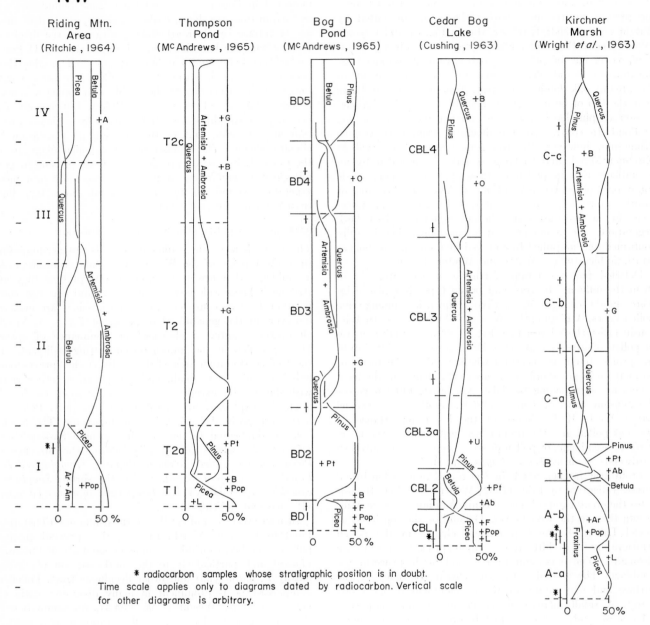

Figure 3. Generalized late- and post-Wisconsin pollen diagrams from selected sites in the Great Lakes region. Location of sites and position of NW-SE transect are shown on Figure 2. Only selected pollen curves are plotted, greatly smoothed; presence of significant quantities of other pollen types is indicated by plus signs. Pollen sum for all diagrams is total pollen except aquatics. Radiocarbon dates are shown by crosses against the time scale at the right; the vertical line indicates the reported standard error of the date. Pollen-zone

as judged from present distributions. This floristic complexity has been explained in various ways. Andersen (1954) proposed that part of the mixture, the deciduous-forest element, was redeposited from older pollen-bearing sediments. This hypothesis cannot, at least, account for the mixture at some of the sites (Cushing, 1964), and the uniformity of the pollen assemblage makes it suspect at the rest. West (1961) suggested that pollen of the deciduous-forest element was blown from distant habitats and, like Andersen, argued that high values of non-arboreal pollen suggested open vegetation near the northern treeline. Fries *et al.* (1961), on the other hand, preferred to interpret the same

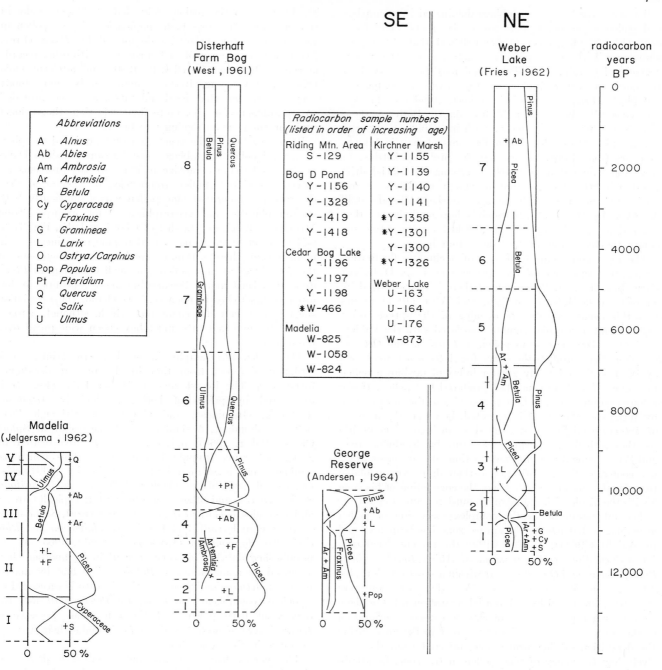

designations to the left of each diagram are those of the original authors. Zone abbreviations at Thompson Pond and Bog D Pond are not used by McAndrews (1965) but are equivalent to his assemblage-zone names as follows: T1 = BD1 = *Picea-Populus* zone, T2 = *Gramineae-Artemisia* zone, T2a = *Pinus-Pteridium* sub-zone, T2c = *Ostrya-Ulmus* sub-zone, BD2 = *Pinus-Pteridium* zone, BD3 = *Quercus-Gramineae-Artemisia* zone, BD4 = *Quercus-Ostrya* zone, BD5 = *Pinus strobus* zone.

assemblage as representing a mixture of vegetation types (swamp coniferous forest, oak savanna, and prairie) in which all the elements could be represented, and Wright *et al.* (1963) argued that the vegetation in southeastern Minnesota during deposition of the spruce-dominated assemblage was a mixed conifer-hardwood forest with nearby areas of grassland. Cushing (1963), Ritchie (1964), and McAndrews (1965) all emphasized the possible diversity of microhabitats—as a result of soil instability and fluctuating levels of soil moisture—that could accommodate a diverse flora on the recently deglaciated landscape.

At Madelia in southern Minnesota the spruce-dominated

pollen zone overlies an assemblage dominated by non-arbo-real pollen, especially Cyperaceae (sedges) and *Salix* (willow) (Fig. 3). Jelgersma (1962) believed that this represented an herbaceous pioneer vegetation on the newly deglaciated terrain. A similar record may be preserved to the north at Norwood (Fig. 2), for leaves of the pioneer heliophyte *Dryas integrifolia* have been found in sediments overlying till (Watts, unpublished data). Both of these records are from shallow basins with incomplete postglacial stratigraphy. Most other pollen diagrams, at least in Minnesota, are from deeper basins that are probably kettles; in these the sediment immediately overlying the glacial drift is often a litter horizon that is similar in character and origin, but not necessarily in age, to the "Allerød mull" described by Hartz (1912). Such a horizon indicates that vegetation was already well established on the landscape before the basin formed and deposition began.

The most convincing evidence for a climatic fluctuation during the deposition of the spruce zone is at Disterhaft Farm Bog (Fig. 3). Pollen zone 3 there is characterized by an increase in *Artemisia* pollen, and West (1961) argues that this event indicates an opening of the spruce forest as the result of a cooler climate associated with the Valders readvance. The increase in pollen of *Fraxinus* and *Ostrya/Carpinus* that parallels the curve for *Artemisia* is explained by West as the relatively greater influx of far-blown pollen to a more open landscape that produced less pollen. If the reconstruction of vegetation proposed for the spruce zone by Wright *et al.* (1963) is accepted, however, the increase of *Artemisia* might be interpreted as an increase in prairie together with the replacement of spruce by deciduous trees, and West's zone 3 would suggest a time of warmer or drier, not cooler, climate. Until radiocarbon dates are available from West's site or a similar one, the correlation of his zone 3 with the Valders glacial advance must remain in doubt.

The interpretation of the complex succession of pollen assemblages that overlie the spruce zone has been reviewed by Wright (1964a). At sites within the present deciduous-forest formation, pollen maxima of *Abies, Betula, Alnus, Pinus, Ulmus,* and *Quercus* occur within a short stratigraphic interval, and Wright suggested that the succession may have been controlled by differential migration rates of these taxa after a rapid warming of climate caused deterioration of the spruce forest. The absence of pine in the area during the deposition of the spruce zone, inferred from the relatively low frequency of pine pollen in the zone, he attributed to the delayed migration of *Pinus* into the Great Lakes region from a full-glacial refuge in the Appalachian Highlands. An alternative hypothesis is that the climate during deposition of the spruce zone was unfavorable for pine throughout the region (Cushing, 1963). Although pine occurs throughout the range of spruce today, it is easily conceivable that the climate in the Great Lakes region during wasting of the Wisconsin ice sheet could have been radically different, for example in the seasonal distribution of temperature and precipitation, from any climate today within the range of the same species. The ecological tolerances of the species involved are too poorly known either to support or contradict such an hypothesis. Of recent pol-

len diagrams in the region, only that at Meyers Lake in Indiana (Fig. 2) shows high frequencies of pine pollen in and below a zone otherwise dominated by *Picea* (Frey, 1959). The significance of such a contrast with other records in central Indiana (Engelhardt, 1960) and adjacent Ohio (Kapp and Gooding, 1964a) remains to be understood; Frey's suggestion that local habitats may have provided an environment for pine more favorable than the regional environment is an intriguing possibility.

Reconstruction of the vegetation that produced the pine-dominated pollen assemblage must be cautious since Davis (1963) used that assemblage to illustrate the problems involved in relating pollen frequencies to vegetation. Yet the relative amount of pine pollen varies sufficiently both stratigraphically and geographically (for example, from Madelia to Kirchner Marsh to Cedar Bog Lake, Fig. 3) to make attractive the hypothesis that pine trees increased in number somewhere within the region. As characteristic of the assemblage as pine pollen is a small maximum of *Pteridium* (bracken) spores. Because bracken is a heliophyte that often occurs today in open pine woodland, the association suggests relatively dry conditions, which, although perhaps limited to small habitats, must have been widespread over the region.

The pollen stratigraphy in northeastern Minnesota is strikingly different from that in the present deciduous-forest area. The lowest zone at Weber Lake (Fig. 3) is dominated by pollen of herbs, particularly *Artemisia, Ambrosia,* Gramineae, and Cyperaceae, although *Picea* pollen is abundant. A similar assemblage occurs at Spider Creek (Baker, 1965) and a nearby site investigated by Saskia Jelgersma (unpublished diagram). This pollen assemblage zone is characterized in addition by a distinctive macrofossil assemblage, which includes *Dryas integrifolia, Salix herbacea,* and other wide-ranging but typically arctic-alpine species as *Carex capillaris* (Cyperaceae), *Silene acaulis* (Caryophyllaceae), and *Vaccinium uliginosum* and *Rhododendron lapponicum* (Ericaceae) (Baker, 1965; Watts, unpublished data). This zone is overlain by another characterized by a maximum of *Betula* pollen and by macrofossils of *Betula glandulosa,* and that in turn is succeeded by a pollen assemblage dominated by *Picea,* with low frequency of herb pollen and the continuous presence of *Larix;* leaves of both *Picea* and *Larix* make their first appearance in this zone also.

The new pollen diagrams and macrofossil discoveries therefore confirm Fries' (1962) interpretation of the Weber Lake stratigraphy, while they provide even stronger contrast with the stratigraphy to the west and south, where macrofossils of *Picea* and *Larix* indicate that conifers were present as soon as the basins were open to sedimentation. Since the radiocarbon dates permit correlation of largely treeless conditions in northeastern Minnesota with forest development to the south, it should be possible to locate what must have been a prominent floristic boundary between the two areas. The search is hampered, however, by the complexity of the glacial sequence in northeastern Minnesota (Wright and Ruhe, this volume); indeed, one hypothesis to explain the persistence of a non-forested landscape in northeastern Minnesota appeals to the local cooling effect of the Superior Lobe in the nearby Lake Superior basin.

The top of the spruce-dominated pollen assemblage zone is sharply defined in much of the Great Lakes region, and the available radiocarbon dates place it between about 10,000 and 11,000 years B.P. (Fig. 3). Additional dates of the same zone boundary in Ohio are similar: 10,600 ± 150 at Sunbeam Prairie Bog (L550B; Kapp and Gooding, 1964a) and about 9,500 and 10,500 at two sites reported by Ogden (1965). In northeastern Minnesota a different but equally sharp zone boundary occurs within the same radiocarbon age span. Whether the variation in age of these zone boundaries across the entire region results from the vagaries of radiocarbon sampling or from geographic variation in the true age of the stratigraphic boundary is unknown. If some sufficiently small subdivision of the region is considered, however, the precision of pollen stratigraphy for time correlation within such a well-defined stratigraphic interval can clearly be greater than the precision of radiocarbon sampling. Partly for this reason, Wright (1964b) suggested that the top of the spruce zone might be used to define the top of the Wisconsin stage in the area of the Michigan Lobe; if adopted at a type locality clearly related to the glacial sequence (for example, at a site on the type Valders till), this proposal would greatly improve time-stratigraphic terminology in the Great Lakes region.

MIDDLE WISCONSIN

Plant fossils older than about 13,000 radiocarbon years B.P. are not rare in the Great Lakes region, but detailed stratigraphic studies of them are. Ogden (1965) summarizes these; only a few phytogeographical problems will be mentioned here.

One interesting record is the identification of *Tsuga* (hemlock) wood, dated from about 12,000 to 16,500 years B.P., reported from four sections in central Iowa by Ruhe and Scholtes (1956; Ruhe *et al.*, 1957). Evidence that hemlock grew as far west and south as Iowa is surprising, since the present range of the tree is in the eastern part of the Great Lakes region. Furthermore, *Tsuga* pollen is not reported in significant amounts from upper-Wisconsin deposits in the region, and hemlock was considered by Sears (1942b) a postglacial immigrant, together with broadleaved genera. Further evidence that *Tsuga* may have been a widespread component of middle-Wisconsin vegetation near the ice border is furnished by a pollen diagram near Canton in west-central Illinois (Voss, 1939), in which *Tsuga* pollen is prominent. Although Voss considered the Canton deposit to be late Sangamon in age, it is now accepted (Kapp and Gooding, 1964b) as Farmdalian in the classification of Frye and Willman (1960). *Tsuga* pollen, together with *Abies*, *Picea*, and *Larix* pollen, has also been reported by Horr (1955) from undated marsh deposits in northeastern Kansas.

Associated with the *Tsuga* finds are other conifers: *Picea* and *Taxus* wood in Iowa (Ruhe and Scholtes, 1956) and *Larix* wood, *Picea* leaves, and *Picea*, *Abies*, and *Pinus* pollen at the Canton site (Voss, 1939) and at three other sites in

central Illinois (Voss, 1933) that also are now considered Farmdalian. The abundance of pine pollen in the Farmdalian deposits in Illinois contrasts again with its scarcity in late-Wisconsin sediments and suggests that the middle-Wisconsin climate may have been quite different from that during deposition of the late-Wisconsin spruce-dominated pollen zone. Both lack of knowledge of the fossil species and lack of autecological information about possible modern alternatives prohibit more than speculation about the difference, however.

PRE-WISCONSIN

The only interglacial pollen diagram in the Great Lakes region that shows a progression of pollen assemblages from dominance by coniferous to deciduous and back to coniferous trees was presented by Kapp and Gooding (1964b) from a Sangamon soil in southeastern Indiana. Although most of the same taxa are involved, the pollen assemblages only superficially resemble those of late- and post-Wisconsin deposits, and interpretation is therefore even more difficult. Indeed, Kapp and Gooding caution against assuming that interglacial plant associations were comparable to recent associations, for even if the available flora were the same it is doubtful that environmental conditions in Sangamon and postglacial times were identical. Thus although the climatic sequence from cool to warm to cool that they suggest for the Sangamon is probably valid, many detailed studies must be made before understanding of either interglacial phytogeography or environment can advance much further.

CONCLUSIONS

The interpretation of the paleobotanical record, like the interpretation of modern plant distributions, has become more inductive in recent years, and some of the confidence inspired by earlier reconstructions of Quaternary vegetation and environment is fading. The difficulties of inferring vegetation from assemblages of pollen grains are appreciated (Davis, 1963 and this volume), and the data of pollen stratigraphy now tend to be used more for their floristic indications than as indices of vegetation. Further, just as glacier fluctuations cannot be related to climatic change in any simple way (Meier, this volume), neither—since the decline of the climax concept—can observed or inferred changes in vegetation be easily interpreted in terms of climate.

Where present vegetation types are well defined and adequate surface pollen samples are available, as in northwestern Minnesota (McAndrews, 1965), the reconstruction of vegetation from the pollen-stratigraphic record is more confident. But as older and older fossil assemblages are considered, the analogy with the present vegetation becomes strained. Such a situation is explicable in terms of modern ecological concepts. For if the individuality of the plant community (Gleason, 1939) is accepted as a working hypothesis, then the assumption of continuous existence through time of a community type must be doubted. The historical interpretation of the present distribution of species and communities then becomes more difficult, and the complexities of the paleobotanical record acquire new significance. The mixture of floristic elements that characterizes the spruce-dominated pollen assemblage in postglacial sediments from Minnesota to Michigan is less unexpected. It suggests that the concept of an orderly clisere at the close of the Wisconsin glaciation, as depicted for example by Dansereau (1957, p. 114) and Martin (1958), may be in error (Benninghoff, 1957). The vegetation south of the ice border during intervals of glaciation may not have been azonal, as Drury (1956) implies, but there is no assurance that floristic provinces and plant communities earlier in the Quaternary Period resembled in any way those of today.

The modern concept of vegetation as a continuous series of populations not only emphasizes the "loosely ordered complexity" of present plant communities (Whittaker, 1957) but also directs attention to the environmental tolerances of the species that make up the communities. Thus Curtis (1959) recognized the importance of summarizing the autecology of at least the major dominants of the vegetation of Wisconsin. This approach is welcome to paleoecologists who hope to reconstruct Quaternary environments from a fragmentary fossil assemblage, for each extension of knowledge about the life history of a species whose presence in a paleoflora can be demonstrated limits further the possible range of environment at the time and place where the plant occurred. The realization that plants react individually to their environment (which includes other plants) and not in collective units such as communities or floristic elements (Faegri, 1963, p. 221) will hopefully call greater attention to the need for increased knowledge about present ecotypes, their environmental tolerance, and the degree to which they are in equilibrium with their present environment. At the same time it calls for both greater detail and greater number in paleobotanical studies. If the present is poorly understood, how much more so must the past be when its records are inadequately sampled.

REFERENCES

Agassiz, Louis, 1850, Lake Superior; its physical character, vegetation, and animals: Boston, Gould, Kendall, and Lincoln, 428 p.

Andersen, S. T., 1954, A late-glacial pollen diagram from southern Michigan, U.S.A.: Danmarks Geol. Undersøgelse, ser. 2, No. 80, p. 140-155

Baker, R. G., 1965, Late-glacial pollen and plant macrofossils from Spider Creek, southern St. Louis County, Minnesota: Geol. Soc. Amer. Bull., v. 76, in press

Benninghoff, W. S., 1957, Interglacial and late-glacial vegetation of the north-central United States (abst.): Geol. Soc. Amer. Bull., v. 68, p. 1888

Borchert, J. R., 1950, The climate of the central North American grassland: Assoc. Amer. Geogr. Ann., v. 40, p. 1-29

Braun, E. Lucy, 1950, Deciduous forests of eastern North America: Philadelphia, Blakiston, 596 p. (reprinted, 1964: New York, Hafner).

—— 1951, Plant distribution in relation to the glacial boundary: Ohio J. Sci., v. 51, p. 139-146

Butters, F. K., and Abbe, E. C., 1953, A floristic study of Cook County, northeastern Minnesota: Rhodora, v. 55, p. 21-55, 63-101, 116-154, 161-201

Cain, S. A., 1944, Foundations of plant geography: New York, Harper Bros., 556 p.

—— 1947, Characteristics of natural areas and factors in their development: Ecol. Monogr., v. 17, p. 185-200

Cooper, W. S., 1958, Terminology of post-Valders time: Geol. Soc. Amer. Bull., v. 69, p. 941-945

Curtis, J. T., 1959, The vegetation of Wisconsin: Madison, Wis., Univ. of Wisconsin Press, 657 p.

Cushing, E. J., 1963, Late-Wisconsin pollen stratigraphy in east-central Minnesota: Univ. of Minnesota Ph.D. thesis, 165 p. Ann Arbor, Mich., Univ. Microfilms (Dissertation Abst., v. 25, p. 2441)

—— 1964, Redeposited pollen in late-Wisconsin pollen spectra from east-central Minnesota: Amer. J. Sci., v. 262, p. 1075-1088

Dansereau, Pierre, 1957, Biogeography, an ecological perspective: New York, Ronald Press, 394 p.

Davis, Margaret B., 1963, On the theory of pollen analysis: Amer. J. Sci., v. 261, p. 897-912

—— this volume, Phytogeography and palynology of northeastern United States

Deevey, E. S., Jr., 1949, Biogeography of the Pleistocene: Geol. Soc. Amer. Bull., v. 60, p. 1315-1416

Deevey, E. S., Jr., and Flint, R. F., 1957, Postglacial hypsithermal interval: Science, v. 125, p. 182-184

Deevey, E. S., Jr., Gross, M. S., Hutchinson, G. E., and Kraybill, H. L., 1954, The natural C^{14} contents of materials from hard-water lakes: Natl. Acad. Sci. Proc., v. 40, No. 5, p. 285-288

Drury, W. H., Jr., 1956, Bog flats and physiographic processes in the Upper Kuskokwim River region, Alaska: Harvard Univ., Gray Herb. Contr., No. 178, 130 p.

Engelhardt, D. W., 1960, A comparative pollen study of two early Wisconsin bogs in Indiana: Indiana Acad. Sci. Proc., v. 69, p. 110-118

Faegri, Knut, 1963, Problems of immigration and dispersal of the Scandinavian flora, *in* Löve, Askell, and Löve, Doris (eds.), North Atlantic biota and their history: New York, Macmillan, p. 221-237

Fassett, N. C., 1931, Notes from the herbarium of the University of Wisconsin, vii: Rhodora, v. 33, p. 224-228

—— 1943, Another Driftless Area endemic: Torrey Bot. Club Bull., v. 70, p. 398-399

Fernald, M. L., 1925, Persistence of plants in unglaciated areas of boreal America: Amer. Acad. Arts Sci. Mem., v. 15, p. 237-342

—— 1935, Critical plants of the upper Great Lakes region of Ontario and Michigan: Rhodora, v. 37, p. 197-222, 238-262, 272-301, 324-341

—— 1942, Misinterpretation of Atlantic coastal plain species: Rhodora, v. 44, p. 238-246

—— 1950, Gray's manual of botany: New York, American Book Co., 8th ed., 1632 p.

Flint, R. F., *et al.*, 1959, Glacial map of the United States east of the Rocky Mountains (scale 1:750,000): Geol. Soc. Amer.

Forman, R. T. T., 1964, Growth under controlled conditions to explain the hierarchical distributions of a moss, *Tetraphis pellucida:* Ecol. Monogr., v. 34, p. 1-25

Fox, W. S., and Soper, J. H., 1954, The distribution of some trees and shrubs of the Carolinian zone of southern Ontario: Roy. Can. Inst. Trans., v. 30, pt. 2, No. 63, p. 99-130

Frey, D. G., 1959, The Two Creeks interval in Indiana pollen diagrams: Inv. Indiana Lakes and Streams, v. 5, p. 131-139

Fries, Magnus, 1962, Pollen profiles of late Pleistocene and Recent sediments from Weber Lake, Minnesota: Ecology, v. 43, p. 295-308

Fries, Magnus, Wright, H. E., Jr., and Rubin, Meyer, 1961, A late Wisconsin buried peat at North Branch, Minnesota: Amer. J. Sci., v. 259, p. 679-693

Frye, J. C., and Willman, H. B., 1960, Classification of the Wisconsinan Stage in the Lake Michigan glacial lobe: Illinois State Geol. Survey Circ. 285, 16 p.

Frye, J. C., Willman, H. B., and Black, R. F., this volume, Outline of glacial geology of Illinois and Wisconsin

Gleason, H. A., 1922, The vegetational history of the Middle West: Assoc. Amer. Geogr. Ann., v. 12, p. 39-85

—— 1939, The individualistic concept of the plant association: Amer. Midl. Nat., v. 21, p. 92-108

Gleason, H. A., and Cronquist, Arthur, 1964, The natural geography of plants: New York, Columbia Univ. Press, 420 p.

Hartz, N., 1912, Allerød-Gytje und Allerød-Mull: Dansk Geol. Foren. Medd., v. 4, p. 85-92

Horr, W. H., 1955, A pollen profile study of the Muscotah Marsh: Univ. Kansas Sci. Bull., v. 37, pt. 1, No. 4, p. 143-149

Jelgersma, Saskia, 1962, A late-glacial pollen diagram from Madelia, south-central Minnesota: Amer. J. Sci., v. 260, p. 522-529

Just, Theodor, 1959, Postglacial vegetation of the north-central United States; a review: J. Geol., v. 67, p. 228-238

Kapp, R. O., and Gooding, A. M., 1964a, A radiocarbon-dated pollen profile from Sunbeam Prairie Bog, Darke County, Ohio: Amer. J. Sci., v. 262, p. 259-266

—— 1964b, Pleistocene vegetational studies in the White-water basin, southeastern Indiana: J. Geol., v. 72, p. 307-326

Küchler, A. W., 1964, Potential natural vegetation of the conterminous United States (map, scale 1:3,168,000): Amer. Geogr. Soc. Spec. Publ. 36

Martin, P. S., 1958, Pleistocene ecology and biogeography of North America, *in* Hubbs, C. L. (ed.), Zoogeography: New York, Amer. Assoc. Adv. Sci., p. 375-420

Maycock, P. F., and Curtis, J. T., 1960, The phytosociology of boreal conifer-hardwood forests of the Great Lakes region: Ecol. Monogr., v. 30, p. 1-35

McAndrews, J. H., 1963, Postglacial vegetation history of the prairie-forest transition of northwestern Minnesota: Univ. of Minnesota Ph.D. thesis, 112 p. Ann Arbor, Mich., Univ. Microfilms

—— 1965, Postglacial history of prairie, savanna, and for-est in northwestern Minnesota: Harvard Univ., Arnold Arbor. J., in press

McLaughlin, W. T., 1932, Atlantic coastal plain plants in the sand barrens of northwestern Wisconsin: Ecol. Monogr., v. 2, p. 335-383

Meier, M. F., this volume, Glaciers and climate

Moss, E. H., and Pegg, George, 1963, Noteworthy plant species and communities in westcentral Alberta: Can. J. Bot., v. 41, p. 1079-1105

Nichols, G. E., 1935, The hemlock–white pine–northern hardwood region of eastern North America: Ecology, v. 16, p. 403-422

Ogden, J. G., III, 1965, Pleistocene pollen records from eastern North America: Bot. Rev., v. 31, in press

Peattie, D. C., 1922, The Atlantic coastal plain element in the flora of the Great Lakes: Rhodora, v. 24, p. 57-70, 80-88

Perring, F. H., 1963, Data-processing for the Atlas of the British Flora: Taxon, v. 12, No. 5, p. 183-190

Potzger, J. E., 1946, Phytosociology of the primeval forest in central-northern Wisconsin and upper Michigan, and a brief post-glacial history of the Lake Forest formation: Ecol. Monogr., v. 16, p. 211-250

—— 1948, A pollen study in the tension zone of lower Michigan: Butler Univ. Bot. Stud., v. 8, p. 161-177

Raup, H. M., 1947, Some natural floristic areas in boreal America: Ecol. Monogr., v. 17, p. 221-234

Ritchie, J. C., 1964, Contributions to the Holocene paleo-ecology of westcentral Canada. I, The Riding Mountain area: Can. J. Bot., v. 42, p. 181-196

Ritchie, J. C., and deVries, Bernard, 1964, Contributions to the Holocene paleoecology of westcentral Canada; a late-glacial deposit from the Missouri Coteau: Can. J. Bot., v. 42, p. 677-692

Rosendahl, C. O., 1947, Studies in *Chrysosplenium*, with special reference to the taxonomic status and distribution of *C. iowense:* Rhodora, v. 49, p. 25-36

Rosendahl, C. O., and Moore, J. W., 1947, A new variety of *Sedum rosea* from southeastern Minnesota and additional notes on the flora of the region: Rhodora, v. 49, p. 197-202

Rowe, J. S., 1959, Forest regions of Canada: Canada Dept. Northern Affairs and Natl. Resources, Forestry Branch, Bull. 123, 71 p.

Ruhe, R. V., Rubin, Meyer, and Scholtes, W. H., 1957, Late Pleistocene radiocarbon chronology in Iowa: Amer. J. Sci., v. 255, p. 671-689

Ruhe, R. V., and Scholtes, W. H., 1956, Ages and development of soil landscapes in relation to climatic and vegetational changes in Iowa: Soil Sci. Soc. Amer. Proc., v. 20, No. 2, p. 264-273

Schuster, R. M., 1958, Boreal Hepaticae, a manual of the liverworts of Minnesota and adjacent regions. III, Phytogeography: Amer. Midl. Nat., v. 59, No. 2, p. 257-332

Sears, P. B., 1942a, Xerothermic theory: Bot. Rev., v. 8, p. 708-736

—— 1942b, Postglacial migration of five forest genera: Amer. J. Bot., v. 29, p. 684-691

—— 1948, Forest sequence and climatic change in northeastern North America since early Wisconsin time: Ecology, v. 29, p. 326-333

Smith, P. W., 1957, An analysis of post-Wisconsin biogeography of the Prairie Peninsula region based on distributional phenomena among terrestrial vertebrate populations: Ecology, v. 38, p. 205-218

Smith, Preston, 1940, Correlations of pollen profiles from glaciated eastern North America: Amer. J. Sci., v. 238, p. 597-601

Soper, J. H., 1955, Some families of restricted range in the Carolinian flora of Canada: Roy. Can. Inst. Trans., v. 31, No. 1, p. 69-90

—— 1964, Mapping the distribution of plants by machine: Can. J. Bot., v. 42, p. 1087-1100

Soper, J. H., and Maycock, P. F., 1963, A community of arctic-alpine plants on the east shore of Lake Superior: Can. J. Bot., v. 41, p. 183-198

Steere, W. C., this volume, The boreal bryophyte flora as affected by Quaternary glaciation

Transeau, E. N., 1935, The Prairie Peninsula: Ecology, v. 16, p. 423-437

Voss, John, 1933, Pleistocene forests of central Illinois: Bot. Gaz., v. 94, p. 808-814

—— 1939, Forests of the Yarmouth and Sangamon interglacial periods in Illinois: Ecology, v. 20, p. 517-528

Watts, W. A., and Winter, T. C., 1965, Plant macrofossils from Kirchner Marsh, Minnesota—a paleoecological study: Geol. Soc. Amer. Bull., v. 76, in press

Watts, W. A., and Wright, H. E., Jr., Late-Wisconsin pollen and seed analysis from the Nebraska sandhills: unpublished manuscript

Weaver, J. E., and Clements, F. E., 1929, Plant ecology: New York, McGraw-Hill, 520 p.

West, R. G., 1961, Late- and postglacial vegetational history in Wisconsin, particularly changes associated with the Valders readvance: Amer. J. Sci., v. 259, p. 766-783

Whittaker, R. H., 1957, Recent evolution of ecological concepts in relation to the eastern forests of North America: Amer. J. Bot., v. 44, p. 197-206

Wright, H. E., Jr., 1964a, Aspects of the early postglacial forest succession in the Great Lakes region: Ecology, v. 45, p. 439-448

—— 1964b, The classification of the Wisconsin glacial stage: J. Geol., v. 72, p. 628-637

Wright, H. E., Jr., and Ruhe, R. V., this volume, Glaciation of Minnesota and Iowa

Wright, H. E., Jr., Winter, T. C., and Patten, H. L., 1963, Two pollen diagrams from southeastern Minnesota; problems in the regional late-glacial and postglacial vegetational history: Geol. Soc. Amer. Bull., v. 74, p. 1371-1396

Wynne-Edwards, V. C., 1939, Some factors in the isolation of rare alpine plants: Roy. Soc. Can. Trans., ser. 3, v. 33, sec. 5, p. 35-42

SUMMARY

Modern ecological concepts stress the reaction of the individual plant, rather than a floristic group or vegetation association, to its environment. Application of this approach to present flora and vegetation and the paleobotanical record in the Great Lakes region makes new interpretations possible. Where they have been objectively mapped, boundaries between floristic provinces in the Great Lakes region appear to be related to environmental— chiefly climatic—gradients, and they suggest that an equilibrium is approached between environment and plant distribution. Floristic elements, such as the coastal-plain element in the Great Lakes region, cannot be assumed to have historical as well as present geographical unity. A disjunct distribution does not necessarily imply that a species once had a more continuous range; whether the disjuncts of the Driftless Area of southwestern Wisconsin are preglacial relicts may be doubted on botanical as well as geological grounds.

In favorable areas, such as northwestern Minnesota, interpretation of pollen assemblages as old as 9,000 years may be successfully based on comparison with modern vegetation. Fossil assemblages from older deposits, however, may have no modern analogues. The spruce-dominated pollen assemblage that marks the lowest late-Wisconsin pollen zone over much of the region is puzzling for its mixture of modern floristic elements; like middle-Wisconsin and interglacial assemblages, it suggests that during much of the Quaternary neither floristic provinces nor plant communities were similar to those of today. For this reason, and because the autecology of the species involved is imperfectly known, reconstruction of climate and environment is largely speculative, even when the stratigraphy of the assemblages is well understood. Geographical variation in the composition of age-equivalent pollen and macrofossil assemblages, illustrated by the contrast between late-Wisconsin assemblages in northeastern and southern Minnesota, can define past floristic boundaries whose relationship to past environmental gradients can hopefully be discovered.

PALYNOLOGY AND PLEISTOCENE PHYTOGEOGRAPHY
OF UNGLACIATED EASTERN NORTH AMERICA*

DONALD R. WHITEHEAD[1]

COMPARATIVELY LITTLE is known concerning Pleistocene vegetational and climatic changes in unglaciated eastern North America. Understandably, most work has been concentrated in the glaciated region. To date we have available sketchy knowledge of postglacial forest development (or, more correctly, of postglacial pollen succession) from scattered localities south of the drift border. Conditions prevailing earlier are less well understood. This is occasioned by the scarcity of basins containing sediments of sufficient age and by problems of dating and correlation associated with those deposits that do antedate the postglacial.

The incompleteness and equivocal nature of the data have helped engender one of the most stimulating controversies in the North American Pleistocene literature—that concerning full-glacial conditions in the region south of the ice margin. Concepts are diverse, ranging from those of Braun (1955), who envisioned essentially no changes except within a few kilometers of the ice margin, to those of Deevey (1949), who suggested that there were migrations of boreal species into Mexico and southern Florida, and Martin (1958a), who indicated that the southern margin of the boreal forest may have been as far south as northern South Carolina (a displacement of over 1,200 km).

The present paper will review the status of this controversy in the light of new evidence and will comment on postglacial and pre-Wisconsin conditions in the unglaciated East as well. The area under consideration (Fig. 1) lies south of the ice margin and east of the 100th meridian. There will be an evident bias in favor of the Southeast, partly because a number of recent studies have been carried out in that region, but also because my own interests lie there. Because much earlier work has been well discussed by Deevey (1949), Braun (1955), Dillon (1956), and Martin (1958a), no attempt will be made to present a comprehensive review.

PHYSIOGRAPHY AND VEGETATION OF THE UNGLACIATED EAST

Before discussing problems of Pleistocene history, the physiography and present vegetation of the region will be outlined briefly. This should permit more meaningful comparisons with past floras.

* The writer wishes to acknowledge the invaluable contributions made by Dr. Johannes Iversen and Dr. Svend Th. Andersen, whose thoughtful discussions were instrumental in orienting much of the early work on the manuscript. The author is especially grateful to W. A. Watts for making available much unpublished information. Support for the project was provided by National Science Foundation Grant G-17277.
[1] Department of Biology, Williams College, Williamstown, Massachusetts.

The region in question can be subdivided into physiographic provinces (Fig. 2) on the basis of topography and subsurface geology (Fenneman, 1938). As one would expect, there is a parallelism between vegetational types and physiographic provinces (Fig. 3). Of greatest significance for the present discussion is the presence of the Appalachian Mountain complex, which extends from within the glaciated region southwestward for over 1,000 km. The highest peaks in the East (over 2,000 m) occur in North Carolina and Tennessee near the southern terminus of this range. The orientation of the chain (basically north-south) creates a situation in marked contrast to that existing in Europe—i.e., the migrational barrier posed by the alps is nonexistent in North America. Evidence of local glaciation within this mountain complex is sketchy. Apparently there were no major alpine glaciers. However, the presence of block fields at high elevations along much of the chain argues for the existence of an intense frost climate at some time in the past, conceivably severe enough for the development of tundra vegetation, perhaps as far south as the Great Smoky Mountains of North Carolina and Tennessee.

East of the Appalachian complex lie the Piedmont Plateau and the Coastal Plain. The former is an area of rolling, well-dissected topography underlain by deeply weathered metamorphic and igneous rocks. The Coastal Plain is a flat-lying region consisting of generally unconsolidated sediments of Mesozoic and Tertiary age. Many of the formations are marine. Characteristic of the coastward border of the Coastal Plain is a series of terrace plains and scarps, apparently related to higher stands of the sea during interglacial times.

West of the mountains is a series of plateau complexes that grade into the vast interior lowlands.

The major vegetational regions (after Braun, 1950) are outlined in Figure 3. The correlation with physiographic provinces is obvious. Of interest to the present discussion are southern extensions of the more "northern" forest types along the Appalachian Mountain complex. This is indicated in a most general way on the map. The boreal forest, dominated by spruce and fir, occurs in a number of mountainous regions from New England and New York southward to North Carolina and Tennessee. In the Great Smoky Mountains it occurs at high elevations (generally above 1,500 m). Similarly, a correlative of the hemlock–white pine–northern hardwoods forest—a complex rich in birch (*Betula lutea, B. papyrifera*), sugar maple (*Acer saccharum*), beech (*Fagus grandifolia*), hemlock (*Tsuga canadensis*), basswood (*Tilia americana*), and occasional pine and spruce is found at intermediate elevations even at the southern terminus of the Blue Ridge complex. Hemlock and beech are particularly abundant in a mixed mesophytic community in the moister, shaded habitats provided by ravines.

The most characteristic vegetational type of the mountainous region as a whole (and of southern New England) is the oak-chestnut forest, a type rich in oaks (many species), formerly the American chestnut (*Castanea dentata*), and numerous other deciduous trees (including *Liriodendron, Fagus, Tilia, Betula, Aesculus,* and *Acer*). As one would expect, there are innumerable local variations within this general forest type, some areas contain species of the northern hardwoods type, others representatives of the rich mixed-mesophytic forests, and still other species of the oak-pine forests of the Piedmont.

East of the mountains and largely coinciding with the Piedmont lies the oak-pine forest region. The dominant trees of this association are oaks and hickories (numerous

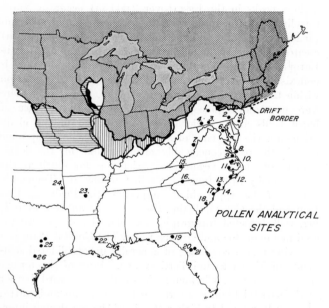

Figure 1. Pollen-analytical sites in the unglaciated east. Drift sheets based on Flint *et al.,* 1945; Cross-hatched = Wisconsin drift; vertical lines = Illinoian; horizontal lines = Kansan; black = Nebraskan. Sites: (1) Bear Meadows, Pa., Sears, 1935; (2) Marsh, Pa., Martin, 1958b; (3) New Paris, Pa., Guilday *et al.,* 1964; (4) Glade Run Bog, Pa., Schrock, 1945; (5) Pine Barrens, N.J., Potzger, 1945; (6) Washington, D.C., Knox, 1962; (7) Cranberry Glades, W.Va., Darlington, 1943; (8) Chesapeake Bay borings, Harrison *et al.,* 1964; (9) Dismal Swamp, Va., Lewis and Cocke, 1929; Cocke *et al.,* 1934, Whitehead, unpubl.; (10) Rockyhock Bay, Dismal Swamp, N.C., Whitehead, 1963; Vick, 1961; (11) Shepard Pond, N.C., Vick, 1961; (12) Flanner's Beach, N.C., J. T. Davis, 1963; (13) Carolina Bays, N.C., Buell, 1945; Frey, 1951, 1953, 1955; Whitehead, 1963, 1964; (14) Boggy Lake, N.C., Vick, 1961; (15) Shady Valley Bog, Tenn., Barclay, 1957; (16) "Buried soils," S.C. and N.C., Cain, 1944; Whitehead and Barghoorn, 1962; (17) Myrtle Beach, S.C., Frey, 1952; (18) Ladson Formation, S.C., Leopold, 1959; (19) and (20), Florida borings, J. Davis, 1946; (21) Mud Lake, Fla., Watts, 1965; (22) Louisiana fluvial deposits, Brown, 1938; (23) Arkansas site, Sears, 1935; Sears and Couch, 1932; (24) Oklahoma site, Sears, 1935; (25) Texas bog, Potzger and Tharp, 1943, 1947, 1954; (26) Texas bog, Graham and Heimsch, 1962.

species of both). Pines are abundant, especially on poorer soils.

Most of the Coastal Plain is occupied by the southeastern evergreen forest, a type characterized by nondeciduous species, both conifers and dicotyledons. Pines are abundant over much of the area, particularly on the extensive areas of sandy soil. On moister, often peaty soils a variety of evergreen shrubs and trees occur. These include *Magnolia, Gordonia, Persea,* and several members of the Ericaceae. Cypress (*Taxodium*) and *Chamaecyparis* are often common. A number of bottomland communities include elm, gum (*Nyssa*), and sweet gum (*Liquidambar*). Oaks and hickories are locally abundant on both drier soils and bottomlands.

West of the mountains lie the mesophytic forests. The mixed-mesophytic forest of the Appalachian Plateau is extraordinarily rich in species (*Fagus, Liriodendron, Tilia, Acer, Aesculus, Castanea, Tsuga, Quercus,* and others), and dominance is generally shared among a number of them. The western mesophytic forest represents a transition between the rich mixed-mesophytic forest region and the oak-hickory region to the west.

West of the mesophytic forests (and just east of the prairies) lies the oak-hickory forest region, a forest extremely similar in structure and general characteristics to the oak-pine forest of the Piedmont. The dominance of oak and hickory reflects the clinal decrease in moisture as one moves westward from the Appalachian Mountains.

The beech-maple forest, lying between the northern harwoods forest region and the mesophytic forests, is dominated by beech and sugar maple. For the purpose of this paper it can best be considered as a more southerly variant of the northern hardwoods forest region. The maple-basswood forest region to the west, positioned between oak-hickory and northern hardwoods forest, can be considered in a similar way.

The preponderance of basically subtropical and tropical species in southern Florida necessitates the delimitation of that area as a separate floristic region.

The prairies lie west of deciduous forests and occupy vast regions of interior North America.

It is important to emphasize that these vegetational zones are arbitrary constructions—nowhere is it possible to draw a sharp line between forest types. In fact, no two phytogeographers will agree as to which types should be recognized (see, for example, Shelford, 1963). The choice of Braun's forest types for this discussion was strictly arbitrary.

FULL-GLACIAL CONDITIONS IN THE SOUTHEAST

In the previous reviews bearing upon the subject an impressive body of biogeographical, paleontological, geological, and geochemical evidence has been assembled, and yet widely divergent views have evolved. There is general agreement among Deevey (1949), Dillon (1956), and Martin (1958a) as to the magnitude of the changes attending periods of maximum glaciation, but the concepts of Braun (1955) stand in marked contrast.

Much has been made of the occurrence of remains, both pollen and macrofossil, of boreal species in scattered localities south of the drift border. This evidence has been termed "impeccable" by Martin (1958a), and it has been taken as an indication of a major displacement of the boreal forest during Wisconsin time. While agreeing in general with Martin, I should question the "impeccability" of much of the earlier evidence.

A major southward displacement of many boreal species and profound climatic changes can no longer be disputed. The paleotemperature evidence presented by Emiliani (1955) further supports this idea. Biotic displacement is indicated by the work of Buell (1945), Frey (1951, 1952, 1953, 1955), and Whitehead (1963, 1964) in eastern North Carolina and South Carolina, Whitehead and Barghoorn (1962) in western North Carolina and South Carolina, Terasmae (*in* Harrison *et al.*, 1964) and Whitehead (unpubl.) in eastern Virginia, and Graham and Heimsch (1960) in Texas. However, whether this evidence can be taken to support the idea of a zonal displacement of boreal forest and deciduous forest formations is open to question.

Among the most significant early reports of boreal species are those of Davis (1946) from Florida, Brown (1938) from Louisiana, and Potzger and Tharp (1943, 1947, 1954) from Texas. Davis reported the presence of spruce and fir pollen in sediments of undoubted Pleistocene age in northern Florida. However, no quantitative study was made, the overall composition of the pollen flora was not discussed, and the stratigraphy of the sections was not elucidated. It is thus extremely difficult to evaluate the significance of this report. This uncertainty is accentuated by the current studies of Watts (1965) on Mud Lake, Marion County, Florida. Watts has analyzed over 9 m of sediment within which rather profound changes in pollen percentages take place. Radiocarbon dates of 5,070 ± 150 (I-1477) (240 cm) and >34,500 (I-1478) (660 cm) are available, yet no grains of spruce, fir, hemlock, or other boreal species have been recovered. However, there is a suggestion of a depositional break at the 490-cm level, hence the full-glacial horizons may be missing.

Brown (1938) identified macrofossil remains of a number of boreal species from fluvial sediments in Louisiana. The remains include cones of *Picea glauca* (plus wood, needles, and seeds of spruce), wood of larch (*Larix laricina*), and branchlets of white cedar (*Thuja occidentalis*). Associated with these boreal species was a substantial number of other species, the majority of which are now found in the Southeast today. Several northern species of moss have also been identified (Steere, 1938). An interpretation is extremely difficult, since it is not yet possible to date the horizons exactly, and since some of the material may have been transported for some distance. Furthermore, the spruce cones, measuring 60-86 mm in length and 15-16 mm in width, pose some interesting questions. To the best of the writer's knowledge, white spruce cones only rarely exceed 60 mm in length. There is no question that spruce occurred in the sediments, but whether the remains represent white spruce is perhaps questionable. If water transport can be ruled out we are left with evidence indicating the existence of several boreal forest species within a "southern" deciduous forest. If the deposits date from full-glacial time, then we have evidence of a forest rather similar to that existing

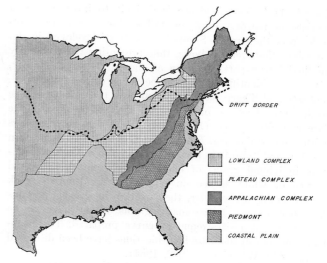

Figure 2. Generalized physiographic provinces in eastern North America. After Fenneman (1938).

today except for a few northern infiltrators. If, however, the sediments date from a late-glacial sequence (not the most recent, however) or another more temperate period, then we have only minimum indications of the magnitude of changes that took place during the glacial maxima.

Another highly significant report of boreal species comes from several bogs in Texas (Potzger and Tharp, 1943, 1947, 1954). In the lower levels of two bogs (Patschke Bog, Lee County; Gause Bog, Milam County), Potzger and Tharp have reported the presence of pollen of *Abies*, *Picea glauca*, and *Picea mariana*. The maximum for the spruce-fir com-

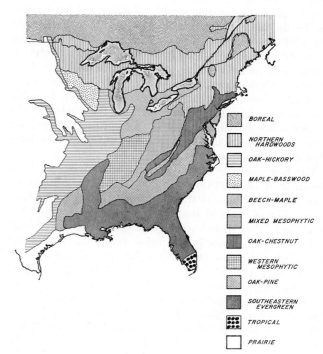

Figure 3. Forest regions, eastern North America. After Braun (1950).

plex is 11%. This evidence is difficult to interpret for a variety of reasons. First, no radiocarbon dates are available from the profile. Secondly, the bogs developed in depressions that were ox-bows, thus presenting the possibility of fluvial transport of pollen at the basal levels. Thirdly, the specific identification of spruce pollen can be questioned. Potzger and Tharp have indicated that the smaller spruce grains are those of black spruce (*P. mariana*) and the larger, white spruce (*P. glauca*). However, other species with large grains, *e.g. Picea rubens*, or any of the western species, could also be represented. It is also difficult to separate individual grains of black spruce from those of red spruce or white spruce on a size basis. Although black spruce grains are smaller, they overlap in size with grains of other species, hence many grains would have to be measured and a size-frequency curve prepared. The problems inherent in such size identifications have been discussed for pine by Whitehead (1962, 1964).

A recent restudy of the deeper levels from the Gause Bog (Graham and Heimsch, 1960) has raised further questions concerning the work of Potzger and Tharp. Using precisely the same samples that were utilized by Potzger and Tharp, Graham and Heimsch obtained rather different results. They encountered no fir pollen at all, and their spruce percentages were decidedly lower (maximum 3%). Moreover, they encountered spruce pollen only at the 13.7-ft level, even though several recounts were made.

Potzger and Tharp had reported a sharp rise in *Castanea* percentages from about 5% at the base of the Gause profile to 20% between 11 and 13 ft, but Graham and Heimsch reported that *Castanea* pollen was completely absent from their Gause samples. Such discrepancies are difficult to reconcile. Whether they are a function of previous misidentifications or the rather primitive and inefficient methods of sample preparation used by Potzger and Tharp cannot be decided. At any rate, it is necessary to re-evaluate the evidence for boreal elements in Texas. Spruce pollen is clearly present, but the percentages are low. By extrapolation from another profile from which dates have been obtained, Graham and Heimsch suggest that the 13.7-ft level dates from about 12,500 years ago. If this is valid, then we have no information concerning the conditions obtaining in full-glacial time, merely an indication that at least some boreal individuals (spruce) had survived into lateglacial time in Texas.

The best evidence of full-glacial conditions comes from the work of Buell (1945) and Frey (1951, 1953, 1955) on Carolina Bay sediments from southeastern North Carolina. In a series of detailed studies Frey has demonstrated beyond doubt that there have been profound changes of both vegetation and climate in the region during late-Pleistocene time. Although many problems of interpretation remain, it is evident that Frey's work has rendered Braun's concepts of full-glacial vegetation untenable. The work is doubly convincing, since similar trends have been demonstrated from a number of different lakes in the same region.

The evidence is as follows. In most of the basins a similar series of alternating organic and inorganic zones can be identified. The uppermost organic horizon, generally the thickest, apparently dates almost entirely from the post-

glacial. A date of 10,224 ± 510 years (C-474) has been obtained from the base of this zone. Beneath this lies a relatively inorganic lake silt that is in turn underlain by a peaty organic horizon from which a date of >38,000 years (W-197) has been obtained. The latter horizon, referred to as the "middle organic horizon," is generally underlain by another inorganic silt zone. From at least one coring station there is evidence of yet another organic zone beneath the lowest inorganic member. The changes in sediment type suggest climatic changes. This is borne out by the pollen diagrams (Fig. 4).

Figure 4 is a generalized pollen diagram prepared by Frey on the basis of a number of individual profiles in southeastern North Carolina. The uppermost pollen zone (Zone C), which coincides largely with the upper organic horizon, is from the postglacial. However, it is interesting to note the maxima of beech and hemlock pollen at the base of the zone, suggesting the existence of a forest type adapted to cooler, more mesic conditions in early postglacial or lateglacial time.

The upper silt horizon, bracketed by C^{14} dates of 10,224 and >38,000, apparently contains sediments that date from Wisconsin time. The pollen zone coinciding with this horizon (M-Zone) is characterized by a pronounced maximum of pine pollen, the occurrence of spruce pollen (maximum 7-9%), marked minima in the curves for all other elements, an extraordinary maximum of *Isoëtes* microspores, and abundant remains of dinoflagellates (mostly *Peridinium limbatum*). The size-frequency curves for pine pollen (Frey, 1951) suggest the presence of a species possessing small pollen grains, possibly the jack pine, *Pinus banksiana*.

At the base of the M-Zone, close to the transition to the middle organic horizon, pine percentages fall sharply, and the curves for birch, oak, and many other deciduous tree species begin to rise. This marks the transition from Zone M to Zone N. The latter zone presumably reflects warmer climate during either an interstadial or an interglacial.

The meaning of the M-Zone is difficult to ascertain, largely because the only boreal element identified with certainty is *Picea*. The small pine grains could be either those of jack pine or red pine (*Pinus resinosa*) (Whitehead, 1962, 1964). The latter species is a "boreal" one, but is distributed somewhat farther south than jack pine. The absence of deciduous-tree pollen may be more apparent than real, possibly a function of pine over-representation, as indicated by the fact that all the curves decline as pine increases (with the exception of *Isoëtes*).

More recent studies of the M-Zone sediments from Singletary Lake (Whitehead, 1963, 1964) have demonstrated the presence of a number of "northern" elements during M-Zone time. These include *Lycopodium annotinum*, *Lycopodium lucidulum*, *Abies*, *Schizaea pusilla*, and *Sanguisorba canadensis*. Hence there can be little doubt of cooler conditions in southeastern North Carolina at that time.

There are other data (Whitehead, 1964) from which one can infer the structure of the vegetation in the area surrounding Singletary Lake (and conceivably in the region as a whole). The curves for *Artemisia*, *Ambrosia*, *Corylus*, and Compositae parallel those for *Pinus* and *Picea*, and

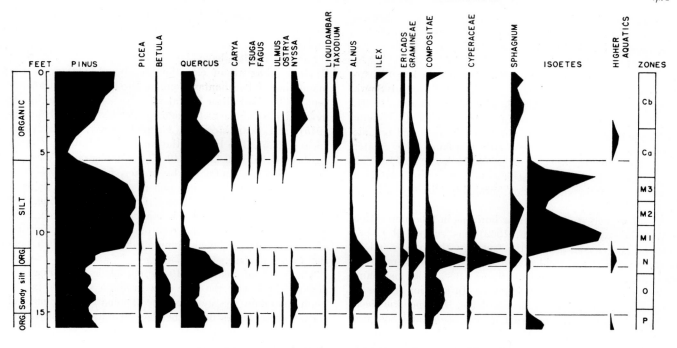

GENERALIZED POLLEN DIAGRAM FOR BLADEN COUNTY, N.C.

Figure 4. Generalized pollen diagram for Bladen County, North Carolina. After Frey (1953).

pollen of other heliophytes such as *Polygonella, Plantago,* Caryophyllaceae (*Arenaria*-type, *Cerastium-Stellaria* type), and Chenopodiaceae occur in the M-Zone. *Polygonella* in particular is a good indicator of areas of uncolonized open sand. It thus seems probable that the coarse sands of the area supported an open vegetation during Wisconsin time, a community dominated by widely spaced pines with heliophytic herbs and shrubs as associates. Because much of the region is underlain by coarse sand, this community may have been widely distributed. Spruce and other more mesic boreal elements may have grown along the shores of the lakes or on the poorly drained inter-bay areas. There is a strong possibility that a number of "austral" elements were present in the area as well, since occasional grains of *Taxodium, Liriodendron,* and *Platanus* were encountered, as well as numbers of *Quercus* and *Carya* grains.

Whether or not one can consider the full-glacial vegetation of the Singletary Lake region to have been boreal forest (as we now know it) is obviously questionable. Hopefully studies presently in progress, involving absolute pollen frequency counts, will shed further light on the meaning of the pine maximum and the apparent absence of other pollen types.

Wells and Boyce have criticized the work of Frey, since they feel that he has not considered the effect that recurrent fires would have on the integrity of a given peat profile and the possible consequences of periodic expansion of bay area through erosion of marginal peat (Wells and Boyce, 1953; Frey, 1954). Such erosion would lead to the redeposition of pollen in limnic sediments forming at that time. However, it is evident from the sediments and the microfossils contained in them that most of the basins have

been lakes for a considerable period of their history and most certainly during full-glacial time. The effect of a fire on lake sediment would be, to say the least, minimal. Furthermore, it is possible that the bays may not have had any marginal peat mat at all. This is suggested by the type of sediment and remains of aquatic plants found in them. It would appear that the lakes were quite clear during Wisconsin time (Whitehead, 1964), not deeply stained by humic materials leaching from the peaty margins as at present. If this is valid, then there would be few problems of redeposition to contend with. The clear trends in Frey's diagrams and the parallelism from lake to lake offer further proof that the changes are real ones reflecting regional vegetational and climatic fluctuations.

The Carolina Bays, which are distributed on the Coastal Plain from southeastern Virginia to northern Florida and contain sediments of appreciable age, present extremely fertile ground for studies of full-glacial conditions in the Southeast. A comprehensive latitudinal transect should provide much information on the zonal character of the biotic displacements.

Frey (1952) has also made an analysis of two undated peat horizons exposed close to sea level at Myrtle Beach, South Carolina. Although the stratigraphic position of the peats is uncertain, the deposits are of great significance because of the presence of spruce pollen. The percentage is particularly high in the "upper peat" (42%), suggesting the abundant presence of spruce, at least locally, in northeastern South Carolina. Tree types also represented include pine (37%), oak (15%), hickory (1.5%), and birch (1.5%). In addition there are high percentages of grass, composite, chenopod, sedge, caryophyll, and water-lily pollen. The association of pollen of a number of relatively thermophilous trees with that of spruce makes it more difficult to think in terms of boreal forest. However, there is as yet no proof that the horizons are full-glacial.

Boreal elements have also been identified in late-Pleistocene sediments from western North Carolina and South Carolina (Cain, 1944; Whitehead and Barghoorn, 1962). Cain reported the presence of spruce pollen (maximum 12%) and fir pollen (maximum 17%) from buried organic horizons near Spartanburg, South Carolina. The greater abundance of the boreal elements in the lower half of each section suggested that the sediments accumulated during a time of climatic amelioration, probably directly after a glaciation.

A subsequent study of similar horizons in the same region (Whitehead and Barghoorn, 1962) has supported Cain's general contention, despite the fact that the spruce and fir percentages were decidedly lower than those reported previously. The maximum for fir was 0.8%, the maximum for spruce 9% (generally below 4%). In addition, grains of *Sanguisorba canadensis, Arceuthobium, Lycopodium lucidulum, L. Selago, L. obscurum, L. clavatum,* and *Schizaea pusilla* were identified. All of these can be considered "northern" elements. Some of them do reach the latitude of the Carolinas, but generally only at higher elevations in the Appalachian Mountains. In addition, single grains of *Ephedra* were identified from each of three sections. It was originally suggested that *Ephedra* could have grown along the drainage divides with other heliophytes in relatively open pine forests. However, recent work by Maher (1964) has suggested that most, if not all, of the *Ephedra* grains found in late-glacial and postglacial sediments in the East have been wind-transported from the Southwest. The trends in the various profiles suggest that the sediments did accumulate during a time of warming climate, as Cain had indicated earlier. However, the radiocarbon dates available (>35,000) from several horizons demonstrate that the period of amelioration was not the present postglacial, but probably one succeeding an earlier glaciation, conceivably an early Wisconsin advance. The correlation of the horizons with the known Pleistocene chronology is still obscure, but indications are that the horizons represent interstadials, perhaps correlating with the Brørup (*ca.* 56,000 before the present) or Amersfoort (*ca.* 64,000 B.P.) of northwestern Europe (Andersen *et al.,* 1960) and the Port Talbot (48,000 B.P.) or St. Pierre (65,000 B.P.) of North America (Dreimanis, 1960). Once again, we have evidence of boreal elements in the Southeast, but apparently not from a full-glacial horizon. Also, it must be remembered that these horizons lie relatively close to the present spruce-fir forests of the Blue Ridge.

Other deposits from within the mountainous region have provided evidence of the lowering of vegetational zones in early postglacial or late-glacial time and have engendered further speculation on full-glacial conditions. A pollen diagram from Shady Valley Bog in Johnson County, Tennessee (Barclay, 1957), shows a distinct maximum of hemlock near the base along with higher percentages of spruce and fir pollen. This level presumably dates from late-glacial time. However, the diagram must be interpreted cautiously, because the bog is at an elevation of 850 m in a mountainous region and spruce currently grows on the bog surface.

Similar results have been obtained from Cranberry Glades, a bog at an elevation of about 1,000 m in the mountains of Pocahontas County, West Virginia (Darlington, 1943), Glade Run Bog at an elevation of 825 m in the mountains of Somerset County, Pennsylvania (Schrock, 1945), and Bear Meadows, Center County, Pennsylvania (Sears, 1935). The base of the profile at Cranberry Glades has been dated at 9,434 ± 840 (C-336). The pollen diagram at that level is dominated by spruce, fir, birch, oak, and hemlock. Above this, pine pollen appears and attains a maximum. Subsequently spruce, fir, and pine decline, and there is a hemlock-oak-birch maximum. Pine, birch, oak, and hickory dominate the rest of the postglacial portion of the diagram, although some spruce and fir pollen persist to the surface.

The work of Schrock (1945) on Glade Run Bog has demonstrated near the base of a profile a spruce-fir maximum underlain by another zone dominated by pine and spruce (with traces of fir, hemlock, birch, and oak). The occurrence of relatively small pine grains suggested the presence of jack pine (or red pine?). No radiocarbon dates are available from this profile. Martin (*in* Guilday *et al.,* 1964) has indicated that the spruce-fir maximum probably dates from a late-glacial advance of ice, not a major maximum as Schrock had believed. This once again gives us an indication of the lowering of vegetational zones but does not indicate the extent associated with full-glacial time.

Sears' (1935) profile shows a pine-fir-spruce zone at the base and maxima of birch and oak in the upper half. Non-Arboreal Pollen (NAP) percentages appear low throughout the section.

More recently Martin (*in* Guilday *et al.,* 1964) has investigated the clays beneath Cranberry Glades and has encountered a pollen assemblage that he believes dates from late-glacial time. In the lower levels of the clay Martin noted maxima of pine and spruce, high percentages of NAP (58%), and small pine-pollen grains. This may indicate a relatively open boreal forest vegetation, perhaps analogous to the subarctic boreal savanna. If this interpretation is valid, then there is reason to speculate on the presence of tundra in the mountains of West Virginia during full-glacial time.

In southeastern Virginia the work of Terasmae (*in* Harrison *et al.,* 1965) on bore-holes from the mouth of Chesapeake Bay, and of Whitehead (unpubl.) on the sediments of the Dismal Swamp, have provided relevant new data. Terasmae has prepared diagrams from two borings containing peaty sediments at depths between 16.6 and 28.8 m below present mean sea level. Radiocarbon dates range from 10,340 ± 130 (ML-90) at −25 m to 15,280 ± 200 (ML-91) at −27.2 m. Terasmae suggests that the lowest pollen spectra date from between 15,000 and 16,000 years before present. The lower spectra are characterized by maxima of pine and spruce (the latter attaining 45% in one spectrum) and smaller quantities of fir pollen. Birch and alder pollen is also frequent. NAP values range between 20% and 30% (principally grasses, composites,

Ambrosia, Artemisia, sedges, and caryophylls). This is excellent evidence for the existence of a forest type with considerable spruce and fir in southeastern Virginia between 11,000 and 16,000 years ago. The NAP percentages are high, but not sufficiently so to warrant suggesting the existence of boreal savanna. Aside from the spruce and fir, no other boreal elements were encountered.

The peat in the Dismal Swamp appears to be entirely postglacial in age. This is supported by dates from the base of two of the deepest peat sections (7,670 ± 60 (Y-1146) and 8,900 ± 160 (Y-1320) and by pollen diagrams from four profiles within the Swamp (Fig. 5). However, spectra from the clays underlying the peat provide evidence of cooler conditions during what was probably late-glacial time. The pollen flora of the clay is quite similar to many spectra obtained by Terasmae. A comparison of the Dismal Swamp and Chesapeake Bay profiles suggests that the pollen flora of the clay is between 10,000 and 12,000 years old. The clay spectra are characterized by high percentages of pine, rising percentages of spruce, maxima of birch and alder, and significant percentages of herb pollen (principally grass, sedge, composite, *Thalictrum,* and *Sanguisorba canadensis*). Spores of *Lycopodium lucidulum* and *L. clavatum* were also encountered. The high percentages of grass and sedge pollen are puzzling, since one would not expect evidence of relatively open boreal forests in sediments from the late-glacial in an area so far from the ice margin. In this case it is probable that the grasses and sedges were growing locally in moist habitats. Certainly the grass and sedge maxima higher in the profile can be explained on this basis. However, it is perhaps premature to rule out the possibility that there was a hiatus between deposition of peat and clay and that the clays actually date from full-glacial time. In such a case a different meaning might be attached to the high grass and sedge percentages.

Knox's (1962) studies of interglacial horizons underlying the terrace formations in the Washington, D.C., area have provided further evidence of the movement of boreal species during times of glacial advances. The peat horizons that Knox has investigated are clearly interglacial and derive from a sizeable cypress swamp, now positioned some 6 m below ground level and approximately 12 m above mean sea level. The pollen spectra corroborate the interglacial age. They are dominated by thermophilous species such as oak, hickory, pine, beech, elm, sweet gum (*Liquidambar*), and tulip tree (*Liriodendron*). However, in the less organic silts and clays overlying and underlying the swamp, pine percentages increase, spruce is represented, and hemlock is present at several levels. This is a clear indication of cooler conditions both preceding and succeeding the deposition of the interglacial horizon. It is interesting that similar pollen zones bracket the interglacial horizon (a pine zone immediately overlying and underlying, and a pine-spruce zone further removed). Spruce attains a maximum of 27% in a coarse horizon above the swamp layer and 70% in a silt below. The only other boreal elements identified were occasional grains of fir and larch. Few data on NAP were presented. One can suggest that the upper-silt pollen flora records the cooling of climate in early-Wisconsin time, and that the lower-silt pollen spectra record cooler conditions at the termination of the Illinoian glaciation. These spectra correlate well with the late-glacial spectra from eastern Virginia. There is thus substantial evidence for the existence of a forest dominated by spruce and pine during both early late-glacial and early-Wisconsin time. Evidence of full-glacial conditions is lacking, but nothing less boreal than spruce-pine forests can be expected.

In an area much closer to the ice margin (Chester County, Pennsylvania) Martin (1958b) has investigated fluvial marsh sediments that he suggests date from full-glacial time. Although the diagrams are extremely difficult to interpret and are apparently influenced by redeposited pollen, Martin feels that they provide evidence of a vegetation transitional between spruce–jack pine savanna and tundra.

The proposed full-glacial pollen zones (F-Zones) are characterized by high NAP (50-75%), plus spruce, fir, and pine pollen. Measurements of pine air sacs suggest that a species possessing small pollen grains was present. This Martin believes was jack pine. NAP in the zone includes *Thalictrum, Artemisia, Sanguisorba canadensis, Polemonium, Polygonum* cf. *bistortoides,* and *Saxifraga* cf. *oppositifolia,* in addition to high percentages of grass and sedge. An interpretation of the F-Zones is complicated by the occurence of distinct maxima for *Alnus, Pinus, Tsuga, Quercus, Ostrya-Carpinus, Ambrosia,* and fern spores in Zones F-1 and F-3. Pollen of other thermophilous species also occurs in these zones. The rank order and ratio of percentages of these more thermophilous types is the same in both F-1 and F-3 and parallels that in the postglacial C-Zones. Martin interprets this as a result of a contamination of Zones F-1 and F-3 by ground-water transport of material from the C-Zone. Further support for this contention is found in the parallelism of the pine air-sac size-frequency curves in Zones C, F-1, and F-3. Air sacs are smaller in Zones F-2 and F-4. The radiocarbon dates are decidedly younger than full-glacial (Y-478, 13,540 ± 270, from F-4, and Y-479, 13,630 ± 230, from F-3), but Martin suggests that contamination with younger material might explain this.

A diagram from a second profile in the Marsh (M2) appears to be less influenced by redeposition and hence is probably of greater significance. It is interesting to note that the NAP percentages are a trifle lower and that they parallel the curve for *Sanguisorba canadensis.*

These diagrams may be full-glacial in age and indicate the presence of spruce–jack pine savanna in southeastern Pennsylvania, but I feel that the evidence is inconclusive. First of all, the evidence for the presence of jack pine is equivocal. There is absolutely no way of separating the grains of jack pine and red pine on a size basis, since the mean sizes are too close (37.01μ and 40.11μ; Whitehead, 1962, 1964). Air sacs are even more closely similar in size (32.83μ and 34.91μ). A size-frequency curve to which both of these species contributed would be perfectly unimodal. Thus the species represented by the smaller grains could equally well be *Pinus resinosa,* a "boreal" species that currently ranges as far south as southeastern Pennsylvania and along the highlands to West Virginia (Munns, 1938).

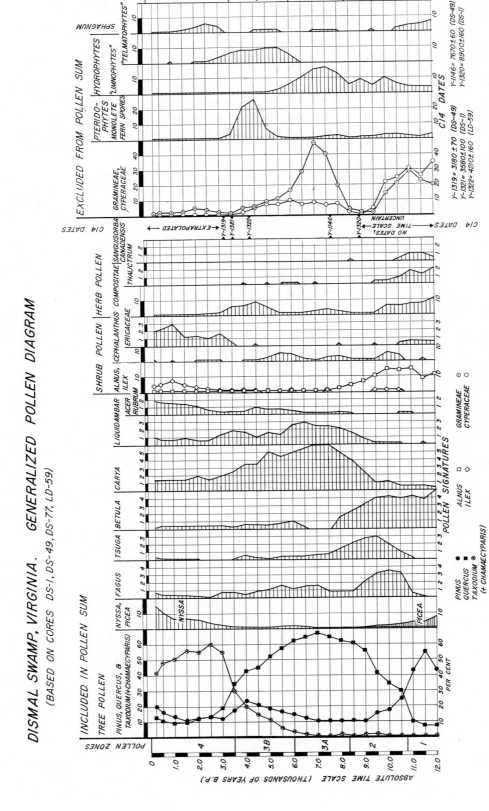

Figure 5. Generalized pollen diagram from the Dismal Swamp. Whitehead, unpublished.

The presence of spruce and fir is incontestable. However, the meaning of the NAP percentages is by no means so clear. The NAP is almost exclusively grass and sedge pollen, which in the writer's experience has often been locally derived. There need not necessarily be high percentages of fern spores and composites in sediments subject to over-representation, as Martin seems to imply. The correlation of the grass and sedge curves with that for *Sanquisorba canadensis* from Core M2 is interesting, since *Sanguisorba* is a plant of boggy and peaty soils.

The proof of tundra or boreal savanna must rest upon more than a demonstration of high percentages of grass and sedge pollen. Fortunately, there is further evidence that bears upon this. The grains of *Polygonum bistortoides* (or *P. viviparum?*) and *Saxifraga* cf. *oppositifolia* indicate the presence of boreal elements, and grains of *Artemisia*, caryophylls, chenopods, and *Rumex* suggest at least some open habitats. However, it must be remembered that the percentages of these elements are low and that we are dealing with sediments in a fluvial marsh, hence water transport might be a factor.

In the absence of unequivocal radiocarbon dates and more clear-cut palynological evidence, it would seem best to make a more conservative interpretation of the Marsh sequence. Cooler conditions cannot be disputed, and a minimum of late-glacial age is indicated. However, the structure of the vegetation is open to question.

Much more convincing evidence of boreal forest and boreal savanna has been obtained recently by Guilday *et al.* (1964) in their investigation of 9 m of cave fill from a sink hole near New Paris, Bedford County, in the Allegheny Mountains of Pennsylvania. The cave deposits have yielded an abundance of vertebrate material in addition to well-preserved pollen and spores. The overwhelming majority of species identified derive from either the Canadian or the Hudsonian Zone. In the upper layers Canadian zone species predominate, in the lower levels Hudsonian zone forms. One species, the Labrador collared lemming (*Dicrostonyx hudsonius*), is now found almost exclusively within the tundra. Several prairie species—the thirteen-lined ground squirrel (*Citellus tridecemlineatus*) and the sharp-tailed grouse (*Pedioecetes phasianellus*)—also occur. Although a number of the species identified are now wide-ranging (extending far south of the boreal forest) it is noteworthy that virtually all the New Paris remains possess characteristics of populations now living in central and southern Canada; *e.g.* in species that currently exhibit a positive Bergmann's response (larger size in the north) the New Paris fossils are almost invariably large; in those that demonstrate a negative response the fossils are small. The abundance of the remains (3,000 specimens) makes the data highly significant. The pollen evidence, by itself a bit equivocal, provides corroborative evidence for the existence of boreal forest or, conceivably, boreal woodland. Two pollen zones can be recognized in the profile, with the lower, Zone B, providing evidence of cooler conditions. Both zones are dominated by pine. Spruce percentages are higher in the lower zone. Pollen of thermophilous trees is more common in the upper zone (Zone A). NAP percentages are slightly higher in the lower zone.

Martin's measurements of pine air sacs suggest that the grains may be slightly smaller in the lower zone, and that jack pine may have been present. A radiocarbon date of 11,300 ± 1,000 (Y-727) has been obtained from charcoal fragments in Zone A. A date of 9,540 ± 500 (M-1067) has been derived from bone in Zone B. The charcoal date is considered to be more accurate, hence late-glacial age is indicated.

Martin considers the zones to be more or less equivalent to the F-Zones from Marsh, Pennsylvania, and to the spectra from the clays underlying Cranberry Glades, West Virginia. The differences can be explained on the basis of topography and edaphic factors. Although one could question the presence of jack pine (red pine would be just as likely), it is hard to argue with the general body of evidence. It would appear that boreal forest and boreal savanna coexisted in the Alleghenies during late-glacial time. The presence of the Labrador collared lemming argues for the presence of tundra, perhaps at higher elevations during full-glacial time.

Many of the other profiles available from the Southeast are of little interest to this discussion, since, almost without exception, they are truncated basally and hence date from postglacial time. This includes the work of Potzger (1945) from the Pine Barrens of New Jersey, the work of Lewis and Cocke (1929) and Cocke *et al.* (1934) from the Dismal Swamp, and the studies of Sears and Couch (1932) from Arkansas. The recent age of these deposits precludes their use to support the argument that thermophilous species persisted close to the ice margin, such as in the Pine Barrens of New Jersey.

PRE-WISCONSIN VEGETATION AND CLIMATE

Only a handful of definite pre-Wisconsin horizons have been studied in the Southeast. These include the Horry Clay horizon of supposed Sangamon age near Myrtle Beach, South Carolina (Frey, 1952), a probable correlative of the Horry Clay exposed at Flanner's Beach, on the Neuse River near New Bern, North Carolina (Whitehead and J. T. Davis, unpubl.; J. T. Davis, 1963), the interglacial (Sangamon?) Walker Cypress Swamp deposit (and associated silts) from Washington, D.C. (Knox, 1962), and a section from the Ladson Formation near Charleston, South Carolina (Leopold, 1959). Other deposits, not well dated, that may provide evidence of pre-Wisconsin conditions include the buried soils from western North Carolina (Cain, 1944; Whitehead and Barghoorn, 1962), the lower levels of the Carolina Bay profiles (Buell, 1945; Frey, 1951, 1953, 1955; Whitehead, 1963, 1964), the fluvial sediments from Louisiana (Brown, 1938), the peats from Myrtle Beach, South Carolina (Frey, 1952), and a variety of undated horizons from which macrofossils have been identified (*e.g.* Berry, 1925).

The most detailed study of an interglacial sequence in the Southeast is that of Knox (1962) on the surficial sediments of the Washington, D.C., area. The most interesting unit contained in the various sections studied is a freshwater peat, called the Walker Cypress Swamp, now known from numerous excavations, which occurs roughly 6 m below ground level and between 7 and 12 m above present mean sea level. The macrofossils and pollen flora suggest a cypress swamp along a slowly flowing stream. Indications are that the climate was at least comparable to the present, conceivably warmer. *Taxodium* stumps are the most striking of the macrofossils (some 8 ft in diameter) and occur with remains of many other temperate herbs, shrubs, and trees. In the pollen flora, *Quercus* (27.8%), grasses (22.0%), *Pinus* (10.2%), *Taxodium* (10.1%), *Carya* (8.7%), *Fagus* (2.9%), *Castanea* (1.33%), and *Liriodendron* (1.4%) are well represented in addition to *Liquidambar, Platanus, Acer, Nyssa,* and others. This suggests a climate and vegetation quite comparable to the present. The abundance of *Taxodium* in the microfossil and macrofossil record argues for slightly warmer and more oceanic conditions, perhaps indicating a higher sea level.

The oak-hickory maximum is well developed in the middle of the interglacial sequence, and correlates with a minimum in the pine curve. As mentioned previously, the sediments underlying and overlying the swamp horizon contain pollen and spores suggesting cooler conditions (spruce, fir, more pine, etc.). It is interesting that there is a pine maximum transitional to the "boreal pollen zone" both above and below the interglacial sequence. It would thus appear that an entire interglacial was represented (probably the Sangamon) along with a waning phase of the Illinoian glaciation and the earliest portion of the Wisconsin.

The two Horry Clay horizons thus far investigated are incomplete in the sense that they span only a small portion of an interglacial. Both of the horizons probably formed at or close to sea level during the warming phase of the Sangamon interglacial. Deposition at each station was halted by marine transgression. There is particularly good evidence of this from the Flanner's Beach section, where 1.3 m of peaty clay (on the upper surface of which are rooted cypress stumps) is overlain by 5.5 m of Pamlico Formation, the lower 2 m of which abound in marine mollusks (Richards, 1950). The clay is rich in freshwater diatoms, but a few unmistakably marine forms occur. This suggests deposition close enough to sea level to allow occasional tidal influence. The pollen diagram is relatively rich in chenopod pollen, also suggesting saline conditions. An increase of "Hystrix" at the top of the clay section indicates the imminent transgression. This is further supported by the distribution of mollusks in the overlying Pamlico Formation. *Rangia cuneata*, a pelecypod found along the southeastern coast in both salty and brackish shallow waters, is common in the lower levels of the Pamlico. Mollusks of somewhat deeper waters abound higher in the section. The pollen diagram from the Flanner's Beach section is relatively uniform and is dominated by pine, cypress, oak, hickory, ash, sweet gum, chenopods, grasses, sedges, and composites. Grains of hemlock and spruce are extremely uncommon. This suggests climatic conditions quite comparable to the present relatively early in Sangamon time.

There is a suggestion of an unconformity between the Pamlico and the Horry Clay, hence the transgression may have been oscillating. Following initial submergence of the region there was apparently a period of lowering of water level during which the surface of the peaty clay was exposed and developed cracks. Conceivably the cypress grew on the surface of the clay at this time. Subsequently sea level rose once again, and the cypress and the Horry Clay were buried beneath marine sediments.

The Horry Clay section at Myrtle Beach differs in that the diatoms contained in the upper meter are entirely marine (Cooke, 1937). However, periods of dominant freshwater influence must have been present to allow germination and growth of the cypress, stumps of which are found on the upper surface of the clay. In addition, a pollen study (Frey, 1952) indicated that the lower portion of the clay is of freshwater origin. The pollen spectra suggest a vegetation and climate comparable to the present and conditions somewhat warmer and moister midway during the period of deposition. There are maxima of oak, hickory, black gum, sweet gum, ash, elm, cypress, and willow in the middle of the section, and maxima of pine at the base and at the top. These data and the occurrence of pollen of *Nuphar, Nymphaea,* and *Myriophyllum* and spicules of freshwater sponges point to the freshwater origin of the clay.

Leopold (1959) has analyzed a 10-m section of the Ladson formation near Charleston, South Carolina. This formation is apparently largely marine and was laid down during a high stand of the sea, probably during the last interglacial. The formation occurs between 3 and 17 m above present sea level. Leopold's study suggests a near-shore depositional environment. The pollen diagram, dominated by pine, oak, and hickory, is thought to be indicative of a climate comparable to the present, hence supporting the interglacial correlation. While certainly agreeing with the correlation and general interpretation, I would suggest that the climate obtaining during deposition of the member studied was not quite so warm as at present. This is suggested by the occurrence of occasional grains of spruce, fir, and hemlock.

The correlation of the four interglacial sections thus far discussed is not yet certain. All appear to date from the Sangamon Interglacial, yet the pollen profiles, while clearly indicating temperate conditions, are dissimilar enough to preclude exact correlation. Actually the changes in the section described by Frey are similar to those reported by Knox from the Washington, D.C., area. However, the Horry Clay cannot date from the middle of an interglacial, since it is overlain by 5.4 m of marine sediment. Further work will be necessary.

As mentioned previously, the lower pollen zones (Zones N, O, P) from the Carolina Bays may also date from pre-Wisconsin time. The problem of correlation has been discussed by Frey (1955). A date of >38,000 is available from the middle organic horizon (Zone N). The pollen flora indicates temperate conditions for this zone and for Zone P. It is possible that the middle organic horizon dates from Sangamon time and that the basal temperate zone is from the second interglacial. It is also conceivable that the middle organic horizon was formed during an early-Wisconsin interstadial, perhaps correlating with the Brørup interstadial (56,000 B.P.) of northwestern Europe (Andersen *et al.,* 1960). If the latter were true, then Pollen Zone P might correlate with either the earlier Amersfoort interstadial (64,000 B.P.) or with the end of the Sangamon Interglacial.

The lower zones from Mud Lake, Florida (Watts, 1965), may also antedate the Wisconsin.

POSTGLACIAL FOREST DEVELOPMENT

As one would expect, diagrams from relatively close to the drift border and in the mountainous region show distinct similarities to those obtained from the glaciated region. In general these diagrams can be differentiated into the characteristic zones (B, C1, C2, and C3). Such a zonation is not so clear in the diagrams from areas farther to the south.

PROFILES FROM THE MOUNTAINS OR CLOSE TO THE DRIFT BORDER

The postglacial portion of the diagrams from Marsh, Pennsylvania (Martin, 1958b), 80 km south of the ice margin, begin with an abbreviated B-zone (pine zone), distinguished by a sharp maximum of pine associated with falling percentages of spruce, some fir, and rising percentages of alder, oak, and hemlock. Whether this pine zone reflects a dominance of pine in early postglacial time or rather the replacement of prolific pollen producers (such as spruce) by less prolific pollinators (beech, sugar maple, etc.; Davis, 1963) cannot be determined at this time. The overlying pollen zone (C1) is characterized by maxima of oak, hemlock, and alder and declining percentages of spruce, fir, birch, and willow, suggesting the presence of a forest type similar to the present hemlock–white pine–northern hardwoods forest region of Braun (1950). However, this zone differs from its counterpart from the glaciated region in having lower percentages of beech and higher percentages of pine. The uppermost zone studied by Martin (C2) is characterized by rising percentages of hickory and abundant oak and chestnut pollen. Pine is common in both C-zones. The rise of hickory and decline of hemlock suggest increasing warmth and decreasing soil moisture during C2 time. Zone C3 is not represented in the diagram, but probably exists in the unstudied upper 24 cm of sediment.

The pollen profiles from the mountains of West Virginia (Darlington, 1943) and Tennessee (Barclay, 1957) are roughly similar but cannot yet be correlated unequivocally with the established postglacial sequence from the glaciated region. At Cranberry Glades, Darlington found a zone rich in spruce and fir pollen at the base of the peat profile. A radiocarbon date of $9,434 \pm 840$ from the top of this zone suggests that it might correlate with the Valders advance. There is a discernible pine zone (also rich in birch pollen) beginning at the level of the C^{14} date. This may well be the vegetational (but not chronological) equivalent of the B-Zone from the glaciated region. A hemlock, birch, and oak zone, possibly the equivalent of Zone C1, occurs above this. Oak, birch, pine, and hickory dominate the rest of the profile, although spruce and fir are consistently represented. The maximum of birch at the top of the profile may be indicative of moister conditions during C3 time.

However, there are no corresponding increases in spruce, fir, and hemlock as might be expected in this zone.

The Shady Valley profile (Barclay, 1957) is shallower, more difficult to interpret, but apparently at least equally old. In fact, the occurrence of an oak maximum beneath a zone rich in pine, spruce, and hemlock allows speculation on the presence of an interstadial antedating the Valders advance. A radiocarbon date of $9,500 \pm 150$ is available from the top of this complex zone; by extrapolation the base of the profile would date from about 11,800 years ago. Barclay has correlated the base of the profile with the B-Zone. However, this seems to be too old. Moreover, pine dominates only one spectrum. A pronounced hemlock maximum ensues just above the base of the profile and continues for roughly a meter. A distinct birch maximum occurs in the lower half of the hemlock zone. Barclay has correlated this zone with C1. However, the base of the zone may also date from Valders time. The upper portion of the profile can be divided into zones C2 and C3. C2 is characterized by an oak-hickory maximum (a distinct *Castanea* maximum occurs early in the zone); C3 by an increase in spruce, hemlock, and fir.

The correlation of this profile with established sequences is therefore difficult. The distinct hemlock-birch zone probably indicates the existence of a hemlock–northern hardwoods forest type in the Shady Valley region, but it is not certain when it developed. The base of this pollen zone may date from the late-glacial, rather than early postglacial as in the northeast. If the latter correlation is valid, then the chestnut maximum in the upper half of Barclay's Zone C1 (the hemlock zone) may be chronologically equivalent to C1 in the Northeast. At any rate, the evidence for climatic deterioration during C3 time is excellent. It would appear that the vegetational zones in the surrounding mountains have been lowered slightly during this period of time, leading to greater growth of hemlock in the vicinity of the bog and growth of spruce on the bog itself.

The profiles from the Pine Barrens of New Jersey (Potzger, 1945) are extraordinarily uniform. Hemlock, spruce, and fir appear to be represented in the lower levels of a few sites, but basically the diagrams are dominated by temperate forest species (oak, pine, birch, chestnut, hickory). Since little differentiation is apparent, it would seem that the bogs developed during C-Zone time, and perhaps quite recently. *Castanea* percentages are a little higher and oak lower in the upper levels of a few of the bogs. Conceivably the chestnut rise might be indicative of moister conditions during C3.

SOUTHEASTERN VIRGINIA

Recent work in southeastern Virginia (Whitehead, unpubl., and Terasmae *in* Harrison *et al.*, 1965) has provided information on the vegetational history of the region. My work in the Dismal Swamp has indicated that the Swamp is younger than formerly believed. Deposition of organic sediment began (roughly contemporaneously) throughout at least the northern half of the Swamp approximately 8,000-9,000 years ago. This is supported by five radiocarbon dates and by pollen diagrams from four widely separated profiles. The correspondence among the diagrams, which is remarkably good, has permitted the preparation of a generalized diagram for the Dismal Swamp (Fig. 5). This has been prepared by smoothing the individual curves from each profile, replotting each on an absolute time scale (this involves a certain amount of extrapolation and interpolation), then superimposing individual replotted curves (e.g. the oak curves from all four profiles) and averaging the trends. The generalized diagram includes only those entities represented most commonly.

Four distinct zones can be recognized in the pollen diagram. The lowest zone (Zone 1), referred to previously in the section on full-glacial conditions, occurs in the clay sediments directly beneath the peat and provides evidence of cooler conditions during late-glacial time (*ca.* 12,000-10,700 years B.P.). Zone 2 occurs in organic sediment overlying the clay and provides evidence of rising water table throughout the Swamp and the existence of a forest similar to the hemlock–northern hardwoods region between 10,700 and 8,300 years B.P. This zone is characterized by declining pine and spruce and rising oak percentages and by maxima of beech, hemlock, birch, and alder. The aquatic vegetation included *Cabomba caroliniana*, a species that now reaches the northern limit of its natural range in Virginia and southern New Jersey. Despite the occurrence of *Cabomba*, it is probable that the climate was slightly cooler than the present, because maxima of hemlock and beech occur along with grains of spruce and *Sanguisorba canadensis*. Zone 3 (8,300-3,500 B.P.), here divided into two subzones, contains significant maxima of oak, hickory, and sweet gum. The subdivisions of the zone are based on the curves of shrubs, herbs, and aquatics. Indications are that during Zone 3A time there was open water over much of the Dismal Swamp. This zone is dominated by pollen of grasses, sedges, and aquatics. The aquatics are virtually all limnophytes—species that grow in areas where there is continuous water. These include *Myriophyllum*, *Potamogeton*, *Proserpinaca*, *Utricularia*, *Nuphar*, and *Nymphaea*. The oak, hickory, and sweet gum doubtless grew on the "ridges" that protruded above the general surface of the Swamp. (The clay surface beneath the Swamp is known to be undulating.) During 3B time, there is good evidence for "shoaling" throughout the Swamp. The deeper-water aquatics were replaced by those that often grow on peaty soils or where the hydroperiod is not continuous. These types include *Orontium*, *Eriocaulon*, *Xyris*, *Sagittaria*, and *Cephalanthus*. Species of boggy soils include *Diodia virginiana* and *Geum* cf. *rivale*. There are also distinct maxima for monolete fern spores (indicating the presence of *Woodwardia*?) and composites. At about this depth throughout the Swamp (1 m) a distinct stump layer occurs. There is thus little doubt that the hydroperiod was considerably shortened at this time. Whether this was a function of a slowing of the water-table rise or an acceleration of the rate of peat development cannot be determined. In the upper portion of the zone there is a gradual decline of oak and hickory and a reciprocal rise of *Taxodium*. This suggests an inundation of the "ridge" habitats on which oak and hickory had been growing and the gradual development of "swamp forest." The spread of *Taxodium* may also be due to increased oceanicity, in turn

a function of sea-level rise. During Zone-4 time (3,500 years B.P. to present) there is evidence of the virtual elimination of both "ridge" and open-water habitats (and the rise to dominance of "swamp forest"). Aquatics are represented infrequently, oak declines sharply, and cypress pollen becomes dominant. There are maxima for *Nyssa*, *Ilex*, *Ericaceae*, and *Acer rubrum*. Pollen of *Itea virginica*, *Magnolia*, *Liriodendron*, and spores of *Polypodium* (*P. polypodioides*?) occur.

The correspondence among the cores is good, indicating that the same vegetational developments have taken place throughout at least the northern half of the Dismal Swamp. A diagram from Lake Drummond (located in the center of the Swamp) indicates that it is a relatively recent feature, dating from the transition between Zones 3 and 4.

Evidence of Indian agriculture has been found in Core DS-1 (just east of Lake Drummond). Five grains of *Zea mays* were identified from the 0.49-cm level. These were associated with a slight maximum for grass, *Ambrosia*, *Myrica*, *Corylus*, and *Pinus*, and occasional grains of *Artemisia*, perhaps indicating the presence of a small clearing in the Swamp. The clearance must have been localized, however, since no evidence of agriculture was encountered in the Lake Drummond core (2 km to the west), even though roughly 1,000 grains were counted per sample. By extrapolation from a C^{14} date at the 0.80-m level (Y-1321, 3,580 ± 100), the "agricultural horizon" would date from about 2,000 B.P. This assumes a uniform rate of peat formation and no loss of surface peat by oxidation. However, the latter assumption may be weak, since there is good evidence from other portions of the Swamp of a recent decrease in peat thickness through oxidation. The age may thus be a minimum one.

Close correlation exists between the diagrams from the Dismal Swamp and the postglacial spectra from the Chesapeake Bay borings studied by Terasmae (*in* Harrison et al., 1965). In Terasmae's diagrams there is a hemlock, birch, alder, and beech zone separating an upper, oak-hickory zone from a late-glacial pine-spruce zone. There is no doubt that Terasmae's hemlock zone is the vegetational and chronological equivalent of Zone 2 from the Dismal Swamp. It would thus appear that beginning approximately 11,000 years ago there was a change from a pine-spruce-birch-alder forest to one similar to the present hemlock–white pine–northern hardwoods association. This type of forest apparently reached its greatest development 9,500 years ago and was then gradually displaced by a more thermophilic oak–hickory–sweet gum forest. The latter was well developed by 8,300 years B.P. Both the Dismal Swamp and Chesapeake Bay diagrams provide evidence of the development of oak–hickory–sweet gum forests in southeastern Virginia.

The upper portion of Terasmae's diagrams are too old to permit comparison with Zones 3B and 4 from the Dismal Swamp. The changes suggested by the Dismal Swamp diagrams (development of a swamp forest dominated by cypress, red maple, black gum, and swamp shrubs) may reflect conditions within the Swamp itself, not those in edaphically different habitats in southeastern Virginia.

It is perplexing to note that there is very little correspondence between the two studies reported above and the other available investigations from the Dismal Swamp region (Lewis and Cocke, 1929; Cocke *et al.*, 1934; Vick, 1961). This is true despite the fact that the several cores I obtained came from virtually the same sites as those reported by Lewis and Cocke. There is an indication of a grass-aquatic phase near the base of their profiles and an indication of a *Nyssa-Taxodium* maximum at the top, but there the resemblances cease. Furthermore, Lewis and Cocke have reported high percentages of *Salix* pollen, a type I rarely encountered (maximum 0.6%) even though up to 1,000 grains were counted per sample. There is also an indication of a salt-water invasion midway in one of the profiles reported by Cocke *et al.* (1934). I discovered no evidence of such an influence. Furthermore, all evidence seems to indicate that sea level in southeastern Virginia at that point in the Swamp's history was as much as 20 m below the present level (Newman, 1964).

The diagram of Vick (1961) from the southern portion of the Dismal Swamp is remarkably similar to those of Lewis and Cocke. However, since Vick did not tabulate herb and shrub pollen, direct comparisons are difficult. His diagram shows a basal pine maximum, relatively constant low percentages of oak, hickory, and sweet gum throughout the profile, and an increase in gum, maple, and cypress at the top. There is also an extraordinary maximum of willow pollen throughout the lower seven-eighths of the profile, with values reaching 40%.

The discrepancies between these studies and those of myself and Terasmae are difficult to explain. In the case of the earlier work, it could be a function of primitive techniques of sample collection and preparation and of pollen identification at that early point in the science's development in North America. Vick's diagrams (from the Dismal Swamp and farther south in coastal North Carolina) present problems that can only be evaluated through further studies of the same basins.

SOUTHEASTERN NORTH CAROLINA

The work of Buell (1945), Frey (1951, 1953, 1955), and Whitehead (1963, 1964) provides fairly comprehensive evidence concerning the postglacial pollen sequence in southeastern North Carolina. By far the most important contribution is that of Frey (1953) in his major paper dealing with the regional pollen sequence. Figure 4, taken from Frey's paper, is a generalized diagram for the Bladen County region, depicting a pollen chronology spanning a considerable period of time from the present to at least early-Wisconsin time.

Frey has designated the post-Wisconsin maximum portion of his regional diagram as Zone C, divisible into subzones Ca and Cb. These are deciduous-forest pollen zones, but certainly not chronologically equivalent to the C-Zones from the Northeast. In fact, much of Zone Ca may not even be postglacial. The C^{14} date of 10,224 ± 510 suggests that much of this zone may date from the late-glacial. Vegetationally, this zone appears to be similar to Zone 2 from the Dismal Swamp. It occurs at the transition between a pine-rich boreal zone (full-glacial?) and a postglacial oak-hickory zone. Maxima of birch, hemlock, beech, elm, alder, and hornbeam occur. Once again, this may indicate the presence of a forest type similar to the present hemlock–northern hardwoods association during late-glacial and early-postglacial time. It is interesting to note that the hemlock percentages are decidedly lower than those from southeastern Virginia, perhaps reflecting the more southerly position of the profiles. The upper half of Zone Ca is dominated by oak, hickory, sweet gum, and, somewhat later, cypress. This zone is quite comparable to Zones 3A and 3B from the Dismal Swamp.

The uppermost zone from the Carolina Bays is characterized by a steady increase in pine percentages with reciprocal decreases of oak, hickory, cypress, and other deciduous-leaved types. There is a maximum of *Nyssa* early in Cb time. *Ilex* and *Ericaceae* are more common at the top of the profile. Thus the uppermost postglacial zone differs from that in southeastern Virginia, where pine percentages remain low. These differences are easy to explain, since the dominant soil type in the Dismal Swamp region is peat and that in southeastern North Carolina is coarse sand.

The diagrams of Vick (1961), ranging from northeastern to southeastern North Carolina, are puzzling. All seem to show an extraordinarily close parallelism to Frey's regional diagram from Bladen County. This homogeneity is unexpected in such widely separated profiles. Furthermore, it is curious that his Dismal Swamp profile (from southeastern Gates County in northeastern North Carolina) differs so sharply from Burnett Pond (Central Chowan County, northeastern North Carolina), for the basins are separated by less than 30 km. Further study, involving larger counts of all pollen and spore types, will have to be carried out in order to assess the significance of these profiles.

FLORIDA

South of the Carolina Bay region few postglacial diagrams are available for study. Watts' (1965) profile of Mud Lake provides the only evidence of postglacial conditions south of the Carolina Bay region. Four distinct zones are evident. The uppermost zone (0-240 cm) contains maxima of pine and cypress. Oak and *Myrica* are also common. Zone II (240-660 cm) is marked by a distinct oak maximum. Zone III (660-760 cm) is characterized by another distinct pine maximum. Zone IV (760-950 cm) contains maxima of oak, hickory, sweet gum, and cypress. It is interesting that grains of beech and sugar maple type, although generally rare in the profile, are most frequently encountered in the basal zone. There is a sharp maximum of NAP types coinciding with Zone II, with chenopod types attaining very high values (up to 528%). A radiocarbon date of 5,070 ± 150 (I-1477) is available from the 240-cm level and a date of >34,500 (I-1478) from the 660-cm level.

An interpretation of the Mud Lake profile is difficult, since a hiatus exists in the depositional record (indicated by the sand at 490 cm). Watts has indicated that the fluctuations observed, while undoubtedly due to climatic change, could be achieved by changes in abundance of species already present near Mud Lake. The results of Watts' further work on this most significant profile will be awaited eagerly. Particularly critical will be his study of an additional three meters of sediment at the base of the profile.

TEXAS

The work of Potzger and Tharp (1947, 1954) had suggested the invasion of Texas by a boreal forest type during full-glacial or late-glacial time and a distinct sequence of climatic changes during postglacial time (*e.g.* warm-dry, with oak and grasses; warm-moist, with alder and chestnut; warm-dry, with oak, hickory, and grasses). The validity of this reconstruction has been challenged by more recent and detailed work (Graham and Heimsch, 1960). It would now appear that a sharp revision must be made in the sequence suggested by Potzger and Tharp. Graham and Heimsch have demonstrated that the vegetation of south-central Texas has been monotonously uniform for the past 8,000 years. Furthermore, as mentioned previously, their study of samples from Gause Bog has indicated that spruce and fir are much less common than was reported by Potzger and Tharp, and that *Castanea*, which played a significant role in the postglacial section of the Potzger and Tharp profiles, was probably not present at all.

ARKANSAS AND OKLAHOMA

Sears (1935) and Sears and Couch (1932) have presented evidence of a climatic shift from warm-dry to warm-moist conditions in Arkansas. This is suggested by a maximum of oak and hickory at the base of a 5-ft profile and a gradual increase in *Nyssa* and *Pinus* upwards. It seems probable that this profile is relatively young, perhaps dating to no more than 6,000 years ago.

The profile from eastern Oklahoma (Sears, 1935) is extremely shallow and homogeneous. No significant changes take place within the section. The diagram is dominated by pine, oak, and hickory.

General Conclusions

As mentioned in the introduction, it is not yet possible to obtain more than the sketchiest impression of Pleistocene vegetational changes in the Southeast. Too few well-dated horizons have been studied. Much of the early work must be disregarded, since subsequent studies have demonstrated that there were serious errors, probably as a function of the relatively primitive palynological techniques employed.

It is possible, however, to present a tentative reconstruction of vegetation from the full-glacial to the present for a transect extending from the Chesapeake Bay region to southeastern North Carolina.

FULL-GLACIAL (25,000-15,000 B.P.)

Assuming that the oldest horizons studied by Terasmae (older than 14,000 years) are reasonably close to full-glacial in age and that the M-Zone from the Carolina Bays is also of Wisconsin age (bracketed by dates of 10,224 and >38,-000), then one can suggest that there were appreciable differences between southeastern Virginia and southeastern North Carolina during full-glacial time. The forests of Virginia were apparently more boreal in aspect (pollen percentages: spruce 45%, pine 40%, fir 3%). It can be suggested that spruce was the dominant tree, and that fir was not uncommon. Terasmae did not report other boreal species, but I have found spores of *Lycopodium lucidulum*

and *L. clavatum* and grains of *Sanguisorba canadensis* in the late-glacial clays underlying the Dismal Swamp. It seems probable that these and other boreal species occurred during full-glacial time in the same region.

The full-glacial forests of southeastern North Carolina differed appreciably. Pine was apparently the dominant species (the most common pines were either red pine or jack pine, perhaps both), spruce was much less abundant (maximum generally about 7%), and fir was very uncommon. A number of other "northern" species did occur. These include *Lycopodium lucidulum*, *L. annotinum*, *Schizaea pusilla*, *Sanguisorba canadensis*, and *Arceuthobium* (the latter may not have occurred during the Wisconsin maximum, but did occur earlier).

The differences between the two regions appear clear, but whether they reflect sharp climatic differences cannot be determined. It is possible that the greater abundance of pine in the Carolina Bay region is a function of edaphic conditions (specifically, the prevalence of coarse sand).

LATE-GLACIAL (15,000-10,000 B.P.)

The late-glacial forests of the Chesapeake Bay region were originally rich in spruce, pine, fir, and birch. The dominance then shifted to pine, with spruce, birch, and alder as associates. These forests gradually gave way to one rich in beech, hemlock, birch, and alder. Oak and hickory also began to play a more important role in the forests. The general indications are for a gradual change from a boreal forest type to a hemlock–northern hardwoods type throughout late-glacial time.

The late-glacial trends in southeastern North Carolina are quite similar to those described above. The full-glacial pine-spruce forests were replaced by forests with abundant oak, hickory, birch, hemlock, beech, elm, and other thermophilous species. Frey indicates that maxima of beech and hemlock are attained early in this transition. By the close of late-glacial time the forests of the region were dominated by oak, hickory, and other deciduous forest species. Percentages of hemlock and beech were already declining. It is interesting that the beech-hemlock zone occurs earlier in the North Carolina profiles and that hemlock is less important quantitatively. This is in keeping with the southerly location of the sites.

POSTGLACIAL (10,000 B.P.-PRESENT)

Early postglacial time in the Chesapeake Bay region witnessed a gradual transformation of the "northern hardwoods" forest type into a forest dominated by oak, hickory, sweet gum, and many other deciduous forest species. These forests reached their maximum development approximately 7,000 years ago. It is hard to generalize on the more recent forest history of the region, because we have only the Dismal Swamp diagrams on which to rely, and these may reflect the rather specialized edaphic situation within the Swamp itself. Within the Swamp region there was a gradual elimination of oak-hickory forest and the development of a swamp forest rich in *Taxodium, Nyssa, Acer rubrum*, and swamp shrubs.

An oak-hickory forest type had attained its maximum development in southeastern North Carolina by early postglacial time, considerably earlier than in southeastern Virginia. Subsequently the areal importance of this forest type decreased as *Nyssa* and *Taxodium* became more abundant. This development may not reflect increased moisture as much as increasing oceanicity and temperature. In the most recent portion of the diagrams there is evidence suggesting the development of the present pine-dominated forests of the region.

REFERENCES

Andersen, S. T., deVries, Hessel, and Zagwijn, W. H., 1960, Climatic change and radiocarbon dating in the Weichselian glacial of Denmark and the Netherlands: Geol. Mijnbouw, v. 39, p. 38-42

Barclay, F. H., 1957, The natural vegetation of Johnson Co., Tennessee, past and present: Univ. Tennessee Ph.D. thesis

Berry, E. W., 1926, Pleistocene plants from North Carolina: U.S. Geol. Surv. Prof. Pap. 140-C, p. 97-119

Braun, E. Lucy, 1950, Deciduous forests of eastern North America: Philadelphia, Blakiston Co., 596 p.

—— 1955, The phytogeography of unglaciated eastern United States and its interpretation: Bot. Rev., v. 21, p. 297-375

Brown, C. A., 1938, The flora of Pleistocene deposits in the Western Florida Parishes, West Feliciana Parish, and East Baton Rouge Parish, Louisiana: Louisiana Dept. Conserv. Bull. 12, p. 59-96

Buell, M. F., 1945, Late Pleistocene forests of southeastern North Carolina: Torreya, v. 45, p. 117-118

Cain, S. A., 1944, Pollen analysis of some buried soils, Spartanburg County, South Carolina: Torrey Bot. Club Bull., v. 71, p. 11-22

Cocke, E. C., Lewis, I. F., and Patrick, Ruth, 1934, A further study of Dismal Swamp peat: Amer. J. Bot., v. 21, p. 374-395

Cooke, C. W., 1937, The Pleistocene Horry clay and Pamlico formation near Myrtle Beach, South Carolina: Wash. Acad. Sci. J., v. 27, p. 1-5

Darlington, H. C., 1943, Vegetation and substrate of Cranberry Glades, West Virginia: Bot. Gaz., v. 104, p. 371-393

Davis, J. H., Jr., 1946, The peat deposits of Florida, their occurrence, development, and uses: Florida Geol. Surv. Geol. Bull., v. 30, 247 p.

Davis, J. T., 1963, A pollen-analytical investigation of the Horry Clay from Flanner Beach, North Carolina: Williams College honors thesis

Davis, Margaret B., 1963, On the theory of pollen analysis: Amer. J. Sci., v. 261, p. 897-912

Deevey, E. S., Jr., 1949, Biography of the Pleistocene: Geol. Soc. Amer. Bull., v. 60, p. 1315-1416

Dillon, L. S., 1956, Wisconsin climate and life zones in North America: Science, v. 123, p. 167-176

Dreimanis, Aleksis, 1960, Pre-classical Wisconsin in the eastern portion of the Great Lakes region, North America: Copenhagen, 21st Intern. Geol. Congr. Rep., Pt. 4, p. 108-119

Emiliani, Cesare, 1955, Pleistocene temperatures: J. Geol., v. 63, p. 538-578

Fenneman, N. M., 1938, Physiography of eastern United States: New York, McGraw-Hill Book Co., Inc., 714 p.

Flint, R. F., et al., 1945, Glacial map of North America: Geol. Soc. Amer. Spec. Pap. 60

Frey, D. G., 1951, Pollen succession in the sediments of Singletary Lake, North Carolina: Ecology, v. 32, p. 518-533

—— 1952, Pollen analysis of the Horry clay and a seaside peat deposit near Myrtle Beach, South Carolina: Amer. J. Sci., v. 250, p. 212-225

—— 1953, Regional aspects of the late-glacial and postglacial pollen succession of southeastern North Carolina: Ecol. Monogr., v. 23, p. 289-313

—— 1954, Evidence for the recent enlargement of the "bay" lakes of North Carolina: Ecology, v. 35, p. 78-88

—— 1955, A time revision of the Pleistocene pollen chronology of southeastern North Carolina: Ecology, v. 36, p. 762-763

Graham, Alan, and Heimsch, Charles, 1960, Pollen studies of some Texas peat deposits: Ecology, v. 41, p. 751-763

Guilday, J. E., Martin, P. S., and McCrady, A. D., 1964, New Paris No. 4; a late Pleistocene cave deposit in Bedford County, Pennsylvania: Natl. Speleol. Soc. Bull. 26, p. 121-194

Harrison, Wyman, Malley, R. J., Rusnak, G. A., and Terasmae, Jaan, 1965, Late-Pleistocene uplift, Chesapeake Bay entrance: J. Geol., in press

Knox, A. S., 1962, Pollen from the Pleistocene terrace deposits of Washington, D.C. (abst.): Pollen et Spores, v. 4, p. 357-358

Leopold, Estella B., 1959, Pollen, spores, and marine microfossils, in Malde, H. E. Geology of the Charleston phosphate area, South Carolina: U.S. Geol. Surv. Bull. 1079, p. 49-53

Lewis, I. F., and Cocke, E. C., 1929, Pollen analysis of Dismal Swamp peat: Elisha Mitchell Sci. Soc. J., v. 45, p. 37-58

Maher, L. J., Jr., 1964, *Ephedra* pollen in sediments of the Great Lakes region: Ecology, v. 45, p. 391-395

Martin, P. S., 1958a, Pleistocene ecology and biogeography of North America, in Hubbs, C. S. (ed.) Zoogeography: Amer. Assoc. Adv. Sci. Publ. 51, p. 375-420

—— 1958b, Taiga-tundra and the full-glacial period in Chester County, Pennsylvania: Amer. J. Sci., v. 256, p. 470-502

Munns, E. N., 1938, The distribution of important forest trees of the United States: U.S. Dept. Agric. Misc. Publ. 287, 176 p.

Newman, W. S., 1964, Holocene biostratigraphy of the lagoon near Wachapreague, eastern shore of Virginia (abst.): Geol. Soc. Amer., Ann. Meetings (1964)

Potzger, J. E., 1945, The Pine Barrens of New Jersey, a refugium during Pleistocene times: Butler Univ. Bot. Stud., v. 7, p. 182-193

Potzger, J. E., and Tharp, B. C., 1943, Pollen record of Canadian spruce and firm from Texas bog: Science, v. 98, p. 584

—— 1947, Pollen profile from a Texas bog: Ecology, v. 28, p. 274-280

—— 1954, Pollen study of two bogs in Texas: Ecology, v. 35, p. 462-466

Richards, H. G., 1950, Geology of the Coastal Plain of North Carolina: Amer. Philos. Soc. Trans., v. 40, p. 1-83

Schrock, A. E., 1945, A preliminary analysis of an unglaciated bog in Pennsylvania: Univ. Pittsburgh Bull., v. 41, p. 1-4

Sears, P. B., 1935, Types of North American pollen profiles: Ecology, v. 16, p. 488-499

Sears, P. B., and Couch, G. C., 1932, Microfossils in an Arkansas peat and their significance: Ohio J. Sci., v. 32, p. 63-68

Shelford, V. E., 1963, The ecology of North America: Urbana, Univ. Illinois Press, 610 p.

Steere, W. C., 1938, Pleistocene mosses from Louisiana: Louisiana Geol. Survey Bull., v. 12, p. 97-101

Vick, A. R., 1961, Some pollen profiles from the Coastal Plain of North Carolina: Univ. Syracuse Ph.D. thesis, 73 p.

Watts, W. A., 1965, Pollen diagram from Mud Lake, Marion County, Florida: unpublished manuscript.

Wells, B. W., and Boyce, S. G., 1953, Carolina bays: additional data on their origin, age, and history: Elisha Mitchell Sci. Soc. J., v. 69, p. 119-141

Whitehead, D. R., 1962, Size-frequency identifications of fossil pine pollen from Pleistocene deposits in eastern North America (abst.): Pollen et Spores, v. 4, p. 387-388

—— 1963, "Northern" elements in the Pleistocene flora of the Southeast: Ecology, v. 44, p. 403-406

—— 1964, Fossil pine pollen and full-glacial vegetation in southeastern North Carolina: Ecology, v. 45, p. 767-776

Whitehead, D. R., and Barghoorn, E. S., 1962, Pollen analytical investigations of Pleistocene deposits from western North Carolina and South Carolina: Ecol. Monogr., v. 32, p. 347-369

SUMMARY

Reconstruction of Pleistocene vegetation and climate in the Southeast remains difficult. Too few well-dated horizons have been studied, and much of the available information is inconclusive. The most comprehensive data are available from southeastern North Carolina and southeastern Virginia. These suggest that there were significant vegetational differences between the two regions. Whether these differences imply comparable climatic differences is not certain, for edaphic factors might have played a role. The full-glacial forests of southeastern North Carolina were dominated by pine (either jack pine or red pine) and spruce. A number of other "northern" species occurred as well. It would appear that the areally dominant vegetational type was an extremely open pine forest. A number of heliophytic herbs and shrubs occurred within this forest type. In contrast, in southeastern Virginia the dominant tree during full-glacial time was spruce, with fir and pine playing subordinate roles. Fewer boreal elements are known from this region, but this is probably a function of less detailed studies. The vegetational changes during late-glacial and postglacial time are quite similar in the two regions, although vegetationally comparable forests occur earlier in North Carolina. For example, a hemlock–northern hardwoods forest developed in North Carolina well over 10,000 years ago, while the same general type attained maximum development in southeastern Virginia only 9,500 years ago. In addition, hemlock was less common in North Carolina.

Although much of the early evidence of boreal species from other areas in the unglaciated East must be disregarded, present work clearly indicates considerable changes in vegetation (and hence climate) during periods of glaciation. The views expressed by Braun are hence untenable. However, whether one can speak of zonal displacement of vegetational types is questionable. Critical information is still lacking, but some investigations suggest that the full-glacial forests may have consisted of a mixture of boreal and more tolerant austral species.

Some new studies from Florida suggest that the full-glacial forests of that region may have been relatively austral in character.

Few interglacial horizons have been studied in detail, but several studies of apparent Sangamon horizons point to climatic conditions as warm as, if not warmer than, the present.

PLEISTOCENE POLLEN ANALYSIS AND
BIOGEOGRAPHY OF THE SOUTHWEST *

PAUL S. MARTIN,[1] PETER J. MEHRINGER, JR.[1]

WEST OF the 100th meridian, south and west of the Central Rockies, and east of the Sierra Nevada of California lies the desert region of the United States. Most of the deserts fall within the Basin-Range Province, which, except near the Lower Colorado River, lies above 300 m elevation. The Basin-Range Province extends into the Great Basin to the northwest, to the Colorado Plateau on the north, and to the High Plains on the east. Relative relief is great, reaching 4,500 m between the bottom of Death Valley and the top of Mt. Whitney, California, 140 km to the west. In addition to extreme climatic diversity caused by physiography there are major regional differences in mean annual temperature and in seasonal distribution of rainfall. The Great Basin is a high, cool desert with largely winter precipitation, the Mohave Desert somewhat lower and warmer, the Sonoran the lowest and hottest with an important summer-rainfall component, and the Chihuahuan higher and cooler with biologically significant rainfall mainly in the summer season.

Following its acquisition by the United States after the war with Mexico, over 100 years ago, intensive geological and biological surveys of the Southwest began under various agencies of the federal government. By the start of the 20th century most of the higher animals and plants of the region were known to science. But even in these groups new species continue to be discovered occasionally, for example the vertebrates *Salmo gilae* Miller (1950), *Plethodon neomexicanus* Stebbins and Riemer (1950), *Gerrhonotus panamintinus* Stebbins (1958), and the oak *Quercus ajoensis* Muller (1954). That parthenogenesis was only recently discovered in the whiptail lizard, *Cnemidophorus*, is a further illustration that much remains to be learned regarding even the "well-known" terrestrial vertebrates.

Ecological studies of the major animal-plant communities in the San Francisco Peaks of Arizona led to the concept of life-zones, which Merriam (1890) divided into Alpine, Subalpine, Hudsonian, Canadian, Neutral, Piñon Zone, and Desert Area. Similar life-zone descriptions in many desert mountains followed, with emphasis in recent years on the detailed pattern of individual species distribution (see Lowe, 1964; Whittaker and Niering, 1964). While the major biotic zones are now familiar to most ecologists, detailed ecological studies of certain distinctive environments of the Southwest are seldom seen in print. These environments include the margins of playa lakes (Potter, 1957), the natural cienegas and undissected floodplains of the desert grassland (Martin, 1963a, p. 23), the spring mounds of southern Nevada (Mehringer, in press), and the ice caves of New Mexico (Lindsey, 1951). Limnology, a more flourishing field of research in the arid Southwest than one might imagine, has been thoroughly reviewed by Cole (1963), who includes bogs, basin-range playas, meteoritic pits, volcanic lakes, mountain lakes (unglaciated), ox-bows, deflation basins, and solution basins in his inventory of the more important natural sediment traps.

The sizable although locally vanishing areas of natural desert in the Southwest offer excellent opportunity for studies of vegetation dynamics. For example, by photographic comparison Hastings and Turner (in press) show a retreat of mesquite, blue palo verde, and creosote bush from their lower range limits and an upward advance of these and other shrubs into the desert grassland during the last 60 years. The authors consider climatic change to be a major cause.

General accounts of the vegetation in parts of the arid Southwest may be found in Lowe (1964), Shreve and Wiggins (1964), Benson and Darrow (1954), Hastings and Turner (in press), Munz and Keck (1949), and Jaeger (1957). Some of the basic problems encountered in relating present to past vegetation through fossil-pollen counts are exposed in papers by Potter and Rowley (1960), Hafsten (1961), Hevly *et al.* (in press), Dixon (1962), Martin (1963a), Maher (1963), and King (1964). The short, superior summary by Malde (1964) covers, from a geologist's viewpoint, recent developments in the study of Late Pleistocene environments since man's arrival in western North America.

THE DEVELOPMENT OF POLLEN ANALYSIS IN ARID AMERICA

Despite its limitations, the fossil-pollen record is an especially revealing technique in the study of Pleistocene biology, and much of our account will focus on recent developments in this field. In the Southwest the use of pollen analysis in paleoecology can be traced to Laudermilk

* For advice or assistance in the preparation of this chapter we gratefully acknowledge the contributions of David P. Adam, Roger Y. Anderson, M. E. Cooley, Paul E. Damon, Emil W. Haury, Richard H. Hevly, C. Vance Haynes, J. R. Hastings, Claude W. Hibbard, J. J. Hester, Leo Heindl, H. C. Fritts, H. K. Gloyd, T. L. Simley, Raymond M. Turner, P. V. Wells, and Fred Wendorf. Several of the points of view we have adopted represent an outgrowth of the Ft. Burgwin Paleoecology Conference (Taos, New Mexico, June 1962). Through Grant GB 1959 the National Science Foundation provided financial support in the preparation of our manuscript, which represents Contribution No. 98, Program in Geochronology, University of Arizona.

[1] Geochronology Laboratories, University of Arizona, Tucson, Arizona.

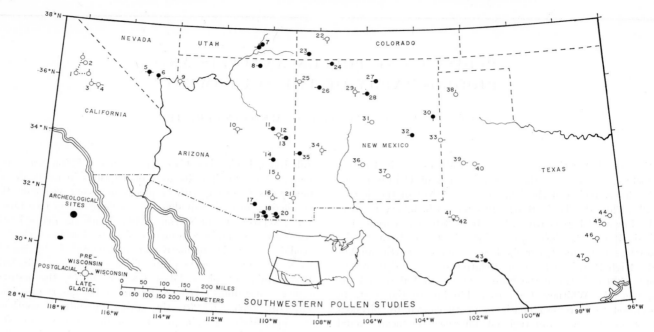

Figure 1. Pleistocene pollen-stratigraphic areas in the Southwest. Numbers refer to areas and bibliographic sources given in Table 1.

and Munz (1934), who illustrated various pollen grains in coprolite of the Shasta ground sloth. An early effort at postglacial pollen stratigraphy, made at the instigation of Ernst Antevs, was that of Sears (1937), who prepared a simple diagram of pollen in alluvial samples found near Kayenta in northern Arizona. The discovery that pollen occurs in sediments from dry lakes (playas) in the Southwest (Sears and Clisby, 1952; Clisby and Sears, 1956) revealed an extraordinarily rich source of fossil pollen in beds once considered largely devoid of organic remains (Tolman, 1909, p. 160). In cave earth Anderson (1955) encountered *Zea* among the pollen associated with archaeological materials. Pollen analysis of the present decade continues to be based on the study of alluvium, playa lake clays, cave earth (including coprolite), and fill of archaeological sites, plus some newly discovered sources such as the buried organic mats and wind-blown silt of spring mounds (Mehringer, in press), and the soil profile of mountain forests (King, 1964).

But each of these environments of deposition has its own effect on the pollen record, and climatic change is not the only major variable that can alter the pollen content of sediments. For example, Tertiary microfossils are a serious contaminant of Pleistocene alluvium in Wyoming (Rohrer and Leopold, 1963). Pollen of *Sarcobatus, Ephedra,* and other xerophytes is carried in dust storms from the desert into conifer-rimmed mountain lakes (Maher, 1963), while tree pollen, notably pine, accounts for as much as 40% of the pollen in certain desert soils. Although pollen is abundant in coprolite, it is greatly affected by phenology and feeding habits of the animal under study. Much remains to be learned about the fossil "pollen pool" and about its most effective use in arid-land paleoecology. Plant macrofossils are needed to supplement the pollen record. A promising

and recently discovered source is the content of desert pack-rat middens which may contain seeds, twigs, and bone cemented with urine and enduring largely intact for over 40,000 years (Wells and Jorgensen, 1964).

All but eight of the Pleistocene pollen stratigraphic records shown in Figure 1 are based on analyses published in the present decade or still in manuscript, making it impossible to develop perspective in our review, which seems destined by the rapid growth of the field for unplanned obsolescence. While the palynological literature of the Southwest is still small enough to summarize easily, the same may not be said for the biogeographic literature, which is voluminous. In the conviction that a major advance in Pleistocene studies of the Southwest over the past decade has been the growth of pollen analysis, we have chosen to stress this part of the fossil record. But there is much to expect from future studies of plant macrofossils, diatoms, mollusks, vertebrates, and other common Pleistocene fossils. The special insight of the taxonomist with a taste for biogeography continues to be worth close attention from all students of the Pleistocene.

DIVISIONS OF THE PLEISTOCENE

The Southwestern fossil-pollen record can be divided into three clearly marked periods: pre-Wisconsin (Sangamon and older), Wisconsin (12,000-70,000 before the present), and postglacial (12,000 years ago to date). Because of the formidable regional variation in climate, vegetation, and therefore in local pollen rain, a detailed Pleistocene chronology of the Southwest will require far more than the 50-odd diagrams reviewed by us at this time (Fig. 1). Certain major guidelines for future study are at hand, and the more obvious features of the Southwestern pollen record can be identified. For example, the dominant Pleistocene

TABLE 1

Pleistocene Pollen-Study Areas in the Southwest That Are
Shown in Fig. 1
(Those marked by an asterisk are also shown on Figs. 3 and 4)

CALIFORNIA
    1. Kennedy Meadows, Bakeoven Knob, Alabama Hills, and Little Lake. Axelrod and Ting, 1961
    2. Owens Lake. Martin, unpubl.
    3. China Lake. Martin, unpubl.
   *4. Searles Lake. Roosma, 1958; Leopold, unpubl.

NEVADA
   *5. Tule Springs. Mehringer, in press
    6. Gypsum Cave. Laudermilk and Munz, 1934

UTAH
    7. Glen Canyon, Colorado River. Martin and Sharrock, 1964

ARIZONA
    8. Navajo National Monument. Leopold, unpubl.; Sears, 1961
    9. Rampart Cave. Martin, Sabels, and Shutler, 1961
  *10. Potato Lake. Whiteside, 1964
  11. Hay Hollow Wash. Hevly, 1964a
 *12. Laguna Salada. Hevly, 1962, 1964; Schoenwetter, 1962
  13. Hooper Ranch, etc. Schoenwetter, 1962
  14. Point of Pines. Martin and Schoenwetter, 1960; Martin, 1963a
  15. Safford. Gray, 1961
 *16. Willcox Playa. Hevly and Martin, 1961; Martin, 1963c
  17. Cienega Creek, Matty Wash. Martin, 1963a
  18. Lewis Springs. Martin, 1963a
  19. Lehner Ranch Arroyo. Mehringer and Haynes, in press
  20. Double Adobe and vicinity. Martin, 1963a
  21. San Simon Cienega. Martin, 1963a

COLORADO
  22. Molas Lake. Maher, 1961
  23. Wetherill Mesa. Byers and Martin, in press

NEW MEXICO
  24. Navajo Dam, San Juan River. Schoenwetter and Eddy, 1964
 *25. Chuska Mountains, Dead Man Lake. Bent, 1960; Bent and Wright, 1963
  26. Chaco Canyon. Martin, unpubl.
  27. Picuris Pueblo. Schoenwetter, unpubl.
  28. Tesuque. Leopold, Leopold, and Wendorf, 1963
  29. Valle Grande. Sears and Clisby, 1952
  30. San Jon Site. Hafsten, 1961
  31. Harold Rud Salt Lake. Hafsten, 1961
  32. Middle Pecos, Ft. Sumner. Jelinek and Martin, unpubl.
  33. Arch Lake. Hafsten, 1961
 *34. San Augustin Plains. Clisby and Sears, 1956; Clisby et al., 1957; Clisby et al., 1962; Clisby, unpubl.
  35. Reserve and vicinity. Schoenwetter, 1962
  36. Malpais Spring. Hafsten, 1961
  37. Wolfe Ranch Canyon. Hafsten, 1961

TEXAS
  38. Rita Blanca Lake. Kirkland and Anderson, 1963
 *39. Rich Lake. Hafsten, 1961
  40. Tahoka Lake. Hafsten, 1961
 *41. Crane Lake. Hafsten, 1961
  42. Juan Cordova Lake. Hafsten, 1961
  43. Damp Cave, Centipede Cave. Johnson, 1963
  44. Franklin Bog. Potzger and Tharp, 1954
  45. Gause Bog. Potzger and Tharp, 1954
  46. Patschke Bog. Potzger and Tharp, 1947
  47. Soefje Bog. Graham and Heimsch, 1960

pollen types to be expected in most sediments include the following groups: (1) cheno-ams (Chenopodiaceae plus *Amaranthus*), (2) Compositae (separable into *Artemisia*, short-spine, and long-spine types), (3) grasses, (4) wind-pollinated trees, especially pine, followed by either spruce, oak, or juniper, depending on location and history of the deposit.

PRE-WISCONSIN PLEISTOCENE

In their pioneering study on the San Augustin Plains, Clisby and Sears (1956) perceived that a major change in pollen content clearly associated with continental glaciation could be found in that part of their core associated by radiocarbon dating with Wisconsin glaciation. The Wisconsin beds can be characterized by a maximum of pine and spruce pollen and are thought to reflect invasion of the arid San Augustin Plains by spruce and other boreal conifers.

The extraordinary feature of Clisby and Sears' record is not the fact that a spruce invasion occurred but that it happened only once. Evidence of a pre-Wisconsin descent of boreal forest into the part of San Augustin Plains now occupied by juniper grassland was not found in deeper parts of the San Augustin Plains core (Clisby et al., 1957; Clisby, written communication), sampled to a depth of over 300 m. Periodic changes in vegetation types that might be assigned to relatively cold versus relatively warm climates through four or more separate glacials are not obvious.

No other playas in the Southwest have been studied to so great a depth as the San Augustin Plains. From pluvial Lake Cochise in southern Arizona the upper 20 m of a 42-m core reveals Wisconsin-age pine parkland and woodland within a region currently dominated by desert grassland and mesquite. Below 20 m grass pollen dominates those strata that contain pollen (Martin, 1963c). Pine-dominated strata are absent, and the pre-Wisconsin pluvial environment shows none of the attributes of the Wisconsin-age beds.

Samples from pluvial Lake Bonneville in two separate drill cores supplied by A. J. Eardley of the University of Utah have been studied to a depth of 30 m; the pine-spruce curves are summarized in Figure 2. Radiocarbon dates of full-glacial age lie at or slightly above the zone in which pine pollen is found in greatest abundance. Presumably, the Wisconsin extends to a depth of 12 m. The zone between 12 and 16 m, in which pollen is not present, is thought to represent an interglacial. Beneath it fossil pollen again marks what should be a glacial, but the maximum in pine pollen (including some spruce) seen at the top of the Wendover core does not reappear.

A drill core from China Lake, California, contains sterile horizons to a depth of 6 m, where pollen of sedge and cattail is associated with a C^{14} date of $28,500 \pm 4,300$ (A-451) on carbonate of the fresh water mussel *Anodonta oregonensis* (P. E. Damon, written communication). Strata lacking pollen again appear between 12 and 16 m and may represent the same sterile zone found in Lake Bonneville. Unlike the record from most Southwestern playas, *Picea* (spruce) is very rare relative to fir in the China Lake core, and there is no reason to believe this boreal tree migrated south along the Sierra Nevada during the Wisconsin (see Adam, 1964, p. 15). Problems and possibilities in correlating playa-lake drill cores are shown in Figure 2.

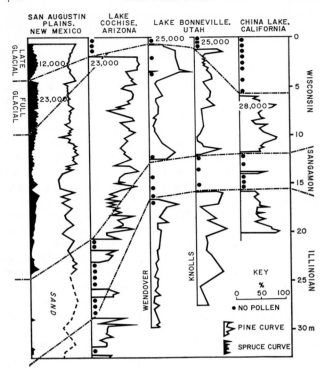

Figure 2. Provisional correlation of Pleistocene drill cores from Southwestern playa lakes. San Augustin Plains record is that of Clisby and Sears (1956) and Clisby (unpubl.); other records are from Martin (1963c; unpubl.).

Most Early Pleistocene and Tertiary lacustrine or alluvial outcrops in Arizona contain little pollen (Gray, 1960). An exception are three short drill-core samples from the Safford Basin in southeastern Arizona, considered to lie below late Blancan and Irvingtonian vertebrates at the 111 Ranch (Gray, 1961). The fossil counts contain more tree pollen (especially Cupressaceae, *Pinus,* and *Quercus*) and *Artemisia* than do modern pollen-rain samples from the region, thus suggesting a cooler or wetter climate and presumably Early Pleistocene pluvial conditions. A correlation with Nebraskan or pre-Nebraskan glaciation is possible. Of considerable biogeographic interest is pollen of *Ostrya* (24 records in about 4,000 determinations) and of *Ulmus* (5 records in 4,000 determinations).

Pollen analysis of a Blancan-age lake near Channing, Texas, by Harbour (Kirkland and Anderson, 1963) indicates over 50% *Artemisia* pollen, far more than is found in the region today and comparable to the high frequencies of *Artemisia* in the Rich Lake Interpluvial (Zone D of Hafsten, 1961). Further evidence of climatic change is seen in the fossil-leaf record, of which about half consists of *Quercus.* All the oaks are deciduous species presently found either east or west of the fossil locality. Other leaves include *Salix, Populus, Morus,* and *Ulmus,* thus establishing beyond doubt a more westerly occurrence of elm (*Ulmus*) in the Late Pliocene or Early Pleistocene.

Presently, the center of abundance for trees found in the Rita Blanca fossil beds is at least 400 km to the east in a much more mesic part of Texas. However, regions shedding high quantities of *Artemisia* pollen today lie to the west, and a mixing of central Texan with Northern Plains elements seems required by both fossil-pollen and leaf records.

An Early Pleistocene pollen record from California in the southern Sierra Nevada and adjacent Owens Valley is claimed by Axelrod and Ting (1961). If their conclusions are correct the deposits predate a 2,000-m uplift of the Sierra Nevada when species of trees not presently found in southern California extended southward along the Sierra. Their interpretation seems discordant with recent potassium-argon dates of Pliocene age for the surface under study (Dalrymple, 1963) and with the glacial chronology of the Sierra Nevada (Sharp and Birman, 1963, p. 1085). But it is possible that major tectonic activity occurred in the Pleistocene and that this will complicate geologic-climatic dating of certain beds.

While both the Safford, Arizona, and Rita Blanca, Texas, deposits contain evidence of cooler and moister conditions than characterize those areas today, they do not equal the dramatic change seen in the Wisconsin full-glacial. As the latter event occurred through only a relatively small part of the Wisconsin, perhaps no more than 6,000 years, it is possible that Early or Middle Pleistocene changes of comparable magnitude will eventually be found. Admittedly, the absence of a well-marked cold-wet Illinoian in the San Augustin Plains or in the shorter cores from Lake Cochise and the Great Salt Lake Desert does not match current climatic interpretations from other regions. For example, from their Savanna de Bogota core in Colombia, van der Hammen and Gonzalez (1960, p. 305) conclude that the next-to-last glacial, the Riss, was very cold with a greater displacement to vegetation zones than is seen in the Würm-Wisconsin. Such a record has yet to be found in the Southwest, making pre-Wisconsin climatic correlations very difficult.

THE WISCONSIN GLACIAL

If unequivocal climatic correlations between continental glaciation and Southwestern pollen stratigraphy cannot be demonstrated for the Early and Middle Pleistocene, correlations within the last glaciation are more promising and can be supported in some cases by radiocarbon dating.

According to Flint (1963) the last glacial began approximately 70,000 years ago, reached a maximum 20,000 years ago, and ended by 8000 B.C. An estimated age of 70,000 years appears reasonable for the Wisconsin portion of drill cores from San Augustin Plains, New Mexico (Clisby and Sears, 1956), Lake Cochise, Arizona (Martin, 1963c), Lake Bonneville, Utah, and China Lake (see Fig. 2) and Searles Lake, California. Despite major fluctuations in the ice margin, presumably accompanied by climatic changes that would be felt in arid regions, there was no warm interval during the last 70,000 years that could be considered as a true interglacial.

In the Texas High Plains the Rich Lake Interpluvial (22,000 to 32,000 years ago) was characterized by high pollen frequencies of grass and *Artemisia,* with small amounts of *Ephedra,* oak, and cheno-ams. According to Wendorf (1961, p. 130), the pollen and invertebrate data indicate a climate slightly cooler and possibly more moist than today's. It is quite likely that this interval corresponds in age to the Clear Creek fauna near Dallas, Texas (Slaughter and Ritchie, 1963), carbon-dated at 29,000 years and showing an easterly movement of small mammals now found in central and west Texas, plus a southerly penetration of the bog lemming *Synaptomys*. A decline in pine pollen older than the full-glacial occurs at Tule Springs (Mehringer, in press). These events argue for an interstadial of relatively mild climate immediately preceding the full-glacial and corresponding to the Plum Point interstadial (Flint, 1963) and the Paudorf oscillation of the European Pleistocene.

Southwestern pollen profiles containing horizons that by radiocarbon dates or on other grounds can be assigned to the interval between 17,000 to 23,000 years ago are designated in Table 1 by an asterisk. Within the Mohave Desert at Searles Lake this was a time when woodland occupied a region presently dominated by creosote bush, white bur-sage, and various species of saltbush (Roosma, 1958). Within another part of the Mohave Desert at Tule Springs (Fig. 5a), Nevada, woodland or possibly yellow-pine parkland is represented in sediments of full-glacial age (Mehringer, in press). Radiocarbon dates show that juniper and other trees and shrubs were growing 600 m below their present lower limits near Frenchman Flat at various times from >40,000 to 7,800 years ago (Wells and Jorgensen, 1964). In the Great Basin the pollen record from Great Salt Lake indicates a maximum of pine and spruce, with very little *Artemisia* or other Great Basin desert shrubs, just below sediments dated as 20,000–24,000 years old. Within the Colorado Plateau, Bent (1960) and Bent and Wright (1963) record a subalpine woodland of spruce and *Artemisia* at Dead Man Lake in the Chuska Mountains, while Whiteside (1964) found a similar dominance of spruce and *Artemisia* in sediments from a small lake behind the Mogollon Rim of central Arizona. Both areas have been dominated by ponderosa pine through most of postglacial time.

In a drier area at lower elevation on the north side of the Mogollon Rim, Hevly (1962, 1964a, 1964b) found pollen of pine and spruce similar to the pine-spruce fossil record recorded by Clisby and Sears in the San Augustin Plains. Hevly's pine-spruce maximum lies stratigraphically beneath a radiocarbon date of 7,300 ± 110 years (A-256). Clisby and Sears' spruce maximum can be directly related to radiocarbon dates of 23,070 ± 650 years (Y-1053). Today both areas are dominated by juniper grassland.

At the bottom of shallow soil profiles, 10 cm or less in depth, in the Sandia Mountains of New Mexico, King (1964) found spruce pollen percentages equivalent to those in the modern pollen rain of the Sandias at higher elevations, in one case implying an 810-m vertical descent of spruce-fir forest. The Sandia profiles are undated; in the absence of an accompanying increase in *Artemisia* they differ from Wisconsin-age deposits in the Chuska Mountains and along the Mogollon Rim. In view of the abundant opportunity for post-depositional alteration of pollen percentages in a soil, it is hard to believe that they do not represent a mixture of pollen rains of different ages. Differential destruction could also account for the apparent increase in spruce with depth. But King's provocative discovery should encourage further interest in the meaning of pollen in the soil profile, and his detailed analysis of the modern pollen rain contained in moss polsters is an important contribution to that neglected subject.

South of the Colorado Plateau in the desert grassland, 20,000-year-old sediments from Lake Cochise, Arizona, are almost exclusively composed of pine pollen with very small amounts of spruce and grass (Martin, 1963c). In west Texas Hafsten records a similar maximum of pine and spruce at about the same time, with very few or no other pollen types represented during the Tahoka pluvial. One radiocarbon date of 17,000 years from Rich Lake indicates full-glacial age. Suspicion that the extremely high pine counts might represent a type of pinyon-juniper woodland (Jelinek, 1962) is not borne out by modern pollen-rain studies in the Sangre de Cristo (Dixon, 1962) and the San Juan Mountains (Maher, 1963). The pine-dominated Tahoka pluvial seems to contain too much spruce pollen and too little juniper to represent a pinyon-juniper woodland. Admittedly macrofossil evidence is badly needed.[2]

Hafsten's pine-spruce Pollen Zone C from the Texas High Plains may be reflected in Potzger and Tharp's (1947) diagram from Patschke Bog in east Texas. The bottom of their profile at 22 ft contains almost 50% pine pollen, with a few percent spruce, in an area in which the postglacial pollen record is dominated by grass and oak with an extremely low frequency of pine. Subsequent work in the east Texas bogs has failed to confirm the initial pine dominance (Potzger and Tharp, 1954; Graham and Heimsch, 1960), but the later studies may not have included sediments of equivalent age.

From what is known of the Southwestern pollen record, especially the localities listed in Table 2 or marked by an asterisk in Figure 1, we have projected a vegetation map for 20,000 years ago (compare Figs. 3 and 4). The result is clearly a first approximation. Furthermore, absolute reliance on radiocarbon dates as criteria for establishing full-glacial age can be hazardous in view of the apparent ages of 17,000 to 25,000 years on *living* aquatic plants in Montezuma Well, Arizona (Damon, Haynes, and Cole, 1964). Fortunately, the Montezuma Well anomaly is a special case related to unusual geochemical and topographic circumstances. For more detailed discussion of procedure, C^{14} dates, and an earlier version of the full-glacial vegetation map, see Martin (1964).

A major difficulty in constructing Figure 4 was the problem of the Sonoran Desert. The sediments from Ventana Cave, in the heart of the Sonoran Desert of southern Arizona, has been carbon-dated at the level of volcanic debris at 11,300 ± 1,200 years (Damon and Long, 1962, p. 246). Apart from the hazards involved when climatic inference is based on large Pleistocene vertebrates—to be discussed later—the date indicates that the associated

---

[2] P. V. Wells has uncovered wood of pinyon, juniper, and *Berberis* of full-glacial age in pack-rat middens of the Big Bend region, Texas (UCLA 785, 18, 750 ± 360, *see* Radiocarbon, v. 7). The region today is part of the Chihuahuan Desert; it falls within the area mapped as pinyon-juniper woodland on Figure 4.

TABLE 2

Modern and Full-glacial (17,000–23,000 B.P.) Vegetation in Arizona, New Mexico, and West Texas
(NAP = non-arboreal pollen)

Present environment	Location and source	Elev. in m	Pollen rain in percent		Dominant vegetation	
			Modern	Full-glacial	Modern	Full-glacial
Cool montane conifers	1. Potato Lake, Ariz. (Whiteside, 1964)	2,340	Pine-65 Grass-20	Spruce-25 Pine-15 *Artemisia*-20	Ponderosa pine forest	Subalpine spruce-woodland
	2. Dead Man Lake, N.M. (Bent, 1960)	2,640	Pine-70 NAP-25 Spruce-tr.	Spruce-8 Pine-30 *Artemisia*-50	Ponderosa pine parkland	Subalpine spruce-woodland
Cool grassland	3. Laguna Salada, Ariz. (Hevly, 1962)	1,900	Pine-20 Juniper-25 NAP-50	Spruce-7 Pine-50 *Artemisia*-10	Juniper-grassland	Spruce-pine forest
	4. San Augustin Plains, N.M. (Clisby and Sears, 1956; Clisby *et al.*, 1962)	2,000	Pine-20 Cheno-ams-60 Composites-5	Pine-85 Spruce-13 Fir-1	Blue grama grassland-saltbush	Spruce-pine forest
Warm grassland	5. Pluvial Lake Cochise, Ariz. (Martin, 1963c)	1,260	Pine-20 NAP-70	Pine-98 Spruce-1	Mesquite-grassland	Pine parkland
	6. Rich Lake, Tex. (Hafsten, 1961)	1,100	Pine-15 NAP-85	Pine-90 Spruce-8	Short grass plains	Pine parkland (with spruce?)

fauna will not shed much light on what the Sonoran Desert was like at the height of continental glaciation. The claim for grassland in the area at the time appears based largely on the abundance of horse bones in both the conglomerate and volcanic debris (Colbert in Haury, 1950, p. 137). But the fossil-pollen content of a sample of volcanic debris (Fig. 6) is similar in proportions to pollen counts of the soil surface of the Sonoran Desert near Tucson and is unlike pollen counts from the desert grassland of southeastern Arizona. Furthermore, the assumption that fossil horses are reliable indicators of grassland loses its validity if one considers the present range of thousands of burros

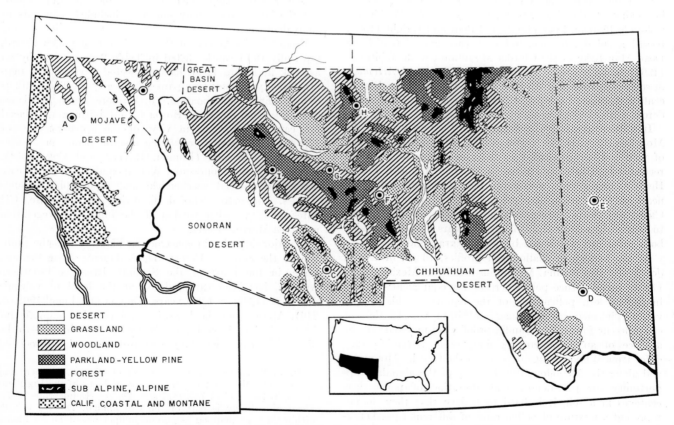

DESERT
GRASSLAND
WOODLAND
PARKLAND-YELLOW PINE
FOREST
SUB ALPINE, ALPINE
CALIF. COASTAL AND MONTANE

Figure 3. Modern vegetation of the Southwest, based on Shantz and Zon (1924).

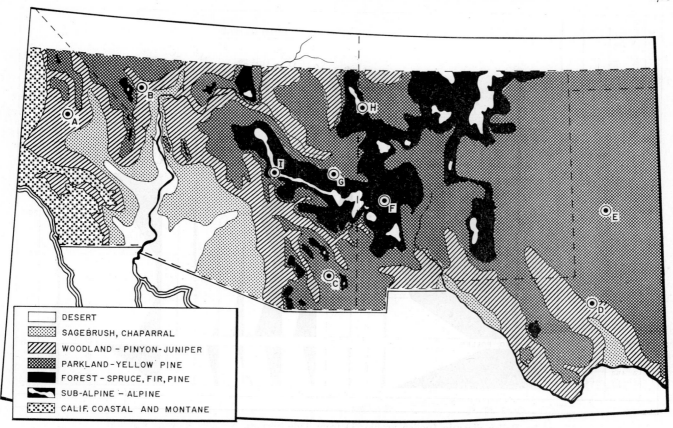

Figure 4. Full-glacial vegetation of the Southwest 17,000-23,000 years ago, based mainly on carbon-dated fossil-pollen spectra from (A) Searles Lake, (B) Tule Springs, (C) Pluvial Lake Cochise, (D) Crane Lake, (E) Rich Lake, (F) San Augustin Plains, (G) Laguna Salada, (H) Dead Man Lake, (I) Potato Lake. See Table 1 for bibliographic sources.

and horses living wild in the Mohave Desert, one of the least grassy parts of western North America.

Despite the fact that the Sonoran Desert was probably in its present position 11,000 years ago, it seems equally likely that it was displaced by earlier full-glacial climatic changes which caused pine parkland to invade the desert grassland and caused woodland to spread through the Great Basin and Mohave Deserts. The plant communities to be expected in the Sonoran Desert 20,000 years ago would be sagebrush and chaparral, with creosote bush persisting along the lower Colorado River. At the same time, applying the expected 900 to 1,200 m of vertical displacement to certain species of the Sonoran Desert creates a peculiar difficulty. Even if sea level were 100 m lower at the time, it appears that any major drop in vertical range would have submerged many desert plants in the waters of the Gulf of California.

This hypothetical fate would not be a hazard in the case of the emblem of the Sonoran Desert, the saguaro (*Cereus giganteus*), which exceeds 1,200 m in its present vertical range, but it would be in the case of those Mexican species that do not enjoy great vertical amplitude, as the cardon (*Cereus pringlei*), boojum (*Idria columnaris*), and the arboreal caper (*Forchammeria watsonii*). Backed against the arid tropics of Sinaloa, with the Sierra Madre Occidental

blocking retreat to the west and with Great Basin chaparral and sagebrush presumably invading from the north, Sonoran Desert plants may have been hard pressed. Hopefully, pollen studies around the Gulf of California begun by Auriel Cross and his students at Michigan State University will uncover the location of Sonoran Desert species 20,000 years ago.

THE POSTGLACIAL, 12,000 B.P. TO PRESENT

On the basis of the pollen-stratigraphic evidence we have chosen to place the beginning of the postglacial in the Southwest at about 12,000 years ago. Thus the early part of our postglacial would fall within late-glacial time of the eastern United States, which is climatically quite distinct from the postglacial of that area (Deevey and Flint, 1957). In the Southwest the last glacial-pluvial pollen records are C[14] dated between 13,000 and 12,000 B.P. There follows a rapid change to pollen spectra resembling more closely those of the rest of the postglacial than of the full-glacial. This rapid change seems to correspond in time to the Two Creeks ice recession of classical Wisconsin glaciation (Broecker and Farrand, 1963). Carbon-dated pollen evidence for a rapid vegetation change in the Southwest at the beginning of the postglacial (*i.e.* from glacial moist-cool

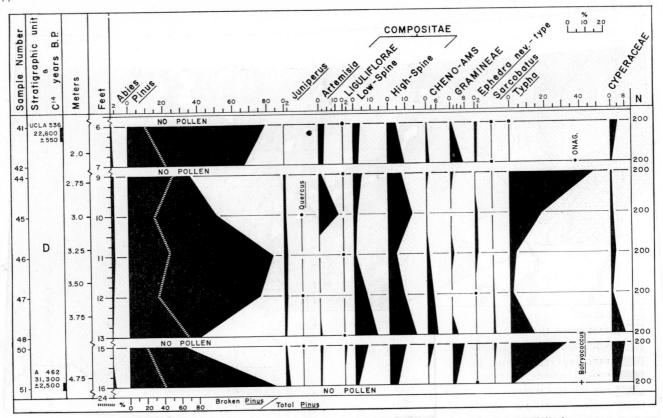

Figure 5a. Pollen diagram (pollen profile II) from Tule Springs, Nevada, showing a full-gla-cial record from lake beds. The changes in *Pinus* and *Typha* pollen are thought to be the result of fluctuating lake levels which may or may not be related to climatic change (for a discussion of the Tule Springs diagrams see Mehringer, in press).

conditions to postglacial drier-warmer conditions) is apparent in the pollen records from Tule Springs, Nevada (Fig. 5b; Mehringer, in press), Potato Lake, Arizona (Whiteside, 1964), San Augustin Plains, New Mexico (Clisby and Sears, 1956), and Crane Lake, Texas (Hafsten, 1961).

In southeastern Arizona, pollen spectra from the Naco, Ventana Cave, and Lehner Early Man sites (Fig. 6) show that by 11,000 years ago the vegetation was similar to today's (for a discussion of the carbon dating of these sites see Haynes, 1964). At the Lehner site the postglacial beds, dating from about 11,200 years ago, contain fossils of mollusks that are found there now. An older stratigraphic unit, separated from the postglacial beds by an erosion surface and C^{14} dated at 11,600 ± 400 B.P. (A-478, Damon, Haynes, and Long, 1964), contains fossils of snails which live today only in the higher mountains of southern Arizona (Mehringer and Haynes, in press).

While there is every reason to expect late-glacial oscillations of the type so familiar to pollen stratigraphers in temperate latitudes, some claims for their existence in the Southwest appear to be based as much on expectation as on evidence. And in view of the recent revision in the long-accepted correlation of the Two Creeks interstadial of the Great Lakes with the Alleröd of western Europe, based on careful stratigraphy and radiocarbon dating (Broecker and Farrand, 1963), the facile naming of an undated pine

fluctuation in the Southwest as correlative with some particular late-glacial fluctuation in Europe or eastern North America seems to us questionable. If worldwide changes are to be hypothesized, the Southwestern pollen record is in accord with the evidence of Broecker *et al.* (1960) for an abrupt change in climate close to 11,000 years ago.

The pollen record of the last 10,000 years shows intriguing but at most minor changes. In east Texas the organic material of spring seeps appears to be mainly of post-glacial age. Graham and Heimsch (1960) found little change in fossil content of a 4.6-m profile. In high-altitude lakes of the southern Colorado Plateau the postglacial pollen record also seems relatively stable (Bent and Wright, 1963; Maher, 1961; Whiteside, 1964). A more variable postglacial record is that of Hevly (1964a), who recognizes five postglacial zones and develops the concept of "sensitive sites" as necessary in uncovering postglacial vegetation shifts of 150-300-m amplitude.

In the Texas High Plains, Hafsten divided his post-glacial Pollen Zone A into four parts, based on minor fluctuations of cheno-ams, composites, and pine. Major fluctuations in the first two types characterized floodplains of southern Arizona, where Martin (1963a) proposed a four-part floodplain chronology with two composite and two cheno-am maxima. In the case of the Lehner site, counts made exclusive of cheno-ams and composites (Fig. 6) re-

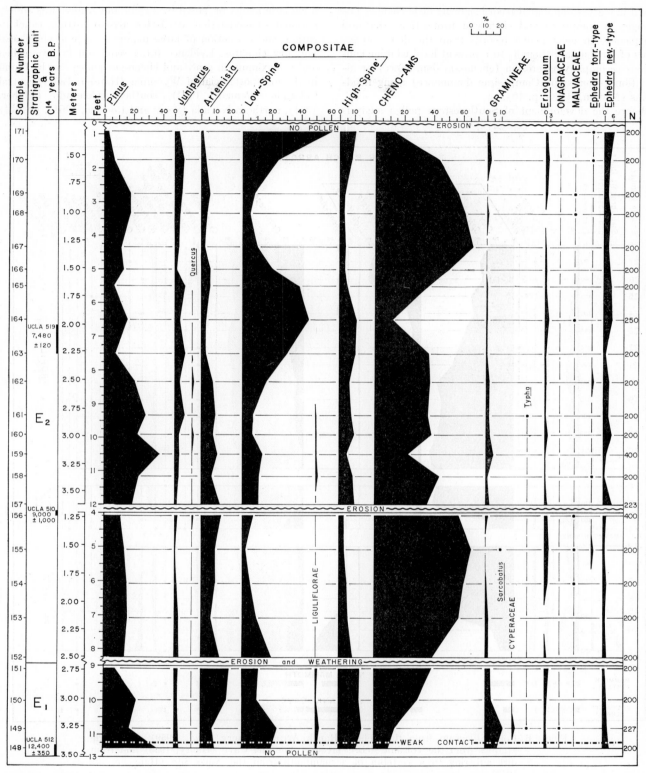

Figure 5b. Pollen diagram (pollen profile IV) from Tule Springs, Nevada, showing a postglacial, alluvial pollen record dominated by NAP. The upper two samples are placed between 6,000-7,000 B.P. on geologic evidence and show pollen spectra similar to the modern pollen rain in the Mohave Desert at the site. The lower samples approach the modern pollen rain of the Great Basin Desert environment.

sulted in a grass-dominated record showing little change. The changes in composite and cheno-am proportions that are conspicuous in most pollen records from the desert grasslands of Arizona are thought to represent local edaphic conditions accompanying erosion (cheno-am dominance) or alluviation (short-spine Compositae dominance) along floodplains (Martin, 1963a, p. 49).

Before the development of Southwestern pollen analysis

a climatic model proposed by Bryan and Antevs was widely adopted—a model that attributed arroyo cutting, calichification, and extinction of large mammals to mid-postglacial hot, dry climates. Evidence for a reduction in tree pollen and a maximum in grass and cheno-am pollen can be found in the mid-postglacial of Wyoming (Hansen, 1951), central Colorado (Pennak, 1963), southern Colorado (Maher, 1961), northern Nevada (Sears and Roosma, 1961), possibly

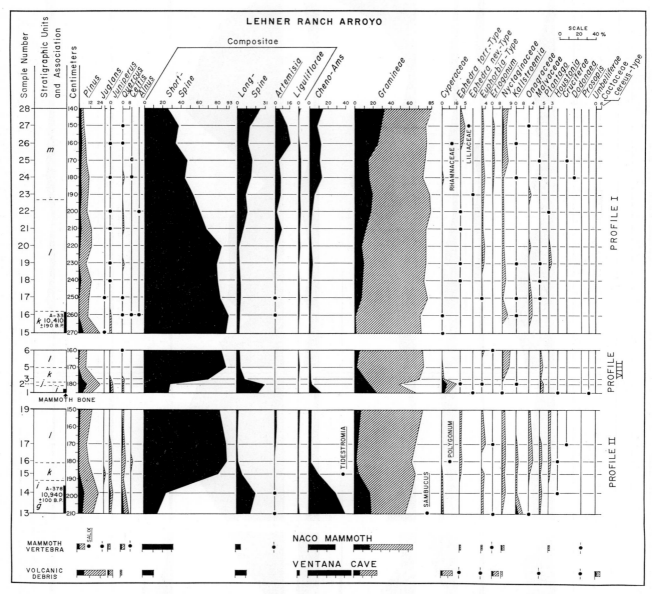

Figure 6. Pollen diagram from the Lehner Ranch Arroyo (Haury *et al.,* 1959) and single samples from the volcanic debris layer of Ventana Cave (Haury, 1950) and from dirt adhering to a vertebra of a mammoth from the Naco Site (Haury *et al.,* 1953).

The Lehner pollen diagram shows portions of three pollen profiles from pre-Altithermal-age beds (Antevs, 1959). The solid portion of the diagram represents the first count (200 grains), which includes all pollen types. The lined portion indicates the second pollen count (100 grains), excluding cheno-ams and composites. The dots (·) indicate less than 1% of a pollen type in the first count or less than 2% in the second count. Both counts are plotted to the same scale and are read from the zero percent line at the left (Mehringer and Haynes, in press).

southern Nevada (Mehringer, in press), and northern Arizona (Hevly, 1964a). How much "drought" is to be read into the records may be less important than establishing whether there was a shift in seasonality, with summer storminess partly compensating for a decrease in winter precipitation (see also Malde, 1964, p. 127).

Along the Mexican border the Antevs-Bryan climatic model of drought as a cause of arroyo cutting has not been substantiated by evidence of marked aridity in the mid-postglacial pollen record (Martin, 1963a). There it is possible that under the influence of the Mexican monsoon the Altithermal actually may have been a time of greater precipitation, at least in summer, rather than of drought. Carbon-dated pollen records falling within the Altithermal (4,000 to 7,500 years) are few, but three gleaned from a total of 13 carbon-dated pollen spectra of postglacial age show slightly higher numbers of either pine or grass pollen, with some ponding evidenced by hygric pollen types (Martin, 1963b). Near the Pecos River in Texas, Johnson (1963) also found a pine rise during the archaic and suggested wetter conditions during the "Altithermal" of that area.

Because of the nature of relative numbers an increase in pine pollen is by no means absolute proof of an increase in growth of pine trees, and under a circumstance in which local pollen production is reduced, conceivably as a result of unfavorable climatic conditions, there could be a *relative increase* in the amount of pine pollen received at the site of deposition. The interpretation of slight changes in pine-pollen frequencies in fossil-pollen records from the arid Southwest presents problems yet to be resolved. In areas of varying relief where coniferous forests are separated from deserts by a thousand or more meters in elevation but by only a few tens of kilometers in distance, a high percentage of wind-blown pine pollen may be found in the modern pollen content of desert soils (Mehringer, in press; Hevly *et al.*, in press). The relative frequency of pine pollen *increases* with the reduction in plant cover as one enters the desert (see Martin and Gray, 1962, Fig. 1). This is also true in areas remote from montane forest. For example, the soil surface of the Sonoran Desert at Yuma, in southwestern Arizona about 110 km from the nearest coniferous forest, contains a higher percentage of pine pollen than do soil surface samples of the desert grassland of southeastern Arizona, which is surrounded by mountains with coniferous forests.

Thus an increase in pine-pollen percentages in an alluvial pollen record from the desert grassland (Martin, 1963a) might mean either an expansion of local forests and more moist conditions, as Martin supposed, or a reduction in local plant cover, the result of drought. Whatever later discoveries may reveal, there is yet no clear evidence from the floodplain pollen record that suggests "deserts on the march" or an Altithermal climate in southern Arizona and New Mexico that was appreciably hotter and dries than today's.

Many pollen studies in the Southwest can be associated with archaeological excavations (see Fig. 1). Pollen occurs in trash mounds, in subterranean ceremonial rooms (kivas), in buried floors of Pueblo rooms or pithouses, and in cave earth. Alluvium contains a pollen record less easily related to man's activities, but some alluvial sites contain corn

(*Zea*) pollen, verifying its presence in the Southwest 2,000 or more years ago (Martin and Schoenwetter, 1960) and suggesting its cultivation behind stone walls constructed as check-dams (Byers and Martin, in press). Pollen of *Cucurbita*, both *pepo* and *moschata-mixta* types, commonly appears in prehistoric sites and human feces, while pollen of beans (*Phaseolus*) and cotton (*Gossypium*) is seldom found. Other pollen types found in abundance only around archaeological sites and thus considered of economic significance—although the plants themselves may not have been cultivated by prehistoric man—include Rocky Mountain beeweed (*Cleome*), cactus (especially *Opuntia*), *Agave*, and Liliaceae. Prehistoric human feces are highly variable in pollen content; they may contain large numbers of pollen grains of most of the foregoing types (Martin and Sharrock, 1964), and may on occasion by dominated by single species used for food only seasonally, such as *Populus*, short-spine Compositae (cf. *Dicoria*), and a large-sized grass pollen.

The pollen content of the sediments of certain archaeological sites may show an increase in pine in the 11th and 13-14th centuries that Schoenwetter (1962) and Hevly (1946a) believe can be associated with climatic changes. If it can be established that these changes are independent of cultural disturbance, or of changes in the non-pine pollen sum (Leopold *et al.*, 1963), it will be possible to interpret cultural history more directly in terms of climate than has been possible previously. Perhaps the best evidence of late prehistoric climatic fluctuation is still that found in the tree-ring record, plus the very fact of Pueblo abandonment.

In summary, the Southwestern pollen record of the Pleistocene indicates (1) difficulties in correlating with continental glaciation of the Early and Middle Pleistocene; (2) direct correlation with Wisconsin glaciation, starting perhaps 70,000 years ago, with biotic zones descending 900-1,200 m; (3) a rapid rather than gradual recovery of postglacial vegetation about 12,000 B.P., and (4) intriguing but relatively minor changes in pollen proportions, suggesting 150-400 m of vertical displacement in vegetation zones over the last 12,000 years. These minor changes in postglacial pollen profiles can be associated with arroyo cutting, Pueblo abandonment, and other significant climatic and cultural events.

PLEISTOCENE BIOGEOGRAPHY

The biogeographic storm long raging in eastern United States regarding the degree to which biotic communities were affected by glaciation can be traced into the Southwest, where the nature of Pleistocene climates has also been a matter of perennial interest, considerable difference in opinion, and some contention (compare Merriam, 1890, p. 20-21; Epling, 1944; Deevey, 1949, p. 1394-1400; McVaugh, 1951; Antevs, 1954; Dillon, 1956; Croizat, 1958, p. 42; Norris, 1958, p. 305; Darrow, 1961, p. 37-41; and Howden, 1963). Among the first to consider the effect of the Pleistocene on plant distribution in the west was John Muir (1877), who observed that groves of the giant sequoias occupy unglaciated areas in California between glaciated valleys such as King's River, Tuolume, and the Merced. Muir concluded that sequoias were not distributed more extensively in the Sierra Nevada in postglacial time.

Recent summaries of Tertiary paleobotany (Axelrod, 1950, 1958; Darrow, 1961; MacGinitie, 1958) present evidence for arid climates from the Miocene to the Late Pliocene, the time when Axelrod assumes the desert vegetation had achieved approximately its present composition. Doubts about such a recent evolution of the desert have arisen in the minds of those biogeographers studying the strikingly diverse, endemic Mexican xerophytes (Rzedowski, 1962), but no serious challenge to Axelrod's thesis of deserts in the Pliocene has appeared. Pollen types associated with arid-land plant communities can be traced to the late Miocene (Martin and Gray, 1962).

Regarding the migrations that led to the development of the present biotic communities in the Southwest it is clear that the late-Tertiary record shows a contraction of humid forest (the "Arcto-Tertiary Geoflora") and the expansion of more xeric communities ("Madro-Tertiary Geoflora") moving north from Mexico. But in historical reconstruction it is logically necessary to place *last* things first, *i.e.* to see if present patterns of distribution can be satisfactorily explained in terms of the most recent climatic events before turning to the effect of older changes. Belief that the present biota of the Southwest attained, and has retained, its present geographic distribution since the end of the Pliocene was based on certain biogeographic inference now largely invalidated by the Pleistocene fossil record.

To be more specific, the fossil pollen record of Wisconsin-age pine parkland with spruce south of the Colorado Plateau means sufficient downward displacement of plant communities to allow several invasions of "Arcto-Tertiary Geofloras" into the desert mountains during the Pleistocene. For example, the extraordinary occurrence of lungless salamanders (*Aneides hardyi*) in the Sacramento Mountains, New Mexico, has been interpreted as the result of late-Tertiary expansion of their favored habitat—mixed conifer forest with Douglas fir (*Pseudotsuga*)—spreading southward through the Rockies from the Pacific Northwest where relatives of these salamanders live now (Lowe, 1950). On paleobotanical grounds Lowe severed the connection in the Pliocene. The Pleistocene fossil record by no means disproves Lowe's interpretation, but, as Murray (1957) pointed out, dispersal of *Aneides* through the Rocky Mountains likely occurred several times since the Tertiary, and it is certainly conceivable that final isolation of *Aneides* in the Sacramento Mountains did not occur until the beginning of the postglacial.

OAKS, WHIP-TAILED LIZARDS, AND CREOSOTE BUSH

Some uncertainty lingers regarding Tertiary versus Pleistocene contacts in widely separated species pairs not closely related, such as the frogs *Rana boylei* and *R. tarahumare* (Zweifel, 1955) and the fringe-toed lizards *Uma exul* and *U. scoparia* (Norris, 1958). But in the case of closely related species most taxonomists have come to view the last stage of interconnection between disjunct populations as probably Late Pleistocene, or even postglacial. In the case of the evening primrose *Clarkia rhomboidea*, Mosquin (1964) postulates a more or less continuous Wisconsin-age distribution through the Great Basin, a region it encircles but largely avoids at present. Double Pleistocene invasions ending in

sympathy in southern California is the case in paired species within the salamander genera *Ensatina* and *Batrachoseps*, frogs of the genus *Rana*, and lizards of the genus *Eumeces* (see Peabody and Savage, 1958, p. 182). The lizard *Uma* most likely found that the Mohave and Great Basin Deserts were uninhabitable during glacial time. Its present range is thought to represent the outcome of a postglacial invasion (Norris, 1958). Findley and Jones (1962) believe that during the Wisconsin pluvial the long-tailed and montane voles (*Microtus longicaudus* and *M. montanus*) were widespread. During postglacial times they found their preferred habitats—cool, mesic grass-sedge meadows and woods' edges near coniferous forest—in the highest and wettest mountains of Arizona and New Mexico. Invasion from the north at a time when the climate was cool and dry can be documented by the fossil record of the sage vole (*Lagurus*) and other mammals in Isleta caves of New Mexico (Harris and Findley, 1964). As a final case among many, hybridization between the whip-tailed lizards, *Cnemidophorus tigris gracilis* and *C. t. marmoratus*, almost surely represents postglacial contact along the Arizona–New Mexico boundary. The two populations were widely separated during the full-glacial. It is possible that the hybrids developed only since the arroyo cutting, overgrazing, and climatic change of the last 70 to 80 years (Zweifel, 1962).

A group recently receiving careful biogeographic and ecologic attention is the western oaks (*Quercus*), represented by 14 species in Arizona and 16 in California. In a determined effort at resolving some of the taxonomic chaos Tucker (1961, 1963) has been studying various populations included within the *undulata* complex. The main contributor is *Quercus gambelii*, the most mesic of the Arizona–New Mexico oaks and one of relatively few deciduous species in the Southwest. It hybridizes occasionally with *Quercus arizonica*. Because of the dependence of *Quercus arizonica* on summer rains, it is likely that it and *gambelii* were not in contact in the Southwest during the Late Pleistocene and that the small number of hybrids known at present are strictly a postglacial development. In the case of the more numerous hybrids between *Quercus turbinella* (scrub oak) and *Q. gambelii* there is a remarkable extension of hybrid populations north to the Wasatch Range of Utah, where *turbinella* itself is absent (Cottam *et al.*, 1959; Tucker *et al.*, 1961).

A similar pattern among shrubs of the Rosaceae is reported by Stutz and Thomas (1964). Intergeneric hybrids of *Cowania* (cliff rose) and *Purshia* occur north of the region where the parent populations are sympatric. *Cowania*-like characters can be found in *Purshia* 300 km north of its present limit. In the case of both the scrub oak and the cliff rose it is possible that the missing parent recently ranged much farther north, perhaps in the Altithermal. On the other hand, Stutz and Thomas suggest that natural selection alone might allow *Cowania* genes to move northward by stepwise backcrossing. Whatever the explanation for the origin of the hybrids, it appears that their pattern of distribution is no older than the postglacial.

Admittedly, in the absence of direct fossil evidence the conclusion that Southwestern plants and animals were on the move during the Wisconsin and earlier in the Pleistocene tells us nothing about species age. Leaves of both *Quercus gambelii* and its near relative *Q. margaretta* contributed to the rich Early Pleistocene fossil record of Rita Blanca Lake in west Texas, presently an oakless region (Kirkland and Anderson, 1963). In the case of *Quercus ajohensis*, a species almost surely left as a postglacial relict after Wisconsin pluvial invasion of chaparral into the Sonoran Desert, fossil leaves show that its ancestors lived at much higher latitudes in central Washington in the Lower Pliocene (Tucker and Muller, 1956).

Finally, although it seems to us that the Pleistocene and in particular the full-glacial and postglacial climates of the last 20,000 years will account for a great deal of what one sees in the present distribution patterns of plants and animals throughout the Southwest, certain paradoxes in distribution as yet defy satisfactory explanation. An inescapable example is the fact that the most abundant of Southwestern desert shrubs, the creosote bush (*Larrea tridentata*), as well as *Koeberlinia spinosa, Celtis tala,* and other distinctive aridland plants of the Southwest, also occurs in the deserts of South America (see Johnston, 1940; Axelrod, 1950; Garcia *et al.*, 1960). The zoologist may find some comfort and a valuable clue in the fact that only xeric plants display this challenging gap in their ranges. "Of the hundreds of species of insects associated with *Larrea* in the two hemispheres, not one is shown to have a range similar to that of *Larrea*" (Raven, 1963, p. 165). It is unlikely that the amphitropical relationships in American desert floras entail Late Pleistocene dispersal.

PLANTS AND ANIMALS IN PREHISTORIC REFUSE

We have emphasized that there is little evidence of major climatic change in the postglacial pollen record of the Southwest. Regarding the non-cultivated-plant record from the oldest occupied prehistoric caves of the Southwest, 70 species identified from Danger Cave, Utah (Jennings, 1957, p. 228), 15 species from Ventana Cave, Arizona (Haury, 1950, p. 168-169), and 44 species from Bat Cave, New Mexico (Smith, 1950), all are to be found today within a day's walking distance of the ancient middens. In the case of vertebrates the pattern is similar. From beds lying above the 11,000-year-old volcanic debris in Ventana Cave, Allen (*in* Haury, 1950, p. 151) examined over 300 pounds of selected mammal bones. Of the species present, only the prairie dog (*Cynomys*) might not have lived near the cave in prehistoric times. Among 13 species of birds, Howard (*in* Haury, 1950, p. 152) found nothing more extraordinary than brown pelican, possibly brought from the Gulf of California. Beyond some suggestion of a size increase in *Neotoma albigula* and *Peromyscus maniculatus*, 7,300 identified bones from Wupatki, Arizona, revealed little change between the fauna of 800 years ago and that of the present, (Lincoln, 1962). Over 3,000 identified bones from prehistoric sites at Point of Pines, Arizona, were mainly deer and antelope (Stein, 1963), as were bones from the Awatovi site, Arizona (Lawrence, 1951). In each case, all the ecologically sensitive small mammals could have come from the immediate vicinity, and no range changes were noted. Minor exceptions are the Pueblo-age middens in northern New Mexico

that Harris (1963) believes show range changes of less than 20 km among the cottontails and long-tailed vole.

In reviewing the results of analysis of bird bones from a number of Indian middens, mainly of postglacial age, Miller (1963) reported only one extinct species, the vulture *Coragyps occidentalis,* and one major range extension, that of the California condor. The ichthyologist may fare better with archaeofaunal material. Miller (1955) reported the recently described hump-backed chub *Gila cypha* from Catclaw Cave along the Colorado River, and Gehlbach and Miller (1961) found *Lepisosteus* and *Cycleptus* in northern New Mexico, in each case from stream reaches where these species are unrecorded within historic times.

A record of biological conservatism appears the main conclusion to be drawn from the postglacial middens examined. Altithermal drought, if it occurred, left no obvious macrofossil evidence. Somewhat drier conditions after the Los Pinos–Sambrito phases of the Pueblo Period (A.D. 1-700) are suggested in northern New Mexico (Harris, 1963). But if the middens are generally undistinguished for the vertebrates they contain, they are intriguing for what they do not. No trace of the large extinct Pleistocene mammals and tortoises has been reliably reported from Southwestern prehistoric sites of the last 6,000 years and none was found in Danger Cave, carbon-dated at over 10,000 B.P. (Jennings, 1957, p. 93).

THE ECOLOGY OF LATE PLEISTOCENE EXTINCTION

The use of radiocarbon dating has established that the distinctive large mammals of the Pleistocene in North America, such as native horses, camels, sloths, elephants, glyptodonts, certain species of peccary, antelope, and bison, disappeared together over 8,000 years ago. In dry caves of the arid Southwest, soft parts such as hair and hide of extinct sloths (*Nothrotherium*) may endure at least 10,000 years (Simons and Alexander, 1964), while sloth dung of similar vintage from Rampart Cave, Arizona, still smells like barnyard manure. In New Mexico unusual polished rocks, evidently opalized by silica from the backs of large mammals that rubbed against them in prehistoric time, are found at the foot of desert mountains (Lang, 1947).

The effect on desert shrubs of large herds of mammals with highly varied forage adaptations is a subject seldom explored in the paleobotanical literature. Although he overlooked the Pleistocene fauna, Ellison (1960, p. 65) felt that ". . . the fact that, under the apparent handicap of millennia of grazing, most of the dominant species of the world's herblands are palatable plants, not only to buffalo and elk but to domestic livestock, is very impressive indeed." Ellison suggested an ecosystem in which plants would benefit by grazing, the implication being that through simple chemical adaptations all native range plants could readily evolve poisonous properties like the famous locoweed (*Astragalus nothoxys* and related species) and theoretically might achieve a high degree of protection against large herbivores.

In the Southwestern deserts the large number of either thorny or resinous shrubs rich in terpenes and other aromatic oils suggests a long history of plant-animal adaptation in which effective defenses against unlimited over-browsing were evolved. While only about 5.5% of the browse plants in national forest ranges possess very considerable forage value to existing animals (Dayton, 1931, p. 3), it is also noteworthy that only about 3.2% are known to be poisonous. The fact that range shrubs typically evolved repellant rather than lethal mechanisms to prevent over-browsing would seem to support Ellison's inference that some benefit was derived by being consumed. Whatever the nature of the equilibrium evolved during the Late Cenozoic between plants and large herbivores, it was suddenly upset early in postglacial time with the extinction of a majority of the native large mammals of the Southwest, and upset again after about 8,000 years by the introduction of range cattle, horses and burros, and sheep and goats. Why the large native mammals disappeared when they did remains one of the major unsolved problems in the study of the Pleistocene.

In a review of Pleistocene biography, Martin (1958) concluded that the Late Pleistocene environment must have had some unique attributes to account for the unique ecological pattern of Late Pleistocene extinction. Only large or relatively large herbivores plus their associated predators, scavengers, and parasites are involved. In the Southwest, extinction of a dozen native genera occurred within about 2,000 years, soon after man arrived in the New World, at a time when the climate and ecology of the region was much like it is at present. Native plants, invertebrates, aquatic vertebrates, small terrestrial vertebrates (except associated species such as cowbirds and vampire bats) were unaffected (Martin, 1958). None of these observations is new, and the suggestion that man's arrival in the New World triggered big-game extinction has been previously made by certain paleontologists without capturing the endorsement of very many archaeologists. One reason is that some rather large problems remain to be solved, or at least explained away, such as the minimum number of hunters and the rate of predation necessary to lead to the extinction of any single species, the fact that rather few associations of man with certain mammals such as mastodon are known, and the fact that big game endured in Africa largely intact despite man's long history of evolution on that continent.

Current studies on the Pleistocene of the Southwest have added to but not basically changed our knowledge of the extinction pattern. Holman (1962) notes that herpetological evidence consistently indicates that fewer amphibians and reptiles became extinct during the Pleistocene than birds and mammals. The relatively large extinct element among birds can be attributed partly to a reduction of scavengers such as *Teratornis* and to extinction of flightless species such as *Chendytes* of the California coast. Hester (1960) thoroughly reviewed the carbon-dated records of all species of extinct mammals, detailing the evidence that most of them disappeared suddenly between about 11,000 and 8,000 years ago.

Confining his analysis to carefully excavated, carbon-dated archaeological sites, Haynes (1964) shows that mammoth extinction evidently occurred in the Rocky Mountains and High Plains about 11,000 years ago, somewhat earlier than Martin (1958) and Hester (1960) in-

dicated and soon after the deglaciation of a mid-Canadian corridor, which Haynes believes was the entry route of Early Man. Folsom bison hunters, who replaced Clovis mammoth hunters 10,500 years ago, were limited to the western plains, while pre-Folsom big-game hunters enjoyed a relatively homogeneous culture and ranged from coast to coast (Mason, 1962). Other cultural attributes are less easy to infer from the record of the artifacts, but Wendorf and Hester (1962, p. 168) note that the butchering techniques of the Paleo-hunters were cruder than those of historic and prehistoric hunters in the Plains, who utilized *Bison bison* more thoroughly. Woodbury (1963, p. 57) infers a considerable degree of cooperative effort among the hunters, with hunting concentrated at waterholes and streams.

Crucial to the claim that climate had little to do with extinction is evidence that Pleistocene herbivores occupied major plant communities such as are found in the Southwest today. The pollen record associated with extinct mammals at Tule Springs (Mehringer, in press) and at the Lehner site, Naco, and Ventana Cave (Fig. 6) points to such a conclusion. In the case of the Shasta ground sloth *Nothrotherium*, the paleobotanical evidence is decisive. Both pollen and macroscopic plant material found in its dung show that 10,000 to 11,000 years ago at Rampart Cave, Arizona, in Gypsum Cave, Nevada, and at Aden Crater, New Mexico, sloths were browsing on many of the desert shrubs dominant in the Southwest at present (Martin *et al.*, 1961; Aden Crater sloth date in Simons and Alexander, 1964).

A more ambiguous case is that of the large tortoises (*Geochelone* and large extinct species of *Gopherus*); extinction apparently occurred before disappearance of the elephants, horses, and sloths. In reviews of tortoise paleoecology, Hibbard (1960) and Brattstrom (1961) conclude that intolerance of freezing temperatures and inability to burrow led to tortoise extinction at the end of the Sangamon, a time when Hibbard (1960) believes the climate became especially severe. *Geochelone* (formerly included with the Old World genus *Testudo*) survived only in South America, including the Galapagos Islands. If the full-glacial is considered, Hibbard's unconventional paleoclimatic interpretation that the Wisconsin was more extreme than earlier glacials is entirely in accord with the Southwestern Pleistocene pollen record. His suggestion that large tortoises can be used as indicators of frostless climates has been widely adopted, for example by Slaughter *et al.* (1962), Wood (1962), and Holman (1962).

Yet the case of the large tortoises provokes some unsettling questions. If freezing temperatures are crucial in large-tortoise extinction, must we assume that no frost-free habitats were available in Mexico, Central America, and the West Indies to harbor tortoises during the height of Wisconsin glaciation? And is *Geochelone* unknown in the Southwest in the Wisconsin? The Clear Creek local fauna contains *Geochelone* of moderate size (Holman, 1963). While Slaughter and Ritchie (1963) correlate the Clear Creek faunas with the Sangamon, they report a radiocarbon date of 28,840 ± 4,740 B.P. on shells in the Clear Creek deposits, much too young to be Sangamon as commonly understood by most Pleistocene geologists. Auffenberg (1962) alludes to other Wisconsin records of *Geochelone*, and Hibbard and Taylor (1960) mention small *Geochelone* from Friesenheim Cave, Texas, a Late Pleistocene (Wisconsin) fauna. Slaughter (manuscript) lists this species (*Geochelone wilsoni*) from late-glacial faunas at Blackwater Draw and Domebo, Oklahoma. While there seems little doubt that *G. wilsoni* disappeared along with the large mammals at the end of the Wisconsin, the extinction of the larger tortoises may have occurred earlier.

Finally, is the claim of *Geochelone* and large *Terrapene* in association with prehistoric hearths at the Lewisville site (Crook and Harris, 1957, 1962) without substance? Admittedly, the radiocarbon dates at Lewisville of over 37,000 years are hard to square with lack of sturdy documentation for man in the New World elsewhere at this time. And most students of prehistory find the report of a Clovis point associated with the Lewisville artifacts too much of a good thing. Perhaps the controversy raging over the Lewisville site will spur efforts to establish—or discount—the provocative interpretations of Crook and Harris.

In brief, the stratigraphic evidence from both caves and alluvial deposits in Texas establishes large-tortoise extinction *after* the end of the Sangamon 70,000 years ago. Whether the event is related to the first arrival of man in the New World, to unusual thermal stress during the Wisconsin full-glacial, or to other yet unidentified causes will require refined geochronological and paleoecological evidence. Hopefully, paleontologists excavating Pleistocene tortoises will not overlook the possibility that dirt adhering to the bones may contain crucial pollen evidence regarding vegetation and climate of the time.

Similar evidence obtained from pollen in matrix containing mammoth, tapir, and sloth bones shows that some highly unwarranted assumptions have been made regarding their paleoclimatic meaning. Despite claims to the contrary, their extinction cannot be laid to drought (Martin, 1963a, p. 64-65). Some conservative ecological assumptions may be reasonable—a shift from browsing mastodon to grazing mammoth appears to accompany desiccation of the Monahans Dunes area (Green, 1961, p. 44), and the fossil record at the foot of the Rocky Mountains suggests the presence of camels on upland ranges while mammoth were grazing the floodplains (Hunt, 1954, p. 119). Different species of large herbivores undoubtedly occupied different ecological niches on the prehistoric range. But in view of the failure to explain satisfactorily large-mammal extinction as a function of climatic change, similar theories applied to the extinction of large tortoises must be viewed with suspicion. Archaeological sites show that extinction closely followed man's arrival in the New World. While the case is by no means closed, this circumstance, in our view, best accounts for the Late Pleistocene "age of overkill."

References

Adam, D. P., 1964, Exploratory palynology in the Sierra Nevada, California: Univ. Arizona Geochronology Lab., Interim Res. Rep. 4, 30 p.

Anderson, R. Y., 1955, Pollen analysis, a research tool for the study of cave deposits: Amer. Antiq., v. 21, p. 84-85

Antevs, Ernst, 1954, Climate of New Mexico during the last glaciopluvial: J. Geol., v. 62, p. 182-191

—— 1959, Geologic age of the Lehner Mammoth Site: Amer. Antiq., v. 25, p. 31-34

Auffenberg, Walter, 1962, A new species of *Geochelone* from the Pleistocene of Texas: Copeia, v. 1962, p. 627-636

Axelrod, D. I., 1950, Evolution of desert vegetation in western North America: Carnegie Instn. Publ. 590, p. 217-306

—— 1958, Evolution of the Madro-Tertiary Geoflora: Bot. Rev., v. 24, p. 433-509

Axelrod, D. I., and Ting, W. S., 1961, Early Pleistocene floras from the Chagoopa surface, southern Sierra Nevada: Univ. California Publ. Geol. Sci., v. 39, p. 1-117

Benson, Lyman, and Darrow, R. A., 1954, Trees and shrubs of the Southwestern deserts: Tucson, Univ. Arizona Press, 437 p.

Bent, Anne M., 1960, Pollen analysis at Deadman Lake: Univ. Minnesota M.S. thesis, 22 p.

Bent, Anne M., and Wright, H. E., Jr., 1963, Pollen analysis of surface materials and lake sediments from the Chuska Mountains, New Mexico: Geol. Soc. Amer. Bull., v. 74, p. 491-500

Brattstrom, B. H., 1961, Some new fossil tortoises from western North America with remarks on the zoogeography and paleoecology of tortoises: J. Paleont., v. 35, p. 543-560

Broecker, W. S., and Farrand, W. R., 1963, Radiocarbon age of the Two Creeks forest bed, Wisconsin: Geol. Soc. Amer. Bull., v. 74, p. 795-802

Broecker, W. S., Ewing, Maurice, and Heezen, B. C., 1960, Evidence for an abrupt change in climate close to 11,000 years ago: Amer. J. Sci., v. 258, p. 429-448

Byers, William, and Martin, P. S., in press, Pollen and archaeology at Wetherill Mesa, Colorado: Amer. Antiq.

Clisby, Kathryn H., and Sears, P. B., 1956, San Augustin Plains—Pleistocene climatic changes: Science, v. 124, p. 537-539

Clisby, Kathryn H., Foreman, F., and Sears, P. B., 1957, Pleistocene climatic changes in New Mexico, U.S.A.: Zürich, Geobot. Inst. Rübel, v. 34, p. 21-26

—— 1962, Palynology–diastrophism–erosion: Tucson, Arizona, Intern. Pollen Conf., Field Excursion, Pleistocene Palynology of the Arid Southwest, p. 28-30

Cole, G. A., 1963, The American Southwest and Middle America, *in* Frey, D. G. (ed.), Limnology in North America: Madison, Univ. Wisconsin Press, p. 393-434

Cottam, W. P., Tucker, J. M., and Drobnick, Ruby, 1959, Some clues to Great Basin postpluvial climates provided by oak distributions: Ecology, v. 40, p. 361-377

Croizat, Leon, 1958, Panbiogeography. Vol. I, The new world: Caracas, Venezuela, 1018 p.

Crook, W. W., Jr., and Harris, R. K., 1957, Hearths and artifacts of Early Man near Lewisville, Texas, and associated faunal material: Texas Archeol. Soc. Bull., v. 28, p. 7-97

—— 1962, Significance of a new radiocarbon date from the

Lewisville site: Texas Archeol. Soc. Bull., v. 32, p. 327-330

Dalrymple, G. B., 1963, Potassium-argon dates of some Cenozoic volcanic rocks of the Sierra Nevada, California: Geol. Soc. Amer. Bull., v. 74, p. 379-390

Damon, P. E., and Long, Austin, 1962, Arizona radiocarbon dates III: Radiocarbon, v. 4, p. 239-249

Damon, P. E., Haynes, C. V., and Cole, G. A., 1964, Carbon-14 content of aquatic plants, Montezuma Well, Arizona (abst.): Amer. Geophys. Union Trans., v. 45, p. 117

Damon, P. E., Haynes, C. V., and Long, Austin, 1964, Arizona radiocarbon dates V: Radiocarbon, v. 6, p. 91-107

Darrow, R. A., 1961, Origin and development of the vegetational communities of the Southwest, *in* Shields, L. M. and Gardner, L. J. (eds.), Bioecology of the arid and semi-arid lands of the Southwest; New Mexico Highlands Univ. Bull., p. 30-47

Dayton, W. A., 1931, Important western browse plants: U.S. Dept. Agr. Misc. Publ. 101, 214 p.

Deevey, E. S., Jr., 1949, Biogeography of the Pleistocene: Geol. Soc. Amer. Bull., v. 60, p. 1315-1416

Deevey, E. S., Jr., and Flint, R. F., 1957, Postglacial hypsitermal interval: Science, v. 125, p. 182-184

Dillon, L. S., 1956, Wisconsin climate and life zones in North America: Science, v. 123, p. 167-176

Dixon, H. M., 1962, Vegetation, pollen rain, and pollen preservation, Sangre de Cristo Mountains, New Mexico: Univ. New Mexico M.S. thesis, 69 p.

Ellison, Lincoln, 1960, Influence of grazing on plant succession of rangelands: Bot. Rev., v. 26, p. 65-66

Epling, Carl, 1944, The historical background. Contributions to the genetics, taxonomy, and ecology of *Drosophila pseudoobscura* and its relatives: Carnegie Instn. Publ. 554, p. 147-183

Findley, J. S., and Jones, C. J., 1962, Distribution and variation of voles of the genus *Microtus* in New Mexico and adjacent areas: J. Mammal., v. 43, p. 154-166

Flint, R. F., 1963, Status of the Pleistocene Wisconsin stage in central North America: Science, v. 139, p. 402-404

Garcia, Enriqueta, Soto, Consuelo, and Miranda, Faustino, 1960, *Larrea* y clima: Anales Inst. Biol., v. 31, p. 133-171

Gehlbach, F. R., and Miller, R. R., 1961, Fishes from archaeological sites in northern New Mexico: Southwestern Naturalist, v. 6, p. 2-8

Graham, Alan, and Heimsch, Charles, 1960, Pollen studies of some Texas peat deposits: Ecology, v. 41, p. 751-763

Gray, Jane, 1960, Micropaleobotanical research on the Late Tertiary sediments of Arizona: Arizona Geol. Soc. Digest, v. 3, p. 145-149

—— 1961, Early Pleistocene paleoclimatic record from Sonoran Desert, Arizona: Science, v. 133, p. 38-39

Green, F. E., 1961, The Monahans Dunes area, *in* F. Wendorf, compiler, Paleoecology of the Llano Estacado: Santa Fe, Mus. New Mexico, p. 22-47

Hafsten, Ulf, 1961, Pleistocene development of vegetation and climate in the southern High Plains as evidenced by pollen analysis, *in* F. Wendorf, compiler, Paleoecology of the Llano Estacado: Santa Fe, Mus. New Mexico, p. 59-91

Hammen, Thomas van der, and Gonzalez, Enrique, 1960, Upper Pleistocene and Holocene climate and vegetation of the "Sabana de Bogota" (Colombia, South America): Leidse Geol. Med., v. 25, p. 261-315

Hansen, H. P., 1951, Pollen analysis of peat sections from near the Finley site, Wyoming, *in* J. H. Moss *et al.*, Early Man in the Eden Valley: Univ. Pennsylvania Mus. Monogr., p. 111-118

Harris, A. H., 1963, Vertebrate remains and past environmental reconstruction in the Navajo Reservoir district: Mus. New Mexico Press, Anthrop. Pap. 11, p. 1-59

Harris, A. H., and Findley, J. S., 1964, Pleistocene-Recent fauna of the Isleta Caves, Bernalillo County, New Mexico: Amer. J. Sci., v. 262, p. 114-120

Hastings, J. R., and Turner, R. M., in press, The changing mile: Tucson, Univ. Arizona Press

Haury, E. W., 1950, The stratigraphy and archaeology of Ventana Cave, Arizona: Tucson, Univ. Arizona Press, 599 p.

Haury, E. W., Antevs, Ernst, and Lance, J. F., 1953, Artifacts with mammoth remains, Naco, Arizona: Amer. Antiq., v. 19, p. 1-24

Haury, E. W., Sayles, E. B., and Wasley, W. W., 1959, The Lehner mammoth site, southeastern Arizona: Amer. Antiq., v. 25, p. 2-30

Haynes, C. V., Jr., 1964, Fluted projectile points: their age and dispersion: Science, v. 145, p. 1408-1413

Hester, J. J., 1960, Late Pleistocene extinction and radiocarbon dating: Amer. Antiq., v. 26, p. 58-77

Hevly, R. H., 1962, Pollen analysis of Laguna Salada, *in* Mogollon Rim region, east-central Arizona: New Mexico Geol. Soc., 30th Field Conf. Guidebook, p. 115-117

—— 1964a, Pollen analysis of Quaternary archaeological and lacustrine sediments from the Colorado Plateau: Univ. Arizona Ph.D. thesis, 124 p.

—— 1964b, Paleoecology of Laguna Salada: Chicago Nat. Hist. Mus., Fieldiana (Anthrop.), v. 55, p. 171-187

Hevly, R. H., and Martin, P. S., 1961, Geochronology of pluvial Lake Cochise, southern Arizona. I, Pollen analysis of shore deposits: J. Arizona Acad. Sci., v. 2, p. 24-31

Hevly, R. H., Mehringer, P. J., Jr., and Yocum, H. G., in press, Modern pollen rain in the Sonoran Desert: J. Arizona Acad. Sci.

Hibbard, C. W., 1960, An interpretation of Pliocene and Pleistocene climates in North America: Michigan Acad. Sci. Rep. (for 1959-1960), p. 1-30

Hibbard, C. W., and Taylor, D. W., 1960, Two Late Pleistocene faunas from southwestern Kansas: Univ. Michigan Mus. Paleont. Contr., v. 16, p. 1-223

Holman, J. A., 1962, A Texas Pleistocene herpetofauna: Copeia, p. 255-261

—— 1963, Late Pleistocene amphibians and reptiles of the Clear Creek and Ben Franklin local faunas of Texas: Dallas, Texas, Grad. Res. Center J., v. 31, p. 152-167

Howden, H. F., 1963, Speculations on some beetles, barriers, and climates during the Pleistocene and pre-Pleistocene periods in some non-glaciated portions of North America: Syst. Zool., v. 12, p. 178-201

Hunt, C. B., 1954, Pleistocene and Recent deposits in the Denver area, Colorado: U.S. Geol. Surv. Bull. 996-C, p. 91-140

Jaeger, E. C., 1957, The North American deserts: Palo Alto, California, Stanford Univ. Press, 308 p.

Jelinek, A. J., 1962, Paleoecology of the Llano Estacado (review): Amer. Antiq., v. 27, p. 432-433

Jennings, J. D., 1957, Danger Cave: Univ. Utah Anthrop. Pap. 27, p. 1-328

Johnson, LeRoy, Jr., 1963, Pollen analysis of two archaeological sites at Amistad Reservoir, Texas: Texas J. Sci., v. 15, p. 225-230

Johnston, I. M., 1940, The floristic significance of shrubs common to North and South American deserts: Harvard Univ., Arnold Arbor. J., v. 21, p. 356-363

King, J. E., 1964, Modern pollen rain and fossil profiles, Sandia Mountains, New Mexico: Univ. New Mexico M.S. thesis, 50 p.

Kirkland, D. W., and Anderson, R. Y., 1963, Environmental reconstruction of a Blancan Lake near Channing, Texas: unpublished manuscript

Lang, W. B., 1947, The polished rocks of Cornudas Mountain, New Mexico: Science, v. 105, p. 65

Laudermilk, J. D., and Munz, P. A., 1934, Plants in the dung of *Nothrotherium* from Gypsum Cave, Nevada: Carnegie Instn. Publ. 453, p. 29-37

Lawrence, Barbara, 1951, Mammals found at the Awatove Site: Harvard Univ., Peabody Mus. Pap. 35, 44 p.

Leopold, L. B., Leopold, Estella B., and Wendorf, Fred, 1963, Some climatic indicators in the period A.D. 1200-1400 in New Mexico: Paris, UNESCO Symp., Changes of Climate, p. 265-270

Lincoln, E. P., 1962, Mammalian fauna from Wupatki Ruin: Plateau, v. 34, p. 129-134

Lindsey, A. A., 1951, Vegetation and habitats in a southwestern volcanic area: Ecol. Monogr., v. 21, p. 227-253

Lowe, C. H., 1950, The systemic status of the salamander *Plethodon hardii*, with a discussion of biogeographical problems in *Aneides*: Copeia, p. 92-99

Lowe, C. H. (ed.), 1964, The vertebrates of Arizona: Tucson, Univ. Arizona Press, 259 p.

MacGinitie, H. D., 1958, Climate since the Late Cretaceous *in* Hubbs, C. L. (ed.), Zoogeography: Amer. Assoc. Adv. Sci., Publ. 51, p. 61-79

McVaugh, Rogers, 1951, Suggested phylogeny of *Prunus serotina* and other wide-ranging phylads in North America: Britonia, v. 7, p. 317-346

Maher, L. J., Jr., 1961, Pollen analysis and postglacial vegetation history in the Animas Valley region, southern San Juan Mountains, Colorado: Univ. Minnesota Ph.D. thesis, 85 p.

—— 1963, Pollen analyses of surface materials from the southern San Juan Mountains, Colorado: Geol. Soc. Amer. Bull., v. 74, p. 1485-1503

Malde, H. E., 1964, Environment and man in arid America: Science, v. 145, p. 123-129

Martin, P. S., 1958, Pleistocene ecology and biogeography of North America, *in* Hubbs, C. L. (ed.), Zoogeography: Amer. Assoc. Adv. Sci., Publ. 51, p. 375-420

—— 1963a, The last 10,000 years, a fossil pollen record

of the American Southwest: Tucson, Univ. Arizona Press, 87 p.

—— 1963b, Early man in Arizona: the pollen evidence: Amer. Antiq., v. 29, p. 67-73

—— 1963c, Geochronology of Pluvial Lake Cochise, southern Arizonia. II, Pollen analysis of a 42-meter core: Ecology, v. 44, p. 436-444

—— 1964, Pollen analysis and the full-glacial landscape: Ft. Burgwin (New Mexico) Research Center Publ. No. 3, p. 66-74

Martin, P. S., and Gray, Jane, 1962, Pollen analysis and the Cenozoic: Science, v. 137, p. 103-111

Martin, P. S., and Schoenwetter, James, 1960, Arizona's oldest cornfield: Science, v. 132, p. 33-34

Martin, P. S., Sabels, B. E., and Shutler, Dick, Jr., 1961, Rampart Cave coprolite and ecology of the shasta ground sloth: Amer. J. Sci., v. 259, p. 102-127

Martin, P. S., and Sharrock, F. W., 1964, Pollen analysis of prehistoric human feces, a new approach to ethnobotany: Amer. Antiq. v. 30, p. 168-180

Mason, R. J., 1962, The paleo-Indian tradition in eastern North America: Curr. Anthrop., v. 3, p. 227-278

Mehringer, P. J., Jr., in press, Late Pleistocene vegetation in the Mojave Desert of southern Nevada: J. Arizona Acad. Sci.

Mehringer, P. J., Jr., and Haynes, C. V., Jr., in press, The pollen evidence for the environment of Early Man and extinct mammals at the Lehner mammoth site, southeastern Arizona: Amer. Antiq.

Merriam, C. H., 1890, Results of a biological survey of the San Francisco Mountain region and desert of the Little Colorado in Arizona: U.S. Dept of Agr., North American Fauna, No. 3, 128 p.

Miller, Loye, 1963, Birds and Indians in the West: South California Acad. Sci. Bull., v. 62, p. 178-191

Miller, R. R., 1950, Notes on the cut-throat and rainbow trout with the description of a new species from the Gila River, New Mexico: Univ. Michigan Mus. Zool. Occ. Pap. 529, p. 1-42

—— 1955, Fish remains from archaeological sites in the Lower Colorado River Basin, Arizona: Michigan Acad. Sci. Arts Lett. Pap., v. 40, p. 125-135

Mosquin, Theodore, 1964, Chromosomal repatterning in *Clarkia rhomboidea* as evidence for post-Pleistocene changes in distribution: Evolution, v. 18, p. 12-25

Muir, John, 1877, On the post-glacial history of *Sequoia gigantea:* Amer. Assoc. Adv. Sci. Proc., 25th meeting, p. 242-253

Muller, C. H., 1954, A new species of *Quercus* in Arizona: Madroño, v. 12, p. 140-145

Munz, P. A., and Keck, D. D., 1949, California plant communities: El Aliso, v. 2, p. 87-105

Murray, K. F., 1957, Pleistocene climate and the fauna of Burnet Cave, New Mexico: Ecology, v. 38, p. 129-132

Norris, K. S., 1958, The evolution and systematics of the iguanid genus *Uma* and its relation to the evolution of other North American desert reptiles: Amer. Mus. Nat. Hist. Bull., v. 114, p. 247-326

Peabody, F. E., and Savage, J. M., 1958, Evolution of a coast range corridor in California and its effects on the origin and dispersal of living amphibians and reptiles, *in* Hubbs, C. L. (ed.), Zoogeography: Amer. Assoc. Adv. Sci. Publ. 51, p. 159-186

Pennak, R. W., 1963, Ecological and radiocarbon correlations in some Colorado mountain lake and bog deposits: Ecology, v. 44, p. 1-15

Potter, L. D., 1957, Phytosociological study of San Augustin Plains, New Mexico: Ecol. Monogr., v. 27, p. 113-136

Potter, L. D., and Rowley, Joanne, 1960, Pollen rain and vegetation, San Augustin Plains, New Mexico: Bot. Gaz., v. 122, p. 1-25

Potzger, J. E., and Tharp, B. C., 1947, Pollen profile from a Texas bog: Ecology, v. 28, p. 274-280

—— 1954, Pollen study of two bogs in Texas: Ecology, v. 35, p. 462-466

Raven, P. H., 1963, Amphitropical relationships in the floras of North and South America: Quart. Rev. Biol., v. 38, p. 151-177

Rohrer, W. L., and Leopold, Estella B., 1963, Fenton Pass formation (Pleistocene?), Bighorn Basin, Wyoming: U.S. Geol. Surv. Prof. Pap. 475-C, p. 45-48

Roosma, Aino, 1958, A climatic record from Searles Lake, California: Science, v. 128, p. 716

Rzedowski, Jerzy, 1962, Contribuciones a la fitogeografia floristica e historica de Mexico. I, Algunas consideraciones acerca del elemento endemico en la flora Mexicana: Soc. Bot. Mexico, No. 27, p. 52-65

Schoenwetter, James, 1962, The pollen analysis of eighteen archaeological sites in Arizona and New Mexico, *in* Martin, P. S. *et al.*, Chapters in the prehistory of eastern Arizona, I: Chicago Nat. Hist. Mus., Fieldiana (Anthrop.), v. 53, p. 168-209

Schoenwetter, James, and Eddy, F. W., 1964, Alluvial and palynological reconstruction of environments—Navajo Reservoir District: Mus. New Mexico Pap. Anthrop. No. 13, 115 p.

Sears, P. B., 1937, Pollen analysis as an aid in cultural deposits in the United States, *in* MacCurdy, G. G. (ed.), Early Man: London, Lippincott & Co., p. 61-66

—— 1961, Palynology and the climatic record of the Southwest: New York Acad. Sci. Ann., v. 95, p. 632-641

Sears, P. B., and Clisby, K. H., 1952, Two long climatic records: Science, v. 116, p. 176-178

Sears, P. B., and Roosma, Aino, 1961, A climatic sequence from two Nevada caves: Amer. J. Sci., v. 259, p. 669-678

Shantz, H. L., and Zon, R., 1924, Natural vegetation, Atlas of American Agriculture, U.S. Dept Agri.

Sharp, R. P., and Birman, J. H., 1963, Additions to classical sequence of Pleistocene glaciations, Sierra Nevada, California: Geol. Soc. Amer. Bull., v. 74, p. 1079-1086

Shreve, Forrest, and Wiggins, Ira, 1964, Vegetation and flora of the Sonoran Desert: Palo Alto, California, Stanford Univ. Press, 2 vols., 1740 p.

Simons, E. L., and Alexander, H. L., 1964, Age of the shasta ground sloth from Aden Crater, New Mexico: Amer. Antiq., v. 29, p. 390-391

Slaughter, B. H., and Ritchie, Ronald, 1963, Pleistocene mammals of the Clear Creek local fauna, Denton County, Texas: Dallas, Texas, Grad. Res. Center J., v. 31, p. 117-131

Slaughter, B. H., Crook, W. W., Jr., Harris, R. K., Allen, D. C., and Seifert, Martin, 1962, The Hill-Schuler local faunas of the upper Trinity River, Dallas and Denton Counties, Texas: Univ. Texas Bur. Econ. Geol. Rep. Inv. 48, 75 p.

Smith, C. E., Jr., 1950, Prehistoric plant remains from Bat Cave: Harvard Univ. Bot. Mus. Leaflets, v. 14, p. 157-180

Stebbins, R. C., 1958, A new alligator lizard from the Panamint Mountains, Inyo County, California: Amer. Mus. Novitates, no. 1883, p. 1-27

Stebbins, R. C., and Riemer, W. J., 1950, A new species of plethodontid salamander from the Jemez Mountains of New Mexico: Copeia, v. 1950, p. 73-80

Stein, W. T., 1963, Mammal remains from archaeological sites in the Point of Pines region, Arizona: Amer. Antiq., v. 29, p. 213-220

Stutz, H. C., and Thomas, L. K., 1964, Hybridization and introgression in *Cowania* and *Purshia:* Evolution, v. 18, p. 183-195

Tolman, C. F., 1909, Erosion and deposition in the southern Arizona bolson region: J. Geol., v. 17, p. 136-163

Tucker, J. M., 1961, Studies in the *Quercus undulata* complex. I, A preliminary statement: Amer. J. Bot., v. 48, p. 202-208

—— 1963, Studies in the *Quercus undulata* complex. III, The contribution of *Q. arizonica:* Amer. J. Bot., v. 50, p. 699-708

Tucker, J. M., and Muller, C. H., 1956, The geographic history of *Quercus ajoensis:* Evolution, v. 10, p. 157-175

Tucker, J. M., Cottam, W. P., and Drobnick, Rudy, 1961, Studies in the *Quercus undulata* complex. II, The contribution of *Quercus turbinella:* Amer. J. Bot., v. 48, p. 329-339

Wells, P. V., and Jorgensen, C. D., 1964, Pleistocene wood rat middens and climatic change in Mohave Desert— a record of juniper woodlands: Science, v. 143, p. 1171-1174

Wendorf, Fred, compiler, 1961, Paleoecology of the Llano Estacado: Santa Fe, Mus. of New Mexico, 144 p.

Wendorf, Fred, and Hester, J. J., 1962, Early Man's utilization of the Great Plains environment: Amer. Antiq., v. 28, p. 159-171

Whiteside, Melvin, 1964, Paleoecological studies of Potato Lake and its environs: Tempe, Arizona State Univ. M.S. thesis

Whittaker, R. H., and Niering, W. A., 1964, Vegetation of the Santa Catalina Mountains, Arizona. I, Ecological classification and distribution of species: J. Arizona Acad. Sci., v. 3, p. 9-34

Wood, P. A., 1962, Pleistocene fauna from 111 Ranch area, Graham County, Arizona: Univ. Arizona Ph.D. thesis, 121 p.

Woodbury, R. B., 1963, Indian adaptations to arid environments, *in* Hodge, Carle, and Duisberg, P. C. (eds.), Aridity and man: Amer. Assoc. Adv. Sci. Publ. 74, p. 55-85

Zweifel, R. G., 1955, Ecology, distribution, and systematics of frogs of the *Rana boylei* group: Berkeley, Univ. California Publ. Zool., v. 54, p. 207-292

—— 1962, Analysis of hybridization between two subspecies of the desert whiptail lizard, *Cnemidophorus tigris*: Copeia, p. 749-766

SUMMARY

Pleistocene pollen analysis in the American Southwest was first attempted in the 1930's. Rapid growth of the field in the present decade has exposed important and occasionally provocative evidence regarding climates of the Pleistocene in arid America. While much remains to be learned about the limitations of pollen analysis, the presence of abundant fossil pollen and spores in a variety of sediments, including playa lake mud, alluvium, cave earth, archaeological trash, and prehistoric coprolite, ensures increasing use of the method in future paleoecological investigation.

From the pollen content of drill cores it appears that prior to Wisconsin glaciation climatic changes corresponding to the advance and retreat of continental glaciers are not easily recognized. Present difficulties may be overcome as our knowledge grows, but the pollen-stratigraphic record of the longest and most thoroughly studied drill core examined to date, that of Clisby and Sears from the San Augustin Plains, is not easily correlated climatically with multiple glaciation.

The difficulties with climatic correlation do not extend into the Wisconsin, where there is a carbon-dated maximum in biotic-zone depression of 900-1,200 m about 20,000 years ago that corresponds to the maximum in Wisconsin ice advance recognized in the eastern United States. Furthermore, the Rich Lake Interpluvial in the Llano Estacado of Texas appears to correspond with the Plum Point Interstadial of the eastern United States. Earlier stadial-interstadial climatic fluctuations can be recognized in the pollen record of Wisconsin-age drill cores. The carbon-dated full-glacial pollen records suggest a vegetation pattern considerably altered from that of the present and one that must have imposed many changes in plant and animal distributions.

A change to warm-dry postglacial climates appears to have occurred rather rapidly around 12,000 B.P. Except perhaps in the High Plains of Texas, the shift from full-glacial to postglacial climates is not clearly marked by late-glacial fluctuations, and no Valders or Younger-Dryas-age return of pluvial climates is evident. Postglacial alluvium of the desert grassland shows sharp changes in composite and cheno-am proportions, changes likely to be related to episodes of arroyo cutting and filling. In juniper-piñon areas of northern Arizona and New Mexico fluctuations in the tree-pollen record include a major rise in tree pollen coincident with or following abandonment of many Southwestern villages 700-500 years ago.

Evidence for an Altithermal drought, which is supported by reduction in tree-pollen counts in profiles from the Great Basin, the Central Rockies, and the Pacific Northwest, is not evident in southern Arizona and New Mexico, where mid-postglacial spectra may contain more rather than less tree pollen. The widely held concept of Altithermal drought in the Southwest is theoretically questionable, and some of the Altithermal phenomena, such as intense arroyo cutting and calichification, may reflect an intensified summer monsoon.

While pre-Pleistocene climatic change is widely recognized as responsible for the origin of arid-land plants, some of which can be traced to the Late Miocene, it now seems likely that many, perhaps all, Southwestern plants and animals were on the move in the Pleistocene. Certainly climatic change in the Wisconsin glacial period must have transformed the range of many species. Broken distributions in the range of boreal or Cordilleran plant and animal populations can be attributed to full-glacial invasion from the north ending 14,000 years ago. The postglacial return of desert, grassland, and Mexican woodland communities took place within the last 12,000 years, some species apparently "overshooting" to leave relict outposts or hybrid populations considerably to the north of the main range of the species.

In the Southwest, as elsewhere in the New World, the extinction of elephants, native horses, camels, sloths, and other large vertebrates is a major event of the Late Pleistocene. Evidently it occurred at least 1,000 years after the change to warm, dry postglacial climates. Generic extinction is not seen in the Late Pleistocene record of plants, invertebrates, or small vertebrates; these endured intact. While doubt remains regarding the association of Early Man and certain of the extinct vertebrates, it appears that most of the large herbivores were hunted by Early Man, whose culture was drastically altered by their disappearance and who may be held responsible for the Late Pleistocene "age of overkill."

PLANT GEOGRAPHY IN THE SOUTHERN ROCKY MOUNTAINS

W. A. WEBER[1]

THE FOLLOWING discussion of plant geography in the Southern Rocky Mountains is an attempt to assemble impressions accumulated during eighteen years of residence in this area. The Southern Rocky Mountains, for the purposes of this discussion, are those mountain ranges lying south of the Wyoming deserts, west of the Great Plains, north of Santa Fe, New Mexico, and westward to and including the Wasatch, Uinta, La Sal, and Abajo Mountains of Utah and the San Francisco Peaks of Arizona. Floristically the area forms a unit, effectively isolated on all sides by lowlands in the form of plains, deserts, or lower mountain ranges. The major development of alpine tundra in the western United States occurs in this area. The Black Hills of South Dakota, while lying well to the northeast, are very closely related to the Southern Rockies by their strong element of the Cordilleran flora and are a key to a detailed understanding of floral migrations during the Pleistocene.

Phytogeographically the Southern Rocky Mountain region is an extremely complicated area. It harbors remnants of the ancient Tertiary flora that existed there in Florissant and Creede (late-Tertiary) times. The mountains themselves have been major highways for north-south movement of plants between the American Arctic and, according to some phytogeographers, the South American Andes. Several of the major river systems draining into the Pacific Ocean and the Gulf of Mexico originate there and provide pathways of migrations for plants, while the divides between the river systems constitute effective barriers at the same time. The mountain area now is effectively isolated on all sides from similar alpine areas by arid steppes or lowlands, but at one time or another different segments of its periphery must have been open to floristic traffic. The Southern Rockies constitute one terminus of a track that once led from the mountains of Central Asia to the Mexican Plateau. On the American continent the area holds the greatest concentration of circumpolar species at their southernmost limits.

The physical attributes of the mountains for this role are exceptional. Aside from the features already mentioned, the Southern Rockies contain the greatest concentration of high peaks, 52 over 14,000 ft (4,240 m) and the largest area of alpine tundra outside Alaska. A wide variety of life-zones, from alpine to Upper Sonoran, are telescoped locally within narrow linear distances. The Continental Divide not only reaches here its easternmost approach on the Continent, but it meets the plains by way of an abrupt escarpment that results in local climatic anomalies critical for the flora.

Several problems arise when one places the outline of the

[1] University of Colorado Museum, Boulder, Colorado.

present vegetation against the background of the Quaternary period, and these have been kept in mind, below, in making a division of the flora into its obvious "elements," or clusters of species whose geographical patterns roughly coincide, for reasons that may be part ecological, part historical. An attempt is then made to place these elements in perspective as to their wider holarctic patterns and as to the possible influences, past and present, that may bear on the history of these plant distribution patterns in the Southern Rockies.

The overriding problem concerns migration. Did the alpine flora move out of the Arctic under the influence of Continental glaciation, as Darwin (1883), Hooker and Gray (1880), Wallace (1900), and others following them have suggested, to climb the mountaintops and become stranded there following the recession of the Pleistocene climate, or did an ancient Tertiary alpine flora already exist here and in the other austral ranges of the Northern Hemisphere? Did not this old flora, aided by a climatic depression of timberline and the availability of unstable virgin soils to the north, form the present arctic flora, as suggested by Tolmachev (1959) and Hultén (1962, p. 4)?

What were the nature and the chronology of the events that have placed certain "Cordilleran" species at isolated stations in the Great Lakes Region and in eastern Canada (Fernald, 1925) and that resulted in the curious mixture of boreal, Cordilleran, eastern-deciduous-forest and Great Plains species in the Black Hills of South Dakota? And how can one explain the fact that many of these eastern species occur in a necklace-like pattern extending in mesic sites along the eastern flank of the Rockies from the Black Hills down through New Mexico and eastern Arizona?

Falling into the same general pattern in the eastern Rockies, a number of ferns, mosses, lichens, and higher plant genera occur as narrow endemics or as worldwide disjuncts. Some of these might be classed as subtropical or sub-oceanic elsewhere in the world. Are these relicts of the old Tertiary flora or have they arrived at odd times by long-distance transport from other continents?

What is the explanation for the modern absence of broad-leaved trees in an area that once supported a mixed broadleaf–coniferous flora probably as rich as that of the southern Appalachians? Can the depletion of this flora be correlated with paleoclimatic or orogenic events?

Are the basic similarities between the floras of the Southern Rockies and the Asiatic Altai simply the result of similar climate, topography, and continental situation—each area in the long run receiving and supporting a common species pool derived by long-distance transport? Or are their floras the surviving remnants of a flora that at one time was more or less continuous over mountain ranges connecting the two areas?

How many modern plant distributions can be traced to migrations of floras ahead of an advancing ice sheet? How many must be attributed to wholesale extinction and recovery from small refugia? Can these problems be successfully attacked on a vegetational basis, or must each species be considered a problem in itself?

In the succeeding paragraphs the reader may be disappointed to find that the well-known species or dominant trees receive little consideration. This is unavoidable because the species critical to a discussion of this sort are those that are relatively homogeneous or not racially complex. Their distribution patterns are most likely to be framed within an area showing obvious correlations with climate or geochronology. Widespread species like *Pinus ponderosa, Pseudotsuga menziesii,* and the like are genetically very complex and racially differentiated. Their heterogeneity has enabled them to radiate adaptively into a large number of ecological situations. A knowledge of their ecology, genetics, and migrations in detail would, of course, be of great value, but at the present time, because of insufficient study, they are part of the enigma.

Taxonomic relationships are questionable, contact between American and Asiatic institutions are difficult, the major literature is hidden in monographs and revisions of isolated genera, and the physical record in the form of herbarium specimens is scattered in hundreds of museums, some of which no longer lend specimens for phytogeographical study. Because of the magnitude of this segment of the field of phytogeography, this paper will be limited to a discussion of the patterns that emerge from study of the Southern Rocky Mountain flora. Other equally important aspects, namely phytosociology, cytotaxonomy, autecology, paleontology, and physiology will be left to those who may find among these patterns problems that may be tackled by use of their disciplines.

HISTORICAL REVIEW

Phytogeographical research began in the Rocky Mountains with the historic journey across America made in 1877 by Joseph Dalton Hooker and Asa Gray. Out of this brief exposure to the living landscape of the area came one of phytogeography's classic papers, "The Vegetation of the Rocky Mountain Region and a Comparison with That of Other Parts of the World" (Hooker and Gray, 1880). In this paper Hooker established the presence of the Boreal, Asiatic, Mexican, and local elements in the Rocky Mountain flora and built the framework of all future discussions.

A few years later, in 1887, another of the greatest biogeographers of all time, Alfred Russel Wallace, spent a few days in Colorado during a lecture tour and happened to meet a young botanical novice who took him on an excursion to Gray's Peak (Wallace, 1905). His companion was a Denver schoolteacher named Alice Eastwood, Colorado's first resident botanist, who later became world-famous for her studies of the California flora and for the part she played in rescuing the type collections of the California Academy of Sciences during the San Francisco earthquake of 1906. The Gray's Peak excursion gave Wallace a number of significant phytogeographical impressions (Wallace, 1900).

Professor T. D. A. Cockerell should also be listed among the early phytogeographers, because, beginning with his sojourn in the Wet Mountain Valley in 1887-1888, he attempted to record the entire spectrum of plant and animal life in the Southern Rockies. This work was prompted by biogeographical considerations, as witnessed by the many papers he later published bearing on the field. Throughout his life Cockerell was a strong disciple of Darwin and Wallace. He published several papers analyzing the alpine vegetation of Colorado (Cockerell, 1887-1906) and was an active collector and describer of fossil plants, particularly from the late-Cenozoic floras of southern Colorado.

For many years the taxonomic philosophy of Per Axel Rydberg dominated thinking about the Rocky Mountain region, later to fall into disrepute because of his reputation as a taxonomic "splitter." Rydberg, nevertheless, was a man of remarkable perception even though his taxonomic categories often were at least one level removed from contemporary taxonomic tastes. Rydberg made substantial contributions to phytogeography, first by his analysis (1896) of the flora of the Black Hills in which he demonstrated the coexistence in that area of a Boreal, a Cordilleran, an eastern woodland–prairie, and a Great Plains element. In a paper on the origin of the alpine flora (1914a) he speculated on the origins of circumpolar species, on dispersal capacities of plants, and on disjunct vicarious species pairs. In a series of papers (1914b-1922) Rydberg analyzed the flora of the altitudinal- or life-zones of the Rockies, but these were essentially phytosociological rather than geographical in substance.

The most sophisticated and broadly based work on Rocky Mountain phytogeography was contributed by the Danish-American botanist Theodore Holm, whose forgotten paper, "Alpine Vegetation of Colorado" (Holm, 1923), is really a classic. Holm spent two summers in Colorado, in 1896 and 1899, and brought to the area personal field experience gained from three Danish arctic expeditions. Holm published tables listing the occurrence of Colorado alpine species in twelve major arctic-alpine regions of the Northern Hemisphere and in many ways anticipated the monumental style of Hultén.

Holm first recognized that a number of Colorado "endemics" were in fact conspecific with Asiatic species or circumpolar species, and he perceived that the alpine species of such genera as *Trifolium* were more closely related to species of the Old World alpine than to local lowland groups; he pointed out the probable Old-World relatives of certain alpine endemic genera such as *Oreoxis* and *Chionophila.* Holm also made significant contributions to the taxonomy and phytogeography of alpine grasses and sedges, which, unfortunately, have not been given full consideration up to the present time. He discovered the arctic-alpine *Juncus biglumis* L. for the first time in the Southern Rockies, but the report went unnoticed until years later when the plant was rediscovered (Weber, 1955). It is a pity that Holm's field work in the region was so brief, for he had the background necessary to make a major contribution.

In August, 1919, the International Phytogeographical

Excursion, under the leadership of Eduard Rübel, was held in the United States. In Colorado the party visited the Pikes Peak area. A photograph was recently published showing a trio of famous botanists—Adolf Engler, Carl Schröter, and Rübel—on the trail near Minnehaha (Lüdi, 1961). It was on this excursion that the Danish botanical explorer, Ove Paulsen, collected the arctic annual *Koenigia islandica* L. for the first time in America outside the Arctic. Incredibly, this record was never published, and the specimen was only discovered in the Copenhagen Herbarium shortly after the writer published his discovery of the species in 1953 (Weber, 1955, 1961).

The Alpine Laboratory of F. E. Clements on Pikes Peak attracted many ecologists and some phytogeographers to the area, including G. Einar DuRietz, who visited it in 1926. The University of Colorado's Institute of Arctic and Alpine Research provides current facilities for research in its subalpine and alpine stations near Boulder. The hemispheric ramifications of plant relationships in the Rockies are very complex, and through visits and exchanges of research workers from the far-flung mountain areas of the northern world much correlative information can be gained and new understandings reached.

Recent local phytogeographical activity has been principally accessory to the publication of up-to-date floras. Modern floras are now available for Colorado (Harrington, 1954), Arizona (Kearney and Peebles, 1960), Idaho (Davis, 1952), and the Pacific Northwest (Hitchcock *et al.*, 1955-1961), while floras are in preparation for Wyoming (Porter), Utah (Holmgren *et al.*), Montana (Booth, 1950), and New Mexico (Dittmer *et al.*). New discoveries of plants in Colorado are reported by Weber (1955, 1961). The Beartooth Plateau of northern Wyoming and adjacent Montana has recently been found to be rich in arctic-alpine rarities (Johnson, 1962), and the Convict Creek area of the southern Sierra Nevada, while outside our area, contains alpine-arctic disjuncts pertinent to our flora (Major and Bamberg, 1963). It would be most desirable to have available annotated lists for the alpine floras of the Uinta and La Sal Mountains of Utah, the high Rockies of New Mexico, and the Beartooth Plateau. A thorough revision of the Black Hills flora is also long overdue.

Professor Hultén's distribution maps (Hultén, 1958, 1962) of the circumpolar flora are of immense importance in clarifying the greater distributional areas of Rocky Mountain plants. As late as 1958, however, the Rocky Mountains was a particularly difficult area for him since many circumpolar species occurring there have passed as local endemics, thus making it hard to recognize them in the literature. In 1959, however, Hultén was able to spend several weeks in the Colorado alpine area, and his visit, together with succeeding visits by other foreign specialists, has helped to clarify taxonomic relationships and microhabitat questions.

Taxonomic monographs usually contain detailed dot-maps, and these are most useful phytogeographical tools. Editorial policy, however, often eliminates documentation of these maps in favor of a perfunctory list of "representative specimens." This, plus the growing reluctance of the major herbaria to lend material for phytogeographic purposes, impedes the progress of research in the field at a time when detailed work should be encouraged. Regional floras, with notable exceptions (Deam, 1940; Jones and Fuller, 1955) provide neither dot-maps nor detailed distributional outlines; such works could be of great value if the importance of local distribution could be brought home to the authors. Careful outlines of local distribution are, of course, more useful than the usual vague compilations of world distribution.

A mapping program for the entire North American flora should be high on the agenda of cooperative taxonomic projects. The enormous number of herbaria on this continent makes mapping particularly difficult, but this is an area where computer methods would make possible a clearing-house for phytogeographical data.

LATE-CENOZOIC FOSSIL PLANT RECORDS FOR COLORADO[2]

The late-Cenozoic vegetation and flora of Colorado is known from only a limited number of localities, but inferences from these and from fossil localities in nearby states are summarized in this brief section.

LATE-TERTIARY FLORA OF COLORADO

A late-Oligocene flora from the Florissant Lake Beds, west of Pike's Peak in central Colorado, is well known. This flora was examined by Lesquereux (1883) and others and later studied intensively by MacGinitie (1953), who described 114 species, comprising 87 genera in 47 vascular plant families. MacGinitie characterized the Florissant flora ecologically as including several types of plants: (1) coriaceous-leaved oaks and genera of pine, scrub, and chaparral, which probably grew locally on dry foothills; (2) a riparian or lakeshore assemblage including *Salix*, *Fagopsis*, Cyperaceae, *Sequoia*, and certain broad-leaved trees (*Carya*, *Ulmus*, *Zelkova*, *Tilia*, *Castanea*) that probably occupied the wet valley margins; and (3) conifers that grew locally on higher peaks.

From the present distribution of genera and species identified from leaves at Florissant, MacGinitie concluded that the vegetation at the site was similar to that which now grows in subhumid warm-temperate areas in the northern Sierra Madre of northeastern Mexico, in part including forms similar to subxeric living species now growing in western Texas and northeastern Mexico. He inferred that the rainfall was not adequate to support a true forest except along streams where ground-water was close to the surface.

In contrast to earlier Tertiary floras of the state, which include subtropical and tropical elements, this flora suggests a warm-temperate and subxeric environment. Other mountainous areas in the state presumably also supported a relatively xeric vegetation during the late Oligocene.

A study of the Florissant pollen and spores (Leopold, unpublished data) identifies other xeric genera (*Eleagnus*, *Sarcobatus*, and *Xylonagra*) and also additional broad-leaved trees (*Eucommia*, *Juglans*, and *Fremontodendron*). The Florissant flora contains a rather large percentage of

[2] This section is by Estella B. Leopold, U.S. Geological Survey, Denver, Colorado. Publication authorized by the Director, U.S. Geological Survey.

angiosperm genera that do not grow now in the Rocky Mountain Province (*ca.* 60%), and thus it differs from late Oligocene floras on the Pacific Coast (72-74% exotic genera; Wolfe and Barghoorn, 1960) that have a more subtropical aspect. However, it resembles a flora of the same age from the Ruby Valley in Montana (Becker, 1961).

Miocene and Pliocene floras of Colorado are less rich than the Oligocene flora, but include relatively more genera still native to Colorado. A leaf flora from Creede in southwestern Colorado in the San Juan Mountains (MacGinitie, 1953, p. 73) is thought to be either Miocene or Pliocene in age. Forms identified by MacGinitie and R. Brown (written communication, 1957), plus those found as fossil pollen and spores (Leopold, unpublished data) are: *Selaginella* cf. *densa, Potamogeton, Pinus florissanti, Picea, Abies longirostris, Ephedra* cf. *E. torreyana,* cf. *E. nevadensis, Juniperus,* cf. *Tsuga,* cf. *Larix, Populus, Salix, Alnus, Quercus, Jamesia* (= *Edwinia*), *Acer, Cercocarpus myricaefolia,* Oenotheraceae, *Sarcobatus, Eleagnus, Mahonia marginata, Carya, Ulmus* and/or *Zelkova, Crataegus,* and *Artemisia.*

Only two of the Creede genera (or 10%) are now foreign to the Rocky Mountain area (*Carya* and *Ulmus-Zelkova*). Except for *Ephedra,* which now grows in very dry sites not much farther west in the pinyon-juniper association and on desert margins, the others are common in the San Juan Mountains today.

The Troublesome Formation (middle Miocene) in Middle Park, north-central Colorado (Izett and Lewis, 1963), yields a pollen assemblage consisting of the following flora (Leopold, unpublished data): *Picea* cf. *engelmanni, Pinus, Picea, Abies, Ephedra, Alnus, Ulmus-Zelkova, Arceuthobium, Carya, Sphaeralcea, Eleagnus,* Compositae cf. *Xanthium, Artemisia,* Gramineae, *Symphoricarpos, Sarcobatus vermiculatus,* and Chenopodiaceae undet.

Like the Creede flora, the assemblage is composed overwhelmingly of pine and spruce pollen. The pollen assemblage resembles the present pollen rain in the area, with the exception of *Ulmus* (or *Zelkova*), *Carya,* and *Juglans,* which are now exotic to Colorado. Thus, the Mio-Pliocene floras of this region contain only a few broad-leaved trees that are late-Tertiary relicts. None of these is known to persist in the Colorado flora after the Pliocene. Pliocene floras from Wyoming, Idaho, and Arizona have a generic aspect similar to those from Colorado.

THE PLIO-PLEISTOCENE BOUNDARY IN SOUTHERN IDAHO

With respect to palynology or paleobotany, the Plio-Pleistocene boundary has not been studied in Colorado, but evidence from south-central Idaho (Axelrod, 1964; Leopold and Brown *in* Mapel and Hail, 1959) may be pertinent. The middle-Miocene (or early-Pliocene) flora at Trapper Creek (Beaverdam Formation of Axelrod, 1964) contains forms such as *Sequoia, Fraxinus, Carya, Ulmus, Zelkova, Persea, Nyssa,* and *Ilex,* which are now foreign to the region, plus many forms now characteristic, *e.g. Pinus, Picea, Tsuga, Abies, Ephedra, Alnus, Quercus, Acer, Populus.* The flora of the Salt Lake Formation (early Pliocene; Mapel and Hail, 1959) and of the Banbury Basalt (middle Pliocene; Leopold, unpublished data) are greatly impoverished compared with the Trapper Creek flora. Broad-leaved trees,

for example, are represented only by *Carya, Juglans,* and *Ulmus-Zelkova* in the Salt Lake, and only by *Carya* and *Ulmus-Zelkova* in the Banbury.

A diverse pollen flora from the Glenns Ferry Formation of Blancan age (latest Pliocene and earliest Pleistocene) in the western Snake River Plain represents plants now native to Idaho, except for rare pollen of *Carya* and *Ulmus-Zelkova* (see stratigraphic summary by Malde, this volume). The flora is dominated by various genera of Pinaceae and includes *Celtis, Populus,* and several xeric shrubs, in addition to water plants and herbs. It suggests a climate slightly wetter than today's (annual precipitation now about 10 in.), which permitted low montane vegetation to grow in this now treeless area. Pollen from the overlying Bruneau Formation (middle Pleistocene) is mainly of the Pinaceae and includes no late-Tertiary relict genera. It suggests a climate somewhat cooler and wetter than today's.

The succession of Miocene, Pliocene, and Quaternary pollen floras from southern Idaho demonstrates gradual loss of broad-leaved tree genera that still persist in central and eastern United States and along the Pacific Coast. This may be expressed in terms of the percentage of the identified flora that is lost progressively with time (Wolfe and Barghoorn, 1960).

For Idaho, the middle-Miocene (or early-Pliocene) Trapper Creek flora contains 35% of genera that are now foreign to the central Rocky Mountain region. The Pliocene floras contain only 2 or 3 genera that are now exotic to the region, but these genera represent about 25% of the total. In the Blancan (Plio-Pleistocene) interval, these exotic genera (including only *Carya* and *Ulmus-Zelkova*) make up only 9% of the flora. Younger pollen floras that have been examined contain no genera that are now foreign to the present regional flora.

The loss of broad-leaved trees from the flora of the central Rocky Mountains was undoubtedly progressive, owing to gradual changes in regional climate and the rise of mountains (particularly the Cascade Range and the Sierra Nevada). The consequent decrease in mesic conditions permitted only a few broad-leaved trees to survive in Idaho and Colorado (*e.g. Populus, Acer grandidentatum,* and *Betula papyrifera*), though shrubby species of many dicotyledonous tree genera are also represented (*Quercus, Celtis, Acer, Alnus,* etc.).

LATE-QUATERNARY POLLEN RECORDS

The reported late-Quaternary pollen records in Colorado are limited to two late-Pinedale and postglacial bog deposits in the San Juan Mountains (Maher, 1961) and four deposits in the Rocky Mountain Front Range west of Boulder (Pennak, 1963).

In the San Juan Mountains, Maher (1961) studied two sites in the subalpine vegetation zone at an elevation of about 3,200 m, or about 300 m below the present tree line. The pollen sequence is as follows. An early interval of clayey sediments is characterized by dominance of *Artemisia* (40-70% of total pollen) and *Pinus.* A radiocarbon date of 15,450 ± 220 years (Y-1147) was obtained from near the top of this zone. Overlying organic sediments, with a date of 13,360 ± 120 (Y-1437) at the very base, are characterized by pollen of many montane forms—*Pinus, Picea, Abies, Pseudotsuga, Betula,* and *Quercus,* and various non-tree taxa. *Ephedra* pollen also was found, but it is thought to represent long-distance transport from arid lowlands. Tundra was apparently replaced locally by subalpine forest about 13,500 years ago. According to data from modern pollen surface samples, Maher (1961, 1963) concluded that before this forestation took place tree-line stood at least 600 m lower than now.

In the Front Range, Pennak (1963) studied four sites ranging in altitude from 2,617 to 3,247 m. C[14] dates indicate that the oldest sediments are nearly 6,700 years old. Pollen diagrams from the four sites have individual features, but the two oldest may bear on interpreting past climate. *Artemisia* pollen is fairly high (*ca.* 30% of the total pollen) in sediments from 6,700 to about 6,000 years old. Otherwise, *Pinus* pollen is dominant. A predominance of grass pollen lasting from 6,000 to 3,000 years ago occurs in one pollen profile. Pennak thought this recorded a warm, dry period, but it could represent local edaphic conditions at a single site.

SUMMARY

The late-Tertiary floristic history of Colorado, reconstructed from a meager fossil record, indicates that a rich temperate flora became impoverished during the Miocene and Pliocene Epochs in Colorado—a pattern common to several western states. Although the post-Blancan Quaternary plant record of Colorado is also scant, no generic extinctions are known within this flora after the Tertiary.

THE ORIGIN OF THE MODERN FLORA

The modern flora of the Southern Rockies forms a complicated patchwork of overlays, the base consisting of what remnants there are from the Oligocene flora as recorded at Florissant, Colorado (MacGinitie, 1953). At the lower altitudes this flora is distinctly of Madro-Tertiary derivation (Axelrod, 1948), but in the high mountains occur remnants of what must have been a more or less continuously distributed high-mountain flora extending from this area across Beringia into the mountain regions of Central Asia— the Boreal-Asiatic element discussed later. The alpine areas are dominated by circumpolar species, which were either in place there before the Pleistocene or migrated there during the Ice Ages.

Modern plant-distribution patterns in the Southern Rockies suggest that the Cordilleran flora once extended considerably down-slope and eastward, possibly coincident with a depression of timberline during cold periods, and that the eastern woodland flora extended westward, probably along the major watercourses, and mingled with the Cordilleran flora along a wide area of the western Great Plains. Today the Cordilleran flora has retreated into the higher areas, leaving relicts in the Black Hills and at scattered points on the Great Plains, while the eastern flora has retreated eastward or been exterminated on the Great Plains, leaving reciprocal relict colonies along the mesic eastern front of the mountains.

Former connections of the Southern Rockies to the northwestward have been severed by the development of the

deserts of southern Wyoming, but relict stands of northwestern species provide traces of the old connection. The Madro-Tertiary xeric floral elements of the Great Basin and Colorado Plateaus have penetrated far into the mountains on the west by way of the warm river valleys and deep canyons, and on the southeast a clearly defined invasion by the west Texas–western New Mexico flora (here called the Chihuahuan element) is actively encroaching on the eastern flanks of the mountains.

The most widely accepted explanation for the presence of boreal and arctic species in the Rocky Mountains was advanced by Darwin (1883), and adopted with little change by Hooker and Gray (1880) and Rydberg (1914c, p. 89). The southward penetration of the Pleistocene climate caused successive vegetational zones to replace each other southward so that a vast displacement and telescoping of the flora occurred. As the ice retreated northward, arctic species found congenial habitats on the mountaintops of the southern mountain ranges, where they now exist widely disjunct from their relatives that moved back to the Arctic. Constant repetition of this idea has given it the aura of truth. However, in recent years Tolmatchev (1959a, b) and Hultén (1962) have attacked it as rather naïve and over simplified.

The influence of a Mexican reservoir in stocking the floristic "streams" of the American Southwest was appreciated very early by Hooker and elaborated by Watson (1890). Hooker and Gray (1880, p. 62) stated: "We infer that the Pacific region, while preserving through all vicissitudes a moderate number of boreal types and receiving a few Eastern Asiatic ones probably at a later date, has been mainly replenished from the Mexican Plateau, and at a comparatively late period. A large part of the botany of California, still more of Nevada, Utah, and western Texas, and, yet more, that of Arizona and New Mexico, may be regarded as a northward extension of the botany of the Mexican Plateau."

Axelrod (1948, p. 139) sums up succinctly his interpretation of the historic events that have resulted in the present-day Rocky Mountain flora: "The histories of montane forest, woodland, chaparral and desert vegetation outlined . . . indicate that the major Tertiary floras of the western United States were differentiated into communities of essentially modern aspect largely by Middle Pliocene and succeeding climates. Differentiation apparently was in response to a trend to lowered yearly rainfall, shifting seasonal distribution of rain, and increased ranges and extremes of temperature. Under the impact of these accelerated post-lower Pliocene climatic changes the Arcto-Tertiary and Madro-Tertiary floras lost their identity, since species formerly shared with other regions became extinct in certain areas of their early Pliocene distribution. As montane forest, woodland, chaparral and arid subtropical scrub were restricted in range as rainfall lessened, open steppe and subdesert environments of subcontinental extent came into existence over the warm-dry and cold-dry regions. Herbaceous and semi-woody plants which had a restricted distribution on the borders of Miocene and early Pliocene communities apparently spread widely and evolved rapidly as these new regional environments were initiated. Only in latest Cenozoic times, in response to the development of more localized environments, were the modern plant formations fully segregated into the regional climaxes, the subregional associations and the more localized communities that now characterize western North America. . . .

"The floristic evolution initiated during the Middle Pliocene has not been completed, but is continuing at the present time. This is shown by inter-relationships displayed by the various modern communities of each plant formation over this region. The relationships between these living derivative communities of Late Tertiary vegetation are expressed by the modern patterns of plant distribution. They occur not only in North America, but extend beyond to other continents in both latitudinal and meridional directions. These distributional patterns are considered to reflect the former occurrence of ancestral Tertiary Floras across the intervening areas. The modern patterns seem to have resulted from world-wide late Cenozoic climatic changes which differentiated generalized Tertiary floras into communities now having more restricted ranges."

PRESENT-DAY COINCIDENT PATTERNS AND THEIR RELATIONSHIPS TO PAST EVENTS

Plant species have genetically determined ranges of tolerance to environmental characteristics, and they are bound to specific areas in which a tolerable set of environmental factors operates. Plant-distribution patterns thus are maps of the environments of the world.

The application of plant-distribution patterns to problems involving long-term climatic changes, orogenies, and continental displacement is based upon the assumption that plants are not capable of quickly colonizing every land area that is suitable for them but are limited by their innate dispersal capacity, competitive ability, and genetic structure (individual and populational) and by physiographic and climatic barriers to their spread. Because of this, the actual distribution patterns of plant species always tend to lag behind geologic evolution, and modern plant-distribution patterns in greater or lesser degree provide "fossil" evidence of ancient distribution patterns.

Mason (1946), in a very important paper on the edaphic factor in narrow endemism, analyzed the dynamics of geographic distribution in plants. He showed that distribution patterns result from the interaction of the physical environment with the physiological reactions and genetic processes of individuals and populations. He insisted that "area as such has no historical significance in vegetation. . . . The pattern of distribution is determined by causes inherent in the locality and most probably has had no correlative relationship with the history of the flora over any wide area. . . . The size and shape of the area occupied are the product of today's facts, both genetic and environmental."

Mason here was attacking the oversimplifications of Willis' "Age and Area" hypothesis, Hultén's model of the "equiformal progressive area," and other phytogeographical dicta concerning the center of origin and dispersal. It is difficult to believe that Mason would deny the historic implications for those classic distribution patterns linking eastern Asia with the southern Appalachians, the Chilean flora with that of Australasia, or the well-known transatlantic biological connections.

Botanical evidence has played an important role in suggesting theories of land bridges between continents, continental drift, and the various other notions of geologic evolution. In this discussion we are concerned only with the presence in the Rocky Mountains of "coincident distribution patterns." These represent assemblages of species with generally homologous areas or with ranges radiating from a more or less restricted area toward other parts of the world, the implication being that these patterns represent traces of past continuities of distribution or paths of migration to or from those regions.

The following analysis of modern distribution patterns is inspired by the more comprehensive work of Hultén, who is mapping the distribution patterns of the entire holarctic flora.

Hultén (1937) proposed a theory of "equiformal progressive areas," briefly described below, which he hoped would provide detailed explanations of the recolonization of the ice-denuded portions of the North following the last glacial period. In essence, he postulated a bare circular area of uniform climate seeded with a number of species and characterized by minimum competition. Depending on the dispersal potential of the various species, these would radiate from the center where they were introduced and eventually develop "equiformal" circular areas that in the end would occupy the total area available. The model is never realized because of the complex biology of plant species, their competitive relations, unequal dispersal capacities, and environmental complexity. But Hultén showed that the theoretical situation could be approximated with maps of the total areas of a large number of species, and in so doing he located a number of centers of these "equiformal progressive areas."

In the Southern Rocky Mountains the historical background is very different from that of the arctic regions with which Hultén was concerned. The region was not affected directly by continental glaciation, and at no time were large land areas completely devoid of plants. Present distribution patterns reflect events much older than Pleistocene, and the flora is much larger than that of the North. Except for a relatively small number of species endemic to this area, the patterns with which one deals represent only the termini of distribution areas of great magnitude. For example, from almost all sides, major distribution patterns converge upon the Southern Rockies. The northern limits of the Mexican Plateau flora are there, as are the southern limits of the arctic flora, the eastern limits of the Great Basin flora, the western limits of the Great Plains flora. Unfortunately, although the patterns are clear, the detailed information from climatology, geology, and paleontology that might justify and explain them has not yet been integrated. The patterns are outlined here in the hope of stimulating investigation and of thus securing the needed information from the other branches of biology and from geology.

In the short time available it has been impossible to provide a complete analysis of the 4,000 or so species of higher plants, not to mention the cryptogams, of the Southern

Rocky Mountain flora. For one thing, our knowledge of distributions is still too incomplete to permit this. At the risk of seeming to bias the record in favor of the proposed hypotheses, those species that have been selected exemplify the patterns, and it is left to future research to determine whether the coincident patterns are real or not.

Hultén (1937) pointed out some of the difficulties in this work. Among the most pertinent is the fact that nothing less than total distribution must be shown, because, whereas one might imagine that a generalized pattern should be adequate, it is the isolated outlier that is often most critical to an understanding of ecological tolerances or history of migration.

Hultén was especially critical of studies that use a single species to solve a biogeographic problem and of ones that concern themselves with only a segment of a distribution pattern. The present analysis is open to criticism on the latter count because very different distribution patterns may have homologous radiant arms into the Rocky Mountains. With some attention to the broader distributional area, some separation of these elements may be effected, but oversimplifications are bound to creep in.

Because the areas being considered here are only portions of the greater world areas, and because no inference is made to "center of dispersal," or direction of migration, the writer prefers not to use Hultén's term, "equiformal progressive areas." Instead the areas described herein are called "coincident areas." A group of species having a coincident area constitutes an *element*. Elements may be further subdivided into sub-elements. Coincident areas are either well-marked or vague to the extent that the species coincide in their ranges to a more or less marked degree.

THE CIRCUMPOLAR ELEMENT AND RELATED CORDILLERAN PATTERNS

It has long been known that many plants of the Northern Hemisphere are found in an almost continuous ring on the fringes of North America, Eurasia, and the intervening islands (see Fig. 1). The occurrence of some of these species in the southern mountains of both continents, either with a continuous connection or as disjunct populations, is also a fact that was obvious to the earliest phytogeographers. Yet the details of their distribution and the sorting of these patterns into groups reveal that there are significant gaps both in their meridional and latitudinal aspects. The circumpolar plants are being mapped by Hultén (1958, 1962, and unpublished), who has presented in some detail (Hultén, 1958, p. 3-6) the theory of the origin and migration of this flora.

Hultén (1958) presents a significant departure from the time-honored concept of the origin of the alpine flora as postulated by Darwin, Hooker, and subsequent investigators (cited earlier in this chapter). He postulates a warm and genial Tertiary climate over the northern world, conducive to circumpolar distributions of many groups now considered to be temperate or subtropical. The onset of the Ice Ages

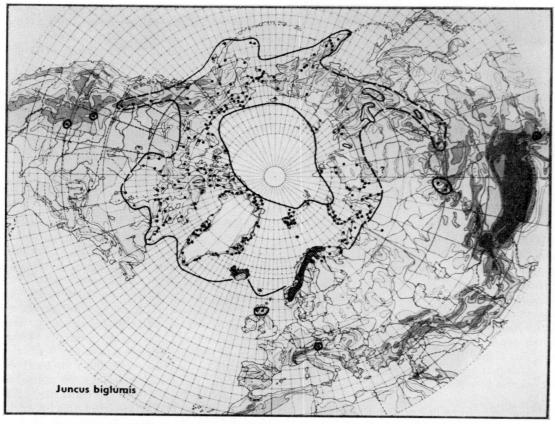

Figure 1. Distribution of *Juncus biglumis,* a typical circumpolar pattern with southern outliers. From Hultén (1962).

not only exterminated many of these plants in their northern areas but eliminated them from even more southerly intermediate areas. The circumpolar areas were broken up, leaving isolated fragments. Hultén does not insist that the present alpine flora migrated out of the Arctic at all but implies that the alpine floras of the Northern Hemisphere, originally more or less circumpolar, were also fragmented by the climatic changes and persisted as isolated remnants in the southern mountains. Comprehensive accounts of the circumpolar species are found in Hultén (1958-1962).

It is likely that the present low-altitude circumpolar arctic flora reached that area by outward migration onto virgin areas left bare by the ice; this migration led them away *from the mountain regions* where they had been surviving as fragmented populations of the old montane segment of the circumpolar Tertiary flora.

In the Southern Rockies the richest alpine communities are situated where high ranges trending east-west lie between or connect the principal north-south ranges. These ranges are all similar in that they are more constantly mesic throughout the year than the contrasting north-south mountains. Here the diurnal insolation through the summer months seems to be less direct or of shorter duration, resulting in a slow run-off, later snow beds, and development of small bogs and lakes at high elevations. These ranges probably escape the severe effects of the winter "Foehn" winds that dry out the slopes of the north-south ranges. Rare species in these places may occur on either north-facing or south-facing slopes, not necessarily on the summits but at some distance below. Cold-air drainage basins are also important relict areas. South Park, for example, harbors a colony of *Salix candida* Flügge, *Primula egaliksensis* Wormskj., and *Halimolobos virgata* (Nutt.) Schulz, and Middle Park supports stands of *Rubus acaulis* Michx., *Cystopteris montana* (Lam.) Bernh., and *Parnassia kotzebuei* Cham. & Schl.

A list of the especially rich alpine areas of Colorado, together with their special attractions, is given below:

1. Mount Evans: *Saxifraga foliolosa* R. Br., *Phippsia algida* (Phipps) R. Br., *Koenigia islandica* L., *Hydrogrimmia mollis* (B.S.G.) Loeske, *Oreas martiana* (Hoppe & Hornsch.) Brid., *Cetraria commixta* (Nyl.) Th. Fr., *Stereocaulon rivulorum* Magn.

2. Hoosier Pass: *Eutrema penlandii* Rollins, *Saussurea weberi* Hultén, *Festuca brachyphylla* Schultes, *Braya humilis* Robinson, *Armeria maritima* (Mill.) Willd., *Oxytropis podocarpa* A. Gray.

3. Elk Mountains: *Erigeron humilis* Grah., *E. lanatus* Hook., *Stellaria irrigua* Bunge, *Senecio porteri* Greene, *Eriophorum scheuchzeri* Hoppe, *E. russeolum* Frise. This area is unusual in its concentration of species that are Canadian Rocky Mountain types.

4. San Juan–San Miguel Range near Silverton: *Cladonia mitis* Sandst., *Adiantum pedatum* L., *Eriophorum scheuchzeri* Hoppe, *Parnassia kotzebuei* Cham. & Schl.

Much of our mountain vegetation can be related, directly or indirectly, to the Circumpolar Element. Local endemics can be linked to relatives that are Northern Rocky Mountain types; these in turn are related to species that have radiated across Boreal America, and these in turn to circumpolar types. The sorting of patterns into sub-elements is accomplished with this understanding always in mind. These sub-elements are listed below, in order of increasing area:

A. Southern Rocky Mountain endemics, derived from Circumpolar Elements
B. Central Rocky Mountain–Pacific Northwest
C. Northern Rocky Mountain
D. American radiants
E. Boreal-Asiatic
F. Circumpolar

Boreal-Asiatic sub-element. The Boreal-Asiatic sub-element comprises species of the general circumpolar distribution that tend to be concentrated in the mountains of western America, Asia, and southern Europe, rare or absent in the American Arctic, and generally absent from Scandinavia. This extremely interesting group in our flora contains the following types:

1. Genera with close relatives in Central Asia: *e.g. Besseya* (Scrophulariaceae), related to Eurasian *Wulfenia* and *Picrorhiza* (*fide* Pennell, 1933); *Chionophila* (Scrophulariaceae), related to *Chelone?*; *Oreoxis* (Umbelliferae), related to *Ligusticum?*

2. Genera with endemic species in the Rockies and different endemics in Eurasia; *e.g. Aquilegia* (Ranunculaceae), several blue-flowered species in Rockies with counterparts in Asia; *Eritrichium* (Boraginaceae), two or three species in the western Cordillera and the rest scattered in alpine and Arctic Eurasia (Fig. 2); *Helictotrichon* (Gramineae), two species in the Rockies, many in Eurasia.

3. Rocky Mountain forms only racially distinct from Eurasian counterparts: *Androsace chamaejasme* Host., *Aster alpinus* L., *Braya humilis* (C. A. Mey.) Rob., *Artemisia arctica* Less.

4. Highly uniform species isolated in widely disjunct areas of the Rocky Mountains and Asia: *Stellaria umbellata* Turcz., *S. irrigua* Bunge, *Draba fladnizensis* Wulf., *Ranunculus gelidus* Kar. & Kar., *Crepis nana* Rich., *Gentiana prostrata* Haenke.

The Boreal-Asiatic sub-element of the circumpolar flora is probably a very old Tertiary one; it has radiated at various times to produce circumpolar types. For example, *Cerastium beeringianum* Cham. & Schlecht., studied by Hultén (1956), has a fairly typical Boreal-Asiatic distribution reinforced in the general area by the related *C. fischerianum* and *C. jeneseiense*, which are Amphi-Beringian and Eastern Asiatic respectively. Other related species in the same group have reached and now occupy segments of the northeast America-Greenland-Scandinavia areas.

Eritrichium aretioides (Cham.) DC. (Boraginaceae), typifies the pattern of Boreal-Asiatic distributions in our area. Lechner-Pock (1956) reviewed the species of the *E. nanum* group (Fig. 2), to which this belongs and showed that the group as a whole occupies four major areas: (1) an Arctic belt in Eurasia with outlying stations as far west

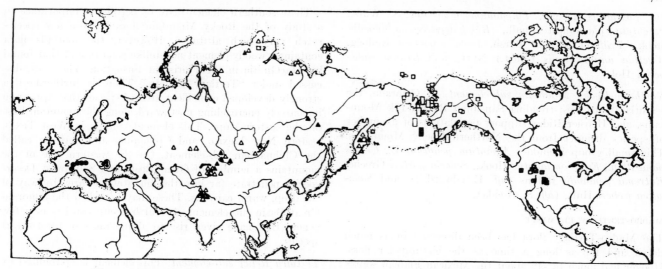

Figure 2. Distribution of the *Eritrichium nanum* group, a Boreal-Asiatic pattern. From Lechner-Pock (1956). Symbols represent different taxa.

as Kola Peninsula; (2) the mountainous regions of Central Asia and Central Europe; (3) the lands on either side of the Bering Sea (Kamchatka, eastern Siberia, and Alaska); and (4) the Rocky Mountains. Thus there are major disjunctions of the same or related species between (1) and (2) on the one hand and (3) and (4) on the other. The group is absent from the American Arctic east of Alaska. Five species comprise the subgenus; three of these are Eurasian: *E. nanum* (Alps), *E. jankae* (Carpathians), and *E. villosum* (Asia, Caucasus, Arctic Europe), and two are American–East Asian: *E. aretioides* (discussed above) and *E. chamissonis* (Bering Strait).

The Boreal-Asiatic sub-element, as far as it seems to be composed of species with close relatives in Asia, tends to be alpine. However, if one extrapolates this element to related genera that are now endemic in western North America, there is a suggestion that this element "seeded" the southwestern desert areas with these groups. It seems likely that *Cryptantha*, *Onosmodium*, *Mertensia*, and other such genera are ultimately related to ancient Asiatic genera.

The alpine members of the Boreal-Asiatic element include species that vary from common and widespread to rare and highly disjunct. This element includes conservative species that appear to be much like their Asiatic counterparts, "racy" species forming intercontinental chains of subspecies, and those species whose relationships to Asiatic counterparts are probably close but untested.

Boreal-American sub-element. A few alpine species belong to a group that has radiated into Boreal America but no farther (Fig. 3). However, all of these are clearly related to Boreal-Asiatic groups, on the one hand, and to circumpolar species on the other. These include: *Arenaria obtusiloba* (Rydb.) Fern., *Carex stans* Drejer, *Festuca baffinensis* Polunin, *Geum rossii* (R. Br.) Ser., *Oxytropis podocarpa* A. Gray, *O. viscida* Nutt., *Potentilla hookeriana* Lehm., *P. rubricaulis* Lehm., and *Stellaria monantha* Hultén.

Central Rocky Mountain–Pacific Northwest sub-element. A small group of Central Rocky Mountain–Pacific North-

west species, isolated from the next northern area of distribution by the Wyoming deserts, occurs in the Park Range north of Steamboat Springs, Colorado, with outliers as far south as Rocky Mountain National Park and Rabbit Ears Pass. This pattern is characterized by *Rhododendron albiflorum* Hook. and *Trillium ovatum* Pursh, which are quite obviously derivatives of Tertiary relicts. This group of species must have had a continuity of range northwestward prior to the desiccation of the southern Wyoming high desert. The assemblage imparts a characteristic northwestern flavor to this regional flora. The environment is considerably more mesic than in the mountains to the south, and the area supports an isolated population of the wood frog, *Rana sylvatica cantabrigensis* Baird (Maslin, 1959). This sub-element includes: *Antennaria luzuloides* T. & G., *Botrychium multifidum* ssp. *coulteri* (Underw.) Clausen, *Cypripedium fasciculatum* Kellogg, *Fritillaria pudica* (Pursh) Spreng., *Ivesia gordonii* (Hook.) T. & G., *Lewisia triphylla* (S. Wats.) Robinson, *Mimulus lewisii* Pursh,

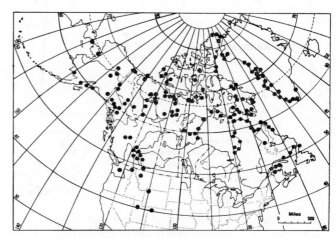

Figure 3. Distribution of *Stellaria monantha,* a Boreal-American pattern. From Porsild (1963). Colorado stations not shown.

M. moschatus Dougl., *Polygonum minimum* S. Wats., *Potentilla glandulosa* Lindl., *Rhododendron albiflorum* Hook., *Trillium ovatum* Pursh, *Viola purpurea* Kellogg, *Wyethia amplexicaulis* (Nutt.) Nutt., and *Bryum sandbergii* Holz.

Northern Rocky Mountain sub-element. In Colorado, the essentially east-west-trending San Juan Range, Elk Mountains, and Hoosier Ridge support populations of a number of species disjunct from the Northern Rocky Mountains. This small group includes: *Adiantum pedatum* L., *Crepis nana* Rich., *Erigeron lanatus* Hook., *Senecio porteri* Greene, *Eutrema penlandii* Rollins (*aff. E. edwardsii*), and *Saussurea weberi* Hult. (*aff. S. viscida*).

MADRO-TERTIARY ELEMENT

The Madro-Tertiary flora has been discussed in as much detail and for as long a time as the circumpolar flora. Hooker had much to say about the Mexican Plateau source of the southwestern flora. Watson (1890) and Abrams (1913) also discussed the origins of southwestern plants, and Axelrod (1948) has developed a general theory of the history of this ancient element in our flora. Locally, MacGinitie's (1953) work on the Florissant fossil flora is a basic source of information on the flora and climate of Oligocene times in Colorado, and Hay (1939) has analyzed the Mexican element in the Colorado flora.

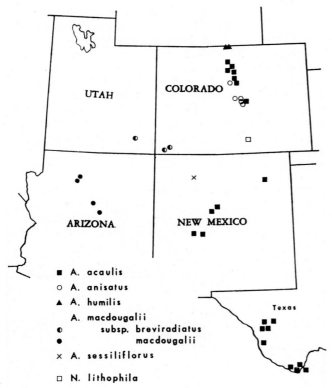

■ A. acaulis
○ A. anisatus
▲ A. humilis
  A. macdougalii
◓   subsp. breviradiatus
●   macdougalii
× A. sessiliflorus

□ N. lithophila

Figure 4. Distribution of *Aletes* and *Neoparrya*, genera with Madro-Tertiary relict patterns. (*Aletes acaulis*, black squares, falls into the Chihuahuan sub-element.) From Theobald *et al.* (1964).

These southern elements are of peripheral importance to a study of the Rocky Mountain flora because few species reach very high altitudes. However, the foothills flora contains a woody element not unlike a portion of that found by MacGinitie in the Florissant formation. These are discussed under "Tertiary Relicts." There is furthermore a strongly developed coincident area of species that appear to be actively encroaching northward along the mountain base on the eastern slope. This element centers in West Texas, eastern New Mexico, and Chihuahua and may be called the Chihuahuan sub-element. On the western side of the mountains a number of Great Basin and Southwest Desert species penetrate far into the mountainous area by way of the deep, warm canyons. These may be called the Sonoran-Great Basin sub-element. A fourth group consists of a few genera that have given rise to alpine races of local desert species.

Tertiary Relict sub-element. This element is epitomized by *Jamesia americana. Jamesia* is a monotypic genus of the Hydrangeaceae with no close relatives in the modern flora of this region, but probably closely related to Asiatic species of *Deutzia*. Leaves of *Jamesia* have been reported from the Creede (Mio-Pliocene) flora by Stewart (1940). The modern distribution of *Jamesia* consists of a continuous area in the eastern foothills of the Colorado Rockies, south to northern New Mexico, and discontinuous areas in the mountains of southern New Mexico to the southeastern corner of Arizona. The species also reappears locally on the east slope of the southern Sierra Nevada of California.

Rubus deliciosus Torr. is similarly restricted to the east slope of the Rockies but has an outlying relative in western Colorado and Utah. *Selaginella weatherbiana* Tryon is limited to cool north-facing canyonsides in the eastern foothills from northern Colorado to southern New Mexico. The umbelliferous genera *Aletes*, *Neoparrya* (Fig. 4), and *Harbouria* have essentially the same distribution, although *Aletes* also has a Colorado Plateau member.

It is significant that a number of the species displaying this distribution are types that have a worldwide Tertiary Relict status. This is especially true of the ferns, some bryophytes, and lichens. The ferns *Asplenium septentrionale* (L.) Hoffm., *A. adiantum-nigrum* L., *Dryopteris filix-mas* (L.) Schott, the moss *Anacolia laevisphaera* (Tayl.) Flowers, and the lichens *Normandina pulchella* (Borr.) Nyl., *Cetraria glauca* (L.) Ach., *Cetraria chlorophylla* (Willd.) Vain., *Sticta weigelii* (Ach.) Vain, *Anaptychia leucomelaena* (L.) Vain. are quite out of place in the present Rocky Mountain flora but show interesting world distributions involving more oceanic or subtropical regions.

This group includes species of peculiar ecological requirements. They evidently were once widespread in the foothill flora of the West but have been eliminated with increasing aridity, leaving isolated remnants in three principal areas: the east slope of the Rockies, the Colorado Plateaus, and the eastern Sierra Nevada. Many of these species are cliff-dwelling types that may combine high water requirements with obligate saxicoly or low competitive ability. On the eastern slope of the Rockies this ecological combination is fulfilled by the steep escarpments which, combined with local atmospheric peculiarities, produce a cloud veil that results in local pockets of temporary high humidity (Ives, 1938).

Several additional species belonging to this old mesic Tertiary flora have persisted in much larger areas in the forested regions. *Pachystima myrsinites* (Pursh) Raf., *Mahonia repens* Lindl., *M. fremontii* (Torr.) Fedde and species of *Populus*, *Ribes*, and *Cercocarpus* represent the more successful survivors of this group. Other Tertiary Relicts include: *Acer grandidentatum* Nutt. ex T. & G., *Asplenium adiantum-nigrum* L., *Asplenium septentrionale* (L). Hoffm., *Dryopteris filix-mas* (L.) Schott, *Epipactis gigantea* Dougl. ex Hook., *Jamesia americana* T. & G., *Pachystima myrsinites* (Pursh) Raf., *Philadelphus microphyllus* A. Gray, *Ptelea trifoliata* L., *Rhamnus smithii* Greene, *Robinia neomexicana* A. Gray, *Rubus deliciosus* Torr., *Selaginella weatherbiana* Tyron, *Harbouria trachypleura* (A. Gray) C. & R., *Neoparrya lithophila* Mathias, *Aletes acaulis* (Torr.) C. & R., *Aletes humilis* C. & R., and *Aletes macdougalii* C. & R.

Chihuahuan sub-element. In the Chihuahuan sub-element is included a group of species that occupy west Texas, eastern New Mexico, and usually Chihuahua and that show a coincident area extending northwest into Colorado along the Arkansas drainage system. Probably this pattern contributes a good number of species to the flora of the southern Great Plains, and in some instances to southeastern United States. It appears to be a more or less distinct group because the species in Colorado are decidedly "eastern" and do not occur in the southwestern corner, nor do most of them occur west of southeastern Arizona.

South from the Boulder area, the flora changes dramatically in several stages. Just south of Denver one encounters the first stands of *Quercus gambelii* Nutt., which becomes an important species to the south. Just north of Colorado Springs, *Pinus edulis* Engelm. appears, and a few miles to the south of that city the candelabra cactus, *Opuntia arborescens* Engelm. becomes conspicuous. Near Walsenburg *Juniperus monosperma* (Engelm.) Sarg. makes its appearance, and when the Arkansas River is reached a number of herbaceous plants and suffruticose species of southern affinities add to the pattern. The number of species belonging to the distribution pattern characteristically including West Texas, eastern New Mexico, and the Chihuahuan desert increases southeastward along the Arkansas River drainage until at the southeastern corner of Colorado the entire flora is dominated by this element.

The distribution pattern of *Pinus edulis* indicates that it belongs to the Madro-Tertiary element, which with Chihuahuan sub-element, appears to fill an expanding rather than a retreating area in eastern Colorado. This peculiarity is explained by Cain (1944): "An expanding area tends to have a relatively continuous boundary and a homogeneous topography, whereas a contracting area tends to have a relatively discontinuous boundary and an irregular and broken topography. . . . The principal reasons for the above relationships are the fact that the expanding area has not reached effective barriers and that the contracting area leaves behind relict colonies in local situations where

frequently edaphic or microclimatic conditions provide at least temporary compensation for a general climatic unfavorableness."

It does not seem necessary to the argument to insist that effective barriers have not been reached, for it is quite obvious that in our flora, at least, the barriers exist and have been reached by many species in this pattern. However, the barriers themselves are very likely moving northward, permitting a slow encroachment, and the differential extensions of the various species indicate that different species are limited in their spread by different combinations of climatic extremes.

In the Southern Rocky Mountains *Pinus edulis* reaches the Wyoming state line (Peterson, 1962) on the west side of the mountains, but on the east slope its limit of maximum continuous distribution is in the Colorado Springs region westward to Monarch Pass. It is therefore anomalous to find a colony of piñon pine about 250 km to the north, in Owl Canyon, 50 km northwest of Fort Collins. This population has been regarded by many botanists as a relict population; this interpretation would be out of harmony with the general theory proposed here and would place it in the general Cordilleran pattern, which is a contracting area. Does this colony really represent the remnant of an ancient extension of the species? Or is there some other explanation?

Wright (1952) mapped the stand, took borings of the trees, and listed the associated vegetation. He found that the age of the six largest trees ranged from 317 to 372 years and that the population radiates out from a small group of old trees in the northwest corner of the grove. In other words, the population can be projected back only 300 years to a small cluster of trees all concentrated in one gully. The associated vegetation contains no species pointing to a southern relict stand; even the juniper associated with this piñon stand is *Juniperus scopulorum* rather than *J. monosperma*, the usual associate of piñon on the eastern slope. Wright held that this isolated stand, instead of representing a relict stand, represents a chance introduction, possibly through the agency of animals that might have rifled supplies of Indians carrying the nuts from place to place. The survival of the piñon on this site may be attributed, in its turn, to a combination of calcareous substrate, eastern exposure, and an open community present in the beginning. In recent times, the piñon has been spread to several nearby localities, probably by jays (Weber, 1961), where isolated individuals ranging from a few years to 100 years old have been found.

Species of the Chihuahuan sub-element include: *Abutilon incanum* (Link) Sweet, *Andropogon saccharoides* Sw., *Argemone squarrosa* Greene, *Asclepias macrotis* Torr., *A. oenotheroides* Cham. & Schlecht., *Asplenium resiliens* Kunze, *Berlandiera lyrata* Benth., *Bouteloua barbata* Lag., *B. eriopoda* (Torr.) Torr., *Cheilanthes eatonii* Baker, *C. wootonii* Maxon, *Croton texensis* (Klotsch) Muell. Arg., *Cucurbita foetidissima* H.B.K., *Dalea lanata* Spreng., *D. nana* Torr., *Desmanthus cooleyi* (Eaton) Trel., *Engelmannia pinnatifida* T. & G., *Eragrostis oxylepis* (Torr.) Torr., *Eriochloa contracta* Hitchc., *Gaillardia pulchella* Foug., *Hoffmanseggia densiflora* Benth., *H. drepanocarpa* A. Gray, *H. jamesii* T. & G., *Juniperus monosperma* (Engelm.) Sarg.,

Krameria spp., *Melampodium cinereum* DC., *Mimosa borealis* A. Gray, *Palafoxia* spp., *Pericome caudata* A. Gray, *Sapindus saponaria* L., *Sarcostemma crispum* Benth., *Stillingia sylvatica* Gard., and *Thelesperma* spp.

Sonoran–Great Basin sub-element. The desert flora that penetrates far into the Rockies by way of the warm river valleys, canyon walls, and arid plateaus is a conspicuous element in Western Colorado, represented by hundreds of species, of which it is sufficient to name only a few genera: *Astragalus, Atriplex, Cryptantha, Phacelia,* and *Gilia.* These groups are evidently elaborations of the old Tertiary flora that radiated into the Great Basin from a Mexican reservoir. The low divides in southern Wyoming and northern New Mexico have permitted a number of species of this western group to overflow into favorable sites on the eastern face of the Rockies, particularly those species that are adapted to shale outcrops. The Pierre and Niobrara shales along the eastern foothills support local stands of essentially western species, *e.g., Physaria australis* (Pays.) Rollins, *Eriogonum campanulatum* Nutt., and *Erigeron canus* A. Gray.

A discussion of this large and complicated group is outside the scope of this paper, because the flora is not chiefly Rocky Mountain in composition. The importance of this element arises from the fact that the Great Basin flora has contributed several species to the Rocky Mountain alpine flora, which will be discussed next.

Alpine-Desert disjunct vicariads. One of the distinct differences between the alpine areas of the Southern Rockies and of the Sierra Nevada of California is the almost total lack of desert annuals in the former. In fact, the Southern Rockies boast a single alpine annual, *Koenigia islandica* L., and this is not at all related to the local desert element but belongs to the circumpolar arctic flora.

On the other hand, several of the common desert perennials are represented in the alpine zone by subspecies or closely related species. Since their distribution from desert to alpine zone is interrupted by the forested belt they may be said to be disjunct races. The presence of such desert types as *Hymenoxys, Gilia (Ipomopsis), Lesquerella,* and *Paronychia* in the alpine flora imparts an anomalous aspect to the tundra. Following is a list of desert species with their alpine counterparts: *Hymenoxys acaulis* (Pursh) Parker and *H. acaulis* var. *caespitosa* (A. Nels.) Parker; *Oreoxis alpina* ssp. *puberulenta* W. A. Weber and *O. alpina* ssp. *alpina* (A. Gray) C. & R.; *Paronychia sessiliflora* Nutt. ssp. *sessiliflora* and *P. sessiliflora* ssp. *pulvinata* (A. Gray) W. A. Weber; *Erysimum capitatum* (Dougl.) Greene and *E. nivale* (Greene) Rydb.; *Gilia spicata* Nutt. and *G. globularis* Brand; *Eriogonum jamesii* Benth. and *E. flavum* Nutt.

The enlargement of this list to include other alpine species belonging to genera found in the adjacent deserts must be done very cautiously. The alpine species of *Trifolium,* for example, are much more closely related to Eurasian alpine counterparts than to local desert-steppe species, and the alpine *Phlox condensata* (A. Gray) A. Nels. is evidently much closer to the western Arctic–eastern Asiatic *Phlox sibirica* or *P. richardsonii* than it is to local species.

EASTERN WOODLAND–PRAIRIE ELEMENT

Along the east face of the Front Ranges of Colorado and New Mexico, and at scattered points in a southwesterly direction into southeasternmost Arizona, characteristic members of the flora of the northeastern United States occur in favorable mesic localities. These localities include forested northeast-facing ravines in the foothills, moist gulches at the junction with the plains, prairie remnants, and open pine forests of gentle topography abutting on the plains. Livingston (1952) was concerned with this group as a problem in ecology rather than historical phytogeography.

Several facts concerning these plants are noteworthy. Most or all of the species also occur in the famous mixed Cordilleran-Boreal-eastern forests and prairies of the Black Hills of South Dakota, and the present distribution in the Rocky Mountains (see Fig. 5) may be considered a fragmentary remnant of this old pattern along the flanks of the Rocky Mountains. In Colorado, the Continental Divide acts as a complete barrier to the westward extension of this pattern, which suggests that the distribution postdates the last uplift of the area.

The mixing of these species with the Cordilleran flora at their present locations might be explained by an extension of the Cordilleran flora along highlands eastward during the Pleistocene, encouraged by the climatic changes at the lower altitudes and the depression of timberline above, accompanied by a westward extension of the eastern flora along the principal watercourses. Postglacial events would have caused each element to retreat toward its original center, leaving remnants in the most favorable sites at each end of the farthest extension. The mixture of Rocky Mountain, Boreal, and eastern elements is most pronounced in the Black Hills. Southward, where increasing aridity has eliminated all but a few species, the pattern occurs in smaller and more widely isolated patches.

The eastern species are favored in areas where the transition from high plains to mountains is especially abrupt. In

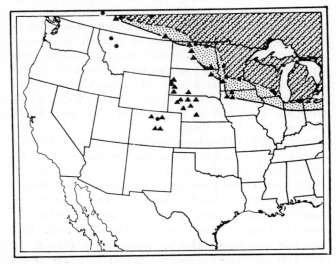

Figure 5. Distribution of *Salix serissima* (hatching and large dots) and *S. petiolaris* (fine dotting and triangles), two eastern woodland species. From Ball (1949).

such areas, exemplified by the prominent face of Green Mountain near Boulder, Colorado, the almost vertical escarpment provides a wall rising from 1,600 m to over 2,400 m. This wall provides steep, cool, sheltered northeast-facing ravines and at certain times of the year intercepts air masses in such a way as to produce a local cloud veil. The concomitant increase of humidity protects eastern relicts of high moisture requirements and encourages the development of local pockets of vegetation quite unlike that in the surrounding foothills. It is interesting to find that this "eastern" element is drawn from the entire taxonomic spectrum, from the lichens on up to the phanerogams.

Probably some of these species were nearly extinct in this area at the time of the arrival of white men. But the white man soon introduced irrigation, and as a result some of these species have spread along the irrigation ditches. It is also possible that some species of eastern distribution have actually been introduced by the early settlers themselves in this way, or have escaped from nurseries featuring wild species.

In some instances it is almost impossible to tell whether a plant was originally native here or was introduced. *Thalictrum dasycarpum* Fisch. & Lall. and *Eupatorium maculatum* L. are almost unquestionably natives and are now established locally along ditches. But it is hard to decide whether this is also true of *Impatiens capensis* Meerb., *Acorus calamus* L., and *Leersia oryzoides* (L.) Sw.

SPECIAL PROBLEMS

ENDEMISM

For such an apparently diversified area, the striking absence of narrow endemism is a remarkable feature of the flora. The reasons for this are complex and little studied.

The following is a reasonably complete list of the high mountain endemics of the southern Rockies; most of these seem to be related to Great Basin species: *Aquilegia saximontana* Rydb., *Arenaria macrantha* (Rydb.) A. Nels., *Artemisia pattersonii* A. Gray, *Astragalus molybdenus* Barneby, *Castilleja haydenii* (A. Gray) Cockerell, *C. occidentalis* Torr., *C. puberula* Rydb., *Chionophila jamesii* Benth., *Draba crassa* Rydb., *D. exunguiculata* (Schulz) C. L. Hitchcock, *D. graminea* Greene, *D. grayana* (Rydb.) C. L. Hitchc., *D. streptocarpa* A. Gray, *Erigeron melanocephalus* A. Nels., *Eriogonum coloradense* Small, *Eutrema penlandii* Rollins, *Gilia globularis* Brand, *Haplopappus clementis* (Rydb.) Blake, *Haplopappus pygmaeus* (T. & G.) Gray, *Helictotrichon mortonianum* (Scribn.) Henr., *Kobresia macrocarpa* Clokey, *Mertensia alpina* (Torr.) G. Don, *Oreoxis bakeri* C. & R., *O. humilis* Raf., *Penstemon hallii* A. Gray, *P. harbourii* A. Gray, *Podistera eastwoodae* (C. & R.) Math. & Const., *Ranunculus macauleyi* A. Gray, *R. adoneus* A. Gray, *Saussurea weberi* Hultén, *Senecio soldanella* A. Gray, *S. taraxacoides* (A. Gray) Greene, *Townsendia rothrockii* A. Gray, *Trifolium attenuatum* Greene, and *T. brandegei* S. Wats.

Most of the endemics of lower elevations are plants of arid lands in the Colorado Plateau country (*Lomatium, Astragalus, Cryptantha, Penstemon, Townsendia*). A few of the mountain endemics (*Gilia globularis, Mertensia al-*

pina, Haplopappus clementis, Hymenopappus newberryi, are obviously derived from the surrounding desert flora, in most instances easily matched to their respective vicariads.

A small remainder are obviously related to arctic species (*Luzula subcapitata, Eutrema penlandii*) or to northern Cordilleran types with further relationship westward across Beringia (*Saussurea weberi* Hultén, aff. *S. viscida* Hultén of Alaska; *Kobresia macrocarpa* Clokey, aff. *K. hyperborea* Porsild). A very few represent remnants of the old Tertiary flora. These are well illustrated by the monotypic genus *Neoparrya*, and by *Rubus deliciosus* Torr., *Aletes anisatus* and *A. humilis, Selaginella weatherbiana*, and the lichen *Candelariella spraguei*, all of which are endemic along the eastern foothills in a line leading from southern Wyoming to northern New Mexico. The list is necessarily somewhat incomplete because of judgment decisions on the "narrowness" of the endemism.

The general problem of edaphic endemism has been thoroughly elaborated by Mason (1946), and specific parts of the problem have been discussed by Trelease and Beath (1949), Johnston (1941), and Persson (1956).

Trelease and Beath's study (1949) of seleniferous plants has particular importance in our area, because a number of species are limited in their distribution by the outcrops of rocks containing selenium. Some species of *Astragalus, Machaeranthera* (*Xylorhiza*), and *Stanleya*, are thus affected, and these plants have played an important part in the history of the cattle industry because of the poisonous qualities of plants containing selenium. *Haplopappus fremontii* A. Gray, *Eriogonum lachnogynum* Torr., and *Parthenium alpinum* (Nutt.) T. & G. appear to be selenophiles in our flora.

Johnston (1941) discusses the occurrence and restriction of plants on gypsum soils in Mexico. In the Rocky Mountain flora, *Cryptantha paradoxa* (A. Nels.) Payson, *Frankenia jamesii* Torr., and *Townsendia annua* Beaman appear to be restricted to gypsum outcrops.

In many parts of the world limestone and calcareous soils are of great importance in plant distribution. It is therefore of interest that many species that are proved to be calciphiles in northern Europe, e.g. *Dryas octopetala* L. and *Kobresia simpliciuscula* (Wahlenb.) Mack., are not so in the Southern Rockies. This is a problem that needs study. Furthermore, the limestone outcrops do not appear to be critical from the standpoint of fern distribution, as they often are in eastern North America. However, certain lichens (*Acarospora glaucocarpa* (Wahlenb.) Koerb., *Placynthium nigrum* (Huds.) S. Gray and certain bryophytes (*Orthotrichum jamesianum* Sull. & Lesq., *Didymodon* spp.), being much more closely tied to substrates, are limited to limestone.

CRYPTOGAMIC DISTRIBUTION PATTERNS

Some information is now available concerning the extent to which the mosses, hepatics, and lichens mirror the distribution patterns of the higher plants. Generally speaking, the ranges of most cryptogams are broader than those of phanerogams, and many more species are widely disjunct over the world. But the reasons for this are not necessarily related to the ease of dispersal by spores or soredia. The striking discontinuities of the desert and subtropical mosses and many crustose lichens argue for Tertiary or older origins for these species, as well as for extraordinary genetic stability.

In the Southern Rockies almost all the bryophyte species in the mountains are well-known circumpolar types. The flora of the alpine and subalpine regions can be analyzed with the help of any of the standard Scandinavian manuals. There is virtually no high-altitude endemism in our moss flora. On the other hand, in the foothills and desert areas one encounters species belonging to the Madro-Tertiary flora, many of which range into Mexico, while some are common to the deserts of America, Central Asia, and North Africa.

The lichen flora is much the same. The mountains have a very strong circumpolar or arctic-alpine element. Somewhat higher percentages of Cordilleran endemism occur, although this may be an illusion, because we know little of the crustose flora of the high mountains of Asia. In the eastern foothills, a few species occur that seem to be correlated with the Eastern Woodland–Prairie element discussed earlier (*e.g. Parmeliopsis placorodia, Umbilicaria pustulata,* and *U. pensylvanica*). The cloud veil so often present on the eastern escarpment of the Front Range creates conditions mesic enough to support several species of high moisture requirement, whose occurrence is extremely unusual so far distant from the coastal influence (*Cetraria glauca, Cetraria chlorophylla*).

One of the striking negative aspects of the lichen flora is the scarcity of epiphytic macrolichens on the coniferous trees of the higher foothills and mountains. Their absence may be associated with the very low humidity of these areas. The intermountain parks, which are cold-air drainage basins, on the other hand, support adequate corticolous elements. The cryptogam-barren upper foothills of the Rockies contrast sharply with the same areas in southern New Mexico and Arizona, where periodic cloud cover on the higher slopes, probably resulting from proximity to moisture-laden air from the Gulf of California, results in a very rich corticolous lichen flora.

CONCLUSION

The elucidation of coincident distribution patterns is only a first faltering step in the elaboration of local phytogeographical theory. As Faegri (1963, p. 221) says: "A common distribution area does not in itself explain anything. On the contrary, it is a problem in itself, and what is generally done, is to consider the hypothetical explanation of the reason why a group of plants occur together as a fact to be used in the analysis of other problems as well. But in nature there is nothing like a flora element behaving as a collective unit. There are only individual plants (not plant species!) reacting each in an individual way. And the more or less fortuitous occurring together may be the result of widely differing histories and ecologic demands."

The foregoing discussion merely draws attention to some obvious patterns of plant distribution in the Southern Rocky Mountains and relates these to some fairly well-established events in Quaternary and Tertiary times. No questions have been answered and few have been raised. Plant-geographical research has only begun, and there is

much to do before the region will take its place among those that may be said to be botanically well known. Future progress will depend upon advances in the fields of traditional taxonomic methodology, mapping, cytology, autecology, and geology in many of its forms.

1. Traditional Taxonomic Methodology. The strong connections between the Southern Rocky Mountain flora and the floras of several widely separated areas necessitate a broad exchange policy for herbarium collections. Cooperation and interest is greatly needed from workers well-informed about the Alps, Pyrenees, Caucasus, and the mountains of the Soviet Union.

2. Mapping. Although the great mapping project of Hultén on the circumpolar plants will be valuable, local mapping projects should be designed to refine the world patterns. In the United States detailed mapping has been left to monographers instead of floristic workers, with the result that many common species have not been mapped simply because they present no taxonomic problems.

Ideally, a major herbarium in each state should be designated as a clearing-house for accurate taxonomic and geographical data, and uniform sets of base maps should be selected for the mapping of the flora on the local level.

3. Cytology. Hultén points out that in many instances Rocky Mountain species seem to be more closely related morphologically to their Eurasian mountain counterparts than they are to their American Arctic counterparts. An analysis of chromosome numbers and polyploidy levels for these species in all segments of their areas would go far to develop a general theory of origin and migrations.

4. Autecology. The strong dominance of community studies in American ecology should be balanced by an equally strong analysis of the ecology of species.

5. Geology. Plant geographers need to know from the physical geologist and geographer the extent, altitude, and time spans of local land masses in detail, as well as information bearing on the ancient climates, presence of highland migration bridges, and barriers. At the present time much of the information available is too general to be of much value to the phytogeographer. It is hoped that the present discussion has suggested points that might lead to a continuing dialogue between botanists and geologists and between botanists concerned with the present flora and paleobotanists concerned with the Pleistocene and Tertiary flora.

REFERENCES

Abrams, LeRoy, 1913, Deserts and desert flora of the West, *in* Nature and science on the Pacific Coast: San Francisco, Paul Elder & Co., p. 168-176

Axelrod, D. I., 1948, Climate and evolution in western North America during middle Pliocene time: Evolution, v. 2, p. 127-144

—— 1964, The Miocene Trapper Creek flora of Southern Idaho: Berkeley, Univ. California Publ. Geol. Sci., v. 51, 148 p.

Ball, C. R., 1949, Two problems in *Salix* distribution: Madroño, v. 10, p. 81-87

Becker, H. F., 1961, Oligocene plants from the Upper Ruby Basin, southwestern Montana: Geol. Soc. Amer. Mem., v. 82, 127 p.

Booth, W. E., 1950, Flora of Montana. I, Monocots: Bozeman, Montana State College, 232 p.

Cain, S. A., 1944, Foundations of plant geography: New York, Harper & Brothers, 556 p.

Cockerell, T. D. A., 1887, British plants in America: Science Gossip, v. 23, p. 214

—— 1888, The boreal flora in Colorado: Science Gossip, v. 24, p. 189

—— 1891, The effect of altitude on plants: Nature Notes (Selborne Society), v. 2, p. 13-15

—— 1906, The alpine flora of Colorado: Amer. Naturalist, v. 40, p. 861-873

Darwin, Charles, 1883, Origin of species: New York, D. Appleton and Co., 458 p.

Davis, R. J., 1952, Flora of Idaho: Dubuque, Iowa, Wm. C. Brown Co., 828 p.

Deam, C. C., 1940, Flora of Indiana: Indianapolis, Dept. Conservation, 1236 p.

Faegri, Knut, 1963, Problems of immigration and dispersal of the Scandinavian flora, *in* Löve, Askell, and Löve, Doris, North Atlantic biota and their history: New York, Pergamon Press, p. 221-232

Fernald, M. L., 1925, Persistence of plants in unglaciated areas of boreal America: Amer. Acad. Arts Sci. Mem., v. 15, p. 237-342

Harrington, H. D., 1954, Manual of the plants of Colorado: Denver, Sage Books, 666 p.

Hay, Dorothy, 1939, The Mexican element in the Colorado flora: Univ. Colorado M.S. thesis, 107 p.

Hitchcock, C. L., Cronquist, Arthur, Ownbey, Marion, and Thompson, J. W., 1955-1961, Vascular plants of the Pacific Northwest: Seattle, Univ. Washington Press, v. 3-5

Holm, Theodore, 1923, The vegetation of the alpine region of the Rocky Mountains in Colorado: Nat. Acad. Sci. Mem., v. 19, p. 1-45

Hooker, J. D., and Gray, Asa, 1880, The vegetation of the Rocky Mountain region and a comparison with that of other parts of the world: U.S. Geol. Surv. Terr., v. 6, p. 1-62

Hultén, Eric, 1937, Outline of the history of arctic and boreal biota during the Quaternary period: Stockholm, A/B Thule, 168 p.

—— 1956, The *Cerastium alpinum* complex, a case of worldwide introgressive hybridization: Svensk Bot. Tidskr., v. 50, p. 411-495

—— 1958, The Amphi-Atlantic plants and their phytogeographical connections: Kgl. Sv. Vetensk.-Akad. Handl., ser. 4, v. 7, 340 p.

—— 1962, The Circumpolar plants. I, Vascular cryptogams, conifers, monocotyledons: Kgl. Sv. Vetensk.-Akad. Handl., ser. 4, v. 8, 275 p.

Ives, R. L., 1938, Weather phenomena of the Colorado Rockies: Franklin Inst. J., v. 226, p. 691-755

Izett, G. A., and Lewis, G. E., 1963, Miocene vertebrates from Middle Park, Colorado: U.S. Geol. Surv. Prof. Pap. 475-B, p. 120-122

Johnson, P. L., 1962, The occurrence of new Arctic-Alpine species in the Beartooth Mountains, Wyoming-Montana: Madrono, v. 16, p. 229-233

Johnston, I. M., 1941, Gypsophily among Mexican desert plants: Harvard Univ., Arnold Arbor. J., v. 22, p. 145-170

Jones, G. N., and Fuller, G. D., 1955, Vascular plants of Illinois: Urbana, Univ. Illinois Press, 593 p.

Kearney, T. H., and Peebles, R. H., 1960, Arizona flora: Berkeley, Univ. California Press, 2nd ed., 1085 p.

Lechner-Pock, Lore, 1956, *Eritrichium nanum* (Amann) Schrader und seine Verwandten: Phyton, v. 6, p. 98-206

Lesquereux, L., 1883, Contributions to the fossil flora of the western territories. III, The Cretaceous and Tertiary floras: U.S. Geol. Survey Terr. Rep., v. 8, 279 p.

Livingston, L. B., 1952, Relict true prairie communities in central Colorado: Ecology, v. 33, p. 72-86

Lüdi, Werner, 1961, Eduard August Rubel, 1876-1960: Zürich, Geobot. Inst. Eidg. Techn. Hochschule Stiftung Rübel Ber., v. 32, p. 5-24

MacGinitie, H. D., 1953, Fossil plants of the Florissant beds, Colorado: Carnegie Instn. Publ. 599, 198 p.

Maher, L. J., 1961, Pollen analysis and postglacial vegetation history in the Animas Valley Region, Southern San Juan Mountains, Colorado: Univ. Minnesota Ph.D. thesis, 85 p.

—— 1963, Pollen analyses of surface materials from the southern San Juan Mountains, Colorado: Geol. Soc. Amer. Bull., v. 74, p. 1485-1504

Major, J., and Bamberg, S. A., 1963, Some Cordilleran plant species new for the Sierra Nevada of California: Madrono, v. 17, p. 93-109

Malde, Harold E., this volume, Snake River Plain

Mapel, P., and Hail, J., 1960, Tertiary geology of the Goose Creek district Cassia County, Idaho, Box Elder County, Utah, and Elko County, Nevada: U.S. Geol. Surv. Bull., 1055-H, p. 217-254

Maslin, T. P., 1959, An annotated check list of the amphibians and reptiles of Colorado: Univ. Colorado Stud., v. 6, p. 1-98

Mason, L., 1946, The edaphic factor in narrow endemism: Madrono, v. 8, p. 209-226, 241-257

Pennak, R. W., 1963, Ecological and radiocarbon correlations in some Colorado Mountain lake and bog deposits: Ecology, v. 44, p. 1-15

Persson, Herman, 1956, Studies in "Copper Mosses": Hattori Bot. Lab. J., v. 17, p. 1-18

Peterson, R. S., 1962, Wyoming pinyon revisited: Madrono, v. 16, p. 269-270

Porsild, A. E., 1963, *Stellaria longipes* Goldie and its allies in North America: Nat. Mus. Canada Bull., v. 186, p. 1-35

Rydberg, P. A., 1896, Flora of the Black Hills of South Dakota: U.S. Nat. Herbarium Contr., v. 3, p. 463-536

—— 1914a, Phytogeography and its relation to taxonomy and other branches of science: Torreya, v. 12, p. 73-85

—— 1914b-1922, Phytogeographical notes on the Rocky Mountain region: Torr. Bot. Club Bull. 1914b, Pt. I, Alpine region: v. 40, p. 677-686; 1914c, Pt. II, Origin of the alpine flora: v. 41, p. 89-103; Pt. III, Formations of the alpine zone: v. 41, p. 459-474; Pt. IV, Forests of the subalpine and montane zones, v. 42 (1915), p. 11-25; Pt. V, Grasslands of the subalpine and montane zones: v. 42, p. 629-642; Pt. VI, Distribution of the subalpine plants: v. 43 (1916), p. 343-364; Pt. VII, Formations in the subalpine zone: v. 44 (1917), p. 431-454; Pt. VIII, Distribution of the montane plants: V. 46 (1919), p. 295-327; Pt. IX, Wooded formations of the montane zone of the Southern Rockies: v. 47 (1920), p. 441-454; Pt. X, Grasslands and other open formations of the montane zone of the Southern Rockies: v. 48 (1922), p. 315-326

—— 1916, Vegetative life zones of the Rocky Mountains: New York Bot. Garden Mem., v. 6, p. 477-499

Stewart, B. K., 1940, Plant ecology and paleoecology of the Creede Valley, Colorado: Univ. Colorado, Ph.D. thesis, 154 p.

Theobald, W. L., Tseng, C. C., and Mathias, M. E., 1964, A revision of *Aletes* and *Neoparrya* (Umbelliferae): Brittonia, v. 16, p. 296-315

Tolmachev, A., 1959a, Sur l'origine de la flore arctique: Quant, ou, et comment surgit la flore arctique?: 9th Intern. Bot. Congr.: Toronto, Univ. Toronto Press, v. 2, p. 399

—— 1959b, Der autochtone Grundstock der arktischen Flora und ihre Beziehungen zu den Hochgebirgsfloren Nord- und Zentralasiens: 9th Intern. Bot. Congr.: Toronto, Univ. Toronto Press, v. 2, p. 400

Trelease, S. F., and Beath, O. A., 1949, Selenium, its geological occurrence and its biological effects in relation to botany, chemistry, agriculture, nutrition, and medicine: New York, authors, 292 p.

Wallace, A. R., 1900, Studies, scientific and social: New York, Macmillan, v. 1, 526 p.

—— 1905, My life, a record of events and opinions, v. 2: New York, Dodd, Mead & Co., 464 p.

Watson, Sereno, 1890, Relation of Mexican flora to that of the United States: Amer. Assoc. Adv. Sci., 39th Meeting Proc., p. 291-292

Weber, W. A., 1955, Additions to the flora of Colorado, II: Univ. Colorado Stud., Ser. Biol., v. 3, p. 65-108

—— 1961, Additions to the flora of Colorado, III: Univ. Colorado Stud., Ser. Biol., v. 7, p. 1-26.

Wolfe, J. A., and Barghoorn, E. S., 1960, Generic change in Tertiary floras in relation to age: Amer. J. Sci., v. 258A, p. 388-399

Wright, C. W., 1952, An ecological description of an isolated piñon pine grove: Univ. Colorado M.S. thesis, 43 p.

Summary

The Southern Rocky Mountain flora contains the following elements and sub-elements: (1) Circumpolar, which includes Boreal-Asiatic, Boreal-American, Central Rocky Mountain–Pacific Northwest, and Northern Rocky Mountain sub-elements; (2) Madro-Tertiary, which includes Tertiary-relict, Chihuahuan, Sonoran–Great Basin, and alpine-desert disjunct sub-elements; and (3) Eastern Woodland–Prairie elements.

In a broad sense the Cordilleran elements display contracting ranges and the Madro-Tertiary elements expanding ones. Several alpine species that impart a special character to the flora are clearly related to vicariads in the desert steppe. The unique association of Cordilleran, Boreal, and eastern elements in the Black Hills extends sporadically along the east slope of the Rockies through New Mexico to southeast Arizona. Several supposedly ancient species, endemics, and monotypes also occupy this area. Present alpine floras of North American mountain systems probably antedate in part the present arctic flora and demonstrate strong connections with the alpine flora of central-Asiatic mountain systems.

Temperate-asiatic, eastern woodland and Madro-Tertiary genera were well represented in the woody flora of Colorado during the Oligocene and Miocene, but many of these were eliminated regionally during the Pliocene.

Optimum sites for alpine rarities or disjuncts are those east-west trending mountain ranges where the highly xeric continental climate is modified by local conditions favoring a higher and more stable moisture level.

A PLEISTOCENE PHYTOGEOGRAPHICAL SKETCH
OF THE PACIFIC NORTHWEST AND ALASKA*

CALVIN J. HEUSSER[1]

VEGETATION PATTERNS that are recognizable today in northwestern North America began to take shape late in the Tertiary and continued to differentiate during the Pleistocene, as uplift of the mountain ranges constituting the western cordillera proceeded. Uplift created greater dryness and continentality to the interior of the cordillera. Plants that were dependent on greater amounts of moisture and that were not adapted to the extremes of continental climate were gradually excluded. In the Pacific Northwest prior to the uplift of the Cascades and Coast Range, for example, redwood (*Sequoia*) forest was widespread and contained many genera of angiospermous trees and shrubs now growing in Asia or eastern North America (Cain, 1944, p. 104). Uplift with resultant environmental modification caused the destruction of the redwood forest and favored the invasion of grasses, sagebrush, and other more xerophytic, non-arboreal plants characteristic of the interior basins. Along the Pacific coast, on the other hand, moisture increased, enabling the segregation of conifer forest. Late in the Tertiary, tree genera composing the modern conifer forest were growing in western Alaska (Hopkins, 1963, p. 33), and it is believed that under the cooler, moister Pleistocene climate they migrated southward and assumed, in a general way, their present ranges. Because of the growth and disappearance of the cordilleran glacier complex at different times during the Pleistocene, their ranges have probably never been stationary for a very long time.

This review concerns the Pleistocene phytogeography of the Pacific Northwest (Washington and Oregon) and Alaska, as developed from palynological reconstructions. Ever since Hansen (1938a, b) pioneered the application of pollen study to interglacial, late-glacial, and postglacial sediments in the Puget Lowland of western Washington, numerous papers by him and by others have dealt with northwestern North America and here contribute to the substance of this review. Within the confines of this chapter, it is not possible to treat this literature in its entirety; rather, only the highlights are stressed.

Botanical nomenclature, unless otherwise indicated, follows Peck (1941) for the Pacific Northwest and Hultén (1941-50) for Alaska.

---

* I wish to thank Dwight R. Crandell and Paul A. Colinvaux for making unpublished manuscripts available for reference.
[1] American Geographical Society, New York.

MODERN VEGETATION AND ENVIRONMENTAL RELATIONSHIPS

PACIFIC NORTHWEST

The northwestern American Pacific slope is covered for the most part by conifer vegetation, which is subdivided by Cooper (1957) into Pacific Coastal and Pacific Subalpine Forests. Elevations near sea level and low-lying foothills of western Washington and Oregon are occupied by Pacific Coastal Forest. In this region the forest exhibits exceptional grandeur, with trees of unusual size and with profuse undergrowth. The western hemlock–western red cedar association is a representative climax, although the inroads made by fire and lumbering have greatly reduced its area and brought about replacement by Douglas fir (*Pseudotsuga menziesii* [Mirb.] Franco). Western hemlock (*Tsuga heterophylla*) is most abundant, with western red cedar (*Thuja plicata*) and lowland white fir (*Abies grandis*) of secondary importance. Western white pine (*Pinus monticola*), also of lesser importance but widely distributed in the forest, is a subclimax species. Along the immediate ocean strip, hemlock in association with Sitka spruce (*Picea sitchensis*) is designated climax (Jones, 1936).

Douglas fir is succeeded by hemlock and other more tolerant conifers over the wetter portion of its area, whereas in drier localities where hemlock is absent or infrequent, as on south-facing exposures in the Oregon Coast Range, it can achieve climax status (Merkle, 1951). Red alder (*Alnus oregona*), under conditions of disturbance, often forms an initial successional stage preceding Douglas fir. The intolerant lodgepole pine (*Pinus contorta*) likewise plays an early successional role, particularly on sand dunes, which, if stabilized for some time, will later be invaded by Sitka spruce and, in turn, as soil humus increases, by hemlock. In the Willamette Valley to the east of the Oregon Coast Range, Douglas fir prevails on north slopes, where the proportion of atmospheric and edaphic moisture is relatively high, and Oregon white oak (*Quercus garryana*) grows on the drier and warmer south-facing hillsides (Hansen, 1947a).

The Pacific Subalpine Forest is manifest at upper elevations in the Pacific Northwest. It occupies a zone from about 450 m to about 1,500 m in the Olympic Mountains, 1,500-2,300 m in the Cascade Range of Washington, and 2,300-3,000 m in the Oregon Cascades. Characteristic trees of this climax are alpine fir (*Abies lasiocarpa*), amabilis fir (*A. amabilis*), mountain hemlock (*Tsuga mertensiana*),

469

and Alaska yellow cedar (*Chamaecyparis nootkatensis*); but Engelmann spruce (*Picea engelmanni*) and whitebark pine (*Pinus albicaulis*), which are found in the Cascade subalpine forest, do not grow in the Olympic Mountains. Several trees of the Pacific Coastal Forest range upward to subalpine elevations, western hemlock and Douglas fir being especially noteworthy in this regard. Fires within the altitudinal limits of the forest in the Cascades frequently cause reversion to temporary occupancy by lodgepole pine. Lodgepole pine also represents an edaphic subclimax on pumice where other species are slow to pioneer and replace it. The Pacific Subalpine Forest extends over to the upper eastern slopes of the Cascades.

At lower elevations on the eastern side, as dryness increases toward the interior of the Columbia Basin, western yellow pine (*Pinus ponderosa*) becomes the dominant arboreal species among trees of Douglas fir, lodgepole pine, and, mostly in Oregon, western juniper (*Juniperus occidentalis*). Yellow pine forest is generally open, with few shrubs and herbs. Progressively eastward the trees give way to sagebrush (*Artemisia tridentata*), which on the upland is associated with juniper. Sagebrush dominates a good deal of the Columbia Basin except in parts of eastern Washington and Oregon, which were formerly covered by prairie of bunch grasses (*Agropyron spicatum, Festuca idahoensis,* and *Poa secunda*) and are now important wheat-growing areas.

The Pacific Northwest has dry summers. Precipitation is generally high west of the Cascades, but rainfall in summer is light, and July and August are the driest months. Despite exceedingly wet or snowy winters near the coast and in the Cascades and Olympics, summer drought is a major cause of forest-fire danger. Precipitation annually reaches 3,300 mm and more in coastal areas but is as low as 300 mm in eastern sectors. Maximum snowfall in the mountains can amount to 12-15 m. The coastal strip is cooler (15° C July average) in summer than the interior (21°) and warmer in winter (6° January average compared to −4°).

ALASKA

The Pacific Coastal and Subalpine Forests merge along the Pacific rim of Alaska. Trees characteristic of these two types associate to an increasingly greater degree northward in British Columbia, and in southeastern Alaska the Subalpine Forest components, namely mountain hemlock, Alaska yellow cedar, and amabilis fir, grow with typically coastal trees close to tidewater. Subalpine species, especially mountain hemlock, nevertheless maintain more distinct continuity on upper slopes and at timber line. Timber line descends from 2,000 m in the northern Cascades of Washington to 700 m in southeastern Alaska, 100-600 m in south-central Alaska, and sea level on Kodiak Island in southwestern Alaska. Douglas fir, lowland white fir, Engelmann spruce, western white pine, and whitebark pine do not extend to Alaska.

Climax forest in southeastern Alaska consists primarily of western hemlock (Taylor, 1932). Western hemlock–western red cedar has been designated climax, but cedar is a minor tree in the forest, reaching the end of its range at 57° N on northern Kupreanof Island in the Alexander Archipelago, and its ability to regenerate itself is questioned (Gregory, 1957). Sitka spruce is by far the most common tree growing with hemlock. It has also been accorded climax status in association with hemlock, especially where cedar does not occur, but its degree of tolerance is not so great, and its tendency is to behave more like a subclimax species. In succession on glacial moraines and outwash, spruce replaces such early pioneers as willow (*Salix barclayi, S. sitchensis,* and *S. alaxensis*), Alaska alder (*Alnus crispa* subsp. *sinuata*), and black cottonwood (*Populus trichocarpa*). As organic matter builds up in the soil, western hemlock invades the stands and gains superiority. Westward around the Gulf of Alaska, however, where western hemlock loses superiority, spruce near the coast and mountain hemlock inland become the predominant trees. On Kodiak Island and on the Alaska Peninsula bordering Shelikof Strait, Sitka spruce represents the last conifer outpost of the forest. Beyond this limit, coastal grassland and tundra obtain to the southwest along the Aleutian Islands.

The forests of coastal Alaska are not extensive and do not attain the magnificence of the forests of the Pacific Northwest. Topography and climate are perhaps the chief reasons for their lesser rank. Generally greater precipitation over almost the entire region and a shorter growing season are less favorable for luxuriance. These factors, however, are propitious for the existence of glaciers, such as the huge Malaspina, Guyot, and Bering complexes northwest of Yakutat, and they are conducive to the formation of muskeg on benches and moderately inclined slopes. Glaciers and especially muskeg delimit the extent of the forest.

Muskeg (a name of local aboriginal derivation) pertains to natural areas where, because of impeded drainage, peat accumulates under a living cover of sphagnum moss, sedge, heath, and scrubby trees. Slope (soligenous), domed (ombrogenous), flat (topogenous), and intermediate types are recognized. Muskeg is rather extensive in southeastern Alaska, chiefly on the islands of the Alexander Archipelago. Lodgepole pine, because of its inability to compete on the forested upland, persists almost entirely on muskeg as far northwest as the Yakutat flats.

The vegetation of interior Alaska is a vast mosaic of forest, muskeg, and tundra. The low country along the river courses (Copper, Susitna, Yukon, Tanana, Kuskokwim, Porcupine, Chandalar, Koyukuk, and Kobuk) support tree growth consisting predominantly of spruce and birch, which in decreasing number follow the tributary streams up into the mountains. White spruce (*Picea glauca*) is generally the timber-line tree at elevations of 600-900 m in the interior, 300-450 m on the south side of the Brooks Range, and 60-240 m in western Alaska (Sigafoos, 1958). Along with black spruce (*P. mariana*), it has spread from the unglaciated interior into glaciated country, and hybrids have resulted where it has made contact with the coastal Sitka spruce in the Cook Inlet area (Little, 1953).

White spruce grows in more or less pure stands or with an intermingling of birch, other broad-leaf trees, and black spruce. Birch is a taxonomically complicated genus in Alaska. According to Hultén (1941-1950, p. 572), the tree (white or paper) birches are *Betula kenaica*, ranging mainly on the Alaska Peninsula, Kenai Peninsula, and Kodiak

Island, and *B. resinifera*, ranging in central Alaska. These hybridize both with each other and with the shrubby dwarf birches *B. nana* subsp. *exilis* and *B. glandulosa*. Some authors (for example Sigafoos, 1958) consider the tree birches to be represented by *B. papyrifera* Marshall and its varieties. Other broad-leaf trees growing with white spruce are quaking aspen (*Populus tremuloides*) and balsam poplar (*P. tacamahacca*). Alder (*Alnus*) and willow (*Salix*) as tall shrubs or small trees are present in varying proportions. With balsam poplar they comprise the border of the meandering river courses. The alders *A. crispa* and *A. incana* are more prominent in central Alaska, whereas *A. crispa* subsp. *sinuata* frequents the Pacific coastal districts. But all three, including hybrids between *A. crispa* and subsp. *sinuata*, are identified at stations in southern, central, and western Alaska (Hultén, 1941-50, p. 585). Willow in Alaska is a large genus with numerous species and varieties. Pure stands of white birch and aspen, as well as white and black spruce, are of frequent occurrence in most parts of the interior forest.

Most of interior Alaska, with long cold winters, receives little precipitation, but trees of merchantable size can thrive in the river valleys owing to summers with long days and to ground water, derived largely from melting snow in the mountains. Permafrost (perennially frozen ground), which is widespread but generally discontinuous or sporadic over most of the interior, impedes subsurface drainage and in doing so also makes water available to the roots of trees and other plants during the growing season. But permafrost, in addition, affects vegetation both adversely and differentially. Under freeze-thaw cycles, for example, forests are caused to revert to successional stages (Benninghoff, 1952). Moreover, distribution and depth of permafrost largely determine the type of plant cover (Hopkins *et al.*, 1955, p. 135).

Equally as profound as permafrost in its effect upon vegetation is fire. Lutz (1953, p. 7) states that extensive fires have burned interior forests from prehistoric times down to the present day. He considers white spruce to be the upland forest climax and interprets the sharp boundaries between different types of vegetation as a reflection of fire history. When burning lays the forest to waste, the successional communities that follow depend on several factors, most important of which appear to be fire intensity and the type and proximity of the seed source. White birch and quaking aspen in relatively pure stands or in admixtures with white spruce represent the frequently observed seral stages.

Sluggishly drained alluvial lowlands back from the meandering rivers are a labyrinth of muskeg (also referred to as flats). Erosion and flooding by rivers plus thawing and growth of permafrost are responsible for the instability revealed by the variety of plant communities. Stability, although only of limited duration, is represented by black spruce forest. In the upper Kuskokwim River region, quaking bogs and intervening ridges and hummocks characterize this type of low terrain (Drury, 1956, p. 13). Bog surfaces are occupied by sedges, heaths, and dwarf birches, growing on dense sphagnum moss, and by open pools of aquatics. Ridges and islands support low heath and dwarf birch,

scattered willow and alder, few white birch, and larch (*Larix laricina*) in a forest dominated by black spruce.

Beyond the forest limits in Alaska, tundra is the principal type of vegetation. Arctic tundra is spread far and wide on the north slope from the Brooks Range to the Arctic Ocean, in western Alaska on the Seward Peninsula as well as north and south on the borderland of the Chukchi and Bering Seas, and on the islands of the Bering Sea (St. Lawrence, St. Matthew, and the Pribilofs). Plant composition and distribution in the arctic tundra are strongly influenced by topography (elevation and exposure), drainage, substratum, and permafrost, with the result that a wide variety of local types is encountered over the extremes of wetness and dryness. According to Britton (1957) a dwarf-shrub heath with tussocks of cotton-grass (*Eriophorum vaginatum* subsp. *spissum*) covers much of the arctic slope north of the Brooks Range. The shrubs crowberry (*Empetrum nigrum*), labrador tea (*Ledum palustre* subsp. *decumbens*), lingen berry (*Vaccinium vitis-idaea* subsp. *minus*), dwarf birch, alder (*Alnus crispa*), and willows and the herbaceous composites, sedges, and grasses are well represented. In the vicinity of Ogotoruk Creek in northwestern Alaska, cotton-grass tussock tundra (classified eastward as part of the overall dwarf-shrub heath type) is estimated to occupy more area than any other type (Johnson *et al.*, 1959, p. 30). With the *Dryas* fellfield and *Eriophorum-Carex* wet-meadow types, it covers over 80% of the drainage system. Dwarf birch, willow, and heath are present in the area, but alder is apparently absent. Sigafoos (1958) maps most of the Seward Peninsula as herbaceous tundra in which cotton-grass tussocks, birch, and heath occupy the poorly drained upland, with sedges in the lowlands and bogs. A small part of the peninsula is mapped as shrub tundra, which occurs as thickets of willow, alder, dwarf birch, and heath on better-drained soils. On most of the Alaska Peninsula, southwestern Kodiak Island, and parts of the Aleutians, subalpine meadow or grassland dominated by *Calamagrostis canadensis* subsp. *langsdorffii* prevails (Hultén, 1937a, p. 36; Cahalane, 1959, p. 13).

Alpine tundra is distributed above timber line in the mountains that form the Pacific border and in the interior ranges. With increasing altitude, its character becomes increasingly xeric. In the Coast Mountains north of the Taku River Valley in southeastern Alaska, for example, heath mats made up largely of *Cassiope mertensiana*, *C. stelleriana*, and *Empetrum nigrum* dominate the tundra between about 1,000 and 1,500 m (Heusser, 1954). Above 1,500 m non-vascular cryptogams are more conspicuous in a sparse cover of *Artemisia arctica*, *Potentilla emarginata* subsp. *nana*, and *Hierochloe alpina*, among a few other vascular species, and at 2,100 m plants are entirely cryptogamic. Heaths, sedges, grasses, rushes, composites, and rosaceous plants comprise the major alpine representatives.

Climate in Pacific coastal districts of Alaska is strongly oceanic with heavy precipitation and cloudiness and without extremes of temperature. Winters are cold and snowy and summers cool and wet. January and July average temperatures are unusually uniform except at stations located inland at the heads of fiords. The January average is a few degrees below freezing over much of the coast, and the July average is 12-13° C except in the southwestern Aleutian area, where it is near 10°. Annual precipitation ranges between about 2,000 and 4,000 mm, of which a considerable portion falls as snow. The interior, by contrast, is comparatively dry with cool, short summers and long, extremely cold winters. January average temperature for the southern and western interior is about −14° C and for the Yukon Valley and northern Alaska −25°. The July average is close to 6° in the north, 12° in the southern and western sectors, and 14° in the Yukon Valley. Precipitation of 100-150 mm is the annual average for the arctic slope and 300-750 mm for other non-mountainous parts of the interior.

LATE-GLACIAL AND POSTGLACIAL RECONSTRUCTIONS

PACIFIC NORTHWEST

Three diagrams redrawn from Hansen (1947a) serve as models for the areas they represent (Fig. 1) and illustrate the vegetation changes in Washington and Oregon during late-glacial and postglacial time (Fig. 2). The late-glacial and postglacial are not differentiated in the diagrams, but from relevant geological and chronological data there is no doubt that Zone I includes late-glacial sediments.

The Granite Falls diagram is from a section in the Puget Lowland. The area of the site was formerly occupied by Pacific Coastal Forest but has been disturbed by lumbering and farming. Lodgepole pine predominantly and some western white pine comprise the spectra in Zone I. Douglas fir replaces pine almost entirely in Zone II and maintains a superior position throughout Zone III. Western hemlock, which progressively increases through Zone III, gains maximum proportions in Zone IV. In the Puget Lowland, as terrain was vacated by the Vashon glacier about 12,000-14,000 B.P. (Crandell, 1962, p. 36), lodgepole pine was the initial invader. Hansen (1947a, p. 72) states that it took this role because of its capacity to set seed at an early age and to grow in different edaphic situations under unstable physiographic conditions. Postglacial warming and physiographic stabilization enabled Douglas fir to succeed lodgepole (Zone II). Postglacial warmth or dryness restricted the development of western

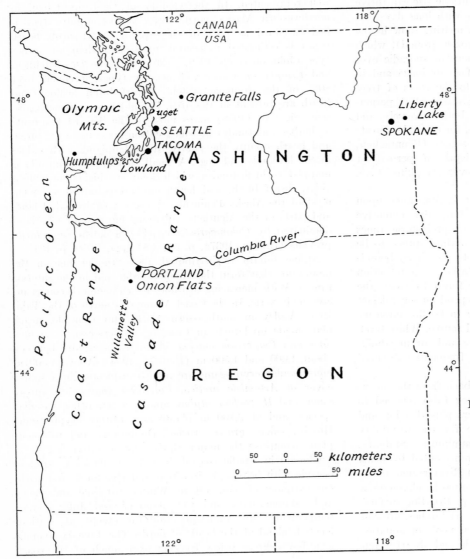

Figure 1. Sketch map of the Pacific Northwest showing the locations of late-glacial and postglacial sections discussed in the text.

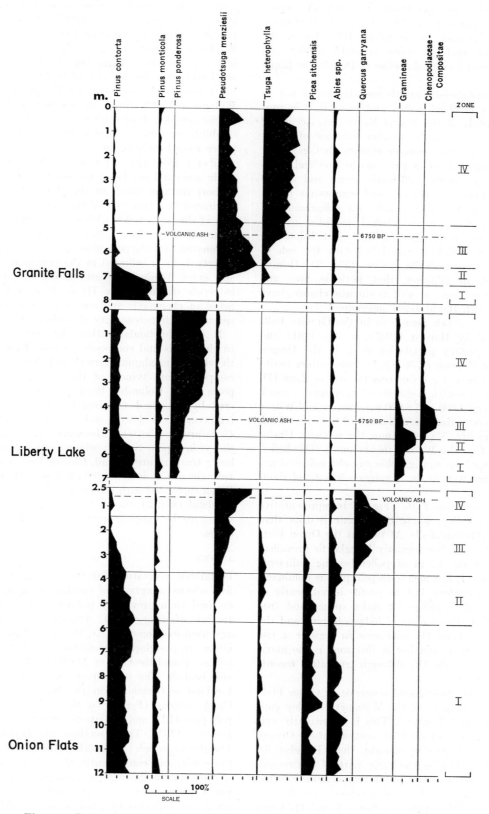

Figure 2. Pollen diagrams of Pacific Northwest sections redrawn from Hansen (1947a).

hemlock with the result that hemlock, a highly tolerant tree requiring fairly moist conditions, was able to succeed Douglas fir only in parts of the Puget Lowland where moisture was not a limiting factor (Zone III). Later, the spread of hemlock under a more favorable cooler and wetter climate caused a gradual decline of Douglas fir (Zone IV).

The effect of postglacial warmth and dryness is not so apparent in Puget Lowland pollen profiles as it is in profiles from other parts of the Pacific Northwest. According to Hansen (1947a, p. 77), the marine influence of Puget Sound tempered the drier, warmer climate that generally prevailed in the region. Certain parts of the Lowland, however, were under a climate sufficiently warm and dry to enable thermophilous oak, grasses, and composites to increase in proportion. In pollen profiles for a bog south of Tacoma, for example, Hansen (1938a) recorded oak to 14% and grass and composites to 32% just below the volcanic ash layer, which is correlated with the ash of Zone III in the Granite Falls section (Fig. 2). Hansen (1947b) observes, in addition, that periodic fires and unfavorable soil conditions, as well as climatic change, have had much to do with the arboreal succession.

Volcanic ash at a depth near 5 m in the Granite Falls section is assigned by Hansen (1947a, p. 24; 1961) and Rigg and Gould (1957) to Glacier Peak in the Oregon Cascades. It is dated about 6,750 B.P. by radiocarbon analysis and provides a basis for estimating the age of Zone III, which Hansen equates with a climate of maximum warmth and dryness between 4,000 and 8,000 B.P. Powers and Wilcox (1964) claim, however, that this ash ascribed to Glacier Peak came instead from Mt. Mazama (now the remnant Crater Lake) in Oregon (see also Wilcox, this volume). This belief, nevertheless, changes the stratigraphic and chronological import in only a minor way, as the Mazama ash is dated about 6,450 B.P.

The section from Onion Flats (Fig. 2) is representative of the Willamette Valley, where the climate is drier than in the area about Granite Falls. At present the Onion Flats locality is being farmed, but formerly Douglas fir prevailed. More than half of the 12 m of pollen-bearing sediments is taken up by Zone I, in which lodgepole pine is dominant. White pine is also evident, but its profile is not nearly so well developed as the profiles for Sitka spruce and true fir. Zone II brackets the decline of lodgepole pine and the rise of Douglas fir. Zone III continues to register a rise of Douglas fir, but more striking in this zone is the maximum of Oregon oak. Zone IV, although truncated, records a Douglas fir maximum.

The middle and late postglacial sequence at Onion Flats reveals the greater dryness of the Willamette Valley contrasted with the Puget Lowland. This is particularly evident in Zone III of the Onion Flats section, where Oregon oak, an indicator of greater drought than Douglas fir, achieves supremacy. During the early part of the record, however, greater moisture and lower temperature affected the valley, as shown by the well-developed profiles for lodgepole pine and Sitka spruce in Zones I and II. From the more than 6 m of sediments below the lodgepole maximum in Zone I, throughout which the proportion of pine

and spruce is high, one suspects that the section extends some distance into Wisconsin sediments older than the late-glacial. This suspicion also applies in the case of Hansen's (1947a, p. 106) section from Fargher Lake in southwestern Washington, about 50 km to the northeast. Onset of sedimentation at Onion Flats (and likely at Fargher Lake, as well) postdates the drainage of backwater from the Columbia River which, according to Allison (1935), flooded the Willamette Valley during the melting of the late-Wisconsin glacier complex. Radiocarbon dates, however, are needed to establish the time backwater subsided, that is, the time the pollen record could begin.

Liberty Lake (Fig. 2) is in the dry, yellow-pine country in the glaciated northeastern corner of the Columbia Basin, a short distance north of the glacier boundary. The lake originated in a tributary of the Spokane River by aggradation of the main valley with outwash during glacial wastage (Hansen, 1944). Zone I, as in the previous two diagrams, is dominated by lodgepole pine, but the drier environment at Liberty Lake is reflected in the percentages of yellow pine and grass. While grass attains its maximum in Zone II, lodgepole declines. Zone III is distinguished by a prominence of chenopods and composites and Zone IV by consistently high percentages of yellow pine.

It is understandable that the succession from grasses to chenopods and composites is considered coincident with the shift to maximum warmth and dryness. Chenopods and composites are typical of the vegetation of the semiarid parts of the Columbia Basin, whereas in the portion covered by grassland (original bunch-grass prairie), average temperature is lower and average precipitation higher (soils are also better). Moreover, this trend continues into the yellow pine timber, where even greater moisture and lower temperature prevail. Glacier Peak (or Mt. Mazama) volcanic ash is intercalated in Zone III at Liberty Lake. When correlated with the Granite Falls section in the Puget Lowland (Fig. 2), the postglacial warm and dry interval is shown to be contemporaneous on both sides of the Cascades.

ALASKA

Postglacial vegetation, for the most part, is portrayed by five selected diagrams of muskeg sections, which are summarized from previously published, more detailed material (mainly Heusser, 1960). Arranged in order of their geographical location (Fig. 3), they reveal the trends and variations in postglacial vegetation from the Alexander Archipelago around the Gulf of Alaska to the islands of Afognak and Kodiak. The pattern of succession seen in the Puget Lowland is recognized in the Ward Creek and Montana Creek sections (Fig. 4) by the early appearance of lodgepole pine (EP) and the late-postglacial profusion of western hemlock (LP). These sections are beyond the range of Douglas fir, which ends south of the Skeena River in British Columbia, and consequently they do not contain a record of this tree. Following the lodgepole zone, succession during a warmer and drier interval (=hypsithermal, HTL) ensues as indicated by prominences of alder, Sitka spruce, and hemlock. This succession is the same as that taking place at present on recently deglaciated ground in south-

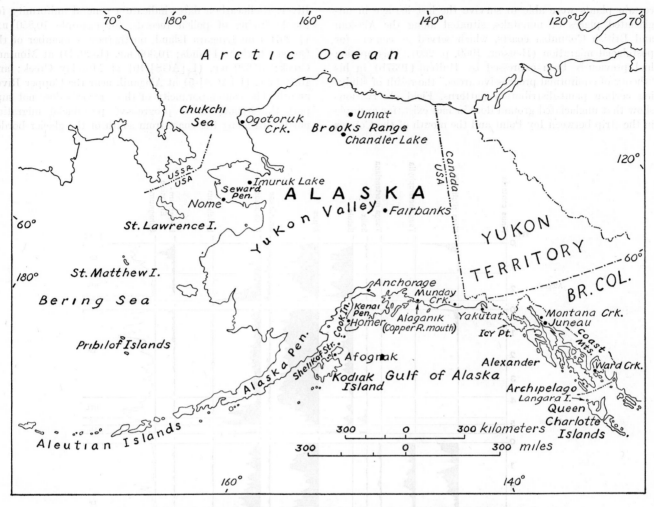

Figure 3. Sketch map of Alaska showing the location of sections discussed in the text.

eastern Alaska. The muskeg plant *Lysichitum*, considered an indicator of stagnation in growth of the muskeg surface because of a change in drainage, was abundant at Ward Creek at that time. Sedge, heath, and *Sphagnum*, like *Lysichitum*, are part of the complex of plant communities growing on the muskeg, and their profile fluctuations constitute a history of local moisture alterations affecting the development of the muskeg. Strengthening of the mountain hemlock profile during zone LP in the Montana Creek section is evidence for a cooler climate during the last several thousand years. The radiocarbon age of the base of the section is 10,300 B.P. (L-297G).

At Munday Creek (Fig. 4), lodgepole pine is barely recorded in the basal sediments and is without doubt wind-transported at least several hundred kilometers from the southeast. The last outlier of pine is at present 150 km to the east about Yakutat. Sedge replaces pine during the early postglacial and in association with heath, willow, and alder suggests the presence of tussock tundra. Later in zone HTL, alder and *Lysichitum* replace sedge. Conifer forest evidently did not develop in the Munday Creek area until the late postglacial, during which time Sitka spruce,

and not hemlock, became the major conifer. The long delay preceding this event enabled alder to persist in abundance for a protracted time. Munday Creek section is dated 10,820 B.P. (I [AGS]-10) at the base.

In the Homer and Afognak diagrams (Fig. 4), as at Munday Creek, sedge, again implying tundra, appears to have been the most prominent constituent of the early postglacial vegetation. And, as the profiles show, the sedge contained a shrub admixture of willow, alder, and birch. Birch in these profiles reflects the proximity of interior Alaska. Noteworthy is the fact that spectra preponderantly of birch come from the base of the Homer section but are overlain by silts that are barren of pollen. These basal spectra, which are distinctively different from the remainder in the section, are accorded a late-glacial age (LG). Alder dominates the middle and upper levels of the sections and becomes invaded by conifers, represented by a mixture of Sitka, white, black, and hybrid spruces. The migration of white spruce in numbers onto the upper Alaska Peninsula is also a late event (Heusser, 1963a). Vegetation about the Homer and Afognak sites is at present largely Sitka spruce.

In a previous paper, I pointed out the likelihood that

certain plants were able to survive the last ice age in un-glaciated places or nunataks, situated along the Alaskan and British Columbia coasts, which served as centers for postglacial migration (Heusser, 1960, p. 200). This opinion had previously been expressed by Hultén (1937b) in his "theory of equiformal progressive areas," the result of study-ing certain plant-distribution patterns. Field observations show that unglaciated ground does in fact exist, for example in the strip between Icy Point and the mouth of the Copper River. Radiocarbon dates indicate a general uniformity for the beginning of pollen records, for example 10,850 B.P. (L-297C) on Langara Island, northernmost member of the Queen Charlotte Islands; 10,300 B.P. (L-297D) at Montana Creek; 10,820 B.P. (I [AGS]-10) at Munday Creek; and 10,390 B.P. (I [AGS]-5) at Alaganik near the Copper River mouth. The contemporaneity of these records does not sup-port the hypothesis of progressive postglacial migration northward along the coast from south of the glacier border

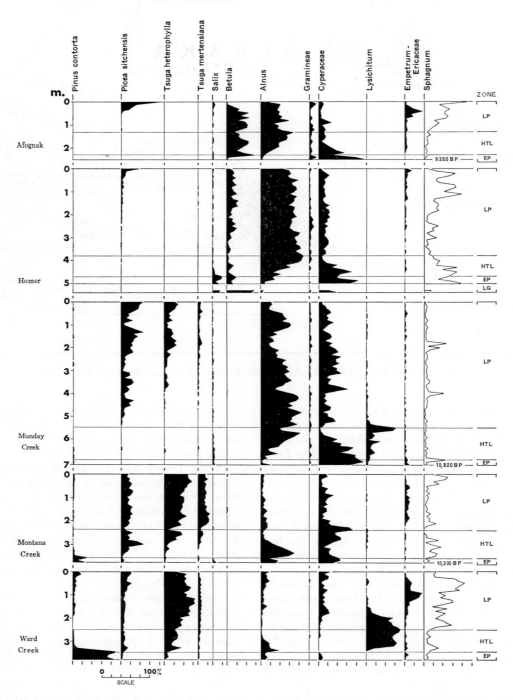

Figure 4. Pollen diagrams for Pacific coastal Alaska. Note that the profile for *Picea sitchensis* (Sitka spruce) in the Homer section is probably constituted by black, white, and hybrid spruces in addition to Sitka spruce.

in Washington. Perhaps the glaciers of coastal Alaska and British Columbia began to recede from their last Wisconsin maximum about the same time Vashon ice began to withdraw from the Puget Lowland (about 14,000 B.P.). Thus the Alaskan sites studied could have been freed of ice and available for rapid colonization by plants migrating from Washington. Glaciers northwestward along the coast apparently readvanced later during the time of the Sumas stade (about 11,000 B.P.), which is recognized in the eastern Fraser Lowland of British Columbia (Armstrong *et al.*; 1964).

Palynological work done in the interior of Alaska was first published by Hansen (1953), who studied numerous sections along the Alaska Highway, between Yukon Territory and Fairbanks, and along the Richardson, Slana-Tok, and Glenn Highways to the vicinity of Anchorage. Hansen's profiles concern arboreal species, and many consist entirely or almost entirely of spruce which, although undifferentiated, must be made up of both black and white spruce. The profiles show that spruce becomes progressively dominant between the Yukon and Fairbanks. Certain sections, in addition, contain an abundance of alder and birch. One near Anchorage shows birch in greater amounts in the lower and upper levels and spruce intervening. Because fire plays a major role in birch regeneration in the interior forest, its behavior in the pollen diagrams is difficult to assess decisively. One is inclined to interpret birch in the lower levels as a result of early postglacial succession on deglaciated ground whereas later birch prominences have more likely resulted from burning.

No further palynological work has been accomplished in the interior forest region. Livingstone's (1955, 1957) studies and those that have followed (Hopkins *et al.*, 1960; Colinvaux, 1963, 1964a, b, personal communication 1964; Heusser, 1963b) concern arctic tundra. Livingstone (1955) established a three-zone chronology at Chandler Lake (Fig. 3) on the north side of the Brooks Range. In the lower zone, sedges, grasses, and composites with some willow and birch represent the tundra. Later in the middle zone, birch becomes a noteworthy shrubby element of the tundra but is partially replaced by alder and minor amounts of spruce in the ensuing upper zone. Alder is overrepresented, however, and the presence of spruce is the result of wind transport from the south slope of the Brooks Range, which is as far north as the tree grows in arctic Alaska.

Colinvaux (1963, 1964a, b, personal communication 1964) confirms the validity of Livingstone's zonation in his work on cores from Imuruk Lake, St. Lawrence Island, and several other localities (Fig. 3). This tends to establish the sequence as the type postglacial vegetation succession for much, if not all, of northern and western Alaska. Pollen diagrams from Umiat (Livingstone, 1957), Nome (Hopkins *et al.*, 1960), and Ogotoruk Creek (Heusser, 1963b), respectively located in northern, western, and northwestern tundra, appear to be truncated because they do not include, or they show only part of, the alder zone. Colinvaux' pollen diagrams for the Pribilof Islands, at present only partially complete, should provide an additional test for Livingstone's zonation for interior Alaska.

WISCONSIN AND PRE-WISCONSIN RECONSTRUCTIONS

PACIFIC NORTHWEST

Hansen (1938b) and Hansen and Mackin (1940, 1949) made several exploratory palynological and stratigraphic studies of nonglacial deposits older than the last glaciation (Vashon = "classical" or late Wisconsin) in the Puget Lowland of western Washington. In a section from the Green River, about 32 km southeast of Seattle, pine (western white and lodgepole), lowland white fir, Sitka spruce, and hemlock (undifferentiated) were identified (Hansen, 1938b). White pine and fir, generally most abundant, suggest a cool and moderately dry climate, which later became wetter as the proportion of spruce increased. Age and stratigraphic relationship of this section, however, have not been ascertained. Another section, located in Seattle, shows lodgepole and western white pine dominating the spectra, grass percentages high at the base, and Sitka spruce prominent in the middle and uppermost levels; hemlock is poorly represented, and Douglas fir is absent (Hansen and Mackin, 1940). Climate, as in the case of the Green River sequence, is considered to have been cool and moderately dry, particularly at the outset, milder and wetter when the proportion of spruce increased. Although the section is interpreted to be Puyallup interglacial in age, Crandell (1962, p. 12) is of the opinion it dates from early to middle Wisconsin time. Two additional sections, one near Everett, 24 km north of Seattle, and the other at Possession Point on Whidbey Island, 15 km southwest of Everett, are the most comprehensively investigated by Hansen and Mackin (1949). Predominance of lodgepole pine with lesser amounts of white pine and Sitka spruce at Possession Point implies an early interglacial cool, and likely moist, climate. In the Everett section, which is considered to be in part stratigraphically equivalent to the section at Possession Point, Douglas fir in the basal levels gives way to western hemlock, which with true fir occupies a position of superiority except toward the upper levels, where lodgepole pine increases. The Everett sequence accordingly is thought to represent the influence of a later ameliorating climate and a subsequent return of coolness with the oncoming of glacial conditions. A major interglacial age is presumably recorded in these sequences and is believed to predate the interglacial that precedes the Vashon.

The Pleistocene glacial sequence recently worked out by Crandell *et al.* (1958) for the Puget Lowland and contiguous Fraser Lowland to the north has added notably to the comprehension of glacial events in the Pacific Northwest. More recent studies (Armstrong *et al.*, 1964) continue to add refinement to the glacial history (see also Crandell, this volume). From the standpoint of palynology, a refined Pleistocene stratigraphy is requisite for a full reconstruction of the vegetation and a critical interpretation of phytogeographical matters.

The Alderton interglacial, the earliest nonglacial interval observed in the Puget Lowland by Crandell *et al.* (1958), is described from a section at Alderton, 40 km south of Seattle. A pollen record derived from beds of peat and peaty silt by Estella Leopold of the U.S. Geological Survey depicts

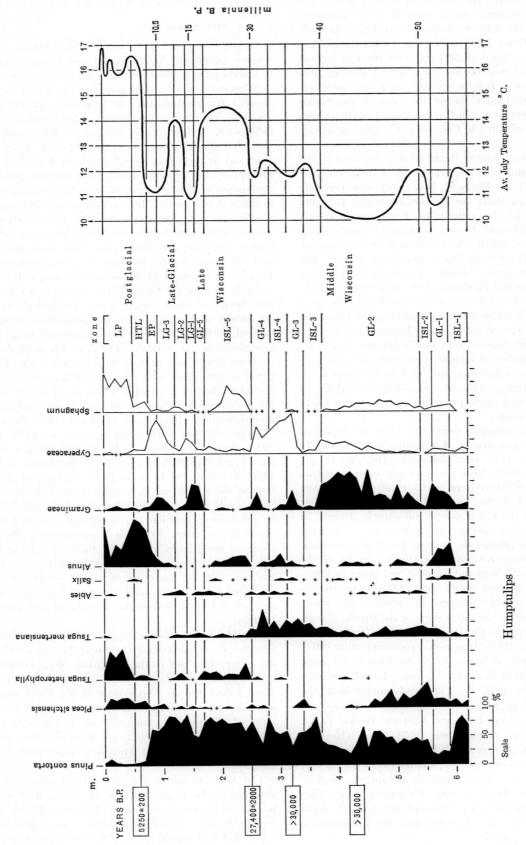

Figure 5. Summary pollen diagram for the Humptulips section showing temperature and chronology interpreted for middle and late Wisconsin, late-glacial, and postglacial pollen zones. Plus signs indicate percentage values of less than two. See text for further explanation.

Engelmann spruce and fir in major proportions at lower levels succeeded by Douglas fir and alder. This record, however, is fragmentary and is looked upon as not representative of the entire span of the Alderton, which separates the early Orting and later Stuck glaciations. Greater coverage is achieved for the next younger nonglacial interval, the Puyallup, which lies between drift of the Stuck and Salmon Springs glaciers. A composite of two sections located in the Alderton area reveals pollen of pine and some Engelmann spruce immediately above Stuck drift, spruce and true fir at higher levels, and fir in maximum numbers in the uppermost horizons (Crandell *et al.*, 1958). Two additional sections of the Puyallup investigated for pollen are from Enumclaw, 24 km southeast of Seattle, and the Des Moines–Zenith area, 10 km south (Leopold and Crandell, 1958). Enumclaw spectra portray a cold environment following Stuck glaciation. Non-arboreal types, especially the Gramineae and Compositae (including *Artemisia*), are abundant with pine and poplar. Later, Engelmann spruce becomes predominant with the decline of the non-arboreal component, and subsequently true fir and, in turn, mountain and western hemlocks follow under a series of cool and moist climatic regimes. The Des Moines–Zenith section, overlying a volcanic mudflow postdating Stuck glaciation, contains pollen assemblages of Douglas fir, true fir, pine, western hemlock, and alder at lower levels and of pine and Engelmann spruce at upper levels. These assemblages imply an interval of greater warmth followed by a cooling trend. They likely constitute a sequel to the Enumclaw record and when taken together are comparable to the Possession Point–Everett pollen stratigraphy (Hansen and Mackin, 1949). Salmon Springs drift overlying Puyallup sediments and interrupted by peat and volcanic ash is exposed near Sumner, 28 km south of Seattle (Crandell *et al.*, 1958). Spectra of pine and true fir, as the principal types present in the peat, can possibly be matched with spectra from the previously discussed Green River locality, about 17 km to the northeast (Hansen, 1938b). One difficulty, however, in attempting correlations between the palynological work done by Hansen and by Leopold concerns pollen identification. Whereas Hansen identified spruce as *Picea sitchensis* and recognized pine and fir largely at the species level, Leopold treated spruce as *P. engelmanni* and pine and fir only as genera.

In view of the absence of finite dates for the interglacial peats, the uncertainty of stratigraphic correlations, and the problem of pollen identification, pollen records thus far assembled present only a discontinuous, partial picture of pre-Vashon vegetation in the Puget Lowland. Their contribution lies in revealing certain facts, among which are that, within the limits of pollen recognition, vegetation components during the interglacials did not differ from those growing at present in western Washington, that plants not included in local floras were not in evidence, and that interglacial climate was never so adverse as to restrict arboreal types.

Outside, but close to the end moraines and related outwash, occur sediments in which pollen preservation has been more or less continuous from sometime prior to the Vashon up to the present day. Records contained in these sediments are especially valuable not only because of their continuity but also because a spectrum from any level can be interpreted in reference to the surface spectrum and existing environment for the same locality. It is hardly to be expected that any deposit of this kind will continuously span the whole of the Pleistocene or will even penetrate uninterruptedly deep into the epoch, and in the long run it will be necessary to piece together many different records before the total picture is at hand.

A bog near Humptulips (Fig. 1) on the Olympic Peninsula is a site at which deposition began during pre-Vashon time and continued with no major hiatus up until the present (Heusser, 1964). Pollen stratigraphy of a 6.2-m section taken at the site is shown in Figure 5. Chronology of the section is controlled by radiocarbon dates, although control is lost at a depth of 3.2 m where a date of >30,000 years B.P. renders the age of the remainder of the section uncertain. Chronology below this level is derived in part from the finite ages of certain correlative glacial and nonglacial events in the Great Lakes–St. Lawrence region and elsewhere (Flint and Brandtner, 1961). It is also derived from the mapping by Crandell (1962, p. 48) of pre-Wisconsin drift near Humptulips bog, early Wisconsin drift less than a kilometer away, and middle Wisconsin drift 3-6 km to the northwest. An early middle Wisconsin age is tentatively assigned the earliest pollen-bearing sediments. According to Crandell (this volume), the bog rests on drift of older Salmon Springs(?) or early Wisconsin age.

Middle Wisconsin spectra at Humptulips are dominated primarily by grass, except where mountain hemlock, Sitka spruce, and lodgepole pine profiles are prominent. Spectra spanning the late Wisconsin (Fraser Glaciation of Armstrong *et al.*, 1964) show this pattern, but pine percentages are higher, and spruce and mountain hemlock profiles are weaker, especially during the middle to late Wisconsin interval ("Olympia Interglaciation" of Armstrong *et al.*, 1964), when the profile for western hemlock begins to develop. Vegetation on ice-free parts of the Olympic Peninsula through much of middle and late Wisconsin glacial intervals probably resembled the edge of the Pacific Coast Forest in Alaska as it looks today where Sitka spruce and mountain hemlock make contact with subalpine grassland or meadow and alpine heath. Interstade vegetation appears to approach that of the present time on the peninsula.

A July average temperature curve is included in Figure 5. It was prepared from records maintained at weather stations scattered along the British Columbia and Alaska coasts where modern pollen spectra could be matched with fossil spectra from various levels in the Humptulips section (Heusser, 1964). The curve discloses that during the middle Wisconsin glacial interval (GL-2) temperature depression was greatest, 6-7° C below the present-day average; in the late Wisconsin (GL-5, LG-1), it was about 6° below; and during the Sumas stade (LG-3), it amounted to about 5° below. The middle to late Wisconsin interstadial (ISL-5) July average temperature was about 2° below today's, and the Vashon-Sumas interval (LG-2; Everson interval of Armstrong *et al.*, 1964) had a temperature of 2-3° below. On the basis of this curve and the probable temperature conditions in refugia on the British Columbia and Alaska coasts over the time represented, it seems likely that certain coniferous trees survived the late Wisconsin, whereas only herbs and shrubs endured the middle Wisconsin glacial environment. Plants appear to have existed close to the middle and late Wisconsin glacier fronts in Washington, and at times of recession, either during an interstade or during postglacial time, vegetation cover appears to have developed rapidly on deglaciated terrain.

Along the sea cliffs of Oregon and Washington, buried Pleistocene peats and highly organic silts crop out from place to place. Pollen diagrams of two peat exposures at Newport, Oregon, 140 km southwest of Portland, are clearly related and depict a succession from lodgepole pine to Sitka spruce, followed by western hemlock and spruce (Hansen and Allison, 1942). This pattern is much the same as the early postglacial succession that has taken place in southeastern Alaska. Wood from sand and silt associated with the peat is dated >38,000 B.P. (W-646). At the present time, I am studying the pollen stratigraphy of some 20 sections from coastal exposures of Pleistocene age in Oregon and Washington. Most of these are from the stretch of coast between the mouths of the Hoh and Queets Rivers on the western Olympic Peninsula. It is believed that a considerable portion of the Pleistocene vegetation and climatic history of this part of the Pacific Northwest is contained in this material.

ALASKA

Until recently, an early study of the Fairbanks "mucks" by Chaney and Mason (1936) was the only attempt to investigate Pleistocene plant deposits in Alaska. "Mucks" occur in different parts of the unglaciated interior and consist of interbedded peat, wood, ice, eolian silt, and volcanic ash, including bones of bison, mammoth, horse, and other animals (Péwé, 1957). Those near Fairbanks (Fig. 3), exposed by gold-dredging operations, have been dated >35,000 B.P. (W-475, W-476). Chaney and Mason did not investigate the pollen and spore content but rather the macroscopic remains of plants. They identified 27 plants, 8 of which were trees, including white spruce, quaking aspen, willows (*Salix glauca* and *S. reticulata*), and birches (*Betula glandulosa* and *B. resinifera*).

Colinvaux' (1963, 1964a) papers presenting results of his work on a core from Imuruk Lake on the Seward Peninsula are the only ones so far which provide more of an insight into late and pre-late Wisconsin vegetation in Alaska. Imuruk Lake, flat-bottomed and no more than 3 m deep and 13 km across, according to Hopkins (1959), is situated in the tundra, about 6 km northwest of the nearest spruce trees (Fig. 3). Hopkins believed the lake should contain a record of continuous pollen deposition beginning in middle Illinoian time and urged that a study of the pollen stratigraphy be undertaken. As a result, Colinvaux brought up an 8-m core of the lake sediments in 1960 for the purpose of a pollen study.

Colinvaux' pollen diagram consists mainly of profiles for birch, alder, spruce, willow, heath, sedge, grass, *Artemisia*, and *Sphagnum*. Five radiocarbon dates apply to the core. Two, at just below a depth of 1 m and at 2-3 m, are,

respectively, >34,500 and >37,000 B.P. (Y-1142 and Y-1143), but one at 7.5 m, 21,700 B.P. (I-415), is anomalous. Because of this anachronism, Colinvaux at first interpreted his results in terms of different chronological schemes, but finally decided that the sequence probably spans the interval beginning during the interglacial preceding the Nome River (= Illinoian) glaciation. More than the lower half of the core covers this interglacial, in which percentage values for birch and spruce, although fluctuating, are relatively high. During the Nome River glacial interval, by contrast, these woody plants become sparse, and the proportion of grass, sedge, willow, and *Artemisia* is high. Spectra for an interglacial succeeding Nome River time display features similar to the early interglacial spectra, except that alder is better represented later. Spectra for the Salmon Lake (= Wisconsin) glacial interval exhibit a greater abundance of grass, but otherwise are much the same as those covering the Nome River glaciation. Colinvaux concludes that the pollen stratigraphy portrays a series of tundra types, ranging from cotton-grass tussock to depauperate grassland, which has never been replaced by forest vegetation.

In most palynological work, certain factors preclude the results from being unequivocal, and the Imuruk Lake diagrams are no exception. One factor concerning these diagrams is the discrepancy in the series of radiocarbon dates, which arouses suspicion regarding any age interpretation that could be made of the core. Another is the variety and frequency of disturbances that can influence sedimentation and cause reworking, resuspension, and redeposition of older pollen-bearing sediments, with the resulting contamination of undisturbed pollen assemblages. According to Hopkins (1959) Imuruk Lake history has involved (1) local faulting and irregular warping, which occurred at least twice during the late Pleistocene; (2) a recent lava flow entering the lake basin on the south side; and (3) a collapse of areas marginal to the lake and modification of the lake's outline, owing to the thawing of permafrost.

SUMMARY OF RECONSTRUCTIONS

LATE-GLACIAL AND POSTGLACIAL

The accompanying correlation table (Fig. 6) summarizes much of the foregoing material covering late-glacial and postglacial vegetation in the Pacific Northwest and Alaska. Correlations that are made reflect the extent of the data now available and are clearer in some areas of the table than in others. Some liberty has been taken in adjusting the correspondence of certain columns, and, consequently, time boundaries do not necessarily express the opinions of the individual authors. Some minor changes over previously published correlations are made for the sake of depicting the broad lines of relationship in a table that includes remotely separated parts of northwestern North America.

Some of the conclusions that emerge from a review of the table in Figure 6 and from portions of the foregoing material are:

1. Vegetation following the withdrawal of glaciers of the last ice age consisted of lodgepole-pine parkland in the

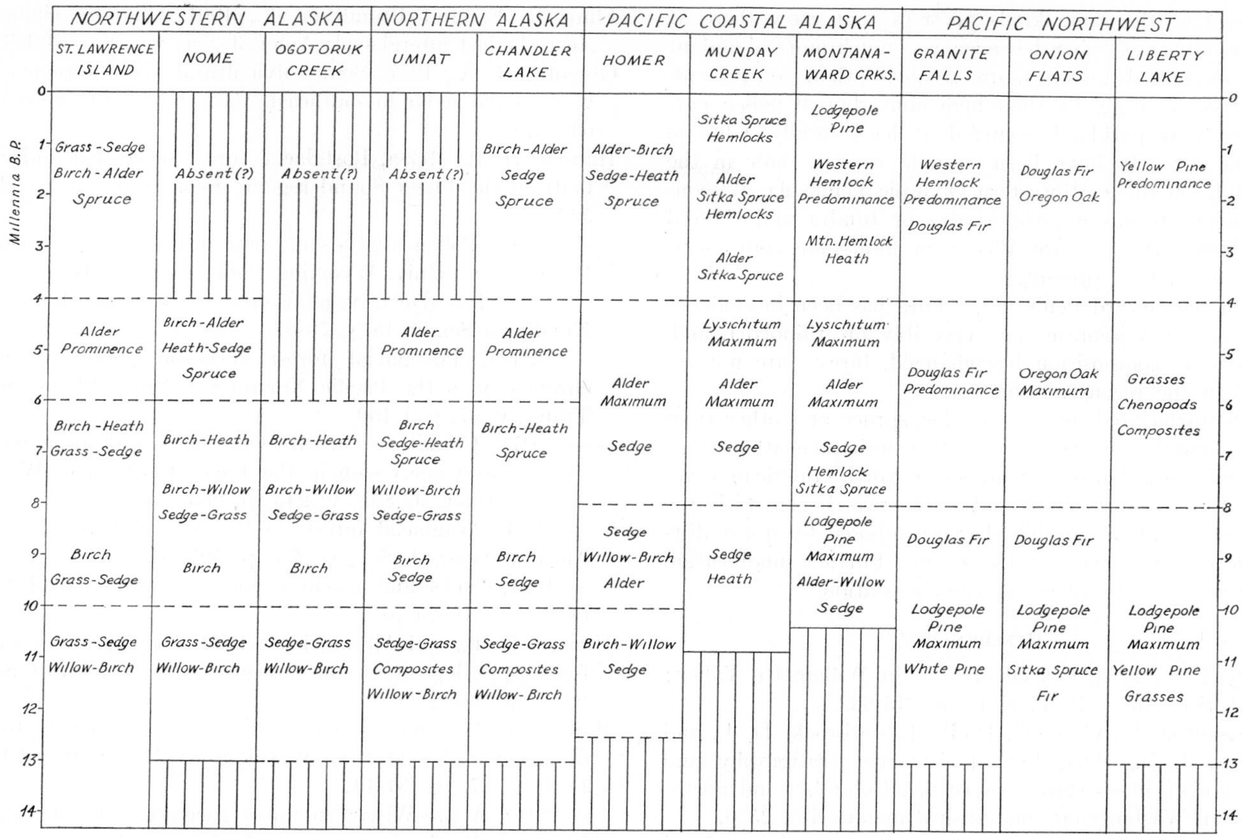

	NORTHWESTERN ALASKA			NORTHERN ALASKA		PACIFIC COASTAL ALASKA			PACIFIC NORTHWEST		
Millennia B.P.	ST. LAWRENCE ISLAND	NOME	OGOTORUK CREEK	UMIAT	CHANDLER LAKE	HOMER	MUNDAY CREEK	MONTANA-WARD CRKS.	GRANITE FALLS	ONION FLATS	LIBERTY LAKE
1	Grass-Sedge Birch-Alder Spruce	Absent (?)	Absent (?)	Absent (?)	Birch-Alder Sedge Spruce	Alder-Birch Sedge-Heath Spruce	Sitka Spruce Hemlocks / Alder Sitka Spruce Hemlocks	Lodgepole Pine / Western Hemlock Predominance / Mtn. Hemlock Heath	Western Hemlock Predominance Douglas Fir	Douglas Fir Oregon Oak	Yellow Pine Predominance
3							Alder Sitka Spruce				
5	Alder Prominence	Birch-Alder Heath-Sedge Spruce		Alder Prominence	Alder Prominence		Lysichitum Maximum / Alder Maximum	Lysichitum Maximum / Alder Maximum	Douglas Fir Predominance	Oregon Oak Maximum	Grasses Chenopods Composites
6						Alder Maximum					
7	Birch-Heath Grass-Sedge	Birch-Heath	Birch-Heath	Birch Sedge-Heath Spruce	Birch-Heath Spruce	Sedge	Sedge	Sedge Hemlock Sitka Spruce			
8		Birch-Willow Sedge-Grass	Birch-Willow Sedge-Grass	Willow-Birch Sedge-Grass							
9	Birch Grass-Sedge	Birch	Birch	Birch Sedge	Birch Sedge	Sedge Willow-Birch Alder	Sedge Heath	Lodgepole Pine Maximum / Alder-Willow Sedge	Douglas Fir	Douglas Fir	
10									Lodgepole Pine Maximum	Lodgepole Pine Maximum	Lodgepole Pine Maximum
11	Grass-Sedge Willow-Birch	Grass-Sedge Willow-Birch	Sedge-Grass Willow-Birch	Sedge-Grass Composites Willow-Birch	Sedge-Grass Composites Willow-Birch	Birch-Willow Sedge			White Pine	Sitka Spruce Fir	Yellow Pine Grasses

Figure 6. Summary of late-glacial and postglacial vegetation for sections discussed in the text. Vertical lines appearing at the bases of most columns cover intervals for which no record is available. Where they terminate above by a solid cross-line, the pollen-bearing sediments are radiocarbon-dated; dash cross-lines indicate age inference from regional dating. Sections from Nome, Ogotoruk Creek, and Umiat appear to be truncated above. Authors responsible for studies shown here are mentioned in the text.

Pacific Northwest and northwestward as far as southeastern Alaska. Treeless vegetation, comprised of sedge and heath or sedge with birch and willow, characterized the deglaciated ground in south-central and southwestern Alaska, and was spread over much of the interior as tundra, made up largely of grass and sedge with some willow and birch.

2. As postglacial climate became warmer, alder and more tolerant coniferous trees displaced pine parkland in the Pacific Northwest and in southeastern Alaska, whereas in the Willamette Valley the succession went to oak, and east of the Cascades it went to grasses, chenopods, and composites. Alder displaced much of the treeless vegetation of the south-central and southwestern Alaska coast. In the interior, birch became a significant part of the tundra before being invaded by alder. Alder ultimately achieved prominence, earlier in the coastal district than in the interior.

3. During the latter part of the postglacial, western hemlock dominated the coastal forest as far to the northwest as southeastern Alaska. Coastal areas in the Pacific Northwest that were too dry for hemlock supported Douglas fir, as they do today, and in eastern Washington yellow pine was favored at this time. In south-central and southwestern Alaska, Sitka spruce and mountain hemlock became the major conifer forest trees, and on the Kenai Peninsula they mixed with birch and white and black spruce from the interior. Spruce in the interior also apparently spread in the direction of the tundra. During the late postglacial, tundra-covered northern and western Alaska became a mosaic of herbaceous and shrub communities.

4. During glacial times vegetation in glaciated areas was overridden by ice and destroyed. However, plants thrived along the glacier border in the Pacific Northwest and, at least during late Wisconsin glaciation, in interior Alaska. Available evidence from Pacific coastal Alaska and British Columbia, although inconclusive, points toward the persistence of plants in refugia. Postglacial recolonization of deglaciated ground by plants proceeded from the unglaciated tracts.

WISCONSIN AND PRE-WISCONSIN

Wisconsin or earlier Pleistocene-age pollen records are few and mostly discontinuous and of uncertain age. The necessarily limited conclusions that can be drawn follow:

1. During interglacial ages in the Puget Lowland (possibly beginning with the early Pleistocene), forests were

composed of the same kinds of trees that grow there at present. Lodgepole pine, however, was much more abundant and mountain hemlock more frequent than at present. Some records imply by their high non-arboreal pollen percentages that parkland occurred at least locally. Climate appears never to have been so mild as it is now in the Lowland. On the southwestern Olympic Peninsula, Wisconsin vegetation was a park tundra or tundra and showed only during the pre-late Wisconsin interstade some semblance to that at present.

2. On the Seward Peninsula, tundra has been in evidence from pre-late Wisconsin time (possibly pre-Illinoian), and, although its composition has changed, forests are not recorded in the reconstruction.

3. In unglaciated interior Alaska, spruce and other trees have endured since before late Wisconsin glaciation.

4. Differentiation of northwestern North American vegetation into modern units and unit areas began with the climatic and physiographic changes imposed by uplift during the late Tertiary and Pleistocene. Further modification took place as a result of repeated glaciation.

REFERENCES

Allison, I. S., 1935, Glacial erratics in Willamette Valley: Geol. Soc. Amer. Bull., v. 46, p. 615-632

Armstrong, J. E., Crandell, D. R., Easterbrook, D. J., and Noble, J. B., 1964, Late Pleistocene stratigraphy and chronology in southwestern British Columbia and northwestern Washington: unpublished manuscript, 25 p.

Benninghoff, W. S., 1952, Interaction of vegetation and soil frost phenomena: Arctic, v. 5, p. 34-44

Britton, M. E., 1957, Vegetation of the arctic tundra, *in* Hansen, H. P. (ed.), Arctic biology: Oregon State Coll. 18th Ann. Biol. Colloq., p. 26-61

Cahalane, V. H., 1959, A biological survey of Katmai National Monument: Smithson. Instn. Misc. Coll., v. 138, p. 1-246

Cain, S. A., 1944, Foundations of plant geography: New York, Harper, 556 p.

Chaney, R. W., and Mason, H. L., 1936, A Pleistocene flora from Fairbanks, Alaska: Amer. Mus. Novitates, v. 887, p. 1-17

Colinvaux, P. A., 1963, A pollen record from arctic Alaska reaching glacial and Bering land bridge times: Nature, v. 198, p. 609-610

—— 1964a, The environment of the Bering land bridge: Ecol. Monogr., v. 34, p. 297-329

—— 1964b, Origin of ice ages: pollen evidence from arctic Alaska: Science, v. 145, p. 707-708

Cooper, W. S., 1957, Vegetation of the northwest-American province: 8th Pacific Sci. Congr., v. 4, p. 133-138

Crandell, D. R., 1962, Glaciation of Washington and Oregon: unpublished manuscript, 138 p.

Crandell, D. R., Mullineaux, D. R., and Waldron, H. H., 1958, Pleistocene sequence in southeastern part of the Puget Sound lowland, Washington: Amer. J. Sci., v. 256, p. 384-397

Drury, W. H., Jr., 1956, Bog flats and physiographic processes in the upper Kuskokwim River region, Alaska: Harvard Univ., Gray Herb. Contr. 178, 130 p.

Flint, R. F., and Brandtner, F., 1961, Climatic changes since the last interglacial: Amer. J. Sci., v. 259, p. 321-328

Gregory, R. A., 1957, Some silvicultural characteristics of western red cedar in southeast Alaska: Ecology, v. 38, p. 646-649

Hansen, H. P., 1938a, Postglacial forest succession and climate in the Puget Sound region: Ecology, v. 19, p. 528-542

—— 1938b, Pollen analysis of some interglacial peat from Washington: Univ. Wyoming Publ., v. 5, p. 11-18

—— 1944, Postglacial vegetation of eastern Washington: Northwest Sci., v. 18, p. 79-87

—— 1947a, Postglacial forest succession, climate, and chronology in the Pacific Northwest: Amer. Philos. Soc. Trans., v. 37, p. 1-130

—— 1947b, Climate versus fire and soil as factors in postglacial forest succession in the Puget Lowland of Washington: Amer. J. Sci., v. 245, p. 265-286

—— 1953, Postglacial forests in the Yukon Territory and Alaska: Amer. J. Sci., v. 251, p. 505-542

—— 1961, Cycles and geochronology: California Acad. Sci. Occ. Pap. 31, 24 p.

Hansen, H. P., and Allison, I. S., 1942, A pollen study of a fossil peat deposit on the Oregon coast: Northwest Sci., v. 16, p. 86-92

Hansen, H. P., and Mackin, J. H., 1940, A further study of interglacial peat from Washington: Torrey Bot. Club Bull., v. 67, p. 131-142

—— 1949, A pre-Wisconsin forest succession in the Puget Lowland, Washington: Amer. J. Sci., v. 247, p. 833-855

Heusser, C. J., 1954, Nunatak flora of the Juneau Ice Field, Alaska: Torrey Bot. Club Bull., v. 81, p. 236-250

—— 1960, Late Pleistocene environments of North Pacific North America: Amer. Geogr. Soc. Spec. Publ. 35, 308 p.

—— 1963a, Postglacial palynology and archaeology in the Naknek River drainage area, Alaska: Amer. Antiq., v. 29, p. 74-81

—— 1963b, Pollen diagrams from Ogotoruk Creek, Cape Thompson, Alaska: Grana Palynologica, v. 4, p. 149-159

—— 1964, Palynology of four bog sections from the western Olympic Peninsula, Washington: Ecology, v. 45, p. 23-40

Hopkins, D. M., 1959, History of Imuruk Lake, Seward Peninsula, Alaska: Geol. Soc. Amer. Bull., v. 70, p. 1033-1046

—— 1963, Geology of the Imuruk Lake area, Seward Peninsula, Alaska: U.S. Geol. Surv. Bull. 1141-C, 101 p.

Hopkins, D. M., Karlstrom, T. N. V., et al., 1955, Permafrost and ground water in Alaska: U.S. Geol. Surv. Prof. Pap. 264-F, p. 113-146

Hopkins, D. M., MacNeil, F. S., and Leopold, E. B., 1960, The coastal plain at Nome, Alaska: a late Cenozoic type section for the Bering Strait region: 21st Intern. Geol. Congr. Rep., Copenhagen, Denmark, pt. 4, p. 46-57

Hultén, E., 1937a, Flora of the Aleutian Islands and westernmost Alaska Peninsula with notes on the flora of the Commander Islands: Stockholm, Bokförlags Aktiebolaget Thule, 397 p.

—— 1937b, Outline of the history of arctic and boreal biota during the Quaternary period: Stockholm, Bokförlags Aktiebolaget Thule, 168 p.

—— 1941-1950, Flora of Alaska and Yukon: Lund, Gleerup, 1902 p.

Johnson, A. W., Viereck, L. A., and Melchior, H. R., 1959, Ogotoruk valley botanical project: Univ. Alaska Dept. Biol. Sci. Prog. Rep., 102 p.

Jones, G. N., 1936, A botanical survey of the Olympic Peninsula, Washington: Univ. Washington Publ. Biol. 5, 286 p.

Leopold, E. B., and Crandell, D. R., 1958, Pre-Wisconsin interglacial pollen spectra from Washington State, USA: Zurich, Geobot. Inst. Rübel Veröff., v. 34, p. 76-79

Little, E. L., Jr., 1953, A natural hybrid spruce in Alaska: J. For., v. 51, p. 745-747

Livingstone, D. A., 1955, Some pollen profiles from Arctic Alaska: Ecology, v. 36, p. 587-600

—— 1957, Pollen analysis of a valley fill near Umiat, Alaska: Amer. J. Sci., v. 255, p. 254-260

Lutz, H. J., 1953, The effects of forest fires on the vegetation of interior Alaska: Alaska For. Res. Cent. Sta. Pap. 1, 36 p.

Merkle, J., 1951, An analysis of the plant communities of Mary's Peak, western Oregon: Ecology, v. 32, p. 618-640

Peck, M. E., 1941, A manual of the higher plants of Oregon: Portland, Binfords & Mort, 866 p.

Péwé, T. L., 1957, Permafrost and its effect on life in the north, *in* Hansen, H. P. (ed.), Arctic biology: Oregon State College, 18th Ann. Biol. Colloq., p. 12-25

Powers, H. A., and Wilcox, R. E., 1964, Volcanic ash from Mount Mazama (Crater Lake) and from Glacier Peak: Science, v. 144, p. 1334-1336

Rigg, G. B., and Gould, H. R., 1957, Age of Glacier Peak eruption and chronology of post-glacial peat deposits in Washington and surrounding areas: Amer. J. Sci., v. 255, p. 341-363

Sigafoos, R. S., 1958, Vegetation of northwestern North America, as an aid in interpretation of geologic data: U.S. Geol. Surv. Bull. 1061-E, p. 165-185

Taylor, R. F., 1932, The successional trend and its relation to second-growth forests in southeastern Alaska: Ecology, v. 13, p. 381-391

Wilcox, R. E., this volume, Volcanic-ash chronology

Summary

When uplift of the western cordillera occurred in late-Tertiary and Pleistocene time, vegetation in the Pacific Northwest and Alaska began to take on the broad aspects of its present distribution. Repeated glaciation further contributed toward molding the modern units, which consist chiefly of coastal Pacific and interior Alaskan forests, arctic tundra in northern and western Alaska, muskeg, alpine tundra above timber line in the cordillera, and sagebrush and grassland in the Columbia Basin of eastern Washington and Oregon.

Late-glacial vegetation in the Pacific Northwest, reconstructed on palynological grounds, constituted an early lodgepole-pine parkland which during the postglacial was replaced west of the Cascades by forests of hemlock where rainfall was pronounced and by Douglas fir and oak where greater dryness prevailed; east of the Cascades, grasses, chenopods, and composites, and later yellow pine, succeeded lodgepole. In Pacific coastal Alaska, early pine parkland in the southeastern sector was subsequently given over largely to hemlock-spruce forest; toward the west as far as Kodiak Island conifer forest developed from an initial tundra of sedge and shrubs. Unglaciated coastal refugia may have served as centra for plant invasion of deglaciated terrain, in addition to the area south of the glacier boundary in Washington. Unglaciated interior Alaska was an extensive refugium for the major forest trees, spruce and birch, as well as for herbs and shrubs of the arctic tundra. Records of late-glacial and early postglacial arctic vegetation show herbaceous tundra in the beginning, later invaded by birch and more recently by alder.

Wisconsin and pre-Wisconsin vegetation in the Pacific Northwest west of the Cascades was composed of the same trees growing there now. Arctic tundra has prevailed in Alaska, much in the same manner as it does at present, through at least the latter part of the Pleistocene.

THE BOREAL BRYOPHYTE FLORA AS AFFECTED
BY QUATERNARY GLACIATION *

WILLIAM C. STEERE[1]

THIS TOPIC is one that invites speculation. Although speculation without evidence can be an empty exercise, it does serve the useful purpose of enabling one to find the various alternative possibilities to account for present circumstances. Fortunately, in this case we do have evidence in the light of which we may examine our various suppositions.

The evidence consists of two very different series of data, one derived from the identification of fossil or subfossil bryophytes in preglacial, interglacial, or postglacial deposits of peats and forest beds, the other derived from a careful analysis of the present geographical distribution of living bryophytes. These two methods or approaches for an investigation of the effect of Quaternary glaciation on the boreal bryophyte flora will be explored and discussed.

SUBFOSSIL MOSSES FROM QUATERNARY DEPOSITS

First of all, it seems a necessary caution to point out that only those subfossil mosses that are found in fossil peats and forest soils that are still in their original position are valid materials for drawing conclusions about earlier distribution patterns, climates, and other environmental conditions. Subfossil mosses found in river silts, especially near areas of high relief, cannot be considered a reliable material for drawing general conclusions, since their origin is so uncertain. In a river as large and as long as the Mississippi, subfossil materials found in the delta may with high probability have been transported for long distances from higher latitudes or altitudes (Steere, 1938b).

Unfortunately, few major reports of original investigations and no comprehensive reviews dedicated to bryophytes identified in Quaternary deposits have been published since Gams' excellent review (1932), concerned largely with the European discoveries, and my own treatment (Steere, 1942) of North American subfossil mosses.

In Europe, progress in the study of Quaternary bryophytes since Gams' review (1932) has consisted primarily of occasional reports of one or a few species of moss from Quaternary or postglacial deposits. Vanden Berghen (1950), for example, has reported *Dicranum bergeri* Bland. to be relatively common in subfossil peats found in the coastal plain of Flanders, in Belgium. Although a common enough species in northern Europe, especially in Scandinavia, it seems to be absent from the present flora of Belgium (Demaret and Castagne, 1961). The one species of *Sphagnum* and two other mosses found in interglacial deposits at Porsi, in Swedish Lapland (Lundqvist, 1960), still occur in the same area, as does the one moss found in interglacial peat at Ale, near Lulea in the same area (Persson, 1960). An extensive list of fossil mosses from the Taimyr Peninsula (Savich-Ljubitskaya and Abramova, 1954) consists of species which inhabit the same area today. Konior (1936) reports from Pleistocene deposits at Dziedzice, Poland, four species of moss that still occur in Poland. A major report of original research on Quaternary mosses, based on the identification of more than 200,000 fossil mosses from Poland, lists and discusses 63 species (Jasnowski, 1957). One of the most significant contributions to our understanding of past climates and past distributions of bryophytes was the fossil discovery (Hesselbo, 1910) in Denmark of *Cinclidium latifolium* Lindb., whose nearest living populations are in Siberia 2,000 km distant. These examples of scattered bits of information illustrate clearly the need for a comprehensive and up-to-date review of the Western European literature on Quaternary mosses, as Jasnowski (1957) has done for Poland.

In Great Britain, most of the emphasis on Quaternary plants, thanks to the great personal and professional influence of Professor Harry Godwin, has been placed on the postglacial flora, because of its enormously important interrelationship with prehistorical and historical events and the activities of man himself. However, the postglacial era and its bryological history have turned out to be of unusual biogeographical significance, because several species of bryophytes have become extinct or nearly so during this relatively brief period. Man's effect on his environment, in a multitude of ways, is generally to make it drier. The inexorable draining of bogs and moors in Great Britain for the exploitation of peat, to develop farm land, and for other reasons, has had a deleterious effect on those environments that are favorable to bog and fen mosses. For example, *Meesia triquetra* (Hook et Tayl.) Aongstr., a moss characteristic of boreal, subarctic, and arctic bogs and fens (Steere, 1931), was a member of the British flora at the time of the Roman Conquest, and undoubtedly through the quite unintentional efforts of man it has become very nearly extinct in the United Kingdom. The comments on this species by Godwin and Richards (1947) deserve to be quoted: "Since it has never previously been found in the British Isles, either living or fossil, the recent discovery of

* For grants in support of field investigations during twelve seasons in arctic and subarctic areas of Alaska, Canada, Lapland, Greenland, and Iceland, I acknowledge with gratitude the generosity of the Office of Naval Research, the National Science Foundation, and the Arctic Institute of North America. I acknowledge with especial appreciation the logistic and other support given generously by the directors of the Arctic Research Laboratory at Point Barrow, Alaska, especially Ira L. Wiggins and Max Brewer.

[1] New York Botanical Garden, Bronx Park, New York.

its remains in considerable quantity in peat of approximately Neolithic age in the Somerset Levels is of great interest." Other bog mosses known from several localities in England a century or more ago have become either extinct or excessively rare through the draining of their habitats, as *Paludella squarrosa* (Hedw.) Brid., *Helodium blandowi* (Web. et Mohr) Warnst., and *Calliergon turgescens* (Th. Jens.) Kindb. Still other boreal species, as *Calliergon trifarium* (Web. et Mohr) Kindb., *Cinclidium stygium* Sw., *Dicranum bergeri* Bland., *Catoscopium nigritum* (Hedw.) Brid., and *Mnium cinclidioides* Hüben., are known today from numerous localities in the Highlands of Scotland, with scattered relic localities in northern England and, more rarely, in northern Wales and Ireland. It is especially to be regretted that Godwin (1956), in his monumental treatment of the post-Quaternary vascular plants of Great Britain, omitted any consideration of the mosses, except for a paragraph or two (p. 331).

In North America, where too few bryologists can keep up with even the day-by-day demands for the identification of recent species collected in all parts of the world, continued investigation of fossil and subfossil material from Quaternary deposits has been sadly neglected, and no major work has appeared since my own pioneer venture (Steere, 1942) on early interglacial mosses of Iowa. Again, space permits the mention only of examples, and for this I choose three representative papers—the comprehensive investigation of the Pleistocene flora of Minnesota by Rosendahl (1948), the further study of fossil mosses from the Two Creeks Forest Bed of Wisconsin by Culberson (1955), and a recent study of pollen and mosses in the Whitewater Basin of southeastern Indiana by Kapp and Gooding (1964). We have in the United States and Canada an enormous backlog of collected and uncollected material of bryophytes from well-known sites—all that is needed is the services of competent bryologists to study this material, which will yield almost at once an enormous amount of information concerning the Quaternary glaciations and their vicissitudes.

Subfossil mosses have not been extensively investigated or used in the interpretation of Quaternary problems outside Europe and North America (Puri, 1958; Hedberg, 1961; van Zinderen Bakker, 1962).

In late years, the studies of subfossil peats and forest beds—as well as the mosses in them—have gained a new and highly modern tool of enormous potential importance, through the development of techniques for radiocarbon dating of subfossil materials. Of course, like every technique, radiocarbon dating has its limitations, of which the primary one is that organic materials more than approximately fifty thousand years old cannot be accurately dated. However, much has happened during the last 50,000 years, including the development of man's present culture. This period has been marked by active glaciation, great fluctuations in the levels of the sea, as well as drastic changes in climate, at least locally. As a consequence, all these events have left their mark on present-day distribution of mosses. Having in hand accurate dates for the time of deposition of subfossil peats should give us new and more trustworthy ideas on the rates of migration of plants during glacial and postglacial times. Moreover, subfossil deposits that are too

ancient for radiocarbon dating alert us to the necessity of interpreting their time of formation by more subjective and intuitive methods.

So far, subfossil peats, even without the useful additional data that radiocarbon dating would have provided, have given us significant evidence of earlier and different patterns of distribution, undoubtedly correlated with a perceptible difference in climate.

In closing this discussion of fossil Quaternary mosses and their distribution, I emphasize again, at the risk of being repetitive, the necessity for prompt and comprehensive study of the abundant materials available for investigation and for general reviews of the scattered, casual, and unrelated papers in the literature of each continent.

SIGNIFICANT PATTERNS IN PRESENT-DAY GEOGRAPHICAL DISTRIBUTION OF BRYOPHYTES

Mosses, being much smaller than higher plants, are more easily overlooked, and there are fewer specialists to collect and identify them. Nevertheless, their patterns of geographic distribution are as clear and as illuminating as those of the higher plants, which they often, but not always, parallel remarkably closely. Because mosses produce numerous small spores easily borne by the wind, their distribution is commonly held to be rather generalized. This belief is erroneous, however; mosses appear to have migrated in the same foot-by-foot manner as higher plants and were probably associated with them. A few species of weedy mosses that follow man's disturbance or that are spread by his activities do have generalized areas of distribution, and from these ubiquitous species has arisen the erroneous impression that *all* mosses have generalized distributions. A quite contrary situation exists; bryophytes show several significant patterns of disjunct distribution, each one of which reflects historical climatic and physical events, some of them occurring before the Quaternary, some during, and some since.

THE HIGH-ARCTIC BRYOPHYTE ELEMENT

During the past two decades an increasingly large amount of field work has been done by bryologists in the polar areas of each continent, so that we now have a good idea, in general, of the distribution of bryophytes in the several arctic land areas of the world. In fact, it has been recognized (Steere, 1953; Gams, 1955; Holmen, 1960) that there exists in the Arctic a coherent group of species of bryophytes that are restricted to arctic regions or that occur in very large part within the Arctic Circle and extend south of it only where high altitude or local climate provides equivalent environmental conditions. At first, as these species were described from arctic Europe, Siberia, Greenland, and arctic North America, they were considered to be endemic to their type areas. However, as field exploration by bryologists has been extended, these species have been found one after another to have a typically circumpolar pattern of distribution (Fig. 1), no matter where originally described, so that of the approximately 500 species of bryophytes known in arctic regions, at least 10% belong to the high-arctic element.

The following species are considered to be members of

the circumpolar, high-arctic element of bryophytes, a few of which still have populations in the Alps and in the Rocky Mountains that may be relics of the Quaternary glaciation, and others of which are presently known from much more restricted areas:

Andreaea obovata Thed.
Arctoa anderssonii Wich.
Arnellia fennica (Gottsche) Lindb.
Aulacomnium acuminatum (Lindb. & Arn.) Paris
Barbilophozia binsteadii (Kaal.) Loeske
Barbula johansenii Williams
Bryobrittonia pellucida Williams
Bryum arcticum (R. Brown) BSG.
Bryum cryophilum Mårt.
Bryum wrightii Sull. & Lesq.
   (plus a large and uncertain number of further species of *Bryum* described from the Arctic)
Calycularia laxa Lindb. & Arn.
Cephaloziella arctica Bryhn & Douin
Ceratodon heterophyllus Kindb.
Cinclidium arcticum (BSG.) C. Müll.
Cinclidium latifolium Lindb.
Claopodium subpiliferum (Lindb. & Arn.) Broth.
Coscinodon latifolius Lindb. & Arn.
Cratoneuron arcticum Steere
Cyrtomium hymenophylloides (Hüb.) Holmen
Cyrtomium hymenophyllum (BSG.) Holmen
Desmatodon leucostomus Berggr.
Didymodon asperifolius (Mitt.) Crum, Steer & Anders.
Distichium hagenii Ryan
Drepanocladus badius (Hartm.) Roth
Drepanocladus brevifolius (Lindb.) Warnst.
Drepanocladus latifolius Lindb.
Drepanocladus lycopodioides (Brid.) Warnst.
Fissidens arcticus Bryhn
Funaria polaris Bryhn
Grimmia tenuicaulis Williams
Haplodon wormskjoldii (Hornem.) R. Brown
Haplozia polaris (Lindb.) K. Müll.
Helicodontium rotundifolium Arn.
Hygrohypnum polaris (Lindb.) Broth.
Hygrolejeunea alaskana Schuster & Steere
Lepicolea fryei Persson
Lophozia hyperarctica Schuster
Lophozia pellucida Schuster
Lophozia quadriloba (Lindb.) Evans
Marsupella arctica Bryhn & Kaal.
Mesoptychia sahlbergii (Lindb. & Arn.) Evans
Mnium andrewsii Steere (1958b)
Mnium blyttii BSG.
Oncophorus glaucescens Lindb. & Arn.
Oligotrichum falcatum Steere (1958a)
Philonotis tomentella Mol.
Philocrya aspera Hagen & Jensen (Steere, 1956)
Plagiochila arctica Bryhn & Kaal.
Polytrichum hyperboreum R. Brown
Pottia obtusifolia (R. Brown) C. Müll.
Psilopilum cavifolium (Wils.) Hagen
Psilopilum laevigatum (Wahlenb.) Limpr.

Pterygoneurum arcticum Steere (1960)
Radula prolifera Arn.
Scapania hyperborea Jørg.
Scapania polaris Schuster
Scapania simmonsii Bryhn & Kaal.
Scapania spitsbergensis (Lindb.) K. Müll.
Seligeria polaris Berggr.
Timmia comata Lindb.
Tortella arctica (Arnell) Crundw. & Nyholm
Trichostomum cuspidatissimum Card. & Thér.
Voitia hyperborea Grev. & Arnott

In addition to those species enumerated above, at least one undescribed genus and several new and undescribed species will eventually add further detail to the picture.

In arctic Alaska, I have found most of the species originally considered to be endemic to Greenland, to the Canadian Eastern Arctic (Steere, 1948), and to Siberia. Conversely, species originally described and known only from

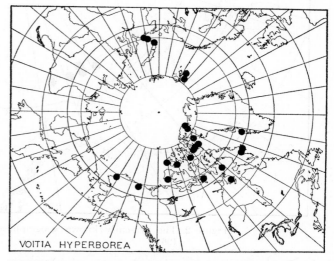

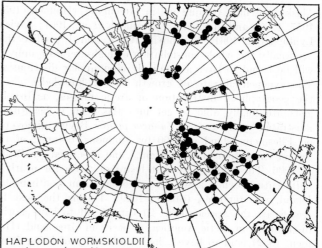

Figure 1. The known distribution of two typically high-arctic species, *Haplodon wormskioldii* and *Voitia hyperborea*, generalized (from Steere, 1953)

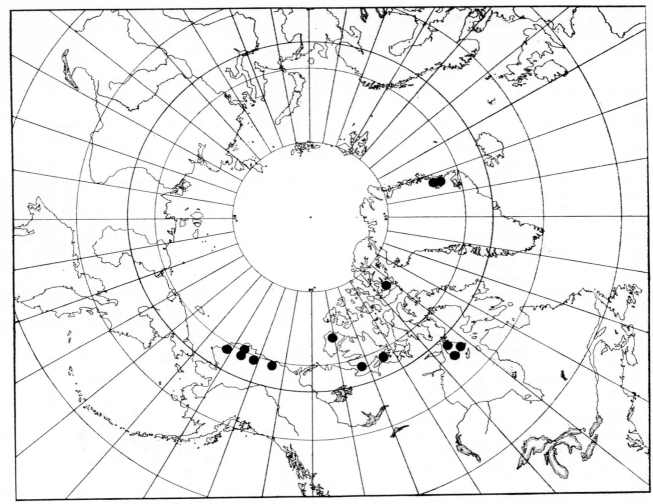

Figure 2. The presently known geographical distribution of *Funaria polaris* (after Steere, 1964)

Alaska are now turning up in Greenland (Holmen, 1952, 1957, 1960) and in Siberia (Abramova *et al.*, 1961; Savich-Lyubitskaya, 1961; Smirnova, 1958), and I predict that eventually the whole constellation of high-arctic bryophytes will be found to have a genuinely circumpolar distribution. The exponential rate of growth of our knowledge about the geographical distribution of arctic mosses, as bryologists are finally able to get into the field, is beautifully illustrated by the case of *Funaria polaris* Bryhn, discovered on Ellesmere Island in 1900 by Simmons, botanist of the second expedition of the "Fram," and described by Bryhn in 1906. This species was not heard of again for nearly a half century, when a second collection, from Southampton Island, was reported (Steere, 1949). During the next fifteen years this species (Fig. 2) turned out to have a wide distribution in arctic America, to occur in Greenland (Holmen, 1952), and to have a high probability of being found in Siberia (Steere, 1964).

The origin of these truly arctic species of bryophytes is an interesting question, as none of them is closely related to the species of more temperate climates to the south, and many of them belong to monotypic genera. Their real relationship appears to be with tropical species of the southern hemisphere (Steere, 1953), which would seem to indicate a very ancient relationship and a very long period of isolation in polar regions. Because of the abundant evidence that not all arctic areas were ice-covered during the Quaternary glacial stages, at least not all at the same time, combined with the great length of time that must have been required for these species to evolve and to become so widely distributed throughout the north polar regions, I believe that they represent the remnants of a Tertiary flora that was much more widely distributed in preglacial times. Moreover, the discovery of *Cinclidium latifolium* Lindb. as a fossil in Denmark (Hesselbo, 1910), a species not now known to occur within 2,000 km of the Danish site, certainly indicates a wider distribution of this species during Quaternary times.

In the open tundra there occur members of several genera of Hepaticae that reach their greatest development in the wet tropics, where they normally grow on the trunks of trees. I have earlier suggested (Steere, 1953) that this situation is not quite the ecological contradiction that it might appear to be at first sight, an idea that Rønning

(1959) has reviewed sympathetically. As the trees disappeared and tundra conditions developed, these hepatics, as *Frullania*, *Lejeunea*, and *Ascidiota*, would find a parallel environment on the tundra tussocks, which lack minerals and nitrogen sources and provide an essentially xeric habitat dependent upon fog and occasional rain for moisture.

DISJUNCT BRYOPHYTES ON CALCAREOUS SILT

One of the special habitats for bryophytes in the tundra of arctic America is the fine-grained calcareous silt that erupts in the form of "frost boils" under the stresses of expansion as the superficial layers, thawed during the brief summer, refreeze. When wet, this silt is soft and sticky, but during the dry and windy arctic summer it dries to a fine white powder. Fully exposed to the wind and sun, the nearly bare frost boils must be xeric habitats, and the bryophytes that characteristically inhabit them are of the type that Gams (1934) has characterized as steppe mosses. In this habitat, as well as on eroding silt banks, one finds *Aloina brevirostris* (Hook. & Grev.) Kindb. and *Stegonia latifolia* (Schwaegr.) Vent. (occasionally with its variety *pilifera*) often growing together, as Gams illustrates them doing in the steppes of Hungary (his Fig. 6). The distribution of these two species is not directly related to the primary topic under discussion, except insofar as Pleistocene and postglacial conditions have resulted in the exposure of silts suitable to their growth, as well as a steppe-like climate. However, two bryophytes of unusual interest and significance in this discussion are, at least in my experience, restricted in their ecological distribution to frost boils. The moss *Pterygoneurum arcticum* Steere, widespread over the Arctic Slope of Alaska (Steere, 1960), belongs to a genus consisting of a few species that tolerate steppe conditions, which tend to be xeric and alkaline. However, *P. arcticum* is apparently a member of the high-arctic element already discussed, as a small collection of it was made on Bathurst Island in the Canadian Arctic Archipelago by Weston Blake during the summer of 1963—the first collection known from outside of Alaska. Figure 3 shows the generalized distribution of the genus in North America, with several species in the more arid continental parts of the United States and Canada, and the one species endemic to what might be considered an arctic steppe. The other species to be considered here is an apparently still undescribed species of *Fossombronia*, also restricted to bare, silty frost boils and now known from a half-dozen localities in the Brooks Range and its northern foothills. The genus *Fossombronia* is most abundant in the Mediterranean type of climate, with wet winters and dry summers, so that in the United States its species are most numerous and conspicuous in the Southwest, especially in California. However, a few species of *Fossombronia* also occur almost throughout the United States and southern Canada, giving much the same picture of overall distribution as *Pterygoneurum* (Fig. 3).

DISJUNCT ARCTIC OCCURRENCE OF TEMPERATE SPECIES

An excellent example of the type of evidence that may be derived from the present distribution of mosses to identify areas that may not have been glaciated, at least in the later stages of the Quaternary epoch, is the occurrence of a whole series of mosses that are to be interpreted as relics from interglacial or preglacial times. These are often found on south-facing sandstone cliffs and ledges at Umiat and elsewhere in the northern foothills of the Brooks Range of arctic Alaska. Their relic character is inferred from the fact that their normal range otherwise in North America is only in much more temperate areas; they never have been thought of by bryologists as occurring in the Arctic. The following are included in this series:

Barbula convoluta Hedw. (Umiat)
Desmatodon obtusifolius (Schwaegr.) Jur. (Umiat)
Grimmia plagiopodia Hedw. (Umiat)
Frullania tamarisci (L.) Dumort. (widespread)
Herberta adunca (Dicks.) S. F. Gray (widespread)
Molendoa sendtneriana (BSG.) Limpr. (Umiat)
Neckera oligocarpa Bruch (Chandler Lake, Peters Lake)
Radula complanata (L.) Dumort. (Chandler Lake, Peters Lake)
Seligeria campylopoda Kindb. (Driftwood, Smith Lakes)
Seligeria diversifolia Lindb. (Umiat, Titaluk, Smith Lakes)

Figure 3. The unexpected occurrence of high-arctic species in otherwise typically temperate genera; showing the generalized distribution in temperate North America of all species of the genera *Fossombronia* (solid line) and *Pterigoneurum* (broken line) and the local distribution of an as-yet-undescribed species of *Fossombronia* in arctic Alaska and of *Pterigoneurum arcticum* in arctic Alaska and on Bathurst Island in the Canadian Arctic Archipelago (shown by spot)

Figure 4. The "Umiat syndrome." The occurrence at Umiat, on the Arctic Slope of Alaska, at 69°22′ N. Lat., 152°09′ W. Long. (indicated by spot) of 5 species of mosses (out of 15) otherwise occurring only in temperate climates, as shown for *Seligeria pusilla* (solid line), *Grimmia plagiopodia* (dotted line), *Molendoa sendtneriana* (broken line; after Iwatsuki and Sharp, 1958), *Desmatodon obtusifolius* (broken line with dots), and *Seligeria campylopoda* (line of ×'s).

Seligeria pusilla (Hedw.) BSG. (Umiat, Grandstand, Anaktuvuk Pass)
Tetraphis pellucida Hedw. (Umiat)
Tetrodontium brownianum (Dicks.) Schwaegr. (Umiat)

The localities given in parentheses are all situated on the Arctic Slope of Alaska. The species of *Seligeria* were kindly identified by Kjeld Holmen. Figure 4 shows the distribution of five species.

This astonishing concentration of bryophytes of otherwise temperate climates I have called quite informally the "Umiat syndrome," because it indicates an overall correlation composed of many diverse bits of information and because so many of the significant species occur at Umiat.

Of the species just listed, a few deserve special elucidation. Nearly 30 years ago, when I began work on a review of the mosses of the Canadian Eastern Arctic (Steere, 1948), I accepted Polunin's report (1934) of *Grimmia plagiopodia* Hedw. from Akpatok Island in Hudson Strait without examination of the specimen, even though it represented the first locality in the American Arctic. I accepted it because this species occurs widely elsewhere in North America, because it was identified by Mr. Sherrin, a bryol-

ogist very familiar with European species, and, finally, because at that time my own ideas of the floristic elements present in North American Bryophyta and their geographical distribution were still not very firm. I realize now that Polunin's specimen must be reviewed carefully, in comparison with material from temperate North America and from Umiat, because the species is not one that we would ordinarily think of as being arctic in its range.

Herberta adunca (Dicks.) S. F. Gray, as so named by Schuster (1958) from my collections, is both widespread and abundant on the Arctic Slope of Alaska. According to Schuster, it is not known elsewhere from North America, and earlier collections so named must now be referred to as *H. sakuraii* (Warnst.) Hatt. Otherwise, *H. adunca* (Dicks.) S. F. Gray is a species of oceanic western Europe that occurs in Ireland, Wales, western England, Scotland, the Shetlands, the Orkneys, the Faroes, and southwestern Norway and has never been found previously above the Arctic Circle. However, the whole story is not clear, apparently, as Schuster does not find that my collections agree completely with collections from western Europe, and Miller (1962), from an examination of type specimens, raises still further questions about the application of names. Consequently, I should stress here that, irrespective of its real identity and name, the species of *Herberta* that occurs so commonly and abundantly on the Arctic Slope of Alaska has, by virtue of its disjunctive pattern of distribution, an important place in the group of species just listed.

The occurrence in an area with a severe continental climate of *Herberta adunca* (Dicks.) S. F. Gray and of several other typically oceanic species whose closest affinities are overwhelmingly with the temperate and tropical floras, especially of Asia, suggests that they may be relics from a northward extension of the Japanese Current into the Bering Sea, a condition that disappeared with the elevation of the Aleutian chain of islands. The presumed antiquity of oceanic species has been discussed by Richards (1957).

The third species that deserves a special note is *Molendoa sendtneriana* (BSG.) Limpr., kindly identified by Kjeld Holmen. Its "fit" here is unclear, primarily because the species itself is not well understood, which fact in turn is reflected by the relatively uncertain geographical distribution. It occurs in the Alps of Switzerland and Austria, in the Tatra Mountains of Central Europe, in the Caucasus, in the Transcaspian area of Asia, as well as in eastern Siberia, China, and Japan (Mönkemeyer, 1927; Nyholm, 1956). However, it has not yet been reported from northern Europe. In North America, likewise, its distribution is not yet well understood or firmly fixed. Nonetheless, the situation is improving, and a relatively recent paper by Iwatsuki and Sharp (1958) reporting its first occurrence in the United States, in Tennessee, North Carolina, and Florida, points up the startling disjunction of geographical range of a species that also occurs in arctic Alaska.

Several other species listed above will also be found to be storm centers insofar as their identity and geographical distribution are concerned, which reinforces rather than weakens their importance as bits of evidence in a large overall pattern of biogeography.

In summary, I emphasize that this group of disjuncts differs from the group treated previously in consisting of *species* that one just does not expect to find in the Arctic, in contrast to the discovery of endemic species in *genera* (*Pterygoneurum* and *Fossombronia*) whose occurrence in the Arctic is surprising.

DISJUNCT ASIATIC BRYOPHYTES IN ALASKA

A further but small floristic element with a disjunct pattern of geographical distribution consists of species that until recently have been considered wholly Asiatic in their distribution, occurring only in China, Japan, and neighboring areas, yet that recently have been discovered, one by one, in northern and central Alaska. This new Alaskan-Asian element is not to be confused with the abundant and conspicuous element farther south, where many species of bryophytes of the wet coastal forests of northern California, Oregon, Washington, British Columbia, and southern Alaska are apparently identical with those of eastern Asia, especially Japan. The new element, although still not well defined, seems to occur in a more continental type of climate. Since the present distribution pattern of these species certainly has some relation to the Quaternary and its climatic history, some discussion of the known geographic ranges seems appropriate.

Habrodon leucotrichus (Mitt.) Perss., a moss of northern Japan, was reported from Alaska nearly 20 years ago (Persson, 1946). Since then, knowledge of its distribution in Alaska has been extended considerably; I have found it at Nome, for example. *Myuroclada maximowiczii* (Borosz.) Steere & Schof., widely distributed in boreal and arctic Asia, was reported (Steere and Schofield, 1956) from the bank of the Naknek River at King Salmon, where it was collected by Schofield. I can now report further collections of my own from the Matanuska Valley east of Anchorage (1949) and from near Cape Thompson, on the Chukchi Sea (1963), the first American collection from north of the Arctic Circle. Another remarkable disjunction of geographic range is illustrated by *Gollania densepinnata* Dixon, which was known only from China until its discovery in the Mt. McKinley region of Alaska in 1951 (Ando *et al.*, 1957). Since then, its range in Alaska, especially on the northern slope of the Brooks Range, has been much extended.

Among the hepatics, also, occur species with unusual or inexplicable distributions. *Ascidiota blepharophylla* Massal. was described from central China during the last century and is still known in Asia only from the type collection. However, I have found it on the north slope of the Brooks Range towards its western extremity, especially at Driftwood in the upper reaches of the Utukok River (Steere and Schuster, 1960). At Driftwood I also collected what I took to be *Frullania jackii* Gottsche, not known previously in North America, although widely distributed in Asia and reaching Europe. My collection agrees better with the Asiatic race or races of that species that have been described under several specific names (Müller, 1957, p. 1247-1250), so perhaps the best name for the Alaskan population is *Frullania jackii* Gottsche subsp. *japonica* (Sande Lac.) Hatt. (Kamimura, 1961). Because its closest

relatives are in Asia, an Alaskan hepatic, *Hygrolejeunea alaskana* Schuster and Steere (1958), may well turn up eventually in Asia and contribute another member to this interesting disjunct group.

DISJUNCT BRYOPHYTES OF HOT SPRINGS IN ICELAND

As noted by Hesselbo (1918) in his monumental work on the bryophyte flora of Iceland, a significant phytogeographical phenomenon in Iceland is the restriction to the immediate vicinity of hot springs of species of mosses and hepatics characteristic of regions much farther south. My own study of Icelandic hot springs not visited by Hesselbo served to confirm still further his observations that a characteristic group of species of bryophytes was enabled by natural heat to exist under climatic conditions that would otherwise preclude them. *Archidium alternifolium* (Hedw.) Mitt., *Anthoceros punctatus* L., and *Fossombronia dumortieri* (Hüb. & Genth) Lindb. show especially remarkable northward extensions of their geographic range and occur at even the northernmost hot springs of Iceland, near Húsavik (66° N. Lat.) and at Reykhólar (65° 28′ N. Lat.), just south of the Arctic Circle. The disjunct distribution of these species in Iceland, completely correlated with the occurrence of hot springs and without intermediate colonies, indicates clearly that under the influence of a warmer climate they must have had a more uniform and generalized distribution but became gradually localized, by climatic deterioration, in the warmer microclimates where they now survive. A significant piece of evidence in the interpretation of these species as relics is provided by their spores, which are much too large to be carried by the wind. *Archidium* has the largest spores (100-200 μ) of any genus of mosses outside the tropics, and the spores of both *Fossombronia* and *Anthoceros* (*ca.* 40 μ) greatly exceed the average size in hepatics. The remarkable correlation between the hot springs of Iceland and species of bryophytes whose normal environmental preferences are out of harmony with the prevailing climate suggests that a comprehensive study of hot springs in North America might also provide significant information for the interpretation of former climates and plant-distribution patterns.

THE ANOMALOUS DISTRIBUTION OF BRYOXIPHIUM

Many species of bryophytes do not seem to have their centers of greatest density of occurrence in those areas that were most recently glaciated, indicating a relatively slow rate of spread to and colonization of newly exposed areas. Nearly thirty years ago, while mapping the known distribution of North American mosses, I became aware that the geographic distribution of the sword moss *Bryoxiphium norvegicum*, terminating so abruptly in the United States at the glacial border, must have some relationship with at least the most recent stage of the Pleistocene (Fig. 5). Moreover, by its occurrence in the far North, this species seemed to reflect some anomaly in the glacial epoch, so that it might be interpreted as a survivor of at least part of the Ice Age in certain unglaciated refugia in Iceland, northern Greenland, and Alaska (Steere, 1937). This concept has been accepted and reinforced by the

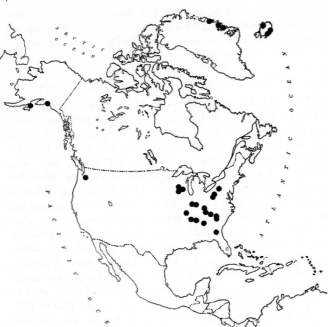

Figure 5. The geographical distribution of *Bryoxiphium norvegicum* (Brid.) Mitt. subsp. *norvegicum* Löve & Löve var. *norvegicum* Löve & Löve (1953). By limitation of the map, the station at Attu is not shown.

weight of new ideas and new discoveries (Löve and Löve, 1953; Löve, 1963).

BRYOPHYTES LARGELY RESTRICTED TO GLACIATED AREAS

Finally, I shall consider briefly a group of bryophytes that, unlike *Bryoxyphium*, appear to be largely restricted in their modern distribution to areas that have been glaciated and do not extend very far south of the border of continental or montane glaciation. Whether this correlation between glaciation and present geographical distribution has anything to do with environmental conditions imposed by the Quaternary is not clear. It is highly probable, however, that the correlation depends as much on physiographic and edaphic conditions produced by glaciation as it does on the climate of the Ice Age, although the two genera that display this type of distribution most clearly, *Drepanocladus* and *Calliergon*, tolerate cold climates and extend northward as far as land goes. On melting, continental glaciers left behind them a terrain full of ponds and shallow lakes, many of which have been transformed by the growth of plants into acid bogs or somewhat calcareous fens, just the habitats in which *Calliergon* and *Drepanocladus* flourish today. South of the limit of continental glaciation, the mature and well-drained physiography, with relatively few natural ponds and lakes, furnishes few appropriate habitats for these aquatic mosses. The historical background of the distribution of these two genera has been thoroughly discussed by Wynne (1944, 1945).

CONCLUDING REMARKS

Evidence from the present geographical range of living bryophytes, especially those with disjunct distributions, has contributed as much to our knowledge of the effects of the Quaternary on plants as has the evidence from fossil materials, if not more. I hope that this paper will provide an additional source of information concerning the response of North American bryophytes to Quaternary conditions, as well as a review of some of the pertinent literature. Other regions of the world provide their own puzzling patterns of disjunct distribution, such as the bicentric occurrence of boreal species in Antarctica, the presence of arctic species on the high equatorial Andes, and the remarkable disjunction of genera and species between southwestern South America and New Zealand. I have not attempted to interpret these anomalous patterns or to derive evidence from them, partly because we do not have enough information about them in spite of Herzog's comprehensive review (1926), and partly because these disjunctions undoubtedly antedate the Pleistocene.

The problems posed by the geographical distribution of higher plants in northern areas have been well summed up in a series of papers resulting from a symposium on the North Atlantic biota held in Iceland (Löve and Löve, 1963), a timely and up-to-date publication that brings all available evidence to bear on the problem of whether plants survived the major glacial stages of the Quaternary in northern latitudes in areas that escaped glaciation. Unfortunately for any final answer, the authors are about equally divided in their opinions, and the reader is left to draw his own conclusions from the large body of evidence presented.

Four major theories have been utilized by phytogeographers to explain anomalous patterns of plant distribution, namely, continental drift, land bridges, long-distance dispersal of spores and seeds, and the survival of plants in unglaciated areas during the Quaternary.

Although a theory of great interest to biogeographers, and one that is gaining momentum, significant continental drift took place so long ago that it can have practically no bearing on problems of Quaternary plant distribution.

Land bridges, on the other hand, may be more germane to our topic here. The Bering Strait bridge has obviously provided a migration route for plants, animals, and man, as deduced from many kinds of biogeographical and archaeological evidence. Geological evidence shows that Asia and North America were joined by dry land during each glacial episode of the Quaternary (Hopkins, 1959). The evidence for land bridges between North America and Europe is far more circumstantial and speculative, and I doubt much that one has existed recently enough to have significance for this report. The bryophyte flora of Iceland is conspicuously European (Meylan, 1940). *Bryoxiphium norvegicum* (Brid.) Mitt., however, has not yet been found in Europe, in spite of its specific epithet, although it occurs in many localities in North America (Fig. 5). The present submarine ridge that runs between the Faroes, Iceland, and Greenland could well have been elevated during the Tertiary, an era of great tectonic activity, and this could explain the almost wholly European character of the flora.

However, any land connection between Iceland and Greenland must have been very brief, if it existed at all, because of the conspicuous disparity between the two floras (Löve, 1958).

The possibility of the creation of disjunct geographical ranges of species by long-distance dispersal of spores, seeds, and other reproductive structures by wind, water, or living organisms is obvious, and many examples can be cited. Adventive plants from the Southwest are not rare in the midwest United States along railroads used by cattle trains carrying livestock to the eastern markets. Many of the present weeds of California are natives of Spain and Portugal that arrived as seeds in the wool of sheep. Weedy species of all groups of plants appear suddenly and conspicuously, far from their original home. The strand flora of tropical islands around the world is remarkably uniform because seeds and fruits of many species of plants are equipped to be carried long distances by ocean currents.

Wind, however, seems to me to be greatly overrated as an agent for plant dispersal over long distances, in spite of the substantial number of plants that have evolved seeds or fruits with wings, hairs, and other specialized structures that enable them to become wind-borne. Unless the reproductive structure falls upon fertile ground, under environmental conditions favorable to the germination of the seed or spore and the development of the young plant, extension of the geographic range of the species cannot occur. The capsules of mosses produce spores in enormous numbers, so abundantly that the microscopic spores become visible as a cloud of dust when a cluster of capsules is disturbed. Nevertheless, the statistical chance for these millions of spores to establish a new colony in a totally different habitat or environment is practically nil.

The bryophyte flora of Iceland presents persuasive evidence against long-distance dispersal of its species by wind, along several lines of reasoning. First of all, as already noted, the bryophyte flora is overwhelmingly European in its composition. It lacks many of the species found in Greenland, yet Greenland is not only much closer to Iceland than is Europe, but the prevailing winds blow from Greenland toward Iceland. With prevailing westerly winds, I find it difficult to believe that the flora of Iceland could have been derived from seeds and spores blown in from Europe; why then are so many Icelandic species absent in Greenland and vice versa?

Seeds pass rapidly through the digestive tract of far-ranging water birds, but they can undoubtedly adhere to feet or feathers for a much longer time, which may explain the botanical truism that the flora of aquatic habitats is much more homogeneous in its composition than the floras of dry land. In spite of the well-substantiated transportation of seeds by birds, one finds it hard to imagine birds flying from Europe to Iceland against the winds, carrying quantities of seeds sufficient to populate newly exposed areas that already contain so many species of European plants, especially in view of the lack of many Greenland plants, which could have been carried in a fraction of the time by birds favored by the wind. I question whether proponents of the concept of long-distance dispersal of plants can produce a tidy answer to this question. Floras appear to move in groups or associations, in which a disjunct species would probably be unable to survive, or, if it did survive, would then evolve races better suited to the new environment. All in all, however, I frankly cannot conceive of the transport for great distances of whole natural associations of plants that would gradually reconstitute themselves as disjunct floras through the accidental introduction of the component species by birds, wind, or other agencies.

Although I believe that the various types of plant distribution discussed have all had a part in the development of our various boreal floras, I am also convinced that the present distribution of many critical bryophytes contributes adequate evidence to the idea that many species survived at least part of the Ice Age *in situ,* in refugia that were situated either on mountains that projected through the continental glaciers (nunataks) or in extensive lowland areas like arctic Alaska where the prevailing precipitation was too low to produce continental ice sheets, although temperatures must have been adequately low. The tolerance of many bryophytes to the extremes of their environment, especially to drought and cold, is well substantiated by experiment and by field observation. Their resistance to environmental stress is well demonstrated by their success in colonizing high mountains and the arctic tundra under conditions that cannot be far different from those that prevailed during the Quaternary glacial epochs.

Biogeographers have long investigated the various agencies and mechanisms for plant dispersal, the environmental conditions needed for the germination of seeds and spores, and the ecological requirements for the development and survival of the plants. The real mystery in the colonization of newly exposed barren land by plants and the evolution of a complex population of many species, the flora, is the amount of time needed. Geological time is almost incomprehensibly long to the biologist, whose concepts are related to living organisms.

Fortunately, biogeographers have recently had thrust upon their attention, literally, a natural laboratory in which to test their hypotheses and theories concerning the dispersal, colonization, and establishment of plants in boreal areas. A submarine volcanic eruption 30 km off the south coast of Iceland, first observed in November 1963, has produced an island already 2 km long and over 200 m high. This emerging island, officially named Surtsey, if properly protected against casual visitors and dedicated amateurs determined to afforest the new land, can well become a unique test area in which to observe the rate at which plants vegetate a brand-new surface. However, seeds and other propagules brought in by careless or well-intentioned visitors can disrupt the controlled observations of scientists to such an extent that Surtsey should be declared off limits to sightseers, whose picnic refuse has already been found. Even though we might have preferred a new island at least a hundred kilometers from the nearest source of plants, Surtsey does provide a unique opportunity, a once-in-a-life-time chance to study the mechanics of plant dispersal.

During the establishment of vegetation on Surtsey, especial attention should be paid to the mosses and hepatics because these plants are almost never transported intentionally by man and therefore reflect much more accurately than higher plants the various natural agencies for dispersal. Certainly, if Surtsey, protected from the too helpful hand of man, develops in the next few decades or even centuries a rich and varied flora similar to that on the "mainland" of Iceland, biogeographers will have an extraordinary opportunity to see in action many phenomena that are now matters of speculation.

REFERENCES

Abramova, Anastasia L., Savich-Lyubitskaya, Lidiya I., and Smirnova, Zoya N., 1961, Opredelitel' listostebel'nykh mkhov arktiki SSSR [Manual of leafy mosses of arctic USSR]: Moscow-Leningrad, Akademiya Nauk SSSR, 715 p.

Ando, Hisatsugu, Persson, Herman, and Sherrard, Elizabeth M., 1957, The first record of *Gollania* in North America: Bryologist, v. 60, p. 326-335

Culberson, W. L., 1955, The fossil mosses of the Two Creeks Forest Bed of Wisconsin: Amer. Midl. Nat., v. 54, p. 452-459

Demaret, Fernand, and Castagne, Émile, 1961, Bryophytes, *in* Robyns, Walter (ed.), Flore générale de Belgique: Brussels, Jardin botanique de l'État, v. 2, p. 113-231

Gams, Helmut, 1932, Quaternary distribution, Chapter XI, *in* Verdoorn, Frans, Manual of bryology: The Hague, Martinus Nijhoff, 486 p.

—— 1934, Beiträge zur Kenntnis der Steppenmoose: Ann. Bryol., v. 7, p. 37-56

—— 1955, Zur Arealgeschichte der arktischen und arktisch-oreophytischen Moose: Feddes Repert., v. 58, p. 80-92

Godwin, Harry, 1956, The history of the British flora, a future basis for phytogeography: Cambridge, Cambridge Univ. Press, 384 p.

Godwin, Harry, and Richards, P. W., 1947, Note on the occurrence of *Meesia triquetra* (Hook. & Tayl.) Aongstr. in postglacial peat in Somerset (England): Rev. Bryol. Lichénol., v. 15, p. 123-130

Hedberg, Olov, 1961, The phytogeographical position of the afroalpine flora, *in* Recent advances in botany: Toronto, University of Toronto Press, 2 v., p. 914-919

Herzog, Theodor, 1926, Geographie der Moose: Jena, Fischer, 439 p.

Hesselbo, Augustus, 1910, Mosrester fra Diluviet ved Skærumhede, *in* En boring gennem de kvartære lag ved Skærumhede: Danmarks Geol. Unders., II Række, v. 25, p. 101-109

—— 1918, The Bryophyta of Iceland, *in* Rosenvinge, L. K., and Warming, Eugenius, The botany of Iceland: Copenhagen, J. Frimodt, v. 1, p. 395-676

Holmen, Kjeld, 1952, *Funaria polaris* in Greenland: Bryologist, v. 55, p. 249-250

—— 1957, Three west arctic moss species in Greenland; on the occurrence of *Cinclidium latifolium, Aulacomnium acuminatum* and *Trichostomum cuspidatissimum:* Medd. om Grønl., v. 156, p. 1-16

—— 1960, The mosses of Peary Land, North Greenland; a list of the species collected between Victoria Fjord and Danmark Fjord: Medd. om Grønl., v. 163, p. 1-96

Hopkins, D. M., 1959, Cenozoic history of the Bering land bridge: Science, v. 129, p. 1519-1528

Iwatsuki, Zennoske, and Sharp, A. J., 1958, *Molendoa sendtneriana* in the United States: Bryologist, v. 61, p. 356-359

Jasnowski, Mieczysław, 1957, Flora mchów z czwartorzedowych osadów torfowisk reofilnych (Moosflora quartärer Flachmoorablagerungen): Acta Soc. Bot. Polon., v. 26, p. 597-629

Kamimura, Minoru, 1961, A monograph of Japanese Frullaniaceae: J. Hattori Bot. Lab., v. 24, p. 1-109

Kapp, R. O., and Gooding, A. M., 1964, Pleistocene vegetational studies in the Whitewater Basin, southeastern Indiana: J. Geol., v. 72, p. 307-326

Karczmarz, Kazimierz, 1962, Rozmieszczenie *Cinclidium stygium* Sw. w Polsce [Distribution of *Cinclidium stygium* Sw. in Poland]: Lublin, Univ. M. Curie-Skiodowska Ann., v. 17, p. 427-431

Konior, Konrad, 1936, Über ein Profil des Pleistozäns in Dziedzice: Kraków, Starunia, v. 11, p. 1-8

Löve, Áskell, 1958, Transatlantic connections and long-distance dispersal: Evolution, v. 12, p. 421-423

—— 1963, Sverðmosinn [The swordmoss]: Náttúrufræðingurinn, v. 33, p. 113-122 [In Icelandic; English summary]

Löve, Áskell, and Löve, Doris, 1953, Studies on *Bryoxiphium:* Bryologist, v. 56, p. 73-94, 183-203

—— (eds.), 1963, North Atlantic biota and their history: New York, Macmillan, 430 p.

Lundqvist, Gösta, 1960, The interglacial ooze at Porsi in Lapland: Sverig. Geol. Unders. Avh., Ser. C, Årsbok, v. 54, p. 1-26

Meylan, Charles, 1940, Contribution à la connaissance de la flore bryologique de l'Islande: Bull. Soc. Bot. Suisse, v. 50, p. 475-499

Miller, H. A., 1962, On the identity of *Herberta adunca:* Nova Hedwigia, v. 4, p. 359-369

Mönkemeyer, Wilhelm, 1927, Die Laubmoose Europas. IV. Ergänzungsband: Leipzig, Akademische Verlagsgesellschaft m.b.H., 960 p.

Müller, Karl, 1957, Die Lebermoose Europas (Musci hepatici): Leipzig, Akademische Verlagsgesellschaft Geest & Portig, K.-G., 3rd ed., v. 6, p. 1247-1250

Nyholm, Elsa, 1956, Illustrated moss flora of Fennoscandia: Lund, C.W.K. Gleerup, v. 2, p. 83-189

Persson, Herman, 1946, The genus *Habrodon* discovered in North America: Svensk Bot. Tidskr., v. 40, p. 317-324

—— 1960, Bryological examination. Appendix 2, p. 12-13, *in* Fromm, Erik, An Interglacial peat at Ale near Luleå, northern Sweden: Sverig. Geol. Unders. Avh., Ser. C, Årsbok, v. 54, p. 1-14

Polunin, Nicholas, 1934, The flora of Akpatok Island, Hudson Strait: J. Bot., v. 72, p. 197-204

Puri, G. S., 1958, Pleistocene research in India: J. Palaeontology Soc. India, v. 3, p. 64-67

Richards, P. W., 1957, The history of the British oceanic bryophytes: 8th Congrès Intern. Bot., Compt. Rend. Séances Rapp. Comm., Sect. 14, 15, 16, p. 63-68

Rønning, O. I., 1959, The vascular flora of Bear Island. Results of Tromsø Museum's biological Svalbardexpeditions 1957 and 1958: Acta Borealia, Ser. A, Scientia, No. 15, 62 p.

Rosendahl, C. O., 1948, A contribution to the knowledge of the Pleistocene flora of Minnesota: Ecology, v. 29, p. 284-315

Savich-Lyubitskaya, Lidiya I., 1961, Notula de *Barbula gigantea* Funck et *Trichostomo cuspidatissimo* Card. et Thér.: Bot. Materialy, Inst. Bot. Komarov., v. 14, p. 262-267

Savich-Lyubitskaya, Lidiya I., and Abramova, Anastasia L., 1954, Iskopaemye mkhi iz raïona raskopok Taïmyrskogo mamonta [Fossil mosses from the district of the excavations of the Taïmyr mammoth]: Bot. Zh., v. 39, p. 594-603

Schuster, R. M., 1958, Notes on Nearctic Hepaticae. XV. *Herberta*. Rev. Bryol. Lichénol., v. 26, p. 123-145

Schuster, R. M., and Steere, W. C., 1958, *Hygrolejeunea alaskana* sp. nov., a critical endemic of northern Alaska: Torrey Bot. Club Bull., v. 85, p. 188-196

Smirnova, Zoya N., 1958, *Lyellia* R. Br.—novyï rod dlya brioflory SSSR [*Lyellia*—a genus new to the bryoflora of USSR]: Bot. Zh., v. 43, p. 850-855

Soper, J. H., and Maycock, P. F., 1963, A community of arctic-alpine plants on the east shore of Lake Superior: Can. J. Bot., v. 41, p. 183-198

Steere, W. C., 1931, *Meesea triquetra*: Rhodora, v. 33, p. 77-78

—— 1937a, *Bryoxiphium norvegicum*, the sword moss, as a preglacial and interglacial relic: Ecology, v. 18, p. 346-358

—— 1937b, Critical bryophytes from the Keweenaw Peninsula, Michigan: Rhodora, v. 39, p. 1-14, 33-46

—— 1938a, Critical bryophytes from the Keweenaw Peninsula, Michigan, II: Ann. Bryol., v. 11, p. 145-152

—— 1938b, Pleistocene mosses from Louisiana, *in* Brown, C. A., Contributions to the Pleistocene history of the Florida Parishes of Louisiana: Louisiana Geol. Surv., Dept. Conserv. Bull., v. 12, p. 97-101

—— 1942, Pleistocene mosses from the Aftonian Interglacial deposits of Iowa: Mich. Acad. Sci. Pap., v. 27, p. 74-104

—— 1948, Musci, *in* Polunin, Nicholas, Botany of the Canadian Eastern Arctic: Natl. Mus. Can. Bull., v. 97, p. 370-490

—— 1949, Bryophyta of arctic America. III, The rediscovery of *Funaria polaris* Bryhn: Bryologist, v. 52, p. 29-32

—— 1953, On the distribution of arctic bryophytes, *in* Arctic Research Laboratory Symposium: Stanford Univ. Publ. Biol. Sci., v. 11, p. 30-47

—— 1956, The taxonomic status and geographic distribution of *Philocrya aspera:* Bryologist, v. 59, p. 161-167

—— 1958a, *Oligotrichum falcatum*, a new species from arctic Alaska: Bryologist, v. 61, p. 115-118

—— 1958b, *Mnium andrewsianum*, a new subarctic and arctic moss: Bryologist, v. 61, p. 173-182

—— 1960, *Pterygoneurum arcticum*, a new species from northern Alaska: Bryologist, v. 62, p. 215-221

—— 1964, The geographic distribution of *Funaria polaris*: Bryologist, v. 66, p. 213-217

Steere, W. C., and Schofield, W. B., 1956, *Myuroclada*, a genus new to North America: Bryologist, v. 59, p. 1-5

Steere, W. C., and Schuster, R. M., 1960, The hepatic genus *Ascidiota* Massalongo new to North America: Torrey Bot. Club Bull., v. 87, p. 209-215

Vanden Berghen, C., 1950, Présence de la mousse *Dicranum Bergeri* Bland., à l'état subfossile, en Belgique: Bull. Inst. Roy. Sci. Nat. Belg., v. 26, p. 1-7

Wynne, Francis E., 1944, Studies in *Drepanocladus*. II, Phytogeography: Amer. Midl. Nat., v. 32, p. 643-668

—— 1945, Studies in *Calliergon* and related genera: Bryologist, v. 48, p. 135-155

Zinderen Bakker, E. M. van, 1962, Botanical evidence for quaternary climates in Africa: Cape Provincial Mus. Ann., v. 2, p. 16-31

SUMMARY

The Quaternary glaciation had many effects upon the present bryophyte flora, as seen from subfossil materials and from several disjunct patterns of geographical distribution. Many species of mosses and hepatics have had little or no success in reinvading areas once covered by continental ice sheets whereas other species, in characteristic associations, have successfully colonized areas formerly glaciated. Emphasis has been placed on the bryophytes of boreal and arctic North America, because they are best known to the author. Several patterns of disjunct geographical distribution of bryophytes are identified, as follows: (1) the high-arctic element probably survived at least part of the Quaternary at high latitudes in unglaciated areas; (2) a small element is typically found on calcareous silt, in which two endemic arctic species belong to genera characteristic of semiarid or steppe areas much farther south; (3) a group of species characteristic of temperate or oceanic climates much farther south is isolated on the unglaciated Arctic Slope of the Brooks Range, especially at Umiat; (4) an element of disjunct Asiatic species occurs; (5) species characteristic of warm climates are now found in Iceland only in the immediate vicinity of hot springs; (6) the anomalous distribution of *Bryoxiphium,* not found in areas most recently glaciated, is discussed; (7) some genera, as *Calliergon* and *Drepanocladus,* are most abundant in glaciated areas.

The various agents active in the dispersal of plants are reviewed, with a sympathetic feeling for the survival of many bryophytes during at least part of the Quaternary in unglaciated areas because of a precipitation level too low for the production of ice sheets. The importance of the new volcanic island emerging off the south coast of Iceland as a laboratory for biogeographers is stressed.

POLYPLOIDY, DISTRIBUTION, AND ENVIRONMENT *

ALBERT W. JOHNSON,[1] JOHN G. PACKER,[2] GERD REESE[3]

POLYPLOIDY IN higher organisms exists when somatic reproductive cells contain more than two haploid sets (genomes) of chromosomes. This can be demonstrated by showing that organisms of the same phylogenetic line possess only two genomes, or, where this is impossible, polyploidy is inferred by the occurrence of chromosome numbers so high that they are considered by specialists of that taxonomic group to be secondarily derived. If all genomes in a polyploid organism are identical genetically, the organism is autopolyploid; if, however, as is usually the case in nature, the genomes are different to some extent (implying genetically different ancestors) some degree of allopolyploidy exists (for a thorough discussion of polyploid nomenclature and origin, see Stebbins, 1950).

Both kinds of polyploid arise in the same ways: (1) by the doubling of the chromosome number of primordial meristematic cells that then give rise to polyploid branch and flower systems; or (2) by the fusion of nonreduced gametes. The genetic, physiologic, and morphologic consequences of polyploidy, *per se,* are unpredictable, even if these characteristics are relatively well known in the ancestral organisms. Statements that polyploid organisms are larger, more vigorous, more tolerant, or otherwise "superior" to their ancestors describe some specific cases, but as generalizations they are unreliable. Each case of polyploidy, whether naturally or artificially produced, must be examined on its own merits.

Polyploidy is of practical and theoretical interest in many branches of botany, especially because of its genetic and evolutionary significance, but also because of its bearing on problems relating to plant taxonomy and distribution. Polyploidy occurs in most plant and in some animal groups, but it has been studied most thoroughly in the flowering plants, where, it is estimated, about one-third to one-half of all species are polyploids. Thus polyploidy has been one of the important evolutionary mechanisms in higher plants, and investigations of polyploid complexes have sought to show where and why polyploid species have been favored by natural selection.

The central and still highly controversial problem of chromosome geography is the well-documented fact that the frequency of polyploidy in angiosperms increases along a south to north gradient in Europe (Tischler, 1935; Löve and Löve, 1957; Reese, 1958, 1961a). The controversy is concerned with whether this results from chance or from intrinsic or extrinsic factors having to do with polyploid species, *per se.* Because evolution occurs most rapidly during periods of climatic and geologic instability and change, explanations invoking Quaternary events as causes for polyploid evolution and spread have attracted considerable attention. Interest in these problems originated in western Europe, and nearly all the important work on them has been done there; therefore, any consideration of the distributional aspects of polyploidy must be discussed in the framework of the extensive European studies on the subject.

As in many problems in plant geography, the reasons for polyploid distribution patterns are nearly impossible to reconstruct. The origins of most modern polyploid species are unknown. The fossil remains of the arctic herbaceous perennial flora are meager, and, in any event, reveal nothing about polyploid levels. Studies on the genetic, physiologic, and morphologic characteristics of extant diploids and related polyploids show that polyploidy can sometimes be correlated with interpopulational differences in some of these traits, but experiments describe only the *status quo* and may be misleading regarding past events and antecedents. The most profitable approach to understanding the interrelationships between polyploidy and Quaternary events is to utilize what is known of the properties of modern polyploids in an ecological and historical context. In this review paper we attempt this kind of synthesis.

HISTORICAL BACKGROUND

The founder of the field of cytogeography is usually recognized to be the Danish cytologist, Hagerup (1931), who described the cytology of some desert plants in the vicinity of Timbuktu in the southern Sahara. Hagerup found that the frequency of polyploidy among 29 species was over 40%, which, at that time, was thought to be rather high. Of special interest was his discovery that in polyploid series, *i.e.* related species with different levels of ploidy, the highest polyploids occurred in the most extreme environments, such as hot, dry, sandy areas. Hagerup (1928)

* The Alaskan work discussed herein was supported, in part, by the United States Atomic Energy Commission under Contract Nos. AT (04-3)-310 and AT (11-1)-34, Project 109. Grateful acknowledgment is also made to F. Harlan Lewis, who supplied assistance and laboratory space and valuable discussions.

The authors share responsibility for the content and the ideas expressed in this paper. Reese contributed most heavily to the discussions on the European background of polyploid studies, and Johnson and Packer assumed responsibility for the relevant North American work.

[1] Department of Biology, San Diego State College, San Diego, California.

[2] University of Alberta, Edmonton, Alberta, Canada.

[3] Botanical Institute of the University, Kiel, Germany.

TABLE 1

Frequency of Polyploidy in the Flowering Plants of Different Parts of the World
(Modified after Löve and Löve, 1949; Reese, 1957)

	Average latitude	Number of angiosperms	% Cytologically known	Percent polyploidy			References
				Monocot	Dicot	Total	
Timbuktu	*ca.* 17°N	138	21.0	67.0	31.0	37.0	Hagerup, 1930, 1931
Canary Islands	*ca.* 28½°N	*ca.* 500	*ca.* 25.8	60.0	25.0	23.0	Larsen, 1960
North Sahara	31°N	250-300	*ca.* 52.0	59.1	33.9	37.8	Reese, 1958
Cyclades	37°N	1184	48.3	44.7	31.2	34.1	Tischler, 1946
Rumania	46°N	2099	67.1	62.7	42.4	46.8	Tischler, 1955
Schleswig-Holstein	54½°N	1081	86.4	72.4	48.1	54.5	Tischler, 1955
Denmark	54½-58°N	1306	90.4	70.2	47.4	53.5	Löve and Löve, 1948
Sweden	55½-69°N	1645	87.3	74.8	48.7	56.0	Löve and Löve, 1948
The Faeroes	62°N	324	90.1	80.0	50.3	61.3	Löve and Löve, 1948
Iceland	63½-66½°N	440	88.2	84.0	52.5	63.8	Löve and Löve, 1948
Northwest Alaska	68°N	291	88.7	84.6	52.9	59.3	Johnson and Packer, 1964
Spitsbergen	77-81°N	135	82.1	95.0	61.4	73.6	Löve and Löve, 1949
Peary Land	*ca.* 82½°N	85	75.3	96.4	77.8	85.9	Holmen, 1952
Macquarie Island	53½°S	31	71.0	88.3	76.9	81.8	Moore, 1960

had previously shown that in Europe the tetraploid of certain "species" pairs in the Ericaceae always grew farther north than the diploid. These observations, and the demonstration that heat and cold shock sometimes induced polyploidy in laboratory populations, led Hagerup to generalize that a cause and effect relationship exists between environmental extremes and polyploidy. Hagerup's ideas led to many later investigations on the distributional aspects of polyploidy. Tischler (1935), for example, explained increased frequency of polyploidy with increasing latitude in four European floras on this basis, and Müntzing (1936) logically extended the Tischler-Hagerup ideas to suggest that polyploidy should also increase with altitude. These and other studies (Table 1) led to the generalization that the degree of polyploidy in the angiosperm flora is greater with higher latitude and altitude and in the more extreme climatic and soil conditions to which the flora is subjected (Reese, 1961a). That this generalization may also hold for the southern hemisphere is suggested by Moore's (1960) report of a frequency of polyploidy of over 60% for the flora of Macquarie Island. Had Moore utilized the bases for calculation employed in the determination of polyploid frequencies in most other studies, his results would have been even higher.

The Tischler-Hagerup hypothesis has been eroded through the years because of discoveries that show that polyploidy is not excessively high in many alpine areas (Favarger, 1954; Knaben, 1950), in snow-beds (Gustafsson, 1948; Pignatti, 1960), or in deserts (Reese, 1957), all of which are extreme by most subjective criteria. This has led Löve and Löve (1957) to suggest that the original concept be limited "mainly to extreme conditions in arctic and subarctic regions," because, in Europe at least, the degree of polyploidy increases as one goes north, the highest percentages being recorded on Spitsbergen and other arctic islands and the lowest on Sicily and other Mediterranean Islands. Studies in arctic Asia (Sokolovskaja and Strelkova, 1960) are in general agreement with those of Europe, and it is probable that North American studies will follow the same pattern (Scott, 1950). Johnson and Packer (1964) report the frequency of polyploidy in a

flora of northwestern Alaska to be about 60%, while Heiser (1950) suggests that the percentage of polyploid species in the Indiana flora is between 40% and 50%.

The studies reported in Table 1 are not strictly comparable for several reasons. Polyploid frequencies for some areas have been determined only or partly from the literature; some studies include all angiosperms, while others omit certain groups in which the existence of polyploidy is uncertain, and some reports of the frequency of polyploidy are for very limited areas with little habitat diversity, while others are for huge areas, the size of Greenland, for example, where a great variety of habitats is considered. Other difficulties in methodology will be discussed below.

From the outset there have been attempts to explain differential diploid-polyploid distributions on more refined grounds than the "tolerance-of-extremes" concept. Cain (1944), Löve and Löve (1949), Stebbins (1950), and Reese (1958, 1961a, 1961b) have discussed these hypotheses and reviewed the literature in considerable detail, so only a brief review is presented here. Before specific proposals are discussed, it may be useful to generalize to the following extent. Either polyploidy has adaptive value that increases with latitude, or its occurrence is related to other morphological or physiological characteristics of the plants, that have adaptive value and are likely to give rise to polyploidy as a natural consequence. That plants have successfully adapted to arctic conditions at the diploid level is illustrated by the presence of such species at the highest latitudes where angiosperms grow. Nevertheless, the high frequencies of polyploid species in the North suggest either that polyploid species were better able to survive at high latitudes in unglaciated refugia, or that they were better able to take advantage of glaciated areas and invade them faster than the diploids, or both.

EXPLANATION BASED ON THE GENETIC CHARACTERISTICS OF POLYPLOIDS

Nearly all natural polyploids that have been investigated have been found to be allopolyploids, which have originated by hybridization of two genetically harmonious entities.

Polyploidy has arisen either at the time of formation of the hybrid by union of two nonreduced gametes or by subsequent somatic doubling of the chromosome number in the hybrid. Genetic variability is thereby increased, and hybrids are able to invade habitats outside the tolerances of the parents or to compete or associate with the parents in the same habitats. The importance of hybridization in plant evolution is well known and heavily documented (Anderson, 1949; Stebbins, 1950; Davis and Heywood, 1963). An otherwise well-adapted hybrid may range from complete sterility to full fertility depending on the extent of the sterility barriers which have evolved between its parents. Once a hybrid has established itself in nature, it may persist and spread in its environment by strictly asexual methods, and, in fact, vegetative reproduction increases the probability of the hybrid's eventually becoming polyploid and fertile. Jones (1958) has shown that sterile pentaploid *Holcus mollis* is the most common of several chromosome races in nature in England. An analogous situation is reported by Strain (1964), who studied isolated male clones of *Populus tremuloides* in California and concluded that vegetative reproduction has probably enabled these plants to persist for hundreds or thousands of years in these isolated stations. Regardless of any other property of polyploids to which their success in nature is attributed, the genetic effects of hybridization must be a first cause, but the survival and spread of the hybrid depends on its adaptedness and the availability of ecological niches.

EXPLANATION BASED ON THE REPRODUCTION AND GROWTH HABIT OF POLYPLOIDS

Gustafsson (1948) proposed that polyploidy in northern environments could be explained by the fact that the arctic flora is largely composed of herbaceous perennial species with efficient means of apomictic (including vegetative) reproduction and that these groups of plants are characteristically highly polyploid wherever they occur. In other words, Gustafsson suggested that the arctic environment selects for growth habit, and polyploidy probably functions primarily to intensify desirable attributes having to do with growth habit and reproduction. He also pointed out that annuals, in which polyploidy is significantly lower, are nearly absent in the North.

Stebbins (1950) was of somewhat the same opinion as Gustafsson, showing that such plant families as the Gramineae and Rosaceae, which are relatively abundant in the Arctic, are high in polyploidy also at low latitudes. Löve and Löve (1949) analyzed these proposals statistically and found that even within these ecological and systematic groups polyploidy increases with latitude.

Two recent studies have relevance to this aspect of polyploidy. Mooney and Billings (1961) show that North American arctic populations of *Oxyria digyna* are rhizomatous, while populations from lower latitudes are not. In this case all populations of *Oxyria* are diploid, but this illustrates the importance of a specific kind of adaptation in the arctic environment. Another study (Mooney, 1963) shows that tetraploid *Polygonum bistortoides* grows at lower altitudes than the alpine diploid and that tetraploidy is related to vegetative reproduction and seed in-

viability, while the diploids reproduce primarily by seed. Mooney points out that environmental severity is relative, and that "for a species originating in a cold environment, a climate that is relatively warm is severe" (see also Manton, 1950). In summary, it is likely that the perennial growth habit and the spread of plants vegetatively is adaptive in an arctic environment. It is also certain that plants possessing these characteristics are more likely to become polyploid than species not possessing these qualities.

EXPLANATIONS BASED ON THE ECOLOGICAL ADAPTEDNESS OF POLYPLOIDS

Stebbins (1950) suggested that the success of polyploids in the North or in glaciated areas can be explained by their better adaptation to different ecological situations than related diploids. Species of a polyploid series or closely related species pairs that differ in their level of ploidy usually have different ecological requirements. Lövkvist (1958), for example, shows that in *Cardamine pratensis*, which in southern Scandinavia has tetraploid, octoploid, and decaploid populations, "the higher chromosome number is correlated with higher water content of the soil." Similarly, *Cardamine hirsuta* ($2n = 16$) grows in dry habitats, while closely related *C. flexuosa* ($2n = 32$) grows in moist shady woods. Dean (1959) reports that in Michigan tetraploid *Tradescantia ohioensis* grows in drier habitats than the diploid, and Lawrence (1947) intimates that hexaploid *Achillea borealis* occupies somewhat wetter habitats than tetraploid *A. lanulosa* in the western United States.

In a study of broader scope, Johnson and Packer (1965) relate the frequency of polyploidy in the flora of Ogotoruk Creek in northwestern Alaska to environmental gradients. They show that the frequency of polyploidy in both monocotyledonous and dicotyledonous plants is highest on cold, wet, disturbed soils and lowest on warmer, drier, relatively undisturbed soils. This study will be discussed more fully below.

Other attempts to correlate polyploidy with ecology have been made by Haskell (1952) and Pignatti (1960). Haskell finds polyploidy increasing in the flora of Britain as moisture increases, for example. His study is broad, but his uncritical use of chromosome numbers from the literature makes his study somewhat less valuable than if cytological observations had accompanied the ecological work. Pignatti (1960) believes that more is to be gained by comparing similar associations as they exist in different areas than by comparing entire floras. He shows, for example, that a single widespread association that exists from Spain to Germany does not show much variation in its relative proportions of diploids and polyploids. On this basis, Pignatti concludes that "it cannot be affirmed that in cold zones polyploidy increases but only that in cold zones associations rich in polyploids increase." He also shows that in pioneer associations there are more diploid species than polyploids, but that the latter are more important as the climax is approached.

Pignatti's work is criticized by Favarger (1961) on several grounds. First, it is questionable if one may compare data from the Alps, where the Braun-Blanquet system of vegetation classification is widely used, and Greenland, where the Scandinavian system is employed. Secondly, the use by Pignatti of species frequency, in calculating the diploid index, weights the index falsely, because the presence of a species, however rare, is of much more significance historically than its abundance.

It is tempting to extend these observations on ecological differences between diploid and polyploid species to account also for differences in their geographic distribution. For example, Lövkvist's observation that decaploid populations of *Cardamine pratensis* grow in cooler, wetter habitats than lower-ploid populations can perhaps be correlated with the fact that high ploids of this species are widely distributed in the Arctic. Lövkvist (1956) states that "this species (the arctic race of *Cardamine pratensis*) grows very well as a semi-aquatic plant in swamps, and alpine pond margins, and often near the edge of the melting ice sheet in glaciated areas." He also notes its "enormous" capacity for vegetative reproduction and reports that it "very seldom flowers and never sets seeds." That these correlations are not always possible is clear from the work of Stebbins (1950), who analyzed 100 examples of naturally occurring polyploid complexes, *i.e.* groups in which polyploids are known to be closely related to extant diploids. He found a tendency for polyploids to be more widespread than diploids, but the reverse is true in many cases. He was unable to make any consistent correlations between northern-southern or glaciated-unglaciated distributions and the level of ploidy.

Polyploid species are initially successful on a local basis only. Unless a widespread ecological niche is available to them and sufficient time has elapsed for them to fill it, there is no reason to expect them to be extensively distributed. Two contrasting examples illustrate this point. In a recent paper, Mosquin (1964) discussed the cytology and distribution of *Clarkia rhomboidea*, an allotetraploid based on *C. virgata* and *C. mildrediae*, two narrowly restricted Sierran diploid species. *C. rhomboidea* is widespread in the western United States, occurring in many populations from southern California to Washington and at scattered localities in Utah, Arizona, Nevada, and Idaho. Mosquin places the time of origin of *C. rhomboidea* as the Wisconsin glaciation and suggests that it became widely distributed because of the existence of favorable habitats during pluvial intervals associated with the glaciation. In this case chromosomal repatterning has also played an important role in the evolution of the tetraploid, and *C. rhomboidea* stands as an excellent example of the combination of genetic and ecologic bases for distribution.

In an earlier study, Smith (1946) compared the distributions and morphologic and physiologic characteristics of diploid, tetraploid, and hexaploid *Sedum pulchellum* in the eastern United States. The hexaploid, she concluded on the basis of physiological experiments, would probably crowd out the other two races if all were growing together. Nevertheless, the hexaploid has the narrowest distribution of all three races because "it has doubtless originated most recently and has not yet had time to become widespread."

The probability also exists that the "same" polyploid taxon may evolve in more than one place and at different times, as has been suggested for the tetraploid based on *Deschampsia caespitosa* (Hedberg, 1958). Other examples of this polytopic origin of polyploid taxa are cited by Ownbey (1950), Heckard (1960), and Tutin (1957).

The bare ground left by retreating glaciers in arctic and alpine areas presented new habitats to surviving and invading plants, and both Stebbins (1950) and Reese (1958, 1961a) attribute at least part of the success of polyploids in invading these habitats to their superior ecological ability, which, as has been pointed out previously, is a consequence of their greater genetic variability. Although Löve (1964) makes a distinction between genetic variability and ecological adaptability, we see them as different aspects of the same basic phenomenon and emphasize that genetic variability cannot function in the absence of favorable ecological conditions.

Löve (1964) has also criticized Stebbins' and Reese's ideas on polyploid success on bare, denuded ground on the basis of studies of weed floras. Heiser and Whitaker (1948) in California and Mulligan (1960) in Canada, for example, show that polyploid species are no more successful as weeds than are diploids, and from this conclude that polyploidy has little to do with the colonization of bare ground. This argument may be spurious, however, for several reasons. First, weedy species have had very different evolutionary histories than species that have not become adapted to man's activities. Second, weedy floras are very high in annual species with relatively low polyploid frequencies, whereas the northern flora has very few annuals. Finally, there is no basis for considering all bare ground as a uniform kind of habitat. After all, agricultural land and newly exposed glacial till are not very similar.

EXPLANATIONS BASED ON THE PHYSIOLOGICAL CHARACTERISTICS OF POLYPLOIDS

Attempts have been made to refine Hagerup's ideas on tolerance of environmental extremes by demonstrating that polyploids are better adapted physiologically in northern environments than their lower ploid relatives (Löve and Löve, 1949; Mooney and Johnson, 1964). Many of these experiments may be criticized because they are based on artificially synthesized polyploids, often in crop plants. Also, the criteria on which "hardiness" is based may be questioned. Finally, the demonstration that a naturally occurring polyploid is different in one or more physiological attributes from its purported diploid relatives describes only the present status of the plants. In one recent study, for example, Mooney and Johnson (1964) show that a triploid population of *Thalictrum alpinum* has greater total growth and net photosynthesis than the diploid population under controlled conditions. Both chromosome races originated from the same area in northwestern Alaska, but the two populations had somewhat different ecological relationships. One cannot conclude from this study (or others like it) that the diploids that gave rise to the triploid were identical to the modern diploids or that they were substantially different from the modern triploid regarding the characteristics in which their diploid and triploid derivatives are now found to differ. The genetic effects of hybridization and polyploidization can be predicted only insofar as the genetics of the parents are known—and even in these ideal circumstances with something less than complete certainty. It is not possible to reason backward in time and conclude that diploids did not survive in extreme environments for physiological reasons alone. In summary, though it is probably safe to generalize that reinforcement of certain desirable diploid physiological properties contributed to the success of polyploids, while the inability of diploids to adjust or adapt to environmental extremes probably contributed to their local extinction, it is impossible to prove this by experiments with extant diploid and polyploid populations. In many cases simpler explanations are possible.

EXPLANATIONS BASED ON HISTORICAL EVENTS

Examination of the intrinsic properties of plants reveals much about the adaptive mechanisms available to species, but these experiments do not fully explain how a species reached its present localities or why it is not in other places. An understanding of the distribution of any species must also be based on the geologic and climatologic events to which that species has been exposed during its history. In recent years, interest has been renewed in historical causes for explaining some aspects of polyploidy. Interest has centered on the composition of the Tertiary flora from which the modern boreal flora has descended, on widespread climatic changes that occurred during both the Tertiary and Quaternary periods, and on glacial events that affected high latitudes both directly and indirectly.

The Arcto-Tertiary Flora is well known from paleobotanical evidence from many northern areas (e.g. Chaney, 1947; Dorofeev, 1963), and most studies agree on its similarity in composition throughout the North. The early- to mid-Tertiary arctic flora was temperate and boreal and contained many still-common and widespread genera and species now found at much lower latitudes. Krystofovich (1929) believed that its species composition in Asia indicated a mean annual temperature of 10° C. The extensive southward migration of the better-known elements of the flora, which began in the late Oligocene, resulted from climatic deterioration, and much constriction in species ranges and widespread elimination of many species continued through the remainder of the Tertiary and the Quaternary. Very few fossils of late Tertiary plants are known from areas now covered by arctic tundra, but it must be assumed from modern distribution records that by the end of the Tertiary a widespread flora at high latitudes was similar in character to the modern circumpolar flora but probably considerably richer in species.

During the Quaternary period fluctuating and sometimes catastrophic climatic and geologic changes modified the flora in various ways. Repeated glaciations probably eliminated many species outright and, according to the ideas of Hultén (1937), eradicated the northern representatives of others. The idea of all northern species migrating southward ahead of the advancing ice and back again following the retreating ice has been considered untenable by Hultén (1937), and in any event it is not required to explain modern distribution patterns in the boreal flora. Other species survived the glacial advances (or at least the most recent of these advances) in refugia even at the highest latitudes (Dahl, 1946; Heusser, 1954), but according to the ideas of Anderson (1936) they suffered severe biotype depletion and with the return of more favorable climates were unable to regain their once more-widespread distribution patterns.

Polyploidy has played an important role in the evolution of the Arcto-Tertiary Flora. It is our belief, however, that in emphasizing polyploidy students of cytogeography have sometimes lost sight of the diploid side of the problem. The highest polyploid frequencies known are from very small arctic floras, which sometimes contain 100 species or less (e.g. Holmen, 1952). Whether these small floras are surviving remnants of the Arcto-Tertiary Flora, or whether they consist of postglacial invaders, or both, is uncertain because the Quaternary histories of places such as Peary Land and Spitsbergen are not completely understood. In either case, however, polyploid species have had a distinct selective advantage in contributing to the composition of the modern floras of these places. Wherever climatic and geologic conditions have favored survival or immigration of larger numbers of species, as in Iceland (Löve and Löve, 1949, 1956), southwest Greenland (Favarger, 1961, based on Jørgensen et al., 1958), or in northwest Alaska (Johnson and Packer, 1965), polyploid frequencies are invariably lower. Thus, the frequency of polyploidy in any area must be considered on the basis of survival of Tertiary diploid and polyploid species, postglacial immigration of diploid and polyploid species, and formation of new polyploids during and following the glacial intervals.

Cytological studies of the plants of known refugia suggest that in some of them, at least, many diploid species have persisted at or near their present locations since the Tertiary. The high frequency of diploid species in the lower unglaciated peripheral Alps (Favarger, 1954) has been explained by the presence of Tertiary survivors. Similar conclusions have been reached from studies from the Eurasiatic arctic (Sokolovskaja and Strelkova, 1960) and northwestern Alaska (Johnson and Packer, 1965). The highest frequency of diploids (77%) in any flora yet studied has been found by Larsen (1960) in the Tertiary endemic species of the Canary Islands.

In both glaciated and unglaciated areas postglacial immigration of diploid species has been important. Reese (1958, 1961a), for example, thinks that although polyploid species were initially more successful on the bare ground following glacial retreat they have been partially replaced in time by diploid species in a way analogous to plant succession in situ. He bases this belief partly on the work of Knapp (1953) and Hermann (1947), who studied polyploidy in relation to plant succession on vegetation-free and artificially cleared ground in Europe. They found that apart from a very short initial phase the polyploids were dominant in the early stages but that diploids invaded the area later, causing a depression of the polyploid frequency until equilibrium was eventually reached. Reese extends these ideas to broader areas and suggests that the high polyploid frequencies of northern glaciated habitats result from the short time that has elapsed since the last glaciation, that the initial even higher frequencies have been reduced in postglacial time by the influx of diploid species, and that there may be a further reduction in the future, barring climatic regression.

It is possible that under the present climatic regime this postglacial invasion may have reached equilibrium. Selander (1950), for example, states that the Scandinavian mountain vegetation has been stable for the past 2,600 years. Löve's (1964) statement that ample time has elapsed since the last glaciation "for the dispersal (to northern Scandinavia) of every species of higher plants met with in the unglaciated parts of Central Europe" may be interpreted in this light, as can Knaben's (1961) demonstration that in Norway it is the lowland species that show closest affinities to the flora of central Europe, while the arctic-alpine flora has east-west affinities. These immigrants from central Europe are both diploid and polyploid, and their lowland localities in Norway, mostly in the south, "must be regarded as terminals for the wanderings of the species . . . after the Ice Age" (Knaben, 1961).

As stated previously, the polyploids in a modern flora must be accounted for either on the basis of survival from Tertiary times, postglacial immigration, formation *in situ* during the Quaternary, or all three of these reasons. Favarger (1961) analyzes both the flora of the peripheral Alps and the flora of southwest Greenland in terms of the age of all of the elements. He recognizes diploids and paleo-polyploids as being the oldest elements in these floras, while mesopolyploids, neopolyploids, and chromosome races are progressively younger. These categories are based on morphological, cytological, and distributional grounds. Paleopolyploids are very ancient species, usually with high chromosome numbers, for which no closely related diploids exist anywhere. Mesopolyploids are well-differentiated, morphologically separate species of a genus in which ancestral diploid species or diploids derived from ancestral types now occur in the same or closely related genus. Neopolyploids are races of a Linnaean species that in a given territory have supplanted the diploid race, whereas chromosome races occur in the same area and differ only in chromosome number, and no morphological distinctions can be found among them.

Fitting all species into this framework requires a certain degree of subjectivity, as Favarger admits, but the method has much to recommend it, because recognition is taken of the fact that polyploidy has occurred repeatedly during the long evolutionary history of the vascular plants and does not result only from the events of one epoch or period. It also provides a relative measure of the age of a flora. In this context, Favarger (1961) finds that the flora of the incompletely glaciated nival zone of the Alps has more of these older elements and fewer of the younger than that of southwestern Greenland, and from this he concludes that the European alpine flora that he studied is older than that of southwestern Greenland. Reese (1958, 1961a) also recognizes that floras with high percentages of diploids are older than those that are mostly polyploid. It should be emphasized that Reese's approach to the age of polyploids is set in an ecological context in which he dates the age of a flora from the time of its establishment, and he is not concerned

with the phylogenetic age of the species of which the flora is composed as is Favarger in his polyploid classification system. These ideas are not conflicting, as Favarger (1961) supposes, but rather concerned with different aspects of the problem of polyploidy.

If we accept as a basic assumption that polyploidy is an adaptive mechanism that sometimes allows species to utilize ecological niches different from those of their ancestors, we are then able to suggest reasons for both the survival of older polyploids and the formation of others in more recent times. The period of climatic deterioration that culminated in the events of the Pleistocene began in mid-Tertiary time and did not affect all plants in the same way, because it is obvious that in all but the most homogeneous areas some habitats are warmer and drier or colder and wetter than the "average." Clements (1916), in his climax terminology, recognized this and referred to such areas as pre- and postclimaxes respectively. In the subarctic forests of Alaska, for example, white spruce (*Picea glauca*) is a mesic species, but in cold bogs within the forested zone species whose main ranges lie to the north of tree-line are common. As Wulff (1943) suggests, there is no reason to think that only regions characterized by extremes support polyploid species, and following the work of Strelkova (1938) and Sokolovaskaja (1937), who noted the proliferation of polyploid species into alpine habitats, he points out that many micro-environmental situations favor the establishment of polyploid forms. Similarly Tolmatchev (1959) suggests that even at times when the better-known elements of the Arcto-Tertiary Flora existed at high latitudes (genera such as *Sequoia, Pinus, Taxodium, Acer, Ulmus,* etc.) places such as alpine fellfields, snow-beds, bogs, and strands supported the herbaceous, perennial ancestors of the modern arctic flora. As the climatic deterioration of the Tertiary continued, habitats that favored these species expanded and became the new "mesic" sites, while the temperate forest species gradually disappeared from the North. During the fluctuating climatic conditions that have characterized the Quaternary, new polyploids have been formed; these have, to some extent, offset the elimination of diploid and older polyploid forms. The modern arctic climate is such that habitat instability is still one of the outstanding features of the North, and it is most likely that new polyploid races are being produced where opportunities for hybridization and successful establishment of new genotypes obtain. The best examples of this are found in areas where introduced species have hybridized with a native species and polyploidy has followed. For example, *Spartina townsendii* in England is a hybrid polyploid derivative of introduced *S. alterniflora* and native *S. maritima*. It is very successful in England and has become widespread even to the point of replacing the parent species.

A synthesis of all of the ideas presented above as explanations for differential diploid-polyploid distributions will be attempted below, but it may be useful first to consider one recent North American study in which several of these problems are considered.

POLYPLOIDY AND ENVIRONMENT AT OGOTORUK CREEK, NORTHWESTERN ALASKA

Two of us, Johnson and Packer (1964), have studied the relationship of polyploidy to environmental gradients in northwestern Alaska. This study is of interest here because it is one of the few North American studies to date (excluding those in Greenland) that report chromosome numbers for a relatively large local flora, and one of the few investigations that consider polyploidy in relationship to modern environment in a quantitative way.

The Ogotoruk Creek–Cape Thompson area is located along the northwestern Alaska coast (68° N; 168° 46′ W) in an unglaciated region of low limestone and sandstone mountains with extensive flat areas covered by unconsolidated Quaternary sediments. The climate is typical of the western Arctic, with cold temperatures in the winter, a short growing season, low annual precipitation, probably about 20 cm, and high winds. Permafrost is present to depths of over 300 m rather generally in the area.

By utilizing extensive physical and biological data that are available from the area we have constructed idealized environmental gradients having to do primarily with topographic and edaphic factors. Organic or fine-grained, cold, wet, mineral soils in which permafrost and frost action play important roles are found in areas of gentle to flat topography and represent one extreme in these factors (Fig. 1). At the opposite extreme are the coarse, well-drained, warmer soils of slopes and ridgetops, in which permafrost is farther from the surface and in which frost action plays only a minor role.

The angiosperm flora of the Ogotoruk Creek Valley includes 291 taxa, 234 of which were analyzed cytologically. In addition, chromosome counts from the literature were utilized for 24 taxa. The monocotyledonous plants at Ogotoruk Creek contain about 85% polyploid species and the dicotyledonous plants about 53% polyploids with an average frequency of polyploidy in the flora of about 60% (Table 2). This is the lowest frequency of polyploidy known for a flora at this latitude.

Polyploidy was correlated with plant distribution along environmental gradients in this study by grouping the taxa according to the habitats in which they occur and then calculating the frequency of polyploidy for each group. The results of this analysis are presented graphically

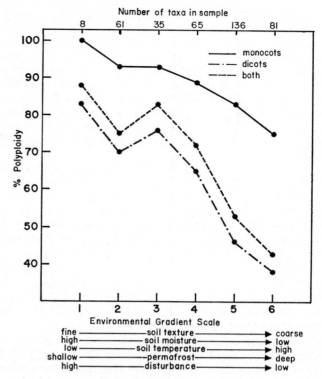

Figure 1. The relationship of the frequency of polyploidy in the angiosperm flora of the Ogotoruk Creek Valley, Alaska, to environmental gradients.

(Fig. 1). Classes one to six along the environmental gradient scale represent points where the physical and biological data show environmental discontinuities. They are usually associated with topographic breaks and are identified in nature most easily by changes in the vegetation.

Polyploid frequencies decrease along the environmental gradient in both monocotyledonous and dicotyledonous plants, with the highest values in wet lowland habitats and the lowest percentages on the well-drained slopes and uplands. The lower polyploid frequency at point two on the gradient scale as compared to point three is due to a small group of diploid dicotyledonous species growing on relatively stable peaty ridges within this general habi-

TABLE 2

Polyploid Frequencies in the Ogotoruk Creek Flora
(All taxa included with the exception of Cyperaceae. Values in parentheses calculated by considering all ambiguous cases as diploids)

	No. of species	Known cytologically	Known cytologically from Ogotoruk Creek	No. of diploids	Percent diploids	No. of polyploids	Percent polyploids
Monocotyledons	52	52	40	8 (9)	15.4 (17.3)	44 (43)	84.6 (82.7)
Dicotyledons	214	206	194	97 (105)	47.1 (51.0)	109 (101)	52.9 (49.0)
Totals	266	258	234	105 (114)	40.7 (44.2)	153 (144)	59.3 (55.8)

tat type, a micro-environmental niche that does not occur in habitat three.

The two most significant results of these studies at Ogotoruk Creek are: first, that the frequency of polyploidy in the flora is correlated with local environmental gradients; and second, that the frequency of polyploidy in the flora of Ogotoruk Creek is lower than in any flora of equivalent latitude yet examined. It is suggested that these two points are related and can be explained on the basis of the Tertiary-Quaternary history of the Ogotoruk Creek Valley.

A great part of Alaska remained unglaciated during the Pleistocene. This includes almost all of the interior between the Alaska Range and the Brooks Range and nearly all of the west and north coasts. Scattered mountain glaciation occurred on the highest of the interior mountains and probably also on the mountains of the Seward Peninsula. Vegetation grew in these areas during all of the Quaternary, as far as is known, and, according to Hultén (1937), "most arctic and numerous boreal plants radiated from the Bering Sea area" to reach their present distributions; this in turn, he adds, was "founded . . . in the geographical distribution of the Tertiary flora." It is most likely, then, that the Ogotoruk Creek flora consists for the most part of species that either survived *in situ* during the Quaternary period or migrated to the area during the Quaternary from other unglaciated refugia in the amphi-Beringian area. The large number of diploid species in this area, then, must be attributed to survival of Tertiary elements, which, as has been pointed out previously, are known in general for their high frequency of diploid species.

The studies at Ogotoruk Creek also show that the majority of diploid species grow on slopes and upland areas, and it is reasoned that these places must be nearly like the Tertiary habitats that occurred in this area. These habitats are relatively stable even today in the extreme arctic climate, as has been demonstrated by analysis of their physical characteristics. Polyploid species also grow in these environments, and it is certain that some of them, at least, are also Tertiary survivors.

Another group of polyploid species occupies habitats at the cold, wet end of the environmental gradient scale. These habitats are much disturbed by frost action and are influenced by shallow permafrost. Of all the kinds of habitat at Ogotoruk Creek, these show most clearly the cumulative effects of a long history of cold and instability that characterized parts of the Pleistocene epoch. The high frequency of polyploids in these environments suggests that they were outside the tolerance limits of the majority of the Tertiary diploid species and that they were invaded during the late Tertiary and Quaternary by Tertiary polyploids as well as by the proliferation of new variable hybrid polyploid taxa.

Thus, it is possible to account for the frequency of polyploidy in the Ogotoruk Creek flora partly on the basis of survival and immigration of diploid and polyploid Tertiary species and partly on the basis of the formation of new polyploid taxa, which were able to spread into new expanding habitats associated with the climatic deterioration of the late Tertiary and Quaternary periods.

SYNTHESIS

The information presented above should make it clear that explanations of polyploid frequencies in floras are complicated and of necessity often speculative. All extant floras are composed of species derived from a variety of sources —old diploids and polyploids that have survived climatic fluctuations, diploid and polyploid immigrants, and new hybrid polyploid species that arise and persist under favorable ecological conditions. In the presence of stable climatic and physiographic conditions, it is likely that the diploid-polyploid ratio in any local area probably remains relatively constant for long periods of time.

In dealing with the central problem of northern cytogeography, *i.e.* the increasing frequency of polyploidy with latitude, we must take into account intrinsic properties of polyploid species that have been and are of selective advantage in the environments in which the species occur. While it is generally accepted that increased genetic variability is a consequence of hybridization, the precise changes that have led to hybrid success must be various. Shifts in ecological adaptability, changes in the reproductive mode (from predominantly sexual to apomictic), and extensions of physiological tolerances have all been associated with polyploid species and invoked as the reasons for their success. Since many diploid species also possess these same characteristics, and also live at high latitudes, one cannot explain high polyploid frequencies in the North solely on this basis. Nevertheless, on the basis of all the evidence available at this time, the possibility remains that, as especially Löve (*e.g.* 1964) suggests, at least part of the reason for the very high polyploid frequencies in small floras of the highest latitudes may be due to the differential survival of polyploid species. At present, the question cannot be resolved conclusively.

If the observed distributions are not simply the result of chance survival (admittedly a possibility), it is assumed (1) that areas at the highest latitudes, if unglaciated, were so drastically changed by the climatic and geologic events of the late Tertiary and Quaternary that diploid species were not able to survive there, or (2) that if these areas were glaciated all plants were eliminated and polyploid species were better able to invade these habitats in interior postglacial time. In the second case, it is possible, as Reese (1961a) suggests, that insufficient time has elapsed since the Wisconsin glaciation to re-establish an equilibrium between diploid and polyploid species in the North.

Wherever more extensive areas remained unglaciated, as in Eurasia or northwestern North America, many more species probably survived from the Tertiary, and, as has been demonstrated, as the flora increases in numbers of species, the number of diploids increases at a more rapid rate than do the polyploids. Also, these continental areas are more accessible to invasion of species from south of the glacial margin; this is especially true in North America, where north-trending mountains provide high-altitude migration routes to the Arctic.

In times of changing environment, then, adaptation, migration, or extinction occur, and the more rapid the change so the more likely it is that extinction will prevail. Hybridization and subsequent polyploidy provide a more rapid method for extending species variation in some cases than gene mutation or chromosome repatterning at the diploid level, and this kind of evolution seems to have been especially important in areas either directly modified by the Pleistocene glaciations or enduring the effects of periglacial climates. That these influences extended far beyond the areas directly affected by the ice sheet is clear from many studies such as the one cited above by Mosquin (1964); the recent discovery of high polyploid frequencies in the alpine and subalpine zone of Mexico and Guatemala (Beaman *et al.*, 1962) may also be related to Pleistocene events.

The demonstration that polyploidy can be related to ecological conditions, even within small areas, provides a key to past conditions having to do with the survival of ancient species as well as the proliferation of polyploid species in recent habitats. It also shows that even adjacent areas with different ecological conditions may have strikingly different polyploid frequencies and that sampling procedures may yield misleading results when ecology is not taken into account.

There is still much to be learned about polyploidy and plant distribution. Statistical studies of diploid and polyploid frequencies in floras do not contribute to the understanding of natural patterns, however, unless they are set in an ecological and an historical context. In North America most attention is being devoted to individual species groups in which differential diploid-polyploid distribution occurs. If these studies are combined with careful analyses of the ecological preferences and historical development in each group, generalizations on the importance of polyploidy as an evolutionary mechanism in Quaternary time should emerge.

REFERENCES

Anderson, Edgar, 1936, The species problem in *Iris:* Missouri Bot. Garden Ann., v. 23, p. 457-509

—— 1949, Introgressive hybridization: New York, John Wiley and Sons, 109 p.

Beaman, J. H., De Jong, D. C. D., and Stoutamire, W. P., 1962, Chromosome studies in the alpine and subalpine floras of Mexico and Guatemala: Amer. J. Bot., v. 49, p. 41-50

Cain, S. A., 1944, Foundations of plant geography: New York, Harper and Bros., 556 p.

Chaney, R. W., 1947, Tertiary centers and migration routes: Ecol. Monogr., v. 17, p. 140-148

Clements, F. E., 1916, Plant succession: Carnegie Instn. Publ. 242, p. 1-512

Dahl, Eilif, 1946, On different types of unglaciated areas during the ice ages and their significance to phytogeography: New Phytologist, v. 45, p. 225-242

Davis, P. H., and Heywood, V. H., 1963, Principles of angiosperm taxonomy: New York, D. Van Nostrand Co., Inc., 556 p.

Dean, D. S., 1959, Distribution of tetraploid and diploid *Tradescantia ohioensis* in Michigan and adjoining areas: Amer. Midl. Nat., v. 6, p. 204-209

Dorofeev, P. I., 1963, The Tertiary forests of western Siberia: Moscow, Acad. Sci. U.S.S.R., Komarov Bot. Inst., 346 p.

Favarger, Claude, 1954, Sur le pourcentage des polyploides dans la flora de l'étage nival des Alpes suisses: 8th Intern. Bot. Cong., Paris, Sect. 9-10, p. 51-56

—— 1961, Sur l'émploi des nombres de chromosomes en géographie botanique historique: Zurich, Geobot. Inst. Eidg. Techn. Hochschule, Stiftung Rübel, Bericht, v. 32, p. 119-146

Gustafsson, Åke, 1948, Polyploidy, life-form and vegetative reproduction: Hereditas, v. 34, p. 1-22

Hagerup, Olaf, 1928, Morphological and cytological studies of Bicornes: Dansk Bot. Arkiv, v. 6, p. 1-27

—— 1930, Études des types biologiques de Raunkaier dans la flore autour de Tombouctou: Kgl. Danske Vidensk. Selsk. Biol. Medd., v. 9, p. 1-116

—— 1931, Über Polyploidie in Beziehung zu Klima, Ökologie und Phylogenie: Hereditas, v. 16, p. 19-40

Haskell, G., 1952, Polyploidy, ecology and the British flora: J. Ecol., v. 40, p. 265-302

Heckard, L. R., 1960, Taxonomic studies in the *Phacelia magellanica* polyploid complex; with special reference to the California members: Berkeley, Univ. California Publ., Bot., v. 32, p. 1-126

Hedberg, Olov, 1958, Cyto-taxonomic studies in Scottish mountain plants, notably *Deschampsia caespitosa* (L.) PB., S. lat.: Svensk Bot. Tidskr., v. 52, p. 37-46

Heiser, C. B., 1950, A comparison of the flora as a whole and the weed flora of Indiana as to polyploidy and growth habits: Indiana Acad. Sci. Proc., v. 59, p. 64-70

Heiser, C. B., and Whitaker, T. W., 1948, Chromosome number, polyploidy, and growth habit in California weeds: Amer. J. Bot., v. 35, p. 179-186

Hermann, G., 1947, Über das Verhalten der polyploiden Arten höherer Pflanzen bei der Besiedlung von Brachland: Planta, v. 35, p. 177-187

Heusser, C. J., 1954, Nunatak flora of the Juneau Ice Field, Alaska: Torrey Bot. Club Bull., v. 81, p. 236-250

Holmen, Kjeld, 1952, Cytological studies in the flora of Peary Land, North Greenland: Medd. om Grønl., v. 128, p. 1-40

Hultén, Eric, 1937, Outline of the history of the arctic and boreal biota during the Quaternary Period: Stockholm, Bokförlags Aktiebolaget Thule, 168 p.

Johnson, A. W. and Packer, J. G., 1965, Polyploidy and environment in arctic Alaska: Science (in press)

Jones, Keith, 1958, Cytotaxonomic studies in *Holcus*. i, The chromosome complex in *Holcus mollis* L.: New Phytologist, v. 57, p. 191-210

Jørgensen, C. A., Sørensen, Th., and Westergaard, M., 1958, The flowering plants of Greenland. A taxonomical and cytological survey: Kgl. Danske Vidensk. Selsk. Biol. Skr., v. 9, p. 1-172

Knaben, Gunvor, 1950, Chromosome numbers of Scandinavian arctic-alpine plant species, i.: Blyttia, v. 8, p. 129-155

—— 1961, Cyto-ecologic problems in Norwegian flora groups; distribution and significance of polyploidy: Hereditas, v. 47, p. 451-479

Knapp, Rudiger, 1953, Über Zusammenhänge zwischen Polyploidie, Verbreitung, systematischer und soziologischer Stellung von Pflanzenarten in Mitteleuropa: Z. Vererbungslehre, v. 85, p. 163-179

Krystofovich, A. N., 1929, Evolution of the Tertiary flora in Asia: New Phytologist, v. 28, p. 303-312

Larsen, Kai, 1960, Cytological and experimental studies on the flowering plants of the Canary Islands: Kgl. Danske Vidensk. Selsk. Biol. Skr., v. 11, p. 1-60

Lawrence, W. E., 1947, Chromosome numbers in Achillea in relation to distribution: Amer. J. Bot., v. 34, p. 538-545

Löve, Áskell, 1964, The biological species concept and its evolutionary structure: Taxon, v. 13, p. 33-45

Löve, Áskell, and Löve, Doris, 1948, Chromosome numbers of northern species: Iceland Univ. Inst. Appl. Sci., Dep. Agric. Rep. B., No. 3, p. 1-131

—— 1949, Geobotanical significance of polyploidy, i. Polyploidy and latitude: Portug. Acta Biol. (A), R. B. Goldschmidt vol., p. 273-352

—— 1956, Cytotaxonomical conspectus of the Icelandic flora: Acta Horti Got., v. 20, p. 65-291

—— 1957, Arctic polyploidy: Gen. Soc. Canada Proc., v. 2, p. 23-27

Lövkvist, Börje, 1956, The *Cardamine pratensis* complex, outlines of its cytogenetics and taxonomy: Symb. Bot. Upsala, v. 14, p. 1-131

—— 1958, Polyploidy and ecological differentiation, *in* Systematics of Today: Stockholm, Almqvist and Wiksells, p. 182-185

Manton, Irene, 1950, Problems of cytology and evolution in the Pteridophyta: Cambridge, England, Cambridge Univ. Press, 316 p.

Mooney, H. A., 1963, Physiological ecology of coastal, subalpine, and alpine populations of *Polygonum bistortoides:* Ecology, v. 44, p. 812-816

Mooney, H. A., and Billings, W. D., 1961, Comparative physiological ecology of arctic and alpine populations of *Oxyria digyna:* Ecol. Monogr., v. 31, p. 1-29

Mooney, H. A., and Johnson, A. W., 1965, Comparative physiological ecology of an arctic and an alpine population of *Thalictrum alpinum* L: Ecology (in press)

Moore, D. M., 1960, Chromosome numbers of flowering plants from Macquarie Island: Bot. Notiser, v. 113, p. 185-191

Mosquin, T. A., 1964, Chromosomal repatterning in *Clarkia rhomboidea* as evidence for post-Pleistocene changes in distribution: Evolution, v. 18, p. 12-25

Mulligan, G. A., 1960, Polyploidy in Canadian weeds: Can. J. Genet. Cytol., v. 2, p. 150-161

Müntzing, Arne, 1936, The evolutionary significance of autopolyploidy: Hereditas, v. 21, p. 263-378

Ownbey, Marion, 1950, Natural hybridization and amphiploidy in the genus *Tragopogon:* Amer. J. Bot., v. 37, p. 487-499

Pignatti, Sandro, 1960, Il significato delle specie poliploidi nelle associazioni vegetali: Ist. Venet., Cl. Sci. Mat. Nat., Atti, No. 118, p. 75-98

Reese, Gerd, 1957, Über die Polyploidiespektren in der nordsaharischen Wüstenflora: Flora, v. 144, p. 598-634

—— 1958, Polyploidie und Verbreitung: Z. Botanik, v. 46, p. 339-354

—— 1961a, Geobotanische Bedeutung der Chromosomenzahl und Chromosomenstruktur: Naturwiss. Rdsch., v. 14, p. 140-145

—— 1961b, Karyotype and plant geography: Rec. Adv. Bot., p. 895-900

Scott, F. I., 1950, Polyploidy among plant species extraneous in Indiana: Butler Univ. Bot. Stud., v. 9, p. 176-187

Selander, Sten, 1950, Floristic phytogeography of southwestern Lule Lappmark: Acta Phytogeogr. Suecica, v. 27, p. 1-200

Smith, H. E., 1946, *Sedum pulchellum:* A physiological and morphological comparison of diploid, tetraploid, and hexaploid races: Torrey Bot. Club Bull., v. 73, p. 495-541

Sokolovskaja, A. P., 1937, Karyo-geographical investigation of the genus Agrostis L.: Bot. Zh., v. 22

Sokolovskaja, A. P., and Strelkova, O. S., 1960, Geographical distribution of the polyploid species of plants in the Eurasiatic Arctic: Bot. Zh., v. 45, p. 369-381

Stebbins, G. L., 1950, Variation and evolution in plants: New York, Columbia Univ. Press, 643 p.

Strain, B. R., 1964, Physiological and morphological variability of local quaking aspen clones: Los Angeles, Univ. California Ph.D. thesis

Strelkova, O. S., 1938, Polyploidy and geographo-systematic groups in the genus *Alopecurus* L.: Cytologia, v. 8

Tischler, Georg, 1935, Die Bedeutung der Polyploidie für die Verbreitung der Angiospermen: Bot. Jb., v. 67, p. 1-36

—— 1946, Über die Siedlungsfähigheit von Polyploiden: Z. Naturforsch., v. 1, p. 157-159

—— 1955, Der Grad der Polyploidie bei den Angiospermen in verschiedenen Grossarealen: Cytologia, v. 20, p. 101-118

Tolmatchev, A. I., 1959, Der autochthone Grundstock der arktischen Flora und ihre Beziehung zu den Hochgebirgsfloren Nord- und Zentralasiens: Bot. Tidsskr., v. 55, p. 269-276

Tutin, T. G., 1957, A contribution to the experimental taxonomy of *Poa annua* L.: Watsonia, v. 4, p. 1-10

Wulff, E. V., 1943, An introduction to historical plant geography: Waltham, Massachusetts, Chronica Botanica Co., 223 p.

SUMMARY

Polyploid species are those whose somatic reproductive cells contain more than two haploid chromosome complements, or which are thought on the basis of cytological data from related species to contain more than two such genomes. Because polyploid species are presumed to have originated from diploid or lower-ploid ancestors, they are phylogenetically younger than lower-ploid species within the same evolutionary line. From one-third to one-half of the flowering-plant species so far investigated are polyploid, and this is taken as evidence that polyploidy has played an important evolutionary role in this plant group.

In the northern hemisphere, the frequency of polyploidy increases with latitude in all areas studied, and this distributional fact has constituted the main problem of cytogeography for several decades. Among the reasons suggested for the high frequency of polyploidy in the North are (1) that polyploid species have been differentially successful over their diploid relatives in occupying the bare ground left behind by retreating glaciers; (2) that polyploid species were better able to survive glacial climates in unglaciated high-latitude refugia than were diploid species; and (3) that the arctic environment selects for combinations of morphological and physiological properties that, though independent of ploidy, are likely for intrinsic reasons to be associated with it.

In polyploid series, polyploids almost always have different ecological requirements than related diploids, but the pattern of difference is inconsistent. In all cases, the diploid is adapted to an environmental mode, and its successful polyploid derivatives have occupied colder-wetter or warmer-drier habitats or both.

These observations and those demonstrating that plants of refugia and areas south of the limits of continental glaciation often have low frequencies of polyploidy suggest that the frequency of polyploidy in any modern flora depends upon the possibility for survival of older elements, the opportunities for inter- or postglacial immigration of both diploid and polyploid species, the characteristics of the modern climate, the possibilities for hybridization, and the availability of ecological niches for new hybrid, polyploid derivatives.

In time of geological and climatic stability, evolutionary rates are retarded; when the reverse obtains, the possibility for the establishment of newly arisen entities is greatly increased. While we recognize that the existence of high polyploid frequencies in the plants of high latitudes is suggestive of the evolution, spread, and differential success of polyploid species in response to the physical changes of the Quaternary Period, the possibility also exists that there has been too little time since the last glaciation for equilibrium in the diploid-polyploid ratios at high latitudes to be reached. The accumulation of morphological and physiological studies of diploid and related polyploid species, especially when set in an ecological and historical context, should help clarify these still unanswered questions.

QUATERNARY MAMMALS OF NORTH AMERICA

C. W. HIBBARD,[1] D. E. RAY,[2] D. E. SAVAGE,[3]
D. W. TAYLOR,[4] J. E. GUILDAY[5]

THE CONSPICUOUS fossil remains of large extinct animals such as mastodons and ground sloths have long held the public interest. Fossils of Quaternary mammals both large and small are common in most parts of North America, but they have not been studied so intensively as those of the earlier Cenozoic. The special advantages that study of Quaternary mammals offers are a relatively full record, the possibility of establishing detailed phyletic lineages, and the opportunity to draw on a vast reservoir of knowledge of ecology, morphology, general biology, and geographic distribution of the living fauna.

The known fossil record of Pleistocene mammals is more nearly complete than that of any other group. Figure 1 shows the distribution of the major faunal localities in North America, herein defined to exclude the Neotropical Region (compare with the much smaller number of Tertiary localities shown by Savage, 1958, Fig. 2). The wide geographic occurrence of the sites and the short time range of many genera and species make mammals the most useful means of correlation within the Quaternary over wide areas of North America. The abundant fossil record, coupled with the fact that so many genera are still living (Table 1), offers hopes for rich synthesis of data from fossil and living mammals.

Previous summaries of North American Quaternary mammals by Hay (1923, 1924, 1927) and Hibbard (in Flint, 1957, p. 458-467; Hibbard, 1958) show the progressive acceleration in knowledge that has been accomplished in the last 25 years by bulk screen-washing or sifting of fossiliferous matrix. In the past 37 years, 49 of 155 genera have been added to the known Quaternary record; 10 are large mammals but 39 are small, being mostly insectivores, bats, and rodents. Despite this progress the knowledge of the North American record lags far behind that of Europe (Flint, 1957, p. 451-455; Fejfar, 1961), even allowing for the different density of paleontologists. Comprehensive taxonomic works on North American Quaternary mammals are rare (Frick, 1937; Klingener, 1963; Osborn, 1936-42;

Simpson, 1941, 1945; Skinner and Kaisen, 1947; Stock, 1925).

The history of mammalian paleontology in North America is largely one of emphasis on comparative morphology, phylogeny, and origin of higher categories. This has led generally to emphasis on the earlier Tertiary record and to the lack of integration of related aspects of geology and biology. We believe that the study of fossil mammals in general, and particularly of Quaternary mammals, must provide a synthesis if it is to be more than descriptive morphology and phylogenetic speculation. Hence we have only briefly summarized the basic data of geographic and stratigraphic occurrences (Fig. 1, Table 2), and we discuss more fully the promising avenues for future research. Common names of all genera mentioned in the text are shown on Table 2.

CHRONOLOGY

SCOPE OF PLEISTOCENE

General agreement in defining the Pliocene-Pleistocene boundary is lacking. Application of potassium-argon radiogenic dates and geomagnetic reversal sequences may bring a consensus in the next decade. Our placement of the lower limit of the Pleistocene is based upon the earliest paleontologic evidence of markedly cooler climate in mid-latitudes. The few radiogenic dates now available (Evernden *et al.*, 1964) imply that the base of the Pleistocene as we define it is probably 2-3 million years old.

Mammalian evidence for recognition of the end of the Pleistocene in North America is based on extinction of such large species as elephants, mastodons, camels, large peccaries (*Mylohyus* and *Platygonus*), *Cervalces*, the larger *Bison*, Woodland Muskox (*Symbos*), Giant Beaver (*Castoroides*), ground sloths, and horses. The gradual extinction of these species occurred through an interval of at least 10,000 years (Hester, 1960); some probably lived as recently as 4000 years B.C. The most conspicuous changes in the North American mammalian fauna thus occurred after the Wisconsin glaciation.

Four chronologies are especially significant for correlation of Quaternary events. They are provided by (a) the biostratigraphic record of land mammals; (b) glacial-interglacial climatic fluctuations, inferred from many sources besides physical-stratigraphic data; (c) geomagnetic-re-

[1] Museum of Paleontology, University of Michigan, Ann Arbor, Michigan.
[2] U.S. National Museum, Washington, D.C.
[3] Department of Paleontology, University of California, Berkeley, California.
[4] Museum of Zoology, University of Michigan, Ann Arbor, Michigan.
[5] Carnegie Museum, Pittsburgh, Pennsylvania.

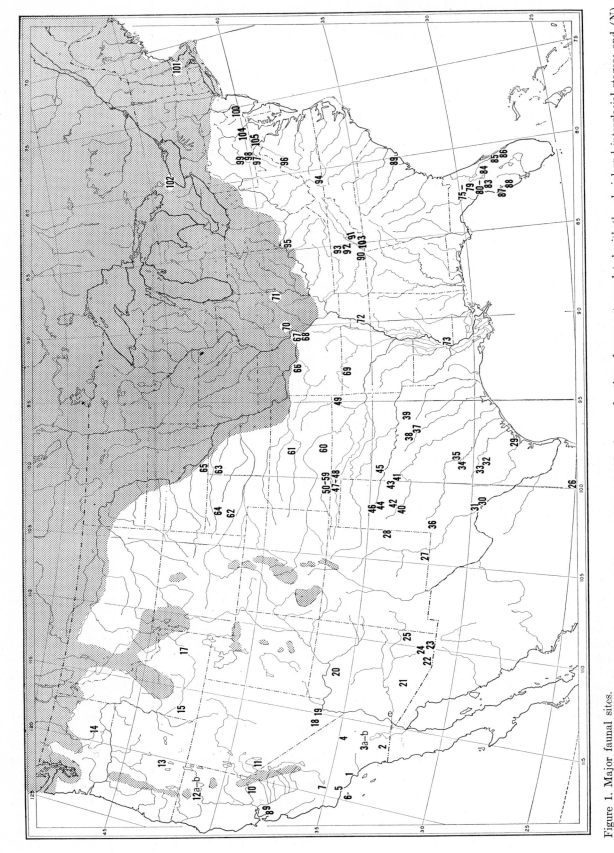

Figure 1. Major faunal sites.

Most of the well-known sites for Pleistocene mammalian assemblages in North America are indicated by numbers, on Figure 1, that correspond with the following list. Following the name of the locality is the age according to the following designations: (LB) Late Blancan, (Ir) Irvingtonian, and (R) Rancholabrean for those faunas not correlated with the glacial and interglacial stages; and (N) Nebraskan, (A) Aftonian, (LA) Late Aftonian, (K) Kansan, (EK) Early Kansan, (LK) Late Kansan, (Y) Yarmouth, (I) Illinoian, (LI) Late Illinoian, (S) Sangamon, (LS) Late Sangamon, (W) Wisconsin, (EW) Early Wisconsin, (MW) Middle Wisconsin, and (LW) Late Wisconsin for those faunas where the glacial chronology is used. C[14] dates are included where available. Further information on dates can be found in references cited or in the appropriate date lists cited in *Radiocarbon* (1959-1963). The last number for each locality designates the paper in the list of references that provides an introduction to the literature on each locality. Thus the publications cited are not necessarily the most important ones, but they include comprehensive bibliographies.

In general, only extensive assemblages have been mapped and listed here. The numerous sites for individual specimens and old collections (often lacking minimal field data) are accessible through summaries by Hay (49, 50, 52). The bibliographies by Hay (53) and Camp *et al.* (14), the latter thoroughly indexed, provide a key to more recent discoveries. Sellards (128) discusses many sites not included here, where Man occurs with Pleistocene vertebrates. Stippled pattern is approximate maximum extent of Pleistocene glaciers. Base map from Goode Base Map Series, Department of Geography, University of Chicago, copyright by the University of Chicago.

1. Rancho La Brea (R), 149
2. Vallecito Creek (Ir), 158
3a. Bautista (Ir), 27
3b. San Timoteo (LB), 27
4. Manix Lake (R), 78
5. Carpinteria (R), 160
6. Channel Islands (R), 147
7. McKittrick (R), 125
8. Livermore Valley (Ir? and R), 120
9. Irvington (Ir), 120
10. Hawver Cave (R), 145
11. Wichman (LB), 89
12a. Samwell Cave (R), 145
12b. Potter Creek Cave (R), 145
13. Fossil Lake (R), 77
14. White Bluffs (LB and later), 151
15. Grand View (LB), 64, 90, 161
17. American Falls (R), 15, 76
18. Tule Springs (R), 45, 130
19. Gypsum Cave (R), 44
20. Anita (LB), 48
21. Ventana Cave (R), 16
22. Papago Springs Cave (R), 135
23. Naco (R), 46
24. Curtis Ranch (LB or Ir), 32
25. Tusker (Ir), 22
26. San Josecito Cave (W), 119
27. Burnet Cave (W), 122
28. Blackwater Draw (LW), 128
29. Sinton (EW), 51
30. Centipede Cave (LW), 88
31. Damp Cave (LW), 88
32. Friesenhahn Cave (LW), 24, 47, 99
33. Cave Without A Name (LW), 106
34. Miller's Cave (LW: A-326, 7,200 ± 300 B.P.), 107
35. Longhorn Cavern (LW), 106, 129
36. Scharbauer (LW), 33

37. Moore Pit (R: Humble, O-235 and 236 37,000 B.P.), 138
38. Clear Creek (MW: SM-534, 28,840 ± 4,740 B.P.), 140
39. Ben Franklin (LW: Loc. 5, SM-532, 9,550 ± 375 B.P.; Loc. 4, SM-533, 11,135 ± 450 B.P.), 139
40. Slaton (R), 97
41. Gilliland (LK), 69
42. Blanco (LB), 78, 96
43. Easley Ranch (R), 20
44. Rock Creek (LK), 155
45. Holloman (LK), 98
46. Cita Canyon (LB), 79, 85
47. Berends (I), 71, 80, 143
48. Doby Springs (I), 71, 80, 101, 144
49. Afton (R), 47, 50
50. Deer Park (A), 57, 62
51. Sanders (LA), 62, 84
52. Seger Gravel Pit (EK), 58
53. Cudahy (LK), 57, 108
54. Borchers (Y), 57, 63, 84
55. Butler Spring (I), 71, 80, 101, 141
56. Mt. Scott (LI), 67, 80, 84, 101, 142
57. Cragin Quarry (S), 23, 57, 71, 80
58. Jinglebob (LS), 60, 71, 80, 84
59. Jones (W: M-1103, > 30,000 B.P.), 57, 71
60. Dixon (N), 62
61. Rezabek (I), 55
62. Broadwater-Lisco (A), 6, 123
63. Sand Draw (A), 65, 95
64. Hay Springs Assemblage (Ir and R), 123
65. Roosevelt Lake (R), 36
66. Enon Sink (W), 100, 132
67. Cherokee Cave (R), 134
68. Herculaneum (W), 103
69. Conard Fissure (Ir and R), 11, 85
70. Alton (R), 47

71. Polecat Creek (LW), 31
72. Island 35 (LW), 159
73. Natchez (W), 49
75. Itchtucknee River (W), 93, 137
76. Santa Fe River Assemblage (LB and R), 10
77. Hornsby Spring and Sink (W: 9,880 ± 270 B.P.), 5, 21
78. Haile (R), 86, 116
79. Arredondo (R), 2, 5, 9
80. Devil's Den (LW?), 3
81. Williston (R), 116
82. Reddick (R), 42, 116
83. Saber-tooth Cave (R), 73
84. Rock Spring (W), 115, 116
85. Melbourne (W), 113, 115, 116
86. Vero (W), 156
87. Seminole Field (W), 2, 4, 12, 113, 116, 132
88. Bradenton Field (W), 112
89. Ashley River (Mixed), 1
90. Little Salt River Cave (W?), 94
91. Craighead Caverns (W?), 94
92. Saltpeter Cave (W?), 94
93. Robinson Cave (LW)
94. Early's Pits (LW), 38
95. Big Bone Lick (W), 124
96. Natural Chimneys (LW), 39
97. Cumberland Cave (R), 35, 85, 117
98. New Paris Sinkholes (LW: Y-727, 11,300 ± 1,000 B.P.), 40
99. Frankstown Cave (R), 37
100. Port Kennedy (Ir), 61, 85, 114, 132
101. Harvard (LW), 118
102. Don Beds (S), 49
103. Little Airplane Cave (W), 105
104. Bootlegger Sink (LW)
105. Cavetown (W), 47

TABLE 1

Late Cenozoic Genera of Non-marine Nearctic Mammals (Counts in the two right-hand columns exclude a few marginal genera that are dominantly Neotropical. The number of genera known as fossils is taken from Table 2)

	Late Pliocene	Early Pleistocene (= post-Pliocene Blancan)	Irvingtonian	Rancholabrean	Wisconsin (= late Rancholabrean)	Living and known also as fossil	Living (with or without fossil record)
Marsupialia	0	0	0	1	1	1	1
Insectivora	7	5	6	9	9	9	10
Chiroptera	1	2	3	12	12	12	23
Primates	0	0	0	1	1	1	1
Edentata	1	3	5	8	8	1	1
Lagomorpha	5	2	4	3	3	3	4
Rodentia	27	25	28	40	39	35	41
Carnivora	19	21	21	22	21	17	20
Proboscidea	4	4	4	4	3	0	0
Perissodactyla	2	3	4	4	4	0	0
Artiodactyla	6	8	13	24	23	9	10
Total	72	73	88	128	124	88	111

versal sequences, which yield a relative chronology that is becoming tied to dates in years (Cox *et al.*, this volume); and (d) potassium-argon radiogenic dates (Evernden *et al.*, 1964). The correlation of these chronologies with each other and with the record of marine sediments and sea-level changes will gain from and richly benefit the study of fossil mammals for the foreseeable future.

Most of the well-known sites of Pleistocene mammalian assemblages in North America are indicated by number in Figure 1, the caption of which provides an entrance to the literature. The faunas we exclude as late Pliocene are Tehama, Tulare, and San Joaquin (California); Hagerman and Sand Point (Idaho); Benson (Arizona); Rexroad and Bender (Kansas); and Red Corral (Texas).

NORTH AMERICAN LAND-MAMMAL AGES

Successive phases in evolution of the North American mammalian fauna are the basis of the land-mammal ages. The most recent three of these are the Blancan, Irvingtonian, and Rancholabrean (Hibbard, 1958; Savage, 1951; Wood *et al.*, 1941). Table 2 shows the combinations of restricted ranges, as based on the first and last appearances that characterize these ages. Outside of central North America, a given fauna is assignable to a land-mammal age even though its place in glacial chronology can scarcely ever be established. Recent potassium-argon radiogenic dates (Evernden *et al.*, 1964) can be correlated roughly with the mammalian ages and thus indirectly with glacial-interglacial events. At present only the earliest Blancan faunas (about 2.5 to 4×10^6 years old) seem to be Pliocene, *i.e.* older than the earliest recognized continental glaciation that reached mid-latitudes. These faunas also are pre-Villafranchian according to the occurrence in North Amer-

ica of more primitive members of phyletic series whose later members occur in Villafranchian faunas of Europe. Such series are the following:

$$Ogmodontomys \rightarrow Cosomys \rightarrow Mimomys \text{ (s.s.)}$$
$$Nekrolagus \qquad \rightarrow Oryctolagus \text{ and } Lepus$$

CORRELATION OF MAMMALIAN FAUNAS
WITH GLACIAL SEQUENCE

The Great Plains region of central North America is the only area where faunas older than the limit of C^{14} dating have been related to glacial-interglacial changes. Most information comes from the intensively studied Meade Basin of southwestern Kansas (Hibbard, 1963b; Hibbard and Taylor, 1960; Taylor, 1960). Correlation of this local faunal and stratigraphic sequence with glacial chronology is based on (a) inferred climatic changes correlated with glacial-interglacial fluctuations, and (b) recognition of lithologic units in southwestern Kansas that can be correlated with those of the glaciated region.

The sequence of diversified vertebrate and invertebrate faunas from southwestern Kansas and the climatic shifts inferred from them (Fig. 2) is the basis for recognizing glacial and interglacial intervals in this area. The magnitude of the faunal shifts, in a vast region of little relief, favors the interpretation that the climatic changes affected most of North America and were probably associated with changes in global circulation. In the southern Great Plains there is evidence of four major episodes of cooler climate separated by three intervals of warmer climate. These intervals are matched with the traditional four glaciations and three interglaciations of the Mississippi Valley.

The petrographically distinctive Pearlette ash (Powers *et al.*, 1958; Swineford, 1949) occurs widely but discontinuously in the Great Plains and is associated at many places with vertebrate and molluscan fossils of the Cudahy fauna, including representatives of many northern or even boreal species (Hibbard, 1949, 1960; Paulson, 1961). These northern elements, and the contrast between this fauna and the immediately younger interglacial Borchers local fauna, indicate that the Pearlette ash is of glacial age. In northwestern Iowa the Pearlette ash occurs stratigraphically above till judged to be Kansan and below Loveland loess (Condra *et al.*, 1950, p. 22-24; Frye *et al.*, 1948).

The Loveland loess in Iowa is younger than Illinoian till and older than Iowan till (Kay and Graham, 1943, p. 50). It has been traced from Iowa westward into Nebraska (Condra *et al.*, 1950; Lugn, 1962) and southward to southern Kansas (Frye and Leonard, 1952, p. 118), where much of the Kingsdown Formation (Cragin, 1896) is correlative with it (Hibbard, 1955a, p. 188; Hibbard *et al.*, 1944). In the Meade Basin the Kingsdown Formation has yielded the Mt. Scott local fauna of late Illinoian glacial age (Hibbard, 1963b) and the Cragin Quarry local fauna of early Sangamon interglacial age (Hibbard and Taylor, 1960), and it is capped by a caliche bed that is interpreted as the Cca horizon of a pedocal soil that formed when the Sangamon soil developed in more humid areas to the north and east. The Sangamon soil has been recognized widely on top of Loveland loess in Kansas and Nebraska (Frye and Leonard, 1952, p. 119-123).

TABLE 2

Range of Late Pliocene and Pleistocene Mammalian Genera Arranged According to First Appearance
(Genera marked with an asterisk (*) are still living, but extinct in the Nearctic Region)

Column headers (both panels): Blancan [Pliocene, Nebraskan, Aftonian, Kansan] | Irvingtonian [Yarmouth, Illinoian] | Rancholabrean [Sangamon, Wisconsin] | Recent [Living]

Left panel:

- Sorex, longtailed shrews
- Bassariscus, ringtail cats
- Peromyscus, white-footed mice
- Mammut, American mastodons
- Hypolagus, extinct rabbits
- Machairodus, sabre-tooth cats
- Scapanus, western moles
- Sciurus, tree squirrels
- Citellus, ground squirrels
- Canis, coyotes and wolfs
- Vulpes, foxes
- Martes, martens and fishers
- Mustela, weasels and minks
- Nannippus, three-toed horses
- Rhynchotherium, mastodons
- Pliauchenia, extinct camels
- Felis, cats
- Lynx, lynx
- Taxidea, badgers
- Marmota, woodchucks and marmots
- Castor, beavers
- Perognathus, pocket mice
- Onychomys, grasshopper mice
- Ochotona, pikas
- Prodipodomys, extinct kangaroo rats
- Bensonomys, extinct mice
- Dipoides, extinct beavers
- Buisnictis, extinct mustelid
- Ogmodontomys, extinct voles
- Notolagus, extinct rabbits
- Baiomys, pigmy mice
- Odocoileus, deer
- Megalonyx, ground sloths
- Tanupolama, extinct llamas
- Paenemarmota, giant woodchuck
- Blarina, shortailed shrews
- Cryptotis, least shrews
- Notiosorex, desert shrews
- Lasiurus, tree bats
- Urocyon, gray foxes
- Procyon, raccoons
- Spilogale, spotted skunks
- Lutra, otters
- Geomys, eastern pocket gophers
- Thomomys, western pocket gophers
- Sigmodon, cotton rats
- Reithrodontomys, harvest mice
- Zapus, jumping mice
- Cuvieronius, extinct mastodons
- Platygonus, extinct peccaries
- Parahodomys, extinct woodrats
- Stegomastodon, mastodons
- Titanotylopus, giant camel
- Pliophenacomys, extinct voles
- Plesippus, zebrine horses
- Borophagus, bone-eating dogs
- Trigonictis, extinct grison
- Ischyrosmilus, sabre-tooth cat
- Chasmaporthetes, extinct hyaena
- Procastoroides, extinct beaver
- Nebraskomys, extinct voles
- Hesperoscalops, extinct moles
- Neterogeomys, extinct gophers
- Pratilepus, extinct rabbits
- Paracryptotis, extinct shrew

- Brachyopsigale, extinct mustelid
- Symmetrodontomys, extinct mouse
- Nekrolagus, extinct rabbit
- Ceratomeryx, extinct pronghorn
- Cosomys, extinct vole
- Canimartes, extinct mustelid
- Pliopotamys, extinct voles
- Synaptomys, bog lemmings
- Cervus, wapiti
- Camelops, extinct camels
- Equus (Asinus?)*, ass-like horses
- Pliolemmus, extinct vole
- Glyptotherium, glyptodons
- Ursus, bears
- Panthera, jaguars
- Cynomys, prairie dogs
- Paramylodon, ground sloths
- Capromeryx, extinct pronghorns
- Castoroides, giant beavers
- Simonycteris, extinct bat
- Hayoceros, extinct pronghorn

Right panel:

- Arctodus, giant short-faced bears
- Microsorex, shrews
- Eptesicus, brown bats
- Gulo, wolverine
- Dipodomys, kangaroo rats
- Ondatra, muskrats
- Phenacomys, phenacomys
- Microtus, voles
- Pedomys, prairie voles
- Pitymys, pine voles
- Neofiber, water rats
- Erethizon, porcupines
- Sylvilagus, cotton-tail rabbits
- Lepus, hares
- Nothrotherium, small ground sloths
- Chlamytherium, giant armadillos
- Dinobastis, sabre-tooth cat
- Smilodon, sabre-tooth cats
- Hydrochoerus,* capybaras
- Mammuthus, mammoths
- Mylohyus, woodland peccaries
- Euceratherium, shrub-oxen
- Preptoceras, shrub-oxen
- Tetrameryx, extinct pronghorns
- Equus (Equus),* modern horses
- Equus (Hemionus?),* hemionus-like horses
- Tapirus,* tapirs
- Stockoceros, extinct pronghorns
- Brachyprotoma, extinct skunk
- Glyptodon, glyptodons
- Osmotherium, extinct skunk
- Tremarctos,* spectacled bears
- Neotoma, woodrats
- Plesiothomomys, extinct gophers
- Etadonomys, extinct kangaroo rat
- Platycerabos, extinct bovid
- Scalopus, eastern moles
- Parascalops, hairytail mole
- Antrozous, pallid bats
- Plecotus, big-eared bats
- Mephitis, striped skunks
- Tamias, eastern chipmunks
- Tamiasciurus, red squirrels
- Clethrionomys, redback voles
- Bison, bison
- Desmodus, vampire bat
- Dasypterus, yellow bat
- Dasypus, armadillos
- Didelphis, opossum
- Myotis, little brown bats
- Tadarida, freetail bats
- Conepatus, hognose skunks
- Glaucomys, flying squirrels
- Bootherium, extinct bovid
- Cervalces, extinct moose
- Brachyostracon, glyptodon
- Boreostracon, glyptodon
- Eremotherium, giant ground sloth
- Paradipoides, extinct beaver
- Oryzomys, rice rats
- Neochoerus, extinct capybara
- Condylura, starnose mole
- Mormoops, leafchin bat
- Leptonycteris, longnose bat
- Pipistrellus, pipistrel bats
- Eumops, mastiff bat
- Aplodontia, sewellel
- Eutamias, western chipmunks
- Cratogeomys, Mexican pocket gopher
- Liomys, Mexican pocket mice
- Dicrostonyx, collared lemmings
- Napaeozapus, woodland jumping mice
- Rangifer, caribou
- Antilocapra, pronghorn
- Oreamnos, mountain goat
- Ovibos, musk-oxen
- Ovis, bighorn sheep
- Heterogeomys,* tropical gophers
- Saiga,* asiatic antelope
- Bos,* yak
- Sangamona, caribou?
- Symbos, woodland musk-ox
- Alces, moose
- Homo, man

EPOCHS	MAMMALIAN AGES	GLACIAL AGES	FAUNAS	CLIMATES AND SIGNIFICANT GEOLOGIC DATA	FAUNAL SHIFTS — Cool-summer elements	Mild-winter elements
RECENT			Living	Mesothermal, semiarid, continental	Many formerly sympatric species now allopatric	Sigmodon hispidus
PLEISTOCENE	RANCHOLABREAN	Wisconsin	Jones	erosional unconformity — Microthermal, subhumid, continental	Ambystoma, neotenic; Sorex cinereus; Citellus richardsoni; Microtus pennsylvanicus	none
		Sangamon	Jinglebob	erosional unconformity — Mesothermal, humid maritime	Sorex cinereus; Microtus pennsylvanicus	Ambystoma, metamorphosed; Terrapene llanensis; Oryzomys fossilis
			Cragin Quarry	caliche bed — Semiarid; Mesothermal, subhumid, maritime	Geochelone; Terrapene llanensis; Holbrookia texana	Crotaphytus collaris; Phrynosoma modestum; Notiosorex crawfordi; Dasypterus golliheri
		Illinoian	Mt. Scott	Microthermal, subhumid, maritime?	Sorex arcticus; S. cinereus; S. palustris; Microtus pennsylvanicus	Terrapene llanensis; Blarina b. carolinensis; Oryzomys fossilis
			Butler Spring	Microthermal, subhumid, continental?	Perca flavescens; Ambystoma, neotenic; Sorex cinereus; Microtus pennsylvanicus	none
	IRVINGTONIAN	Yarmouth	Borchers	erosional unconformity — caliche bed — Semiarid; Mesothermal, subhumid, maritime	none; Ambystoma, metamorphosed; Geochelone; Sigmodon hilli; Spilogale cf. S. ambarvalis	
		Kansan	Cudahy	Pearlette ash bed; Microthermal, subhumid, maritime	Ambystoma, neotenic; Sorex cinereus; S. lacustris; S. megapalustris	Microsorex pratensis; Synaptomys (Mictomys); Microtus paroperarius / none
			Seger		No climatically significant species	
	BLANCAN	Aftonian	Sanders	erosional unconformity — Mesothermal, subhumid, maritime	Some warm-temperate and subtropical	Ambystoma, metamorphosed; Sigmodon intermedius; Bensonomys meadensis; Pliolemmus antiquus
			Deer Park	caliche bed — Semiarid; Mesothermal, maritime	elements from Rexroad fauna absent	Geochelone; Pliopotamys meadensis; Pliolemmus antiquus
		Nebraskan	Unnamed		No climatically significant species	
PLIOCENE			Bender	erosional unconformity — Mesothermal, subhumid, maritime	none	Mammalian fauna not published
			Rexroad	caliche bed — Semiarid; Mesothermal, subhumid, maritime	none	Geochelone rexroadensis; Notiosorex jacksoni; Baiomys spp.; Sigmodon intermedius; Nerterogeomys minor; Bassariscus casei

Figure 2. Late Cenozoic faunal shifts and inferred climatic changes in the southern Great Plains.

BIOGEOGRAPHY

Changes in geographic distribution of species through geologic time are usually accompanied by morphological changes. Hence biogeography is scarcely separable from evolution. We consider three aspects of these topics: faunal shifts, which are changes in distribution associated with ecological changes but with little taxonomic differentiation; historical biogeography, involving changes in distribution over much of North America (including the Bering Straits area), associated with some taxonomic differentiation; and evolution, in which geographic distribution is relatively insignificant.

FAUNAL SHIFTS

The fossil record is so discontinuous that virtually no well-documented evolutionary sequence of American Pleistocene mammals have been described. Even at the generic level the number of first appearances seems to be correlated with the number of known localities (Table 3). One of the principal reasons for the discontinuous record is the large-scale faunal shifts that include such occurrences as tapirs in Pennsylvania (Simpson, 1945), ground sloths in Alaska (Stock, 1942), and boreal lemmings in the southern Great Plains (Hibbard, 1949).

The most detailed studies of Pleistocene faunal sequence come from the Great Plains, mainly southwestern Kansas and northwestern Oklahoma. A general hypothesis of major climatic shifts in this region has been developed by Hibbard and Taylor (Hibbard, 1944, 1949, 1960, 1963b; Taylor, 1960, 1965; Hibbard and Taylor, 1960). The inferred climatic sequence explains a wide variety of data, such as the former association of species that are now allopatric (living in widely separated areas), the repetitive stratigraphic occurrence of species, and the present-day relic occurrence of others. It applies to (and is drawn from) such diverse groups as fishes, amphibians, reptiles, birds, mammals, and mollusks. The same hypothetical climates are unlikely to have occurred outside central North America, but they unify so many facts and interpretations in this area that they will be a useful tool for future research.

Climate can affect individual mammals directly by lethal extremes of temperature or by drought, but its effects on species or genera of mammals through geologic time are probably indirect, acting through the soils and vegetation of the habitat. Smaller mammals, with a narrower range of habitat and individual home range than the larger carnivores or herbivores, are influenced more by the microclimate in which they live than by regional climatic change (Burt, 1958). Hence it is reasonable and a justification of uniformitarian interpretations that the ecological conclusions drawn from rodents and insectivores are similar to those drawn from the associated lower vertebrates, mollusks, and plants. The consistency of inferences from different elements of late Cenozoic biotas in the Great Plains is decisive proof (and the only test possible) of the validity of the method.

Figure 2 summarizes the latest Cenozoic sequence of faunas and inferred climates in southwestern Kansas (see Taylor, this volume, for a similar summary of associated

TABLE 3

Earliest North American Records of Eurasian Immigrants

GENERA	EARLIEST RECORDS
Ursus	Late Blancan (Loc. 46)
Mammuthus	Late Kansan (Loc. 45)
Preptoceras?	Late Kansan (Loc. 44)
Bison	Illinoian (Loc. 48)
Smilodon	Irvingtonian (Loc. 100)
Gulo	Irvingtonian (Loc. 100)
Euceratherium	Irvingtonian (Loc. 9)
Cervalces	Rancholabrean (Loc. 99)
Rangifer	Wisconsin (Hibbard, 1958)
Oreamnos	Wisconsin (Hibbard, 1958)
Ovibos	Wisconsin (Hibbard, 1958)
Ovis	Wisconsin (Hibbard, 1958)
Alces	Wisconsin (Hibbard, 1958)
Bos	Wisconsin (Hibbard, 1958)
Saiga	Wisconsin (Hibbard, 1958)
Bootherium	Wisconsin (Loc. 95)
Symbos	Wisconsin (Loc. 95)

mollusks). The climatic interpretations are drawn from a variety of organisms, including mammals. These interpretations are the simplest possible based on the assumption that fossils imply past habitats like those of their living morphological equivalents. A consistent application of this assumption suggests that present-day climates, with their seasonal extremes of temperature and aridity, are geologically atypical, even of the Pleistocene. Most of the specific fossil associations would be inexplicable if the climate of the present were taken as the key to the past. But if different distributions of precipitation and seasonal extremes are considered as separate variables, seemingly anomalous associations of species are rationalized.

The first major southward faunal shift of ecological significance is shown by some of the mammals of the Cudahy fauna (Hibbard, 1949, p. 1421) of late Kansan age. Some living species of mammals of the Boreal Subregion extended their ranges southward during Illinoian and/or Wisconsin time. Their remains have been recovered in southern localities, *e.g. Ovibos*, Muskox (Fig. 3); *Microtus xanthognathus* (Fig. 4); *Sorex arcticus* (Fig. 5); and *Dicrostonyx*, Collared Lemming (Fig. 6). Remains of *Sorex cinereus*, Masked Shrew, and *Synaptomys cooperi*, Bog Lemming, are found as far south as San Josecito Cave, Mexico (Fig. 1, Loc. 26); and *Sorex palustris*, Northern Water Shrew, is known from Oklahoma, Kansas, and north-central Tennessee (Fig. 1, Loc. 48, 56, and 93).

The Yellow-cheeked Vole (*Microtus xanthognathus*) and the Rock Vole (*M. chrotorrhinus*) lived in the same area in Pennsylvania and Virginia (Fig. 4) during late Wisconsin time; they now live in widely separated areas in Boreal North America. Guilday (1963) recovered fossil remains of *Dicrostonyx* (*Misothermus*) *hudsonius*, Labrador Collared Lemming, in Pennsylvania (Fig. 6). He considered the present tundra population of this species to be a probable relic of a former Holarctic pre-Wisconsin distribution.

Southward and southwestward retractions of ranges of ecological significance during the later Pleistocene are shown by the present distribution of *Dasypterus*, Yellow Bat (Fig. 4); *Hydrochoerus*, Capybara; *Oryzomys*, Rice Rat (Fig. 3); *Neofiber*, Water Rat (Fig. 1, Loc. 40, 61, **and**

Figure 3. Recent distribution (A) of the Muskox, *Ovibos moschatus,* with fossil records (99, and unnumbered circles). Open circles indicate questionable identifications. Data from reference citations 28, 43, 49, 50, 52, 83. Northerly portion of the Recent distribution (B) of the Marsh Rice Rat, *Oryzomys palustris* (including *O. couesi,* fide E. R. Hall, 1960, Southw. Nat., v. 5, No. 3, p. 171-173), with fossil records for *O. fossilis* (43, 56, 58). Data from reference citations 20, 43, 60, 67. *Oryzomys palustris* is known also from several post-Pleistocene prehistoric localities, not mapped, east of the Mississippi River and north of its modern limits.

100); *Conepatus,* Hognose Skunk (Fig. 5); *Felis pardalis,* Ocelot (Fig. 7); *Panthera onca,* Jaguar (Fig. 8).

The presence of maritime climates and extensive broad, marshy, undissected valleys seems to have provided the habitat for the northern ranges of the Capybara, Rice Rat, and Water Rat.

Neofiber, the Water Rat, is a good example of a form whose range has become greatly restricted because of the lack of habitat or because of competition with *Ondatra,* the Muskrat, or for both reasons (Birkenholz, 1963). *Neofiber* is not closely related to *Ondatra,* and in middle Pleistocene faunas (Port Kennedy Cave, Fig. 1, Loc. 100, and Rezabek, Fig. 1, Loc. 61) these two forms were associated, although at the present time their ranges do not overlap. It is of interest to note that the range of the Jaguar during the Pleistocene has been approximately that of the peccaries.

Westward shifts in ranges are shown by *Mormoops,* Leaf-chinned Bat (Fig. 6); *Desmodus,* Vampire Bat (Fig. 1, Loc. 26, 78, 79, and 82); *Citellus,* Ground Squirrel (Fig. 1,

Loc. 93, 96, 97, 98, and 104); *Taxidea,* Badger (Fig. 1, Loc. 97 and 100); *Conepatus,* Hognose Skunk (Fig. 5); and *Ochotona,* Pika (Fig. 7).

HISTORICAL BIOGEOGRAPHY

The Nearctic Region (Canada, continental United States, northern Mexico, including the central plateau but not the coastal lowlands on either side) is inhabited by 111 genera of mammals. These have various patterns of distribution and are variably distinct from the mammals of the Palaearctic and Neotropical Regions. The most marked endemism is at the family level: the pronghorn (Antilocapridae) and sewellel (Aplodontidae) are restricted to the Nearctic. At the other extreme 21 species may be common to North America and Eurasia (Rausch, 1963), and many more to the southern Nearctic and the Neotropical Regions. These different patterns of distribution and different degrees of endemism imply different histories. The Cenozoic (mainly pre-Quaternary) differentiation and spread of the North American families and many genera of mammals have been summarized by Burt (1958), Savage (1958), and Simpson (1947). We comment on the Quaternary spread of mammals (a) between the Neotropical and Nearctic Regions, (b) between the Palaearctic and Nearctic Regions in the Bering Straits area, and (c) within the Nearctic.

Figure 4. Recent distribution (A) of the Rock Vole, *Microtus chrotorrhinus,* with fossil records (96, 98, 104), (B) of the Yellow-cheeked Vole, *M. xanthognathus,* with fossil records (96, 98, 104), and the northerly portion of the Recent distribution (C) of the yellow bat, *Dasypterus,* with fossil records (57, 82). Data from reference citations 39, 42-43, 71.

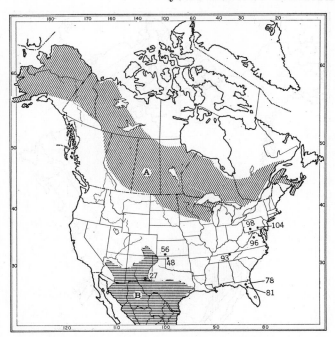

Figure 5. Recent distribution (A) of the Arctic Shrew, *Sorex arcticus,* in North America, with fossil records (48, 56, 93, 96, 98, 104), and the northerly portion of the Recent distribution (B) of the Hognose Skunks, *Conepatus* (including the nominal species *C. mesoleucus* and *C. leuconotus*) with fossil records (27, 78, 81). Data from reference citation 43 and from those cited under each locality in the explanation to Fig. 1.

Neotropical-Nearctic relationships. The fossil record in Central America and Mexico is so little known that times of faunal interchange in Pliocene and Pleistocene times can scarcely be defined. Some groups of ultimate South American ancestry (hystricomorph rodents and edentates) extended their ranges northward into the Nearctic Region during this time. Quaternary events may have had little effect on these genera except in changing the limits of habitable areas during glaciations.

Some genera that are now Neotropical (for example, the peccaries and tapir, *Tapirus* [*Tapirella*]) occurred during Quaternary time far north of their present range. They are most reasonably regarded not as tropical or subtropical elements in Quaternary faunas but as genera that were once widespread in the southern Nearctic Region and that have been extinguished in much of their range by late Quaternary climatic changes.

Palaearctic-Nearctic relationships. During late Pliocene and Quaternary times the spread of mammals between the Old and New Worlds could only have occurred in the Bering Straits region, although for the early Tertiary we cannot categorically exclude faunal connections around the North Atlantic. The clearest paleontologic evidence is the appearance in North America of groups with ancestors in

Eurasia. Such immigrations are particularly noticeable at the family level (Elephantidae and Bovidae) but range through lower taxonomic ranks. Table 3 summarizes the earliest known occurrences of genera that probably entered North America as the same or closely related genera during Quaternary or immediately pre-Quaternary times. A recent study by Kurtén (1963) points the way toward future refinements.

Zoogeographical studies of living and fossil mammals (Burt, 1958; Rausch, 1963; Savage, 1958; Simpson, 1947; Stokes and Condie, 1961) have cast light on the approximate times and range of habitats in Quaternary faunal dispersal in the Bering Straits region. Direct paleontologic and stratigraphic evidence in the Seward Peninsula athwart the path of mammalian spread has become available only recently (Hopkins, 1959a, b).

Table 3 shows that half of the immigrant genera listed have an earliest known record in the Wisconsin. These genera are predominantly those characteristic or tolerant of arctic-alpine environments. The relative predominance of fossil deposits in Alaska of Wisconsin age is partly responsible for the first records of such forms, but the relative severity of Wisconsin-age climates is probably a significant cause also. Fossils of latest Pleistocene mammoth, bison, and horse in a region then vegetated with

Figure 6. Recent mainland distribution (A) of the Collared Lemming, *Dicrostonyx groenlandicus,* (B) of the Labrador Collared Lemming *D. hudsonius,* with fossil record (98), and the northerly portion of the Recent distribution (C) of Peters' Leaf-chinned Bat, *Mormoops megalophylla,* with fossil record (84). Data from reference citations 40, 43, 116. Rausch (1963) regards the above forms of *Dicrostonyx* as conspecific with *D. torquatus.*

tundra (Hopkins, 1959b) show that many of these mammals could have crossed the emergent Bering-Chukchi Platform during a time of lowered sea level in the late Pleistocene.

An earlier immigration that will be of significance both to regional stratigraphy in North America and to chronology of the Bering Straits region is that of *Mammuthus*. Two separate stocks of this genus seem to have entered North America. The later was *M. primigenius*, the Woolly Mammoth, during the Rancholabrean. The earlier was the stock first seen as *Mammuthus haroldcooki* in Kansas and Oklahoma in late Kansan deposits. It may have given rise to all later American species except *M. primigenius*. These early mammoths were not boreal animals; they are rare in southwestern Kansas (Hibbard, 1953) and in Oklahoma (Meade, 1953), and are common in the Seymour Formation of north-central Texas (Hibbard, in preparation). The passage of these animals across the Bering Strait during a glacial interval seems most unlikely, and yet the morphological grade of the first immigrants seems to preclude a Pliocene age. Perhaps the early Pleistocene of our definition precedes the early Pleistocene of Hopkins' (1959a) usage.

Intra-Nearctic relationships. The present patterns of distribution and the composition of the living fauna are the

Figure 8. Northerly portion of the Recent distribution of the Jaguar, *Panthera (Jaguarius) onca*, with fossil records including *P. (J.) onca augusta* but excluding *P. (J.) atrox*. The locality in Nebraska represented by the unnumbered solid circle is the type locality ("Niobrara River") for *P. (J.) onca augusta*. Open circles indicate questionable identifications. Data from reference citations 43, 94, 105, 129, 131.

Figure 7. Recent distribution (A) of the Pika, *Ochotona (Pika)*, in North America, with fossil record (97), and the northerly portion of the Recent distribution (B) of the Ocelot, *Felis (Leopardus) pardalis*, with fossil record (82). Data from reference citations 35, 43, 116.
      The fossil *Ochotona* belongs to the subgenus *Pika* on the basis of partial separation of the incisive and palatine foramina.

product of extinction and evolution as well as of considerable restrictions in distribution. Such changes can be studied most effectively by synthetic biogeographic studies of the type made by Blair (1958) and Neill (1957). The frequent disagreements about the chronology of range changes and about the age of a given pattern of distribution indicate that biogeography is unlikely to be a fruitful area of research without an objective method of analyzing its data.

Quaternary restrictions of range are known in many genera. The gopher, *Geomys*, and shrew, *Blarina*, which formerly occurred west of the continental divide but are now eastern (Hibbard, 1959; White and Downs, 1961) probably were affected by the regional disappearance of their habitat. Late Pleistocene aridity that deprived them of moist soil and humus is a plausible cause. In other cases the reasons remain obscure.

EVOLUTION

The Pleistocene fossil record of mammals in North America is more nearly complete than that of any other class of organisms. As shown in Table 4, only 20% of the extant genera are unrepresented as fossils. Despite this relatively full record, the phyletic development of practically no

TABLE 4

First and Last Appearances of Late Cenozoic
Mammalian Genera Shown in Tables 1 and 2
(*N* = number of localities that are shown in Fig. 1. Late Pliocene
localities are listed in the text under Scope of Pleistocene)

	First appearance		Last appearance	
	Per-cent	Number	Per-cent	Number
Late Pliocene (*N* = 9)	52	37 of 72	18	13 of 72
Early Pleistocene (= post-Pliocene Blancan) (*N* = 14)	19	14 of 73	23	17 of 73
Irvingtonian (*N* = 14)	36	32 of 88	12	10 of 88
Rancholabrean (*N* = 81)	40	50 of 128	31	40 of 128
Wisconsin (*N* = 59)	25	31 of 124	30	36 of 124
Living	20	22 of 111	—	— —

species has been documented. Evidently changes in habitat and geographic range have added to the other gaps in the record caused by geologic and human factors.

PHYLETIC SEQUENCES

The better-documented phyletic sequences include species of the Jumping Mouse, *Zapus*, and of the White-footed Mouse, *Peromyscus*. Klingener (1963) described a series of four successional subspecies leading from the late Pliocene *Zapus sandersi rexroadensis* to the Recent *Zapus hudsonius* (Fig. 9). Hibbard (1955a, p. 212; Hibbard and Taylor, 1960, p. 175) found that the Sangamon *Peromyscus progressus* is closely related to the living *P. leucopus* but has more primitive tooth characters. *P. leucopus* may therefore have evolved during the latest Sangamon and Wisconsin.

Less well documented but plausible lineages have been inferred for several other genera of mammals. These phyletic lines are the simplest and shortest that are consistent with the available fossil record and the data of comparative anatomy, and hence their errors will prove mainly due to oversimplification. Such synthesis of fossil interpretation with data from related fields, and the discovery of more fossils, will favor the inference of longer stratigraphic ranges and of slower rates of change and geographic spread. Students of evolution, biogeography, and Pleistocene stratigraphy should understand that the mammalian evolutionary sequences are only the simplest interpretations of a fragmentary record. Such phyletic lines have been proposed, mainly on dental characters, in many genera of which we list only a sample.

1. Hibbard (1963a) has interpreted evolution of some rabbit genera as taking place in the early Pleistocene—*Sylvilagus*, *Caprolagus*, *Oryctolagus*, and *Lepus* from a "pro-*Sylvilagus*" stock.

2. The stratigraphic succession of fossil mammoths is consistent with an interpretation of progressive increase in number of enamel plates in the teeth. Hibbard (1953) suggested that the oldest known American species, *Mammuthus haroldcooki* from the late Kansan of southwestern Kansas and Oklahoma, is ancestral to *M. imperator*.

3. Kurtén (1963) has discussed Old World–New World lineages in the saber-toothed cats of the *Homotherium-Dinobastis* and *Megantereon-Smilodon* lines and in the black bears of the *Ursus thibetanus–U. americanus* line.

A possible example of apparent evolutionary change that results only from ecological changes has been described by Hibbard (1963b). Stratigraphically distinct samples of the Short-tailed Shrew, *Blarina*, represent different-sized animals that would be ascribed to an evolving lineage in conventional study. Similar differences can be found in the large northern and small southern subspecies of *Blarina brevicauda*, and associated faunas support the interpretation that the observed morphological differences are due to shifts of a cline.

MODERNIZATION OF QUATERNARY FAUNA

The progressive modernization of the Quaternary Nearctic mammalian fauna has taken place through the evolution of new genera and species from autochthonous stocks, through immigration from the Neotropical and Palaearctic Regions, through elimination by absolute extinction, or through extinction of widespread groups in the Nearctic Region but with survival elsewhere, *e.g.* camels and horses.

The only extant species known from pre-Quaternary deposits is the badger, *Taxidea taxus*, in the Rexroad local fauna. The known fossils include only lower jaws, and if a skull is found it will probably reveal specific differences. Even if not, the generalization that mammalian species are of Quaternary origin is valid. (The modernization of genera and species in the faunal sequence of southwestern Kansas

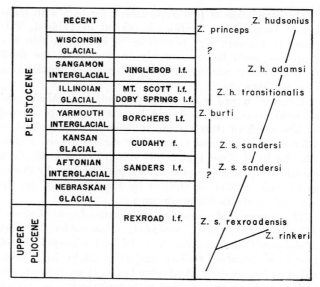

Figure 9. Evolution of the species and subspecies of the jumping mouse, *Zapus*, after Klingener (1963). The Pleistocene fossils are from localities 48, 51, 53, 54, 56, and 58 (Fig. 1) in southwestern Kansas and adjacent Oklahoma, but *Zapus* lives only farther north and east in the Great Plains.

has been contrasted by Taylor, this volume, with the record of mollusks.)

Taking the stratigraphic ranges (Table 2) at face value one might wrongly infer the evolution of many new genera during the Pleistocene. The ecologic replacement of some genera by others, the inverse correlation of number of known fossil localities with age, and the immigration of animals into areas where fossiliferous sediments have been preserved are all more likely causes of the known range than taxonomic evolution.

The following pairs of genera occur in successive strata, with no zone of overlap or with a relatively short interval of joint occurrence. Their morphologic differences are great enough to preclude ancestral-descendant relationship, but their similarities are such that they may have overlapped ecologically. In such cases the first appearance of the younger genera in the fossil record may be due primarily to ecological replacement.

OLDER GENERA		YOUNGER GENERA
Plesippus (zebrine) *Nannippus* (three toed)	replaced by	*Equus* s.s., large horse *Equus* (*Asinus?*) and *Equus* (*Hemionus?*), smaller horse-like forms
Stegomastodon	replaced by	*Mammuthus*, mammoth
Capromeryx	replaced by	*Antilocapra*, pronghorn
Hypolagus	replaced by	*Sylvilagus*, rabbit and *Lepus*, hare
Pliophenacomys	replaced by	*Microtus*, vole
Arctodus	replaced by	*Ursus* (brown and grizzly bear but not the black bear)

The correlation of first appearance of genera with number of known fossil localities is evident in Table 4. This shows that a very high percentage of Pleistocene first appearances could be due entirely to quality of the fossil record, without any evolutionary changes or immigration from outside areas.

The fossil record is so scanty, particularly in Alaska and adjacent areas, that we do not know when groups arrived or how much of their taxonomic differentiation took place after their arrival and before their earliest record as fossils. Study of these immigrants can be carried out most effectively by biogeographic studies such as those by Stokes and Condie (1961) on *Ovis* or by Rausch (1963) on the mammals of the Bering Straits area.

The genera and subgenera *Sylvilagus, Lepus, Lagurus, Microtus, Dinobastis, Smilodon, Mammuthus, Equus, Mylohyus, Camelops, Rangifer, Alces, Antilocapra, Bison, Oreamnos, Symbos, Ovibos,* and *Ovis* might have originated as late as early Pleistocene times. If so, they are the highest-ranking groups that are geologically so young. Although mammalian evolution might have been accelerated during the Pleistocene in some groups, this time-span was so short that differentiation hardly ever went beyond the species-group level. If *Ondatra* is derived from *Pliopotamys* this would be the latest origin of a genus that can be documented in the Pleistocene of North America. In general, the Pleistocene record is conspicuous by the

elimination of old stocks rather than the development of new ones.

PROBLEMS

The problems available for future research include a heritage of old, unsolved ones, along with newly raised questions that result from an increase in knowledge in paleontology as well as in other fields.

The most obvious old problem is as old as the study of Quaternary mammals. Why did the most conspicuous extinctions occur so late and after the last glaciation? Recent studies (Hester, 1960; Martin, 1958; Martin *et al.,* 1961) and the application of C^{14} dates have provided a wealth of data but no consensus. We suggest that any plausible explanation of late Pleistocene extinction cannot be *ad hoc,* but must also shed light on previous mammalian extinctions, contemporaneous non-mammalian extinctions, and on contemporaneous range changes in organisms that did not become extinct.

Newly apparent topics, and those that can be newly attacked with profit, have come from new techniques as well as the gradual accumulation of data. All problems of Quaternary chronology and correlation, and all topics that involve these matters, will be influenced by the results of C^{14} and K/Ar dating and by research on geomagnetic polarity. Study of rates of evolution, of geographic spread, and of regional changes in habitat are particularly dependent upon a refined chronology.

A particularly worthwhile study with worldwide ramifications would be paleoecological analysis of the biota associated with the Pearlette ash. This ash provides a unique, virtually contemporaneous datum throughout much of the Great Plains for a time when a continental ice sheet covered part of northern North America and the climate and its zonation was radically different from that of today. Such a study would require the long-term collaboration of diverse specialists; it thus reflects our belief that knowledge of Quaternary mammals will be most advanced through studies devoted to geology and entire biotas, and not solely to Quaternary mammals.

Examples of a few recent studies that exemplify valuable data gained from a synthetic approach are given below. It is no coincidence that some of the most valuable work is by those not trained as mammalian paleontologists.

The occurrence of beaver-cut wood in peat deposits of New England led Kaye (1962) to suggest that the region in early postglacial time was less swampy than today. If beavers were responsible for providing sites of accumulation for pollen-bearing sediments perhaps they also account for irregularities in pollen stratigraphy.

Late Pleistocene wood rat (*Neotoma*) middens in southern Nevada include twigs and seeds of juniper not now living in the low desert mountains. The relatively large size of the plant remains makes them more significant indicators of local vegetation than windblown pollen; hence Wells and Jorgensen (1964) were able to infer late Pleistocene changes in climate and in distribution of wood rat and juniper woodland.

In an area near Denver, Colorado, Scott (1962, 1963) studied Quaternary history in a particularly thorough way.

The fossil mammals he recorded do not include great diversity of species, but the integration of fossil mammals with geomorphology, buried soils, detailed physical stratigraphy, and the record of other fossil organisms points the way for future research of this kind.

The most abundant and detailed information about glacial-interglacial changes in climate and habitats comes from the Illinoian and Sangamon faunas of southwestern Kansas and northwestern Oklahoma (see references to faunas 47, 48, 55-58). Fossils representing angiosperms, mollusks, fishes, amphibians, reptiles, birds, and mammals provide a wide variety of sources of ecological and stratigraphic data. From these studies far more information about environmental changes has been gained than the study of any one group could yield, and far more information about mammals than a strictly mammalogical study would produce.

REFERENCES

Numbers in parentheses refer to list of faunas in explanation of Figure 1.

1. Allen, G. M., 1926, Fossil mammals from South Carolina: Harvard Univ. Mus. Comp. Zool. Bull., v. 67, p. 447-467 (**89**)
2. Arata, A. A., 1959, Revaluation of the Pleistocene *Urocyon seminolensis* from Florida: Florida Acad. Sci. Quart. J., v. 22, p. 133 (**79, 87**)
3. —— 1961, Meadow vole (*Microtus pennsylvanicus*) from the Quaternary of Florida: Florida Acad. Sci. Quart. J., v. 24, p. 117-121 (**80**)
4. Arata, A. A., and Hutchison, J. H., 1964, The raccoon (*Procyon*) in the Pleistocene of North America: Tulane Stud. Geol., v. 2, p. 21-27 (**87**)
5. Bader, R. S., 1957, Two Pleistocene mammalian faunas from Alachua County, Florida: Florida Mus. Biol. Sci. Bull., v. 2, p. 53-75 (**77, 79**)
6. Barbour, E. H., and Schultz, C. B., 1937, An early Pleistocene fauna from Nebraska: Amer. Mus. Novitates 942, 10 p. (**62**)
7. Birkenholz, D. E., 1963, A study of the life history and ecology of the round-tailed muskrat (*Neofiber alleni* True) in north-central Florida: Ecol. Monogr. 33, p. 187-213
8. Blair, W. F., 1958, Distributional patterns of vertebrates in the southern United States in relation to past and present environments: *in* C. L. Hubbs (ed.), Zoogeography: Amer. Assoc. Adv. Sci. Publ. 51, p. 433-468
9. Brodkorb, Pierce, 1959, The Pleistocene avifauna of Arredondo, Florida: Florida Mus. Biol. Sci. Bull., v. 4, p. 269-291 (**79**)
10. —— 1963, A giant flightless bird from the Pleistocene of Florida: Auk, v. 80, p. 111-115 (**76**)
11. Brown, Barnum, 1908, The Conard fissure, a Pleistocene bone deposit in northern Arkansas: with descriptions of two new genera and twenty new species of mammals: Amer. Mus. Nat. Hist. Mem., v. 9, p. 155-208 (**69**)
12. Bullen, R. P., 1964, Artifacts, fossils, and a radiocarbon date from Seminole Field, Florida: Florida Acad. Sci. Quart. J. (1963), v. 26, p. 293-303 (**87**)
13. Burt, W. H., 1958, The history and affinities of the Recent land mammals of western North America: *in* Hubbs, C. L. (ed.), Zoogeography: Amer. Assoc. Adv. Sci. Publ. 51, p. 131-154
14. Camp, C. L., *et al.*, 1940-1961, Bibliography of fossil vertebrates, 1928-1953: Geol. Soc. Amer. Spec. Pap. 27, 503 p.; Spec. Pap. 42, 663 p.; Mem. 37, 371 p.; Mem. 57, 465 p.; Mem. 84, 532 p.
15. Carr, W. J., and Trimble, D. E., 1963, Geology of the American Falls quadrangle, Idaho: U.S. Geol. Surv. Bull. 1121-G, 44 p. (**17**)
16. Colbert, E. H., 1950, The fossil vertebrates: *in* E. W. Haury and collaborators, The stratigraphy and archaeology of Ventana Cave, Arizona: Tucson, Univ. Arizona Press, p. 126-148 (**21**)
17. Condra, G. E., Reed, E. C., and Gordon, E. D., 1950, Correlation of the Pleistocene deposits of Nebraska: Nebraska Geol. Surv. Bull. 15A, 74 p.
18. Cox, Allan, Doell, R. R., and Dalrymple, G. B., this volume, Quaternary paleomagnetic stratigraphy
19. Cragin, F. W., 1896, Preliminary notice of three late Neocene terranes of Kansas: Colorado Coll. Stud. 6, p. 53-54
20. Dalquest, W. W., 1962, The Good Creek Formation, Pleistocene of Texas, and its fauna: J. Paleont., v. 36, p. 568-582 (**43**)
21. Dolan, E. M., and Allen, G. T., Jr., 1961, An investigation of the Darby and Hornsby Springs sites, Alachua County, Florida: Florida Geol. Surv. Spec. Publ. 7, p. 1-124 (**77**)
22. Downey, J. S., 1962, Leporidae of the Tusker local fauna from southeastern Arizona: J. Paleont., v. 36, p. 1112-1115 (**25**)
23. Etheridge, Richard, 1958, Pleistocene lizards of the Cragin Quarry Fauna of Meade County, Kansas: Copeia, 1958, p. 94-101 (**57**)
24. Evans, G. L., 1961, The Friesenhahn Cave: Texas Mem. Mus. Bull. 2, p. 1-22 (**32**)
25. Evernden, J. F., Savage, D. E., Curtis, G. H., and James, G. T., 1964, Potassium-argon dates and the Cenozoic mammalian chronology of North America: Amer. J. Sci., v. 262, p. 145-198
26. Fejfar, Oldrich, 1961, Review of Quaternary Vertebrata in Czechoslovakia: Warsaw, Inst. Geol., Prace 34, p. 109-118
26a. Flint, R. F., 1957, Glacial and Pleistocene geology: New York, John Wiley & Sons, 553 p.
27. Frick, Childs, 1921, Extinct vertebrate faunas of the badlands of Bautista Creek and San Timoteo Canon, southern California: Univ. California Dept. Geol. Bull., v. 12, p. 277-424 (**3a, 3b**)
28. —— 1937, Horned ruminants of North America: Amer. Mus. Nat. Hist. Bull., v. 69, 669 p.
29. Frye, J. C., and Leonard, A. B., 1952, Pleistocene geology of Kansas: Kansas Geol. Surv. Bull. 99, 230 p.
30. Frye, J. C., Swineford, A., and Leonard, A. B., 1948, Correlation, Pleistocene of Great Plains with glacial section: J. Geol., v. 56, p. 501-525
31. Galbreath, E. C., 1938, Post-glacial fossil vertebrates from east-central Illinois: Field Mus. Nat. Hist. Geol. Ser., v. 6, p. 303-313 (**71**)

32. Gazin, C. L., 1942, The late Cenozoic vertebrate faunas from the San Pedro Valley, Arizona: U.S. Natl. Mus. Proc., v. 92, p. 475-518 (**24**)

33. —— 1955, Identification of some vertebrate fossil material from the Scharbauer Site, Midland, Texas: in Wendorf, Fred, Krieger, A. D., and Albritton, C. C., The Midland discovery: Austin, Univ. Texas Press, Appendix 2, p. 119 (**36**)

34. —— 1957, Exploration for the remains of giant ground sloths in Panama: Smithson. Instn. Rep. for 1956, Publ. 4279, p. 341-354

35. Gidley, J. W., and Gazin, C. L., 1938, The Pleistocene vertebrate fauna from Cumberland Cave, Maryland: U.S. Natl. Mus. Bull. 171, 99 p. (**97**)

36. Green, Morton, 1963, Some late Pleistocene rodents from South Dakota: J. Paleont., v. 37, p. 688-690 (**65**)

37. Guilday, J. E., 1961, *Plecotus* from the Pennsylvania Pleistocene: J. Mammal., v. 42, p. 402-403 (**99**)

38. —— 1962a, Notes on Pleistocene vertebrates from Wythe County, Virginia: Carnegie Instn. Pittsburg Mus. Ann., v. 36, p. 77-86 (**94**)

39. —— 1962b, The Pleistocene local fauna of the Natural Chimneys, Augusta County, Virginia: Carnegie Instn. Pittsburg Mus. Ann., v. 36, p. 87-122 (**96**)

40. —— 1963, Pleistocene zoogeography of the lemming, *Dicrostonyx:* Evolution, v. 17, p. 194-197

42. Gut, H. J., and Ray, C. E., 1964, The Pleistocene vertebrate fauna of Reddick, Florida: Florida Acad. Sci. Quart. J., v. 26, p. 315-328 (**82**)

43. Hall, E. R., and Kelson, K. R., 1959, The mammals of North America: New York, Ronald Press, 1084 p.

44. Harrington, M. R., 1933, Gypsum Cave, Nevada: Southwest Mus. Pap. 8, p. 1-197 (**19**)

45. Harrington, M. R., and Simpson, R. D., 1961, Tule Springs, Nevada, with other evidences of Pleistocene man in North America: Southwest Mus. Pap. 18, 146 p. (**18**)

46. Haury, E. W., Antevs, Ernst, and Lance, J. F., 1953, Artifacts with mammoth remains, Naco, Arizona: Amer. Antiq., v. 19, p. 1-24 (**23**)

47. Hay, O. P., 1920, Descriptions of some Pleistocene vertebrates found in the United States: U.S. Natl. Mus. Proc., v. 58, p. 83-146 (**32, 49, 70, 105**)

48. —— 1921, Descriptions of species of Pleistocene Vertebrata, types or specimens of most of which are preserved in the United States National Museum: U.S. Natl. Mus. Proc., v. 59, p. 599-642 (**2**)

49. —— 1923, The Pleistocene of North America and its vertebrated animals from the states east of the Mississippi River and from the Canadian Provinces east of longitude 95°: Carnegie Instn. Publ. 322, 499 p. (**73**, p. 389-393; **102**, p. 281-283; and others)

50. —— 1924, The Pleistocene of the middle region of North America and its vertebrated animals: Carnegie Instn. Publ. 322A, 385 p. (**49**, p. 254-255; and others)

51. —— 1926, A collection of Pleistocene vertebrates from southwestern Texas: U.S. Natl. Mus. Proc., v. 68, p. 1-18 (**29**)

52. —— 1927, The Pleistocene of the western region of North America and its vertebrated animals: Carnegie Instn. Publ. 322B, 346 p.

53. —— 1929-30, Second bibliography and catalogue of the fossil Vertebrata of North America: Carnegie Instn. Publ. 390, v. I, 916 p.; v. II, 1074 p.

54. Hester, J. J., 1960, Late Pleistocene extinction and radiocarbon dating: Amer. Antiq., v. 26, p. 58-77

55. Hibbard, C. W., 1943, The Rezabek fauna, a new Pleistocene fauna from Lincoln County, Kansas: Kansas Univ. Sci. Bull., v. 29, pt. 2, p. 235-247 (**61**)

56. —— 1944, Stratigraphy and vertebrate paleontology of Pleistocene deposits of southwestern Kansas: Geol. Soc. Amer. Bull., v. 55, p. 707-754 (**53**)

57. —— 1949, Pleistocene vertebrate paleontology in North America: Geol. Soc. Amer. Bull., v. 60, p. 1417-1428 (**50, 53, 54, 57, 59**)

58. —— 1951, Vertebrate fossils from the Pleistocene Stump Arroyo member, Meade County, Kansas: Univ. Michigan Mus. Paleont. Contr., v. 9, p. 227-245 (**52**)

59. —— 1953, *Equus* (*Asinus*) *calobatus* Troxell and associated vertebrates from the Pleistocene of Kansas: Kansas Acad. Sci. Trans., v. 56, p. 111-126

60. —— 1955a, The Jinglebob interglacial (Sangamon?) fauna from Kansas and its climatic significance: Univ. Michigan Mus. Paleont. Contr., v. 12, p. 179-228 (**58**)

61. —— 1955b, Notes on the microtine rodents from the Port Kennedy Cave deposit: Philadelphia Acad. Nat. Sci. Proc., v. 107, p. 87-97 (**100**)

62. —— 1956, Vertebrate fossils from the Meade Formation of southwestern Kansas: Michigan Acad. Sci. Pap., v. 41 (1955), p. 145-200 (**50, 51, 60**)

63. —— 1958, Summary of North American Pleistocene mammalian local faunas: Michigan Acad. Sci. Pap., v. 43 (1957), p. 3-32 (**54**)

64. —— 1959, Late Cenozoic microtine rodents from Wyoming and Idaho: Michigan Acad. Sci. Pap., v. 44 (1958), p. 3-40 (**15**)

65. —— 1960, An interpretation of Pliocene and Pleistocene climates in North America: Michigan Acad. Sci. Ann. Rep. 62, p. 5-30

66. —— 1963a, The origin of the P_3 pattern of *Sylvilagus, Caprolagus, Oryctolagus* and *Lepus:* J. Mammal., v. 44, p. 1-15

67. —— 1963b, A late Illinoian fauna from Kansas and its climatic significance: Michigan Acad. Sci. Pap., v. 48 (1962), p. 187-221 (**56**)

68. —— 1964, A contribution to the Saw Rock Canyon local fauna of Kansas: Michigan Acad. Sci. Pap., v. 49 (1963), p. 115-127

69. Hibbard, C. W., and Dalquest, W. W., 1962, Artiodactyls from the Seymour Formation of Knox County, Texas: Michigan Acad. Sci. Pap., v. 47 (1961), p. 83-99 (**41**)

70. Hibbard, C. W., Frye, J. C., and Leonard, A. B., 1944, Reconnaissance of Pleistocene deposits in north-central Kansas: Kansas Geol. Surv. Bull. 52, pt. 1, p. 1-28

71. Hibbard, C. W., and Taylor, D. W., 1960, Two late Pleistocene faunas from southwestern Kansas: Univ.

Michigan Mus. Paleont. Contr., v. 16, p. 1-223 (**47, 48, 55, 57, 58, 59**)

72. Hinton, M. A. C., 1926, Monograph of the Voles and Lemmings (Microtinae) living and extinct: Brit. Mus. (Nat. Hist.), v. 1, 488 p.

73. Holman, J. A., 1958, The Pleistocene herpetofauna of Saber-tooth Cave, Citrus County, Florida: Copeia, 1958, p. 276-280 (**83**)

74. Hopkins, D. M., 1959a, Cenozoic history of the Bering land bridge: Science, v. 129, p. 1519-1528

75. —— 1959b, History of Imuruk Lake, Seward Peninsula, Alaska: Geol. Soc. Amer. Bull., v. 70, p. 1033-1046

76. Hopkins, M. L., 1955, Skull of fossil camelid from American Falls lake bed area of Idaho: J. Mammal., v. 36, p. 278-282 (**17**)

77. Howard, Hildegarde, 1946, A review of the Pleistocene birds of Fossil Lake, Oregon: Carnegie Instn. Publ. 551, p. 141-195 (**13**)

78. —— 1955, Fossil birds from Manix Lake, California: U. S. Geol. Surv. Prof. Pap. 264-J, p. 199-205 (**4**)

79. Johnston, C. S., and Savage, D. E., 1955, A survey of various Late Cenozoic vertebrate faunas of the panhandle of Texas. Part I, introduction, description of localities, preliminary faunal lists: Univ. California Dept. Geol. Bull., v. 31, p. 27-50 (**42, 46**)

80. Kapp, R. O., in press, Illinoian and Sangamon vegetation in southwestern Kansas and adjacent Oklahoma: Univ. Michigan Mus. Paleont. Contr. (**47, 48, 55, 56, 57, 58**)

81. Kay, G. F., and Graham, J. B., 1943, The Illinoian and post-Illinoian Pleistocene geology of Iowa: Iowa Geol. Surv., v. 38, p. 1-262

82. Kaye, C. A., 1962, Early postglacial beavers in southeastern New England: Science, v. 138, p. 906-907

83. Kitts, D. B., 1953, A Pleistocene musk-ox from New York and the distribution of the musk-oxen: Amer. Mus. Novitates 1607, 8 p.

84. Klingener, David, 1963, Dental evolution of *Zapus*: J. Mammal. v. 44, p. 248-260 (**51, 54, 56, 58**)

85. Kurtén, Björn, 1963, Notes on some Pleistocene mammal migrations from the Palaearctic to the Nearctic: Eiszeitalter u. Gegenwart, v. 14, p. 96-103 (**46, 69, 97, 100**)

86. Ligon, J. D., in press, A Pleistocene avifauna from Haile, Florida: Florida Mus. Bull. (**78**)

87. Lugn, A. L., 1962, The origin and sources of loess: Univ. Nebraska Stud., n.s., v. 26, p. 1-105

88. Lundelius, E. L., Jr., 1963, Non-human skeletal material: *in* J. F. Epstein, Centipede and damp caves: excavations in Val Verde County, Texas, 1958: Texas Arch. Soc. Bull., v. 33, p. 127-129 (**30, 31**)

89. Macdonald, J. R., 1956, A Blancan mammalian fauna from Wichman, Nevada: J. Paleont., v. 30, p. 213-216 (**11**)

90. Malde, H. E., and Powers, H. A., 1962, Upper Cenozoic stratigraphy of western Snake River Plain, Idaho: Geol. Soc. Amer. Bull. v. 73, p. 1197-1220 (**15**)

91. Martin, P. S., 1958, Pleistocene ecology and biogeography of North America: *in* C. L. Hubbs (ed.), Zoogeography: Amer. Assoc. Adv. Sci. Publ. 51, p. 375-420

92. Martin, P. S., Sabels, B. E., and Shutler, Dick, Jr., 1961, Rampart Cave coprolite and ecology of the Shasta ground sloth: Amer. J. Sci., v. 259, p. 102-127

93. McCoy, J. J., 1963, The fossil avifauna of Itchtucknee River, Florida: Auk, v. 80, p. 335-351 (**75**)

94. McCrady, Edward, Kirby-Smith, H. T., and Templeton, Harvey, 1951, New finds of Pleistocene jaguar skeletons from Tennessee caves: U.S. Natl. Mus. Proc., v. 101, p. 497-511 (**90, 91, 92**)

95. McGrew, P. O., 1944, An Early Pleistocene (Blancan) fauna from Nebraska: Field Mus. Nat. Hist. Geol. Ser., v. 9, p. 33-66 (**63**)

96. Meade, G. E., 1945, The Blanco Fauna: Univ. Texas Publ. 4401, p. 309-556 (**42**)

97. —— 1952, The water rat in the Pleistocene of Texas: J. Mammal., v. 33, p. 87-89 (**40**)

98. —— 1953, An early Pleistocene vertebrate fauna from Frederick, Oklahoma: J. Geol., v. 61, p. 452-460 (**45**)

99. —— 1961, The saber-toothed cat, *Dinobastis serus*: Texas Mem. Mus. Bull. 2, pt. II, p. 23-60 (**32**)

100. Mehl, M. G., 1962, Missouri's Ice Age animals: Missouri Geol. Surv. Educ. Ser. 1, p. 1-104 (**66**)

101. Miller, B. B., in press, Five Illinoian molluscan faunas from the southern Great Plains: Malacologia (**47, 48, 55, 56**)

102. Neill, W. T., 1957, Historical biogeography of present-day Florida: Florida Mus. Biol. Sci. Bull., v. 2, p. 175-220

103. Olson, E. C., 1940, A late Pleistocene fauna from Herculaneum, Missouri: J. Geol., v. 48, p. 332-357 (**68**)

104. Osborn, H. F., 1936-1942, Proboscidea: New York, Amer. Mus. Press, 1675 p.

105. Parmalee, P. W., 1961, A recent find of jaguar bones in a Tennessee cave: Tennessee Acad. Sci. J., v. 36, p. 81-85 (**103**)

106. Patton, T. H., 1963a, Fossil remains of Southern Bog Lemming in Pleistocene deposits of Texas: J. Mammal., v. 44, p. 275-277 (**33, 35**)

107. —— 1963b, Fossil vertebrates from Miller's Cave, Llano County, Texas: Texas Mem. Mus. Bull. 7, p. 1-41 (**34**)

108. Paulson, G. R., 1961, The mammals of the Cudahy fauna: Michigan Acad. Sci. Pap., v. 46 (1960), p. 127-153 (**53**)

109. Powers, H. A., Young, E. J., and Barnett, P. R., 1958, Possible extension into Idaho, Nevada, and Utah of the Pearlette ash of Meade County, Kansas (abst.): Geol. Soc. Amer. Bull., v. 69, p. 1631

110. Radiocarbon, 1959-1963, New Haven, Yale Univ. (suppl. Amer. J. Sci.), v. 1-5 (continuing ser.)

111. Rausch, R. L., 1963, A review of the distribution of Holarctic Recent mammals: *in* J. L. Gressitt (ed.), Pacific Basin Biogeography: Honolulu, Bishop Mus. Press, p. 29-44

112. Ray, C. E., 1957, A list, bibliography, and index of the fossil vertebrates of Florida: Florida Geol. Surv. Spec. Publ. 3, p. 1-175 (**88**, p. 78; and others)

113. —— 1958, Additions to the Pleistocene mammalian fauna from Melbourne, Florida: Harvard Univ. Mus. Comp. Zool. Bull., v. 119, p. 421-449 (85)

114. —— 1964, *Tapirus copei* in the Pleistocene of Florida: Florida Acad. Sci. Quart. J., v. 27, p. 59-66 (87, 100)

115. —— 1964, The jaguarundi in the Quaterny of Florida: J. Mammal., v. 45, p. 330-332 (84, 85)

116. Ray, C. E., Olsen, S. J., and Gut, H. J., 1963, Three mammals new to the Pleistocene fauna of Florida, and a reconsideration of five earlier records: J. Mammal., v. 44, p. 373-395 (78, 81, 82, 84, 85, 87)

117. Richmond, N. D., 1963, Evidence against the existence of crocodiles in Virginia and Maryland during the Pleistocene: Biol. Soc. Washington Proc., v. 76, p. 65-68 (97)

118. Romer, A. S., 1951, *Bison crassicornis* in the late Pleistocene of New England: J. Mammal., v. 32, p. 230-231 (101)

119. Russell, R. J., 1960, Pleistocene pocket gophers from San Josecito Cave, Nuevo León, México: Univ. Kansas Mus. Nat. Hist. Publ. v. 9, p. 539-548 (26)

120. Savage, D. E., 1951, Late Cenozoic vertebrates of the San Francisco Bay region: Univ. California Dept. Geol. Bull., v. 28, p. 215-314 (8, 9)

121. —— 1958, Evidence from fossil land mammals on the origin and affinities of the western Nearctic fauna: *in* C. L. Hubbs (ed.), Zoogeography: Amer. Assoc. Adv. Sci. Publ. 51, p. 97-129

122. Schultz, C. B., and Howard, E. B., 1935, The fauna of Burnet Cave, Guadalupe Mountains, New Mexico: Philadelphia Acad. Nat. Sci. Proc., v. 87, p. 273-298 (27)

123. Schultz, C. B., and Stout, T. M., 1948, Pleistocene mammals and terraces in the Great Plains: Geol. Soc. Amer. Bull., v. 59, p. 553-588 (62, 64)

124. Schultz, C. B., Tanner, L. G., Whitmore, F. C., Jr., Ray, L. L., and Crawford, E. C., 1963, Paleontologic investigations at Big Bone Lick State Park, Kentucky: A preliminary report: Science, v. 142, p. 1167-1169 (95)

125. Schultz, J. R., 1938, A late Quaternary mammal fauna from the tar seeps of McKittrick, California: Carnegie Instn. Publ. 487, p. 111-215 (7)

126. Scott, G. R., 1962, Geology of the Littleton quadrangle, Jefferson, Douglas, and Arapahoe Counties, Colorado: U.S. Geol. Surv. Bull. 1121-L, p. 1-53

127. —— 1963, Quaternary geology and geomorphic history of the Kassler quadrangle, Colorado: U.S. Geol. Surv. Prof. Pap. 421-A, 70 p.

128. Sellards, E. H., 1952, Early Man in America—a study in prehistory: Austin, Univ. Texas Press, 211 p. (28)

129. Semken, H. A., Jr., 1961, Fossil vertebrates from Longhorn Cavern, Burnett County, Texas: Texas J. Sci., v. 13, p. 290-310 (35)

130. Simpson, G. G., 1933, A Nevada fauna of Pleistocene type and its probable association with man: Amer. Mus. Novitates 667, 10 p. (18)

131. —— 1941, Large Pleistocene felines of North America: Amer. Mus. Novitates 1136, 27 p.

132. —— 1945, Notes on Pleistocene and Recent tapirs: Amer. Mus. Nat. Hist. Bull., v. 86, p. 33-82 (66, 87, 100)

133. —— 1947, Holarctic mammalian faunas and continental relationships during the Cenozoic: Geol. Soc. Amer. Bull., v. 58, p. 613-687

134. —— 1949, A fossil deposit in a cave in St. Louis: Amer. Mus. Novitates 1408, 46 p. (67)

135. Skinner, M. F., 1942, The fauna of Papago Springs Cave, Arizona, and a study of *Stockoceros*; with three new antilocaprines from Nebraska and Arizona: Amer. Mus. Nat. Hist. Bull., v. 80, p. 143-220 (22)

136. Skinner, M. F., and Kaisen, O. C., 1947, The fossil *Bison* of Alaska and preliminary revision of the genus: Amer. Mus. Nat. Hist. Bull., v. 89, p. 123-256

137. Slaughter, B. H., 1963, Some observations concerning the genus *Smilodon*, with special reference to *Smilodon fatalis*: Texas J. Sci., v. 15, p. 68-81 (75)

138. Slaughter, B. H., Crook, W. W., Jr., Harris, R. K., Allen, D. C., and Seifert, Martin, 1962, The Hill-Shuler local faunas of the Upper Trinity River, Dallas and Denton Counties, Texas: Univ. Texas Bur. Econ. Geol. Rep. Inv. 48, p. 1-75 (37)

139. Slaughter, B. H., and Hoover, B. R., 1963, Sulphur River Formation and the Pleistocene mammals of the Ben Franklin local fauna: So. Methodist Univ., Grad. Res. Center J., v. 31, p. 132-148 (39)

140. Slaughter, B. H., and Ritchie, Ronald, 1963, Pleistocene mammals of the Clear Creek local fauna, Denton County, Texas: So. Methodist Univ., Grad. Res. Center J., v. 31, p. 117-131 (38)

141. Smith, C. L., 1958, Additional Pleistocene fishes from Kansas and Oklahoma: Copeia, 1958, p. 176-180 (47, 48, 55)

142. Smith, G. R., 1963, A late Illinoian fish fauna from southwestern Kansas and its climatic significance: Copeia, 1963, p. 278-285 (56)

143. Starrett, Andrew, 1956, Pleistocene mammals of the Berends fauna of Oklahoma: J. Paleont., v. 30, p. 1187-1192 (47)

144. Stephens, J. J., 1960, Stratigraphy and paleontology of a late Pleistocene basin, Harper County, Oklahoma: Geol. Soc. Amer. Bull., v. 71, p. 1675-1702 (48)

145. Stock, Chester, 1918, The Pleistocene fauna of Hawver Cave: Univ. California Dept. Geol. Bull., v. 10, p. 461-515 (10, 12a, 12b)

146. —— 1925, Cenozoic gravigrade edentates of western North America, with special reference to the Pleistocene Megalonychinae and Mylodontidae of Rancho La Brea: Carnegie Instn. Publ. 331, 206 p.

147. —— 1935, Exiled elephants of the Channel Islands, California: Sci. Monogr., v. 41, p. 205-214 (6)

148. —— 1942, A ground sloth in Alaska: Science, v. 95, p. 552-553

149. —— 1956, Rancho La Brea, a record of Pleistocene life in California: Los Angeles Co. Mus. Sci. Ser. 20, Paleont. Publ. 11, 6th ed., 83 p. (1)

150. Stokes, W. L., and Condie, K. C., 1961, Pleistocene bighorn sheep from the Great Basin: J. Paleont., v. 35, p. 598-609

151. Strand, J. R., and Hough, M. Jean, 1952, Age of the

Ringold formation: Northwest Sci., v. 26, p. 152-154 **(14)**

151a. Swineford, A., 1949, Source area of Great Plains Pleistocene volcanic ash: J. Geol., v. 37, p. 307-311

152. Taylor, D. W., 1960, Late Cenozoic molluscan faunas from the High Plains: U.S. Geol. Surv. Prof. Pap. 337, 94 p.

153. —— this volume, The study of Pleistocene nonmarine mollusks in North America

154. Toepfer, V., 1963, Tierwelt des Eiszeitalters: Leipzig, Akad. Verlagsges., Geest & Portig, 240 p.

155. Troxell, E. L., 1915, The vertebrate fossils of Rock Creek, Texas: Amer. J. Sci., v. 39, p. 613-638 **(44)**

156. Weigel, R. D., 1963, Fossil vertebrates of Vero, Florida: Florida Geol. Surv. Spec. Publ. 10, p. 1-59 **(86)**

157. Wells, P. V., and Jorgensen, C. D., 1964, Pleistocene wood rat middens and climatic change in Mohave Desert: a record of juniper woodlands: Science, v. 143, p. 1171-1174

158. White, J. A., and Downs, T., 1961, A new *Geomys* from the Vallecito Creek Pleistocene of California: Los Angeles Co. Mus. Contr. Sci. 42, 34 p. **(2)**

159. Williams, Stephen, 1957, The Island 35 mastodon: its bearing on the age of archaic cultures in the East: Amer. Antiq., v. 22, p. 359-372 **(72)**

160. Wilson, R. W., 1933a, The Pleistocene mammalian fauna from the Carpinteria asphalt: Carnegie Instn. Publ. 440, p. 59-76 **(5)**

161. —— 1933b, A rodent fauna from later Cenozoic beds of southwestern Idaho: Carnegie Instn. Publ. 440, p. 117-135 **(15)**

162. Wood, H. E., *et al.*, 1941, Nomenclature and correlation of the North American continental Tertiary: Geol. Soc. Amer. Bull., v. 52, p. 1-48

163. Zeuner, F. E., 1959, The Pleistocene Period; its climate, chronology and faunal successions: London, Hutchinson and Co., 447 p.

SUMMARY

Only 22 out of 111 living Nearctic mammalian genera are unknown as fossils, so mammals are the best known Quaternary group of animals in North America. The 155 Quaternary genera have restricted and overlapping ranges that are the basis for the Blancan (only the latter part is Quaternary), Irvingtonian, and Rancholabrean mammalian ages. The chronology based on mammals can now be related to those of glacial-interglacial climatic changes, geomagnetic-polarity epochs, and potassium-argon dates, from which it appears that the Quaternary of our definition began about 2.5 million years ago.

The basic data of stratigraphic ranges (177 genera) and geographic occurrences (104 localities) are summarized with 160 references that provide entrance to a much larger literature. Most of the text is devoted to discussion of promising avenues for future research and examples of the kinds of synthetic study that have proved fruitful.

Faunal shifts correlated with glacial-interglacial climatic changes have been documented thoroughly only in the southern Great Plains. Interpretations based on small mammals are consistent with those based on lower vertebrates, mollusks, and plants. Immigration from the Old World via the Bering Straits is most marked among hardy boreal forms that may have crossed when sea level was lower.

In spite of the relatively full fossil record, well-documented phyletic sequences of species are unknown outside the rodents. Although many genera are first known from Quaternary sediments, in practically all cases they probably lived before then. Probably all Recent mammalian species originated during the Quaternary, but generic change was by extinction rather than evolution into new genera.

AVIAN SPECIATION IN THE QUATERNARY [*]

ROBERT K. SELANDER[1]

IN THIS review I have attempted to survey knowledge of the North American Pleistocene avifauna, to indicate some of the changes that occurred in the transition to the Recent, and to illustrate ways in which events in the Quaternary have influenced avian distribution and speciation.

THE FOSSIL RECORD

EVOLUTION OF BIRDS

Adaptive radiation of the orders of birds occurred in the Cretaceous near the Tertiary boundary (Howard, 1950; Brodkorb, 1963a), and most orders known today were established by the Eocene. Modern families, with the possible exception of the Fringillidae (Brodkorb, 1960) and some others of the order Passeriformes, are believed to have existed by the Miocene. Many modern genera are represented in Miocene faunas, and probably most modern genera had evolved by the Pliocene (Wetmore, 1959b, p. 19). However, modern species first appear in the late Pliocene and are not numerous until the Pleistocene (Brodkorb, 1955, p. 31; Howard, 1955b, p. 205). From middle and upper Pleistocene deposits, three-quarters or more of the species represent living forms (Moreau, 1954; Brodkorb, 1960).

Little is known of pre-Tertiary avifaunas, for 97% of the 840 species of extinct fossil birds are from the Tertiary and Pleistocene (Brodkorb, 1963a, p. 55). However, avian paleontologists believe that birds (with the possible exception of the passerines) achieved maximum abundance in the Tertiary, with the Quaternary being a period of reduction in numbers of adaptive types and species. From data for late Pleistocene avifaunas of North America and the West Indies (Wetmore, 1956), Brodkorb (1960) estimates that 11,600 species lived contemporaneously in the world in the late Pleistocene.

There are approximately 8,650 living avian species, probably less than 1% of which are undescribed (Mayr, 1946a). By 1960, 732 were already recorded from Pleistocene deposits, together with 272 extinct species, giving a total of 1,004 species known from the Pleistocene (Brodkorb, 1960, p. 41).

There is no consensus among avian paleontologists regarding the age of living bird species. Wetmore (1951, p. 63) expressed a "firm belief that . . . our living kinds

had their evolution both as genera and as species in the Miocene and Pliocene periods." Later (1959b, p. 20), he modified this opinion slightly, suggesting that "most of the species of our present avifauna had attained development by the beginning of the Pleistocene, and that the major changes since have come through extinction of numerous kinds." Even so, evolution in the Quaternary has been mainly at the subspecific level, according to Wetmore (1959b). But Brodkorb (1955, 1960, 1963a) and Moreau (1963) believe that most living species of birds arose in the Pleistocene, and Brodkorb notes (1960, p. 47) that "almost no avian species are known to cross epochal lines." To estimate the average longevity of avian species, Brodkorb (1960) used data for North American Pleistocene birds shown in Table 1. Because extinction rates (which are considered equal to the average longevity of species) for the fourth (last) glacial age are unaccountably high and cannot be typical for the whole Pleistocene, Brodkorb relied on data for the first interglacial and third glacial stages, adopting a mean value of 500,000 years. The maximum longevity for avian species is considered to be approximately 1,000,000 years. From these data, Brodkorb (1960, p. 50) estimates that 23,000 species evolved during the Pleistocene, and he calculates that the 9,500 known living and extinct species represent 0.5% of the

TABLE 1

Estimates of Average Longevity of Avian Species
(From Brodkorb, 1960, p. 49)

Locality and Pleistocene stage	Years before present	Total species recorded	Percent extinct	Estimated average longevity (years)
Florida:				
Mid-fourth glacial[a]	17,000	63	9.5	89,474
California:				
Fourth glacial[b]	25,000	121	18.2	68,681
Florida:				
Third glacial[c]	184,000	70	21.9	420,091
Idaho: First interglacial[d]	691,500	9	66.7	518,366

[a] Combined avifaunas of Seminole Field, Melbourne, and Rock Spring, Florida (Wetmore, 1931; Woolfenden, 1959). Years for stage based on radiocarbon averages (Horsberg, 1955).

[b] Rancho La Brea, McKittrick, and Carpinteria, California (Miller and DeMay, 1942; with additions by A. H. Miller, 1947, and Dawson, 1948). Years for stage based on radiocarbon averages (Horsberg, 1955).

[c] Reddick, Arredondo, Haile, and Williston, Florida (Brodkorb, 1953, 1957, 1959; Holman, 1959). Years for stage based on geological evidence (Kay, 1931).

[d] Hagerman, Idaho, avifauna (Brodkorb, 1958). Years for stage based on geological evidence (Kay, 1931).

[*] The author's research is supported by the National Science Foundation (Grant GB-1624); and this review was written during tenure of a Guggenheim Fellowship. Dr. Pierce Brodkorb read the manuscript and corrected several errors, and Dr. M. D. F. Udvardy kindly supplied a number of references to the literature.

[1] Department of Zoology, University of Texas, Austin, Texas.

TABLE 2

Major North American Pleistocene Avifaunas

	No. species identified	Percent extinct	References
I. Early Pleistocene			
Hagerman Lake beds, Idaho	10	60	Wetmore, 1933; Miller, 1948; Brodkorb, 1958
Benson, Arizona	6	83	Wetmore, 1924
II. Middle Pleistocene			
Vallecito, California	16	62	Howard, 1963
Williston, Florida	5	40	Holman, 1959
Reddick, Florida	63	21	Brodkorb, 1957, 1963e; Hamon, 1964
Arredondo, Florida	43	20	Brodkorb, 1959b
III. Late Pleistocene			
San Josecito Cave, Nuevo Leon	37	30	L. Miller, 1943
Rancho La Brea, California	140	15	Howard, 1962a
McKittrick, California	64	16	Wetmore, 1959b
Carpinteria, California	48	21	Wetmore, 1959b
Fossil Lake, Oregon	60	25	Howard, 1946
Smith Creek Cave, Nevada	44	14	Howard, 1952
Seminole, Florida	46	9	Wetmore, 1931
Itchtucknee, Florida	52	15	McCoy, 1963
Rock Spring, Florida	35	0	Woolfenden, 1959
Natural Chimneys, Virginia	38	0	Wetmore, 1962; Guilday, 1962

1,634,000 species estimated to have existed since the origin of the class Aves.

The poorly known late Pliocene avifauna provides little evidence bearing on the age of modern species. Only five living North American species are reported from the Pliocene (Wetmore, 1959b, p. 20), and apparently none of these records can be taken as unequivocal proof of a pre-Pleistocene occurrence of living forms. Four modern species have been reported from the Rexroad formation of Kansas (Wetmore, 1944), which, although assigned to upper Pliocene, may actually be lower Pleistocene or transitional (Bardack, 1962). One of these species, originally reported as the modern turkey, has been reidentified as an extinct species of *Agriocharis* (Brodkorb, 1964b), and the three remaining forms may also prove to be incorrectly assigned. The fifth species is the eared grebe (*Podiceps caspicus*), from middle-Pliocene beds in Kansas, the identification of which is questioned by Brodkorb (1963c, p. 229).

The problem of the age of modern species of birds will be solved only when we have better knowledge of late Pliocene and Pleistocene avifaunas. Meanwhile, it is well to bear in mind that there is no "standard" rate of speciation (Mayr, 1963b, p. 581); although speciation often proceeds very slowly, under special conditions it may be completed in a few thousand years. Measured in terms of major adaptive modification, avian evolution in the late Tertiary and Quaternary has been comparatively slow (A. H. Miller, 1940; Howard, 1947b, 1950), but, considering the fossil record and the indirect evidence of Pleistocene speciation provided by studies of the relationships and distributions of living forms, it is difficult to accept the view that avian species formation was essentially suspended one million years ago. Therefore, I believe Brodkorb's and Moreau's interpretation of the age of species will prove to be correct.

NORTH AMERICAN PLEISTOCENE AVIFAUNAS

It is difficult to visualize the North American avifauna in the early Quaternary, since the bulk of Pleistocene fossil

material comes from middle and upper levels. Wetmore (1959b, p. 20-21) suggests that the number of species in the United States and Baja California at the beginning of the Pleistocene may have equalled the number found now in Mexico, or roughly a thousand species, representing 89 families (Blake, 1953). The present avifauna of North America north of mainland Mexico (but including Baja California) consists of 697 native species of regular occurrence, 87 reported as strays from other regions, and 12 introduced by man (A.O.U. Check-list, 1957). Summarizing North American Pleistocene avifaunas in 1959, Wetmore noted that 198 (28%) of the 697 native species had been found in Pleistocene deposits. In addition, 83 extinct species had been described, making a total of 281 species known from the Pleistocene of North America, of which the extinct forms constituted 30%. (Because many additional species have been recorded from the Pleistocene by Brodkorb, Howard, and others since 1959, these figures are now only approximations.)

Major Pleistocene avifaunas of North America are listed in Table 2. Owing to differing interpretations of tentative identifications, numbers of forms reported for avifaunas are not strictly comparable (Howard, 1963, p. 30), but Table 2 at least provides some indication of the relative proportions of living and extinct forms in the various avifaunas.

Early Pleistocene avifaunas. Hagerman Lake beds, Twin Falls County, Idaho: Although originally assigned to upper Pliocene (Wetmore, 1933), these deposits apparently correspond to the first (Aftonian) interglacial stage (Hibbard, 1958, p. 11). If a record (A. H. Miller, 1948) of the whistling swan (*Olor columbianus*) does not pertain to **Olor hibbardi*,[2] later described by Brodkorb (1958, p. 238), the avifauna includes at least 17 species (4 of them modern), only 10 of which have been determined specifically.

Benson, Cochise County, Arizona: From deposits which

---

[2] Extinct forms are indicated by an asterisk.

may be upper Pliocene, Wetmore (1924) named four extinct species and assigned 7 or 8 other forms to modern genera, without specific designation. Howard (1963, p. 31) considers 11 species identified, but Brodkorb (1955, p. 31) indicates only 6.

Middle Pleistocene avifaunas. Reddick, Marion County, Florida: In deposits formed during the Illinoian glacial stage, 63 species have been identified (Brodkorb, 1957; Hamon, 1964). The only forms absent from the present avifauna of Florida are the extinct species, one of which is the recently extirpated passenger pigeon (*Ectopistes migratorius*).

In the Reddick avifauna are several species with affinities to the Pleistocene or Recent arid subtropical or Sonoran fauna of the Southwest. These include *Protocitta dixi*, which, with *Henocitta brodkorbi* of the Williston fauna (Holman, 1959), is allied to the living Mexican and Central American jays of the *Cyanocorax* complex; an icterid, *Pandanaris floridana*, representing a genus also known from the Pleistocene of Rancho La Brea (*P. convexa*; A. H. Miller, 1947) and allied to modern cowbird genera; and the widely distributed scavengers *Coragyps occidentalis*, *Gymnogyps amplus*, and *Caracara prelutosa*.

The southwestern element in the middle Pleistocene avian and mammalian faunas of Florida is believed to have reached the eastern United States in the late Tertiary or during the warm and dry Yarmouth or Aftonian interglacial stages. Subsequently, "climatic deterioration during the glacial ages and the repeated insularity or inundation of much of Florida during the interglacial stages both undoubtedly contributed to the partial extermination or restriction of this fauna" (Brodkorb, 1957, p. 137).

The small avifauna from Haile, Florida (7 modern species; Brodkorb, 1953), is now considered to be of Illinoian age and contemporaneous with Reddick (Brodkorb, 1957, p. 136).

Arredondo, Alachua County, Florida: From sediments presumably deposited under cooler conditions during the Illinoian glacial stage, Brodkorb (1959b) has identified 43 species. Regarded as interglacial relicts are a lapwing, *Dorypaltus prosphatus* (representing the only Nearctic record of the subfamily Vanellinae); a falcon, *Falco readei*; a quail, *Colinus suilium*; an oropendola, *Cremaster tytthus* (belonging to a group of icterids presently Neotropical in distribution); and the modern jay *Aphelocoma coerulescens*.

Vallecito Creek, San Diego County, California: This avifauna includes at least 28 forms, but only 16 have been identified to species (Howard, 1963). Notable elements are the turkey *Agriocharis anza* (belonging to a genus now confined to Central America); an Old World vulture, *Neophrontops vallecitoensis*; a tadornine duck, *Brantadorna downsi*; and the vulture *Teratornis incredibilis*, the last being, apart from the modern forms, the only species appearing in other fossil avifaunas.

Late Pleistocene avifaunas. Space limitations preclude discussion of all the numerous North American late Pleistocene and subfossil Quaternary avifaunas. Among late Pleistocene avifaunas not listed in Table 2 are the following, all of which consist of modern species, except as noted: Crystal Springs, Florida (Brodkorb, 1956a); Eichelberger Cave, Florida (age?, Brodkorb, 1956b); Jones fauna, Kansas (Downs, 1954); Schuiling Cave, California (*Gymnogyps amplus* and 14 modern species; Downs et al., 1959); Kentuck locality, McPherson County, Kansas (possibly middle Pleistocene; Galbreath, 1955); Shorts Creek, Kansas (Stettenheim, 1958); American Falls, Idaho (Brodkorb, 1963d); Manix Lake, California (10 species, 3 of which are extinct; Howard, 1955b); Hamilton, Ontario (Wetmore, 1958).

As shown in Table 2, most elements of the late Pleistocene avifaunas represent modern species. The Rancho La Brea (Howard, 1955a) is typical in this respect and is noteworthy as the only large avifauna analyzed quantitatively in terms of species and individuals.

An early census of the Rancho La Brea avifauna was presented by Howard (1930), who has recently (1962a) analyzed 13 pits containing 85,000 skeletal parts representing 5,845 individuals of at least 133 species (19 extinct). Falconiformes and Strigiformes comprise 68% of the combined avifaunas, this well-known preponderance of predators and scavengers in the Rancho La Brea deposits being, as noted by Howard (1962a, p. 9) "the result of the nature of the tar accumulations, which acted as traps, baited with carcasses or struggling animals."

The pits vary in faunal content (Fig. 1) and were active at different times over a period of thousands of years (Marcus, 1960; Howard, 1962a), but unfortunately their chronological sequence is undetermined. Pit number 3, which contains the "typical" Pleistocene fauna, has been dated by carbon-14 at 14,500 B.P. (Howard, 1960, p. 713), and Pits 10, 28, and 37, yielding relatively few extinct Pleistocene forms, are thought to have been active in Recent times. The avifauna of Pit 10, in which human bones were found, was previously analyzed by Howard and Miller (1939).

Compared with the avifauna of Pit 3, those of Pits 10, 28, and 37 contain fewer individuals of extinct species and greater numbers of small *versus* large raptors (Howard, 1962a, Figs. 3 and 4); and in each the living turkey vulture (*Cathartes aura*) outnumbers the extinct vulture *Coragyps occidentalis*, whereas the converse is true in the case of Pit 3. Pits 10, 28, and 37 also show an increase over Pit 3 in the relative abundance of grassland-inhabiting western meadowlarks (*Sturnella neglecta*), with an accompanying decrease in yellow-billed magpies (*Pica nuttalli*).

A group of eight presumably older pits (3, 4, 13, 16, 60, 61-67, 77, and Acad.) contained a combined total of 109 species. Omitting the passerines, which have been incompletely studied, Howard (1962a, p. 14) designated those species found in all eight older pits as the "nucleus" of the typical Rancho La Brea Pleistocene avifauna; extinct forms are 8 falconiforms, a turkey, *Parapavo californicus*; a true stork, *Ciconia maltha*; and an owl. "Nucleus" species reportedly constitute from 37% to 92% of the total non-passerine assemblage per pit, and those not common to all 13 pits are considered "critical markers of a typical Pleistocene pit avifauna."

There is an inconsistency in Howard's treatment of "nucleus" species, for the owl *Strix brea* is listed as one of 17

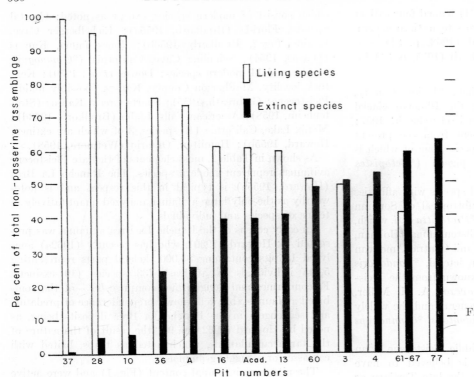

Figure 1. Numbers of individuals of living and extinct avian species in each of 13 Rancho La Brea pits expressed as percentages of total non-passerine assemblages. (From Howard, 1962a, p. 12)

"nucleus" species, although Howard (1962a, p. 16 and Table 1, p. 23) notes that it was absent from Pits 13, 60, and 77. Apparently, it should not have been considered one of the "nucleus" or "critical" species, and, accordingly, the number of "nucleus" species is reduced to 16, of which 12 are "critical."

For comparative purposes, Howard expressed for each pit the number of individuals of the "critical" species as a percentage of the total number of non-passerine individuals represented. I have calculated comparable percentages (from data in Table 1 of Howard, 1962a), using 12 "critical" species (*Strix brea* not included), and have also recalculated the percentages based on 13 "critical" species. For several pits (*e.g.* 28, 10, Acad., 60), our figures do not agree, but the error involved does not seriously affect any of the conclusions reached by Howard. The 13 pits fall into two groups, a presumably younger one (Pits 37, 28, 10, 36, A, and Acad.) with from 1% to 39% of the individuals belonging to the 12 "critical" species, and a presumably older one (Pits 61-67, 3, 16, 4, 13, 77, and 60) with 61% to 78% of the individuals belonging to "critical" species. Pit 10 (13.5%) apparently is less well set apart from Pits 36 and A (28-29%) than was indicated by Howard's percentages (7.9% for Pit 10).

Bahamas and Bermuda. The primary relationship of the relatively rich late Pleistocene and the depauperate Recent avifaunas of the Bahamas is with the Greater Antilles rather than Florida, owing, apparently, in part to exposure of the Grand Bahama Bank during Wisconsin glaciation (Brodkorb, 1959a, p. 350). Of the known 21 resident late Pleistocene and pre-Columbian Recent birds (Wetmore, 1937, 1938; Brodkorb, 1959a), 43% are extinct; included are two

large hawks (*Titanohierax* and *Calohierax*) and an owl (*Tyto pollens*), which exploited the large rodents of the islands.

From presumed Pleistocene deposits in Bermuda, Wetmore (1960) reports a small avifauna, including a duck (*Anas pachyscelus*) and a crane (*Baeopteryx latipes*), both of which exhibit weakened wing structure.

SOME EXTINCT PLEISTOCENE TYPES

Wetmore (1959b) has summarized information on the Pleistocene forms of the avian orders, and I shall not repeat his effort here. However, any review of Pleistocene birds must give special note to the Falconiformes and especially the vultures, many of which passed from the scene with the extinction of the large Pleistocene mammals.

The New World condors and vultures (suborder Cathartae) were represented in the Pleistocene by *Gymnogyps amplus* (surviving as the modern California condor, *G. californianus*), *Coragyps occidentalis* (representing the modern *C. atratus*), and the modern turkey vulture (*Cathartes aura*). In addition, there are four species that failed to survive: *Breagyps clarki* of the late Pleistocene of Rancho La Brea and Smith Creek Cave, Nevada; *Cathartornis gracilis* of Rancho La Brea; and two giant species, *Teratornis merriami*, widely distributed in North America in the late Pleistocene, and *Teratornis incredibilis*, described by Howard (1952) from Nevada and recently identified in the middle Pleistocene fauna of Vallecito Creek, California. Another condor, *Pliogyps fisheri*, from the Rexroad formation, apparently is not ancestral to any of the Pleistocene species (Tordoff, 1959).

Three of the 11 extinct species of the hawk family Accipitridae recorded from Pleistocene North America belong to the Old World Vulture group (Aegypiinae, or Gypaëtinae of Brodkorb, 1964a) occurring today in Eurasia and Africa. These are *Neogyps errans, *Neophrontops vallecitoensis (Howard, 1963, p. 17) of middle Pleistocene southern California, and *N. americanus, a form abundantly represented in late Pleistocene asphalt deposits in California and found also in Neuvo Leon. *N. americanus, together with other extinct species, survived into early Recent time at Rancho La Brea, as evidenced by bones found in Pit 10 (Howard and Miller, 1939; Howard, 1962a).

Another group well represented in Pleistocene faunas is the Anseriformes, recently reviewed by Howard (1964a). For the United States there are Pleistocene records of 39 species, of which 9 are extinct, and, on a worldwide basis, the corresponding figures are 90 and 32. Among the more unusual types are the flightless, scoter-like "diving geese," *Chendytes lawi from upper Pleistocene marine beds in southern California (L. Miller, 1925, 1960; Howard, 1947c, 1949, 1964b; L. Miller et al., 1961), and the less specialized * C. milleri (Howard, 1955c) from lower Pleistocene deposits on San Nicolas Island, California.

The most remarkable Pleistocene find in recent years is *Titanis walleri (Brodkorb, 1963b) from northern Florida, a new genus of the giant flightless birds of the superfamily Phorusrhacoidea, otherwise known only from Argentina and Uruguay (Oligocene to early Pleistocene). The Florida bird was found in association with a mammalian and avian fauna that suggests a late Pleistocene age.

CHRONOCLINES

Chronoclinal relationships (Simpson, 1961, p. 102) involving late Tertiary, Pleistocene, and Recent forms have been suggested but generally have not been expressed in the nomenclature. As Howard (1947a) notes, many additional Pleistocene-Recent chronoclines will appear when larger series of specimens are available. But in this connection it should be noted that the paleontologist, whose species are necessarily morphological, will not readily detect forms that have achieved the biological species level of differentiation without obvious or consistent skeletal modification. Certainly, comments by avian paleontologists regarding difficulties in distinguishing elements of closely related living species do not provide confidence that all Pleistocene remains are correctly assigned to species (see Moreau, 1954, p. 420). Research on fossil forms, and especially on successional clines, would be facilitated by quantitative studies of variation in skeletons of modern taxa, such as those of Linsdale (1928), Adams (1955), Baumel (1953), and Woolfenden (1961).

A good example of a chronocline is provided by the quail genus Colinus, in which there is progressive reduction in size and change in qualitative characters from *C. hibbardi of the late Pliocene (Kansas) through *C. suilium (pre-Wicomico Pleistocene of Florida) to C. virginianus, a polytypic species widely distributed in North America and recorded from the upper Pleistocene in Florida and Texas (Holman, 1961). The transition from *C. suilium to C. virginianus occurred in Wicomico time and was perhaps initiated by a change from a glacial to an interglacial climate.

Following are some other accepted, presumed, or tentatively suggested ancestral sequences involving Pleistocene and Recent populations: golden eagle (Aquila chrysaëtos) of Rancho La Brea ancestral to smaller modern golden eagle (Howard, 1947a); great horned owl (Bubo virginianus) of late Pleistocene California ancestral to smaller modern great horned owl (Howard, 1947a; Downs et al., 1959; but see Wetmore, 1959b, p. 19); *Gymnogyps amplus ancestral to Gymnogyps californianus (Fisher, 1944, 1947; but see L. Miller, 1957, p. 61); *Fulica hesterna possibly ancestral to *F. (a.) shufeldti, which is ancestral to F. americana (Howard, 1946, 1963; but see Wetmore, 1959b, p. 19); *Caracara prelutosa ancestral to *C. lutosa and C. cheriway (Howard, 1940); *Podilymbus (p.) magnus ancestral to P. podiceps (Howard, 1946); *Aechmophorus (o.) lucasi ancestral to A. occidentalis (Howard, 1946); *Tachycineta speleodytes ancestral to T. bicolor (Brodkorb, 1959b); *Neophrontops vallecitoensis ancestral to *N. americanus (Howard, 1963).

DISTRIBUTIONAL CHANGES

Pleistocene avifaunas of North America, like those of Europe (Moreau, 1954) and Russia (Dementiev, 1960), are to a large degree composed of species occurring in the same areas today, perhaps in part because most of them come from southern areas in which environmental changes in the Pleistocene were relatively moderate. However, the fossil record provides a few examples documenting a southward shift of ranges during stages of glaciation, although little to match the extensive mammalian and piscine evidence reviewed by Blair (1958) for the southern United States.

For the sharp-tailed grouse (Pedioecetes phasianellus), which in historical time ranged in the eastern United States no farther south than Michigan and Illinois (Aldrich, 1963), a former range in late Wisconsin time through the valleys of the northern Appalachian region is demonstrated by fossils from Pennsylvania (Wetmore, 1959a, p. 181-182) and Virginia (Wetmore, 1962). And even more indicative of boreal conditions in Virginia near the end of Wisconsin time are records of the spruce grouse (Canachites canadensis) and the gray jay (Perisoreus canadensis), species occurring now in the eastern United States in northern hardwood-conifer forests north of a line from northern Wisconsin east to northern New Hampshire (Aldrich, 1963; A.O.U. Check-list, 1957, p. 366).

The ruffed grouse (Bonasa umbellus), with a modern distribution extending only as far south as Arkansas and, in the Appalachians, South Carolina and Georgia (Aldrich, 1963), is recorded in the Pleistocene fauna of presumed Illinoian age of Arredondo, Florida (Brodkorb, 1959b, p. 276). Also recorded in this fauna and in the Reddick fauna (Illinoian age) of Florida (Brodkorb, 1957) are young individuals of the swallow *Tachycineta speleodytes, a temporal representative of the tree swallow (T. bicolor), which in the eastern United States breeds regularly only as far south as Missouri, northwestern Tennessee, Virginia, and Maryland but nests casually farther south to Arkansas, Louisiana, and Mississippi (A.O.U. Check-list, 1957, p. 359). On the basis of the occurrence of this and other northern genera in the Reddick deposit, Brodkorb (1957, p. 138) suggests that the climate in northern Florida during the Illinoian glacial stage was at least as cool as that of Virginia today.

A number of changes in distribution of Californian birds from late-Pleistocene to Recent times are noted by A. H. Miller (1937). A major change along the Pacific coast is shown by the crow *Corvus caurinus*, which occurred at Carpinteria and Rancho La Brea in the late Pleistocene but now ranges south only to the Puget Sound region, Washington (A. H. Miller, 1940). In this case, the species now apparently has a narrower ecological range than it did in the Pleistocene.

By correlating information on the occurrence and relative abundance of passerine species in deposits (assigned to Wisconsin time) at Carpinteria, McKittrick, and Rancho La Brea, California, with knowledge of the geographic and ecological distributions of their modern representatives, A. H. Miller (1929, 1932, 1937, 1940; see also Dawson, 1948, and Sibley, 1939) was able to describe Pleistocene floral and climatic environments at these sites. The passerines of Carpinteria, on the coast of Ventura County, indicate a cooler, more humid Pleistocene climate, with isotherms depressed 200 miles south on the coast (A. H. Miller, 1940, p. 809). But at McKittrick, on the eastern side of the coast range, they suggest an arid climate similar to that prevailing there today. At Rancho La Brea, the fauna of the "typical" Pleistocene pits reflects a climatic and vegetational complex found today slightly northward and to the interior, and analysis of the passerines in several pits indicates a replacement of live-oak and brushland associations by grassland prior to the period of activity of Pit 10, which was open in Recent times.

There are several modern genera and species for which the fossil record is adequate to show that they were widespread in the Pleistocene but have since experienced drastic reductions in range.

The Holarctic magpie *Pica pica*, currently in North America a western form ranging east to Manitoba, Kansas, and Oklahoma (A.O.U. Check-list, 1957, p. 376), occurred in late Wisconsin time in Virginia (Wetmore, 1962). A record of this species from the lower Pleistocene of Texas (A. H. Miller and Bowman, 1956), according to Brodkorb (personal communication), is based on a specimen of an undescribed *Protocitta* jay. The Californian species *Pica nuttalli* may be the product of an earlier invasion of the genus from Asia (Parkes, 1958, p. 428).

The Pleistocene vulture *Coragyps occidentalis*, which is a temporal representative of the modern black vulture (*C. atratus*), ranged from Florida to California and is recorded from an Indian midden at Five Mile Rapids, Oregon, dated by carbon-14 at 8,000 B.P. (L. Miller, 1957, p. 61). The modern form ranges in the United States west only as far as Texas (and also occurs in southern Arizona), but there is a Recent subfossil record from New Mexico. The woodrail *Aramides cajanea* occurred in Florida in the late Pleistocene (Wetmore, 1931) but now ranges north only to Tamaulipas, Mexico.

In upper-Pleistocene deposits *Caracara prelutosa* is recorded from Florida to California and, as a racially distinct form, *C. p. grinnelli*, from Nuevo Leon (Howard, 1940;

see Brodkorb, 1959a, for nomenclature). Related extinct forms are known from the upper Pleistocene of New Providence Island, Bahamas (Brodkorb, 1959a), and a Quaternary cave in Puerto Rico (Wetmore, 1922, p. 303). The modern representatives of the *C. prelutosa* complex are *C. lutosa*, an endemic species of Guadalupe Island last reported in 1903, and *C. cheriway*, a tropical form ranging north to Arizona and Texas (casual in Louisiana and New Mexico), with disjunct populations in Florida, Cuba, and the Isle of Pines.

Among North American species that were widely distributed in the Pleistocene but now face extinction are the California condor and the whooping crane (*Grus americana*). Owing at least in part to man's activities, several species, including the great auk (*Pinguinus impennis*), passenger pigeon, Carolina paroquet (*Conuropsis carolinensis*), and Labrador duck (*Camptorhynchus labradorium*), have become extinct within the past 100 years; and 50 additional species are considered to be in danger of extinction. This unhappy history is chronicled by Greenway (1958), and reports on the current status of rare species are published annually in the *Auk* and the *Wilson Bulletin*.

There are few data on the effect of man's activities in increasing population densities and ranges of native species, but certainly many forms, including the granivorous blackbirds and grackles, have benefited from human modification of the environment (Welty, 1962).

THE RECENT AVIFAUNA

BIOGEOGRAPHIC STUDIES

There is space for only brief mention of avian biogeographic studies in North America. The distribution of birds in relation to major biotic communities and biomes was studied by Pitelka (1941) and Odum (1945), respectively, and the distribution of California birds was analyzed in detail by Miller (1951) in relation to life zones, ecologic formations, and faunal groupings.

In a major biogeographic contribution, Mayr (1946b, 1963a, 1964) has analyzed (mainly at the familial and generic levels) the North American avifauna in terms of geographic areas of origin. His contention that North America in the Tertiary was a major center of origin or, at least, of radiation of tropical genera and families (the autochthonous North American avifauna) is disputed by Darlington (1957, p. 279-287) but has been generally accepted by ornithologists. Bond (1948, 1963) relies on Mayr's analysis in discussing the derivation of the avifauna of the West Indies, and several authors, including Johnston (1964), have studied the avifaunas of local regions of North America in relation to Mayr's postulated geographic areas of origin. Parkes (1958) commented on the New World radiation of certain families and genera of Old World origin.

Udvardy (1958) presents a valuable ecological analysis of North American avifaunas and a comparison with Palearctic avifaunas. Surprisingly, he finds that only 3.1% of the 229 temperate forest and woodland species of North America are common to the Old World. (Incidentally, his suggestion of a late-Pleistocene entrance of the wood warblers into the taiga biome is at variance with the interpretations of Mengel, 1964; see beyond.) Recently, Udvardy (1963a) has undertaken a "causal analysis" of species' ranges, employing a method used by plant geographers and classifying the passerines north of Mexico into 17 ecogeographical groups.

The distribution of subspecies in the Great Basin region has been analyzed by A. H. Miller (1941a) and Behle (1963) in terms of "centers of differentiation," following Grinnell's application (1928) of this concept to the avifauna of Baja California. In a convincing reinterpretation of Grinnell's work, Davis (1959) has shown that the Cape region of Baja California is not, as Grinnell believed, a "potent" center of differentiation of races and species but rather "a center of relatively weak differentiation . . . presumably for the reason that the habitat [Madro-tertiary flora] with which the stocks pioneering into the Cape region were associated has been relatively little altered in the Cape highlands, whereas this same earlier habitat has become much more altered on the Pacific coast." Davis' interpretation may also be applied to certain lowland species of the Cape region (Selander, 1964, p. 220).

Compared with the Old World, the colonization of North American deserts by birds appears to have been less extensive and to have involved in greater degree behavioral adjustments rather than physiological and morphological specializations (Bartholomew and Cade, 1964; Bartholomew, 1958; A. H. Miller, 1963). By way of explanation, Udvardy (1958, p. 62) stresses the relatively recent origin (late Pliocene and Pleistocene) of North American deserts, while Dixon (1959) emphasizes ecological factors, including a presumed reduction in numbers of unoccupied niches caused by populations of euryoecious species ranging into desert scrub habitats from more arborescent formations.

PLEISTOCENE SPECIATION

Although numerous authors have invoked Pleistocene climatic events as direct or indirect causes of extrinsic (geographic) isolation of populations, the meager fossil record has made it impossible to determine the roles of the different glacial and interglacial periods (Mayr, 1963b, p. 560). Rather than attempting to review all the relevant literature for North America, I have selected a few cases (mostly involving species occurring in the United States) to illustrate some of the ways in which events of the Pleistocene are believed to have affected avian populations. In reviewing these examples, I have purposely refrained from discussing the ecological, behavioral, and genetic aspects of species evolution; these topics have been examined in detail by Mayr (1951, 1963b).

In the first major paper on Pleistocene speciation in North American birds, Rand (1948b) showed how certain arctic and boreal semi-species and subspecies could have arisen through geographic isolation in northern refugia during glacial periods. Patterns of distribution were related to refugia postulated by botanists as occurring southeast of the ice sheet, east and west of the Rocky Mountains, in the Rocky Mountain area south of the ice, and in the Yukon–Bering Sea region. Additionally, Rand (1948b, p. 315) postulated the existence of refugia in the Arctic Islands to account for the present distribution of the *Larus* gull

complex. For additional information on avian distribution and speciation in relation to northern refugia, see Austin (1932), Pitelka (1950), Cade (1955), Drury (1953), and Fay and Cade (1959).

White-crowned sparrow. Rand (1948a, 1948b) interprets the systematic and distributional relationships of the four major subspecies of this sparrow in terms of a pattern of isolation in four refugia during Pleistocene glaciation (presumably Wisconsin), as follows: the population ancestral to *Zonotrichia leucophrys gambelii* in the Yukon-Bearing Sea area; the western segment of *Z. l. leucophrys* (*Z. l. "oriantha"*) in the Rocky Mountain area; the eastern segment of *Z. l. leucophrys* in the northeastern United States; and the *Z. l. pugetensis–Z. l. nuttalli* segment in the Pacific coastal area. With deglaciation, *Z. l. gambelii* extended its range southward, establishing a zone of hybridization with the Rocky Mountain population in southeastern British Columbia and southwestern Alberta, and contacting the eastern segment of the species in central Canada. The eastern segment of *Z. l. leucophrys* moved northward to its present range in Canada but left a relict population in the extreme northeastern United States, and the Pacific coastal and Rocky Mountain populations moved northward to their present positions. An alternate scheme proposed by Banks (1964, p. 115) differs mainly in that the *gambelii* and *pugetensis-nuttalli* break is thought to have occurred before the *gambelii-leucophrys* disjunction was effected, an interpretation based on the assumption that equal rates of evolution occurred in all populations. As noted by Rand (1948b), the distributional pattern of the races of this sparrow resembles that of the four closely related species of spruces (*Picea*), as studied by Halliday and Brown (1943), and the pattern of isolation and postglacial spread is generally similar to that postulated by Peterson (1955, p. 14-18) for the North American races of the moose (*Alces alces*).

Wood warblers (Parulidae). Mengel (1964) has developed a bold and convincing interpretation of the biogeography and systematics of 46 species of North American wood warblers in relation to late-Pliocene and Pleistocene history. The story begins in the late Pliocene, with a northern element of the Parulidae adapted to temperate, deciduous Arcto-tertiary forest in eastern North America, and a southern element inhabiting disjunct western and eastern sclerophyll and pine woodlands derived from the relatively xerophytic, deciduous Madro-tertiary flora. The history of the latter element has not been traced in detail, but the members of the yellow-throated superspecies (*Dendroica dominica* of the eastern United States, *D. graciae* of southwestern North America, and *D. pityophila* and *D. adelaidi* of the West Indies) are differentiates presumably stemming from this early isolation. Possibly the Kirtland warbler (*D. kirtlandii*), now inhabiting jack-pine reproduction in burned areas in central Michigan (Mayfield, 1960), is also a derivative of the Madro-tertiary element, some members of which may have secondarily become adapted to the Arcto-tertiary forests and now show no evidence of their southern origin.

The history of the warbler element originally inhabiting the temperate Arcto-tertiary forest is considered by Mengel in relation to a "model sequence" of events in the

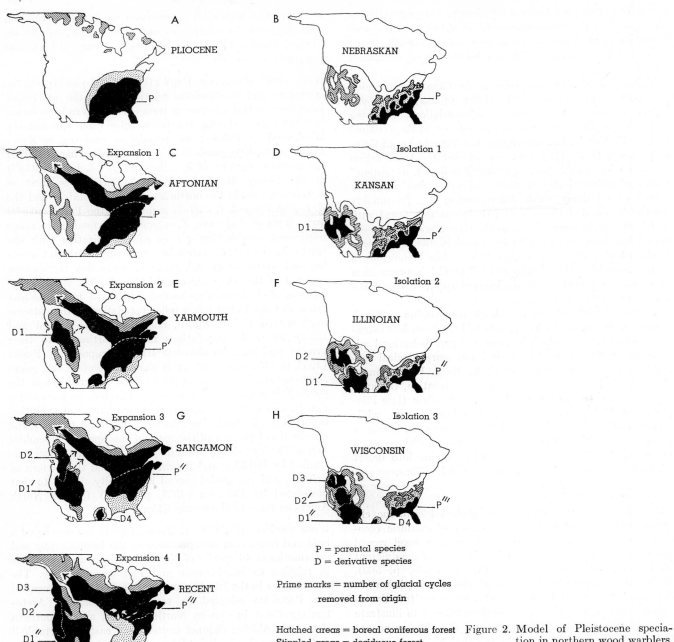

P = parental species
D = derivative species

Prime marks = number of glacial cycles
removed from origin

Hatched areas = boreal coniferous forest
Stippled areas = deciduous forest
Black areas = ranges of birds

Figure 2. Model of Pleistocene speciation in northern wood warblers.
(From Mengel, 1964)

Pleistocene (Fig. 2). With the first (Nebraskan) glaciation, components of the northern, boreal (coniferous) Arcto-tertiary forest moved deep into southeastern North America, invading a "compacted" deciduous Arcto-tertiary forest (related to today's eastern deciduous forest) and providing an opportunity for some of the warblers to adapt to coniferous forest or its seral stages. In the following interglacial period, a broad, transcontinental band of boreal Arcto-tertiary forest was established, permitting these warblers to achieve continent-wide ranges and setting the scene for disjunction of these stocks into eastern and western segments upon subsequent glacial advance. And in the western United States, montane forests replaced glaciers during the interglacial periods, creating islands of habitat in which differentiation could proceed. A few western differentiates apparently extended their ranges eastward in the transcontinental coniferous forest, only to become disjunct again, but the number of eastern "reinvasions" was small, perhaps due in part to competitive interactions with members of the rich warbler fauna of eastern North America.

Repetition of this process through the four glacial cycles of the Pleistocene resulted in the differentiation of most or all 12 endemic western species of warblers. Results predicted by the model are best shown by the black-throated green warbler superspecies (Fig. 3), in which the western forms *Dendroica townsendi*, *D. occidentalis*, and *D. nigres-*

cens show progressive degrees of differentiation from the eastern *D. virens* and may represent the products of three interglacial invasions from the east. However, both *D. occidentalis* and *D. townsendi*, which hybridize in their small area of sympatry, may stem from the same western invasion; *D. nigrescens* possibly represents a Pliocene disjunct of an ancestral Madro-tertiary form that subsequently gave rise to *D. virens* in the eastern Arcto-tertiary forest. *Dendroica chrysoparia* of the Edwards Plateau of Texas, which inhabits a relict of the eastern deciduous forest, is viewed as an offshoot of *D. virens* or its ancestor, which may have reached Texas during Wisconsin glaciation. (Mengel, 1964, believes that *D. chrysoparia* is not derived from *D. nigrescens*, as claimed by Stein, 1962.)

Among other examples interpreted in relation to the "model" are the western Audubon warbler (*D. auduboni*) and the eastern and northern Myrtle warbler (*D. coronata*), which hybridize where they are in contact in British Columbia and may have differentiated in the Wisconsin glacial period. Many of the clinal subspecies of wood warblers are thought to have evolved since the Wisconsin glacial period.

According to Mengel's analysis (1964), between 22% and 27% of the 46 species of continental wood warblers achieved specific status directly as a result of Pleistocene events, and Mengel suggests that no less than 12 species arising in the Pleistocene have become extinct.

A well-studied case of hybridization involves the blue-winged warbler (*Vermivora pinus*) and the golden-winged warbler (*V. chrysoptera*), which are broadly sympatric in parts of northeastern North America (Parkes, 1951; Berger, 1958). Although the present zone of sympatry runs largely east to west, Short (1963) believes the situation is the result of secondary contact between formerly isolated western (*pinus*) and eastern (*chrysoptera*) populations. According to his historical interpretation, the ancestral warbler population was separated into eastern and western segments at the height of Wisconsin glaciation by glacial ice and the Mississippi Embayment (Hobbs, 1950). He suggests that differentiation occurred in this period of isolation, with *pinus* presumably inhabiting prairie forest edge and *chrysoptera* occupying habitats along the southeastern coast of the United States, but the forms could have evolved prior to this time. With postglacial amelioration of the climate in the east, *chrysoptera* moved northward to New England and extended its range westward to the Great Lakes region. Short (1963) suggests that *pinus*, moving northward in the Mississippi region, was prevented from reaching the Great Lakes region by grasslands of the Prairie Peninsula, but it seems possible that the two warblers made contact in this area during the warm, mesic phase of the Climatic Optimum. In any event, as suggested by Short, the two forms were probably to a large degree geographically isolated during the Xerothermic interval when grasslands of the Prairie Peninsula extended to the northeastern states (Smith, 1957). The present western segment of the zone of sympatry is thought to have been established by *pinus* moving northward into the Prairie Peninsula at the end of the Xerothermic period, but the history of the eastern parts of the zone is difficult to assess.

A recent and continuing northward extension of the range

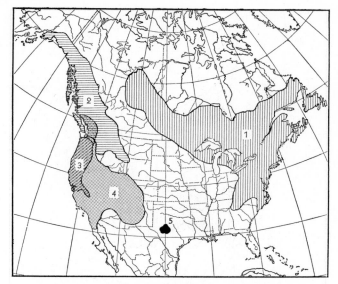

Figure 3. Breeding distribution of black-throated green warbler superspecies. 1, *Dendroica virens*; 2, *D. townsendi*; 3, *D. occidentalis*; 4, *D. nigrescens*; 5, *D. chrysoparia*. (From Mengel, 1964)

of *pinus*, attributed in part to man's activities, has increased the extent of the zone of sympatry. These warblers inhabit clearings, forest edge, and abandoned fields rather than climax forest, and, according to Mayr (1963b, p. 117), hybridization "presumably began some 200 years ago when the natural habitat barrier between the species was obliterated by deforestation and farming." Within this century, several formerly *chrysoptera*-like populations in New York, Connecticut, Massachusetts, and Michigan have shifted toward *pinus* as a result of hybridization. Among samples from the breeding populations in sympatry, hybrids outnumber individuals of the parental types, and 42% of the 1,028 adult specimens of the two forms examined by Short (1963) were identified as "definite hybrids."

Black-capped and Carolina chickadees. The black-capped chickadee (*Parus atricapillus*) of northern North America is replaced in the mid-eastern and southeastern United States by the Carolina chickadee (*P. carolinensis*). Where they are in contact in Illinois and Missouri, hybridization occurs in a narrow zone (Brewer, 1963); but in the Great Smoky Mountains of Tennessee and North Carolina, where *P. atricapillus* occurs at higher elevations than *P. carolinensis*, there is no evidence of interbreeding (Tanner, 1952, p. 412).

From Kansas east to central Illinois, the breeding ranges of the two forms appear to be contiguous, and in this region *P. carolinensis* may be moving northward and replacing *P. atricapillus*. Eastward from central Illinois to the Atlantic coast, where the position of the line of contact appears to be stabilized, there is evidence of a gap of several miles between the ranges of the two chickadees, which Brewer (1963, p. 42) interprets as a "reproductive isolating mechanism" dependent upon low reproductive success of hybrids

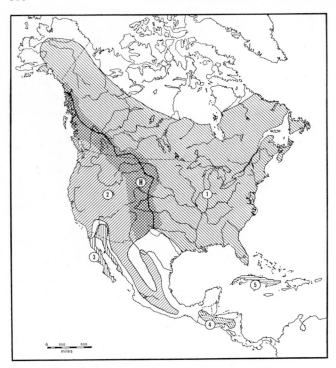

Figure 4. Breeding distribution of subspecies groups of flicker (*Colaptes auratus*). 1, *auratus*; 2, *cafer*; 3, *chrysoïdes*; 4, *mexicanoïdes*; 5, *chrysocaulosus*. H, zone of hybridization between *auratus* and *cafer* in which "pure" individuals are absent. (From Short, 1965)

and selection against tendencies for the parental types to disperse from their ranges into the gap.

Brewer (1963) proposes that the stock giving rise to *P. atricapillus* and *P. carolinensis* crossed the Bering land bridge from Asia into North America in the Pliocene or early Pleistocene. In some pre-Wisconsin glacial period, possibly the Illinoian, the segment ancestral to *P. atricapillus* may have been restricted to montane forests of western North America, while that giving rise to *P. carolinensis* was isolated south of the glacier in eastern North America. In the ensuing interglacial period (the Sangamon, if divergence began during Illinoian glaciation), the two populations came into secondary contact, and, with subsequent glaciation (Wisconsin), both *P. carolinensis* and an eastern segment of *P. atricapillus* moved southward to positions in which the former occurred north of the Gulf of Mexico and the latter occupied a range extending from the range-boundary with *P. carolinensis* north to the glacier. Presumably in this period, as now, the two forms were ecologically incompatible and therefore occupied strictly allopatric ranges. When deglaciation occurred, both forms moved northward, with *P. carolinensis* replacing *P. atricapillus* over much of its former range, but not in the Appalachian highlands, including the Great Smoky Mountains, where a relict population of *P. atricapillus* remains today.

North American flickers. Hybridization of *Colaptes* flickers, previously studied in part by Tavener (1934), Dickinson

(1953), and Dillon (1956), has recently been analyzed by Short (1965), whose monograph should be consulted by all persons concerned with introgression and the historical aspects of speciation in North America. According to Short's interpretation, all North American flickers belong to a single species, *Colaptes auratus*, composed of several subspecies groups, as shown in Figure 4.

The original geographic separation of the ancestral *auratus-cafer* populations may have occurred in the Illinoian glacial age, if not earlier, and divergence presumably continued during subsequent glacial periods but was perhaps halted or reversed due to increased contact and hybridization during interglacial periods. Short suggests that, with the waning of the last major advance of the Wisconsin glacier, the eastern form *auratus* moved northwestward into Canada while *cafer* was restricted to the area south of the receding ice sheet in the western United States. Later the two populations established a broad contact in British Columbia, where the present zone of hybridization bisects the area where the center of the Cordilleran ice sheet lay during Wisconsin time. (Several other pairs of races and semi-species of birds show similar patterns of contact; McCabe, 1936; Rand, 1948b; A. H. Miller, 1941b; Aldrich, 1943; Howell, 1952; Johnson, 1963.) Contact along rivers in the Great Plains probably existed through much of the Pleistocene but was perhaps obliterated during the Xerothermic interval of the Climatic Optimum. Under present conditions, the Plains river valleys afford only a small fraction of the total contact between the two forms. Introgression is extensive and affects *cafer* more than *auratus*.

Colaptes a. chrysoïdes is considered by Short (1964) an offshoot of an early *cafer* population that reached woodlands of the Cape region of Baja California in a Pleistocene glacial period. Isolated there by increasing aridity on the peninsula and a rise in sea level, the population adapted to desert conditions and later extended its range northward to contact and hybridize with *cafer* in Arizona and Sonora.

Species and subspecies pairs in the Great Plains region. A considerable volume of information is available on secondary contact of east-west subspecies and species pairs in the Great Plains. The pairs studied are as follows: western meadowlark (*Sturnella neglecta*) and eastern meadowlark (*S. magna*) (Lanyon, 1956, 1957; Szijj, 1963); indigo bunting (*Passerina cyanea*) and lazuli bunting (*P. amoena*) (Sibley and Short, 1959); rose-breasted grosbeak (*Pheucticus l. ludovicianus*) and black-headed grosbeak (*P. l. melanocephalus*) (West, 1962); Baltimore oriole (*Icterus g. galbula*) and Bullock oriole (*I. g. bullockii*) (Sibley and Short, 1964); and races of the rufous-sided towhee (*Pipilo erythrophthalmus*) (Sibley and West, 1959).

In each case, eastern and western populations are presumed to have been isolated by unsuitable environmental conditions in the Plains region during some Pleistocene glacial period, but in no case is it possible to state when isolation first occurred or secondary contact was first established. In the meadowlarks, hybridization is infrequent, but extensive interbreeding is recorded for the other pairs. The age of the zones of hybridization is unknown, but, to greater or lesser degree for each pair, man's activities in planting shade trees and shelter-belts and in controlling prairie fires and the flooding of river plains has increased the available habitat, with the result that the extent of interchange of genetic material through hybridization has increased in historical times.

Relevant to the influence of agriculture and other human activities in modifying avian habitats and, in particular, to their effect in removing extrinsic barriers to gene exchange between populations, attention is directed to the complex pattern of introgressive hybridization in the red-eyed towhees (*Pipilo erythrophthalmus* and *P. ocai*) in Mexico (Sibley, 1950, 1954; Sibley and West, 1958; Sibley and Sibley, 1964). Breakdown of ethological and ecological barriers between the two semi-species in central Mexico (they are sympatric without interbreeding in Oaxaca) was at first believed to have occurred within the last 300 years; but, after considering archaeological and historical demographic evidence from the Valley of Mexico and adjacent areas, Sibley and Sibley (1964, p. 499) concluded that "the extensive areas of second-growth brush and resulting interdigitation of *ocai* and *erythrophthalmus* habitats that seem important in increasing the probability of hybridization have existed for at least a thousand years and possibly longer."

Another situation in Mexico in which human activities have facilitated secondary contact and hybridization between populations occurs on the Pacific coastal plain of Chiapas, where recent clearing of forests has created "edge" and second-growth thickets supporting populations of hybrids between strongly differentiated subspecies of the rufous-naped wren (*Campylorhynchus rufinucha*) (Selander, 1964, p. 77-111). In this, as in other hybrid situations, it is possible that interbreeding occurred occasionally long before human activities modified the habitats and permitted establishment of the zone of hybridization in its present form.

Tufted and black-crested titmice. In Texas, the tufted titmouse (*Parus b. bicolor*) of the eastern United States hybridizes with a more arid-adapted subspecies, the black-crested titmouse (*P. b. sennetti* of the *atricristatus* group) along a zone of climatic transition (Fig. 5) (Dixon, 1955). The contact presumably is secondary, following an east-west Pleistocene disjunction of an ancestral population, which could have been effected by more extensive distribution of prairie in central Texas. Interbreeding probably antedates the environmental disturbances caused by the settlement of Texas by the white man. Along the Arkansas River, there has been a shift in hybrid character of the population toward *sennetti* since the late 1800's, correlated with an increase in winter temperatures (Dixon, 1955, p. 178).

Other examples of presumed east-west Pleistocene disjunctions in the southern United States are found in *Centurus* woodpeckers (Selander and Giller, 1959, 1963); common grackles (Chapman, 1940; Huntington, 1952); great-tailed and boat-tailed grackles (Selander and Giller, 1961); and orioles (Beecher, 1950).

Brown and Abert towhees. In an important contribution emphasizing the role of environmental change in speciation, Davis (1951) reconstructed the series of events leading to formation of the brown towhee (*Pipilo fuscus*) and Abert

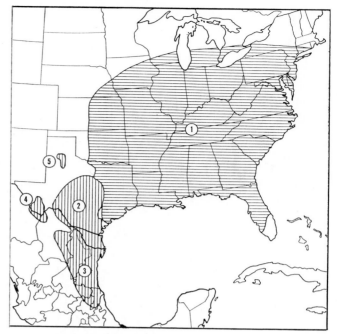

Figure 5. Distribution of tufted titmouse (*Parus bicolor*). 1, gray-crested subspecies *P. b. bicolor*. 2-5, black-crested subspecies of *atricristatus* group: 2, *P. b. sennetti*; 3, *P. b. atricristatus*; 4, *P. b. dysleptus*; 5, *P. b. paloduro*. (From Dixon, 1955)

towhee (*P. aberti*) in Mexico and the southwestern United States (Fig. 6). Spreading northwestward from Mexico to Oregon, Colorado, and Oklahoma in association with the Madro-tertiary flora, the ancestor of *P. fuscus* became separated into the *crissalis* and *perpallidus* racial groups when this flora was disjoined by formation of the Mohave and Colorado deserts in the middle Pliocene. Although the *crissalis* and *perpallidus* groups presumably have never been in secondary contact, their morphological, ecological, and behavioral similarities indicate that they have remained conspecific (Davis, 1951; Marshall, 1964).

With recession of the Madro-tertiary flora from the Colorado desert region in the middle Pliocene, towhees ancestral to *P. aberti* became confined to desert watercourses, but they probably maintained periodic contact with towhees of the *crissalis* group to the west, becoming totally isolated with the uplift of the mountains of southern California to their present height in the Pleistocene. Subsequently, *P. aberti* invaded the drainages of the Colorado and Gila rivers, becoming sympatric with *fuscus* towhees of the *perpallidus* group. The comparatively rapid evolution of *P. aberti* is attributed to the fact that the ancestral population "was isolated in a region of rapid environmental change and was confined . . . to a growth form quite unlike that utilized by the eastern or western groups of *fuscus*" (Davis, 1951, p. 100).

Scrub jay. Speciation in the scrub jay (*Aphelocoma coerulescens*), which, like the brown towhee, is associated with

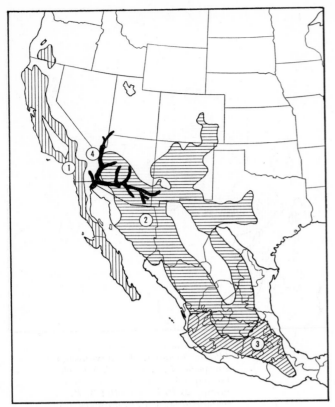

Figure 6. Distribution of brown and Abert towhees. 1, *crissalis* subspecies group of *P. fuscus*; 2, *perpallidus* subspecies group of *P. fuscus*; 3, *fuscus* subspecies group of *P. fuscus*; 4, *P. aberti*. (From Davis, 1951)

derivatives of the Madro-tertiary flora, has been studied by Pitelka (1951). Disjunction in the distribution of the ancestral form which led to differentiation of the western *"californica"* subspecies group, the interior *"woodhouseii"* group, and the isolated Florida form *A. c. coerulescens* is believed to antedate the Pleistocene, while isolation and differentiation of the large Santa Cruz Island form, *A. c. insularis*, occurred in the Pleistocene.

Other examples. Following are references to additional examples in which glaciation or other events of the Pleistocene are presumed to have caused disjunctions of populations, leading to differentiation in geographic isolation: alcids (Storer, 1952; Udvardy, 1963b); herons (Mayr, 1956); color morphs of snow goose (Cooch, 1963); mallards (Johnsgard, 1961); woodpeckers (Voous, 1947); Canada jays (Austin, 1932); *Agelaius* blackbirds (Orians, 1961); *Ammospiza* sparrows (Beecher, 1955); song sparrows on Mexican Plateau (Dickerman, 1963); horned larks (Behle, 1942); vireos (Hamilton, 1959).

CONCLUSIONS

Although there is abundant circumstantial evidence that environmental changes in the Pleistocene profoundly influenced avian speciation in North America, we can only speculate on rates of evolution of the modern subspecies and species which show patterns of distribution and contact suggesting former geographic isolation. That so many of the cases cited in the foregoing review involve populations that have not achieved the full species level of differentiation is perhaps due in part to the fact that forms that hybridize or are ecologically incompatible naturally attract the attention of systematists. Many Pleistocene isolates presumably achieved specific status and are now broadly sympatric, showing little evidence of former isolation, while other species have become extinct, in part due to competitive interactions with closely allied forms. And still others, which reached only the racial level of differentiation, have perhaps established broad clines of intergradation that do not reflect former patterns of isolation. A consideration of all lines of evidence suggests that few forms reached the full species level as a result of geographic isolation in the late Pleistocene. However, many of the more strongly differentiated subspecies may have evolved in Wisconsin time isolation, and many of the more weakly defined subspecies recognized by North American ornithologists have probably arisen in Recent times. In 1930 Moreau estimated 5,000 years as the minimum time required for evolution of avian races, but, in line with recent work in ecological genetics (Ford, 1964) demonstrating suprisingly great selective forces operating to maintain or to adjust the adaptations in natural populations, research on the introduced house sparrow (*Passer domesticus*) in North America (Johnston and Selander, 1964) has shown that geographic differentiation of a level generally accepted as subspecific by avian taxonomists may occur in less than 100 years. Thus, racial evolution may be extremely rapid, but, as noted by Mayr (1963b), we cannot extrapolate from racial to specific rates of evolution.

REFERENCES

Adams, C. T., 1955, Comparative osteology of the night herons: Condor, v. 57, p. 55-60

Aldrich, J. W., 1943, Relationships of the Canada jays in the Northwest: Wilson Bull., v. 55, p. 217-222

—— 1963, Geographic orientation of American Tetraonidae: J. Wildlife Management, v. 27, p. 528-545

A.O.U. Check-list, 1957, Check-list of North American birds, Baltimore, Amer. Ornithol. Union, 5th ed.: 691 p.

Austin, O. L., Jr., 1932, The birds of Newfoundland Labrador: Nuttall Ornithol. Club. Mem. 7, 229 p.

Banks, R. C., 1964, Geographic variation in the white-crowned sparrow *Zonotrichia leucophrys*: Univ. California Publ. Zool., v. 70, p. 1-123

Bardack, D., 1962, A review of the fossil birds of Kansas: Kansas Ornithol. Soc. Bull., v. 13, p. 9-14

Bartholomew, G. A., 1958, The role of physiology in the distribution of terrestrial vertebrates, *in* Hubbs, C. L. (ed.), Zoogeography: Amer. Assoc. Adv. Sci. Publ. 51, p. 81-95

Bartholomew, G. A., and Cade, T. J., 1963, The water economy of land birds: Auk, v. 80, p. 504-539

Baumel, J. S., 1953, Individual variation in the white-necked raven: Condor, v. 55, p. 26-32

Beecher, W. J., 1950, Convergent evolution in the American orioles: Wilson Bull., v. 62, p. 51-86

—— 1955, Late-Pleistocene isolation in salt-marsh sparrows: Ecology, v. 36, p. 23-38

Behle, W. H., 1942, Distribution and variation of the horned larks (*Otocoris alpestris*) of western North America: Univ. California Publ. Zool., v. 46, p. 205-316

—— 1963, Avifaunistic analysis of the Great Basin region of North America: XIII Intern. Ornithol. Congr. Proc., p. 1168-1181

Berger, A. J., 1958, The golden-winged–blue-winged warbler complex in Michigan and the Great Lakes area: Jack-Pine Warbler, v. 36, p. 37-73

Blair, W. F., 1958, Distributional patterns of vertebrates in the southern United States in relation to past and present environments, *in* Hubbs, C. L. (ed.), Zoogeography: Amer. Assoc. Adv. Sci. Publ. 51, p. 433-468

Blake, E. R., 1953, Birds of Mexico; a guide for field identification: Univ. Chicago Press, 644 p.

Bond, J., 1948, Origin of the bird fauna of the West Indies: Wilson Bull., v. 60, p. 207-229

—— 1963, Derivation of the Antillean avifauna: Philadelphia Acad. Nat. Sci. Proc., v. 115, p. 79-98

Brewer, R., 1963, Ecological and reproductive relationships of black-capped and Carolina chickadees: Auk, v. 80, p. 9-47

Brodkorb, P., 1953, Pleistocene birds from Haile, Florida: Wilson Bull., v. 65, p. 49-50

—— 1955, The avifauna of the Bone Valley formation: Florida Geol. Surv., Rep. Inv. No. 14, p. 1-57

—— 1956a, Pleistocene birds from Crystal Springs, Florida: Wilson Bull., v. 68, p. 158

—— 1956b, Pleistocene birds from Eichelberger Cave, Florida: Auk, v. 73, p. 136-137

—— 1957, New passerine birds from the Pleistocene of Reddick, Florida: J. Paleont., v. 31, p. 129-138

—— 1958, Fossil birds from Idaho: Wilson Bull., v. 70, p. 237-242

—— 1959a, Pleistocene birds from New Providence Island, Bahamas: Florida State Mus. Bull., v. 4, p. 349-371

—— 1959b, The Pleistocene avifauna of Arredondo, Florida: Florida State Mus. Bull., v. 4, p. 269-291

—— 1960, How many species of birds have existed?: Florida State Mus. Bull., v. 5, p. 41-53

—— 1963a, Birds from the Upper Cretaceous of Wyoming: XIII Intern. Ornithol. Congr. Proc., p. 55-70

—— 1963b, A giant flightless bird from the Pleistocene of Florida: Auk, v. 80, p. 111-115

—— 1963c, Catalogue of fossil birds. ı, Archaeopterygiformes through Ardeiformes: Florida State Mus. Bull., v. 7, p. 179-293

—— 1963d, Pleistocene birds from American Falls, Idaho: Florida Acad. Sci. Quart. J., v. 26, p. 280

—— 1963e, A new Pleistocene grebe from Florida: Florida Acad. Sci. Quart. J., v. 26, p. 53-55

—— 1964a, Catalogue of fossil birds. ıı, Anseriformes through Galliformes: Florida State Mus. Bull., v. 8, p. 195-335

—— 1964b, Notes on fossil turkeys: Florida Acad. Sci. Quart. J., v. 27, p. 223-229

Cade, T. J., 1955, Variation of the common rough-legged hawk in North America: Condor, v. 57, p. 313-345

Chapman, F. M., 1940, Further studies of the genus *Quiscalus*: Auk, v. 57, p. 225-233

Cooch, F. G., 1963, Recent changes in distribution of color phases of *Chen c. caerulescens*: XIII Intern. Ornithol. Congr. Proc., p. 1182-1194

Darlington, P. J., Jr., 1957, Zoogeography; the geographical distribution of animals: New York, John Wiley & Sons, Inc., 675 p.

Davis, J., 1951, Distribution and variation of the brown towhees: Univ. California Publ. Zool., v. 52, p. 1-120

—— 1959, The Sierra Madrean element of the avifauna of the Cape District, Baja California: Condor, v. 61, p. 75-84

Dawson, W. R., 1948, Records of fringillids from the Pleistocene of Rancho La Brea: Condor, v. 50, p. 57-63

Dementiev, G. P., 1960, Espèces aviennes récentes trouvées à l'état fossile au post-tertiaire dans l'URSS: XII Intern. Ornithol. Congr. Proc., p. 162-166

Dickerman, R. W., 1963, The song sparrows of the Mexican Plateau: Minnesota Mus. Nat. Hist. Occ. Pap. 9, p. 1-71

Dickinson, J. C., Jr., 1953, Report on the McCabe collection of British Columbian birds: Mus. Comp. Zool. Bull., v. 109, p. 123-209

Dillon, L. S., 1956, Wisconsin climate and life zones in North America: Science, v. 123, p. 167-176

Dixon, K. L., 1955, An ecological analysis of the interbreeding of crested titmice in Texas: Univ. California Publ. Zool., v. 54, p. 125-206

—— 1959, Ecological and distributional relations of desert scrub birds of western Texas: Condor, v. 61, p. 397-409

Downs, T., 1954, Pleistocene birds from the Jones fauna of Kansas: Condor, v. 56, p. 207-221

Downs, T., Howard, H., Clements, T., and Smith, G. A., 1959, Quaternary animals from Schuiling Cave in the Mojave Desert, California: Los Angeles Mus. Contr. Sci., No. 29, p. 1-21

Drury, W. H., Jr., 1953, Birds of the Saint Elias quadrangle in the southwestern Yukon Territory: Can. Field-Nat., v. 67, p. 103-128

Fay, F. H., and Cade, T. J., 1959, An ecological analysis of the avifauna of St. Lawrence Island, Alaska: Univ. California Publ. Zool., v. 63, p. 73-150

Fisher, H. I., 1944, The skulls of cathartid vultures: Condor, v. 36, p. 272-296

—— 1947, The skeletons of Recent and fossil *Gymnogyps*: Pacific Sci., v. 1, p. 227-236

Ford, E. B., 1964, Ecological genetics: London, Methuen, 335 p.

Galbreath, E. C., 1955, An avifauna from the Pleistocene of central Kansas: Wilson Bull., v. 67, p. 62-63

Greenway, J. C., Jr., 1958, Extinct and vanishing birds of the world: Amer. Comm. Intern. Wild Life Protection Spec. Publ. 13, 518 p.

Grinnell, J., 1928, A distributional summation of the ornithology of Lower California: Univ. California Publ. Zool., v. 32, p. 1-300

Guilday, J. E., 1962, The Pleistocene local fauna of the Natural Chimneys, Augusta County, Virginia: Pittsburg, Carnegie Mus. Ann., v. 36, p. 87-122

Halliday, W. E. D., and Brown, A. W. A., 1943, The distribution of some important forest trees in Canada: Ecology, v. 24, p. 353-373

Hamilton, T. H., 1959, Adaptive variation in the genus *Vireo*: Wilson Bull., v. 70, p. 307-346

Hamon, J. H., 1964, Osteology and paleontology of the passerine birds of the Reddick, Florida, Pleistocene: Florida Geol. Surv. Bull. 44, p. 1-120

Hibbard, C. W., 1958, Summary of North American Pleistocene mammalian local faunas: Michigan Acad. Sci., Arts, Lett. Pap., v. 43, p. 3-32

Hobbs, W. H., 1950, The Pleistocene history of the Mississippi River: Science, v. 111, p. 260-262

Holman, J. A., 1959, Birds and mammals from the Pleistocene of Williston, Florida: Florida State Mus. Bull., v. 5, p. 1-24

—— 1961, Osteology of living and fossil New World quails (Aves, Galliformes): Florida State Mus. Bull., v. 6, p. 131-233

Horsberg, C. L., 1955, Radiocarbon dates and Pleistocene chronological problems in the Mississippi Valley region: J. Geol., v. 63, p. 278-286

Howard, H., 1930, A census of the Pleistocene birds of Rancho La Brea from the collections of the Los Angeles Museum: Condor, v. 32, p. 81-88

—— 1940, A new race of caracara from the Pleistocene of Mexico: Condor, v., 42, p. 41-44

—— 1946, A review of the Pleistocene birds of Fossil Lake, Oregon: Carnegie Instn. Publ. 551, p. 143-195

—— 1947a, An ancestral golden eagle raises a question in taxonomy: Auk, v. 64, p. 287-291

—— 1947b, A preliminary survey of trends in avian evolution from Pleistocene to Recent time: Condor, v. 49, p. 10-13

—— 1947c, Wing elements assigned to *Chendytes*: Condor, v. 49, p. 76-77

—— 1949, Avian fossils from the marine Pleistocene of southern California: Condor, v. 51, p. 20-28

—— 1950, Fossil evidence of avian evolution: Ibis, v. 92, p. 1-21

—— 1952, The prehistoric avifauna of Smith Creek Cave, Nevada, with a description of a new gigantic raptor: Southern California Acad. Sci. Bull., v. 51, p. 50-54

—— 1955a, Fossil birds, with especial reference to the birds of Rancho La Brea (revised): Los Angeles County Mus., Sci. Ser. No. 17, Publ. No. 10, p. 1-40

—— 1955b, Fossil birds from Manix Lake, California: U.S. Geol. Surv. Prof. Pap. 264J, p. 199-205

—— 1955c, New records and a new species of *Chendytes*, an extinct genus of diving geese: Condor, v. 27, p. 137-143

—— 1960, Significance of carbon-14 dates for Rancho La Brea: Science, v. 131, p. 712-714

—— 1962a, A comparison of avian assemblages from individual pits at Rancho La Brea, California: Los Angeles County Mus. Contr. Sci. No. 58, p. 1-24

—— 1962b, Bird remains from a prehistoric cave deposit in Grant County, New Mexico: Condor, v. 64, p. 241-242

—— 1963, Fossil birds from the Anza-Borrego Desert: Los Angeles County Mus. Contr. Sci. No. 73, p. 1-33

—— 1964a, Fossil Anseriformes, *in* Delacour, J., The waterfowl of the world: London, Country Life Ltd., v. 4, p. 233-326

—— 1964b, Further discoveries concerning the flightless "diving geese" of the genus *Chendytes*: Condor, v. 66, p. 372-376

Howard, H., and Miller, A. H., 1939, The avifauna associated with human remains at Rancho La Brea, California: Carnegie Instn. Publ. 514, p. 39-48

Howell, T. R., 1952, Natural history and differentiation in the yellow-bellied sapsucker: Condor, v. 54, p. 237-282

Huntington, C. E., 1952, Hybridization in the purple grackle, *Quiscalus quiscula*: Syst. Zool., v. 1, p. 149-170

Johnsgard, P. A., 1961, Evolutionary relationships among the North American mallards: Auk, v. 78, p. 3-43

Johnson, N. K., 1963, Biosystematics of sibling species of flycatchers in the *Empidonax hammondii-oberholseri-wrightii* complex: Univ. California Publ. Zool., v. 66, p. 79-239

Johnston, R. F., 1964, The breeding birds of Kansas: Univ. Kansas Publ., Mus. Nat. Hist., v. 12, p. 575-655

Johnston, R. F., and Selander, R. K., 1964, House sparrows; rapid evolution of races in North America: Science, v. 144, p. 548-550

Kay, G. F., 1931, Classification and duration of the Pleistocene epoch: Geol. Soc. Amer. Bull., v. 42, p. 425-466

Lanyon, W. E., 1956, Ecological aspects of the sympatric distribution of meadowlarks in the north-central states: Ecology, v. 37, p. 98-108

—— 1957, The comparative biology of the meadowlarks (*Sturnella*) in Wisconsin: Nuttall Ornithol. Club. Publ. No. 1, p. 1-67

Linsdale, J. M., 1928, Variations in the fox sparrow (*Passerella iliaca*) with reference to natural history and osteology: Univ. California Publ. Zool., v. 30, p. 251-393

Marcus, L., 1960, A census of the abundant large Pleistocene mammals from Rancho La Brea: Los Angeles County Mus. Contr. Sci. No. 38, p. 1-11

Marshall, J. T., 1964, Voice in communication and relationships among brown towhees: Condor, v. 66, p. 345-356

Mayfield, H. F., 1960, The Kirtland's warbler: Bloomfield Hills, Michigan, Cranbrook Inst. Sci. Bull. 40, 242 p.

Mayr, E., 1946a, The number of species of birds: Auk, v. 63, p. 64-69

—— 1946b, History of the North American bird fauna: Wilson Bull., v. 58, p. 3-41

—— 1951, Speciation in birds: X Intern. Ornithol. Congr. Proc., p. 91-131

—— 1956, Is the great white heron a good species?: Auk, v. 73, p. 71-77

—— 1963a, The fauna of North America, its origin and unique composition: XVI Intern. Congr. Zool. Proc., v. 4, p. 3-11

—— 1963b, Animal species and evolution: Cambridge, Belknap Press, Harvard, 797 p.

—— 1964, Inferences concerning the Tertiary American bird faunas: Natl. Acad. Sci. Proc., v. 51, p. 280-288

McCabe, T. T., 1936, Endemism and the American Northwest: Wilson Bull., v. 48, p. 289-302

McCoy, J. J., 1963, The fossil avifauna of Itchtucknee River, Florida: Auk, v. 80, p. 335-351

Mengel, R. M., 1964, The probable history of species formation in some northern wood warblers (Parulidae): Living Bird, v. 3, p. 9-43

Miller, A. H., 1929, The passerine remains from Rancho La Brea in the paleontological collections of the University of California: Univ. California Publ. Dept. Geol. Sci. Bull., v. 19, p. 1-22

—— 1932, The fossil passerine birds from the Pleistocene of Carpinteria, California: Univ. California Publ. Dept. Geol. Sci. Bull., v. 21, p. 169-194

—— 1937, Biotic associations and life-zones in relation to the Pleistocene birds of California: Condor, v. 39, p. 248-252

—— 1940, Climatic conditions of the Pleistocene reflected by the ecologic requirements of fossil birds: Sixth Pacific Sci. Congr. Proc., 1939, p. 807-810

—— 1941a, A review of centers of differentiation for birds in the western Great Basin region: Condor, v. 43, p. 257-267

—— 1941b, Speciation in the avian genus *Junco*: Univ. California Publ. Zool., v. 44, p. 173-434

—— 1947, A new genus of icterid from Rancho La Brea: Condor, v. 49, p. 22-24

—— 1948, The whistling swan in the upper Pliocene of Idaho: Condor, v. 50, p. 132

—— 1951, An analysis of the distribution of the birds of California: Univ. California Publ. Zool., v. 50, p. 531-644

—— 1963, Desert adaptations in birds: XIII Intern. Ornithol. Congr. Proc., p. 666-674

Miller, A. H., and Bowman, R. I., 1956, A fossil magpie from the Pleistocene of Texas: Condor, v. 58, p. 164-165

Miller, L., 1925, *Chendytes*, a diving goose from the California Pleistocene: Condor, v. 27, p. 145-147

—— 1943, The Pleistocene birds of San Josecito Cavern, Mexico: Univ. California Publ. Zool., v. 47, p. 143-168

—— 1957, Bird remains from an Oregon Indian midden: Condor, v. 59, p. 59-63

—— 1960, Notes on the Pleistocene flightless goose, *Chendytes*: Southern Calif. Acad. Sci. Bull., v. 59, p. 57-61

Miller, L., and DeMay, I., 1942, The fossil birds of California: Univ. California Publ. Zool., v. 47, p. 47-142

Miller, L., Mitchell, E. D., and Lipps, J. H., 1961, New light on the flightless goose, *Chendytes lawi*: Los Angeles County Mus. Contr. Sci. No. 43, p. 1-11

Moreau, R. E., 1930, On the age of some races of birds: Ibis, v. 6, p. 229-239

—— 1954, The main vicissitudes of the European avifauna since the Pliocene: Ibis, v. 96, p. 411-431

—— 1963, The distribution of tropical African birds as an indicator of past climatic changes, *in* Howell, F. C., and Bourlière, F. (eds.), African ecology and human evolution: Chicago, Aldine Publ. Co., p. 28-42

Odum, E. P., 1945, The concept of the biome as applied to the distribution of North American birds: Wilson Bull., v. 57, p. 191-201

Orians, G. H., 1961, The ecology of blackbird (*Agelaius*) social systems: Ecol. Monogr., v. 31, p. 285-312

Parkes, K. C., 1951, The genetics of the golden-winged × blue-winged warbler complex: Wilson Bull., v. 63, p. 5-15

—— 1958, The Palaearctic element in the New World avifauna, *in* Hubbs, C. L. (ed.), Zoogeography: Amer. Assoc. Adv. Sci. Publ. 51, p. 421-432

Peterson, R. L., 1955, North American moose: Toronto, Univ. Toronto Press, 280 p.

Pitelka, F. A., 1941, Distribution of birds in relation to major biotic communities: Amer. Midl. Nat., v. 25, p. 113-137

—— 1950, Geographic variation and the species problem in the shore-bird genus *Limnodromus*: Univ. California Publ. Zool., v. 50, p. 1-108

—— 1951, Speciation and ecologic distribution in American jays of the genus *Aphelocoma*: Univ. California Publ. Zool., v. 50, p. 195-464

Rand, A. L., 1948a, Birds of southern Alberta: Natl. Mus. Canada Bull., v. 111, 105 p.

—— 1948b, Glaciation, an isolating factor in speciation: Evolution, v. 2, p. 314-321

Selander, R. K., 1964, Speciation in wrens of the genus *Campylorhynchus*: Univ. California Publ. Zool., v. 74, p. 1-305

Selander, R. K., and Giller, D. R., 1959, Interspecific relations of woodpeckers in Texas: Wilson Bull., v. 7, p. 107-124

—— 1961, Analysis of sympatry of great-tailed and boat-tailed grackles: Condor, v. 63, p. 29-86

—— 1963, Species limits in the woodpecker genus *Centurus* (Aves): Amer. Mus. Nat. Hist. Bull., v. 124, p. 213-274

Short, L. L., Jr., 1963, Hybridization in the wood warblers *Vermivora pinus* and *V. chrysoptera*: XIII Intern. Ornithol. Congr. Proc., p. 147-160

—— 1965, Hybridization in the flickers (*Colaptes*) of North America: Amer. Mus. Nat. Hist. Bull. (in press)

Sibley, C. G., 1939, Fossil fringillids from Rancho La Brea: Condor, v. 41, p. 126-127

—— 1950, Species formation in the red-eyed towhees of Mexico: Univ. California Publ. Zool., v. 50, p. 109-194

—— 1954, Hybridization in the red-eyed towhees of Mexico: Evolution, v. 8, p. 252-290

Sibley, C. G., and Short, L. L., Jr., 1959, Hybridization in the buntings (*Passerina*) of the Great Plains: Auk, v. 76, p. 443-463

—— 1964, Hybridization in the orioles of the Great Plains: Condor, v. 66, p. 130-150

Sibley, C. G., and Sibley, F. C., 1964, Hybridization in the red-eyed towhees of Mexico; the populations of the southeastern plateau region: Auk, v. 81, p. 479-504

Sibley, C. G., and West, D. A., 1958, Hybridization in the red-eyed towhees of Mexico; the eastern plateau populations: Condor, v. 60, p. 85-104

—— 1959, Hybridization in the rufous-sided towhees of the Great Plains: Auk, v. 76, p. 326-338

Simpson, G. G., 1961, Principles of animal taxonomy: New York, Columbia Univ. Press, 247 p.

Smith, P. W., 1957, An analysis of post-Wisconsin biogeography of the Prairie Peninsula region based on distributional phenomena among terrestrial vertebrate populations: Ecology, v. 38, p. 205-218

Stein, R. C., 1962, A comparative study of songs recorded from five closely related warblers: Living Bird, v. 1, p. 61-71

Stettenheim, P., 1958, Bird fossils from the late Pleistocene of Kansas: Wilson Bull., v. 70, p. 197-199

Storer, R. W., 1952, A comparison of variation, behavior and evolution in the sea bird genera *Uria* and *Cepphus*: Univ. California Publ. Zool., v. 52, p. 121-222

Szijj, L. J., 1963, Morphological analysis of the sympatric populations of meadowlarks in Ontario: XIII Intern. Ornithol. Congr. Proc., p. 176-188

Tanner, J. T., 1952, Black-capped and Carolina chickadees in the southern Appalachian Mountains: Auk, v. 69, p. 407-424

Taverner, P. A., 1934, Flicker hybrids: Condor, v. 36, p. 34-35

Tordoff, H. B., 1959, A condor from the upper Pliocene of Kansas: Condor, v. 61, p. 338-343

Udvardy, M. D. F., 1958, Ecological and distributional analysis of North American birds: Condor, v. 60, p. 50-66

—— 1963a, Bird faunas of North America: XIII Intern. Ornithol. Congr. Proc., p. 1147-1167

—— 1963b, Zoogeographical study of the Pacific Alcidae. Symposium on "Pacific Basin Biogeography": Honolulu, Bishop Museum Press, p. 85-111

Voous, K. H., 1947, The history of the distribution of the genus *Dendrocopos*: Amsterdam, 142 p.

Welty, J. C., 1962, The life of birds: Philadelphia, W. B. Saunders Co., 546 p.

West, D. A., 1962, Hybridization in the grosbeaks (*Pheucticus*) of the Great Plains: Auk, v. 79, p. 399-424

Wetmore, A., 1922, Bird remains from the caves of Porto Rico: Amer. Mus. Nat. Hist. Bull., v. 46, p. 297-333

—— 1924, Fossil birds from southeastern Arizona: U.S. Natl. Mus. Proc., v. 64, p. 1-18

—— 1931, The avifauna of the Pleistocene in Florida: Smithson. Misc. Coll., v. 85, p. 1-41

—— 1933, Pliocene bird remains from Idaho: Smithson. Misc. Coll., v. 87, p. 1-12

—— 1937, Bird remains from cave deposits on Great Exuma Island in the Bahamas: Mus. Comp. Zool. Bull., v. 80, p. 427-441

—— 1938, Bird remains from the West Indies: Auk, v. 55, p. 51-55

—— 1944, Remains of birds from the Rexroad fauna of the upper Pliocene of Kansas: Univ. Kansas Sci. Bull., v. 30, p. 89-105

—— 1951, Recent additions to our knowledge of prehistoric birds, 1933-1949: X Intern. Ornithol. Congr. Proc., p. 51-74

—— 1956, A check-list of the fossil and prehistoric birds of North America and the West Indies: Smithson. Misc. Coll., v. 131, p. 1-105

—— 1958, Miscellaneous notes on fossil birds: Smithson. Misc. Coll., v. 135, p. 1-11

—— 1959a, Notes on certain grouse of the Pleistocene: Wilson Bull., v. 71, p. 178-182

—— 1959b, Birds of the Pleistocene in North America: Smithson. Misc. Coll., v. 138, p. 1-24

—— 1960, Pleistocene birds in Bermuda: Smithson. Misc. Coll., v. 140, p. 1-10

—— 1962, Notes on fossil and subfossil birds: Smithson. Misc. Coll., v. 145, p. 1-17

Woolfenden, G. E., 1959, A Pleistocene avifauna from Rock Spring, Florida: Wilson Bull., v. 71, p. 183-187

—— 1961, Postcranial osteology of the waterfowl: Florida State Mus. Bull., v. 6, p. 1-129

Summary

Although the Pleistocene in North America was a period of reduction in total numbers of species and adaptive types of birds, it was also a time of active speciation. The theory of a Pliocene origin for most or all modern bird species is not supported by the fossil record. Patterns of distribution and secondary contact of modern populations provide strong circumstantial evidence that glaciation and other events of the Quaternary profoundly influenced avian speciation. The speciation process is characterized by great variation in rate, depending importantly upon factors of population size, isolation, and rate and degree of environmental change.

AMPHIBIAN SPECIATION*

W. FRANK BLAIR[1]

THE WORKING premise of this review is that the origins of present-day distributions of organisms can be understood only by reference to climatic events of the Pleistocene and that recently evolved species and populations in incipient stages of speciation are reflections of Pleistocene events. Deevey (1949) has somewhat oversimplified this premise in his statement, "Nearly all well-studied cases of subspeciation and speciation point to the Pleistocene as the time of such previous isolation, and the occurrence of closely related forms in the same area is therefore attributed to post-Pleistocene alterations in geography and in biogeography." Deevey's statement is perhaps overly inclusive, but otherwise basically defensible. This same working premise has governed me (W. F. Blair, 1958a) in analyzing patterns of distribution of most groups of terrestrial vertebrates in the southern United States. The present discussion surveys the apparent effects of the Pleistocene on present distributions and on speciation of amphibians of the United States and adjacent areas of Canada and Mexico. For a few species complexes that have been studied in relatively great depth it is possible to hypothesize their Pleistocene evolutionary history in some detail.

A basic argument in Deevey's (1949) analysis and in my own (Blair, 1958a) is that glacial advances in continental North America were accompanied by climatic effects far south of the glacial border and that the consequent latitudinal displacement of biotas was such that warmth-adapted species suffered fragmentation of ranges as they retreated to refuges in Florida and Mexico. The degree of displacement of biotas below the glacial boundary has been argued *pro* and *con,* with some plant ecologists (*e.g.* Braun, 1955) holding strongly against significant displacement. Reopening of this argument is not pertinent here; evidence for displacement is summarized in the two above-mentioned papers. However, two recent major contributions involving pollen analyses from the previously poorly known arid Southwest are pertinent. Work on late Pleistocene deposits of the Llano Estacado of western Texas and eastern New Mexico by Wendorf and associates (1961, p. 130) indicates that this area, presently dominated by arid short-grasslands, supported "open boreal woodlands or forest" an estimated 15,000 to 22,500 years ago. "The pollen spectra are dominated by pine and spruce, with very minor representation from grass, composites, and Artemisia." Martin (1963a, p. 66) states, "Palynological evidence of major environmental shifts in the late Pleis-

tocene of the Southwest includes (1) an interlude of juniper-pine woodland in the Mohave Desert, (2) a past forest of spruce and pine in the San Augustin Plains, (3) pine woodland or forest in the Texas High Plains and southeastern Arizona. . . . From the evidence of radiocarbon dates the last major pluvial maximum would be slightly older than 20,000 years, with pluvial conditions ending by 12,000 B.P." Martin (1963b) has found the fossil pollen above the 14-m level in the Willcox Playa of southeastern Arizona comparable to the pollen rain in the Chuska Mountains of northwestern New Mexico, 1,400 m higher in elevation and 700 km to the north, where the mountains are covered by open stands of *Pinus ponderosa* with an understory including *Artemisia frigida* and with *Picea, Abies,* and *Pseudotsuga* on north slopes. The present vegetation in the area of the Willcox Playa is desert grassland and shrub.

The southward and northward shifting of biotas in relation to glacial and interglacial stages, dominated by temperature changes, is only one of the biogeographic phenomena stemming from the great variability of Pleistocene climates. Changes in moisture regimes were also of great importance. All of the subtleties of Pleistocene change are impossible to reconstruct, and the best we can hope for is to determine the relation of present distribution and present evidence of speciation to major shifts in climatic conditions. The probable diversity of Pleistocene climates in the central grasslands has been referred to by W. F. Blair (1958a) as follows: "It seems reasonable to hypothesize that under the vast shifts of climatic regimes that characterized the Pleistocene a wide spectrum of conditions from moist to arid might be expected to have existed in the present grasslands in various combinations with temperature conditions." MacGinitie (1958, p. 74) has generalized even further: "Almost any type of erratic distribution and almost any inconsistency of distribution appear possible when the effects of climatic changes in the later Tertiary and Pleistocene are considered."

The two orders of amphibians considered in this review are ecologically very different kinds of animal, and consequently they would be expected to respond quite differently to climatic flux (W. F. Blair, 1958a, p. 462). Most of the urodeles are relatively well adapted to cold and wet conditions, with present centers of distribution in remnants of the Arcto-Tertiary forest. They would be expected to have tended to move with this forest as it shifted position under Pleistocene climatic shifts. Relative to the urodeles, the anurans are warmth-adapted, and in all families the number of genera and/or species decreases along a gradient of decreasing temperature, whether the

* Much of my own work reported here has been supported by grants from the National Science Foundation.
[1] Department of Zoology, University of Texas, Austin, Texas.

gradient is latitudinal or montane. In general the anurans are more tolerant of moisture deficiency than are the urodeles, but, even in these, many groups meet xeric boundaries either because of direct effects of lack of moisture or because of its effect on vegetation.

LATE TERTIARY PRELUDE TO PLEISTOCENE SPECIATION

General world cooling of climates in the late Tertiary and extensive orogeny that reached its peak at the close of this period (MacGinitie, 1958) must have had profound effects on distributions that were formerly much more extensive under the less rigid climatic zonation of the early and middle Tertiary. Development of the central grasslands in the Pliocene interposed a major barrier to east-west dispersal of many kinds of organism. These late Tertiary events undoubtedly enforced broad disjunctions that are still in existence today, but some of these probably cannot be distinguished from disjunctions that have resulted from Pleistocene events.

The fossil record of Cenozoic amphibians is so fragmentary and identification to species level even in Pleistocene material is often so dubious that it is of little help toward our main objective of assessing the effects of the Pleistocene on biogeography and speciation of these animals. It is useful, however, in indicating ranges of genera formerly greater than those now occupied and in indicating the level of evolution of genera and higher taxa at the beginning of the Pleistocene.

A survey of the available evidence indicates that the diversification of both urodeles and anurans into families, genera, and even species groups within genera had taken place long before the beginning of the Pleistocene. Hecht (1963) in reviewing the anuran evidence concluded that, "By Oligocene times the major features of modern world anuran fauna had developed." Major evolutionary lines recognizable in living forms within the genus *Bufo* apparently existed well before the close of the Tertiary. Auffenberg (1956) has considered *Bufo praevius* Tihen from the Miocene Thomas Farm fauna of Florida to be a member of the *B. americanus* group; the present author concurs with this interpretation, but Tihen (1962) disagrees. Estes and Wassersug (1963) regard a fossil *Bufo* from the late Miocene La Venta fauna of Colombia as specifically inseparable from modern *B. marinus*. Tihen (1962) has suggested that *Neoprocoela edentata* Schaeffer from Lower Oligocene of Argentina is actually a *Bufo* of the *calamita* complex and that *B. alienus* Tihen from the middle Pliocene of Kansas is possibly a member of this complex. For other anuran genera, with the exception of the pelobatid genus *Scaphiopus*, the fossil material is too unsatisfactory to be of much help.

Auffenberg (1956) reported the subgenus *Scaphiopus* from the Thomas Farm fauna and regarded this Lower Miocene form from Florida as close to *S. holbrooki*, which occurs there today. Tihen (1960) regards all four fossil pelobatids known from the Pliocene of North America as being *Spea*, which he regards as generically distinct from *Scaphiopus*. Zweifel (1956) has constructed a series of postulates relating subgeneric and specific differentiation

of *Scaphiopus* to events of the late Tertiary. He has suggested that "the evolution of [subgenus] *Spea* may be correlated with the establishment of grassland as a distinct and wide-ranging formation at least as early as the lower Pliocene and perhaps as far back as mid-Miocene." He has suggested that the living species *S. couchi* (subgenus *Scaphiopus*), "possibly evolved in association with the thorn scrub and mesquite-grass formations that were being established in the southwestern interior region by mid-Oligocene." He suggested that the evolution of *S. hurteri* (regarded by W. F. Blair, 1958b, as a subspecies of *S. holbrooki*) may be correlated with the early development of grasslands (late Tertiary) and establishment of the forest-grasslands ecotone. Alternative probabilities will be discussed in a later section.

The evidence for urodele evolution to the level of species groups well prior to the opening of the Pleistocene is equally as convincing as that for the anurans. On the basis of material from the late Cretaceous Lance formation of Wyoming, Estes (1964) has shown that the subfamily Desmognathinae of the family Plethodontidae had differentiated by late Mesozoic time. Goin and Auffenberg (1955, 1957, 1958) have traced the family Sirenidae back to the Lower Cretaceous of Texas and the genus *Siren* back to the Eocene of Wyoming. Estes (1963) reported a *Notopthalmus* (family Salamandridae) from the early Miocene Thomas Farm fauna of Florida and considered that it could have given rise to the species that occurs in Florida today. Tihen (1955) presented evidence for his statement: "The genus *Ambystoma* was certainly established by Upper Pliocene time, probably much earlier, and differentiation into species groups was well under way, possibly completed, during or before Upper Pliocene time." Tihen and Chantell (1963) later supported the latter conclusion by identification of an apparent member of the *A. maculatum* group from the Valentine formation (Miocene-Pliocene boundary) of Nebraska.

As mentioned earlier, the fossil record is also pertinent to our objectives in that it indicates formerly extensive distributions that were subsequently affected by events of the late Tertiary and Pleistocene, but this information is applicable almost exclusively to genera and higher taxa. One of the most interesting records is that of the family Rhinophrynidae. The single living species occurs today in the tropics and ranges northward to Tamaulipas. Hecht (1959) described a rhinophrynid (*Eurhinophrynus*) from an atlas from the middle Eocene Bridger formation of Wyoming. Holman (1963) described from the lower Oligocene Cypress Hill formation of Saskatchewan a *Rhinophrynus* said to be difficult to distinguish from living *R. dorsalis* except by its much smaller size. Of equal interest is the record of the genus *Siren* from the Eocene of Wyoming (Goin and Auffenberg, 1957), for the genus and family are presently restricted to the Gulf of Mexico coastal plain, southern Atlantic coastal plain, and Mississippi Embayment. These records are consistent with other evidence of broad distributions and markedly less climatic zonation prior to the climatic deterioration in the late Tertiary.

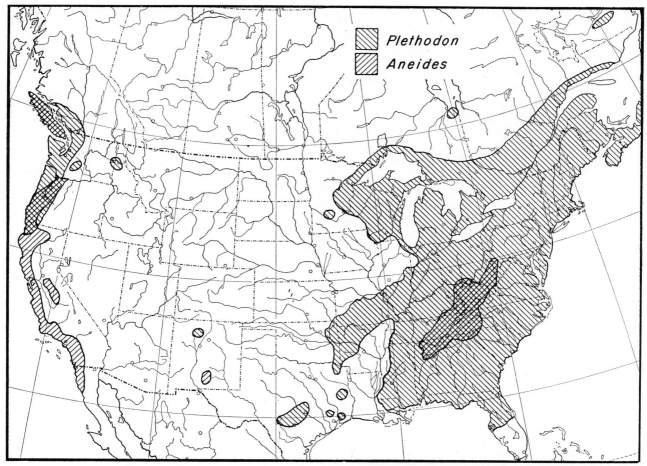

Figure 1. Distribution of two genera of plethodontid (lungless) salamanders, illustrating dicentric pattern of distribution imposed by arid grasslands and deserts of Tertiary origin and illustrating post-Pleistocene relicts in the Rocky Mountains and along the border of eastern and western centers. Adapted with permission from maps by Stebbins (1951, copyright by Houghton Mifflin Co.). Base map with permission from Goode Base Map Series, Department of Geography, University of Chicago (copyright by University of Chicago).

Pre-Pleistocene Disjunctions

Urodele distributions clearly reflect the late Tertiary drying of the interior and development of grasslands and deserts. The possible pre-Pleistocene evolution of the Ambystomatidae has been discussed by Tihen (1958). Appearance of the family in North America in "late Mesozoic or very early Tertiary" is hypothesized, with establishment of the various species groups before the Pliocene and major aspects of their distributions before the end of the Pliocene. Main centers are the eastern, forested half of the United States and the forested Pacific coastal strip. "The relatively arid, unforested conditions of the Plains region through much of the Tertiary prevented an extensive spread [from the eastern center] to the west." A southward spread from the eastern center is postulated to explain the origin of a Mexican group, the *Ambystoma tigrinum–A. mexicanuam–Bathysiredon* complex, which, by evolution of neoteny, has been able to surmount and occupy the arid interior. Details of distribution within these centers presumably reflect Pleistocene events; the main patterns appear to be Tertiary in origin, as Tihen (1958) has postulated.

The salamandrids show a similar east-west distribution, with the dry interior intervening between the west-coast *Taricha* and eastern-forest *Notopthalmus* (= *Diemictylus*), and there is no suggestion that this basic pattern has any different history than that of the ambystomatids. The lungless salamanders (Plethodontidae) show a pattern comparable to that of the ambystomatids, with eastern and western centers and with a southern element that, in this case, extends into South America. The consensus opinion (Dunn, 1926; Martin and Harrell, 1957; Brame and Wake, 1963) is that this basic pattern was established in the Tertiary. The genera are mostly endemic to one or another of the three areas, but two genera (*Plethodon* and *Aneides*) are common to the east and the west. Both have relict species in the Rocky Mountains of New Mexico, *Plethodon neomexicanus* in the Jemez Mountains of northern New

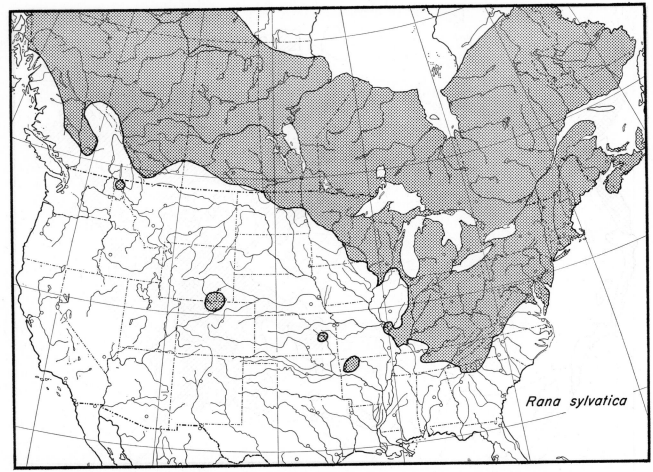

Figure 2. Distribution of *Rana sylvatica*, a northern frog, illustrating pattern of southern relicts as a result of southward shift in the Wisconsin and subsequent withdrawal. With permission after Conant (1958, copyright by Houghton Mifflin Co.). Base map with permission from Goode Base Map Series, Department of Geography, University of Chicago (copyright by University of Chicago).

Mexico and *Aneides hardyi* in the Sacramento Mountains of southern New Mexico (Fig. 1). Stebbins and Riemer (1950) have suggested that *P. neomexicanus* arrived by dispersal southward through the Rocky Mountains, although it is described as "close to *Plethodon cinereus* of the eastern United States and Canada." Lowe (1950) has theorized that *A. hardyi* became isolated during the early Pliocene. W. F. Blair (1958a) has suggested that the two Rocky Mountain relicts could date from the Pleistocene and that connections with the eastern segments of the genus could have existed as recently as the late Pleistocene. The work of Wendorf and associates (1961) indicating boreal forest on the Llano Estacado in the Wisconsin adds support to this possibility.

The pattern of anuran distribution is very different from that of the urodeles. The ancient relict, *Ascaphus*, of the Pacific northwest and the tropical elements (*Hypopachus, Leptodactylus, Eleutherodactylus, Syrrhophus,* and *Pternohyla*), which barely enter the Southwest from Mexico, are not immediately pertinent. Among the seven remaining genera, five (*Microhyla, Scaphiopus, Bufo, Pseudacris,* and *Rana*) find the arid interior no barrier. One eastern

genus, *Acris*, finds the central grasslands region a barrier to its westward distribution. The seventh genus, *Hyla,* the only arboreal genus in the United States, has species to the east and to the west of the central grasslands and has its center of greatest present differentiation in the tropics to the south. That the eastern United States has long been a center of differentiation for *Hyla* is indicated by the presence of the genus in the Lower Miocene Thomas Farm fauna of Florida (Auffenberg, 1956). Of the four United States species of *Hyla* west of the central grasslands, two occur in isolated populations in mountain ranges east of the Sierra Nevada, mostly in Arizona and New Mexico and adjacent Mexico. One, *H. arenicolor*, appears to be a member of the *versicolor* group, which has four species in the eastern United States. Bogert (1960, p. 305) considers it closest to *H. versicolor* on the basis of morphology and call structure. W. F. Blair (1959a) interprets the same evidence to indicate closer relationship to *H. femoralis*. Progeny of crosses between ♀ *H. arenicolor* and ♂ *H. femoralis*, and *H. avivoca* (= *phaeocrypta*) of the *versicolor* group metamorphosed, but it was not possible to test them for fertility, nor have the reciprocal crosses been made. This kind of evidence will be necessary before one can hazard an educated guess as to the length of time *H. arenicolor* has been isolated. It could have been as late as in the Pleistocene; it could have been in the Tertiary. The other desert-mountain species, *H. wrightorum*, is closely related to, if not conspecific with, *H. eximia* of Mexico and undoubtedly represents a Pleistocene, probably Wisconsin, relict of the southern population. *H. californiae* and *H. regilla* also appear to be members of the *eximia* group (see Bogert, 1960; W. F. Blair, 1960) and presumably had their origins to the south. It is true that one eastern species, *H. squirella*, also appears to belong to this same species group (W. F. Blair, 1960), but any estimate of how long the species has been in the eastern United States would be pure conjecture.

Distributions and Speciation
through Post-Pleistocene Southern Isolation

Presently disjunct southern populations of species that are relatively northern in their distributions provide indisputable evidence for a southward shift of these species, and this may account for some of the speciation in the southern United States. Several species of amphibians are represented by disjunct southern populations that are slightly or undetectably differentiated. These presumably reflect southward displacement in the Wisconsin and subsequent return northward of the main body of the population after the close of the Wisconsin. A nominal species of toad, *Bufo houstonensis*, occupies a limited range in the vicinity of Houston, Texas, while the southern limit of the present range of *B. americanus* is 340 miles to the north in the Ouachita Mountains of southeastern Oklahoma (Fig. 4). *B. houstonensis* is little differentiated morphologically from *B. americanus*, with which it is interfertile (W. F. Blair, 1959b) and from which its mating call is not significantly differentiated (W. F. Blair, 1962). Another toad, *B. hemiophrys*, occurs as a relict on the Laramie Plateau of Wyoming some 500 miles south of the present range of the species. I have been unable to detect any morphological difference between these toads and individuals from Delta, Manitoba, and northwestern Minnesota within the main body of the range.

The wood frog (*Rana sylvatica*), one of the northernmost anurans in North America, ranges from coastal and central Alaska across Canada and southward in the eastern United States (Fig. 2). Three widely disjunct populations, and thus three potentially incipient species, are known from the central United States, one in the Rocky Mountains of northern Colorado and southeastern Wyoming (Maslin, 1947; Baxter, 1947), one in the Flint Hills of Kansas (Smith, 1950), and one in the Ozark Highlands of northwestern Arkansas. The pickerel frog (*Rana palustris*) of the eastern United States shows less extensive southern disjuncts (see Conant, 1958, map 239). Brown and Boschung (1954) discovered one of these populations in the twilight zone of a cave in Conecuh County, Alabama, and attributed survival of this population to the ability to retreat to the cave during the hot, dry summers. Brode (1958) made similar observations in three caves in Mississippi.

The disjunct ranges discussed above surely represent remnants of Wisconsin ranges. Earlier southern disjunctions may well account for part of the complex speciation that has taken place in the chorus frogs of the *Pseudacris nigrita* group (see Mecham, 1961, p. 39), *e.g.* the speciation of *P. brimleyi* and *P. nigrita* of the southeastern Gulf coastal plain as isolates from *P. triseriata*. Speciation of *Bufo terrestris*, another coastal-plain species (Fig. 4), from the far-northward-ranging *B. americanus* may have had a similar history.

Urodele distributions in the eastern United States also show evidence of north-south disjunctions, but for the most part they also bear the imprint of east-west disjunctions related to moisture and are more appropriately discussed elsewhere. Present distribution of *Hemidactylium scutatum* illustrates this pattern; there are widely disjunct populations in southwestern Georgia, southeastern Louisiana, western Arkansas, and eastern Missouri, and the main body of the species is to the northeast of this semicircle of disjunct populations. Another plethodontid, *Desmognathus fuscus*, is reportedly disjunct in southern Mississippi and southwestern Alabama (Valentine, 1963). *D. auriculatus* of the coastal plain and *D. brimleyorum* of the Ouachita Mountains in Oklahoma and Arkansas, under Valentine's (1963) classification, perhaps represent earlier isolations from the *D. fuscus* stock. The ranges of *D. fuscus* and *D. auriculatus* presently overlap on the Gulf coastal plain (Valentine, 1963).

Northern Relicts

Extensive northern relicts of presently existing species would be unexpected, for the last major climatic upheaval of the Quaternary was the one that saw the retreat northward of the Wisconsin glacier and the return northward of the displaced biota. However, there are presently existing northern relicts of southern warmth-adapted species; these apparently reflect minor post-Wisconsin fluctuations of climates and of species ranges. If this conclusion is valid, then this group is relatively young by comparison with the southern relicts of northern species. Bleakney (1958, p. 46) has suggested that northern species also extended their ranges northward during the "climatic optimum."

One group involves Atlantic coastal-plain forms such as *Hyla cinerea* (Conant, 1958, map 224), *Rana virgatipes* (Conant, 1958, map 243), and *Microhyla carolinensis* (Conant, 1957) and has disjunctions imposed by the intrusion of Chesapeake Bay into the coastline and, for the *Rana*, by Delaware Bay as well. A second species of the *Hyla cinerea* group, *H. andersoni*, is broadly disjunct, with one population in the New Jersey pine barrens and others in southern North Carolina and eastern Georgia (Conant, 1958, map 218).

A few northern disjuncts of southern warmth-adapted species in the eastern United States (*Microhyla carolinensis* and *Ambystoma talpoideum*) have been discussed by P. W. Smith (1957) as attributable to northward shift of these populations during the post-Wisconsin warm, moist "Climatic Optimum." Similarly (P. W. Smith, 1957), the occurrence of relicts of a chorus frog, *Pseudacris streckeri*, as far northeastward as the sand plains of west-central

Illinois is attributed to a northeastward spread of this species in the subsequent "Xerothermic period." If so, this would make the disjuncts in this species the youngest of those under discussion.

EAST-WEST DISJUNCTS AND SPECIATION IN EASTERN UNITED STATES

The existence of species pairs oriented east-west in the southern United States has been discussed by Deevey (1949, p. 1374) and explained on the basis of differentiation after isolation in glacial-stage refuges in Florida and Mexico. These distribution patterns in terrestrial vertebrates have been discussed by W. F. Blair (1958a). In addition to these species pairs, there are various lesser disjuncts of as-yet-little-differentiated populations of anurans. These last undoubtedly reflect relatively recent climatic change and minor shift of range. The eastern narrow-mouth frog (*Microhyla carolinensis*) is known to have a series of disjunct populations in local, relatively mesic situations from the Gulf coastal plain in Texas to northeastern Oklahoma and 80 or more km west of the western limits of the main body of the range (W. F. Blair, 1955; A. P. Blair and Laughlin, 1955). This situation could have resulted from relatively minor increase in xeric conditions along the forest-grassland boundary and was perhaps conditioned by man's influence in this direction (W. F. Blair, 1955). An apparently disjunct population of the green-frog (*Rana clamitans*) exists along Alum Creek in Bastrop County, Texas. The most extensive disjunct is a population of *Hyla avivoca* in southeastern Oklahoma and about 250 km west of the main range (A. P. Blair and Lindsay, 1961). Disjunct populations of the gray treefrog (*Hyla chrysoscelis*) occur to the west of its main range from southern Texas to Canada (*e.g.* Fargo, North Dakota: A. P. Blair, 1952; Gillespie, Llano, and Throckmorton Counties, Texas: author's data). If one is unwilling to accept the evidence for major climatic change in the far south during Pleistocene glacial stages of sufficient magnitude to disrupt transcoastal distributions of warmth-adapted species, he can turn to these minor disjuncts as evidence that the opportunities for east-west speciation exist and have existed in the past without major north-south displacement of biotas.

The urodeles of the eastern United States show patterns of east-west disjunction that are consistent with major displacement of biotas in the Pleistocene, because these would have been expected to move southward and westward with the Arcto-Tertiary forest during glacials and become relict to the west during interglacials (W. F. Blair, 1958a, p. 463). The Ozark Highlands of Oklahoma, Arkansas, and Missouri and the Ouachita Mountains of Oklahoma and Arkansas are jointly a main center for urodele relicts (Dowling, 1956). Relict species of *Plethodon* and *Eurycea* that have related species centering on Appalachia, as well as disjunct populations of the previously mentioned *Hemidactylium scutatum*, occur there. A lesser center (apparently because of its presently less favorable conditions for urodele existence) is the Edwards Plateau of central Texas. *Eurycea* is able to exist there in neotenic populations, which closely parallel the neotenic *Eurycea* populations of the Ozarks.

Plethodon glutinosus survives in mesic pockets, particularly around springs. As mentioned earlier, the paleoclimatic evidence becomes increasingly indicative that salamanders such as *Plethodon* might have found conditions favorable for their spread far west of these present relicts as late as Wisconsin time; this situation could account for the relict populations of *Plethodon* and *Aneides* in the southern Rocky Mountains. Tihen (1958) has suggested that *Ambystoma schmidti* of the southern Mexican Plateau reached there coincident with a major glacial advance. The nearest member of the group to which Tihen assigns *A. schmidti* is *A. texanum*, which presently ranges westward to the eastern edge of the Edwards Plateau.

There remains a sizeable group of species or near-species pairs of anurans whose initial eastern and western disjuncts have been attributed to glacial-stage climatic shifts that fragmented formerly continuous ranges (W. F. Blair, 1958a). These differ from the minor anuran disjuncts discussed earlier in this section in that speciation has proceeded considerably further. There is another important difference. The minor disjuncts exist in pockets of favorable environment (surrounded by seemingly hostile environments) sufficiently similar to the environment occupied by the main body of the species that they are able to persist in these pockets. Some of the species pairs, on the other hand, show marked ecological divergence, and grasslands-adapted and forest-adapted species meet or approach one another along the forest-grasslands boundary. Others are maintained as disjunct, allopatric populations by the Mississippi Embayment and occupy relatively similar environments on opposite sides of it. We shall examine these two groups in some detail, as most of the species in them have been subjected to fairly intensive investigation of their stage of speciation.

The simplest pattern involving the Mississippi Embayment is that of the spadefoot toads, *Scaphiopus holbrooki* and the nominal species *S. hurteri* (Fig. 3). These anurans have breeding habits adapted to xeric conditions, but as mentioned earlier a probable ancestor was in Florida in the early Miocene (Auffenberg, 1956). Both populations are arenicolous and find their respective westward and eastward distributions limited by the alluvial soils of the Mississippi Embayment (Wasserman, 1958). The two populations are moderately differentiated morphologically, and, as Wasserman (1958) has shown, they are interfertile. Furthermore, the mating calls are essentially similar, and ecological isolating mechanisms are not discernible (W. F. Blair, 1958b), all of which implies that these populations would not behave as separate breeding systems under sympatry, and hence they are regarded as subspecies. The sum of this evidence suggests separation of these east-west populations no earlier than the Pleistocene, and the relatively southern distribution of both populations points to the likelihood of a disruption of ranges by glacial-stage climate. The third population of this complex, *S. couchi*, ranges largely to the west of *S. h. hurteri* (although there is limited sympatry in Texas and Oklahoma) and on into non-mountainous and non-tropical parts of Mexico. Greater morphological differentiation and relatively high (but not complete) genetic incompatibility (Wasserman, 1957) sug-

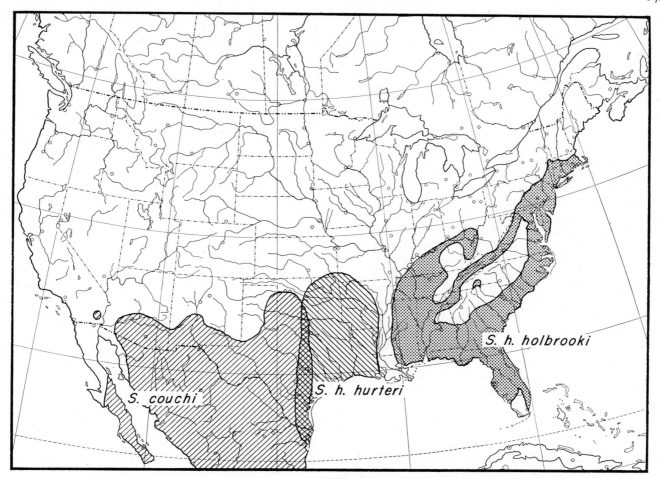

Figure 3. Distribution of spadefoots of subgenus *Scaphiopus,* illustrating speciation through east-west disjunction (for discussion see text). With permission after Conant (1958, copyright by Houghton Mifflin Co.) with modifications from Wasserman (1958). Base map with permission from Goode Base Map Series, Department of Geography, University of Chicago (copyright by University of Chicago).

gest an earlier origin for *S. couchi* than for the separation of *S. h. holbrooki* and *S. h. hurteri*. The separation of *S. couchi* may have come in an early Pleistocene glacial stage and the separation of the two presently disjunct allopatric populations of *S. holbrooki* may have come as late as the Wisconsin.

The pattern of distribution of a pair of chorus frogs, *Pseudacris ornata* and *P. streckeri* differs in that the hiatus is wider. *P. ornata* is limited in its westward range by the Mississippi Embayment; *P. streckeri* is a grasslands inhabitant that reaches its eastward limit at the border of the forest, thus leaving a wide gap between its eastern limit and the Mississippi Embayment. This pair is only moderately differentiated in morphology, but they have evolved genetic incompatibility (Mecham, 1957, 1959). The mating call is moderately differentiated, but the differentiation has been shown to be adequate for discrimination by the females (tested only in *P. streckeri:* W. F. Blair and Littlejohn, 1960). No significant ecological isolating mechanisms are apparent. Nevertheless, the general picture is either very rapid evolution or initial isolation presumably predating the Wisconsin.

An east-west pair of frogs (*Rana*) have the Mississippi Embayment complexly involved in their present distribution. The eastern *R. capito* has the typical coastal-plain distribution of a population that might have survived the Wisconsin glacial stage in a Florida refuge; it presently ranges west to the Mississippi Embayment. The western species, *R. areolata*, is a grasslands-adapted frog that ranges northward along the forest border, eastward in the "Prairie Peninsula," and southward along the eastern side of the Mississippi River. It apparently does not contact the range of *R. capito* (Conant, 1958, map 242). The two populations are regarded as conspecific by some workers, but the relationships of these populations have not been investigated by methods other than those of morphology.

Even such relatively complex distributional relationships as those of the two species of cricketfrogs (*Acris*) could be traceable to previous east-west disjunction. One species, *A. gryllus*, has the distribution of spread from a presumed glacial-stage refugium in Florida; it ranges west on the Gulf coastal plain to the Mississippi River. The other species, *A. crepitans*, ranges from northeastern Mexico to southeastern South Dakota and east to the Atlantic coast, overlapping the range of *A. gryllus* along the border of the coastal plain. The ubiquitous *A. crepitans* could have spread to its present range from a glacial-stage refuge in Mexico. Hybridization occurs in the zone of overlap, and there is evidence for strong reinforcement there of premating isolating mechanisms (W. F. Blair, 1958c).

An east-west species pair in which there is differentiation into forest and grassland types is found in the narrow-mouth frogs, *Microhyla* (= *Gastrophryne*), with the forest-adapted *M. carolinensis* and grasslands-adapted *M. olivacea* overlapping narrowly from the Gulf coast to northeastern Oklahoma. Limited hybridization and reinforcement of isolating mechanisms are occurring in the overlap zone (W. F. Blair, 1955). These are warmth-adapted members of a family that has its North American distribution centering in the tropics of Middle America, and consequently one would suspect them of having been highly susceptible to east-west disjunction during Pleistocene glacial stages. An alternative origin could have been by way of a minor disjunction such as those discussed earlier in *M. carolinensis*, followed by adaptation to and spread into the surrounding "hostile" environment.

A different origin seems likely for a grasslands-adapted chorus frog, *Pseudacris clarki*, because the species complex to which it belongs ranges far northward and is one of the most cold-adapted groups of anurans. The range narrowly overlaps that of *P. triseriata* along the forest-grassland border from the Gulf coast to southeastern Kansas and in the grasslands of central Kansas, and rare hybrids occur. *P. clarki* is morphologically well differentiated, and it is differentiated in mating call, with the difference providing a premating isolating mechanism (Michaud, 1962). Fertility of interspecific hybrids has been demonstrated (Lindsay, 1958). *P. clarki* could have had its genesis as a far southern relict after populations of *P. triseriata* in the central grasslands moved southward during a glacial stage and then retreated northward. This would involve no major change of the vegetation type occupied, as *P. triseriata* currently ranges across the northern grasslands and also occurs in forests. The degree of differentiation suggests origin of *P. clarki* during one of the pre-Wisconsin glacial advances.

The distribution patterns of the cryptic species *Hyla versicolor* and *H. chrysoscelis* involve east-west contacts that were believed by W. F. Blair (1958c) to reflect east-west fragmentation in the Pleistocene. Johnson (1961, 1963) has demonstrated genetic incompatibility between these species, which are markedly differentiated in mating call but not in morphology. In view of the genetic incompatibility and differentiation in mating call it seems likely that the speciation of these frogs was pre-Wisconsin, with present morphological similarities the result of parallelism. Distributional relationships of these species in the critical area of Missouri and Iowa are unknown, but it is possible that the apparently disjunct population of otherwise northern *H. versicolor* known to range from the Ozark Highland southward to the Gulf of Mexico is actually a relict from a southward extension of *H. versicolor* during the Wisconsin. Only additional work will solve this problem.

A salamander, *Notopthalmus meridionalis*, is disjunct in southern Texas and northeastern Mexico, with a grassland gap between its range and that of *Notopthalmus viridescens*, which ranges west to the forest border.

POST-PLUVIAL RELICTS IN THE SOUTHWEST

Anuran distributions in the arid Southwest show patterns of distribution comparable to those for fishes discussed by Hubbs and Miller (1948) and Miller (this volume). In general, the desert relicts appear to be relatively recent in origin (from Wisconsin distributions), although the evidence is largely from morphology, because these taxa have been relatively little investigated by the methods of experimental and non-morphological systematics. Moisture is the critical factor, of course, in limiting amphibian distributions in this part of the continent. Prehistoric irrigation practices, as well as naturally occurring bodies of permanent water, appear to have been important to the survival of the desert relicts (A. P. Blair, 1955).

Most of the pluvial relicts belong to the genus *Bufo*. A much greater range during the Wisconsin pluvial is suggested for *B. microscaphus* (Fig. 4). I have compared living and preserved material from the populations of western Chihuahua, western New Mexico, and southwestern Utah, and insignificant morphological differentiation exists. The coastal California population has been treated as a subspecies by Stebbins (1951) and as a separate species by earlier workers.

The *B. boreas* group shows greater morphological differentiation among its pluvial relicts than does *B. microscaphus*. The range of *B. boreas* extends along the Pacific coast from northern Baja California to southern Alaska, and inland it extends southward in the main mountain chains. One relict population in Deep Springs Valley, Inyo County, California, has been described as a species, *B. exsul*, by Myers (1942) and from morphological evidence has been variously regarded as a species or subspecies. Another relict population in Oasis Valley, Nye County, Nevada, has been variously treated as a species, *B. nelsoni*, or as a subspecies. Schuierer (1962, 1963) has discussed these desert endemics and has curiously interpreted statements by Hubbs and Miller (1948, p. 89) as indicating that *B. exsul* became endemic "before 'Lahontan' time." The latter authors were discussing water connections that would have permitted dispersal by fish; absence of such connections does not mean that the regional environment was such as to exclude *B. boreas*-type toads from the present desert at the time that Lake Lahontan existed. Structural similarities (W. F. Blair, 1963a) and hybridization data (W. F. Blair, 1964) suggest that *B. alvarius* of the Sonoran desert may be a derivative of *B. boreas*. If so, its origins were presumably earlier than those of the endemics discussed above, perhaps through isolation following one of the earlier Pleistocene pluvials

A relict population of *Bufo punctatus* has been reported by Miller (1944) from Saline Valley, which is adjacent to the valley in which the relict *Bufo exsul* occurs. This species ranges widely in the Southwest. Banta (1962) has examined toads from this population and has commented on the fact that this population appears "to have undergone no or very slight evolution" by contrast with that shown

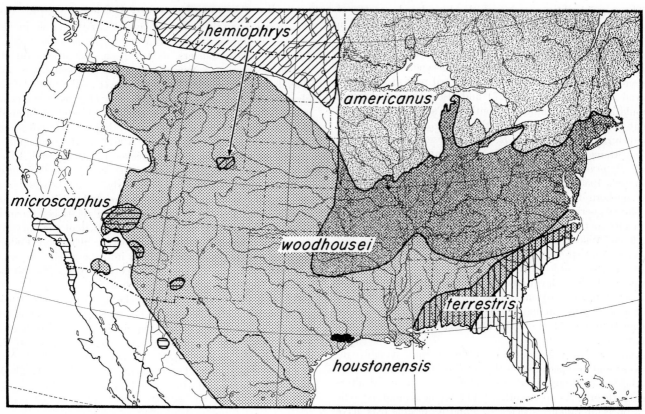

Figure 4. Distribution of *Bufo americanus* group of toads, illustrating possibly four different times of speciation (for discussion see text). Base map with permission from Goode Base Map Series, Department of Geography, University of Chicago (copyright by University of Chicago).

by *B. exsul*. It may not be safe to assume that the greater differentiation in the *boreas* group implies greatly longer isolation. The relics of this group exist in small populations (*e.g.* Schuierer, 1962, estimated the total population of *B. exsul* in 1954 to be "in excess of 10,000 adults," which by point of reference is less than the probable egg complement of a single female). It is possible that small population size (Schuierer, 1962, reported "fewer toads in 1958," and Myers, 1942, estimated the population at 600 to 700 toads), and the marginal conditions of existence have resulted in more rapid differentiation than in the case of the *B. punctatus*.

A disjunct population of *Bufo woodhousei* west of the main range of the species (see Stebbins, 1951, p. 502) occurs in southeastern California, where the lowlands of the Colorado River apparently have been instrumental in permitting survival and where present irrigation favors continued survival of this population. Mayhew (1962) has reported a disjunct population of a spadefoot, *Scaphiopus couchi*, from the Imperial Valley of southern California. Both of these anurans, as well as *B. punctatus*, are relatively well adapted to xeric conditions for anurans, and one would assume that their present disjunctions postdate the Wisconsin, as the areas involved became the most xeric areas in North America. By contrast the disjunctions in the *B. boreas* complex may have had their origins as the Wisconsin came to a close.

Milstead (1960) has summarized information about pluvial relics in the Chihuahuan desert. These also appear to be post-Wisconsin in origin, for with the exception of *Acris crepitans* they (*Eleutherodactylus, Syrrhophus, Bufo valliceps*) belong to subtropical taxa that presumably moved northward after the Wisconsin. Pluvial conditions must also have favored greater continuity of distribution of *Hyla arenicolor*, which now exists in numerous highly isolated montane populations from southern Utah southward into Mexico and eastward to trans-Pecos Texas. The nominal species *Hyla wrightorum* of the Colorado Plateau in Arizona and New Mexico is an isolate from *Hyla eximia* of the Mexican Highland that surely reached its present position during a pluvial, probably in the Wisconsin, since it is essentially undifferentiated in mating call (W. F. Blair, 1960) or in morphology.

MONTANE SPECIATION

Climatic shifts in the main mountain chains appear to have been important in initiating species in anuran and urodele groups. It is beyond our scope to attempt an exhaustive treatment of Pleistocene and post-Pleistocene montane speciation in North America, but some of the well-studied examples are adequately illustrative. The greatest amount of attention has been given to the history of speciation in groups inhabiting the Cascade–Sierra Nevada chain of western North America.

The possible history of two closely related species of frogs, *Rana boylei* and *R. muscosa*, has been discussed in detail by Zweifel (1955), who holds the opinion that the "separation of *R. boylei* and *R. muscosa* dates from the uplift of the Sierra Nevada in the Pliocene." *R. muscosa* presently occupies essentially the glaciated part of the Sierra Nevada (Zweifel 1955, Fig. 27) and also occurs in disjunct populations in mountains of southern California; displacement down the west slope of the Sierra Nevada is postulated during glacial stages. *R. boylei* presently occupies the Coast Ranges and the Sierra Nevada at lower elevations than *R. muscosa* and has disjuncts in southern California (Zweifel, 1955, Fig. 15). For various reasons, isolation of the southern disjuncts of *R. muscosa* are postulated "during a pluvial period concurrent with some glacial maximum previous to the most recent one," while disjunction of the *R. boylei* relicts is attributed to the drying after the last pluvial. Another species pair, *R. aurora* and *R. cascadae*, show a comparable altitudinal relationship, with *R. cascadae* at higher elevations in the Cascade Mountains of Washington and Oregon and *R. aurora* at lower elevations to the west and ranging south to Baja California. Genetic incompatibility (Porter, 1961) suggests relatively long separation.

Another Sierra Nevadan distribution that possibly involves montane speciation is that of *Bufo canorus*, a member of the *boreas* group. Karlstrom (1962) has discussed alternative theories as to its origin: (1) "it is a montane relic of a once far ranging species . . . and its origins may have been far north of its present range," (2) it is "a montane differentiate of an ancestral *boreas*-like toad which became isolated in or near its present range in the Sierra." He rejects the first hypothesis, but the fact that *B. canorus* retains the mating call (Karlstrom, 1962) whereas the wide-ranging *B. boreas* has nearly lost it favors this argument instead. Favoring the second theory, Karlstrom has suggested origin of *B. canorus* on an unglaciated "island . . . somewhere in the Sierra during the early Pleistocene." Karlstrom (1962, p. 84) demonstrated metamorphosis of F_1 hybrids between female *B. canorus* and male *B. boreas*. The reciprocal hybrids show high percentage of metamorphosis (W. F. Blair, 1964), and F_1 males are fertile in backcrosses to *B. boreas* (author's data).

Dispersal of salamanders across the Central Valley of California under pluvial conditions has been postulated by Stebbins (1949) for the plethodontid *Ensatina* and by Riemer (1958) for the salamandrid *Taricha*.

The Rocky Mountains are largely depauperate of amphibians. However, both *Bufo boreas* and *Pseudacris triseriata*, which range southward along this chain, exist in isolated populations toward their southern limits. These potentially speciating populations have been essentially uninvestigated.

There is evidence for much montane speciation among urodeles in the Appalachian Mountains, with the *Plethodon jordani* group (Hairston and Pope, 1948) illustrating the greatest fragmentation. There is one example among anura in *Pseudacris brachyphona*, a member of the highly speciated *P. nigrita* complex.

THE GLACIAL BORDER AND GLACIATED AREAS

Pleistocene climatic changes played their main role in amphibian evolution south, even far south, of the farthest advances of the glaciers, as has been documented in the preceding sections. Nevertheless, glacial boundaries and glacial-stage refugia in "driftless" areas to the north of the glacial boundary appear to have been of some significance in speciation, particularly for urodeles. The most interesting and thoroughly analyzed case is that of the *Ambystoma jeffersonianum* complex (Uzzell, 1964). Uzzell's convincing argument is that the diploid species *A. laterale* and *A. jeffersonianum* arose through disjunction by the Wisconsin ice sheet, with the former, presently a cold-adapted species, finding a refuge in the unglaciated "driftless area" of Wisconsin and the latter, presently a relatively warmth-adapted species, originating from that part of the ancestral population that was driven south by the glaciation. Following post-Wisconsin spread of both into the glaciated region, hybridization may account for the origin of the two triploid species, *A. tremblayi* and *A. platineum*.

Thurow (1961) has attributed the fixation of an erythristic allele in *Plethodon cinereus* to small-population effects along the oscillating glacial margin in the eastern United States. Evidence is presented to suggest origin of this variant in the area of Litchfield County, Connecticut, after the Cary glaciation and subsequent spread along the glacial boundary during and after the Mankato glaciation.

EVOLUTIONARY HISTORIES

The biogeographical and other evidence presented in the preceding sections is indicative of extensive speciation in both orders of amphibians during the Pleistocene. Climatic oscillations involving both temperature and moisture and combinations of the two during the course of the Pleistocene can account for disruptions of range that could have been the beginning of most of the diversification within species group. In general, as discussed earlier, it is likely that the diversification into existing species groups occurred in the Tertiary, with diversification within the groups being mostly a Pleistocene phenomenon. For the most part, it is possible from existing distributions to make a reasonable estimate of the specific mode of origin of a species (*i.e.* through southern or montane isolation or east-west disjunction, etc.); the relatively few exceptions involve cases where one or both species appear to have undergone major expansion of range subsequent to their speciation. For the most thoroughly studied species groups it is possible to reconstruct the sequence of dichotomies with some confidence, but any attempted dating of these dichotomies falls largely in the realm of speculation. This discussion will be limited to the anurans. There is no reason to suppose that the urodeles underwent any less extensive speciation in the Pleistocene than did the anurans, but for the most part our assessment of this group would have to be based on morphology alone, whereas for the anurans there is a considerable body of additional evidence from hybridization experiments and from investigation of the presence and strength of pre-mating isolating mechanisms.

The most thoroughly studied species group in North American anurans is the *Bufo americanus* group (Fig. 4), in which there appears to be a sequence of possibly four time levels of dichotomies among the six species (W. F. Blair, 1963a). Five of the nominal species are distributed allopatrically, and the sixth, *B. woodhousei*, occurs sympatrically in part at least with all except the far northern *B. hemiophrys*. Two eastern species, *B. terrestris* and *B. americanus*, replace one another from south to north, and *B. houstonensis* is a Gulf-coast relict. *B. microscaphus*, a western species, was only recently recognized as a member of this group by A. P. Blair (1955) and confirmed by W. F. Blair (1957). The oldest dichotomy seems to have separated *B. woodhousei* from the remainder of the complex. The evidence is found in: (1) its different throat coloration in males from that common to the five other species (W. F. Blair, 1963a); (2) its greater genetic incompatibility with the other species (W. F. Blair, 1963b), although all species combinations tested are at least partially interfertile; (3) its present sympatry with four of the five other species; and (4) evidence of a relatively long history for *B. woodhousei* as seen in the secondary interbreeding of eastern and western sections of the species along the forest grassland boundary (A. P. Blair, 1942; Meacham, 1962). The eastern species have relatively longer mating calls than do *B. hemiophrys* and *B. microscaphus;* this fact suggests the possibility of a second dichotomy into ancestral long-calling eastern and short-calling western toads. A subsequent dichotomy would have separated *B. terrestris* and *B. americanus* in the east and *B. hemiophrys* and *B. microscaphus* in the west. Finally, such relicts as *B. houstonensis* and the disjunct populations of *B. hemiophrys* and *B. microscaphus* split off, almost certainly at the close of the Wisconsin. The weakest part of this argument is the assumed affinity of *B. hemiophrys* and *B. microscaphus*. When external characters are considered these species represent extremes of differentiation in opposite directions. *B. hemiophrys* has the bright color pattern of northern populations of *B. americanus* and has the head crests developed into more or less of a boss, whereas *B. microscaphus* has lost most of the color pattern and has the crests reduced below those of any other member of the group. Adaptation to its rather specialized environment (watered areas in an otherwise xeric region) may account for the marked differentiation of *B. microscaphus* and may provide an explanation for this apparent discrepancy.

Space prohibits as detailed an analysis of other U.S. species groups as that presented above, but it is possible to summarize briefly the apparent effects of the Pleistocene on speciation within the species groups. Discussion will be limited to the genus *Bufo* and to U.S. members of the family Hylidae (see W. F. Blair, 1959a, 1963a, for designation of species groups in these taxa). The *B. valliceps* group, centering in Middle America, has a history equally as long and as complex as that of the *B. americanus* group, as judged from its diversification, and shows evidence of extensive speciation in the late Pleistocene (Porter, 1964; author's data). Several other groups show evidence of intragroup

diversification similarly spanning the Pleistocene and involving probably more than one time-level of dichotomies. These include the *B. punctatus, B. boreas, B. marinus, Hyla versicolor, H. eximia,* and *Pseudacris nigrita* groups. The three species of the *B. cognatus* group are suspect of having been separate a relatively long time, because of their low degree of genetic compatibility (W. F. Blair, 1961) and their high degree of differentiation in morphology and mating call (Bogert, 1960, p. 271). For similar reasons, the two species of the *Pseudacris ornata* group appear to be pre-Wisconsin in origin, as discussed earlier. Only two complexes, the two species of *Acris* (W. F. Blair, 1958c; Mecham, 1964) and the three species of the *Bufo debilis* group (Bogert, 1962) have only species that are in such stages of speciation as to suggest speciation in the relatively late Pleistocene and that are without near relatives that might suggest earlier Pleistocene dichotomies. Three species are without near relatives, implying either no Pleistocene speciation of their ancestral stocks or, if dichotomies occurred, the survival to the present of only a single species. Two of these, *Bufo quercicus* and *Hyla ocularis,* are southeastern coastal-plain forms that may have found a glacial-stage refugium in Florida. The third is *H. crucifer,* which spans a huge range of environmental conditions from the Gulf coast into Canada.

REFERENCES

Auffenberg, Walter, 1956, Remarks on some Miocene anurans from Florida, with a description of a new species of *Hyla:* Breviora, No. 52, p. 1-11

Banta, B. H., 1962, A preliminary account of the herpetofauna of the Saline Valley hydrographic basin, Inyo County, California: Wasmann J. Biol., v. 20, p. 161-251

Baxter, G. W., 1947, The amphibians and reptiles of Wyoming: Wyoming Wild Life, v. 1947, p. 30-34

Blair, A. P., 1942, Isolating mechanisms in a complex of four species of toads: Biol. Symp., v. 6, p. 235-249

—— 1952, Notes on amphibians from Oklahoma and North Dakota: Copeia, v. 1952, p. 114-115

—— 1955, Distribution, variation, and hybridization in a relict toad (*Bufo microscaphus*) in southwestern Utah: Amer. Mus. Novitates, No. 1722, p. 1-38

Blair, A. P., and H. E. Laughlin, 1955, Range extension of *Gastrophryne carolinensis:* Copeia, v. 1955, p. 311

Blair, A. P., and H. L. Lindsay, 1961, Hyla avivoca (Hylidae) in Oklahoma: Southwest. Nat., v. 6, p. 202

Blair, W. F., 1955, Mating call and stage of speciation in the *Microhyla olivacea–Microhyla carolinensis* complex: Evolution, v. 9, p. 469-480

—— 1957, Structure of the call and relationships of *Bufo microscaphus* Cope: Copeia, v. 1957, p. 208-212

—— 1958a, Distributional patterns of vertebrates in the southern United States in relation to past and present environments *in* Hubbs, C. L. (ed.), Zoogeography: Amer. Assoc. Adv. Sci. Publ. 51, p. 433-468

—— 1958b, Mating call and stage of speciation in two allopatric populations of spadefoots (*Scaphiopus*): Texas J. Sci., v. 10, p. 484-488

—— 1958c, Mating call in the speciation of anuran amphibians: Amer. Nat., v. 92, p. 27-51

—— 1959a, Call structure and species groups in U.S. treefrogs (*Hyla*): Southwest. Nat., v. 3, p. 77-89

—— 1959b, Genetic compatibility and species groups in U.S. toads (*Bufo*): Texas J. Sci., v. 11, p. 427-453

—— 1960, Mating call as evidence of relationships in the *Hyla eximia* group: Southwest. Nat., v. 5, p. 129-135

—— 1961, Further evidence bearing on intergroup and intragroup genetic compatibility in toads (genus *Bufo*): Texas J. Sci., v. 13, p. 163-175

—— 1962, Non-morphological data in anuran classification: Syst. Zool., v. 11, p. 72-84

—— 1963a, Evolutionary relationships of North American toads of the genus *Bufo;* a progress report: Evolution, v. 17, p. 1-16

—— 1963b, Intragroup genetic compatibility in the *Bufo americanus* species group of toads: Texas J. Sci., v. 15, p. 15-34

—— 1964, Evidence bearing on relationships of the *Bufo boreas* group of toads: Texas J. Sci., v. 16, p. 181-192

Blair, W. F., and Littlejohn, M. J., 1960, Stage of speciation of two allopatric populations of chorus frogs (*Pseudacris*): Evolution, v. 14, p. 82-87

Bleakney, J. S., 1958, A zoogeographical study of the amphibians and reptiles of eastern Canada: Natl. Mus. Can., Bull. 155, p. 1-119

Bogert, C. M., 1960, The influence of sound on the behavior of amphibians and reptiles: Amer. Inst. Biol. Sci., Publ. 7, p. 137-320

—— 1962, Isolation mechanisms in toads of the *Bufo debilis* group in Arizona and western Mexico: Amer. Mus. Novitates, No. 2100, p. 1-37

Brame, A. H., and Wake, D. B., 1963, The salamanders of South America: Los Angeles Mus., Contr. Sci., No. 59, p. 1-72

Braun, E. Lucy, 1955, The phytogeography of unglaciated eastern United States and its interpretation: Bot. Rev., v. 21, p. 297-375

Brode, W. E., 1958, The occurrence of the pickerel frog, three salamanders and two snakes in Mississippi caves: Copeia, v. 1958, p. 47-48

Brown, J. S., and Boschung, H. T., Jr., 1954, *Rana palustris* in Alabama: Copeia, v. 1954, p. 226

Conant, Roger, 1957, Notes on the herpetology of the Delmarva Peninsula: Copeia, v. 1957, p. 50-52

—— 1958, A field guide to reptiles and amphibians of the United States and Canada east of the 100th meridian: Boston, Mass., Houghton Mifflin, 366 p.

Deevey, E. S., Jr., 1949, Biogeography of the Pleistocene: Geol. Soc. Amer. Bull., v. 60, p. 1316-1416

Dowling, H. G., 1956, Geographic relations of Ozarkian amphibians and reptiles: Southwest. Nat., v. 1, p. 174-189

Dunn, E. R., 1926, The salamanders of the family Plethodontidae: Northampton, Mass., Smith Coll. Anniv. Ser., 441 p.

Estes, Richard, 1963, Early Miocene salamanders and lizards from Florida: Florida Acad. Sci. Quart. J., v. 26, p. 234-256

—— 1964, Fossil vertebrates from the late Cretaceous Lance formation, eastern Wyoming: Berkeley, Univ. California Publ. Geol. Sci., v. 49, p. 1-187

Estes, Richard, and Wassersug, Richard, 1963, A Miocene toad from Colombia, South America: Breviora, No. 193, p. 1-13

Goin, C. J., and Auffenberg, Walter, 1955, The fossil salamanders of the family Sirenidae: Harvard Univ., Mus. Comp. Zool. Bull., v. 133, p. 497-514

—— 1957, A new fossil salamander of the genus *Siren* from the Eocene of Wyoming: Copeia, v. 1957, p. 83-85

—— 1958, New salamanders of the family Sirenidae from the Cretaceous of North America: Chicago Nat. Hist. Mus. Fieldiana, Geol., v. 10, p. 449-459

Hairston, N. G., and Pope, C. H., 1958, Geographic variation and speciation in Appalachian salamanders (*Plethodon jordani* group): Evolution, v. 2, p. 266-278

Hecht, M. K., 1959, Amphibia and reptiles, *in* McGrew, P. O., The geology and paleontology of the Elk Mountain and Tabernacle Butte area, Wyoming: Amer. Mus. Nat. Hist. Bull., v. 117, p. 130-146

—— 1963, A reevaluation of the early history of the frogs, Part II: Syst. Zool., v. 12, p. 20-35

Holman, J. A., 1963, A new rhynophrynid frog from the early Oligocene of Canada: Copeia, v. 1963, p. 706-708

Hubbs, C. L., and Miller, R. R., 1948, The zoological evidence; correlation between fish distribution and hydrographic history in the desert basins of western United States, *in* The Great Basin, with emphasis on glacial and postglacial times: Univ. Utah Bull., v. 38, p. 18-166

Johnson, F. C., 1961, Cryptic speciation in the *Hyla versicolor* complex: Austin, Univ. Texas Ph.D. thesis, 120 p.

—— 1963, Additional evidence of sterility between call-types in the *Hyla versicolor* complex: Copeia, v. 1963, p. 139-143

Karlstrom, E. L., 1962, The toad genus Bufo in the Sierra Nevada of California, ecological and systematic relationships: Berkeley, Univ. California Publ. Zool., v. 62, p. 1-104

Lindsay, H. L., 1958, Analysis of variation and factors affecting gene exchange in *Pseudacris clarki* and *Pseudacris nigrita* in Texas: Austin, Univ. Texas Ph.D. thesis, 60 p.

Lowe, C. H., Jr., 1950, The systematic status of the salamander *Plethodon hardii*, with a discussion of biogeographical problems in *Aneides*: Copeia, v. 1950, p. 92-99

MacGinitie, H. D., 1958, Climate since the Late Cretaceous: Amer. Assoc. Adv. Sci. Publ. 51, p. 61-79

Martin, P. S., 1963a, The last 10,000 years, a fossil pollen record of the American Southwest: Tucson, Ariz., Univ. Arizona Press, 87 p.

—— 1963b, Geochronology of pluvial lake Cochise, southern Arizona II. Pollen analysis of a 42-meter core: Ecology, v. 44, p. 436-444

Martin, P. S., and Harrell, B. E., 1957, The Pleistocene history of temperate biotas in Mexico and eastern United States: Ecology, v. 38, p. 468-480

Maslin, T. P., 1947, *Rana sylvatica cantabrigensis* Baird in Colorado: Copeia, v. 1947, p. 158-162

Mayhew, W. W., 1962, *Scaphiopus couchi* in California's Colorado desert: Herpetologica, v. 18, p. 153-161

Meacham, W. R., 1962, Factors affecting secondary intergradation between two allopatric populations in the *Bufo woodhousei* complex: Amer. Midl. Nat., v. 67, p. 282-304

Mecham, J. S., 1957, Some hybrid combinations between Strecker's chorus frog, *Pseudacris streckeri*, and certain related forms: Texas J. Sci., v. 9, p. 337-345

—— 1959, Experimental evidence of the relationship of two allopatric chorus frogs of the genus *Pseudacris:* Texas J. Sci., v. 11, p. 343-347

—— 1961, Isolating mechanisms in anuran amphibians, *in* Blair, W. F., Vertebrate speciation: Austin, Univ. Texas Press, p. 24-61

—— 1964, Ecological and genetic relationships of the two cricket frogs, genus *Acris*, in Alabama: Herpetologica, v. 20, p. 84-91

Michaud, T. C., 1962, Call discrimination by females of the chorus frogs, *Pseudacris clarki* and *Pseudacris nigrita:* Copeia, v. 1962, p. 213-215

Miller, R. R., 1944, Northward occurrence of the spotted toad and the northern crested lizard in California: Copeia, v. 1944, p. 123

Milstead, W. W., 1960, Relict species of the Chihuahuan desert: Southwest. Nat., v. 5, p. 75-88

Myers, G. S., 1942, The black toad of Deep Springs Valley, Inyo County, California: Univ. Michigan Mus. Zool. Occ. Pap., no. 460, p. 1-13

Porter, K. R., 1961, Experimental crosses between *Rana aurora aurora* Baird and Girard and *Rana cascadae* Slater: Herpetologica, v. 17, p. 156-165

—— 1964, Morphological and mating call comparisons in the *Bufo valliceps* complex: Amer. Midl. Nat., v. 71, p. 232-245

Riemer, W. J., 1958, Variation and systematic relationships within the salamander genus *Taricha:* Berkeley, Univ. California Publ. Zool., v. 56, p. 301-390

Schuierer, F. W., 1962, Remarks upon the natural history of *Bufo exsul* Myers, the endemic toad of Deep Springs Valley, Inyo County, California: Herpetologica, v. 17, p. 260-266

—— 1963, Notes on two populations of *Bufo exsul* Myers and a commentary on speciation within the *Bufo boreas* group: Herpetologica, v. 18, p. 262-267

Smith, H. M., 1950, Handbook of amphibians and reptiles of Kansas; Univ. Kansas Mus. Nat. Hist. Misc. Publ. 2, p. 1-336

Smith, P. W., 1957, An analysis of post-Wisconsin biogeography of the prairie peninsula region based on distributional phenomena among terrestrial vertebrate populations: Ecology, v. 38, p. 205-218

Stebbins, R. C., 1949, Speciation in salamanders of the plethodontid genus Ensatina: Berkeley, Univ. California Publ. Zool., v. 48, p. 377-526

—— 1951, Amphibians of western North America: Berkeley, Univ. California Press, 539 p.

Stebbins, R. C., and Riemer, W. J., 1950, A new species of plethodontid salamander from the Jemez Mountains of New Mexico: Copeia, v. 1950, p. 73-80

Thurow, G. R., 1961, A salamander color variant associated with glacial boundaries: Evolution, v. 15, p. 281-287

Tihen, J. A., 1955, A new Pliocene species of *Ambystoma* with remarks on other fossil ambystomids: Univ. Michigan Mus. Geol. (Paleont.) Contr., v. 12, p. 229-244

—— 1958, Comments on the osteology and phylogeny of ambystomatid salamanders: Florida State Mus., Biol. Sci. Bull., v. 3, p. 1-50

—— 1960, On *Neoscaphiopus* and other Pliocene pelobatid frogs: Copeia, v. 1960, p. 89-94

—— 1962, A review of New World fossil bufonids: Amer. Midl. Nat., v. 68, p. 1-50

Tihen, J. A., and Chantell, C. J., 1963, Urodele remains from the Valentine formation of Nebraska: Copeia, v. 1963, p. 505-510

Uzzell, T. M., Jr., 1964, Relations of the diploid and triploid species of the *Ambystoma jeffersonianum* complex (Amphibia, Caudata): Copeia, v. 1964, p. 257-300

Valentine, B. D., 1963, The salamander genus *Desmognathus* in Mississippi: Copeia, v. 1963, p. 130-139

Wasserman, A. O., 1957, Factors affecting interbreeding in sympatric species of spadefoots (*Scaphiopus*): Evolution, v. 11, p. 320-338

—— 1958, Relationships of allopatric populations of spadefoots (genus *Scaphiopus*): Evolution, v. 12, p. 311-318

Wendorf, Fred (ed.), 1961, Paleoecology of the Llano Estacado: Santa Fe, New Mexico, Mus. New Mexico Press, 144 p.

Zweifel, R. G., 1955, Ecology, distribution, and systematics of frogs of the Rana boylei group: Berkeley, Univ. California Publ. Zool., v. 54, p. 207-292

—— 1956, Two pelobatid frogs from the Tertiary of North America and their relationships to fossil and recent forms: Amer. Mus. Novitates, No. 1762, p. 1-45

SUMMARY

Speciation within species groups of North American amphibians is attributable to initiation by Pleistocene climatic changes, with anurans (relatively adapted to warmth) and the urodeles (relatively adapted to cold and moisture) responding differently to regional change. The fossil record suggests that diversification down to the level of species groups had occurred before the end of the Tertiary, and some presently existing distribution patterns, such as the dicentric one involving the central grassland barrier, undoubtedly have existed since the Tertiary. Most present distribution patterns, however, seem to have had their origins in the Pleistocene, and the increase in number of species within species groups is largely attributable to Pleistocene events. Presently existing southern disjunct populations of relatively northern species reflect southward displacement during the Wisconsin glaciation and suggest the mechanism whereby various species have originated as a result of earlier Pleistocene glaciations. Northern disjuncts are rare, as might be expected, and are attributable to minor post-Wisconsin fluctuations in climate. The existence of various east-west species pairs of anurans in the eastern United States is attributed to splitting of previous ranges in these warmth-adapted animals through southward shift of climatic zones during glacial stages. Minor disjuncts along the forest-grasslands border suggest a possible, alternative source for such pairs. East-west disjunction of urodeles presumably involved spread during glacial stages, followed by disjunction during interglacials. Anuran relicts in the southwestern deserts represent remnants of pluvial-stage distributions. There is evidence for extensive montane speciation in connection with Pleistocene climatic change in the Sierra Nevada and in the Appalachian Mountains but not in the Rocky Mountains. There is limited evidence for the role of the glacial boundaries in urodele evolution. For the most thoroughly studied species groups of anurans it is possible to postulate the sequence of Pleistocene dichotomies that led to the present composition of the group.

REPTILES IN THE QUATERNARY
OF NORTH AMERICA

WALTER AUFFENBERG,[1] WILLIAM W. MILSTEAD[2]

THE PLEISTOCENE EPOCH dawned on a reptilian fauna not too different from that of today. The "ice age" was a period of rapid adaptive radiation, speciation, and extinction in the mammals, but not in the reptiles. If there is any one thing that characterizes the reptiles of the entire last half of the Cenozoic it is their stability. Modernization of the reptilian fauna of North America is a Mio-Pliocene phenomenon (Auffenberg, 1958a, 1963a). The main effects of the Pleistocene on North American reptiles were those changes in range resulting from a fluctuating ecology, along with some speciation, principally at the subspecies level, and some extinction. Most of the present species had already been established shortly after the beginning of the Pleistocene (Auffenberg, 1958b, 1955, 1956, 1963a; Holman, 1958, 1959a, b, 1963; Ethridge, 1958, 1960a, b; Mecham, 1958; Milstead, 1956; Dowling, 1958; Brattstrom, 1953a, b, c, 1954a, b, 1955a, b).

Major ecological fluctuations affecting reptilian distribution in the Quaternary have been: (1) expansion and contraction of frigid temperautre zones, (2) expansion and contraction of both xeric and mesic climates, including the opening and closing of xeric and mesic dispersal routes, and (3) changes in sea level, including the influence of the Mississippi Embayment and the Florida Archipelago.

The general trend of climatic change throughout the Pleistocene has apparently been toward a progressively colder climate. However, this trend has not been uniform. It has been marked by at least three major setbacks (the interglacials) between each of the progressively cooler periods (the glacials). Correlated with these fluctuations of glacial and interglacial conditions were changes in sea level. Also significant, but with less direct correlation, were fluctuations in humidity. Thus the Pleistocene is characterized by its dynamic temperature, humidity, and sea-level changes, while the preceding Pliocene Epoch was relatively more stable with regard to these factors.

On the basis of reptilian distribution Hibbard (1960) suggests that winter temperatures failed to fall below freezing as far north as South Dakota during the Lower Pliocene (Claredonian); as far north as Nebraska in the Middle Pliocene (Hemphillian); and as far north as Kansas in the Upper Pliocene (Early Blancan). Thus, though the Pliocene was much warmer than our present climate, the trend

toward isothermic compression and cooler climates had already begun.

This cooling trend was apparently accelerated during the last part of the Pliocene, culminating in the first of the Pleistocene glacial stages (Nebraskan). The compression and redistribution of climatic zones may have eventually brought about a deterioration and reversal of the isothermic patterns, initiating the first of the so-called interglacial ages (Aftonian). Ultimately there were produced three additional glacial ages, each presumably colder than the preceding. The interglacial ages are thought to have followed the same pattern, for each was probably colder than the one before.

The fluctuating ecological conditions during the Pleistocene must have modified the distribution of reptiles more than that of mammals or birds living in the same geographic area. However, the same general pattern is evident; that is, with each glacial period the northern limits of distribution of various reptiles were forced southward, followed by northward movement during each interglacial period.

Throughout the entire span of the Pleistocene the reptiles as a group were pushed farther south with each succeeding glacial age, and returned less far northward with each interglacial. Thus, the present northern boundary lines of many species mark the extent of invasion from more southerly areas since maximum Wisconsin glaciation. Degree of modification of range as the result of fluctuating Pleistocene climates was probably greatest in the periglacial zones (narrower in the East, wider in the Middle West). There was probably very little change in the Southeast (Auffenberg, 1963) and Southwest.

With each glacial age the level of the sea was lowered, while with each interglacial it rose. These fluctuations had considerable influence on the geographic ranges of species living in coastal areas. The main effect of high sea-level stages was in providing a physical mechanism for isolation and subsequent speciation. Low sea levels made available certain types of dispersal routes unavailable during high levels (e.g. Neill, 1957; Auffenberg, 1958b). However, the major effects of sea-level changes were virtually limited to those reptiles inhabiting the lands bordering the Gulf of Mexico and the Gulf of California.

Throughout both the Pliocene and the Quaternary, significant fluctuations in humidity were important in modifying the ranges of reptiles and amphibians. These humidity changes are correlated with the contraction and expansion of temperature isotherms. Such fluctuating humidity bound-

[1] Florida State Museum, University of Florida, Gainsville, Florida.
[2] Department of Biology, University of Missouri, Kansas City, Missouri.

557

aries were important in opening or closing certain east-west dispersal routes, as well as in providing physical mechanisms for isolation and speciation. Though they undoubtedly occurred throughout North America, these changes were apparently most important to those reptiles inhabiting central and southern United States.

In subsequent pages we plan to begin our discussions with a general review of reptiles and Pleistocene stratigraphy. This will be followed by sections on (1) the effects of a fluctuating ecology, (2) speciation, and (3) extinction. The literature references are mainly to those publications dealing with fossil and present-day reptiles.

In many cases examples of corroborative conclusions based on studies of other organisms would have been included, except for a necessity to be brief. We do not plan to list all the reptilian species that have been recorded as fossils, or the localities in which they are known to occur. This information has been recently compiled by Gehlbach (1961). We have relied on his work for many of our comparisons, and on the distribution maps of Recent species given by Stebbins (1954) and Conant (1958). Some of the work mentioned on tortoises and box turtles is previously unreported. It was supported by National Science Foundation research grants to the authors (Auffenberg, G 17613; Milstead, G 19421 and GB 2232).

REPTILES AND PLEISTOCENE STRATIGRAPHY

The known fossil history of Pleistocene reptiles is far less extensive than that for the mammals. The reptiles, being ectothermous, have a more restricted ecologic and geographic range. Speciation is a more southern phenomenon (Darlington, 1948, 1957). Thus the best reptilian fossil record is considerably removed from the periglacial zones, and the Pleistocene is accordingly less known. Thus fossil reptiles are known from fewer localities than mammals, and the deposits in which they are particularly common are often difficult to correlate with those of the periglacial zones. In addition, the extent of variation in the type of fossil elements available for study is less well known in the present species of reptiles than in recent species of mammals, and their study is currently less popular than that of the fossil mammals. Finally, reptilian species seem to have a longer temporal range than many mammal species, and they are thus less useful in biostratigraphic correlation.

Even so, the number of publications on Pleistocene reptiles in the last two decades is almost greater than all previous publications in this area up to that time. According to some workers, Pleistocene paleomammalogy in North America is lagging behind that in Europe. This is not true of Pleistocene paleoherpetology in North America. The main reason is, of course, that there is less diversification in the European Pleistocene reptiles. However, comprehensive taxonomic works on North American Quaternary reptiles are still rare, and the emphasis has been on descriptive morphology. Phylogenetic speculation must often be based on a fossil record that is spotty and usually represented by relatively few specimens. Except for the turtles, where the fossil record is more nearly complete, synthetic approaches are presently out of the question.

Because of the nature of the material, the long temporal existence of reptilian species, and their restricted geographic distribution, they can never be so important as mammals in Pleistocene biostratigraphic studies of temperate areas. As a result, even those deposits particularly rich in reptiles are of little biostratigraphic value, unless accompanied by chronologically restricted mammalian species. Therefore, the biostratigraphic aspects of Quaternary reptilian evolution must be interpreted on the basis of the North American land-mammal ages of the Quaternary: Late Blancan, Irvingtonian, Rancholabrean, and Recent (see Hibbard *et al.*, this volume).

However, the fact that reptiles are more restricted ecologically suggests that they will be found to play an exceedingly important role in Quaternary paleoecological studies. This importance is just starting to be realized (*e.g.* Hibbard, 1960; Auffenberg, 1962, 1963a; Brattstrom, 1961; Milstead, 1960, unpubl. ms.; Milstead and Tinkle, unpubl. ms.).

There is some evidence that in most Quaternary reptiles the transition from Late Blancan to Irvingtonian was probably the most important on the basis of degree of speciation and/or extinction per unit time (Auffenberg, 1963a, and unpubl. ms.). On the other hand, the Irvingtonian and Rancholabrean Ages are apparently characterized by successive expansions and contractions of ranges. Speciation and extinction seem minor (Auffenberg, 1958b, unpubl. ms.; Milstead, unpubl. ms.; Milstead and Tinkle, unpubl. ms.). Except on the subspecies level, the Wisconsin Glaciation witnessed the most drastic contractions of range of southern types, as well as the southward or westward movement of forest forms (*e.g.* Auffenberg, 1962, 1963a, unpubl. ms.; Neill, 1957; Milstead, 1953, unpubl. ms.; Milstead and Tinkle, unpubl. ms.). Extinction of reptile species during the Wisconsin was apparently less common than in mammals (Auffenberg, 1962, 1963a; Brattstrom, 1953a, 1954a). During post-Wisconsin time northern United States witnessed an extension of grassland types into the Prairie Peninsula and the concomitant disjunction of more mesic reptiles in the same area (Conant, 1960). The same pattern is evident in the southern portion of the Great Plains during this same period.

EFFECTS OF A FLUCTUATING ECOLOGY

The dependence of ectothermous organisms on environmental conditions causes us to consider the fluctuating ecology of the Pleistocene as the most important single factor in determining the ranges and evolution of reptilian species during the Quaternary.

Much has been written on the effects of the frigid Pleistocene glacial climates on the faunas of North America and Europe. We take the rather conservative position that temperature fluctuations caused by at least the three earliest major glaciations were largely restricted to the periglacial zones. Thus they were of little immediate importance to most reptiles, since relatively few species inhabited these areas. On the other hand, fluctuations in humidity and sea level, correlated with the presence or absence of continental glacial masses, are here believed to have been extremely important factors in reptilian evolution throughout all of southern North America.

REPTILES AND THE PERIGLACIAL ZONES

There is very little fossil evidence bearing on the distribution of reptiles in northern United States during glacial and interglacial periods. First, the reptile fauna of this area was probably never very diversified even during the interglacial periods. Second, no reptilian species are known to have become extinct in the Pleistocene of northeastern North America or the highlands of the eastern half of the country. Third, of all the fossil reptiles recorded from this area only a few are found outside the same area today, and these from regions not too distant (Auffenberg, personal observation, and 1955c, 1958b; Dowling, 1958; Hecht, 1954). It is obvious that during glacier retreat there was northward movement of a few species of forest-adapted reptiles in north-central and northeastern United States, and a northward movement of prairie-inhabiting types in the northern Great Plains. There was also a post-Wisconsin northeastward extension of a grassland reptilian fauna along the old glacial outwash plains as far as western Pennsylvania (e.g. Transeau, 1935; Ruthven, 1908a; Conant, 1938; Schmidt, 1939).

It is rather obvious that disjunction probably occurred during all parts of the Pleistocene, arising from a variety of causes and involving a variety of species. However, in northern periglacial zones such disjunction obviously dates from post-Wisconsin time, when trans-Mississippi River disjunction took place in the ranges of certain mesic upland species of reptiles in north-central United States (Conant, 1960). The disjunction across the short-grass prairie as noted in other species may also have occurred at the same time (Grobman, 1941). All these movements in northern United States were probably minor, however, when the entire North American reptile fauna is considered. Their extent was largely determined by changes in temperature and humidity and the expansion or contraction of certain floral types associated with periglacial or near-periglacial conditions.

REPTILES AND ECOLOGICAL FLUCTUATIONS IN THE CENTRAL AND SOUTHERN GREAT PLAINS

In the Midwest the effects of fluctuating cooler and warmer climates discussed in the preceding section were felt primarily in the northern states. The central and southern Great Plains and the Southwest were apparently more affected by fluctuations in east-west humidity boundaries.

During the Lower Pliocene the climate was of a moist, subtropical type, becoming progressively more arid in the Southwest and southern Midwest until the Middle Pliocene. Mesic conditions returned during the early part of the Upper Pliocene but again gave way to aridity in the later part of the period (Hibbard, 1960). The Nebraskan Glacial brought a gradual return of humid conditions to central United States. This was followed by another arid period in the Aftonian Interglacial. The same pattern was followed throughout the Pleistocene (mesic or pluvial conditions in the Southwest and southern Midwest during the glacial ages and semiarid conditions during each interglacial age). The

TABLE 1

Suggested Directions of Movements of Some Species over the Gulf Coast Corridor at Times during the Quaternary

(Eastward movements are presumed to have occurred during arid periods and westward movements during mesic periods. The names used merely indicate the modern species. For more exactness at the time of movement, each species name should be followed by the phrase "or ancestor")

Species	Direction of movement
Kinosternon subrubrum	W
Pseudemys concinna	E
Pseudemys scripta	E
Terrapene carolina	W
Deirochelys reticularia	W
Gopherus polyphemus	E
Anolis carolinensis	W
Sceloporus undulatus	E
Lygosoma laterale	W
Cnemidophorus sexlineatus	E
Natrix sipedon	W
Natrix rigida	W
Natrix cyclopion	W
Farancia abacura	W
Masticophis flagellum	E
Pituophis melanoleucus	E
Micrurus fulvius	E
Sistrurus miliaris	E
Crotalus adamanteus	E

formation of the present North American deserts is apparently a post-Wisconsin phenomenon.

These Plio-Pleistocene humidity fluctuations had a pronounced influence on reptilian faunas. During pluvial periods the ranges of some of the more mesic species were expanded, while those of xeric species were contracted. The formation of east-west mesic corridors permitted some mesic species to migrate well beyond former boundaries. The alternate arid conditions allowed geographic extension of many desert and grassland types and concomitant contraction of many mesic species. During the drier periods there were established arid east-west corridors which permitted species to migrate beyond their former limits. The alternating semiarid and mesic dispersal corridors brought about an interdigitation and mixing of eastern and western herpetofaunal elements (Tables 1 and 2). Shifts in humid-

TABLE 2

Suggested Directions of Movements of Some Species through the Rocky Mountain Corridor at Times during the Quaternary

(Eastward movements are presumed to have occurred during arid periods and westward movements during mesic periods. The names used merely indicate the modern species. For more exactness at the time of movement, each species name should be followed by the phrase "or ancestor")

Species	Direction of movement
Terrapene nelsoni	W
Gopherus agassizi	E
Trionyx spinifer	W
Crotaphytus collaris	E
Sceloporus magister	E
Urosaurus ornatus	E
Cnemidophorus tigris	E
Heloderma suspectum	E
Crotalus atrox	W
Crotalus molossus	W

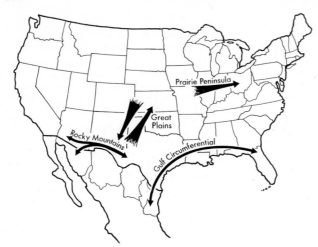

Figure 1. Generalized map of disperal routes used by reptiles during the Quaternary. The Circumferential Gulf Coast Corridor shown here with a single arrow may have included two actual corridors: an inland forested corridor during pluvial and/or high-sea-level periods, and a more coastal grassland corridor during arid and/or low-sea-level periods. The Great Plains and Prairie Peninsula Corridors are shown with broad arrows to indicate general movements throughout the areas involved. The Rocky Mountains Corridor was a restricted corridor through mountain passes. All of the corridors are presumed to have reversed their directions as climatic conditions shifted in the Quaternary (see text).

ity boundaries coupled with associated faunal shifts often left relict populations stranded in high- or low-humidity islands.

There were three important dispersal routes for reptiles during various parts of the Pleistocene (Fig. 1): the Circumferential Gulf Coast Corridor from Mexico to Florida; the Southern Rocky Mountains Corridor, an area of relatively low elevation across the Continental Divide in southern New Mexico and Arizona; and the Southern Great Plains Corridor (Kansas, eastern Colorado, Oklahoma, Texas, eastern New Mexico). An important corridor in the post-Pleistocene was the Prairie Peninsula Corridor in Illinois, Indiana, Ohio, etc. (Schmidt, 1939).

The most important of these was probably the Circumferential Gulf Coast Corridor. Of the three major corridors, it was probably the only one in existence throughout the entire Pleistocene and the most easily established under conditions of either aridity or humidity.

The available record of Pleistocene reptiles in Florida indicates that this area possessed a sufficiently equable climate so that many cold-sensitive types existed there throughout the Pleistocene until the Wisconsin, perhaps even until near its closing (Auffenberg, 1962, 1963a, unpubl. ms.; Hibbard, 1960). This conclusion is mainly based on the continued

presence of large reptiles such as giant tortoises and crocodilians throughout almost the entire Pleistocene. In addition, there is no evidence that the Austroriparian reptile fauna was diminished. Pollen of fir and spruce (Davis, 1946) and various Transitional species of birds and mammals have been reported from some of the same deposits containing large, cold-sensitive reptiles. However, most of these are from deposits of Wisconsin age (*e.g.* Gazin, 1950; Sellards, 1916), when large reptiles such as *Geochelone* are believed to have been the most affected by lowering temperatures anyway. Some of these more northern plants and animals, such as fir and spruce, *Microtus* (Arata, 1961), and *Synaptomys* (Simpson, 1929), may have extended their ranges into the peninsula more because of an increase of moisture during the glacial ages than because of temperature alone (Neill, 1957; Oosting and Hess, 1956; Dillon, 1956).

It is fairly certain, however, that temperatures were markedly decreased in southeastern United States during and after the Wisconsin, as indicated by foraminiferal studies in the Gulf of Mexico (Trask *et al.*, 1947), the occurrence of *Erethizon, Ondatra, Cervus* in deposits of this age in Florida (Simpson, 1929; Lawrence, 1942; Gazin, 1950), and pollen analyses (Davis, 1942; Frey, 1951). This drastic climatic change is well correlated with the disappearance of the largest reptiles from the same area (Auffenberg, 1962, 1963a).

On the other hand, some mid-Pleistocene cooling is also indicated by hibernating accumulations of *Terrapene* in one of the Irvingtonian (Illinoian?) deposits at Reddick, Florida (Auffenberg, 1959), in which *Synaptomys* was also found (Gut and Ray, 1964). The same deposit contains two reptiles (*Eumeces fasciatus* and *Carphophis amoena*) that at the present time are found only north of the fossil deposit (Auffenberg, 1956, 1963a; Neill, 1957).

There is some evidence that during the post-Wisconsin interval of maximum warmth (7,500 to 5,000 B.P.) *Anolis carolinensis* attained a larger size than at the present time (Auffenberg, 1956). Larger size in fossil representatives of modern reptiles is often interpreted as an indication of warmer climate. Examples include *Crotalus potterensis* from several stratigraphic levels in Potter Cave, California (Brattstrom, 1953a), and *Crotalus viridis* in the McKittrick Asphalt deposits. It is also noteworthy that the largest specimens of Pleistocene *Geochelone* and *Gopherus* known from North America originate from deposits representing the early part of the period, when climates are thought to have been more equable than in the middle and particularly the later portions of the Pleistocene.

Much more important than north-south shifting in southeastern North America was the east-west dispersal made possible by one or more circumferential Gulf Coast Corridors. A shift toward more xeric conditions would have allowed grassland types from western United States to move eastward. Conversely, more humid conditions would extend the forest westward, allowing for an expansion of forest-dwelling reptiles to move in that direction (Table 1). Such corridors in south-central United States must have been in existence many times in the past, even before the Pleistocene. Such corridors were undoubtedly the routes over which many of the ectotherms migrated from their ancestral homes in northern Mexico (*e.g.* Blanchard, 1921; Neill, 1949; Ruthven, 1908b). Thus certain more characteristically "western" reptiles and amphibians were already present in peninsular Florida by the Lower Miocene (Auffenberg, 1956a, 1964) and had increased in number by the Middle Pliocene (Auffenberg, 1955, 1957, 1963a). Many of the rather distinctive modern xeric Florida reptila genera (*Stilosoma, Neoseps, Rhineura,* etc.) moved eastward at this time. They are not Pleistocene immigrants, as is often stated.

However, xeric and grassland east-west corridors were probably formed during each of the interglacial ages of the Pleistocene as well. This is suggested by the prairie flora of the Black Belt of Alabama (Harper, 1943), the coastal "Cactus Gardens" of southwestern Florida (Small, 1921), certain genera and species of plants, as well as a number of vertebrate and invertebrate animals (Neill, 1957). Many of the xeric reptiles of Florida are first recorded in this area from deposits representing the Irvingtonian mammal stage (Holman, 1958, 1959a, b; Auffenberg, 1963, unpubl. ms.).

Two closely related types of mesic circumferential corridors were probably operative during the Pleistocene. One was a more inland, open forest corridor, and the other a grassland-dominated type near sea level. Certain species of reptiles undoubtedly followed the coastal grassland or open forests in both directions as the broad, flat, continental shelf of the Gulf region was exposed during glacial periods by low sea levels. These related mesic corridors were important in the dispersion of *Terrapene* in the Gulf Coast area during the Pleistocene (Auffenberg, 1958b), and probably also in that of many other reptiles for which we presently lack fossil material. The sometimes fragmented Circumferential Gulf Coast distribution of several Recent Florida organisms (Neill, 1957) and the pattern of geographic variation (gene flow) of other reptiles within the peninsula suggest a similar interpretation, *e.g. Elaphe* (Neill, 1949), *Coluber* (Auffenberg, 1955a), *Lampropeltis* (Blanchard, 1921).

With each interglacial period, the Florida peninsula was inundated by high seas as the glaciers melted back from their maximum extent (Cooke, 1945; MacNeil, 1950). The islands that resulted and their effects on reptilian populations on or adjacent to them have been admirably summarized by Neill (1957) and utilized in interpreting the Pleistocene history of several reptile groups (Neill, 1964; Carr and Goin, 1942; Highton, 1956). Some of the inland Pleistocene deposits of Florida possess certain reptiles presently restricted to coastal dunes or sea-level forests, suggesting the existence of former high sea levels (Auffenberg, 1955b, 1958b).

Of all the physical features of the Florida Archipelago during glacial periods that were of importance to reptile distribution and speciation, the Suwanee Strait is perhaps most significant. This lowland, often flooded with salt water during the Pleistocene, served to connect Gulf and Atlantic coastal and lowland reptile communities during high sea levels, and also limited the southward or northward dispersion of some terrestrial species (Neill, 1959).

A corridor similar to that found in the circumferential Gulf area existed across the Continental Divide in southern New Mexico and Arizona during the Pleistocene. However, it was much less extensive in both geographic area and in

faunal exchange. Today this corridor is a semiarid grassland between the Sonoran Desert to the west and the Chihuahuan Desert to the east (Dice, 1943). During Pleistocene pluvial periods this area was probably more mesic and the desert on each side considerably less inhospitable. Thus, Great Plains grassland reptiles could move westward over the corridor. During arid periods it was probably much more like the Sonoran Desert, permitting the invasion of western desert reptile species into the Chihuahuan Desert and the Great Plains.

The Rocky Mountains Corridor was much narrower geographically and more restricted ecologically than the Gulf Corridor, particularly during pluvial periods. Reptiles for which this corridor is believed to have been important as a dispersion route are listed in Table 2.

The picture for the central United States is not so clear as it is for the Rocky Mountain and Gulf Corridors. There is considerable evidence regarding the sequence of events in the Midwest and Southwest during most of the Pleistocene. Unfortunately, it is frequently conflicting. Blair (1958) and others have taken the view that the central United States was heavily forested during pluvial periods and that a number of mesic species now occurring in the Southeast moved westward during the Pleistocene. On the other hand, Martin and Harrel (1957) and Martin (1958) have concluded that vegetational changes were not extensive during pluvial periods. At most, they envision central United States as supporting an open woodland, believing that the more mesic forms now occurring west of the Great Plains immigrated in pre-Pleistocene times. Both views are based on pollen samples and large numbers of selected distributional records of plants and animals.

Milstead (1956, unpubl. ms.) concluded from the large numbers of the Forest Box Turtle (*Terrapene carolina*) found in the post-Wisconsin deposits of Friesenhahn Cave in central Texas that this area was more mesic at the close of the Wisconsin than at present. On the basis of other fossil species from the same cave, Mecham (1958) stated that whereas some species indicated greater humidity others indicated greater aridity. However, subsequent to these two studies the Forest Box Turtle has been recorded from post-Wisconsin localities in western Texas and in New Mexico (Milstead, unpubl. ms.). These finds extend the range of the species completely across the state of Texas, indicating that a forest corridor existed across the southern plains in the Late Pleistocene. The area need not have been more heavily forested than the open woodlands of the Texan Biotic Province (Blair, 1950) in east-central Texas and Oklahoma today.

The Grassland Box Turtle (*Terrapene longinsulae*) also seems to fit a pattern of alternating forests and grasslands across the Great Plains. Only three clearly identifiable specimens of this species have been found (Milstead, unpubl. ms.; Milstead and Tinkle, unpubl. ms.). They are from an Early Pleistocene and two Pliocene deposits in Kansas. Though the deposits are widely spaced in time, each of them coincides with the arid periods proposed by Hibbard (1960). The species is apparently absent from pluvial deposits in the same area (presumably forested conditions).

The same deposit in New Mexico from which the Forest

Box Turtle was recorded also contains *T. ornata*, the successor to *T. longinsulae*. This is the only fossil site in which *T. carolina* and *T. ornata* occur together. Today the two species come in contact along an irregular north-south line on the eastern border of the Great Plains.

On examining the Late Pleistocene amphibians and reptiles of two areas in north-central Texas, Holman (1963) found that the fossil fauna of both deposits was very similar to those occurring in the same areas today, with the exception of *Arizona elegans*. This species now occurs about 65 km west of Holman's Sangamon deposit at Clear Creek. A slightly drier climate than now is indicated. Etheridge (1960a) recorded *Ophisaurus attenuatus* from the Illinoian of Oklahoma in an area 80 km west of the present range, indicating a slightly wetter climate than now. Tihen (1954) and later Etheridge (1958, 1960b) reported two lizards from the Cragin Quarry site in the Kansas Sangamon, *Holbrookia texana* and *Phrynosoma modestum*, which today occur far to the southwest. Thus a portion of the Kansas Sangamon evidently was considerably more arid than it is today. These two species moved northeast during the Sangamon as far as the Forest Box Turtle moved westward immediately after the Wisconsin. Fourteen present-day eastern (mesic) species have been recorded as relict populations in the Chihuahuan Desert (Milstead, 1960). Smith (1961) recorded several species of amphibians and reptiles in Illinois that appear to be western grassland relicts.

The present geographic and ecologic distributions of the species mentioned above clearly indicate that most are ecotonal species. That is, they are species that live on the margins of the major vegetational types characteristic of their distribution. The expansion or contraction of their ranges would not require a marked change in humidity. Thus they do not provide any positive evidence on the extent of forested areas in central United States during pluvial times or of desert areas in arid times (Milstead, 1960). Many other species appear to have been more widely distributed in the Midwest, as is apparent from present distribution maps (Conant, 1958; Stebbins, 1954). Most of these species are also ecotomal.

SPECIATION

Very little speciation took place in the reptiles between the Pliocene and Recent, and that which did was largely at the subspecific level. The Pleistocene deleted more reptilian species from the North American faunal lists than it added. This might be expected when one compares reptilian faunas of the recent American tropics with those of the recent American temperate zones. In most tropical environments there are many species, each of which is closely adapted to a particular niche. On the other hand, in temperate areas, where there are fewer species, most of the species are broadly adapted to the extremes of the environment. Thus the reduction of species numbers from the Pliocene to the present in North America is to be expected in a transition from subtropical to temperate reptile faunas.

Several patterns of speciation are represented by Pleistocene and fossil reptiles. Simple replacement of one species by another through selection of another phenotype in the gene pool is generally thought to take place over a long period of time, although it may occur fairly rapidly in some animals, as Dobzhansky (1963) has shown in *Drosophila*.

Pleistocene reptiles illustrating this pattern of speciation include several turtles and lizards. In Kansas *Terrapene longinsulae* (Hay, 1908) has been recorded from the Middle and Upper Pliocene and the Pleistocene Aftonian Interglacial (Milstead, unpubl. ms.; Milstead and Tinkle, unpubl. ms.). There are no subsequent records of this species, but a similar, only slightly differentiated turtle, *Terrapene ornata*, has been recorded from the Sangamon and Wisconsin of New Mexico and is presently widespread in central United States. In another example, *Sceloporus robustus* (Twente, 1952) of the Kansas Pliocene was followed by the closely related *Sceloporus undulatus*, which is now widespread in the eastern half of the United States. The fossil turtle *Emydoidea twenti* (Taylor, 1943) of the Illinoian of Kansas was followed by *Emydoidea blandingi* of the Wisconsin of Kansas, and *Clemmys owyhenis* (Brattstrom and Sturn, 1959) of the Middle Pliocene of Oregon was followed by *Clemmys marmorata* of the Upper Pliocene to Recent of California.

One of the most nearly complete replacement sequences known is in the tortoises of the Turgida series in south-central United States. *Geochelone turgida* of the Middle Pliocene was replaced by the closely related Late Pliocene *G. riggsi*, followed by the Lower Pleistocene *G. johnstoni*, then by the Middle Pleistocene *G. equicomes*, and finally by the Late Pleistocene *G. wilsoni* (Auffenberg, 1963b).

Among Pleistocene and Recent North American reptiles there are only a very few examples of a pattern of speciation involving intense selective pressure on small populations. The best example is probably *Terrapene coahuila*. Today this species lives in a series of small springs and ponds in a bolson in central Mexico with interior drainage (Webb *et al.*, 1963). Its nearest relative is *Terrapene carolina*, whose closest populations occur in southeastern Texas and southeastern Mexico (Milstead, 1960, unpubl. ms.; Milstead and Tinkle, unpubl. ms.). At the present time a hiatus of several hundred kilometers exists between *T. coahuila* and either of the two populations of *T. carolina*. However, Pleistocene representatives of *T. carolina* occurred in southwestern Texas over much of the intervening area less than 150 km from the bolson where *T. coahuila* occurs today. Certain of the characters of *T. coahuila* are known to occur in some of the Texas fossil *T. carolina* and in Gulf Coast representatives of living *T. carolina*. Thus it appears that during pluvial periods in the Pleistocene, *T. carolina* ranged from the coast of Texas and Mexico west to the Rocky Mountains and Sierra Madre, and that what is now *T. coahuila* is the result of isolation during an arid period of the Pleistocene (Milstead, 1956, 1960, unpubl. ms.). Progressive aridity appears to have brought about intense selection for characters of some value in an aquatic existence, producing in this relict population the only aquatic species known in the genus. These characters already existed in a modified form within the gene pool of *T. carolina* (Milstead, unpubl. ms.).

Another example of this pattern of speciation is the separation of *Terrapene ornata* (or *longinsulae*) and *T. nelsoni*. The former is found predominantly in grasslands. During one of the Pleistocene pluvial periods the humid conditions may have caused both expansion of woodland in the Great Plains and the extension of open, grassy forests over the Rocky Mountains Corridor in southern New Mexico and Arizona. Over this route a species of the Ornata complex migrated to the western foothills of the Sierra Madre. Increasing aridity at a later date closed the corridor. Selection acting on the small, isolated southwestern population ultimately led to the establishment of *T. nelsoni*. The latter species is adapted to an oak-grassland association such as occurs at approximately the same altitude as that of the old Rocky Mountains Corridor (Milstead and Tinkle, unpubl. ms.).

Terrapene ornata probably crossed the Rocky Mountains Corridor several times during the Pleistocene, perhaps with each major shift of the east-west humidity boundaries. These shifts were probably extremely important in the replacement of *T. longinsulae* by *T. ornata* and in the subspeciation of the latter.

Terrapene ornata is presently divided into two subspecies: *T. o. ornata* in the northern part of the species range, and *T. o. luteola* in the southwestern part (Legler, 1960). *Terrapene o. luteola* more closely resembles the ancestral *T. longinsulae* and recent *T. nelsoni* than does *T. o. ornata*, and this appears to represent the older stock. *Terrapene o. ornata* probably arose from a relict population established to the north or east of the main population during a Pleistocene pluvial period. An evolutionary history involving Pleistocene pluvial and non-pluvial periods has also been suggested as the basis for the evolution of the *Thamnophis cyryopis* complex in southwestern Texas and Central Mexico (Milstead, 1953).

Increasing aridity in the same general area is believed to be largely responsible for fragmenting the ranges of the present North American land tortoises, *Gopherus agassizii*, *G. berlandieri*, *G. polyphemus*, and *G. flavomarginatus*. The two former and the two latter species together form two distinct species groups on the basis of morphologic similarity. Pleistocene species ancestral to each of the two Recent species groups are now known to have been sympatric throughout at least the southern half of what is now the Chihuahuan Desert. *G. polyphemus* and *G. flavomarginatus* were apparently separated during a Pleistocene pluvial age (perhaps Wisconsin). A fossil tortoise that is closely related to *flavomarginatus* occurs in the Sangamon of Kansas. A species intermediate between *G. agassizii* and *G. berlandiari* was sympatric with a *G. flavomarginatus* type in the Sangamon of the southern part of the Mexican plateau, and the separation of these two forms probably resulted from increasing aridity in the Wisconsin. *G. berlanderieri* is modified the most from the basic stock and probably exhibited the fastest evolutionary rate of all four of the present species, for its evolution seems almost entirely post-Sangamon. *G. agassizii* and *G. flavomarginatus* are apparently most closely related to the pre-Pleistocene ancestral stock (all after Auffenberg, unpubl. ms.).

There is some fossil evidence that there has been considerable reduction in the range of some species of *Gopherus* since the end of the Wisconsin, presumably post-Altithermal. Thus the eastern edge of the range of *G. agassizii* has moved westward (Brattstrom, 1964), and the northernmost edge

of *G. polyphermus* southward (Auffenberg, unpubl. ms.) from 10,000 to 6,000 B.P.

The present distribution of other North American reptiles suggests many other cases that may represent this form of speciation during the Pleistocene. Thus, during one part of the Pleistocene many species appear to have expanded their ranges, while during a subsequent period they were fragmented by the opening or closing of xeric and mesic corridors (by the formation of arid grasslands or deserts during non-pluvial periods, and forests of several different types in pluvial periods). Some of the North American species exhibiting this general pattern are *Kinosternon flavescens*, *Chrysemys picta*, *Pseudemys concinna*, *Pseudemys scripta*, *Trionyx spinifer*, *Eumeces anthracinus*, *Ophisaurus attenuatus*, *Coluber constrictor*, *Opheodrys vernalis*, *Pituophis melanoleucus*, *Elaphe guttata*, *Lampropeltis getulus*, and *Natrix septemvittata*.

REPTILIAN EXTINCTION IN THE PLEISTOCENE

Many species of reptiles have remained relatively unchanged during all or almost all of the Pleistocene. Several species of present-day snakes extend back into the Pliocene (Auffenberg, 1963a; Brattstrom, 1955a), and at least two species of lizards into the Miocene (Estes, 1961, 1962). A number of genera extend into the Eocene, and there is some reason to believe that at least a few had their beginnings in the Cretaceous.

No reptilian genera are definitely known to have evolved or to have become extinct during the Pleistocene. On the other hand, several species and many subspecies evolved during the same period. A number of Pleistocene species presently believed to have become extinct will probably be found to be synonyms of Recent species when they are thoroughly studied. (Table 3).

Among the Pleistocene turtles (the only group for which an adequate record is available) only two periods seem to be marked by extinction. These are (1) the end of the Late Blancan land-mammal Age and (2) the time from the Wisconsin maximum to the waning phases of the Wisconsin approximately 11,000 years ago. As far as is known, no reptilian species has become extinct during the past 8,000 years, though some are admittedly on the brink of extinction through the activities of man. Hunting for flesh is not nearly so important in bringing about a truly significant change in the status of reptilian species as are human projects that completely change the environment (extensive lumbering, agriculture, etc.). This is because usually only the larger, non-secretive species of reptiles are conscientiously sought for food. Turtles and their eggs are perhaps most commonly preyed upon by man in North America at the present time (Carr, 1953; Legler, 1959), though aboriginal New World men certainly consumed a great variety of reptiles (Neill, 1956). The questions are frequently asked, "Why did so many Pleistocene species become extinct?" and, because man is a product of Pleistocene evolution, "Was he responsible for this extinction?"

The extinction of several reptilian groups in the New World near the end of the Late Blancan land-mammal Age, notably species of the North American tortoise *Gopherus* (Auffenberg, 1962a, unpubl. ms.), obviously rules out man

TABLE 3

Extinction in North American Pleistocene Turtles, Probably
not so Extensive as the Present Literature Indicates

Extinct taxa	Age			
	Blancan	Irving-tonian	Rancho-labrean	Recent
Turtles:				
1. *Chelydra laticarinata*			×	0?
1. *Chelydra sculpta*			×	0?
2. *Pseudemys bisornata*			×?	0?
2. *Pseudemys petrolei*			×?	0?
2. *Pseudemys trulla*			×?	0?
2. *Pseudemys sculpta*		×	×	0
2. *Pseudemys jarmani*			×?	0?
2. *Pseudemys euglypha*			×?	0?
3. *Pseudemys delicata*			×?	0?
3. *Pseudemys extincta*			×	0?
Geochelone crassiscutata		×	×	0
Geochelone campester	×	0	0	0
4. *Geochelone annae*			×?	0
4. *Geochelone francesi*			×?	0
Geochelone johnstoni	×	0	0	0
Geochelone equicomes		×?	×	0
Geochelone wilsoni			×	0
Geochelone incisa		×	×	0
Gopherus pertenuis	×	0	0	0
5. *Gopherus laticaudata*	×	0	0	0
5. *Gopherus canyonensis*	×	0	0	0
Gopherus hexagonata		×	×	0
6. *Gopherus atascosae*		×?	0?	0?

1. = *C. serpentina?* 2. = *P. scripta?* 3. = *P. floridana* and/or *nelsoni?* 4. = *G. crassisentata?* 5. = *G. pertinuis?* 6. = *G. polyphemus?*

×, Species present; 0, species extinct

as a causative agent. Most important, the extinction was selective: only the large species of *Gopherus* in the southern part of the central plains were affected. These giant forms were apparently replaced by smaller, related species that had had a more northern distribution in previous periods. The disappearance of the larger forms and their replacement by smaller, related forms undoubtedly resulted from changes in temperature and/or humidity. In view of the fact that smaller forms succeeded the larger this climatic change was probably toward cooler, more humid conditions.

At the present time *Gopherus* inhabits arid to mesic grassland conditions. It is not a dweller of dense forests. The moisture-tolerant Florida species, *G. polyphemus*, inhabits the most xeric communities within its range (Carr, 1952) and can best be described as an ecotonal form, found in open forest or bushy country that is provided with an understory of abundant, edible grasses. A close relative is also found in relict grasslands in the Mapimi Bolson of the Chihuahuan Desert today (*G. flavomarginatus*), and a close relative of both these species was the replacement form in the southern Great Plains after the Late Blancan. This same general trend is witnessed throughout the remainder of the Pleistocene; that is, larger southern forms are replaced by smaller forms from a previously more northern range, probably with each glacial period.

The second genus of North American land tortoises, *Geo-*

chelone, is also represented by at least one small and one large species in the southern central plains throughout almost all of the Pleistocene. As in *Gopherus*, the northern limit of the range of the larger species receded southward with each interglacial and glacial period, so that even by the Sangamon it appears to have been restricted to an essentially circumferential Gulf Coast Range. This uneven but nonetheless eventual restriction in range was apparently brought about by changes in temperature and/or humidity.

In areas of equable climate throughout most of the Pleistocene the larger *Geochelone* (such as *G. crassiscuttata*) were sympatric with a smaller species (such as *G. incisa*) in Florida (Auffenberg, 1962). However, in the Great Plains the larger forms had already disappeared by the Sangamon, while a representative of the smaller group still lived there (*G. equicomes*, in Kansas; Auffenberg, 1962b). By late Wisconsin the large species were already extinct, though by approximately 11,000 B.P. a smaller species (*G. wilsoni*) was still present in the open forests of Oklahoma, Texas, and eastern New Mexico (Auffenberg, 1964). The eastern diminutive form (*G. incisa*) probably became extinct along with its large relative, *G. crassicuttata* during the Wisconsin, whereas the extinction of the southern central plains form (*G. wilsoni*) will probably be found to be correlated with increasing aridity and the disappearance of the open forests in that area.

Thus it seems certain that the reduction of area occupied by large species of tortoises restricted to more or less ideal conditions, and concomitant reduction in the range of smaller, related forms in peripheral habitats, was a trend already well established by the Middle Pleistocene, and perhaps even earlier. If, as is postulated by Hibbard (1960), there was a general trend toward decreasing temperatures throughout the Pleistocene, we would eventually expect: (1) the extinction of all the less cold-tolerant, larger species, and (2) the eventual restriction of the ranges of the smaller peripheral species as well.

The peripheral species of *Gopherus* (closely related to the present day relict species) undoubtedly escaped the colder winter temperatures of the peripheral areas they inhabited by retiring into burrows they themselves constructed. A fossil Sangamon form, closely related to *G. polyphemus* of the Pleistocene to Recent of southeastern United States, was actually taken from a "fossil burrow" in Kansas. All the Recent species of the genus are known to escape temperature extremes in this same manner. Thus, *G. agassizii, G. flavomarginatus* and *G. polyphemus* dig extensive burrows, which they inhabit during at least a part of the year. The smallest present-day species, *G. berlanderi*, usually passes the coldest days of the year in pack-rat houses or brush piles. The giant species of tortoises are restricted to subtropical and tropical conditions, partly because their size makes it physically impossible for them to dig hibernation burrows. In addition, with larger size it becomes increasingly difficult to obtain an effective natural hibernating den (Auffenberg, 1962a; Brattstrom, 1961). Thus these large land tortoises are forced to spend the winter on the surface, with relatively little protection in suboptimal conditions, except for their mass. Large aquatic reptiles, like alligators, can manage in somewhat more temperate areas, because they take advantage of the moderating effects of the water in which they live.

Recent species of *Geochelone* are restricted to more equable conditions than *Gopherus*. Personal observations of several species of captive *Geochelone* at Gainesville show that no non-burrowing *Geochelone* can exist through one of the colder Florida winters of the present time (see also Hibbard's, 1960, discussion of an account of Galapagos Islands tortoises kept in outside pens in Florida and other places in the southern United States). Furthermore, the burrowing habit is less well developed (if present at all) in *Geochelone* than in *Gopherus*. This suggests that as conditions became less equable the range of *Geochelone* in North America became more and more reduced. Extinction was inevitable when conditions became subminimal. Man, with a predilection for the flesh of the tortoises, would certainly have hastened the process in at least the larger species of *Geochelone*, but there is still no direct evidence that Paleo-Indians and giant *Geochelone* lived together in North America or that man preyed upon these animals. But in every one of those instances in which remains of giant species of *Geochelone* have been found with those of man, the contemporaneity of the entire assemblage has always been doubted (Vero Beach, Melbourne, Seminole Field, etc.; Bullen, 1958). That man was contemporaneous with a smaller extinct species (*G. wilsoni*) is certain. Whether he caused its extinction is open to doubt.

A larger species (*G. costaricensis*) is known from Central America, where climate would certainly have been sufficiently warm for continual existence of such forms. However, the exact age of the deposit from which these remains were taken is unknown. They may be earlier than Late Pleistocene. Thus they would predate the entry of man into the New World, and their extinction may then have been brought about by a trend toward more mesic, forested conditions. On the other hand, these fossils may be contemporaneous with man in Central America, and the tortoise may have become extinct as a direct result of his activities. Perhaps this Central American population represents the culmination of the trend toward the reduction in distribution of the larger species of *Geochelone* in the New World, a trend that has its roots in the earlier part of the Cenozoic (Brattstrom, 1961).

Although there would seem to be a significant geographic hiatus between this Central American record of *Geochelone* and those of the Late Pleistocene of North America, this may, of course, reflect a lack of knowledge concerning the fossils in the intervening area. Several insular species of *Geochelone* in the Caribbean Basin (*G. cubensis*, *G. monensis*, and *G. sombrerensis*) could very easily have been brought to extinction by the activity of man. However, no definite contemporaneous association has been proved. The decimation of the Galapagos tortoise populations by man in his activities over just a few centuries shows how easily this may be accomplished in an insular situation.

REFERENCES

Arata, Andrew, 1961, The Meadow vole (*Microtus pennsylvanicus*) from the Quaternary of Florida: Florida Acad. Sci. Quart. J., v. 24, p. 117-121.

Auffenberg, Walter, 1955a, A reconsideration of the racer, *Coluber constrictor*, in eastern United States: Tulane Stud. Zool., v. 2, p. 89-115

—— 1955b, Glass lizards (*Ophisaurus*) in the Pleistocene and Pliocene of Florida: Herpetologica, v. 11, p. 133-136

—— 1955c, The status of the fossil snake *Coluber acuminatus*: Copeia, 1955, p. 65-67

—— 1956a, Remarks on some Miocene anurans from Florida, with a description of a new species of *Hyla*: Breviora, v. 52, p. 1-11

—— 1956b, Additional records of Pleistocene lizards from Florida: Florida Acad. Sci. Quart. J., v. 19, p. 157-167

—— 1957, A new species of *Bufo* from the Pliocene of Florida: Florida Acad. Sci. Quart. J., v. 20, p. 14-20

—— 1958a, A new genus of colubrid snake from the Upper Miocene of North America: Amer. Mus. Novitates, No. 1874, p. 1-16

—— 1958b, Fossil turtles of the genus *Terrapene* in Florida. Florida State Mus., Biol. Sci. Bull., v. 3, p. 53-92

—— 1959, A Pleistocene *Terrapene* hibernaculum: Florida Acad. Sci. Quart. J., v. 22, p. 49-53

——1962a, A redescription of *Testudo hexagonta* Cope: Herpetologica, v. 18, p. 25-34

—— 1962b, A new species of *Geochelone* from the Pleistocene of Texas: Copeia, 1962, p. 627-636

—— 1963a, The fossil snakes of Florida: Tulane Stud. Zool., v. 10, p. 131-216

—— 1964, A new fossil tortoise from the Texas Miocene, with remarks on the probable geologic history of tortoises in eastern U.S.: Texas Mem. Mus., Pierce-Sellards Ser., v. 3, p. 1-11

—— Unpubl. ms., The Pleistocene and Recent tortoises of the genus *Gopherus*

Blair, W. F., 1950, The biotic provinces of Texas: Texas J. Sci., v. 2, p. 93-117

—— 1958, Distributional patterns of vertebrates in the southern United States in relation to past and present environments, *in* Hubbs, C. L. (ed.), Zoogeography: Amer. Assoc. Adv. Sci. Publ. 51, p. 433-468

Blanchard, F. N., 1921, A revision of the king snakes, Genus *Lampropeltis*: U.S. Natl. Mus., Bull. 114, p. 1-260

Brattstrom, B. H., 1953a, Records of Pleistocene reptiles from California: Copeia, 1953, p. 173-179

—— 1953b, The amphibians and reptiles from Rancho La Brea: San Diego Soc. Nat. Hist. Trans., v. 11, p. 365-392

—— 1953c, Records of Pleistocene reptiles and amphibians from Florida: Florida Acad. Sci. Quart. J., v. 16, p. 243-248

—— 1954a, The fossil pit vipers (Reptilia: Crotalidae) of North America: San Diego Soc. Nat. Hist. Trans., v. 12, p. 31-46

—— 1954b, Amphibians and reptiles from Gypsum Cave, Nevada: So. California Acad. Sci. Bull. 53, p. 8-12

—— 1955a, Pliocene and Pleistocene amphibians and reptiles from southeastern Arizona: J. Paleo., v. 29, p. 150-154

—— 1955b, Records of some Pliocene and Pleistocene reptiles and amphibians from Mexico: So. California Acad. Sci. Bull. 54, p. 1-4

—— 1961, Some new fossil tortoises from western North

America with remarks on the zoogeography and paleoecology of tortoises: J. Paleontology, v. 35, p. 543-560

—— 1964, Amphibians and reptiles from cave deposits in south-central New Mexico: So. California Acad. Sci. Bull. 63, p. 93-103

Brattstrom, B. H., and Sturn, Ann., 1959, A new species of fossil turtle from the Pliocene of Oregon, with notes on other fossil *Clemmys* from western North America: So. California Acad. Sci. Bull. 58, p. 65-71

Bullen, R. P., 1958, More Florida radiocarbon dates and their significance: Florida Anthrop., v. 11, p. 76

Carr, A. F., Jr., and Toin, C. J., 1942, Rehabilitation of *Natrix sipedon taeniata* Cope: New England Zool. Club Proc., v. 21, p. 47-54

Conant, Roger, 1938, Reptiles of Ohio: Amer. Midl. Nat., v. 20, p. 1-200

—— 1958, A field guide to reptiles and amphibians of eastern North America: Boston, Houghton Mifflin Co., 366 p.

—— 1960, The queen snake, *Natrix septemvittata*, in the interior highlands of Arkansas and Missouri, with comments upon similar disjunct distributions: Acad. Nat. Sci. Philos. Proc., v. 112, p. 25-40

Cooke, C. W., 1945, Geology of Florida: Florida Geol. Surv., Geol. Bull., v. 29, 339 p.

Darlington, P. J., Jr., 1948, The geographical distribution of cold blooded vertebrates: Quart. Rev. Biol., v. 13, p. 274-300

—— 1957, Zoogeography—The geographical distribution of animals: New York, John Wiley and Sons, 675 p.

Davis, J. H., Jr., 1946, The peat deposits of Florida: Florida Geol. Surv. Bull. 30, 247 p.

Dice, L. R., 1943, The biotic provinces of North America: Ann Arbor, Michigan, Univ. Michigan Press, 78 p.

Dillon, L. S., 1956, Wisconsin climate and life zones in North America: Science, v. 123, p. 167-176

Dobzhansky, Theodosius, 1963, Genetics of natural populations xxxiii. A progress report on genetic changes of *Drosophilia pseudoobscura* and *Drosophilia persimulis* in a locality in California: Evolution, v. 17, p. 333-339

Dowling, H. G., 1958, Pleistocene snakes of the Ozark Plateau: Amer. Mus. Novitates, No. 1882, p. 8

Estes, Richard, 1961, Miocene lizards from Colombia, South America: Breviora, No. 143, p. 1-11

—— 1962, A fossil gerrhosaur from the Miocene of Kenya (Reptillia: Cordylidae): Breviora, No. 158, p. 1-10

Etheridge, Richard, 1958, Pleistocene lizards of the Cragin Quarry Fauna of Meade County, Kansas: Copeia, 1958, p. 94-101

—— 1960a, The slender glass lizard, *Ophisaurus attenuatus*, from the Pleistocene (Illinoian Glacial) of Oklahoma: Copeia, 1960, p. 46-47

—— 1960b. Additional notes on the lizards of the Cragin Quarry fauna: Michigan Acad. Sci. Arts Lett., v. 45, p. 113-117

Frey, D. G., 1951, Pollen succession in the sediments of Singletary Lake, North Carolina: Ecology, v. 32, p. 518-533

Gazin, C. L., 1950, Annotated list of fossil mammalia associated with human remains at Melbourne, Florida: Washington Acad. Sci. J., v. 40, p. 397-404

Gehlbach, F. R., 1961, Summary of North American Plio-

cene and Pleistocene herpetofaunas: private circulation

Grobman, A. B., 1941, A contribution to the knowledge of variation in *Opheodrys vernalis* (Harlan), with the description of a new subspecies. Univ. Michigan Mus. Zool., Mise. Publ., v. 50, p. 1-38

Gut, H. J., and Ray, C. E., 1964, The Pleistocene vertebrate funa of Reddick, Florida: Florida Acad. Sci. Quart. J., v. 26, p. 315-328

Harper, R. M., 1943, Forests of Alabama: Geol. Surv. Alabama Monogr., v. 10, p. 1-230

Hay, O. P., 1908, Descriptions of five species of North American fossil turtles, four of which are new: U.S. Natl. Mus. Proc., No. 1640, p. 161-169

Hecht, M. K., 1954, Fossil rattlesnakes of the genus *Crotalus* from northern Massachusetts: Copeia, 1954 p. 158-159

Hibbard, C. W., 1960, An interpretation of Pliocene and Pleistocene climates in North America: Michigan Acad. Sci. Arts Lett., 62nd Ann. Rep., p. 1-30

Hibbard, C. W., Ray, D. E., Savage, D. E., Taylor, D. W., and Guilday, J. E., this volume, Quaternary mammals of North America

Highton, Richard, 1956, Systematics and variation of the endemic Florida snake *Stilosoma*: Florida State Mus. Bull. 1, p. 73-96

Holman, J. A., 1958, The Pleistocene herpetofauna of Sabertooth Cave, Citrus County, Florida: Copeia, 1958, p. 276-280

—— 1959a, A Pleistocene herpetofauna from Orange Lake, Florida: Herpetologica, v. 15, p. 121-125

—— 1959b, Amphibians and reptiles from the Pleistocene (Illinoian) of Williston, Florida: Copeia, 1959, p. 96-102

—— 1963, Late Pleistocene amphibians and reptiles of the Clear Creek and Ben Franklin local faunas of Texas: So. Methodist Univ., Grad. Res. Center J., v. 31, p. 152-157

Lawrence, Barbara, 1942, The muskrat in Florida: New England Zool. Club Proc., v. 19, p. 17-20

Legler, J. M., 1959, A new tortoise, genus *Gopherus*, from north central Mexico: Univ. Kansas, Mus. Nat. Hist. Publ., v. 11, p. 335-343

—— 1960, Natural history of the Ornate Box Turtle, *Terrapene ornata* ornata Agissiz: Univ. Kansas, Mus. Nat. Hist. Publ., v. 10, p. 527-669

MacNeil, F. S., 1950, Pleistocene shore lines in Florida and Georgia: U.S. Geol. Surv. Prof. Pap., v. 221-F, p. 95-107

Martin, P. S., 1958, Pleistocene ecology and biogeography of North America, *in* Hubbs, C. L. (ed.), Zoogeography, Amer. Assoc. Adv. Sci. Publ. 51, p. 375-420

Martin, P. S., and Harrell, B. E., 1957, The Pleistocene history of temperate biotas in Mexico and eastern United States: Ecology, v. 38, p. 468-480

Mecham, J. S., 1958, Some Pleistocene amphibians and reptiles from Friesenhahn Cave, Texas: Southw. Naturalist, v. 3, p. 17-27

Milstead, W. W., 1953, Geographic variation in the garter snake, *Thamnophis cyrtopsis*: Texas J. Sci., v. 5, p. 348-379

—— 1956, Fossil turtles of Friesenhahn Cave, Texas, with the description of a new species of *Testudo*: Copeia, 1956, p. 162-171 (See also Copeia, 1959, p. 88)

—— 1960, Relict species of the Chihuahuan Desert: Southw. Naturalist, v. 5, p. 75-88

—— Unpubl. ms., Fossil box turtles (*Terrapene*) of central North America and box turtles of eastern Mexico.

Milstead, W. W., and Tinkle, D. W., Unpubl. ms., Box turtles (*Terrapene*) of western Mexico, with comments on the species groups in the genus

Neill, W. T., 1949, A new subspecies of rat snake (genus *Elaphe*) and notes on related forms: Herpetologica, v. 12, p. 1-12

—— 1957, Historical biogeography of present day Florida. Florida State Mus., Bull. Biol. Sci., v. 2, p. 175-220

Neill, W. T., and Gut, H. J., 1956, Animal remains from four preceramic sites in Florida: Amer. Antiq., v. 21, p. 383-395

Oosting, H. J., and Hess, D. W., 1956, Microclimate and a relic stand of *Tsuga canadenis* in the lower piedmont of North Carolina. Ecology, v. 37, p. 28-39

Ruthven, A. G., 1908a, The faunal affinities of the prairie region of Central North America: Amer. Nat., v. 42, p. 388-393

—— 1908b, Variations and gentic relationships of the garter snakes: U.S. Natl. Mus. Bull. 61, 201 p.

Schmidt, K. P., 1939, Herpetological evidence for the post-glacial eastward extension of the Steppe in North America: Ecology, v. 19, p. 396-407

Sellards, E. H., 1916, Human remains and associated fossils from the Pleistocene of Florida: Florida State Geol. Surv., 8th Ann. Rep., p. 121-160

Small, J. K., 1921, Old trails and new discoveries: New York Bot. Garden J., v. 22, p. 22-40, 49-64

Smith, P. W., 1961, The amphibians and reptiles of Illinois: Illinois Nat. Hist. Surv., v. 28, 298 p.

Stebbins, R. C., 1954, Amphibians and reptiles of western North America: New York, McGraw-Hill Book Co., 539 p.

Taylor, E. H., 1943, An extinct turtle of the genus *Emys* from the Pleistocene of Kansas: Univ. Kansas, Sci. Bull., v. 29, p. 249-254

Tihen, J. A., 1954, A Kansas Pleistocene herpetofauna: Copeia 1954, p. 217-221

Transeau, E. N., 1935, The prairie peninsula: Ecology, v. 16: p. 423-437

Trask, P. O., Phleger, F. B., and Stetson, H. C., 1947, Recent changes in sedimentation in the Gulf of Mexico: Science, v. 106, p. 460-461

Twente, J. W., Jr., 1952, Pliocene lizards from Kansas: Copeia, 1952, p. 70-73

Webb, R. G., Minckley, W. L., and Craddock, J. E., 1963, Remarks on the Coahuilan Box Turtle, *Terrapene coahuila* (Testudines, Emydidae): Southw. Naturalist, v. 8, p. 89-99

SUMMARY

The main effects of the Quaternary on North American reptiles were those changes in range resulting from a fluctuating ecology, along with some speciation, principally at the subspecies level, and some extinction. The general trend of climatic change throughout the Pleistocene was apparently toward a progressively colder climate from the maritime conditions of the Pliocene to the temperate conditions of today. The trend was not uniform but was marked by glacial and interglacial ages. Correlated with these ages were changes in sea level and, to a lesser extent, changes in humidity.

The effects of the temperature changes on reptiles were probably the least important of the Pleistocene changes. Colder climates contributed to the extinction of some species and had some slight influence in the speciation of a few forms, but the major effect was in modifying the northern range of the reptiles as a group. Throughout the entire span of the Pleistocene the reptiles as a group were pushed farther south with each succeeding glacial age, and they reinvaded less far northward with each interglacial. This effect was felt primarily in the periglacial zones, however, and relatively few species were involved.

With each glacial age the level of the sea was lowered, while with each interglacial it rose. These fluctuations had considerable influence on the geographic ranges of species living in coastal areas. The main effect of high sea-level stages was in providing a physical mechanism for isolation and subsequent speciation. Low sea levels made available certain types of dispersal routes unavailable during high levels.

Throughout both the Pliocene and the Quaternary there were significant changes in humidity that modified the reptilian faunas across the entire southern United States. Conditions were at times more mesic and at other times more arid than those of today. Such fluctuations were important in opening and closing certain east-west dispersal routes. These alternating arid and mesic routes brought about an interdigitation and mixing of eastern and western herpetofaunal elements. The shifts and mixings also left relict populations stranded in high- or low-humidity islands, and they thus provided a physical mechanism for speciation.

Although the Quaternary was a period of extensive speciation and extinction in the mammals, the reptiles emerged with little change. Very little speciation took place in the reptiles between the Pliocene and Recent, and that which did was largely at the subspecific level. Most of the present species had already been established shortly after the beginning of the Quaternary. The Pleistocene deleted more species from the North American faunal lists than it added, but even so, extinction was not extensive. The groups most affected were the North American tortoises. Some extinction or replacement occurred in all other reptilian groups except the crocodiles, but few species were involved when compared with the number of species that survived.

QUATERNARY FRESHWATER FISHES OF NORTH AMERICA*

ROBERT RUSH MILLER[1]

EXCEPT FOR a few ancient relicts—the sturgeons (*Acipenser, Scaphirhynchus*), paddlefish (*Polyodon*), gars (*Lepisosteus*), and bowfin (*Amia*), which have survived in and spread from old lowlands represented today by the Mississippi Valley—the origin of the freshwater fish fauna of North America barely antedates the Cenozoic Era. The most abundant family, the minnows (Cyprinidae), with approximately 250 species, appears no earlier in North America than the Miocene (Table 1). A diverse assemblage of species of widely different ages comprises this fauna, which may be divided into the true freshwater fishes and those that inhabit fresh water but tolerate salinities of various degrees. This division is in part arbitrary because some species and genera in the second group appear to be as restricted to fresh water as those in the first, but the distinction is important in understanding distributional patterns. Fishes long and sharply restricted to fresh water are able to disperse widely only with the relatively slow physiographic changes of the land itself.

The strictly freshwater (stenohaline) or Primary[2] fishes of North America (from the Rio Usumacinta basin of Guatemala-Mexico northward) comprise 15 families, about 90 genera, and approximately 500 species. (These figures are original estimates and include undescribed as well as described species.) The immediate precursors of 49 of these genera and 317 of the species, or about 60% of the living fauna, may well be no older than late Miocene or early Pliocene. The Secondary, Diadromous, Vicarious, Sporadic, and Complementary freshwater fishes include those that are salt-tolerant, regularly migrate between fresh water and the sea, are essentially freshwater representatives of chiefly marine groups, occur sporadically in fresh water, or invade fresh water chiefly where Primary fishes are reduced or absent. Some arbitrary decisions on the inclusion or exclusion of species were made. These fishes are treated here because some of them enter the fossil record. The North

American fishes in this second group of categories comprise 25 families, about 100 genera, and approximately 400 species. (This includes, for Guatemala and Mexico, only those families recorded from fresh water north of the boundary between Mexico and United States.) When added to those in the first group, the total for all categories in North America (as restricted above) is about 940 species.

Considering only Primary freshwater fishes, the North American fauna includes seven endemic families: Amiidae (bowfin), Hiodontidae (mooneyes), Ictaluridae (North American catfishes), Amblyopsidae (cavefishes), Percopsidae (trout-perches), Aphredoderidae (pirate perches), and Centrarchidae (sunfishes). All except the Amblyopsidae are known from Cenozoic deposits and all except *Amia* are Recent or fossil only in North America; *Amia* is reported also from the Paleocene of Europe. Seven Primary families are shared with Eurasia: Polyodontidae (paddlefishes), Esocidae (pikes), Umbridae (mudminnows), Dalliidae (blackfishes), Cyprinidae (minnows), Catostomidae (suckers), and Percidae (perches). No fossils of the Umbridae are known in North America (but there are early Cenozoic records for Europe), and no known fossil record exists in either continent for the Arctic Dalliidae. The remaining five families have living representatives in both areas, and all but the Polyodontidae have a fossil record in Eurasia and North America; fossil paddlefishes are known from North America only (Cretaceous and Eocene, see MacAlpin, 1947). Only one freshwater family, the Characidae (characins), is common to North and South America, and the single species that occurs in the United States, *Astyanax fasciatus* (Cuvier), is able to tolerate brackish water (I found it living with euryhaline fishes around mangroves in Campeche, Mexico, in 1959).

Five secondary families that have known representatives in sea water or that may include salt-tolerant species (Goodeidae) are considered here especially for their zoogeographic interest. The Lepisosteidae (gars) and Goodeidae (Mexican livebearers) are North American endemics, the gars occurring as far southward as Costa Rica. The principally tropical Poeciliidae (livebearers) occur both in North and South America (Rosen and Bailey, 1963, p. 35, map 1), but have radiated from Middle America and probably originated there (Miller, 1959, p. 195; Rosen and Bailey, 1963, p. 144). The Cyprinodontidae (killifishes), chiefly of tropical and warm-temperate distribution (Lagler *et al.*, 1962, map, p. 465), occur on all continents save Australia; their comparative osteology has been treated by Sethi (1960), with some recent amplification by Uyeno and Miller

* I am grateful to the following for assistance in the preparation of this paper: J. R. Alcorn, Shelton P. Applegate, Reeve M. Bailey, Robert C. Bright, Ted M. Cavender, William L. Cristanelli, W. I. Follett, Maurice J. Grolier, Eugene R. Hampton, Claude W. Hibbard, F. D. Holland, Jr., David M. Hopkins, P. F. Karrow, C. C. Lindsey, Richard H. Olson, R. B. Peters, Donald E. Savage, Gerald R. Smith, R. H. Tedford, Teruya Uyeno, and Eugene Van Buren. Financial assistance was generously provided through grants from the National Science Foundation (G-15914, GB-735).

[1] Museum of Zoology, University of Michigan, Ann Arbor, Michigan.

[2] Myers (1951, p. 12) has defined this and the following terms.

(1962b) and by Rosen and Bailey (1963, p. 25, Figs. 3, 4). The Cichlidae (mojarras), also chiefly tropical in the Old World as well as the New (Lagler *et al.*, 1962, map, p. 466), are common to North and South America—but in this hemisphere all known fossils and all but one species occur south of the United States border.

North American fishes are of various ages, but in general they may be conveniently divided into (1) an Old Fauna and (2) a New Fauna. Included in (1) are the sturgeons, gars, bowfin, mooneyes, trout-perches, pirate perch, and sunfishes. Of these, only the sturgeons are not strictly fresh-water fishes, and they are known as Recent and fossil in both Eurasia and North America (fossil from Cretaceous to late Pleistocene; see Wilimovsky, 1956, and Applegate, in press, for early fossil history). The mooneyes (Hiodontidae) are represented by the Middle Eocene fossil *"Leuciscus" rosei* Hussakof (Cavender, MS). A fossil (at the University of Alaska) related to the trout-perch and pirate perch families (Percopsidae and Aphredoderidae) occurs in beds near Homer, Alaska, that are dated floristically as Early Miocene (D. M. Hopkins, personal communication, 1963). The oldest remains of these fishes are from the Middle Eocene Green River shales; *Trichophanes,* an extinct aphredoderid genus from Colorado and Nevada, is of Oligocene or Miocene age. Perhaps the cavefishes (Amblyopsidae), unknown as fossils, belong to the Old Fauna. Sunfishes are not uncommonly represented in Miocene and Pliocene deposits (Uyeno and Miller, 1963, p. 9), and their earliest known remains at Sentinel Butte, North Dakota, may be of Paleocene age (Wilson *et al.*, 1959, p. 519). Also to be included in the Old Fauna, at least in part, are the suckers and the North American catfishes. Catostomids are known in this continent as early as the Eocene by the extinct genus *Amyzon* (my phylogenetic tree of the Catostomidae—Miller, 1959, p. 202—erred in showing *Amyzon* as Miocene only). The Ictaluridae are plausibly of early-Cenozoic origin, with a long history of development inferred for the genera *Ictalurus* and *Noturus* (Taylor, 1955, p. 436); the earliest unquestioned fossil record for the family is from the Miocene of South Dakota (Smith, 1961). The larger species of the Percidae (the line containing the living genera *Perca* and *Stizostedion*) are reasonably assumed to belong to the older fauna also, since the fossil genus *Mioplosus* appears to represent that phyletic line in Eocene deposits of North America (Bailey, 1938, p. 56), and *Perca* is known from the Eocene of Europe (though only from the latter part of the Pleistocene in North America). In summary, the Old Fauna includes some ancient relicts of pre-Tertiary origin (*Acipenser, Polyodon, Lepisosteus, Amia*) as well as Hiodontidae, Umbridae, Catostomidae, Ictaluridae, Percopsidae, Aphredoderidae, Centrarchidae, Percidae (Percinae), and possibly the Amblyopsidae, which are known or presumed to occur first in the early Tertiary.

The New Fauna comprises the trouts (Salmonidae), the four species of South American characins (representing the genera *Astyanax, Brycon, Hyphessobrycon,* and *Roeboides*) that have reached the Isthmus of Tehuantepec or crossed the United States border (*Astyanax*), the minnows, the later evolutionary lines of the suckers (see below), the killifishes (Cyprinodontidae), the livebearers (Poeciliidae), the darter line (Etheostomatinae) of the Percidae, the freshwater sculpins (Cottidae), and some Neotropical cichlids, of which only *Cichlasoma cyanoguttatum* (Baird and Girard) has managed to penetrate the United States. The origin of this fauna appears to be no earlier than the Miocene, which marks the first known appearance of trouts (*Salmo*), minnows (*Gila*), and killifishes (*Fundulus*). By Pliocene time the suckers of the subfamily Catostominae (Miller, 1959, Fig. 11, p. 202), as represented by *Catostomus* and its close allies and, probably, by *Moxostoma,* had begun to evolve toward the subsequent flowering of these groups that is so evident today (together they comprise 55 of the 75 living species of catostomids). The sculpin genus *Cottus,* represented by about 25 Recent species concentrated in northwestern United States, is known as fossil no earlier than the Pliocene, and much of the proliferation of this group may have occurred in the Pleistocene. Since there is no fossil record for the darters, one can only make an inference as to whether they represent a geologically recent development; their diversification into an assemblage of more than 100 species is suggestive of a relatively late event. The Poeciliidae, almost unknown in the fossil record, have diversified chiefly south of our border and apparently this proliferation is a rather recent development.

The fortuitous nature of fossil preservation, the small size of most freshwater fishes, and the habitat predilections of many species tend to render fossilization unlikely; for many groups, therefore, we may expect little or no help from the fossil record in deciphering phylogenetic history.

In the space available for this contribution I summarize what is known of the occurrence and distribution of North American late Pliocene and Pleistocene fishes from freshwater deposits and discuss the ecological and evolutionary significance of representatives from the Great Plains and from west of the Rocky Mountains. Lacustrine speciation in Bear Lake, relict distributions, and the contribution of the Recent and fossil faunas to paleohydrology in the arid Western United States are also treated.

THE FOSSIL RECORD

The study of Cenozoic continental fishes has lagged woefully behind that of the higher vertebrates (Miller, 1959, p. 192). In the first half century since 1900, the year that approximates the close of the period of initial study of American fossil fishes by Cope and Leidy (1870-1894), only sporadic reports were published. Not until the past decade was a diversified fish fauna of post-Oligocene age described for North America (Smith, 1954). Paleoichthyologists have just begun to scratch the surface of a challenging field that holds promise of rich and significant rewards.

Lack of adequate osteological collections of Recent species, inadequate methods for recovering smaller vertebrates, and ignorance of the comparative osteology of major fish groups have been the chief deterrents to advancing the knowledge of the fossil fishes of the past 50 million years or so. Recently, however, this long neglected field, and that of fossil cold-blooded vertebrates in general, has become activated by a number of investigators. Since a thorough knowledge of the modern fauna is prerequisite to proper interpretation of late-Cenozoic fishes, it is the students of the living forms that are currently doing most of the research on Pleistocene and late-Tertiary fish faunas.

Although the time is far from ripe for a comprehensive synthesis of American paleoichthyology, considerable progress has been made in recent years toward broadening the scope of investigations so that they now focus on and contribute to related disciplines in both the biological and geological sciences. Hopefully we may expect to find some "index fossils" among the fishes that will provide evidence on the age and correlation of beds, although more secure evidence is likely to come from the composition of faunas. The horizons are unlimited, and I eagerly anticipate that much of what is presented here will rapidly become obsolete—particularly the information in Table 1, which marks the first attempt at such a tabular summary for fishes.

Only very recently have the published records of late Cenozoic continental fishes been summarized for North America, along with an evaluation of their classification and dating (Uyeno and Miller, 1963). The present chapter represents, in part, an updating and expansion of that paper. No fishes have yet been described from Pleistocene freshwater deposits in Mexico, but a fossil catfish from the bottom of Lago de Chapala, close to and possibly identical with the living species *Ictalurus dugesii*, is under study by W. I. Follett of the California Academy of Sciences; fish remains have also been recorded from the adjacent Chapala formation (Downs, 1958; Clements, 1963). The fossils discussed herein are all from deposits in the continental United States and Canada (Fig. 1).

Fifteen families of American freshwater fishes are represented by 49 genera that are either living today (45) or became extinct near the onset of the Pleistocene. These 49 genera comprise 95 species, of which 5 belong to the 4 extinct genera (Table 1). Seven of the families, 34 of the genera, and 65 of the species are Primary fishes. The extinct genera, all from Plio-Pleistocene lake beds (the "Idaho Lake") in southern Idaho, are treated in the section on Paleohydrology. The three families of pre-Tertiary origin that include the sturgeons, gars, and bowfin are indicated (for my purposes here) as ubiquitous in the fossil record, although the known data show gaps for the late Cenozoic (Uyeno and Miller, 1963, p. 5). The 45 living genera comprise some 90 species, an increase of 6 genera and 19 species over the comparable data given by Uyeno and Miller (1963). Unlike that summary, however, the present one includes much unpublished information. In contrast to the 90 species of these 45 living genera that are now known as fossil, the same genera are represented by 418 living species —a strong indication of the incompleteness of the fossil record. Nearly half (41) of the known fossil species are extinct. Considering only the Pleistocene representatives of living genera, there are 14 families (eliminating the Atherinidae, not known fossil later than the Pliocene), 41 genera, and 69 species. These fishes are treated in the following section.

PLEISTOCENE FISHES

The known fossil record of North American late-Pliocene and Pleistocene freshwater fishes is indicated in Table 1 and by the sites shown in Figure 1. Only at relatively few of these localities—sites 11, 14-17, 25-32, and 34—are the recovered fossils sufficiently diversified to be regarded as comprising a fauna. Most if not all of the Pleistocene fishes recovered thus far, especially post-Nebraskan remains, are osteologically indistinguishable from living species; the few exceptions pertain chiefly to the "Idaho Lake" fauna, which includes some minnows, suckers, a catfish, and a sunfish that range in age from late Pliocene to early Pleistocene (Miller and Smith, MS). A few middle- to late-Pliocene species, other than ancient types, have been identified with existing forms (Uyeno and Miller, 1963, Table 1). Since the fossil records of sturgeons, gars, and bowfin contribute no new information concerning their distribution, evolution, or paleoecology, these relict forms are not considered further here.

Salmonidae. The trouts and their allies are represented by one or two species of Pacific salmon, genus *Oncorhynchus,* from the Klamath River basin of Oregon and the Thompson River of British Columbia, but this genus has not yet been identified from deposits older than the Pleistocene. The genus *Salmo* (of which a Miocene species has recently been described by La Rivers, 1964) is represented by the cutthroat (*S. clarki*) in Lahontan and possibly in Bonneville deposits of Nevada and Utah, the Atlantic salmon(?) (*S. salar?*) in Quebec, and an extinct species, *S. copei* Uyeno and Miller (1963)—formerly *Rhabdofario lacustris* Cope— from Plio-Pleistocene lake beds in southern Idaho. As suggested by Nordon (1961, p. 749) on osteological grounds and here supported by its relatively early fossil appearance, *Salmo* is probably close to the basal ancestor of its subfamily (the Salmoninae). The late trout (*Salvelinus namaycush*) has been recorded from interglacial clays that perhaps represent the Yarmouth interglacial at Menomonie, Wisconsin. The Bonneville cisco of Bear Lake, Idaho-Utah (*Prosopium gemmiferum*), has recently been discovered in the late-Wisconsin Bonneville terrace of Pluvial Lake Bonneville near Salt Lake City (Stokes *et al.,* 1964); this find constitutes the first fossil record for *Prosopium.*

Esocidae. Among the pikes, only the muskellunge (*Esox masquinongy*) has been definitely identified from Pleistocene deposits, in Texas, Oklahoma, and Kansas, but fossils probably referable to another species (*E. americanus* or *E. niger*) have been reported from Texas.

Cyprinidae. As expected, the ubiquitous minnows, which are of Asiatic origin, have the largest number (24) of fossil species, and not all of those recovered have yet been identified (see, *e.g.,* Smith, 1958: 178). Three genera (*Diastichus, Mylocyprinus,* and *Sigmopharyngodon*) and nine species are extinct, all but one of which lived in the "Idaho Lake," discussed later. Seven of the 14 genera, representing 17 species, are from western United States; the remainder are from Saskatchewan, Kansas, Oklahoma, and Texas.

The genus *Gila,* as here broadly interpreted, appears earliest in the record and contains the most fossil species. Two subgenera are recognized and may be distinguished by the number of pharyngeal tooth rows: 2 in *Gila* and 1 in *Siphateles.* The genus includes generalized forms, such as the living Utah chub (*Gila atraria*), also known as fossil

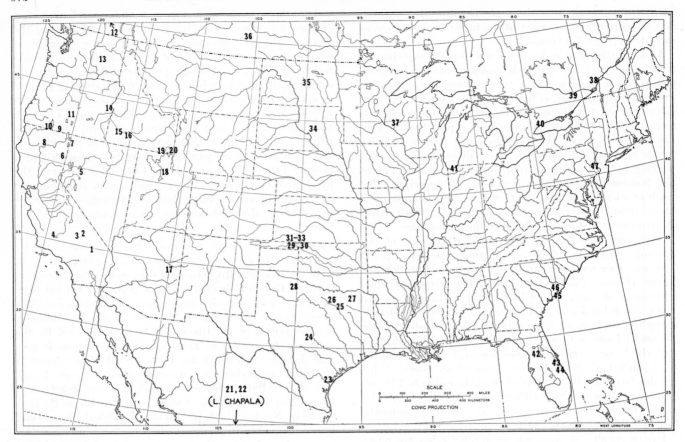

Figure 1. Late-Pliocene and Pleistocene sites for American freshwater fishes. The locations of Plio-Pleistocene and Pleistocene sites where fishes have been recovered in North America are shown by number on Figure 1 and in the list that follows. Following the name of the locality is the probable age, according to these abbreviations: (Int) = Interval of Late Pliocene to Early Pleistocene in southern Idaho and Oregon, (K) = Kansan, (Y) = Yarmouth, (I) = Illinoian, (LI) = Late Illinoian, (P) = Pleistocene, (EP) = Early Pleistocene, (MP) = Middle Pleistocene, (LP) = Late Pleistocene, (S) = Sangamon, (LS) = Late Sangamon, (W) = Wisconsin, (EW) = Early Wisconsin, (MW) = Middle Wisconsin, and (LW) = Late Wisconsin. Radiocarbon datings are given where available. Age assignments for those sites that contain both mammals and fishes are as given by Hibbard *et al.* (this volume). Key references to the literature are indicated for each locality. For certain localities that lack published information, the site is identified in appropriate detail. Three sites, 12 (in Canada) and 21-22 (in Mexico), could not be plotted but are indicated on the map.

(Stokes *et al.*, 1964), and the Mio-Pliocene *Gila turneri*. The nearest Old World relative of *Gila* may be *Tribolodon*, which lives in Japan. A related genus *Ptychocheilus* is known fossil from the Early Pliocene near Juntura, Oregon (Shotwell, 1963, p. 15) and, as *P. prelucius*, from the Middle Pliocene of northern Arizona (Uyeno and Miller, 1965). The 3 widely distributed living representatives of the genus had evidently evolved by late-Pliocene to early-Pleistocene times, since fossils from deposits of this time appear to be osteologically indistinguishable from the Recent forms.

The query in Table 1 after the number of species attributed to *Mylopharodon* results from the uncertainty (Uyeno and Miller, 1963, p. 13) as to whether *"Leucus" condonianus* (Middle Pliocene) is referable to the genus *Mylopharodon*. Similarly, the query after *Notropis* indicates tentative identification to this the most abundant genus of American minnows (over 100 living species).

Catostomidae. The suckers are the second most abundant group in the Pleistocene record. Ten of the 14 species occur in western United States, chiefly in the "Idaho Lake." Only the river carpsucker (*Carpiodes carpio*), a species of buffalo (*Ictiobus*), the white sucker (*Catostomus commersoni*), and the black redhorse (*Moxostoma duquesnei*) have been

Key to Figure 1:

1. Manix Lake (LW: 19,500 ± 500), Howard, 1955; Hubbs *et al.*, 1962
2. Lake Searles (LW: ±11,000), Flint and Gale, 1958
3. White Hills (K), Tedford, R. H., pers. com., 1964, fishes associated with an early Irvingtonian mammal fauna near China Lake, Calif.
4. Lake Tulare (LW or MW), Jordan, 1927; Feth, 1961
5. Lake Lahontan (W), La Rivers, 1962
6. Secret Valley (P?), about 34 km on U.S. Hwy 395 W and N of Litchfield, at NW end of Secret Valley, Lassen Co., Calif. (UM-CALIF-2-63).
7. Duck Valley (P?), sand dune and tufa ridge .5 km NW of jct. of State Hwy 81 and road to SW to Madeline Plains, Washoe Co., Nev. (UM-NEV-5-63).
8. Potter Creek Cave (MP), Stock, 1918
9. Lost River (W), Uyeno and Miller, 1963
10. Lower Klamath Lake (LW), Uyeno and Miller, 1963
11. Fossil Lake (W; Int?), Howard, 1946; Uyeno and Miller, 1963
12. Thompson River (LW), Lindsey, C. C., pers. com., 1964, based on salmon remains in Prov. Mus. Victoria, Cat. No. 470-474, 526, British Columbia.
13. Ringold, Moses Lake (EP or MP), Grolier, M. J., pers. com., 1964, fishes from Moses Lake area, Wash.
14. Willow Creek (Int), Uyeno and Miller, 1963
15. Grand View (Int), Hibbard, 1959; Uyeno, 1961
16. Glenns Ferry (Int: 3.1 m.y. B.P.), Malde and Powers, 1962; Evernden *et al.*, 1964; Miller and Smith, MS
17. Snowflake (EP), Lance, 1960; Miller and Uyeno, MS
18. Lake Bonneville (LW), Stokes *et al.*, 1964
19. Provo formation (LW: 13,900 ± 400 B.P.), Bright, 1963
20. Lake Thatcher (MW: 33,700 — 27,000 B.P.), Bright, 1963
21. Chapala formation (Int), Downs, 1958; Clements, 1963
22. Lago de Chapala (LP), Downs, 1958; Clements, 1963
23. Sinton (EW), Hay, 1926
24. Miller's Cave (LW: 7,200 ± 300 B.P.), Patton, 1963
25. Moore Pit (EW: >37,000 B.P.), Slaughter *et al.*, 1962; Uyeno and Miller, 1962a
26. Clear Creek (MW: 28,840 ± 4,740 B.P.), Slaughter and Ritchie, 1963; Uyeno, 1963
27. Ben Franklin (LW: 12,000 — 9,000 B.P.), Slaughter and Ritchie, 1963; Uyeno, 1963
28. Easley Ranch (EW), Dalquest, 1962
29. Berends (I), Smith, 1954
30. Doby Springs (I), Smith, 1958; Stephens, 1960
31. Butler Spring (I), Smith, 1958; Hibbard and Taylor, 1960
32. Mt. Scott (LI), Smith, 1963
33. Jinglebob (LS), Hibbard, 1955
34. Ree Heights (P), Cope, 1891; Uyeno and Miller, 1963
35. Prophet Mts. (LW), Sherrod, 1963
36. Lillestrom (LW: *ca.* 10,000 B.P.), Uyeno and Miller, 1963
37. Menomonie (Y?), Hussakof, 1916
38. Goose River (P), Lambe, 1904
39. Ottawa Valley (P), Dawson, 1872
40. Don beds (S), Coleman, 1933
41. Lake Michigan (P), Hay, 1923
42. Williston (MP), Hay, 1919; Ray *et al.*, 1963
43. Melbourne (W), Hay, 1927
44. Vero (W), Hay, 1917; Weigel, 1963
45. Young Island (P), Hay, 1923
46. Ashley River (P), Hay, 1923
47. Durham Cave (LP), Leidy, 1889

uncovered east of the Rocky Mountains, in North Dakota, Kansas, Oklahoma, and Texas. The distributional significance of the lakesuckers of the genus *Chasmistes,* which now comprises a few relict species, is treated in the section on Paleohydrology.

Ictaluridae. Among the North American freshwater catfishes known as Pleistocene fossils are two bullheads (*Ictalurus melas* and *I. nebulosus*) and the channel catfish (*I. punctatus*) of eastern United States (Uyeno and Miller, 1963, p. 8), an extinct and yet undescribed species of *Ictalurus* from the Plio-Pleistocene "Idaho Lake" (Miller and

Smith, MS), and an *Ictalurus* from Lago de Chapala, Mexico, now being described by W. I. Follett. The significance of the former occurrence and extinction of catfish west of the present main range of the family (Fig. 2) is treated in the discussion of the "Idaho Lake" fauna. A fossil record for the large and distinctive flathead catfish (*Pylodictis olivaris*) has only recently been published (Uyeno and Miller, 1962a; the Sangamon age interpretation is now revised to Middle Wisconsin).

Cyprinodontidae. The killifishes, well represented in Pliocene deposits, are definitely known in the Pleistocene by

TABLE 1

Known Geologic Range of Living Families and Genera of American Freshwater Fishes, Including Four Genera Known
Only from the Late-Pliocene to Early-Pleistocene Interval

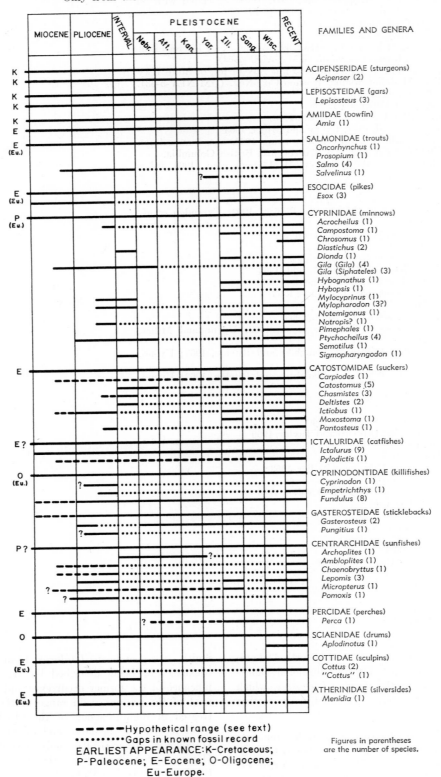

only a single species, the banded killifish (*Fundulus diaphanus*), in South Dakota (Uyeno and Miller, 1963, p. 17).

Gasterosteidae. The marine and freshwater stickleback genus *Gasterosteus* is known from Pleistocene beds in the Ottawa Valley of Ontario, Canada.

Centrarchidae. Sunfishes and basses are represented by 5 species in Pleistocene deposits, 3 of which are members of the genus *Lepomis*, the most speciose of living centrarchids. All fossil and Recent records are for eastern United States (the preliminary identification of the "Idaho Lake" sunfish as *Lepomis*—Miller, 1959, p. 194—was wrong; this fossil is an undescribed species of *Archoplites*). The basses of the genus *Micropterus*, regarded by Bailey (1938, p. 77-78) as an early evolutionary development in the family, are known from fragmentary remains in the Early Pliocene of Oklahoma (Laverne formation) and the Late Miocene of Nebraska (Smith, 1962, p. 509; Uyeno and Miller, 1963, p. 10, 23).

Percidae. Perches are represented in the American fossil record only by the yellow perch (*Perca flavescens*) in the Pleistocene of South Dakota, Kansas, and Oklahoma. The abundant and diversified darters, widespread in eastern North America, live largely in habitats poorly suited for fossilization.

Sciaenidae. The freshwater drum (*Aplodinotus grunniens*), an eastern North American species derived from marine forms, is known only from Wisconsin glacial deposits in Michigan and Texas.

Cottidae. The sculpins of the genus *Cottus*, also derived from a predominantly marine family, are known in the Pleistocene thus far only from the late-Wisconsin Bonneville terrace of Utah (Stokes *et al.*, 1964). A related but different and as yet unnamed genus ("*Cottus*" in Table 1), occurs in Plio-Pleistocene beds of the "Idaho Lake" (Uyeno and Miller, 1963, p. 20).

Faunal shifts. Because so few Pleistocene sites have yielded a diversified assemblage of fishes, only limited opportunity exists to demonstrate faunal shifts for these animals. C. L. Smith (1954) described the first diversified Pleistocene fish fauna for North America—the Illinoian Berends fauna of Oklahoma (Fig. 1, Loc. 29), which also includes a variety of mammals and mollusks (Hibbard and Taylor, 1960). The fishes comprise 8 families, 9 genera, and 12 species. By superimposing the ranges of these species where they are presently sympatric it is found that the comparable living fauna occurs from Minnesota to western New York and from the north shore of Lake Huron to central Iowa, central Indiana, and northern Ohio—well to the north of Oklahoma. The inference that the time of the Berends fauna was one of a cooler and moister climate is supported by the present distributional patterns of the associated mollusks and mammals and by the occurrence of spruce, fir, and pine pollen. The yellow perch (*Perca flavescens*) is the fish species that most closely restricts the southern limit of the fauna, for its natural range today lies several hundred miles to the north of northern Oklahoma (Rostlund, 1952, p. 282).

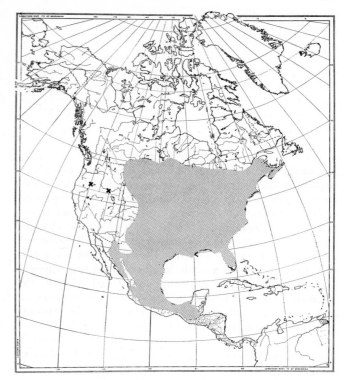

Figure 2. Distribution of the North American freshwater catfishes. Fossil records (X) are indicated for western North America only. (From Miller, 1959, Fig. 5.)

The Mt. Scott local fauna in southwestern Kansas (Fig. 1, Loc. 32), also of Illinoian age, has yielded 14 species of fishes in seven families (Smith, 1963). The majority of these species do not live in the area today. Three of them, the muskellunge (*Esox masquinongy*), brassy minnow (*Hybognathus hankinsoni*), and yellow perch, represent a northern element that occurs today considerably to the north and east of southwestern Kansas. Northern mammals also are associated with the fishes. The inference drawn from the several zoological groups is that the Mt. Scott fauna enjoyed a more extensive aquatic habitat, cooler temperatures, and greater moisture—a climate that is generally similar to that occurring today in southern Wisconsin.

Effects of Pleistocene events. The progressive trend toward increasing aridity and marked seasonal changes associated with the Quaternary has brought about the extinction of some species and sharp restrictions in the ranges of many forms, particularly in the now-arid Great Basin—an area dominated by relict species and populations (Hubbs and Miller, 1948). Withering and desiccation of stream systems and lakes have destroyed aquatic habitats, and the lowering of temperatures during the glacial periods precluded the survival of species whose spawning requirements could not adjust to the new thermal maxima (Miller, 1959, p. 194). On the other hand, glaciation may have also provided the stimulus for the evolution and speciation of such cold-loving genera as the salmons (*Oncorhynchus*) and sculpins (*Cottus*), just as successive lacustrine stages likely triggered the speciation of whitefishes of the genus *Prosopium* in Bear Lake (Idaho-Utah) and the minnows of the subgenus *Siphateles* in the Great Basin. As in other groups of animals, the Pleistocene was a time of diminution of faunas, and the chief changes since then have been largely associated directly or indirectly with man's activities (Miller, 1961; Smith, this volume).

PALEOHYDROLOGY

Knowledge of both fossil and living fishes may contribute important evidence for the existence of former lakes and streams and of their interrelationships with now-separated drainage systems. On the premise that habitat preferences and ecological tolerances of living species have not changed significantly during the period (chiefly the Pleistocene) when morphology has similarly shown little or no evolution, fossils may also provide information on past climates and paleoecology. Such data supplement and reinforce the interpretations that have been made largely by mammalian and avian paleontologists and, more recently, by students of fossil molluscan faunas (Taylor, 1960a; this volume).

In this section the evidence from the fossil record is integrated with knowledge of the distribution and ecology of existing populations.

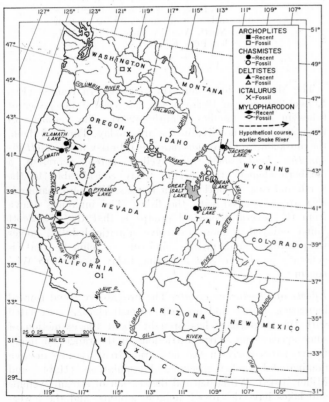

Figure 3. Part of western North America, showing the Recent and fossil distribution of five genera of fishes of the "Idaho Lake" fauna, and the hypothetical course of the Pleistocene Snake River.

THE IDAHO LAKE FAUNA

During late-Pliocene time the waters of an earlier Snake River were impounded to create a large Idaho lake in southwestern Idaho and adjacent parts of Oregon (Wheeler and Cook, 1954, Fig. 1; see also Feth, 1961, Fig. 47.1, lake no. 8). This lake, first called the Idaho Pliocene Lake by Cope (1883), evidently persisted into early-Pleistocene times, when it was drained through capture by, or spill-over into, the Columbia River basin via the Salmon River. The outlet of Idaho Lake cut the impressive gorge of Hell's Canyon of the present Snake River, along the Oregon-Idaho line (Fig. 3).

The fish fauna of Idaho Lake, as essentially represented in the Plio-Pleistocene Glenns Ferry formation (Malde and Powers, 1962, p. 1206), was first summarized by Cope (1883). Later it was briefly mentioned by Miller (1959, p. 194), and has been studied recently by Uyeno (1961) and by Uyeno and Miller (1963). As now known (Miller and Smith, MS), the fauna comprises 6 families, 15 genera, and at least 20 species, as follows: Salmonidae, *Salmo copei* (formerly *Rhabdofario lacustris*—see Uyeno and Miller, 1963, p. 12); Cyprinidae, 7 or more genera and 10 species, including at least 3 extinct genera (*Diastichus*, *Mylocyprinus*, and *Sigmopharyngodon*) and the first fossil referable to the Columbia River genus *Acrocheilus*; Catostomidae, 4 genera and about 7 species, including the first fossil records for *Deltistes* and *Pantosteus*; Ictaluridae, 1 species of *Ictalurus*; Centrarchidae, 1 species of *Archplites*, constituting the first fossil record of this relict Californian genus; and Cottidae, "*Cottus*" *divaricatus* (see Uyeno and Miller, 1963, p. 20). Because the fauna has yet to be studied in detail in its entirety and more material is accumulating, further additions to and modifications of this list may be anticipated.

Excluding such semi-marine types as lampreys, sturgeons, and salmon (*Oncorhynchus*), the fishes living today in this area comprise 4 families, 14 genera, and 21 species—a less diversified assemblage than is represented by the presently known fossil record.

The Idaho Lake fauna is of diverse origin. The trout (*Salmo copei*) is noncommittal, as it is close to the modern cutthroat, *S. clarki*, a species widely distributed today in western North America. Among the minnows is a genus, *Mylopharodon*, restricted today to central California (Sacramento–San Joaquin and Russian River basins—see Fig. 3); the Idaho representative was recently described as distinct from the California species (Uyeno, 1961, p. 338), and a second Idaho species, "*Leucus*" *condonianus*, may pertain to the same genus (Uyeno and Miller, 1963, p. 13). Another Idaho fish that has its nearest living relative in California belongs to the sunfish genus *Archoplites* (Fig. 3), the fossil representative of which is being studied by Miller and Smith (MS). These disjunct sunfishes—of which the Idaho representative seems to have survived in Washington (Fig. 1, Loc. 13) until perhaps the Early or possibly the Middle Pleistocene—represent relicts of a once more widespread distribution of this and other genera of centrarchids (Miller, 1959, p. 199-200).

The genera *Mylopharodon* and *Archoplites* are of particular interest in connection with the pre-Pleistocene waterway between the ancestral Snake River and the Pacific that was hypothesized by Wheeler and Cook (1954, p. 354; see also Fig. 3 herein). At the time they wrote there was no ichthyological evidence to support their view that a river flowed in a southwesterly course via the present lower part of the Malheur River into or near what is now the Klamath or the Sacramento basin of southern Oregon and northern California. Taylor (1960b) reviewed the evidence from the distribution patterns of living mollusks and fishes to support such an independent course of the former Snake River, concluding that the route to the Pacific was by way of the Klamath rather than the Sacramento basin. The present fossil-fish evidence suggests that the history was complex, since neither *Mylopharodon* nor *Archoplites* lives in the Klamath drainage today although other "Idaho Lake" genera occur there now.

The known fossil and present occurrence of the two sucker genera *Chasmistes* and *Deltistes* (Fig. 3) suggests that their distribution—especially that of *Chasmistes*—is likely older than the hypothetical course of the former Snake River, which Taylor concluded was at least as old as Early Pleistocene. The Recent distribution of *Chasmistes* is restricted to six known localities: (1) Snake River near Jackson Lake, Wyoming, based on a specimen at The University of Michigan; (2) Utah Lake, Utah (population extinct); (3) Upper Klamath Lake, Oregon; (4) Lake of the Woods, Oregon (population extinct); (5) Klamath River in Copco Reservoir, California; and (6) Pyramid Lake and, formerly, the adjacent Winnemucca Lake, Nevada. All of these populations, comprising 3 and possibly 5 species (the Lake of the Woods and Snake River samples may represent distinct forms), are usually restricted to lakes during all but the brief spawning period of about two or three weeks; apparently rarely, they may also occur in large rivers. All are large fishes, not infrequently attaining lengths up to 2 ft and weights to 6 lbs (Snyder, 1917, p. 52). The known fossil records clearly demonstrate that *Chasmistes* formerly enjoyed a much wider distribution, extending to the south as far as southern California (Fig. 1, Loc. 3) and inhabiting 5 drainage basins (Death Valley system, Madeline Plains, Duck Flat, Fossil Lake, and Bear River—numbers 1-4 and 6 on Fig. 3), where the genus no longer survives. This distributional pattern, referred to as the "Fishhook Pattern" by D. W. Taylor (personal communication), probably dates back to the Pliocene and indicates that the disjunct localities were formerly connected by a series of rivers and lakes, though they were not necessarily all interconnected with each other at one time.

The minnow subgenus *Siphateles* has similarly correlated past and present distributions (Hubbs and Miller, 1948, p. 79), although fishes of this group have not been identified from Idaho Lake beds (unless critical study of *Diastichus* will show that it represents the phyletic line from which evolved the *Siphateles* division of *Gila*). Other fossil fishes (*Fundulus*, *Empetrichthys*) also demonstrate that waterways connected western Nevada southward to the Death Valley region and westward into southern California probably in late-Miocene or early-Pliocene times (Uyeno and Miller, 1962b, p. 529 and Fig. 7).

Another source for the Idaho Lake fauna and for other beds to the west and north is revealed by the occurrence of fossil catfish of the genus *Ictalurus* (Fig. 3). The family to which this genus belongs is almost exclusively eastern American, with limited crossover to the west of the Continental Divide only in western Mexico (Fig. 2). However, from the Early Pliocene to Early Pleistocene (and possibly around Moses Lake, Washington, into middle-Pleistocene time) *Ictalurus* inhabited southern Idaho, the Juntura basin of adjacent western Oregon, and the middle Columbia basin of Washington (Fig. 3). The area now occupied by the upper Missouri River drainage is the most likely source from which these stocks were derived.

Many other Idaho Lake fishes appear to have been autochthonous—e.g. the minnows *Mylocyprinus*, *Sigmopharyngodon*, and *Diastichus*, and possibly the sculpin "*Cottus*" *divaricatus*. Their extinction seems definitely to be correlated with the disappearance of the extensive lacustrine habitat. This seems especially true for the specialized genus *Mylocyprinus*, whose very large and robust pharyngeal bones supported heavy molariform teeth admirably suited for crushing the abundant mollusks that inhabited the lake. The very large molluscan fauna vanished when the lake was drained (Taylor in Uyeno, 1961, p. 334).

Why the squawfish genus *Ptychocheilus*, represented by abundant remains referable to *P. oregonensis* in the Idaho Lake, does not occur in the Klamath system is difficult to explain if the pre-Snake connection was through that basin. This genus has wide ecological tolerance and is probably as old as the early Pliocene (Uyeno and Miller, 1965).

The comparative ages of the fossils associated with the Idaho Lake, their relationships and ecology, and the timing and possible multiple outlets of the pre-Snake drainage will have to be known in much more detail before the fish evidence can be properly appraised.

SPECIATION IN BEAR LAKE

Bear Lake, which crosses the Idaho-Utah line northwest of Great Salt Lake (Fig. 3), is a rather cold and deep oligotrophic body of water, about 20 miles long and 4 to 8 miles wide, with a maximum depth of 208 ft (McConnell et al., 1957). Its relationship to Bear River is unusual in that the river entirely bypasses the lake, entering Bear Valley on the northeastern side and flowing out of the valley directly to the north. At higher lake levels, however, as indicated by old shorelines, Bear River flowed directly into the lake. Detailed knowledge of the geological history of Bear Lake is lacking, but it has been suggested that the valley was occupied by three lakes during Pliocene, early-Pleistocene, and Pluvial times (see Hubbs and Miller, 1948, p. 32).

Four species are endemic to the lake. Three represent whitefishes of the genus *Prosopium*: the Bonneville cisco, *P. gemmiferum*, the Bonneville whitefish, *P. spilonotus*, and the Bear Lake whitefish, *P. abyssicola*; the fourth is the Bear Lake sculpin, *Cottus extensus*, recently described by Bailey and Bond (1963). The Bonneville cisco was long thought to be a zoogeographical enigma (Hubbs and Miller, 1948, p. 31) because it was classified in the cisco genus *Leucichthys*, a group otherwise largely restricted to eastern North America. Despite its elongate body, projecting lower jaw, and numerous gill rakers—features in which it resembles ciscos—Norden (1961, p. 713) demonstrated that it possesses all of the technical characteristics of the genus *Prosopium*.

Our concern here is with the origin of this species flock in Bear Lake, including an explanation for the coexistence there of a fourth, widely distributed species of the genus *P. williamsoni*. The history of the Bear River and of its associated lakes is critical to the interpretation of this phenomenon and is here summarized from the recent study by Bright (1963). Prior to 34,000 years B.P. (before the present), the Bear River flowed northwestward into the Snake River via the ancestral Portneuf River, near Pocatello, Idaho. Subsequently, but still prior to 34,000 B.P., basaltic lava flows began to obstruct the northern end of the gorge of ancestral Portneuf River near the present town of Soda Springs. Bear River was then gradually forced into a southern course leading into Gentile Valley where it formed Lake Thatcher. Eventually successive lava flows at the northern end of the Thatcher basin built a barrier higher than the lowest rim at the southern end of the lake (elevation 5,445 ft), and Lake Thatcher overflowed into Cache Valley (an arm of Pluvial Lake Bonneville) about 25,000 years B.P. The outlet of Lake Thatcher cut its channel into the resistant rock of Oneida Narrows at least as deep as the present gorge, during which time all of the water from the Bear River basin flowed into Lake Bonneville. Approximately 18,000 years B.P., that lake rose to its highest level, 5,100 ft, and overflowed its barrier at Red Rock Pass to enter Snake River. It then receded to the Provo level.

Thus there were three opportunities for fishes to enter Bear Lake: (1) early in the history of the Bear Valley when Bear River was a direct tributary of the early Snake River; (2) when the connection was first established with Lake Bonneville; and (3) after Lake Bonneville had overflowed into the Snake River. There were also at least three distinct lakes in which ancestral whitefishes could have developed in geographic isolation and later come to coexist in Bear Lake: (1) Bear Lake, (2) Lake Thatcher, and (3) Lake Bonneville. With the exception of Lake Thatcher, these lake basins probably had a long (Pleistocene or earlier) history of successive lake stages.

Prosopium gemmiferum, a small fish seldom more than 7 in. long, is specialized for lacustrine life and is sharply distinct from the other Bear Lake whitefishes in its morphology and habits; it is a filter feeder and spawns at temperatures between 36° and 38° F in late January and early February close to shore and to the bottom. It could have developed either in the Bear Lake or the Bonneville basin; it has recently been discovered in Bonneville deposits (Stokes *et al.*, 1964). *Prosopium abyssicola* is a depwater form, spawning in water 50 to 100 ft deep at temperatures between 35° and 39° F in January and February (or later); it usually lives at depths greater than 75 ft and is a small species, seldom exceeding 9 in. It too could have originated in either the Bonneville or the Bear Lake basin. *Prosopium spilonotus*, the only species caught by anglers, usually spawns over rocky shallows when the water is about 45° F in early December; it is most closely related to *P. williamsoni*, which is scarce in Bear Lake. The latter species is common in larger lakes in the northern part of its range but more

frequently inhabits rivers, and all lake populations migrate up inlet streams to spawn on gravel and rubble riffles when the water temperature is about 40° F, from October to early December (Sigler, 1951). Thus all four species are now able to coexist because of differences in feeding habits, spawning time and place, and probably behavioral traits. *Prosopium spilonotus* may have been derived from an early invasion of Bear Valley by *P. williamsoni* or its ancestral form; or it could have developed in Lake Thatcher and have moved into Pluvial Bear Lake when Lake Thatcher was drained by downcutting of its outlet. Further work on the history of the lakes and additional finds of fossil fishes should clarify and will probably modify the interpretation presented here. That the evolution of the three species of *Prosopium* took place during the Quaternary seems probable.

FUTURE STUDIES

Paleoichthyology has much to offer for the modern investigator since it has now entered a period of stimulating rebirth and is progressing from an isolated discipline to one that is able to contribute to, as well as gain from, the growing fund of knowledge in paleoecology, biogeography, and evolution. Modern technical advances such as dating by radiometric methods are contributing importantly to the promising avenues for future research.

A basic need is to continue studies of the identification and evaluation of fossil remains, using increasingly refined morphological and taxonomic approaches. The nomenclature and classification of numerous groups are very much in need of revision because almost no fossil described twenty years ago can now be taken at face value as properly defined. Studies of new fossil sites and revision of earlier work by the examination of new and better material from known sites are needed and will benefit from the use of multiple, broad-based approaches. Additional comparative studies of the osteology of living forms are essential before the fossil relatives can be properly evaluated. Also critical is the need for comprehensive research on the habits, ecology, and life history of many elements of the existing fish fauna. Close collaboration among paleontologists, geologists, and ichthyologists is required for significant and rapid advances of knowledge in paleoichthyology. Information about changing climates and habitats has the greatest and most lasting significance when a broad spectrum of specialists can exchange data and ideas as they focus their attention on beds of common interest. Such an approach greatly strengthens the contributions from the many special fields.

REFERENCES

Numbers in parentheses refer to locations
on Figure 1.

Applegate, S. P., in press, The vertebrate fauna of the Selma Chalk formation of Alabama—Part 7, the fossil fishes: Fieldiana, Geol. Mem., v. 3, No. 7

Bailey, R. M., 1938, A systematic revision of the centrarchid fishes, with a discussion of their distribution, variations, and probable interrelationships: Univ. Michigan Ph.D. thesis, 256 p.

Bailey, R. M., and Bond, C. E., 1963, Four new species of

freshwater sculpins, genus *Cottus*, from western North America: Univ. Michigan Mus. Zool. Occ. Pap. 634, p. 1-27

Bright, R. C., 1963, Pleistocene Lakes Thatcher and Bonneville, southeastern Idaho: Univ. Minnesota Ph.D. thesis, 292 p. (**19, 20**)

Cavender, T. M., manuscript, Systematic position of the American Eocene hiodontid fish *"Leuciscus" rosei* Hussakof

Clements, Thomas, 1963, Pleistocene history of Lake Chapala, Jalisco, Mexico, *in* Essays in honor of K. O. Emery: Los Angeles, Univ. Southern California Press, p. 35-49 (**21, 22**)

Coleman, A. P., 1933, The Pleistocene of the Toronto region: Ontario Dept. Mines Ann. Rep., v. 41, p. 1-55 (**40**)

Cope, E. D., 1883, On the fishes of the Recent and Pliocene lakes of the western part of the Great Basin, and of the Idaho Pliocene lake: Philadelphia, Acad. Nat. Sci. Proc., p. 134-166

—— 1891, On some new fishes from South Dakota: Amer. Naturalist, v. 25, p. 654-658 (**34**)

Dalquest, W. W., 1962, The Good Creek formation, Pleistocene of Texas, and its fauna: J. Paleontology, v. 36, p. 568-582 (**28**)

Dawson, J. W., 1872, Notes on the post-Pliocene geology of Canada, with especial reference to the condition of accumulation of the deposit and the marine life of the period: Montreal, 112 p. [not seen] (**39**)

Downs, Theodore, 1958, Fossil vertebrates from Lago de Chapala, Jalisco, Mexico: 20th Intern. Congr. Geol., Mexico, 1956, sec. 7, p. 75-77 (**21, 22**)

Evernden, J. F., Savage., D. E., Curtis, G. H., and James, G. T., 1964, Potassium-argon dates and the Cenozoic mammalian chronology of North America: Amer. J. Sci., v. 262, p. 145-198 (**16**)

Feth, J. H., 1961, A new map of western conterminous United States showing the maximum known or inferred extent of Pleistocene lakes: U.S. Geol. Surv. Prof. Pap. 424-B, p. 110-112 (**4**)

Flint, R. F., and Gale, W. A., 1958, Stratigraphy and radiocarbon dates at Searles Lake, California: Amer. J. Sci., v. 256, p. 689-714 (**2**)

Hay, O. P., 1917, Vertebrata mostly from stratum no. 3, at Vero, Florida, together with descriptions of new species: Florida Geol. Surv. Rep., v. 9, p. 43-68 (**44**)

—— 1919, Description of some mammalian and fish remains from Florida, of possibly Pleistocene age: U.S. Natl. Mus. Proc., v. 56, p. 103-112

—— 1923, The Pleistocene of North America and its vertebrate animals from the states east of the Mississippi River and from the Canadian provinces east of longitude 95°: Carnegie Instn. Publ. 322, 499 p. (**41, 45, 46**)

—— 1926, A collection of Pleistocene vertebrates from southwestern Texas: U.S. Natl. Mus. Proc., v. 68, p. 1-18 (**23**)

—— 1927, The Pleistocene of the western region of North America and its vertebrated animals: Carnegie Instn. Publ. 322B, 346 p. (**43**)

Hibbard, C. W., 1955, The Jinglebob interglacial (Sanga-

mon?) fauna from Kansas and its climatic significance: Univ. Michigan Mus. Paleont. Contr., v. 12, p. 179-228 (**33**)

—— 1959, Late Cenozoic microtine rodents from Wyoming and Idaho: Michigan Acad. Sci. Pap., v. 44, p. 3-40 (**15**)

Hibbard, C. W., and Taylor, D. W., 1960, Two late Pleistocene faunas from southwestern Kansas: Univ. Michigan Mus. Paleont. Contr., v. 16, 223 p. (**31**)

Howard, Hildegarde, 1946, A review of the Pleistocene birds of Fossil Lake, Oregon: Carnegie Instn. Publ. 551, pt. 8, p. 141-195 (**11**)

—— 1955, Fossil Birds from Manix Lake, California: U.S. Geol. Surv. Prof. Pap. 264-J, p. 199-205 (**1**)

Hubbs, C. L., Bien, G. S., and Suess, H. E., 1962, La Jolla natural Radiocarbon measurements II: Radiocarbon, v. 4, p. 204-238 (**1**)

Hubbs, C. L., and Miller, R. R., 1948, The zoological evidence; correlation between fish distribution and hydrographic history in the desert basins of western United States: Univ. Utah Bull., v. 38, No. 20 (Biol. Ser., v. 10, No. 7), p. 17-166

Hussakof, Louis, 1916, Discovery of the Great Lake trout, *Cristivomer namaycush*, in the Pleistocene of Wisconsin: J. Geol., v. 24, p. 685-689 (**37**)

Jordan, D. S., 1927, The fossil fishes of the Miocene of southern California: Stanford Univ. Publ., Univ. Ser., Biol. Sci., v. 5, p. 85-99 (**4**)

Lagler, K. F., Bardach, J. E., and Miller, R. R., 1962, Ichthyology: New York, John Wiley and Sons, Inc., 545 p.

Lambe, L. M., 1904, Progress of vertebrate paleontology in Canada: Roy. Soc. Can. Trans., ser. 2, v. 10, p. 13-56 (**38**)

Lance, J. F., 1960, Stratigraphic and structural position of Cenozoic fossil localities in Arizona: Arizona Geol. Soc. Dig., v. 3, p. 155-159 (**17**)

La Rivers, Ira, 1962, Fishes and fisheries of Nevada: Carson City, Nevada Fish and Game Comm., 782 p. (**5**)

—— 1964, A new trout from the Barstovian (Miocene) of western Nevada (Isospondyliformes, Salmonoidei, Salmonidae): Biol. Soc. Nevada Occ. Pap. 3, 4 p.

Leidy, Joseph, 1889, Notice and description of fossils in caves and crevices of the limestone rocks of Pennsylvania: Pennsylvania Geol. Surv. Ann. Rep. (1887), p. 1-20 [not seen] (**47**)

MacAlpin, Archie, 1947, *Paleopsephurus wilsoni*, a new polyodontid fish from the upper Cretaceous of Montana, with a discussion of allied fish, living and fossil: Univ. Michigan Mus. Paleont. Contr., v. 6, No. 8, p. 167-234

Malde, H. E., and Powers, H. A., 1962, Upper Cenozoic stratigraphy of western Snake River Plain, Idaho: Geol. Soc. Amer. Bull., v. 73, p. 1197-1219 (**16**)

McConnell, W. J., Clark, W. J., and Sigler, W. F., 1957, Bear Lake, its fish and fishing: Utah Dept. Fish and Game, Idaho Dept. Fish and Game, and Utah State Agric. Coll., 76 p.

Miller, R. R., 1959, Origin and affinities of the freshwater fish fauna of western North America, *in* Hubbs, C. L. (ed.), Zoogeography: Amer. Assoc. Adv. Sci., Publ. 51, p. 187-222

—— 1961, Man and the changing fish fauna of the American Southwest: Michigan Acad. Sci. Pap., v. 46, p. 365-404

Miller, R. R., and Smith, G. R., manuscript, New fossil fishes from Plio-Pleistocene lake beds in Idaho and Oregon **(16)**

Miller, R. R., and Uyeno, Teruya, manuscript, Pleistocene fishes from Snowflake, Arizona **(17)**

Myers, G. S., 1951, Fresh-water fishes and East Indian zoogeography: Stanford Ichthyol. Bull., v. 4, p. 11-21

Norden, C. R., 1961, Comparative osteology of representative salmonid fishes with particular reference to the grayling (*Thymallus arcticus*) and its phylogeny: Can. Fish. Res. Bd. J., v. 18, p. 679-791

Patton, T. H., 1963, Fossil vertebrates from Miller's Cave, Llano County, Texas: Texas Mem. Mus. Bull., v. 7, p. 1-41 **(24)**

Ray, C. E., Olsen, S. J., and Gut, H. J., 1963, Three mammals new to the Pleistocene of Florida, and a reconsideration of five earlier records: J. Mammal., v. 44, p. 373-395 **(42)**

Rosen, D. E., and Bailey, R. M., 1963, The poeciliid fishes (Cyprinodontiformes), their structure, zoogeography, and systematics: Amer. Mus. Nat. Hist. Bull., v. 126, p. 1-176

Rostlund, Erhard, 1952, Freshwater fish and fishing in native North America: Berkeley, Univ. California Publ. Geogr., v. 9, p. 1-313

Sethi, R. P., 1960, Osteology and phylogeny of oviparous cyprinodont fishes (Order Cyprinodontiformes): Univ. Florida Ph.D. thesis, 275 p.

Sherrod, Neil, 1963, Late Pleistocene fish from lake sediments in Sheridan County, North Dakota: North Dakota Acad. Sci. Proc., v. 17, p. 32-36 **(35)**

Shotwell, J. A. (ed.), 1963, The Juntura basin; studies in earth history and paleoecology: Amer. Phil. Soc. Trans., n. s., v. 53, pt. 1, p. 1-77

Sigler, W. F., 1951, The life history and management of the mountain whitefish *Prosopium williamsoni* (Girard) in Logan River, Utah: Utah State Agric. Coll. Bull. 347, p. 1-21

Slaughter, B. H., Crook, W. W., Jr., Harris, R. K., Allen, D. C., and Seifert, Martin, 1962, The Hill-Shuler local faunas of the upper Trinity River, Dallas and Denton counties, Texas: Univ. Texas Bur. Econ. Geol., Rep. Inv. 48, 75 p. **(25)**

Slaughter, B. H., and Ritchie, Ronald, 1963, Pleistocene mammals of the Clear Creek local fauna, Denton County, Texas: So. Methodist Univ., Grad. Res. Center J., v. 31, p. 117-131 **(26, 27)**

Smith, C. L., 1954, Pleistocene fishes of the Berends fauna of Beaver County, Oklahoma: Copeia, 1954, p. 282-289 **(29)**

—— 1958, Additional Pleistocene fishes from Kansas and Oklahoma: Copeia, 1958, p. 176-180 **(30, 31)**

—— 1961, An ictalurid catfish, *Ictalurus decorus* (Hay), from the Miocene of South Dakota: J. Paleont., v. 35, p. 923-926

—— 1962, Some Pliocene fishes from Kansas, Oklahoma, and Nebraska: Copeia, 1962, p. 505-520

Smith, G. R., 1963, A late Illinoian fish fauna from southwestern Kansas and its climatic significance: Copeia, 1963, p. 278-285 **(32)**

Snyder, J. O., The fishes of the Lahontan system of Nevada and northeastern California: U.S. Bur. Fish. Bull., v. 35, p. 31-86

Stephens, J. J., 1960, Stratigraphy and paleontology of a late Pleistocene basin, Harper County, Oklahoma: Geol. Soc. Amer. Bull., v. 71, p. 1675-1702 **(30)**

Stock, Chester, 1918, The Pleistocene fauna of Hawver Cave: Berkeley, Univ. California Dept. Geol. Bull., v. 10, p. 461-515 **(8)**

Stokes, W. L., Smith, G. R., and Horn, K. F., 1964, Fossil fishes from the Stansbury level of Lake Bonneville, Utah: Proc. Utah Acad. Sci., v. 41, p. 87-88

Taylor, D. W., 1960a, Late Cenozoic molluscan faunas from the High Plains: U.S. Geol. Surv. Prof. Pap. 337, 94 p.

—— 1960b, Distribution of the freshwater clam *Pisidium ultramontanum*; a zoogeographic inquiry: Amer. J. Sci., v. 258-A (Bradley vol.), p. 325-334

Taylor, W. R., 1955, A revision of the genus *Noturus* Rafinesque with a contribution to the classification of the North American catfishes: Univ. Michigan Ph.D. thesis, 583 p.

Uyeno, Teruya, 1961, Late Cenozoic cyprinid fishes from Idaho with notes on other fossil minnows in North America: Michigan Acad. Sci. Pap., v. 46, p. 329-344 **(15)**

—— 1963, Late Pleistocene fishes in the Clear Creek and Ben Franklin local faunas of Texas: So. Methodist Univ., Grad. Res. Center J., v. 31, p. 168-171 **(26, 27)**

Uyeno, Teruya, and Miller, R. R., 1962a, Late Pleistocene fishes from a Trinity River terrace, Texas: Copeia, 1962, p. 338-345 **(25)**

—— 1962b, *Empetrichthys, erdisi*, a Pliocene cyprinodontid fish from California, with remarks on the Fundulinae and Cyprinodontinae: Copeia, 1962, p. 519-531

—— 1963, Summary of late Cenozoic freshwater fish records for North America: Univ. Michigan Mus. Zool. Occ. Pap. 631, 34 p. **(9, 10, 11, 14, 34, 36)**

—— 1965, Middle Pliocene cyprinid fishes from the Bidahochi formation, Arizona: Copeia, 1965, p. 28-41

Weigel, R. D., 1963, Fossil vertebrates of Vero, Florida: Florida Geol. Surv. Spec. Publ., v. 10, 59 p. **(44)**

Wheeler, H. E., and Cook, E. F., 1954, Structural and stratigraphic significance of the Snake River capture, Idaho-Oregon: J. Geol., v. 62, p. 525-536

Wilimovsky, N. J., 1956, *Protoscaphirhynchus squamosus*, a new sturgeon from the upper Cretaceous of Montana: J. Paleont., v. 30, p. 1205-1208

Wilson, Druid, Keroher, G. C., and Hansen, B. E., 1959, Index to the geologic names of North America: U.S. Geol. Surv. Bull. 1056-B, p. 407-622

SUMMARY

The origin of the freshwater fish fauna of North America scarcely antedates the Cenozoic, except for a few ancient relicts. Fifteen families are represented by 49 genera that are either living today (45) or became extinct near the onset of the Pleistocene. The 49 genera comprise 95 species, of which 5 belong to the 4 extinct genera. In contrast to the 90 species of extant genera that are known as fossil, these same genera are represented by 418 living species. About 60% of the existing fauna may be no older than late Miocene or early Pliocene.

Current knowledge of the occurrence and distribution of North American late-Pliocene and Pleistocene fishes is summarized, and the ecological and evolutionary significance of representatives from the Great Plains and areas west of the Rocky Mountains are discussed. Lacustrine speciation in Bear Lake (Idaho-Utah), relict distributions, and the contribution of the Recent and fossil faunas to paleohydrography in arid Western United States are also treated. Many unpublished data are included.

The first tabular summary of the known geologic range of living families and genera of American freshwater fishes is attempted, along with a map showing late-Pliocene and Pleistocene collection sites. The latter are documented by references.

Most if not all Pleistocene fossils are osteologically indistinguishable from living species. Few sites have sufficiently diversified remains to constitute faunas. Consequently only limited opportunity exists to demonstrate faunal shifts for these animals. As in groups other than fishes, the Pleistocene was a time of diminution of faunas. However, glaciation may have provided the impetus for the evolution and speciation of salmonoids and sculpins (*Cottus*).

The Idaho Lake fauna (Plio-Pleistocene) of southern Idaho is discussed in some detail, although studies of the fish remains are incomplete. The hypothetical former drainage of an earlier Snake River to the Pacific is supported by both fossil and zoogeographic evidence.

Paleoichthyology is now entering a period of challenge, promise, and stimulating rebirth. Much is yet to be learned, however, of the comparative osteology and the habits, ecology, and life history of the living fauna before additional advances can be made in interpreting Quaternary fishes.

PLEISTOCENE EVENTS AND INSECTS *

HERBERT H. ROSS[1]

INSECTS

IN NORTH AMERICA only a few Pleistocene insect fossils have been studied so that it is impossible to bring together syntheses comparable to those made for parts of Europe (Coope et al., 1961; Pearson, 1963). Because of this sparse fossil information, present contributions to a knowledge of the Pleistocene through the study of North American insects must be based on (1) comparative distribution patterns of existing species, (2) relationships between existing species, (3) correlations of insect species with species of other groups for which paleontological information is known, and (4) correlations between insect species and the physical and ecological characteristics of the land that offer a basis for explaining the phenomena exhibited by the insects. All these bases entail difficulties in interpretation. Ranges may appear disjunct because of a lack of collecting or because human land use has annihilated the species over large areas. Especially in the insects, new species may be found that will necessitate changes in our phylogenies. Ecological and physical correlation may be of recent origin.

If fossils from well-dated deposits are lacking, extrapolation from living species into the past requires one other assumption: that three is in general a correlation between the quantitative passage of time and the amount of morphological difference between related phylogenetic lines. Although evidence is incontrovertible that different lineages change at individual and therefore different rates (Simpson, 1944), it seems true that on the average a correlation between time and change does exist. Where this factor is used, therefore, the more similar the examples that bear on the same point, the more probable will be the correlation between time and change.

Much of the evidence concerning the insects is based on disjunct ranges of species. Many insect species are highly vagile and can disperse long distances by their own sustained flight or passively by moving air masses. Populations of such species can cross wide areas inimical to them ecologically and establish disjunct populations in suitable ecological areas long distances from the species' parental range. Disjunct ranges of this type provide no evidence of an historical nature. Other insect species appear to move only a relatively short distance from their point of origin. Some of these are wingless and heavy-bodied, whereas others are strong fliers and are not carried aloft by thermal currents. When these species of low vagility have disjunct ranges, there is a good possibility that the disjunctions are the result of the disruption by ecological change of a once-continuous range. Even in these instances, there is frequently the possibility that man may have caused the ecological change resulting in the disjunction. In this paper every effort has been made to employ as historic examples only disjunctions due to natural ecological breaks and involving either species of low vagility or disjunctions of such great distances that dispersal between the disjunct areas seems virtually impossible. The examples have further been drawn wherever possible from those groups that have been extensively collected and whose known ranges have therefore a good chance of being close to the real ranges.

In spite of the limitations of interpretation, living insects can contribute greatly to a knowledge of Pleistocene events, simply because there is such a large number of insect species (probably 150,000 in North America) and because most of them have rigid ecological requirements. No other group of organisms has this amazing array of almost countless ecological indicators; it is almost impossible to conceive of a land or freshwater situation about which some group of insects will not eventually give us relatively precise insights into the past. Because of the tremendous number of both species and individuals confronting the insect taxonomist, however, interpretive insect studies in this area of investigation are scattered or sketchy. The present paper must therefore be considered at most a provisional progress report.

Clues about Pleistocene events offered by insects are especially cogent concerning intercontinental dispersals, intracontinental dispersals between eastern and western North America, and intraregional movements in both the West and East. Eastern North America is considered first because more is known about its insects, and many conclusions based on data from this area are useful as background information in considering the other areas. The distribution of the insect fauna of eastern North America cannot be understood, however, without a knowledge of certain topographic conditions that prevailed prior to the Pleistocene.

* Sincere thanks are hereby extended to Dr. W. E. Ricker, Canada Fisheries Research Board, for permission to incorporate into this manuscript data from our cooperative project endeavoring to deduce Pleistocene climates south of the glacial lobes through an analysis of distribution patterns of winter stoneflies; and to Mr. J. D. Unzicker, University of Illinois and Illinois Natural History Survey, for permission to use certain information from our cooperative project concerning the caddisfly fauna of the Ozark-Ouachita region.

Gratefully acknowledged is assistance on the manuscript and bibliography by Mrs. Bess White and Mrs. Bernice Sweeney and on the maps and mapping by Mrs. Alice Prickett and Mr. George Rotramel.

This paper is based to a large extent on findings supported by a research grant from the National Science Foundation.

[1] Illinois Natural History Survey, Urbana, Illinois.

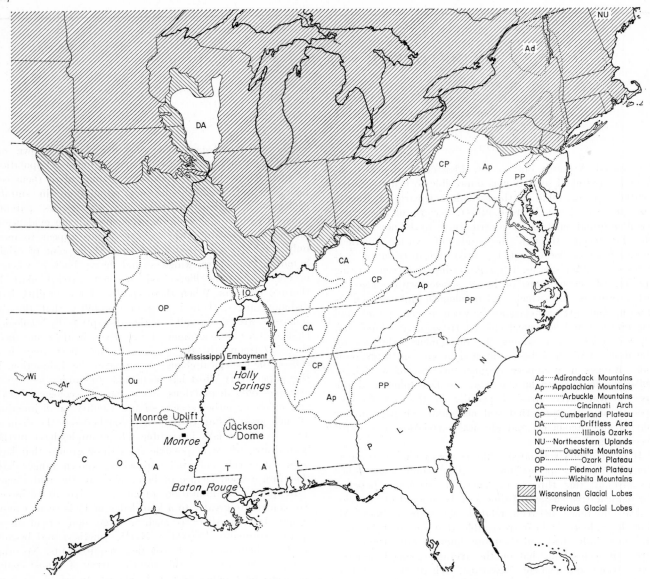

Figure 1. Late Cenozoic tectonic setting of the south-central United States. (Adapted from Tectonic Map of the United States and Glacial Map of North America.)

EASTERN INTRAREGIONAL EFFECTS

LATE-CENOZOIC TOPOGRAPHIC AND CLIMATIC CHANGES[2]

Because the present distribution of insect faunas is in large part related to late-Cenozoic changes in climate and topography, the following brief summary attempts to present background information for a more complete understanding of the ecological mechanisms for insect evolution and distribution in the central states. In the nonglaciated regions ecological changes are related to the tectonic, sedimentary, and physiographic history as well as to climatic changes. The area under consideration includes such major topographic features as the Ozark Plateau, Ouachita Mountains, Interior Low Plateaus, Cumberland Plateau, Appalachian Mountains, Northeastern Uplands, and related

[2] This section was written by Charles A. Ross, Western Washington State College, Bellingham, Washington.

features as described by Fenneman (1938), as well as the broad alluvial valley of the Mississippi River (Fig. 1).

Suggestions for the time and amount of movement on the tectonic features have been the subject of considerable discussion and debate for more than 80 years and are based almost entirely on two types of evidence, erosional surfaces and their related alluvial deposits. No general agreement has been reached concerning all aspects of the problems, particularly those relating to ages and interrelationships. Fossils useful to date the deposits are generally lacking in the higher levels of gravels except in the High Plains, and neither the deposits nor the erosional surfaces are traceable with much certainty from one tectonic unit to the next. In the Gulf Coastal Plain, they intertongue with or are overlapped by marine fossiliferous strata (Doering, 1956, 1958).

The late Cenozoic physiographic and sedimentary history of this area results from the activity of several interconnected tectonic features. Several small uplifted areas such as the Sabin Uplift, Monroe Uplift, and Jackson Dome separate the Mississippi Embayment Syncline from the more active syncline underlying the Gulf Coastal Plain (Fig. 1). The axis of this syncline follows closely the Mississippi River from Cairo, Illinois, as far south as the mouth of the Arkansas River; the structure was most active in late Cretaceous and early Cenozoic time (Stearns and Marcher, 1962; Ross, 1963). The low plateaus and the Appalachian Highlands to the east have been involved in a series of uplifts since Cretaceous time.

The Ozark Uplift, the Ouachita Mountains, and the intervening Arkoma Basin were differentially uplifted also and appear to have behaved as a unit during the late Cenozoic, although tectonically each is quite a different geologic feature. Similar Cenozoic uplift took place in the Arbuckle Mountains of the southern High Plains and in the Red River Valley of Texas.

Five prominent terrace surfaces have been recognized by Fisk (1938, 1940, 1951) in and adjacent to the Mississippi alluvial valley southward from its junction with the Ohio River. To these Fisk assigned a Pleistocene age, each surface representing valley-filling associated with the rise of sea level during times of glacial melting. In the upper part of the Mississippi Embayment and farther north, Leighton and Willman (1949) recognize three erosional surfaces and a number of terrace deposits, of which the first two erosional surfaces were considered pre-Pleistocene and the third surface and the terraces were considered Wisconsin. Horberg (1946, 1950a, b) also recognized several Cenozoic erosional levels in Illinois that predated glaciation.

Topographic changes. The topography of the area was apparently very subdued by middle Cenozoic time, although probably it was not a featureless plain. Although not so high as at present, the Rocky Mountains to the west and the Appalachians, Adirondack Mountains, and Northeastern Uplands on the east of this plain were areas of greater height and relief than the Central interior plains. Late-Cenozoic uplift was greatest along the Rocky Mountains and the Appalachian Mountains and decreased irregularly toward the Mississippi Embayment and Gulf Coast synclines. The Ozark Uplift, Ouachita Mountains, Arbuckle and Wichita Mountains, and Nashville Dome were local centers of uplift on this gently sloping surface, and the Jackson, Sabine, and Monroe uplifts are just north of the Pliocene-Pleistocene hinge line at the northern edge of the Gulf Coastal geosyncline.

The late Tertiary physiographic conditions apparently were considerably different from those that prevail there at present. The late Tertiary (Pliocene) deposits in most of the area south of the glacial limit, and presumably once present also in the area north of this limit (Horberg, 1950a, b), were broad, sheet-like deposits of hydrous iron oxide-bearing gravel locally as thick as 15 m, deposited on extensive erosional surfaces that sloped gently toward the Gulf Coast or Mississippi Embayment from adjacent higher areas (Potter, 1955). Comparable gravels were deposited on the Atlantic side of the Appalachians and in the Great Plains. Below this highest late-Cenozoic surface are several other gravel terraces, which have resulted from the erosion and subsequent redeposition of the higher gravels at lower levels. Of particular ecological interest was the deep erosion that followed the uplifts. The steep-sided valleys that formed in many of the uplifted areas resulted in a marked increase in the diversity of local ecological habitats. Erosion breached the previous water table and greatly increased the groundwater outflow in springs; this resulted in special habitats characterized by nearly constant stream flow and water temperature closer to the annual average soil temperature.

Climatic fluctuations. Late Cenozoic climatic changes are clearly indicated by the nearly cyclical erosional and depositional record of this large region. In the Miocene and Pliocene, the renewed uplift of the Rocky Mountains most likely influenced the circulation of the westerly winds and, during late Pliocene, shifted biomes as much as 300 km eastward. The early Pliocene of the High Plains was about 3° C warmer and had 25 cm more rainfall than at present, as indicated by plant fossils (Chaney and Elias, 1936, p. 25). The middle Pliocene of western Kansas had about 12 cm less rainfall, and grasslands adjacent to river floodplains formed the predominant biome. The whole of the south-central states probably had a somewhat similar trend during the Pliocene.

During the advances of the Pleistocene glaciers the average temperatures were reduced, but to what extent and how far south is a matter of conjecture. The summer temperatures may have been decreased more than winter temperatures because of increased cloud cover. These climatic changes caused shifts in the vegetational belts southward. The tundra zone may have been very narrow, perhaps extending only a few kilometers in front of the ice sheets during their maxima (Frye and Willman, 1958; Ekblaw and Willman, 1955). However, climates cooler than the present extended considerably south of the glacial lobes (Buell, 1945; Frey, 1953) during the Wisconsinan. Presumably a similar southward extension occurred during the preceding glacial maxima.

During interglacial times a northward shift in the ecological belts repopulated the areas exposed by the melting ice. A late interglacial fauna and flora near Toronto, Canada, indicates a climate 2° to 3° C warmer than present (Flint, 1957, p. 340), and Dorf (1959, p. 197) cites other evidence suggesting that interglacial periods were notably warmer than the present.

Differences in the distribution of precipitation between different Pleistocene substages are also likely. Eolian "cover sands" in the High Plains of Yarmouthian and Illinoian age indicate a sharp change in climate at the end of the Kansan to more arid conditions (Frye and Leonard, 1957, p. 28; Leonard and Frye, 1962, p. 15). Major shifts in the location of maximal ice advances between different substages suggest changes in the circulation pattern that supplied moisture for glacier growth.

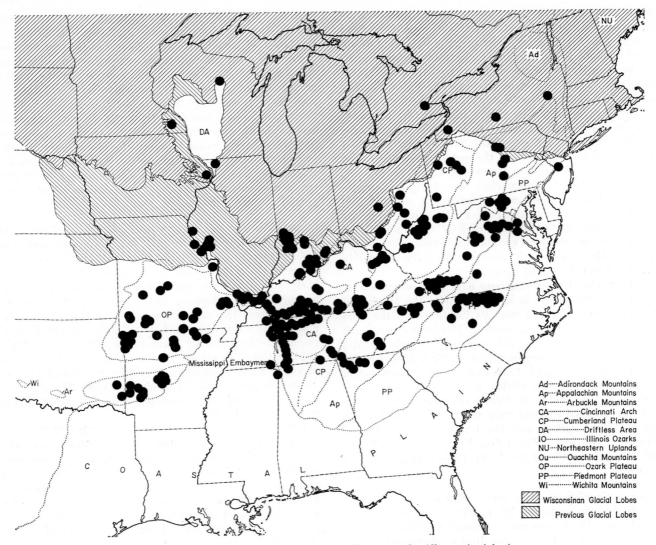

Ad----Adirondack Mountains
Ap----Appalachian Mountains
Ar------Arbuckle Mountains
CA----------------Cincinnati Arch
CP----Cumberland Plateau
DA----------------Driftless Area
IO------------------Illinois Ozarks
NU---Northeastern Uplands
Ou----------Ouachita Mountains
OP----------------Ozark Plateau
PP----------Piedmont Plateau
Wi----------------Wichita Mountains

Wisconsinan Glacial Lobes
Previous Glacial Lobes

Figure 2. Known distribution for the winter stonefly *Allocapnia rickeri*.

INSECT CORRELATIONS

Colonization after deglaciation. It is evident from the abundant insect fauna now present in formerly glaciated areas that an extremely varied fauna representing diverse ecological types persisted in unglaciated areas and moved into previously glaciated areas after the ice dissipated.

The leveling action of the glaciers produced physical conditions in at least Ohio, Indiana, Illinois, and Iowa that have prevented certain insect species from recolonizing these areas. This is shown by several species of forest-floor thrips (Stannard, 1963) that have been able to spread only a few miles into the Wisconsin drift and then only along the well-drained bluff forests of a few rivers. Poor drainage apparently produces ecological conditions of the forest floor that are inimical to these tiny insects. The winter stonefly *Allocapnia rickeri* has not spread into any of the drift area in these same states except along rivers and streams running through exposed outcrop areas; the species cannot exist in the sluggish, silty streams occurring over most of the formerly glaciated area (Fig. 2).

The ranges of the great majority of insect species occurring in eastern North America show no correlation with these glacial boundaries but occur in suitable habitats through both glaciated and unglaciated country. In the case of insects such as mosquitoes, deer flies, and a large number of marsh flies, a poorly drained deglaciated area inimical to *Allocapnia rickeri* would have offered unusually good opportunities for proliferation and dispersal.

Outpost colonies. A number of boreal insects have distributions that coincide fairly well with the northern coniferous forest, extend southward through the Appalachian Mountains and along the Cumberland Plateau, and have in addition outpost colonies south or west of the main range. Most spectacular of these are species such as *Allocapnia pygmaea* that have abundant populations in the streams arising in the large springs of the Missouri Ozarks (Fig. 3). These species apparently have a very low vagility. The spring-fed streams in which their Missouri populations live maintain summer temperatures considerably below those of normal streams fed entirely by surface runoff.

Thus in summer they simulate the ecological conditions of the fast, cool streams that the species occupy in their northern and eastern range. The simplest explanation for these outposts is that, during the period of glacial advance, the surface streams between central Wisconsin and central Missouri became colder and possibly faster, allowing the northern *A. pygmaea* and its ecological neighbors to disperse southward through the intervening area. During deglaciation, these boreal species presumably spread northward, repopulated the streams of country to the north, but left thriving populations in the spring-fed streams of Missouri. Large numbers of caddisflies, for example, *Diplectrona modesta, Pycnopsyche subfasciata, Setodes vernalia,* and *Glossosoma intermedium,* have this same general type of Ozark-plus-boreal distribution but differ from more restricted relicts such as *Allocapnia pygmaea* in that local populations still occur in spring-fed streams and cool ravines of Illinois and Indiana scattered along the presumed route of northern dispersal.

In their movement into deglaciated country, these aquatic insects would have had to spread between streams that did not originate with the glaciers themselves. Glacial meltwater normally carries a heavy load of glacial "flour," forming a fine suspension that kills practically all aquatic insects in a stream.

Speciation. The Ozark Plateau and Ouachita Mountains contain certain species that are closely related only to boreal species now occurring considerably to the north. Examples are *Glyphopsyche missouri,* known only from the large spring-fed streams of southern Missouri and having a holarctic, boreal sister species, *G. irrorata,* known in eastern North America only as far south as extreme northern Michigan (Leonard and Leonard, 1949); and *Hydropsyche*

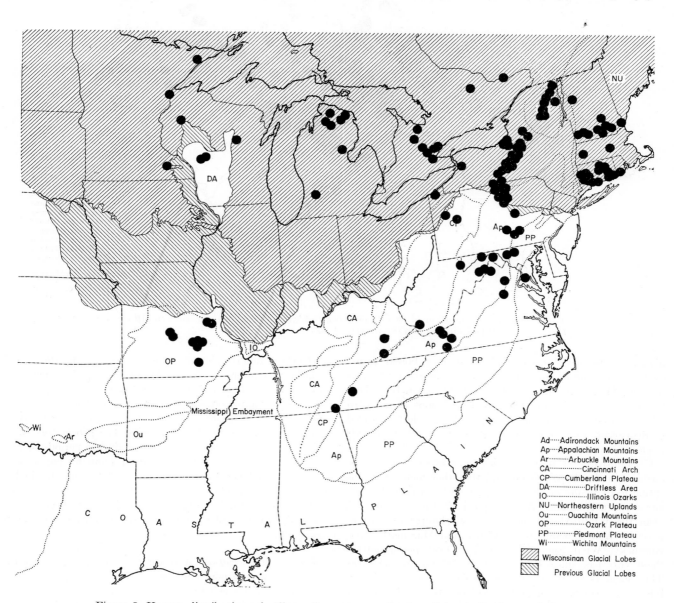

Figure 3. Known distribution of *Allocapnia pygmaea,* showing disjunct Ozark populations.

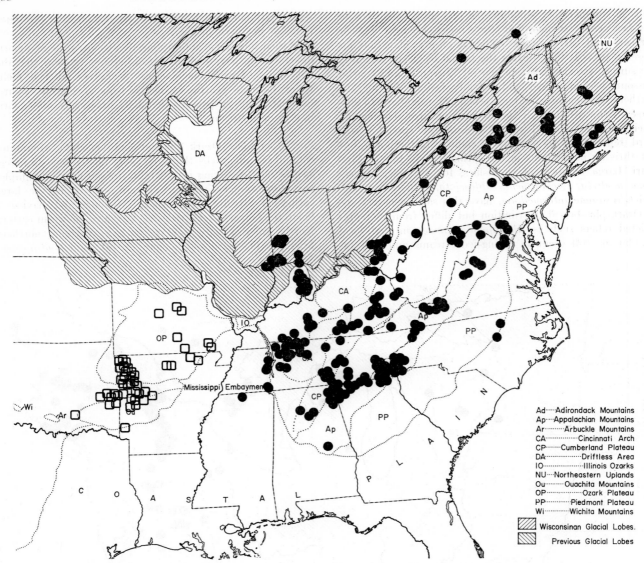

Figure 4. Known distribution of two sister species of winter stoneflies, the eastern *Allocapnia recta* (black circles) and the western *A. mohri* (open squares).

piatrix, whose close relative, *H. vexa*, is a boreal transcontinental species known as far south as northern Minnesota and Wisconsin (Ross, 1944). It would seem that these two Ozark species originated from populations of northern relatives that reached the Ozarks and were left stranded there earlier than the relict populations of *Allocapnia pygmaea*.

Certain pairs of insect species or subspecies have one member in the Appalachians and the other member in the spring-fed streams of the cave region of southern Indiana and western Kentucky. An example is *Rhyacophila banksi*, from the White Mountain area, New Hampshire, and *R. parantra* from Bloomington, Indiana, and Mammoth Cave, Kentucky. What appears to be a hybrid population of these two has since been taken at Maynooth, Ontario. This suggests a Wisconsin age isolation and speciation, but with a colonization of the deglaciated area before the two segregates had become genetically incompatible.

Certain other pairs of species occur as northern and southern counterparts in the Appalachian region. The caddisfly *Rhyacophila teddyi* and the stonefly *Allocapnia aurora*, for example, appear to be species that evolved in the Great Smoky Mountains area of the Appalachians from progenitors related to boreal species. The progenitors could have moved down the Appalachians during periods of glacial advance, and after deglaciation remnant populations of each phylogenetic line became isolated in the higher southern Appalachians, evolving there into new species. The evidence further suggests that there has been a considerable mixture of the resultant species during subsequent cool climates.

Non-boreal speciation. Another type of speciation in the Ozarks concerns non-boreal insects. For example, *Allocapnia recta* occurs chiefly in the hills and mountains east of the Mississippi Embayment and lives in small, clear, rocky streams (Fig. 4); its sister species *A. mohri* lives in the same type of stream in the Ozark Plateau–Ouachita Mountains area. The range of *Allocapnia rickeri* (Fig. 2) points out a phenomenon common to these and all other clear, rocky-stream species occurring in this general area. West of the Appalachians they extend little into the glaciated areas and, except under special conditions, do not occur in the Mississippi Embayment area and the coastal plain. The ranges of these species thus are shaped like an hourglass, with the constriction in the narrow hilly area of southernmost Illinois. Because *Allocapnia recta* and *mohri* arose from the same immediate ancestor, it seems certain that this ancestor once had a range in general like that of *rickeri* and that for some reason conditions in the Illinois corridor later became unfavorable to the *recta-mohri* ancestor and resulted in a division of its range. The western part of the range has evolved into *mohri*, the eastern part into *recta*.

Similar examples occur in the caddisflies. In the *Rhyacophila carolina* complex, four species occur in the Appalachian Mountains and the Cumberland Plateau, and two have apparently relict western populations in the Illinois Ozarks; a fifth species, *R. kiamichi*, occurs only in the Ozark Plateau–Ouachita Mountain area. In the caddisfly genus *Agapetus*, the two species *artesus* and *medicus* that occur only in the Ozark Plateau–Ouachita Mountain region are close relatives of species known only from the hill and mountain country of central and eastern Tennessee. The origin of these and other caddisflies showing the same relationship can be explained most plausibly by the same mechanism used to explain the evolution of *Allocapnia recta* and *mohri*.

Because the Mississippi Embayment area has been a feature of long standing with little topographic change, it seems safe to assume that there was no direct dispersal of these aquatic insects across the Embayment south of Illinois. It therefore seems reasonable that changes in the ecological conditions of the Illinois Ozarks associated with Pleistocene events alternately permitted the dispersal of ancestral forms between the eastern and western areas and then broke the ranges at this point and produced geographic isolation between the eastern and western populations of the species.

The gate-like effect of the Illinois Ozarks appears to have caused speciation in the caddisfly genera *Chimarra* and *Polycentropus*. The results are now highly complex, because the species that presumably evolved in the Ozarks have spread into the northern and eastern parts of the continent and now have ranges that partially overlap their sister eastern species.

Local endemics. Two species of caddisfly, *Pycnopsyche rossi* and *Triaenodes smithi*, are known from only one spring at the base of the limestone bluffs 20 miles north of the southern tip of Illinois. Each seems to be a primitive member of a cluster of species that evolved in the temperate deciduous forest of eastern America. It is possible but not demonstrable that these and perhaps other as-yet-undiscovered forms reached these local areas during glacial maxima, and now are stranded there and may be on the verge of extinction.

Near Holly Springs, Mississippi, Monroe, Louisiana, and Baton Rouge, Louisiana, occur springs having peculiar endemic species. These springs are in the coastal plain area, perhaps associated with faulting or local tectonic movements. To my knowledge they are isolated by a considerable distance from the main ranges of the few other caddisflies found in them. Each of the two Louisiana spring streams harbors a distinctive endemic species of *Chimarra*, closely related to species now occurring in the Ouachita Mountains or the Appalachians. It is possible that these local endemic species originated from wind-blown vagrants. It is also possible that during the glacial maxima some of the connecting streams from the Ouachita Mountains were cool enough to afford avenues of dispersal by which caddisflies reached their present spring habitats.

Enrichment of Ozark fauna. The many species of boreal or Appalachian extraction found in the freshwater insect fauna of the Ozarks and Ouachitas give the impression of a balanced fauna, indicating that entire communities of organisms dispersed and were isolated in unison. To date no extensive lineages appear to have evolved within the Ozarks, indicating that this faunal element is fairly young. It might be argued that the first east-west movement of the more southern species such as the ancestor of *Rhyacophila kiamichi* dispersed across this area far earlier than the Pleistocene. To this question the history of the topography offers excellent evidence. Before the Pliocene, when Illinois and much of the terrain around the Mississippi Embayment was an area of low relief, it is difficult to see how these cool-water, clear-stream species could have dispersed westward. They were probably restricted in their distribution to the Appalachian area and a few neighboring areas of hill country. It was not until the margins of the Mississippi Embayment were elevated and these elevations eroded into cool valleys having spring-fed streams that genera such as *Allocapnia, Agapetus, Glossosoma*, and the like would have found suitable habitats to spread westward. Of especial importance in this spread were the streams along the eroded edges of the Cincinnati Arch and those of the Shawnee Hills of Kentucky and of the Illinois Ozarks. Because certain of these species of boreal affinities now occur in only a few small areas of highest elevation in Missouri, Arkansas, and Oklahoma, it is doubtful if even these mountains were high enough before their re-elevation in pre-Pleistocene or early Pleistocene time to produce the cool streams necessary for the survival of these species.

This does not, of course, provide a firm dating for the initiation of these insect dispersals, because the geotectonic activity is not dated exactly and also because we do not know in what part of North America the insects occurred at that time. It is possible that these essentially cool-temperate insects were confined in late Tertiary to areas of the continent far north of the area under discussion. There seems little doubt, however, that this topographic history dates the possible initiation of dispersals from the boreal zone and the Appalachians to the Ozark-Ouachita area at a period not earlier than late Pliocene or early Pleistocene.

The shortness of the phylogenies so far attributable to evolution within this area suggests a Pleistocene rather than a Pliocene dating.

Floridian speciation. Although far removed from the glacial fronts, Florida and adjoining areas appear to have been broken into islands, then reunited, as a result of changes in sea levels during the Pleistocene. Distribution patterns of insects of low vagility such as scarab beetles of the genus *Mycotrupes* and wingless grasshoppers (Olson *et al.*, 1954; Neill, 1957) indicate that these Pleistocene sea level oscillations produced considerable speciation in faunal elements of the Floridian region. Although evidence of these evolutionary events is now discernible only in groups having a low vagility, unquestionably other groups were affected in like manner, but the species produced have since dispersed sufficiently to obscure their history.

Dispersals in the Central Plains

The effects of Pleistocene events on insects of the Great Plains are difficult to detect. The grassland insects now inhabiting the formerly glaciated northern areas are similar to those found in the unglaciated areas, with a gradual change of fauna northward such as would be expected from ecological considerations alone. This suggests that the insect fauna of this part of the world simply oscillated in a north-south direction in phase with changes in climate associated with glaciation. The few exceptions to the purely north-south movement are a group of insects found in the Black Hills of South Dakota. The caddisflies of this area are almost all species that are mainly confined to the Rocky Mountain area, indicating that the dry area between the Black Hills and the Big Horn Mountains of Wyoming was wetter and cooler than it is now. Even so, it is puzzling that these Black Hills caddisfly populations show no evidence of morphological change from their Rocky Mountain relatives. On the face of it, this similarity would indicate (1) that the species reached the Black Hills only once and quite recently, (2) that there have been quite frequent cold-water stream connections between the Black Hills and the Rockies through most of the Pleistocene, or (3) that vagrant specimens are continually being blown into the Black Hills area.

Also in the Black Hills are a few species of tree-inhabiting leafhoppers that otherwise occur throughout the eastern deciduous forest. Phylogenetic considerations indicate that these species evolved in the eastern deciduous forest and probably reached the Black Hills at a time when greater rainfall provided avenues of hosts westward from Minnesota or Wisconsin to the Black Hills. These avenues need have been only narrow gallery forests along stream banks. One of these leafhoppers, *Erythroneura carmini*, occurs also on the scrub oaks along the eastern foothills of the Rocky Mountains south to central Colorado; its dispersal from the Black Hills westward to the Rockies fits in well with changes indicated by the Black Hills caddisflies.

Western Intraregional Effects

The West is here considered as that large area between the Great Plains and the Pacific Ocean, extending from about the Mexican border to Alaska. It is unfortunate that the detailed distribution records needed to gain an understanding of intraregional Pleistocene effects in this area have been extremely difficult to compile. Even so, some remarkably interesting suggestions can be made concerning insects and the Pleistocene in this western area.

RECOLONIZATION OF DEGLACIATED AREAS

The entire deglaciated area from Alaska southward has been repopulated by an abundant insect fauna. Certain species presumably restricted to areas south of the glaciers during the last glacial maximum have now dispersed to Alaska, and it is probable that some of the species that persisted in the unglaciated parts of Alaska have dispersed southward through British Columbia and perhaps farther. There has likewise been a dispersal of species, at least in certain caddisflies, between the eastern parts of the region and the western parts in areas along the United States–Canada border that were formerly separated by at least mountain glaciers. Many species occurring to the south, especially in Oregon and California, appear to have moved northward very little and might indicate that few temperature changes occurred in some of the lowland Pleistocene climates of that area.

DISJUNCT RANGES

Distribution patterns in the caddisfly genera *Anagapetus* and *Glossosoma* indicate that the interior Great Basin, separating the ranges associated with the Rocky Mountains proper to the east and the Cascade–Sierra Nevada group to the west, has been a barrier to the east-west movement of coolwater caddisflies probably to a time considerably antedating the Pleistocene (Ross, 1956). A few species such as the caddisfly *Rhyacophila rotunda* do occur on both sides of this basin. This is suggestive that during a fairly recent pluvial period there was a band of cool streams, possibly at about the latitude of the San Francisco Mountains in Arizona, that offered a dispersal route for cool-adapted forms such as the caddisflies. The pluvial periods very likely date from the Pleistocene (Martin, 1959).

In aquatic insects, a conspicuous feature is the occurrence of relict populations on widely separated mountains or small mountain groups. For example, the caddisfly *Imania tripunctata* occurs in Alaska with disjunct populations recorded from Wellington, British Columbia, and Laramie, Wyoming. Similar examples have been recorded among the wingless grasshoppers and especially the curious wingless genus *Grylloblatta* (Gurney, 1937b). These disjunctions are most easily explained by assuming that temperatures along the mountain chains were sufficiently lower during times of glacial advance that species now restricted to high mountains could survive at lower elevations and disperse to new areas. During warmer interglacial periods these species would again be restricted to higher mountain elevations and thus be divided into isolated populations.

SPECIATION

Isolated populations of the sort just described, but presumably originating from earlier dispersals, have evolved into many distinct species that are still locally distributed. Again examples of such speciation are abundant in the aquatic insects, especially in the caddisfly genera *Imania* and *Farula* (Ross, 1950a), *Homophylax* (Denning, 1964), and *Rhyacophila* (Ross, 1956) and in many western stoneflies (Ricker, 1943).

Certain of these local endemics suggest an interesting possibility. *Rhyacophila unimaculata* has been found to date only near Mt. Robson, British Columbia, several hundred miles north of the former southern edge of the ice sheet. Such records raise the possibility that some species evolving in the northern Cordillera persisted through the periods of glaciation on unglaciated peaks and ridges rising above the Cordilleran ice fields.

Pleistocene events apparently caused a fracturing of the ranges of many more widely distributed western species and produced isolation of sufficient duration that the isolated populations evolved into either distinctive subspecies or species. For example, the mosquito *Aedes bicristatus*, restricted to central California, is a sister species of *A. trichurus*, widely distributed throughout the northern United States and southern Canada (Carpenter and LaCasse, 1955). It seems likely that *A. bicristatus* originated as a West Coast population isolated by Pleistocene events.

Striking evidence of Pleistocene speciation is offered by the sawfly genus *Tenthredo*. In many instances what appear to be distinctive species occur in adjacent areas, with intergradation along presumed lines of contact. Because of insufficient collections, the history of these entities is largely unresolved, but continued analysis of the genus should produce highly interesting results. One pair of species of *Tenthredo* appears to offer firm evidence of a Pleistocene separation. The species *T. stricklandi* occurs in Canada in the more eastern ranges and foothills of the Rockies; its sister species *T. rhammisia* is abundant from southern British Columbia to northern California throughout the Cascade Mountain area and has been collected also in northwestern Wyoming. The common ancestor of these two species was apparently divided into eastern and western segments, and these two segments evolved into different species; *T. rhammisia* now appears to be moving eastward.

The same situation applies to the caddisfly pair *Rhyacophila alberta*, known from the Rocky Mountain region, and *R. tucula*, abundant on the West Coast in the Cascades but with one record in northwestern Wyoming. The progenitor of *R. alberta* and *tucula* very likely was divided into western and eastern segments, with subsequent speciation of the two (Ross, 1950b). The Wyoming record of *R. tucula* could represent a glacial relict population resulting from a dispersal and disjunction subsequent to that which divided the *alberta-tucula* ancestor. The species pair *Glossosoma alascense* and *G. wenatchee* apparently speciated on either side of the Great Basin from a common, more northern ancestor that had moved south during the glacial maximum and divided into population segments on each side of the Basin. Since the two species evolved, each has moved far to the north, and presumably their ranges mingle in the yet uncollected Cascade Mountain area of British Columbia (Fig. 5).

INTERREGIONAL EFFECTS

A number of insects spread between the western and eastern parts of the continent almost certainly because of changes associated with the Wisconsin glaciation. Several species of the caddisfly genus *Rhyacophila* spread from west to east. In each case the species belonged to a monophyletic cluster that had evolved in the West, and in each cluster only its most widespread species seems to have made the eastern journey. In one of these, *R. acropedes*, the eastern populations exhibit slight morphological differences from western populations, perhaps suggesting that the species

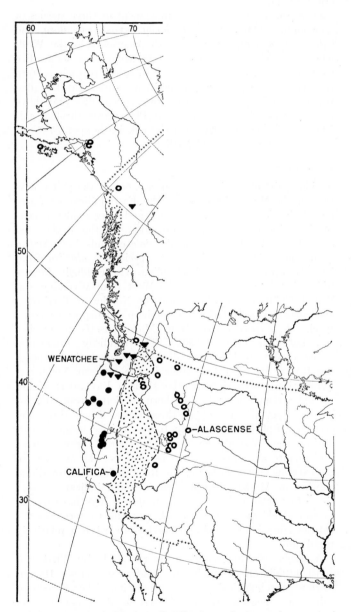

Figure 5. Known distribution of the caddisflies *Glossosoma alascense, wenatchee,* and *califica.* (From Ross, *Evolution and classification of the mountain caddisflies,* 1956, by permission of the University of Illinois Press.)

moved east during the earliest phases of the Wisconsin. Species of the caddisfly genera *Athripsodes, Triaenodes,* and *Banksiola* moved from eastern North America into the western mountain region. *Hydropsyche bifida* apparently moved west across the top of the Great Plains into the foothills of the Rocky Mountains.

It is interesting that there is no evidence of the typically mountainous boreal Appalachian fauna moving westward. The caddisflies that did make the journey are all marsh, pond, or hill-country species that occur in the flatter terrain of northern Wisconsin, Michigan, and adjacent southern Canada.

Of especial interest was the movement of three species of scorpionflies (Mecoptera), *Panorpa venosa, maculosa,* and *submaculosa,* from eastern North America into the West, where they now occur in the Uinta Mountains, Utah. The western populations appear to be identical to their eastern relatives (Gurney, 1937a, 1938), suggesting that this dispersal is of very recent date. The scorpionflies may have moved across the northern Great Plains area through gallery forests concurrently with the oak leafhopper *Erythroneura carmini* mentioned earlier.

SPECIATION

Various pairs of species or subspecies, one of the pair occurring in the West, the other in the East, indicate a fairly recent division of parental ranges and offer evidence concerning the routes of recolonization of the deglaciated area. The caddisfly *Hydropsyche riola* extends from Alaska to northern Michigan, its sister species *H. alhedra* from New Hampshire to North Carolina. The caddisfly *Limnephilus batchawana* occurs in the West from Wyoming and British Columbia to Alberta and the Northwest Territories and eastward to Ontario and northern Michigan; its sister species *L. curtus* occurs from Massachusetts to Quebec and Labrador (Ross, 1950a). The caddisfly *Triaenodes grisea* appears to be of one distinct morphological type in the Rocky Mountains, another in the western Northwest Territories, and a third in the Hudson Bay area; highly variable populations in southern Saskatchewan suggest intergrading mixtures of all three types. These three and other examples of essentially boreal species suggest that, during the Wisconsinan, ancestral boreal species were broken into as many as three isolated populations, one in the extreme east, another in the Rocky Mountain area, and another in Alaska. Present records would indicate further that after deglaciation the eastern species may have tended to spread chiefly northward, whereas the western isolated entities spread westward and northwestward at a relatively rapid rate.

A similar picture emerges from the study by Wirth and Jones (1957) on the midge *Culicoides variipennis.* Its numerous morphological types, representing either species or subspecies, suggest several interregional dispersals and isolations of populations, followed by subsequent mixing and hybridization (Ross, 1962).

Species of the leafhopper genus *Erythroneura* offer several examples of intercontinental dispersal followed by subsequent isolation and speciation. About 500 species of this genus **feed** on trees, vines, and shrubs in North America, and all but a handful of the species are confined to the eastern deciduous forest. The phylogeny of this entire genus has been worked out in sufficient detail that the few western species can be regarded with a high degree of probability as offshoots of phylogenetic lines otherwise restricted to the eastern part of the country. Several lineages of the *obliqua* group dispersed westward long enough ago that each lineage has since evolved into two or three species.

In the *Erythroneura comes* group, three lines have evolved into distinctive species in California and Arizona; in the small *E. vulnerata* group, one line has evolved into a separate species in the same area; and in the small *E. maculata* group, one line has evolved into a separate species in California. These three groups feed on *Vitis* and its allies and *Rhus.* This group of leafhoppers is most abundant in the southern part of the deciduous forest, suggesting that they spread westward across the southwestern United States during a pluvial period of some time ago. Similar evidence is found in several paired western species of the caddisfly genera *Ochrotrichia* and *Chimarra;* in each case one species of the pair occurs in the Rocky Mountain region and the other species occurs in the hill and mountain country from southern Texas northward and eastward.

A few insect species are extremely puzzling. The caddisfly *Wormaldia sisko* occurs along the Pacific coast from California to British Columbia and in the Great Smoky Mountains of North Carolina–Tennessee. The two populations are virtually identical morphologically. The scorpionfly genus *Brachypanorpa* has two species in the western mountain region, one of which also occurs in the Great Smoky Mountains. Both species are relict groups phylogenetically. It is difficult to associate this very peculiar disjunction with Pleistocene events.

INTERCONTINENTAL EVENTS

Insect species that are distributed continuously across the holarctic region are not in themselves evidence of Pleistocene effects except for the obvious colonization of deglaciated areas by these species. Those northern species that have a discontinuity of range between the continents or that occur on one continent and have a closely related species on the other do offer evidence of prehistoric intercontinental movements.

DISJUNCT RANGES

Among mosquitoes several northern species occur across the entire holarctic region in what appears to be a continuous band, for example *Aedes cinereus, stimulans, flavescens,* and others. *Aedes vexans, sticticus,* and *dorsalis* have this same general range but it is broken in the Alaska area. The morphological similarity of the isolated populations of a species would indicate that the break was relatively recent and that it reflects a complete transcontinental dispersal during warmer climates a few thousand years ago, with a subsequent southern movement and disjunction of the range. An exact knowledge of the range of these northern species might, by elimination, give us moderately exact figures concerning the temperatures in Alaska during the recent climatic optimum. At the present time fairly accurate distributional records are available for only a few points in the north (Rempel, 1953; Vockeroth, 1954a, b; Gjullin *et al.*, 1961; Ross, 1964).

SPECIATION

A goodly number of insect species have either poorly defined subspecies or pairs of questionable species that indicate evolutionary change after intercontinental isolation. In the caddisfly genus *Hydropsyche*, *H. guttata* occurs across Eurasia and *H. separata* across northern North America; the two are remarkably similar except for one slight but constant difference in the male genitalia. It is likely that the parental population of these two species spread from Eurasia to North America; later the range was broken, and these two very slightly different entities evolved. In the holarctic sawfly *Dolerus gessneri*, Alaskan populations differ from other North American populations but resemble Eurasian populations in certain characters of the genitalia. In *Dolerus similis*, several morphologically similar subspecies occur in North America and Eurasia. In the larch sawfly *Pristiphora erichsoni*, a European, an Asiatic, and a North American form can be delineated on the basis of relative measurements (Coppel and Leius, 1958). The situation in these latter two sawfly species can be explained most plausibly by assuming fairly recent intercontinental dispersal and subsequent isolation and subspeciation.

In the sawflies of the genus *Neodiprion*, the North American *nanulus* line evidently dispersed into Eurasia, and the Eurasian population became isolated and ultimately evolved into the distinctive but closely related species *N. sertifer*.

In the mosquito genus *Aedes*, *A. melanimon* is a central western species in North America with a sister species *A. caspius* distributed from western Europe to the Near East and the Gobi Desert. *A. nigrinus*, occurring in Europe east to western Russia, has two sister species in North America, *A. spenceri* occurring from the Great Plains to the dry belt of British Columbia, and *A. ventrovittis* occurring in the western mountains. Both of these examples indicate a Pleistocene division of previously transcontinental ancestors, followed by speciation.

The leafhopper genus *Macrosteles* is primarily a northern but not an arctic genus whose species feed on a wide variety of herbaceous hosts. A phylogenetic analysis of the 50 world species (Moore and Ross, 1957) offers remarkable evidence for at least 15 intercontinental dispersals, 5 of them are apparently quite recent, because the New and Old World populations are still identical morphologically, and 6 of them represent an earlier and possibly synchronous intercontinental dispersal, because each line is now represented by a closely related but distinctive pair of sister species, one on each continent; the other dispersals were undoubtedly earlier. The same phenomenon is shown by one arctic caddisfly, *Limnephilus kennicotti*, occurring across the subarctic from the East Coast to western Northwest Territory, that has a sister species *L. miser* occurring from Alaska across Eurasia to Scandinavia.

Other pairs of closely related species, one of the pair occurring in Eurasia, the other in North America, are more southern in distribution and have considerably greater differences between the two species of each pair. Many of the North American representatives are restricted in their distribution to the temperate deciduous forest. Whereas these offer indubitable evidence of intercontinental dispersal, the circumstances indicate a much earlier dispersal than that of the more northern species considered. Because of ecological associations, pre-Pleistocene dispersals are usually invoked. This explanation harmonizes well with the discovery of Mills (1939) that the more southern the species of North American Collembola, the more distant their relationship to Eurasian relatives.

Many instances have been reported of the Pleistocene dispersal of insects between Europe and eastern North America. Lindroth (1957) has assembled convincing evidence that a large number of these were the result of transport of European species in ship ballast. It seems likely, however, that a few boreal, littoral, and shore insects, especially beetles and flies (Vockeroth, 1958), spread between western Europe and eastern North America during this period. Because of Lindroth's evidence, however, it may be difficult to decide which species reached North America naturally and which ones were brought by man.

The tacit assumption in the foregoing discussion is that intercontinental dispersal of insects was primarily across the Bering Bridge area. The chief evidence for this assumption is the similarity between the Alaskan and Eurasian faunas, implying that the "intercontinental" separation was not between the continents themselves but between the unglaciated area of Alaska and the remainder of unglaciated North America.

THE ARCTIC

Due to the special efforts of the Entomology Institute of Canada, much is now known about North American arctic insects (Freeman, 1958a). The majority of them are holarctic, and it is difficult to deduce from their distribution alone where these species lived during the glacial maxima. Six species of fleas now radiate around a large area of Alaska and Yukon that was not glaciated, and it seems probable that these fleas were restricted to the northwestern unglaciated area (Holland, 1958). Other fleas occurring both in the Canadian low arctic and Kamchatka indicate the same area of midglacial occurrence. Of these arctic fleas that are known only from the Alaska area, all have their closest relatives in arctic Eurasia, indicating that they were the results of Pleistocene isolation and speciation.

A surprising number of butterflies occur almost entirely within the arctic. Some are widespread, some western arctic, and some eastern arctic. From a study of their distribution patterns Freeman (1958b) suggested three main areas of occurrence of the species during the glacial maxima: (1) in the western mountain system, particularly in the northwest, (2) south of the ice, at least in the Appalachian region, and (3) north of the ice in the eastern Queen Elizabeth Islands and Greenland.

In the interesting, almost entirely arctic beetle subgenus *Cryobius* of the genus *Pterostichus* (family Carabidae), Ball (1963) has elucidated many intercontinental holarctic dispersals of species pairs and certain dispersals and isolations between western and eastern North America. The distribution patterns of *Cryobius* given by Ball show no indication of the occurrence of these beetles either during or after the glacial maxima in the Queen Elizabeth Islands or Greenland.

TIME CORRELATIONS

Attempting to correlate these insect dispersals and isolations with geologic time is perplexing. Northern holarctic species such as *Aedes vexans* that have their ranges broken only in the Bering Bridge area might represent intercontinental dispersals during the climatic optimum of about 5,000 years ago.

The warmer ocean temperature recorded between Altonian and Woodfordian time (Rosholt *et al.,* 1961) may not have been associated with a marked increase in continental temperatures; rather, a relatively small elevation of ocean temperature can be explained at least partially by a decrease in rainfall and less runoff from glaciated areas into the ocean. Even if land temperatures did rise as much as ocean temperatures, during that interval they would not have reached a level nearly so high as at present. It seems logical to suppose that the ancestors of species pairs such as *Aedes melanimon* and *caspius* would not have dispersed far enough to the north to have reached the Bering Bridge at that time (in the event that sufficient deglaciation afforded such a corridor), and that the ancestors of such pairs dispersed between Eurasia and North America during pre-Wisconsin time.

Dispersals resulting in the isolation of boreal species in the Ozarks include two types: (1) those exemplified by *Allocapnia pygmaea* (Fig. 3), in which the isolated population is still identical morphologically with the northern population, and (2) those such as *Glyphopsyche missouri,* in which the Ozark population has become morphologically distinct from its boreal relatives. These two types suggest that successive cooler periods occurred, the more recent one producing the disjunct ranges, the earlier one the disjunction resulting in speciation. Perhaps dispersals of type 1 occurred during the Wisconsin, and those of type 2 occurred during the Illinoian. There is a possibility, however, that type-1 dispersals occurred during the Woodfordian substage of the Wisconsin and those of type 2 occurred during the Altonian substage.

In studies of cave beetles, Krekeler (1958, 1959) believed that the most closely related morphological species of these beetles have been separated since Kansan time. Because cave-beetle populations are small in number and genetic change in them would presumably not be rapid, it might take longer (though not necessarily so) for cave beetles to evolve into definitive species than it would for species having larger populations, such as the caddisflies and other examples treated above. Nevertheless, Krekeler's data do suggest a time at least as old as the Illinoian for the second group of boreal dispersals.

REFERENCES

Ball, G. E., 1963, The distribution of the species of the subgenus Cryobius (Coleoptera, Carabidae, Pterostichus), *in* J. L. Gressitt (ed.), Pacific Basin biogeography: Pacific Sci. Assoc., Bishop Museum Press, p. 133-151

Buell, M. F., 1945, Late Pleistocene forests of southeastern North Carolina: Torreya, v. 45, p. 117-118

Carpenter, S. J., and LaCasse, W. J., 1955, Mosquitoes of North America: Berkeley, Univ. California Press, 360 p.

Chaney, R. W., and Elias, M. K., 1936, Late Tertiary floras from the High Plains: Carnegie Instn., Contr. Paleont., pt. I, Publ. No. 476, 72 p.

Coope, G. R., Shotton, F. W., and Strachan, Ian, 1961, A late Pleistocene fauna and flora from Upton Warren, Worcestershire: Roy. Soc. London Philos. Trans. B, v. 244, p. 379-421

Coppel, H. C., and Leius, K., 1958, Morphological variations in populations of the larch sawfly, *Pristiphora erichsonii* (Htg.) (Hymenoptera: Tenthredinidae) from Canada, Great Britain, and Japan: 10th Intern. Congr. Entomol., v. 1, p. 231-238

Denning, D. G., 1964, The genus *Homophylax* (Trichoptera: Limnephilidae): Entomol. Soc. Amer. Ann., v. 57, p. 253-260

Doering, J. A., 1956, Review of Quaternary surface formations of Gulf Coast region: Amer. Assoc. Petroleum Geologists Bull. 40, p. 1816-1862

—— 1958, Citronelle age problem: Amer. Assoc. Petroleum Geologists Bull. 42, p. 764-786

Dorf, Erling, 1959, Climatic changes of the past and present: Univ. Michigan Mus. Paleont. Contr., v. 13, p. 181-210

Ekblaw, G. E., and Willman, H. B., 1955, Farmdale drift near Danville, Illinois: Illinois Acad. Sci. Trans., v. 47, p. 129-138

Fenneman, N. M., 1938, Physiography of eastern United States: New York, McGraw-Hill, 714 p.

Fisk, H. N., 1938, Geology of Grant and LaSalle parishes: Louisiana Geol. Surv. Bull. 10, 246 p.

—— 1940, Geology of Avoyelles and Rapides parishes: Louisiana Geol. Surv. Bull. 18, 240 p.

—— 1951, Loess and Quaternary geology of the lower Mississippi Valley: J. Geol., v. 59, p. 333-356

Flint, R. F., 1957, Glacial and Pleistocene geology: New York, John Wiley & Sons, 553 p.

Freeman, T. N., 1958a, A historical account of insect collecting in northern Canada: 10th Intern. Congr. Entomol., v. 1, p. 613-617

—— 1958b, The distribution of arctic and subarctic butterflies: 10th Intern. Congr. Entomol., v. 1, p. 659-672

Frey, D. G., 1953, Regional aspects of the Late-glacial and Post-glacial pollen succession of southeastern North Carolina: Ecol. Mongr., v. 23, p. 289-313

Frye, J. C., and Leonard, A. B., 1957, Studies of Cenozoic-geology along eastern margin of Texas High Plains, Armstrong to Howard Counties: Univ. Texas Bur. Econ. Geol., Rep. Inv. 32, 62 p.

Frye, J. C., and Willman, H. B., 1958, Permafrost features near the Wisconsin glacial margin in Illinois: Amer. J. Sci., v. 256, p. 518-524

Gjullin, C. M., Sailer, R. E., Stone, Alan, and Travis, B. V., 1961, The mosquitoes of Alaska: U.S. Dept. Agric., Agric. Handbook 182, 98 p.

Gurney, A. B., 1937a, A new species of *Panorpa* from

Utah, with notes on other nearctic species (Mecoptera): Entomol. Soc. Washington Proc., v. 39, p. 222-227

—— 1937b, Taxonomy and distribution of the Grylloblattidae: Entomol. Soc. Washington Proc., v. 50, p. 86-102

—— 1938, Synonymy in the genus *Panorpa* (Mecoptera): Entomol. Soc. Washington Proc., v. 40, p. 52

Holland, G. P., 1958, Distribution patterns of northern fleas (Siphonaptera): 10th Intern. Congr. Entomol., v. 1, p. 645-658

Horberg, Leland, 1946, Preglacial erosion surfaces in Illinois: J. Geol., v. 54, p. 179-192

—— 1950a, Preglacial gravels in Henry County, Illinois: Illinois Acad. Sci. Trans., v. 43, p. 171-175

—— 1950b, Bedrock topography of Illinois: Illinois State Geol. Surv. Bull. 73, 111 p.

Krekeler, C. H., 1958, Speciation in cave beetles of the genus *Pseudanophthalmus* (Coleoptera, Carabidae): Amer. Midl. Nat., v. 59, p. 167-189

—— 1959, Dispersal of Cavernicolous beetles: Syst. Zool., v. 8, p. 119-130

Leighton, M. M., and Willman, H. B., 1949, Itinerary of field conference—late Cenozoic geology of Mississippi Valley, southeastern Iowa to central Louisiana: Illinois State Geol. Surv., 86 p.

Leonard, A. B., and Frye, J. C., 1962, Pleistocene molluscan faunas and physiographic history of Pecos Valley in Texas: Univ. Texas Bur. Econ. Geol. Rep. Inv. 45, 42 p.

Leonard, J. W., and Leonard, Fannie A., 1949, An annotated list of Michigan Trichoptera: Univ. Michigan Mus. Zool. Occ. Pap. 522, 35 p.

Lindroth, C. H., 1957, The faunal connections between Europe and North America: New York, John Wiley & Sons, 344 p.

Martin, P. S., 1959, Pleistocene ecology and biogeography of North America, *in* Hubbs, C. L. (ed.), Zoogeography: Amer. Assoc. Adv. Sci. Publ. 51, p. 375-420

Mills, H. B., 1939, Remarks on the geographical distribution of North American Collembola: Brooklyn Entomol. Soc. Bull., v. 34, p. 158-161

Moore, T. E., and Ross, H. H., 1957, The Illinois species of *Macrosteles*, with an evolutionary outline of the genus (Hemiptera, Cicadellidae): Entomol. Soc. Amer. Ann., v. 50, p. 109-118

Neill, W. T., 1957, Historical biogeography of present-day Florida: Florida State Mus. Bull. 2, p. 175-220

Olson, Ada L., Hubbell, T. H., and Howden, H. F., 1954, The burrowing beetles of the genus *Mycotrupes* (Coleoptera: Scarabaeidae: Geotrupinae): Univ. Michigan Mus. Zool. Misc. Publ. 84, 59 p.

Pearson, R. G., 1963, Coleopteran associations in the British Isles during the late quaternary period: Biol. Rev.: v. 38, p. 334-363

Potter, P. E., 1955, The petrology and origin of the Lafayette Gravel: J. Geol., v. 63, p. 1-38, 115-132

Rempel, J. G., 1953, The mosquitoes of Saskatchewan: Saskatoon, Sask., Can. J. Zoology, n 31, p. 433-509

Ricker, W. E., 1943, Stoneflies of southwestern British Columbia: Indiana Univ. Publ., Sci. Ser. 12, p. 1-145

Rosholt, J. N., Emiliani, C., Geiss, J., Koczy, F. F., and Wangersky, P. J., 1961, Absolute dating of deep-sea cores by the Pa^{231}/Th^{230} method: J. Geol., v. 69, p. 162-185

Ross, C. A., 1963, Structural framework of southernmost Illinois: Illinois State Geol. Surv. Circ. 351, 28 p.

Ross, H. H., 1944, The caddisflies, or Trichoptera, of Illinois: Illinois State Nat. Hist. Surv. Bull. 24, p. 1-96

—— 1950a, Synoptic notes on some nearctic Limnephilid caddisflies (Trichoptera, Limnephilidae): Amer. Midl. Nat., v. 43, p. 410-429

—— 1950b, New species of Nearctic Rhyacophila (*Trichoptera, Rhyacophilidae*): Washington Acad. Sci. J., v. 40, p. 260-265

—— 1956, Evolution and classification of the mountain caddisflies: Urbana, Univ. Illinois Press, 213 p.

—— 1962, A synthesis of evolutionary theory: Englewood Cliffs, New Jersey, Prentice-Hall, 387 p.

—— 1964, The colonization of temperate North America by mosquitoes and man: Mosquito News, v. 24, p. 103-118

Simpson, G. G., 1944, Tempo and mode in evolution: New York, Columbia Univ. Press, 237 p.

Stannard, L. J., 1963, Post-Wisconsin biogeography in eastern North America, based, in part, on evidence from thrips (Insecta): Entomol. Soc. Amer., North Central Branch Proc., v. 18, p. 31-35

Stearns, R. G., and Marcher. M. V., 1962, Late Cretaceous and subsequent structural development of the northern Mississippi Embayment area: Geol. Soc. Amer. Bull., v. 73, p. 1387-1394

Vockeroth, J. R., 1954a, Notes on the identities and distributions of *Aedes* species of northern Canada, with a key to the females (Diptera: Culicidae): Can. Entomol., v. 86, p. 241-255

—— 1954b, Notes on northern species of *Aedes*, with descriptions of two new species (Diptera: Culicidae): Can. Entomol., v. 86, p. 109-116

—— 1958, Distribution patterns of the Scatomyzinae (Diptera, Muscidae): 10th Intern. Congr. Entomol., v. 1, p. 619-625

Wirth, W. W., and Jones, R. H., 1957, The North American subspecies of *Culicoides variipennis*: U.S. Dept. Agric. Tech. Bull. 1170, p. 1-35

Summary

Climatic changes associated with Pleistocene events set the stage for a remarkable array of insect dispersals that resulted in an increase in number of species or produced isolated populations that have the potential to evolve into future new species. Better-documented dispersals include (1) intraregional dispersals in eastern North America between the Appalachians and the Ozarks, or from the north into the Ozarks or southern Appalachians; (2) intraregional dispersals between various mountain systems of western North America; (3) interregional, transcontinental dispersals between eastern and western North America;

and (4) intercontinental dispersals, chiefly between western North America and Asia. For boreal or sub-boreal species, tenuous evidence suggests that isolations resulting in disjunct populations occurred during the Wisconsin and those resulting in speciation occurred earlier.

During the late Pliocene or early Pleistocene, the erosion of geotectonically uplifted areas produced a series of ravine and gorge habitats having cool streams, this belt of habitats extending from the Appalachians to the Ozarks across a previously largely peneplained region. During Pleistocene times of cooler climate, many eastern cool-stream species apparently dispersed through this belt into the Ozarks and Ouachitas and became established there. This concatenation of geotectonic uplifts, land-surface sculpturing, and Pleistocene climatic fluctuations thus appears to have brought about a remarkable Pleistocene colonization of the Ozark and Ouachita region in Missouri, Arkansas, and Oklahoma by an extensive fauna of boreal and temperate insects.

THE STUDY OF PLEISTOCENE NONMARINE MOLLUSKS IN NORTH AMERICA*

D. W. TAYLOR[1]

Most North American Pleistocene shells can be referred to living species. This generally established observation determines the strengths and weaknesses of mollusks for geologic studies. It leads also to the tacitly accepted principle that the basis of interpretation of the fossils includes knowledge of the details of morphology, classification, ecology, and geographic distribution of living mollusks.

Local variations in fauna and sediments make the methods and faunistic literature of one area often unsuited to another area. For the sake of generality I therefore restrict this essay to some broader principles, observations, and conclusions from the study of Pleistocene nonmarine mollusks. The comparisons with the central European record are based on publications by Vojen Ložek and on his extensive comments on a first draft of this paper.

Both in Europe and North America relatively few late Pliocene and early Pleistocene nonmarine molluscan faunas have been described, and generalizations about this interval in both continents are necessarily crude. Rate of differentiation seems to have been more rapid in land snails than in aquatic mollusks, and more rapid in Europe than in central North America. As a corollary the contrast between Pliocene and Pleistocene faunas is more marked in Europe.

The differences between the two regions are probably due mostly to two factors: the different geography of the regions, and their geologic histories. The broad central lowland of North America has practically no sharp ecological boundaries, so the molluscan faunas have consisted almost entirely of widespread species that have survived for a long time. The topographic and ecologic diversity of Europe provides practically no room for such major changes in range as those seen in many faunas of central North America, and it has favored more local differentiation. The Alpine Revolution during the Tertiary may have stimulated the rich and local differentiation of such speciose groups as

Helicidae and Clausiliidae. Perhaps one of the consequences of the rapidly changing late Tertiary landscape of Europe was that many molluscan groups in that region were and still are evolving more rapidly than are those in the stable lowland area of central North America.

If rapid ecological changes and local isolation are significant factors in evolution of nonmarine mollusks, then North America has three main areas where late Cenozoic differentiation is likely to have been most rapid: (1) the Great Lakes region, where frequent isolation and reunion of lake and stream habitats has occurred through the Quaternary; (2) the region of Florida and the Bahamas, where sea-level changes can join or isolate many small islands in the archipelagoes situated on shallow platforms; and (3) the Great Basin and central west-coast region of North America, where the Middle Pleistocene orogeny of the Coast Ranges, eustatic changes in sea level, block faulting in the Great Basin, Pleistocene desiccation, and volcanism have changed habitats more rapidly and drastically than in other parts of North America. The Great Plains region is the area where there is the most detailed knowledge of late Cenozoic (particularly Pleistocene) nonmarine mollusks in North America, but the conservative character of its fauna is probably not representative of all of the continent.

I have commented on the interpretation of Quaternary mollusks previously (Taylor, 1960b), but crudely and superficially as it seems in retrospect. Anyone concerned with the principles of paleoecologic interpretation should take the essay by G. H. Scott (1963) as a starting point. The conventional approach to paleoecology (usually tacit) is to interpret former environments upon the assumption that they have changed and that the species have changed less so or not at all. Scott made the telling point that this frame of mind is in ill accord with the evolutionary approach of the biostratigrapher. He concluded (G. H. Scott, 1963, p. 524), "Lyell's particular principle of ecological uniformity is neither a sufficient nor even a necessary condition for paleoecology to be called a science."

Quaternary shells are so like those of living mollusks that interpretation of the past in terms of the present has seemed a commonplace. It is significant both for the general methods of paleoecology and for the Pleistocene history of North America that such a seemingly simple procedure in such a geologically young interval is not straightforward.

Pleistocene assemblages that are referable to living assemblages pose no interpretive problems. Those that are referred to living species, not all of which can be found living in close proximity, require one or another assump-

*Publication authorized by the Director, U.S. Geological Survey. Thanks are due to the following persons, who have reviewed the manuscript and helped to eliminate errors. They are not responsible for any remaining factual or interpretive flaws: Don Allen, Dallas, Texas; E. P. Cheatum, Department of Biology, Southern Methodist University, Dallas, Texas; C. W. Hibbard, Museum of Paleontology, University of Michigan, Ann Arbor, Michigan; D. M. Hopkins, U.S. Geological Survey, Menlo Park, California; Aurèle LaRocque, Department of Geology, Ohio State University, Columbus, Ohio; Bob H. Slaughter, Shuler Museum of Paleontology, Southern Methodist University, Dallas, Texas. Special thanks are due to Vojen Ložek, Quaternary Department, Geological Institute of the Czechoslovak Academy of Sciences, Prague, Czechoslovakia.
[1] U.S. Geological Survey, Washington, D.C.

tion: either some species have changed their environmental tolerances, or they have not. To take the first stand is to lessen the precision with which these species can be used in the fossil record. To take the second is to say in effect that some environments only a few thousand years old, in which all the species were those still living, cannot be found and studied today. In either case the present is not, in detail, the key to the past.

Pragmatically I am suspicious of strict adherence either to the idea of ecologic nonevolution or to the idea that present environments are standards for the past. As a taxonomic conservative I believe fossils should be referred to living species unless they can be shown to be different; but surely all evolutionary changes in mollusks are not necessarily reflected in their shells. Most fossil assemblages of living species can be rationalized by supposing the species have not changed their ecologic tolerances and that past environments were not precisely like those of today. Even so there are cases (for example the wide Pleistocene distribution of species such as *Omalodiscus pattersoni* (Baker), *Bulimnea megasoma* (Say), *Acroloxus coloradensis* (Henderson), and *Pupilla sinistra* (Franzen) that cannot be disposed of so readily.

Regional Differences in Pleistocene Faunas

The regional differences in the living molluscan fauna of North America are shown also by Pleistocene faunas. In arid areas the fossil assemblage may be more diverse than the modern fauna, but generally the living species are found in adjacent areas. Pleistocene faunas from different faunal provinces may share no species in common, just as with present-day faunas.

Faunal divisions of North America were drawn by Pilsbry (1948) for land snails and by Henderson (1931) for western, land and freshwater mollusks. The faunal differences expressed by such provinces are mainly of pre-Pleistocene origin, as shown by direct fossil evidence, by correlation with geologic structure, and by inferred correlation with probable past events. The major geographic differences in the living fauna probably have their beginnings at least in the Cretaceous, as Henderson (1931) noted. Lesser geographic differences may not be so ancient, but many are of Tertiary origin. The Recent Holarctic element among land snails has been interpreted as the relict Mesozoic to early Tertiary fauna of northern latitudes (Waldén, 1963, p. 163). Local endemism, disjunct distribution, and much observable geographic variation may as readily be of Tertiary as of Pleistocene origin. The fossil record by its nature will never provide all the documentation one could wish and so must be interpreted against a sound biogeographic background.

MODES OF INTERPRETATION OF PLEISTOCENE FAUNAS

The composition of any assemblage of animals and plants is determined by three factors. *Geologic Time* determines the stages present in the myriad lines of descent of various evolving organisms—what genetic combinations are available. *Habitat* includes the range of environments and the physical and biotic factors affecting individuals in an assemblage throughout their lives. *Biogeographic history* includes antecedent factors of regional distribution and dispersal that determine what organisms can occupy newly available habitats in a particular area or can gradually enter and adapt to already present environments.

So far as fossil shells can demonstrate, nearly all species of mollusks have remained virtually unchanged throughout the Pleistocene. The recurrence of similar habitats is the simplest explanation for the known recurrent assemblages. Within the Pleistocene, mollusks show the effects of passing time almost entirely by the gradual extinction of species that were already present in the Pliocene.

Regional differences in geologic history and molluscan fauna, *i.e.* biogeographic differences, are so great that in different parts of North America different problems loom large, calling for different techniques of study and interpretation. The mainly lacustrine faunas of pluvial Lakes Bonneville and Lahontan led Call (1885) to biometric analysis; considerations of the effects of salinity, temperature, and elevation on freshwater mollusks; and study of the living fauna of the now-arid region. Ponds and small lakes that existed in the glaciated region of the eastern United States have been studied by quantitative analysis of stratigraphic sequences by LaRocque and his students (*e.g.* Mowery, 1961), who emphasize limnology. The alluvial deposits of the unglaciated southern Great Plains have favored study of large samples with emphasis on climatic inferences (Hibbard and Taylor, 1960; Taylor, 1960b). Nowhere have studies of buried soils and fossiliferous alluvium and loess reached the refinement and precision of those by Ložek in Czechoslovakia (*e.g.* Kukla *et al.*, 1961, Kukla and Ložek, 1961), although the combined pedological-stratigraphic-paleontological approach promises equally detailed results in parts of North America. Cave-fills and travertine have yielded abundant fossil assemblages in Europe, but so far are virtually unstudied in North America.

Some of the differences among these various studies are no doubt personal, and others reflect unequal knowledge of different regions. Still for the most part they are reflections of different circumstances. Tectonic events, hydrographic changes, and local endemism are salient problems in the western part of North America (see Taylor, 1960a). Local changes in drainage, vegetation, climate, soil, and geographic distribution of mollusks are stronger themes in the east. Thus west of the Rocky Mountains biogeographic problems are dominant in Pleistocene studies, but to the east the elements of ecology are more conspicuous. The data from the west are fewer and less amenable to generalization. I have emphasized the Great Plains and Midwest region for this reason.

Knowledge of Living North American Mollusks

The ready reference of most Pleistocene shells to living species is an attribute of mixed value. On the one hand it offers a means of interpreting in some detail an ancient environment. But ecologic interpretation of fossils depends on knowledge of the identity and habitat of living species. An illustration will show not only that present knowledge of the living fauna is imprecise, but that at least some recent and widely accepted work is seriously erroneous.

THE *Lymnaea "palustris"* GROUP

"*Lymnaea palustris*" is a name that has been applied widely to pond snails in much of the Northern Hemisphere. Under various generic names it occurs in the following general works on mollusks in northern Eurasia: Kennard and Woodward, 1926, p. 56 (Britain); Germain, 1931, p. 497 (France); Nobre, 1941, p. 188 (Portugal); Adam, 1947, p. 47 (Belgium); van Benthem Jutting, 1933, p. 200 (Netherlands); Mandahl-Barth, 1949, p. 68 (Denmark); Boettger, 1944, p. 255 (Germany); Frömming, 1956, p. 107 (central Europe); Ložek, 1956, p. 239 (Czechoslovakia); Soós, 1943, p. 83 (Hungary); Grossu, 1955, p. 101 (Roumania); Zhadin, 1952, p. 173 (U.S.S.R.). In his monograph on "The Lymnaeidae of North and Middle America", Baker (1911) identified the species as living in most of North America, but later (1928) considered the American snails to represent subspecies different from those of Europe. Hubendick (1951) reviewed the Lymnaeidae as a whole, maintained the species was valid, and extended it to include a number of forms previously considered separate by Baker. These works show that in recent years there has been general agreement on the concept of one species distributed in northern Eurasia and North America, even though some authors have recognized varieties while others have not.

In evidently the first careful study of "*L. palustris*," based on thorough anatomical study of 686 specimens from 75 localities in Poland, Jackiewicz (1959) found that it included three distinct biological entities. These differ in several characters of genitalia and radula and show different but overlapping ecologic and geographic distribution. One can be distinguished often but not always by shell features; two cannot be distinguished by shell features. These three entities were reasonably called separate species by Jackiewicz. Previously applied varietal names were available for *Lymnaea corvus* (Gmelin) and *L. turricula* Held, but no name could be applied surely to the third, named as new *L. occulta* (Jackiewicz). Use of the name *L. palustris* (Müller) does not aid understanding of this complex group or clarity in communication and should be discontinued.

The status of all the North American members of the *Lymnaea "palustris"* group is thus open to question. Perhaps there are no species common to America and Eurasia, or if some are they cannot be recognized in the present state of knowledge. Perhaps the finely dividing classification by Baker (1928) goes too far, perhaps not far enough. Until a detailed morphological study of American representatives of this group is available the number and characteristics of the species will be uncertain. Identification of fossils, and their ecologic interpretation, will likewise be of doubtful value. Clearly, however, the more narrowly drawn species are more likely to prove useful than broad, composite categories such as "*Lymnaea palustris*" or "*L. humilis*".

LIVING SPECIES FIRST DESCRIBED AS FOSSILS

Theoretically the knowledge of living mollusks should precede study of Pleistocene mollusks. In practice the study of the recent North American fauna has advanced so slowly that paleontology has run ahead even at the elementary

TABLE 1

Living Species Considered Extinct When First Described

Helicinidae
Hendersonia occulta (Say, 1831). Shimek, 1904.
Hydrobiidae
Amnicola pilsbryana Baily and Baily, 1952. Taylor and Bright, unpublished data.
Fluminicola avernalis Pilsbry, 1935. Gregg, 1941.
Pyrgulopsis letsoni (Walker, 1901). Berry, 1943.
Tryonia clathrata Stimpson, 1865. Stearns, 1893.
Tryonia protea (Gould), 1855. Stearns, 1901.
Physidae
Physa skinneri Taylor, 1954. Taylor, 1960b.
Pupillidae
Pupilla sinistra Franzen, 1946. Hibbard and Taylor, 1960.
Endodontidae
Discus macclintocki (Baker, 1928). Morrison, 1940; Hubricht, 1943, 1955.
Discus shimeki (Pilsbry, 1890). Shimek, 1901.
Polygyridae
Stenotrema hubrichti Pilsbry, 1940. Hubricht, 1943.

stage of describing species, and some extant species were first known as fossils. Such discoveries were understandable in the last century, when so much of North America was unknown malacologically. Nevertheless, they are still being made, and other supposedly extinct forms may yet be found alive. The references in Table 1 include original descriptions and authority for occurrence of the species alive.

LATEST CENOZOIC MOLLUSCAN FAUNAS IN CENTRAL NORTH AMERICA

Most of the known, independently dated late Pliocene and Pleistocene molluscan faunas of central North America are listed in Table 2 in stratigraphic order. The compilation is

TABLE 2

Latest Cenozoic Molluscan Faunas
in Central North America (Fig. 1)

A. Late Pliocene (complete)
  1. Saw Rock Canyon local fauna, Rexroad Formation, Seward County, Kansas (Taylor, 1960b).
  2. Red Corral local fauna, Oldham County, Texas (Taylor, 1960b).
  3. Rexroad local fauna, Rexroad Formation, Meade County, Kansas (Miller, 1964; Taylor, 1960b).
  4. Bender local fauna, Rexroad Formation, Meade County, Kansas (Taylor, 1960b).
B. Nebraskan (complete)
  5. Sand Draw local fauna, Brown County, Nebraska (Taylor, 1960b).
  6. David City gravel and Nebraskan till, Doniphan County, Kansas (Frye and Leonard, 1952).
C. Late Nebraskan–early Aftonian (complete)
  7. Dixon local fauna, Kingman County, Kansas (Taylor, 1960b).
D. Aftonian (complete)
  8. Sanders local fauna, Missler Silt Member of Ballard Formation, Meade County, Kansas (Taylor, 1960b).
E. Kansan (incomplete)
  9. Cudahy fauna, associated with the Pearlette ash bed in various locally named formations. Many localities, Iowa to Texas (Leonard, 1950); Phillips County, Kansas (Frye and Leonard, 1954); Randall County, Texas (Johnston and Savage, 1955); Jefferson County, Colorado (Scott, 1962).

Continued

TABLE 2 (*cont.*)

10. Cagle Loess Member of Atherton Formation, Putnam County, Indiana (Wayne, 1958, 1959, 1963).
11. Cloverdale Till Member of Jessup Formation, Parke County, Indiana (Wayne, 1959, 1963).

F. Yarmouth
12. Borchers local fauna, Atwater Silt Member, Crooked Creek Formation, Meade County, Kansas (Hibbard, 1949). This assemblage includes only vertebrates. No mollusks surely referable to the Yarmouth in the light of modern stratigraphy are known.

G. Illinoian (incomplete)
13. Berends local fauna, Sanborn Group, Beaver County, Oklahoma (Miller, in press).
14. Doby Springs local fauna, Harper County, Oklahoma (Miller, in press).
15. Butler Spring local fauna, Sanborn Group, Meade County, Kansas (Miller, in press).
16. Mt. Scott local fauna, Kingsdown Formation, Meade County, Kansas (Miller, 1961, in press).
Kansas (Frye and Leonard, 1954; Leonard, 1952).
Oklahoma (Kitts, 1959).
Illinois (Rubey, 1952).
Indiana (Gooding, 1963; Wayne, 1958, 1959).

H. Sangamon (complete)
17. Slocum alluvium, Douglas and Jefferson counties, Colorado (Scott, G. R., 1962, 1963).
18. Cragin Quarry local fauna, Kingsdown Formation, Meade County, Kansas (Hibbard and Taylor, 1960).
19. Slaton local fauna, Lubbock County, Texas (Taylor, unpublished data).
20. Jinglebob local fauna, Kingsdown Formation, Meade County, Kansas (Hibbard and Taylor, 1960).
21. Don beds, Toronto, Ontario, Canada (Baker, 1931a; Watt, 1954).

I. Wisconsin (incomplete)
29. Jones local fauna, Vanhem Formation, Meade County, Kansas (Hibbard and Taylor, 1960).
Colorado (Scott, 1962, 1963).
Illinois (Leonard and Frye, 1960; Rubey, 1952).
Indiana (Wayne, 1959, 1963; Gooding, 1963).
Kansas (Goodrich, 1940; Hibbard and Taylor, 1960; Leonard, 1952).
Minnesota (Tuthill, 1963).
Nebraska (Miller and Scott, 1955, 1961).
North Dakota (Tuthill, 1961; Tuthill *et al.*, 1964).
Ohio (Clark, 1961; Cornejo, 1961; LaRocque, 1952; LaRocque and Conley, 1956; LaRocque and Forsyth, 1957; Leonard, 1953; Mowery, 1961).
Oklahoma (Kitts, 1959).
Texas (Cheatum and Allen, 1963; Dalquest, 1962; Frye and Leonard, 1964; Slaughter *et al.*, 1962; Wendorf, 1961).

intended primarily to show how few late Pliocene, Nebraskan, and interglacial assemblages there are on which to base inferences about effects of the first glaciation, long-term climatic trends, glacial-interglacial shifts in range, or progressive faunal changes. Illinoian faunas are relatively abundant compared to interglacial assemblages, and I have listed only a sample, principally the more reliably dated ones. Some fossil shells of Wisconsin or post-Wisconsin age can be found nearly anywhere. Their study can become most meaningful as local sequences with detailed stratigraphy and radiocarbon dates are described. A few of these are available and listed, but most localities of Wisconsin mollusks have been omitted. For access to older literature, with stratigraphy of variable reliability, see Baker (1920).

REVISED OR QUESTIONED AGES

Some assemblages have been omitted from Table 2 or appear there under a revised age assignment, for reasons discussed below. The list is arranged from younger to older:

22. Mollusks attributed to the Yarmouth in Howard County, Nebraska (Miller and Scott, 1955) have been shown by radiocarbon dates to be of late Wisconsin age (Miller and Scott, 1961). The fossils attributed to the late Wisconsin originally are also younger than supposed, but still of late Wisconsin age.
23. The Sulphur River Formation (of Slaughter and Hoover, 1963) in Delta County, Texas, ranges in age from about 12,000 to 9,000 years B.P. Mollusks from this unit were identified as both late Kansan and early Wisconsin by Frye and Leonard (1963, locality 12 and section 6), according to Slaughter and Hoover.
24. Mollusks from the Hardeman terrace, Hardeman County, Texas, were assigned a late Kansan age by Frye and Leonard (1963, p. 34, locality 8; p. 38, section 7). Shells collected by W. W. Dalquest from the locality cited by Frye and Leonard yielded a radiocarbon date of 16,775 ± 565 years B.P. (Socony Mobil laboratory, mean of five dates, including comparison of interior and exterior of shells; Dalquest, personal communication, 1964).
25. Mollusks from near Byers, Clay County, Texas, were described by Allen and Cheatum (1961) as of Illinoian age. Frye and Leonard (1963) considered the assemblage as Kansan on the basis of the fauna as well as geomorphic evidence (tracing of the Hardeman terrace). Shells of *Physa gyrina* Say from this locality were dated as 16,920 ± 665 years old (SM-694, SMU-P 17).
26. The Clear Creek local fauna, Denton County, Texas (Slaughter and Ritchie, 1963; Cheatum and Allen, 1963), has been dated as 28,840 ± 4740 years B.P. (SM-534; Slaughter and Ritchie, 1963, p. 129). Of the interglacial *vs.* interstadial alternatives considered by Slaughter and Ritchie, this date tends to favor an interstadial early Wisconsin age.
27. The Hill-Shuler local faunas, Dallas and Denton counties, Texas, were ascribed to "the last interglacial or a major interstadial of the last glacial" (Slaughter *et al.*, 1962, p. 10). They occur in the T-2 terrace fill, representing the same episode of alluviation as that which yielded the Clear Creek local fauna (Slaughter and Ritchie, 1963, p. 129), and like that fauna are referred here to an early Wisconsin interstadial. Occurrence of such now-northern mollusks as *Gyraulus circumstriatus, Lymnaea caperata,* and *Aplexa hypnorum* is also more consistent with a Wisconsin than Sangamon age. A radiocarbon date of greater than 37,000 years B.P. (Slaughter *et al.*, 1962, p. 52) is in keeping with an interstadial age.
28. The Good Creek Formation of Dalquest (1962), in Foard County, Texas, is referred here to the early Wisconsin instead of the Sangamon interglacial. Occurrence of several mollusks in the Easley Ranch local fauna now found only considerably to the north (especially striking is *Pupilla muscorum*) is more consistent with a Wisconsin than Sangamon age. The mammalian fauna most similar to that from the Good Creek Formation is the Jinglebob local fauna, Meade County, Kansas, ascribed to the late Sangamon (Hibbard and Taylor, 1960). At this level of precision I think the mammals may not be age-diagnostic—not sufficiently different to permit one to distinguish early Wisconsin from late Sangamon, and I prefer to rely on ecological interpretation of the mollusks.
29. The Jones local fauna, Meade County, Kansas (Hibbard and Taylor, 1960), has been dated as more than 30,000 years old (M-1103; Crane and Griffin, 1961). In terms of the local sequence the fauna is Wisconsin, and from the radiocarbon date evidently early Wisconsin. If molluscan assemblages like that of the Jones occurred as far south as central Texas, they are older than those referred to an early Wisconsin interstadial.

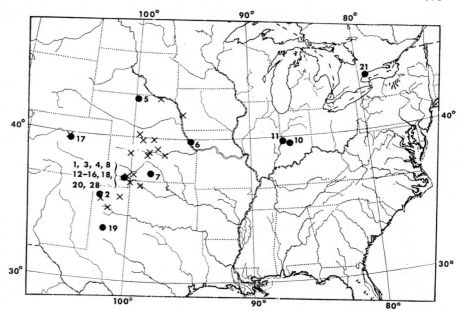

Figure 1. Location of fossil molluscan faunas in central North America. Numbers correspond to those in Table 2. ×'s mark localities of the Cudahy fauna (9, Table 2) associated with Pearlette ash.

30. The Rezabek local fauna, Lincoln County, Kansas (Hibbard, 1943) is considered of Illinoian age (Hibbard, 1963, and personal communication). A sample of the shells in the University of Michigan Museum of Paleontology collected by Hibbard seems to me to be reworked from older Pleistocene deposits, probably Kansan. Most of the shells are worn or etched in contrast to those of other Pleistocene assemblages from the Great Plains that I have studied. Possibly both Illinoian and Kansan shells are represented, but for the present they had better be ignored.

31. Mollusks from the Swingle locality, Kingman County, Kansas (Lane, 1960), were interpreted previously as Nebraskan or Aftonian. There is still no basis for a more precise age assignment.

GENERAL OBSERVATIONS ON THE FOSSIL RECORD

Analysis of the late Pliocene and Pleistocene molluscan assemblages in central North America (Table 2) leads to the following generalizations.

1. Nearly all species in the Pleistocene faunas are still living, either locally or in adjacent areas (Table 4).

2. Percentage of extinct species in general decreases gradually with time. Irregularities in detail can be ascribed to variably complete samples of the fauna.

3. Evolutionary novelties are rare. The only species for which evidence is adequate to support a Pleistocene origin is the freshwater snail *Promenetus exacuous exacuous*. It may have developed in the late Pleistocene from the Pliocene to Middle Pleistocene *P. exacuous kansasensis* (Hibbard and Taylor, 1960; Miller, in press).

4. The faunas may represent a terrestrial environment only, as in most loess, but ordinarily consist of aquatic mollusks of a pond or small stream together with a sample from some adjacent terrestrial habitats. Large-stream faunas are unknown; those of large lakes are known only from the latest Pleistocene Great Lakes.

5. Extant species mostly occur in associations that can be duplicated today. Exceptions can nearly all be grouped in two classes. (i) Late Pleistocene assemblages, especially from loess, in the central Great Plains and Ohio River valley include several elements now restricted far to the north or at high elevations in the Rocky Mountains. Species such as *Pupilla muscorum*, *Columella columella alticola*, and *Discus shimeki* are found as fossils in the lowlands in association with species with which they do not now coexist. (ii) Many Pleistocene assemblages in the southern Great Plains include species now found only far to the north of their fossil occurrences, such as *Lymnaea stagnalis*, *Gyraulus deflectus*, and *Physa skinneri*. In interglacial or interstadial faunas these may be found associated with species of generally southern distribution, whose range they do not now overlap.

6. Differences between successive faunas are more conspicuous toward the south and west. As Wayne (1963, p. 58) noted in Indiana, "nearly identical ecologic conditions near the ice margin prior to, during, and following each glaciation have resulted in the recurrence of relatively similar faunas at successively higher stratigraphic positions. Distinctions between faunal assemblages in the Pleistocene formations in Indiana are more subtle than those recorded for Kansas." The more conspicuous faunal contrasts to the south and west can be explained simply as due to fluctuations from semiarid to humid and from continental to maritime climates that had little or no expression in more humid eastern regions. A corollary is that the stratigraphic value of Pleistocene mollusks will be greatest where climatic variations were most extreme, hence generally in the semiarid southern Great Plains.

PARALLELISM WITH EUROPE

There are some clear, even striking, parallels between the Pleistocene molluscan faunas of Czechoslovkia and those of central North America. These parallels are instructive in showing how generally different molluscan faunas have reacted to events of the Pleistocene in similar ways. Interpretations of the better-known European assemblages are also pertinent to interpretation of analogous aspects of the

American record. Abundant literature on the Czech mollusks is available through Ložek (1955, 1961, 1963), Ložek and Kukla (1959), and Kukla *et al.* (1961).

1. The major features of change in molluscan faunas are similar: progressively smaller numbers of extinct or regionally extinct species, and changes in composition associated with major shifts in temperature and precipitation.

2. Postglacial aridity is marked in both central Europe and the southern High Plains. In southwestern Kansas the living molluscan fauna is poorer in species than any of the adequately sampled Pleistocene faunas. "The present-day relatively continental climate of Meade County is similar to no known ancient climate that is to be inferred from fossils in the area" (Hibbard and Taylor, 1960, p. 24-25).

3. The Last Glacial in Czechoslovakia is characterized by the widespread and abundant *Columella*-fauna, named after the dominant species *Columella columella columella.* This assemblage is a subarctic steppe fauna made up of several wide-ranging, ecologically tolerant species together with arctic and arctic-alpine species. *C. columella columella* lives in Scandinavia north of 67° and eastward in Siberia to the Yenisei between 61° and 69° 15′; it is known in central Europe in lower Pleistocene deposits but is most common in those of the Last Glacial (Forcart, 1959).

A later Wisconsin cold-steppe fauna is likewise known in the northern Great Plains. It includes two species, now living in the higher Rocky Mountains, that are unknown from the earlier parts of the Pleistocene. These alpine elements are *Columella columella alticola* and *Discus shimeki.* Characteristic associates in the assemblage are other northern and montane species known also from earlier glacial deposits, such as *Pupilla muscorum, P. blandi,* and *Vertigo modesta. Oreohelix strigosa cooperi,* living in the Black Hills of South Dakota and Cypress Hills of Alberta, occurred also in this cold-steppe fauna far to the east into Iowa. As in the European *Columella* fauna the association is not one found living today; it is a combination of arctic-alpine elements together with widely tolerant species and lacks southern and hygrophilous species (for discussion and different interpretation see Shimek, 1930, 1931). Available stratigraphic data suggest that these arctic-alpine species spread eastward only, or most commonly, in the "classical" or post-Farmdale Wisconsin interval.

4. The last interglacial assemblages in Czechoslovakia include *Banatica* faunas, named after *Helicigona banatica.* This species and some of its associates are extinct in the region or are found only in local populations. The interglacial faunas have a high percentage of warmth- and moisture-loving species. Kukla *et al.* (1961, p. 24) interpreted these assemblages as indicating a climate like that of the present, or 2° − 3° C warmer, but with annual precipitation at least 50% greater than at present. The climate approximated that of the northern Balkan Peninsula.

In southwestern Kansas the late Sangamon Jinglebob local fauna provides a parallel to the Riss-Würm *Banatica* faunas. The climate was more humid than that of today and had no marked seasonal extremes. Thermophiles occur among the vertebrates though not the mollusks.

The amplitude of climatic change is more marked in some areas than in others. Central Europe shows the greatest differences in that continent between the warm and cold intervals. The warm ones are often of submediterranean character, while the cold intervals have a subarctic fauna. To the north and south, climatic shifts are not so evident. In Czechoslovakia the interglacials are very moist-maritime, the glacials more or less dry-continental. Only the late postglacial is dry, so that the lowlands are a cultivated chernozem steppe, whereas in the interglacials they were woodland with gray-brown podzolic soils.

In North America relatively few sequences of Pleistocene faunas are known, but the record is consistent with the belief that climatic shifts were strongest in the southern High Plains.

The significance of the ecological similarities and differences in Pleistocene molluscan faunas of Europe and North America can be evaluated soundly only when their chronological correspondence has been established. At present no intercontinental glacial or interglacial correlations older than the limit of C_{14} dating are reliable.

CLIMATIC INTERPRETATION OF LATEST CENOZOIC FAUNAS IN HIGH PLAINS REGION

Knowledge of nonmarine fossil mollusks in North America is insufficient for more than a few generalizations. That of widest interest to students of Pleistocene phenomena is the inferred sequence of climatic changes in the High Plains region, for it can be checked by many lines of evidence and is pertinent to general hypotheses of Pleistocene climatic change.

The span of Pleistocene time has been brief compared to the duration of molluscan species as identified by shells. Hence if one can eliminate the effects of biogeographic history, then the composition of a Pleistocene fauna is largely determined by the range of habitats available. The High Plains region is a large, relatively featureless area with no sharp biogeographic discontinuities; it is all in one "faunal province." Within this area regional climate and local habitats are the main variables, and if local habitat is understood then regional climate can be evaluated.

Inferences about the climatic significance of mollusks come from geographic distribution, habitat, and associated species. There are virtually no experimental data. The plausibility of such inferences can be tested by comparison with similarly derived inferences from other kinds of animals associated with the mollusks, by whether or not diverse faunal elements can be reconciled, and by comparison with ecologic interpretation of associated plant remains. The mollusks and several groups of associated vertebrates of various faunas in southwestern Kansas and northwestern Oklahoma can be interpreted simply and plausibly under an hypothesis of major climatic shifts (Hibbard and Taylor, 1960; Taylor, 1960b). Associated pollen, so far as known, is consistent with these inferences and confirms the principle of interpretation (Kapp, in press). As more information about recent mollusks becomes available and as more fossils are studied, the rather broad climatic inferences summarized in Table 3 can be refined. Writing of the Pleistocene mollusks of Czechoslovakia, Ložek (1961, p. 119) stated: "Although in the older literature their significance is underestimated with reference to assessing the climate it still is possible to state, on the basis of all observations carried out with due care, that they are equally sensitive from this point of view as plants."

SEQUENCE OF INFERRED CLIMATES

The climates inferred from the series of late Pliocene and Pleistocene faunas of southwestern Kansas and northwestern Oklahoma are summarized in Table 3. Most of the elements of the former hypothetical climates are given in terms of contrast with the present local climate.

Meade County, in southwestern Kansas, now has a continental, temperate, generally moisture-deficient climate. Precipitation and temperatures are variable, both from year to year and within a given year. Mean annual rainfall is 19.66 in. (49 mm) for 45 years. The lowest recorded annual precipitation is 9.35 in. (337 mm), for 1910; the highest, 31.62 in. (803 mm), for 1915. The climate is dry, with no seasonal water surplus; Meade County is on the boundary between semiarid and dry subhumid climatic types. Summer is the wettest season, and nearly three-quarters of the annual precipitation comes during the warmer half year. Mean annual temperature is about 56° F (13° C). January, the coldest month, has a mean temperature of about 32° F (0° C); July, the hottest month, has a mean temperature of about 80° F (26° C). Recorded temperature extremes are −20° F (−29° C) and 110° F (43° C). Normal annual evaporation from pans is slightly over 90 in. (about 2,290 mm); from May to October 65 in. (about 1,650 mm) (Hibbard and Taylor, 1960).

A conservative approach has been employed in interpreting earlier climates. The inferred climates differ from the present one only by the minimum differences considered necessary to account for observed faunal differences. Names of the animals interpreted as especially significant climatic indicators are listed under the heading "Significant fossils" in Table 3; not all are mollusks. In general, a given species has been regarded as significant for only one climatic element or pair of elements, such as minimum winter temperature, effective warm-season precipitation, temperatures of summer hot spells, and the like.

GENERAL OBSERVATIONS ON PLEISTOCENE CLIMATES

The inferred Pleistocene climates of central North America (Table 3; Hibbard, 1960; Hibbard and Taylor, 1960; Taylor, 1960b) have significance not only for hypotheses of Pleistocene climatic change but also for stratigraphy. The general observations that follow illustrate the close interaction between theoretical research (geologic history and Pleistocene climatology) and applied research (stratigraphy of Pleistocene deposits).

1. Through all of Pleistocene time prior to the Wisconsin, glacial-interglacial changes were broadly similar. The record is consistent with the hypothesis of cyclic changes (Taylor, 1960b) but inadequate to document such an interpretation beyond reasonable doubt. Significantly, however, Karlstrom (1961) considered the Pleistocene record most simply interpreted as a system of harmonic or near-harmonic cycles of climatic change.

2. All of the pre-Wisconsin climates were more maritime than the modern climate at the sites where the fossils were collected. None of the pre-Wisconsin faunas known could live in the present combination of hot summers and bitterly cold spells during the winter. Recurrence of similar climates —all different from that of the present—produced similar molluscan faunas at various times.

3. "If the circulation of air masses in the Sangamon was generally like that today, in that there were winter incursions of air from Canada and the Arctic southward over the Plains, the Jinglebob and Cragin Quarry assemblages imply that there were no continental glaciers and no ice on the Arctic Ocean. Aside from the matter of much milder winters, the considerably greater precipitation suggested by the pine pollen and vertebrate fauna from the Jinglebob site can be explained most simply by the postulation that the moisture was derived from an ice-free Arctic Ocean" (Hibbard and Taylor, 1960, p. 24).

4. The land snail *Columella columella alticola*, living at high elevations in the Rocky Mountains (Leonard, 1952, p. 33; Pilsbry, 1948), appears in the Pleistocene of the Great Plains only in the Wisconsin. This snail and its associates make up a cool-steppe fauna that seems to reflect a time when summers were cooler and mean annual temperature lower than at any other time in the Pleistocene. The correlative *Columella-fauna* in Czechoslovakia is a similar association due to the same cause. The synchroneity of these cool-steppe faunas suggests more extreme glacial climates during the Wisconsin-Würm than previously in the Pleistocene.

5. The present is a poor guide to the past so far as geographic distribution and faunal associations of mollusks go. In southwestern Kansas all of the adequately sampled Pleistocene faunas, glacial as well as interglacial, are more diverse than the living molluscan fauna (Hibbard and Taylor, 1960, p. 18-19). The record there is more detailed than elsewhere, but in general everywhere in the arid and semiarid regions of North America the Pleistocene faunas are richer than the local living assemblages. Aridity and strong seasonal contrast are a late Wisconsin or post-Wisconsin development, not only in the Great Plains but generally in the American Southwest (Malde, 1964). Sure these unprecedented climatic changes, following hard on the most intense of the glacial climates, played a role in extinction of the large vertebrates.

6. In summary the fossil record can be interpreted most simply and consistently by hypothesizing major climatic fluctuations. Pre-Wisconsin climates, both glacial and interglacial, were less continental than those of today and differed among themselves mainly in amount and effectiveness of mean annual precipitation, and summer temperatures. Perhaps glacial climates became gradually more severe through the Pleistocene; at any rate the Wisconsin seems to have been most severe. The dry, seasonal climates of today are a late Wisconsin or post-Wisconsin development. The events that brought about these changes evidently affected global circulation to a considerable extent, though not necessarily by altering its pattern. The most plausible speculation I can make is that during the Wisconsin the Arctic Ocean became frozen and has remained so longer than at any time previously, if indeed it was ever frozen

TABLE 3

Late Cenozoic Climates Inferred from Fossil Assemblages in Southwestern Kansas and
Northwestern Oklahoma and Compared with Modern Climate
(Numbers refer to Table 2 and Fig. 1)

Age	Local fauna	Climate	Significant fossils
Recent		Semiarid to dry subhumid, generally moisture deficient, continental, temperate. January mean 32° F, July mean 80° F. Mean ann. precip. 19.35 in.; mean ann. pan evaporation 90+ in.	
Early Wisconsin	29. Jones	Semiarid to dry subhumid. Mean ann. precip. no greater, perhaps less. Summers much cooler. Continentality reduced	Mammals: *Sorex cinereus, Microtus pennsylvanicus;* mollusks: *Pisidium ferrugineum, P. lilljeborgi, Valvata tricarinata, Lymnaea stagnalis, Pupilla blandi*
Late Sangamon	20. Jinglebob	Humid, no seasonal moisture deficiency. Mean ann. precip. 40-45 in. Winters much milder. Summers much wetter, slightly cooler. Continentality much reduced	Tortoise: *Terrapene llanensis;* mammals: *Oryzomys, Microtus pennsylvanicus;* mollusks: *Laevapex kirklandi, Strobilops labyrinthica, Punctum minutissimum*
Early Sangamon	18. Cragin Quarry	Semiarid. Mean ann. precip. little different. Freezing temperatures rare or absent. Summers slightly cooler. Continentality much reduced	Tortoises: *Terrapene llanensis,* medium-sized *Geochelone;* lizards: *Phrynosoma cornutum, P. modestum;* shrew: *Notiosorex crawfordi;* snail: *Gastrocopta pellucida hordeacella*
Late Illinoian	16. Mt. Scott	Moist subhumid. Mean ann. precip. slightly greater (20-25 in.). Summers much cooler, winters slightly warmer. Continentality reduced	Fishes: *Esox masquinongy, Perca flavescens;* tortoise: *Terrapene llanensis;* mammals: *Sorex cinereus, S. arcticus, Blarina brevicauda carolinensis, Oryzomys fossilis;* mollusks: *Pisidium subtruncatum, P. variabile, Valvata tricarinata, Physa skinneri, Gastrocopta cristata, G. pellucida hordeacella*
Illinoian	15. Butler Spring	Dry subhumid. Mean ann. precip. little different. Summers much cooler, winters perhaps like those today. Continentality reduced	Fishes: *Ictalurus* cf. *I. punctatus, Perca flavescens;* mollusks: *Valvata tricarinata, Probythinella lacustris, Lymnaea stagnalis, Physa skinneri, Pupilla muscorum, Vertigo elatior, Vallonia cyclophorella*
Illinoian	14. Doby Springs	Dry subhumid. Mean ann. precip. little different. Summers much cooler, winters perhaps like those today. Continentality reduced	Fishes: *Catostomus commersoni, Perca flavescens;* mammals: *Sorex arcticus, S. cinereus, Blarina brevicauda brevicauda;* mollusks: *Sphaerium sulcatum, Valvata tricarinata, Probythinella lacustris, Lymnaea stagnalis, Gyraulus deflectus, Pupilla muscorum, Vertigo elatior*
Illinoian	13. Berends	Dry subhumid. Mean ann. precip. little different. Summers much cooler. Continentality reduced	Fishes: *Perca flavescens, Esox masquinongy;* mammals: *Sorex* cf. *S. cinereus, Blarina* cf. *B. brevicauda, Microtus pennsylvanicus;* mollusks: *Valvata tricarinata, Physa skinneri*
Early Yarmouth	12. Borchers	Dry subhumid. Freezing temperatures rare or absent. Mean ann. precip. slightly greater or summers slightly cooler. Continentality much reduced	Tortoise: *Geochelone* (large); mammals: *Sigmodon hilli, Spilogale ambarvalis*
Kansan	9. Cudahy	Dry subhumid. Mean ann. precip. little different. Summers much cooler. Continentality reduced	Mammals: *Sorex cinereus, S. lacustris, Microsorex pratensis, Microtus paroperarius, Synaptomys meltoni;* mollusks: *Valvata tricarinata, Gyraulus deflectus, Planorbula campestris, Physa skinneri, Pupilla muscorum, Vallonia pulchella, V. cyclophorella*
Late Aftonian	8. Sanders	Subhumid. Mean ann. precip. greater, but perhaps only slightly. Summers cooler. Winters no cooler. Continentality reduced	Mammals: *Sigmodon* cf. *S. intermedius, Bensonomys meadensis;* mollusks: *Lymnaea bulimoides techella, L. caperata, Promenetus umbilicatellus, Physa skinneri, Aplexa hypnorum, Helicodiscus singleyanus*
Late Pliocene	4. Bender	Semiarid-dry subhumid. Mean ann. precip. little different. Summers slightly cooler. Winters little if at all cooler. Continentality reduced	Mollusks: *Lymnaea bulimoides techella, L. caperata, L.* cf. *L. exilis, Promenetus umbilicatellus, Gastrocopta cristata, Helicodiscus singleyanus, Polygyra rexroadensis*
Late Pliocene	3. Rexroad	Dry subhumid. Mean ann. precip. slightly greater. Freezing temperatures rare or absent. Summers slightly cooler. Continentality much reduced	Tortoise: *Geochelone rexroadensis;* lizard: *Phrynosoma cornutum;* mammals: *Notiosorex jacksoni, Baiomys* spp., *Sigmodon intermedius;* mollusks: *Lymnaea exilis, Helisoma anceps, Nesovitrea electrina*

TABLE 3 (cont.)

Age	Local fauna	Climate	Significant fossils
Early late Pliocene	1. Saw Rock Canyon	Dry subhumid. Mean ann. precip. slightly greater. Winters slightly warmer. Summers slightly cooler. Continentality reduced	Turtle: *Kinosternon flavescens;* mammals: *Baiomys sawrockensis, Onychomys larrabeei;* mollusks: *Marstonia* spp., *Helisoma anceps, Strobilops labyrinthica, Gastrocopta holzingeri*

TABLE 4

Progressive Change in Late Cenozoic Mammals and Mollusks of Southern Kansas and Northwestern Oklahoma
Data from Hibbard (1963), Hibbard and Taylor (1960), Miller (in press), and Taylor (1960b)

	Extinct genera				Extinct species			
	Mammalia		Mollusca		Mammalia		Mollusca	
Local fauna	Percent	Number	Percent	Number	Percent	Number	Percent	Number
Jones (Wisconsin)	13	2	0	0	23	3	0	0
Jinglebob (Sangamon)	14	3	0	0	50	9	2	1
Cragin Quarry (Sangamon)	25	7	0	0	50	14	6	2
Mt. Scott (Illinoian)	0	0	0	0	28	5	1	1
Butler Spring (Illinoian)	0	0	0	0	0	0	4	2
Adams (Illinoian)	50	4	0	0	85	6	5	1
Doby Springs (Illinoian)	12	3	0	0	39	8	3	2
Berends (Illinoian)	29	3	0	0	54	5	2	1
Sanders (Aftonian)	62	8	0	0	100	13	20	4
Dixon (Nebraskan)	27	3	0	0	100	7	16	7
Rexroad (late Pliocene)	54	30	0	0	98	64	25	9
Saw Rock Canyon (late Pliocene)	67	8	0	0	100	11	28	7

before. The Arctic air masses that dominate the central part of North America throughout the colder half-year are thus drier and colder than previously, and seasonal contrasts are intense.

EFFECTS OF PLEISTOCENE EVENTS ON MOLLUSKS IN CENTRAL NORTH AMERICA

Within the limitations imposed by the scarcity of faunas of pre-Wisconsin age and the state of taxonomic knowledge, some generalizations can be made about the effects of the Pleistocene on mollusks.

1. The net effect has been a reduction in variety of the fauna. Many more species became extinct than developed during the Pleistocene. These extinctions were most marked in western North America; in central North America they are not nearly so conspicuous as in the west and much less marked than among mammals (Table 4, 5). The number of supposedly extinct invalid and dubious species is greater by far than that of the extinct valid species.

2. Environmental changes of the Pleistocene may have stimulated evolution of *Promenetus exacuous exacuous* from *P. exacuous kansasensis* (Hibbard and Taylor, 1960). This interpretation is entirely speculative; if valid, it would be the only exception to the statement that the effects of the Pleistocene have been entirely destructive, not creative, at the specific level.

3. Over large areas of the arid Great Plains, mollusks were more diversified and abundant in the Pleistocene than now (Table 6). There is no such contrast with Pliocene mollusks, however. It is more accurate to say that the Recent has brought adverse conditions than to claim that the

TABLE 5

Extinct Valid Species of Pleistocene Mollusks in Central North America
(Many other described forms are synonyms or dubiously valid)

A. Species terminating with no descendents

Planorbidae
Omalodiscus pattersoni (Baker). Pliocene to Wisconsin. Leonard, 1953; Taylor, 1958, 1960b.

Strobilopsidae
Strobilops sparsicostata Baker. Pliocene to Nebraskan. Taylor, 1960b.
Strobilops lonsdalei Ho and Leonard, 1961. Kansan to Wisconsin.
Strobilops lonsdalei cansasiana Ho and Leonard, 1961. Kansan.

Pupillidae
Gastrocopta chauliodonta Taylor. Nebraskan to Aftonian. Taylor, 1960b.
Gastrocopta paracristata Franzen and Leonard. Pliocene to Aftonian. Taylor, 1960b.
Gastrocopta scaevoscala Taylor. Pliocene to Nebraskan or Aftonian. Taylor, 1960b.
Vertigo gouldi hannai Pilsbry. Pleistocene. Pilsbry, 1948.

Limacidae
Deroceras aenigma Leonard. Pliocene to Wisconsin. Hibbard and Taylor, 1960; LaRocque and Conley, 1956.

B. Species becoming extinct through evolution

Planorbidae
Promenetus kansasensis (Baker). Pliocene to Sangamon. Hibbard and Taylor, 1960.

Pleistocene brought favorable ones. Many mollusks with present northern distributions are known in the southern High Plains and probably do represent southward faunal dispersal. Yet the magnitude of such changes in range dur-

TABLE 6

Number of Species of Mollusks in Late Cenozoic Faunas
of Southwestern Kansas and Northwestern Oklahoma
Data from Hibbard and Taylor (1960), Miller (in press),
Taylor (1960b).

Fauna	Pelecypoda	Prosobranchia	Basommatophora	Stylommatophora	Total Mollusca
Recent, Meade County	4	0	8	17	29
Jones (Wisconsin)	5	1	15	10	31
Jinglebob (Sangamon)	10	1	17	24	52
Cragin Quarry (Sangamon)	2	0	12	21	35
Mt. Scott (Illinoian)	15	1	20	28	64
Butler Spring (Illinoian)	9	2	19	24	54
Adams (Illinoian)	2	1	5	14	22
Doby Springs (Illinoian)	11	2	21	26	60
Berends (Illinoian)	8	1	17	17	43
Sanders (Aftonian)	0	0	10	13	23
Bender (late Pliocene)	3	0	15	19	37
Rexroad (late Pliocene)	3	1	12	23	39

ing, say, the Sangamon and Wisconsin may have been much less than one would judge using present distribution patterns as a standard.

4. The southward and eastward spread in the Great Plains and Ohio Valley of a cold-steppe fauna during part of Wisconsin glacial times is an event that is unknown previously in the Pleistocene. The alpine Rocky Mountain land snail *Columella columella alticola* "has not been found in deposits older than Wisconsin in Kansas, Illinois, Indiana, or Ohio" (LaRocque and Forsyth, 1957, p. 87).

5. Virtually all the Pliocene nonmarine mollusks of northern North America must have been extinguished or displaced by the ice sheets. Perhaps most of the endemic species were destroyed. The most likely remnants or descendents of the preglacial northern fauna are the locally endemic forms occurring within the limits of glaciation or close to it, and species in northern areas (Alaska, Newfoundland, etc.) that might have survived in their present areas of distribution. The slow rate of differentiation in most mollusks (Table 4) would seem to imply that local endemics in a glaciated area are more likely preglacial relicts than postglacial novelties. In the Great Plains region the locally endemic snails *Pupilla sinistra* and *Oreohelix strigosa cooperi* are known to have been much more widespread in the late Pleistocene than now. Perhaps they were also more widespread in the Pliocene than in the Pleistocene.

GLACIAL-INTERGLACIAL CHANGES

Pleistocene molluscan assemblages within the same area of the Great Plains or Central Lowland that show different proportions of locally extinct northern and southern elements have been interpreted in terms of glacial-interglacial changes. Strict superposition in one exposure of a single depositional sequence is rare. The mollusks from three horizons in one such exposure in southwestern Kansas are listed in Table 7, together with the local Recent fauna. The

stratigraphically lowest locality is UM-K2-59, ascribed to the Mt. Scott local fauna of late Illinoian age. It has yielded more than twice as many species as are now living in the county. The higher localities are referred to the Cragin Quarry local fauna of early Sangamon age. They have about as many species as are living in the vicinity, and virtually all occur in the older Mt. Scott assemblage. In this stratigraphic section the changes from Illinoian glacial to Sangamon interglacial fauna were principally the local extinction of many species now living only to the north and/or east of the fossil locality. The Sangamon fauna has practically no immigrants; it is the Illinoian fauna reduced by more than half, with different relative abundance of species. (The fossil localities are in the SE¼ sec. 18, T.32S., R.28W., Meade County, Kansas. See Miller, in press; Hibbard, 1963; and Hibbard and Taylor, 1960, for geology, measured section, relative abundance of species, present distribution of species, and associated fauna.)

THE COURSE OF FUTURE WORK

The most profitable lines of future research on Pleistocene nonmarine mollusks in North America can now be seen, even though only in broad outlines. I have selected those problems and methods which may benefit other areas of research and those which may resolve current difficulties in stratigraphic study of mollusks.

1. In many ways the most significant of all problems involving Pleistocene mollusks would entail a detailed study of the biota associated with the Pearlette ash, with special attention to climatic zonation. The wide area over which the fauna is known (crosses, Fig. 1) and the stratigraphic contemporaneity established by the ash provide a unique opportunity to study zonation of climate during a glacial interval.

2. Refinement of stratigraphic application of mollusks will accompany increasingly detailed knowledge of the geographic shifts of various species. Establishing when, how often, and how far south and east such species as *Pupilla muscorum, P. blandi, Vertigo alpestris oughtoni, Vallonia cyclophorella,* and *Discus shimeki* have moved would not only increase their value for stratigraphy but provide rich data for understanding Pleistocene climatic changes.

3. The recurrence of similar assemblages of mollusks at various times necessitates the use of independent sources of evidence to establish the stratigraphic horizon of such assemblages. Detailed and relatively complete stratigraphic sections are rarely available. In the present state of knowledge fossil mammals provide the most useful data. The far more rapid progressive change of Pleistocene mammals compared to mollusks is shown in Table 4.

4. Collecting Pleistocene mollusks without stratigraphic data, or studying fossil mollusks while ignoring the associated biota, is analogous to collecting stream-drift for a survey of living mollusks. In regions poorly known scientifically such collections may have some value. In the present state of knowledge none of these practices is worthwhile, for the information gained lacks the detail necessary for incorporation into the body of scientific data. Study of Pleistocene history will be most advanced by combined re-

TABLE 7

Faunal Change in Meade County, Kansas.
The Three Fossil Localities Are in a Single Exposure

	Mt. Scott loc. UM-K2-59	Cragin Quarry loc. 2	Cragin Quarry loc. 3	Recent, Meade County
Unionidae				
Anodonta grandis Say				X
Uniomerus tetralasmus (Say)				X
Sphaeriidae				
Sphaerium occidentale Prime	X			
partumeium (Say)	X			
striatinum (Lamarck)	X			
sulcatum (Lamarck)	X			
transversum (Say)	cf.			X
Pisidium casertanum (Poli)	X		X	X
compressum Prime	X			
nitidum Jenyns	X			
obtusale (Lamarck)	X			
variabile Prime	X			
Valvatidae				
Valvata tricarinata (Say)	X			
Ellobiidae				
Carychium exiguum (Say)	X	X	X	
Lymnaeidae				
Fossaria dalli (Baker)	X	X		X
obrussa (Say)	X			X
Lymnaea caperata Say	X	X	X	
exilis Lea	X			
reflexa Say	X			
Lymnaea bulimoides techella (Haldeman)				X
cockerelli (Pilsbry & Ferriss)				X
Ancylidae				
Ferrissia meekiana (Stimpson)	X			
Laevapex fuscus (Adams)	X			
kirklandi (Walker)	X			
Planorbidae				
Gyraulus circumstriatus (Tryon)	X	X	X	
parvus (Say)	X			X
Armiger crista (Linnaeus)	X		X	
Planorbella trivolvis (Say)	X			X
Promenetus exacuous exacuous (Say)	X			X
exacuous kansasensis (Baker)		X		
Promenetus umbilicatellus (Cockerell)	X			
Physidae				
Physa anatina Lea	X	X	X	X
gyrina Say	X			
skinneri Taylor	X			
Aplexa hypnorum (Linnaeus)	X			
Strobilopsidae				
Strobilops labyrinthica (Say)	X			
Pupillidae				
Gastrocopta armifera (Say)	X	X	X	X
contracta (Say)	X	X	X	
cristata (Pilsbry & Vanatta)	X	X	X	
holzingeri (Sterki)	X	X	X	
pellucida hordeacella (Pilsbry)	X	X	X	
procera (Gould)	X			X
tappaniana (Adams)	X	X	X	
Pupoides albilabris (Adams)	X	X	X	X
Pupilla blandi Morse	X		X	
Vertigo milium (Gould)	X	X	X	
ovata (Say)	X	X	X	X
Valloniidae				
Vallonia gracilicosta Reinhardt	X	X	X	
parvula Sterki	X	X	X	X
Succineidae				
cf. *Succinea*	X			X
Oxyloma cf. *O. retusa* (Lea)	X			X
Endodontidae				
Discus cronkhitei (Newcomb)	X			
Helicodiscus parallelus (Say)	X	X	X	X
singleyanus (Pilsbry)			X	X
Zonitidae				
Hawaiia minuscula (Binney)	X	X	X	
Nesovitrea electrina (Gould)	X	X	X	
Zonitoides arboreus (Say)	X	X	X	
nitidus (Müller)	X			
Limacidae				
Deroceras aenigma Leonard	X	X	X	
laeve (Müller)				X
Euconulidae				
Euconulus fulvus (Müller)	X	X	X	
Polygyridae				
Stenotrema leai (Binney)	X	X	X	
Number of species	55	22	27	26

TABLE 7 (cont)

Mt. Scott. loc. UM-K2-59	%
Cragin Quarry loc. 2	%
Cragin Quarry loc. 3	%
Recent, Meade County	%

searches on stratigraphy, soils, fauna, and flora; through such investigations research on fossil mollusks will not only yield more but receive more from neighboring sciences.

5. Anyone attempting to interpret in detail the environment represented by Pleistocene mollusks finds abruptly how little is known of the living American fauna. In studying a late Wisconsin assemblage in Ohio, LaRocque (1952) provided a model study that wrung as much as possible from available ecological data. It is a measure of the primitive state of malacology that there was only one study of freshwater mollusks on which he could draw for measurements of pH and simple water quality, that by Morrison (1932).

6. Theoretically it might seem a straightforward matter to begin gathering ecological data on mollusks. To a considerable extent this is true; many geologists and paleontologists who began the study of Pleistocene shells have also collected Recent shells for ecological or distributional data. Qualitative analysis should precede quantitative analysis, however; it would be fruitless to gather detailed ecologic data on a composite species. Refined morphologi-

cal and taxonomic studies are a necessary prelude to meaningful ecologic studies, and these in turn to detailed paleoecologic interpretations.

7. The lack of detailed systematic analysis of living mollusks has already begun to hinder study of Pleistocene fossils, as illustrated by the discussion, earlier in this chapter, of the *Lymnaea "palustris"* group. This is not an isolated example. Virtually none of the species supposed to be common to North America and Eurasia, or pairs of related species with this distribution, has been studied critically with material from representative localities. Such studies are prerequisites for evaluating the extent and timing of possible faunal exchanges between the continents, and for understanding similarities and differences in ecology of supposedly identical species. Especially rewarding subjects for detailed study would seem to lie in the genera *Pupilla* and *Columella*. One can scarcely doubt that analysis of these groups as careful as that which has been carried out in Europe (Forcart, 1959; Ložek, 1954, 1955) would result in useful refinement of current American classification.

Mere describing of new species is not an illuminating response to the lack of systematic study of mollusks. Shimek's (1930, p. 682) words have even greater force, alas, today: "It is true that recent efforts have been made to segregate as species certain fossil forms of several variable species, but the variation in the fossils is duplicated in the modern forms and there is no warrant for the separation." Such spurious species are a disservice to taxonomy by distorting the relative rank of morphologic units, to stratigraphy by establishing supposedly extinct forms, and to paleoecology by depriving it of the evidence of variation within a living species.

8. If paleontological study of Pleistocene mollusks suffers now from lack of basic biological research, it will do so to a much greater degree in the immediate future. This gloomy prediction is based on the belief that Pleistocene research is still in an early stage; on the complete absence from this field of individuals qualified to deal with gross morphology of living mollusks, ecology, biogeography, and stratigraphy all together; and on the observation that there is no prospect for such students soon. Conventional conchological-stratigraphic research has proved to have some use, but in the long run strictly zoological study will advance Pleistocene paleontology more.

Finally it should be noted that Ložek (1961, p. 123) considered that, in Czechoslovakia, "the research methods and the application of Quaternary molluscs are in a test stage at present and they will require considerable improvement." By this standard, in America only a few wistful glances have been cast at the subject.

References

Adam, William, 1947, Revision des mollusques de la Belgique. I, Mollusques terrestres et dulcicoles: Mus. Hist. Nat. Belg. Mém., v. 106, p. 1-298

Allen, Don, and Cheatum, E. P., 1961, A Pleistocene molluscan fauna near Byers, Clay County, Texas: So. Methodist Univ., Grad. Res. Center J., v. 29, p. 137-169

Baily, J. L., Jr., and Baily, R. I., 1952, *Amnicola pilsbryana*, new name: Nautilus, v. 65, p. 144

Baker, F. C., 1911, The Lymnaeidae of North and middle America, recent and fossil: Chicago Acad. Sci. Spec. Publ., v. 3, p. 1-539

—— 1920, The life of the Pleistocene or glacial period as recorded in the deposits laid down by the great ice sheets: Urbana, Univ. Illinois Bull., v. 17, 476 p.

—— 1928, The fresh water Mollusca of Wisconsin. Part I, Gastropoda: Wis. Geol. Nat. Hist. Surv. Bull., v. 70, pt. 1, p. 1-507

—— 1931, A restudy of the interglacial molluscan fauna of Toronto, Canada: Illinois Acad. Sci. Trans., v. 23, p. 358-366

Benthem Jutting, Tera van, 1933, Mollusca (I). A. Gastropoda Prosobranchia et Pulmonata: Fauna Nederl., v. 7, p. 1-387

Berry, E. G., 1943, The Amnicolidae of Michigan; distribution, ecology, and taxonomy: Univ. Mich. Mus. Zool. Misc. Publ. 57, p. 1-68

Boettger, C. R., 1944, Basommatophora: Tierwelt Nord- u. Ostsee, v. 9b, p. 241-478

Call, R. E., 1885, On the Quaternary and recent Mollusca of the Great Basin, with descriptions of new forms. Introduced by a sketch of the Quaternary lakes of the Great Basin by G. K. Gilbert: U.S. Geol. Surv. Bull. 11, p. 1-66

Cheatum, E. P., and Allen, Don, 1963, An ecological comparison of the Ben Franklin and Clear Creek local molluscan faunas in Texas: So. Methodist Univ., Grad. Res. Center J., v. 31, p. 174-179

Clark, A. L., 1961, Pleistocene molluscan faunas of the Castalia deposit, Erie County, Ohio: Sterkiana, No. 3, p. 19-39

Cornejo, John, 1961, Pleistocene molluscan faunas of the Souder lake deposit, Franklin County, Ohio: Sterkiana, No. 4, p. 35-49

Crane, H. R., and Griffin, J. B., 1961, University of Michigan radiocarbon dates VI: Radiocarbon, v. 3, p. 105-125

Dalquest, W. W., 1962, The Good Creek Formation, Pleistocene of Texas, and its fauna: J. Paleont., v. 36, p. 568-582

Forcart, Lothar, 1959, Die palaearktischen Arten des Genus *Columella* (Moll., Styll., Pupillidae): Naturf. Ges. Basel Verh., v. 70, p. 7-18

Franzen, Dorothea S., 1946, A new fossil pupillid: Nautilus, v. 60, p. 24-25

Frömming, Ewald, 1956, Biologie der mitteleuropäischen Süsswasserschnecken: Berlin, Duncker & Humblot, 313 p.

Frye, J. C., and Leonard, A. B., 1952, Pleistocene geology of Kansas: Kansas Geol. Surv. Bull. 99, 230 p.

—— 1954, Significant new exposures of Pleistocene deposits at Kirwin, Phillips County, Kansas: Kansas Geol. Surv. Bull. 109, p. 29-48

—— 1963, Pleistocene geology of Red River basin in Texas: Univ. Texas Bur. Econ. Geol. Rep. Inv. 49, p. 1-48

—— 1964, Relation of Ogallala Formation to the southern High Plains in Texas: Univ. Texas Bur. Econ. Geol. Rep. Inv. 51, p. 1-25

Germain, Louis, 1931, Mollusques terrestres et fluviatiles, pt. 2: Faune Fr., v. 22, p. 479-897

Gooding, A. M., 1963, Illinoian and Wisconsin glaciations in the Whitewater Basin, southeastern Indiana, and adjacent areas: J. Geol., v. 71, p. 665-682

Goodrich, Calvin, 1940, Mollusks of a Kansas Pleistocene deposit: Nautilus, v. 53, p. 77-79

Gould, A. A., 1855, New species of land and fresh-water shells from western (N.) America: Boston Soc. Nat. Hist. Proc., v. 5, p. 127-130

Gregg, W. O., 1941, *Fluminicola avernalis* and *Fluminicola avernalis carinifera* from Nevada: Nautilus, v. 54, p. 117-118

Grossu, A. V., 1955, Gastropoda Pulmonata: Fauna Rom., Moll., v. 3, pt. 1, p. 1-518

Henderson, Junius, 1931, Molluscan provinces in the western United States: Univ. Colorado Stud., v. 18, p. 177-186

Hibbard, C. W., 1943, The Rezabek fauna, a new Pleistocene fauna from Lincoln County, Kansas: Univ. Kansas Sci. Bull., v. 29, p. 235-247

—— 1949, Pleistocene stratigraphy and paleontology of Meade County, Kansas: Univ. Michigan Mus. Paleont. Contr., v. 7, p. 63-90

—— 1960, An interpretation of Pliocene and Pleistocene climates in North America: Michigan Acad. Sci., 62nd Ann. Rep., p. 5-30

—— 1963, A late Illinoian fauna from Kansas and its climatic significance: Michigan Acad. Sci. Pap., v. 48, p. 187-221

Hibbard, C. W., and Taylor, D. W., 1960, Two late Pleistocene faunas from southwestern Kansas: Univ. Michigan Mus. Paleont. Contr., v. 16, p. 1-223

Ho, Tong-Yun, and Leonard, A. B., 1961, Two new strobilopids from the Pleistocene of the High Plains: Nautilus, v. 75, p. 43-49

Hubendick, Bengt, 1951, Recent Lymnaeidae; their variation, morphology, taxonomy, nomenclature, and distribution: K. svenska Vetensk. Akad. Handl., ser. 4, v. 3, p. 1-223

Hubricht, Leslie, 1943, Hunting *Stenotrema hubrichti:* Nautilus, v. 56, p. 73-75

—— 1955, *Discus macclintocki* (F. C. Baker): Nautilus, v. 69, p. 34

Jackiewicz, Maria, 1959, Badania nad zmiennością i stanowiskiem systematycznym *Galba palustris* O. F. Müll.: Poznan, Prace Kom. Biol., v. 19, No. 3, p. 1-54

Johnston, C. S., and Savage, D. E., 1955, A survey of various late Cenozoic vertebrate faunas of the Panhandle of Texas. Part I, introduction, description of localities, preliminary faunal lists: Univ. California Publ. Geol. Sci., v. 31, p. 21-49

Kapp, R. O., in press, Illinoian and Sangamon vegetation in southwestern Kansas and adjacent Oklahoma: Univ. Michigan Mus. Paleont. Contr.

Karlstrom, T. N. V., 1961, The glacial history of Alaska: its bearing on paleoclimatic theory: New York Acad. Sci. Ann., v. 95, p. 290-340

Kennard, A. S., and Woodward, B. B., 1926, Synonymy of the British nonmarine Mollusca (Recent and post-Tertiary): London, British Museum, 447 p.

Kitts, D. B., 1959, Cenozoic geology of northern Roger Mills County, Oklahoma: Oklahoma Geol. Surv. Circ. 48, p. 5-26

Kukla, Jiří, and Vojen Ložek, 1961, Quaternary deposits of Czechoslovakia; loesses and related deposits: Warszawa, Prace Geol. Inst., v. 34, p. 11-28

Kukla, Jiří, Vojen Ložek, and Quido Záruba, 1961, Zur Stratigraphie der Lösse in der Tschechoslowakei: Quartär, v. 13, p. 1-29

Lane, C. W., 1960, Geology and ground-water resources of Kingman County, Kansas: Kansas Geol. Surv. Bull. 144, 174 p.

LaRocque, Aurèle, 1952, Molluscan faunas of the Orleton Farms mastodon site, Madison County, Ohio: Ohio J. Sci., v. 52, p. 10-27

LaRocque, Aurèle, and J. F. Conley, 1956, Two Pleistocene molluscan faunules from Hunter's Run, Fairfield County, Ohio: Ohio J. Sci., v. 56, p. 325-328

LaRocque, Aurèle, and Forsyth, Jane L., 1957, Pleistocene molluscan faunules of the Sidney Cut, Shelby County, Ohio: Ohio J. Sci., v. 57, p. 81-89

Leonard, A. B., 1950, A Yarmouthian molluscan fauna in the midcontinent region of the United States: Univ. Kansas Paleont. Contr. 8, p. 1-48

—— 1952, Illinoian and Wisconsinan molluscan faunas in Kansas: Univ. Kansas Paleont. Contr. 9, p. 1-38

—— 1953, Molluscan faunules in Wisconsinan loess at Cleveland, Ohio: Amer. J. Sci., v. 251, p. 369-376

Leonard, A. B., and Frye, J. C., 1960, Wisconsinan molluscan faunas of the Illinois Valley region: Illinois Geol. Surv. Circ. 304, p. 1-32

Ložek, Vojen, 1954, Noví měkkýši československého pleistocénu: Anthropozoikum, v. 3, p. 327-342

—— 1955, Měkkýši Československého Kvartéru: Rozpr. Úst. Ústav. Geol., v. 17, p. 1-509

—— 1956, Klíč Československých měkkýšů: Bratislava, Slovensk. Akad. Vied, 373 p.

—— 1961, Survey of Czechoslovak Quaternary: Mollusca: Warszawa, Prace Geol. Inst., v. 34, p. 119-124

—— 1963, Malakozoologicky významná území Slovenska z hlediska ochrany prírody: Čsl. Ochr. Prír., v. 1, p. 76-113

Ložek, Vojen, and Kukla, Jiří, 1959, Das Lössprofil von Leitmeritz an der Elbe, Norböhmen: Eiszeitalter u. Gegenwart, v. 10, p. 81-104

Malde, H. E., 1964, Environment and man in arid America: Science, v. 145, p. 123-129

Mandahl-Barth, G., 1949, Bløddyr III. Ferskvandsbløddyr: Danm. Fauna, v. 54, p. 1-249

Miller, B. B., 1961, A late Pleistocene molluscan faunule from Meade County, Kansas: Michigan Acad. Sci. Arts Lett., Pap., v. 46, p. 103-125

—— 1964, Additional mollusks from the late Pliocene Bender local fauna, Meade County, Kansas: J. Paleont., v. 38, p. 113-117

—— in press, Five Illinoian molluscan faunas from the southern Great Plains: Malacologia

Miller, R. D., and Scott, G. R., 1955, Sequence of alluviation along the Loup rivers, Valley County area, Nebraska: Geol. Soc. Amer. Bull., v. 66, p. 1431-1448

—— 1961, Late Wisconsin age of terrace alluvium along

the North Loup River, central Nebraska; a revision: Geol. Soc. Amer. Bull., v. 72, p. 1283-1284

Morrison, J. P. E., 1932, A report on the Mollusca of the northeastern Wisconsin lake district: Wisconsin Acad. Sci. Arts Lett. Trans., v. 27, p. 359-396

—— 1940, Another Pleistocene snail is not extinct: Nautilus, v. 53, p. 123

Mowery, D. H., 1961, Pleistocene molluscan faunas of the Jewell Hill deposit, Logan County, Ohio: Sterkiana, No. 4, p. 1-21

Nobre, Augusto, 1941, Fauna malacológica de Portugal. II, Moluscos terrestres e fluviais: Univ. Coimbra Mus. Zool. Mem., v. 124, p. 1-277

Pilsbry, H. A., 1890, New and little known American mollusks, No. 3: Philadelphia Acad. Nat. Sci. Proc., v. 42, p. 296-302

—— 1935, Western and southwestern Amnicolidae and a new *Humboldtiana:* Nautilus, v. 48, p. 91-94

—— 1940, Land Mollusca of North America (north of Mexico), v. 1, pt. 2: Philadelphia Acad. Nat. Sci. Monogr., v. 3, pt. 1, p. 575-994

—— 1948, Land Mollusca of North America (north of Mexico), v. 2, pt. 2: Philadelphia Acad. Nat. Sci. Monogr., v. 3, pt. 2, p. 521-1113

Rubey, W. W., 1952, Geology and mineral resources of the Hardin and Brussels quadrangles (in Illinois): U.S. Geol. Surv. Prof. Pap. 218, p. 1-179

Say, Thomas, 1831, Descriptions of several new species of shells, and of a new species of *Lumbricus:* Transylvan. J. Med., v. 4, p. 525-529

Scott, G. H., 1963, Uniformitarianism, the uniformity of nature, and paleoecology: New Zealand J. Geol. Geophys., v. 6, p. 510-527

Scott, G. R., 1962, Geology of the Littleton quadrangle, Jefferson, Douglas, and Arapahoe counties, Colorado: U.S. Geol. Surv. Bull. 1121-L, p. 1-53

—— 1963, Quaternary geology and geomorphic history of the Kassler quadrangle, Colorado: U.S. Geol. Surv. Prof. Pap. 421-A, p. 1-70

Shimek, Bohumil, 1901, *Pyramidula shimekii* (Pils.) Shim: Univ. Iowa Labs. Nat. Hist. Bull., v. 5, p. 139-145

—— 1904, *Helicina occulata* Say: Davenport Acad. Sci. Proc., v. 9, p. 173-180

—— 1930, Land snails as indicators of ecological conditions: Ecology, v. 11, p. 637-686

—— 1931, Ecological conditions during loess-deposition: Iowa Univ. Stud. Nat. Sci., Stud. Nat. Hist., v. 14, p. 38-54

Slaughter, B. H., Crook, W. W., Jr., Harris, R. K., Allen, D. C., and Seifert, Martin, 1962, The Hill-Schuler local faunas of the upper Trinity River, Dallas and Denton Counties, Texas: Univ. Texas Bur. Econ. Geol. Rep. Invest. 48, p. 1-75

Slaughter, B. H., and Hoover, B. R., 1963, Sulphur River Formation and the Pleistocene mammals of the Ben Franklin local fauna: So. Methodist Univ., Grad. Res. Center J., v. 31, p. 132-148

Slaughter, B. H., and Ritchie, Ronald, 1963, Pleistocene mammals of the Clear Creek local fauna, Denton County,

Texas: So. Methodist Univ., Grad. Res. Center J., v. 31, p. 117-131

Soós, Lajos, 1943, A Kárpat-medence Mollusca-faunája: Budapest, Magyar Tudományos Akad., 478 p.

Stearns, R. E. C., 1893, Report on the land and fresh-water shells collected in California and Nevada by the Death Valley Expedition, including a few additional species obtained by Dr. C. Hart Merriam and assistants in parts of the southwestern United States: North Amer. Fauna, v. 7, p. 269-283

—— 1901, The fossil fresh-water shells of the Colorado Desert; their distribution, environment, and variation: U.S. Natl. Mus. Proc., v. 24, p. 271-299

Stimpson, William, 1865, Diagnoses of newly discovered genera of gasteropods, belonging to the sub-fam. Hydrobiinae, of the family Rissoidae: Amer. J. Conch., v. 1, p. 52-54

Taylor, D. W., 1954, A new Pleistocene fauna and new species of fossil snails from the High Plains: Univ. Michigan Mus. Zool. Occ. Pap. 557, p. 1-16

—— 1958, Geologic range and relationships of the fresh-water snail *Anisus pattersoni:* J. Paleont., v. 32, p. 1149-1153

—— 1960a, Distribution of the freshwater clam *Pisidium ultramontanum;* a zoogeographic inquiry: Amer. J. Sci., v. 258-A, p. 325-334

—— 1960b, Late Cenozoic molluscan faunas from the High Plains: U.S. Geol. Surv. Prof. Pap. 337, 94 p.

Tuthill, S. J., 1961, A molluscan fauna and late Pleistocene climate in southeastern North Dakota: North Dakota Acad. Sci. Proc., v. 15, p. 19-26

—— 1963, Molluscan fossils from upper Glacial Lake Agassiz sediments in Red Lake County, Minnesota: North Dakota Acad. Sci. Proc., v. 17, p. 96-101

Tuthill, S. J., Clayton, Lee, and Laird, W. M., 1964, A comparison of a fossil Pleistocene molluscan fauna from North Dakota with a Recent molluscan fauna from Minnesota: Amer. Midl. Nat., v. 71, p. 344-362

Waldén, H. W., 1963, Historical and taxonomical aspects of the land Gastropoda in the North Atlantic region, *in* Löve, Askell, and Löve, Doris (ed.), North Atlantic biota and their history: New York, MacMillan, p. 153-171

Walker, Bryant, 1901, A new *Amnicola:* Nautilus, v. 14, p. 113-114

Watt, A. K., 1954, Correlation of the Pleistocene geology as seen in the subway with that of the Toronto region, Canada: Can. Geol. Assoc. Proc., v. 6, No. 2, p. 69-81

Wayne, W. J., 1958, Early Pleistocene sediments in Indiana: J. Geol., v. 66, p. 8-15

—— 1959, Stratigraphic distribution of Pleistocene land snails in Indiana: Sterkiana, No. 1, p. 9-18

—— 1963, Pleistocene formations in Indiana: Indiana Geol. Surv. Bull., v. 25, p. 1-85

Wendorf, Fred (ed.), 1961, Paleoecology of the Llano Estacado: Ft. Burgwin Res. Cent. Publ., No. 1, p. 1-144

Zhadin, V. I., 1952, Molliuski pryesnykh i solonovatykh vod SSSR: Tabl. Anal. Faune U.R.S.S., v. 46, p. 1-376

SUMMARY

Regional differences shown by the living North American molluscan fauna are shown also by Pleistocene faunas, so that widely separated fossil assemblages may have no species or even genera in common. Such differences, and the more numerous data, have led herein to an emphasis on central North America. Most of the fossil shells can be referred to living species, so that their interpretation rests largely on knowledge of the Recent fauna. As exemplified by the discovery of supposedly extinct species still alive, and of composite Recent "species," there is much to learn even at the level of descriptive taxonomy.

Most of the independently dated late Pliocene and Pleistocene molluscan faunas of central North America have been summarized. The basic faunal data permit some generalizations about rates of change, local habitat, regional environments, and parallelism with the much better known record in Czechoslovakia.

Inferred pre-Wisconsin climates all had less seasonal contrast than that of today. Wisconsin glacial climates were more extreme than any previous, and the aridity and strong seasonal contrasts of the present are a late Wisconsin or post-Wisconsin development. In general Pleistocene events extinguished pre-existing species, and scarcely any evolutionary replacement has occurred.

Numerous problems of value to Pleistocene geology await the student of fossil mollusks; but the mollusks should be studied as part of broader stratigraphic and ecologic problems. In the long run strictly zoological studies will advance Pleistocene conchology more by adding to the foundations for interpretation of the fossils.

OTHER INVERTEBRATES—AN ESSAY IN BIOGEOGRAPHY *

DAVID G. FREY[1]

RATIONALE

THE QUATERNARY has been a time of dynamic unrest for organisms as well as for the earth's surface and climate. The successive loading and unloading of the land by glaciers has profoundly affected the distribution of organisms on the continents and in the adjacent oceans, and the consequent fragmentation of formerly continuous ranges has provided the mechanism for genetic differentiation leading to speciation. Except in the vertebrates and mollusks, and perhaps the beetles, the fossil record is presently so meager that we cannot reconstruct previous distributions directly but must deduce them from present distributions and our general understanding of the response of organisms to changing environmental conditions during the Quaternary. Regretably, it is almost as true now as it was 15 years ago when Deevey (1949) wrote his lengthy summary on Pleistocene biogeography that many groups of organisms are so poorly known systematically and distributionally they can contribute little to the topic. This is particularly true of most groups of invertebrates, and hence in the development and documentation of various ideas I shall have to rely in part on vertebrates, mollusks, and insects, which are treated separately in detail elsewhere in this book. Furthermore, since organisms in their changing distributions are not limited by national boundaries, there is no logic in restricting discussion to any present political unit. Although much of the development will be concerned with the continental United States—the conterminous 48—by necessity it cannot be confined to this region.

Previous reviews of the subject, although with relatively little attention to invertebrates, have been presented by Deevey (1949, 1961), Dillon (1956), Martin and Harrell (1957), Martin (1958, 1963), and Dorf (1959). In addition there have been a number of symposia on various aspects of Quaternary biogeography, which will be referred to in this report.

Within the vast areas formerly covered by the Laurentide and Cordilleran ice sheets there now exist well-developed biotas that obviously have immigrated there in the relatively short span of time since the wasting of the most recent glaciers. Intuitively, the predecessors of these biotas must have been displaced southward during the growth and spread of the glaciers, and, considering the relatively great durations of the interglacials (e.g. perhaps 80,000 years for the Sangamon Interglacial: see Broecker et al., 1958), this sequence of forced migration and recolonization must have occurred in each glacial-interglacial couplet. Less extensive, although no less significant, adjustments of distribution undoubtedly occurred during the various interstadials. Present distributions of organisms give us information regarding only the most recent phase of colonization. Interglacial deposits eventually will yield what information is available regarding the previous biotas, and, at least for the aquatic biotas, terrestrial mollusks, beetles, and vertebrates, this promises to be quite extensive (Frey, 1964).

There is always the possibility that at least some of the biotal elements in the glaciated regions are not postglacial immigrants from the trans-glacial regions to the south but rather survivors from local nonglaciated refugia or nunataks. Unequivocal demonstration of such supposed instances is difficult, although many are claimed among both plants and animals on the basis of present distributions. For Scandinavia, Iceland, and Greenland such instances are summarized by Ball (1963b), who in turn claims survival of certain flightless carabid beetles in unglaciated refugia in Alaska (Ball, 1963a, 1963b). Similar claims are made for some carabids in Newfoundland (Lindroth, 1963b) and fleas in Alaska (Holland, 1963). There are many other instances. Although this is an important aspect of historical biogeography, no attempt was made to seek out other instances and evaluate the evidence.

Peripheral to the ice margins organisms have not been static in their distributions throughout the Quaternary, contrary to opinions held even recently by some (see Deevey, 1949, and Martin, 1958, for recent discussions of this matter). Their responses to changes in regional climate (chiefly temperature in the Southeast, temperature and precipitation in the Southwest) have been almost equally dramatic although intuitively less obvious. Depression of temperatures in the South during the Wisconsin Glaciation is indicated by reduced surface seawater temperatures even in the tropical mid-Atlantic based on O^{16}/O^{18} ratios of surface-dwelling Foraminifera (Broecker et al.,

* Numerous specialists have variously contributed encouragement, apologies, condolences, and occasionally even suggestions or information in my assignment. To all of them I am truly grateful: G. E. Ball, E. L. Bousfield, J. L. Brooks, G. E. Gates, C. J. Goodnight, W. J. Harman, R. R. Hessler, H. H. Hobbs, P. C. Holt, W. Knülle, H. W. Levi, P. S. Martin, Frank Maturo, Jr., W. R. Murchie, P. T. Paine, Mary D. Rogick, and N. L. Rumpp. I can merely hope that this review will encourage them and other specialists to intensify their studies on the systematics and distribution of their special groups, so that when the subject of Quaternary biogeography is reviewed again at some indefinite time in the future, there will be no need for another profusion of apologies.

This paper represents Contribution 764 from the Department of Zoology, Indiana University.

[1] Department of Zoology, Indiana University, Bloomington, Indiana.

1958), by the widespread occurrence of elements of boreal forest and northern deciduous forest in the South (see Martin, 1958, and Whitehead, this volume, for reviews), by the occurrence of relict populations of marine organisms with more northern affinities in the northern portions of the Gulf of Mexico and the Gulf of California (discussed later in this paper), and by various elements of the Pleistocene megafauna (*e.g.* Richards, 1962) in the Southeast. Increased rainfall during the pluvial (= glacial) periods in the Southwest is indicated in part by the history of the interior-drainage lakes of the Great Basin. Lowering of the temperature in the Southwest during the pluvial periods resulted in a downward displacement of altitudinal plant zones by as much as 1,200 m (Martin, 1963), which would have permitted the continuous distribution of floral and faunal elements previously represented by isolated populations on the tops of mountains, as today.

There are still other features of Quaternary history that have affected the distribution and evolution of organisms. The formation and subsequent melting of the glaciers resulted in a eustatic lowering and raising of sea level, from a measured 100 m below present level in the Gulf of Mexico (Shepard *et al.*, 1960) or a calculated 160 m during the penultimate glaciation (Donn *et al.*, 1962) to 10 m above present sea level in the Carolinas (Richards, 1962). Although there is a series of terraces along the Atlantic Coast at higher elevations than this, no marine fossils have been found, except for a possibly Pliocene locality in South Carolina, that would substantiate the common opinion that these are older Pleistocene marine terraces (Richards, 1962). A broad marginal region along the coast was alternately exposed and inundated by the sea and thus alternately colonized by terrestrial and marine biotas. Potentially this could have resulted in migrational corridors for organisms or at the other extreme in at least temporary isolation of populations with subsequent genetic differentiation.

At low sea stands eastern Asia and western North America were connected *via* a land bridge over the present Bering Strait, thus permitting the migration of man (*e. g.*, Haynes, 1964) and other organisms, chiefly in an eastward direction. The environmental conditions on these land bridges are largely unknown, except for the most recent one during the maximum of Wisconsin glaciation 18,000 years B.P. (before the present). Colinvaux (1963, 1964) showed by pollen analysis that only a treeless tundra existed at this time.

On the other side of the Continent a more controversial land bridge connecting Europe with North America has been espoused by some biogeographers. A recent review of biogeographic and physical evidence on this topic suggests, although there is by no means complete agreement, that if such a land bridge existed it may have extended from Europe to Iceland and perhaps to Greenland but probably not to continental North America (see Löve and Löve, 1963). Davis Strait between Greenland and the mainland has been continuously a migrational barrier during the Pleistocene.

Besides the eustatic changes in sea level there have been isostatic changes in land elevation caused by the weight of the ice and even by the weight of water of the largest pluvial lakes of the Great Basin (King, this volume). Melting of the ice proceeded faster than the isostatic rebound, one result of which was that in postglacial time there was a transgression of the sea up the St. Lawrence River to the vicinity of Montreal—the Champlain Sea—with arms north along the Ottawa River and south into Lake Champlain, and also a proglacial sea in James Bay and southern Hudson Bay—the Tyrrell Sea. These marine waters provided the opportunity for westward migration and subsequent isolation of salt-associated organisms, such as salt-marsh sparrows (Beecher, 1955). Moreover, especially the Laurentide Ice Sheet developed a series of large proglacial and glacial lakes along its southern and western margins, which are believed to be the means whereby such "glacial relicts" as the amphipod *Pontoporeia affinis* and the mysid *Mysis relicta* attained their present discontinuous distribution on the Continent (Ricker, 1959). Other organisms, too, undoubtedly used such east-west corridors.

Major and minor drainage patterns in the glaciated and periglacial regions have been changed by the glaciers and their sluiceways and by renewed cycles of stream and karst activity.

This flux of environmental conditions in the Quaternary has resulted in the migration, isolation, and differentiation of organisms, the patterns of which are beginning to appear in certain groups, and especially in those where the degree of genetic differentiation is actually being measured by cross-breeding experiments (Blair, 1958, this volume). The pattern of today is the resultant of all the spatial displacements and evolutionary developments during all the various episodes of the Quaternary and of previous geological time as well. This truism is difficult to provide with a sound chronological and sequential framework beyond the limits of radiocarbon dating, but many distributional studies are quite suggestive, nevertheless.

DISJUNCT MARINE DISTRIBUTIONS

Some of the most suggestive information concerning redistribution and genetic differentiation of organisms occasioned by events of the Quaternary, although regretably still not satisfactorily tied in with specific events, comes from the present distributions of marine organisms along the east and west coasts, and particularly in the Gulf of Mexico and the Gulf of California.

GULF OF MEXICO

One of the striking features of the inshore fauna of the northern Gulf of Mexico is that many of its species also occur at higher latitudes along the Atlantic Coast—north to Cape Hatteras or even Cape Cod—but do not occur around the tip of the Florida peninsula. The ranges, instead of being continuous, therefore, are interrupted or disjunct (Fig. 1). Marine organisms occupying continuous ranges are probably limited at their extremes mainly by annual maximum and minimum temperatures as affecting survival, growth, and reproduction (Hutchins, 1947; Deevey, 1950). Where ranges are discontinuous, historical factors must be suspected and looked for. In the present

TABLE 1

Extent of Disjunction in South Florida and the West Indies of Various Groups of Invertebrates Occurring in the Gulf of Mexico between the Mouths of the Mississippi River and the Rio Grande, and also the Number of Endemic Species in the Gulf

(From Hedgpeth, 1953)

Group	Total number of species	Endemic in Gulf	Number of species disjunct in Florida region		
			Distributed north to Woods Hole	Distributed north to Cape Hatteras	Wide ranging
Hydroids	40	2	—	—	2
Actinaria	13	3	—	1	1
Nemertea	16	2	4	—	9
Mollusca					
Pelecypoda	101	11	14	10	—
Gastropoda	71	7	9	3	—
Polychaeta	58	12	5	9	2
Crabs					
Oxystomes	15	3	—	—	—
Spider	11	—	—	—	—
Cancroid	27	1	2	—	—
Grapsoid	20	2	4	2	—
Echinoderms	24	3	2	—	—
Totals	396	46	40	25	14

instance the most satisfactory explanation is the infiltration of Atlantic Coast species into the Gulf during periods of lowered sea temperatures contemporaneous with the glacial ages and the subsequent isolation of the Gulf populations as the sea temperatures rose during the interglacials.

Specialists in various groups of invertebrates have long recognized this phenomenon of coastwise disjunction without necessarily appreciating its origin and significance. Its magnitude was not apparent until Hedgpeth (1953) summarized the geographic distribution of various groups of organisms in the Louisiana-Texas portion of the Gulf Coast. Of the 396 species of invertebrates then known from this region, 198 have distributions extending northward for varying distances along the Atlantic Coast, and of these, 65% or 33% have their ranges interrupted in the Florida region (Table 1). In addition, one-quarter of the 48 species that are not confined in their overall distribution to the Gulf and the Western Atlantic also show disjunctions in the same general region.

The number of species of invertebrates occurring only in the Gulf of Mexico—the so-called endemics—is less than 12% of the total, which is lower than would be expected for such a region. Hedgpeth considered that the Gulf has always been a transitional region between the Temperate and Tropical Zones, brought about by fluctuating environmental conditions encompassing much of Tertiary as well as Quaternary time. This would favor the development of wide-ranging eurytopic species at the expense of indigenous restricted species.

Subsequent more detailed studies on particular groups of organisms suggest that the extent of endemism may be considerably greater than this. Hartman (1951) reported 182 species of polychaetes from the Gulf, including new genera and a surprising number of new species and subspecies. She emphasized that the fauna is still very incompletely

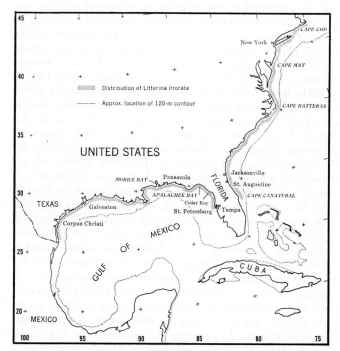

Figure 1. Gulf of Mexico and the east coast of the United States, showing the distribution of the common marsh snail *Littorina irrorata* (after Hedgpeth, 1953) as an example of many species of east-coast organisms with a generally northern distribution that also occur in the northern portion of the Gulf of Mexico but do not occur around the tip of the Florida peninsula. The 120-m contour shows the approximate coastline of this region during maximum eustatic lowering of sea level in the Quaternary.

known and that even the novice collector might expect to turn up new records and even new species. Assuming that the Gulf populations have been isolated from their Atlantic Coast counterparts for a sufficiently long period of time, one would expect differences in morphology and physiology to have developed. Such differences, when they become known through careful and critical studies, will help answer the questions of length of isolation of the populations and rates of evolution in the various groups. With present information we can only assume that most of the disjunctions have occurred since the most recent rise in surface sea temperatures about 11,000 years ago (Emiliani, 1955).

The information in Hedgpeth (1953) is supplemented and frequently given in greater detail in the book edited by Galtsoff (1954), in which specialists in the various groups of organisms have summarized the faunistic information for the entire Gulf of Mexico. For the purposes of historical biogeography our present knowledge of the various groups is discouragingly incomplete, as indicated by the all-too-frequently recurring apologetic statement at the beginning of most chapters.

Deevey (1950) in his first analysis of the Gulf Coast hydroids suggested that among the coelenterates at least two of the 39 species known from the northwest Gulf—*Podocoryne carnea* and *Tubularia crocea*—are disjunct in the south Florida region, and that our knowledge of the ecology of *T. crocea* indicates it could not flourish under present conditions in southern Florida. In a later paper Deevey (1954) listed another disjunct species—*Cladocarpus flexilis* —which is known from three localities near Mobile Bay in the Gulf but is not known south of Cape May on the Atlantic Coast. The anemones are not a good group for showing disjunctions because of their generally wide distribution, although Carlgren and Hedgpeth (1952) list one species that occurs in the Gulf and along the Atlantic Coast north to Cape Hatteras but is disjunct in southern Florida, and in a later paper Hedgpeth (1954a) suggests that four other species may have a similar distribution. The gorgonian corals along the lower west coast of Florida represent an attenuated West Indian assemblage (Bayer, 1953, 1954). In the Tampa region it is replaced by a distinctly temperate fauna, dominated by *Leptogorgia virgulata*, *L. setacea*, and *Muricea pendula*. These three species are abundant along the Carolina coast and south to northern Florida, but all of them are absent from the lower east coast of Florida. *L. virgulata* extends north to New York.

Coe (1951, 1954) noted that south Florida disjunction is pronounced among the nemertean worms. The species occurring at Pensacola on the Gulf Coast of Florida are similar to those at St. Augustine on the Atlantic Coast, but the southern peninsula of Florida separating these two localities contains a different assemblage. Five of the 17 species are known only from the Gulf and Atlantic coasts, but even species that are more widely distributed tend to show a disjunction in southern Florida. The nemerteans afford striking examples of the general principle that Gulf Coast individuals of "northern" species are smaller at maturity than individuals of the same species from more northern and colder climates.

The horseshoe crab (*Limulus polyphemus*) shows an anomalous distribution in that it apparently occurs in abundance along the Atlantic Coast around the tip of Florida to St. Petersburg but only in isolated pockets to the west (Hedgpeth, 1954b).

Rehder (1954) divided the mollusks of the Gulf of Mexico into two major groups. Those having an affinity with the Carolinian Province extend from Cape Hatteras south to about Cape Canaveral on the east coast of Florida and from Tampa Bay on the west coast along the Gulf to about Corpus Christi, Texas. Although Rehder does not state so specifically, he implies that these species are disjunct in southern Florida. Forty species are listed as Carolinian in origin. The remainder are members of the Caribbean Province to the south.

Two northern species of tunicates—*Molgula manhattensis* and *Bostrichobranchus pilularis*—are common in the Middle Atlantic states and also occur on the Louisiana coast but have not been found yet in southern Florida (Van Name, 1954). Lacking really adequate data on distribution one must always be cautious that a presumed interruption in range reflects the actual condition in the species rather than merely the patchiness of fortuitous collections.

Fishes also exhibit disjunctions in this region. Rivas (1954) listed the sturgeon *Acipenser sturio* and the gizzard shad *Dorosoma cepedianum* in this category. He also suggested that the shad *Alosa alabamae* on the Gulf Coast, which is closely related to *Alosa sapidissima* on the Atlantic Coast, originated through the development of southern Florida as a dispersal barrier in a previously continuous population. Neither species now occurs in southern Florida. Reid (1954) found that the fish fauna at Cedar Key, Florida, was a mixture of tropical and temperate elements, whereas that at Apalachee Bay only 160 km to the north was distinctly more temperate. The sciaenoid fishes in particular tend to be disjunct in southern Florida, and three species of triglids (sea robins) living in shallow Gulf water are represented by closely related forms on the Atlantic Coast (Ginsburg, 1950).

Another striking example of relict species in the Gulf of Mexico is provided by the planktonic Foraminifera. The 20 species presently occurring there constitute a mixed fauna, consisting of both mid- and low-latitude Atlantic elements (Phleger, 1960). The mid-latitude forms, such as *Globorotalia truncatulinoides*, tend to have their maximum abundance in the northwestern part of the Gulf at maximum distance from sites of entrance of tropical Caribbean water, whereas the low-latitude forms, such as *Globigerinoides sacculifer*, have their greatest abundance more to the south. However, all the species occur over the entire area of the Gulf although in different relative abundance. Phleger (1954) had suggested earlier that the mid-latitude species entered the Gulf during one or more of the glacial ages, at which times the planktonic fauna consisted entirely of mid-latitude species.

This conjecture is substantiated in part by the stratigraphy of the sediments of the Gulf (Phleger, 1960). The upper portion of undisturbed cores contains the modern mixed planktonic fauna. This overlies a fauna considered to be mid-latitude in aspect and late-glacial in age (Phleger, 1951). The age of this faunal transition in the Atlantic has been radiocarbon-dated at 10,000-12,000 years B.P., which agrees nicely with the increase in sea-surface temperatures at this time (Emiliani, 1955). Rates of postglacial sedimentation can be inferred from the thickness of the sediments containing the modern mixed planktonic assemblage.

The continental shelf in the Texas-Louisiana region contains many extensive areas with little or no sedimentation during the past 15,000 years or so. Shells of shallow-water mollusks in these areas have provided material for radiocarbon dating, for interpretation of past temperatures, and for interpretation of former shoreline features, now covered by great depths of water (Curray, 1960; Parker, 1960). Sea level was about 90 m lower than at present 17,000 years ago and, by extrapolation, about 120 m lower than at present 20,000 years ago. This exposed a broad, flat area of continental shelf up to 210 km wide. The transgression from this low seastand was interrupted by two and possibly three regressions, the middle one of which correlates well with the glacial advance in post-Two Creeks time. At about this time the littoral drift pattern shifted from counterclockwise to clockwise under the influence of southwest winds, which is believed to have warmed appreciably the uppermost 20 m of water. This is correlated with the immigration of many warm-water mollusks from the region of Middle America, which presently either do not occur along the Texas coast at all or else are rare in deeper water offshore.

By contrast, during the Wisconsin Glaciation 20,000-18,000 years ago, when sea level was perhaps 110-120 m lower than at present, a temperate climate is indicated by the mollusks. From 18,000-16,000 years ago, when sea level rose from its low of 120 m to about 80 m, the climate was even more strongly temperate. Most of the mollusks from this time interval presently live along the Atlantic Coast from northern Florida to Cape Hatteras. According to Emiliani (1958) the earth was probably colder during the late-glacial maximum about 20,000 years ago than at any time since the Permo-Carboniferous glaciation, and perhaps even the coldest of all time.

GULF OF CALIFORNIA

The south-opening Gulf of California (Fig. 2), lying between the Mexican mainland and the 1,300-km-long Baja California affords a situation similar to the Gulf of Mexico for the isolation of northern species that migrated southward during periods of thermal depression in the Quaternary. A recent symposium on "The biogeography of Baja California and adjacent seas" (see Dawson, 1960; Garth, 1960; Hubbs, 1960; Soule, 1960; and Walker, 1960) summarizes for a number of groups of organisms their present distributions and the inferences that can be drawn concerning past events that affected these distributions.

The outer coast of Baja California is very interesting biogeographically, because it represents the transition between a tropical biota originating to the south—generally referred to as Panamic—and a warm-temperate (San Diegan) or cool-temperate (Montereyan) biota originating to the north. These two biotas exhibit alternating dis-

Figure 2. General geographic relationships of the south-opening Gulf of California, which contains many disjunct populations of Pacific Coast organisms in its northern portion.

continuities along the coast, because areas of upwelling, which favor the northern biota, alternate with protected bays having high insolation, which favor the southern biota. Thus, upwelling is strong along the northwest coast south to about Punta Baja and again south of Bahia Vizcaino to about Punta Abreojos. South of here upwelling gradually declines, although a certain amount is still present to the extreme tip of the peninsula at Cabo San Lucas (Dawson, 1960). On the south side of headlands upwelling is particularly strong, and it is mainly in such locations that disjunct populations of northern species occur. Contrariwise, in regions protected from upwelling, such as Bahia Magdalena and Bahia Vizcaino and especially the still more highly protected lagoons off the latter bay, disjunct populations of southern species can occur far north of their continuous ranges.

Such disjunct outliers can be explained purely on the basis of ecology, as Dawson (1960) has attempted for the algae, or on the basis of major population adjustments in response to temperature changes in the Quaternary. Substantiation for the latter idea is afforded by a late-Pleistocene fauna of more than 100 species of marine mollusks, and a few other invertebrates, that indicates a significantly colder hydroclimate than today (Addicott and Emerson, 1959). Dawson (1960) regards the northern disjunct populations of southern species as dating no earlier than the last interglacial, when isotherms shifted northward.

It is likely, however, that the biogeographic balance along the Pacific coast of Baja California is extremely sensitive to even short-term thermal changes, and that most of the present disjunct populations, at least those of southern species, are postglacial in origin. Hubbs (1948), for example, showed that during a warm period in the mid-1800's tropical and subtropical fishes and invertebrates were able to move as far north as Monterey. Similarly, in the recent warm period of 1957-1959 upwelling along northwestern Baja California was sufficiently weakened to permit the northward movement of numbers of fishes and other organisms, largely restricted to more southern latitudes (Hubbs, 1960).

Some organisms are isothermal in their distribution along the California–Baja California coast. They submerge to greater depths in southern California, where the surface temperatures are warmer, and then recur in shallow water in northwestern Baja California (Hubbs, 1960). Hubbs also postulated that during the thermal depressions of the glacial ages, even the tropical waters of the eastern Pacific were sufficiently cooled to enable various "northern" species to cross the equator and become established in the Southern Hemisphere. Subsequent warming has resulted in disjunction in range, which has enabled genetic differences to develop in the population isolates. Specific examples of such cognate species are cited for the sharks, teleosts, pinnipeds, cetaceans, and possibly some birds, invertebrates, and the giant kelp *Macrocystis*.

Of greater interest, however, is the situation inside the Gulf of California. Whereas on the outer coast, especially on the northwestern portion, the biota is distinctly temperate in aspect, in the Gulf the biota is dominated by Panamic species that have moved in from the south. However, in the northernmost portion of the Gulf are disjunct populations of temperate species that do not occur in the southern portion of the Gulf or in the southern portion of the outer coast of Baja California but do occur in the northwestern portion and more generally to the north. These populations isolated in the Gulf can be regarded as remnants or relicts of periods when the outer-coast and Gulf populations were continuous with one another around the tip of the peninsula or through an oceanic connection across the peninsula in the La Paz region that may have developed in late-Pleistocene time (Beal, 1948). Hubbs (1960) favors the former route, whereas Walker (1960) seems to favor the latter.

Temperature fluctuations in the northern part of the Gulf of California, as in the northern Gulf of Mexico, are more extreme than farther south, being warmer in summer and cooler in winter. The northern species isolated here have been able to survive alongside purely tropical forms, because the winter temperatures are sufficiently cool to enable spawning and early development (Hutchins, 1947).

Of 230 species of brachyuran crabs known from the Gulf of California (Dawson, 1960), 131 (57%) are Panamic in origin, 80 (35%) are indigenous, and 19 (8%) are northern. In general, any north-temperate genus is represented by only a single species in the Gulf, and when a northern genus is represented by several species along the outer coast of Baja California, the species that occurs farthest south along the coast is the one most likely to occur in the Gulf. For such cognate populations the southern limit of range is almost always farther north in the Gulf

than along the open coast, which is explained by the generally lower temperatures resulting from upwelling in the latter location.

Differentiation between the cognate populations varies from none at all, through populational, to subspecies, and even to full species in the case of the *Libinia setosa–L. mexicana* pair. The degree of differentiation seems related to temperature tolerance. Those species that are eurythermal and widely ranging are undifferentiated, whereas those that are stenothermal and more narrowly ranging are the most strongly differentiated.

Interestingly, in the highly protected lagoons of Bahia Vizcaino and in the bay itself a number of disjunct populations of tropical species have been found that are widely ranging in the Gulf of California. The three spider crabs and two xanthids included here were formerly considered Gulf endemics. Their West Coast cognates are different at the subspecies level or below. Garth (1960) considers these isolates as relicts of a former advance up the West Coast.

Walker (1960) reported 526 species of fishes from the continental-shelf waters of the Gulf of California. Of these, 384 (73%) range mainly to the south, many of them to Panama and beyond, 92 (17%) are endemic in the sense that they have not been taken outside the Gulf, and 50 (10%) are species occurring elsewhere only to the north. More than half the latter occur as relict populations in the Gulf. Nine species are confined to the upper Gulf, including the giant sea bass *Stereolepis gigas* and the large shark *Cetorhinus maximus*, which elsewhere has a worldwide distribution in north-temperate and subarctic seas. Thirteen species are abundant in the upper Gulf but also occur less commonly to the south. For the most part, the degree of differentiation of these isolated populations from the outer coast populations is slight, often only color differences, which argues for recency of isolation. However, two genera —*Leuresthes* and *Girella*—have endemic species in the San Diegan fauna and closely related endemic species in the Gulf, which undoubtedly derive from a much earlier isolation. Although there are 92 endemic species in the Gulf, there are only four endemic genera, all monotypic, which Walker considers evidence for the relatively recent origin of these species.

Along the rocky southeastern shore of Baja California are disjunct populations of rocky-shore fishes that elsewhere occur only along the mainland coast south of Mazatlan. Walker (1960) argues that these species could not have reached their present position by migrating around the head of the Gulf, because the long stretch of east coast between Mazatlan and Guaymas is mainly mud and sand, with an almost complete lack of rocky areas. Improbable as it seems, the species must have crossed the deep open water between the mainland and Cabo San Lucas. These population isolates show even less differentiation from their parent cognates than do the relict temperate populations in the north. Hence, logically, they are more recent in origin.

At least three levels of differentiation of fishes occur in the Gulf: the oldest are the endemic species, the next oldest are the relict northern populations at the head of the Gulf, and the youngest are the disjunct southern populations along the southeast peninsula. Walker argues that a depression of isotherms sufficient to permit warm-temperate and cool-temperate species to enter the Gulf around Cabo San Lucas might well have eliminated the endemic species from the Gulf, whereas an oceanic connection across the peninsula near La Paz would require only a relatively slight cooling to enable the northern species to enter the Gulf without the thermal elimination of the endemics. The invasion of the rocky shore at the tip of the peninsula by mainland species is the most recent event.

A more recent study (Parker, 1964a, 1964b) on the macroinvertebrates, chiefly mollusks, of the Gulf of California demonstrates the same pattern of distribution, with isolated populations of more northern outer-coast species occurring toward the head of the Gulf or in deeper, colder water. Even more common are the fossil shells of northern species that up to now have not been collected alive in the Gulf. Shells of shallow-water species at present water depths of 110-115 m, radiocarbon-dated at 17,000-19,000 years B.P., indicate a lowering of sea level by this amount, as in the Gulf of Mexico, during the classical Wisconsin. During the cold phases of the Quaternary, organisms were able to migrate as much as 1,100 km south of their present position.

Information on other groups of marine organisms either is not available at all or else is insufficient for determining the presence of relict populations and the degree of their differentiation from parent populations. Among the ectoproct Bryozoa, relict populations probably occur, although Soule (1960) did not discuss this matter. Twenty-eight species of Pacific Coast origin occur in the Gulf, and species of this group comprise 57% of the total ectoproct fauna in the northern third of the Gulf.

LAND BRIDGES BETWEEN NORTH AMERICA AND EURASIA

Eustatic lowering of sea level during glacial ages is a means whereby land connections may have become established between continents or between continents and present islands, thereby permitting the dispersal of organisms. Geological evidence for such a connection between North America and Siberia is secure, whereas the suggestion by some biologists that a land bridge through the Faroe Islands to Iceland and even Greenland must have existed at some time during the Quaternary is still unacceptable to geologists.

NORTH AMERICA–SIBERIA LAND BRIDGE

At present the Bering Strait separates North America from Asia, but during nearly all of Tertiary time except in the middle Eocene a broad land connection existed (Hopkins, 1959), providing an important migrational corridor for organisms. Sometime after the middle Pliocene and before the beginning of the Pleistocene, as deduced from the distributions of fossil marine mollusks and Foraminifera, the land connection became interrupted. It presumably was re-established during each glacial age through eustatic lowering of sea level, and interrupted during each interglacial.

On the basis partly of sea-level data from the Gulf of Mexico and partly of local radiocarbon-dated materials, Hopkins concluded that in early-Wisconsin time, when sea level was more than 90 m lower that at present, a land platform more than 1,600 km wide existed between Alaska and Siberia. This connection narrowed and possibly was even severed when sea level rose higher than −45 m during the prolonged interstadial 35,000-25,000 years ago. During the late-Wisconsin glacial advances sea level again fell to about −60 m, re-establishing the land bridge, which persisted until about 11,000-10,000 years ago.

Since the land bridge existed in the Quaternary only during glacial ages, Hopkins argues that the climate was never less severe than in late-Wisconsin time. Fossil frost features on the Seward Peninsula indicate that the summers at this time were shorter and cooler than at present and that the winters were at least as severe. Only treeless tundra existed on the land bridge in late-glacial time, and Hopkins believes that at no time during the Pleistocene was the platform forested. Evidence for this opinion comes from a comparison of the vegetation of Alaska and eastern Siberia and from fossil floras. Whereas the tundra floras (and presumably faunas as well) of the two continents intermigrated during each glacial age, the forest floras have probably not been in contact with one another since early-Pleistocene or even Pliocene time.

Direct evidence of the existence of harsh climatic conditions during land-bridge intervals has been provided by the pollen analyses of Colinvaux (1963, 1964) on cores from Imuruk Lake on Seward Peninsula, an area offshore in Kotzebue Sound, and on St. Lawrence Island. The Imuruk core possibly represents continuous sedimentation from Yarmouth time to the present. All the evidence indicates that at least the northern portion of this broad land platform, regardless of altitude, had a tundra climate more severe than the present, and certainly inhospitable for the intermigration of any except cold-adapted organisms. There may have been a coastal maritime strip along the south shore with a somewhat warmer climate, but even here there is no suggestion of the development of a forest cover. The southwest portion of Kodiak Island has been free of ice since the end of Illinoian time, and hence it could have served as a refugium for the survival of Sangamon biota during Wisconsin time. However, there is no evidence for the survival of any organisms here except the hardiest species of flightless carabid beetles (Ball, 1963a).

In spite of these very severe environmental conditions, the land connection between Alaska and Siberia has been used as a migrational corridor by many groups of organisms, perhaps mainly in Tertiary time during milder climates, although inferentially in more recent times as well. Some of this evidence is summarized in the recent volume edited by Gressitt (1963). The discrepancies between the severe climate of the Quaternary land-bridge periods and the environmental requirements of the organisms that may have used the bridge at these times still must be resolved, but this cannot be done until the time relations of the migrations are more firmly established.

Stegmann (1963) has analyzed the taiga avifaunas on the two sides of the Bering Strait, now separated by almost 1,000 km. Various ages of interchange are indicated. Two species suggest quite recent interchange, 12 species with different subspecies on the two continents represent an earlier interchange, and five species pairs suggest a still earlier crossing. Faunal similarities among the deciduous-forest species to the south are still more remote in origin. Thus, Stegmann postulates interchanges at various times from early Tertiary up to the end of the Quaternary.

Kessel (1963) is concerned with the tundra avifauna of Alaska. Of 89 species, 71 also occur in northeast Siberia, although 15 of the Panboreal species are represented by different subspecies on the two continents, suggesting a reasonably long period of genetic isolation.

Ball (1963b) studied the distribution of flightless carabids, which have their center of abundance in the tundra of Alaska and eastern Siberia. The seven species that occur on both sides of the Bering Strait argue for a fairly recent intermigration. Others that are differentiated at the subspecies level suggest an earlier period of faunal continuity. Interestingly, although the Aleutian chain has been used rather extensively as a migrational corridor by plants, it has not been so used by lower animals (Lindroth, 1963c).

Of the 46 species of fleas known from Alaska (Holland, 1963), 50% occur on both sides of the Bering Strait, being differentiated at most at the subspecies level. Their distribution is not strictly a function of the distribution of their vertebrate hosts, since the ranges of host and parasite are not completely congruent, indicating that the fleas are controlled at least in part by external factors as well.

Eight of the 15 species of *Daphnia* occurring in North America also occur in Eurasia (Brooks, 1957). Because these Holarctic species are concentrated in the northwestern part of North America, Brooks concluded that the faunal exchange took place between Siberia and Alaska rather than across the Atlantic. In fact, western Europe and eastern North America lie at opposite ends of any morphological clines that have developed. In only one instance is the morphological differentiation great enough to merit subspecific recognition.

This is at best a very incomplete discussion of the Beringia problem. The evidence is overwhelming that there have been numerous and extensive interchanges in the past, but the timing and magnitude of these interchanges in the Quaternary are still very much unresolved.

NORTH AMERICA–EUROPE LAND BRIDGE

In many groups of organisms the same species occur in western Europe and eastern North America. These are the so-called amphi-Atlantic species. The resemblance between the biotas on the two sides of the North Atlantic becomes progressively greater at higher latitudes, until in the fringe of continents and islands surrounding the Arctic Ocean the biota is virtually circumpolar. Such distributions have been used as arguments for the existence of a former land bridge between Europe and North America, stretching from Great Britain through the Faroe Islands, Iceland, and Greenland to the North American mainland. This whole question has recently been examined in a symposium (Löve and Löve, 1963).

With present topographic relationships a land connection between the North Atlantic islands could not have existed during the Pleistocene (Heezen and Tharp, 1963). During the penultimate glaciation, which was the greatest and hence brought about the greatest eustatic lowering of sea level, sea level was lowered a maximum of about 160 m (Donn et al., 1962), which would still have left water gaps about 300 km wide and 200 m deep between the Faroes and Iceland and between Iceland and Greenland. The less extensive earlier and later glaciations would have left even greater water gaps. Thus, eustatic lowering of sea level by itself was insufficient to create a land bridge. If such a connection did exist during the penultimate glacial, the ridge must have subsided more than 200 m during the past 200,-000 years, and there is no geologic or oceanographic evidence for this. Furthermore, Shotton (1965) considers it unlikely that a ridge of Tertiary basalts, as proposed by some biogeographers, could have functioned as a land bridge at any time during the Pleistocene.

Nevertheless, biological dispersal has occurred by some means, mostly from the east to the west, with only a small component in the reverse direction. Lindroth (1963a), for example, points out that the beetle faunas of the Faroes, Iceland, and Greenland have a high percentage of species occurring in northern Europe. Greenland and Iceland have relatively few species in common with North America. On the other hand, Baffin Island, only 350 km from Greenland, has a distinctly North American fauna. From this evidence Lindroth regards Davis Strait between Greenland and the rest of North America as the most effective faunal barrier in the entire circumpolar region.

Because many of the beetles are flightless or otherwise have low mobility and because the dispersal along this island chain has occurred contrary to prevailing winds and currents, Lindroth concludes they must have dispersed along a continuous or near-continuous land connection. There is little evidence for speciation of beetles in the Pleistocene (this is also argued by Shotton, 1965, on the basis of fossil material, although not agreed to by Ball, 1964). Since there are so few endemic species on these islands, Lindroth argues that dispersal must have occurred after species formation, hence at some time during the Pleistocene and probably during one of the interglacials.

Hultén (1963) concluded from a detailed analysis of the distribution of plants occurring on the North Atlantic islands and elsewhere that there is little evidence for a land bridge in late-Tertiary or Quaternary time. On the other hand, Dahl (1963) argued for the existence of such a bridge no earlier than Pliocene time. The amphi-Atlantic plants are mainly arctic-subarctic in distribution, which Dahl considers evidence for severe climatic conditions at the time the bridge existed. He considers a basaltic land connection in Pliocene time or later as a likely possibility.

Waldén (1963) claims that the land gastropods offer no evidence for a Pleistocene land bridge to Iceland. However, Omodeo (1963) favors continental drift to account for similarities in the earthworm faunas of the southern continents and a land bridge across the North Atlantic, over which many eastern species moved westward to North America, but only a few rare western species moved eastward. Evolution has been slow in the earthworms, and there appears to be relatively little interspecific competition. Thus, Omodeo regards the European species in North

America as an integral part of the Holarctic ancient fauna.

G. E. Gates (in correspondence) considers it likely that all earthworms were wiped out in the glaciated regions of North America, with no survivors in refugia or nunataks, and that the species presently occurring there, chiefly European, were introduced by man. "Today, all megadrile species of Alaska, Canada, Newfoundland, as well as Greenland and Iceland, are present in those regions . . . because they were accidentally introduced by man. The megadrile fauna of New England differs from that of Canada only by the presence in greenhouses of South and Central American exotics as well as Asiatic, or outdoors by the presence of two American endemics that also were introduced by man." W. R. Murchie (in correspondence) considers that there is as yet too little definite information available on the species and distribution of North American earthworms to resolve this problem.

More recently Einarsson (1964) has concluded from a re-examination of all available geological and biological evidence that there is no justification or even necessity for postulating a late-Tertiary or Quaternary bridge to explain the present distribution of organisms along the North Atlantic island chain.

Undoubtedly many species of insects and other invertebrates have accidentally been transferred from one region to another. Lindroth (1957), in a fascinating bit of biological sleuthing, demonstrated convincingly that a considerable number of species of insects (chiefly carabid beetles), centipedes, millipedes, oniscid isopods, and lesser numbers of other terrestrial groups were passively introduced into Newfoundland along with ballast in the holds of fishing vessels. Before any permanent settlements existed in Newfoundland or adjacent areas, the ships took on rocks, old bricks, dirt, etc. as ballast for their westward voyage. When this material was dumped on shore rather than in the water, the included animals had a chance to become established. After steam vessels came into use and especially after the development of colonies in New England, which made ballast unprofitable in favor of cash cargoes, ballast introductions ceased, but other introductions were made in association with livestock (such as various dung beetles) or agricultural plants.

As a final embellishment of this idea, Hedgpeth (1953) has suggested that the disjunct populations of some of the northern hydroids in the northern Gulf of Mexico may not be natural but may have become established through passive winter transport on the hulls of oil tankers plying between Wilmington, Delaware, and Port Aransas, Texas.

GREAT PLAINS

A north-south strip, about 300 km wide by 1,100 km long, extending from central-western Texas to South Dakota is currently a semiarid treeless expanse. The southern portion, although unglaciated, contains deposits consisting of four members of coarse clastic sediments laid down during colder climate, separated by three members of finer materials deposited during warmer climates. This sequence has been correlated with the till and moraine sequence of the Mississippi Valley on the basis of its vertebrate (Hib-

bard *et al.*, this volume) and molluscan (Taylor, 1960, this volume) assemblages and their climatic implications.

The record of mollusks for this region indicates that climatic conditions gradually deteriorated after Miocene time, resulting at the end of the Pliocene in conditions probably more adverse to plants and animals than at any other time in the Cenozoic (Frye and Leonard, 1957). Branchiate snails, which require permanent surface water, were absent. The snails that were present are kinds that can withstand long periods of desiccation.

At the beginning of the Pleistocene there was a marked climatic improvement, culminating in Kansan time. Branchiate snails reappeared, and there was a considerable increase in the total gastropod fauna. The terrestrial gastropods indicate a dominant prairie vegetation, with belts of trees and shrubs along the valleys. The large helicine gastropods that flourish in the deciduous forests a few hundred kilometers to the east of the Great Plains are not present, however, suggesting that at no time in the Quaternary were the southern Great Plains forested.

In post-Kansan time the climate again deteriorated, until today it is considered to be almost as extreme as at the end of the Pliocene. But whereas then the region was largely a featureless plain, now at least the streams in deeply incised through-valleys are perennial. Both the Yarmouth and Sangamon interglacials were moister than at present, although gradually declining (Leonard, 1950; Frye and Leonard, 1957). During the glacial ages the climate was much more severe than at present. For example, during the Illinoian Glaciation, Harper County in Oklahoma is considered to have had a climate roughly comparable to that of North Dakota today (Taylor and Hibbard, 1955). During the Illinoian maximum, spruce seems to have been established in the region (Kapp, 1963).

Virtually no work has been done on other groups of animals, although they are certainly represented in these sections and should eventually be studied. For example, beetles would be expected to be abundant and of great use in deciphering past climates and vegetations. Ostracods eventually may be helpful (Gutentag and Benson, 1962), although at present the fossil freshwater ostracods are not well enough known to be used as stratigraphic indices for the subdivisions of the Quaternary, or for interpreting past conditions. An exception is *Candona nyensis*, which appears to be restricted to Pleistocene deposits, not occurring at all in the Pliocene. Actual documentation by fossil records of the changing distributions of various groups of organisms during the Quaternary will be available from these sections when they are finally studied by specialists.

GREAT BASIN AND THE SOUTHWEST

Increased rainfall and lowered temperatures in the Southwest during the glacial ages are indicated in part by the history of the interior-drainage lakes of the Great Basin. The sediments of Searles Lake, California, contain two sequences of lake mud representing pluvial periods, each overlain by evaporites representing drier periods without inflow from Owens Lake at higher elevation (Flint and Gale, 1958). Radiocarbon dates show that the more recent period of inflow from Owens Lake began prior to 23,000

B.P. and ended about 10,000 B.P., which roughly coincide with the limits of the classical Wisconsin in the central United States. In a note published before any radiocarbon dates were available, Roosma (1958) had already concluded from the pollen diagram that the upper lake mud (the Parting Mud) probably derived from Two Creeks time.

The lower Bottom Mud derives from an earlier major glaciation in Wisconsin time (Flint and Gale, 1958; Flint and Brandtner, 1961), which at the time of those studies was not yet recognized in the glacial sequence of the Mid-continent. The bottommost Mixed Layer is considered pre-Wisconsin, possibly Sangamon and Illinoian (Smith, 1962). Thus, here there is an alternation of moist-cool conditions (glacial or stadial) with warmer-dry conditions (interglacial or interstadial). According to Broecker and Orr (1958), a twofold increase in precipitation and a 5° C decrease in temperature would be sufficient for the development of these pluvial conditions. Taylor (in Flint and Gale, 1958) concluded from an examination of the mollusks in the Parting Mud that July temperatures were about 4.5° C lower than at present.

A core from Great Salt Lake (Eardley and Gvosdetsky, 1960), believed to encompass all of Quaternary time since the Aftonian except for the last postglacial, exhibits five strong pluvial cycles. The only animals in the core studied to date are the mollusks and ostracods, although it was noted that the fecal pellets of the brine shrimp *Artemia gracilis* were abundant during the very saline and shallow-water phases.

These basin systems are extremely interesting from the standpoints of paleolimnology and zoogeography, although these aspects are almost completely unexplored. The lakes in these basins not only experienced great fluctuations in water volume—Lake Bonneville at its maximum, for example, being almost as large as Lake Michigan (Morrison, this volume)—but also fluctuations in mineral content of their water from strictly fresh to highly saline, and occasionally they experienced external connections with through-systems. The latter would permit the immigration of various groups of aquatic and aquatic-associated organisms. Lake Bonneville is believed to have overflowed into the Snake River only at the time of highest lake level in late-Wisconsin time (Morrison, this volume).

Such alternation of pluvial and interpluvial periods, with all the contrasts in environmental conditions they connote, and the occasional external connections at high water levels surely afforded many opportunities for immigration, expansion of range, and then subsequent fragmentation of range during the ensuing interpluvial periods, thereby providing the basis for genetic differentiation. This is undoubtedly the history in brief of the remarkable endemic fishes in the Great Basin (Hubbs and Miller, 1948).

Reduced temperatures during the pluvial periods resulted in the downward displacement of vegetational zones, permitting the re-establishment of continuous ranges of biotal elements that had been isolated on mountain tops. During the interpluvials these ranges contracted, again isolating population segments from one another. Thus, here is another recurrent mechanism of geographic isolation that could have led to genetic differentiation of the isolates.

Studies of the mollusks from several localities in Monahans Dunes and at Lubbock in the Llano Estacado suggest that January and July temperatures were 8-11° C cooler than at present during the Tahoka Pluvial 23,500-16,000 years B.P. (Wendorf, 1961). The extent of the altitudinal depression of vegetational zones is generally given as ranging between 1,200 m, according to pollen (Martin, 1963), and 600 m, according to boreal elements in the Burnet Cave assemblage (Murray, 1957) and the presence of *Juniperus osteosperma* in fossil *Neotoma* middens (Wells and Jorgensen, 1964). The animal microfossils and pollen in a lake in the Chuska Mountains, New Mexico, indicate alpine conditions here during the last glaciopluvial period (Megard, 1964). In spite of such an extensive lowering of vegetational zones, however, there is no evidence that the present arid barrier of western Texas and northern Mexico was replaced by humid deciduous forest at any time during the Quaternary (Martin and Harrell, 1957).

The occurrence of disjunct isolates of northern species on mountain tops well south of their continuous range is well documented among the vertebrates, but there are relatively few instances known as yet among the invertebrates. There is no reason to doubt, however, that when the region has been adequately studied faunistically, many examples of altitudinal isolates will have been discovered. Lacking fossil evidence, one can only assume that the degree of differentiation between such vicars is more or less directly proportional to the duration of isolation.

In southern Arizona are some allopatric populations of flightless beetles of the genus *Scaphinotus*, which feed exclusively on snails. These are primarily northern beetles, which in this region are confined to coniferous forests at elevations greater than 2,100 m. Ball (1964), from a close study of these populations, has postulated that this region was invaded by a stock from the north during a pluvial age, and that in the following interpluvial subpopulations were isolated on the mountain tops. Quite likely all the peaks initially harbored the beetles, but they have been eliminated from all except two. Another pluvial-interpluvial cycle resulted in the immigration and subsequent isolation of stocks adapted to somewhat less severe conditions, and these have persisted as other populations on mountain tops. Unlike Shotton (1965), who believes there has been virtually no speciation of beetles in the Pleistocene, Ball conceives of all this differentiation as having occurred in this time interval.

Klots (1964) has proposed the same kind of explanation for southward isolation of populations of Lepidoptera, not only in the western mountains but also in the Appalachians and in the high central area of Mexico.

In the Sonoran and Chihuahuan deserts occur some interesting burrowing scarabaeid beetles, in which dispersal appears to be accomplished entirely by the heavy-bodied flightless females being washed out of their burrows during flood stages (Howden, 1963). Their present distributions are linear in relation to old drainage channels or shorelines of Pleistocene lakes. Although much of the differentiation occurred in the Tertiary, Howden believes that at least some occurred in the Pleistocene associated with dispersals and isolations occasioned by the pluvial-interpluvial cycles.

These beetles give no indication that the east-west desert barrier was ever completely interrupted during the Quaternary, thereby permitting the free north-south movement of organisms.

Twelve species of tiger beetles (*Cicindela*) currently occur in the Estancia Valley in central New Mexico (Rumpp, 1961). Most of these species are limited in their distribution by the moisture requirements of the subterranean larvae and pupae, and hence the species occur close to the margins of wet playas. In this respect they resemble the fishes studied by Hubbs and Miller (1948) in being limited by moisture rather than by temperature. On the basis of faunal resemblances Howden concluded that Estancia Valley was connected hydrographically with the Pecos River in late-Pleistocene time and with a northern drainage system in more remote time. Pleistocene uplift probably isolated these southern migrants. Elsewhere, likewise, the ecologically restricted species of tiger beetles in the arid Southwest are represented by various subspecies that seem to reflect genetic differentiation during various periods of interpluvial isolation (Rumpp, 1956, 1957).

CRAYFISHES

The crayfishes are particularly suitable for working out patterns of distribution because of their restriction to water itself or to moist soils adjacent to water or along river channels. Moreover, as a result of increased attention they have received in the past few decades their distributions and phylogenetic relationships are becoming quite well understood. More than half of all the species and subspecies of crayfishes in North America have been described since 1930 (Fitzpatrick, 1964). Only two major papers will be summarized in this review, although attention might well be called to the papers of Williams (1954, 1960), Williams and Leonard (1952), Hobbs (1958), and Hobbs and Barr (1960) for additional studies relating distribution and evolution to events of the Quaternary.

FLORIDA

The study of Hobbs (1942) on the crayfishes of Florida demonstrates the necessity for intensive faunistic work preceding biogeographic speculation. By his intensive collecting in all parts of Florida the list of known forms was increased from 8 or 10 to 42 species and subspecies, most of them new. Many of these taxa are extremely localized in distribution, being restricted to small watersheds or portions of watersheds within the state.

The largest genus is *Procambarus*, with 32 forms. Consideration of these by species groups shows that the localized populations of closely related species are largely allopatric. Five regions of well-drained soils in northern Florida presently act as east-west or north-south migrational barriers to many species. Since it is likely these regions experienced significant expansions and contractions during eustatic sea-level changes in the Quaternary, it might be inferred that much of this speciation has been quite recent. This would be particularly true for those forms that are obligate burrowers.

The original crayfishes of Florida are considered to have come from stocks inhabiting the upper coastal plain of Georgia and Alabama. Hobbs postulates that at least twice after insular Florida first became joined to the mainland the Suwannee Strait across the northern portion of the peninsula was re-established, thereby isolating from the mainland parent populations any organisms that had crossed the land bridge. He postulates that one of these early migrants to the Pliocene "Ocala Island" differentiated into the troglobitic species presently occurring in the caverns of that region. In post-Suwannee Strait time the crayfishes immigrated from the north by six different routes along various river systems and their adjacent poorly drained flatlands.

The Barbatus Section of *Procambarus* is represented by 10 species in northern Florida. The more primitive members of this complex, and hence inferentially the ones that immigrated earliest from the dispersal center north of Florida, are peripheral in distribution, whereas the species that immigrated and evolved later are located farther north.

The general pattern of migration and evolution presented by Hobbs is logical and quite convincing, although he did not attempt to relate it to specific climatic or eustatic events of the Quaternary. Although he considers that most of this differentiation occurred after the early Pleistocene, it might well have been earlier than this if the Tertiary age of "terraces" above the Pamlico in North Carolina (Oaks and Coch, 1963) can be extrapolated to Florida.

EAST-CENTRAL UNITED STATES

Rhoades (1962) has attempted to explain the present distribution of 13 related species and subspecies of crayfishes of the genus *Orconectes* section *limosus*. These crayfishes are characteristic of high-gradient upland streams, mostly in the present Ohio River basin. The genus *Orconectes* is believed to have split off from *Procambarus* in the Ozarkian Highlands in late-Miocene time, and then the progenitor of the *limosus* section is believed to have reached the Teays River and the Ohio River in Pliocene time. The population in the more northern Teays River developed recurved hooks on the gonopods characteristic of the group *limosus*, whereas the population of the Pliocene Ohio River developed divergent tips characteristic of the group *rafinesquei*.

The *rafinesquei* group contains seven species, one of which, *O. pellucidus*, is represented by four subspecies in caverns beneath the Cumberland Plateau. All the surface species are presently isolated as Pliocene–early-Pleistocene relicts in small drainages in unglaciated Kentucky and Tennessee, surrounded by more widely distributed species of other groups. The only exception to this general pattern of distribution is one pre-Pleistocene relict in southeastern Missouri. The isolation of the populations that led to the differentiation of these species is believed to have been accomplished primarily by the restriction of habitat by alluviation of the lower stream courses during the Kansas and Illinoian glacial ages and in part by pressure from such other species as *Procambarus blandingi acutus* and *Orconectes immunis*, both adapted to low-gradient streams that subsequently invaded these altered habitats. Rhoades regards *O. pellucidus* as having become widespread in the caves of the Cumberland Plateau at least by the beginning of the Quaternary, and that fragmentation into the present four subspecies resulted from aggradation of the major streams, chiefly in Illinoian time. Interestingly, though, the subspecies *O. p. pellucidus* still occurs on both sides of the Ohio River, suggesting either that this stream is not a complete barrier to gene transfer or else that it has become so only relatively recently.

The Teays was the master Tertiary river of the eastern interior part of the United States. Draining roughly 500,000 km², it extended from the eastern side of the Blue Ridge in Virginia and North Carolina across West Virginia, Ohio, Indiana, and Illinois. It lay far enough north to be affected directly by the continental glaciers. The Kansan ice sheet split the *limosus* population of this river into three segments. *O. limosus* persisted in the upstream portion east of the terminal moraine in southeastern Ohio, later taken over as part of the Ohio River, whereas two other species migrated separately via sluiceways into the Ohio River drainage in southern Indiana, where they have persisted up to the present. One of these immigrants from the north actually overlies in southern Indiana a troglobitic population of *O. pellucidus* from the south.

Much of the modern Ohio River was formed in Kansan time. Aggradation of the lower portion of the Ohio resulted in the immigration of three species of crayfish adapted to low gradients and the subsequent restriction of *O. limosus* to upper elevations in the Appalachians. When the Illinoian ice impounded the Ohio River above Louisville, the flow of the river was supposedly reversed, thereby enabling *O. limosus* to get into the Chesapeake Bay drainage. Since then it has spread through the Delaware River system into the lower Hudson River. At the same time the subspecies *sanborni* of *O. propinquus*, which differentiated during the Sangamon is believed to have been responsible for the complete elimination of *O. limosus* west of the Allegheny Divide.

In contrast to the situation in Florida, where the speciation of *Procambarus* inferentially seems to have been relatively recent but the various stages in the attainment of the present faunal pattern have not been related to specific events of the Quaternary, in the *limosus* section of *Orconectes* the species are mostly quite ancient, except for possibly fairly recent subspeciation in the cavernicolous *O. pellucidus*, but the changing patterns of distribution have been quite closely related to the glacial changes in drainage pattern and alluviation of streams.

Fossil Remains

Except for the vertebrates and mollusks, speculations regarding the Quaternary distributions and differentiation of various groups of animals have been based almost exclusively on their present distributions, unsupported by evidence from fossils. Hence, the temporal aspects of migration, isolation, and differentiation are often highly speculative, dependent largely on current understanding of the Quaternary geology of the pertinent regions. There are many potential sources of fossil material, however, and these promise to be rewarding when adequately studied.

Most extensive, of course, are lacustrine sediments. A recent review (Frey, 1964) has demonstrated that all groups of freshwater animals, except possibly the coelenterates, are capable of leaving some morphological remains in sediments. In the Cladocera, ostracods, and rhizopods, at least, the remains can be identified positively to species, and it is likely that with attention by specialists the same degree of precision will eventually be attained for a number of other groups. Terrestrial animals can also be preserved in lake sediments. Probably most important here are beetles, chiefly carabids, which can be identified to species and which because of their narrow ecological tolerances are very useful in interpreting past environmental conditions (see Coope, 1961, and Pearson, 1961, for a general discussion of the problems involved). Even such soft-bodied animals as spiders have been reported from lacustrine sediments.

Besides lacustrine sediments, the sediments of the Great Plains that have already yielded such rich material of vertebrates and mollusks (Hibbard *et al.*, this volume; Taylor, this volume) should contain other groups, and also the accumulations in caves and sinkholes (Guilday *et al.*, 1964; Murray, 1957). Tills and alluvia, since they frequently contain mollusks, might also be expected to contain remains of other animals if knowingly searched for. Even the fossil packrat middens (Wells and Jorgensen, 1964) hold promise. This, then, is a plea for the more extensive and intensive exploitation of such deposits by specialists in the various groups of organisms.

In many respects subaqueous basin sediments are most satisfactory, because they permit the working out of detailed biostratigraphies, showing not only the presence or absence of particular species but also community composition and its change from level to level associated with changing internal and external environmental conditions. Such detailed fossil stratigraphies can have three major applications: (1) elucidation of changes in distribution in response to glaciation or deglaciation where records are available from enough widely scattered localities, (2) aid in interpreting external events such as climate and geomorphic processes, and (3) elucidation of the changing ecology of the lake itself and of its watershed.

Studies on the remains of beetles in British Quaternary sediments (see Frey, 1964, for a summary of the work by Shotton, Coope, and Pearson) have shown very nicely the adjustments of the ranges of species in response to climatic changes in the Quaternary. The notostracan *Lepidurus arcticus* has been recovered from late-glacial deposits in Great Britain far south of its present arctic range between 65° and 80° N (Mitchell, 1957; Morrison, 1959). Wright (1932) attempted to determine the successive immigration of species of mollusks into the Tippecanoe River basin in northern Indiana in postglacial time on the basis of their sequential occurrence in cores of lake sediments.

Sparks (see review of papers in Frey, 1964) has used the detailed stratigraphy of mollusks and the ecology of the species in helping to resolve various geomorphic problems. As an example, he was able to demonstrate that certain flat-bottomed valleys in the chalk were formed by spring sapping (Sparks and Lewis, 1957). Megard (1964) concluded from the ecology of fossil Cladocera and midges in its sediments that Dead Man Lake had probably never been deeper than 5 m, even though the sediments have a thickness of roughly 10 m. This helps to substantiate a theory of bedrock subsidence for the origin of this and similar basins.

Since the pioneer study of Deevey (1942) on the animal microfossils in Linsley Pond, Connecticut, our knowledge of the occurrence and significance of cladoceran and midge fossils has expanded rapidly. During the climatic amelioration of the Alleröd there was a rapid immigration of Cladocera into a north-German lake, and then a subsequent decline with the return of tundra conditions (Frey, 1958). Permanent temperate lakes apparently acquired nearly their complete modern assemblage of Cladocera very early in postglacial time (Frey, 1961). Subsequent changes have concerned mainly internal adjustments in the population in response to naturally occurring ecological changes in the lake or to man-induced changes in the watershed (Goulden, 1964). Immigration of new species may accompany eutrophication.

Interpretation of past conditions on the basis of the present ecology of species is strengthened by a study demonstrating a marked morphological and ecological stability of the Cladocera since at least the last interglacial and possibly back into the Tertiary (Frey, 1962). Furthermore, even though most species of the group are widely distributed, usually even intercontinental, quantitative studies of the sedimentary communities do show progressive latitudinal changes in community composition (DeCosta, 1964). There are variations in the distribution of remains over the floor of a lake, and hence it is important to understand these in selecting sites for coring lakes (Mueller, 1964). Contrary to an early assumption (Frey, 1960), the remains are never completely integrated.

Work is really just beginning on the ostracods (Winkler, 1960, 1962; Staplin, 1963a, 1963b), and only one study on close-interval biostratigraphy has been done (Benson and MacDonald, 1963). The latter study seems to indicate a progressive warming of Lake Erie and also suggests that *Candona caudata* in the early history of the lake gradually evolved into *Candona novacaudata* in more recent time.

Midges are important indicators of past environmental conditions in lakes because of the close control of at least deepwater species by oxygen content of the water and redox potential. Unfortunately, at the present state of our knowledge the head capsules of the larvae usually can be identified only to genus and sometimes only to subfamily, but even these imprecise identifications are useful. Types requiring high oxygen levels, which occur early in a lake's history, are replaced by types tolerating low oxygen levels, demonstrating the progressive reduction in deepwater oxygen as a lake ages (Deevey, 1942; Stahl, 1959). Where only polyoxybionts occur, it can be concluded that the oxygen never reached very low levels (Megard, 1964).

The necessity for time control in biostratigraphy is demonstrated by the uncertainty of interpreting some insect remains from a deposit in Florida (Young, 1959b). Many of the remains were almost fresh in appearance, suggesting that they might be intrusive into the older sediments. And yet they included a species of grouse locust that is now absent from Florida, being restricted presently to the Coastal Plain of Texas and eastern Mexico.

MISCELLANEOUS STUDIES

As early as 1902 Ortmann contended that it was erroneous to establish zoogeographic regions exclusively on the basis of present distributions without considering the historical aspects of the development of these distributions. Because of their close similarity Ortmann concluded that the crayfishes of western North America were derived from eastern Asia via the Bering land bridge. In only one instance has a species of the western crayfishes penetrated east of the Continental Divide—in the region of Yellowstone National Park; this Ortmann regards as evidence of stream capture. Normally the Continental Divide is virtually an absolute barrier to the dispersal of higher aquatic organisms (Taylor, 1964).

In a somewhat later, yet still early, significant study, Ortmann (1913) attempted to discover the importance of the Alleghenian Divide in the distribution of freshwater organisms; this study was based in large part on personal field work. He regarded the freshwater mussels (naiads) as most important in this study. Although the fauna of these in the Ohio River is fairly uniform, there is a gradual decrease in number of species upstream, from about 60 near Cincinnati to 47 in Pennsylvania. At least 17 genera in the upper Ohio River have not been able to get over the Alleghenian Divide, even though they extend into the headwaters of the Allegheny River. Only two genera on the Atlantic side do not occur in the interior. Six Atlantic species have closely related species in the upper Ohio River and one in the upper Tennessee River. Four species are identical on the Atlantic and western sides.

Related species east and west of the Alleghenies are explained by the interior species having made their way around the northern end of the mountains in preglacial time and then being separated into eastern and western populations by the glaciers. On the Atlantic side these are mainly northern in distribution. Following deglaciation they migrated northward, accompanied by a number of species of southern origin. Species that are identical or only slightly differentiated on the two sides of the Divide and tend to be rather localized on one side are explained on the basis of stream capture. Capture of certain southern headwater tributaries of the Tennessee River by the Coosa River seems well substantiated by the naiad distribution.

Another significant early study is that of Baker (1920), which is valuable for its compilation of records of fossil vertebrates (chiefly large mammals) and mollusks from glaciated United States and Canada east of the Rockies, and for Baker's own detailed studies of the Lake Chicago sediments. The latter are based on personal collecting at numerous stations along the newly cut North Shore Channel at Chicago. The total list of fossils included 98 species of aquatic mollusks, 1 specimen of the crayfish *Procambarus blandingi acutus* (this is unusual because there are so few fossil records of freshwater decapods), 1 beetle, 3 fishes, 1 bird, and 5 mammals. A summary table shows that except for beetles from the Scarborough beds of Ontario, there was at that time virtually no record of invertebrates other than mollusks from the freshwater Pleistocene of North America east of the Rockies. From his studies Baker attempted a rather detailed reconstruction of the history of Glacial Lake Chicago.

As examples of the potentially rapid response of organisms to climatic change, Smith (1957) has described the distributions of several amphibians and reptiles with main ranges in the glaciated region and relict populations in the south, or with main ranges in the south and relict populations in the north. The latter are believed to have arisen by the expansion of southern ranges during the postglacial warm period and then the subsequent contraction during cooling, leaving the biotal pockets in the north.

Similarly, Smith cites examples of eastward dispersion and subsequent isolation of prairie species, presumably during the postglacial xerothermic phase, although Guilday *et al.* (1964) conclude from the fossil records of certain prairie vertebrates, particularly the 13-lined ground squirrel and the sharp-tailed grouse, in a radiocarbon-dated sequence, that the eastward steppe expansion occurred in late-glacial time or even earlier. The authors also conclude that there was no refugium for temperate biota in this part of the eastern mountains during the Wisconsin glacial. The invertebrates recovered from this cave deposit—3 millipedes and 26 species of terrestrial gastropods—are perhaps partly intrusive and indicate little except for the dramatic decrease in numbers of a large woodland snail below the 7-m level, correlated with the occurrence of a taiga vegetation at this time.

On the other hand, there have been changes in invertebrate distribution even during the past 100 years, apparently correlated with the warming and drying trend during this interval, although the exact controls are difficult to demonstrate. Walker (1957) collected Orthoptera intensively in the DeGrassi Point region of Lake Simcoe over a 60-year period, during which 7 species, chiefly northern, disappeared from the region, and 5 species, chiefly southern, became established. Even making due allowance for disturbances brought about by man, there still seems clear evidence for a general northward movement of species.

In contrast to the crayfishes of Florida studied by Hobbs (1942), the several genera of flightless fossorial beetles in the Southeast reported on by Howden (1963) are confined to well-drained inland sand ridges—the so-called "sand hills." The genus *Mycotrupes* is represented by five allopatric species in the Southeast, three of which occur in Florida. The species burrow deep in the ground and have their peak of surface activity as adults in winter. Howden reasons from their ecology that the mean summer temperatures in Florida during the glacial ages were perhaps 16-18° C, roughly similar to Marquette, Michigan, today. He also reasons that although some of the pertinent sand-hill areas might have been restricted by higher seastands during the interglacials, they could not have been completely covered by the sea. This is contrary to the opinion prevailing some years ago that much of Florida was transgressed by the sea during the interglacials.

Young (1959a) points out that there are relict populations of northern water beetles in northern Florida and in the Gulf Coastal Plain, and that some formerly isolated populations have been reunited during or since the Pleistocene and are now interbreeding. Young suggests that such secondary introgression in insects is probably more common than generally realized.

The problem of "glacial relicts" has already been alluded to in the reference to the paper by Ricker (1959). More recently, Johnson (1964) has discussed the distribution of all potential glacial relicts in the Arctic—the amphipods *Gammaracanthus* (2 species), *Pontoporeia affinis*, and *Pallasea quadrispinosa*, the mysid *Mysis relicta*, the isopod *Mesidothea entomon*, a copepod *Limnocalanus macrurus*, a fish *Myoxocephalus quadricornis*, and the ringed seal *Phoca hispida*. The center of relict populations in North America is in the central Arctic in the vicinity of Victoria and Somerset islands. Victoria has 5 of 7 relict species and Somerset, 3. None is known from Devon and Cornwallis islands except *Limnocalanus* and likewise none from Greenland, although here *Mysis litoralis* occurs in two lakes. Relicts in the arctic islands occur only in areas of marine inundation. Colonization has not been from the mainland because of the absence there of *Gammaracanthus* and *Mesidothea* and the presence of *Pontoporeia* there but not on the islands. Johnson suggests that the islands and mainland were colonized separately, with a considerable time interval between, the mainland at least in early-Wisconsin time and the islands not until virtually the end of Wisconsin time.

This is a difficult problem. Bousfield (in correspondence) agrees with Holmquist (1959): "The so-called 'glacial relicts' are not relicts at all, since they have very wide pan-arctic distributions and did not likely evolve from marine progenitors in the relatively brief (10,000-year) period since the Wisconsin retreat. Crustaceans, particularly freshwater forms, are relatively primitive and evolve very slowly, particularly where physical conditions are severe as in the temporary (and even permanent) fresh waters of glaciated arctic and subalpine regions. In my opinion, the reason why cold freshwater bodies contain such a high percentage of crustacean phylogenetic relicts is that more highly specialized crustaceans, evolving mainly in warm marine, or less rigorous aquatic environments, have not yet solved the physiological problems of existing in harsh environments (*e.g.* by resting eggs) and are thus unable to replace the ancient forms through direct competition."

Destruction of surface and subsurface drainages by glaciation in Canada and the United States resulted in the elimination or forced migration southward of the amphipods formerly living there (Bousfield, 1958). Thirty species and subspecies, chiefly of the ancient freshwater *Crangonyx* section of the Gammaridae, have now moved back into the region to the limit of the hard-water drainage, and a few have invaded the soft waters of the Precambrian Shield and the boreal forest region. On the Pacific Slope a small number of populations have been isolated by locally glaciated and ecologically unsuitable watersheds. Of the amphipods of relatively recent marine origin, which are abundant in the southern part of the continent, only *Pontoporeia affinis* and *Hyalella azteca* have been able to invade the northland, the latter being the most common and widely distributed freshwater amphipod in North America.

REFERENCES

Addicott, W. O., and Emerson, W. K., 1959, Late Pleistocene invertebrates from Punta Cabras, Baja California, Mexico: Amer. Mus. Novitates, No. 1925, p. 1-33

Baker, F. C., 1920, The life of the Pleistocene or glacial period as recorded in the deposits laid down by the great ice sheets: Univ. Illinois Bull., v. 17, No. 41, p. i-xiv, 1-476

Ball, G. E., 1963a, Kodiak beetles and bears (abst.): 11th Ann. Meeting Entomol. Soc. Alberta Proc., p. 8

—— 1963b, The distribution of the species of the subgenus *Cryobius* (Coleoptera, Carabidae, *Pterostichus*); with special reference to the Bering Land Bridge and Pleistocene refugia, *in* Gressitt, J. L. (ed.): Pacific Basin biogeography: Honolulu, Bishop Mus. Press, p. 133-151

—— 1964, The genus *Scaphinotus* (Coleoptera, Carabidae) and the Pleistocene Epoch in southwestern United States (abst.): 12th Intern. Congr. Entomol., London, p. 70 (manuscript of complete paper examined through courtesy of author)

Bayer, F. M., 1953, Zoogeography and evolution in the octocorallian family Gorgoniidae: Mar. Sci. Gulf and Caribb. Bull., v. 3, p. 100-119

—— 1954, Anthozoa: Alcyonaria, *in* Galtsoff, P. S. (ed.), Gulf of Mexico; its origin, waters, and marine life: U.S. Fish and Wildl. Serv., Fish. Bull., v. 89, p. 279-284

Beal, C. H., 1948, Reconnaissance of the geology and oil possibilities of Baja California, Mexico: Geol. Soc. Amer. Mem., v. 31, p. 1-138

Beecher, W. J., 1955, Late-Pleistocene isolation in salt-marsh sparrows: Ecology, v. 36, p. 23-28

Benson, R. H., and MacDonald, H. C., 1963, Postglacial (Holocene) ostracodes from Lake Erie: Univ. Kansas Paleont. Contr., Arthropoda, art. 4, p. 1-26

Blair, W. F., 1958, Distributional patterns of vertebrates in the southern United States in relation to past and present environments, *in* Hubbs, C. L. (ed.), Zoogeography: Amer. Assoc. Adv. Sci., Publ. 51, p. 433-468

—— this volume, Amphibian speciation

Bousfield, E. L., 1958, Fresh-water amphipod crustaceans of glaciated North America: Can. Field-Nat., v. 72, p. 55-113

Broecker, W. S., and Orr, P. C., 1958, Radiocarbon chronology of Lake Lahontan and Lake Bonneville: Geol. Soc. Amer. Bull., v. 69, p. 1009-1032

Broecker, W. S., Turekian, K. K., and Heezen, B. C., 1958, The relation of deep sea sedimentation rates to variations in climate: Amer. J. Sci., v. 256, p. 503-517

Brooks, J. L., 1957, The systematics of North American *Daphnia:* Connecticut Acad. Arts Sci. Mem., v. 13, p. 1-180

Carlgren, Oskar, and Hedgpeth, J. W., 1952, Actinaria, Zooantharia and Ceriantharia from shallow water in the northwestern Gulf of Mexico: Inst. Mar. Sci. Texas Publ., v. 2, p. 143-172

Coe, W. R., 1951, The nemertean faunas of the Gulf of Mexico and of southren Florida: Mar. Sci. Gulf and Caribb. Bull., v. 1, p. 149-186

—— 1954, The nemertean fauna of the Gulf of Mexico, *in* Galtsoff, P. S. (ed.), Gulf of Mexico; its origin, waters, and marine life: U.S. Fish and Wildl. Serv., Fish. Bull., v. 89, p. 303-309

Colinvaux, P. A., 1963, A pollen record from arctic Alaska, reaching glacial and Bering land bridge times: Nature, v. 198, p. 609-610

—— 1964, The environment of the Bering land bridge: Ecol. Monogr., v. 34, p. 297-329

Coope, G. R., 1961, On the study of glacial and interglacial insect faunas, *in* Symposium on Quaternary ecology: Linn. Soc. London Proc., v. 172, p. 62-65

Curray, J. R., 1960, Sediments and history of Holocene transgression, Continental Shelf, northwest Gulf of Mexico, *in* Shepard, F. P. *et al.*, Recent sediments, northwest Gulf of Mexico: Amer. Assoc. Petroleum Geologists, p. 221-266

Dahl, Eilif, 1963, Plant migrations across the North Atlantic Ocean and their importance for the paleogeography of the region, *in* Löve, A. and Löve, D. (eds.), North Atlantic biota and their history: London, Pergamon, p. 173-188

Dawson, E. Y., 1960, A review of the ecology, distribution, and affinities of the benthic flora, *in* Symposium—The biogeography of Baja California and adjacent seas: Syst. Zool., v. 9, p. 93-100

DeCosta, J. J., 1964, Latitudinal distribution of chydorid Cladocera in the Mississippi Valley, based on their remains in surficial lake sediments: Inv. Indiana Lakes and Streams, v. 6, p. 65-101

Deevey, E. S., Jr., 1942, Studies on Connecticut Lake sediments. III, The biostratonomy of Linsley Pond: Amer. J. Sci., v. 240, p. 233-264, 313-324

—— 1949, Biogeography of the Pleistocene, Part I, Europe and North America: Geol. Soc. Amer. Bull., v. 60, p. 1315-1416

—— 1950, Hydroids from Louisiana and Texas, with remarks on the Pleistocene biogeography of the western Gulf of Mexico: Ecology, v. 31, p. 334-367

—— 1954, Hydroids of the Gulf of Mexico, *in* Galtsoff, P. S. (ed.), Gulf of Mexico; its origin, waters, and marine life: U.S. Fish and Wildl. Serv., Fish. Bull., v. 89, p. 267-272

—— 1961, Recent advances in Pleistocene stratigraphy and biogeography, *in* Blair, W. F. (ed.), Vertebrate speciation: Austin, Univ. Texas Press, p. 594-623

Dillon, L. S., 1956, Wisconsin climate and life zones in North America: Science, v. 123, p. 167-176

Donn, W. L., Farrand, W. R., and Ewing, Maurice, 1962, Pleistocene ice volumes and sea-level lowering: J. Geol., v. 70, p. 206-214

Dorf, E., 1959, Climatic changes of the past and present: Univ. Michigan Mus. Paleont. Contr., v. 13, p. 181-210

Eardley, A. J., and Gvosdetsky, Vasyl, 1960, Analysis of Pleistocene core from Great Salt Lake, Utah: Geol. Soc. Amer. Bull., v. 71, p. 1323-1344

Einarsson, Trausti, 1964, On the question of Late-Tertiary or Quaternary connections across the North Atlantic, and the dispersal of biota in that area: J. Ecol., v. 52, p. 617-625

Emiliani, Cesare, 1955, Pleistocene temperatures: J. Geol., v. 63, p. 538-578

—— 1958, Paleotemperature analysis of core 280 and Pleistocene correlations: J. Geol., v. 66, p. 264-275

Fitzpatrick, J. F., Jr., 1964, The evolution and geography of the crawfish genus *Orconectes:* Soc. Syst. Zool. Symposium, Knoxville, Tennessee, 28 Dec. 1964, abstracts of papers, No. 7

Flint, R. F., and Brandtner, Friedrich, 1961, Climatic changes since the last interglacial: Amer. J. Sci., v. 259, p. 321-328

Flint, R. F., and Gale, W. A., 1958, Stratigraphy and radiocarbon dates at Searles Lake, California: Amer. J. Sci., v. 256, p. 689-714

Frey, D. G., 1958, The late-glacial cladoceran fauna of a small lake: Arch. Hydrobiol., v. 54, p. 209-275

—— 1960, The ecological significance of cladoceran remains in lake sediments: Ecology, v. 41, p. 684-699

—— 1961, Developmental history of Schleinsee: Intern. Assoc. Limnol. Proc., v. 14, p. 271-278

—— 1962, Cladocera from the Eemian Interglacial of Denmark: J. Paleont., v. 36, p. 1133-1154

—— 1964, Remains of animals in Quaternary lake and bog sediments and their interpretation: Arch. Hydrobiol., suppl. Ergebn. der Limnol., No. 2, p. 1-114

Frye, J. C., and Leonard, A. B., 1957, Ecological interpretations of Pliocene and Pleistocene stratigraphy in the Great Plains region: Amer. J. Sci., v. 255, p. 1-11

Galtsoff, P. S. (ed.), 1954, Gulf of Mexico; its origin, waters, and marine life: U.S. Fish and Wildl. Serv., Fish. Bull., v. 89, 604 p.

Garth, J. S., 1960, Distribution and affinities of the brachyuran Crustacea, *in* Symposium—The biogeography of Baja California and adjacent seas: Syst. Zool., v. 9, p. 105-123

Ginsburg, Isaac, 1950, Review of the western Atlantic Triglidae (fishes): Texas Acad. Sci. Proc., v. 2, p. 489-527

Goulden, C. E., 1964, The history of the cladoceran fauna of Esthwaite Water (England) and its limnological significance: Arch. Hydrobiol., v. 60, p. 1-52

Gressitt, J. L. (ed.), 1963, Pacific Basin biogeography: Honolulu, Bishop Mus. Press, 563 p.

Guilday, J. E., Martin, P. S., and McCrady, A. D., 1964, New Paris No. 4—A Pleistocene cave in Bedford County, Pennsylvania: Nat. Speleol. Soc. Bull., v. 26, p. 121-194

Gutentag, E. D., and Benson, R. H., 1962, Neogene (Plio-Pleistocene) fresh-water ostracodes from the Central High Plains: Kansas State Geol. Surv. Bull., v. 157, pt. 4, p. 1-60

Hartman, Olga, 1951, The littoral marine annelids of the Gulf of Mexico: Inst. Mar. Sci. Texas Publ., v. 2, p. 7-124

Haynes, C. V., Jr., 1964, Fluted projectile points; their age and distribution: Science, v. 145, p. 1408-1413

Hedgpeth, J. W., 1953, An introduction to the zoogeography of the northwestern Gulf of Mexico, with reference to the invertebrate fauna: Inst. Mar. Sci. Texas Publ., v. 3, p. 107-224

—— 1954a, Anthozoa; the anemones, *in* Galtsoff, P. S. (ed.), Gulf of Mexico; its origin, waters, and marine life: U.S. Fish and Wildl. Serv., Fish. Bull., v. 89, p. 285-290

—— 1954b, Xiphosura, *in* Galtsoff, P. S. (ed.), Gulf of Mex-

ico; its origin, waters, and marine life: U.S. Fish and Wildl. Serv., Fish. Bull., v. 89, p. 423

Heezen, B. C., and Tharp, Marie, 1963, The Atlantic floor, *in* Löve, A. and Löve, D. (eds.), North Atlantic biota and their history: London, Pergamon Press, p. 21-27

Hibbard, C. W., Ray, D. E., Savage, D. E., Taylor, D. W., and Guilday, J. E., this volume, Quaternary mammals of North America

Hobbs, H. H., Jr., 1942, The crayfishes of Florida: Univ. Florida Publ., Biol. Sci. Ser., v. 3, No. 2, 179 p.

—— 1958, The evolutionary history of the Pictus group of the crayfish genus *Procambarus* (Decapoda, Astacidae): Florida Acad. Sci. Quart. J., v. 21, p. 71-91

Hobbs, H. H., Jr., and Barr, T. C, Jr., 1960, The origins and affinities of the troglobitic crayfishes of North America (Decapoda, Astacidae). I, The genus *Cambarus:* Amer. Midl. Nat., v. 64, p. 12-33

Holland, G. P., 1963, Faunal affinities of the fleas (Siphonaptera) of Alaska, with an annotated list of species, *in* Gressitt, J. L. (ed.), Pacific Basin biogeography: Honolulu, Bishop Mus. Press, p. 45-61

Holmquist, Charlotte, 1959, Problems on marine-glacial relicts on account of investigations on the genus *Mysis:* Lund, Berlingska Boktryckeriet, p. 1-270

Hopkins, D. M., 1959, Cenozoic history of the Bering land bridge: Science, v. 129, p. 1519-1528

Howden, H. F., 1963, Speculations on some beetles, barriers, and climates during the Pleistocene and pre-Pleistocene periods in some nonglaciated portions of North America: Syst. Zool., v. 12, p. 178-201

Hubbs, C. L., 1948, Changes in the fish fauna of western North America correlated with changes in ocean temperature: J. Mar. Res., v. 7, p. 459-482

—— 1960, The marine vertebrates of the outer coast, *in* Symposium—The biogeography of Baja California and adjacent seas: Syst. Zool., v. 9, p. 134-147

Hubbs, C. L., and Miller, R. R., 1948, The zoological evidence, correlation between fish distribution and hydrographic history in the desert basins of western North America, *in* Blackwelder, Eliot, *et al.*, The Great Basin, with emphasis on glacial and postglacial times: Univ. Utah Bull., v. 38, p. 17-166

Hultén, Eric, 1963, Phytogeographical connections of the North Atlantic, *in* Löve, A. and Löve, D. (eds.), North Atlantic biota and their history: London, Pergamon Press, p. 45-72

Hutchins, L. W., 1947, The bases for temperature zonation in geographical distribution: Ecol. Monogr., v. 17, p. 325-335

Johnson, Lionel, 1964, Marine-glacial relicts of the Canadian Arctic islands: Syst. Zool., v. 13, p. 76-91

Kapp, R. O., 1963, Pollen analytical investigations of Pleistocene deposits on the Southern High Plains: Dissertation Abst., v. 24, p. 1359

Kessel, Brina, 1963, West-east relationships in the birds of northern Alaska, *in* Gressitt, J. L. (ed.), Pacific Basin biogeography: Honolulu, Bishop Mus. Press, p. 79-84

King, P. B., this volume, Tectonics of Quaternary time in Middle North America

Klots, A. B., 1964, Some glaciation-isolated populations of

Lepidoptera in North America (abst.): 12th Intern. Congr. Entomol., London, p. 70

Leonard, A. B., 1950, A Yarmouthian molluscan fauna in the midcontinent region of the United States: Univ. Kansas Paleont. Contr., Mollusca, art. 3, p. 1-48

Lindroth, C. H., 1957, The faunal connections between Europe and North America: Stockholm, Almqvist & Wiksell, p. 1-344

—— 1963a, The problem of late land connections in the North Atlantic area, *in* Löve, A. and Löve, D. (eds.), North Atlantic biota and their history: London, Pergamon Press, p. 73-85

—— 1963b, The fauna history of Newfoundland illustrated by carabid beetles: Opuscula Entomol., Suppl., v. 23, p. 1-96

—— 1963c, The Aleutian Islands as a route for dispersal across the North Pacific, *in* Gressitt, J. L. (ed.), Pacific Basin biogeography: Honolulu, Bishop Mus. Press, p. 121-131

Löve, Askell, and Löve, Doris (eds.), 1963, North Atlantic biota and their history: London, Pergamon Press, 430 p.

Martin, P. S., 1958, Pleistocene ecology and biogeography of North America, *in* Hubbs, C. L. (ed.), Zoogeography: Amer. Assoc. Adv. Sci., Publ. 51, p. 375-420

—— 1963, The last 10,000 years. A fossil pollen record of the American Southwest: Tucson, Univ. Arizona Press, 87 p.

Martin, P. S., and Harrell, B. E., 1957, The Pleistocene history of temperate biotas in Mexico and eastern United States: Ecology, v. 38, p. 468-480

Megard, R. O., 1964, Biostratigraphic history of Dead Man Lake, Chuska Mountains, New Mexico: Ecology, v. 45, p. 529-546

Mitchell, G. F., 1957, Late-glacial finds of *Lepidurus arcticus* (Pallas) in the British Isles: Nature, v. 180, p. 513

Morrison, M. E. S., 1959, *Lepidurus arcticus* in the Irish late-glacial: Nature, v. 184, p. 739

Morrison, R. B., this volume, Quaternary geology of the Great Basin

Mueller, W. P., 1964, The distribution of cladoceran remains in surficial sediments from three northern Indiana lakes: Inv. Indiana Lakes and Streams, v. 6, p. 1-63

Murray, K. F., 1957, Pleistocene climate and the fauna of Burnet Cave, New Mexico: Ecology, v. 38, p. 129-132

Oaks, R. Q., Jr., and Coch, N. K., 1963, Pleistocene sea-levels, southeastern Virginia: Science, v. 140, p. 979-983

Omodeo, P., 1963, Distribution of terricolous oligochaetes on the two shores of the Atlantic, *in* Löve, A. and Löve, D. (eds.), North Atlantic biota and their history: London, Pergamon Press, p. 127-151

Ortmann, A. E., 1902, The geographical distribution of freshwater decapods and its bearing upon ancient geography: Amer. Philos. Soc. Proc., v. 41, p. 267-400

—— 1913, The Alleghenian Divide and its influence upon the freshwater fauna: Amer. Philos. Soc. Proc., v. 52, p. 287-395

Parker, R. H., 1960, Ecology and distributional pattern of marine macro-invertebrates, northern Gulf of Mexico, *in* Shepard, F. P. *et al.*, Recent sediments, northwest Gulf

of Mexico: Amer. Assoc. Petroleum Geologists, p. 302-337

—— 1964a, Zoogeography and ecology of macroinvertebrates, particularly mollusks, in the Gulf of California and the continental slope off Mexico: Vid. Medd. Dansk Naturh. Foren., v. 126, p. 1-178

—— 1964b, Zoogeography and ecology of macro-invertebrates of Gulf of California and continental slope of western Mexico: p. 331-376, *in* Marine geology of the Gulf of California, van Andel, T. H., and Shor, G. C., Jr. (eds.), Amer. Assoc. Petroleum Geologists, Mem. 3, p. 331-376

Pearson, R. G., 1961, The ecology of the Coleoptera from some late-Quaternary deposits, *in* Symposium on Quaternary ecology: Linn. Soc. London Proc., v. 172, p. 65-71

Phleger, F. B, 1951, Ecology of Foraminifera, northwest Gulf of Mexico. Part I, Foraminifera distribution: Geol. Soc. Amer. Mem., v. 46, p. 1-88

—— 1954, Foraminifera and deep-sea research: Deep-Sea Res., v. 2, p. 1-23

—— 1960, Sedimentary patterns of microfauna in northern Gulf of Mexico, *in* Shepard, F. P., *et al.*, Recent sediments, northwest Gulf of Mexico: Amer. Assoc. Petroleum Geologists, p. 267-301

Rehder, H. A., 1954, Mollusks *in* Galtsoff, P. S. (ed.), Gulf of Mexico; its origin, waters, and marine life: U.S. Fish and Wildl. Serv., Fish. Bull., v. 89, p. 469-474

Reid, G. K., Jr., 1954, An ecological study of the Gulf of Mexico fishes in the vicinity of Cedar Key, Florida: Mar. Sci. Gulf and Caribb. Bull., v. 4, p. 1-94

Rhoades, Rendell, 1962, The evolution of crayfishes of the genus *Orconectes* Section *Limosus* (Crustacea: Decapoda): Ohio J. Sci., v. 62, p. 65-96

Richards, H. G., 1962, Studies on the marine Pleistocene. Part I, The marine Pleistocene of the Americas and Europe. Part II, The marine Pleistocene mollusks of eastern North America: Amer. Philos. Soc. Trans., v. 52, p. 1-141

Ricker, K. E., 1959, The origin of two glacial relict crustaceans in North America, as related to Pleistocene glaciation: Can. J. Zool., v. 37, p. 871-893

Rivas, L. R., 1954, The origin, relationships, and geographical distribution of the marine fishes of the Gulf of Mexico, *in* Galtsoff, P. S. (ed.), Gulf of Mexico; its origin, waters, and marine life: U.S. Fish and Wildl. Serv., Fish. Bull., v. 89, p. 503-505

Roosma, Aino, 1958, A climatic record from Searles Lake, California: Science, v. 128, p. 716

Rumpp, L. N., 1956, Tiger beetles of the genus *Cicindela* in southwestern Nevada and Death Valley, California, and description of two new subspecies (Coleoptera-Cicindelidae): Southern California Acad. Sci. Bull., v. 55, p. 131-144

—— 1957, Notes on the *Cicindela praetextata-californica* tiger beetle complex. Description of a new subspecies from Death Valley, California (Coleoptera-Cincindelidae): Southern California Acad. Sci. Bull., v. 58, p. 144-154

—— 1961, Three new tiger beetles of the genus *Cicindela* from southeastern United States (Cicindelidae-Coleoptera): Southern California Acad. Sci. Bull., v. 60, p. 165-187

Shepard, F. P., Phleger, F. B, and van Andel, T. H. (eds.), 1960, Recent sediments, Northwest Gulf of Mexico. A symposium summarizing the results of work carried out in Project 51 of the American Petroleum Institute 1951-1958: Tulsa, Amer. Assoc. Petroleum Geologists, 394 p.

Shotton, F. W., 1965, The movements of insect populations in the British Pleistocene: Geol. Soc. Amer. Spec. Pap. (in press)

Smith, G. I., 1962, Subsurface stratigraphy of late Quaternary deposits, Searles Lake, California; a summary: U.S. Geol. Surv. Prof. Pap. 350-C, p. 65-69

Smith, P. W., 1957, An analysis of post-Wisconsin biogeography of the Prairie Peninsula region based on distributional phenomena among terrestrial vertebrate populations: Ecology, v. 38, p. 205-218

Soule, J. D., 1960, The distribution and affinities of the littoral marine Bryozoa (Ectoprocta), *in* Symposium—The biogeography of Baja California and adjacent seas: Syst. Zool., v. 9, p. 100-104

Sparks, B. W., and Lewis, W. V., 1957, Escarpment dry valleys near Pegsdon, Hertfordshire: Geol. Assoc. London Proc., v. 68, p. 26-38

Stahl, J. B., 1959, The developmental history of the chironomid and *Chaoborus* faunas of Myers Lake: Inv. Indiana Lakes and Streams, v. 5, p. 47-102

Staplin, F. L., 1963a, Pleistocene Ostracoda of Illinois. Pt. I, Subfamilies Candoninae, Cyprinae, general ecology, morphology: J. Paleont., v. 37, p. 758-797

—— 1963b, Pleistocene Ostracoda of Illinois. Pt. II, Subfamilies Cyclocyprinae, Cypridopinae, Ilyocyprinae; families Darwinulidae and Cytheridae. Stratigraphic ranges and assemblage patterns: J. Paleont., v. 37, p. 1164-1203

Stegmann, Boris, 1963, The problem of the Beringian continental land connection in the light of ornithogeography, *in* Gressitt, J. L. (ed.), Pacific Basin biogeography: Honolulu, Bishop Mus. Press, p. 65-78

Taylor, D. W., 1960, Late Cenozoic molluscan faunas from the High Plains: U.S. Geol. Surv. Prof. Pap. 337, 94 p.

—— 1964, Historical analysis of distribution of west American freshwater molluscs: Soc. Syst. Zool. Symposium, Knoxville, Tennessee, 28 Dec. 1964, abstracts of papers, No. 4

—— this volume, The study of the Pleistocene nonmarine mollusks

Taylor, D. W., and Hibbard, C. W., 1955, A new Pleistocene fauna from Harper County, Oklahoma: Oklahoma Geol. Surv. Circ. 37, p. 1-23

Van Name, W. G., 1954, The Tunicata of the Gulf of Mexico, *in* Galtsoff, P. S. (ed.), Gulf of Mexico; its origin, waters, and marine life: U.S. Fish and Wildl. Serv., Fish. Bull., v. 89, p. 495-497

Waldén, H. W., 1963, Historical and taxonomical aspects of the land Gastropoda in the North Atlantic region, *in* Löve, A., and Löve, D. (eds.), North Atlantic biota and their history: London, Pergamon Press, p. 153-171

Walker, B. W., 1960, The distribution and affinities of the marine fish fauna of the Gulf of California, *in* Symposium—The biogeography of Baja California and adjacent seas: Syst. Zool., v. 9, p. 123-133

Walker, E. M., 1957, Changes in the insect fauna of Ontario (with special reference to the Orthoptera), *in* Urquhart, F. A. (ed.), Changes in the fauna of Ontario: Roy. Ontario Mus., Contr. Div. Zool. and Paleont., p. 4-12

Wells, P. V., and Jorgensen, C. D., 1964, Pleistocene wood rat middens and climatic change in the Mojave Desert; a record of juniper woodlands: Science, v. 143, p. 1171-1173

Wendorf, Fred, 1961, Invertebrate collections, *in* Wendorf, Fred (ed.), Paleoecology of the Llano Estacado: Santa Fe, Mus. New Mexico Press, p. 105-114

Whitehead, D. R., this volume, Palynology and Pleistocene phytogeography: unglaciated eastern North America

Williams, A. B., 1954, An explanation for the distribution of a North American crayfish: Ecology, v. 35, p. 573-575

—— 1960, Speciation and distribution of the crayfishes of the Ozark Plateaus and Ouachita Provinces. Univ. Kansas Sci. Bull., v. 36, pt. 1, p. 803-918

Williams, A. B., and Leonard, A. B., 1952, The crayfishes of Kansas: Univ. Kansas Sci. Bull., v. 34, p. 961-1012

Winkler, E. M., 1960, Post-Pleistocene ostracodes of Lake Nipissing age: J. Paleont., v. 34, p. 923-932

—— 1962, Two late Pleistocene (Cary) freshwater ostracode faunas: J. Paleont., v. 36, p. 1021-1034

Wright, H. P., 1932, Aquatic mollusca of the Tippecanoe River system. Pt. I, The post-glacial migration and present distribution of four species of snails: Ecol. Monogr., v. 2, p. 233-259

Young, F. N., 1959a, Distributional patterns of North American water beetles and their significance (abst.): Anat. Rec., v. 134, p. 660

—— 1959b, Fossil beetles from the Vero Pleistocene: Coleopterists' Bull., v. 13, p. 103-106

SUMMARY

The biological flux of the Quaternary is still largely unknown in detail although inferred in its gross aspects from the forced migrations, isolations, differentiations, and recolonizations that must have occurred repeatedly during this period of time. In most groups of animals the faunistics and present distributions are insufficiently known for any meaningful speculations on these matters, and only in the vertebrates and mollusks is the fossil record sufficiently good at present to aid in the reconstruction of past distributions and evolution. There is reason to hope, however, that the insects (particularly the carabid beetles) and crustaceans (particularly the Cladocera and ostracods, and to a lesser extent the phyllopods, amphipods, isopods, and other lesser groups) are well enough represented in inland sediments to yield important information eventually. Other groups, such as rhizopods, Turbellaria, oribatid mites, etc., may likewise prove valuable.

One major effect of the climatic cycles of the Quaternary, which has included depression of sea as well as land temperatures during the glaciopluvial ages, is the occurrence of numerous disjunct populations of northern species of various invertebrates and fishes in the northern portions of the Gulf of Mexico and the Gulf of California. Certain groups suggest a number of distinct times of such entrapment, based on the degree of differentiation between populations in the gulf and their cognate populations along the open coast to the north. In the Gulf of Mexico such speculations based on distribution and phenotypic differences are nicely substantiated by fluctuations in sea level, changes in circulation pattern, and changes in paleotemperatures as deduced from offshore studies and cores of sediments. The present and past Foraminifera are particularly useful in these interpretations.

During the eustatic lowerings of sea level in the glacial ages, Alaska was broadly joined to Siberia, permitting the migration of organisms adapted to the environmental conditions prevailing at these times. Present evidence suggests that the Quaternary land-bridge climate was very severe, so that only cold-adapted organisms could have moved easily. Exchange of other organisms occurred mainly in the Tertiary. In the Atlantic region there is no compelling evidence for the existence of a land connection even to Greenland, much less to mainland North America, at any time during the Quaternary.

Interpretation of the evolution of present distributions of inland invertebrates, chiefly crayfishes and flightless or fossorial beetles, is based on a floating time scale largely dependent on the state of understanding of the Quaternary geology of the regions in question. Without fossil material a greater precision may never be realized, except possibly through serological or genetic studies.

Some of the greatest potentialities concern lacustrine organisms, many of which are abundantly represented by morphological remains in lake sediments, thereby permitting the construction of close-interval biostratigraphies. Although the individual species are often quite eurytopic, fluctuations in community composition provide valuable insight into changing local and even regional conditions.

RECENT ADJUSTMENTS IN ANIMAL RANGES*

PHILIP W. SMITH[1]

IF 5,000 B.P. (before the present) is arbitrarily accepted as a starting date, the present essay is spared commitment upon the controversial issues of late-Wisconsin chronology, climate of the periglacial belt, and the degree of biological displacement during glacial maxima. However, at 5,000 B.P., it does commence with a controversial event near the close of a warm period, variously called Hypsithermal, Altithermal, or Xerothermic Interval, Climatic Optimum, and Thermal Maximum (see Wright *et al.*, 1963, p. 1390-1391, for summary of C^{14} datings of this phase, and Cooper, 1958, p. 942, for relative merits of the terms).

There has been some disagreement on the duration of the post-Wisconsin warm period, and each term proposed for it has been justifiably criticized. Smith (1957), for the sake of convenience, chose to restrict the term Climatic Optimum to the warm-moist phase of *ca.* 8,000 to 6,000 B.P. and the term Xerothermic Interval to the warm-dry phase of *ca.* 6,000 to 4,000 B.P. This restriction is retained herein, purely for the sake of having terms to distinguish humid and dry phases of the warm period. The present discussion thus commences at the Xerothermic maximum.

By this time, the ice had retreated to the polar region, and the topography and drainage patterns were essentially those of today. The present landscape and drainage features are believed by Broecker *et al.* (1960, p. 441) to date back about 11,000 years. The Archaic Indian culture was declining, the Early Woodland culture developing (Bluhm, 1959). Fires, particularly in grassland and savanna areas, were undoubtedly more frequent than before the arrival of man in the New World and may or may not have been significant in modifying stands of climax vegetation (Martin, 1958, p. 395). Many of the late-Pleistocene animals were extinct, the remaining flora and fauna modern but probably distributed somewhat differently from today. In fact, it is the adjustment during the past 5,000 years of geographic ranges of organisms comprising one important segment of the biota, the vertebrate animals, that is the subject of this chapter.

The most significant of the many events to which animal ranges have had to adjust have almost certainly been the Xerothermic Interval, the subsequent return of a climate like that of today, and the development of modern European civilization on this continent. Accordingly, for the sake of discussion the time under consideration is arbitrarily divided into three parts: the Xerothermic and early post-Xerothermic Period (6,000-3,000 B.P.), the Prehistoric Period (3,000 to 200 B.P.), and the Historic Period (200 B.P. to present). For the first of these the data are derived principally from the field of palaeoecology, for the second from archaeozoology, and for the third from the abundant historical record.

THE XEROTHERMIC AND EARLY POST-XEROTHERMIC PERIOD

Among biologists and archaeologists, there is rather general agreement that since deglaciation the major climatic sequence has been cool–warm–cool (Deevey, 1949), and there is a tacit assumption that the warm phase consisted of a period of humid climate (here termed Climatic Optimum) and one of more arid climate (Xerothermic Interval).

The vegetational cover of eastern North America is suggested primarily by studies of pollen profiles, plant macrofossils, and analyses of present distributional patterns, but it is supported also by some nonbiological evidence. It is believed to have been of a mesic nature during the Climatic Optimum, at which time the ranges of some southern components extended farther north than they do at present. During the Xerothermic Interval, the mesophytic cover was generally supplanted by vegetation of a more xeric type, fragmenting formerly continuous areas of deciduous forest and permitting encroachment of aridity-tolerant trees and nonarboreal plants (Deevey, 1949). In western North America, the vegetational responses to climate were manifested altitudinally (on mountain slopes) as well as latitudinally (Cottam *et al.*, 1959). Evidence that the Xerothermic Interval prevailed in the West is somewhat less plentiful and has, in fact, recently been challenged for the Southwest (Martin, 1963).

Although the climatic and phytogeographic sequences are best documented in eastern and central United States (Deevey, 1949; Thomas, 1951; Frey, 1953; Smith, 1957), evidence of the Climatic Optimum, Xerothermic Interval, or both, is also available for such areas as eastern Canada (Bleakney, 1958), the Pacific Northwest (Heusser, 1960), and the Great Basin (Cottam *et al.*, 1959). Opinion varies widely on the magnitude of these events, embracing, at one extreme, the view that 6,000 years ago the Midwest was semi-desert and, at the other extreme, a denial that the climate then was any warmer than it is today. Perhaps the

---

* I have profited from discussing this subject with Drs. Harlow B. Mills, Sherman A. Minton, Paul W. Parmalee, Richard R. Graber, M. Raymond Lee, Donald F. Hoffmeister, John C. Frye, and Mr. Marvin E. Braasch and from helpful suggestions inadvertently supplied in correspondence with Drs. Robert R. Miller and John E. Guilday. The editors of this volume contributed numerous suggestions of value. None of these persons can be accused of agreeing with this paper in its entirety.

[1] Illinois Natural History Survey, University of Illinois, Urbana, Illinois.

most dramatic illustration of the uncertainty of the sequences for the continent as a whole are Martin's (1958, p. 389) reference to the warm period as the most important event in postglacial history and his (1963, p. 61) assertion that he finds in the Southwest no evidence for a climate warmer and drier than that of the present.

If the premises are accepted that biotas occurred at higher latitudes and altitudes during the Climatic Optimum than at present and that a more arid climate fragmented and reduced mesic forest and increased the extent of steppe and arid-type forest, an explanation is readily available for the major disjunctions in the ranges of many deciduous-forest animals and for the isolation of the numerous relict populations of such animals. With the return of the cooler and moister climate, particularly in eastern North America, the habitats of mesic-forest animals have expanded at the expense of grassland and open-woodland types. Their ranges have moved westward, especially by way of gallery forest along the major rivers (Smith and Minton, 1957, p. 350).

Zoological evidence for this series of events is fortunately abundant and, although somewhat outside the scope of the present paper, so important in setting the stage that a few of the more significant sources may be briefly summarized. Along the east coast, Bleakney (1958) cited disjunct populations in peninsular Nova Scotia of butterflies, amphibians, reptiles, and the white-footed mouse,[2] as well as numerous plants, none of which occurs at corresponding latitudes in adjacent Quebec, New Brunswick, or northern New England. For these elements to enter the peninsula via the narrow Isthmus of Chignecto, their northernmost limits of distribution on the mainland would need to be transposed an average distance of 300 km north of their present range limits. In the floodplain forests and swamps of the Mississippi River valley, Smith (1957) cited relict populations of amphibians and reptiles that require a northern transposition of about 150 to 300 km beyond the northern limits of the main populations of these species. Utilizing another source of data, he analyzed geographic variation in certain snakes and could account for the aberrant, and otherwise inexplicable, patterns of intergradation by assuming that during the Climatic Optimum the more southern subspecies had occurred some 300 km farther north than at present.

Evidence that the climate of the Xerothermic Interval fragmented the widespread deciduous forest is seen in the presently disjunct ranges of numerous fishes and amphibians, which occur on the Interior Low Plateaus and Ozark Plateaus but do not occur in the lower Mississippi River embayment or in the central Illinois prairie (Conant, 1960). Recent work in the Midwest indicates that the list of fishes with this hiatus is even larger than previously believed. Another important relict area is in the Black Hills of South Dakota, where pockets of forest animals surrounded by prairie indicate a formerly extensive forest cover at that latitude (Smith, 1957; Conant, 1960). A number of lesser disjunctions is known, particularly for cold-blooded vertebrates.

Coincidental with the fragmentation in ranges of forest animals, as already noted, the ranges of grassland, forest-

[2] Scientific names of animal species mentioned in the text are listed in the appendix.

edge, and aridity-tolerant forest animals moved eastward. As the climate became cooler and moister, these western components retreated to the west, leaving disjunct populations where edaphic features and other local details of habitat have permitted their survival. A great number of distributional illustrations among cold-blooded vertebrates and mammals have been cited (Schmidt, 1938; Thomas, 1951; Trautman, 1957; Smith, 1957); although some of them may represent a pre-Climatic Optimum eastward dispersal, others probably date back to the Xerothermic Interval. An illustration from the study of geographic variation, based on character clines in prairie snakes, was reported by Smith and Smith (1962), who found trans-Mississippi River relicts clearly derived from Great Plains populations that presently occur at lower latitudes. To match the scutellation features of relict and plains populations, a 150-450-km transposition of isotherms and animal communities is required, conditions evidently prevailing when the snakes moved into the Prairie Peninsula.

Although some recent and careful studies (Martin, 1963; Guilday and Tanner, 1962) threaten the Xerothermic hypothesis, a vast and overwhelming amount of evidence has been assembled to support it, and it provides, for the present time, the best answers to many of the biogeographic questions that face the American student. Nevertheless, it is merely hypothesis, and a growing body of evidence casts doubt that the Xerothermic was any more arid than the present and perhaps less so than the early postglacial.

Prior to the arrival of European man on this continent, animal ranges were thus adjusting to an unusually significant series of climatic events, which had produced complex assemblages of faunas and considerable disruption of ranges of individual species. As populations responded to expanding and contracting optimal habitats, the ranges of many species were in all likelihood abnormally unstable but adjusted to the developing climaxes of present-day climates in different parts of the country well before the impact of European civilization.

THE PREHISTORIC PERIOD

During the 17th and 18th centuries, extremely sketchy accounts of animals were made by early explorers on this continent; references to animals in their expedition narratives were confined to the most conspicuous species and were so infrequent that they contribute little to the knowledge of the total fauna of that period.

Most of the information available for the 2,000- to 3,000-year period prior to European colonization of this country is contributed by studies of animal remains in Indian refuse middens and of bones found in dry caves and rock fissures that served as death traps for animals tumbling into the crevices over many years. The middens tend to reflect only those animals utilized by the Indians. Bones of large mammals and shells in the middens must be interpreted with a certain amount of caution. Parmalee (1958) found 325 specimens of over 20 species of marine mollusks mixed among the shells of native mollusks at the Cahokia Site in Madison County, Illinois. Moreover, both midden and cave deposits may be contaminated by subsequent entries and deaths of burrowing animals. Many of the deposits are not accurately dated, and they are seldom sufficiently extensive to form a picture of faunal associations of the area and period. Some very early cave assemblages, such as the remarkable Pleistocene fauna of Natural Chimneys, Virginia (Guilday, 1962), are notable exceptions.

Despite the drawbacks just listed, the bone material and other animal remains provide evidence of the presence of a great many kinds of animal at specific sites, and many of the species represented are known from a number of different localities. Chiefly through the researches of Parmalee in the Midwest and Guilday in the East, an impressive list of animals (which Parmalee has kindly helped me to compile) is available from many areas where these species no longer occur or appear only as occasional migrants. Among the fishes are the buffalo and the freshwater drum (Trautman, 1957, p. 5). Among the birds are the brown and white pelicans, trumpeter and whistling swans, swallow-tailed kite, ruffed grouse, greater prairie chicken, sharp-tailed grouse, turkey, sandhill crane, long-billed curlew, whimbrel, marbled godwit, ivory-billed woodpecker, common raven, and the extinct Carolina parakeet and passenger pigeon. Among the mammals are the eastern mole, black bear, marten, fisher, coastal mink, wolverine, river otter, spotted skunk, gray wolf, jaguar, mountain lion, bobcat, thirteen-lined ground squirrel, Franklin's ground squirrel, plains pocket gopher, marsh rice rat, eastern wood rat, porcupine, elk, and bison. Many of these animals, such as the white-tailed deer, are known to have occurred in these regions from many thousand years ago well into historic times; others apparently held rather brief tenure in the areas of the fossil records. An illustration of the latter situation is the bison, which Griffin and Wray (1945, p. 25) have pointed out did not appear in numbers east of the Mississippi River until about A.D. 1600 and was eliminated in the East by A.D. 1800. Significant also are the usual omissions of domestic animals, except dog, and, in some parts of their present ranges, the red fox and the American opossum (Guilday, 1958).

In other parts of the United States, ecological conditions as reflected by faunal remains show less change in recent times. Neill *et al.* (1956, p. 393) noted that vertebrate remains in four central Florida sites, dated *ca.* 5,000 to 3,500 B.P., indicate a fauna virtually identical with that occurring in central Florida today "even to certain minutiae of distribution." In the western half of the country, a large number of midden records of considerably later date indicate some ecological change. A rather long list of animals known as Recent fossils in regions where the species have since been extirpated includes the turkey, prairie dog, grizzly bear, ocelot, jaguar, mountain sheep, pronghorn, moose, and caribou (P. W. Parmalee, personal communication). The longnose gar and blue sucker are known from archaeological sites in northern New Mexico, where neither genus presently occurs (Gehlbach and Miller, 1961, p. 2). An assemblage of bird remains from the Upper Sonoran Life Zone of southern Utah, dated from *ca.* 1,260 to 660 B.P., was reported by Hargrave (1939, p. 209) as similar to the bird fauna of the area today, whereas several sites near the Transition Zone in the vicinity of Flagstaff, Arizona, yielded remains from the same time period of a rather different bird fauna than that presently in the area. Animals of southern origin were represented in middens dated *ca.* 1,000 B.P. in the Southwest (Smiley, 1961, p. 702). Thus evidence of a certain amount of ecological change in the West is available, but it is apparently much less dramatic than that for the eastern and central United States, where more pronounced climatic shifts and a greater amount of human modification of the environment have profoundly affected the native fauna.

In view of the voluminous archaeological literature and the great number of fossil records known, the failure of the midden and cave remains to corroborate the climatic chronology outlined in the preceding section of this paper is rather surprising. Although a southward displacement of boreal animals in the East is clearly established by the recent researches of Guilday, the subsequent stages indicate a replacement of boreal by Carolinian elements. Guilday and Tanner (1962) have shown an early eastward spread of grassland components, suggesting that an open-woodland or forest-glade habitat may have prevailed. These forms were soon succeeded by a deciduous forest fauna similar to that occurring in the area today. In the Midwest, the early stages are usually missing; among the later faunas, there are few records to suggest the postulated sequence of warm-moist, warm-dry, and cool-moist. Of the many archaeozoological records known, the best evidence to substantiate an eastward spread of prairie during the Xerothermic Interval is the southwestern Illinois records of the spotted skunk and plains pocket gopher (Parmalee and Hoffmeister, 1957, p. 261; Parmalee *et al.*, 1961, p. 119) and the western Pennsylvania record of the eastern mole (Guilday, 1961, p. 117). None of these species occurs at these sites today, all of them currently occupying more westerly ranges. In the West, faunal assemblages tend to show only local changes in distribution, and climatic correlations, at least for the past 5,000 years, are even more obscure. However, it should be pointed out that large and wide-ranging birds and mammals, which are the types most often encountered in midden remains, are not sensitive ecological indicators, as are many amphibians, reptiles, and small mammals. Moreover, Indian camps tended to be located along water courses, where grassland species of animals would not be expected.

Tempting as it is to correlate former distributions with appropriate climatic phases for the isolated records of certain species, such correlations are unwarranted in the absence of dates for the fossils. A case in point was my own error (Smith, 1957, p. 210) in assuming that undated remains of the marsh rice rat at Peoria, Illinois, some 200 miles north of its present range, dated back to the Climatic Optimum. Guilday (1961, p. 118) and others have found that the rice rat accompanied the northward spread of maize agriculture by Indians 4,000 to 5,000 years after the Climatic Optimum, although the shrinkage of its range since strongly suggests a gradually cooling climate over the past 1,000 years.

Within the Prehistoric Period, as here defined, climatic oscillations are well documented. The presumed extremes, represented by the 11th and 16th centuries, were the subject of a conference held in 1962 in Aspen, Colorado, where an attempt was made to assess all the evidence available regarding the climates of the two periods. An influx of subtropical mammals in southwestern sites, dated at *ca.* 900 to 1,000 years B.P., and an influx of northern birds in similar sites, dated at *ca.* 600 to 700 years B.P., were cited as evidence of climatic extremes, but the consensus of the symposium members was that known faunal remains have serious limitations for climatic inference. Some bizarre distributional phenomena, such as the Recent occurrence of the jaguar in Tennessee (Parmalee, 1961) and the porcupine in southwestern Illinois (Parmalee *et al.*, 1961) may date to minor warm and cool phases of the Prehistoric Period, but in the absence of precise dates such assignment is not justified. On the basis of archaeozoology alone, the sum of the limited evidence available indicates relatively little about climatic change during the past 5,000 years.

The Historic Period

With the arrival and subsequent spread of European civilization in this country, the most conspicuous effects upon the native fauna have been destruction of habitats and an increasingly accelerated fragmentation of animal ranges. The multitude of ways in which man has modified the environment is staggering and cannot be cited in these few pages. It is axiomatic that human progress has meant diminishing wilderness areas and decimation of many elements in the native fauna. At the same time, many animals have shown an amazing resilience and a remarkable ability to adjust to the environmental changes. Throughout the Historic Period there has fortunately been a succession of authors to record the animal life of their time and place and other authors to summarize the scattered observations and speculate upon the changes taking place.

EXTIRPATED AND NOTABLY ENDANGERED SPECIES

Perhaps the most dramatic examples of the effects of human civilization upon native animals are those formerly wide-ranging but now extinct species, such as the harelip sucker, great auk, Labrador duck, passenger pigeon, Carolina parakeet, and coastal mink. Unable to adjust habits or ranges, these species have disappeared within historic times, although some of them were probably doomed to extinction through natural causes even before the arrival of European man. A long list of once-widespread but now endangered species, including the Colorado squawfish and some other southwestern fishes, the American crocodile, whooping crane, Eskimo curlew, Everglade kite, California condor, ivory-billed woodpecker, some eastern species of grouse, the black-footed ferret, swift fox, and numerous species of larger mammals, has aroused the concern of conservationists. Obviously this list could be greatly extended, particularly if those species, with more restricted ranges, that tend to be known only to specialists on the various animal groups were included.

Extinct species are automatically excluded from any discussion of range adjustments. Consideration of endangered species is hardly more appropriate in this paper, inasmuch as range adjustments are largely at the mercy of human foresight and the responses of these species to corrective management practices.

INTRODUCED SPECIES

More appropriate to the subject under discussion are the deliberate and accidental introductions into this country of exotic species and the widespread transplanting of American species into areas outside their natural ranges. Classic examples of naturalized exotics among the fishes are the carp, goldfish, and brown trout; among the amphibians, the marine toad and greenhouse frog; among the birds, the house sparrow, rock dove, starling, ring-necked pheasant, chukar, and gray partridge; among the mammals, the house mouse, Norway rat, nutria, black rat, European hare, and the wild horse. Various other animals, representing all the vertebrate classes, have established toeholds in certain parts of the country but have not spread extensively from the sites where they were initially introduced. In a manner not clearly understood, a correlation between success of the introduced species and the amount of disturbance in the natural environment is usually apparent, the most widespread of the exotics being those that quickly occupied habitats after they had been altered to some degree by the hand of man. The exotics have had varying effects upon the native species; they have not, insofar as is known, completely eliminated any native animal in this country through direct competition or predation.

The transplanting of species into areas outside their natural ranges has been most extensive in the fishes. Virtually all the food and game species in the families Salmonidae, Osmeridae, Esocidae, Centrarchidae, Serranidae, Percidae, and Ictaluridae, some forage species in the families Catostomidae and Clupeidae, and certain miscellaneous fishes, such as the Poeciliidae, have been repeatedly stocked in many different parts of the country. If the species represented in the nonselective stocking practices and minnow-bucket releases are added, the number of transplanted species of fishes becomes enormous.

The effect of planted species upon native fishes cannot be evaluated without, at the same time, a careful consideration of the amount of human alteration of the waters and watersheds. In general, the effects of introductions and environmental change vary with different geographic regions. Saturated faunas in well-watered areas tend to have well-developed defense mechanisms and much better opportunity for dispersal and repopulation than do depauperate faunas in arid regions (Miller, 1961, p. 366). For example, in the American Southwest, Miller (1961) noted that within the past 100 years almost 20% of the native species were endangered, or brought to extinction, as a result of modification of habitats in the area and the introduction of 36 exotic species, whereas Larimore and Smith (1963) found a less profound effect on the native fish fauna of Champaign County, Illinois, despite a vast amount of environmental change and repeated introductions of more than half a dozen exotics over a 60-year period.

Fortunately, a great many of the plantings of fishes are failures, the introduced species sometimes being unable to compete successfully with native species already adapted to a particular environment. However, the ubiquitous carp is ample proof that some plantings do succeed. Some transplanted American species, once in a new region, have an amazing capacity to appear suddenly and explosively in waters where they were never introduced. This saltatorial type of colonization of new territory is especially evident in the present ranges of the mosquitofish and the threadfin shad in the central and western states and the American smelt in the Great Lakes basin.

Among the higher vertebrates, introductions of American species outside their natural ranges have been on a smaller scale. The bullfrog now occurs widely in the western states; the spiny softshell turtle has spread into the lower Colorado River; the opossum now occupies much of California. All three are native to eastern North America. Another eastern species, the bobwhite, and the California quail have been planted in the Pacific Northwest. The armadillo, once native to Texas, was introduced in Florida and is now common in many parts of the state and in other localities on the Gulf Coast. Some introduction has probably occurred through the restocking of turkey, bobwhite, ruffed grouse, beaver, white-tailed deer, and other large game mammals. Whether or not the introduced and restocked species have appreciable effects upon the remaining indigenes is unknown, and evidence that they have a detrimental effect is surprisingly rare. However, they comprise an important segment in the present composition of the fauna in any given area, and such exotics as the house sparrow, rock dove, house mouse, and Norway rat have surely shown remarkable adjustments in their ranges.

OTHER RANGE ADJUSTMENTS

Distributional adjustments are by no means limited to the shrinking ranges of endangered species and the expanding ranges of adaptable exotics. There are many examples of native species adapting to the changing environments and displaying a remarkable tenacity for survival. Adjustments of range in relation to human alteration of the environment and to recent climatic fluctuations, as indicated by weather records and studies of dendrochronology, have been carefully analyzed for the Toronto, Canada, region (Urquhart, 1957). In this series of papers, shifting ranges of such animals as butterflies suggest a relationship with vacillating climate, but human modification of the environment has been so profound that it overshadows and obscures most relationships of range adjustment to climatic change.

Aquatic organisms, especially the fishes, have responded to removal of natural barriers by invading new waters, although the long period sometimes required for entry in foreign waters and the short time required for the species to mushroom, once entry is effected, remains a paradox. An excellent illustration is the recent explosive spread of the sea lamprey and the alewife in the Great Lakes (Scott, 1963, p. 112). Opportunity to bypass a natural barrier (the Niagara Escarpment) came with the completion of the Welland Canal in 1824, but the spread of these species into the western lakes, at least in great numbers, has occurred only in the past few decades. The several other navigation canals, most of which were constructed in the first half of the 19th century, have not yet resulted in appreciable intermingling of faunas from different basins. Occasional stragglers have been reported, but there are no known dispersals paralleling those of the sea lamprey and alewife.

Natural recanalization, stream piracy, and related phenomena would seem to be too infrequent to be instrumental in providing avenues for fishes to expand their ranges. Yet quite recent invasions are well documented, particularly of southern forms northward and western species eastward (Trautman, 1957, p. 127, 376; Scott, 1963, p. 114; Larimore and Smith, 1963, p. 331). Except in arid regions, where natural barriers are more formidable, fish dispersal is primarily contingent upon availability of suitable habitat. When alteration of the stream habitat is sufficient to produce favorable habitat, a species is often able, over a period of years, to find its way into a new drainage system. Human modification of watersheds and habitats, principally through deforestation, has tended to cause a shrinkage in the ranges of eastern forms and to favor an eastward dispersal of the usually more tolerant prairie and plains species. Through various activities, man has created conditions generally less favorable for cold-water fishes and more favorable for heat-tolerant species.

Because of their low vagility and their inability to be active above and below a rather limited temperature range, amphibians and reptiles are comparatively slow to change their ranges. Some data on range adjustments are available; but, except for those indicating range shrinkage, these data are speculative and based on the assumption that the species are expanding because apparently suitable habitats for them are expanding. For example, Thomas (1951, p. 162) noted that in Ohio the clearing of timber and the subjugation of the land to agriculture converted cool, moist forest to hot, dry "prairies" and that forest species such as the Jefferson salamander and the wood frog were consequently being replaced by grassland species such as the small-mouthed salamander and the chorus frog. This reasoning is equally valid for other central states, but the data actually demonstrate changes in abundance more than in range. It is reasonable to assume, however, that breeding sites for desert species are increased with irrigation of new areas and that grassland and forest-edge species can utilize the increasing number of drainage ditches, farm ponds, and artificial lakes, whereas breeding sites for many forest-dwellers (vernal ponds) are rapidly disappearing.

Like the amphibians, some reptiles may find new habitat to invade in the simulated prairies and newly created forest-edge, where there was once forest. It is also possible that rodent-eating snakes have the opportunity to increase their ranges as irrigated alfalfa fields with their hosts of rodents replace desert wastes with their smaller populations of rodents. It is conceivable that the widely introduced earthworm *Lumbricus terrestris* ensures a food supply for small species of snakes and that the trash and litter in urban and suburban vacant lots, where they may abound, provides more habitat than was available to them before human settlement. There is no doubt that the ranges of large poisonous snakes in many parts of this country have been reduced as a result of systematic persecution and destruction of their habitats.

Birds have received more attention within historic times and offer abundant illustrations of recent adjustments in ranges. Snyder (1957, p. 26-42) summarized the known extirpations, examples of range shrinkage, and introductions in Ontario and discussed in greater detail the numerous cases of range expansion in the Province. He noted that the most conspicuous directional movement was from south to north and cited the classic examples of cardinal, mockingbird, and tufted titmouse as well as the snowy egret, turkey vulture, mourning dove, black-billed cuckoo, Bewick's wren, Carolina wren, bobolink, eastern meadowlark, brownheaded cowbird, and numerous species of warblers and native sparrows. Adding the bobwhite, Thomas (1951, p. 162) cited several of the same species as illustrations of birds moving northward in Ohio. Graber and Graber (1963, p. 508) reported that several of the species mentioned above, as well as the red-bellied woodpecker, Acadian flycatcher, Bell's vireo, and Carolina chickadee, had extended their ranges northward in Illinois, and they implied (p. 496), by citing the decline of breeding populations toward the south, that the savannah sparrow was moving northward. Perhaps the most publicized example of this trend, at least in the popular literature, has been the phenomenal northward spread of the cattle egret in recent years.

The reasons for this gradual northward expansion are not clear. Graber and Graber (1963, p. 508) noted that the ranges of some species are deteriorating in the south, suggesting a recent change in climate; however, they commented that the ranges of others remain unchanged in the south despite a pronounced spread to the north, thus suggesting that the birds are expanding northward for reasons other than climate. The reasons for the northward "invasion" probably include, in addition to climatic factors, the appearance of new habitat types and an increase in the number of seral stages in areas that were previously clothed with relatively uniform climax vegetations, the adaptation to, and preference for, such human innovations as orchards, pastures, fence rows, and tilled land by some species, and perhaps even the so-called city effect (temperature elevation in urban areas).

Snyder (1957) considered the second most common trend in Ontario to be an invasion from west to east and cited the horned lark, red-necked grebe, ring-necked duck, western meadowlark, Brewer's blackbird, evening grosbeak, clay-colored sparrow, western kingbird, and double-crested cormorant. Thomas (1951, p. 163) noted that human disturbance of the land resulted in areas of bare ground or scantily vegetated soil that provide optimal habitat for campestrian species such as the horned lark; he suggested that the vesper sparrow, as well as the lark, was moving eastward in Ohio. Graber and Graber (1963, p. 509) pointed out that in Illinois the breeding ranges of the western meadowlark, yellow-headed blackbird, and Brewer's blackbird were extending eastward.

Examples of eastern birds extending their ranges westward are evidently uncommon. Snyder (1957, p. 29-30) believed that only the black duck and great black-backed gull illustrated such a trend in Ontario. Northern birds that appear to be extending their ranges southward are even less common; no instances were reported by Snyder, who interpreted the return of the pileated woodpecker and common raven as a reoccupation of former ranges after local extirpation rather than as a shift in ranges. However,

Thomas (1951, p. 163) believed that the savannah sparrow is moving southward in Ohio, and Graber and Graber (1963, p. 509) reported similar trends for the bobolink and barn swallow in Illinois.

Adjustments in ranges of the native mammals tend to parallel those outlined for birds and cold-blooded vertebrates. Hall (1958, p. 373) pointed out that during the past 40 years the armadillo, hispid cotton rat, and southern bog lemming had extended their ranges appreciably northward in the prairie and plains states. Guilday (1958) has summarized the evidence for believing that the American opossum is spreading northward throughout its range. Thomas (1951, p. 162, 165) cited the eastern mole, deer mouse, and fox squirrel as examples of mammals extending their ranges eastward in Ohio, although these species may be exhibiting more of a change in local abundance than in actual range. It is reasonable to assume that prairie and forest-edge inhabitants may be moving eastward, but supporting data are far less convincing for mammals than for the birds. Thomas (1951, p. 164) suggested that the least weasel and the red fox are northern species gradually moving southward in Ohio.

Certain mammals, like many birds, may have become so closely associated with human modification of the land that they may follow on the heels of civilization. Others have stubbornly tolerated changes, accepting drain tiles in lieu of hollow trees as den sites and maintaining high populations, despite heavy mortality by automobiles, even in suburban areas. On the other hand, there are numerous examples of mammals being repelled by advancing modern man and ranges that have been tremendously reduced in recent times.

In all animals, range adjustments depend on the availability of suitable habitats, vagility of the organism and size of the barrier to be crossed, and the reproductive potential of the species. Unless the range is bounded by insurmountable physiographic features, oscillations in its periphery are certain to be occurring. These small-scale contractions and expansions, not to be confused with cyclic fluctuations, are direct responses to local environmental factors. All short-term observations that suggest changes in animal ranges must be interpreted with caution, for one day of adverse circumstances can erase a decade of range expanding.

There are countless conditions of variable complexity and duration that may have affected animal ranges, but in the absence of data the distributional adjustments can only be speculative. It would seem that, after the extreme deforestation in central and eastern North America in the late 19th century, the current practices of reforestation and establishment of wildlife preserves should result in an increase in range, as well as numbers, of forest animals. The comparative ease of re-establishing deer, beaver, and turkey in areas where they were once extirpated suggests that conditions are becoming more favorable for a forest fauna.

It could be assumed that fossorial animals, such as some of the reptiles, might have benefited by the dust-bowl era of the 1930's, when drought and agricultural malpractice increased the acreage of loose soils. Similarly, such species probably found expanding habitat when the sand prairies were first plowed; for soil-holding vegetation had, through succession, almost eliminated the "blow-outs" and stretches of bare sand that these burrowers prefer. However reasonable the assumption, there is no real evidence to document these short-term adjustments.

Because of the time lapse required for animal distributions to respond to environmental changes, there is considerably less information available on range adjustments in the West than in the central and eastern states. The diminishing desert-grassland and its replacement by shrub and scrubby trees where overgrazing occurs has altered habitat over hundreds of square miles, but the faunal changes discernible are primarily instances of range fragmentation and range shrinkage. Other habitats that have undergone tremendous modification, especially in recent decades, provide examples only of range disruption and the decimation of certain species. There is a similar lack of data for marginal waters. For example, the rate at which estuarine habitats are being destroyed is currently a subject of great concern to the National Academy of Sciences. The loss of these valuable fisheries is well known; the adjustments of individual species within the habitats are almost totally unknown.

Of all the events of the Historic Period, the one that stands out most clearly and unequivocally is the wholesale fragmentation of animal ranges. In many parts of the country, almost every population of vertebrate animals is a relict, separated from its neighbors by as little as the width of a paved highway or by as much as hundreds of square miles of inhospitable habitat. Despite efforts to preserve the vanishing native fauna, the trend toward relict distribution cannot be reversed. There is reason to believe that many of the adjustments described in the paragraphs above will continue in much the same directions for an unknown number of years, perhaps until survival, rather than adjustment, becomes the principal function of the animal population.

Appendix

Scientific Names of Animals Cited in Text

FISHES

Sea lamprey
  Petromyzon marinus Linnaeus
Longnose gar
  Lepisosteus osseus (Linnaeus)
Alewife
  Alosa pseudoharengus (Wilson)
Threadfin shad
  Dorosoma petenense (Günther)
Brown trout
  Salmo trutta Linnaeus
American smelt
  Osmerus mordax (Mitchill)
Goldfish
  Carassius auratus (Linnaeus)
Carp
  Cyprinus carpio Linnaeus
Colorado squawfish
  Ptychocheilus lucius Girard
Blue sucker
  Cycleptus elongatus (Lesueur)
Buffalo
  Ictiobus, species not cited

Harelip sucker
  Lagochila lacera Jordan and Brayton
Mosquitofish
  Gambusia affinis (Baird and Girard)
Freshwater drum
  Aplodinotus grunniens Rafinesque

AMPHIBIANS

Jefferson salamander
  Ambystoma jeffersonianum (Green)
Small-mouthed salamander
  Ambystoma texanum (Matthes)
Marine toad
  Bufo marinus (Linnaeus)
Greenhouse frog
  Eleutherodactylus ricordi Duméril and Bibron
Chorus frog
  Pseudacris triseriata (Wied)
Bullfrog
  Rana catesbeiana Shaw
Wood frog
  Rana sylvatica LeConte

REPTILES

Spiny softshell turtle
  Trionyx spiniferus Lesueur
American crocodile
  Crocodylus acutus Cuvier

BIRDS

Red-necked grebe
  Podiceps grisegena (Boddaert)
White pelican
  Pelecanus erythrorhynchos Gmelin
Brown pelican
  Pelecanus occidentalis Linnaeus
Double-crested cormorant
  Phalacrocorax auritus (Lesson)
Cattle egret
  Bubulcus ibis (Linnaeus)
Snowy egret
  Leucophoyx thula Molina
Whistling swan
  Olor columbianus (Ord)
Trumpeter swan
  Olor buccinator Richardson
Black duck
  Anas rubripes Brewster
Ring-necked duck
  Aythya collaris (Donovan)
Labrador duck
  Camptorhynchus labradorius (Gmelin)
California condor
  Gymnogyps californianus (Shaw)
Turkey vulture
  Cathartes aura (Linnaeus)
Swallow-tailed kite
  Elanoides forficatus (Linnaeus)
Everglade kite
  Rostrhamus sociabilis (Viellot)
Ruffed grouse
  Bonasa umbellus (Linnaeus)
Greater prairie chicken
  Tympanuchus cupido (Linnaeus)
Sharp-tailed grouse
  Pedioecetes phasianellus (Linnaeus)
Ring-necked pheasant
  Phasianus colchicus Linnaeus
Gray partridge
  Perdix perdix (Linnaeus)
Chukar
  Alectoris graeca (Meisner)

Bobwhite
  Colinus virginianus (Linnaeus)
California quail
  Lophortyx californica (Shaw)
Turkey
  Meleagris gallopavo Linnaeus
Whooping crane
  Grus americanus (Linnaeus)
Sandhill crane
  Grus canadensis (Linnaeus)
Long-billed curlew
  Numenius americanus Bechstein
Whimbrel
  Numenius phaeopus (Linnaeus)
Eskimo curlew
  Numenius borealis (Forster)
Marbled godwit
  Limosa fedoa (Linnaeus)
Great black-backed gull
  Larus marinus Linnaeus
Great auk
  Pinguinus impennis (Linnaeus)
Rock dove
  Columba livia Gmelin
Passenger pigeon
  Ectopistes migratorius (Linnaeus)
Mourning dove
  Zenaidura macroura (Linnaeus)
Carolina parakeet
  Conuropsis carolinensis (Linnaeus)
Black-billed cuckoo
  Coccyzus erythropthalmus (Wilson)
Pileated woodpecker
  Dryocopus pileatus (Linnaeus)
Red-bellied woodpecker
  Centurus carolinus (Linnaeus)
Ivory-billed woodpecker
  Campephilus principalis (Linnaeus)
Western kingbird
  Tyrannus verticalis Say
Acadian flycatcher
  Empidonax virescens (Viellot)
Horned lark
  Eremophila alpestris (Linnaeus)
Barn swallow
  Hirundo rustica Linnaeus
Common raven
  Corvus corax Linnaeus
Tufted titmouse
  Parus bicolor Linnaeus
Carolina chickadee
  Parus carolinensis Audubon
Bewick's wren
  Thryomaneus bewicki (Audubon)
Carolina wren
  Thryothorus ludovicianus (Latham)
Mockingbird
  Mimus polyglottos (Linnaeus)
Starling
  Sturnis vulgaris Linnaeus
Bell's vireo
  Vireo belli (Audubon)
House sparrow
  Passer domesticus (Linnaeus)
Brown-headed cowbird
  Molothrus ater (Boddaert)
Yellow-headed blackbird
  Xanthocephalus xanthocephalus (Bonapart)
Brewer's blackbird
  Euphagus cyanocephalus (Wagler)
Eastern meadowlark
  Sturnella magna (Linnaeus)

Western meadowlark
  Sturnella neglecta Audubon
Bobolink
  Dolichonyx oryzivorus (Linnaeus)
Cardinal
  Richmondena cardinalis (Linnaeus)
Evening grosbeak
  Hesperiphona vespertina (Cooper)
Savannah sparrow
  Passerculus sandwichensis (Gmelin)
Clay-colored sparrow
  Spizella pallida (Swainson)
Vesper sparrow
  Pooectes gramineus (Gmelin)

MAMMALS

American opossum
  Didelphis marsupialis Linnaeus
Eastern mole
  Scalopus aquaticus (Linnaeus)
Nine-banded armadillo
  Dasypus novemcinctus Linnaeus
European hare
  Lepus europaeus Pallas
Fox squirrel
  Sciurus niger Linnaeus
Prairie dog
  Cynomys, species not cited
Thirteen-lined ground squirrel
  Citellus tridecemlineatus (Mitchill)
Franklin's ground squirrel
  Citellus franklini (Sabine)
Plains pocket gopher
  Geomys bursarius (Shaw)
Beaver
  Castor canadensis Kuhl
Marsh rice rat
  Oryzomys palustris (Harlan)
Deer mouse
  Peromyscus maniculatus (Wagner)
White-footed mouse
  Peromyscus leucopus (Rafinesque)
Hispid cotton rat
  Sigmodon hispidus Say and Ord
Eastern wood rat
  Neotoma floridana (Ord)
Southern bog lemming
  Synaptomys cooperi Baird
Norway rat
  Rattus norvegicus (Berkenhout)
Black rat
  Rattus rattus (Linnaeus)
House mouse
  Mus musculus Linnaeus
Porcupine
  Erethizon dorsatum (Linnaeus)
Nutria
  Myocastor coypus (Molina)
Dog
  Canis familiaris Linnaeus
Gray wolf
  Canis lupus Linnaeus
Red fox
  Vulpes fulva (Desmarest)
Swift fox
  Vulpes velox (Say)
Grizzly bear
  Ursus horribilis Ord
Black bear
  Ursus americanus Pallas
Least weasel
  Mustela rixosa (Bangs)

Coastal mink
   Mustela macrodon (Prentiss)
Black-footed ferret
   Mustela nigripes (Audubon and Bachman)
Marten
   Martes americana (Turton)
Fisher
   Martes pennanti (Erxleben)
Wolverine
   Gulo luscus (Linnaeus)
Spotted skunk
   Spilogale putorius (Linnaeus)
River otter
   Lutra canadensis (Schreber)
Jaguar
   Felis onca (Linnaeus)
Ocelot
   Felis pardalis Linnaeus
Mountain lion
   Felis concolor Linnaeus
Bobcat
   Lynx rufus (Schreber)
Wild horse
   Eques caballus Linnaeus
Elk
   Cervus canadensis Erxleben
White-tailed deer
   Odocoileus virginianus (Zimmerman)
Moose
   Alces alces (Linnaeus)
Caribou
   Rangifer tarandus (Linnaeus)
Pronghorn
   Antilocapra americana (Ord)
Bison
   Bison bison (Linnaeus)
Mountain sheep
   Ovis canadensis Shaw

REFERENCES

Bleakney, J. S., 1958, A zoogeographical study of the amphibians and reptiles of eastern Canada: Natl. Mus. Can. Bull. 155, 119 p.

Bluhm, Elaine A. (ed.), 1959, Illinois archaeology: Illinois Arch. Surv. Bull. 1, 61 p.

Broecker, W. S., Ewing, Maurice, and Heezen, B. C., 1960, Evidence for an abrupt change in climate close to 11,000 years ago: Amer. J. Sci., v. 258, p. 429-448

Conant, Roger, 1960, The queen snake, *Natrix septemvittata*, in the Interior Highlands of Arkansas and Missouri, with comments upon similar disjunct distributions: Philadelphia Acad. Nat. Sci. Proc., v. 112, p. 25-40

Cooper, W. S., 1958, Terminology of post-Valders time: Geol. Soc. Amer. Bull., v. 69, p. 941-945

Cottam, W. P., Tucker, J. M., and Drobnick, Rudy, 1959, Some clues to Great Basin postpluvial climates provided by oak distributions: Ecology, v. 40, p. 361-377

Deevey, E. S., Jr., 1949, Biogeography of the Pleistocene: Geol. Soc. Amer. Bull., v. 60, p. 1315-1416

Frey, D. G., 1953, Regional aspects of the late-glacial and post-glacial pollen succession of southeastern North Carolina: Ecol. Monogr., v. 23, p. 289-313

Gehlbach, F. R., and Miller, R. R., 1961, Fishes from archaeological sites in northern New Mexico: Southwest. Nat., v. 6, p. 2-8

Graber, R. R., and Graber, Jean W., 1963, A comparative study of bird populations in Illinois, 1906-1909 and 1956-1958: Illinois Nat. Hist. Surv. Bull., v. 28, p. 383-528

Griffin, J. W., and Wray, D. E., 1945, Bison in Illinois archaeology: Illinois Acad. Sci. Trans., v. 38, p. 21-26

Guilday, J. E., 1958, The prehistoric distribution of the opossum: J. Mammal., v. 39, p 39-43

—— 1961, Prehistoric record of *Scalopus* from western Pennsylvania: J. Mammal., v. 42, p. 117-118

—— 1962, The Pleistocene local fauna of the Natural Chimneys, Augusta County, Virginia: Carnegie Inst., Pittsburgh Mus. Ann., v. 36, p. 87-122

Guilday, J. E., and Tanner, D. P., 1962, Animal remains from the Quaker State Rockshelter (36 Ve 27), Venango County, Pennsylvania: Pennsylvania Archaeologist Soc., Pennsylvania Arch. Bull., v. 32, p. 131-137

Hall, E. R., 1958, Introduction, Part II, in Hubbs, C. L., Zoogeography: Amer. Assoc. Adv. Sci. Publ. 51, p. 371-373

Hargrave, L. L., 1939, Bird bones from abandoned Indian dwellings in Arizona and Utah: Condor, v. 41, p. 206-210

Heusser, C. J., 1960, Late Pleistocene environments of North Pacific North America: Amer. Geog. Soc. Spec. Publ. 35, 308 p.

Larimore, R. W., and Smith, P. W., 1963, The fishes of Champaign County, Illinois, as affected by 60 years of stream changes: Illinois Nat. Hist. Surv. Bull., v. 28, p. 299-382

Martin, Paul S., 1958, Pleistocene ecology and biogeography of North America, in Hubbs, C. L. (ed.), Zoogeography: Amer. Assoc. Adv. Sci., Publ. 51, p. 375-420

—— 1963, The last 10,000 years. A fossil pollen record of the American southwest: Tucson, Arizona, Univ. Arizona Press, 87 p.

Miller, R. R., 1961, Man and the changing fish fauna of the American Southwest: Michigan Acad. Sci. Arts Lett., v. 46, p. 365-404

Neill, W. T., Gut, H. J., and Brodkorb, Pierce, 1956, Animal remains from four preceramic sites in Florida: Amer. Antiq., v. 21, p. 383-395

Parmalee, P. W., 1958, Marine shells of Illinois Indian sites: Nautilus, v. 71, p. 132-139

—— 1961, A recent find of jaguar bones in a Tennessee cave: Tennessee Acad. Sci. J., v. 36, p. 81-85

Parmalee, P. W., Bieri, R. A., and Mohrman, R. K., 1961, Mammal remains from an Illinois cave: J. Mammal., v. 42, p. 119

Parmalee, P. W., and Hoffmeister, D. F., 1957, Archaeozoological evidence of the spotted skunk in Illinois: J. Mammal., v. 38, p. 261

Schmidt, K. P., 1938, Herpetological evidence for the post-glacial eastward extension of steppe in North America: Ecology, v. 19, p. 396-407

Scott, W. B., 1963, A review of the changes in the fish fauna of Ontario: Roy. Can. Inst. Trans., v. 34, p. 111-125

Smiley, T. L., 1961, Evidences of climatic fluctuations in southwestern prehistory: New York Acad. Sci. Ann., v. 95, p. 697-704

Smith, P. W., 1957, An analysis of post-Wisconsin biogeography of the Prairie Peninsula region based on distributional phenomena among terrestrial vertebrate populations: Ecology, v. 38, p. 205-218

Smith, P. W., and Minton, S. A., Jr., 1957, A distributional summary of the herpetofauna of Indiana and Illinois: Amer. Midl. Nat., v. 58, p. 341-351

Smith, P. W., and Smith, H. M., 1962, The systematic and biogeographic status of two Illinois snakes: C. C. Adams Center Ecol. Stud. Occ. Pap. 3, 10 p.

Snyder, L. L., 1957, Changes in the avifauna of Ontario, in Urquhart, F. A. (ed.), Changes in the fauna of Ontario: Toronto, Canada, Univ. Toronto Press, 75 p.

Thomas, E. S., 1951, Distribution of Ohio animals: Ohio J. Sci., v. 51, p. 153-167

Trautman, M. B., 1957, The fishes of Ohio: Columbus, Ohio State Univ. Press, 683 p.

Urquhart, F. A. (ed.), 1957, Changes in the fauna of Ontario: Toronto, Canada, Univ. Toronto Press, 75 p.

Wright, H. E., Jr., Winter, T. C., and Patten, H. L., 1963, Two pollen diagrams from southeastern Minnesota. Problems in the regional late-glacial and postglacial vegetational history: Geol. Soc. Amer. Bull., v. 74, p. 1371-1396

Summary

During postglacial time, the major events to which animal ranges have adjusted have been the Xerothermic or Hypsithermal Interval (warmer and drier than at present), the subsequent return of relatively cool-moist climate in the eastern half of North America, and development of modern civilization. Evidence from palaeoecology indicates that, prior to the Xerothermic Interval, deciduous forest occurred more continuously and at slightly higher (at least 150 to 450 km) latitudes than at present. Arid climate fragmented ranges of forest animals, left numerous forest relicts, and, at the same time, enabled steppe and xeric-type forest animals to become more widespread in eastern North America. The return of a cool-moist climate and vegetational cover of a more mesic type fragmented ranges of some western components and left relicts of grassland and forest-edge animals. In western North America, a warm period, usually termed Altithermal, left some relicts on mountain slopes, although greater aridity during the period in the extreme Southwest is now questioned. Climatic and vegetational changes from ca. 5,000 to 3,000 B.P. over most of the country resulted in many range disjunctions and complex patterns of relict populations.

Evidence from archaeozoology indicates that, during the 2,000 to 3,000 years prior to European settlement of North America, biotas had adjusted to environmental conditions of the different parts of this country and that animal ranges were presumably similar to those prevailing when European man first penetrated the American wilderness. A few distributional vagaries, represented by midden and cave remains, may or may not indicate dispersal during phases of unusually warm or cool climate. Faunal remains are seldom precisely dated. Abundant but loosely related archaeozoological data in general do not confirm the climatic chronology postulated by many palaeoecologists.

The introduction and development of modern civilization in this country have resulted in extirpation of several species, endangering of many others, introduction of several exotics, and transplanting of numerous American species outside their natural ranges. Widespread and usually drastic modification of habitats has fragmented animal ranges, but many native species have adjusted their ranges to environmental change. Fishes have been able to bypass natural barriers and have been widely transplanted. Amphibians and reptiles have responded chiefly through range shrinkage. Many birds and mammals have ranges gradually shifting northward; several have ranges extending eastward. Relatively few ranges appear to be moving westward or southward. Human modification of habitats is probably more responsible for these expansions than recent climatic change.

Many well-known alterations of habitats within historic times could result in predictable adjustments of animal ranges, but actual data on these occurrences are not yet available. Adjustments in range are well documented in eastern and central North America. Except for many instances of range fragmentation and withdrawal, they are less certain in the West and in estuaries of both coasts. The most striking result of man's effect upon animal ranges is an increasingly accelerated trend toward relict distribution of all vertebrate populations.

GENERAL

PLEISTOCENE NONMARINE ENVIRONMENTS

EDWARD S. DEEVEY, JR.[1]

THE CHIEF early proponent of widespread former glaciation was a biologist, and ever since Agassiz's day the role of biology in Pleistocene research has been one of full partnership with physical geology. Other kinds of geology also depend heavily on biological data, but Pleistocene studies are primarily ecological, whereas the biology of older and longer time units is primarily evolutionary. The distinction is one of emphasis only, for the subjects are not sharply separable, but ecologists and evolutionists usually have different questions in mind. Similar or identical data—the occurence of fossils in geologic settings—lead them to different inferences about the history of environments on the one hand, and about the phyletic history of organisms on the other.

It is true that organic changes that occurred during the Pleistocene are of exceptional interest to students of evolution, if only because the environmental setting of these changes is relatively well understood. The epoch was short, however, and the amount of morphologic and taxonomic change was slight, so that the leading problems are those of microsystematics rather than those of phylogeny. The evolutionist therefore can shift his attention from the deployment of organic variety to the mechanisms that produce and maintain the variety. However valuable its legacy to theory, the usefulness of this kind of evolution to stratigraphy and chronology is minimal. In other words, the evolutionary biologist expects to learn more from Pleistocene geology than he contributes to it.

By contrast, the history of environments is and must be inferred equally from physical and biological data. It is well known, even to meteorologists who have no concern with the geologic past, that vegetation is often a surer guide to the climate of a region, or to the microclimate of a locality, than any physical measurement yet devised. The central concern of Pleistocene research being the record of climatic variations, the ranges of animals and plants, when known to be environmentally determined and inferred to have changed from the distribution of fossils, are indispensable geologic documents. For the ecologists who provide and interpret these data it is a distinct advantage to be able to discount evolutionary change. It means that Pleistocene paleoecology deals for the most part with known or knowable species, and therefore proceeds in a more strictly

uniformitarian way than is possible in other kinds of paleoecology.

Pleistocene ecology is in fact nothing but an extension of present-day ecology into the most recent past. Major advances of ecological thought therefore tend to be reflected at once in Pleistocene studies, and the converse is also true. Because modern ecology is preoccupied with developing concepts of populations and ecosystems, a holistic viewpoint about life-in-environment is increasingly prevalent, and the metaphorical language of information theory is being usefully applied to systems, such as lakes and the ocean, that transmit biochemical order from the Pleistocene to the present. The systems approach is powerful, and it has the great merit that it appeals to the geochemists, whose recent contributions to paleoecology have been spectacular. As a less happy consequence, however, the autecologies of particular species of animals and plants are seen as trivial by comparison, and they are being less actively studied than formerly. Modern ecology is also undergoing a phase of intense self-criticism, and the current disenchantment with many long-established concepts, such as succession and the climax and ecogeographic rules like Bergmann's, is forcing a newly critical attitude in Pleistocene research. One result is that whereas two generations of workers have added huge quantities of information to a substantial base built by such works as those of Hay (1923, 1924, 1927) and Baker (1920), the basis of ecological inference from a given fossil is often less certain now than it seemed in the golden days when there were fewer fossils to consider.

The function of this essay is not to give a comprehensive account of Pleistocene ecology, but to introduce and comment upon the contributions of biologists who review existing data on Pleistocene biogeography, including biological stratigraphy, in the United States. What emerges from these chapters, or at least from these comments, is a regrettable conclusion: extremely little is reliably known about Pleistocene habitats, especially at times and in places where there were no glaciers. Though it may surprise physical geologists, such a conclusion does not alarm general ecologists, who are aware of how little is reliably known about *any* habitat, ancient or modern. At all events, factual data are much more abundant than they were forty years ago, and the taxonomic quality of fossil identifications has been measurably improved. Skepticism in the

[1] Department of Biology, Yale University, New Haven, Connecticut.

643

geologic interpretation of these data is a healthy sign of scientific maturity, which the paleoecologist shares with the physical geologist.

BIOGEOGRAPHY

DEFINITION

In the literal meaning of the term, *biogeography* embraces all aspects of the distribution of animals and plants, ancient and modern. It therefore can include such microgeographic features as the differences in vegetation on north- and south-facing slopes, which are rarely thought of as geographic by ecologists. Although Andrewartha and Birch (1954) point out that *distribution* and *abundance* are twin facets of the same phenomenon in space-time, absence of an organism from a locality being the special case of zero abundance, most ecologists do not find this abstraction helpful, and certainly *plant ecology* and *plant geography* are different subjects, practiced by different people. Geologists tend to use *biogeography* in its widest meaning, as the heading of this group of chapters shows, but ecologists who practice *stratigraphy* and/or *paleoecology* usually use those terms, reserving *biogeography* for the study of existing ranges of organisms, the great majority of which have little or no fossil record. In this restricted sense the subject is a branch of the "new systematics" and is making major contributions to evolutionary theory, but its relevance to paleoecology is slight, even when it is called *historical biogeography*.

METHODOLOGY

This morose but considered opinion reflects certain weaknesses inherent in biogeographic methodology. Ranges that are continuous, in the sense that a species or other taxon occurs in every suitable habitat within the mapped range, are said to present "purely" ecological problems. One assumes, as the simplest postulate, that the limits of environmental variation are stable, and he inquires which environmental parameters, or factors, have greatest relevance in limiting the range of the species at any segment of its margin. The factors that may be critical are innumerable in principle, being in fact the *n* dimensions of niche hyperspace, and it is fortunate for paleoecology that most ranges seem to be limited mainly by physical factors—temperature and salinity for aquatic organisms, temperature and moisture for terrestrial ones. By assumption, however, these ecological problems are nonhistorical. Historical problems arise when there are demonstrable gaps or disjunctions in the range for which the known autecology provides no explanation. Apart from limitations in our knowledge of autecologies and of means and probabilities of dispersal across gaps, to focus on disjunctions is to insist on the essential value of negative evidence; it amounts to using voids in ranges as negative fossils. The innumerable possible reasons for disjunction then become subjects of speculative argument, frequently interesting and sometimes passionate, but seldom susceptible of proof. Finally, if one grants the reality of an historical problem exposed by such reasoning, and inquires further into the history, it turns out to have no built-in chronology. If present-day environmental

relations fail to explain the range, former ones must do so, but the argument ends when a "past" is reached that was different from the "present." Thus the ranges of animals and plants "prove" many times over that central Europe was glaciated, or that the Great Basin was appreciably moister during a pluvial age, but no airtight biogeographical argument has yet proved the occurrence of more than one glacial or pluvial age.

Repeated glaciation is an established fact, and most existing species are probably old enough to have lived through more than one glacial age. The common occurrence of genera containing many sympatric species, and the rarer but clearer evidence given by double invasions, make it almost axiomatic that floras and faunas are made up of species of different ages, or whose ranges have been established at different times. To prove which species or ranges are older, however, is virtually impossible without fossils, because the "proof" ordinarily rests on unverifiable assumptions about rates of taxonomic differentiation. Thus Ross (this volume), discussing the distribution of hillstream caddisflies, suggests that Ozark-Appalachian disjunctions are older for the species-pairs *Glossopsyche missouri–G. irrorata* and *Hydropsyche piatirx–H. vexa* than for the single disjunct stonefly species *Allocapnia pygmaea*. His dating of the older separation as Illinoian and of the younger as Wisconsin rests primarily on the conclusions of Krekeler (1958) about rates of speciation in cave-dwelling carabid beetles. Depending on one's attitude toward such data, Krekeler's conclusions are as firm or as weak as Ross's, and both biogeographers are echoing the standard contention, also based on taxonomic differentiation (see Deevey, 1949), that European boreo-alpine disjunctions are older by at least one glacial age than the boreo-British pattern. As isolation of a disjunct population is likely in itself to accelerate taxonomic change (though not to the same degree even in closely related species), such reasoning is inevitably partly circular.

JUSTIFICATION

The merit of such arguments is not to be judged by their service to paleoecology. Of course the stratigraphic evidence of loesses in the Mississippi lowland, between the Ozarks and the Appalachian plateau, is surer proof of Illinoian and Wisconsin glaciation than gaps in the ranges of insect taxa can ever be. That is not the point, as the biologist sees it, though what the point is is commonly misunderstood by geologists. The problems at issue are evolutionary, not ecological, and the popularity of historical biogeography among taxonomists needs no other justification. The specialist in flatworms or millipedes has no hope of attacking microevolutionary problems directly, from fossils; when he turns biogeographer he uses all available data on Pleistocene environments, in conjunction with new or nonobvious features of ranges, in an indirect attempt to decipher the rates and especially the modes of speciation. The answers to these purely biological questions are not the same for birds as for butterfles or mosses, and every systematist needs to answer them in terms appropriate to his specialty. It is no part of his concern as systematist, however, that *phyletic* histories should point to former land bridges or pluvial climates or to any particular aspect of environment. Such deductions require inversion of the biogeographic argument, with attendant risk of circularity.

SOME APPLICATIONS

Nevertheless, the inversion is sometimes permissible, at least in Pleistocene contexts, when much is already known about modes of speciation, and of course biogeographic evidence of former environments automatically gains cogency in situations where stratigraphic methods fail (Deevey, 1949). Geologic evidence of former land connections is mainly drowned, and direct indications of former watercourses are scarce or ambiguous in regions of active erosion or volcanism. Even where a glacial history is well established, as in Scandinavia, intelligent study of existing ranges can add significant geologic detail. The elegant work of Svärdson (1961) on fishes and of Segerstråle (1954, 1957) on amphipods provides examples, and Segerstråle (1962) has argued convincingly (from ranges, not from taxonomic distinctness) for a two-stage Siberian origin of the famous ice-lake relicts in northern Europe. Comparable American works are less closely linked to adequate geologic data, but the papers of Gerking (1945) and Ricker (1959) should be cited as typical.

The distinction between continental and oceanic islands in terms of their land mammals, established by A. R. Wallace, remains valid today, and some of the best-founded land bridges, such as those to the British Isles, to Sicily, and to the Greater Sunda Islands, are still largely dependent on mammalian evidence. The paradoxical inclusion of Newfoundland among oceanic islands (Cameron, 1958; Deevey, 1961) does no violence to geologic data, though it emphasizes the importance of dating in such matters. Newfoundland's oceanicity is obviously very recent (late Pleistocene), whereas the continentality of the Greater Antilles, like that of the Balearics and the Ryu-kyus, is of Tertiary age. Cameron's studies in eastern Canada have yielded a textbook example of faunal imbalance on oceanic islands: the Magdalen group in the Gulf of St. Lawrence has four carnivorous species to one species of herbivore. Unfortunately there appears to be no up-to-date treatment of the mammals of Cuba or Hispaniola, or of Antillean biogeography in general.

In the other kind of situation where distributional data have unquestioned paleoecological relevance—former stream connections through presently arid regions—the outstanding American work remains that of Hubbs and Miller (1948) on the fishes of the Great Basin. Miller (this volume) has added some extremely valuable details, but the most informative of these are not biogeographic, in the narrow sense, but stratigraphic. Without the rich fossil finds from the Glenns Ferry formation, or the geologic work of Bright on the history of Bear Lake, inferences from existing fish distribution would be more ambiguous. Even where fossil evidence is relatively ample, as in Taylor's study (1960) of the mollusk *Pisidium*, ambiguities remain; for example, Pleistocene hydrologic connections of the Klamath basin are still unsettled, as the fishes and the mollusks suggest different (not necessarily contemporaneous) patterns. Taylor's full description and analysis of the

Glenns Ferry mollusks (see Malde and Powers, 1962) is awaited with interest, especially in view of Malde's statement (this volume): "Lakes and streams of the Glenns Ferry nourished an exceptionally large and diverse molluscan fauna, comparable in variety and degree of endemism to the fossil mollusks from the former Pontian, Dacian, and Levantine basins of southeastern Europe."

When the widely disjunct ranges of aquatic animals in deserts are considered, interpretations are complicated by widespread extinction and by endemism, but one can at least be sure that every indigenous species is a Pleistocene relict of some sort. The species of humid temperate regions are also Pleistocene relicts, but it solves no problems to say so. The biota of glaciated territory can be examined for clues to routes and times of dispersal, as in a particularly interesting discussion of the flora of Manitoba by Doris Löve (1959), but the biogeography of regions beyond the drift borders lacks even this degree of manageability. By taking postglacial paleoecology as given by pollen stratigraphy, Smith (1957) and Martin (1958) have made plausible interpretations of some disjunctions, boreal relicts in the South being inferred to be longer established in their present habitats than are hypsithermal relicts in the North and East, but this methodology cannot yield independent information on Pleistocene environments. It is self-evident that most recolonization of glaciated country was from southern refuges, and peninsula Nova Scotia has a special relation, being a near-island whose persistent land bridge (the Isthmus of Chignecto) connects to its northern tip. Bleakney (1958) argued that the use of this bridge by amphibians and reptiles required a northward displacement of present climatic zones by *ca.* 200 miles—a useful datum when post-Hypsithermal cooling is being called into question (Davis, this volume). The peninsula that closes Chesapeake Bay to the east has a similar relation to the mainland, as discussed by Smith (1957), and it deserves more careful scrutiny.

Farther beyond the glacial limits, however, the biogeography is fascinating but amorphous, and in the near-absence of stratigraphic data the Pleistocene ecology of the whole southeastern region is beset by unresolved controversy (Braun, 1955). A substantial contribution was made by Martin and Harrell (1957), who demonstrated that Appalachian-Mexican disjunctions, though numerous among plants, are essentially absent among forest-dwelling vertebrates. The clear implication is that Mexican cloud-forest plants, which include such familiar eastern species as the tulip tree (*Liriodendron tulipifera*) and the partridgeberry (*Mitchella repens*), were isolated in Mexico long ago, probably in late-Tertiary time, and have evolved more slowly than the vertebrates. It follows that the intervening steppe country of southeastern Texas and northeastern Mexico has probably *not* been forested in Pleistocene time. Though negative in character, and founded as usual on negative evidence, this conclusion is useful in setting limits to speculation. It appears not to be in conflict with Blair's (1958) evidence, also drawn from disjunct populations of vertebrates, of substantial westward penetration of forests across the central Texas savanna; environments like that around the Lower Pleistocene Rita Blanca lake near Channing, Texas (Kirkland and Anderson, 1963), were probably mesic enough to account for Blair's examples.

CONCLUSION

Martin (this volume) and others are vigorously pursuing Pleistocene biogeography in the southwestern deserts, though largely by stratigraphic methods. The rest of southern United States, from the Gulf South to the glacial boundary, contains some of the most celebrated biogeographic puzzles on earth (magnolias, Theaceae, plethodontid salamanders, alligators, ganoid fishes, etc.). Where these archaic and mainly warmth-demanding types survived the Pleistocene, and what their present habitats were like during glacial ages, are questions that purely biogeographic methods are incompetent to answer.

POSTGLACIAL STRATIGRAPHY

HOLOCENE

Postglacial pollen sequences are less well known in glaciated eastern North America than in Europe, the number of sections being a few hundred instead of several thousand, but the main outlines have been clear since the work of Paul B. Sears in Ohio in the 1930's. His five-part division as extended to Connecticut (Deevey, 1939, 1943)— A, boreal coniferous; B, pines; C-1, oak-hemlock; C-2, oak-hickory; and C-3, oak-chestnut-spruce—has been found to serve very well over most of this enormous region, correlations between zones being based on botanically appropriate modifications in regions where hemlock or hickory or chestnut are replaced as forest dominants by other tree species. It has been generally accepted that the implied climatic sequence— A, cool; B, warm, dry; C-1, warm, moister; C-2, warm, drier; C-3, cooler, moister—prevailed over an area much wider than the present range of any tree species; hence transatlantic and even worldwide correlations have been attempted without diffidence, on the lines laid down by the master (von Post, 1946) in his Vega Lecture. It was also clear very early that a sequence beginning with a time of conifers must be all postglacial in the sense of Firbas and Iversen, and the search for older treeless or late-glacial pollen zones was successful (Deevey, 1951) as soon as the techniques of those workers were applied.

Radiocarbon dating was brought into use as early as 1950 (Flint and Deevey, 1951; Deevey and Potzger, 1951) and verified the general synchrony of major pollen-analytical events on both sides of the Atlantic. Although the most direct test of correlation (comparison of Zone L-2 in Maine with the Alleröd zone) required impracticably large C^{14} samples, it was possible to demonstrate equivalence of early Boreal time between Europe and southern New England or Michigan. Deevey and Flint (1957) therefore were able to discount the time-transgressive nature of the North American pine-pollen zone in defining the Hypsithermal interval (von Post's maximum-warmth period) as the time of Danish pollen-zones V through VIII.

LATE-GLACIAL

Several studies (Andersen, 1954; Leopold, 1956; Davis, 1958; Livingstone and Livingstone, 1958; Ogden, 1959; summary of dates by Deevey, 1958) were concentrated on late-glacial stratigraphy, in an effort to strengthen correlations by defining the zone of influence of the Valders glaciation. As it became clearer (Terasmae, 1959; MacClintock and Terasmae, 1960) that Valders ice probably did not occupy New England, unless as isolated remnant ice caps, southern New England became an obvious place in which to search for evidence of pre-Alleröd climatic oscillations.

By Two Creeks time southern New England and New York, like the type locality at Manitowoc, Wisconsin, but unlike Europe north of Spain, were evidently forested. Evidence of cooling beyond a periglacial belt was therefore to be sought, not in a classic tundra to park tundra to tundra sequence, but in some form of vegetational disturbance short of deforestation. In this situation it was essential to decide by what pollen-statistical criteria such disturbance could be recognized. European experience, with a different late-glacial geography and a floristically much simpler forest, provided no helpful parallels; moreover, the problem is not purely stratigraphic, but requires paleoecological interpretation of a kind that conventional pollen stratigraphy is poorly equipped to handle.

STATISTICAL TRAPS

Pollen percentages form a closed statistical universe, in which variation of one component affects numerical values for all others. Parallel trends of percentages over time at different sites define homotaxial zones, so accounting for the great success of the method as a stratigraphic tool; but as different plants vary enormously in production and dissemination of pollen, changing pollen percentages have no definable ecological meaning. This point was well understood by von Post, but his successors have tended to lose sight of it (Davis, 1963). It arose in acute form in connection with late-glacial variations of the ratio of spruce to nonarboreal pollen (Davis, 1961; Ogden, 1963), when inferences from pollen stratigraphy were sharply contradicted by radiocarbon dates at several sites on Martha's Vineyard and Block Island. Conifer pollen grains in a nonarboreal context are peculiarly liable to misinterpretation, because some or perhaps all of them have been blown for long distances over treeless country; but if the Totoket (Leopold, 1956) and Vineyard (Ogden, 1959) oscillations were statistical artifacts, other interpretations of changing percentages are equally questionable. For example, during postglacial warming (Zone B), when an aspen-birch woodland containing much spruce collects the pollen or such poor producers as larch and fir and then maple before the oaks arrive, one of the least obvious consequences is a rise of pine pollen from *ca.* 20% to *ca.* 60%.

The real meaning of the pine maximum is almost certainly *absence of oak*, but American palynologists have been prevented from seeing this by the undoubted stratigraphic validity of the pine zone. Perhaps, too, they have been misled by the abundance of megafossils of *Pinus sylvestris* in European peat bogs, where the Boreal zone was defined before pollen analysis was invented. The "Sub-Atlantic climatic deterioration" (Zone C-3) is another problem demanding careful reconsideration of the meaning of pollen percentages; Davis (this volume; see also Smith, this volume) finds no evidence of this event, at least in New England pollen diagrams, that cannot be attributed with equal plausibility to the spread of agriculture in the first millennium B.C.

UNIFORMITARIAN APPROACH

Late-Pleistocene paleoecology has the advantage of being able to work directly backward from the present. Martin and his co-workers in the Southwest, as is proper in any newly studied region, interpret buried pollen assemblages only in the light of the modern pollen rain in various habitats, and the lack of comparable information in the Northeast, though embarrassing, is repairable. Several studies (*e.g.* Carroll, 1943) have attempted to relate pollen rain to vegetation in quantitative terms, but moss polsters and the uppermost surfaces of bogs are unsatisfactory samplers of modern pollen, because they represent indefinite times of accumulation. Glass slides and air filters work well for public-health purposes in cities, but their data are not easily translated into rates of natural pollen sedimentation. Analysis of the uppermost surfaces of lake deposits has become the method of choice, cattle tanks being used where natural lakes are not available, and although the limnology of pollen deposition (and redeposition) needs much more study, promising results are being obtained in several areas. Fortunately, as most pollen of paleoecological interest was waterlaid, it is sufficient for most purposes to measure pollen deposition on the lake bottom, so bypassing serious aerodynamic problems posed by other kinds of fallout.

As present-day vegetation is reasonably well known in much of the Northeast, rapid reconnaissance in the lakes of several different regions gives useful results. Ogden (manuscript) has devised a surface-mud sampler for this purpose that is easily operated from a portable boat. So far as it relies on pollen percentages, however, the method is no different from Aario's (1940), as applied to surface peats by Wilson, Hansen, and other American workers; it relates pollen dominance to plant cover in a nonquantitative way, but it is of little help in the difficult situation where a forest dominant such as aspen or maple is virtually unrepresented by pollen. Dramatic examples of the lack of fit between pollen and vegetational frequencies are given by Davis and Goodlett (1960; so also Davis, 1963).

POLLEN-FALLOUT RATES

To escape from the statistical straitjacket of percentage composition, chronological control is necessary. The fallout of each pollen type per unit area and time can be measured independently of other pollen types, if the sedimentation rate of unit volume or mass of pollen-bearing deposit is known. Radiocarbon dating is the newest of several methods applicable to older deposits, and it has now yielded an absolute pollen diagram for the late-glacial history of Rogers Lake, Connecticut (Davis and Deevey, 1964). Current sedimentation rates in most lakes of cultivated regions differ sharply from those of a few centuries ago, however, and must be measured in many habitats if ratios of pollen to vegetation are to be given ecological meaning. Some progress is being made in this direction, but the task is formidable, in view of the necessity of including arctic lakes.

Present-day sedimentation rates can be measured experimentally, in sediment traps, or, less directly, by dating short mud cores. Radiocarbon dating is too insensitive for this purpose, but other natural isotopes such as tritium and Pb^{210} offer promise. Annual laminae of the Zürichsee type (see discussion by Bradley, 1963) occur mainly in meromictic lakes, which are uncommon, but other stratigraphic markers that can be used include the incoming of European weed pollen, the post-1920 decline of chestnut (Castanea), and the post-1954 increase of artificial isotopes.

Direct measurement of pollen fallout in sediment traps suspended over the lake bottom has so far given ambiguous results in Rogers Lake (Davis and Deevey, 1962), mainly because of statistical uncertainties in counting. However, subfossil *Bosmina* carapaces and organic matter in the same traps (Deevey, 1964) give mutually consistent figures averaging 3 years per milliliter (3.3 mm/yr) for the fresh sediment, compared to *ca.* 1 mm/yr for the postglacial section (and 0.36 ± 0.03 mm/yr for the dated late-glacial section; Davis and Deevey, 1964). If these figures prove to be typical of small temperate lakes (Thomas, 1955; Tutin, 1955), *i.e.* if the variance of sedimentation rates is no greater than that of pollen counts, fallout rates may be adequately estimated from counts in standard volumes of surface sediment, without further refinement.

ABSOLUTE POLLEN FREQUENCY

Even in default of calibration between surface pollen frequencies and present-day vegetation, absolute pollen frequency (APF), or pollen per unit mass or volume, can be informative. On the assumption of constant deposition of dry matter, Tsukada (1958) has attempted to deduce relative pollen-dissemination rates of Japanese trees from changes of APF in different habitats. The practice of measuring and publishing APF values is to be encouraged, because they can be calibrated eventually, whereas percentages discard information that can not be recovered. When percentages and APF both change sharply, however, as they can be expected to do at the late-glacial–postglacial boundary, pollen frequencies remain equivocal as indicators of ecology.

CONCLUSION

Many other fossils besides pollen grains contribute to postglacial stratigraphy, and some, like small vertebrates in caves, terrestrial mollusks in loess, or seeds in swamps and salt marshes, are richly informative for paleoecology. Ross (this volume) emphasizes the high indicator value of insects, very many species of which have strict environmental requirements. This discussion has been confined to *pollen* stratigraphy because airborne pollen is nearly universal, and because a pattern of changing climax vegetation on uplands, inferrable in principle from pollen, points more directly to climatic change than do events in lakes, swamps, or caves. To work out this pattern in quantitative terms has seemed eminently worth while to historians of all sorts, not least to archaeologists; and because of the primacy of plants in the environment of animals, including man, pollen stratigraphers have been able to think of themselves as custodians of the history of ecosystems. Other paleoecologists are aware that quantitative methods developed in postglacial stratigraphy are more or less directly applicable to countable assemblages of the remoter past, such as foraminiferans and diatoms in marine deposits as well as the pollen of lignite and the spores of coal. It turns out that the extreme ease with which pollen can be recovered, identified, and counted is one of nature's more seductive tricks. It has permitted a valid and useful stratigraphic division of late-Pleistocene deposits, now largely superseded by radiocarbon dating, while the changing pattern of vegetation remains as elusive as ever.

THE OLDER PLEISTOCENE

WHAT HAPPENED TO THE YARMOUTH?

Pre-Wisconsin organic deposits are not common in North America, or, if they occur in nonglaciated regions, they are difficult to recognize. Sections that span a full interglacial age are extremely rare, and several of the better-known ones are not well placed stratigraphically. Of those studied pollen-analytically by Voss (1933, 1939) and Fuller (1939), the majority have been reassigned to different stages. This is ordinarily done on glacial-geologic grounds, because Pleistocene pollen and other plant evidence lacks any built-in evolutionary clues to age, and interglacial sequences are inevitably much alike.

Apart from the Aftonian beds of Iowa (Steere, 1942), well-studied eastern sections (Terasmae, 1960; Engelhardt, 1960; Kapp, 1964; Kapp and Gooding, 1964; Whitehead and Barghoorn, 1962) fall into two groups. Those dominated throughout by subarctic and boreal plants, implying a climate cooler than today's, are called interstadial. Only those with evidence of deciduous forest near the middle are considered to be interglacial, although this classic criterion breaks down in the far north (Terasmae, 1957). The problems of interpreting pollen percentages are no easier in truncated pre- or intra-Wisconsin sections than in postglacial deposits, but the clear and consistent dominance of hardwood pollen in Sangamon diagrams from southern Indiana (Kapp and Gooding, 1964) leaves little doubt that that region had a rich hardwood forest, probably richer than today's, in middle-Sangamon time. In the famous Don beds near Toronto, now also regarded as Sangamon, the presence of warmth-demanding plants was established on the basis of megafossils, and the pollen evidence is confirmatory. It may seem from the literature that the vegetation of the Northeast is better known in Sangamon than in Holocene time, but this is an illusion. Almost unconsciously, one expects ecological detail to be increasingly blurred in the remoter past, so that "hardwood forest," though acceptable as an index to interglacial climate, is much too imprecise for Hypsithermal time.

In the stratigraphic reassessment of many interglacial deposits, the Yarmouth interglacial appears to be a casualty. The concept of an American equivalent of the Great Interglacial is not to be dispensed with lightly, yet it is remarkable that no plant-bearing deposits can safely be called Yarmouth. The Puyallup interval in the Pacific Northwest (Crandell, this volume; see also Heusser, this volume) may be an equivalent, but there is no evidence from organic

remains that this or any other nonglacial interval was warmer than today in the Puget lowland. In fact, it is difficult to distinguish glacial from interglacial times in pollen assemblages from this region, where strong topographic contrasts and an unusual variety of wind-pollinated conifers contribute to the ambiguity. In the mid-continent region, south of the glacial boundaries, the deposits of Meade County, Kansas, have been studied by paleoecologists with particular care, yet Kapp (1964) describes no pollen-bearing strata from this district older than Illinoian. As Taylor (this volume) knows no mollusk faunas of Yarmouth age, and as Hibbard et al. (this volume) can list only one mammal fauna (the Borchers) from this interval, a keystone of American Pleistocene stratigraphy is seen to be astonishingly loose.

A skeptical review of the data from the Great Plains, well summarized in chapters by Taylor, by Hibbard et al., and by Frye and Leonard, reinforces suspicion that the Yarmouth is a myth, or at least unrecognizable away from its type area, where it is mainly known as a profile of weathering. Evidence of alternating alluviation and erosion is abundant throughout the Plains, but the difficulties of correlating independent bodies of alluvium are notorious. Evolution having been too slow to be useful, even in mammals, ecological inferences have been used for correlation. The southern Plains were clearly better watered through much of the Pleistocene than they are today, and moisture-demanding faunas are assigned to glacial stages while semiarid conditions more similar to the present are classed as interglacial. It is not necessary to challenge the well-established assumptions underlying this procedure, but the matching of these more and less pluvial episodes with particular stages in the glaciated districts depends on the further assumption that there were only four glacial and three interglacial ages, and the possible circularity is evident.

FAUNAL SHIFTS ON THE GREAT PLAINS

Changes in rainfall in semiarid Kansas during the Pleistocene are made obvious by the periodic abundance of fishes, aquatic mammals and mollusks, and ostracods (for the last, see Staplin, 1963). Such changes in a mid-continent region point to marked variation in degree of continentality, but not necessarily to net changes of temperature, and in fact there is little indication of climates much cooler or much warmer than today's in nonglaciated parts of the Plains. Taylor (this volume) points to the contrast in this respect between southwestern Kansas and such eastern regions as Indiana, and he notes that aridity becomes more important than temperature to animal ecology, in the Pleistocene as today, in the vicinity of the 100th meridian. In this situation the evidence from faunal shifts (Miller, this volume) is more equivocal than is generally realized.

For example, by mapping existing ranges of fossil fish species, and noting their area of overlap, Smith (1954) inferred that Kansas in Illinoian time was most like Wisconsin today, but although this was probably true in terms of fish habitats, the *climatic* similarity need not have been very close. More commonly, when assemblages of tens or hundreds of species are considered (Taylor, this volume), no exact modern counterpart of the fossil fauna can be found. By an interesting inversion of the principle of parsimony, the simplest explanation—random reshuffling of ranges—is regarded by ecologists as the least likely. If only a few of the fossils seem out of context, and they are predominantly of northern distribution, one infers that the summer temperatures were cooler; conversely, southern species in otherwise uninformative assemblages imply that the winters were milder; and when extralimital species of both kinds occur together as fossils, the climate is thought to have been less continental. This reasoning is not inherently fallacious, but it assumes more knowledge of present-day ecology than can be obtained from maps. If species' present ranges were known to be at equilibrium, and the limits were known to be controlled by climate, latitudinal arrangements could be taken at face value. Unfortunately, even if one neglects such biotic factors as competition and sociality, it is possible for every segment of the limit of a mapped range to have a different control, as lacustrine species need standing water of the right chemistry, terrestrial animals need certain kinds of plants and/or trace minerals, and homoiothermal vertebrates have various ways of tempering the effects of climate.

Aware of all these difficulties, and others, Hibbard (1960) pictures Pleistocene climates in the southern Plains as not very different from today's, except for the periodically greater rainfall, and he suggests that glacial-interglacial contrasts were notably less sharp beyond the drift borders than is implied by the glacial sequence itself. Like Taylor (this volume), Hibbard considers the Wisconsin as the time of maximum climatic stress, so accounting for the relatively abrupt extinction of many animals, and particularly of such thermophiles as the tortoise *Geochelone*, that had persisted through earlier cycles. Although this view seems to have been arrived at rather reluctantly, it is consistent with the botanical data from the Southwest (Martin, this volume), where spruce pollen and other indications of cool climate are strangely lacking in pre-Wisconsin levels.

Between Meade County, Kansas, where Hibbard and Taylor have worked, and the San Augustin Plains, New Mexico, the site of the deep boring of Clisby and Sears (1956), two pre-Wisconsin lake deposits in Oklahoma and in Texas have been studied with great skill by Stephens (1960) and by Kirkland and Anderson (1963). The lacustrine sequences are short, of different ages, and dated only roughly as Late and Early Pleistocene by their few mammalian fossils and their relation to the Pearlette ash. Both imply pluvial conditions, but the only indications of cooling are those that would be expected to accompany increased moisture. Despite the discontinuities in the record from the southern Plains, it begins to seem that this prairie and semi-desert region was at most a warm savanna, never a cold steppe, throughout the Pleistocene.

PLIO-PLEISTOCENE BOUNDARY

As in the interpretation of the late-glacial in the Northeast, American paleoecologists have been influenced, and possibly misled, by the Pleistocene of central and southeastern Europe. It is easy for Americans to underrate the significance of Europe's transverse mountain system, and of the access it gives, even today, to a cold-steppe fauna and

flora from Asia. A natural supposition that American glacial ages ought to be as cold as Europe's, combined with an *a priori* belief in four glaciations, with Nebraskan equal to Günz, may have encouraged correlations between Kansas and Illinois that have little factual basis. If so, the Yarmouth interglacial may not be the only casualty of the coming stratigraphic reassessment; the Aftonian of the Plains also needs to be re-examined.

The scanty vertebrate faunas called Nebraskan and Aftonian are also Blancan, and they therefore may be of Villafranchian age if not older (Evernden *et al.*, 1964). The case for a pre-Günz Pleistocene in Europe does not rest on the problematical Donau glaciation, but on clear faunistic and floristic evidence that the Villafranchian fauna is older than the Cromerian interglacial. If there are American equivalents of the pre-Cromerian, early-Pleistocene cold phases of the Netherlands (Zagwijn, 1960), they are probably to be sought above the "Aftonian" of Kansas, though the type Aftonian beds of Iowa may still be Cromerian, and the Nebraskan still correlative with Günz.

Long persistence of an "archaic" or Pliocene fauna, once thought to have been an African peculiarity, is now rather generally accepted for regions that never experienced continental glaciations; western North America is not atypical in having the Blancan faunal zone, Pleistocene only in its upper part. It need not follow from this that the Nebraskan glaciation is Middle Pleistocene, but the possibility can no longer be discounted. Among other attractions, it would harmonize the shorter and the current longer estimates of the duration of the Pleistocene by dividing the epoch into glacial and nonglacial portions of nearly equal length. Moreover, despite the way in which the classical stage-names are used in sea-floor stratigraphy (Ericson *et al.*, 1961, 1963, 1964), the suggestion appears not to conflict with the data of that field. Correlation of cold and warm foraminiferan assemblages, particularly the older ones, is hampered by unconformities and reduplications and the paucity of stratigraphic markers—a situation reminiscent of alluvial stratigraphy on the Plains—and the assignment of these marine faunas to continental stages, by the Lamont group as by Emiliani (1955), seems to reflect standard nomenclatural preconceptions.

If parts of the extraglacial American Pleistocene are older than has been believed, as well as more similar climatically to the present, similarity to the upper Pliocene would not be remarkable; before extensive continental glaciation occurred, neither the range of environments nor the stage of mammalian evolution should show any major discontinuity. The Plio-Pleistocene boundary is as inconspicuous in the long pollen sequence beneath the San Augustin Plains (Clisby and Sears, 1956) as it is in the Blancan faunal zone.

The apparent complacency of the early record in this core, and the increase of spruce pollen in and only in the Wisconsin levels, have been attributed to late-Pleistocene uplift of the basin (Clisby and Foreman, 1958). Although late-Tertiary local and regional upwarping of the Cordillera is generally accepted and is commonly invoked to account for increased continentality and regional climatic differentiation toward the east, there is no independent evidence that New Mexico was uplifted so recently by the magnitude required (several thousand feet) to bring its summits from the juniper to the spruce belt. Moreover, the Holocene diminution of spruce pollen, well established throughout the Southwest, is unlikely to have been the result of crustal subsidence.

Wherever else it lies, the Plio-Pleistocene boundary is somewhere between the bottom of the Glenns Ferry formation in Idaho (Malde, this volume) and the bottom of the overlying Bruneau beds, *i.e.* between potassium-argon dates of 3.5 and 1.4×10^6 yr, and there is good reason to expect it within the exposed 2,000 ft of the fabulous Glenns Ferry. When studies of the pollen, by Estella Leopold, and of the mollusks, by Dwight Taylor, are complete, the boundary will probably turn out to be as obscure as it is in the San Augustin core.

If these tentative, unorthodox views of Pleistocene ecology and stratigraphy are verified, delayed onset of continental glaciation and its apparent culmination in the Wisconsin age will demand explanation, and the explanations may not be the same. Late-Tertiary uplift may account for the first, while the oceanography of the Arctic basin may hold the key to the second, as Taylor (this volume) suggests. Studies of the submarine stratigraphy of that basin are awaited with great interest.

REFERENCES

Aario, Leo, 1940, Waldgrenzen und subrezenten Pollenspektren in Petsamo Lappland: Acad. Sci. Fenn., Ann., ser. A, v. 54, No. 8, 120 p.

Andersen, S. T., 1954, A late glacial pollen diagram from southern Michigan: Danmarks Geol. Unders., ser. 2, No. 80, p. 140-155

Andrewartha, H. G., and Birch, L. C., 1954, The distribution and abundance of animals: Chicago, Univ. Chicago Press, 782 p.

Baker, F. C., 1920, The life of the Pleistocene or glacial period: Univ. Illinois Bull., v. 17, No. 41, 476 p.

Blair, W. F., 1958, Distributional patterns of vertebrates in the southern United States in relation to past and present environments, *in* Hubbs, C. L. (ed.), Zoogeography: Amer. Assoc. Adv. Sci., Publ. 51, p. 433-468

Bleakney, J. S., 1958, Zoogeographical study of the amphibians and reptiles of eastern Canada: Natl. Mus. Canada Bull. 155, 119 p.

Bradley, W. H., 1963, Paleolimnology, *in* Frey, D. G. (ed.), Limnology in North America: Madison, Univ. Wisconsin Press, p. 621-652

Braun, E. Lucy, 1955, The phytogeography of unglaciated eastern United States and its interpretation: Bot. Rev., v. 21, p. 297-375

Cameron, A. W., 1958, Mammals of the islands of the Gulf of St. Lawrence: Natl. Mus. Canada Bull. 154, 165 p.

Carroll, Gladys, 1943, The use of bryophytic polsters and mats in the study of recent pollen deposition: Amer. J. Bot., v. 30, p. 361-366

Clisby, K. H., and Foreman, Fred, 1958, Pleistocene climatic changes in New Mexico, U.S.A.: Zürich, Geobot. Inst. Rübel, Veröff., No. 34, p. 21-26

Clisby, K. H., and Sears, P. B., 1956, San Augustin Plains–Pleistocene climatic changes: Science, v. 124, p. 537-538

Crandell, D. R., this volume, The glacial history of western Washington and Oregon

Davis, Margaret B., 1958, Three pollen diagrams from central Massachusetts: Amer. J. Sci., v. 256, p. 540-570

—— 1961, Pollen diagrams as evidence of late-glacial climatic change in southern New England: New York Acad. Sci. Ann., v. 95, p. 623-631

—— 1963, On the theory of pollen analysis: Amer. J. Sci., v. 261, p. 897-912

—— this volume, Phytogeography and palynology of northeastern United States

Davis, Margaret B., and Deevey, E. S., Jr., 1962, Quantitative pollen sedimentation in Rogers Lake, Connecticut (abst.): Geol. Soc. Amer. Spec. Pap. 73, p. 136-137

—— 1964, Pollen accumulation rates: estimates from late-glacial sediment of Rogers Lake: Science, v. 145, p. 1293-1295

Davis, Margaret B., and Goodlett, J. C., 1960, Comparison of the present vegetation with pollen-spectra in surface samples from Brownington Pond, Vermont: Ecology, v. 41, p. 346-357

Deevey, E. S., Jr., 1939, Studies on Connecticut lake sediments. I, A postglacial climatic chronology for southern New England: Amer. J. Sci., v. 237, p. 691-724

—— 1943, Additional pollen analyses from southern New England: Amer. J. Sci., v. 241, p. 717-752

—— 1949, Biogeography of the Pleistocene. Part I, Europe and North America: Geol. Soc. Amer. Bull., v. 60, p. 1315-1416

—— 1951, Late-glacial and postglacial pollen diagrams from Maine: Amer. J. Sci., v. 249, p. 177-207

—— 1958, Radiocarbon-dated pollen sequences in eastern North America: Zürich, Geobot. Inst. Rübel, Veröff., No. 34, p. 30-37

—— 1961, Recent advances in Pleistocene stratigraphy and biogeography, *in* Blair, W. F. (ed.), Vertebrate speciation: Austin, Univ. Texas Press, p. 594-623

—— 1964, Preliminary account of fossilization of zooplankton in Rogers Lake: Intern. Ver. Limnol. Verh., v. 15, p. 981-992

Deevey, E. S., Jr., and Flint, R. F., 1957, Postglacial hypsithermal interval: Science, v. 125, p. 182-184

Deevey, E. S., Jr., and Potzger, J. E., 1951, Peat samples for radiocarbon analysis; problems in pollen statistics: Amer. J. Sci., v. 249, p. 473-511

Emiliani, Cesare, 1955, Pleistocene temperatures: J. Geol., v. 63, p. 538-578

Engelhardt, D. W., 1960, A comparative pollen study of two early Wisconsin bogs in Indiana: Indiana Acad. Sci. Proc., v. 69, p. 110-118

Ericson, D. B., Ewing, Maurice, and Wollin, Goesta, 1963, Plio-Pleistocene boundary in deep-sea sediments: Science, v. 139, p. 727-737

—— 1964, The Pleistocene epoch in deep-sea sediments: Science, v. 146, p. 723-732

Ericson, D. B., Ewing, Maurice, Wollin, Goesta, and Heezen, B. C., 1961, Atlantic deep-sea sediment cores: Geol. Soc. Amer. Bull., v. 72, p. 193-286

Evernden, J. F., Savage, D. E., Curtis, G. H., and James, G. T., 1964, Potassium-argon dates and the Cenozoic mammalian chronology of North America: Amer. J. Sci., v. 262, p. 145-198

Flint, R. F., and Deevey, E. S., 1951, Radiocarbon dating of late-Pleistocene events: Amer. J. Sci., v. 249, p. 257-300

Frye, J. C., and Leonard, A. B., this volume, Quaternary of the southern Great Plains

Fuller, G. D., 1939, Interglacial and postglacial vegetation of Illinois: Illinois Acad. Sci. Trans., Presidential address, v. 32, p. 5-15

Gerking, S. D., 1945, The distribution of the fishes of Indiana: Indiana Dept. Conserv., Inv. Indiana Lakes and Streams, v. 3, p. 1-137

Hay, O. P., 1923, The Pleistocene of North America and its vertebrated animals from the States east of the Mississippi River and from the Canadian provinces east of longitude 95°: Carnegie Instn. Publ. 322, 499 p.

—— 1924, The Pleistocene of the middle region of North America and its vertebrated animals: Carnegie Instn. Publ. 322A, 385 p.

—— 1927, The Pleistocene of the western region of North America and its vertebrated animals: Carnegie Instn. Publ. 322B, 346 p.

Heusser, C. J., this volume, A Pleistocene phytogeographical sketch of the Pacific Northwest and Alaska.

Hibbard, C. W., 1960, An interpretation of Pliocene and Pleistocene climates in North America: Michigan Acad. Sci. Ann. Rep., Presidential address, 1959-60, v. 62, p. 5-30

Hibbard, C. W., Ray, D. E., Savage, D. E., Taylor, D. W., Guilday, J. E., this volume, Quaternary mammals of North America

Hubbs, C. L., and Miller, R. R., 1948, The zoological evidence, in The Great Basin, with emphasis on glacial and postglacial times: Univ. Utah Bull., v. 38, No. 20, p. 18-166

Kapp, R. O., 1964, Illinoian and Sangamon vegetation in southwestern Kansas and adjacent Oklahoma: Univ. Michigan Mus. Paleont. Contr. (in press)

Kapp, R. O., and Gooding, A. M., 1964, Pleistocene vegetational studies in the Whitewater basin, southeastern Indiana: J. Geol., v. 72, p. 307-326

Kirkland, D. W., and Anderson, R. Y., 1963, Environmental reconstruction of a Blancan lake near Channing, Texas: Univ. New Mexico, Prelim. Rep. to Natl. Sci. Fdn. (processed)

Krekeler, C. H., 1958, Speciation in cave beetles of the genus Pseudanophthalmus (Coleoptera, Carabidae): Amer. Midl. Nat., v. 59, p. 167-189

Leopold, Estella B., 1956, Two late-glacial deposits in southern Connecticut: Natl. Acad. Sci. Proc., v. 42, p. 863-867

Livingstone, D. A., and Livingstone, Bertha G. R., 1958, Late-glacial and postglacial vegetation from Gillis Lake in Richmond County, Cape Breton Island, Nova Scotia: Amer. J. Sci., v. 256, p. 341-359

Löve, Doris, 1959, The postglacial development of the flora of Manitoba—a discussion: Can. J. Bot., v. 37, p. 547-585

MacClintock, Paul, and Terasmae, Jaan, 1960, Glacial history of Covey Hill: J. Geol., v. 68, p. 232-241

Malde, H. E., this volume, Snake River Plain

Malde, H. E., and Powers, H. A., 1962, Upper Cenozoic stratigraphy of western Snake River Plain, Idaho: Geol. Soc. Amer., Bull., v. 73, p. 1197-1220

Martin, P. S., 1958, Pleistocene ecology and biogeography of North America, in Hubbs, C. L. (ed.), Zoogeography: Amer. Assoc. Adv. Sci. Publ. 51, p. 375-420

Martin, P. S., and Harrell, B. E., 1957, The Pleistocene history of temperate biotas in Mexico and eastern United States: Ecology, v. 38, p. 468-480

Martin, P. S., and Mehringer, P. J., Jr., this volume, Pleistocene pollen analysis and biogeography of the Southwest, U.S.A.

Miller, R. R., this volume, Quaternary freshwater fishes of North America

Ogden, J. G., III, 1959, A late-glacial pollen sequence from Martha's Vineyard, Massachusetts: Amer. J. Sci., v. 257, p. 366-381

—— 1963, The Squibnocket Cliff peat; radiocarbon dates and pollen stratigraphy: Amer. J. Sci., v. 261, p. 344-353

Post, Lennart von, 1946, The prospect for pollen analysis in the study of the Earth's climatic history: New Phytol., v. 45, p. 193-217

Ricker, K. E., 1959, The origin of the glacial relict crustaceans in North America, as related to Pleistocene glaciation: Can. J. Zool., v. 37, p. 871-893

Ross, H. H., this volume, Pleistocene events and insects

Segerstråle, S. G., 1954, The freshwater amphipods, Gammarus pluex (L.) and Gammarus lacustris G. O. Sars, in Denmark and Fennoscandia—a contribution to the late- and post-glacial immigration history of the aquatic fauna of northern Europe: Soc. Scient. Fenn. Comm. Biol., v. 15, No. 1, 91 p.

—— 1957, On the immigration of the glacial relicts of northern Europe, with remarks on their prehistory: Soc. Scient. Fenn. Comm. Biol., v. 16, No. 16, 117 p.

—— 1962, The immigration and prehistory of the glacial relicts of Eurasia and North America. A survey and discussion of modern views: Intern. Rev. Ges. Hydrobiol., v. 47, p. 1-25

Smith, C. L., 1954, Pleistocene fishes of the Berends fauna of Beaver County, Oklahoma: Copeia, 1954, p. 282-289

Smith, P. W., 1957, An analysis of post-Wisconsin biogeography of the Prairie Peninsula region based on distributional phenomena among terrestrial vertebrate populations: Ecology, v. 38, p. 205-218

—— this volume, Recent adjustments in animal ranges

Staplin, F. L., 1963, Pleistocene Ostracoda of Illinois: J. Paleont., v. 37, p. 758-797, 1164-1203

Steere, W. C., 1942, Pleistocene mosses from the Aftonian interglacial deposits of Iowa: Michigan Acad. Sci. Arts Lett. Pap., v. 27, p. 75-104

Stephens, J. J., 1960, Stratigraphy and paleontology of a late Pleistocene basin, Harper County, Oklahoma: Geol. Soc. Amer. Bull., v. 71, p. 1675-1702

Svärdson, Gunnar, 1961, Young sibling fish species in Northwestern Europe, in Blair, W. F. (ed.), Vertebrate speciation: Austin, Univ. Texas Press, p. 498-513

Taylor, D. W., 1960, Distribution of the freshwater clam *Pisidium ultramontanum;* a paleo-zoogeographical inquiry: Amer. J. Sci., v. 258A (Bradley vol.), p. 325-334

—— this volume, The study of Pleistocene non-marine mollusks in North America

Terasmae, Jaan, 1957, Paleobotanical studies of Canadian nonglacial deposits: Science, v. 126, p. 351-352

—— 1959, Notes on the Champlain Sea episode in the St. Lawrence lowlands, Quebec: Science, v. 130, p. 334-336

—— 1960, Contributions to Canadian palynology No. 2, Part ɪ. A palynological study of post-glacial deposits in the St. Lawrence lowlands; Part ɪɪ. A palynological study of Pleistocene interglacial beds at Toronto, Ontario: Geol. Surv. Canada Bull. 56, p. 1-41

Thomas, E. A., 1955, Stoffhaushalt und Sedimentation im oligotrophen Aegerisee und im eutrophen Pfäffiker- und Greifensee: Ist. Ital. Idrobiol. Mem., Suppl., v. 8, p. 357-465

Tsukada, Matsuo, 1958, Untersuchungen über das Verhältnis zwischen dem Pollengehalt der Oberflächenproben und der Vegetation des Hochlandes Shiga: Osaka City Univ., J. Inst. Polytechnics, ser. D, v. 9, p. 217-234

Tutin, Winifred, 1955, Preliminary observations on a year's cycle of sedimentation in Windermere, England: Ist. Ital. Idrobiol. Mem., Suppl., v. 8, p. 467-484

Voss, John, 1933, Pleistocene forests of Illinois: Bot. Gaz., v. 94, p. 808-814

—— 1939, Forests of the Yarmouth and Sangamon interglacial periods in Illinois: Ecology, v. 20, p. 517-528

Whitehead, D. R., and Barghoorn, E. S., 1962, Pollen analytical investigations of Pleistocene deposits from western North Carolina and South Carolina: Ecol. Monogr., v. 32, p. 347-369

Zagwijn, W. H., 1960, Aspects of the Pliocene and early Pleistocene vegetation in the Netherlands: Geol. Stichting, Mededel., ser. C, III-1, No. 5, 78 p.

SUMMARY

In these comments on biological chapters, *biogeography,* as distinct from *paleoecology* or *stratigraphy,* is understood to be the study of existing ranges of organisms. It recognizes historical problems only when voids exist in ranges, and because of this and other methodological difficulties its relevance to paleoecology is slight; its popularity is justified on purely biological grounds. Postglacial and earlier Pleistocene environments are best studied by stratigraphic methods, but for a number of reasons no clear picture of the sequence of environments can be drawn for North America. Pollen stratigraphers, though in principle able to interpret postglacial vegetation in quantitative terms, have only recently realized that pollen percentages convey no definite information about plant abundance, and they have begun to gather more meaningful data on modern pollen rain. For the earlier Pleistocene, especially the pre-Wisconsin part, most organic records lie outside the glaciated territory, and their correlation with the glacial sequence is unclear. The Wisconsin stands out as the time of maximum climatic stress, both in faunal records from the Plains and in the long San Augustin pollen core in New Mexico, and the older record is unexpectedly complacent. It is particularly puzzling that fossils of Yarmouth age are almost unknown. These facts may mean that the widely accepted division of the Pleistocene into four glacial and three interglacial stages is based on incorrect preconceptions. If the Nebraskan glaciation postdates the Blancan fauna and begins the glacial portion of the Pleistocene, it is easier to understand why Pleistocene environments on the Plains are not clearly differentiated from each other or from Pliocene environments.

PART III ARCHAEOLOGY

LATE QUATERNARY PREHISTORY IN THE NORTHEASTERN WOODLANDS

AN OUTLINE OF SOUTHEASTERN UNITED STATES PREHISTORY WITH PARTICULAR
   EMPHASIS ON THE PALEO-INDIAN ERA

QUATERNARY HUMAN OCCUPATION OF THE PLAINS

POSTGLACIAL CLIMATE AND ARCHAEOLOGY IN THE DESERT WEST

PACIFIC COAST ARCHAEOLOGY

LATE QUATERNARY PREHISTORY IN THE
NORTHEASTERN WOODLANDS *

JAMES B. GRIFFIN[1]

THE AREA to be covered by this survey of the early Indian inhabitants of the northeastern United States and southeastern Canada extends from Iowa east to the Atlantic and from Missouri, the Ohio River, and Pennsylvania north to the present boreal forest of southern Canada (Fig. 1). The Pleistocene geology of this area has been intensively studied, but the complexity of the problems involved is such that an adequate interpretation of the Pleistocene history is still many years in the future. As current work is carried on, the constant revisions make it difficult for an archaeologist to keep pace with new interpretations of the age and correlation of the geologic features. This northeastern area has also been that most intensively studied by palynologists, and many papers record and interpret the late-glacial and postglacial vegetation. These have been of considerable significance in the efforts of archaeologists to understand the environment in which the early Indian lived.

In contrast to many areas of the eastern hemisphere, this northeastern area, as most of North America, does not have evidence of man incorporated in or covered by glacial deposits. It does, however, have evidence of early Indian groups in apparent association with lake beaches and other geologic phenomena of late-glacial and postglacial time. The major theme of this chapter is the gradual occupation of the northeastern area by Paleo-Indian groups as the ice withdrew and the forest and associated vegetation cover moved north. The later association of prehistoric Indian cultures with recent geologic features is also considered.

The earliest primitive hunters recognized in the Northeast will be called the Fluted Point Hunters. This name is derived from the shape and technique of manufacture of their most diagnostic artifact. The term "Fluted Flint Blade Culture Complex" was proposed by Shetrone (1936) as a

designation to apply to what was then called the "Folsom Complex." The term "Fluted Point Hunters" is used to avoid the term "blade," which has a specific connotation in Old World archaeology. Since 1936 a series of fluted point types has been recognized and described both in the High Plains and Southwest and in the eastern United States. This primarily hunting complex will be regarded in this paper as the only clearly recognized culture of the Paleo-Indian period. This period begins with the first occupation by man in North America and ends, as arbitrarily considered in this paper, with the passing out of style of the fluted points, which seems to have taken place in the northeast about 9000-8000 B.C. Earlier cultures may eventually be recognized, or ones that are contemporary with that of the Fluted Point Hunters of the Paleo-Indian period, but up to the present that is not the case.

The exact time period during which the Paleo-Indian first entered the area north of the Ohio River and east of the Missouri River is not so firmly established as is desirable. This earliest occupation of the northeastern area could have been about 15,000 B.C., for the ice had begun its retreat northward by that time. These earliest occupants may have come from the Southeast, which would have been a suitable area for the early hunters for several thousand years before. We know that most of the Southeast was occupied by Fluted Point Hunters and that the number and variety of the projectile points implies that the occupation lasted a few thousand years. At present, however, radiocarbon dates for Early Archaic cultures in the Southeast extend only to 8000-7000 B.C. It is a reasonable inference that the earlier Fluted Point Hunters occupied the Southeast before 8000 B.C., perhaps as early as 10,000 to 12,000 B.C. The earliest northern Paleo-Indians probably moved into the northeast during the retreat of the ice and the gradual spread of vegetation and animal life.

The Fluted Point cultural complex was first identified and dated in the western High Plains and Southwest, and for some years it has been assumed that this was the area of development of the complex and that it later spread from there into the East. The earliest sure dates, however, are from about 9500 to 8900 B.C. in the West for the Fluted Point Hunters using the Clovis style points, and up to about 8000 B.C. for those using the Folsom style. Current dating assignments of this same hunting complex in the Northeast are between 11,000 and 9000 B.C. Thus it is possible that the earliest soundly established American cultural complex developed first in the Southeast, spread from there into the Northeast, and westward into the

* My first debt is to the many individuals who have published the data cited in the references for this paper. I have also been able to employ the findings of a large number of individuals, primarily archaeologists, whose contributions have not yet appeared in print. I am particularly indebted to the editors of this volume for their substantial contributions, corrections, rejections, and mutilations of this paper. Support has been granted to the Museum of Anthropology of the University of Michigan over the past five years from the Division of Anthropology and the Undergraduate Education in the Sciences Program of the National Science Foundation. Without this support, much of the data correlating the prehistoric cultures with changes in the level of Lake Huron would not have been available.

[1] Museum of Archaeology, University of Michigan, Ann Arbor, Michigan.

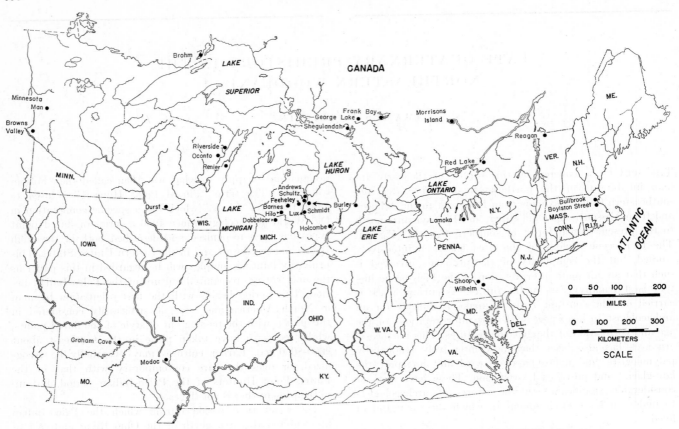

Figure 1. Location of Paleo-Indian and Archaic sites in the Northeast. The dashed line shows the approximate northern boundary of the Fluted Point Hunters.

Plains and Southwest. The available evidence for such a temporal placement in the Northeast will be given below.

The general way of life of the Fluted Point Hunters, and their technology, is derived from that of the Advanced Paleolithic hunters of central Siberia (Griffin, 1962), modified by cultural developments and eliminations during the movement across the Bering Straits and into the area of the United States. The particular cultural expressions found in this latter area are, of course, not duplicated anywhere else, but their Asiatic origins are fairly clear.

EARLY NORTHEASTERN FAUNA AND ITS PROBABLE CONTEMPORANEITY WITH EARLY MAN

The environment of the Northeast during the late-Pleistocene and Recent times is described by a number of other authors in this volume so that the subject will be treated relatively briefly in this paper. It is assumed here that Fluted Point Hunters were in the eastern United States south of the ice front by approximately 12,000 B.C., and that the area south of the Ohio and Missouri Rivers was also occupied. In the absence of firm dates on this occupation, but with imagination controlled by presumed association with geologic features, one can make some reasonable reconstructions.

The term 'hunters" is commonly used as a part of the title of this Paleo-Indian group. Many archaeologists have

stressed the association of these hunters in the West with extinct big-game animals. This, of course, is because of the discovery of "kill" sites in that area, but knowledge of the total food supply exploited over the year is unfortunately lacking. In the northeastern area, I believe there is no sound evidence of the direct association of man with extinct species. This subject has recently been reviewed by Williams (1957), who, however, accepted the association of man and mastodon at a number of sites. The Island 35 mastodon in northeastern Arkansas may have had a projectile point and a scraper under the pelvis, but the time of this association in the deposit in the Mississippi floodplain is difficult to ascertain. The projectile points with the Koch mastodons in Missouri I regard on typological grounds as predominantly Late Archaic. The makers of these points can hardly have been associated with the live beasts, for they had moved north of Missouri by this time. The most extreme example of mastodon bones associated with an archaeological site, and a much-better-documented one, is at the Herrell village site of about A.D. 1200 in Jefferson County, Missouri (Adams, 1949, p. 31), where the bones were found in three separate refuse pits and had obviously been carried there from a nearby bone bed. The Archaic projectile points near the Richmond mastodon near Cromwell, Noble County, Indiana (Burmaster, 1932; Sanford, 1935), or near the Orleton Farms mastodon, Madison County, Ohio (Thomas, 1952), are not in clear association with the skeletons nor can they be so old as the death of the beasts at 10,000 and 7600 B.C., respectively.

One of the major problems in the late Pleistocene ecology of early man in the Northeast concerns the available food supply that was obtainable with his technology. As the latest Wisconsin ice advanced into the New York–New England area and the central part of the Middle West, the fauna was certainly displaced to the south, and northern types were eliminated. The advance of the ice into Ohio, for example, seems to have covered an open spruce forest near the ice margin (Goldthwait, 1959, p. 195). The climatic regime during these advances, within some hundreds of miles of the glacial margin, must have been more severe than during the period of the general retreat. There is relatively little evidence of permafrost in areas near the retreating Wisconsin ice front and, although cold-adapted vegetation may have initially existed there, it should not be described as arctic tundra. During the intermittent retreat, the climatic regime may have been distinctly warmer, and plant species adapted to the newly opened terrain may have advanced more rapidly than some authorities have thought. The vegetational record provided by pollen from bottom sediments of many lakes and bogs may have been retarded in its start, for such areas may have held slowly melting ice blocks covered by glacial drift.

By the time of the ice retreat to the Cary Wabash moraines of northwestern Ohio and in the Michigan Basin between 13,000 to 12,000 B.C., most of the Ohio, Indiana, and Illinois areas were open to vegetation and the accompanying animal life. Close to the ice front were spruce, fir, larch, and some hemlock in Ohio, but in the southern parts of Ohio, Indiana, and Illinois there were strong elements of a deciduous forest, with a greater variety of vegetal foods and animals to support the Paleo-Indian groups.

One of the more interesting facets of the late-glacial fauna in the Great Lakes and St. Lawrence River is the presence of marine mammals. Whales, walrus, and seals have been found in beach and other deposits in Michigan, Ontario, and Quebec (Handley, 1953; Sternberg, 1951). None of these sea mammals has been adequately dated, but the most likely time for their appearance would be during the intrusion of the early Champlain Sea. From there, the sea mammals could have moved into the Great Lakes by the Ottawa-Mattawa Channel during the Algonquin discharge of about 9000 B.C.

Among the first major terrestrial mammals to move up into the central Great Lakes were the mammoth and muskox. Finds of muskox are concentrated in the area from Illinois to Ohio and north into Michigan in the periglacial region. Muskox is adapted to a cold climate and is probably intolerant of warm temperatures. It feeds on tundra-like vegetation or open forest. The Climax muskox (*Symbos cavifrons*) from Kalamazoo County, Michigan, is dated as 11,250± 300 B.C. (Hibbard and Hinds, 1960). Pollen from marl imbedded in a muskox vertebra was the basis for the following interpretation: "The pollen flora . . . indicates that this woodland muskox lived in an extensive spruce forest that may have contained small proportions of balsam fir, larch, and possibly birch. Local openings in the forest probably occurred on gravelly flood plains and sand plains,

where there would have been stands of grasses, with ragweed, sage, goldenrod, other herbs and willows. Ponds and lakes were occupied by pondweeds and probably by other aquatic plants, and their shores were bordered, in at least some places, by catails and sedges" (Benninghoff and Hibbard, 1961, p. 158). There were also significant amounts of pollen of oak and hop-hornbean and minor counts of pine, maple, hickory, and butternut. Partly because of Andersen's (1954) interpretation of deciduous pollen in deposits of about the same time period as "rebedded," Benninghoff was reluctant to consider that the deciduous elements actually occurred in the area.

A more recent find is the Scotts muskox, also from Kalamazoo County, Michigan, which has been dated at 9150 ± 400 B.C. (M-1402). The pollen in a sample of calcareous peaty silt from the brain cavity was studied. Pine was found to be the dominant pollen type, but oak was the next most common, followed by spruce, balsam fir, larch, birch, elm, and a little maple. On the basis of the pollen, the date of the Scotts muskox was originally estimated by Semken et al. (1964) to be about 9000 B.C., but the pollen may not actually be the same age as the muskox.

The closest association found of a muskox with prehistoric Indians was in Fulton County, Illinois, where the skull and horns of *Symbos cavifrons* were discovered during the excavation of an Indian mound (Cole and Deuel, 1937, p. 73). Writers on Early Man have not been misled by this find, for careful excavation proved that the skull was in undisturbed loess one and a half feet below the mound.

The greatest concentration of mammoth finds is in the same general area as the muskox and mastodon. As a feeder on open grassland and open forest the mammoth was probably closer to the retreating ice front than the mastodon and moved north with the early vegetation. A Jefferson mammoth in Jackson County, Michigan, was dated by associated wood at 10,350 ± 350 B.C. (M-507), a Two Creeks date. There are now 32 records of Jefferson mammoth in Michigan and 163 of the mastodon (Skeels, 1962).

The mastodon is described as a browser and forest feeder that lived in mixed coniferous and hardwood forests. The Wells mastodon near Rochester, Fulton County, Indiana, is dated at 10,050 B.C. (I-586) by a wood sample just below the skeletal parts. Pollen from the base of the peat above the mastodon reflects a rapid shift from dominantly coniferous to dominantly deciduous forest of immediately post-Valders time. The Richmond mastodon, Noble County, Indiana, which some archaeologists have thought was associated with Indian projectile points, was first dated by wood fragments at 3350 ± 200 B.C. (M-138), and this may not be far from the age of the projectile points. The tusk, however, is dated 10,680 ± 250 B.C. (M-139), making it about the same age as the Wells mastodon. One of the more significant mastodon dates was obtained from near Chatham, Ontario, where wood and vegetal muck were dated at 9450 and 10,050 B.C. (S-29, 30). These dates are correlated with the advance and retreat of the Valders ice, and the mastodons could easily have moved from Michigan into southwestern Ontario during the Two Creeks low-water stage. This view is supported by Dreimanis' (1964) interpretation of the vegetation growing during the same low-water stage in Lake St. Clair, which was covered after 10,050 B.C. by the rise to the Lake Algonquin II level during the Valders advance.

Another example of the association of mastodon and forest is shown by the Kings Ferry find, Cayuga County, New York, where spruce wood was dated 9460 B.C. (Y-460). At this site, "the fossil flora appears to record a boreal coniferous forest with mosses, but included *Ulmus* and *Acer* as well as *Picea* and *Abies*" (Deevey *et al.*, 1959, p. 147). One of the latest mastodon dates is from Tupperville, Ontario, where the skeletal remains were in gyttja and peat samples of this material from directly above the animal gave a date of 4300 B.C. (S-16). It is strange indeed that there are no valid associations of Early Man with these extinct pachyderms in the Northeast if man was responsible for their disappearance. This is probably their major area of concentration, and it is certain that they were contemporary with man. The cultural level of the people in the Northeast is essentially that of the hunting groups in the High Plains, where the kill sites are known. Many of the elephant finds in the Northeast were in bogs where hunters might have been able to kill them without too much difficulty. If man was responsible for the disappearance of some of the Late Pleistocene fauna in the Northeast, he must have used magic rather than implements. This magic was not very effective for it took some 6000 years to eliminate the animals.

Additional faunal elements that were probably contemporary with muskox, mastodon, and mammoth in the Late Glacial include the barren-ground caribou, giant beaver, peccary, giant moose, and probably other species now in the boreal forest or tundra. Certainly this smaller game would have been numerically more abundant and easier for the early hunters to kill. By the time of the somewhat denser populations of 4000 to 1000 B.C. at the close of the Archaic, the animal species were essentially what they were in the early historic period in the deciduous to boreal forest zones. The only radiocarbon date on woodland caribou is 3820 ± 200 B.C., from near Flint, Michigan (M-294).

THE PALEO-INDIAN FLUTED POINT OCCUPATION

Shetrone (1936) was the first archaeologist to study the distribution of fluted points in the Northeast. On the basis of his analysis of the 140 Ohio specimens in the Ohio State Museum, he emphasized the lateral and basal grinding, recognized that the Ohio points were often made of Upper Mercer flint, first proposed the term "Fluted Flint Blade Culture Complex," and suggested terms such as "Folsom Variant" and "Lindenmeier Variant." He also stated, "It is natural and proper to seek for origins and evolutions, and too often in American archaeology they are hard to find. Since nothing fully analogous to the Fluted Blade has been reported for the Old World, it is likely to be presumed, temporarily at least, that the technique of fluting evolved in America."

A more recent study of fluted points from Ohio describes nearly 500 specimens (Prufer and Baby, 1963). An attempt is made in this publication to determine the age of appearance of the projectile points by plotting their distribution and comparing this with end moraines and beach deposits in northern Ohio. Little or no beach-level control in this area exists, however, and dating of archaeological complexes is not yet satisfactorily accomplished. The majority of the fluted forms are in south-central and southwestern Ohio, while the majority of the Early Archaic forms such as Holcombe and Hi-Lo points are in northern and northwestern Ohio. As is common in much of the Northeast, fluted points in the Delaware Valley are found on upland locations and not in the valley floors, where stream action and other disturbances have tended to remove evidence of the earliest occupations. The presence of fluted points on the bottom of Glacial Lake Passaic in New Jersey, which was drained at least by early Cary time is an indication that this point style was at least as late as Cary.

Witthoft's (1952) detailed study of the Shoop site resulted in a definition of the Enterline Chert Industry. There was no possibility of associating this complex with Pleistocene features, because the material is entirely a surface collection, the site is south of the Wisconsin glacial border, and no faunal or other materials were recovered that might date the complex. The Enterline Chert Industry at the Shoop site is composed of six tool types and discarded spalls. The points are leaf-shaped, with concave base, and have multiple-channelled fluting. They have basal and lower side-edge grinding. Small graver points are retouched from one face on small flakes. Similar graving points were developed on other tools, particularly on the ends of the beveled faces of end scrapers. The gravers are a distinctive part of the flint assemblage of Fluted Point Hunters across the United States. Short end scrapers made from thick, blade-like flakes are usually trianguloid or rectangular, and the broad, steeply retouched working edge is opposite the bulb of concussion. A more distinctive tool of the Enterline Chert Industry is a pointed scraper made on a blade with the bulbar end rechipped on the lateral edges to produce a scraping and gouging implement. Small prismatic flakes thought to be knives are chipped on lateral edges and on one tip. A few bifacially flaked tools with a shape like that of the fluted points may have been knives, and others are clearly unfinished points. Witthoft regards the Enterline Industry as a blade-and-core technology.

The Bull Brook site (Byers, 1954, 1955) west of Ipswich, Massachusetts, is located on a kame terrace, 40 ft above sea level, overlooking the Pine Swamp Road bog (McIntire and Morgan, 1962, Figs. 8 and 9). The bog at the time of the occupation of the site seems to have been a small freshwater pond or swamp. Byers regards Bull Brook as quite close typologically to the Enterline Chert Industry and as having many close similarities to the Lindenmeier Folsom complex. However, he believes that the Bull Brook fluted points resemble Clovis forms of the High Plains. Radiocarbon determinations on charcoal from Bull Brook give a date of about 7000 B.C. for some part of the early Indian occupation at the site (Byers, 1959). The many minute charcoal samples were not clearly in direct association with a fireplace or with an occupation surface, and I believe that the Bull Brook Fluted Point occupation may well have been significantly earlier than the radiocarbon dates.

While the evidence is far from clear, it would seem at current writing that New England was essentially clear of glacial ice from the main northern sources by at least Late Cary–Port Huron time of about 11,000 B.C., and perhaps earlier. Assuming that the early Fluted Point Hunters were in the area west and south of southern New England by 9000 B.C., there was ample time for the development of forest conditions and the fauna of associated game animals. Not only spruce but also white and red pine, balsam fir, hemlock, red cedar, black birch, and oak are indicated both by pollen profiles and by beaver-cut wood (Kaye, 1962).

In addition to Bull Brook, a number of other sites in Massachusetts, such as Wapanucket No. 8 (Robbins and Agogino, 1964), have a Fluted Point complex. This cultural complex is found as far north as Nova Scotia, where Byers (personal communication) is currently excavating the Debert site (Dennis, 1926).

Some movement of man into New England and the Maritime Provinces of Canada may have taken place along the coastal shelf, following the vegetation advance, for eustatic sea level was *ca.* 160-115 ft lower than the present from 10,000 to 8000 B.C. (Kaye and Barghoorn, 1964, Fig. 5).

The most northern site in the northeastern United States to have an occupation by Fluted Point Hunters is in northwestern Vermont overlooking the Champlain lowland. The Reagen site (Ritchie, 1953) probably represents a late phase of this complex because of the presence of points similar to those of the Early Archaic Holcombe occupations in Michigan and Ohio, as well as other artifact types not normally associated with fluted points. The significance of the site is that it was located on beaches of the Champlain Sea about 300 ft above the old Champlain Sea floor. Ritchie (1957) followed the interpretation of the age of the Champlain Sea at 5000 B.C., which was the then current opinion of geologists (Flint, 1957, p. 347). He also observed that 41% of the New York State fluted points had been found on the former bottoms of Lakes Iroquois, Frontenac, and Vermont. More recent work in the St. Lawrence lowland by Terasmae (1960, 1961) and in the Ontario Basin by Karrow *et al.* (1961), in combination with the new Two Creeks dates (Broecker and Farrand, 1963) and the recent paper on the prehistoric Great Lakes (Hough, 1963), indicates that the Champlain Sea was formed after the retreat of the ice across the St. Lawrence during a phase corresponding to the retreat from the Mankato–Port Huron moraines. The Champlain Sea existed in various stages from about 10,000 B.C. to about 8800 B.C., or somewhat later according to my present interpretations. If there is a true association of the Reagen site with the Champlain Sea, it should be about 9000 B.C. The new dates for Lake Iroquois suggest that its floor was available for vegetation, animal life, and man shortly after 9000 B.C.

Since 1955, archaeologists have postulated that the Fluted Point Hunters were in the lower peninsula of Michigan between the time of the withdrawal of the ice and before the lake level began to drop from the Algonquin beach (Griffin, 1956; Mason, 1958). This hypothesis still seems valid. Roosa (1963) has recently proposed that fluted points from Barnes in Midland County, Michigan, are possibly associated with the late Lake Warren beach, while Enterline-style points in Michigan are seemingly associated with a much lower Lake Lundy beach at 620-ft elevation. If these tentative correlations are valid, they would place the Paleo-Indian hunters in southern Michigan by about 11,000 B.C., for these beaches were formed during the retreat from the Port Huron moraine and before the Two Creeks low-water interval.

It would have been possible for the Fluted Point Hunters to have entered Ontario easily from southeastern Michigan during the Two Creeks low-water stage, for at that time only local streams drained into the St. Clair River, Lake St. Clair, and the Detroit River. Entry could also have been made following the post-Valders drop from Lake Algonquin after 9000 B.C. The water barrier, however, even during the high lake levels would have been relatively narrow and almost certainly frozen during the winter. Only eleven fluted points have been reported in Ontario (Kidd, 1951), but their distribution extends from Elgin and Middlesex Counties in southwestern Ontario to Lanark, the second county west of Ottawa. In central Ontario they do not extend north of the southern part of Lake Simcoe, so that their northern border corresponds roughly to the northern distribution of similar points in Michigan. The specimen from the Rice Lake shore in Hamilton County was probably on an area under Lake Iroquois in the Ontario Basin, and the specimen from either southeastern Simcoe County or the northern part of York County may have been under Lake Algonquin or near the shores of that lake. This latter association is also likely for the specimen from Adelaide township in Middlesex County. The specimen from Lanark County could have been found on the west side of the Champlain Sea. These suggestions are to be regarded as possibilities only.

The earliest dated presence of man in the Upper Great Lakes area is at the Durst Rock Shelter in Sauk County, Wisconsin. In Stratum R of the deposit were charcoal fragments interpreted as possibly the result of a campfire in the shelter, although no artifacts were found at this level. The charcoal is dated at 9660 ± 300 B.C. (M-812), and level R was assigned by Black (1959, p. 81) to the Two Creeks interval. A short distance above this level, in Stratum O, there was a well-defined firebed with split animal bones and flakes of basalt. This level should date about 9000 to 8000 B.C., according to Wittry (1959, p. 59). Fluted points in Wisconsin are located in areas that suggest man was present there before and during the Valders advance and retreat (Quimby, 1958). The radiocarbon age of this association is of course earlier on current estimates than it was thought to be in the middle 1950's, for at that time the Valders was dated at 9000 B.C. It should clearly be recognized that the above interpretation of the age of the Fluted Point Hunters in the Northeast is based on presumed correlations with late Wisconsin geologic events.

The location of the Reagen site in Vermont in dune sand on a hill slope about 300 ft above water is not a normal location for a prehistoric site, for usually they are located closer to water. If the technique of fluting points was still in existence for any significant period of time following the retreat of the Valders, archaeologists feel that fluted points should be found in the southern parts of the area uncovered by the Valders ice. This does not seem to be the case, and the earliest archaeological material within the Valders area is that of the Early Archaic. Fluted points are not found on present land areas around the Great Lakes that were covered by Lake Algonquin, but they are found on the land areas uncovered by the drop in level from higher beaches. Furthermore, Early Archaic cultures are consistently associated with Lake Algonquin beaches and with beaches formed during the drop from Lake Algonquin to the Chippewa-Stanley stage. This evidence is presented in the next section. Until we can obtain a series of radiocarbon dates from tight associations with the Fluted Point complex, we are vulnerable to the mistakes inherent in the reasoning that has been employed. At present, however, the best interpretation of the age of Fluted Points in the Northeast is that they are primarily older than 9000 B.C.

For some time, I have made an arbitrary division between the Paleo-Indian period and the Early Archaic cultures of the eastern United States at the time of the disappearance of the technique of "fluting" projectile points. This division can be recognized with some success also in the High Plains and Southwest. There is no cultural break and no clear indication of major population movements that would account for the minor and gradual changes in tool typologies or for the introduction and spread of new cultural developments. The Early Archaic points in the Great Lakes are very similar to some of the Plano-complex forms from the High Plains, and there is a marked blending of Plains and Eastern Woodland forms along the border between the two regions. Many archaeologists speak of Paleo-Indian cultures or traditions that include the Plano complexes of the High Plains from *ca.* 8000 to 4000 B.C. and include also those eastern complexes that have many projectile-point styles similar to the Plano forms of the West. While the cultural continuity is valid both in the East and the West, I prefer to regard the changes as the beginning of a series of regional adaptations that are increasingly emphasized through the long Archaic period. In general terms the Archaic corresponds to the culture level of the Mesolithic in Europe.

EARLY ARCHAIC COMPLEXES OF THE NORTHEAST AND THEIR ASSOCIATION WITH GREAT LAKES ANCIENT BEACHES

In southeastern Michigan the Holcombe and related sites are located in Macomb County, about 6 miles west of Lake St. Clair, along a beach ridge with an elevation of 610 ft. It is assumed that the occupation was contemporaneous with Lake Algonquin, for the complex does not occur to the east within the area covered by the ancient lake. The only food remains were small fragments of animal bone, one of which has been identified by C. C. Cleland as barren-ground caribou. The Holcombe point resembles western Plano forms in having basal and lateral grinding. The base of the point is thinned on both surfaces. Some of the points resemble true fluted points. They are made of Bayport chert from the Upper Grand Rapids Series, probably from

Huron County, Michigan. There are also finely worked points with rounded tips, side scrapers, spoke-shave scrapers, an end scraper, and some possible graver fragments (Fitting, 1964).

Another projectile point of about the same age has been described by Fitting (1963) as the Hi-Lo point. This is similar to the Holcombe point but is, in general, shorter and broader; it has the same basal thinning and lateral and basal grinding. Both the Holcombe and Hi-Lo points are found in northern and northwestern Ohio, where they may be regarded as typologically transitional from fluted forms into ones that belong to the slightly later Early Archaic.

The first attempted association and correlation of early Indian groups with the changing levels of the Great Lakes was made by Greenman and Stanley (1940, 1941, 1943) on sites near Killarney, Ontario, on the north side of Lake Huron. The oldest of the industries in this area was associated with a beach formed during the drop of water level from the Lake Algonquin beach. This event resulted from the opening of the Kirkfield outlet into Lake Ontario and of the North Bay outlet into the Champlain Sea. It began about 9000 B.C. The George Lake quartzite industry was associated initially with a beach now at an elevation of 320 ft above Lake Huron, but most of the workshop material is connected with a beach of the Wyebridge to Cedar Point stages at 297 ft above the modern lake. The cultural evidence includes a number of semi-lunar knives or scrapers, ovate knives, possible perforators, utilized flakes, cores, and thousands of quartzite fragments. Two stemmed-point bases are clearly of the Eden-Yuma styles, and the base of a side-notched point is like those of ones that were deposited at the Modoc Rock Shelter in Illinois by perhaps 7000 B.C. (Fowler, 1959, Fig. 7) and that were also found at the Renier site in Wisconsin (Mason and Irwin, 1960), to the discussed below. Greenman has interpreted the worn and smoothed condition of eleven artifacts as being the result of water-rolling on the beach. Some of the chipping techniques have been compared to Levalloisian and others to "mesolithic" (Greenman, 1948), but the physical placement of the sites and the projectile points that are associated rather clearly date the sites and indicate the cultural associations.

The Sheguiandah site on the eastern end of Manitoulin Island in northern Lake Huron at elevations from 145 to 110 ft above modern Lake Huron was not available for occupancy until after the water level had dropped about 150 ft from its position at nearby George Lake. It has many more finds in the form of finished scrapers, drills, ovate bifacial knives or points, and trianguloid points than does the George Lake site (Lee, 1954, 1955, 1956, 1957). One specimen resembles the Eden Point, and good side-notched Archaic forms occur. I consider this complex to be a part of the George Lake industry. The interpretation of the variety of deposits excavated by Lee has been difficult. Artifacts in "till" prompted the suggestion that the Sheguiandah site had been occupied before the Valders ice advance (Lee, 1957). An alternative interpretation adopted here is that the "till" was deposited secondarily during an early phase of the occupation. The similarity of artifact forms at the

George Lake and the Sheguiandah sites on Lake Huron indicates a close temporal association. The time interval between the formation of the Cedar Point group of beaches and the early occupation of the Sheguiandah site is probably not very great.

The base of a 5-ft deposit of peat in the area called Swamp 3 of the Sheguiandah site was date at 7180 ± 250 B.C. (W-345; Lee, 1956). The pollen record of Terasmae for this level (Lee, 1957, p. 131) has pine dominant, with spruce, birch, and oak. In the 3- to 4.5-ft levels, a marked rise of spruce and drop in pine and birch may reflect a somewhat colder period following the dated level. The Sheguiandah date initially seemed too old, because the drop from Lake Algonquin was thought to be about 6000 B.C., implying that the site was either under ice or under Lake Algonquin at the time of the dated peat. If, however, Lake Algonquin began to drop about 9000 B.C., ample time was available for human activity and for peat formation. Since the Sheguiandah site is at such a low elevation, it was close to the lake until well after the Nipissing period. Long occupation is reflected by the much greater variety of material on the site.

Another location on the north side of the Great Lakes is the Brohm site, about 20 miles northeast of Port Arthur in the Thunder Bay district of Ontario. The culture-bearing area, containing leaf-shaped points, scrapers, and other tools, is in a beach 100 ft wide and about 225-230 ft above the present 605-ft level of Lake Superior (MacNeish, 1952; Burnford, 1964).

MacNeish emphasized the similarity of the Brohm projectile points with Plainview forms and the fact that the cultural material of the Brohm site was deposited on the beach before the humus had begun to form. The site cannot be earlier than the Minong group of beaches, and it is a reasonable inference that it was occupied close to the time when the waters of Lake Superior were at the Minong level or slightly below it.

According to T. L. Tanton, the group of beaches from 245 to 195 ft above the lake at Thunder Bay may be correlated with the Early to Middle Lake Algonquin times (MacNeish, 1952, p. 26). Quimby (1960, p. 35-38) suggests a correlation with the Minong group of beaches in Lake Superior, which appear to correlate with the Lake Payette beaches in the Huron basin (Hough, 1963, Fig. 6A). This correlation is also that of Farrand (1960), whose study of the Lake Superior basin has brought that area into better accord with the Michigan-Huron sequence.

The estimates of the age of Lake Algonquin and the drop to the Chippewa-Stanley low-water stage have varied considerably in the last fifteen years. At the time of the initial correlations of fluted points with Lake Algonquin (Griffin, 1956, p. 21), this lake stage was thought to date about 6500 B.C., and the low-water stage that followed at 3000 B.C. Hough (1958) placed late Lake Algonquin at 6000 B.C. and the low-water stage at about 3000 B.C. Later Hough (1963, p. 103) used a date of 7500 B.C. for the Chippewa-Stanley low-water stage. But these dates are too recent for the following reasons. Broecker and Farrand (1963) place the drowning of the Two Creeks forest bed by the rising waters of Lake Algonquin II (Hough, 1963, p. 97) at *ca.*

9900 B.C. A synchronous low-water stage between Lakes Algonquin I and II in Lake St. Clair has been dated at 10,050 B.C. (Dreimanis, 1964) from plant remains growing on silt in the Sydenham delta area. The rise in the water level in Lake Michigan would not have begun until the outlet into the Huron basin was closed, and the rise in the Huron basin would not have started until the eastern outlets of Lake Huron had been closed.

There seems to be general agreement that the drop from Lake Algonquin to the Chippewa-Stanley low-water stage was rapid. The shorelines of the beaches are not well developed, and about 8000 B.C. may be regarded as an acceptable date for the lowest level of the low-water stage. This is 500 years earlier than the date Hough (1963, p. 103) and Quimby (1963) suggested, and 5,000 years earlier than that of Zumberge and Potzger (1956).

The Door Peninsula of northeastern Wisconsin is the location of the Renier site, which is situated "in windblown sand on top of beach deposits consisting of stratified sand, silt and gravel" (Mason and Irwin, 1960, p. 49). The beach, at an elevation of 616 ft, is regarded as the highest Algonquin beach. The site is believed to have been occupied shortly after the waters of the Michigan basin began to drop from the Lake Algonquin level, thus about 9000-2500 B.C. in the revised chronology presented here. The site contains cremated burial with burned burial goods, including Eden-Scottsbluff points, large quartzite bifacial implements, a side-notched point, and two flake scrapers. The attribution of this site to the dropping Lake Algonquin level would date it at 9000-8500 B.C. In the Plains these projectile points are dated 7500 to 4000 B.C.

Preliminary archaeological work around the Lake Agassiz basin has provided a correlation of a number of Plano projectile point forms with the Campbell beach phase of Lake Agassiz II. It is said that these points do not occur on the floor of the Campbell-phase lake (Elson, 1962, p. 12).

A recent date places the Campbell beach at Williams, Minnesota, at 7250 B.C. (W-1057). This means that the points could only have been placed in the lake basin at a subsequent period.

The Fluted Point Hunter occupation of the Great Lakes and the Northeast has not been securely dated by carbon-14, and the suggested date of 9000 B.C. or older may be in error. Similarly the dating proposed for the Early Archaic sites is not based on radiocarbon, with the possible exception of Sheguiandah, but on typology and correlations with the levels of the Great Lakes from Lake Algonquin to the Chippewa-Stanley low-water stage. The surprising indication of much greater age for the Plano-Early Archaic projectile point forms in the Great Lakes area than in the West is difficult to accept. There is no good reason to expect a time lag of one to three thousand years between the adoption of new projectile styles in the Great Lakes area and their appearance in the Plains.

"Early" Prehistoric Burials

There are only three candidates for early Indian burials in the Northeast. The first of these is "Minnesota Man," interpreted by Jenks (1936) as the skeleton of a 15-year-old female who drowned in Glacial Lake Pelican in Ottertail

County, Minnesota, and was covered by varved sediment. If this skeleton was blanketed by varves, death should have taken place at roughly 11,000 to 10,000 B.C. The artifacts found with this burial were an elk-antler dagger, a perforated pendant of the marine shell *Busycon perversum*, an incisor of an eastern timber wolf, a loon metatarsal, and carapace fragments of turtle. The pendant is highly similar to specimens in Late Archaic shell heaps in Kentucky of about 2000 B.C., and this period marks the beginning of the spread of marine-shell ornaments into the Middle West and Great Lakes area (*cf.* Wormington, 1957, p. 232-233; Johnson, 1962, p. 148-149). In 1957, a radiocarbon date of about 3000 B.C. (W-530) was obtained, which was not formally published for various reasons. One of these was that the bone sample had been preserved with shellac, although great care was taken at the University of Minnesota to remove it chemically before the assay was made. Another reason was that the carbon sample was below the minimum size required by the laboratory. Those who have faith in the excavating skill of the highway road crew that found the burial months before any systematic study was made of the location will believe the radiocarbon date is too young. I believe it is too old because of the associated artifacts.

A representative of the fairly early Archaic populations is the Union Lake skull, recovered from a peat bog in Oakland County, southeastern Michigan, during commercial excavation (Black and Eyman, 1963). Comparison of pollen from the ear and nasal cavities with a pollen diagram from a carefully collected core in nearby Sodon Lake (Cain and Slater, 1948) indicates that the skull derived from the later phases of the pine maximum, which was dated in the Sodon Lake core at 5050 ± 200 B.C.

Of about the same age is the burial of Browns Valley Man, Traverse County, Minnesota, which was made in a gravel knoll that had been formed during the Tintah stage of Lake Agassiz I. The age of the burial is inferred from the associated six projectile points or knives (Jenks, 1937), which place the burial about 6000 to 5000 B.C. The skull is morphologically similar to the Union Lake skull and, in general, to Neumann's Otamid variety (1952).

THE NIPISSING BEACH DEVELOPMENT
AND THE LAKE FOREST AREA

A major geologic event in prehistoric times was the gradual rise of the Upper Great Lakes from the Chippewa-Stanley low-water stage of about 8500 B.C. to the Nipissing stage (elevation of *ca.* 605 ft). The isostatic rebound of the land closed the outlets from the southeastern and finally the northeastern outlets for the Huron basin. A date of 2200 to 2000 B.C. will be used for the Nipissing beach development. There can be little question that during the intervening 6,000 years not only vegetation but also animals and man occupied a large land area now under the surface of the Great Lakes. Communication among Indian bands located around these lowered bodies of water would also have been easier then than later.

Relatively little cultural material in the Great Lakes–St. Lawrence area represents the period *ca.* 7000 to 3000 B.C. This is the earlier time of the development of the Archaic cultures. The Late Archaic in the Northeast begins *ca.*

3000 B.C., but it is best known from the Late Archaic and Terminal Archaic groups, about 2000 to 1000 B.C. This period of time also coincides with the most northward distribution of southern plants as indicated by pollen studies. Probably the increase in the number of aboriginal sites and the greater population density of this time resulted from this amelioration of the climate. The northern spread and development of the deciduous and Lake Forest environment allowed the people and their culture, adapted to these environments, to flourish in the Northeast.

The Lake Forest Formation is a term used by Potzger (1946, p. 215-216) for the forest that extends from the Great Lakes eastward to New England. In Canada, the term Great Lakes–St. Lawrence Forest Region has been used for the mixture of northern hardwoods and boreal-forest species occurring in this area (Rowe, 1959). Dice (1938, p. 503-505) called this region the Canadian Biotic Province and included the animal species in his definition. The term Lake Forest is used in this paper to refer to the cultural complexes that have a very high degree of relationship and interconnection from at least Late Archaic times up to the historic period. The peoples in the area adapted to a strongly lacustrine environment, obtained much of their food from the lakes and streams, and used these waters as highways for movement from western Lake Superior into the St. Lawrence. The term "Boreal Archaic" is not applicable to the complexes of this area, because by the time of the development of the Late Archaic complexes the Boreal Forest, *sensu strictu*, was north of the area. The deciduous forest lies south of the Lake Forest Formation, and the dividing line between them is somewhat arbitrary and decidedly jagged. Biological crossovers and also cultural penetrations occur from the deciduous into the Lake Forest Formation. These are probably most clearly recognized during the Terminal Archaic of *ca.* 1000 to 500 B.C., during the Hopewellian expansion of 100 B.C. to A.D. 200, and during the Mississippian spread into the Upper Great Lakes around A.D. 1000 to 1200.

The time of the Nipissing and Algoma beach developments are important in archaeological correlations and preliminary age determinations. The age of these lake stages is important because of the normal association of camp, village, and burial sites with the beaches.

When the Upper Great Lakes reached the Nipissing level of *ca.* 605 ft, the water covered prehistoric sites that had been located at lower levels. Relatively few sites have been identified as belonging to the time period of the Nipissing beach. When the lake level dropped to the Algoma beach of 595 ft, a large area of land became available again for occupation. Good correlation exists between successive archaeological complexes and the lake-level changes from Nipissing to Algoma. These are based on radiocarbon dates for materials from the beaches and the archaeological sites.

Reference to the Nipissing Lake stage and its age has been varied. For example, Quimby (1960, p. 61) includes some part of the period of the rise to the Nipissing beach as well as the period of the beach development when he says, "The Nipissing stage . . . lasted [from] shortly after 3000 to about 1500 B.C." Zumberge and Potzger (1956) considered that the peat development at South Haven was terminated by the Nipissing beach and that the 605-ft level was reached shortly after 2050 B.C. At Evanston, Illinois, a log supposedly from the Toleston period of Lake Algonquin at 605 ft yielded a date of 2080 B.C. (W-725). On the east side of Lake Michigan, near Muskegon, Michigan, the series of dates from the Michillinda Bog give a close check on the Nipissing beach. A white-pine branch near the top of buried peat gave an age of 2150 B.C. ± 125 (M-472). The peat bog was covered by bedded sands and gravels of the lake just before the Nipissing crest. Sears and Bopp (1960, p. 104) state that "The Michillinda peat seam near Muskegon, Michigan, despite its frequent low pollen counts, affords a classic record of the mesophytic interval, from about 5000 to 4000 B.P. . . ."

Two white-oak logs buried by a beach bar of the rise to the Nipissing beach at Blackwell and Bright Grove, Ontario, in the southern tip of Lake Huron, were dated at 2700 and 2650 B.C. (McCallum and Dyck, 1960). These dates suggest that the rise had reached levels of roughly 580 and 590 ft, about 25 to 15 ft below the Nipissing beach. Farrand (1962, p. 183) used the Blackwell–Bright Grove dates in placing the Nipissing beach at 2250 B.C. Other radiocarbon dates suggest a slightly later date. It is important to recognize that the maximum Nipissing level was short-lived and that there were probably short-term fluctuations at this level.

THE LATE ARCHAIC CULTURES

The Lamoka culture of the central New York area was the first to be described as an Archaic culture (Ritchie, 1932). For many years it was regarded as relatively old, but it may now be regarded as a distinctive Northeastern Late Archaic complex. Because of favorable conditions of preservation, a wide variety of bone and antler tools was found at the type site along with a distinctive, shallow, side-notched, thick-base projectile point, expanded base drills, planoconvex adzes, grinding stones, net sinkers, and some painted and notched bone tablets. This complex has been dated about 2500 to 2000 B.C. in New York. It has been known for some time that in the Saginaw basin and in southeastern Michigan there were adzes, beveled adzes, and projectile points similar to the Lamokoid. The Schmidt site in Saginaw County, currently under excavation by the University of Michigan, should date very close to the New York type site because it has a similar cultural complex. It is located just above the Nipissing level. It is the only association known to me of a Lamokoid culture with one of the prehistoric Great Lake beaches, for Lamoka sites are located primarily in the northern part of the northeastern deciduous forest.

Along the east coast correlation has been attempted between the location of archaeological sites and sea level during the gradual rise of the sea from its low stage of the Wisconsin maximum. The best known of these is the famous Boylston Street Fishweir site, which has been the subject of an unusual amount of well-conceived and integrated study by many scientists attempting to interpret the ecology of this coastal fishing station (Johnson, 1942, 1949). A large series of stakes, which had been placed in shallow bay waters of the Charles River, has been excavated from depths of 31-32 ft below the present filled level of the Back Bay area of Boston. The stakes are carbon-dated at about 2650 B.C. (Kaye and Barghoorn, 1964, p. 74).

The whole question of sea-level position during the last 6,000 years and its relation to possible crustal movements in New England is in such a state of uncertainty (Kaye and Barghoorn, 1964; Shepard, 1964) that archaeologists should be more wary than Griffin (1960, 1961d) and Salwen (1962) were in attempting to correlate prehistoric culture change with the fluctuations in sea level proposed by Fairbridge (1958, 1960). In addition to the probably slow rise in sea level during the last 6,000 years, coastal subsidence has occurred in the New England area, so that presumably many Archaic coastal shell heaps are submerged or have been washed away, and later shell heaps are badly eroded. Archaeologically, the real value of Fairbridge's interpretations and correlations has been to stimulate archaeologists along the Atlantic coast to pay more attention to ecological data that will help interpret the ecology of their prehistoric sites (Salwen, 1964).

The prehistoric material most closely connected with lake-level changes of this 2000-1000 B.C. period is rather loosely called the Old Copper culture. One of the striking features of aboriginal North America was the utilization of the almost pure native copper from the Lake Superior area to make implements and ornaments. Some copper could have been obtained from the glacial drift, but the thousands of prehistoric pits on the Keewenaw Peninsula and on Isle Royale in Lake Superior were the primary source of this metal. The copper was cold-hammered or heated and hammered into a variety of spear points and knife forms, into awls, fishhooks, gaffs, axes, adzes, and celts, and into beads, rings, bracelets, and gorgets. Many of these copper forms are similar to ones in flint, stone, and bone. This relationship may mean in some cases that older forms were copied in copper but also that the greater malleability of copper may have stimulated production of new forms such as the rings and bracelets. The copper implements of the Lake Archaic have a wide distribution from South Dakota and Saskatchewan east to Montreal, New York, and New England and from central Manitoba south to central Kentucky. The major area of concentration, however, was in eastern Wisconsin.

The distribution of copper implements in Wisconsin, Michigan, and Ontario is clearly associated with a trade and communication network from the Upper Great Lakes to Lake Nipissing and the Ottawa River. Lake Erie was the last of the Great Lakes to be discovered by the French. They followed an old established Indian route from Montreal up the Ottawa River and from there west into the Upper Great Lakes. This pattern was in existence at least as early as the Old Copper culture.

The age of this metal industry has been the subject of some disagreement. The first radiocarbon dates were on solid carbon from the Oconto site, 5560 ± 600 B.C. (C-837) and 3650 ± 600 B.C. (C-836). Some archaeologists have accepted the dates, but others have felt that they were much too early because the lithic materials associated with the copper implements belong in the Late Archaic. Quimby and Spaulding (1957, p. 200) believed that the Old Copper culture was essentially pre-Nipissing. There is increasing evidence, however, that although some of the sites with this tool complex may go back as far as 3000 B.C., most of them are between the Nipissing and Algoma stages of 2200 to 1100 B.C. (Griffin, 1961a, 1962).

When the ship canal was excavated across the Keewenaw Peninsula of northern Michigan in the early 1890's, a copper pike was recovered under sand drift at least 25 ft deep. In the marsh areas cut by the canal "were found three distinct forests, one growing on top of the other, to a depth of 14 feet" (Packard, 1893, p. 184). This evidence is taken to support a pre-Nipissing age for Old Copper, for this means there was a low-water stage in Lake Superior comparable to that of the Michigan-Huron basin. Further evidence for this is presented by Quimby and Griffin (Griffin, 1961b, p. 103-117). The oldest apparently acceptable date for Old Copper tools is one recently obtained on charcoal from a site on Morrison's Island in the Ottawa River near Pembroke, Ontario (2750 ± 150 B.C., GSC-162).

Most of the copper implements are in sites of the Lake Forest Archaic of the St. Lawrence–New York–New England area, which belong to the 2500-1000 B.C. period. The Riverside Cemetery site on the north side of the Menominee River near its mouth is located on a sandy ridge. A radiocarbon date on the organic fraction of human bone from feature 6 is 1090 ± 150 B.C. (M-658); this burial was probably made about the time of the formation of the Algoma beaches. The Oconto site, a short distance to the south in Oconto County, Wisconsin, is also probably just above the Algoma level.

In the Saginaw basin the University of Michigan has excavated the Feheeley site, which is located at about the 605 ft to 600 ft elevation. The cultural complex is Late Archaic, with a large number of copper beads and large copper awls and celts. It could not have been occupied until shortly after the drop from the Nipissing stand. It is dated with maple charcoal at 1980 ± 150 B.C. (M-1139). Vegetal remains include grape, acorns, hickory nuts, and walnuts. White and red oak are the predominant charcoal, but beech, basswood, hickory, maple, pine, sycamore, white and black ash, and white and slippery elm also occur. This conforms very well with a pollen study at Milan in southeastern Michigan, with a radiocarbon date on a red-oak log of 2130 B.C. (M-1149). This was interpreted as the period of maximum development of vegetation during the warming trend, with oak pollen 28%, basswood 18%, walnut 14%, elm 12%, sycamore 11%, butternut 7%, hickory 6%, and beech and ash ca. 5%. The soil conditions were interpreted as reflecting the rise to the Nipissing level (Kapp and Kneller, 1962).

TERMINAL ARCHAIC AND LATER CULTURES

Near the Feheeley site on the Algoma beach is the Andrews site, on the east side of the Tittabawassee River. It has a Terminal Archaic complex, with the last phases of Old Copper culture. Archaeologically it postdates Feheeley and has a radiocarbon date of 1220 ± 150 B.C. (M-941).

Across the river to the west from the Andrews site are the Stroebel and Frazer sites, where similar cultural materials of the Terminal Archaic are located at or just below the Algoma level. The Pomranky site, near Midland, Michigan, is on the south side of the Tittabawassee River. The burials and grave goods at this site were in a sand ridge at about 610 ft. The cultural material indicates very clearly that the site was probably occupied during the Algoma stage. These four sites contain highly similar cultural complexes and can be dated about 1000 to 700 B.C.

This Terminal Archaic burial complex extends into Ontario, New York, and New England. In these areas it does not seem to be associated with specific Quaternary geologic features, but the time period is about the same, for the cultural complex was very close to that of the peoples in the Lake Huron to Michigan area. At the Red Lake site, Jefferson County, New York (Ritchie, 1955), a solid-carbon date of 2450 ± 260 B.C. (C-794) was 1,000 years too early (Griffin, 1961c, p. 93), although it was used by Ritchie and others for almost ten years. The more acceptable date of 852 ± 68 B.C. (Y-981, Ritchie, 1962) conforms to other indications of the age of the Red Ochre burial complex throughout the area.

The Frank Bay site in western Lake Nipissing (the modern lake) has an elevation of about 640 ft, so the area of the site was underneath the Nipissing and probably under the Algoma levels of the Lake Huron basin. This also was a stratified site. The lowest level was the pre-ceramic Mattawan complex (Ridley, 1954), which I believe is a distinctive Late Archaic complex with some possible connections with the pre-Dorset cultures of the eastern Arctic but more particularly with some of the Terminal Archaic flint-working industries. A date of 970 ± 150 B.C. (M-363) on charcoal from the Mattawan level indicates that the earliest occupation at this site was after the Algoma drop.

An archaeological site near the mouth of the Tittabawassee River south of Saginaw has provided good evidence of the termination of the Algoma lake level. A former small knoll at the Schultz site, at an elevation of 581 ft, was occupied by an Indian group whose cultural material indicated an age of about 1000 to 500 B.C. It belongs to the Terminal Archaic and Early Woodland complexes of the Saginaw basin. A large charcoal deposit furnished a radiocarbon sample (M-1432), with a date of 530 ± 120 B.C. The interpretation given is that the small land area near the water level was utilized for a short time in the fall for collecting nuts, fruits, and small game and for fishing and mollusk-gathering (Wright, 1964). Two squash seeds from this location are the earliest evidence of agriculture in the Great Lakes. If further radiocarbon dates from this site and other locations bear out the interpretation of this sample, it would mean that the down-cutting of the Port Huron sill to the 580-ft level or below was accomplished before 500 B.C. It would also mean that Terminal Archaic and Early Woodland sites around the shores of Lakes Michigan and Huron should be found between the 595-ft and 580-ft elevations.

One of the first archaeological sites in Ontario to be dated was the Burley site, north along the coast from Sarnia near Port Franks. The site was near the mouth of the Ausable River and recorded three periods of occupation (Jury and Jury, 1951). The lowest level, at 592 ft to 594 ft above sea level, containing pottery and other artifacts of the Middle Woodland period was given an age of 669 ± 220 B.C.

(C-608). At the time of the excavation, it was thought that the 595-ft beach was Nipissing and therefore that the earliest occupation at 592-594 ft was above the level of the lake in pre-Nipissing times, for the sandy layers above Occupation I were interpreted as alluvial sands deposited during the Nipissing stand. The second occupation took place after the retreat from the Nipissing level (Dreimanis, 1951). The current interpretation of the changes in the Lake Huron basin and their dates make this older interpretation invalid. The 12-ft-deep sands on which Occupation I rested must be both Nipissing and Algoma deposits, and the whole sequence of levels with cultural material is post-Algoma. The solid-carbon date is geologically possible, but I believe it to be about 800 years too early on the basis of my current interpretation of the age of the Middle Woodland culture in this area. Some archaeologists, however, accept the date.

Summary

This report has emphasized the possible association of prehistoric Indian cultural groups with late Pleistocene and Recent geologic events in the Northeast. Most of these correlations involve the Great Lakes area, the area which has been most intensively studied by Pleistocene geologists and where the early Indian inhabitants adapted closely to environmental changes only now being discovered by scientific research.

The correct time placement of the Paleo-Indian and Early Archaic cultures is uncertain. The evidence as it is now understood would indicate an occupation from about 12,000 B.C. in the southern part of the Northeast to as early as 11,000 B.C. in the southern half of the Lower Peninsula of Michigan. A more conservative position, based on archaeological typology, would place the Fluted Point Hunters at about 9000 to 8000 B.C. and the Early Archaic complexes from about 8000 to 6000 B.C., so that they would conform in age to their Plains counterparts, which are securely dated by radiocarbon analysis.

The northward spread and establishment of the present biotic zones allowed the prehistoric peoples to develop cultures with a more secure and varied economic base and provided for a gradual population increase. The cultural growth is seen as being primarily one of indigenous development supplemented by increments from the west and south. No significant addition came into the Northeast from the Boreal Forest area. The introduction of agriculture between 500 B.C. and A.D. 500 in the Northeast was what stimulated the marked changes characterizing the last 2,000 years of aboriginal history in the area.

References

Adams, R. McC., 1949, Archaeological investigations in Jefferson County, Missouri: Missouri Arch., v. 11, p. 1-72

Andersen, S. T., 1954, A late-glacial pollen diagram from southern Michigan, U.S.A.: Danmarks Geol. Unders., ser. 2, No. 80, p. 140-155

Benninghoff, W. S., and Hibbard, C. W., 1961, Fossil pollen associated with a late-glacial woodland musk ox in Michigan: Michigan Acad. Sci. Pap., v. 46, p. 155-159

Black, M. J., and Eyman, C. E., 1963, The Union Lake Skull, a possible early Indian find in Michigan: Amer. Antiq., v. 29, p. 39-48

Black, R. F., 1959, Geology of the Raddatz Rockshelter, Sk5, Wisconsin: Wisconsin Arch., v. 40, p. 69-82

Broecker, W. S., and Farrand, W. R., 1963, Radiocarbon age of the Two Creeks forest bed: Geol. Soc. Amer. Bull., v. 74, p. 795-802

Burmaster, E. R., 1932, Reports of archaeological field work in North America during 1931: Amer. Anthrop., v. 34, p. 491

Burnford, S., 1964, Time out of mind: Atlantic Monthly, v. 214, p. 38-43

Byers, D. S., 1954, Bull Brook—a fluted point site in Ipswich, Massachusetts: Amer. Antiq., v. 19, p. 343-351

—— 1955, Additional information on the Bull Brook Site, Massachusetts: Amer. Antiq., v. 20, p. 274-276

—— 1959, Radiocarbon dates for the Bull Brook Site, Massachusetts: Amer. Antiq., v. 24, p. 427-429

Cain, S. A., and Slater, J. V., 1948, Palynological studies at Sodon Lake, Michigan. Part III, the sequence of pollen spectra, profile I: Ecology, v. 29, p. 492-500

Cole, F. C., and Deuel, Thorne, 1937, Rediscovering Illinois: Chicago, Ill., Univ. Chicago Press, 297 p.

Deevey, E. S., Gralenski, L. J., and Hoffren, V., 1959, Yale natural radiocarbon measurements IV: Amer. J. Sci. Radiocarbon Suppl., v. 1, p. 144-172

Dennis, W. A., 1962, Notes and news: Amer. Antiq., v. 27, p. 456

Dice, L. R., 1938, The Canadian Biotic Province with special reference to the mammals: Ecology, v. 19, p. 503-514

Dreimanis, A., 1951, Age determination of the Burley Site at Port Franks, Ontario, by geological methods: Ontario Hist. Soc., v. 43, p. 72-75

—— 1964, Lake Warren and the Two Creeks interval. J. Geol., v. 72, p. 247-250

Elson, J. A., 1962, History of glacial Lake Agassiz; problems of the Pleistocene and Arctic: McGill Univ. Mus. Publ., v. 2, p. 1-16

Fairbridge, R. W., 1958, Dating the latest movements of the Quaternary sea level: New York Acad. Sci. Trans., ser. 2, v. 20, p. 471-482

—— 1960, The changing level of the sea: Sci. Amer., v. 202, p. 70-79

Farrand, W. R., 1960, Former shorelines in western and northern Lake Superior basin: Univ. Michigan Ph.D. thesis, 226 p.

—— 1962, Postglacial uplift in North America: Amer. J. Sci., v. 260, p. 181-199

Fitting, J. E., 1963, The Hi-Lo Site, a Paleo-Indian site in western Michigan: Wisconsin Arch., v. 44, p. 87-96

—— 1964, Some characteristic projectile point bases from the Holcombe Site, Macomb County, Michigan: Michigan Acad. Sci. Pap., v. 49, p. 231-238

Flint, R. F., 1957, Glacial and Pleistocene geology: New York, John Wiley and Sons, Inc., 553 p.

Fowler, M. L., 1959, Summary report of Modoc Rock Shelter: Illinois Mus. Nat. Hist., Rep. Inv. 8, 72 p.

Goldthwait, R. P., 1959, Scenes in Ohio during the last ice age: Ohio J. Sci., v. 59, p. 193-216

Greenman, E. F., 1948, The Killarney sequence and its Old World connections: Michigan Acad. Sci. Pap., v. 32, p. 313-332

Greenman, E. F., and Stanley, G. M., 1940, A geologically dated camp site Georgian Bay, Ontario: Amer. Antiq., v. 5, p. 194-199

—— 1941, Two post-Nipissing sites near Killarney, Ontario: Amer. Antiq., v. 6, p. 305-313

—— 1943, The archaeology and geology of two early sites near Killarney, Ontario: Michigan Acad. Sci. Pap., v. 28, p. 505-531

Griffin, J. B., 1956, The reliability of radiocarbon dates for late glacial and recent times in central and eastern North America: Univ. Utah Anthrop. Pap., v. 26, p. 10-34

—— 1960, Climatic change; a contributory cause of the growth and decline of northern Hopewellian culture: Wisconsin Arch., v. 41, p. 21-33

—— 1961a, Post-glacial ecology and culture changes in the Great Lakes area of North America: Univ. Michigan Great Lakes Res. Publ. 7, p. 147-155

—— 1961b, Lake Superior copper and the Indians; miscellaneous studies of Great Lakes prehistory: Univ. Michigan Mus. Anthrop., Anthrop. Pap. 17, 189 p.

—— 1961c, Comments on Edmunson's Neolithic diffusion rates: Curr. Anthrop., v. 2, p. 92-93

—— 1961d, Some correlations of climatic and cultural change in eastern North American prehistory: New York Acad. Sci. Ann., v. 95, p. 710-717

—— 1962, Similarities and connections between Arctic and Temperate zones of North America, *in* Campbell, J. M. (ed.), Prehistoric cultural relations between the Arctic and Temperate zones of North America: Arctic Inst. Tech. Pap., p. 154-163

Handley, C. O., Jr., 1953, Marine mammals in Michigan Pleistocene beaches: J. Mammal., v. 34, p. 252-253

Hibbard, C. W., and Hinds, F. J., 1960, A radiocarbon date for a woodland musk ox in Michigan: Michigan Acad. Sci. Pap., v. 45, p. 103-108

Hough, J. L., 1958, Geology of the Great Lakes. Univ. Illinois Press, 313 p.

—— 1963, The prehistoric Great Lakes of North America: Amer. Scientist, v. 51, p. 84-109

Jenks, A. E., 1936, Pleistocene man in Minnesota; a fossil *Homo sapiens*: Minneapolis, Minn., Univ. Minnesota Press, 197 p.

—— 1937, Minnesota's Browns Valley Man and associated burial artifacts: Amer. Anthrop. Assoc. Mem., No. 49, 49 p.

Johnson, Elden, 1962, The prehistory of the Red River Valley: Minnesota History, v. 38, p. 146-155

Johnson, F., *et al.*, 1942, The Boylston Street fishweir: Phillips Acad., Peabody Fdn. Archaeol. Pap., v. 2, 212 p.

—— 1949, The Boylston Street fishweir II: Phillips Acad., Peabody Fdn. Archaeol. Pap., v. 4, 133 p.

Jury, W. W., and Jury, E. Mc., 1951, The Burley Site: Ontario History, v. 43, p. 57-71

Kapp, R. O., and Kneller, W. A., 1962, A buried biotic-assemblage from an old Saline River terrace at Milan, Michigan: Michigan Acad. Sci. Pap., v. 47, p. 135-145

Karrow, P. F., Clark, J. R., and Terasmae, Jean, 1961, The age of Lake Iroquois and Lake Ontario: J. Geol., v. 69, p. 659-667

Kaye, C. A., 1962, Early postglacial beavers in southeastern New England: Science, v. 138, p. 906-907

Kaye, C. A., and Barghoorn, E., 1964, Lake Quaternary sea-level change and crustal rise at Boston, Massachusetts, with notes on the auto-compaction of peat: Geol. Soc. Amer. Bull., v. 75, p. 63-80

Kidd, K. E., 1951, Fluted points in Ontario: Amer. Antiq., v. 16, p. 260

Lee, T. E., 1954, The first Sheguiandah expedition, Manitoulin Island, Ontario: Amer. Antiq., v. 20, p. 101-111

—— 1955, The second Sheguiandah expedition, Manitoulin Island, Ontario: Amer. Antiq., v. 21, p. 63-71

—— 1956, The position and meaning of a radiocarbon sample from the Sheguiandah Site, Ontario: Amer. Antiq., v. 22, p. 79

—— 1957, The antiquity of the Sheguiandah Site: Can. Field Nat., v. 71, p. 117-137

MacNeish, R. S., 1952, A possible early site in the Thunder Bay District, Ontario: Natl. Mus. Canada Bull., v. 126, p. 23-47

Mason, R. J., 1958, Late Pleistocene geo-chronology and the Paleo-Indian penetration into the lower Michigan peninsula: Univ. Michigan, Mus. Anthrop., Anthrop. Pap. 11, 48 p.

Mason, R. J., and Irwin, C., 1960, An Eden-Scottsbluff burial in northern Wisconsin: Amer. Antiq., v. 26, p. 43-57

McCallum, K. J., and Dyck, W., 1960, University of Saskatchewan radiocarbon dates II: Amer. J. Sci. Radiocarbon Suppl., v. 2, p. 73-81

McIntire, W. G., and Morgan, J. P., 1962, Recent geomorphic history of Plum Island, Massachusetts and adjacent coasts. Louisiana State Univ. Atlantic Coastal Stud., Contr., 62-67, 44 p.

Neumann, G. K., 1952, Archeology and race in the American Indian, *in* Griffin, J. B. (ed.), Archeology of eastern United States: Chicago, Ill., Univ. Chicago Press, 392 p.

Packard, R. L., 1893, Pre-Columbian copper mining in North America: Smithson. Instn. Rep., p. 175-198

Potzger, J. E., 1946, Phytosociology of the Primeval forest in central-northern Wisconsin and upper Michigan, and a brief post-glacial history of the Lake Forest formation: Ecol. Monogr., v. 16, p. 211-250

Prufer, Olaf, and Baby, R. S., 1963, Paleo-Indians of Ohio: Ohio Hist. Soc., 68 p.

Quimby, G. I., 1958, Fluted points and geochronology of the Lake Michigan basin: Amer. Antiq., v. 23, p. 247-254

—— 1960, Indian life in the upper Great Lakes, 11,000 B.C. to A.D. 1800: Chicago, Ill., Univ. Chicago Press, 182 p.

—— 1963, A new look at geochronology in the upper Great Lakes region: Amer. Antiq., v. 28, p. 558-559

Quimby, G. I., and Spaulding, A. C., 1957, The Old Copper Culture and the Keewenaw waterway: Chicago Nat. Hist. Mus., Fieldiana Anthrop., v. 36, p. 189-201

Ridley, F., 1954, The Frank Bay site, Lake Nipissing, Ontario: Amer. Antiq., v. 20, p. 40-50

Ritchie, W. A., 1932, The Lamoka Lake site; the type station of the Archaic Algonkian period in New York: New York State Arch. Assoc. Res. Trans., v. 7, p. 79-134

—— 1953, A probable Paleo-Indian site in Vermont: Amer. Antiq., v. 18, p. 249-258

—— 1955, Recent discoveries suggesting an Early Woodland burial cult in the northeast: New York State Mus. Sci. Service, No. 40, p. 133

—— 1957, Traces of early man in the northeast: New York State Mus. Sci. Service, No. 358, p. 91

—— 1962, The antiquity of pottery in the northeast: Amer. Antiq., v. 27, p. 583-584

Robbins, Maurice, and Agogino, G. A., 1964, The Wapanucket No. 8 Site; a Clovis-Archaic site in Massachusetts: Amer. Antiq., v. 29, p. 509-513

Roosa, W. B., 1963, Michigan fluted point sites and types: Michigan Arch., v. 9, p. 44-48

Rowe, J. S., 1959, Forest regions of Canada: Canada Forestry Branch Bull. 123, 71 p.

Salwen, B., 1962, Sea levels and archaeology of the Long Island Sound area: Amer. Antiq., v. 28, p. 46-55

—— 1964, Notes and news: Amer. Antiq., v. 29, p. 541

Sanford, J. T., 1935, The Richmond mastodon: Rochester Acad. Sci. Proc., v. 7, p. 135-156

Sears, P. B., and Bopp, M., 1960, Pollen analysis of the Michillinda peat seam: Ohio J. Sci., v. 60, p. 149-154

Semken, H. A., Miller, W. B., and Stevens, J. B., 1964, Pollen associated with the Scotts, Michigan musk ox: J. Paleont., v. 38, p. 823-835

Shepard, F. P., 1964, Sea level changes in the past 6000 years; possible archaeological significance: Science, v. 143, p. 574-576

Shetrone, H. C., 1936, The Folsom phenomena as seen from Ohio: Ohio State Arch. Hist. Soc. Quart., v. 45, p. 240-256

Skeels, M. A., 1962, The mastodons and mammoths of Michigan: Michigan Acad. Sci. Pap., v. 47, p. 101-126

Sternberg, C. M., 1951, White whale and other Pleistocene fossils from the Ottawa Valley: Natl. Mus. Canada Bull. 123, p. 259-261

Terasmae, J., 1960, Contributions to Canadian Palynology, No. 2: Geol. Surv. Canada, Bull. 56, 41 p.

—— 1961, Notes on late-Quaternary climatic changes in Canada: New York Acad. Sci. Ann., v. 95, p. 658-675

Thomas, E. S., 1952, The Orleton Farms mastodon: Ohio J. Sci., v. 52, p. 1-5

Williams, Stephen, 1957, The Island 35 mastodon; its bearing on the age of the Archaic cultures in the east: Amer. Antiq., v. 22, p. 359-372

Witthoft, J., 1952, A Paleo-Indian site in eastern Pennsylvania; an early hunting culture: Amer. Philos. Soc. Proc., v. 96, p. 464-495

Wittry, W. L., 1959, The Raddatz Rockshelter, Sk5, Wisconsin: Wisconsin Arch., v. 40, p. 33-69

Wormington, H. Marie, 1957, Ancient man in North America: Denver Mus. Nat. Hist., Pop. Ser., No. 4, 322 p.

Wright, H. T., 1964, A transitional Archaic campsite at Green Point (20 SA 1): Michigan Arch., v. 10, p. 17-22

Zumberge, J. H., and Potzger, J. E., 1956, Late Wisconsin chronology of the Lake Michigan basin correlated with pollen studies: Geol. Soc. Amer. Bull., v. 67, p. 271-288

SUMMARY

Prehistoric Indians first occupied the southern part of the Northeastern Woodland area between *ca.* 12,000 and 9000 B.C. With the gradual withdrawal of the Wisconsin ice, they slowly occupied the entire area. They were contemporaries of the late Pleistocene fauna, of a lowered sea level, of striking changes in the water level and drainage pattern of the Great Lakes, and of the slow changes in vegetation in the glaciated area. Their hunting and gathering gradually changed in detail as regional adaptations reflected changes in the environment and as new techniques and styles were developed or introduced.

Man's dependence on the available vegetal and animal foods compelled him to live in locations close to the water level in the Great Lakes area. The opportunity is thus provided for close correlations of successive prehistoric cultures with the dramatic changes in the Great Lakes during postglacial times. The reforestation of the Northeast and successive movement north of abundant food sources enabled the prehistoric Indians to increase numerically and to develop a more varied hunting-gathering economy.

The emphasis in this paper is on assessing the correlation and dating of successive pre-agricultural levels of Paleo-Indian and Archaic societies with geologic changes and with the changes in forest composition. Little or no attempt is made to characterize fully the cultural levels or to document the complex history of the cultural changes.

AN OUTLINE OF SOUTHEASTERN UNITED STATES PREHISTORY WITH PARTICULAR EMPHASIS ON THE PALEO-INDIAN ERA

STEPHEN WILLIAMS,[1] JAMES B. STOLTMAN[1]

INTRODUCTION

THE AREA to be covered in this chapter is that generally referred to as the Southeast; it includes the states (Fig. 1) south of the Ohio River and the first tier of states west of the lower Mississippi River. One might argue that such geographical division is arbitrary in the extreme, especially because state boundaries generally do not reflect important cultural or physiographic divisions. However, this is an area that is bounded on the north to a great extent by glaciated areas and on the east and south by the Atlantic Ocean and the Gulf of Mexico. The western boundary is that of the transition into the Great Plains area and is a sound physiographic line.

The temporal dimension encompasses the duration of man's occupation of this area. In all probability this segment of time exceeds 15,000 years, but no certain evidence of human habitation for such a long period of time has so far been discovered in this portion of the continent. For the purpose of this paper, the time span of human occupation has been divided into three eras (Fig. 2): a Paleo-Indian Era, beginning prior to 15,000 B.C. and lasting until 6500 B.C.; a Meso-Indian Era, from 6500 to 2000 B.C.; and a Neo-Indian Era, which extends from 2000 B.C. to the present. Because of the intent of this review, the majority of the discussion will be devoted to our knowledge of the Paleo-Indian Era within this area, and to the nature of the fluted-point tradition that spans this era. Only a brief mention of the archaeological events during the last two eras will be included.

STATUS OF KNOWLEDGE OF PALEO-INDIAN ERA

In dealing with the evidence of Early Man, we must first set forth the basic fact that the Southeast is not exceedingly rich in terms of excavated habitation sites or documented kill sites that have produced remains of Indian occupation in this earliest era. One can further state that in the entire area east of the Great Plains there has never been a single authenticated and well-documented find showing contemporaneity of Indians with now-extinct fauna. This fact is something of a paradox because, as will be shown, many artifacts point to substantial occupation of the area at a time when a now-extinct fauna was probably prevalent in the area. Explanation of this lack of association is not easy. Because many finds of megafauna found with man in the Great Plains have been recorded, one is tempted to invoke natural causes; that is, the kinds of erosion that have

exposed numerous finds in the Great Plains are not so operative in the more heavily forested East. Or one is tempted to suggest that the excavations of many of these Pleistocene faunas unfortunately have not been careful enough to reveal the often scanty evidences of man's associations with the extinct fauna.

No previous publications are devoted solely to the topic of Early Man in the Southeast. More general sources that cover this material in more or less detail are the works of Sellards (1952), Wormington (1957), Willey and Phillips (1958), Mason (1962), and Krieger (1964). Only Mason's article deals with artifact typology and site locations in any specific way, and his bibliography covers the majority of specific data utilized in this review.

PHYSIOGRAPHIC AND GEOLOGIC BACKGROUND

With regard to physiographic divisions, we have followed Fenneman (1938). That some of these provinces (Fig. 3) have significant correlation with archaeological manifestations during the Paleo-Indian Era will be detailed below. In a broad sense one can see five major physiographic divisions: (1) the Coastal Plain, (2) the Mississippi Alluvial Plain, (3) the Ozark Plateau and the contiguous Boston and Ouachita Mountains and the Arkansas Valley, (4) the Appalachian Mountains, with the Piedmont on the southeast and the Plateau on the west, and (5) the Interior Low Plateau Areas of Kentucky and Tennessee.

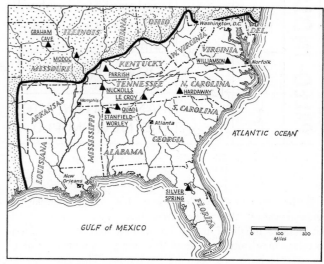

Figure 1. The southeastern United States as considered in this paper, with principal site locations.

[1] Peabody Museum, Harvard University, Cambridge, Massachusetts.

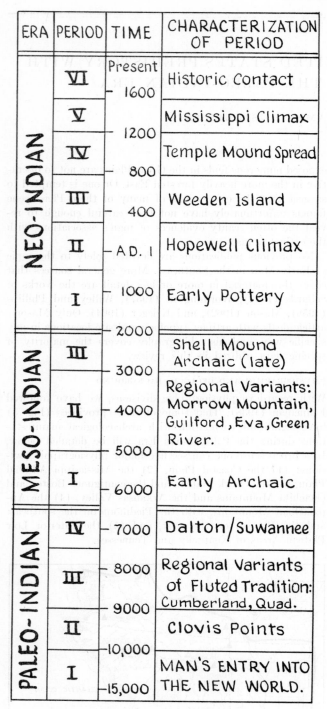

ERA	PERIOD	TIME	CHARACTERIZATION OF PERIOD
NEO-INDIAN	VI	Present — 1600	Historic Contact
NEO-INDIAN	V	— 1200	Mississippi Climax
NEO-INDIAN	IV	— 800	Temple Mound Spread
NEO-INDIAN	III	— 400	Weeden Island
NEO-INDIAN	II	— A.D. 1	Hopewell Climax
NEO-INDIAN	I	— 1000 — 2000	Early Pottery
MESO-INDIAN	III	— 3000	Shell Mound Archaic (late)
MESO-INDIAN	II	— 4000 — 5000	Regional Variants: Morrow Mountain, Guilford, Eva, Green River.
MESO-INDIAN	I	— 6000	Early Archaic
PALEO-INDIAN	IV	— 7000	Dalton/Suwannee
PALEO-INDIAN	III	— 8000 — 9000	Regional Variants of Fluted Tradition: Cumberland, Quad.
PALEO-INDIAN	II	— 10,000	Clovis Points
PALEO-INDIAN	I	— 15,000	MAN'S ENTRY INTO THE NEW WORLD.

Figure 2. The outline of the prehistory of the Southeast.

With regard to the geology as a whole, one can make the generalizations that this area has been rather stable throughout much of man's occupation and that attempts to relate man's occupation of this area to significant geological events have not been too numerous. The most significant work in this area has been with regard to various geological features and physiographic forms within the Lower Mississippi Valley (Gagliano, 1964a) and particu-

larly in peninsular Florida (Goggin, 1948; Rouse, 1952) where changes in sea level caused significant changes in conditions in both underground caves and wells. It would be useful to make a study of sites along some of the major rivers to see if there are some uniformities in stream regimens, especially on the edge of the Piedmont, thus following up the work of Coe (1964) in North Carolina and that of the National Park Service (Ingmanson, 1964) at Ocmulgee National Monument, Macon, Georgia.

Finds of Pleistocene fauna by paleontologists have been quite numerous in the Southeast (Hay, 1923). The majority of these finds have been in Florida, the Mississippi and Ohio Valleys, the Coastal Plain, particularly its eastern edge along the Atlantic shore, and the Ridge and Valley Province. Areas where there are notable absences of such finds are the Piedmont and the rugged western half of the state of Arkansas.

PALEO-INDIAN ERA

This discussion will limit itself to the Southeast. Recent papers by Mason (1962) and Krieger (1964) have dealt with this general time period on a broader scope, and the contiguous areas to the north and west are specifically covered by Griffin and Stephenson in this volume.

PERIOD I: EARLIEST EVIDENCE OF MAN

Period I (Fig. 2) includes man's entry into the New World from a time well before 15,000 B.C. until 10,000 B.C. There are no carbon-14 dates this old associated with archaeological locations anywhere in the Southeast. The only kind of evidence bearing on this period is that of possible association of man with extinct fauna. The major localities that have shown some archaeological merit but are still of uncertain age are (1) the bluffs in Natchez, Mississippi, where a human pelvis apparently associated with extinct fauna has been found (Quimby, 1956), (2) the Vero and Melbourne sites in peninsular Florida (Sellards, 1952, p. 90-94; Rouse, 1951, p. 151-165, 171-189), where human skeletal materials of considerable age have been found, but apparently not directly associated with extinct fauna, unless these forms persisted much later than the time period now under consideration, and (3) the site of the Island 35 mastodon (Williams, 1957) in the Lower Mississippi Valley. Sites of recent study are that at Petite Anse in Coastal Louisiana (Gagliano, 1964b) and several underwater sites in Florida, including Devils Den. It is logical to delineate this period, which, however, is unfortunately now devoid of data.

PERIOD II: CLOVIS POINTS

Points of the Clovis type have been found in great number throughout the Southeast, as will be detailed below. There is considerable range in size (Fig. 4). The points are dated only by analogy with the finds in the Great Plains and Southwest, where several carbon-14 dates center around 9000 B.C. (see Haynes, 1964, for a recent discussion of the age of the Clovis horizon). The typological relationships to the well-dated Arizona–New Mexico finds are so close that "the possibility of their independent origin in the

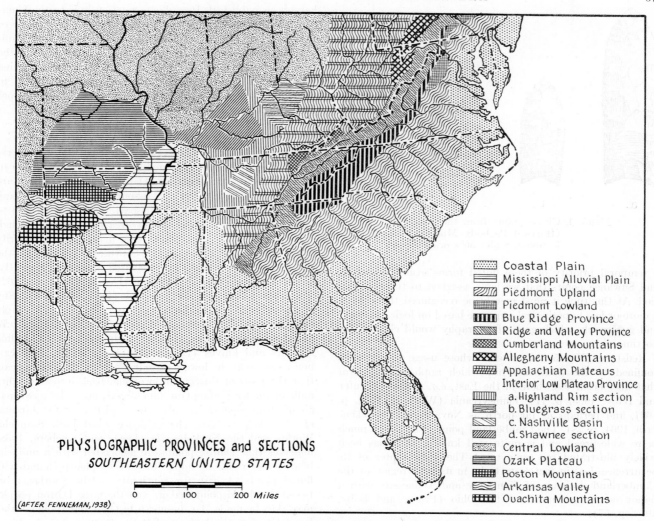

Figure 3. Physiographic provinces of the Southeast, after Fenneman, 1938.

East and in the West is so remote as to be ridiculous" (Mason, 1962, p. 234).

The Williamson site in Dinwiddie County, Virginia (Fig. 1), is one of the few giving an indication of the complex of traits accompanying these distinctive points. Its assemblage of small stone tools can be compared to those found with the Clovis points at the Bull Brook site in Ipswich, Massachusetts (Griffin, this volume). Beveled bone points, which resemble those from Blackwater, New Mexico, have been found at Itchtucknee Springs, Columbia County, Florida (Sellards, 1952, p. 127).

The Clovis points in the Southeast are geographically widespread. Their distinctive outline, well-defined fluting, and basal grinding make a clear typological group. Point size is at present a variable that is not completely understood. In both Massachusetts and Arizona, single-component sites seem to indicate that projectiles of very different lengths were contemporaneous. However, in some localities, such as on the eastern bluffs of the Lower Mississippi Valley, only small Clovis points are found, but whether this distinction is temporal or merely areal is not presently known.

PERIOD III: REGIONAL VARIATIONS OF FLUTED POINTS

It must be admitted that the typological homogeneity of the preceding period and the heterogeneity of the various fluted forms allocated to this post-Clovis period are much more functions of our typology than facts based on stratigraphic evidence. In point of fact, no such stratigraphy exists anywhere in the East, and our segmentation of these data is again based on analogy with Western finds, where the Clovis-Folsom sequence has been observed in the ground.

One can say with some certainty that classic Folsom points do not exist in the Southeast proper. They are, indeed, known only from northwest Louisiana, where they surely came into the area from the Plains. The other projectile points in the Southeast that apparently fall into the post-Clovis time period (Fig. 5) show considerable variations in shape, with only a general lanceolate form holding the group together. It is indeed tempting to set up an historical and genetic sequence of these forms with Redstone and Cumberland points, considered early, and Quad points, which are known both fluted and unfluted, considered as later. Some workers in Alabama have done just this, but the data are too few as yet to show definitely even

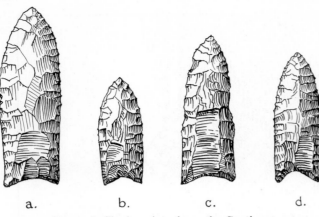

Figure 4. Clovis points from the Southeast (Harvard Peabody Museum Collections). Scale: 50% original size.

a temporal priority of these fluted forms over the Dalton and Suwanee points that we have assigned to the next period. At this time it must merely be recognized that this is a more or less hypothetical sequence based on logic, analogy, and guesswork, which good stratigraphy would clear up in no time.

Redstone (Fig. 5a) is a term whose usage is presently confined to the Southeast but which applies to a form that does occur elsewhere in the East, *e.g.* in Ohio (Prufer and Baby, 1963, p. 17), Pennsylvania (Witthoft, 1952, p. 469), and perhaps as far north as Nova Scotia (Stuckenrath, 1964, p. 28). The Cumberland point (Fig. 5b) is much more widespread and is quite well known, as it has been widely illustrated for some time. The main center of its occurrence does in fact seem to be in its type region of the Cumberland drainage of Kentucky and Tennessee, with a minor occurrence north of the Ohio (Prufer and Baby, 1963, p. 57).

The Quad point (Fig. 5c) occurs mainly in northern Alabama, Kentucky, and Tennessee and is considered to exist with and without flutes. Points of this type have been found stratigraphically early at Flint Creek Rock Shelter (Cambron and Waters, 1959, 1961) and possibly at the Hardaway site (Coe, 1964, p. 64), but no radiocarbon dates

have been published. Its stylistic relationships to the Cumberland point are obvious. One can easily follow the logic of these relationships and invest them with temporal significance as Prufer and Baby (1963, p. 63) have done in the area to the north, with "unfluted" lanceolate points being considered a very late form. There is certainly little to quarrel with in such an arrangement—and here again more dates will prove useful.

PERIOD IV: DALTON-SUWANEE POINTS

In contrast to the earlier periods, data and dates have recently been published that make this fourth period one of the soundest of the sequence. Dalton points (Fig. 5e) are named for Judge Dalton of Missouri, who collected many of these points from central Missouri. Their relationship to the Meserve points of the Plains area is obvious, although again these points were known for many years primarily from surface collections in the Southeast, whereas in the West they were found in excavated material. Recently, however, during work in Alabama (DeJarnette *et al.*, 1962) and in the Lower Mississippi Valley (Ford, in press), many of these points have been excavated from quite deeply buried strata. The Stanfield-Worley site (Fig. 1) has produced a definite Dalton complex with small tools including scrapers and knives (DeJarnette *et al.*, 1962). Radiocarbon dates from the lowest of four levels on the site indicate that the roots of this tradition extend back into the eighth millennium B.C.; abundant faunal remains were recovered, all of them modern, mainly white-tailed deer (DeJarnette *et al.*, 1962, p. 85). The evidence from both Stanfield-Worley and the Nuckolls site (Lewis and Kneberg, 1958) indicates that Dalton points are associated with a unifacial blade-flake tradition similar to that frequently found with fluted points. A case for continuity in the Southeast between the fluted-point makers and the later Dalton peoples may thus be made. To the north in Ohio and Indiana other lanceolate forms (Prufer and Baby, 1963) called the Plano Complex apparently fill the post-fluted-point time period there, but Dalton points are well known to the northwest in southern Illinois and Missouri, and to the west, where they merge with the form called Meserve. Their major concentration is in the central part of the Southeast, with near absence of the form in the eastern Atlantic Coastal Plain.

In the south, particularly in peninsular Florida, there are what appear to be contemporary and perhaps related projectile points called Suwanee (Fig. 5d). These points as presently described (Bullen, 1962) include forms that are slightly fluted as well as others that definitely grade toward the standard Dalton form. Some of this gradation may be a result of the typing of this projectile point, but it must be noted that within the Dalton class itself at least three varieties have already been set up, namely Nuckolls, Greenbrier, and Hardaway (DeJarnette *et al.*, 1962), so that considerable variation is to be found in what is now broadly called "Dalton."

Despite the problem of widespread distribution without too fine a typological breakdown in all that has been called Dalton, it is impressive to note the broad distribution of a single form or group of closely related forms over a large

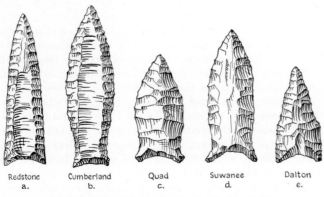

Figure 5. Redstone, Cumberland, Quad, Suwanee, Dalton points, after various sources. Scale: 35% original size.

geographic area, which includes Graham Cave in Missouri and Modoc Rock Shelter in Illinois (Fig. 1), where Dalton points are found in deep stratigraphic position with radiocarbon dates before 7000 B.C. Griffin has recently discussed the problems of dealing with these dates (1964, p. 228).

Within the Southeast itself, Hardaway Dalton is the earliest well-defined point type on the Carolina Piedmont (Coe, 1964, p. 64-67). A similar situation apparently obtains at Russell Cave in northern Alabama and in the Ocmulgee Bottoms at Macon, Georgia. Within the Lower Mississippi Valley, all varieties of Dalton point are found in considerable numbers on many of the older land surfaces within the Alluvial Valley itself (Ford, in press). A similar situation is known from the Cache River valley in southernmost Illinois at the head of the valley (Howard Winters, personal communication).

From these data, it is quite apparent that we are dealing with a broad-gauged horizon marker that apparently marks the end of the fluted-point tradition. It seems to serve as a breaking point in the general continuity of the technical tradition that began in Clovis times. That this break in tradition seems to come at a time that generally correlates with the beginning of what is called the Hypsithermal may not be sheer coincidence.

THE FLUTED-POINT TRADITION

The fluted projectile point is generally accepted as a type fossil of the Paleo-Indian Era throughout most of North America. Indeed, in some usages Paleo-Indian and fluted point are employed interchangeably. Worldwide attention was first focused on these distinctive points between 1926 and 1928 when they were found near Folsom, New Mexico, in direct association with extinct bison (Wormington, 1957, p. 23).

In eastern North America fluted points were known to collectors well before this time, but their significance was not then realized. For example, Thruston (1890, p. 232) pictures a definite Cumberland fluted point from Tennessee, which he terms "a specialty of Maury county." The point is discussed in a context of other very sophisticated chipped flints that we now recognize as dating to Period V of the Neo-Indian Era, yet Thruston states, "No finer flint forms are to be found in the Mississippi Valley" (1890, p. 231). Another early picture of a fluted point appears in Holmes (1897, Pl. 32b) where it is included in a context of "cache forms" (blanks) and "rejects" recovered from the Potomac–Chesapeake Bay region. In 1935 Bushnell announced the discovery of two fluted points in Virginia, calling them "Folsom" in recognition of their similarity to the western points. Since this time, a steadily mounting inventory of finds has accumulated in both East and West, and a considerable variety has been recognized within the fluted-point tradition in the East (Figs. 4 and 5).

It is our feeling that in the eastern United States fluted points are the product of a single technological tradition, and with present data they are best discussed within such a framework. The great complexity of this artifact type, its physical homogeneity over a vast area, and its continuous geographic distribution all argue for a radiation from a single source. At the base of this technological tradition, we would place the Clovis points.

After wide dispersal throughout the Southeast, the Clovis horizon may have provided a foundation from which a number of regional variations developed, namely Cumberland, Redstone, Quad, and Suwanee. Whether these suggested post-Clovis forms should be arranged in a single lineal sequence or in four parallel lines is not known at present. What does seem certain is that all partake of the same technological tradition.

At what time this tradition arrived, or developed, in the Southeast is still a matter of conjecture. Some say that the tradition extended into Archaic times (our Meso-Indian Era) in western Kentucky (Thompson, 1954) and that it persisted as late as Early Woodland times (our Neo-Indian Era) in eastern Tennessee (Lewis and Kneberg, 1957, p. 20). In Louisiana the San Patrice point, placed in a late-Archaic horizon by Webb (1946, p. 15), may also be a terminal product of the fluted-point tradition.

The culture of the peoples of the Paleo-Indian Era was certainly characterized by much more than a single technological tradition in stone working. In fact, there may very well have been people living at this time who did not share in this tradition at all; this is certainly true of the latest periods of the Paleo-Indian Era. Unfortunately, however, relatively little data exist about other aspects of these earliest Southeastern cultures.

A number of factors contribute to the paucity of knowledge about the cultures of the Paleo-Indian Era. First, the majority of fluted points occur as isolated surface finds, thus giving no information about the cultural matrix from which they were derived. Second, most Southeastern sites that have produced fluted points are shallow and multicomponent, so that stratigraphically defined or geographically isolated pure Paleo-Indian *assemblages* are very rare indeed.

The Williamson site of Virginia is one of the best candidates in the Southeast for a pure, single-component Paleo-Indian site. McCary (1951, 1954) provides two of the very few quantified descriptions of a Paleo-Indian assemblage in his reports on this important site. In the assemblage is included a great variety of tools, such as snub-nosed scrapers, side scrapers, gravers, spoke-shave scrapers, and knives, all of which, if examined as rigorously as fluted points, would no doubt prove to be equally diagnostic of the Paleo-Indian Era.

More important than these various tool *forms*, however, is the basic blank upon which most are made, for this reflects a second technological tradition, which appears also to be largely a product of the Paleo-Indian Era. The flake-blade-core elements of this technological tradition have not yet been adequately studied, but the characteristic unifacial tools that are produced are so rarely found in the later Archaic assemblages for which we have good information that they seem safely datable to the Paleo-Indian Era.

In discussing the distribution pattern of the peoples of the Paleo-Indian Era we should prefer to deal with tool assemblages rather than specific artifact types. Unfortunately, very little is published on the distribution of the unifacial blade-flake tradition, so the analysis must be limited to the fluted-point tradition. The ensuing discussion of the geographic distribution of the fluted-point tradition applies *only* to that tradition; no claim is made that all people who lived during the Paleo-Indian Era are thereby included.

The way of life of the fluted-point makers of the Paleo-Indian Era is generally accepted as being that of roving, big-game hunters. As in so many other instances in the Southeast, the evidence for this assertion is all secondary, for no well-authenticated association with extinct fauna is presently known, as was pointed out above. We feel, however, that the discovery of such an association is only a matter of time and more concerted effort. Sooner or later, one of the mounting number of not-quite-provable finds (Williams, 1957; Neil, 1964) will materialize into a fully authenticated association of man and extinct fauna. Other indirect evidence suggesting a mobile, hunting life-way include the complete lack of intensive occupation sites and the very wide dispersal of fluted points. To these may be added a third, the marked correspondence between the geographic range of fluted points and of mastodon, mammoth, and extinct bison, as will be discussed in more detail later.

DISTRIBUTION OF FLUTED POINTS

Fluted points have been found in each of the thirteen Southeastern states discussed in this paper. Moreover, with the exception of the Blue Ridge, Ouachita Mountains, and Ozark Plateaus, these points are well represented in every major physiographic province in the area. In all (not counting Suwanee, Candy Creek, and San Patrice types) 1,142 fluted points from the Southeast have been recorded in this study. In terms of conventional typologies, the vast majority of these fall into the Clovis, Cumberland, or Redstone categories, or variants thereof. With the exception of the Northeast, centering around Ohio, this constitutes the greatest concentration of fluted points presently known in North America.

Like a giant blanket draped over the Southeast, the distribution pattern of fluted points extends into nearly every corner of the area; yet in many places the fabric is threadbare (*e.g.*, the East Gulf Coastal Plain and the Cumberland Plateau), while in others it is marred by gaping holes (*e.g.*, the Mississippi Alluvial Valley and South Florida). Any discussion of the pattern of fluted-point distribution in the Southeast, it is felt, must take into consideration these three basic features: (1) wide geographic range, (2) overall absolute intensity, and (3) internal unevenness.

GEOGRAPHIC RANGE

As already indicated, it is generally held that the makers of Clovis fluted points were big-game hunters and the earliest occupants of the Southeast. Mason (1962, p. 245) has suggested that the widespread distribution of Clovis points reflects just this situation, not only in the Southeast but over most of North America. That is, if a group of hunting peoples is introduced into a country rich in migratory big game, but largely devoid of human occupants, a logical result would be a wide dispersal of the big-game-hunting tradition. No massive migration of peoples need be postu-

lated but only a gradual filling up of the country in response to the *natural* processes that can reasonably be inferred to have been operative, *e.g.* (1) roving game would naturally attract mobile huntsmen into new territories; (2) lack of resistance by prior human occupants would faciliate expansion; (3) normal population growth under favorable conditions would lead to geographic expansion; (4) pressures from the West as more and more people arrived from Asia could create a push toward the East.

OVERALL PATTERN INTENSITY

The large concentration of fluted points in the Southeast would seem to reflect either a long period of Paleo-Indian occupation, a large population, or a combination of both factors. There is presently available no direct evidence bearing on this problem, but some indirect evidence may be cited.

On typological grounds eastern Clovis points are commonly ascribed to the same time horizon as the well-dated classic Clovis forms of Arizona and New Mexico. In fact, employing the age-area hypothesis, Mason (1962, p. 235) has proposed that the intensity and diversity of fluted-point styles suggests the southeastern United States "as a possible 'homeland' of the Clovis complex."

Wherever the homeland of the fluted-point tradition, typological evidence does suggest at least a terminal Pleistocene age for the Southeastern Clovis horizon. Radiocarbon dates from Russell Cave (8,160 ± 300 years, Miller, 1956, p. 542) and from the Stanfield-Worley Bluff Shelter (9,640 ± 450 years, M-1152, and 8,920 ± 400 years, M-1153, DeJarnette *et al.*, 1962, p. 85-87) date archaeological assemblages that, on typological grounds, are generally accepted as postdating most of the Southeastern fluted-point tradition.

On the other end of the time scale, much evidence suggests the persistence into recent times of many elements of the megafauna upon which the early Paleo-Indian presumably preyed (Martin, 1958; Hester, 1960). Florida, especially, is commonly cited as the last outpost of the giant Pleistocene herbivores (Martin, 1958, p. 405). Although Bullen (1963) has recently challenged the carbon-14 dating of the Seminole Field bed (2,040 ± 90 years, L-211) on the basis of disturbances produced by tidal stream action, Martin's position still receives considerable support from the datings of the Melbourne fauna. Rouse (1951 and 1952), on the basis of eustatic changes in sea level, has assigned a postglacial age to the Melbourne interval; specifically, he argues for an extinction of the Melbourne megafauna about 4000 B.C. (1952, p. 296-297).

Florida thus provides an interesting case of convergence of the faunal evidence and the line of inference frequently employed by the archaeologist, that of typology. Suwanee points, a heterogeneous category of lanceolate points with fluting "extremely rare" (Bullen, 1962, p. 87), are the oldest types presently known in Florida. Their placement relative to other Florida assemblages rests on good stratigraphic evidence (Neil, 1958; Bullen, 1958). On typological grounds they show Clovis affinities (Bullen, 1958, p. 16; Mason, 1962, p. 239). It is perhaps no coincidence that projectile points that fall typologically at the most recent end of the fluted-point tradition occur in one of the last, if not the last, refuge of the North American megafauna.

It would appear, then, that the meager evidence at our disposal favors an interpretation that attributes the overall intensity of Southeastern fluted points, in large part, to the long time interval of the Paleo-Indian Era beginning sometime before 10,000 B.C. and persisting in some marginal areas until perhaps 6000 B.C.

INTERNAL PATTERN DIVERSITY

In order to study the regional patterning of the Paleo-Indian occupation of the Southeast, we first surveyed the literature for all published accounts of fluted, Suwanee, and Dalton points. The bulk of the data was tabulated from the various state archaeological journals (see Mason, 1962, for detailed bibliography). From these, and from any other sources that could be found, the location of each point was plotted according to county. We elected to work at the county level because more than 95% of the published points could be incorporated into our study without too great a sacrifice of analytical precision. A second important source of information has been our colleagues, especially those in attendance at the Twentieth Southeastern Archaeological Conference, who have generously provided much additional data on many unpublished finds.

Before discussing these data further, we must point up some important limitations that are inherent in this approach. The aggregate of fluted points about which we now have information can be regarded only as a *sample* of a larger population that includes all the Southeastern fluted points that have ever been made. How representative this sample is of the population from which it is drawn cannot be said, but we are operating under the hypothesis that the sample fairly approximates the distribution pattern of the larger population. Future work may very well fill in many gaps in the present sample, thus necessitating a revision of this hypothesis. One area in particular, the Mississippi Alluvial Valley, constitutes a notable hiatus in the distribution

map. The absence of fluted points here is probably related to rapid recent alluviation that has covered most of the surfaces available for occupation by Paleo-Indians, *e.g.* McFarlan (1961, p. 137) records a carbon-14 date of 5,600 years on recent alluvium about 30 miles south of Baton Rouge from a depth of 23 ft.

Table 1 presents a state-by-state tabulation of the 1,142 fluted points, with an added breakdown into major physiographic provinces (see Fig. 3) as defined by Fenneman (1938). The physiographic province of every county containing a fluted point was determined from state geologic maps. Where counties straddled two physiographic provinces, an attempt was made to ascertain which province contained the points. In many cases the geographic location of the finds was not recorded precisely enough to resolve such problems; in these instances the points are recorded in a separate column in Table 1 indicating the possibility of their being from either of two provinces. A hunch that the fall line might somehow have been an attractive zone for big-game hunters accounts for a failure to separate fall-line county points into specific provinces.

Sixty-one Suwanee points from Florida are recorded separately. Candy Creek and San Patrice points of Archaic or even ceramic contexts, some of which are fluted, have not been included in the sample. The fluted points thus tabulated generally fall into Clovis, Cumberland, or Redstone types, but no attempt was made to differentiate them into such types. It might be added here that a carefully constructed typology, giving due consideration to the permissible range of variation subsumed under any type name, remains to be established, not only for the Southeast, but also for the East as a whole.

Because an analysis by state of the distribution of fluted points would be no less arbitrary than the boundaries that separate them, a more natural framework of analysis was sought. It is felt that the major physiographic provinces, along with the major river systems, provide such a natural frame of reference. From Table 1 it is apparent that the

TABLE 1

Fluted-Point Distribution by Physiographic Provinces

State	1. Interior Low Plateau	2. Appalachian Plateaus	3. Ridge and Valley	4. Blue Ridge	5. Piedmont	5/6. Fall Zone	6. Coastal Plain	Points from counties straddling two provinces						Totals
								1/2	2/3	3/4	4/5	1/6	?	
Ala.	81	17			1	11		31					4	7	152
Ark.							1							1
Del.							11							11
Fla.							[61]							[61]
Ga.					8		20							28
Ky.	163	1					7	2					5	178
La.							18							18
Md.					4									4
Miss.							2							2
N. C.			2		65		3							70
S. C.					4	5	9							18
Tenn.	164	3	44	2			19	3	8	5		38		286
Va.		1	22		127	118	40				22		2	332
W. Va.		37	3							1			1	42
Totals	408	59	69	4	209	134	130	36	9	5	22	42	15	1,142

Interior Low Plateau, with 36% of the recorded fluted points, contains the greatest concentration in the Southeast.

The Piedmont has the next highest concentration of fluted points, nearly twice as many as the Coastal Plain. The Fall Zone does seem to have a significant concentration of points, but this is really true only in Virginia. More information from the Carolinas and Georgia is desirable before the significance of this can be properly evaluated.

We have recorded only four fluted points from the Blue Ridge province, but this is not too surprising considering the ruggedness of the terrain. The Appalachian Plateaus, too, reveal a great paucity of Paleo-Indian materials. Considering the massive area of the Appalachian Plateaus, the number of recorded fluted points (59, or 5%) seems all the smaller.

Within the Appalachian Plateaus Province the distribution pattern of fluted points was seen to follow rather closely the major river systems. In West Virginia, of 37 points found in the province, 33 came from counties that contact either the Ohio or Kanawha Rivers. Thirteen of the 17 Appalachian Plateau fluted points of Alabama came from two counties that are bisected by the Tennessee River. Two of the three Tennessee points were found in the Sequatchia valley.

Such a distribution seemed to us to be far from random, so we reviewed our data on the other physiographic provinces to see if there were any correlations elsewhere between fluted-point distributions and major river systems. The results of this survey are recorded in Table 2.

Louisiana is not entered in the table because the provenience data on the 18 published points do not permit quantification by counties. According to Webb (1948, p. 230), the 18 fluted points are distributed among eight parishes, seven of which are located in northwestern Louisiana on or very near the Red River. Additional finds of fluted points, bringing the Lousiana total to at least 40, conform to this same pattern, occurring primarily in northwestern and central Louisiana (Gagliano and Webb, personal communication).

Attention has frequently been drawn to the common association of Suwanee points with rivers and springs, especially in the central Florida region (Simpson, 1948, p. 13; Neil, 1964, p. 19). According to our county tally, 53 of 61 Suwanee points come from the central Florida region (as defined by Goggin, 1947), and 43 of these 53 were found in counties that lie on the Suwanee or Sante Fe Rivers.

Table 2 shows more than a casual relationship between the distribution of fluted points in the Southeast and the major drainage systems of the area. No claim is made that *all* fluted points in the table come directly from the various river valleys, although this is in fact the case in the majority of instances where precise provenience data are available. Indeed, the Williamson site, the most productive single Paleo-Indian locality in the Southeast, occurs in a county (Dinwiddie) that borders on neither the James nor Roanoke Rivers, although it does lie between these two major rivers and thus is in the same general drainage system. The high but by no means exclusive concentration of fluted points in areas bordering the major river systems thus suggests that large river valleys provided the main arteries of communication during the Paleo-Indian Era.

The concentration of fluted points along major riverways and water courses has important theoretical implications regarding the vicissitude of the fluted-point tradition. Because major Archaic, Woodland, and Mississippi sites tend also to cluster along many of the very same river valleys,

TABLE 2

Fluted Point Distribution by Drainage Systems

Rivers	N. C.	Ky.	Ga.	S. C.	Va.	Tenn.	Ala.	W. Va.	Del.	Md.	Totals
Roanoke	65				123						188
James					43						43
Counties between James & Roanoke					124						124
Savannah		10		4							14
Santee-Wateree				10							10
Shenandoah					8			2			10
Tennessee		2				126	125				253
Duck						29					29
Cumberland		18				67					85
Alabama							11				11
Ohio		18						26			44
Kanawha								7			7
Susquehanna									11		11
Delaware										4	4
Green-Barren		58									58
Kentucky		24									24
Licking		34									34
Mississippi		4				2					6
Totals	65/70[a]	158/178	10/28	14/18	298/332	224/286	136/152	35/42	11/11	4/4	953/1,121
	92.9%[b]	88.8%	35.7%	77.8%	89.8%	78.3%	89.5%	83.3%	100%	100%	85.0%

[a] Numerator: fluted points in each state found in counties bordering rivers listed. Denominator: total fluted points recorded from each state.

[b] Percentage of total fluted points from each state found in counties bordering listed rivers.

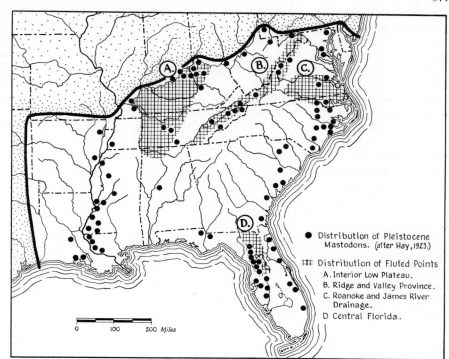

Figure 6. Distribution of mastodons and fluted points.

and because most sites lack enough cultural accumulation to give well-defined stratigraphic assemblages, the probability of fluted points occurring in shallow sites mixed with late materials is extremely high. More often than not fluted points are found with no other artifacts, and more often than not fluted points turn up in or near river valleys. In view of these two facts, one fluted point (or even more) occurring in an otherwise Archaic (or later) assemblage *could* very well be intrusive from an earlier time period. This does not mean that one cannot visualize continuity between the fluted-point tradition and later Archaic cultures. However, extreme caution must be exercised before fluted points are accepted as part of an Archaic assemblage in many of the shallow, multi-component sites that dot the Southeast.

One other aspect of the relationship between fluted points and river valleys bears mention. In Virginia, as Table 2 points out, 290 of the 332 fluted points occur in counties along or between the James and Roanoke Rivers. These are the only two rivers south of the Potomac that penetrate the Blue Ridge, thus gaining access to the Ridge and Valley province. The supposition that these two arteries were part of a major link between the Interior Low Plateau and coastal Virginia is given support by the nearly continuous distribution of fluted points along the Great Valley from northwestern Virginia to Chattanooga.

It is our thesis that the distribution pattern of fluted points in the Southeast becomes intelligible under the hypothesis that during the Paleo-Indian Era fluted-point makers roved the countryside in pursuit of big game, primarily the mastodon. If the hypothesis is valid, the geographic range of mastodon could be expected to coincide with that of fluted points. Figure 6 records the distribution of mastodon-producing localities in the Southeast and also the areas of major concentration of fluted points. Other elements

of the Late Pleistocene megafauna (principally mammoth and bison) duplicate almost exactly the distribution of mastodon in the Southeast, except that the pattern of the latter is more widespread and intense (*cf.* Hay, 1923, p. 415). Hence we can, without any appreciable distortion, include mammoth and bison in our discussion of the mastodon. According to Hibbard (1958, p. 20), all mastodon beds that are well dated should be no older than the Wisconsin glaciation, and they could be as recent as 6000-4000 B.C. (Hester, 1960; Williams, 1957). That is, we have every reason to suspect that the mastodons and fluted points plotted in Figure 6 coexisted at least partly temporally as well as geographically. This correlation between mastodon and fluted-point time and geographic range has been noted elsewhere in the East by Quimby in Michigan (1960, p. 31) and by Prufer in Ohio (personal communication).

The four areas of fluted-point concentration outlined in Figure 6, although clearly not of equal size, are more or less well-delimited natural areas that encompass more than 73% of the fluted and Suwanee points in our sample (882 of 1,203). By area the breakdown of fluted points is as follows: area A contains 408, area B has 69, area C has 352, and area D has 53 (Suwanee). In three of these four areas a very high concentration of mastodon fossils is apparent. Two other areas rich in mastodon remains, however, are notably poor in fluted points, namely, the Lower Mississippi Valley and the North Carolina Fall Zone. Our sentiments about the Mississippi Alluvial Valley have already been expressed. The paucity of fluted points in North Carolina, we feel, reflects more the status of our knowledge than the real situation. When we realize that 65 of the 70 North Carolina fluted points in our sample come from a single collection from a single county on the Virginia border (McCary, 1948), it is apparent that we know as yet very little about the fluted-point tradition in North Carolina. An interesting fact has been brought to our attention by Joffre Coe (personal communication), whose impression from the North Carolina materials is that most Clovis points in that state occur on the coastal plain, but inland from the tidewater—precisely where the general concentration of mastodon remains is found.

Considering the fragmentary nature of both the archaeological and the faunal records, there seems to be an overall pattern correspondence between the distribution of fluted points and mastodons in the Southeast. Such evidence can hardly be considered compelling, but we cite it here because it is consistent with the other lines of indirect evidence upon which we are presently so heavily dependent in our attempts to understand something about the people of the Paleo-Indian Era.

The sparse representation of the fluted-point tradition in the Appalachian plateaus province is perhaps a reflection of the unsuitability of this region for the large herbivores upon which these Paleo-Indians preyed. According to Braun (1950, p. 39-40), this province is blanketed by the Mixed Mesophytic Forest, "a climax association in which dominance is shared by a number of species." Moreover, she considers it "the most complex and the oldest association of the Deciduous Forest Formation" (1950, p. 39), "the lineal descendant of the mixed Tertiary forest" (1950, p. 256). Not all paleoecologists (e.g. Deevey, 1949; Martin, 1958) are in accord with Braun's conception of such forest stability and continuity throughout the Pleistocene. Martin (1958, p. 389), however, feels that the modern distribution of major vegetation zones in the eastern United States was attained prior to the onset of the Hypsithermal about 7500 B.C. How far back into the Pleistocene the present heterogeneity of the Mixed Deciduous Forest can be pushed we do not know. Botanists themselves seem to disagree on this point. But, what does seem generally accepted is the fact that a heterogeneous forest did occupy the Appalachian plateaus province by the closing stages of the Paleo-Indian Era and it *could* date back to the era's very inception.

An area with a heterogeneous forest composition, with individual tree species widely dispersed, could not provide a concentrated enough food supply to support large numbers of herbivores. Perhaps it is for this reason that only rare traces of presumably browsing animals like the mastodon exist, along with their main predator, the Paleo-Indian. A similar situation no doubt prevailed during the Meso-Indian Era, when man himself apparently turned to a more herbivorous existence. The wide dispersal of potential food-providing trees (oak, hickory, walnut, and chestnut in the case of man) must have been as unattractive to man of the Meso-Indian Era as it had been for mastodons earlier. It is not until the Neo-Indian Era and the introduction of agriculture that we get any really intensive occupation of the Appalachian plateau province.

DISTRIBUTION OF DALTON AND OTHER NON-FLUTED POINTS

There are far fewer data on the Dalton tradition. Its geographic distribution is much more circumscribed than that of the fluted-point tradition, but this perhaps partly reflects the nature of the data. Dalton points have not captured so much attention as have fluted points, so that there is considerably less published material on them. Generally speaking, the Dalton tradition is restricted in the East to areas south of the Ohio River. With the publication of the radiocarbon dates from Stanfield-Worley, the earlier belief that Dalton points represent a late-Paleo-Indian tradition in the Southeast that roughly parallels the Plano tradition of the Great Lakes Basin seems substantiated.

Prufer and Baby (1963, p. 22) report three Dalton points from Ohio. At least two Dalton-like points have been reported from southern Virginia, and Bullen (personal communication) now feels that some Florida points, formerly classed as Suwanees, belong in the Dalton category. However, the only really quantitative information on Dalton points presently comes from Alabama, Kentucky, and Tennessee.

It is difficult to assess the reliability of the obviously incomplete information on the Dalton tradition, but some interesting contrasts with the fluted-point tradition do emerge. Of the 253 Alabama Dalton points on record, all were found in counties bordering on the Tennessee River. This same pattern carries northward into western Tennessee, where 89 of the 95 Dalton points in the sample come from Tennessee River counties. The interesting aspect of the Tennessee pattern is that *not one* Dalton point has been reported from the Interior Low Plateau, except where it is adjacent to the Tennessee River. In Kentucky, 19 of 39 Dalton points (49%) reported by Rolingson (1964, p. 42) come from the Western Coalfield (Shawnee section of Fenneman) while only 5 of 39 (13%) have been reported in the Bluegrass section. This is in contrast to the combined distribution of Clovis and Cumberland points, which shows 36% (64 of 178) in the Bluegrass section and only 14% (26 of 178) within the Western Coalfield.

Besides a general contraction in areal distribution of the Dalton tradition compared to the earlier fluted point traditions, available evidence suggests an increasing Dalton concentration into the Tennessee Valley of northwestern Alabama and western Tennessee and into the Green River basin of western Kentucky. Since it is in exactly these three areas that we later find the classic expression of the Shell Mound Archaic culture, we offer as a working hypothesis that the Dalton distribution pattern reflects the onset of a new economic adjustment. With the depletion of the herds of big game animals, new sources of food were sought, or more likely, old supplementary subsistence patterns were intensified in favorable localities. As a result, the Dalton peoples laid the foundations for the subsistence pattern we are to recognize later as "Archaic" in northern Alabama and western Tennessee and Kentucky. Needless to say, in the absence of comparative studies of Dalton and Shell Mound Archaic assemblages, we would not wish to push the implications of geographic continuity too far.

Mention should also be made here of various nonfluted lanceolate forms, e.g. unfluted Clovis and unfluted Cumberland (Beaver Lake). There are very little data on these, and, once again, they are confined to Alabama, Kentucky, and Tennessee. In Alabama all 69 lanceolate points (this includes 42 of the Quad type) were found in counties adjacent to the Tennessee River. The 41 lanceolate points from Tennessee conform more closely to the distribution pattern of the fluted-point tradition, 10 of the 41 occurring in the Interior Low Plateau in counties not bordering the Tennessee River. The distribution of 47 Quad points in Kentucky closely parallels that of Clovis and Cumberland fluted points, but 20 other lanceolate points are confined mainly to northern and northwestern Kentucky, suggesting possible ties with the Plano tradition of the Great Lakes region (Rolingson, 1964, p. 30, 48).

With the exception of some of the northern Kentucky points, there is not much evidence to suggest that these lanceolate forms are in any way related to the Plano tradition. It is even uncertain whether or not they constitute a separate horizon in Southeastern culture history. Lewis and Kneberg (1954), viewing the Tennessee data, have suggested that at least some of these points are unfluted simply because they were too thin.

Meso-Indian Era (6500-2000 b.c.)

Varied criteria suggest a convenient, albeit somewhat arbitrary, line between the Paleo- and Meso-Indian Eras at approximately 6500 b.c. These data include the fact that most of the megafauna are gone by this time, and the warmer Hypsithermal climate period is now well established. Archaeologically, the era seems to be marked by the end of the last remnants of the fluted-point tradition with Dalton and Suwanee forms. The usage herein places a significant break later than some recent writers; *e.g.* Krieger (1964, p. 33) starts his continental "Protoarchaic" at 8000 b.c., and Griffin (1964, p. 224) begins his Northeastern Archaic at the same time. Their criteria for period separation are slightly different from those used here. Rouse (1964, p. 393) begins his "Meso-Indian Era" in the Caribbean area 1,500 years later at 5000 b.c. It is apparent, nonetheless, that a significant change does take place that is characterized by a new life-way and new artifact forms.

As a whole, the Meso-Indian Era can be characterized as one in which positive evidence on the varied nature of artifact assemblages and primitive economies abounds, in contrast to the slim stone-tool complexes of the Paleo-Indian, where only reasonably intelligent guesses can be made as to life-ways. In fact, the data from the southeastern United States provides the archaeologist with some of the richest information on this time period anywhere in the New World. The well-known Mayan and Incaic areas, for example, are virtually a blank for this long time interval.

During this era the basic economic patterns included hunting, fishing, and gathering. Hunting exploited the significant quantities of white-tailed deer and emphasized the riverine environment wherever possible, utilizing fish and freshwater shellfish. Gathering focused on the nuts of the hardwood forests. None of these was a new pursuit, to be sure, although the evidence for any of these activities is admittedly exceedingly rare, if not totally absent, for the preceding Paleo-Indian Era. Cultural changes did take place, however, enabling the peoples of the Meso-Indian

Era to live a much more sedentary existence. Caldwell (1958, p. 6; 1962, p. 288) has focused attention on these economic developments, terming this exploitation of the eastern woodlands "Primary Forest Efficiency."

In artifact forms, stemmed and side-notched projectile points apparently made their first appearances. Positive evidence for the atlatl or spear thrower is noted midway through the era, and ground stone axes and pestles come into the sequence about the same time. The number and variety of bone and antler artifacts exceeds that of the following Neo-Indian Era, but ornaments and art forms are quite rare, consisting mainly of stone beads and simple engraved designs.

PERIOD I: EARLY ARCHAIC

This period is still difficult to separate from the Dalton period, but that such a separation can be made seems apparent at the falls of the Yadkin River in North Carolina where Coe (1964) has outlined the first well-developed stratigraphic sequence of this time period in the East. From Coe's data it seems clear that projectile-point forms changed rather markedly from one archaeological phase to another. Thus some of the Archaic assemblages with a variety of vastly different projectile-point forms, published in the older literature, can be seen as representing post-depositional mixing—not an historical event wherein the Indian had a variety of points from which to choose.

At the bottom of the sequence Hardaway Dalton points are found. The details of the sequence (Kirk and Stanley points) cannot be described in such a brief review, but it is apparent that other areas, such as northern Alabama, reflect the same situation, although the stratigraphy is not so neatly separated. At the Stanfield-Worley site (DeJarnette *et al.*, 1962), side-notched Big Sandy points are found in the lowest Dalton level, but some very recent evidence suggests that these two complexes have been found areally segregated (D. L. DeJarnette, personal communication). Other data that may fit into this period could be W. S. Webb's Early Shell Mound Archaic of the Tennessee Valley (Webb and DeJarnette, 1948).

PERIOD II: REGIONAL VARIATIONS

This period includes the best-known Southeastern Archaic cultures, such as the Eva phase in Tennessee (Lewis and Kneberg, 1961), the Green River phase in Kentucky (Willey and Phillips, 1958, p. 115), and the mid-section of Coe's (1964) Yadkin River sequence in North Carolina. There are abundant data here on what has often been termed the "Shell Mound" Archaic, and indeed considerable emphasis certainly was placed on the utilization of freshwater mussels, although deer were always a substantial part of the diet. The characteristic artifacts include large-stemmed projectile points, ground-stone atlatl weights, and an assortment of bone tools including awls, needles, and fishhooks.

PERIOD III: LATE SHELL-MOUND ARCHAIC

In the Savannah River Valley and on the adjacent Georgia Coast, abundant evidence of this last period of the era is to be found. Both here and in northern Florida these late "pre-ceramic" cultures serve as a foundation for the early ceramic cultures that follow. Sites such as Stallings Island (Claflin, 1931) in Georgia indicate a smooth transition, as pottery is added to such Archaic cultures that have counterparts in much of the Southeast. The enigmatic Poverty Point culture (Ford and Webb, 1956) of Louisiana, with its large earthen ceremonial structures, dates from this period as well and indicates the continuation of artifact forms from earlier times along with elaboration of techniques in ground stone.

Neo-Indian Era (2000 b.c. to the Present)

There seems to be no segmentation of the archaeological time scale that does not bring forth argument. Although the division used here roughly matches that of the Late Archaic–Early Woodland transition as utilized by Griffin (1946, 1952, 1964) and others, most of these authors have insisted that the addition of pottery to the well-established cultures of the preceding era made little or no difference to the way of life. If one could suggest that agriculture was also added at this time, the force of this line of argument would be altered. However, the data presently available seem to indicate that agricultural plants became a significant addition to Southeastern cultures only about the first century a.d. Caldwell (1958) would argue for an even later date for *significant* crop utilization.

Although it is the shortest era of all, the Neo-Indian Era is also the most finely divided. Here we have at work a principle that holds true in geology as well, for we are able to segment the latest time period, the Pleistocene, with a considerable degree of refinement despite many differences of opinion. So too in archaeology the quantity of data in the most recent periods allows a very finely drawn time sequence.

PERIOD I: EARLY POTTERY

The Southeast does not take a backward position as far as the chronology of early pottery in the New World is concerned. The well-dated fiber-tempered ware (Bullen, 1961) found in Georgia and Florida at the 2nd millennium b.c. ranks as the oldest ceramics in North America, with only a few finds in Middle and South America earlier. After 1000 b.c. other grit-tempered ceramics with impressed surfaces are widespread through the whole area, accompanying rather simple cultures.

PERIOD II: HOPEWELL CLIMAX

The Ohio and the Illinois Valleys to the north of our area were the centers for an elaborate burial-oriented culture that was characterized by some truly artistic developments in stone sculpture-in-the-round and wide trade connections. Large conical burial mounds with central log-lined tombs are characteristics of this culture, whose distinctive rocker-stamped pottery and artifacts of copper, including bicymbal ear ornaments and panpipes, were widespread over the East. The trade, which included marine shells from the Florida Gulf Coast region, apparently accounts for the penetration of this culture into the Southeast proper. The

Swift Creek culture of central Georgia and the Santa Rosa culture of Florida (Willey, 1949) represent the regional developments during this period of Hopewellian culture climax and share some of the exotic items of copper traded from the north. In south-central Louisiana the Marksville culture shows even closer ties with the northern centers, and gives rise to a locally widespread late variant of this complex, while showing ties with the Florida Gulf Coast. The economic base of Hopewell and its southern relatives remains a major area of inquiry, but recent finds of corn in Ohio and western Missouri (Yarnell, 1964, p. 104) indicate that by the first century a.d. agriculture must have played an important part in this widespread culture, which indeed blanketed most of the area south of the Great Lakes where maize agriculture was possible.

PERIOD III: WEEDEN ISLAND

While the cultures of the rest of the East suffered something of a decline in the post-Hopewellian period, the Florida Gulf Coast was the center for a vibrant and expanding culture, termed Weeden Island (Willey, 1949, p. 396), which was noted for elaborate funeral ceramics found in pottery caches on the edge of burial mounds. The exotic effigy forms mark a high point in ceramic sculpture in the Southeast and contrast with the drab "backwoods" cultures that characterize the rest of the area at this time.

PERIOD IV: TEMPLE MOUND SPREAD

The question of possible Middle American influence on the Southeast can be raised with regard to some of the earlier cultures such as Hopewell, but the evidence is not very definite. However, with the introduction of large flat-topped pyramidal mounds of earth used as a substructure for ceremonial buildings and set around a sacred plaza, one can hardly term this complex of ideas an independent invention unrelated to the high civilization to the south. These "temple mounds" are one of the most distinctive culture forms of many of the late Southeastern cultures, and their size alone (more than half a dozen scattered through the area exceed 50 ft in height) argues for a high degree of social control. A firm agricultural base utilizing corn, beans, and squash provided for a large aggregate of people in towns and in surrounding hamlets. The best known culture of this time period is Coles Creek in Louisiana (Ford, 1951) and Mississippi; nascent Mississippian culture was probably coeval in some centers farther to the north.

PERIOD V: MISSISSIPPIAN CLIMAX

The Mississippian culture, named for its well-known examples in the Mississippi River Valley, became widespread throughout the whole area, exceeding the earlier Hopewell expansion and bringing a relative homogeneity in some of the cultural forms to much of the area. These widely dispersed items include shell-tempered pottery and palisaded villages with temple mounds and plazas.

In late times, but surely well before DeSoto's arrival in 1542, the Southeast was the scene of a well-developed ceremonial complex, often termed the "Southern Cult" (Waring and Holder, 1945). Intricate work in incised shell, elaborate *repoussé* copper ornaments and stone sculpture-in-the-round are but a few of the elaborate objects of ritual paraphernalia that represent sacred items of this religious complex. Major centers at Spiro, Oklahoma (Burnett, 1945; Hamilton, 1952), Moundville, Alabama (Moore, 1905), and Etowah, Georgia (Moorehead, 1932) have produced artistic specimens that rank with the finest in the New World. There are indications that by A.D. 1500 this elaborate ceremonialism was on the wane; by the historic period, decadent forms in this same art style testify to a pre-Columbian decline that European contact only hastened but did not provoke.

PERIOD VI: HISTORIC

With the advent of European exploration the once-vibrant Southeastern cultures fell easy prey to disease and cultural maladjustments that saw agriculture give way once again to hunting and gathering for many of the fading remnants of a once-proud aboriginal population. The 19th century brought territorial abandonment for most via the "Trail of Tears" to Oklahoma. Today only the Seminole of southern Florida, some Cherokee in North Carolina, and a few Choctaw in Mississippi are the last substantial groups left in the Southeast to testify to a native heritage of more than ten thousand years.

REFERENCES

Braun, E. Lucy, 1950, Deciduous forests of eastern North America: Philadelphia, Pa., The Blakiston Co., 596 p.

Bullen, R. P., 1958, The Bolen Bluff site on Paynes Prairie, Florida: Florida State Mus. Contr. Social Sci., No. 4, 38 p.

—— 1961, Radiocarbon dates for Southeastern fiber-tempered pottery: Amer. Antiq., v. 27, p. 104-106

—— 1962, Suwanee points in the Simpson collection: Florida Anthropologist, v. 15, p. 83-88

—— 1963, Artifacts, fossils, and a radiocarbon date from Seminole Field, Florida: Florida Acad. Sci. Quart. J., v. 26, p. 293-303

Burnett, E. K., 1945, The Spiro Mound collection in the Museum: New York, Heye Foundation, Mus. Amer. Indian Contr., v. 14, p. 9-47

Bushnell, D. I., Jr., 1935, The Manahoac tribes in Virginia, 1608: Smithson. Instn. Misc. Coll., v. 94, 56 p.

Caldwell, J. R., 1958, Trend and tradition in the prehistory of the eastern United States: Amer. Anthrop., Mem. 88, v. 60, 88 p.

—— 1962, Eastern North America, *in* Braidwood, R. H., and Willey, G. R. (eds.), Courses toward urban life: Viking Fund Publ. No. 32, p. 288-307

Cambron, James W., and Waters, Spencer A., 1959, Flint Creek Rock Shelter, Part I: Tennessee Arch., v. 15, No. 2, p. 72-87

—— 1961, Flint Creek Rock Shelter, Part II: J. Alabama Arch., v. 7, No. 1, p. 1-50

Claflin, W. H., Jr., 1931, The Stalling's Island Mound, Columbia County, Georgia: Harvard Univ. Peabody Mus. Pap., v. 14, 47 p.

Coe, J. L., 1949, The oldest culture in North Carolina: Southern Indian Stud., v. 1, p. 15-16

—— 1964, The formative cultures of the Carolina Piedmont: Amer. Philos. Soc. Trans., v. 54, 130 p.

Deevey, E. S., Jr., 1949, Biogeography of the Pleistocene: Geol. Soc. Amer. Bull., v. 60, p. 1315-1416

DeJarnette, D. L., Kurjack, E. B., and Cambron, J. W., 1962, Stanfield-Worley Bluff Shelter excavations: Alabama Arch., v. 8, 124 p.

Fenneman, N. M., 1938, Physiography of eastern United States: New York, McGraw-Hill, 714 p.

Ford, J. A., 1951, Greenhouse: A Troyville–Coles Creek Period site in Avoyelles Parish, Louisiana: Amer. Mus. Nat. Hist. Anthrop. Pap., v. 44, 132 p.

—— in press, Archaeological research in preceramic culture of the Lower Mississippi Valley: Amer. Mus. Nat. Hist. Anthrop. Pap.

Ford, J. A., and Webb, Clarence, 1956, Poverty Point: A Late Archaic site in Louisiana: Amer. Mus. Nat. Hist. Anthrop. Pap., v. 46, 136 p.

Gagliano, S. M., 1964a, Post-Pleistocene occupation of southeastern Louisiana terrace lands: Southeastern Arch. Conf. Bull. 1, p. 18-26

—— 1964b, A preliminary report on the archaeology of Avery Island: Southeastern Arch. Conf. Bull. 1, p. 12-13

Goggin, J. M., 1947, A preliminary definition of archaeological areas and periods in Florida: Amer. Antiq., v. 13, p. 114-128

—— 1948, Florida archaeology and recent ecological changes: Washington Acad. Sci. J., v. 38, p. 225-233

Griffin, J. B., 1946, Cultural change and continuity in eastern United States, *in* Johnson, Frederick (ed.), Man in northeastern North America: Phillips Acad., Peabody Fdn. Arch. Pap., v. 3, p. 37-95

—— (ed.), 1952, Archaeology of eastern United States: Chicago, Univ. Chicago Press, 392 p.

—— 1964, The northeast woodlands area, *in* Jennings, Jesse, and Norbeck, Edward (eds.), Prehistoric man in the New World: Chicago, Univ. Chicago Press, 633 p.

—— this volume, Late-Quaternary prehistory in the northeastern woodlands

Hamilton, H. W., 1952, The Spiro mound: Missouri Arch., v. 14, p. 17-276

Hay, O. P., 1923, The Pleistocene of North America and its vertebrated animals from the states east of the Mississippi River and from the Canadian province east of longitude 95°: Carnegie Instn. Publ. 322, 499 p.

Haynes, C. Vance, Jr., 1964, Fluted projectile points; their age and dispersion: Science, v. 145, p. 1408-1413

Hester, J. J., 1960, Late Pleistocene extinction and radiocarbon dating: Amer. Antiq., v. 26, 57 p.

Hibbard, C. W., 1958, Summary of North American Pleistocene mammalian local faunas: Michigan Acad. Sci. Arts Lett. Pap., v. 43, p. 3-32

Holmes, W. H., 1897, Stone implements of the Potomac–Chesapeake Tidewater province: Bur. Amer. Ethnology Ann. Rep. 15, p. 3-152

Ingmanson, Earl, 1964, The Archaic sequence in the Ocmulgee Bottoms: Southeastern Arch. Conf. Bull. 1, p. 31-32

Krieger, A. D., 1964, Early man in the New World, *in* Jennings, Jesse, and Norbeck, Edward (eds.), Prehistoric man in the New World: Chicago, Univ. Chicago Press, 633 p.

Lewis, T. M. N., and Kneberg, Madeline (eds.), 1954, Editors' comments: Tennessee Arch., v. 10, p. 21-23

—— 1957, The Camp Creek site: Tennessee Arch., v. 13, p. 1-48

—— 1958, The Nuckolls site: Tennessee Arch., v. 14, p. 61-69

—— 1961, Eva, an Archaic site: Univ. Tennessee Stud. Anthrop. 174 p.

Martin, P. S., 1958, Pleistocene ecology and biogeography of North America: Amer. Assoc. Adv. Sci. Publ. 51, p. 375-420

Mason, R. J., 1962, The Paleo-Indian tradition in eastern North America: Curr. Anthrop., v. 3, p. 227-278

McCary, B. C., 1948, A report on Folsom-like points in Granville County, North Carolina: Arch. Soc. Virginia Quart. Bull., v. 3

—— 1951, A workshop site of Early Man in Dinwiddie County, Virginia: Amer. Antiq., v. 17, p. 9-17

—— 1954, A Paleo-Indian workshop in Dinwiddie County, Virginia: Southern Indian Stud., v. 5, p. 9-10

McFarlan, E., Jr., 1961, Radiocarbon dating of later Quaternary deposits, south Louisiana: Geol. Soc. Amer. Bull., v. 2, p. 129-158

Miller, C. F., 1956, Life 8000 years ago uncovered in an Alabama cave: Natl. Geogr. Mag., v. 110, p. 542-558

Moore, C. B., 1905, Certain aboriginal remains of the Black Warrior river: Acad. Nat. Sci. J., v. 13, p. 125-144

Moorehead, W. K., 1932, Etowah papers: New Haven, Yale Univ. Press

Neil, W. T., 1958, A stratified early site at Silver Springs, Florida: Florida Anthrop., v. 11, p. 33-52

—— 1964, The association of Suwanee points and extinct animals in Florida: Florida Anthrop., v. 17, p. 17-32

Prufer, O., and Baby, R. S., 1963, Paleo-Indians of Ohio: Columbus, Ohio Hist. Soc., 68 p.

Quimby, G. I., 1956, The locus of the Natchez Pelvis find: Amer. Antiq., v. 22, p. 77-79

—— 1960, Indian life in the Upper Great Lakes: Chicago, Univ. Chicago Press, 182 p.

Rolingson, M. A., 1964, Paleo-Indian culture in Kentucky: Univ. Kentucky Stud. Anthrop. No. 2

Rouse, Irving, 1951, A survey of Indian River archaeology, Florida: Yale Univ. Publ. Anthrop. 44, 296 p.

—— 1952, The age of the Melbourne Interval: Texas Arch. Paleont. Soc. Bull., v. 23, p. 293-299

—— 1964, The Caribbean area, in Jennings, Jesse, and Norbeck, Edward (eds.), Prehistoric man in the New World: Chicago, Univ. Chicago Press, 633 p.

Sellards, E. H., 1952, Early man in America: Austin, Univ. Texas Press, 211 p.

Simpson, J. C., 1948, Folsom-like points from Florida: Florida Anthrop., v. 1, p. 11-15

Stephenson, Robert L., this volume, Quaternary human occupation of the Plains

Stuckenrath, Robert, Jr., 1964, The Debert Site; Early Man in the Northeast: Expedition, v. 7, No. 1, p. 20-29

Thompson, R. H., 1954, Archaic cultures in Kentucky: Southern Indian Stud., v. 6, p. 7-8

Thruston, Gates P., 1890, The antiquities of Tennessee, Cincinnati, Robert Clarke and Co.

Waring, A. J., and Holder, Preston, 1945, A prehistoric ceremonial complex in the southeastern United States: Amer. Anthrop., v. 47, p. 1-34

Webb, C. H., 1946, Two unusual types of chipped stone artifacts from northwest Louisiana: Texas Arch. Paleont. Soc. Bull., v. 17, p. 9-17

—— 1948, Evidences of pre-pottery cultures in Louisiana: Amer. Antiq., v. 13, p. 227-232

Webb, W. S., and DeJarnette, David, 1948, The Flint River Site, Ma□ 48: Alabama Geol. Surv. Mus. Pap. 23, 87 p.

Willey, G. R., 1949, Archaeology of the Florida Gulf Coast: Smithson. Instn. Misc. Coll., v. 113, 600 p.

Willey, G. R., and Phillips, P., 1958, Method and theory in American archaeology: Chicago, Univ. Chicago Press, 269 p.

Williams, Stephen, 1957, The Island 35 mastodon: its bearing on the age of Archaic cultures in the East: Amer. Antiq., v. 22, p. 359-372

Witthoft, J., 1952, A Paleo-Indian site in eastern Pennsylvania, an early hunting culture: Amer. Philos. Soc. Proc., v. 96, p. 464-495

Wormington, H. M., 1957, Ancient man in North America: Denver, Denver Mus. Nat. Hist., 322 p.

Yarnell, R. A., 1964, Aboriginal relationships between culture and plant life in the Upper Great Lakes region: Ann Arbor, Univ. Michigan Mus. Anthrop. Pap. 23, 218 p.

SUMMARY

The prehistory of the southeastern United States is reviewed from the earliest signs of human occupation to the time of historic contact. Based on what seem to be major shifts in cultural orientation, the prehistory of the Southeast is subdivided into three major eras: the Paleo-Indian Era from the earliest occupation to 6500 B.C.; the Meso-Indian Era from 6500 to 2000 B.C.; and the Neo-Indian Era from 2000 B.C. to historic times. Most emphasis is given to the Paleo-Indian Era, and within it attention is focused on the fluted-point tradition. It is suggested that Southeastern fluted points are the product of a single technological tradition that was part of the tool kit of the earliest migrants to the area. This tradition flourished mainly during the Paleo-Indian Era, with possibility of localized later survival in some areas.

The geographic distribution of the fluted-point tradition was outlined by gathering all available published information concerning Clovis, Cumberland, Quad, Redstone, and Suwanee point types. A total of 1,142 points was recorded from 13 states. Provenience data on each point were tabulated on the county level within each state, and the physiographic province and drainage system of each fluted-point-producing county was determined from geologic maps. The distribution of fluted points was then studied within the natural framework of physiographic provinces and river systems. In addition, the geographic distribution of fluted points was compared with that of mastodon-producing fossil localities. It was found that fluted points tend to be most heavily concentrated in the Interior Low Plateau, along the major river systems, and in areas rich in mastodon remains. The Meso-Indian and Neo-Indian Eras are sketched briefly to complete the time sequence.

QUATERNARY HUMAN OCCUPATION OF THE PLAINS *

ROBERT L. STEPHENSON[1]

Any comprehensive statement about the Quaternary human occupation of the Great Plains area that is brief enough for inclusion in such a review volume as this and yet broad enough in its spatial and temporal coverage to fulfill the commitments of the title must, in large part, be a review of reviews—a summary of summaries. The present paper is intended to be just that. It is intended to be, in as simple terms as possible, a chronologically oriented discussion of what is now known, or thought to be known, of the story of man in this area. Much of the story is very nebulous, even in the thinking of the specialists most intimately involved in the current researches in this field. Much of the story is highly controversial, and good cases can be made for two or more interpretations of a given set of data. I shall attempt to indicate, where appropriate, the more nebulous portions of the story and to avoid plunging the reader into any more controversial interpretations than are essential for clarity and fairness to the varying points of view. In short, I shall attempt to simplify in very brief form a most complex and poorly known story—with what success only the reader can judge.

Human occupations of the New World, like those of the Old World, especially on the earliest levels, are difficult to limit within geographic regions. They are continental phenomena—even hemispherical phenomena—and any limitation to spatial confines must be rather arbitrary. There are, though, certain physiographic and ecological regions in which the early complexes bear closer relationships to each other than they do to complexes in other regions. The Great Plains of the interior of the North American continent is one such region. It has a degree of internal consistency throughout the time span of human occupancy in regard to its physiographic, ecologic, climatic, floral, and faunal characteristics. It also has a degree of internal consistency in its cultural content. Many subdivisions of the region may be distinguished readily in any of these aspects, yet a generalized cohesiveness throughout tends to unite the region. Conversely, there are intimate relationships of all these aspects of the Great Plains with the rest of the continent and even with the rest of the hemisphere. These relationships are no less apparent in their cultural content than they are in their physiographic, ecologic, climatic, and other aspects. Thus our discussions will be confined to a relatively cohesive areal unit but will extend occasionally to the rest of the hemisphere for purposes of clarification or amplification.

In general the boundaries of the Great Plains as outlined by Wedel (1961) are quite satisfactory for our discussion, though I should prefer to extend the southern border through central Texas. By title the discussions are limited on the north and south by the borders of the United States, so I shall confine my remarks largely to that area. The western limits are roughly the eastern foothills of the Rocky Mountains, and the eastern limits follow generally a line angling westward from about 95° west longitude at the Gulf of Mexico to 98° west longitude at the Canadian border (Fig. 1).

The temporal coverage of this discussion will embrace the entire time span of human occupation in the Great Plains. This whole span, though, is but a small fraction of the Quaternary. Our colleagues in geology and paleontology have more than a million years to consider. The archaeologists have only the last three or four percent of this time at the very most. Yet during these 30,000 or 40,000 years a great deal has happened to make this small segment of time a most significant one. Rocks do not change very fast; neither do animal species. Man, the human animal, with his tool-making culture, does. The story of that change, even on the basis of the flimsy fragments of data now available, is an intricate and complex one.

Many schemes and many sets of terms have been devised by American archaeologists for sorting the cultural manifestations within this time span. Willey and Phillips (1958) and Krieger (1964) have discussed these in some detail. I prefer to use a rather simplified scheme of sorting that embraces the concept of culture stages and, by reference to various methods of dating, fits the manifestations of these stages into a cultural sequence. I prefer to work from the general to the specific, and I find it most illuminating to work with a minimum number of broad categories that can be subdivided in various ways, depending upon the scope of the presentation and the orientation of the audience. In short, I prefer the simplest organization that is amenable to the data. This allows a discussion of the entire human occupation of the Great Plains under three broad headings. (1) The Paleo-Indian Stage begins with the first peopling of the area and ends with the general extinction of the big game animals, the disappearance of the well-made lanceolate projectile points, and a general economic dependence upon small game. This stage probably occupies well over half the time span of man's occupation of the Plains, and more than half the discussion in this paper will be devoted to it. (2) The Archaic Stage begins with the end of the Paleo-Indian Stage and ends with the development of agriculture, ceramics, the bow and arrow, and the estab-

* Submitted with permission of the Secretary of the Smithsonian Institution.
[1] Smithsonian Institution, Washington, D.C.

685

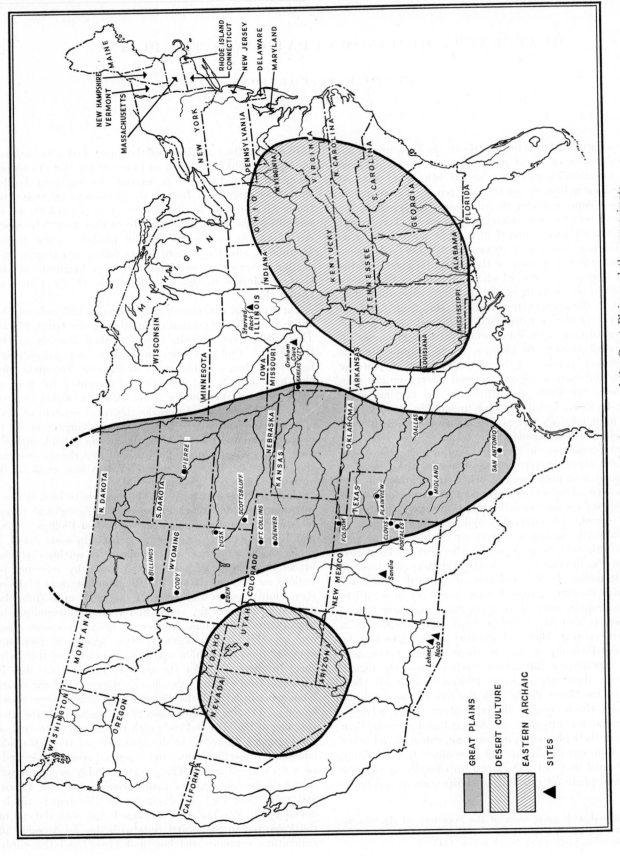

Figure 1. Map of the United States showing area of the Great Plains and the approximate heartlands of the Eastern Archaic and Desert Cultures. Sites outside the Great Plains mentioned in the text are also shown.

lishment of a semi-sedentary village life. (3) The Sedentary Stage begins with the end of the Archaic Stage and ends with the domination of Europeans on the Plains.

THE PALEO-INDIAN STAGE

Many excellent syntheses of Early Man in America (the Paleo-Indian Stage) have been published. Among the most comprehensive of these are Roberts (1940b, 1945, 1953), Sellards (1940, 1947, 1952), Macgowan (1950), Hurt (1953), Willey and Phillips (1955, 1958), Wormington (1957), Macgowan and Hester (1962), Mason (1962), and most recently Krieger (1964). Each of these covers material from the Plains area along with that from the rest of the continent, but none treats the Plains area exclusively. Basic reports, describing and interpreting the material from individual sites in the Plains, number in the hundreds. The

interested student who is not already familiar with this material should begin with the above titles and then examine some of the original sources listed in the bibliographies, especially those that report the more significant finds. Many of the latter will be discussed in the present paper (Fig. 2), and others are discussed by the authors mentioned above.

The modern scientific study of Early Man in America is actually less than forty years old. It was in the Plains area that this study was first established on a firm scientific basis with clearly documented evidence to support the interpretation of the data. This is not to say that a concern with the problem had not been shown previously or that significant discoveries of "Early Man" materials had not been made before the mid-1920's. There had been concern with the origins of the New World aborigines since Euro-

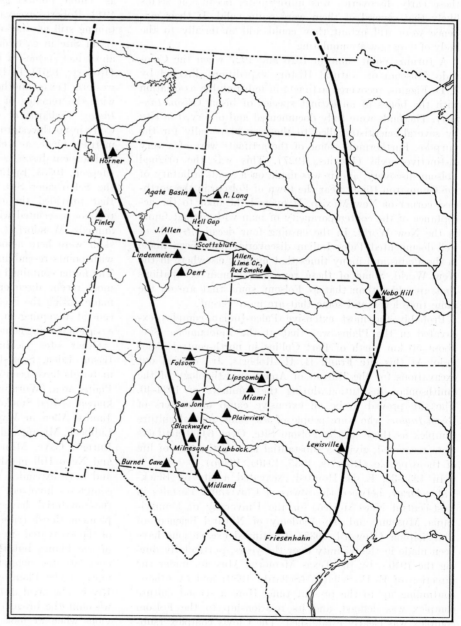

Figure 2. Map of the Great Plains area showing location of Paleo-Indian Stage sites.

peans first began to settle here. Bits of evidence were found on which theories were built to explain those origins. During the last half of the 19th century and the early part of the 20th century several dozen discoveries of man-made tools were reported in apparent association with extinct species of animals or in geological deposits suggesting considerable antiquity (Hrdlicka, 1918, 1923). More than a dozen of these were in the Plains area (Sellards, 1940). With each of these discoveries there was some question as to the actual association of the tools with the bones, the age of the deposits, or the correlation of the deposits with valid temporal sequences. At best the discoveries were not clearly documented by the investigators. At worst there was suspicion of actual fraud. Various ages were attributed to the material, ranging from as recent as a few thousand years to as old as the Pliocene. The general doubt cast upon these early discoveries was unfortunate, because it seems likely that several of them were quite valid. If their evidence were still extant they could add materially to the body of data now accumulating.

A turning point came in 1926 and 1927 when the Colorado Museum of Natural History expedition, directed by J. D. Figgins, recovered artifacts in indisputable association with the bones of an extinct species of bison (*Bison taylori*). The finds were fully documented and observed *in situ* by several scientists called to the scene especially for the purpose. Furthermore, some of the artifacts were of a very distinctive style (Figgins, 1927). This was the original Folsom discovery, and it was made on a small tributary of the Cimmaron River, near the town of Folsom in the northeast corner of New Mexico. It opened the door to the acceptance of the contemporaneity of man with extinct fauna in the New World. In the ensuing four decades, scores of well-documented Paleo-Indian discoveries have been made in the Plains and many times that number elsewhere in the New World. Some of these represent human occupations that are older than that at Folsom, some that are on the same time level, and some that are more recent.

Probably the most extensive Paleo-Indian complex excavated in the Plains was that at the Lindenmeier Site, about 50 km north of Fort Collins in north-central Colorado. At this site Frank H. H. Roberts, Jr., carried out excavations for the Bureau of American Ethnology of the Smithsonian Institution during the summers of 1934-40. The site proved to be an extensive camp of hunters of *Bison taylori* who were people of the same general culture complex as those at the Folsom Site. Over 6,000 artifacts were recovered, giving a substantial idea of the way of life of these people (Roberts, 1935, 1940a, 1940b).

In 1932-33, E. B. Howard excavated a site on Blackwater Draw, between the towns of Clovis and Portales in west-central New Mexico, for the University of Pennsylvania Museum and the Academy of Natural Sciences of Philadelphia (Howard, 1935). Continued excavations have been made in this vicinity over the years, particularly during the 1940's, by the Texas Memorial Museum under the direction of E. H. Sellards (Sellards, 1952) and by others, continuing up to the present time. Here a second culture complex was defined, and its relationship to the Folsom complex was clearly established. The Clovis complex (sub-

sequently defined as the Llano complex, including Clovis points) was identified as a hunting culture that subsisted in part on the now-extinct *Parelephas columbi*. The remains of this complex underlay the remains of a Folsom occupation at this site, and the latter was associated with bones of *Bison taylori*. The two were clearly separated by a sterile zone. Thus, by the mid-1930's, at least two distinct culture complexes had been carefully excavated, well documented, and demonstrated to have been contemporaneous with two separate, extinct faunal assemblages.

Other early culture complexes were also being identified in the Plains during that decade and since (Wormington, 1957). Excavations in 1931 near Scottsbluff in western Nebraska and in 1940 at the Finley Site near Eden in central Wyoming provided an assemblage containing the Eden and Scottsbluff types of points (then referred to collectively as Yuma Points) in association with extinct bison. In 1942, Roberts excavated an assemblage of specimens containing still another distinctive style of point at the Agate Basin Site in east-central Wyoming near Lusk, and again an extinct species of bison was associated with the artifacts (Roberts, 1961). In 1944, at the edge of Plainview in northwestern Texas, another style of lanceolate point was found with the remains of over 100 animals identified as *Bison taylori* (Sellards *et al.*, 1947). At the Horner Site, near Cody in northwestern Wyoming, a distinctive style of asymmetrical blade, as well as Eden and Scottsbluff type points and ancient bison, was excavated in 1949, 1950, and 1952 (Jepson, 1953). In 1953 and 1954, discoveries were made at the Scharbauer Site near Midland in west-central Texas that provided the only well-documented human skeletal remains associated with early styles of artifacts and extinct animals (Wendorf *et al.*, 1955). Portions of a human female skull were here associated with Folsom fluted points and with points resembling the Folsom type but without flutes. The fauna contained extinct antelope, bison, and horse. The most recent discovery of a distinctive artifact style was made during the excavations at the Hell Gap Site in west-central Wyoming in 1960 and 1961 (Agogino, 1961). Excavation is being continued at this site.

Other sites yielding Folsom, Clovis, Plainview, Agate Basin, Eden, Scottsbluff, Cody, Midland, and Hell Gap materials have been excavated and well documented in the Plains area (Wormington, 1957; Krieger, 1964). The sites known as Red Smoke, Lime Creek, and Allen in Nebraska; Jimmy Allen in Wyoming; Ray Long in South Dakota; Lubbock, Miami, and Lipscomb in Texas; Dent in Colorado; Burnett Cave, Milnesand, and San Jon in New Mexico; and Nebo Hill in Missouri are all prominent among these and have expanded and amplified the data on the culture complexes involved. Literally thousands of surface finds of these materials have been made in the Plains area that supplement the distribution pattern of these complexes. Most of the excavated sites are located along the western portion of the Plains, but the surface finds and a few of the excavated sites suggest that these complexes extended over most of the Plains area, south and west of the Missouri River. The areal distribution seems to be extensive, even if we omit the broad distributional implications that are obvious when we look outside the Plains area. The temporal span, though, if we are to take the carbon-14 determinations as meaningful, is surprisingly short. In the 1930's archaeologists based their dating on geological implications of the stratigraphy in the sites and on the suggested dates of extinction of the associated fauna. They could demonstrate stratigraphically that the Clovis material was older than the Folsom and that the Eden, Scottsbluff, and similar material was somewhat younger than Folsom. They generally centered their suggested dates for the Folsom material somewhere around 10,000 years ago, but usually made it quite clear that these were "guess dates."

The carbon-14 determinations on many of these sites have subsequently supported the "guess dates" to a considerable degree. The mammoth found near Dent, Colorado, associated with Clovis Points, has recently been dated at 11,200 years ago (Krieger, 1964), and Clovis materials from the Naco and Lehner sites in Arizona (Fig. 1) have provided dates in the range 11,000-12,000 years ago (Haury et al., 1959). Charcoal from the Lindenmeier Site recently was dated at 10,780 ± 375 years ago (Haynes and Agogino, 1960), and a date of 9,883 ± 350 has been obtained from the Folsom occupation at the Lubbock Site (Sellards, 1952). Dates from the Scharbauer Site are at such variance with each other that it seems premature to assign any carbon-14 age to the site at this time. The Plainview Site has yielded a date of 9,800 ± 500 years ago (Wendorf and Krieger, 1959). The Plainview horizon at the Lime Creek Site in Nebraska has been dated at 9,524 ± 450 years ago (Davis, 1953), and the same horizon at the nearby Allen Site has been dated at 8,274 ± 500 and 10,493 ± 1,500 (Davis and Schultz, 1952; Davis, 1962). The Agate Basin Site has provided dates of 9,350 ± 450 and 9,990 ± 450 years ago (Crane and Griffin, 1963). The Hell Gap Site (the Hell Gap level, below an Agate Basin level) is dated at 10,850 ± 550 years ago (Agogino, 1961).

I am impressed with the rather tight clustering of dates for these Paleo-Indian sites, covering a span of only about 4,000 years and encompassing the three major groups of materials. Of the three basic cultures recognized by Krieger (1964), (1) the Llano Culture, with large, rough, fluted points and fauna containing elephants, is in the range 12,000-11,000 years ago (though some of the investigators believe this should extend to two or three thousand years earlier); (2) the Lindenmeier Culture, with smaller, well-made fluted points and a fauna that included extinct bison, is in the range 11,000-10,000 years ago; and (3) the Plano Culture, with large, well-made, unfluted, lanceolate points and a fauna that included extinct bison, is in the range 10,000-8,000 years ago, though the Hell Gap material suggests that this culture may extend back another thousand years to be contemporaneous with the Lindenmeier Culture, at least in some localities.

The materials so briefly discussed above represent the best-known Paleo-Indian remains thus far found in the Great Plains. We can be fairly certain, though, that these are not the remains of the earliest inhabitants of the New World, nor even of the Great Plains. Evidence for earlier occupations is illusive, indeed, and any discussion of such occupations must be based, in large part, on theoretical considerations. Yet there can be little doubt that there was a long period of human occupation here that preceded the big-game hunters discussed above.

The earliest specifically identifiable culture complexes that we find in the Great Plains are each based upon a diagnostic projectile-point style (Clovis Fluted points for the Llano Culture; Folsom Fluted points for the Lindenmeier Culture; and Plainview, Agate Basin, Scottsbluff, and similar points for the Plano Culture), accompanied by a large or small inventory of relatively non-diagnostic artifacts and associated with a stratigraphic position and faunal assemblage that may or may not be dated by carbon-14. The projectile-point styles are quite specific, and they each exhibit a high degree of technical skill in stone working. It is of interest that these specific styles are not found, so far as I am aware, in central or northeast Asia, where the early immigrants to the New World presumably originated. Neither are they found along the several routes through Alaska and Canada that have been proposed for early migrations, except occasionally in contexts that appear to be later than those in which they are found farther south (Hurt, 1953; MacNeish, 1959). This would suggest a New World origin for these tool styles. Haynes' (1964) suggestion of an arctic origin for fluted points may have merit, but his evidence is certainly tenuous. We must also consider the extensive distribution of the early, fluted, lanceolate points over not only North America but South America as well. They are found either in excavated context or as surface finds over most of the United States and in central Mexico and various localities in South America.

American archaeologists have speculated for years on the length of time that should be allowed for man to make his way into central North America, where we find him about 12,000 or more years ago, or perhaps 2,000 to 5,000 years earlier if we consider the Sandia Cave Site in central New Mexico (Fig. 1) or the Scharbauer Site as having reliable dates. We may also speculate on the length of time required to develop a sophisticated stone-working technology culminating in specialized projectile-point styles. A third time span to consider is that required for man with his specialized stone-working technology to spread over the vast area in which we have found fluted points. The fact is that we have very little evidence on which to base a judgment. Krieger has recently discussed this at some length (1964) and proposed that all the material, both theoretical and actual, of Early Man prior to the first appearance of the well-made projectile points be referred to as the "Pre-Projectile Point Stage," which preceded the "Paleo-Indian Stage." This suggestion has merit, as certainly a different stage of technology appears to have been involved. I am not yet prepared, though, to accept a "stage" of cultural development based on as little evidence as there is at present, especially in the Plains. In the entire Plains, the Lewisville Site and the Friesenhahn Cave seem to provide the best evidence for human occupation on a cultural level and at a time period prior to any of the specialized projectile-point levels.

The Lewisville Site, just northwest of Dallas, Texas, has provided several large hearths containing artifacts and broken animal bones of both extinct and living species (Crook and Harris, 1958). Charcoal from the hearths has been dated by carbon-14 at *more than* 37,000 years ago (Krieger, 1957). This date was justifiably questioned, and a subsequent carbon-14 test yielded a date of *more than* 38,000 years ago (Krieger, 1957). Both the fauna and the geology of the site appear to support these dates. The artifacts consist of a crude chopper, a hammerstone, a flake scraper, three worked flakes, and a Clovis Fluted point. Questions, of course, have been raised about a Clovis point on this time level, and the reasonable inclination of many archaeologists is to disregard the whole site as highly questionable. However, there seems to be good reason to suspect that the Clovis point was actually instrusive into the site. If this can be granted, I think we must seriously consider the *possibility* that this site provides evidence of human occupation in the Plains more than twice as long ago as the earliest fluted point sites that have yet been found.

The Friesenhahn Cave, 38 km north of San Antonio in central Texas, has yielded a wealth of extinct fauna including elephant, mastodon, horse, bison, peccary, tiger, and dire wolf. Associated with the bones were several flints that appear to have been intentionally flaked into crude scrapers and some small bones that appear to have been cut and polished (Sellards, 1952; Evans, 1961). Unfortunately, no carbon-14 date has been obtained for the site, but if these actually are man-made tools, as I believe they are, there is certainly a good case here for man's appearance in the Plains well back in the Wisconsin Age.

This is certainly thin evidence of Early Man in the Great Plains prior to the Llano Culture, but it *is some* evidence. Taken in conjunction with the equally thin evidence from a couple of dozen sites elsewhere in the New World and the theoretical considerations mentioned above, I suggest that it must be considered seriously.

In summary then, the Paleo-Indian Stage in the Great Plains, as I view it here, begins with the earliest immigrants to the area with a poorly known inventory of crude tools at a time when a now-extinct Wisconsin Age fauna was abundant, and beginning *perhaps* as much as 40,000 years ago. It includes the Llano Culture, with its highly developed stoneworking technology, at a time when elephants and extinct species of bison were still being extensively hunted and at a date that can safely be placed at 12,000 years ago at least. It also includes the even more sophisticated Lindenmeier Culture of approximately 10,000 years ago when the elephants were no longer extant but the now-extinct bison was still an item of diet, and the Plano Culture of 10,000 to 8,000 years ago, with its unfluted, lanceolate points and continued hunting of the same bison species. I view the Paleo-Indian Stage as ending with the general disappearance of the large, lanceolate points and the general extinction of the big game animals. This appears to have been about 7,000 or 8,000 years ago in the Plains, but a terminal date must remain flexible, depending upon the local area.

The Archaic Stage

There has been much discussion among American students as to the meaning and use of the term "archaic" and in particular of its application within the Great Plains. Sears (1948), Griffin (1946, 1952, 1964), Willey and Phillips (1958), and Mayer-Oakes (1959) have gone into the subject at length. In 1959, *American Antiquity* devoted most of an entire issue to the subject, with articles by Byers, Fowler, Baerreis, Kelley, and Meighan. Many others have discussed "the archaic" in more or less detail. In general a tendency is expressed or implied among most of these writers to accept a broad "archaic stage" that is applicable to the entire continent or even to the western hemisphere, and to separate the local manifestations of this stage into regional subdivisions. For example, Mayer-Oakes (1959) discusses "The Plains Archaic Concept," and Byers writes of the "Coastal Archaic" and the "Boreal Archaic." Some writers avoid the terms "archaic" and "stage" but seem to have a similar concept in mind. Wedel (1964), for instance, writes of the "Hunters and Gatherers" but does so in the sense of an archaic stage of cultural development that encompasses a specific temporal position. An apparently different approach is taken by Griffin (1952, 1964). He specifically refers to "The Early Archaic Period" and "The Late Archaic Period." This seems to emphasize time period rather than culture stage. Likewise, Mulloy (1958) covers the archaic, without using the term, as a time period under the headings of the Early and the Late Middle Prehistoric Periods.

There appears to be a conflict between the concept of archaic as a stage of technological development and the concept of archaic as a time period. I suggest that the conflict is more apparent than real. Those who embrace the stage concept do so on the basis of a cultural inventory and then attempt to place the material thus categorized into a chronological framework. The adherents of the time-period concept identify the cultural inventory as it appears within a specified time period. In either concept the definition of "archaic" depends primarily upon the cultural materials that the investigator includes within it. Griffin (1964), for example, using the concept of time periods, includes the material of the Plano Culture as a part of the archaic. These are materials that I have included, above, within the Paleo-Indian Stage. Krieger (1964, p. 38), using the concept of stages, includes this same material in a "Protoarchaic Stage" and discusses it in an article on "Early Man," clearly implying that this is not archaic.

I prefer to follow the thinking of Willey and Phillips (1958) in a concept of archaic as a developmental stage, the manifestations of which may be placed in temporal position when, as, and if chronological data are obtained from the included sites. Because the Plano Culture and related materials in the Plains area are usually associated with an extinct fauna, implying ecological relationship to the Lindenmeier Culture and other earlier manifestations, I prefer to exclude those materials. This allows a beginning for the Archaic Stage, with the introduction of corner-notched projectile points at a time when the general ecological situation in the Plains had shifted and man's economy could no longer depend upon the large game animals. As Wedel (1964) rightly states, this ". . . appears to correspond rather well with the estimated time of the Altithermal. . . ." As with the Paleo-Indian Stage, we are limited in the artifact inventory that may be considered as diagnostic of the Archaic Stage in the Plains. The styles of corner-notched projectile points are about the only really diagnostic tools, but they are accompanied by a fauna that is distinct from that of the preceding stage. It is a fauna of small animals and there are implications of a greatly increased economic dependence upon a large variety of foods such as rodents, birds, small mammals, fish, and especially vegetable products. Peoples of the preceding stage utilized these foods too, but only as secondary items in the economy.

Mayer-Oakes' suggestion (1959) that a Plains Archaic Stage developed out of an acculturation between the last remnants of the big-game hunters and the westward expansion of an already established eastern archaic (Fig. 1) people has much merit. This hypothesis helps to explain the similarities to both the big-game hunters of the Plains and the eastern archaic cultures that are found in such sites as Starved Rock in northern Illinois (Mayer-Oakes, 1951), Graham Cave in central Missouri (Logan, 1952), and cer-

tain sites in the eastern parts of the Plains area. It implies an archaic development in the East prior to that in the Plains, and substantial evidence from the eastern states is accumulating to support this implication. It is less helpful in a consideration of archaic materials in the western Plains. Jennings (1957) has suggested that the Desert Culture of the Great Basin (Fig. 1) may have been dominant in the Plains at the height of the Altithermal. This theory also has possibilities, especially for the western Plains, where there seems to have been heavier dependence upon the use of vegetal products in the economy than upon the products of the hunt.

It thus seems reasonable to suggest that the Great Plains, at this time of hotter, drier climate than before, was witnessing the demise of the big-game-hunting economy and the development of a new way of life. The latter seems to have derived a part of its composition from the eastern archaic

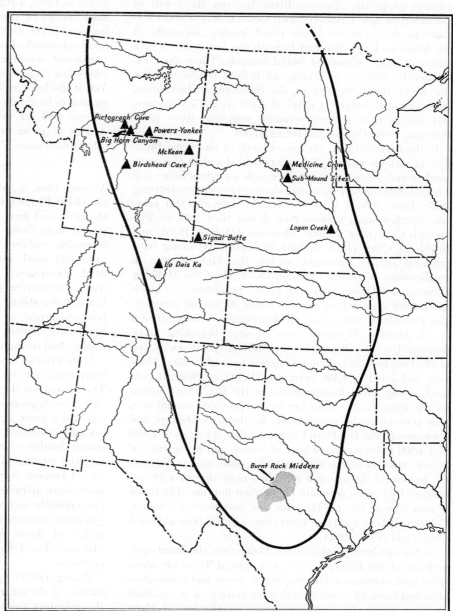

Figure 3. Map of the Great Plains showing location of some Archaic Stage sites.

and a part from the Desert Culture to the west. One point seems certain; the old theory of abandonment of the Plains during the Altithermal can no longer be supported. Data from carefully excavated, well-documented sites of this period have long been lacking, but in recent years more and more sites are being excavated that produce archaic materials and that can be dated sufficiently to support the idea of a substantial occupation of the Plains at that time.

Among the most informative sites in the eastern Plains (Fig. 3) is the Logan Creek Site in northeastern Nebraska, recently excavated by Marvin F. Kivett for the Nebraska State Historical Society. Here corner-notched points reminiscent of eastern archaic forms, along with a modest fauna including small game animals and modern species of bison, were found in a superposed series of campsites. The several cultural layers have provided carbon-14 dates of 6,600 to 8,000 years ago. Similar material has been obtained from the terraces along the Missouri River between the towns of Chamberlain and Pierre in South Dakota, only a short distance northwest of the Logan Creek locality, especially at the Medicine Crow Site and beneath the lowest levels of a series of Plains Woodland burial mounds. These sites, excavated by William N. Irving and Robert W. Neuman for the River Basin Surveys of the Smithsonian Institution, have provided carbon-14 dates of 4,400 to 2,475 years ago, and the terrace geology strongly supports these dates (Coogan, 1960; Coogan and Irving, 1959).

In the western Plains the lowest levels of the Signal Butte Site, in extreme western Nebraska, yielded a seris of corner-notched and ovate points together with a modern fauna and a considerable inventory of non-diagnostic artifacts (Strong, 1935; Bliss, 1950b) with a carbon-14 date of 4,600 years ago. Farther west, various rock-shelter sites such as Pictograph Cave near Billings, Montana (Mulloy, 1958), and Birdshead Cave (Bliss, 1950a) in central Wyoming have provided similar materials, as has the McKean Site in northeastern Wyoming (Mulloy, 1954). Here the McKean, Duncan, and Hanna projectile points are diagnostic, but a substantial quantity of various forms of milling stones is also prominent. The potentials of numerous bison trap sites in the Montana-Wyoming area are only beginning to be developed, as is indicated by the McKean points excavated at the Powers-Yonkee Bison Trap Site in south-central Montana and dated at 4,450 years ago (Bentzen, 1962). Recent work of the River Basin Surveys in the Big Horn Canyon on the Montana-Wyoming border has provided several sites that promise to be illuminating. In the rock shelters and open sites of the Big Horn Canyon, carbon-14 dates of 7,800 and 4,900 years ago have been obtained, and a sequence of hearth styles as well as the projectile points appear diagnostic. In general the material resembles more that of a Desert Culture than of an economy based upon hunting. The latter is also true of the Lo Dais Ka Site just west of Denver, Colorado, where a date of 4,880 years ago has been obtained (Irwin and Irwin, 1961).

In the southern portion of the Plains area the burnt-rock middens of the Edwards Plateau in central Texas are identified with corner-notched projecticle points and a considerable emphasis on food-gathering suggestive of a modified Desert Culture. Geological estimates of the age of these middens are between 6,000 or 7,000 years ago and 1,000 or 2,000 years ago. Here, as elsewhere in the Plains, a time range of considerable extent for the Archaic Stage seems to be indicated. It may well be proposed that throughout the Plains, varying in different localities, a time range beginning about 7,000 or 8,000 years ago and lasting to as recently as 1,000 or 2,000 years ago would be reasonable. Likewise a broad geographical range for the materials indicative of a mixed hunting-gathering-foraging culture is apparent from the numerous surface collections made over nearly all parts of the Plains area.

The Archaic Stage in the Great Plains is by no means a clearly understood cultural unit. It is identifiable on the basis of a small number of diagnostic artifacts, most of which are varying styles of corner-notched projectile points, and a faunal assemblage of modern species. It is a simple-culture stage and is, perhaps, best identified by some of the things it lacks. Large, well-made, lanceolate points and extinct species of large mammals, diagnostic of the preceding stage, are lacking. Pottery, agricultural implements, small side-notched projectile points, and permanent or semi-permanent dwelling structures, all representative of the succeeding stage, are not to be found in Archaic Stage sites. Yet, it did have an identity of its own that is only now beginning to be clarified. The very near future appears to hold a great deal for us in an understanding, not only of the Archaic Stage on the Plains, but of regional, temporal, and other subdivisions of that stage.

THE SEDENTARY STAGE

At some time, as yet undetermined, the archaic cultures of the Great Plains gradually began to be replaced by a more elaborate and more complex way of life. Larger groups of people were living together in communities of gradually increasing stability, with semi-permanent dwelling structures and much attention placed upon the burial of the dead. Experiments with the planting of crops gradually developed into an economic dependence upon agriculture. Pottery containers became a household necessity, and the bow and arrow, as indicated by small side-notched projectile points, replaced the atlatl and dart as a weapon of warfare and the hunt.

More evidence upon which cultural reconstructions can be based exists for this stage than for either of its predecessors. The reasons for this are obvious. The cultures contained not only a much greater variety of material objects than before, but also a great many more of each kind. There were considerably increased numbers of people in the area, living in specific localities for longer periods, thus concentrating more material remains in one place. The remains are better preserved because they are more recent, and, being more obvious, have attracted more attention from the archaeologist. Consequently many papers have been published on the sedentary cultures of the Great Plains, and even a cursory review of them would be too lengthy to attempt here. Mention should be made, though, of a few of the major syntheses.

Strong (1935) early recognized a sequence of cultural entities in the central Plains and their clear relationships to the sedentary cultures of the eastern Woodlands. A decade later Krieger (1946) was able to distinguish the several subdivisions of sedentary cultures in the southern Plains, and Bell and Baerreis (1951) amplified this in an extensive treatment of the Oklahoma area. Lehmer (1954a) treated the northern Plains in broad outline in a most useful synthesis and expanded upon this in detail in his report of certain Oahe Reservoir excavations (1954b). Mulloy (1958) outlined the cultural sequences of the northwestern Plains, although it is a matter of definition as to whether any of the cultures in this area can be considered as actually a part of a Sedentary Stage of cultural development. In 1959, Wedel assembled the data from Kansas and summarized the cultural sequences in that state. Griffin (1952) included the Plains area as a part of his broad synthesis of cultures of the eastern United States. The latest, and most thorough, synthesis of the Plains is given us by Wedel (1961), and more than half of the entire volume is devoted to the sedentary cultures.

All these students have recognized intimate relationships between the semi-sedentary cultures of the Plains and similar cultures of the eastern Woodlands. The latter are generally assumed to have been a gradual development out of the eastern archaic with, perhaps, the addition of some new groups of people from elsewhere. They are discussed under the headings of Early, Middle, and Late Woodland cultures. That the Woodland cultures in the east preceded the semi-sedentary cultures of the Plains is becoming increasingly apparent with the excavation of more sites in both areas. The evidence indicates that the already developed Woodland groups of the East expanded into the Plains and either replaced or merged with the Archaic peoples to bring about an entirely new series of culture complexes.

Sites of incipient sedentary cultures, resembling the Early Woodland sites of the East, appear to be absent in the Plains, or at least have not been clearly identified. The earliest semi-sedentary cultures in the Plains that have been identified with certainty are the Plains Woodland sites. These are clearly related to the Middle Woodland cultures of the Mississippi and Ohio valleys and farther east. Several small village sites in Kansas, Nebraska, the Dakotas and, to a limited extent, eastern Colorado and Oklahoma, have been grouped into several subdivisions of the Plains Woodland culture. In Kansas and Nebraska especially, these subdivisions are the Sterns Creek, Valley, Keith, and Loeske Creek foci (Kivett, 1952). Distinctive styles of pottery are diagnostic of sites within these groupings. Evidence for agriculture and substantial dwelling structures, though, is more suggestive than specific, but corn has been recovered from Loeske Creek sites, and post-hole patterns indicate semi-permanent structures. Carbon-14 dates for sites of these foci are inconclusive but suggest a general time span of 2,500-1,500 years ago.

Along the Missouri River and in the eastern Dakotas a series of burial mounds has been excavated that represents a part of the Plains Woodland culture and suggests a close relationship to burial mounds to the east (Neuman, 1960). Carbon-14 dates for these low, conical mounds with their rather elaborate, log-covered, sub-floor, burial chambers lie within the same general time span as the Valley, Keith, and Loeske Creek sites in Nebraska and Kansas. Recent excavations along the Missouri River by the River Basin Surveys provide evidence of villages that appear to belong to this burial-mound complex, and considerable clarification of this part of the Plains Woodland way of life is anticipated for the near future.

In the area centering around Kansas City, Missouri, a series of sites has been recorded that is rather clearly a western extension of the elaborate Hopewell Culture (Middle Woodland) of the Mississippi and Ohio valleys (Wedel, 1943). These villages have been dated within the period 1,800-1,600 years ago.

Following these early semi-sedentary cultures in the Plains is a series of complexes that may be referred to as fully sedentary in that they include permanent villages that appear to have been occupied continuously for at least a generation or two. Large, permanent dwelling structures were built in fortified or unfortified villages concentrated along the major rivers and streams. The economy was based upon agricultural crops, but hunting, gathering, and fishing were almost equally important, and food was stored from season to season in large underground storage pits. Social, political, and religious life was developed to a considerable extent, though apparently not to the extent of establishing priesthoods or political federations. Well-made pottery was abundant, and many kinds of stone, bone, shell, and wood tools and implements were in use.

Along the middle Missouri River in North and South Dakota, the earliest of these sedentary cultures have been grouped into a Middle Missouri tradition (Lehmer, 1954b). Included within this tradition are the sub-groups referred to as the Monroe, Anderson, Over, Thomas Riggs, and Huff foci. The sites are identified primarily on the basis of distinctive pottery and villages of semi-subterranean, long-rectangular houses, sometimes situated in rows within the village. Some of the villages were fortified with a distinctive rectangular palisade, surrounded by a dry moat, and strengthened by regularly spaced, loop bastions. The villages are usually large, especially the later ones of the tradition, with as many as a hundred houses in a single village. Carbon-14 and dendrochronological dates suggest a time span of 1,300-500 years ago for this tradition.

To the south, in Nebraska and Kansas, a somewhat similar Central Plains tradition has been identified (Wedel, 1961) that includes the sub-groups of Upper Republican, Nebraska, and Smoky Hill cultures. These sites are identified on the basis of distinctive pottery and small unfortified villages of generally square, earth-covered houses. The dates here seem to range from about 900 to 500 years ago and thus appear to have been somewhat later in beginning than the villages to the north.

Still farther south, in Oklahoma, the Washita River and Custer foci appear to be similar manifestations, and the few dates so far available indicate a temporal position comparable to that of the Central Plains tradition (Bell and Baerreis, 1951). Of rather special interest in western Oklahoma and northwestern Texas are the Antelope Creek and Optima foci. On the basis of pottery and other artifacts, sites of these foci clearly relate to the Central Plains tradition. The architecture, however, is of stone masonry, indicating relationships to the Pueblo architecture of New Mexico (Krieger, 1946). Thus it appears that still another major cultural influence, that from the Southwest, made itself felt within the Plains area at least as early as 700 or 800 years ago.

A final development in the prehistoric Sedentary cultures of the Plains is represented along the middle Missouri River by villages of circular earth-lodges, with or without fortifications. The circular, earth-covered house, with four central roof-support posts, a central fireplace, and covered entryway was a very different type of dwelling from the earlier rectangular house. When fortifications were present in these villages they, too, were of a different style, being oval in pattern, with bastions the exception rather than the rule. The villages ranged in size from only a few houses in some sites to as many as 200 or 300 houses in others. There were a great many of these villages. Some were compact clusters of houses, others were widely dispersed settlements. Pottery styles changed, too, as did some of the other items of the artifact inventory, but changes were by no means as dramatic as were the changes of house and village pattern, and there is no indication that the basic economy changed at all. Dated sites indicate that the circular-house villages made their appearance in this area about 500 to 600 years ago and that the earliest of these were contemporaneous with the latest of the villages with long-rectangular houses. Whether this represents a new people moving into the Plains or a development out of the earlier cultural pattern is not clear, but the former appears to be much more probable, as no developmental sequence between the two has been demonstrated. In any event, this was a time of heavy population density along the middle Missouri River Valley, a density that must have been comparable to the white population of the area some fifty years ago. With numerous minor variations, the circular earth-lodge villages dominated the area well into the historic period, ultimately becoming the villages of the people known historically as the Mandan, Arikara, and Hidatsa. The last such village of these three tribes, known as Like-a-Fishhook Village, in central North Dakota, was abandoned less than a century ago.

In Nebraska and Kansas, too, similar changes were taking place in village and house patterns at this time with but little change in general artifact styles and basic economy. The circular house of the protohistoric Pawnee replaced the earlier square house, and population centers shifted to the major stream valleys. Farther south in southern Kansas and Oklahoma the change was to the large, circular, grass-covered houses of the peoples known historically as the Wichita.

Along the extreme eastern fringe of the Plains area, one other culture complex should be mentioned as related, both temporally and culturally, to the complexes listed above. This is the Oneota culture, which appears to represent a Mississippian intrusion into the margin of the Plains culture area. The shell-tempered Oneota pottery is quite different from the grit-tempered Plains pottery. The Oneota house style is not well known, but much of the rest of the Oneota culture seems to resemble the Plains material.

With the influx of white explorers, traders, and settlers into the Plains area during the 19th century the aboriginal sedentary way of life gradually came to an end. Briefly an incursion of horse nomads, such as the Sioux, Cheyenne, Comanche, and others, swept the Plains, contributing to the demise of the sedentary cultures. But they, too, were reduced to virtual oblivion by the overpowering civilization of the White man.

References

Agogino, G. A., 1961, A new point type from Hell Gap Valley, eastern Wyoming: Amer. Antiq., v. 26, p. 558-560.

Baerreis, D. A., 1959, The Archaic as seen from the Ozark Region: Amer. Antiq., v. 24, p. 270-275

Bell, R. E., and Baerreis, D. A., 1951, A survey of Oklahoma archeology: Texas Arch. Paleont. Soc. Bull., v. 22, p. 7-100

Bentzen, Raymond, 1962, The Powers-Yonkee bison trap: Plains Anthropologist, v. 7, p. 113-118

Bliss, W. L., 1950a, Birdshead Cave, a stratified site in Wind River Basin, Wyoming: Amer. Antiq., v. 15, p. 187-196

—— 1950b, Early and late lithic horizons in the Plains: 6th Plains Arch. Conf. Proc. (1948), p. 108-114

Byers, D. S., 1959a, An introduction to five papers on the Archaic Stage: Amer. Antiq., v. 24, p. 229-232

—— 1959b, The Eastern Archaic: some problems and hypotheses: Amer. Antiq., v. 24, p. 233-256

Coogan, A. H., 1960, Geological age of Soldier Creek, Buffalo County, South Dakota: Iowa Acad. Sci. Proc., v. 67, p. 314-325

Coogan, A. H., and Irving, W. N., 1959, Late Pleistocene and Recent Missouri River terraces in the Big Bend Reservoir, South Dakota: Iowa Acad. Sci. Proc., v. 66, p. 317-327

Crane, H. R., and Griffin, J. B., 1963, University of Michigan radiocarbon dates VIII: Radiocarbon, v. 5, p. 228-253

Crook, W. W., Jr., and Harris, R. K., 1958, A Pleistocene campsite near Lewisville, Texas: Amer. Antiq., v. 23, p. 233-246

Davis, E. M., 1962, Archeology of the Lime Creek Site, in southwestern Nebraska: Univ. Nebraska Spec. Publ. 3, 106 p.

Davis, E. M., and Schultz, C. B., 1952, An archeological and paleontological salvage program at the Medicine Creek Reservoir, Fremont County, Nebraska: Science, v. 115, p. 288-290

Evans, G. L., 1961, The Friesenhahn Cave: Texas Mem. Mus. Bull. 2, 68 p.

Figgins, J. D., 1927, The antiquity of man in America: Nat. Hist., v. 27, p. 229-239

Fowler, M. L., 1959, The Modoc Rock Shelter; an Early Archaic site in southern Illinois: Amer. Antiq., v. 24, p. 257-269

Griffin, J. B., 1946, Culture change and continuity in eastern United States archaeology, in Johnson, Frederick (ed.), Man in northeastern North America: Phillips Acad., Peabody Fdn. Arch. Pap., v. 3, p. 37-95

—— 1952, Culture periods in eastern United States archaeology: in Griffin, J. B. (ed.), Archaeology of the eastern United States: Chicago, Univ. Chicago Press, p. 352-364

—— 1964, The northeast Woodlands area: in Jennings,

J. D., and Norbeck, Edward (eds.), Prehistoric Man in the New World: Chicago, Univ. Chicago Press, p. 223-258

Haury, E. W., Sayles, E. B., and Wasley, W. W., 1959, The Lehner Mammoth site, southeastern Arizona: Amer. Antiq., v. 25, p. 2-30

Haynes, C. V., Jr., 1964, Fluted projectile points; their age and dispersion: Science, v. 145, p. 1408-1413

Haynes, C. V., Jr., and Agogino, George, 1960, Geological significance of a new radiocarbon date from the Lindenmeier Site: Denver Mus. Nat. Hist. Proc., No. 9, p. 5-23

Howard, E. B., 1935, Evidence of Early Man in North America: Univ. Pennsylvania Mus. J., v. 24, p. 61-175

Hrdlicka, Ales, 1918, Recent discoveries attributed to Early Man in America: Bur. Amer. Ethnol. Bull. 66, p. 9-67

—— 1923, Origin and antiquity of the American Indian: Smithson. Instn. Ann. Rep. (1923), p. 481-494

Hurt, W. R., Jr., 1953, A comparative study of the pre-ceramic occupations of North America: Amer. Antiq., v. 18, p. 204-222

Irwin, H. J., and Irwin, C. C., 1961, Radiocarbon dates from the Lo Dais Ka Site, Colorado: Amer. Antiq., v. 27, p. 114-115

Jennings, J. D., 1957, Danger Cave: Soc. Amer. Arch. Mem., No. 14, 328 p.

Jepsen, Glenn L., 1953, Ancient buffalo hunters of northwestern Wyoming: Southwestern Lore, v. 19, p. 9-25

Kelley, J. C., 1959, The Desert Culture and the Balcones Phase; archaic manifestations in the Southwest and Texas: Amer. Antiq., v. 24, p. 276-288

Kivett, M. F., 1952, Woodland sites in Nebraska: Nebraska State Hist. Soc. Publ. Anthrop., No. 1, 102 p.

Krieger, A. D., 1946, Culture complexes and chronology in northern Texas, with extensions of Pueblo datings to the Mississippi Valley: Univ. Texas Publ. 4640, 366 p.

—— 1957, Notes and news; Early Man: Amer. Antiq., v. 22, p. 321-323

—— 1964, Early Man in the New World, in Jennings, J. D., and Norbeck, Edward (eds.), Prehistoric Man in the New World: Chicago, Univ. Chicago Press, p. 23-84

Lehmer, D. J., 1954a, The Sedentary Horizon of the northern Plains: Southw. J. Anthrop., v. 10, p. 139-159

—— 1954b, Archeological investigations in the Oahe Dam area, South Dakota, 1950-51: Bur. Amer. Ethnol. Bull. 158, R.B.S. Pap. 7, 190 p.

Logan, W. D., 1952, Graham Cave, an Archaic site in Montgomery County, Missouri: Missouri Arch. Soc. Mem. 2, 101 p.

Mason, R. J., 1962, The Paleo-Indian tradition in eastern North America: Current Anthrop., v. 3, p. 227-278

Macgowan, Kenneth, 1950, Early Man in the New World: New York, Macmillan Co., 260 p.

Macgowan, Kenneth, and Hester, J. A., Jr., 1962, Early Man in the New World: New York and Garden City, N. J., Amer. Mus. Nat. Hist. and Doubleday & Co., 160 p.

Mayer-Oakes, W. J., 1951, Starved Rock Archaic: A pre-pottery horizon from northern Illinois: Amer. Antiq., v. 16, p. 313-324

—— 1959, Relationship between Plains Early Hunter and Eastern Archaic: Washington Acad. Sci. J., v. 49, p. 146-156

MacNeish, R. S., 1959, Men out of Asia, as seen from the northwest Yukon: Univ. Alaska Anthrop. Pap., v. 7, p. 41-70

Meighan, C. W., 1959, California cultures and the concept of an Archaic Stage: Amer. Antiq., v. 24, p. 289-318

Mulloy, William, 1954, The McKean Site in northeastern Wyoming: Southw. J. Anthrop., v. 10, p. 432-460

—— 1958, A preliminary historical outline for the northern Plains: Univ. Wyoming Publ., v. 22, 235 p.

Neuman, R. W., 1960, The Truman Mound site, Big Bend Reservoir area, South Dakota: Amer. Antiq., v. 26, p. 78-92

Roberts, F. H. H., Jr., 1935, A Folsom campsite and workshop: Smithson. Instn. Explorations and Field Work in 1934, p. 61-65

—— 1940a, Excavations at the Lindenmeier Site contribute new information on the Folsom Complex: Smithson. Instn. Explorations and Field Work in 1939, p. 87-92

—— 1940b, Developments in the problem of the North American Paleo-Indian: Smithson. Instn. Misc. Coll., v. 100, p. 51-116

—— 1945, The New World Paleo-Indian: Smithson. Instn. Ann. Rep. (1944), p. 403-434

—— 1953, Earliest Man in America: Paris, J. World Hist., v. 1, p. 255-277

—— 1961, The Agate Basin complex, Mexico, in Homenaje a Pablo Martinez del Rio, en el xxv aniversario de la edicion de Los origenes americanos: p. 125-132

Sears, W. H., 1948, What is the Archaic?: Amer. Antiq., v. 14, p. 122-124

Sellards, E. H., 1940, Early Man in America, index to localities and selected bibliography: Geol. Soc. Amer. Bull., v. 51, p. 373-431

—— 1947, Early Man in America, index to localities and selected bibliography, 1940-45: Geol. Soc. Amer. Bull., v. 58, p. 955-978

—— 1952, Early Man in America; a study in prehistory: Austin, Univ. Texas Press, 211 p.

Sellards, E. H., Evans, G. L., and Meade, G. E. (with a description of the artifacts by Krieger, A. D.), 1947, Fossil bison and associated artifacts from Plainview, Texas: Geol. Soc. Amer. Bull., v. 58, p. 927-964

Strong, W. D., 1935, An introduction to Nebraska archeology: Smithson. Instn. Misc. Coll., v. 93, 323 p.

Wedel, W. R., 1943, Archeological investigations in Platte and Clay Counties, Missouri: U.S. Natl. Mus. Bull. 183, 284 p.

—— 1959, An introduction to Kansas archeology: Bur. Amer. Ethnol. Bull. 174, 723 p.

—— 1961, Prehistoric man on the Great Plains: Norman, Univ. Oklahoma Press, 355 p.

—— 1964, The Great Plains, in Jennings, J. D., and Norbeck, Edward (eds.), Prehistoric man in the New World: Chicago, Univ. Chicago Press, p. 193-222

Wendorf, Fred, Krieger, A. D., Allbritton, C. C., and Stewart, T. D., 1955, The Midland discovery: Austin, Univ. Texas Press, 139 p.

Wendorf, Fred, and Krieger, A. D., 1959, New light on the Midland discovery: Amer. Antiq., v. 25, p. 66-78

Willey, G. R., and Phillips, Philip, 1955, Method and theory

in American archeology. II, Historical-developmental interpretation: Amer. Anthropologist, v. 57, p. 723-819
—— 1958, Method and theory in American archaeology: Chicago, Univ. Chicago Press, 270 p.

Wormington, H. M., 1957, Ancient man in North America: Denver Mus. Nat. Hist., Popular Series No. 4, 4th ed., 322 p.

SUMMARY

A study of prehistoric man in the Great Plains must be based upon a general consideration of man in the entire western hemisphere. The Great Plains area of central North America, though, provides a cultural, ecological, and physiographic unit that can be discussed separately within this hemispheric perspective. The region has been occupied by man for at least 15,000 or 20,000 years and perhaps for as much as twice that long. The sequence of human cultural development here may be considered within a framework of three sequential culture stages, each of which is amenable to further subdivision in various ways. The Paleo-Indian Stage includes the earliest human inhabitants of the New World, of whom there is very little specific evidence, and the big-game hunters of the Llano, Lindenmeier, and Plano cultures. The Archaic Stage includes the nomadic foragers who subsisted by gathering, fishing, and the hunting of small game animals. The Sedentary Stage includes the incipient and developed agriculturalists whose economy depended upon farm crops as well as hunting, gathering, and fishing, who lived in semi-permanent or permanent communities, and who made pottery and hunted with the bow and arrow.

POSTGLACIAL CLIMATE AND ARCHAEOLOGY IN THE DESERT WEST *

MARTIN A. BAUMHOFF,[1] ROBERT F. HEIZER[2]

THE DISCUSSION in this paper will center on the problem of the nature of postglacial climatic change (*i.e.* the past 10,000-11,000 years) and its effect on prehistoric cultures. About 11,000 years ago man made his first known appearance in the Desert West at such sites as Naco and Lehner in Arizona; Danger Cave in Utah; Leonard Rock Shelter and Fishbone and Guano caves in Nevada; Fort Rock Cave in Oregon; and Five Mile Rapids in Washington. The artifacts from these sites and others are listed by Jennings (1964).

The ecologic dependence of Early Man on his climatic environments in the areas west of the Rocky Mountains has recently been a subject of spirited debate. We discern two main elements in this controversy: first, the physical and biologic evidence of climatic change and, second, the archaeologic signs of cultural change. The discussion of past climate centers on the reality of the Anathermal, Altithermal, and Medithermal sequence of Antevs (1948), and the discussion of past culture revolves on the actuality of the stable "Desert Culture" of Jennings (1957). Any considerable climatic change should be reflected in cultural change, but this response may not be automatic. Cultural-climatic relations for particular periods and areas must be established independently.

We discuss first the matter of postglacial climate, and then we turn to archaeologic evidence of cultural change.

SUBDIVISIONS OF POSTGLACIAL TIME IN THE DESERT WEST

Some investigators regard the temperature sequence of Antevs (Table 1) as either wrong or, in any case, too simple for use as a standard classification of postglacial time in the Desert West. The principal objections have come from Aschmann (1958), Jennings (1957, 1964), Martin (1963a, b), and Bryan and Gruhn (1964). On the other hand Malde (1964), in an excellent review of the pertinent biologic and geologic evidence, infers that the middle postglacial interval was "at first rather arid and then gradually became wetter."

SUGGESTED MODIFICATIONS OF THE ANTEVS CHRONOLOGY

Aschmann (1958) is opposed to the Antevs scheme because of theoretical meteorologic considerations, and he argues

* For editorial and informational aid we wish to acknowledge the kindness of E. Antevs, R. B. Butler, R. D. Daugherty, D. G. Frey, R. Fryxell, J. D. Jennings, H. E. Malde, R. B. Morrison, and H. E. Wright, Jr.

[1] Department of Anthropology, University of California, Davis, California.

[2] Department of Anthropology, University of California, Berkeley, California.

that geologic evidence can be variously interpreted. He suggests that seasonal change in precipitation would have greater ecologic effect than temperature change. Thus an increase in winter rain in the northern Great Basin, which could result from more frequent penetration of Pacific air into the area, would be accompanied by higher rather than lower temperatures. Similarly, Aschmann argues that storms occurring in the southern part of the Great Basin are brought in by very warm air from the Gulf of Mexico and are accompanied by higher temperatures. The evidence of arroyo cutting and dune building in the Southwest that is relevant to the question is not discussed by Aschmann. Thomas (1962) has more recently reviewed the evidence for drought conditions in the Southwest in the years 1942-1956 and finds no relation between drought and temperature. He accepts, but does not review, the detailed evidence for the warm and dry interval of 5000-2500 B.C.

Jennings (1957) objects to the Antevs scheme because it does not jibe with radiocarbon dates from Danger Cave, an important archaeologic site that exhibits an occupation record of long duration in the Lake Bonneville basin. The Antevs chronology, if strictly followed, requires the assumption that Lake Bonneville stood at an elevation higher than Danger Cave about 9,500 years ago. However, three radiocarbon dates from the deepest cave deposits show that the lake level had dropped below Danger Cave for the last time more than 11,000 years ago. Jennings therefore could not accept both the radiocarbon dates and this part of the Antevs scheme. Although Jennings (1957) did not at first categorically reject the Antevs sequence, he emphasized the unchanging character of Great Basin culture since Pleisto-

TABLE 1

Subdivisions of Postglacial Time
(Antevs, 1948, 1952, 1955)

Time	Temperature age	Moisture conditions
Present		
	Medithermal	Moderately warm; arid and semi-arid. Rebirth of Great Basin Lakes.
2500 B.C.		
	Altithermal	Arid; disappearance of Great Basin Lakes. Distinctly warmer than at present.
5000 B.C.		
	Anathermal	Climate at first like today but growing warmer. Probably subhumid and humid. Great Basin Lakes higher than in Medithermal.
7000 B.C.		

cene times and correspondingly minimized the changing consequences of ecologic conditions. Jennings later (1964) rejected Antevs' proposals in their entirety.

The objections of Martin (1963a, 1963b) to the Antevs scheme are based upon palynological evidence. He concludes that relatively sparse pine pollen, recovered from beds correlated with the Sulphur Springs Stage of the Cochise culture in southern Arizona, dated by radiocarbon about 8,000 years old, does not indicate pluvial conditions as Antevs (1962) supposed. Furthermore, Martin believes that Antevs' Altithermal, rather than being a period of drought, was a relatively humid time, as shown by several pollen indicators of moisture recovered from deposits dated from 2170 B.C. to 3330 B.C. (A-186, A-193) (*cf.* Malde and Schick, 1964, p. 71). Martin interprets certain zoogeographic data as supporting his belief that the Altithermal was a moist period; some lizards, snakes, and rodents in the Chiricahua Mountains of Arizona are isolated outliers of larger populations resident in the Sierra Madre Mountains of Mexico. Martin conjectures that these forms moved north during times when there was more rainfall and a continuous belt of oak-pine woodland. This period, he believes, may have been the Altithermal, which was characterized by subtropical monsoons. How firm this evidence is we cannot say. Cottam *et al.* (1959) have cited the warm and dry Altithermal as the probable period for northward migration of *Quercus turbinella* in Utah.

Ancient wood rat (*Neotoma*) middens in southern Nevada that have been dated by radiocarbon demonstrate juniper woodlands as old as 40,000 years and offer one means of amplifying and verifying the records of pollen-bearing sediments (Wells and Jorgensen, 1964). These "fossil" nests provide important clues to restricted stands of mountain woodland during middle-postglacial times. The presence of leafy twigs and seeds of juniper dated from 7,800 to 40,000 years ago in a region now characterized by desert shrubs "indicates a local Pleistocene woodland climate" and provides the evidence for a lower limit of woodland about 800 m higher than at present during the warm phase of the middle postglacial. This inference we take as supporting Antevs' climatic scheme.

Finally, Bryan and Gruhn (1964) propose that although the climatic sequence of Antevs is generally verified, the time boundaries are not necessarily everywhere the same. In particular they suggest that corresponding climatic shifts were earlier in the south than in the north. They also caution that the climatic record is a product of local, continental, and global conditions, so that climatic changes detected in one locality need not apply to another. The past climate of each area must be determined independently. The evidence of warm and wet conditions toward the end of Altithermal times (summarized by Malde, 1964) illustrates this point of regional variation.

Thus two quite distinct issues involve post-Pleistocene climate: (1) dating the onset of post-Pleistocene climate as, recorded by desiccation of Great Basin lakes, extension of xerophytic plant communities over large areas of the Desert West, and other evidence; and (2) the reality and dating of later climatic changes.

With regard to the first problem, it seems evident that the onset of postglacial conditions was earlier than Antevs inferred in 1948 from the data then available to him. A low lake level in the Bonneville basin prior to 11,000 years ago is shown by the radiocarbon dates from Danger Cave (Jennings, 1957; Tanners *et al.*, 1964, p. 156), and concurrent desiccation of other pluvial lakes is shown by radiocarbon-dated tufas in the Lake Lahontan basin (Broecker and Orr, 1958; Shutler, 1961), at Searles Lake (Flint and Gale, 1958), and at Leonard Rock Shelter, where gastropod shells from a beach deposit underlying archaeological levels date at 11,050 ± 1000 B.C. (UCLA-298). Archaeological evidence favors the view of Bryan and Gruhn that the onset of postglacial climate may have been earlier in the south than in the north. In the west, therefore, the beginning of the Anathermal may be moved downward from 9000 B.C. (Table 1) to about 7000 B.C.

As to the sequence of post-Pleistocene climatic phases, we shall discuss only archaeologic matters, but we wish to point out that the theoretical basis of Antevs' scheme is irrelevant to archaeologists. Thus when Aschmann, as a climatologist, says that a period of increased winter rain may be responsible for an increase in mean annual temperature, we assert that this is beside the point. Rather, the archaeologist looks for a change in climatic or ecologic conditions during some period of time that may help to account for some observed culture change. If geologic and/or biologic evidence for a change in climate coincides with considerable culture change, then this may be regarded as evidence *a priori* that the two are related, regardless of the precise nature of the climatic change.

ARCHAEOLOGICAL CULTURES AND CHRONOLOGY

Archaeologists can contribute most usefully to the understanding of postglacial climates by reviewing the cultural sequences known from various parts of the Desert West to see what archaeology indicates about past environment. We are mostly concerned with two points in time: (1) 5000 to 6000 B.C., which marks the onset of the Altithermal, and (2) 2000 to 2500 B.C., the onset of the Medithermal, always remembering that the precise timing may differ from place to place. For these times we shall review evidence for marked cultural change that could have resulted either from large-scale migration or from local changes in culture. When changes of either of these two types coincide with climatic change inferred from other evidence, then we may conclude that the two events are related.

Our review will largely ignore the time before 10,000 B.C., and we shall not discuss the Big Game Hunters. Some archaeologists believe, on the basis of the Lewisville site, Texas, that man was present in the Far West for something like 40,000 years. The Lewisville "hearths," however, may not be firepits attributable to human agency but may be carbonized remains of wood rat (*Neotoma*) nests. No artifacts whatsoever (except for a Clovis fluted projectile point alleged to have been planted as a hoax) were found in any of the "hearths." There are also many problems about the date and causes of extinction of the large Pleistocene game animals. Evidence of man's contemporaneity with these animals in the Desert West is confined to southernmost Arizona, the Naco and Lehner sites being the best known

(Haury *et al.*, 1953, 1959). Although remains of ground sloth are reported as associated with artifacts in Gypsum Cave, southern Nevada (Harrington, 1933), the archaeological evidence for this is not so clear as might be desired, and only pieces of sloth dung (not the artifacts) have been dated by radiocarbon. All we really know is that the ground sloth occupied Gypsum Cave about 8500 B.C. (C-221). Alleged associations of man and *Equus* in some Nevada and Oregon cave deposits are not adequately demonstrated. In brief, if uncertain associations of man and extinct Pleistocene mammals are ignored, evidence is still lacking that man knew or hunted or ate such animals in the western desert region other than in southern Arizona. The simplest conclusion is that the large herbivores disappeared in the Great Basin before man's entry into the area.

SOUTHERN PART OF DESERT WEST

In southern Arizona and New Mexico, at times later than the Big Game kill sites, which appear to date in the range of 7000 to 9000 B.C., the succeeding cultures are classified as stages of the Cochise culture by Sayles and Antevs (1941). The specimens representing the Cochise culture are based on additional collections, and further analysis assigns these artifacts to the successive Sulphur Springs, Cazador, Chiricahua, and San Pedro Stages. We have not seen the newer analysis, but it is summarized by Martin (1963a, p. 71) as follows:

"Sulphur Spring Stage, an assemblage of grinding stones with flat metates, unshaped pebbles serving as manos, and few percussion-flaked tools; (2) Cazador Stage, moderately large basin metates, small, shaped manos, and the first appearance of flaked projectile points; (3) Chiricahua Stage, basin metates, shaped manos, percussion-flaked tools and pressure-flaked points, distinguished from the preceding by a greater frequency of flaked implements; (4) San Pedro Stage, deep basin metates, large manos, pressure-flaked projectile points, percussion and pressure-flaked scraper, axes and knives; pit houses and storage pits are diagnostic. Around 2,000 B.C. [error for 200 B.C.?] pottery appears."

It is difficult to tell much without further information, but the major cultural change, if any, may be marked by an increase in the abundance of sites at the beginning of the San Pedro Stage. Antevs thought that the San Pedro began about the end of the Altithermal, and Martin appears to agree with this chronological placement (Fig. 1). This suggests a cultural change coinciding with the end of the Altithermal. On present evidence there is no corresponding cultural change at the beginning of the Altithermal. It is notable, however, that the Anathermal interval of increasing desiccation from Pleistocene to Altithermal time coincides on Martin's chart (1963a, Fig. 37) with a phasing out of the Big Game Hunters and a replacement by the Cochise culture. Martin (1963a, p. 70) denies that this resulted from climatic change; rather he suggests that the large mammals became extinct in this period because of over-hunting by man. This seems to us a rather radical proposal, because it is difficult to imagine survival of large herds of these mammals in an ecological regime that presumably resembled

that of the present Desert West, and such would seem to be a logical corollary of Martin's position. If, on the other hand, the large Pleistocene mammals were present only as remnants, their numbers having been drastically reduced by environmental restraints, then man may have been instrumental in causing their final disappearance.

The long-discussed site of Tule Springs near Las Vegas in southern Nevada, once thought to demonstrate occupation of great antiquity, now proves, after recently completed excavations, to show no evidence of man older than 10,000 or 11,000 B.C. Problematic fire hearths have been shown to be natural deposits of "lignitized" wood (Cook, 1964). The reports on the geology (by C. Vance Haynes) and archaeology (by R. Shutler) are not yet published. An open site near Tule Springs, called Corn Creek Dunes site, was apparently occupied during the Altithermal, judging from seven radiocarbon dates ranging from 5200 B.C. to 4030 B.C. (Williams and Orlins, 1933). The site, apparently visited sporadically rather than having been continuously occupied, lies about 2 km from a spring area. In the dry middle postglacial such live springs may have been more important to man than during the climatic regimes of earlier or later times.

WESTERN GREAT BASIN

The cultural sequence in the western Great Basin (Fig. 2) can be discussed by referring to Lanning's chronology (1963, Table 9). At Owens Lake and in western Nevada, where the chronology is most firmly based (either on radiocarbon dates or on archaeologic cross-dating), the period between 3000 and 2000 B.C. (*i.e.* the time Antevs proposes as the onset of the Medithermal) corresponds with the earliest abundant evidence of human occupance. Evidence of man before then is extremely scanty, although Lanning has found near Owens Lake a few surface specimens that he presumes to be older than the deepest material in the Rose Spring archaeological deposit. At Death Valley and Mohave Desert also, the abundant signs of man date from about 3000 B.C., but the archaeological evidence comes mostly from surface sites, and isolation and "dating" of the cultures involves considerable assumption, predilection, and hypothesis-upon-hypothesis reasoning (Warren and De Costa, 1964). These sequences may be correct, but they must still be judged to be hypothetical. It is mainly in the Lovelock-Fallon region of western Nevada that archaeologic specimens are dated earlier than the Medithermal. From the Anathermal layers of cave and shelter sites there are about a dozen artifacts from Leonard Rock Shelter (some projectile points, blades, wooden atlatl darts, pieces of fine netting) and two projectile points from Hidden Cave (Grosscup, 1956; Morrison, 1964, p. 105). Deposits, interpreted as Altithermal, at Leonard Rock Shelter yielded a single infant burial associated with twined basketry (Heizer, 1951, 1956). Artifacts from Fish Bone and Guano caves on the north shore of Winnemucca Lake are reported to date from 9250 B.C., which is about the time that the final lowering of Lake Lahontan waters freed the caves for occupancy (Broecker and Orr, 1958; Wormington, 1957, p. 196), and man may have lived in these caves between 5000 B.C. and 2000 B.C.

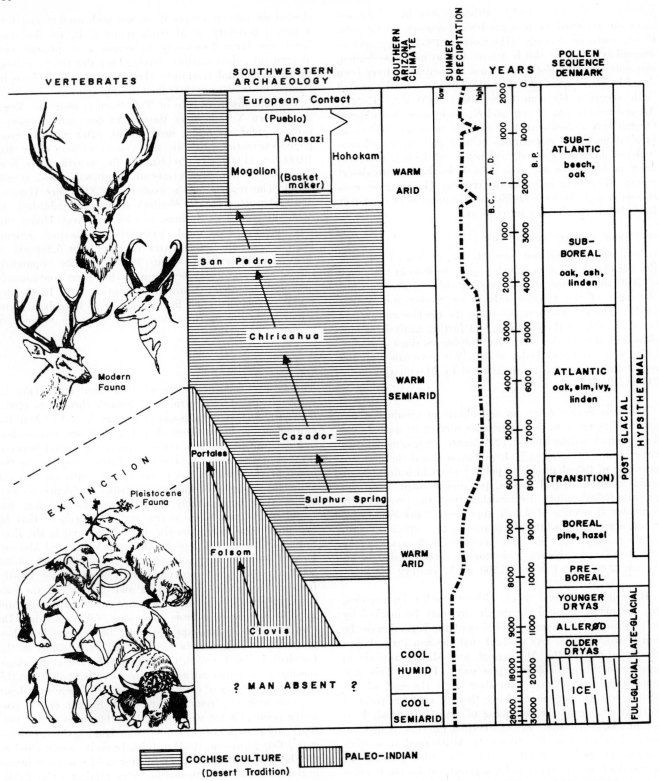

Figure 1. Archaeological cultures, climate, rainfall, and chronology in the Southwest. (After Martin, 1963a).

during a dry interval that is implied by the proportion of tree pollen (Sears and Roosma, 1961).

When these finds are compared with those of the period beginning at 2500 B.C., the marked contrast is apparent. Not only does the type of artifact change, but there is an enormous increase in specimens and in numbers of occupied cave and open sites. For this region, at least, it seems to us that there is abundant cultural evidence for improvement

Climatic Stage	Date	Central California	Owens Lake	Mohave Desert	Death Valley	Yosemite Valley	Lake Tahoe	Lassen County	Western Nevada
Medithermal	AD 1000	Late Horizon 2	Cottonwood	"Desert Mohave"	DV IV	Mariposa	Kings Beach	Amedee	Dune Springs
		Late Horizon 1	Late Rose Spring		DV III	Tamarack		Tommy Tucker	Late Lovelock
	BC–AD		Middle Rose Spring	Amargosa	Late DV II		Martis		Trans. Lovelock
	BC 1000	Middle Horizon	Early Rose Spring		Early DV II	Crane Flat		Karlo	Early Lovelock
	2000	Early Horizon	Little Lake	Pinto					
Altithermal	3000								Carson
	4000								Leonard
	5000		(Owens Lake II)*	Lake Mohave	DV I				Fallon
Anathermal	6000	Farmington							Humboldt
	7000		(Owens Lake I)*						Hidden Cave

* ( ) = tentative archaeological complex.

Figure 2. Chronology of archaeological cultures in the western Great Basin and California. (After Lanning, 1963)

in climatic-biotic conditions after the Altithermal. If this is attributed to a rebirth of Humboldt Lake as a result of lowered temperatures and increased moisture, the same may be said of many of the other lakes of western Nevada (Morrison, 1961, p. 113). For instance, an open site at the mouth of the Humboldt River shows settled occupation in 733 B.C. (M-649), but how much earlier the site was occupied we cannot now say. The earliest radiocarbon date for human occupation of Lovelock Cave is 1218 B.C. (C-735). Bat guano carbon-dated at 2498 B.C. (C-277) and 4054 B.C. (C-278) from beneath the lowest cultural deposits indicates that the cave was available in this period but presumably not occupied (Grosscup, 1944). Thus, in the western Great Basin, cultural evidence indicates marked improvement in living conditions following the Altithermal interval. Archaeologic evidence for a comparable change at the beginning of the Altithermal is lacking. From the climatic sequence relatively abundant evidence of man might be anticipated in the Anathermal and scarce evidence in the Altithermal. However, the archaeologic evidence is scarce in both periods. It is true that there are one or two hints that the human population during the Anathermal may have been more plentiful than during the Altithermal; for example, Wallace (1958) believes that his Death Valley I culture was separated from Death Valley II by a period of non-occupance (Fig. 2), but the Death Valley archaeological dates are not firm. Again, in western Nevada there are perhaps three or four times as many specimens from pre-Altithermal as from Altithermal time, but the numbers are too small for accurate comparison. On the whole, present evidence indicates that population was extremely sparse in the region before 2500 B.C.

COLUMBIA PLATEAU AREA

In the Columbia Plateau, particularly the part in eastern Washington and adjacent northern Idaho, Daugherty (1962), Butler (1962), and Fryxell and Daugherty (1963) accept Antevs' scheme or some modification of it, but Bryan and Gruhn (1964) do not. However, it should be noted that data for the Columbia Plateau area differ from data discussed for other regions, in the sense that the work of Fryxell and Daugherty (1963) represents a long-range integrated program of combined geological and archaeological study involving examination of more than fifty sites in an area from which much palynological data have been collected (Hansen, 1947) and in which regional correlation of deposits is materially aided by widespread volcanic-ash horizons of known radiocarbon age. Here the relationship of cultural and geological materials has been most thoroughly studied. Particularly at Marmes Rock Shelter, located at the confluence of the Palouse and Snake Rivers, the combined analysis of geological and cultural stratigraphy (Fryxell and Daugherty, 1962, Figs. 5-6, Table IV) indicates change of culture accompanied by change in sedimentation within the rockshelter. Fryxell (personal communication) considers that a striking decrease in the amount of rockfall and coincident increase in eolian sedimentation in rockshelters throughout the area resulted from decreased frost activity and minimum effective precipitation at a time correlated by him with Hansen's "Thermal Maximum" and Antevs' "Altithermal."

Daugherty (1962) divides the cultural sequence as follows:

1. Early Period (*ca.* 9000-6000 B.C.): Occupation by hunting, fishing, and collecting peoples with lanceolate projectile ("Cascade") points, a variety of scrapers and scraper planes, and some bone tools. Evidently there were a few manos and metates.

2. Transitional Period (6000-2500 B.C.): This period would coincide with Antevs Altithermal. People probably lived mostly along the major streams and their tributaries. There was a change in projectile-point type from lanceolate to side-notched. Storage pits became of greater importance, and the flat mortar, basketry hopper, and conical pestle came into use.

3. Developmental Period (2500 B.C.–A.D. 1): The economy did not fundamentally change during this period, the trend being in the direction of increased riverine specialization. Apparently there was no marked change in artifact inventory.

Daugherty meant this sequence to apply to the entire intermontane region, including the Great Basin, and we have simply extracted data relative to the Plateau. It should be noted that dates for the sequence vary from place to place. In particular, Butler's (1962) Weis Rock Shelter sequence is as follows (Fig. 3):

1. Craig Mountain Phase (5500-1500 B.C.):[3] Characterized by lanceolate points, edge-ground cobbles, and various forms of scrapers; apparently a hunting culture.

2. Grave Creeks Phase (1500-100 B.C.): The dates are estimated from the inferred rate of sedimentation. Side-notched projectile points occur with the mano and metate.

Thus Daugherty's early phase, which he believes ended about 6000 B.C., seems at Weis site to have lasted several thousand years longer. It is probable that one or both of these schemes requires chronological adjustment.

It is interesting to note that both Daugherty and Butler identify periods of cultural change that coincide fairly closely with inferred periods of climatic change. Thus Daugherty detects changes at the beginning and end of the Altithermal, and Butler's Craig Mountain Phase meshes quite neatly with a period of "maximum warmth and dryness." Is it possible that these archaeologists have interpreted the archaeological material so that the cultural periods coincide with an assumed climatic sequence? Daugherty's paper, a frankly theoretical study, does not have sufficient detail to allow this question to be judged adequately, but some of his field work in the Columbia Plateau does support the Antevs scheme (Fryxell and Daugherty, 1963; Fryxell and Cook, 1964). Butler's climatic sequence is essentially based on correlation with Pacific Northwest pollen records (using two radiocarbon dates), but he reports changes in lithology and faunal re-

---

[3] The initial date is determined from radiocarbon and from relation to volcanic ash from Mount Mazama; the closing date is estimated from another radiocarbon date of 2500 B.C. (TBNC-114) and from the inferred rate of sedimentation.

mains (presumably related to climate) that coincide with cultural change.

The same holds for Leonard Rock Shelter in western Nevada, where a clear stratigraphy can be matched with Antevs' chronology by radiocarbon dates (Heizer, 1951).

To summarize, some cultural evidence in the Columbia Plateau supports Antevs' climatic sequence, but it is not without contradictions or at least enigmas. An interesting point about the Plateau sequences is that there is a great deal more evidence of human occupancy in the period before 2500 B.C. than during the corresponding period farther south. This is, of course, exactly what would be expected if Antevs' sequence is correct. In a period of increasing desiccation, the Great Basin could offer fewer advantages for life compared to the Plateau region.

EASTERN GREAT BASIN

Danger Cave, on the Utah-Nevada border just north of Wendover (Jennings, 1957), is a large, dry cave with a very rich inventory of artifacts extending through a period that, according to a series of eleven radiocarbon dates, lasted from about 9000 B.C. into the Christian era. Such a sequence, with its abundant artifacts and dates, should provide a fairly complete cultural-climatic history of the region. However, Jennings (1957, p. 287) writes:

"The suggestion that the Desert Lifeway is old and stable is rooted in the archaeological evidence. Most artifact types persist throughout the deposits; no dramatic changes in content occur. Material traits, at least, are added to the full assemblage but nothing can be interpreted as pointing to significant changes in orientation toward nature, unless the shift in chipped flint from early dominance of the small triangular notched point to the larger lanceolate stemless blade of D IV and D V [the latest Danger Cave strata] times can be so interpreted. The usefulness of this concept of stability is debatable; re-examination will be necessary."

Again, in his most recent discussion of the nature of the Desert Culture, Jennings (1964, p. 153) refers to "a stable, successful adjustment to a special environment, an environment characterized by chronically deficient moisture." To us, this emphasis on the arid environmental adaptation by man in the Great Basin directs attention to secondary rather than primary factors. Nearly all of the ancient archaeologic sites in the Great Basin are in caves on the borders of lakes of the Bonneville and Lahontan basins; hence the fundamental ecological adjustment of Early Man in the Great Basin can be seen as oriented toward water rather than the waterless desert as emphasized by Jennings. This is not a new idea. The importance of the Great Basin lakes as sites of early settlement has been discussed earlier by Jennings and Norbeck (1955), Heizer and Krieger (1956), and most recently by Rozaire (1963). Whether such modern pluvial lakes as Humboldt, Carson, Pyramid, Winnemucca, Walker, Abert, Summer, and Owens were completely dry in the Altithermal has been studied stratigraphically in only a few places. Some of these lakes were completely dry during the Altithermal (Morrison, 1964, p. 75, 102); others may have been lowered to much smaller water bodies (Antevs, 1948,

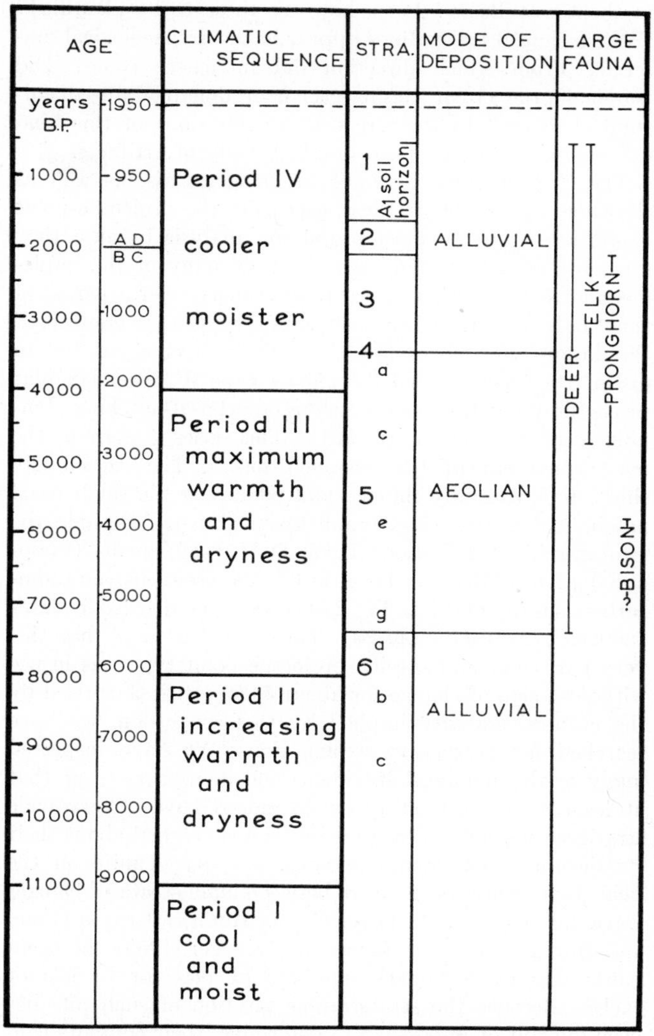

AGE		CLIMATIC SEQUENCE	STRA.	MODE OF DEPOSITION	LARGE FAUNA
years B.P.	1950				
1000	950	Period IV	1 (A₁ soil horizon)		
2000	A.D. / B.C.	cooler	2	ALLUVIAL	DEER — ELK — PRONGHORN
3000	1000	moister	3		
4000	2000		4 / a		
5000	3000	Period III maximum	c		
6000	4000	warmth and dryness	5 / e	AEOLIAN	BISON ?
7000	5000		g		
8000	6000	Period II increasing	6 / a / b		
9000	7000	warmth and dryness	c	ALLUVIAL	
10000	8000				
11000	9000	Period I cool and moist			

Figure 3. Climatic sequence and archaeological cultures at Weis Rock Shelter, Idaho. (After Butler, 1962)

p. 11). The distribution of endemic fish in lakes, streams, and springs in these desert basins (Hubbs and Miller, 1948) shows that few areas have been literally waterless since the end of the Pleistocene. In so far as the dry valley and mountain areas of the Great Basin were exploited by Indians, this adjustment to aridity may have been achieved first during the dry Altithermal rather than during the more humid early-postglacial period.

We agree wholeheartedly with Jennings that the general economic pattern of existence at Danger Cave may have been rather stable, and we have argued elsewhere (Heizer and Baumhoff, 1962, p. 7), in accord with the ideas of Steward (1938), that "the harshness of Great Basin environment imposed restrictions so severe that to live there at all (with a hunting-gathering economy), the Indians were forced into a rather narrowly prescribed set of subsistence and social customs." Such aphorisms, however, leave unanswered a number of important archaeological questions. Were there any prehistoric migrations and/or population replacements in the Great Basin? If so, how are these to be identified? What technical innovations appear in the archaeological material? From which direction did influences come? Did people in the Great Basin receive or donate diffused cultural elements? In the Great Basin questions of this kind can be answered only from detailed study of artifacts.

The chipped-stone artifacts in Danger Cave as well as elsewhere in the Desert West, especially the projectile-point types, are probably most useful for analysis because they are most abundant. Why is it that so many of the implement forms at Danger Cave are unchanged over a period of thousands of years when such is never the case elsewhere? We do not refer to nondescript scrapers or choppers but to distinctive types. Consider Jennings' type W28, a triangular projectile point with side-notching and basal-notching. Jennings comments (1957, p. 122): "This series is perhaps the most consistent of the stemmed pieces. The exceedingly short stem, carefully thinned and possessing the small basal notch, makes this class unmistakable." Now consider the stratigraphic distribution: Level D II, 9 specimens (radiocarbon date 7837 B.C.); Level D III, 23 specimens (no radiocarbon date); Level D IV, 2 specimens (radiocarbon dates 2850 B.C., 2050 B.C., A.D. 20). Thus Jennings says that this very particular and specific projectile point type was in use without a sign of change for about 5,000 years. Surprised by the cultural stability implied by this conclusion, we have searched for alternative explanations. We have inspected many of the Jennings' specimens and it appears to us that at least a few distinct types do indeed have a very wide stratigraphic range. But we were then concerned about their stratigraphic placement. Jennings is quite definite on the point that significant mixture between main strata of Danger Cave did not occur. In Lovelock and Humboldt caves (Loud and Harrington, 1929; Heizer and Krieger, 1956) the occupants dug extraordinary numbers of pits for burials or caches. Because the stratigraphic position of such pits has been difficult or impossible to determine, their contents cannot be accurately placed in the depositional sequence. Pits in Danger Cave were rare, and Jennings has told us that while the excavations were in progress all possible attention was paid to recognizing and recording intrusive pits. The kind of mixture noted was within, rather than between, levels (Jennings, 1957, p. 63). We cannot provide any good reason to refute the Danger Cave data and can only point out that they do not fit with findings of cultural change at other Great Basin sites. The uniqueness, so far as our present knowledge of Great Basin prehistory now stands, of the Danger Cave sequence may, as Jennings has suggested to us, be a reflection of the separateness of the Danger Cave culture subcenter.

A further problem at Danger Cave is the stratigraphic distribution of the radiocarbon dates. There are eleven dates from Level D I: 9503, 9201, 9050, 8650, 8450, 8320 (two dates), 8200, 7790, 7100, 7020 B.C.; two dates from Level D II: 7839, 7010 B.C.; one date from Level D IV: 1869 B.C.; and three dates from Level D V: 2950, 2050 B.C., A.D. 20 (Jennings, 1957, p. 93; Tamers *et al.*, 1964, p. 156). Thus Level D III, which forms a large part of the center of the deposit, has not been carbon-dated. Presumably its age falls between the latest D II date (7020 B.C.) and the oldest

D IV or D V date (2950 B.C.). Thus Level D III seems to fall within the Altithermal even though its duration and placement within this interval are undetermined. A series of radiocarbon dates for Level D III from Danger Cave is urgently needed for the light it will throw on man's presence in middle-postglacial times in the Great Basin. Jennings (1957, p. 60, 64, 93) recognizes a period of non-occupancy after the deposition of Level D II and before the D III layer was accumulated. Further, he suggests that this period of non-occupancy was "dry and no ponds, marshes or lakes were nearby—as opposed to conditions during which D II accumulated where the recurrent guano deposits argue for much shallow water nearby and climate moister than now. The break in [cave] use, regardless of its length, probably testifies to a period of regional desiccation and the temporary abandonment of the area by man." This period of non-occupancy might coincide with part of the Altithermal. Radiocarbon dates for 5 samples from Level D III submitted to UCLA by Jennings might tell.

Finally, we mention some unpublished information we have for the eastern Great Basin region. During 1958 and 1959 we surveyed extensively in eastern Nevada, and we excavated four sites in various degrees of completeness. All four sites seemed to be relatively late. One of these sites, South Fork Rock Shelter, is a midden deposit 3 m deep on a low bench near the mouth of the South Fork of the Humboldt River at Elko, Nevada, not far west of Danger Cave. Projectile points are the most common artifact at the shelter and show a definite typologic sequence from bottom to top that parallels the one noted by Lanning (1963) at Rose Spring, Inyo County, California, in the western Great Basin. The radiocarbon dates for the shelter are as follows: depth 72 in., 1359 B.C. (LJ-212); depth 94-100 in., 2347 B.C. (UCLA-296); depth 120 in., 2397 B.C. (UCLA-295). These dates indicate that occupation at the shelter began about 2500 B.C. Thus, in the Elko area, as in the western Great Basin, people apparently began to move in at the end of the Altithermal.

In summary, the cultural evidence for ecologic change in the eastern Great Basin is still uncertain, although results from South Fork Rock Shelter tend to confirm what is known in the western Great Basin. The record at this site, however, is short compared to the sequence at Danger Cave. The Danger Cave sequence, as interpreted by Jennings, shows no marked cultural change in the postglacial period, although Jennings detects signs of ecologic change. We doubt that the evidence is entirely conclusive, but further discussion will depend on radiocarbon dating of Level D III.

FINAL CONSIDERATIONS ON CLIMATES AND GREAT BASIN CULTURES

At this point we return to the questions posed by Aschmann, Jennings, Martin, and Bryan and Gruhn. Aschmann's objections to the Neothermal climatic sequence are essentially based on theoretical climatology. Aschmann (1958, p. 35) says: "The evidence for the so-called Altithermal from 5000 B.C. to 2000 B.C., when the Great Basin was supposed to be uninhabitable, I find lacking. On Meighan's [unpublished] correlation chart of May 1955, the period is well documented with dated sites as one would expect considering its temporal

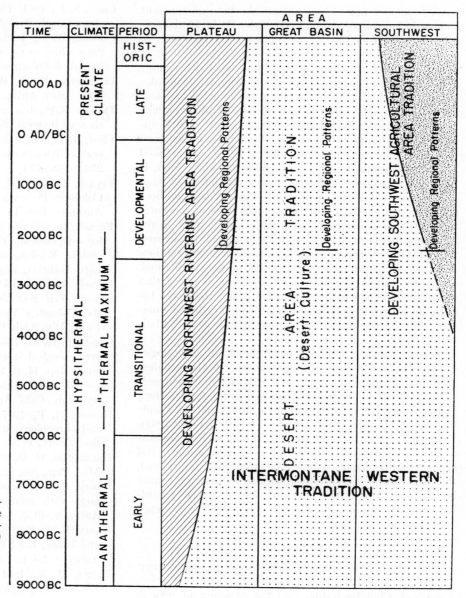

Figure 4. Schematic pattern of development of the Intermontane western archaeological tradition. (After Daugherty, 1962)

remoteness." While it may be true that there were people living in the Great Basin during the Altithermal, the evidence of occupation becomes very much more abundant after 2500 B.C., indicating a marked increase in population density. This seems to us to argue strongly that there was an improvement in climate. Whether this improvement involved rising temperature or increasing precipitation, or both, we are not able to say, but we assume that the indicated increase in population reflects more surface water and greater amounts of plant and animal food.

Jennings' objections stem from his interpretation of archaeological evidence at Danger Cave, which does not seem to fit with signs of climatic change. We have mentioned the undated Level D III in the sequence at Danger Cave and continue to feel justified in using the Antevs scheme elsewhere because it fits well with archaeological facts. Danger Cave may be an archaeological anomaly, for reasons not understood at this time.

In Figure 4 the "Developing Regional Patterns" in the Columbia Plateau, the Great Basin, and the Southwest are indicated as beginning at 2500 B.C. or at about the end of the Altithermal. If so, is this to be accounted for by a massive migration over the entire area? Probably not, because different artifact types were introduced in different regions. Even if the changes are accountable as the result of migration, why did this occur at this particular time? There appears to us to be much evidence suggesting that Antevs' scheme is still useful and will continue to be so in the future.

Martin's objections (1963a, 1963b), as we have noted, are based primarily upon pollen profiles from the Southwest. We are not competent to question the biologic or climatic inferences drawn from his data. We point out, however, a lack of dated pollen for the period from 7,900 to 5,300 years ago—the major part of the Altithermal. Martin believes that pollen from 5,300 to 4,100 years old indicates an increase in moisture rather than a decrease, which he attributes to increased summer rain. This is about the time of apparent increase in human population in the Great Basin. His botanical inferences from this are as follows (Martin, 1963a, p. 67): "What did the desert grassland look like in Altithermal time? Increased summer rain would produce a richer cover of perennial gramma grasses and would bring the blue oaks, Emory oaks, and Chihuahua pines to lower elevations." Martin goes on to describe a marvelous landscape which "sparkled emerald, the color of a spring pasture on a Pennsylvania farm" during the month of August. That must have been very pleasant in August, but the plants used as food may have depended not on summer but on winter rain. If the winter rain decreased as the summer rain increased—and Martin does not argue against this—then living conditions may have worsened in spite of a net increase in precipitation. The pine-nut crop in particular, a crucial item in the Southwestern aboriginal diet, may have suffered. In any case the cultural record in southern Arizona shows that conditions improved for some reason at the end of the Altithermal. Bryan and Gruhn, it seems to us, are right in saying that the postglacial climate was not everywhere the same, because there may have been a variety of local or broad situations differing from place to place or from latitude to latitude.

Actually, much of the local establishment of chronologies has already been done by scientists in other fields, including both geology and palynology, and striking parallel chronologies appear from areas as far removed as the southwestern United States (summarized by Malde, 1964) and the Pacific Northwest (Hansen, 1947; Heusser, 1960; Fryxell, 1963). Unless the great mass of data indicating that there was a postglacial climatic interval of maximum warmth and drought can be demonstrated to be erroneously interpreted, the basic Antevs concept of the Altithermal interval cannot be discarded. The implications of ecological changes regarding interpretation of archaeological evidence likewise cannot be ignored.

REFERENCES

Antevs, Ernst, 1948, Climatic changes and pre-white man: Univ. Utah Bull., v. 38, p. 168-191

—— 1952, Climatic history and the antiquity of man in California: Berkeley, Univ. California Arch. Surv. Rep. 16, p. 23-31

—— 1955, Geologic-climatic dating in the West: Amer. Antiq., v. 20, p. 317-335

—— 1962, Late Quaternary climates in Arizona: Amer. Antiq., v. 28, p. 193-198

Aschmann, H. H., 1958, Great Basin climates in relation to human occupance: Berkeley, Univ. California Arch. Surv. Rep. 42, p. 23-40

Broecker, W. S., and Orr, P. C., 1958, Radiocarbon chronology of Lake Lahontan and Lake Bonneville: Geol. Soc. Amer. Bull., v. 69, p. 1009-1032

Bryan, A. T., and Gruhn, Ruth, 1964, Problems relating to the Neothermal climatic sequence: Amer. Antiq., v. 29, p. 307-315

Butler, B. R., 1962, Contributions to the prehistory of the Columbia Plateau: Idaho State Coll. Mus. Occ. Pap. 9, 86 p.

Cook, S. F., 1964, The nature of charcoal excavated at archaeological sites: Amer. Antiq., v. 29, p. 514-517

Cottam, W. P., Tucker, J. M., and Drobnick, Rudy, 1959, Some clues to Great Basin postpluvial climates provided by oak distribution: Ecology, v. 40, p. 361-377

Daugherty, R. D., 1962, The intermontane western tradition: Amer. Antiq., v. 28, p. 144-150

Deevey, E. S., Jr., and Flint, R. F., 1957, Postglacial hypsithermal interval: Science, v. 125, p. 182-184

Flint, R. F., and Gale, W. A., 1958, Stratigraphy and radiocarbon dates at Searles Lake, California: Amer. J. Sci., v. 256, p. 689-714

Fryxell, Roald, 1964, Summary of postglacial history of the Columbia Plateau: Pullman, Washington State Univ., Lab. Anthrop., Rep. Inv. No. 27, p. 30-31

Fryxell, Roald, and Cook, E. F., 1964, A field guide to the loess deposits and channeled scablands of the Palouse area, eastern Washington: Pullman, Washington State Univ., Lab. Anthrop., Rep. Inv. No. 27, 32 p.

Fryxell, Roald, and Daugherty, R. D., 1963, Late glacial and postglacial geological and archaeological chronology of the Columbia Plateau, Washington: Washington State Univ., Div. Arch. Geochron., Rep. Inv. No. 23, 22 p.

Grosscup, G. L., 1954, Radiocarbon dates from Nevada of archaeological interest: Berkeley, Univ. California Arch. Surv. Rep. 44, p. 17-31

—— 1956, The archaeology of the Carson Sink area: Berkeley, Univ. Calif. Arch. Surv. Rep. No. 33, p. 58-64

Hansen, H. P., 1947, Postglacial forest succession, climate and chronology in the Pacific Northwest: Amer. Philos. Soc. Trans., v. 37, 130 p.

Harrington, M. R., 1933, Gypsum Cave, Nevada: Southwest Mus. Pap., No. 8, 197 p.

Haury, E. W., Antevs, Ernst, and Lance, J. F., 1953, Artifacts with mammoth remains, Naco, Arizona: Amer. Antiq., v. 19, p. 1-24

Haury, E. W., Sayles, E. B., Wasley, William, Antevs, Ernst, and Lance, J. F., 1959, The Lehner mammoth site: Amer. Antiq., v. 25, p. 1-42

Heizer, R. F., 1951, Preliminary report on the Leonard Rockshelter site, Pershing County, Nevada: Amer. Antiq., v. 17, p. 89-98

—— 1956, Recent cave explorations in the lower Humboldt Valley, Nevada: Berkeley, Univ. California Arch. Surv. Rep. No. 33, p. 50-57

Heizer, R. F., and Baumhoff, M. A., 1962, Prehistoric rock art of Nevada and eastern California: Berkeley, Univ. California Press, 412 p.

Heizer, R. F., and Krieger, A. D., 1956, The archaeology of Humboldt Cave, Churchill County, Nevada: Berkeley, Univ. California Publ. Amer. Arch. Ethnal., v. 47, No. 1, p. 1-190

Heusser, C. J., 1960, Late Pleistocene environments of North Pacific North America: New York, Amer. Geogr. Soc., Spec. Publ. 35, 308 p.

Hubbs, C. L., and Miller, R. R., 1948, The zoological evidence; correlation between fish distribution and hydrographic history in the desert basins of western United States: Univ. Utah Bull., v. 38, p. 18-166

Jennings, J. D., 1957, Danger Cave: Univ. Utah Anthrop. Pap., No. 27, 328 p.

—— 1964, The desert west, *in* Jennings, J. D. and Norbeck, Edw. (eds.), Prehistoric Man in the New World: Chicago, Univ. Chicago Press, p. 149-174

Jennings, J. D., and Norbeck, Edward, 1955, Great Basin prehistory; a review: Amer. Antiq., v. 21, p. 1-11

Lanning, E. P., 1963, Archaeology of the Rose Spring site, Iny-372: Berkeley, Univ. California Publ. Amer. Arch. Ethnal., v. 49, p. 237-336

Loud, L. L., and Harrington, M. R., 1929, Lovelock Cave: Berkeley, Univ. Calif. Publ. Amer. Arch. Ethnal., v. 25, No. 1, 183 p.

Malde, H. E., 1964, Environment and man in arid America: Science, v. 145, p. 123-129

Malde, H. E., and Schick, A. P., 1964, Thorne Cave, northeastern Utah; geology: Amer. Antiq., v. 30, p. 60-73

Martin, P. S., 1963a, The last 10,000 years; a fossil pollen record of the American Southwest: Tucson, Univ. Arizona Press, 87 p.

—— 1963b, Early man in Arizona; the pollen evidence: Amer. Antiq., v. 29, p. 67-73

Morrison, R. B., 1961, Lake Lahontan stratigraphy and history in the Carson Desert (Fallon) Area, Nevada: U.S. Geol. Surv. Prof. Pap. 424-D, p. 111-114

—— 1964, Lake Lahontan: Geology of southern Carson Desert, Nevada: U.S. Geol. Surv. Prof. Pap. 401, 156 p.

Rozaire, C. E., 1963, Lake-side cultural specializations in the Great Basin: Nevada State Mus. Anthrop. Pap. 9, p. 72-77

Sayles, E. B., and Antevs, Ernst, 1941, The Cochise culture: Medallion Pap., v. 29, p. 1-81

Sears, P. B., and Roosma, Aino, 1961, A climatic sequence from two Nevada caves: Amer. J. Sci., v. 259, p. 669-678

Shutler, Richard, 1961, Correlation of beach terraces with climatic cycles of Pluvial Lake Lahontan, Nevada: New York Acad. Sci. Ann. v. 95, p. 513-520

Steward, J. H., 1938, Basin-plateau aboriginal sociopolitical groups: Smithson. Instn., Bur. Amer. Ethnal. Bull. 120, 346 p.

Tamers, M. A., Pearson, F. J., Jr., and Davis, E. M., 1964, University of Texas Radiocarbon dates II: Radiocarbon, v. 6, p. 138-159

Thomas, H. E., 1962, The meteorologic phenomenon of drought in the Southwest: U.S. Geol. Surv. Prof. Pap. 372-A, 42 p.

Wallace, W. J., 1958, Archaeological investigations in Death Valley Monument, 1952-1957: Berkeley, Univ. California Arch. Surv. Rep. 42, p. 7-22

Warren, C. N., and de Costa, John, 1964, Dating Lake Mohave artifacts and beaches: Amer. Antiq., v. 30, p. 206-209

Wells, P. V., and Jorgensen, C. D., 1964, Pleistocene wood rat middens and climatic change in the Mohave Desert; a record of juniper woodlands: Science, v. 143, p. 1171-1173

Williams, P. A., and Orlins, Robert, 1963, The Corn Creek Dunes site: Nevada State Mus. Anthrop. Pap. No. 10, 48 p.

Wormington, H. Marie, 1957, Ancient man in North America: Denver Mus. Nat. Hist., 4th ed., 322 p.

SUMMARY

Examination is made of some of the views, notably those of Achmann, Jennings, Martin, and Bryan and Gruhn, recently expressed in opposition to or substantial modification of the postglacial climatic sequence proposed by Antevs. Evidence of climatic changes and synchronous cultural changes in the Desert West are summarized. The four-stage Cochise culture sequence of southern Arizona appears to show reflections of climatic change. The sequence in the western Great Basin and the Columbia Plateau gives clear support for the Antevs scheme. In the eastern Great Basin the evidence from Danger Cave appears to contradict the notion of post-Pleistocene climatic change, but it is open to question. In general, the archaeological evidence supports the Antevs climatic sequence.

PACIFIC COAST ARCHAEOLOGY *

CLEMENT W. MEIGHAN[1]

THE PACIFIC COAST has experienced a great deal of active archaeological investigation since World War II, and although there remain large gaps in our knowledge (both of areal coverage and of chronological periods) it is possible to present a general outline of human prehistory for the region. Previous summaries and general articles relevant to the archaeology of the Pacific Coast include Krieger (1962), Heizer (1950, 1952), and Meighan (1959). Because these articles are already out of date in some particulars, it is unnecessary to repeat here the detailed chronological charts and other information they contain.

The present summary cannot review comprehensively all of the previous summary articles, let alone the dozens of individual site reports and other studies now available. The focus here is on the Pacific Coast proper, primarily the margin of the Pacific Ocean extending inland to the Sierra Nevada and Cascade Ranges but not beyond. Most of the relevant work has been done within a few miles of the Pacific shore. Inland sites, particularly in southern California, eastern Oregon, and eastern Washington, are properly dealt with as part of Great Basin cultural history. The discussion here will also concentrate on recent work. For finds on which no new information has been obtained recently (such as the Borax Lake site in northern California) adequate details are available from one of the general summaries of North American archaeology, such as that of Wormington (1957).

In time, the emphasis will be on sites older than five thousand years. Sites less than 5,000 years old are relevant primarily for their ecology and have little to contribute to knowledge of the earliest human settlement. This time limitation results in a very brief commentary for much of the Pacific Coast, since we have no documented sites older than 5,000 years for much of the coastline. This does not mean that such sites do not exist; even the most conservative scholar believes much of the Pacific Coast to have been settled and inhabited by at least 8,000 to 10,000 years ago. The relative scarcity of older sites is therefore a reflection of the present state of our archaeological knowledge rather than a true picture of cultural history.

The general emphasis on more recent sites can be seen in the distribution of radiocarbon dates. For California alone, 164 published radiocarbon dates (most of them tabulated in Jelinek, 1962) are distributed in the following time periods:

* For letters and consultations concerning recent work, I am much indebted to A. C. Spaulding, R. E. Greengo, R. S. Kidd, and R. Berger. C. L. Warren and D. L. True kindly permitted use of their illustrations of San Dieguito artifacts.
[1] Department of Anthropology, University of California, Los Angeles, California.

Less than 4,000 years ago:	122
4,000-7,500 years ago:	30
7,500-9,500 years ago:	0
9,500-12,500 years ago:	5
More than 12,500 years ago:	7

A more detailed breakdown, by millennia, is given in Table 1. It is clear that most of our chronological information comes from relatively recent remains. There are several reasons for this: (1) Older sites are harder to find and are more apt to be buried or destroyed by erosional processes. (2) Many of the older sites have not yielded anything that can be used to provide a radiocarbon date; no organic material has survived. (3) The oldest sites often have such crude and limited cultural remains as to yield little information for the cultural historian. Beyond proving that man was at a given place at an early date, they provide no real information about man's way of life. Many archaeologists therefore prefer to deal with more recent sites yielding more abundant cultural evidence.

ORIGINS OF MAN ON THE PACIFIC COAST

The questions of origin of human settlement are of course of great interest and have drawn much study and more speculation. Out of the welter of conflicting statements about Early Man along the Pacific Coast, there is developing a most interesting and exciting picture. However, only the general outlines of the picture are beginning to emerge, and considerably more study will be necessary before conclusions can be stated with real assurance. The time span about which we know something is steadily increasing. Ten years ago, prior to extensive excavations and a broad program of radiocarbon dating, a history of man acceptable to all scholars could not go back more than about 4,000 years on the Pacific Coast, even though we knew from older dates in the Great Basin and elsewhere that Pacific Coast history must

TABLE 1

Distribution of West Coast Radiocarbon Dates by Millennia

Years ago	California	Oregon & Washington
<2,000	60	17
2,000-3,000	14	2
3,000-4,000	27	0
4,000-5,000	23	0
5,000-6,000	8	0
6,000-7,000	13	1
7,000-8,000	7	2
8,000-9,000	0	1
9,000-12,000	4	1
>12,000	7	0

have greater antiquity. At present our knowledge of Pacific Coast history is relatively firm back to about 8,000 years in some areas, with scattered indications that our cultural continuum will be firmly documented to at least 10,000 to 12,000 years in the near future. Although this is not very exciting news to the Early Man enthusiasts, some of whom consider a 10,000-year-old site to be quite late in the sequence, the general picture is one of developing scholarly knowledge.

Conclusions about human origins along the Pacific Coast are influenced by two factors. One is a universal problem—unpublished data. For many of the radiocarbon dates, the evidence for human association or cultural context has not been presented beyond newspaper accounts and brief assertions. Some of the most important radiocarbon dates, and many of the older ones, are in this category. Their significance is not open to analysis until the discoverers have had time to present the full scholarly evidence, and some of the potentially important dates must therefore be ignored here.

A second problem, and one directly relevant to the above questions of evidence presented, lies in the nature of the evidence for human activity. What constitutes unquestionable evidence of man's presence? Some investigators have uncritically accepted the presence of charcoal as evidence of man (a completely fallacious assumption); some have held that a burned or partially carbonized animal bone is evidence of man; and some will not accept evidence of man short of actual human skeletons or an assemblage of unquestionable man-made objects. Skeletons and unquestionable tools may be regarded as definitive evidence, charcoal and burned bone as only "possible," with greater or lesser degree of probability depending upon subsidiary lines of evidence.

The search for origins of man on the Pacific Coast has been considerably obscured by the assumption that charcoal is indicative of man's presence and that any pocket of charcoal can be identified as a "hearth." Not only is this assumption invalid, but in several cases the collector of the charcoal has not taken adequate care to be sure that his black stuff *is* charcoal before sending it to the dating laboratory. Dates have been requested on samples of asphaltum, for example. Recent studies of these problems have been published by Cook (1964) and Cruxent (1962).

A special mention must be made here of the work of Carter, "Pleistocene Man at San Diego" (1957), since the reconstruction of cultural history given in this work differs from that of all other scholars. The question of human origins on the Pacific Coast in this work is treated as a question of geological history in which claims are made of the discovery of man in the last interglacial age in San Diego County. This is stated to mean human evidence over 60,000 years ago and beyond the reach of radiocarbon dating. If these claims are valid, the whole picture of human origins in the New World will be subject to drastic revision. However, the evidence for the claimed ancient man has not been acceptable to most writers. The work has been critically reviewed by several archaeologists, including Krieger (1958) and Johnson and Miller (1958). The present paper cannot discuss Carter's work in detail, but without regard to his interpretations of geology and soil it can be demonstrated that the archaeological part of this study is largely erroneous as to dates, sequence, and content of southern California archaeological sites. This blunt statement can now be made on the basis of new evidence not available to Carter at the time of his work. He was able to cite only 20 radiocarbon dates and had entirely inadequate site descriptions to work with. There are now some 100 radiocarbon dates for the region and much more detailed descriptions of the associated artifact inventories. The thesis of Warren (1964) largely supplants Carter's version of San Diego archaeology and should be consulted for an up-to-date summary. No firm evidence for interglacial man exists on the Pacific Coast, despite the claims for such a discovery.

DATES OVER 12,500 YEARS AGO

In the broad time periods previously mentioned in the tabulation of radiocarbon dates, there are 7 dates over 12,500 years ago. Two additional dates greater than 32,000 years ago are on Jelinek's (1962) list of dates but clearly do not apply to human activity. All of the 7 dates here considered are in southern California—4 from Santa Rosa Island, 1 from La Jolla, and 2 from the Lake Manix shoreline. No radiocarbon dates in this time range are asserted to be associated with man anywhere else on the Pacific Coast. Of the dates given, the Lake Manix and La Jolla dates apply to geological phenomena and are not applicable in any firm way to Early Man. The Santa Rosa dates have been published only in a preliminary way; some are apparently dates of geological significance only, but evidence may eventually link these dates to human occupation of the West Coast. Until the evidence is published and evaluated, it would be premature to accept or reject these dates as applying to human activity.

9,500 TO 12,500 YEARS AGO

More useful at present for questions of Early Man are the dates in the time range 9,500 to 12,500 years ago. California has 5 published dates in this time range; they include 3 from Santa Rosa Island, 1 from Lake LeConte and 1 from Lake Mohave. One of the Santa Rosa dates has been published by Orr (1962a, b) and is claimed to apply to some weathered human bones from Arlington Springs site. The other Santa Rosa dates are not firmly attached to human activity.

A recently published date (Berger *et al.*, 1964) indicates the survival of dwarf mammoth on Santa Rosa Island until as recently as 8,000 years ago (UCLA-705). Association of human and mammoth remains is already accepted in several localities outside California in the time range 11,000 to 13,000 years ago. Association between man and mammoth has been claimed by Orr (1964) in the same time range (*ca.* 12,500 years) within California. This 8,000-year date is of considerable interest because of the 7,500-year dates for the beginning of the La Jolla culture. Since the La Jolla assemblage represents a seed-grinding, small-game-hunting, shellfish-collecting people and is quite different from the preceding San Dieguito material, it may be possible to correlate the sharp cultural change with the demise of the Pleistocene-type fauna, occurring at different times in different regions but apparently relatively late in time in southern California.

There is another important significance to the 8,000-year

date for mammoth on Santa Rosa. On the one hand, such a late date seems feasible, since the dwarf form of mammoth (6 ft high) on Santa Rosa is presumably the end product of some considerable time spent in evolutionary change (the full-size mammoth persisting in the Southwest until 11,000 or 12,000 years ago). It is therefore conceivable that the island dwarf form could have persisted into recent times. On the other hand, it is barely conceivable that human hunters could have subsisted on this form for several thousand years in a restricted island environment of only 52,000 acres. Rainer Berger has reminded me that Santa Rosa has fluctuated in area with recent sea-level changes and that the island may have been as much as ten times its present size 8,000 to 10,000 years ago. However, the island has not been connected to the mainland during the history of man, so the general point is still valid, namely, that large and slow-breeding animals confined to a limited area are highly vulnerable to primitive hunters. Hence, if the 8,000-year date for mammoth proves valid, it makes a man-mammoth association more likely for the island but makes those dates greater than 12,000 years much less likely for this situation.

The finds from the La Brea tar pits should also be mentioned here because this site with its rich Pleistocene fauna would appear an ideal place to find evidence of ancient man. Some artifacts and one human skeleton were found in the LaBrea tar pits, but four manufactured wooden objects believed to be spear fragments gave a radiocarbon date of 4,400 years ago. Trees from the La Brea material have been dated at over 14,000 years ago. It is thus clear (Howard, 1960) that the Indian specimens are younger than the Pleistocene fossils.

The two lake-shore datings in this group of old dates are not taken from archaeological material and cannot be directly applied to man. However, indirectly they may be good evidence for man of the time. The Lake Mohave date, in particular, is of considerable importance if it can be related to the Lake Mohave site (Campbell *et al.*, 1937). Considerable argument has been spent on the question of whether the Lake Mohave site was occupied at a time when the lake was full of water. The original describers of the site assumed that it was occupied when the lake was full. This assumption was challenged by Rogers (1939), who believed that the site was below the level of the overflow channel of the lake and hence would have been under water when the lake was full. Later Brainerd (1953), on the basis of careful contour mapping, showed that the overflow channel crossed the site but did not cover it. With all the evidence together, there is no reason to deny the contemporaneity of human occupation and lake filling; hence the date of 9,640 ± 200 years ago (LJ-200) can be applied with some confidence to the artifact complex of the Lake Mohave culture. Lake Mohave is properly a Great Basin site, but the characteristic artifacts are comparable to those of the San Dieguito site and culture, so this material and the date are relevant to the coastal sequence as well. The interpretations just made are not inconsistent with the stratigraphy and dates for the San Dieguito and subsequent La Jolla material (Moriarty *et al.*, 1959; Warren and True, 1961; Warren, 1964; Shumway *et al.*, 1961).

The Lake LeConte date (9,630 ± 300 years ago, LJ-528)

also does not apply directly to human activity. The date is noteworthy for its remarkable closeness to the Lake Mohave date. The implications for the archaeologist are clear: the lake terraces of southern California are the places to look for Early Man sites, although the same terraces have remains of different ages on them, as discussed later.

Other West Coast dates in this time range include 9,785 years ago for the bottom of the site at The Dalles, Oregon (Cressman, 1960, p. 66). Cressman believes the earliest occupation of the site began 11,000 or more years ago. Most of the collection from his early horizon, however, appears to fall in the period 6,000 to 8,000 years ago and hence belongs in the time period discussed below. The culture is a riverine one emphasizing salmon-fishing, bird-hunting, and some mammal-hunting.

7,500 TO 9,500 YEARS AGO

The time range 7,500 to 9,500 years ago is represented by radiocarbon-dated sites in Oregon, British Columbia, and the Aleutians, but there is virtually no dated evidence for man in this time period from sites south of Oregon. This does not mean that the southern areas were unoccupied until later, for dates older than this period do exist for southern California, as mentioned previously.

Besides The Dalles, referred to above, a similar kind of site and ecological situation is in the Fraser Canyon, British Columbia, with a radiocarbon date of 8,150 years ago (Borden, 1960). Finally, the site of Anangula in the Aleutians has 3 radiocarbon dates of 8,425, 7,990, and 7,660 years ago (Black and Laughlin, 1964). Although this site is contemporaneous with the others mentioned, it is apparently quite different in artifact content, and the ecological adaptations of the people are not clear. The site appears to be a place where stone flake tools were manufactured.

In the south, a single radiocarbon date of 7,530 years ago (LJ-454) presumably applies to the La Jolla culture and is at the very end of this two-millennia period. Perhaps chance and inadequate data are responsible for this gap in the record of human occupation, but because there are 12 radiocarbon dates of greater age and no fewer than 30 for the subsequent period in California there may be something significant in human history that explains the apparent gap in the historical record. Some pure speculation on this point: (1) Possibly the coastal strip was not occupied until 7,500 years ago (conceivable, but seems unlikely). (2) The diminution of Pleistocene big game may have caused a reduction in population so that there are fewer sites in this time period. (3) Some ecological change of regional importance (west of the Sierra Nevada) may have restricted or inhibited human activity during this period.

Whether or not this time period is truly a gap in the record of human activity, it is clear that some explanation of what was going on during these 2,000 years is important to our understanding of human development on the West Coast.

The best-described cultural complex for this period is that of the San Dieguito site and culture. The type site is the C. W. Harris site on the San Dieguito River, excavated originally by M. J. Rogers, defined in considerably more detail by later excavations of Warren and True (1961), and currently under investigation by Ezell and Moriarty. Although San Dieguito artifact types are found widely in the coastal region and in the deserts of southern California—the Lake Mohave–Playa material (True, 1958)—the Harris site is the only one so far excavated where a large sample of adequately published material has a stratigraphic context. The San Dieguito specimens occur in the gravel deposits of the San Dieguito River but are not rolled or waterworn. They probably result from a campsite that was located in the wide bed of the San Dieguito River and was later buried under alluvium from the adjacent hills. Over the San Dieguito material occurs a layer of river silt slightly less than a meter thick containing no cultural material. Above this is a thicker cultural deposit, which has La Jolla cultural materials in it (radiocarbon dated at 6,300 years ago) and in the upper levels pottery of the recent Indians in this region. The site is of great importance because it clarifies a number of controversial questions in coastal archaeology and permits us to draw the following conclusions:

1. San Dieguito is older than La Jolla on the basis of the stratigraphy and the radiocarbon date (this sequence has been reversed by some writers).

2. San Dieguito must precede, by an unknown amount, 7,500 years ago because that date represents the beginnings of the subsequent La Jolla culture. At the moment, the Lake Mohave date previously mentioned is an indirect indicator of where San Dieguito culture may fall in time. On the basis of this and the stratigraphy, an estimate of 7,500 to 9,500 years ago for the San Dieguito culture is not unreasonable (Warren and True, 1961, p. 261, estimate the age as 8,000 to 11,000 years).

The artifact assemblage from the San Dieguito site includes large leaf-shaped points, cutting and scraping tools, and little else. One grinding stone is reported in dubious association; it seems likely that the San Dieguito people did not have seed-grinding implements. No objects of bone or shell have been found, probably because of poor conditions for preservation of such items. An inventory of this type clearly represents a culture dependent upon hunting for subsistence and comparable in a general way to such North American finds as Folsom and Clovis (Llano). In the latter examples, the bones of large game animals of the terminal Pleistocene are associated with the artifacts. No such find is yet available for San Dieguito, but presumably the artifacts were used in the hunting of some sort of large game animal.

4,000 TO 7,500 YEARS AGO

This time period is represented by 30 radiocarbon dates in California, most of them for sites on the south coast from north of Santa Barbara down into Baja California. The two dates from central California apply to the Early Central California cultural horizon.

The southern dates clearly apply to a widespread cultural horizon to which Wallace (1955) gave the term Early Milling Stone Horizon. Various site names and cultural terms have been applied to this horizon: Oak Grove, Topanga, Zuma Beach, and La Jolla. Although some regional differences can be seen, a general cultural uniformity exists from

Avila (San Luis Obispo County) to about half way down the peninsula of Baja California. Not only are the characteristic materials concentrated in this 3,500-year period, but many basic similarities can be seen. What is involved here is a basically land-oriented, seed-using complex with milling stones or metates as the common household implement, abundant crude stone core tools, few stone projectile points, and little evidence of utilization of marine resources even though many of the sites overlook the Pacific. Although the sites contain shell and fishbones and thus the people were not entirely ignorant of the sea and its resources, such finds are scarce and limited in variety as compared to those of later peoples.

4,000 YEARS AGO TO THE PERIOD OF WHITE CONTACT

The past 4,000 years of the archaeological record show increasing population, diversification of culture, adaptation to many specialized ecological niches, and a general (although not universal) shift toward the greater use of marine resources. Several of the cultures in this time period represent communities in which fishing was the primary economic activity; such communities are not demonstrable prior to about 4,000 years ago.

ANCIENT HUMAN SKELETONS

Several finds of human bones or skeletons have been made on the West Coast in contexts suggesting an antiquity of at least several thousand years. These finds are regrettably unaccompanied by artifacts that would permit us to associate the skeletal remains with one of the older tool industries. Further, while some finds suggest contemporaneity with extinct animals, a completely certain association with Pleistocene fauna is not yet demonstrable for the human remains. This is a perennial problem in archaeology because of the common practice of grave-digging, which results in the transfer of the skeleton to a deeper layer than that on which the individual had lived. Finally, dating of these finds is extraordinarily difficult, and none has been directly dated. The recently developed dating technique using the organic components of bone (Berger *et al.*, 1964) may permit direct dating of some of these early skeletons.

Because of these various difficulties, the presumed early skeletons are not very informative beyond indicating man's presence at an early date. A brief summary of the major finds is sufficient here (see also the summary of Heizer, 1950).

ARLINGTON SPRINGS MAN

Two human femora plus an unidentified third bone were found in the bank of Arlington Canyon, Santa Rosa Island, California (Orr, 1962a, b). Charcoal "in direct contact with the bones" was dated at 10,390 years ago, and a second sample from a foot away was dated at 9,950 years ago. The charcoal dates the level but not necessarily the skeletal remains.

STANFORD MAN

A human skull was found at a depth of *ca.* 6 m in the gravels of San Francisquito Creek on the campus of Stanford University in Central California. No direct evidence of age is available, although the find is described as a "probable early man" (Heizer and McCown, 1950).

LOS ANGELES MAN

An incomplete skeleton was found at a depth of 4 m in the sediments of the Los Angeles Valley, California. In the same stratum some distance away were found remains of *Archidiskodon*, the Imperial elephant. Heizer (1952, p. 7) believes that fluorine dating confirms the contemporaneity of the human and elephant bones. No artifacts were associated.

GENERAL HISTORICAL RECONSTRUCTION

From the evidence now available, a broad picture of West Coast prehistory can be attempted. In the beginning, the coastal area was settled from inland regions at a time preceding 8,000 years ago. This statement is based on the generally land-oriented tool assemblages and the present knowledge of chronology. The geographic barriers of the West Coast mountains may have delayed the settlement of the coastal areas until some time after man's entry into the New World.

The earliest West Coast peoples, along the entire length of the coast, appear to have been hunters who concentrated on larger game and had no particular interest in or involvement with the resources of the sea. By about 7,500 years ago, at least part of the coastal region was widely settled, and a shift took place to a more varied and diversified kind of economy, with close adaptation to the resources of the numerous ecological niches of the western coastline. In general, however, plant foods appear to have been basic, and a generalized hunting-gathering economy flourished, dependent on broad utilization of many plant and animal varieties (including the lesser ones). There is some indication that specialized riverine and lakeshore adaptations began to develop at this time in the areas where such adaptation was possible. Adaptation to the Pacific Ocean also began then and included the gathering of shellfish, hunting of sea mammals (probably largely on the beaches and thus with the same weapons and techniques as were used for land animals), and a limited amount of ocean fishing. The latter implies the development of some sort of boat. Compared to later peoples, however, they exploited the sea much less, and the ocean provided only supplemental food until about 4,000 to 5,000 years ago. From 4,000 years ago to the disappearance of Indian culture, all areas of the West Coast have had some peoples who were primarily dependent on ocean resources. The general picture is one of increasing familiarity with the ocean and increasing skill at exploiting it.

General syntheses of West Coast prehistory have tended to assume that an inland orientation prevailed, at least for the early settlements of the region. This view is seen in such general terms as "Intermontane Western Tradition" (Daugherty, 1962), "Trans-Cascadian" (Swanson, 1962), "Old Cordilleran" (Butler, 1961), and "Desert Culture" (Jennings and Norbeck, 1955). All of these terms have been applied to aboriginal occupation in the west, and all of them bear the implications of origin in a non-coastal situation.

The progressive shift toward ocean resources is abundantly documented for southern California. The same conclusion has been reached by Cressman (1960, p. 7) for Oregon:

"Interior Oregon was occupied from approximately the end of the Pleistocene, about 11,000 years ago. . . . Oregon coastal cultural manifestations, even at the ethnographic level, indicate an interior orientation in its social complexity. . . . Therefore, the hypothesis is advanced that population movements from the earlier occupied interior down the river valleys were responsible for the initial occupation of the Oregon coast."

Farther north, some quite old dates are reported for coastal locations in the Aleutians. The site of Anangula in the eastern Aleutians has 3 radiocarbon dates, averaging 8,025 years ago. In reporting the geology of the site, Black and Laughlin (1964) comment on the culture as follows: "It is apparent that ancient man in this region, if he was sea-oriented, would usually have had his home along the edge of the Bering Sea platform that is now under many meters of water. That he was sea-oriented at Anangula is the most reasonable interpretation."

The cultural remains from Anangula have not yet been reported in sufficient detail to support this tentative suggestion of a sea-oriented group.

Not quite so far north, another ancient site is known near Yale, British Columbia, on the Fraser River (anonymous, 1960; Borden, 1960). The site, excavated by Borden in 1959 and 1960, has an early date of 8,150 years ago. The culture was presumably riverine; the site is a favorite salmon-fishing spot in a narrow defile of the river.

From the sparse and scattered evidence available, it appears that the Cascade–Sierra Nevada ranges were a formidable obstacle to the spread of Early Man. Travelling on foot and living off the land, ancient man found the high elevations were impassable in winter and poor in plants and game in the summer. The original route of settlement of the New World is generally considered to have passed east of these mountains across ice-free land. The flow of human settlement then travelled through the river valleys to the West Coast and around the southern end of the Sierra Nevada to southern California. No doubt this population movement reached the shore of the Pacific at different times in different places —apparently by 8,000 years ago in British Columbia and the Aleutians, and about the same time in southern California. The middle coast (northern California, Oregon, southern Washington) seems on present evidence to have been settled somewhat later. Movement along the coast appears to have been remarkably limited at any time. It must be pointed out, however, that negative evidence is most unreliable in archaeology, particularly for Early Man, and that older coastal sites may yet be discovered.

EARLY TOOL ASSEMBLAGES

The assemblage of tools found in sites of Early Man provides evidence of the stage of his cultural development and his way of making a living. In addition, the tools are sometimes distinctive in form or style so that they permit comparative studies with finds from other areas. The older West Coast artifacts are of interest in these matters.

Two general classes of finds have been of particular importance—projectile points for the hunting of game and milling stones for the grinding of plant foods. Since both are relatively late in man's cultural history, some believe

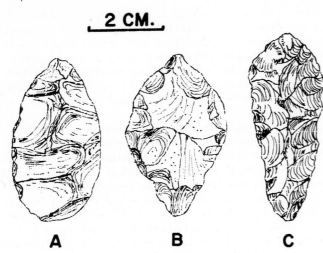

Figure 1. Projectile points from the Lake Mohave site, southern California. Materials from this site are apparently related, culturally and temporally, to the San Dieguito specimens from the southern California coastal region. A radiocarbon date of 9,640 ± 200 years ago applies to the filling of the lake and presumably to the associated cultural remains. Redrawn after Campbell *et al.* (1937, Pl. 51a, Pl. 43a, c).

that a New World culture lacking in one or both of these devices and hence of an age comparable to remains of similar simplicity in the Old World may be found. Krieger (1962) discusses the possibility of a "pre-projectile point" culture in the western United States. He feels that the evidence for such a stage is fairly abundant in both North and South America. However, in the western United States there are some major problems in identifying a "pre-projectile point" assemblage, with its implications of age and cultural simplicity. These problems, which have so far not been solved adequately for a single western location, include the following:

1. Many of the simpler western tribes in recent times made the great majority of their projectile points, to tip their arrows, of sharpened hardwood foreshafts. Archaeological samples of these cultures would appear to be "pre-projectile point" unless a large sample of specimens were obtained.

2. That this same practice may well have existed in the past is shown by the low frequency of projectile points in the milling-stone horizons of southern California, where the ratio of projectile points to other artifacts is as low as 1 to 400. Thus a collection of many hundred specimens is necessary before a "pre-projectile point" culture can be identified.

3. Quarry sites, chipping stations, and "workshops" may have abundant coarse and primitive worked-stone debris without any finished projectile points. These do not necessarily represent "pre-projectile point" horizons but merely specialized occupation sites.

The far-western sites that have been tentatively put forward as "pre-projectile point" can be disposed of, in my opinion, as follows:

1. Tule Springs, Nevada (Baumhoff and Heizer, this volume). Not of the age originally proposed; cultural sample inadequate for description of man's activities at the site.

2. Texas Street, San Diego County. In my opinion, not a site at all but a terrace of naturally fractured gravels.

3. Various Santa Rosa Island localities. Too little cultural evidence to permit conclusions—what has been presented so far is one scraper (Orr, 1964), a fragmentary human skeleton, some mammoth bones, and possible "hearths."

4. Scripps Campus of University of California. A charcoal lens in the side of the cliff. No human evidence is associated, and the lens may or may not be of human origin.

5. Lake Manix, California. All surface finds; inadequately described at present. This is the best contender for a tradition of great age that is not a projectile-point tradition; the

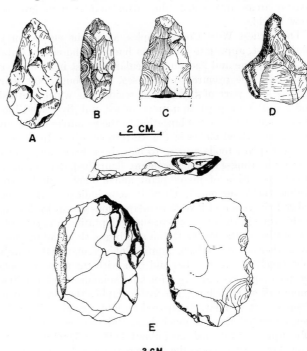

Figure 2. Specimens from the Farmington area, California. A-D, Projectile points and drill from site Sta-5, which may be related to the Farmington workshop sites; redrawn after Treganza (1952, Pl. 2B,E,H,O). E, Three views of a scraper from the Farmington complex. Abundant tools of this sort are found in the reworked Arroyo Seco gravels of Pleistocene age. No projectile points like A-C have been found in the gravels. Treganza and Heizer (1953, p. 32) estimate the age of the Farmington Complex at 9,000 to 7,000 years; redrawn after Treganza (1952, Pl. 1A). (Note that E is not drawn to same scale as A-D).

assemblages merit the most careful study and description.

6. Chapala Basin, Baja California. The early horizon is represented by a sample of only a few dozen artifacts. Presence of projectile points in the culture is still an open question.

7. Farmington Complex, in western foothills of the Sierra Nevada, central California. Krieger (1962, p. 142) refers to this as "another situation in which only crude core tools and large flakes have been recovered from no less than 58 sites, with projectile points absent." These sites are referred to in the original report (Treganza, 1952) as "Quarry-Workshops" to distinguish them from village sites. Treganza specifically states, "It is possible that sites such as Sta. 5, 6 and 10 located adjacent to some of the larger Quarry-Workshops may represent the villages occupied by the people who frequented the quarry sites." It is therefore uncertain whether the Farmington Complex represents a "pre-projectile point" culture for three reasons: (i) Of 19 quarry-workshops for which collections are tabulated (Treganza, 1952, p. 7), the collections range in number of specimens from 0 to 67 and average a dozen or so specimens per site (these were collected from stream-cut gravel banks, not excavated). These samples are too small to be certain that projectile points are absent. (ii) The describer identifies the sites as quarry-workshops, not villages. (iii) The village sites suggested for the Farmington Complex do contain projectile points (quite like those of the San Dieguito site, incidentally).

In sum, there may be a "pre-projectile point" horizon in the Far West, but I agree with Wallace (1962, p. 174) that it is certainly not convincingly demonstrated at the present time. Stone projectile points are known to be present in the oldest dated *assemblages* along the entire Pacific Coast.

A pre-milling-stone culture on the West Coast has also been hard to prove but seems now well established, being represented by the San Dieguito site, which had only one

2 CM.

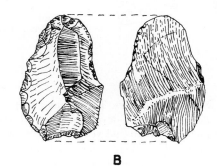

A   B

Figure 3. Projectile point and scraper from site DjRi 3, in the Fraser Canyon, British Columbia, about 160 km inland from the Gulf of Georgia. The levels from which the specimens came were dated at 8,150 ± 310 years ago; redrawn from Borden (1960, Pl. IV, Fig. 1a, b; Fig. 3b).

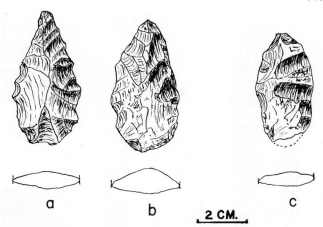

a   b   **2 CM.**   c

Figure 4. Projectile point from site SDi-149, type site of the San Dieguito culture of southern California. Estimated age: 8,000 to 11,000 years (Warren and True, 1961, p. 261, Fig. 4).

mano or hand stone in dubious association (Warren and True, 1961), and by the Lake Mohave material (Campbell *et al.*, 1937). Similar sites of hunting orientation are known for the Great Basin and the Southwest.

For some San Diego County sites, a somewhat curious argument has been followed in which absence of stone points is presumed to be evidence of great age while presence of milling stones in the same site does not preclude great age. Such argument, based on a collection of a dozen or fewer specimens, is completely meaningless.

The general assemblage of artifacts from west of the Cascade–Sierra Nevada ranges differs in detail from the forms found in the Great Basin and Southwest. The early hunting horizons of the interior are typified by fluted projectile points of the Clovis-Folsom tradition. The early hunting cultures of the western mountains and coast have been noted as using bi-pointed or leaf-shaped projectile points (anonymous, 1960; Daugherty, 1962; Butler, 1961). A variety of stone scrapers is also found, but so far no bone or shell objects. Unfortunately, the early sites of the West Coast have not yielded the bones of the animals hunted, and so far the stone tools have been found in one place and the animal bones in another. There is no association on the West Coast of an assemblage of tools with the bones of Pleistocene animals, unlike the Plains, Basin, and Southwest, where such associations can be demonstrated in at least a few sites of each region.

ARCHAEOLOGICAL CORRELATIONS OF
GEOLOGICAL AND CLIMATOLOGICAL PHENOMENA

Climatological associations. The relationship between archeological remains and climatic changes has been explored or mentioned by many western archaeologists, following the information presented by such writers as Antevs (1955) and Hubbs (1960). The interpretations of Antevs have provided a detailed frame of reference for the last 13,000 years, the period of most concern to western archaeology. The recent spate of publications concerned with critical review

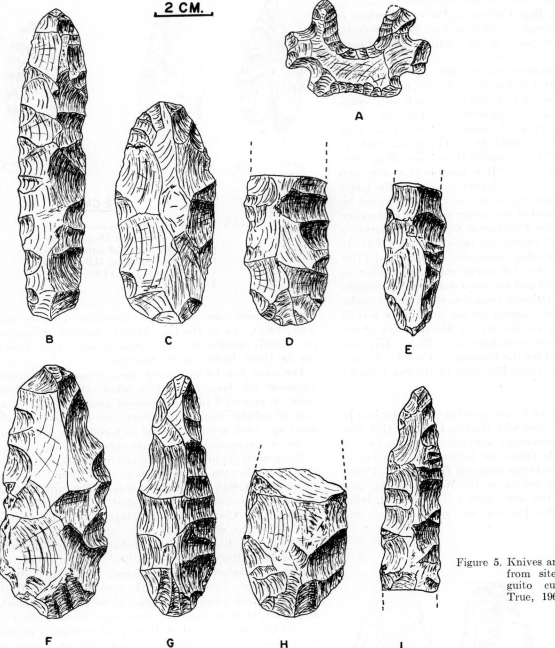

Figure 5. Knives and a crescentic object from site SDi-149, San Dieguito culture (Warren and True, 1961, Fig. 3).

of Antevs' work, and particularly with the nature of an "Altithermal" period, will no doubt force some revisions of archaeological thinking. So far as the West Coast archaeology is concerned, there is no real *archaeological* evidence of climatic fluctuations over the past several thousand years, and archaeologists have used the climatologist's schemes without contributing evidence of importance.

It should be noted that Antevs' Altithermal, from 4,000 to 7,500 years ago, corresponds fairly closely to the duration of the milling-stone cultures of coastal southern California. These cultures are markedly different from the cultures that preceded and followed them. To what extent the "cultural altithermal" can be explained in climatic terms, however, remains to be seen.

Sea-Level changes. The recent paper of Shepard (1964) indicates that sea level has risen at the rate of about one meter per thousand years for the past 6,000 years. In stable areas where there is no earth movement, this means that beach-line archaeological sites will be under water except for very recent settlements. That many sites are in fact submerged is well known, and it is also true that most sites found on modern beaches are quite late in time. However, this does not mean that all Early Man sites are accessible only with diving equipment. Instability of the land has been even greater in many Pacific areas, so that ancient beach sites are now often above the water. In addition, there was a common tendency for primitive man to live on an elevated spot with a good view of the sea, and accordingly most of the 4,000–7,000-year-old sites along the southern California coast are on the Pleistocene marine terraces. Nobody lives exactly at sea level, and the level of water in the ocean (or a lake) is not going to be the same as the level of a human encampment unless the people are living on a raft. Exact correlations should not be expected. The significance of the sea-level changes is clear, however, and must be taken into account by archaeologists seeking early sites along the coast.

An interesting archaeological site at Willow Creek, Monterey County, in the middle of the California coastline, has a bearing on the sea-level observations of Shepard. The archaeological site is on a buried beach *ca.* 1.5 m below the modern beach. The radiocarbon date of 1,900 years indicates the rise of sea level to be about at the rate Shepard reports. The site is not under water because it was on the uphill edge of the beach above the tide zone.

Lagoon silting. A common observation on West Coast shell middens is a shift from more open-water shellfish such as mussels to mud-dwellers such as clams. This has been reported for San Francisco Bay (Greengo, 1951), the Santa Barbara area (Greenwood, 1961), and the San Diego area (Warren, 1964). The explanation appears to lie in the silting in of bays and lagoons as alluvium is carried into them. The rising sea level mentioned above presumably causes the silt to pile up rather than carried out to sea.

Archaeologically, the sites of more than a couple of thousand years ago are therefore apt to be farther from open water now than they were originally (in some cases a distance of several kilometers inland). The apparent environmental resources of today are not those that led to the settlement pattern observed archaeologically.

Stream gravels. In a few cases, archaeological remains in California have been found in stream gravels in situations somewhat analogous to the common occurrence of artifacts in the glacial gravels of western Europe. However, the geology of the gravels is not worked out in detail, and they cannot be correlated with major glacial events at present. Two well-known examples may be mentioned: the materials of the Farmington Complex in central California (in the western foothills of the Sierra Nevada) and the San Dieguito site in San Diego County. In addition, the find of a human skull described as "Stanford Man" is also from stream gravels. The Texas Street site described by Carter (1957) is also a gravel terrace of immense proportions but critics of this find, including the writer, do not regard the site as containing man-made objects.

Ocean terraces. The West Coast ocean terraces of the Pleistocene are liberally sprinkled with archaeological sites, but so far the age of the sites seems to have no correlation with the age of the terraces. The terraces have been favored camping spots for thousands of years, but because people have legs and a common wish to live on level ground, there is no reason to assume that their camps represent anything but selection of a level area, often with a good view of the surroundings. The 12- and 30-m terraces in southern California contain many of the older sites; sites less than 2,000 years old are commonly on or immediately above the beach. Sites of any age can occur on any terrace.

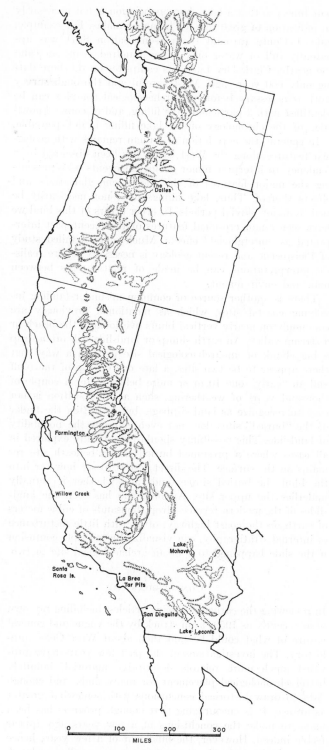

Figure 6. Map showing location of sites referred to in text.

Dry lakes. The common association of archaeological sites with shores of lakes now dry is well known. This is primarily a feature of the Great Basin and is not so useful on the Pacific Coast. Many important Early Man locations are associated with the various pluvial lakes. However, intermittent filling of some basins has continued into quite recent times, so that a lake-shore association is not necessarily an indication of great age for human remains. For example, Lake LeConte (around the present Salton Sea) was apparently full of water only a few hundred years ago, and the nearby Clark Dry Lake has campsites on its shore dating only 600 years ago. Most careful and thorough survey work is necessary before an archaeological complex can be identified with a particular lake filling, and of course knowledge of the chronology of the lake filling is indispensable.

In general, the correlation of human remains with geological features along the West Coast has been obscured by a tendency to interpret minor geological events as representing the major features of the Pleistocene glaciations and effects thereof. Thus, lake fillings need not necessarily be tied to major pluvial periods. In other errors of this kind we have seen minor erosional features of the recent past interpreted as "interglacial" effects. Much more detailed study of Pleistocene and recent geology is necessary before realistic interpretations can be made of relationships between man and environment.

There is another source of common misunderstanding involving coastal sites, which as mentioned previously are commonly on nearly vertical bluffs overlooking the beach or a stream valley. An earth slump or landslide will often drop a big chunk of an archaeological site in such a way that there appear to be two sites, a late one on top of the bluff and an "early" one 10 m or more below. After a couple of thousand years of weathering, such a superposition is not easy to recognize as land slippage, but too often the finder of the "buried" sites does not even consider the possibility of landslide. This possibility should be carefully explored in all cases where a presumed buried site is beneath site remains on the surface. The direct test is to see how far into the bluff the buried site extends and whether it actually underlies the upper site. Anyone who has seen the landslides of the modern terraces drop thousands of cubic meters of earth on the coast highway, often with little disturbance of internal stratigraphy, can visualize the possible confusion if the slide happened to split an archaeological site in two.

CONCLUSIONS

In reviewing the earlier summary articles, including my own of as recently as 1959, I am struck by the vague and general nature of what could be said then about West Coast prehistory. The investigations of the past few years have provided much more reliable descriptive material, infinitely better chronological placement for many finds, and enough data to draw historical conclusions with somewhat greater assurance. It is encouraging that enough progress has been made to make the conclusions of a few years ago appear feeble indeed. However, the hindsight of a few years hence will no doubt make the current summary equally outdated, and immense amounts of information are needed before even the broad outlines of cultural history of the Pacific Coast can be clearly seen.

From central California north, coastal archaeology is very limited, and most of what has been reported falls in the past few thousand years. If older sites exist on these hundreds of miles of coast, they have yet to be found.

Knowledge of the older sites west of the Cascade–Sierra Nevada ranges is very meager in comparison with what is known of ancient man inhabiting those mountain areas and the interior regions to the east of the mountains.

Studies of West Coast physical environment must also be greatly expanded in order to find, identify, and understand the locations occupied by ancient man. Pollen analyses, so useful in other regions, are not available for the West Coast. The diversity of West Coast environments requires detailed geological and climatological studies for each small region—virtually none have been published for the Pleistocene and post-Pleistocene features likely to be associated with Early Man.

We also do not know the subsistence basis for the early West Coast humans. Presumably they were hunters of large animals, and we may guess that mammoth and other large Pleistocene forms fell victim to man's weapons along the Pacific Coast as they did elsewhere. However, the bones of Pleistocene fauna have so far not been found associated with human tools in this area.

From this brief list of major gaps in our archaeological knowledge, it is clear that the next few years should see many important discoveries and investigations. Our progress to date has reached the point where we can ask intelligent questions, but most of the answers still lie in the future.

REFERENCES

Anonymous, 1960, The present state of archeology in western Canada: Calgary, Glenbow Fdn., Western Canadian Arch. Council, No. 1, 11 p.

Antevs, Ernst, 1955, Geologic-climatic dating in the West: Amer. Antiq., v. 20, p. 317-335

Baumhoff, Martin A., and Heizer, Robert F., this volume, Postglacial climate and archaeology in the Desert West

Berger, Rainer, Horney, A. G., and Libby, W. F., 1964, Radiocarbon dating of bone and shell from their organic components: Science, v. 144, p. 999-1001

Black, R. F., and Laughlin, W. S., 1964, Anangula; a geologic interpretation of the oldest archeologic site in the Aleutians: Science, v. 143, p. 1321-1322

Borden, C. E., 1960, An early site in the Fraser Canyon, British Columbia: Natl. Mus. Can. Bull. 162 (Anthrop. Ser. No. 45), p. 101-118

Brainerd, G. W., 1953, A re-examination of the dating evidence for the Lake Mohave artifact assemblage: Amer. Antiq., v. 18, p. 270-271

Butler, R. B., 1961, The Old Cordilleran Culture in the Pacific Northwest: Idaho State Coll. Mus. Occ. Pap., 5, 111 p.

Campbell, E. W., Campbell, W. H., Antevs, Ernst, Amsden, C. A., Barbieri, J. A., and Bode, F. D., 1937, The Archeology of Pleistocene Lake Mohave: Los Angeles, Southw. Mus. Pap., 11, 118 p.

Carlson, R. L., 1960, Chronology and culture change in the San Juan Islands, Washington: Amer. Antiq., v. 25, p. 562-586

Carter, G. F., 1952, Interglacial artifacts from the San Diego area: Southw. J. Anthrop., v. 8, p. 444-456

Carter, G. F., 1957, Pleistocene man at San Diego: Baltimore, Johns Hopkins Press, 400 p.

Cook, S. F., 1964, The nature of charcoal excavated at archaeological sites: Amer. Antiq., v. 29, p. 514-517

Cressman, L. S., 1960, Cultural sequences at The Dalles, Oregon: Amer. Philos. Soc. Trans., v. 50, No. 10, 108 p.

Cruxent, J. M., 1962, Phosphorus content of the Texas Street "Hearths": Amer. Antiq., v. 28, p. 90-91

Daugherty, R. D., 1962, The intermontane western tradition: Amer. Antiq., v. 28, p. 144-150

Greengo, R. E., 1951, Molluscan species in California shell middens: Berkeley, Univ. California Arch. Surv. Rep. 13, 29 p.

Greenwood, Roberta S., 1961, Excavations at Goleta. Part IV, Shell analysis: Los Angeles, Univ. California Arch. Surv. Ann. Rep. 1960-1961, p. 409-422

Heizer, R. F., 1950, Observations on early man in California: Berkeley, Univ. California Arch. Surv. Rep. 7, p. 5-10

—— 1952, A review of problems in the antiquity of man in California: Berkeley, Univ. California Arch. Surv. Rep. 16, p. 3-17

Heizer, R. F., and McCown, T. D., 1950, The Stanford skull, a probable early man from Santa Clara County, California: Berkeley, Univ. California Arch. Surv. Rep. 6, 18 p.

Howard, Hildegard, 1960, Significance of carbon-14 dates for Rancho La Brea: Science, v. 131, p. 712-714

Hubbs, C. L., 1960, Quaternary paleoclimatology of the Pacific Coast of North America: California Cooperative Oceanic Fisheries Inv., v. 7, p. 105-112

Jelinek, A. J., 1962, An index of radiocarbon dates associated with cultural materials: Chicago, Curr. Anthrop., v. 3, p. 451-480

Jennings, J. D., and Norbeck, Edward, 1955, Great Basin prehistory: a review: Amer. Antiq., v. 21, p. 1-11

Johnson, Frederick, and Miller, J. P., 1958, Review of "Pleistocene Man at San Diego": Amer. Antiq., v. 24, p. 206-210

Krieger, A. D., 1958, Review of "Pleistocene Man at San Diego": Amer. Anthrop., v. 60, p. 974-978

—— 1962, The earliest cultures in the western United States: Amer. Antiq., v. 28, p. 138-143

Meighan, C. W., 1959, Californian cultures and the concept of an archaic stage: Amer. Antiq., v. 24, p. 289-305

Moriarty, J. B., Shumway, George, and Warren, C. N., 1959, Scripps Estates Site I (SDi-525): Los Angeles, Univ. California Arch. Surv. Ann. Rep. 1958-1959, p. 185-216

Orr, P. C., 1960, Radiocarbon dates from Santa Rosa Island, II: Santa Barbara, Mus. Nat. Hist. Dept. Anthrop., Bull. 3, 10 p.

—— 1962a, The Arlington Spring site, Santa Rosa Island, California: Amer. Antiq., v. 27, p. 417-419

—— 1962b, Arlington Spring man: Science, v. 135, p. 219

—— 1964, Pleistocene chipped stone tool on Santa Rosa Island, California: Science, v. 143, p. 243-244

Rogers, M. J., 1939, Early lithic industries of the lower basin of the Colorado River and adjacent desert areas: San Diego Mus. Pap. 3, 75 p.

Shepard, F. P., 1964, Sea level changes in the past 6000 years; possible archeological significance: Science, v. 143, p. 574-576

Shumway, George, Hubbs, C. L., and Moriarty, J. R., 1961, Scripps Estate site, San Diego, California; a La Jolla site dated 5460 to 7370 years before the present: Ann. New York Acad. Sci., v. 93, p. 37-132

Swanson, E. H., 1962, Early cultures in northwestern America: Amer. Antiq., v. 28, p. 151-158

Treganza, A. E., 1952, Archaeological investigations in the Farmington Reservoir area, Stanislaus County, California: Berkeley, Univ. California Arch. Surv. Rep. 14, 25 p.

Treganza, A. E., and Heizer, R. F., 1953, Additional data on the Farmington Complex, a stone implement assemblage of probable early postglacial date from central California: Berkeley, Univ. California Arch. Surv. Rep. 22, p. 28-41

True, D. L., 1958, An early complex in San Diego County, California: Amer. Antiq., v. 23, p. 255-263

Wallace, W. J., 1955, A suggested chronology for Southern California Coastal Archaeology: Southw. J. Anthrop., v. 11, p. 214-230

Wallace, W. J., 1962, Prehistoric cultural development in the Southern California deserts: Amer. Antiq., v. 28, p. 172-180

Warren, C. N., 1964, Cultural change and continuity on the San Diego coast: Los Angeles, Univ. California Ph.D. thesis, 264 p.

Warren, C. N., and True, D. L., 1961, The San Dieguito Complex and its place in California prehistory: Los Angeles, Univ. California Arch. Surv. Ann. Rep., 1960-61, p. 246-338

Wormington, H. M., 1957, Ancient man in North America: Denver, Colorado, Denver Mus. of Nat. Hist., Popular Ser. No. 4, 4th ed., 322 p.

SUMMARY

Investigations in Pacific Coast archaeology have established a firm chronology for Early Man based on radiocarbon dates extending back to 8,000 years ago in scattered locations from the eastern Aleutians to southern California. On stratigraphic and other grounds, older finds are reported for southern California and western Oregon, but cultural evidence is meager in all such cases and questionable in some. Arguments presented for "interglacial man" and "pre-projectile point cultures" and similar claims that man's antiquity on the West Coast is greater than 15,000 years are so far not supported by acceptable evidence.

The oldest West Coast peoples were land-oriented hunters, presumably of big-game animals of the terminal Pleistocene, although convincing association of man and specific animal forms cannot yet be demonstrated on the Pacific Coast. The earliest hunters apparently reached the West Coast by crossing the Cascade–Sierra Nevada ranges from the Great Basin, starting at an unknown time prior to 8,000 years ago. The central and northern California coasts may have been settled later than southern California and the northern coasts.

The early hunters were succeeded by a variety of cultures (from about 7,500 to 4,000 years ago) adapted to specialized ecological niches, particularly riverine (fishing, bird-hunting) economies on the North Coast and plant-using, seed-grinding economies in southern California. More recent aborigines have continued these specializations but have also developed a successful boat-using oceanic adaptation in several coastal areas.

Association of archaeological remains with geological and climatological features has been developed in only a preliminary way. Studies relating ancient man to sea-level changes, lake and marine terraces, lagoon silting, and deposition of stream gravels are developing.

PART IV: MISCELLANEOUS STUDIES

LATE QUATERNARY HISTORY, CONTINENTAL SHELVES OF THE UNITED STATES

ISOTOPE GEOCHEMISTRY AND THE PLEISTOCENE CLIMATIC RECORD

QUATERNARY PALEOPEDOLOGY

GEOCHEMISTRY OF SOME QUATERNARY LAKE SEDIMENTS OF NORTH AMERICA

QUATERNARY PALEOHYDROLOGY

GLACIERS AND CLIMATE

VOLCANIC-ASH CHRONOLOGY

QUATERNARY PALEOMAGNETIC STRATIGRAPHY

TECTONICS OF QUATERNARY TIME IN MIDDLE NORTH AMERICA

DENDROCHRONOLOGY

THEORETICAL PALEOCLIMATOLOGY

LATE QUATERNARY HISTORY, CONTINENTAL SHELVES
OF THE UNITED STATES *

JOSEPH R. CURRAY[1]

THE *continental shelf* (Fig. 1) is the shallow submerged platform bordering the continents. It slopes gently seaward to an increase in slope at a worldwide average depth of about 130 m. There is considerable variation in depth of this change in gradient, or *shelf break*, from a few tens of meters to several hundred meters, but use of the term shelf is retained for those features which terminate at a depth of less than 550 m (300 fathoms) (Shepard, 1963a, p. 206). The steeper slope below the shelf break is the *continental slope*. It is a topographic feature of first order on the face of the earth, with a total length of over 300,000 km and a height of almost 4 km. The continental slope marks the structural edge of the continent and overlies the change from thick continental crust to thin oceanic crust; it is the surface manifestation of the greatest structural discontinuity in the crust of the earth. The *continental rise* is the gently sloping fan of sediments lapping up on the foot of the continental slope and sometimes extending seaward hundreds of kilometers over the floor of the ocean. Continental rises are not present everywhere at the base of the slope; this position is frequently occupied by oceanic or deep-sea *trenches*.

The *continental terrace* is defined as the sediment and rock mass underlying the continental slope, the continental shelf, and the coastal plain. The continental shelf and coastal plain are parts of the same geologic province, the upper part of the continental terrace, and are separated by the shoreline, a constantly moving feature that undergoes wide fluctuations at the whim of local and eustatic sea level, deposition, and erosion. The term *continental margin* is frequently used to include the continental terrace and the adjacent continental rise or trench.

The depositional and physiographic products of the most recent wide fluctuations in eustatic sea level during the late Quaternary form the subject matter of this paper. During maximum glacial advance, most of the continental shelves of the United States were subaerially exposed and subjected to alluvial deposition and erosion. During these same periods the depositional regime of the upper continental slopes changed drastically under the increased depositional load over the shelf edge or shoreline at the time. This abruptly increased rate of deposition on these steeper gradients resulted locally in instability, slumping, sliding, and generation of turbidity currents, which in turn produced a greatly increased rate of supply of terrigenous sediments to the continental slope and rise and to the deep sea.

During recession of continental glaciers sea level rose, producing a transgression across the shelves that was probably extremely rapid by geological standards. Deposition could not keep pace with the migration of the shoreline, and relict subaerial and shallow-water sediments lie exposed on much of the surface of the wider shelves. Since the time sea level arrived at essentially its present position, there has not yet been time to bring these wide shelves (and slopes) into equilibrium with present conditions, and much of what we observe in our modern oceans is not truly in equilibrium.

LATE QUATERNARY SEA LEVEL

Changes in sea level during the past 30,000 to 40,000 years have been studied by means of radiocarbon dates of deposits with known close relationships with sea level. These include peat deposits and shells of organisms with known shallow-water habitat that are now found well below sea level either in borings or in relict shallow-water sediments of the outer shelf. Many compilations of these dates have been published with curves of sea-level fluctuations, as postulated from the dates and from other indirect geological evidence (see, for example: van Straaten, 1954; Shepard and Suess, 1956; Godwin *et al.*, 1958; Curray, 1961; McFarlan, 1961; Jelgersma, 1961; Fairbridge, 1961; Scholl, 1964; Shepard, 1964).

A new compilation and re-evaluation of about 150 carefully selected published and unpublished dates have been made for this paper. The dates and sources are not presented at this time, but the postulated curve of sea-level fluctuations for the past 40,000 years is shown in Figure 2. The plot of dates shows considerable scatter because of errors of the dates, contamination of the carbon in the dated material, errors in the assumed living-depth ranges of organisms and depth of accumulation of peat, reworking and redeposition of the dead shells, local crustal instability, and compaction of underlying sediments. Despite these many sources of error, a general trend emerges, which is represented by the dotted and solid lines of the graph. The dashed line represents probable fluctuations postulated by indirect geological evidence, to be discussed later.

The curve separates rather logically into several parts for the following discussion: prior to 18,000 B.P. (before

* Contribution from the Scripps Institution of Oceanography, University of California, La Jolla, California. This study was supported by the Office of Naval Research (NONR 2216-01) and by various grants of the National Science Foundation. I am grateful to many people for discussions of ideas expressed herein and for reading and commenting upon parts of the manuscript, particularly D. L. Inman, D. G. Moore, F. B. Phleger, F. P. Shepard, Tj. van Andel, E. L. Winterer, and H. E. Wright. K. O. Emery kindly made several unpublished manuscripts available during the investigation
[1] Scripps Institution of Oceanography, La Jolla, California.

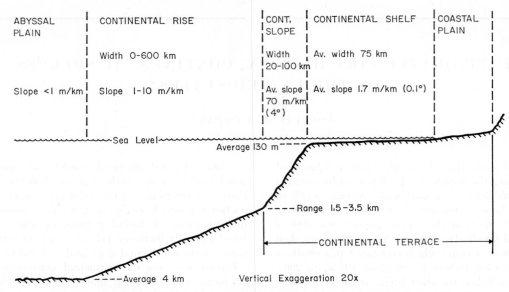

Figure 1. Diagrammatic profile of continental terrace with continental rise, showing average or range of depth, width, and slope of component parts.

present), including the mid-Wisconsin Transgression and
late-Wisconsin Regression; the Holocene Transgression,
from about 18,000 to 7,000 B.P.; and the period following
7,000 B.P. with more nearly stable sea level.

PRIOR TO 18,000 B.P.

This portion of the curve (dotted line, Fig. 2) is largely
speculation. It is based on a few dates suggesting an interstadial high stand of sea level sometime between about
22,000 and 35,000 B.P. (Curray, 1961, and unpublished
dates; Shepard, 1963b) and on correlation with continental
Pleistocene events. This interstadial stand of sea level probably lay slightly below present sea level. On the basis of
indirect geological evidence, it is suggested that the maximum lowering of sea level during the early-Wisconsin glaciation was about −145 m, but the time of this lowering
is not known. Dating by Pa^{231}/Th^{230} is now placing the
Sangamon interglacial preceding the glaciation in the vicinity of 100,000 B.P. (H. H. Veeh, personal communication;
Rosholt *et al.*, 1961).

18,000 TO 7000 B.P.

The maximum late-Wisconsin low stand of sea level occurred between about 20,000 and 17,000 B.P. at a level of
about −120 to −125 m (Curray, 1961; Curray and Moore,
1964). The sea-level evidence agrees well with late-Wisconsin continental glacial chronology. Depth of the low stand
is not well established, however, but it appears that the
maximum lowering was at least 110 m. Figure 1 shows my
estimate of −124 m.

The transgression following this low level is called the
Holocene Transgression. By normal geological standards,
this was most certainly an extremely rapid transgression,
representing a eustatic change in sea level of over 100 m in
less than 20,000 years. The solid curve (Fig. 2) is an estimated mean of the dates. There are very few reliable dates
older than 10,000 years, so the bend in the curve at about

17,000 B.P. may not be real. The pronounced bend in the
curve at about 7,000 B.P., however, is based on many dates
and is believed to represent a real slowing in the rise of sea
level.

The dashed curve is modified slightly from Curray (1960,
1961). The general trend of this curve was based on radiocarbon dates from the continental shelf of the Gulf of
Mexico, and the fluctuations were postulated from detailed
analysis of the bathymetry and sediment distribution on the
shelf off Texas. Some confirming evidence for the existence
and levels of the latter two fluctuations was presented by
van Andel and Sachs (1964) from a subsurface study of
sediments in the Gulf of Paria, Venezuela. Other similar
fluctuations have been postulated by Fairbridge (1961).
We can be confident that some such fluctuations must have
occurred and that the general period of the Holocene
Transgression was climatically very complex. But we can be
equally confident that the levels and times of fluctuations
we can postulate in the present state of our knowledge will
ultimately not prove correct in detail. For purposes of this
paper it is sufficient to keep in mind the probable complexity of this period of time, as well as that of the previous
transgressions and regressions.

Deep-sea micropaleontological and geochemical work in
the Atlantic and Caribbean has suggested a rather abrupt
change in climate and oceanic circulation centering around
11,000 B.P. (Broecker *et al.*, 1960). For this reason the
date 11,000 B.P. is now frequently cited as the end of the
Pleistocene and the beginning of the Holocene or Recent,
and it had been anticipated that we should find an abrupt
rise of sea level corresponding to this date. Published studies
of sea-level changes have thus far shown no abrupt rise in
the curve at this time and have shown that 11,000 B.P. occurs in the middle of the Holocene Transgression. This was
probably a period of extreme variation in climate on the
continents, with local advance and recession of glaciers.
These may not necessarily correlate between continents nor

with eustatic sea-level fluctuations, which represent the worldwide integrated amount of water in glaciers. A change in Atlantic circulation might have been one of many changes. Another alternative explanation is that perhaps the change was not so abrupt as generally assumed—that there was a period of transition between 15,000 and 7,000 B.P. In any event, it seems an unnecessary oversimplification to consider 11,000 B.P. as the end of the Pleistocene.

7,000 B.P. TO PRESENT

A rather pronounced slowing in the rate of rise of sea level occurred at 7,000 B.P., when sea level lay approximately 10 m below its present level. This portion of the curve is well substantiated with dates, although there is some disagreement about the precise position of sea level. The most controversial part of the entire curve is the past 5,000 years, for which we have the most data but are trying to resolve finer differences. There are basically three schools of thought: (1) Sea level has been slowly and continuously rising throughout this time and has reached its present position asymptotically only very recently (Shepard, 1960, 1964; Scholl, 1964). (2) Sea level reached its present position and has been stable for the past 3,000 to 5,000 years (Fisk, 1944; LeBlanc and Bernard, 1954; Gould and McFarlan, 1959). (3) Sea level first reached its present position 3,000 to 5,000 years ago and has been fluctuating above and below its present position since that time (see especially Fairbridge, 1961).

The curve in Figure 2 is shown asymptotically approaching present sea level because this is approximately the mean of the published dates. These dates, however, probably show some bias, in that the best-studied areas such as the Gulf Coast, the Netherlands, and the east coast of the United States may be slowly subsiding. Some other parts of the world show historical, archaeological, and radiocarbon evidence of brief stands of the sea higher than the present.

The writer considers these higher oscillations quite probable, although they are not shown in Figure 2. For purposes of the present paper, it is sufficient to consider the past 7,000 years as a period of slow rise of sea level followed by relative stability. Conditions of *modern* deposition of sediment commenced locally at different times during this period depending upon the local rate of supply of sediment, local tectonic stability, and the intensity of the oceanographic agents of sediment dispersal (van Andel and Curray, 1960; Curray, 1964).

SEDIMENTS AND MORPHOLOGY OF THE SHELF

EFFECTS OF SEA-LEVEL FLUCTUATIONS

The effects of Quaternary sea-level fluctuations have long been realized in the study of sediments of continental shelves. Shepard (1932) made one of the first thorough studies of shelf sediments, in which he stressed the existence and importance of relict sediments from glacially lowered sea level. Emery (1952) described the surface sediments on several shelf areas off Southern California in terms that are generally applicable to other areas. He grouped shelf sediments into the following five types: (1) *authigenic, e.g.* glauconite and phosphorite, which formed *in situ*; (2) *organic, e.g.* Foraminifera and other shells, the skeletal matter of organism; (3) *residual*, having weathered from underlying rocks; (4) *relict*, or remnant from a different earlier environment; and (5) *detrital*, presently being supplied by rivers, currents, or wind.

I shall use this same classification in this paper but concentrate particularly on the latter two groups, *relict* and *detrital*. I shall consider *detrital sediments* as those currently being supplied from the continent or other sources and transported to the area of deposition. In this sense, these are the sediments now in equilibrium with environmental conditions of the depositional area; they will be

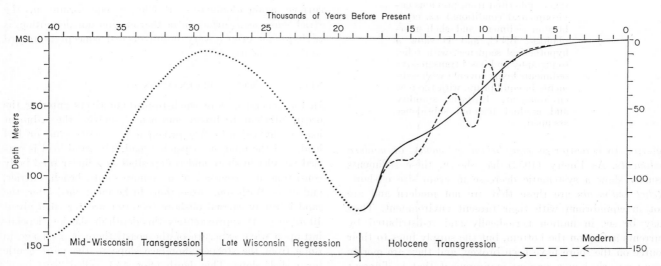

Figure 2. Late-Quaternary fluctuations of sea level, from compilation of published and unpublished radiocarbon dates and other geologic evidence. Dotted curve estimated from minimal data. Solid curve shows approximate mean of dates compiled. Dashed curve slightly modified from Curray (1960, 1961). Probable fluctuations since 5,000 B.P. not shown here.

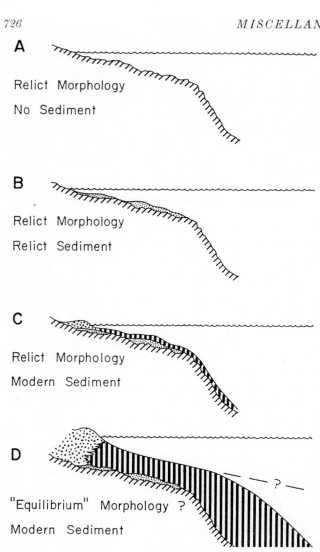

A

Relict Morphology

No Sediment

B

Relict Morphology

Relict Sediment

C

Relict Morphology

Modern Sediment

D

"Equilibrium" Morphology ?

Modern Sediment

Figure 3. Diagrammatic representation of relict (inherited from previous environmental conditions) *vs.* equilibrium sediment and shelf morphology. B, C, and D show a hypothetical sequence, with relict topography and basal transgressive sediments being covered with sediments in equilibrium with the new environment. Eustatic stability and gradual regional subsidence assumed.

referred to hereafter as *equilibrium sediments*, or *modern sediments*. As Emery (1952) has shown, these sediments usually show a systematic decrease in grain size offshore. *Relict sediments* are those that are not modern and are not in equilibrium with their present environment. They may be set in motion periodically and redistributed by currents acting on the bottom, but the supply lines to their source on the shore have been broken, and they are merely being reworked in a present environment that is different from the environment that prevailed at that spot at the time they were originally transported and deposited there.

Morphology or topography also is not in equilibrium with its present environment. The configuration of the present

surface of the continental shelf and upper continental slope is a product of erosion and deposition during sea-level fluctuations of the Quaternary. Indeed the rather close correspondence of the depth of the shelf break throughout the world is probably the effect of deposition and erosion during lowered sea level.

We may represent the possible combinations of relict vs. equilibrium sediments and morphology of the shelf surface diagrammatically as in Figure 3. Possibility A is relict morphology without any sediment cover. The surface shown is assumed to have resulted from erosion of older underlying sediments and rocks during a time of lowered sea level. B shows this same surface locally veneered with relict sediment deposited during the period of rising sea level. C shows more extensive deposition of sediment after sea level reached essentially its present position, but not yet great enough to subdue completely the underlying relict morphology. Finally D shows the same feature after enough more deposition, accompanied by uniform gradual subsidence, to produce a profile of equilibrium.

The concept of marine profile of equilibrium has been discussed on the basis of recent field evidence by Dietz (1963, 1964) and Moore and Curray (1964). Such equilibrium profiles probably exist today only locally in nearshore regions of abundant supply of sediment. In a strict sense, even these may not be profiles of equilibrium, but rather profiles of deposition. Moore and Curray believe that some shelf profiles in regions of abundant supply of sediment are starting to approach profiles of deposition and are more rounded than are other shelf profiles. In theory a profile of equilibrium should be concave upward, flattening seaward, so perhaps the complete equilibrium profile can never be attained because the continental terrace overlies the discontinuity between oceanic and continental crust. A pronounced change in level is therefore inevitable, and the thick blanket of sediment can be concave upward only out to the point where the underlying original convex-upward surface again dominates. Profile of equilibrium in the strict sense, as a surface of neither erosion nor deposition, is perhaps not even a very useful or real concept in regard to the continental shelf.

NERITIC DETRITAL SEDIMENTATION

In the general case of small-to-medium rivers entering the ocean adjacent to broad continental shelves, the sediment load is divided into two principal parts, the sand or bed load, and the mud or suspended load. The sand load is carried parallel to shore and is deposited as a linear sand body consisting of a complex of nearshore sands, beach, barrier, and dune. With some exceptions to be mentioned later, the sand is rarely carried offshore to water greater than about 10 m deep. At approximately this depth or shoaler, depending upon wave exposure of the coast, there is a change in slope from the steeper shoreface slope to the more gentle inner shelf slope. This depth (Fig. 4A), called "surf base" or "surge base," has been recently discussed by Dietz and Menard (1951) and Dietz (1963).

The suspended or mud load is carried continuously or intermittently in suspension farther seaward as well as parallel to the shore and is deposited as a thin blanket of open-shelf facies, ultimately to become marine shales. The inner edges of these mud blankets usually lie not shoaler than surf base, or 10 m; but depending upon current systems and wave exposure, the inner edge may be farther offshore and separated from the modern nearshore sands by a band of relict sediments.

Careful study of the patterns of these blanket-shaped deposits on modern shelves demonstrates that they rarely cover the pre-existing relict bottom sediments on the shelf farther than 30 to 40 km from shore. The outer edge of the deposit pinches out to zero thickness, and the underlying relict basal sands of the preceding Holocene Transgression lie at the surface beyond this point. Some of the mud certainly is transported beyond this pinch-out, but the rate of deposition in most cases appears to be slow with respect to the rate of reworking of the muds into the underlying sands by both current surges and the activities of burrowing organisms. In these transition zones, the relict sands are muddy, mottled with mud-filled burrows, and irregularly interbedded with mud layers.

The region in which this "marine shale" deposition occurs, called the "shelf depositional region" in Figure 4A, is only the region of maximum deposition of the muds today. Sea level and shorelines have been stabilized for only a few thousand years. Even in the case of shorelines stabilized by the upward growth of barrier islands, the sea level rise that followed establishment of the barrier islands created larger and larger lagoons and estuaries that have served as traps, minimizing the amount of sediment coming to the shelf. With prolonged future stabilization of sea level, these estuaries and lagoons will be filled, more sediment will escape to the shelf, and the width of the depositional region will probably increase. Considerable variations in the width of this region exist off major rivers, such as the Mississippi, and in regions where current systems act to transport the muds offshore rather than parallel to shore.

The region of shelf deposition is controlled both by distance from shore and by depth of water. Orbital velocity associated with wave action decreases exponentially with depth of water; there is no abrupt decrease with depth as implied by the old theory of wave base. Tidal and permanent oceanic currents on which these oscillatory currents are superimposed may attain the same velocities at the bottom as on the surface. Variation in bottom-current intensity with depth of water and distance from shore should control the transport and deposition of these suspended sediments. This control decreases the grain size and rate of deposition to the outer edge of this region. This concept has been recently discussed more fully by Curray and Moore (1964) and Moore and Curray (1964) in an attempt to modify and update the concept of wave base.

Deposition may occur all the way across narrow shelves and on down the upper continental slope. On a wide shelf, on the other hand, beyond the region of mud deposition lies the region of non-deposition. Here the exposed relict sediments are basal transgressive sediments of the Holocene rise in sea level (Fig. 4B). The rise of sea level was so rapid during the period 18,000 to about 7,000 years B.P. that time was insufficient for deposition of a shelf facies to cover the basal sands. In most regions the blanketing by shelf facies did not commence until about 7,000 years ago or even later.

If this model of neritic sedimentation applied everywhere, all shelves would show the same pattern, or parts of the same pattern, depending upon their width. But shelves vary in their amount of exposure to wave action, amount of supply of sediment, width, gradient, tides, and permanent current systems. Thus some shelves have no shelf facies overlying the relict sediments, whereas some wide shelves off the deltas of major rivers are blanketed with Holocene muds. Furthermore, the sediments we find on shelves today do not represent simply two static periods of sea level, namely low Pleistocene level and the present level. Much of the surface sediment is the product of changing conditions: a general period of transgression, interrupted by brief periods of regression and followed by the present relatively stable sea level.

The model presented is grossly oversimplified, with respect to both local variations and complexity of the events.

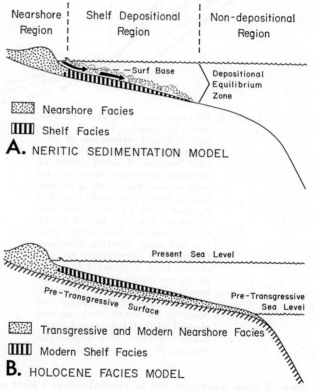

Figure 4. Models of neritic terrigenous sedimentation and resulting Holocene facies on a broad continental shelf. Nearshore sand facies is confined to within a few kilometers of shore. Shelf mud facies is deposited beyond the nearshore facies, but not at a high enough rate to cover the underlying transgressive nearshore facies all the way across the shelf. The same sedimentation model applied to a shelf that is half the width can result in complete burial of the underlying transgressive nearshore facies.

SEDIMENT BY-PASSING

Case I: Shelf Edge Turbulence

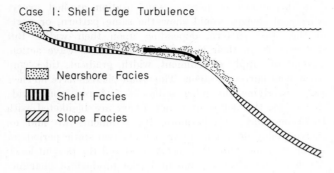

Case 2: Submarine Canyons

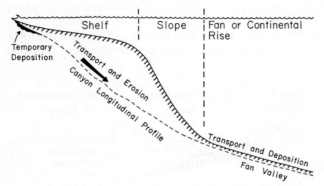

Figure 5. Two common mechanisms of sediment by-passing. Case 1 shows prevention of deposition of suspended fine sediments on the shelf edge because of development of excessive turbulence by wave and tidal action. The result is deposition of slope-facies muds. Case 2 is transportation of sand and fine sediments down the axis of a submarine canyon that heads near the surf zone. Sand in longshore transport is intercepted by the canyon head. Suspended fine sediments are trapped by settling into canyon farther out on the shelf. Transportation of these sands and muds to the continental rise and abyssal plain takes place by turbidity currents, slow glacier-like flowage, or by current action.

Some of these differences will be pointed out in a later section.

SEDIMENT BY-PASSING

By-passing of sediment across an area where no sediment or a texturally different sediment is being deposited can be accomplished in two possible manners (Fig. 5). Case 1 shows by-passing of fine suspended sediment across the outer shelf beyond the pinch-out of the shelf muds, to ultimate deposition on the continental slope. This may be locally an important process, especially on shelves of narrow to medium width, where increase of turbulence at the shelf edge prevents deposition on the outer shelf. This tur-

bulence may be caused in part by concentration of tidal current and wave action at the shelf edge.

Cause and effect must be evaluated in considering Case 1 by-passing. At first glance this would appear to be simple reconfirmation of the classic wave-base theory, with prevention of deposition on the shelf and final deposition on the slope. It is here suggested, however, that in many cases deposition of these same suspended muds would occur in these places if the shelf surface were already blanketed with muds. The presence of the relict sediments (sand, shell deposits, and gravels) produces a hydrodynamically rough bottom, which creates enough weak turbulence to prevent permanent deposition of the muds. With sufficient time or with increase of the rate of supply of the muds, this surface will eventually be smoothed by deposition, and the rate of deposition will increase accordingly. Rate or even occurrence of deposition thus reflects the nature of the substrate.

The second case of by-passing is transport of sediment off the continental terrace through submarine canyons (Fig. 5, Case 2). As has been shown by Shepard (1963a, p. 314) and many others, sediment can accumulate temporarily in the heads of submarine canyons. Canyons heading near the shoreline intercept the longshore drift of sand. The oblique drift of suspended muds on a shelf is also intercepted by the canyon farther out on the shelf. These sediments accumulate temporarily and are later moved through the canyon for deposition on the fan, on the rise at the base of the slope, or on the abyssal plain. The mechanism of transport may be turbidity currents, slow glacier-like creep, simple flushing down-canyon by tidal and other currents, or by combinations of these processes. For our purposes, it is important only that both coarse and fine sediments are transported by these means past the shelf to deeper water. This deposition may occur on the continental rise even adjacent to a shelf where no significant deposition occurs. Indeed this is probably the principal mechanism of transportation of sand to the deep sea during either glacial or interglacial periods.

The continental slope is locally a region of deposition today but locally a region of no significant deposition. Where sediment is carried in suspension to the shelf, some may be carried over the shelf edge to the slope for deposition. A narrow shelf completely blanketed with modern sediment will most certainly grade into a slope of active deposition, with rate of deposition decreasing continuously seaward. By-passing of sediment across the outer shelf and shelf break also contributes sediment to the upper slope.

The effects of Quaternary sea-level fluctuations were profound on both the shelf and slope. Shelf surfaces were periodically inundated and subaerially exposed. The upper slope, on the other hand, was continuously under water, but the rate of deposition must have varied by several orders of magnitude. During times of lowest sea level, essentially all marine deposition occurred on the upper slope, where river mouths discharged at the shelf edge or into submarine canyons. Stability of sediments is primarily a function of rate of deposition and slope (Moore, 1961), so these periods of rapid deposition must have resulted in extensive slumping, sliding, and generation of turbidity currents. The

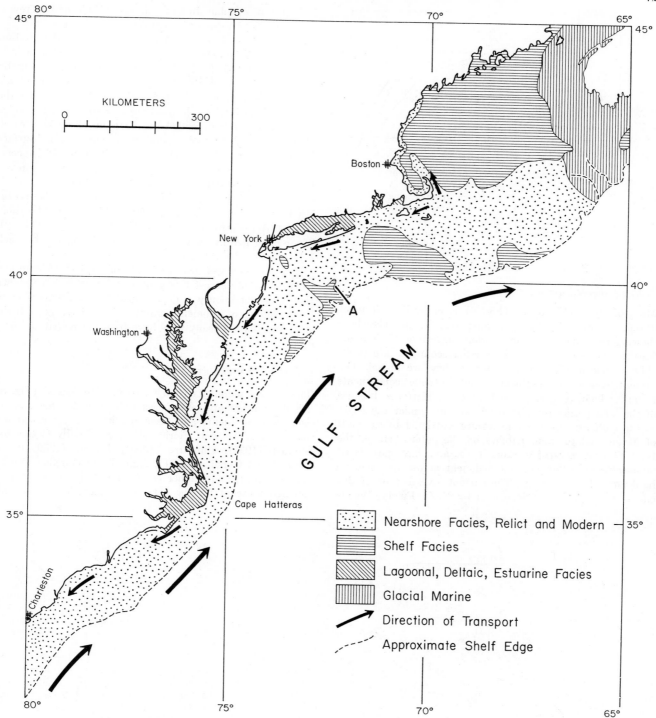

Figure 6. Distribution of surface-sediment facies on the continental shelf off northeast and east-central United States; modified from Shepard (1932), Stetson (1938, 1949), Gorsline (1963), Uchupi (1963), and Emery (in press). For section along line A, see Figure 7.

results are probably threefold. First, some permanent progradation or seaward building of the shelf edge must have resulted (Ewing *et al.*, 1963; Curray and Moore, 1964). Second, the rate of supply of sediments to the deep sea must have been considerably higher (Broecker *et al.*,

1958). And third, the topography of the continental slope and rise would be expected to show the scars of these periods of instability. This is quite probably the case, as topographic irregularities are well known from many of the well-surveyed slopes of the world.

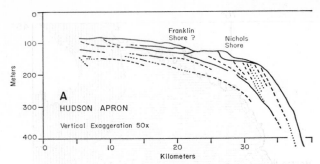

Figure 7. Acoustic reflection record near shelf edge off New York, (line A on Fig. 6) redrawn from Ewing *et al.* (1963, Fig. 2), showing sediment reflecting layers, erosional terraces, and surface ridges.

SHELVES OF THE UNITED STATES

EASTERN UNITED STATES

Most of the shelf surface (Fig. 6) is covered with relict nearshore sands, locally containing gravels, and elsewhere showing low topographic expression suggestive of shoreline features. Off Nova Scotia these relict sediments are probably of glacial origin, but elsewhere they are fluvial. The present content of authigenic and biogenic constituents is rather high, especially south of Cape Hatteras, because of the long period of submarine exposure under the edges of the Gulf Stream. Shelf facies are restricted to the Gulf of Maine and to small patches on the outer shelf off the New York area. Most workers in the area have postulated large-scale by-passing of fine sediment across the shelf to be deposited on the slope. The current investigation of this entire shelf and upper-slope area by K. O. Emery, Woods

Hole Oceanographic Institution, should ultimately reveal the nature and volumetric significance of this process.

An acoustic-reflection profile (Fig. 7) across the Hudson Apron reveals steeply dipping layers, interpreted as a low-sea-level delta of the Hudson River, truncated on top by an erosional terrace at −165 (to −130) m (Ewing *et al.*, 1963). This terrace is covered with a low ridge called the Nichols shore by Veatch and Smith (1939). Another ridge at −103 to −112 m, called the Franklin shore by Veatch and Smith, did not correspond to a consistent subsurface feature. These features are presumed to be Pleistocene. Shells from the terrace underlying the Nichols shore proved to be too old to date by radiocarbon. Perhaps the Nichols shoreline is early Wisconsin, corresponding to the postulated low sea-level stand at −145 m, and the Franklin shore is a late-Wisconsin low stand of about 18,000 B.P. (Fig. 2). These older features have not been buried because this shelf is largely non-depositional.

Two higher-power acoustic-reflection profiles (Moore and Curray, 1963a) across this continental terrace have shown that it is dominantly a depositional feature, consisting of thick sections of sediment conformably underlying both the shelf and slope. Locally they have been uncovered and outcrop on the slope.

SOUTHERN UNITED STATES

The surface sediments from Charleston to Miami (Fig. 8) are relict nearshore sand facies rich in authigenic and biogenous constituents and becoming increasingly calcareous off Florida. The west Florida shelf, studied by Gould and Stewart (1955), Ginsburg (1956), Tanner (1960, 1961), Goodell and Gorsline (1961), Kofoed and Gorsline (1963), Scholl (1963), and Tanner *et al.* (1963), is predominantly calcareous except for the nearshore region. The calcareous

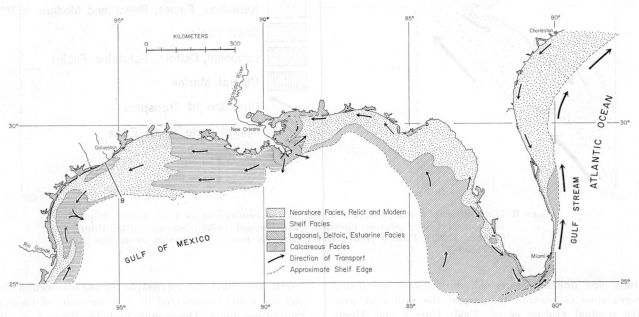

Figure 8. Distribution of surface-sediment facies on the continental shelf off southern and southeastern United States. The Atlantic shelf is from same source as Figure 6. For section along line B, see Figure 9.

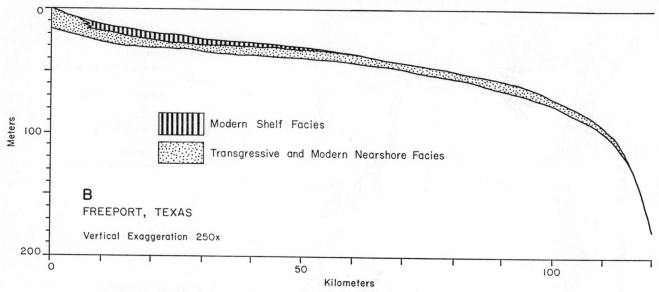

Figure 9. Cross section showing facies interpretations off Freeport, Texas (line B on Fig. 8).

facies include oolitic, shelly, algal, and foraminiferal facies zoned by depth. As shown by Gould and Stewart (1955), much is to be learned about late-Quaternary history from these sediments and from shelf morphology.

West of 85° W Long. the broad calcareous zone narrows to shelf-edge calcareous and reef facies, studied in detail by Ludwick and Walton (1957) and Ludwick (1964). Here again, there is essentially no modern shelf facies present over the non-depositional surface of the transgressive nearshore sands.

The Mississippi delta (Shepard, 1956; Fisk and Mc-Farlan, 1955) is built essentially to the shelf edge. The bottomset beds on the shelf are shown here as shelf facies, and some bottomset deposition occurs on the upper continental slope also, producing instability and slumping on an extremely gentle slope (Shepard, 1955).

The pattern of the northwestern Gulf of Mexico (Fig. 8) is simplified from Curray (1960). The broad mud-covered shelf west of the Mississippi Delta is related to earlier subdeltas of the Mississippi that started to form adjacent to this part of the shelf about when the rise of sea level slowed, 7,000 B.P. Even today, with the birdfoot delta lying far to the east, an abundant supply of fine sediment is probably carried by the current system for deposition on this wide shelf. This and some other major river deltas are exceptions to the offshore limit of 30 to 40 km for deposition of shelf-facies muds.

The broad shelf of relict nearshore sands off Galveston is the region in which detailed work on sediment distribution and topography suggested the sea-level fluctuations shown with a dashed line in Figure 2. The lens or tongue of shelf mud trending southwest from near Galveston is supplied today from the Brazos and Colorado Rivers. North of the Rio Grande is a region of extensive cover by shelf-facies muds adjacent to a portion of the coast without significant rivers. This is apparently related to the current system and convergence shown, with probable long-distance transport from more remote river sources.

The cross section (Fig. 9) is based on interpretation of scattered cores and borings and the assumed stratigraphic relationships of the facies. This is rather typical of many broad shelves, with modern shelf muds found overlying the relict sands only on the inner part of the shelf.

The sedimentary framework of portions of the northwestern Gulf of Mexico was studied, by Moore and Curray (1963b), by means of higher-power acoustic reflection. Thick conformable sections of sediment underlie both the slope and shelf. Topographic irregularities beneath the slope and faulting beneath the shelf have resulted from salt-dome intrusion.

PACIFIC COAST

Surface sediments of the shelf off the Pacific Coast (Fig. 10) have not been so thoroughly studied as on the east and Gulf coasts, with the exception of several narrow shelves in the southern California area. Nevertheless, the patterns appear basically rather simple, although they are undoubtably very complex in detail.

The entire shelf is much narrower than on the east and Gulf coasts, ranging from about 50 km wide near the Columbia River to as narrow as 1 km off southern California. Because of this relatively narrow width, the modern shelf-facies muds appear to cover the outer shelf and shelf break in many places. The nearshore sands may not be modern all the way from the shoreline out to the inner edge of the shelf muds, but they may be modern closer to shore, separated from the muds by a band of relict sands. The muds thus might by-pass these relict sands before reaching the outer shelf for deposition. This by-passing might be attributed to turbulence created by the rather intense wave action of the northern coastal region.

Sediments on the shelf off Vancouver Island at the northern edge of the chart are analogous to those on the east coast in being of probable glacial origin (Shepard, 1932). They consist of gravels, sands and clays variably mixed.

An acoustic-reflection profile across the narrow shelf off

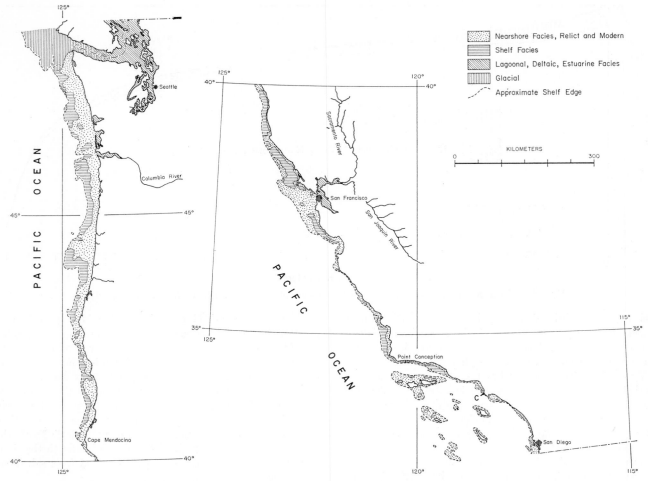

Figure 10. Distribution of surface sediment facies on the continental shelf off western United States, from Shepard (1932), Emery (1960), and the writer's studies of chart notations. For section along line C, see Figure 11.

Palos Verdes (Fig. 11), north of San Diego (line C, Fig. 10) shows a thick lens of Holocene shelf muds on the narrow shelf, thinning both offshore and toward shore. It overlies a unit interpreted by Moore (1960) as probable alluvial and nearshore facies over eroded bedrock. This shelf is narrow enough that the entire width is thickly blanketed with shelf-facies silts and clays.

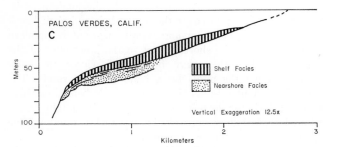

Figure 11. Line drawing of acoustic-reflection record across continental shelf off Palos Verdes, California, redrawn from Moore (1960, Pl. 3), showing facies interpretations (line C on Fig. 10).

Higher-power acoustic-reflection studies in progress by the writer between Cape Mendocino and Point Conception have shown that the continental terrace is dominantly a depositional feature, with thick masses of sediment lying approximately conformable to the surfaces of the shelf and slope. A basement high, locally known to be granitic, occurs in some places beneath the outer shelf and elsewhere beneath the slope.

DISCUSSION

A dilemma in nomenclature exists among the three groups most interested in Pleistocene-Holocene stratigraphy:

1. Some continental Pleistocene geologists (Frye and Leonard, 1953) recommend definition of a glacial age as encompassing the entire period of growth and retreat of continental glaciers. Applying this definition to the sea-level curve of Figure 2, the Pleistocene would extend to the last few thousand years, when sea level became more nearly stable. Sediments of what has been here called the Holocene Transgression would be Pleistocene, and the only Holocene sediments on the shelf would be the *modern* sediments.

2. Deep-sea stratigraphers have stressed the climatic and

faunal change in the Atlantic and Caribbean and have encouraged definition of the dividing line between Pleistocene and Holocene at 11,000 B.P. (Broecker *et al.*, 1960; Ericson *et al.*, 1961). For their purposes this is quite satisfactory regardless of how abrupt or gradual the change might have been because it places the dividing line in the middle of the transition. For purposes of continental and shelf geologists, this definition is quite unsatisfactory because it would separate "rock" and "time-rock" units in the middle.

3. Marine geologists concerned with shelf sediments have usually used the marine transgressive unconformity to distinguish marine "rocks" units, such as the transgressive nearshore facies and the shelf facies, from the underlying alluvial facies. Arbitrary definition of an age would necessitate splitting lithologic units and considering some parts Pleistocene and other parts Holocene.

The only practical compromise among these groups would be to accept the recommendation of Frye and Leonard (1953). This would place the end of the Pleistocene at the time when continental ice sheets had retreated to their present more or less stable volumes and sea level had risen essentially to its present position. Some Pleistocene geologists (Frye and Willman, 1960) have used 5,000 years as the line between Pleistocene and Recent, apparently because of early estimates by Fisk (1944, etc.) that sea level stabilized at this time. Today we cannot agree when or if sea level has stabilized at its present level, but the curve of Figure 2 seems to agree with other published date compilations and curves in showing a pronounced flattening in the curve at about 7,000 B.P. Some plots would place this at 6,000, some perhaps at 8,000, but all show a break in the curve. This would appear to be a logical time to define as the boundary between Pleistocene and Holocene or Recent.

This definition would have the effect in deep-sea stratigraphy of putting the contact at the end of the period of transition from cold- to warm-water faunal assemblages rather than in the middle and would appear to be just as satisfactory a definition. This revised definition would have its most drastic effect upon terminology of shelf sediments. Most of the shelf facies would still be called Holocene, but most of the relict nearshore facies would then be considered Pleistocene. The transgression from 18,000 to 7,000 B.P. would no longer be called the Holocene Transgression, but would be renamed latest-Wisconsin Transgression, or some other similar name.

This revised nomenclature has not been used in this paper, and usage of terminology has been continued from that of many previous shelf studies. The change could be made simply if the need for uniformity of terminology is necessary. In the meantime, it is more important to define terms clearly.

A eustatic sea-level curve need not necessarily correlate with Pleistocene events of any given area. It represents the integrated worldwide total of water locked into continental glaciers, and as such it is probably the best source of information on worldwide climatic fluctuations. Similarly, surface temperatures, circulation, and faunal assemblages of any given portion of the ocean will not necessarily correlate with sea-level fluctuations or with continental events. If standard Quaternary stratigraphic nomenclature is to be established, it is here proposed that sea-level fluctuations should be one of the major considerations rather than local or regional manifestations of the climatic transition.

A complete record of Quaternary events exists somewhere on or under our continental shelves and coastal plains. It must be sought by the proper means and evaluated carefully in the light of possible local variations. As an example, it is quite illogical to attempt to solve problems of sea-level fluctuations from study only of areas such as the Mississippi Delta that are known to be subsiding. Tectonic instability may not be so obvious in other regions, but this factor should be carefully evaluated in all such studies.

Another approach to the problem of delineating sea-level fluctuations is by estimation of ice volumes on the continents. A revised estimate (Donn *et al.*, 1962) shows good agreement with direct estimates of maximum sea-level lowerings during the Wisconsin. The agreement seems all the more remarkable, however, when the nature of some of the estimates of area and thickness of ice are considered. It is obvious that much greater precision is possible by more direct observation of depositional and erosional levels on the edges of stable shelves.

REFERENCES

Andel, Tj. H. van, and Curray, J. R., 1960, Regional aspects of modern sedimentation in northern Gulf of Mexico and similar basins, and paleogeographic significance, *in* Shepard, F. P., (ed.), Recent sediments, northwest Gulf of Mexico: Amer. Assoc. Petroleum Geologists, p. 345-364

Andel, Tj. H. van, and Sachs, P. L., 1964, Sedimentation in the Gulf of Paria during the Holocene transgression; a subsurface acoustic reflection study: J. Mar. Res., v. 22, p. 30-50

Broecker, W. S., Turekian, K. K. and Heezen, B. C., 1958, The relation of deep sea sedimentation rates to variations in climate: Amer. J. Sci., v. 256, p. 503-517

Broecker, W. S., Ewing, Maurice, and Heezen, B. C., 1960, Evidence for an abrupt change in climate close to 11,000 years ago: Amer. J. Sci., v. 258, p. 429-448

Curray, J. R., 1960, Sediments and history of Holocene transgression, continental shelf, northwest Gulf of Mexico, *in* Shepard, F. P., *et. al.* (eds.), Recent sediments, northwest Gulf of Mexico: Amer. Assoc. Petroleum Geologists, p. 221-266

—— 1961, Late Quaternary sea level; a discussion: Geol. Soc. Amer. Bull., v. 72, p. 1707-1712

—— 1964, Transgressions and regressions, *in* Miller, R. L. (ed.), Papers in marine geology (Shepard commemorative vol.): New York, Macmillan Co., p. 175-203

Curray, J. R., and Moore, D. G., 1964, Pleistocene deltaic progradation of continental terrace, Costa de Nayarit, Mexico *in* van Andel, Tj. H. and Shor, G. G. Jr. (eds.), Marine geology of the Gulf of California: Amer. Assoc. Petroleum Geologists, Mem. 3, p. 193-215

Dietz, R. S., 1963, Wave-base, marine profile of equilibrium, and wave-built terraces; a critical appraisal: Geol. Soc. Amer. Bull., v. 74, p. 971-990

—— 1964, Wave-base, marine profile of equilibrium, and wave-built terraces; reply: Geol. Soc. Amer. Bull., v. 75, p. 1275-1282

Dietz, R. S., and Menard, H. W., Jr., 1951, Origin of abrupt change in slope at continental shelf margin: Amer. Assoc. Petroleum Geologists Bull., v. 35, p. 1994-2016

Donn, W. L., Farrand, W. R., and Ewing, Maurice, 1962, Pleistocene ice volumes and sea-level lowering: J. Geol., v. 70, p. 206-214

Emery, K. O., 1952, Continental shelf sediments of southern California: Geol. Soc. Amer. Bull., v. 63, p. 1105-1108

—— 1960, The sea off southern California, a modern habitat of petroleum: New York, John Wiley and Sons, 366 p.

—— in press, The continental shelf off the Atlantic coast of the United States, U.S. Geol. Surv.

Ericson, D. B., Ewing, Maurice, Wollin, Goesta, and Heezen, B. C., 1961, Atlantic deep-sea sediment cores: Geol. Soc. Amer. Bull., v. 72, p. 193-285

Ewing, John, Le Pichon, Xavier, and Ewing, Maurice, 1963, Upper stratification of Hudson apron region: J. Geophys. Res., v. 68, p. 6303-6316

Fairbridge, R. W., 1961, Eustatic changes in sea level, *in* Physics and chemistry of the Earth, v. 4: New York, Pergamon Press, p. 99-185

Fisk, H. N., 1944, Geological investigation of the alluvial valley of the lower Mississippi River: Vicksburg, Mississippi River Comm., 78 p.

Fisk, H. N., and McFarlan, Edward, Jr., 1955, Late Quaternary deltaic deposits of the Mississippi River—local sedimentation and basin tectonics, *in* Poldervaart, Arie (ed.), Crust of the Earth: Geol. Soc. Amer. Spec. Pap. 62, p. 279-302

Frye, J. C., and Leonard, A. B., 1953, Definition of time line separating a glacial and interglacial age in the Pleistocene: Amer. Assoc. Petroleum Geologists Bull., v. 37, p. 2581-2586

Frye, J. C. and Willman, H. B., 1960, Classification of the Wisconsinan stage in the Lake Michigan glacial lobe: Illinois State Geol. Surv., Circ. 285, 16 p.

Ginsburg, R. N., 1956, Environmental relationships of grain size and constituent particles in some south Florida carbonate sediments: Amer. Assoc. Petroleum Geologists Bull., v. 40, p. 2384-2427

Godwin, Harry, Suggate, R. P., and Willis, E. H., 1958, Radiocarbon-dating of the eustatic rise in ocean-level: Nature, v. 181, p. 1518-1519

Goodell, H. G., and Gorsline, D. S., 1961, A sedimentologic study of Tampa Bay, Florida: 21st Intern. Geol. Congr., pt. 23, p. 75-88

Gorsline, D. S., 1963, Bottom sediments of the Atlantic shelf and slope off the southern United States: J. Geol., v. 71, p. 422-440

Gould, H. R., and McFarlan, Edward, Jr., 1959, Geologic history of the Chenier Plain, southwestern Louisiana: Gulf Coast Assoc. Geol. Soc. Trans., v. 9, p. 261-270

Gould, H. R., and Stewart, R. H., 1955, Continental terrace sediments in the northeastern Gulf of Mexico, *in* Hough, Jack, and Menard, H. W. (eds.), Finding ancient shorelines: Soc. Econ. Paleont, Min. Spec. Publ. 3, p. 2-20

Jelgersma, Saskia, 1961, Holocene sea level changes in the Netherlands: Maastright, van Aelst, Geol. Stichting, Ser. C-VI, 101 p.

Kofoed, J. W., and Gorsline, D. S., 1963, Sedimentary environments in Apalachicola Bay and vicinity, Florida: J. Sed. Petrology, v. 33, p. 205-223

LeBlanc, R. J., and Bernard, H. H., 1954, Résumé of late. Recent geological history of the Gulf coast: Geol. Mijnbouw, v. 16e, n.s., p. 185-194

Ludwick, J. C., 1964, Sediments in northeastern Gulf of Mexico, *in* Miller, R. L. (ed.), Papers in marine geology. (Shepard commemorative vol.): New York, Macmillan Co., p. 204-238

Ludwick, J. C., and Walton, W. R., 1957, Shelf-edge, calcareous prominences in northeastern Gulf of Mexico: Amer. Assoc. Petroleum Geologists Bull., v. 41, p. 2054-2101

McFarlan, Edward, Jr., 1961, Radiocarbon dating of late Quaternary deposits, south Louisiana: Geol. Soc. Amer. Bull., v. 72, p. 129-158

Moore, D. G., 1960, Acoustic-reflection studies of the continental shelf and slope off southern California: Geol. Soc. Amer. Bull., v. 71, p. 1121-1136

—— 1961, Submarine slumps: J. Sed. Petrology, v. 31, p. 343-357

Moore, D. G., and Curray, J. R., 1963a, Sedimentary framework of continental terrace off Norfolk, Virginia, and Newport, Rhode Island: Amer. Assoc. Petroleum Geologists Bull., v. 47, p. 2051-2054

—— 1963b, Structural framework of the continental terrace, northwest Gulf of Mexico: J. Geophys. Res., v. 68, p. 1725-1747

—— 1964, Wave-base, marine profile of equilibrium, and wave-built terraces; discussion: Geol. Soc. Amer. Bull., v. 75, p. 1267-1274

Rosholt, J. N., Jr., Emiliani, Cesare, Geiss, J., Koszy, F. F., and Wangersky, P. J., 1961, Absolute dating of deep-sea cores by the Pa^{231}/Th^{230} method: J. Geol. v. 69, p. 162-185

Scholl, D. W., 1963, Sedimentation in modern coastal swamps, southwestern Florida: Amer. Assoc. Petroleum Geologists Bull., v. 47, p. 1581-1603

—— 1964, Recent sedimentary record in mangrove swamps and rise in sea level over the southwestern coast of Florida, Part i: Marine Geol., v. 1, p. 344-366

Shepard, F. P., 1932, Sediments of the continental shelves: Geol. Soc. Amer. Bull., v. 43, p. 1017-1039

—— 1955, Delta-front valleys bordering the Mississippi distributaries: Geol. Soc. Amer. Bull., v. 66, p. 1489-1498

—— 1956, Marginal sediments of Mississippi Delta: Amer. Assoc. Petroleum Geologists Bull., v. 40, p. 2537-2623

—— 1960, Rise of sea level along northwest Gulf of Mexico, *in* Shepard, F. P., *et al.* (eds.) Recent sediments, northwest Gulf of Mexico: Amer. Assoc. Petroleum Geologists, p. 338-344

—— 1963a, Submarine geology: New York, Harper & Row, 2nd ed., 557 p.

—— 1963b, Thirty-five thousand years of sea level, *in* Essays in marine geology in honor of K. O. Emery: Los Angeles, Univ. Southern California Press, p. 1-10

—— 1964, Sea level changes in the past 6000 years: possible archeological significance: Science, v. 143, p. 574-576

Shepard, F. P., and Suess, H. E., 1956, Rate of postglacial rise of sea level: Science, v. 123, p. 1082-1083

Stetson, H. C., 1938, The sediments of the continental shelf off the eastern coast of the United States: Massachusetts Inst. Tech. and Woods Hole Oceanogr. Inst. Pap. Phys. Oceanogr. Met., v. 5, 48 p.

—— 1949, The sediments and stratigraphy of the east coast continental margin, Georges Bank to Norfolk Canyon: Massachusetts Inst. Tech. and Woods Hole Oceanogr. Inst. Pap. Phys. Oceanogr. Met., v. 11, p. 1-60

Straaten, L. M. Van, 1954, Radiocarbon datings and changes of sea level at Velzen (Netherlands): Geol. Minbouw, n.s., v. 16e, p. 247-253

Tanner, W. F., 1960, Florida coastal classification: Gulf Coast Assoc. Geol. Soc. Trans., v. 10, p. 259-266

—— 1961, Offshore shoals in area of energy deficit: J. Sed. Petrology, v. 31, p. 87-95

Tanner, W. F., Evans, R. G., and Homes, C. W., 1963, Low-energy coast near Cape Romano, Florida: J. Sed. Petrology, v. 33, p. 713-722

Uchupi, Elazar, 1963, Sediments on the continental margin off eastern United States: U.S. Geol. Surv. Prof. Pap. 475-C, p. 132-137

Veatch, A. C., and Smith, P. A., 1939, Atlantic submarine valleys of the United States and the Congo submarine valley: Geol. Soc. Amer. Spec. Pap. 7, 101 p.

SUMMARY

Continental shelves, the shallow submerged borders of the continents, were alternately exposed subaerially and inundated during the Quaternary. The most recent maximum subaerial exposure occurred about 18,000 years ago during late-Wisconsin glacial advance and was followed by a rapid marine transgression. The rate of rise of sea level decreased markedly about 7,000 years ago, and during the last few thousand years sea level has been approximately at its present position, possibly with some minor fluctuations above and below.

The sediments that are now being deposited on the shelf include elongate bodies of near-shore sands and offshore deposits of muddy shelf facies. Beyond the extent of these *modern* sediments the shelf surface is covered with nearshore sands relict from lower stands of sea level.

The shelf off eastern United States is covered almost entirely with relict nearshore sands of the transgression. The present mud supply is trapped in estuaries, although some of it may be transported across the shelf surface to the continental slope. Much of the Florida and northeastern Gulf of Mexico shelf is covered with calcareous facies. The northwestern Gulf of Mexico and Pacific coast shelves are covered with patches of both shelf muds and relict nearshore sands.

It is suggested that eustatic sea-level fluctuations may be the best basis for world-wide classification and correlation of late-Quaternary events.

ISOTOPE GEOCHEMISTRY AND THE PLEISTOCENE CLIMATIC RECORD *

WALLACE S. BROECKER[1]

THE ESTABLISHMENT of an absolute chronology for the climatic fluctuations that characterize Pleistocene time is eagerly awaited by both the geophysicist interested in determining the cause of glaciation and by the stratigrapher interested in reconstructing the events that took place. The postwar boom in isotope geochemistry, which brought into being methods for measuring both time and paleotemperature, has greatly accelerated progress toward this end. As with all new approaches to earth science, valid results are accompanied by numerous erroneous ones. Such seeming vacillations by the geochemist become confusing to the consumer; thus periodic papers such as this summarizing the status of the research serve a purpose. Dead-

* Lamont Geological Observatory Contribution No. 792.
[1] Lamont Geological Observatory, Palisades, New York.

wood can be cleared away, the reliability of existing techniques evaluated, and the direction of future research pointed out. Because of the rapid current progress in this field much of what is said here will more than likely be out of date within a few years.

AGE METHODS

Ten methods of determining the absolute age of Pleistocene events have been conceived and explored. The first portion of the paper will summarize their underlying principles and their major assumptions (Table 1).

1. The radiocarbon method. Libby and his co-workers (see Libby, 1955) first demonstrated that the isotope C^{14} with a 5,730-year half-life, could be used for dating organic and carbonate materials. Produced by cosmic-ray neutron in-

TABLE 1

Summary of Pleistocene Age-Dating Methods

Isotope	Half-life, 10^3 yrs	Method	Range, 10^3 yrs	Materials	Ocean temp.	Sea level	Glacier extent	Arid lakes	Pollen sequence	Text No.	Ref.
C^{14}	5.7	Decay	0-35	Organics-$CaCO_3$	+	+	+	+	+	1	A
			35-70*	Organics							B
Pa^{231}	32	Decay	5-120	Red clay	+	0	0	0	0	5	C
		Integration	5-120	or						5	D
		Th^{230} normal	5-120	*Glob.* ooze						4	E
Th^{230}	75	Decay	5-400	Red clay	+	0	0	0	0	2	F
		Integration	5-400	or						2	—
		Th^{230} normal	5-400	*Glob.* ooze						2	G
		Growth	0-200	$CaCO_3$-(organics)	0	+	0	+	+	3	H
U^{234}	250	Decay	50-1000	Coral	0	+	0	0	0	6	I
He^4	—	Growth	No limit	Mollusks or coral	0	+	0	+	0	7	J
Ar^{40}	—	Growth	No limit	Volcanics	+	+	+	+	+	8	K
Cl^{36}	300	Growth	50-500	Ign. or met. rock	0	0	+	0	0	9	L
Be^{10}	2500	Decay	100-8000	Red clay	+	0	0	0	0	10	M

A. Libby (1955), Broecker and Kulp (1956)
B. DeVries (1959)
C. Sarma (1964)
D. Sackett (1965)
E. Rosholt *et al.* (1961 and 1962), Sackett (1961 and 1965)
F. Piggot and Urry (1941), Volchok and Kulp (1957)
G. Goldberg and Koide (1962, 1963)

H. Barnes *et al.* (1956), Thurber *et al.* (1965), Kaufman and Broecker (1965)
I. Thurber (1962), Thurber *et al.* (1965)
J. Fanale and Schaeffer (1965)
K. Evernden *et al.* (1964), Evernden and Curtis (in press)
L. Schaeffer and Davis (1960)
M. Merrill *et al.* (1960)

* With ultra-low-background detectors and pre-enrichment of C^{14}

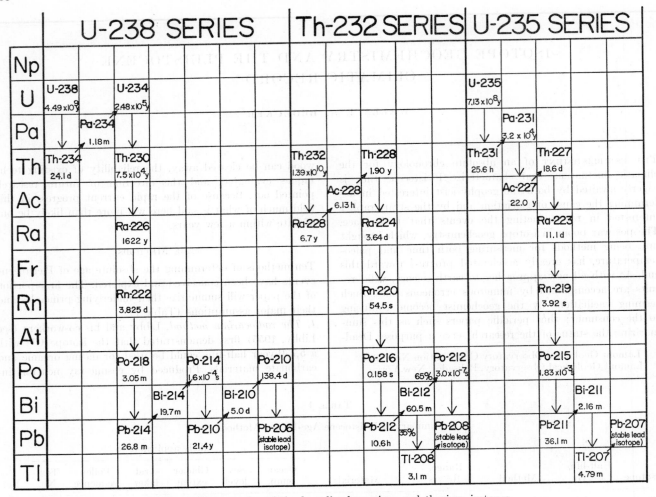

Figure 1. Decay series of the long-lived uranium and thorium isotopes.

teractions with atmospheric nitrogen, C^{14} is found in nearly uniform abundance in the carbon of all living organisms. By assuming that (1) materials formed in the past had this same initial C^{14}/C^{12} ratio and (2) that these materials have remained closed systems to the introduction of extraneous carbon, the present-day residual of C^{14} in fossil materials can be used to estimate their age. Most laboratories can detect this residual in samples as old as 40,000 years. By pre-enrichment of the C^{14} in the sample carbon and through the use of somewhat more sensitive detectors deVries (1959) was able to extend the measurement sensitivity to 70,000 years. Although the vast majority of ages obtained are almost certainly valid, two sources of uncertainty must be stressed: (1) contamination by younger carbon is known to be a serious potential source of error for organic materials greater than 40,000 years in age and for carbonates greater than 20,000 years in age, and (2) lower than normal initial C^{14} concentrations are to be expected for all materials deriving carbon from terrestrial waters. In the first case, ages beyond the stated limits must, without independent evidence, be considered minima, and, in the second, ages uncorrected for this effect could be as much as 3,000 years too great. Further mention of these problems is made below.

2-7. URANIUM SERIES METHODS

As shown in Figure 1, the long-lived uranium isotopes, 238 and 235, decay through a series of short-lived products to stable isotopes of lead. Whereas most of the members of these series have half-lives too short to be useful for geochronology, U^{234} (half-life 250,000 years) and Th^{230} (75,000 years) in the U^{238} series and Pa^{231} (32,000 years) in the U^{235} series have decay times appropriate for Pleistocene dating. In addition the eight helium atoms produced by the decay of U^{238} also have proved useful as hourglass type age indicators. (Because of its low abundance a negligible amount of He is generated by U^{235}.)

Application of the intermediate daughter products depends on the existence of natural separations of these isotopes from their parent uranium. Fortunately this takes place on a grand scale in the hydrologic cycle. Whereas uranium is quite soluble in natural waters, thorium and protactinium are virtually insoluble. Thus the daughter products are enriched relative to their parents in the detrital phases of sediments, whereas the parents are enriched with respect to the daughters in authigenic phases. If the original enrichment (or depletion) of the daughter is known, the extent to which equilibrium has been re-established in a fossil material can be used to estimate its age.

The several methods of application of these isotopes are outlined in the following sections.

2. The ionium-excess method. Beginning with the discovery by Pettersson (1930) that significant amounts of short-lived Ra^{226} unsupported by its long-lived parent U^{238} existed in recently deposited deep-sea sediments, numerous attempts have been made to use uranium-series inequilibria to date deep-sea sediments. Subsequent work has indicated that the excess Ra^{226} was not primary but was produced by an excess of Th^{230}, its immediate parent. The first age method was based on the assumptions that (1) the concentration of excess Th^{230} in recently formed sediment has remained constant with time at any point on the ocean floor and (2) Th^{230} does not migrate within the sedimentary column. Thus the level in a core at which the Th^{230} concentration reached half that at the surface is assigned an age of 75,000 years (the half-life of Th^{230}), that where it reached one quarter, 150,000 years, and so forth. The quantities of excess Th^{230} in such sediment are sufficient for measuring ages up to several hundred thousand years. Even though the basic chronology for Atlantic cores provided by the early work of Piggot and Urry (1941) has been confirmed by C^{14} measurements, the limited number of cores analyzed and the use of the potentially mobile Ra^{226} (1,600-year half-life daughter of Th^{230}) as an indicator of its parent's concentration caused these results to be cast into disrepute and to be largely forgotten. The recent extensive measurements by Goldberg and co-workers (Goldberg and Koide, 1962, 1963; Goldberg et al., 1964; Goldberg and Griffin, 1964) of the Th^{230}/Th^{232} ratio in deep-sea cores constitutes an extension of this early work. Their innovation of expressing the Th^{230} results as ratios to the Th^{232} rather than to total sediment is of minor consequence, because measurements show that Th^{232} remains essentially constant with depth in the core. The considerable internal consistency of these results, demonstrated by the smooth exponential decrease of Th^{230} with depth in many cores and the systematic distribution of deposition rates throughout the ocean, gave Goldberg and co-workers confidence in the reliability of this method. However, recent direct comparisons with the radiocarbon method show that ages based on Th^{230} can be as much as five to ten times too great (Goldberg and Griffin, 1964).

3. The ionium-deficiency method. The discovery by Barnes et al. (1956) that marine coral formed with several parts per million uranium but with negligible Th^{230} gave rise to a method of dating carbonate materials up to 200,000 years old. If fossil carbonates formed free of Th^{230} and if they have remained closed systems with respect to isotopes in the uranium series, then the extent to which Th^{230} has grown toward equilibrium with the uranium present in a fossil carbonate is a measure of its age. Measurements (Barnes et al., 1956; Sackett, 1958; Broecker, 1963; Rosholt et al., 1963; Blanchard, 1963; Thurber et al., 1965; Broecker and Thurber, 1965; Kaufman and Broecker, 1965) have shown that, whereas ideal materials do exist in many samples, one or both the assumptions are often violated. Tatsumoto and Goldberg (1959) and Kaufman and Broecker (1965) have shown that the Th^{232} concentration in the shell provides a valuable means for evaluating whether Th^{230} was added to the sample by processes other than the radioactive decay of the uranium present. Blanchard (1963), Kaufman and Broecker (1965), and Thurber et al. (1965) have shown that lack of equilibrium between Ra^{226} and its parent Th^{230} is a useful indicator of interaction between the sample and its surroundings. The discovery by Russian workers (Cherdyntsev et al., 1955) and confirmation in this country by Thurber (1962) that U^{234} (half-life 250,000 years) undergoes considerable separation from its parent U^{238} during weathering makes necessary a U^{234}/U^{238} measurement on each sample for which a Th^{230} age is to be measured. Details regarding this effect are given below. Kaufman and Broecker (1965) and Thurber et al. (1965) have shown that where the checks based on Th^{232} and Ra^{226} are favorable, samples yield Th^{230} ages in agreement with radiocarbon. Where Th^{230} ages are in error, they are generally too low. The reason for these deviations appears to be secondary addition of uranium.

Results obtained on peats of known radiocarbon age show a similar initial deficiency and subsequent growth of Th^{230} toward equilibrium with its parent uranium, suggesting that the Th^{230} growth method can be applied to organic materials as well as carbonates. However, as not all peats contain appreciable authigenic uranium (as opposed to that in the ever present detrital silicate), this method will certainly not be universally applicable.

4. The protactinium-ionium method. Sackett (1960) and Rosholt et al. (1961) independently conceived the idea of using Pa^{231}, the daughter of U^{235}, with 32,000-year half-life, in conjunction with Th^{230} for dating. Ages based on the Pa^{231}/Th^{230} ratio instead of Th^{230} alone in deep-sea cores should be less sensitive to changing oceanic conditions. The reasoning is as follows. As the majority of the excesses of Th^{230} and Pa^{231} found in deep-sea sediments are generated within the sea by the decay of the dissolved uranium, the ratio of Pa^{231} to Th^{230} added to the sediment should be fixed by the half-lives and abundances of U^{235} and U^{238} in sea water. Because these quantities are universally constant, then, if the processes removing Pa^{231} and Th^{230} from seawater do not distinguish between the two species and if they remain fixed once in the sediment, the ratio of Pa^{231} to Th^{230} in newly formed sediment should be constant. Because the excess Pa^{231} disappears roughly twice as fast as that of Th^{230}, the ratio of these two isotopes should decrease with a half-time of 58,000 years. The method is applicable over the last 120,000 years; beyond this limit detection of the residual excess Pa^{231} becomes difficult. Measurements by Rosholt et al. (1962, 1963) and by Sackett (1960, 1965) largely confirm these assumptions, yielding Pa^{231}/Th^{230} ratios for core tops close to the predicted values and ages for fossil material in agreement with radiocarbon. However, several core tops yielded finite ages of up to 100,000 years. Correspondingly high ages are encountered farther down. Whereas Rosholt et al. (1962) attributed these anomalies to the introduction of reworked sediment, the preferential concentration of Th^{230} toward the core top through migration could also explain the observations (Sackett, in press).

5. The protactinium method. Because of the apparently anomalous behavior of Th^{230} in some deep-sea cores, Sackett (in press) has developed an age method based on the disappearance of Pa^{231} analogous to the original Th^{230} method. In order to avoid the requirement that both Pa^{231} and sediment are deposited either at constant rates or at rates that vary sympathetically, Sackett (in press) used a model assuming a constant rate of Pa^{231} deposition. By determining the ratio of the amount of excess Pa^{231} above any given level in the core to total excess Pa^{231} in the core, ages can be obtained that are independent of variations in sedimentation rate and depend only on the constancy of the Pa^{231} deposition rate. Sackett (in press) has shown that ages obtained in this manner are in satisfactory agreement with C^{14} ages even in cores showing anomalously high Th^{230}/Th^{232} and Pa^{231}/Th^{230} ages. Because of the low abundance of Pa^{231} and its relatively short half-life, the method covers only the last 120,000 years.

6. The U^{234} method. The discovery by Cherdyntsev *et al.* (1955) that U^{234} is more easily released to ground waters during weathering than its parent U^{238} raised the possibility of an age method based on the disappearance of the excess U^{234} incorporated into carbonate minerals deposited from natural waters (Thurber, 1962). As U^{234} decays with a 250,000-year half-life, the method would be potentially applicable to events over the last million years. Beyond the usual closed-system assumption, ages would depend on the reliability of the estimate of the initial excess of U^{234} in a sample. Evidence accumulated to date (Thurber *et al.*, 1965; Broecker and Kaufman, 1965; Kaufman and Broecker, 1965) suggests (1) that conditions in fresh waters are too variable to warrant precise estimates of the initial excess, (2) that marine mollusks receive a sizeable contribution of uranium from the sediment in which they are buried, a reservoir so heterogeneous that again initial excesses cannot be reliably estimated, and (3) that marine coral appears to yield U^{234} ages consistent with independent age formation.

7. The helium method. Fanale and Schaeffer (1965) have recently demonstrated that ages based upon the amount of helium accumulated in carbonate materials are in many cases consistent with the Cenozoic time scale or with those obtained by the Th^{230} method. Whereas for samples beyond a million years in age the estimate is made by measuring the total helium and uranium for younger samples the U^{234}/U^{238} ratio must also be known in order to correct for the influence of inequilibrium in the uranium series on the rate of helium production. Experimental evidence suggests that major errors are toward low ages (secondary uranium and/or helium loss). This method is limited in age range only by the availability of suitably preserved material.

OTHER METHODS

8. The potassium-argon method. The work of Evernden *et al.* (1964) and Evernden and Curtis (in press) clearly demonstrates that the K-Ar method can yield reliable ages for Pleistocene events. The following assumptions appear to be well grounded: (1) volcanic minerals form free of Ar^{40}, (2) the Ar^{40} produced in the mineral by decay of potassium is quantitatively retained; and (3) the argon thus generated can be reliably distinguished from that absorbed from the atmosphere. The main drawbacks of the method are (a) that the inclusion of slight amounts of old rock detritus within the sample can cause significant increases in age, and (b) that suitable volcanic material occurs only rarely in direct association with deposits of known climatic significance.

9. The beryllium method. Be^{10} with a half-life of 2.5 million years, is produced by cosmic rays in the atmosphere as is C^{14}. Like other nonvolatile species, Be^{10} will be rapidly washed out of the atmosphere by rain and will largely end up in deep-sea sediments. Goel *et al.* (1957) and Merrill *et al.* (1960) investigated the possibility of using the decrease of the concentration of this isotope with depth in deep-sea cores as a means of determining their age. As in the case of the Th^{230} and Pa^{231} decay methods, the assumptions regarding the initial concentration of Be^{10} to be assigned to any sample and the absence of secondary migration must be experimentally proved. Perhaps a model with a constant Be^{10} deposition rate analogous to the model used by Sackett for Pa^{231} will prove most nearly reliable. Because the extremely low abundance of this isotope makes its precise measurement exceedingly difficult, the results to date demonstrate only that it exists in deep-sea cores in roughly the predicted amount.

10. The chlorine method. Schaeffer and Davis (1955) devised an ingenious method for measuring the length of time a given silicate rock has been exposed at the earth's surface. Cosmic-ray bombardment produces the isotope Cl^{36} (half-life 300,000 years) in surface rocks through interaction of the neutrons with stable chlorine. The ratio of Cl^{36} to the stable chlorine present would then be related to the time of exposure. Since cosmic-ray neutrons penetrate only a few meters into the earth's surface, a rock buried below this depth and then exposed by glacial action could conceivably record the age of the glaciation. Whereas the existence of Cl^{36} in roughly the predicted amounts has been demonstrated, the chlorine content of most rocks is so low that detection of the Cl^{36} therein has proved impractical. As the method offers one of the few hopes for establishing the ages of mountain glaciations, further attempts to isolate sufficient quantities of chlorine from igneous rocks are certainly warranted.

CLIMATE RECORDS

A number of records of world climate exist to which these age-dating methods can be applied. The five indicators most extensively used are: (1) surface-ocean temperature as recorded in deep-sea sediments, (2) the volume of glacial ice as recorded by fluctuations in sea level, (3) the extent of major ice sheets as recorded by glacial deposits, (4) the aridity of desert areas as recorded by the size of closed-basin lakes, and (5) plant-growth environment as recorded by the type of pollen grains in Pleistocene sediments.

Of prime importance to the stratigrapher is the glacial record. The four major glacial periods and three interglacials recognized form the framework for Pleistocene history. Because this record includes only glacials of intensity comparable to or greater than that of the last major ice advance, it by no means necessarily forms a complete record of world climate. Numerous brief or less intense cold periods may not be recorded.

To the geophysicist the record in deep-sea sediments has more appeal, because ideally it should be complete, showing the relative lengths and amplitudes of all, rather than only the major cold periods. Naturally a strong temptation exists among students of climatic history to correlate these two records. Much confusion has ensued. Emiliani's (1955, 1964) correlation, for example, leads to a short time scale, the first glacial period dating about 300,000 years, while that of Ericson *et al.* (1964) leads to a long time scale, with the first period dating 1,500,000 years. Because of the fundamental differences between these two climatic records, a really firm correlation awaits the establishment of absolute ages for key tie points in both sequences. Similar problems are encountered in correlating the other three records mentioned above. Progress toward fixing the ages of key time points in each system is summarized in the sections that follow.

SURFACE OCEAN TEMPERATURE

The tests of planktonic Foraminifera found in deep-sea sediments record climatic change through shifts both in species assemblage (Schott, 1935; Ericson *et al.*, 1961, 1964) and in oxygen-isotope ratio (Emiliani, 1955, 1964). For example, a typical equatorial Atlantic core contains at its top the tests of forams currently inhabiting tropical waters. At a depth of about 30 cm an abrupt transition to species currently inhabiting the cold water of the northern Atlantic occurs. The O^{18}/O^{16} ratio in $CaCO_3$ tests of any given species persisting across this transition undergoes a change of a little more than 0.1%. Both effects appear to be the result of a shift in surface ocean temperature. The cold-water species from the northern Atlantic are assumed to have displaced the tropical species in the equatorial region as the result of glacial cooling of the surface Atlantic.

As the degree of enrichment of O^{18} with respect to O^{16} in precipitating $CaCO_3$ increases 0.02% per 1° C temperature drop, then, if the isotopic composition of the equatorial Atlantic remained constant, the observed isotopic change in the foram tests must reflect a change in water temperature of 6° to 8° C.

As pointed out by Emiliani (1955) the isotopic composition of the ocean undergoes a sympathetic change. Because of the progressive depletion of O^{18} that occurs in air masses as the result of moisture loss through precipitation, the residual water precipitating in the cold regions of the earth is 1-3% deficient in O^{18} with respect to seawater. Thus, for example, if at the height of glaciation the amount of water stored in ice (beyond that stored today) were equal in volume to a layer of ocean water 100 m thick and if this ice had an O^{18}/O^{16} ratio 2% lower than that of mean seawater, then the mean O^{18} concentration in the oceans would be increased by 0.06%. This effect, if averaged over the oceans, would cause a change in the isotopic composition of foram tests equivalent to a 3° C decrease in temperature.

The concentration of salt caused by the extraction of this amount of water would raise the mean salinity of the sea by 3%. If water density rather than temperature controls the present-day distribution of forams, then, other factors being equal, a foram would have to migrate to water about 3.5° C warmer in order to counteract the salinity-induced density rise. Thus it is conceivable that the mean temperature of the ocean remained constant and that both the observed species change and the isotope shift reflect glacially induced density increases.

With this in mind, it is of interest to examine the available data. Four regions of the oceans will be considered: the surface of the equatorial Atlantic and of the east equatorial Pacific (as recorded by pelagic forams) and the deep Atlantic and deep Pacific oceans (as recorded by benthic forams). Pertinent paleontologic and isotope data are given in Table 2. The absence of measureable isotope or

TABLE 2

Limiting Cases for Interpretations of the Glacial to Interglacial Oxygen Isotope and
Faunal Changes Observed in Deep Sea Cores

Limiting case	Temperature increase necessary to produce observed		Salinity decrease necessary to produce observed	
	O^{18}/O^{16} change	Faunal change	O^{18}/O^{16} change[a]	Faunal change[b]
Surface equatorial Atlantic	~7°C	~10°C	~7%	~10%
Bottom equatorial Atlantic	~3°C	—	~3%	—
Surface equatorial Pacific	~2°C	<3°C	~2%	<3%
Bottom equatorial Pacific	~2°C	—	<2%	—
Volume weighted mean	<3°C	—	<3%	—
Ind. est.	ΔT = (none available)		ΔS = 3% (sea-level lowering)	

[a] Calculated assuming that glacial ice is 2% depleted in O^{18} with respect to mean sea water.
[b] Calculated assuming that the faunal change represents a migration to cooler (hence more dense) water that took place in order to nullify the density decrease caused by glacial melting.

TABLE 3

Comparison of Radiocarbon Ages on Types of Coexisting Material in Deep-Sea Cores

Core No.	Lat.	Long.	Depth (m)	Sediment type	Material	Age	Material	Age	Reference
V12-97	10°35'N	65°04'W	—	Green lutite	CaCO₃	7,350 ± 200	Organic	7,930 ± 150	Olson and Broecker (1961)
V10-LDC64	34°24'N	24°06'E	2,300	Organic-rich *Glob.* ooze	Forams	8,700 ± 1,000	Organic	8,400 ± 250	Olson and Broecker (1959)
A180-32	29°07'N	26°15'W	1,529	*Glob.* ooze	Forams	12,000 ± 300	Coccolith	11,200 ± 300	Broecker (unpubl.)
A254-BR-C	15°57'N	72°54'W	2,968	*Glob.* ooze	Forams	12,500 ± 200	Coccolith	12,800 ± 250	Rosholt *et al.* (1962)
A180-76	00°46'S	26°02'W	3,510	*Glob.* ooze	Forams	9,800 ± 200	Coccolith	10,300 ± 350	Ericson *et al.* (1956)
A172-2	16°12'N	72°19'W	3,070	*Glob.* ooze	Forams	11,500 ± 250	Coccolith	14,400 ± 400	Rubin and Suess (1955)
A179-4	16°36'N	74°48'W	2,965	*Glob.* ooze	Forams	11,800 ± 300	Coccolith	13,500 ± 400	Rubin and Suess (1955)

species variations in equatorial Pacific cores is of particular interest. Emiliani's (1955) explanation for the difference in response of the two equatorial oceans calls on a circulation change in the surface Pacific to balance out the temperature effect. This is most unlikely. As the basic patterns of circulation are very similar in the two equatorial oceans, any climate-induced changes in the Pacific Ocean should be as pronounced as in the Atlantic. The observed difference must reflect a basic change in either the thermal or the density regime of the Atlantic Ocean that failed to take place in the Pacific. The difference is almost certainly related to the proximity of the continental ice sheets to the Atlantic Ocean. This proximity could have caused either cooling or increased density. Whereas cooling is intuitively reasonable, density effects merit consideration. Because the continental glaciers were probably nourished primarily by waters evaporated from the Atlantic or its adjacent seas, if intermixing between the two oceans had a time constant similar to or longer than the length of a glacial period, a larger salinity increase would take place in the Atlantic than in the Pacific.

Despite the uncertainty regarding the cause of the species and isotopic changes observed in equatorial Atlantic cores, they are internally consistent and clearly related to climatic changes associated with periods of glaciation. Hence their chronology is of considerable significance. Examination of the publications of Ericson and co-workers (1961, 1964), who base their conclusions primarily on paleontologic evidence, and of Emiliani (1955, 1964), who bases his conclusions largely on oxygen-isotope data, reveal several basic problems encountered in constructing continuous records of Pleistocene climate.

1. Climatic curves constructed by Emiliani agree with those constructed by Ericson over only the upper few meters of the core (hence over about 120,000 years). As made apparent by contrasting the idealized climate curves (see Fig. 2) of Emiliani (1955) and Ericson *et al.* (1964), beyond Ericson's zone "w" quite different interpretations are obtained.

2. The climatic curves for the deep-sea cores fail to show the detailed climatic fluctuations revealed in other records. For example, whereas the retreat of the ice sheets and the sequence of pollen abundance in adjacent areas show that the end of the last glacial period was characterized by significant oscillations in climate, the oceanic record shows only a unidirectional and rather abrupt transition from cold to warm. Perhaps the oscillations observed in the other records are so small compared to the total magnitude of the climatic changes that they fail to show up in the oceanic record. Or perhaps the oceans fail to record the full amplitude of the oscillations and change only from one limiting condition to another at the onset and termination of glacial periods.

3. Attempts to apply standard continental stratigraphic terminology to the climatic fluctuations as observed in deep-sea cores lead to widely divergent conclusions (see Fig. 2) even over the last 120,000-year period where no important disagreement exists regarding the temperature curves or the chronology. Thus this exercise cannot be taken too seriously until reliable absolute ages provide a few meaningful tie points.

4. As continuous sections of *Globigerina* ooze longer than 10 m have not been obtained, and as sedimentation rates in *Globigerina* ooze average several centimeters per 1,000 years the record in any one core covers no more than 500,000 years. Records of earlier events can be found only in areas where erosion has eliminated much of the Pleistocene record. Extension of the record thus requires correlation of sections in the incomplete cores with those in the complete cores. The danger of course is that the erosive processes that brought this material within reach of the corer may have altered the sections of interest.

The absolute time scales applied by Ericson and Emiliani to their respective climatic curves are based on C¹⁴, Pa²³¹/Th²³⁰, and Pa²³¹ ages. Before the reliability of the ages used is discussed, mention should be made as to why the other methods summarized above have not been applied. The three methods involving products of the uranium

TABLE 4

Radiocarbon Ages for the Midpoint of the "y-z" Climatic Transition in Deep-Sea Cores

Core No.	Lat.	Long.	Water depth (m)	Length "z" zone (cm)	Age midpoint "y-z" trans.	Lab.[a]
			North Atlantic			
R10-10	41°24'N	40°06'W	4755	110	10,920	L
A179-15	24°48'N	75°56'W	3110	110	10,450	L
A179-8[b]	20°29'N	72°49'W	4060	270	13,500	L
			Equatorial Atlantic			
A180-74	00°03'S	24°10'W	3320	18	10,750	L
A180-73	00°10'N	23°00'W	3750	18	11,300	W
A180-76	00°46'S	26°02'W	3510	20	10,750	L
A180-48[b]	15°19'N	18°06'W	1450	457	12,100	L
			Caribbean			
A179-4[b]	16°36'N	74°48'W	2965	24	11,000	W
			Cariaco Trench			
V12-99	10°35'N	65°04'W	—	450	10,850	L
			Gulf of Mexico			
A185-35[b]	24°34'N	92°37'W	3630	105	10,900	L
V3-126	23°45'N	92°28'W	3485	40	10,900	L
V3-127	23°38'N	92°40'W	3540	40	12,900	L

[a] L = Lamont Geological Observatory
W = U.S. Geol. Surv. Lab., Washington, D.C.
[b] Cores that might contain a substantial amount of reworked carbonate material. Ages quoted are hence maxima.

series in carbonates, *viz.* Th^{230} growth, U^{234} decay, and He^4 growth, cannot be used because the main carbonate phases in deep-sea cores (the tests of Foraminifera and coccoliths) contain negligible amounts of uranium. Whereas the K-Ar method is potentially useful for dating volcanic-ash layers, the rarity of significant concentrations of this material, as well as the large dilution with argon-rich detrital silicate fragments, have discouraged application of this method to ocean sediments. Goldberg and Bieri (personal communication) are currently exploring this possibility with the use of a high-sensitivity cycloidal mass spectrometer capable of analyzing very small amounts of volcanic material. The Cl^{36} method as described above is clearly not applicable, and the Be^{10} method has not been adequately investigated because of the difficulties in obtaining reliable measurements. As detailed below, Th^{230} ages on cores of *Globigerina* ooze are generally of doubtful validity.

The age of mid-point of the transition from the "cold" oceanic climate characterizing Ericson's "y" period to the "warm" climate of the present or "z" period has been reliably established at 10,800 years by radiocarbon dating. The results upon which this conclusion is based are summarized in Tables 3 and 4. Agreement of the ages on the coarse (foram) and the fine (coccolith) fractions of carbonate material in the cores and of ages on coexisting carbonate and organic phases demonstrates that contamination is unimportant. The consistency of the mid-point age from core to core also provides strong evidence that secondary alteration and primary incorporation of reworked material have not altered the age. Considering also the agreement of this age for the end of the last cold period with ages obtained for corresponding events in the other systems, this result appears to be as reliable as any based on radiocarbon.

Attempts have been made to date this transition by the Th^{230}/Th^{232}, Pa^{231}/Th^{230}, and Pa^{231} decay methods. These results are summarized in Table 5. Included for comparison are ages calculated from Th^{230} decay with assumption of

TABLE 5

Comparison of Ages Obtained on Deep-Sea Cores by the Radiocarbon and Uranium-Series Inequilibrium Methods

Core No.	Lat.	Long.	Depth (m)	Mean % $CaCO_3$	Depth to "y-z" trans. (cm)	Age of "y-z" boundary in 10^3 yrs by various methods					Ref.
						C^{14}	Th^{232}/Th^{230}	Pa^{231}/Th^{230}	$Th^{230}/\Sigma Th^{230}$	$Pa^{231}/\Sigma Pa^{231}$	
A254-BR-C	15°57'N	72°54'W	2968	50	20	12,000	12,000	12,000	8,000	6,000	1
Zep 15	21°06'N	44°57'W	3255	80	12[a]	17,000	90,000	—	32,000	—	2
Zep 18	23°45'N	44°14'W	4950	60	18[a]	15,000	100,000	—	40,000	—	2
A180-32	29°07'N	26°15'W	1529	65	16	13,000	50,000	130,000	—	14,000	3

1. Rosholt *et al.*, 1962
2. Goldberg *et al.*, 1964
3. Sackett, 1965

[a] No paleontologic data are available. The depths are those at which the C^{14} age measurements were made.

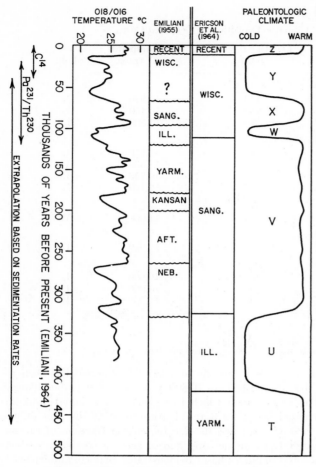

Figure 2. Comparison of climatic curves of Emiliani (1955, 1964) and Ericson *et al.* (1964). Although the two generally agree in their assignment of ages to various levels in the core, they seriously disagree as to (1) the climate characterizing the period from 120,000 to 300,000 and (2) the correlation with the continental glacial sequences. For example, Ericson *et al.* consider the "x" zone to be an interstadial within the Wisconsin, and Emiliani correlates it with the Sangamon interglacial. Emiliani assigns the Nebraskan to a level in the core with an age of about 300,000 years, and Ericson *et al.* to one with an age of 1,500,000 years.

constant Th^{230} deposition similar to the assumption of Sackett (1965) for his Pa^{231} ages. The plots of Th^{230}/Th^{232} given in Figure 3 are typical of cores showing gross discordancy between the methods and of those showing near concordancy. The following generalizations appear valid. Plots of Th^{230}/Th^{232} versus depth for cores yielding discordance depart strongly from the ideal smooth exponential decrease predicted if both the rate of sedimentation and the input of thorium isotope have remained constant with time. If interpreted simply as the result of variations in

sedimentation rate with no corresponding changes in initial Th^{230}/Th^{232} ratios, as done by Goldberg and his co-workers, then the results show very high ages for the transition.

Other equally acceptable explanations not nearly so contradictory with independent evidence are possible. For example, Goldberg and Koide's (1962) assumption that the Th^{230}/Th^{232} ratio in sediment deposited at any point in the ocean floor remains constant with time regardless of changes in rates of sedimentation has no impelling geochemical basis. Because Th^{230} is generated within the ocean, whereas Th^{232} is almost certainly an integral part of the continental detritus carried to the sea floor, temporal changes in the net amount of detritus added to the ocean would necessarily lead to a change in the average Th^{230}/Th^{232} ratio in depositing sediment (unless a corresponding proportional change in the uranium content of the sea occurred). Broecker *et al.* (1958), using radiocarbon data, have shown that the rate of deposition of detritus in the equatorial Atlantic was three times greater during the "y" than during the "z" period. If the rate of Th^{230} deposition remained constant, the initial Th^{230}/Th^{232} during the "z" period would be three times higher than during the "y" period. In this case the sharp decrease in Th^{230}/Th^{232} ratio observed by Goldberg would merely reflect a change in sedimentation rate. Walton and Broecker (1959) demonstrated in one equatorial core that a threefold abrupt decrease in Th^{230}/Th^{232} occurs at the "y-z" transition. Koczy (1961) has also emphasized this possibility. If this were the case, however, ages calculated by either the Pa^{231} (or Th^{230}) decay method of Sackett or by the Pa^{231}/Th^{230} method should be valid. The failure of these ages to agree internally or with the C^{14} ages in the anomalous cores indicates that changes in sedimentation rate alone cannot explain the anomaly.

Two other possibilities exist. The Pa^{231} and Th^{230} deposition rates also change with time. In this case, the Th^{230} and Pa^{231} ages would be invalid, but the Pa^{231}/Th^{230} ages would be correct. Upward concentration of Th^{230} in the cores would yield the anomalously high gradients of Th^{230} and correspondingly high Pa^{231}/Th^{230} and Th^{230}/Th^{232} ages without altering the Pa^{231} ages. The incorporation of reworked sediment could also contribute to the anomalies. At present the information available does not allow these possibilities to be evaluated adequately. It does seem clear, however, that where differences exist the uranium-series ages and not the C^{14} ages are in error.

In light of the above evaluation the following conclusions regarding the Th^{230} decay method are appropriate. Results are probably valid only in cores showing simple logarithmic decreases with depth. They should be trusted only when verified in the upper portions of the core by Pa^{231} data (yielding Pa^{231} ages agreeing with the Th^{230} ages). Additional cross-checks by C^{14} dating and by stratigraphic correlation with other cores are also desirable. If these checks are positive, then Th^{230}/Th^{232} ages in the 150,000 to 500,000-year age range can be given significance. It should be emphasized, however, that, because cores yielding evidence for climatic change are also subject to greater variability in sedimentation conditions, determinations of Th^{230} age and of climate are to some extent mutually ex-

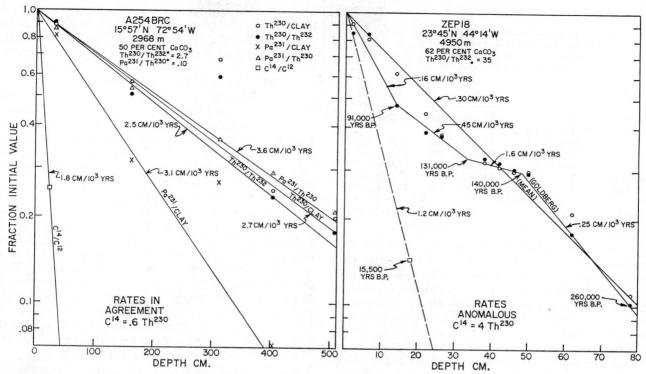

Figure 3. Comparison of sedimentation rates derived from uranium series and from radiocarbon data on two deep-sea cores. Whereas in core A254BRC, studied by the Miami group (Rosholt *et al.*, 1963), the rates are in satisfactory agreement, the rate based on Th^{230}/Th^{232} given by Goldberg *et al.* (1964) for the top of ZEP18 is 8 times lower than that obtained by C^{14}. The departure of the 315-cm point in core A254BRC from the $Th^{230}/clay$, $Pa^{231}/clay$, and Th^{230}/Th^{232} curves but not from the Pa^{231}/Th^{230} curve points out the basic advantage of the last-named method. It appears that rates and ages derived from the Th^{230}/Th^{232} cannot be valid unless the points fall on a straight line in such plots. Departure from a straight line indicates that the assumption of constant initial Th^{230}/Th^{232} ratio has been violated.

clusive. Only a fraction of existing cores will prove satisfactory for both methods. As valid Th^{230}/Th^{232} ages require that the sequence be continuous to the present, reliable dating of composite sections will prove even more difficult.

The age of Ericson's "x-z" boundary (*i.e.* the beginning of the last oceanic "cold" period) has been independently established in two different ways. Suess (1955), Emiliani (1955), and Broecker *et al.* (1958) have used sedimentation rates established in the upper portion of the cores by C^{14} dating to extrapolate the age of this boundary. These investigators agree on an age of about 65,000 years. Direct Pa^{231}/Th^{230} ages (Rosholt *et al.*, 1961) and Pa^{231} ages (Sackett, 1965) yield about the same result. Thus the age of this boundary appears to be well established.

The same two approaches have been taken to establish the ages of the "w-x" and "v-w" boundaries. The estimates are however not in agreement. Emiliani (1955), using average sedimentation rates of 30,000 years or so covered by C^{14}, obtains ages of 105,000 and 125,000 respectively. Broecker *et al.* (1958) took into account the variation of sedimentation rate with climate (rates in the equatorial Atlantic were only half as great during the "z" as during the "y" period, for example) and obtained estimates of 150,000 and 175,000 respectively. Pa^{231}/Th^{230} ages by

Rosholt *et al.* (1961, 1963) yield values of 98,000 and 125,-000 respectively and hence agree nicely with Emiliani's extrapolations. Although the Pa^{231}/Th^{230} ages are probably correct, these ages are less certain than those for the two overlying boundaries.

The only way ages for earlier boundaries can presently be obtained is by extrapolation of sedimentation rates. Although such estimates are valid indicators of the magnitude of these ages, they are potentially subject to rather large errors. As any errors are cumulative, the uncertainty increases with increased extrapolation. Hence reliable establishment of these ages awaits the successful application of the Be^{10} or Ar^{40} methods or of Th^{230}/Th^{232} ages that fit the requirements given above. Hopefully the basic disagreement regarding the construction of a climatic curve for these portions of the core will be resolved by the time reliable ages are available.

THE AREAL EXTENT OF GLACIERS

Precise dating of the climatic curve based on the extent of the ice sheets is limited almost completely to the last 25,000 years. Radiocarbon ages on wood largely from glacial tills (marking the position of an advancing ice front), from the beaches of proglacial lakes, and from basal bog deposits have yielded a fairly detailed picture of temporal

TABLE 6

Summary of Precise C[14] Age Comparisons Made
on Lignin and Cellulose Fractions of Woods
Associated with the Two Creeks Forest
(Broecker and Farrand, 1963)

Locality	Horizon	Cellulose age	Lignin age
Two Creeks	Forest bed	11,850 ± 100	11,790 ± 100
Two Creeks	Sediment below forest bed	11,890 ± 100	11,850 ± 100
DePere	Forest bed	11,820 ± 100	11,850 ± 100
DePere	Forest bed	11,820 ± 100	11,990 ± 100
Menasha	Till	11,760 ± 100	11,820 ± 100
Appleton	Till	11,820 ± 100	11,760 ± 100
Average	—	11,830	11,840

variations in the position of the ice front in the North American midcontinent. As demonstrated by careful C[14] determinations on lignin and cellulose fractions of wood samples from the Two Creeks Forest (which was overridden by the Valders ice), very precise ages can be obtained on such material (Broecker and Farrand, 1963) (Table 6). These results indicate that the ice was undergoing a significant advance during the period 23,000 to 20,000 years ago and achieved its maximum extent about 18,000 years ago. The retreat initiated shortly after attainment of this maximum was characterized by at least one major fluctuation (the Valders readvance 11,800 years ago), which was followed by a rapid retreat beginning about 11,500 years ago, corresponding in time to the *cold-warm* ("y-z") transition observed in ocean sediments. As mentioned above, other details revealed by the fluctuations of this retreat are not recorded in deep-sea sediments.

Studies of the deposits exposed on the north side of Lake Erie permitted Dreimanis (1957) and deVries and Dreimanis (1960) to reconstruct the fluctuations of the continental ice margin during the extended radiocarbon range. As shown in Table 7, four tills separated by interstadial deposits are recognized. The stratigraphic boundaries were dated by C[14] measurements on wood incorporated into the tills and on organic materials in the interstadial deposits.

TABLE 7

Summary of Radiocarbon Results for the Till Sequence
Exposed along the North Shore of Lake Erie
(Dreimanis, 1957, and deVries and Dreimanis, 1960)

Deposit	Stratigraphic name	Material dated	C[14] age
Till	Port Stanley	—	—
Contact		—	—
Interstadial	Lake Erie	Wood	12,660 ± 440
Till	Catfish Creek	—	—
Contact		Wood	27,000 ± 1,500
Interstadial	Plum Point	—	—
Till	Southwood	—	—
Contact		Wood	44,200 ± 1,500
Interstadial	Port Talbot	Gyttja (upper half of section)	47,500 ± 250
Till	Dunwich	—	—

The upper two tills are equivalent to the main Wisconsin ice advance and Valders readvance mentioned above. If the ages for material for the Southwood till and underlying Port Talbot gyttja are valid, then moderately warm periods about 48,000 and 28,000 years ago were separated by an important cold interval beginning 44,000 years ago.

In the absence of concrete data regarding the absolute ages of earlier glacial periods, a great deal of speculation has taken place. As mentioned above, Emiliani (1964) and Ericson *et al.* (1964) have attempted to relate the record observed in ocean cores to the classical glacial periods. Ericson's inferred age for the Nebraskan is, for example, five times Emiliani's age. This difference does not reflect differences regarding the assignment of absolute ages to any given level in a particular deep-sea core but rather to differences in matching given levels in the core with a given glacial period. The only absolute age measurements that bear on this long (Ericson) *versus* short (Emiliani) glacial time scale are Evernden and Curtis' (1964, in press) K-Ar dates. Their age of 1.8 million years for the lower middle Pleistocene Olduvai Gorge deposits, of 1.0 million for the Bishop tuff (which presumably postdates the deposits of one of the major mountain glaciations), and of 450,000 years for an ash deposited between the Tyrrhenian and Sicilian high sea stands support the long chronology. As Emiliani's correlation involves the rather questionable assumption that every prominent cold period in deep-sea cores has a recognized equivalent in the glacial record, acceptance of a longer time scale in no way violates the oceanic evidence.

SEA LEVEL

The use of the level of the sea as an indicator of climate suffers from the major drawback that factors other than the total volume of water locked in glacial ice can alter sea level at any point on the earth's surface. However, only climatic change should lead to fluctuations that are universally recorded. Hence, if concurrence can be achieved among records from different areas the results should provide one of the best climatic records.

Although similar, in the sense that it also gauges the volume of glacial ice, the sea-level record supplements the glacial record in that the deposits available for inspection are largely from "warm" rather than "cold" periods. The records are similar in that lesser fluctuations will be lost.

Although disagreement exists on the details, it is broadly accepted that the sea rose rapidly during the interval 12,000 to 8,000 years ago and more slowly thereafter, reaching within 3 m of its present level between 6,000 and 3,500 years ago. Since that time it has remained within ±3 m of its present level. Lack of agreement on the details of this curve stem largely either from uncertainties regarding the relationship between sample elevation and mean sea level at the time of deposition or the possibility of non-eustatic effects. Here, then, is an example of where geochronometric capabilities have advanced well beyond the capability to apply them.

Beyond 12,000 years uncertainties become much greater. There appear to be no reliable C[14] ages that place sea level within 50 ft of its present level back to the limits of the method. Where finite ages have been obtained for deposits close to or above the present level of the sea they (1) are on carbonates greater than 20,000 years in age, or (2) come from areas affected by glacial rebound. Where comparisons with other methods are available the finite ages have proved to be the result of secondary contamination.

The Th²³⁰ growth method and the U²³⁴ and He⁴ methods offer the possibility of dating carbonates from shorelines formed during the higher-than-present stands of the sea that occurred during previous interglacial periods. Results published by Thurber *et al.* (1965) and by Broecker and Thurber (1965) suggest, for example, that the sea stood close to its present level in the Bahama-Florida region and on Eniwetok Atoll about 120,000 years ago (Tables 8 and 9). Several He⁴ ages by Fanale and Schaeffer (1965) confirm this result. Whereas no evidence for high sea stands between 120,000 and 6,000 years ago has been found at Eniwetok, one coral sample from the Bahamas yields an age of 80,000 years. As this sample fulfills all the internal check requirements established by Thurber *et al.* (1965), the probability is high that the age is correct. The fact that the coral is deposited on a terrace in an oolite dune dating 120,-000 years adds weight to the validity of this date. Unpublished results by Lowenstam and Goldberg (personal communication) for Bermuda, by Broecker and Kaufman (personal communication) for southern California, and by Thurber and Stearns (personal communication) for the western Mediterranean also suggest positive sea stands between about 80,000 and 150,000 years ago. As considerable effort is currently being made in this area, definitive information should became available within the next few years. Hopefully, by combination of the three methods (*i.e.*, Th²³⁰, U²³⁴, and He⁴), valid ages over the entire Pleistocene range can be obtained.

PLUVIAL LAKE LEVELS

Variations in the size of lakes confined to closed basins are undoubtedly to a large extent related to climatic change. As summarized below, radiocarbon ages clearly demonstrate that high stands broadly correlate with "cold" periods and low with "warm." Thus if the absolute chronologies of these fluctuations could be established it would provide a first approximation to the world climatic curve. The lakes receiving the most extensive study to date are Searles in California, Lahontan in Nevada, and Bonneville in Utah. As the absolute chronologies of these lakes have until recently been based entirely on radiocarbon dates on lacustrine materials, the problem of choice of a suitable initial C¹⁴ concentration arises. Broecker and Walton (1959), on the basis of extensive studies of the present day C¹⁴/C¹² ratio in Great Basin waters, concluded that 500 years should be subtracted from ages for Lahontan and Bonneville samples that had been calculated with the usual initial ratio obtained from tree rings of known age. The uncertainty in this correction should not exceed 500 years. Whereas results published on bicarbonate-rich Searles Lake (Flint and Gale, 1958; Stuiver, 1964) are based on the usual control, Broecker and Kaufman (1965) suggest that 2,000 years be subtracted. The uncertainty in this correction is about 1,000 years. The adjusted chronologies based on the C¹⁴ re-

TABLE 8

Comparison of C¹⁴ and Th²³⁰ Ages on Samples of Coral from Borings on Eniwetok Atoll
(Thurber *et al.*, 1965)

Number	Depth (ft)	Th²³⁰ age	C¹⁴ age
Loc 15	Surface	400 ± 100	<200
MU7-4	13-24	4,500 ± 900	3,800 ± 150
MU7-10	24-26	6,600 ± 400	5,600 ± 150
MU7-11	24-36	5,000 ± 300	5,000 ± 150
MU7-12	34-36	5,700 ± 600	5,900 ± 150
MU7-13	48-51	100,000 ± 10,000	—
MU7-23	64-69	115,000 ± 15,000	33,000 ± 1,500
MU7-23	64-69	120,000 ± 15,000	—
MU7-32	80-85	>220,000	>38,000

TABLE 9

Th²³⁰ Growth Ages for Marine Carbonates from Pleistocene Deposits in the Bahamas and Florida Keys
(Broecker and Thurber, 1965)

Number	Description	Th²³⁰ age
Berry Islands, Bahamas		
L-717F	Coral from marine terrace cut in eolianite II	80,000 ± 8,000
L-717M	Oolite from eolianite II	140,000 ± 20,000
L-717N	Oolite from eolianite I	165,000 ± 20,000
L-717A	Coral from platform rock	195,000 ± 20,000
Florida Keys		
L-744D	Miami oolite, West Key	90,000 ± 9,000
L-744C	Miami oolite, West Key	120,000 ± 10,000
L-765A	Coral from Key Largo limestone, Windley Key	95,000 ± 9,000
L-801D	Key Largo coral	130,000 ± 20,000
L-801F	Key Largo coral	130,000 ± 15,000
L-801C	Key Largo coral	140,000 ± 15,000

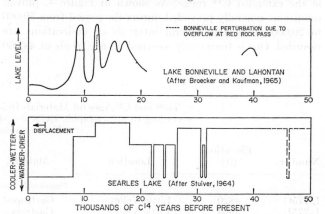

Figure 4. Curves of climate *versus* time, based on the fluctuation in level of lakes in the Great Basin. Stuiver's (1964) curve for Searles Lake is based on radiocarbon ages on samples from sediment cores, and Broecker and Kaufman's (1965) curve on radiocarbon and uranium-series dates on raised strandline deposits from Lakes Lahontan and Bonneville.

TABLE 10

Comparison of C[14] and Th[230] Ages on Carbonates
from Lakes Lahontan and Bonneville
(Kaufman and Broecker, 1965)

Number	Material	Location	Th[230]	C[14]
		Lake Bonneville		
	(carbonates associated with Gilbert's white marl)			
L-775I	Gastropods	Little Valley, Utah	16,700	15,400
L-775J	Gastropods	Little Valley, Utah	18,000	15,300
L-774N	Gastropods	Leamington, Utah	17,100	14,500
L-774A	Gastropods	Big Gully, Utah	11,000	17,000
L-672B	Tufa	Big Gully, Utah	21,400	17,100
L-774C	Gastropods	Big Gully, Utah	9,400	17,100
L-774R	Gastropods	Table Mtn., Utah	17,000	18,000
L-774I	Gastropods	McCornick, Utah	17,300	17,600
L-774H	Gastropods	Delta, Utah	16,700	15,000
		Lake Lahontan		
	(carbonates associated with white marl deposits)			
L-772K	Gastropods	Elder Ranch, Nevada	16,100	17,900
L-772NA	Gastropods	Elder Ranch, Nevada	12,200	19,100
L-772NB	Chara	Elder Ranch, Nevada	13,700	17,900
L-772B	Gastropods	Fishbone Cave, Nevada	11,900	17,300
L-772A	Chara	Fishbone Cave, Nevada	21,600	17,100
L-772F	Gastropods	Crypt Cave, Nevada	15,400	17,600
L-772GA	Gastropods	Big Gully, Utah	16,200	16,800
L-772HA	Chara	Llyndyll, Utah	24,400	18,400

sults, as shown in Figure 3, are not greatly different from that obtained for the glacial fluctuation, the major transition from large to small lakes occurring about 9,000 years ago.

Stuiver (1964) has presented a chronolgy for Searles Lake in the extended C[14] range. As shown in Figure 4, pluvial conditions generally prevailed during the period from 50,000 to 20,000 years ago, several intervals of desiccations are recorded. One is tentatively assigned an age of about 48,000

years, and four more are definitely dated at 33,000, 28,000, 26,000, and 24,000 years.

Kaufman and Broecker (1965) have recently shown that Th[230] growth ages for carbonates from Lakes Lahontan and Bonneville agree favorably with radiocarbon ages (Table 10). These results not only demonstrate the validity of C[14] ages of lacustrine carbonates from these lakes but also open the possibility of using the Th[230] method to date earlier pluvials.

Results of C[14] and Th[230] measurements are summarized in Table 11 for pluvial lake samples that are thought, on the basis of geological studies, to be beyond the range of C[14]. The unreliability of finite C[14] ages on carbonates in the range greater than 25,000 years is evident. As the deposits containing these samples were all formed during periods of pluviation, the ages should reflect times of "cold" climate.

Perhaps the most significant age obtained is that of 40,000 years for the upper Alpine deposits exposed at the Provo level in Little Valley. The concurrence of radiocarbon and uranium-series results provide good evidence for pluviation at this time. This conclusion is in accord with Stuiver's.

The ages of approximately 93,000 and 120,000 years respectively for the Lake Lahontan sample of Eetza age from the Fallon area (Morrison, 1964) and for the pre-Alpine Lake Bonneville sample from Little Valley provide evidence for a pluviation corresponding to the "w" cold period found in deep sea-cores.

POLLEN STRATIGRAPHY

Perhaps the most extensively studied record of world climate is that based on the relative abundances of various types of pollen found in terrestrial and lacustrine deposits. Whereas the complexity of interpretation of these records makes evaluations by non-experts of little value, a few of the more obvious hazards of this approach might be mentioned. (1) Because these records are almost always fragmentary, the establishment of a complete climatic curve involves correlation of records for numerous localities; for periods beyond the last major interglacial these correlations

TABLE 11

Th[230] and C[14] Ages on Materials from Lakes Lahontan and Bonneville which,
according to Stratigraphic Evidence, should be beyond the Range of Radiocarbon
(Kaufman and Broecker, 1965)

Number	Elevation (ft)	Location	Material	Stratigraphic age	C[14] age	Th[230] age
			Bonneville (present elev. 4,200 ft)			
L-775G	4820	Little Valley	Gastropod	Upper Alpine	40,000 ± 2,000[a]	38,500 ± 3,000
L-775L	4864	Little Valley	Gastropod	Pre Alpine[b]	28,500 ± 1,600	93,000 ± 10,000
L-775M	4760	Little Valley	Gastropod	Pre Alpine[b]	25,400 ± 2,500	>105,000
			Lahontan (present elev. 3,800 ft)			
L-773L	4080	Fallon area	Gastropod	Eetza[c]	>38,000	128,000 ± 10,000
L-772P	4050	Truckee Canyon	Gastropod	Unknown	{>34,000, 23,000 ± 2,000}	290,000 ± 90,000
L-773B	4070	Fallon Area	Gastropod	Pre-Eetza[c]	>40,000	>250,000

[a] Rubin and Alexander (1958)
[b] Morrison (pers. comm.)
[c] Morrison (1964)

can often be legitimately questioned. (2) Because the rate of accumulation of the host sediment can be extremely variable in any given locality, conclusions regarding the relative lengths of various "warm" and "cold" periods based on the thickness of the deposits is questionable. (3) Direct ties between pollen curves and the glacial record are rare and hence, as in the case of ocean cores, correlations must be accomplished largely by curve matching.

So far all radiometric ages on pollen sequences are based on C^{14} dates on organic matter from the host sediment. As in many cases the organic material dated is lacustrine in origin, the problem of the initial C^{14}/C^{12} ratio to be used in computing the result must be considered. Work by Deevey *et al.* (1954), Broecker and Walton (1959), Keith and Anderson (1963) makes it clear that corrections equivalent to age subtractions of up to 3,000 years may certainly be necessary. This problem has not been given the attention it merits. In the absence of any information regarding the geochemistry of the water body involved, subtraction of 1,500 years from results on limnic peats should yield ages good to ±1,500 years. As the correction is independent of sample age this problem is most serious in the case of pollen profiles representing postglacial time. Thus results on samples consisting of organic matter largely formed by plants using atmospheric CO_2 are certainly to be preferred. For samples in the range greater than 25,000 years, the 1,500-year uncertainty becomes comparable to that resulting from measurement.

As the available C^{14} results for samples in the extended range (35,000 to 70,000 years) are restricted largely to material from pollen profiles, mention of the reliability of these results is pertinent at this point. The obvious problem is the extent to which contamination of the sample with recent carbon alters the age measurement. The incorporation of 1% by weight of recent material will cause a 100,000-year-old sample to yield an apparent age of 38,000 years, 0.1%, an age of 57,000 years, and 0.01% 76,000 years. Thus, if in error, ages in the extended range are too low. The age of 64,000 years obtained by deVries (1959) on a piece of wood from an Amersfoort interstadial deposit is of particular importance to climate chronologies. Is the C^{14} that deVries found (0.04% of that in a recently grown wood) residual initial C^{14} or does it represent contamination? The "humic acids" removed from this sample during a NaOH pretreatment contained enough contamination to give them an apparent age of 42,300 years. If 94% of the contaminant were removed by the pretreatment, the remaining 6% would alone yield the observed age of 64,000 years for the treated wood. Hence only by the internal consistency of results from different chemical fractions (for example, from lignin and cellulose separates) and from numerous deposits representing the same event can the absence of contamination in the treated sample be proved. In the absence of such checks these ages are only reliable minima.

A well-documented pollen record for the last 13,000 years is available for northern Europe. The C^{14} chronology obtained is summarized in Figure 5. As in the case of the glacial and closed-basin lake records the transition from the last cold to the present warm climate is an oscillating one.

As the oscillations cover a period of only 2,000 years, centered about 11,000 years ago, the timing of the transition corresponds to that of the "y-z" oceanic warming.

The period between 13,000 years and at least 46,000 is characterized by pollen of tundra plants (Zagwijn, 1961). Although Brandtner (1956) found evidence for an interstadial between 25,000 and 30,000 years ago in an Austrian loess sequence, no definitive evidence for this fluctuation has been found in the Dutch profiles (Zagwijn, 1961). On the basis of the radiocarbon dates of deVries (1959), Zagwijn (1961) assigns an age of about 59,000 years to the Brørup interstadial ("warm"), whose end marks the onset of the long Weichselian pleniglacial ("cold") mentioned above. As this age assignment is based on an interpolation between the one 64,000-year result on the preceding Amersfoort interstadial and the two ages of 46,500 and 44,500 years for a humic layer within the overlying pleniglacial, its validity is subject to considerable question. If, for example, the wood dated at 64,000 years contained residual contamination, then both the age of 53,000 years assigned for the Brørup and of 64,000 years for the Amersfoort interstadial could be far too low. This danger is emphasized by the 43,700-year age deVries obtained on an Eemian peat (stratigraphically older than Amersfoort) and by the 50,000 ± 3,000-year age obtained on a sample dating the cold period separating the Amersfoort and Brørup interstadials. Until these uncertainties are removed, correlation of the pollen record with the oceanic record in the extended C^{14} range is dangerous.

Thus far no other methods have been successfully applied to pollen profiles. Preliminary measurements by Robert Kay (personal communication), showed that the Th^{230} growth method may also apply. He found that two out of

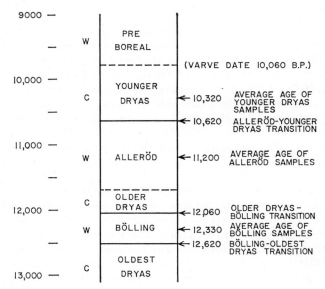

Figure 5. Sequence of climatic periods inferred from pollen profiles from Denmark, based on diagram given by Barendsen *et al.* (1957). Warm periods are indicated by W and cold by C. No radiocarbon data are available for the dotted transitions.

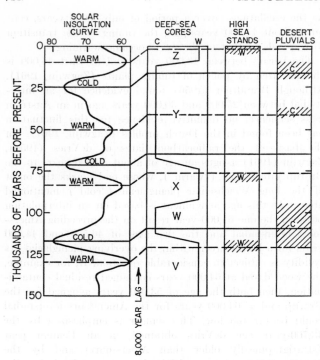

Figure 6. Comparison of the solar insolation curve of Brouwer and van Woerkem (1953) with the deep-sea climate surve of Ericson *et al.* (1964). Periods of high sea stands (hence warm climate) and of pluviation (hence cold climate) are also given. A better match is obtained if the earth's response is assumed to lag the insolation change by 8,000 years.

six samples of peat he examined contained appreciable amounts of "authigenic" uranium. The Th^{230} present could be accounted for by decay of uranium during the time since formation of the peats (11,000 years in each case as measured by C^{14}). As this method would provide an obvious cross-check for the 64,000-year C^{14} ages on Brørup peats, further work is being carried out along these lines. A further possibility is to apply the Th^{230} and He^4 methods to mollusks from the marine facies of pollen-bearing deposits. K-Ar ages on ash layers within pollen sequences will also prove invaluable.

As pointed out by Emiliani (1955), there is a rather striking correspondence between the solar-insolation curve as derived by Brouwer and van Woerkem (1955) and the climatic curves for ocean cores. This comparison is made in Figure 6. Except for the warm maximum centered around 50,000 years, the agreement is quite good if a lag of about 8,000 years between the radiation change and the terrestrial response is incorporated. The prominent warm insolation maximum at 127,000 years is recorded by the 120,000-year high stands of sea level measured at many points on the globe, and also by the latter part of Ericson's "v" zone (Emiliani's zone 7), which dates about 130,000 years. The 117,000 insolation minima appears to be recorded by the pluviation of the Great Basin tentatively dated at about

100,000 years (Kaufman and Broecker, 1965; Broecker and Kaufman, 1965) and by Ericson's zone "w" (Emiliani's zone 6) in deep-sea cores. The slightly less prominent warm maximum at 85,000 years ago also seems to be recorded by the high sea stand at 80,000 years reported by Broecker and Thurber (1965) and by Ericson's "x" zone (Emiliani's zone 5) in the deep-sea cores. If an 8,000-year response time is assumed, the 25,000-year minimum and 10,000-year insolation maximum correspond well with the sequence of events recorded in the various earth systems dated by the radiocarbon method. Thus only the 50,000-year maximum offers a real problem.

The deep-sea cores show a change from warm to cold about 65,000 years ago. The cold period continues to about 11,000 years ago. Figure 7 shows a typical paleontological curve published by Ericson *et al.* (1961) and three oxygen-isotope and coarse-fraction curves given by Emiliani (1955, 1964) for the "y" zone. The radiation curve (displaced by 8,000 years) is given for comparison. Neither Ericson's nor Emiliani's curve shows any evidence of a pronounced warm interval 30,000 to 50,000 years ago. The coarse-fraction curves, which, as pointed out by Emiliani (1955), show a striking resemblence to oxygen-isotope curves, in many cases show a coarse maximum in this range. Broecker *et al.* (1958), using radiocarbon data, have explained the relationship between coarse fraction and climate as follows. Sedimentation rates of clay and coccoliths (hence fine) were considerably higher in the equatorial Atlantic during the latter part of the "y" period (25,000 to 11,000 years ago) than during the "z" period, whereas the rate of Foraminifera (hence coarse) deposition was nearly constant. If this relationship is true in general, then the percent coarse fraction will be higher in warm than cold period. Too much weight cannot be given this evidence until it has been demonstrated that the percent coarse material varies only with climate.

Evidence from the other systems is also ambiguous. Several marine deposits close to present-day sea level have been tentatively dated at about 40,000 years by the uranium-series inequilibrium method. These include shells dredged from the Cape May Canal in New Jersey, shells from the lowest Tyrrhenian terrace in the Mediterranean, shells from Tomales Bay north of San Francisco, and shells from the marine deposits at the base of the Quadra Beds in British Columbia. However, as both the validity of the ages and of a warm-climate assignment can in each case be questioned, only secondary significance can be attached to these results. As mentioned above, Zagwijn (1961) finds no suggestion of warm climates during this period from his pollen studies in the Netherlands. Whereas deVries and Dreimanis (1960) provide evidence for a prominent ice retreat about 48,000 years ago, they also show that a rather prominent glacial advance occurred around 40,000 years ago. Searles Lake apparently desiccated about 48,000 years ago, but a significant pluvial apparently took place in both Searles Lake and Lake Bonneville about 40,000 years ago.

If the existence of a significant warm period 50,000 to 35,000 years ago is demonstrated and if the present chronology for the least 120,000 years stands the test of time, then the very close correlation between the insolation curves and

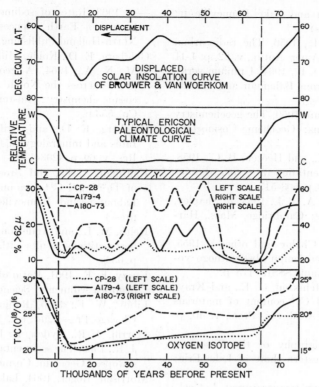

Figure 7. Detailed comparison of ocean-core climatic curves with the solar-insolation curve during the time interval 75,000 to 5,000 years ago (Ericson's "y" zone). Although neither the paleontologic or oxygen-isotope curves show the prominent warm period between 55,000 and 35,000 suggested by the insolation curve, plots of coarse fraction (hence the ratio of forams to clay and coccoliths) in some cases very nicely match the insolation curve. Again the match is only obtained if a lag of 8,000 years is introduced between the insolation change and the terrestrial response.

the earth's climate curve can hardly be attributed to coincidence.

Conclusions

The absolute Pleistocene chronology, established by the radiocarbon method, for the last 25,000 years is in the process of being extended to cover the entire Pleistocene. The application of the K-Ar method to volcanic-ash deposits, the Th^{230} growth and He^4 accumulation methods to carbonates, the Pa^{231} and Th^{230} decay methods to deep-sea cores, and the extended C^{14} method to woods has already provided much valuable information.

Further applications of these methods along with new ages that hopefully will be provided by Be^{10} decay measurements on deep-sea cores, Th^{230} growth measurements on peat deposits, and possibly Cl^{36} measurements on moraines left by mountain glaciers should within the next few years provide the absolute ages necessary to complete the framework.

Considerable geological work will be necessary in order to remove ambiguities in the climatic curves to which these ages are applied. For example, the conflict between Ericson's and Emiliani's interpretations regarding the climatic conditions that existed during the deposition of deep-sea sediments more than 120,000 years ago must be resolved.

The results available to date support the contention that the solar-insolation mechanism of Milankovitch must in some way contribute to the timing of climate changes.

References

Barendsen, G. W., Deevey, E. S., and Gralenski, L. J., 1957, Yale natural radiocarbon measurements III: Science, v. 126, p. 908-919

Barnes, J. W., Lang, E. J., and Potratz, H. A., 1956, Ratio of ionium to uranium in coral limestone: Science, v. 124, p. 175-176

Blanchard, R. L., 1963, Uranium decay series disequilibrium in age determination of marine calcium carbonates: St. Louis, Missouri, Washington Univ. Ph.D. thesis

Brandtner, Friedrich, 1956, Lösszstratigraphie und palaolithische Kulturabfolge in Niederösterreich und in den angrenzenden Gebieten: Eiszeitalter u. Gegenwart., v. 7, p. 127-175

Broecker, W. S., 1963, A preliminary evaluation of uranium series inequilibrium as a tool for absolute age measurement on marine carbonates: J. Geophys. Res., v. 68, p. 2817-2834

Broecker, W. S., and Farrand, W. R., 1963, The radiocarbon age of the Two Creeks Forest Bed, Wisconsin: Geol. Soc. Amer. Bull., v. 74, p. 795-802

Broecker, W. S., and Kaufman, Aaron, 1965, Radiocarbon

chronology of Lake Lahontan and Lake Bonneville II: Geol. Soc. Amer. Bull. (in press)

Broecker, W. S., and Kulp, J. L., 1956, The radiocarbon method of age determination: Amer. Antiq., v. 22, p. 1-11

Broecker, W. S., and Thurber, D. L., 1964, Uranium series dating of corals and oolites from Bahaman and Florida Key limestones: Science (in press)

Broecker, W. S., and Walton, Alan, 1959, The geochemistry of C^{14} in fresh water systems: Geochem, Cosmochim. Acta, v. 16, p. 15-38

Broecker, W. S., Turekian, K. K., and Heezen, B. C., 1958, The relation of deep sea sedimentation rates to variations in climate: Amer. J. Sci., v. 256, p. 503-517

Brouwer, J., and van Woerkom, A. J. J., 1953, in Shapley, Harlow (ed.), Climatic change: Cambridge, Mass., Harvard Univ. Press, 318 p.

Cherdyntsev, V. V. (with P. I. Chalov and others), 1955, Tr. III sessii komissii po. opredeleniyu absolyutnogo voziasta: Moscow, Izd. Akad. Nauk SSSR, 175 p.

Deevey, E. S., Gross, M. S., Hutchinson, G. E., and Kraybill, H. L., 1954, The natural C^{14} content of materials from hard-water lakes: Natl. Acad. Sci. Proc., v. 40, p. 285-288

Dreimanis, Aleksis, 1957, Stratigraphy of the Wisconsin glacial stage along the northwestern shore of Lake Erie: Science, v. 126, p. 166-168

Emiliani, Cesare, 1955, Pleistocene temperatures: J. Geol., v. 63, p. 538-578

—— 1964, Paleotemperature analysis of the Caribbean cores A254-BR-C and CP-28: Geol. Soc. Amer. Bull., v. 75, p. 129-144

Ericson, D. B., Ewing, Maurice, Wollin, Goesta, and Heezen, B. C., 1961, Atlantic deep sea sediment cores: Geol. Soc. Amer. Bull., v. 72, p. 193-286

Ericson, D. B., Ewing, Maurice, and Wollin, Goesta, 1964, The Pleistocene epoch in deep sea sediments: Science, v. 146, p. 723-732

Ericson, D. B., and Wollin, Goesta, 1956, Correlation of six cores from the equatorial Atlantic and Caribbean: Deep-Sea Res., v. 3, p. 104-125

Evernden, J. F., and Curtis, G. H., 1965, The potassium-argon dating of Late Cenozoic rocks in East Africa and Italy: Curr. Anth. (in press)

Evernden, J. F., Savage, D. E., Curtis, G. H., and James, G. T., 1964, Potassium-argon dates and the Cenozoic mammalian chronology of North America: Amer. J. Sci., v. 262, p. 145-198

Fanale, F. P., and Schaeffer, O. A., 1965, The helium-uranium method for dating marine carbonates: Science (in press)

Flint, R. F., and Gale, W. A., 1958, Stratigraphy and radiocarbon dates at Searles Lake, California: Amer. J. Sci., v. 256, p. 689-714

Goel, P. S., Kharkar, D. P., Lal, Devendra, Narsappaya, N., Peters, B., and Yatirajam, V., 1957, The beryllium-10 concentration in deep-sea sediments: Deep-Sea Res., v. 4, p. 202

Goldberg, E. D., and Koide, Minoru, 1962, Geochronological studies of deep-sea sediments by the Io/Th method: Geochim. Cosmochim. Acta, v. 26, p. 417-450

—— 1963, Rates of sediment accumulation in the Indian Ocean, in Earth sciences and meteoritics: Amsterdam, North-Holland Publishing Co., 90 p.

Goldberg, E. D., Koide, Minoru, Griffin, J. J., and Peterson, M. N. A., 1964, A geochronological and sedimentary profile across the North Atlantic Ocean, in Isotopic and cosmic chemistry: Amsterdam, North-Holland Publishing Co., 553 p.

Goldberg, E. D., and Griffin, J. J., 1964, Sedimentation rates and mineralogy in the South Atlantic: J. Geophys. Res., v. 69, p. 4293-4309

Kaufman, Aaron, and Broecker, W. S., 1965, Comparison of Th^{230} and C^{14} ages on carbonate materials from lakes Lahontan and Bonneville: Geol. Soc. Amer. Bull. (in press)

Keith, M. L., and Anderson, G. M., 1963, Radiocarbon dating: fictitious results with mollusk shells: Science, v. 141, p. 634

Koczy, F. F., 1961, Ratio of thorium-230 to thorium-232 in deep sea sediments: Science, v. 134, p. 1978

Libby, W. F., 1955, Radiocarbon dating: Chicago, Univ. Chicago Press, 2nd. ed., 175 p.

Merrill, J. R., Lyden, E. F. X., Honda, M., and Arnold, J. R., 1960, The sedimentary geochemistry of the beryllium isotopes: Geochim. Cosmochim. Acta, v. 18, p. 108-129

Morrison, Roger, 1964, Lake Lahontan: Geology of southern Carson Desert, Nevada: U.S. Geol. Surv. Prof. Pap. 401, 156 p.

Olson, E. A., and Broecker, W. S., 1959, Lamont natural radiocarbon measurements V: Radiocarbon, v. 1, p. 1-29

—— 1961, Lamont natural radiocarbon measurements VII: Radiocarbon, v. 3, p. 141-175

Pettersson, H., 1930, Teneur en radium des depots de mer profonde: Campagnes Sci. Monaco, v. 81

Piggott, C. S., and Urry, W. D., 1941, Radioactivity of ocean sediments: Amer. J. Sci., v. 239, p. 81-91

Rosholt, J. N., Emiliani, Cesare, Geiss, Johannes, Koczy, F. F., and Wangersky, P. J., 1961, Absolute dating of deep-sea cores by the Pa^{231}/Th^{230} method: J. Geol., v. 69, p. 162-185

—— 1962, Pa^{231}/Th^{230} dating and O^{18}/O^{16} temperature analysis of core A254-BR-C: J. Geophys. Res., v. 67, p. 2907-2911

—— 1963, Absolute dating of deep-sea cores by the Pa^{231}/Th^{230} method and accumulation rates; a reply: J. Geol., v. 71, p. 810

Rubin, Meyer, and Alexander, Corinne, 1958, U.S. Geol. Surv. radiocarbon dates IV: Science, v. 127, p. 1476-1487

Rubin, Meyer, and Suess, H. E., 1955, United States Geological Survey natural radiocarbon measurements II: Science, v. 121, p. 481-488

Sackett, W. M., 1958, Ionium-uranium ratios in marine deposited calcium carbonates and related materials: St. Louis, Washington Univ. Ph.D. thesis

—— 1960, Protactinium-231 content of ocean water and sediments: Science, v. 132, p. 1761-1762

—— 1965, Deposition rates by the protactinium method: Kingston, Rhode Island, 3rd Ann. Symposium on Marine Geochem., Proc. (in press)

Sarma, T. P., 1964, Dating of marine sediments by ionium and protactinium methods: Pittsburgh, Pennsylvania, Carnegie Inst. Tech. Ph.D. thesis

Schaeffer, O. A., and Davis, Ray, 1955, Cl-36 in nature: New York Acad. Sci. Ann., v. 62, p. 105

Schott, W., 1935, Die Foraminiferen in dem aequatorialen Teil des Atlantischen Ozeans: Meteor, v. 3, Pt. 3, p. 43-134

Stuiver, Minze, 1964, Carbon isotopic distribution and correlated chronology of Searles Lake sediments: Amer. J. Sci., v. 262, p. 377-392

Suess, H. E., 1955, Radiocarbon concentration in modern wood: Science, v. 122, p. 415-417

Tatsumoto, M., and Goldberg, E. D., 1959, Some aspects of the marine geochemistry of uranium: Geochim. Cosmochim. Acta, v. 17, p. 201-208

Thurber, D. L., 1962, Anomalous U^{234}/U^{238} in nature: J. Geophys. Res., v. 67, p. 4518-4520

Thurber, D. L., Broecker, W. S., Potratz, H. A., and Blan-chard, R. L., 1965, Uranium series ages of coral from Pacific atolls: Science (in press)

Volchok, H. L., and Kulp, J. L., 1957, The ionium method of age determination: Geochim. Cosmochim. Acta, v. 11, p. 219-246

deVries, Hessel, 1959, Measurement and use of natural radiocarbon, *in* Abelson, P. H. (ed.), Researches in geochemistry: New York, John Wiley & Sons, 511 p.

deVries, Hessel, and Dreimanis, Aleksis, 1960, Finite radiocarbon dates of the Port Talbot Interstadial deposits in southern Ontario: Science, v. 131, p. 1738

Walton, Alan, and Broecker, W. S., 1959, A contribution to the geochemistry of ionium in deep sea cores (abst.): Intern. Oceanogr. Congr. Proc., Sept. 1959, Woods Hole, Mass.

Zagwijn, W. H., 1961, Vegetation, climate and radiocarbon datings in the late Pleistocene of the Netherlands. Part I, Eemian and early Weichselian: Geol. Fdn. Netherlands, Mem., n. s., No. 14, p. 15-45

SUMMARY

The current status of isotope techniques employed for the determination of Pleistocene chronology and climate is summarized. Results derived from the application of these methods are evaluated. The conclusion is drawn that a generally reliable climatic record for the past 150,000 years has been obtained and that this record bears a remarkable resemblance to that predicted by Milankovitch-type insolation curves.

QUATERNARY PALEOPEDOLOGY

ROBERT V. RUHE[1]

PALEOPEDOLOGY IS the study of paleosols. A paleosol (from Greek, *palaio* ancient, and Latin, *solum* soil) is a soil that formed on a landscape of the past. *Relict soils* are soils that formed on pre-existing landscapes but were not buried by younger sediments. Formation of such soils dates from the time of the initial landscape. *Buried soils,* also formed on pre-existing landscapes and were subsequently covered by younger sediment or rock. These soils crop out in natural or man-made excavations, such as stream or roadcuts, and on hill slopes. Buried soils are particularly common in the United States. They occur beneath loess and till in the Midwest, beneath alluvial-fan gravel in the Southwest, and between basaltic lava flows in Hawaii (Fig. 1). *Exhumed soils* are those that were buried but have been re-exposed on the land surface by erosion of the covering mantle. These soils may have wide extent and be juxtaposed geographically with other soils that are more in harmony with the present environment.

RECOGNITION OF PALEOSOLS

Paleosols are recognized by the same kind, arrangement, and distribution of features that occur in soils on the present landscape. A soil is a three-dimensional body and commonly is composed of horizons that parallel the land surface. A vertical section downward through the soil is a soil profile; it contains one or more horizons that are differentiated on the basis of color, texture, structure, consistence, mineralogical and chemical composition, thickness, nature of horizon boundaries, and the like. The same criteria are applicable to paleosols.

There is no problem in recognizing a buried soil as a paleosol. Recognition of relict and exhumed soils as paleosols, however, is more difficult and must be done by geomorphic and stratigraphic means. Relict soils are soils on landscapes older than the present, so it must be demonstrated that the landscape is old, that the older surface has been stable and subject to little erosion since its formation, and that the soil on it dates from the time of origin of the surface.

For example, Ruston, a Red-Yellow Podzolic soil, has widespread distribution on coastal-plain sediments from Virginia to the Mississippi River Valley (Fig. 2). The Ruston soil abuts loess deposits paralleling the valley in Mississippi, Tennessee, and Kentucky, and a soil similar to Ruston passes under the loess. The Ruston-like soil is buried beneath Wisconsin loess in Carroll County, Mississippi (Simonson, 1954), and beneath Loveland (Illinoian) loess in Obion County, Tennessee (Wascher *et al.*, 1948), and near Memphis, Tennessee (Thorp *et al.*, 1951). Consequently the

[1] Soil Conservation Service, Iowa State University, Ames, Iowa.

Ruston soil on stable landscapes beyond the limits of the loess mantle must date in part from pre-Illinoian or Yarmouth time and is a relict soil or paleosol.

In Kansas and to the south, Sangamon paleosols emerge from beneath Wisconsin loess and become the surface soils (Frye and Leonard, this volume). These soils traced to southwestern Texas are the Chestnut, Reddish Chestnut, Brown, Reddish Brown, and Red Desert soils (Fig. 2). The Sangamon paleosols also can be traced from beneath Wisconsin loess in Kansas where they become the surface Reddish Prairie soils (Thorp *et al.*, 1951) that extend southward into Oklahoma and Texas. All of these great-group soils then can be in part relict soils that date from Sangamon time.

Exhumed soils are recognized by tracing a soil under a sediment and demonstrating that where it is uncovered the mantle was stripped. For example, Pleistocene paleosols are on interfluve summits and crop out on shoulders of slopes in Adair County, Iowa. Loess discontinuously mantles the paleosols and adjacent slopes. The paleosols pass under the loess as buried soils. Patchy distribution of loess through a wide elevation range, occurrence on wide summits but absence on narrow summits, absence from topographic saddles, absence on shoulders of slopes but presence on adjacent lower slopes and higher summits all indicate that erosion of the loess caused the outcrop pattern of the paleosols. In these areas the paleosols are exhumed.

STUDY OF PALEOSOLS

The study of paleosols as soils *per se* began about 30 years ago. Prior to that time and even today paleosol profiles have been confused with weathering profiles. A paleosol profile is the uppermost part of the weathering profile (Fig. 3) and can be described, defined, analyzed, and interpreted as any land-surface soil (Fig. 4). Commonly one finds that paleosols are analogues of land-surface soils but not necessarily in the same area. If one knows something about the environmental factors, *i.e.* climate, vegetation, material, topography, and time that controlled formation of the land-surface soil, an analogous paleosol may be similarly interpreted. This is not possible if the entire paleosolum is broadly lumped into one or two zones of the weathering profile.

In Decatur County, Iowa, the morphology of a buried soil is similar to Edina and Putnam surface soils formed from loess under grass in southern Iowa and northern Missouri (Simonson, 1954). Colors and thicknesses of horizons of the paleosol are similar to the Edina except that the buried A1-horizon is thinner and the A2-horizon is thicker. However, these horizons are very similar to those in the Putnam. Clay distribution and cation exchange capacities

755

Figure 1. Paleosols: (A) Buried soil formed partly in till beneath loess in Adair County, Iowa. (B) Buried soil formed in alluvium beneath alluvial-fan gravel in Dona Ana County, New Mexico. Carbonate in Bbca horizon is radiocarbon-dated at $20,300 \pm 800$ years (W-796) and in Ccab horizon $>30,000$ years (W-797). (C) Buried soil formed in pyroclastics beneath basalt lava flow near Kapaa, Kauai, Hawaii: *A* is alluvium; *B*, basalt; *P*, paleosol; and *Y*, pyroclastics. Soil horizons indicated in photos (A) and (B); scale in feet.

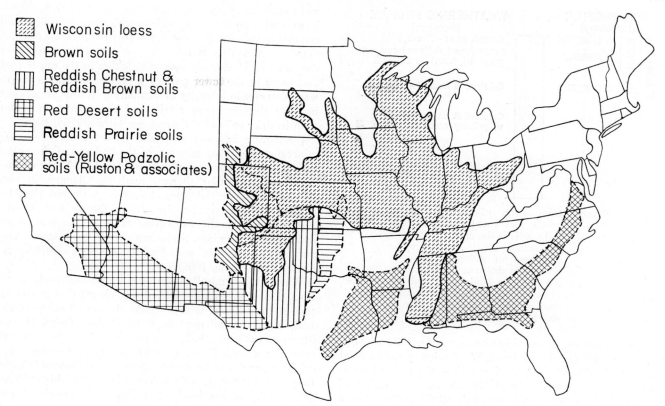

Figure 2. Major distribution of Wisconsin loess and of certain soils in United States. Loveland loess (Illinoian) is less widespread than Wisconsin loess. From maps of Pleistocene Eolian Deposits of the United States, Geol. Soc. America, 1952, and a map of Soil Associations of the United States, U.S. Dept. Agriculture, 1938.

in the buried soil also are similar to the Putnam. As Edina and Putnam are Planosols, the buried soil is a paleo-Planosol, and one may infer that genetic pathways and environments were similar on the present and buried landscapes.

METHODS OF ANALYSIS

Relict soils are studied, mapped, sampled, and analyzed as any soil on the land surface. Often it may be difficult to determine what properties are related to the past or what properties to the present. Certain features within the soil may demonstrate its history. For example, along the Rio Grande in Dona Ana County, New Mexico, and on the Picacho surface of late-Pleistocene age, a surface soil has a prominent subsurface carbonate horizon (Fig. 5). Within the upper 1 in. of this horizon, *organic* carbon sealed in the indurated horizon is dated by radiocarbon at $9,550 \pm 300$ years (I-616). *Inorganic* carbon of calcium carbonate of the same sample is dated at $13,850 \pm 600$ years (I-392). Carbonate from the top of the 1-in. layer is $4,575 \pm 170$ years (I-375) and from the base of the layer is $18,300 \pm 600$ years (I-391). Other inorganic carbon dates are shown in the figure. Organic carbon and clay-distribution curves are sub-parallel to an apparent illuvial horizon between 4 and 18 in., but the carbonate curve is discordant. Calcium carbonate apparently has engulfed the lower parts of illuvial horizons of organic carbon and silicate clay. As the organic carbon of 9,550 years is sealed in carbonate, such sealing occurred

after the illuvial horizon of the soil formed. Consequently the illuvial horizon is a relict feature that predates the carbonate deposition. The 9,550-year date also represents the latest date at which eluviation of organic carbon could have begun and thus the minimum age of the B-horizon (Perrin *et al.*, 1964). Consequently, the Picacho surface must have been stabilized and soil formation begun before that time. The Picacho surface must be as old as late Wisconsin.

Buried and exhumed soils offer different problems. Soil-chemical analyses may be meaningless as representing the original chemical nature of the paleosol. Some buried soils under loess in southern Iowa are completely saturated with bases (Simonson, 1941). Analogous land-surface soils in the same area have base saturations of only 40% in the B-horizon and 100% at depths of 4 to 5 ft in the C-horizon. Values of pH may be over 6.0 throughout the buried soils. Yet pH values in similar land-surface soils are 5.3 in the A1-, 4.0 in the B-, and 5.0 in the C-horizon.

Morphologic study in the field shows that carbonate nodules descend from the overlying calcareous loess into a buried soil although the paleosol matrix is leached. Vertically elongate iron-oxide pipestems ascend from the paleosol into the overlying loess. Such field data and supporting laboratory data show that the buried soil has been secondarily enriched with bases, carbonates, and iron oxide by solutions percolating downward through the overlying loess (Ruhe, 1956).

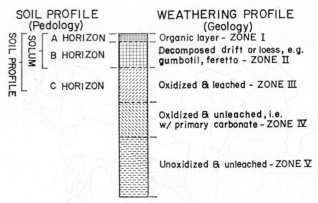

Figure 3. Comparison of the weathering profile and the soil profile. The soil profile is the upper part of the weathering profile and may be composed of different kinds of horizon in different combinations. All of these kinds and combinations of soil horizons are considered in the weathering profile as simple zones. *Cf.* Figure 4.

Where chemical characterization is not feasible, mineralogy of the soil may be analyzed. Weathering of the paleosol may be evaluated by weathering ratios—the ratio of number of grains of relatively stable minerals to number of grains of relatively unstable minerals (Ruhe, 1956). Zircon

and tourmaline, for example, are more resistant than amphiboles and pyroxenes. These minerals are identified and counted systematically under the petrographic microscope. Samples are analyzed and ratios calculated for horizons of the paleosol. Commonly ratios are higher in the upper part and lower in the lower part of a profile, showing a downward decrease in intensity of weathering. Ratios are greater in older than in younger soils and also greater in wetter than in drier soils of the same age (Ruhe, 1956, 1960).

Weathering intensity may also be determined by clay-mineral studies. Clay minerals of the horizons of the paleosol are identified and quantities estimated by X-ray diffraction and differential thermal analysis. Changes in clay mineralogy within the paleosol may be evaluated (Bhattacharya, 1962, 1963; Brophy, 1959; Droste and Tharin, 1958) as well as the weathering ratios of the coarser silt and sand-size fractions. Such data permit quantitative comparison of paleosols and land-surface soils (Millet and Drew, 1963; Ruhe, 1956).

Where the chemical nature of a mantle differs distinctly from that of a subjacent buried soil, chemical characterization of the paleosol is feasible. At the type locality of the Waipio paleosol adjacent to Pearl Harbor, Oahu, Hawaii, Stearns (1935, p. 49-55) reported Salt Lake basaltic tuff overlying a buried soil, 4 to 12 in. thick, developed in a subjacent reef limestone and attributed "considerable time" to soil development. This paleosol is part of his evidence for a stand of sea level 60 ft below the present during

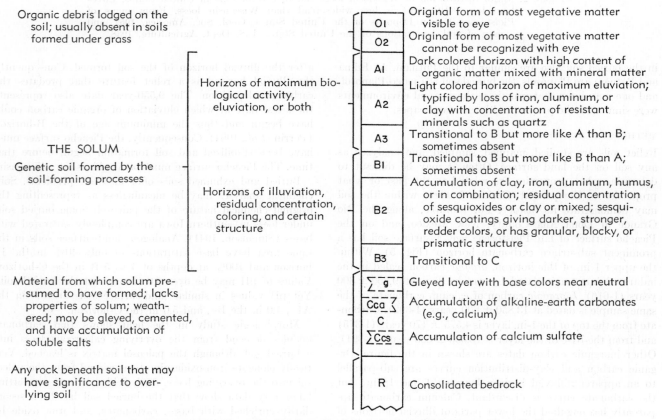

Figure 4. Hypothetical soil profile that has all of the principal soil horizons. Not all of these horizons are present in any profile, but every profile has some of them. Modified from Soil Survey Manual (1951).

Waipio (Illinoian) time (Stearns, 1961, p. 10). However, chemical analysis of the paleosol shows little if any soil development (Table 1). Soils on the youngest landscapes of Oahu contain 1% to more than 3% organic carbon and 10% to 15% free Fe_2O_3. Calcium carbonate is lacking in the solum even though coral limestone may be at shallow depths.

Unfortunately most studies of paleosols are mainly descriptive. Even in work where paleosols have been used extensively (Richmond, 1962; Morrison, 1964), few quantitative analytical data have been presented. In studies where quantitative data are adequate (Brophy, 1959), weathering profiles have been used rather than the paleosol and its subjacent weathering profile.

PALEOSOLS AND STRATIGRAPHY

Weathered layers have long been used to separate stratigraphically Pleistocene deposits, particularly those in the Midwest. In the classic studies of gumbotils a distinction was drawn between soil and gumbotil (Kay and Apfel, 1929; Leighton and MacClintock, 1930). Gumbotil was not considered as part of a soil profile (Scholtes *et al.*, 1951; Simonson, 1954). Pedologically, a gumbotil is part of a paleosol and may be the B-horizon of a paleo-Planosol or paleo-Gray Brown Podzolic soil or the A3- and B-horizons of a paleo-Humic Gley soil or paleo-Grumusol (Simonson, 1954; Ruhe, 1956). These paleosols are analogues of kinds of soil on the land-surface (Fig. 6). In general, a Planosol has a thin organic surface horizon over a layer, lighter in color and relatively depleted of clay, that sharply overlies a clayey subsoil horizon. A Gray-Brown Podzolic soil is somewhat similar in the two upper horizons, but the change to the clayey subsoil is gradual. A Humic Gley soil and Grumusol have thicker organic surface horizons that overlie clayey subsoils without distinct differences in clay content.

TABLE 1

Some Chemical Properties of Buried Soil under Salt Lake Basaltic Tuff, Type Locality of Waipio Paleosol, Oahu, Hawaii

Horizon (in.)	Organic carbon[a] (%)	Free Fe_2O_3[a] (%)	$CaCO_3$[a] (%)	Material
0-2	0.09	2.4	47.3	Clay
2-3	0.09	3.2	63.2	Clay
3-5	0.08	0.4	99.2	Coral
5-9+	0.05	0.4	90.0	Coral

[a] Determined by Walkley-Black method, sodium dithionite extraction, and gravimetric loss of CO_2 respectively. Appreciation is expressed to T. E. Fenton for the analyses.

The clayey subsoils, particularly if gray in color, are the gumbotil. These kinds of soil occur adjacent to each other and grade from one to another on the paleosolic surfaces of the older glacial tills. Therefore, the lateral variation of the gumbotil must be known and can be identified and recognized. When the variations are known, the paleosol can be used for stratigraphic purposes (Richmond and Frye, 1957; Amer. Comm. Strat. Nomen., 1961).

"GUMBOTIL DILEMMA"

Gumbotil has recently become the subject of a lively controversy (Frye, Shaffer, *et al.*, 1960; Frye, Willman, and Glass, 1960; Trowbridge, 1961; Allen, 1962; Leighton and MacClintock, 1962; Frye and Willman, 1963). As aptly pointed out by Frye, Shaffer, *et al.* (1960), the original definition by Kay (1916a) was dual, one part based on morphology and the other on genesis, and herein lies the so-called dilemma. There is no need to repeat Kay's (1916a) original definition, as all writers in the argument have done so, but Trowbridge's (1961, p. 154) ten points on definitive character (morphology) of gumbotil are well taken. Objec-

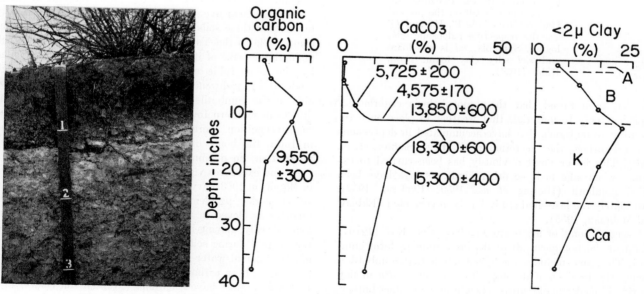

Figure 5. Properties of soil on Picacho surface along Rio Grande in Dona Ana County, New Mexico, illustrating relict nature of some of the properties. Radiocarbon dates of *organic* and *inorganic* carbon fitted to curves. Scale in photo in feet. Data from Soil Survey Laboratory, Soil Conservation Service.

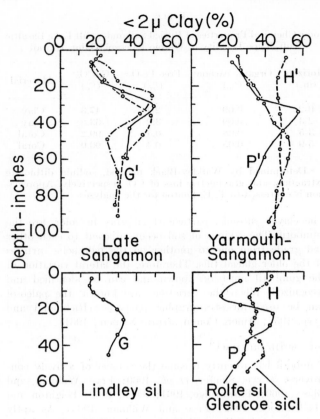

Figure 6. Comparison of clay-distribution curves of paleosols and of soils of land surface. Yarmouth-Sangamon paleosols are the gumbotil of Pleistocene-geology terminology, and, Late Sangamon paleosols are the feretto till. Rolfe is a Planosol (P), Glencoe a Humic Gley soil (H), and Lindley a Gray-Brown Podzolic soil (G), formed in till on the present land surface. Soils P', H', and G' are the respective paleosolic analogues. Symbols: *sil* is silt loam and *sicl* silty clay loam. From Ruhe (1956).

tion has been raised that these morphologic criteria can apply not only to materials that weather in place on a till plain but to materials that have accumulated in depressions on a till surface, the "accretion-gley" (Frye, Shaffer, et al., 1960). This latter point obviously has been carried to extremes when lake beds or other kinds of clays have been called gumbotil (Hseung et al., 1950; Eveland, 1952). Fortunately the last-cited study has been corrected (Ekblaw and Willman, 1955).

A second point of argument involves what Kay (1916a) meant or did not mean about decomposition to form gumbotil. This, too, includes the specification that gumbotil is largely the product of decomposition of till *in situ* in flat, poorly drained upland areas (Leighton and MacClintock, 1930, p. 37). The latter authors apparently are very restrictive in their requirement for weathering in place as they (1962, p. 286) took the present writer to task for assuming

accretion in gumbotil in Iowa (Ruhe, 1956, p. 448-449). Yet, two of the profiles discussed previously and also in this present paper (Fig. 6) are sites of Kay (Kay and Apfel, 1929, p. 128). Frye, Shaffer, et al. (1960) also demanded that gumbotil "be restricted to material resulting from *in situ* development" and further emphasized the following point (Frye and Willman, 1963, p. 10): "Although accretion-gley is common, the presence of such depositional soils was not noted in the writings of either Kay or Leighton and MacClintock. If they had differentiated them from gumbotil, they certainly would have called attention to the possibility of confusing them." On the contrary, Kay (1916b and repeated in Kay and Apfel, 1929, p. 109) clearly stated: "The gumbo is believed to be essentially the result of the thorough chemical weathering of the Kansan drift; but, subordinately, other factors, such as the wind, freezing and thawing, burrowing of animals, slope wash, etc., have undoubtedly contributed to its formation. The Kansan drift which has been changed to gumbo may have differed somewhat from the normal Kansan drift that lies below the gumbo." Without doubt, Kay permitted other agents and processes besides weathering in place in the formation of gumbotil. The present writer has concluded from the study of many of Kay's own gumbotil sites in Iowa that gumbotil includes various kinds of paleosol that can be categorized as analogues of soils on the present land surface (Ruhe, 1956), and others have presented the same opinion (Simonson, 1941, 1954; Thorp et al., 1951; Frye and Leonard, 1952, p. 21-22).

On any younger drift surface, e.g. Cary of the Des Moines lobe in Iowa, slope wash affects slopes, and sediment accumulates in lower adjacent closed depressions (Wallace and Handy, 1961). Clarion, Nicollet, and Webster soils, for example, are in catenary association from knolls down slight slopes into the depressions, respectively. It is recognized that, in places, the Clarion is formed in till, the Nicollet in colluvium over till on the slopes, and Webster in accretionary sediment over till in the depression. One can readily understand these soils advancing to a stage of development comparable to the Yarmouth-Sangamon paleosols but each maintaining some of its individual characteristics controlled by the geomorphic evolution of the landscape although modified by pedogenesis. These phenomena are recognizable in the gumbotils of Kay's gumbotil plain on tabular divides in southern Iowa. If such phenomena were accorded such recognition, there would be no gumbotil dilemma, and in Iowa, the home of the gumbotil, where there is such recognition, no dilemma exists.

Among exposures visited on a Pleistocene field conference in Illinois in 1963 (Frye and Willman, 1963), in part on the accretion-gley problem, only one (the Rochester section) qualifies as gleyed in the pedological sense, in my opinion. Pedologically, gleying is believed to indicate intensive reduction of iron during soil development, or reducing conditions due to stagnant water as shown by base colors that are near neutral, with or without mottles (Soil Survey Staff, 1962). Base colors must have a chroma (Munsell soil colors) of 2 or less in aggregated materials or 1.0 or less in non-aggregated material. In the Hipple School section (Frye and Willman, 1963, p. 31-34) the "accretion-gley" has a base color of 2.5Y 5/4, a considerable variance from the pedological color requirement of gley. The present writer was impressed that "accretion-gley" may contain as many different things as gumbotil, so instead of a gumbotil dilemma there now may be an accretion-gley dilemma.

It is suggested that many of the gumbotil and accretion-gley problems could be resolved if they were approached from a combined geomorphologic-pedologic approach. These two fields of study complement each other. Maintaining a distinct separation of pedology and geology, as advocated by some (Leighton, 1958, p. 704-706; 1959, p. 595; Leighton and MacClintock, 1962, p. 289-291), can only preclude development of meaningful, complementary information and delay solution of the problems.

SOIL-STRATIGRAPHIC UNITS

If a paleosol has distinctive features and stratigraphic relations that permit its consistent recognition and mapping as a stratigraphic unit, it is a useful stratigraphic tool. The lateral variation of the paleosols must be fully known (Amer. Comm. Strat. Nomen., 1961, p. 654; Richmond, 1962, p. 23-25). Such variation can be determined only by careful study from a pedological approach and not by gross study as a zone in a weathering profile. For example, the Sangamon paleosol separating underlying Loveland loess from overlying Wisconsin loess in southwestern Iowa has an overall gross morphology. A light-colored, weak platy A2-horizon overlies a brown (10YR hue) B-horizon with strongly developed coarse subangular blocky structure and with dark reddish-brown (5YR hue) coatings on peds. The subjacent C-horizon is yellowish brown (10YR hue) and massive. On successive primary and secondary divide ridges to the east in cuts 50 to 25 along Rock Island Railroad, Pottawattamie County (Ruhe, 1954), the clay content in the B-horizon progressively increases (Fig. 7). As Loveland loess thins from 26 ft in cut 50 to 16 ft in cut 25 through a distance of 18 miles, clay content in the B-horizon increases from 33% to 55%. Loess thickness decreases with distance as expressed by the equation $Y = 1/(0.043 + 0.00104X)$, where Y is thickness in feet and X is distance in miles, and clay content of the B-horizon in the Sangamon paleosols increases as loess thickness decreases as expressed by the equation $Y = 1/(0.0016 + 0.0011X)$, where Y is clay content in percent and X is thickness in feet. Clay content in the C-horizon of the paleosol also increases eastward, and clay content in the B-horizons is related to clay content in the C-horizons as $Y = -(19.24 - 1.9X)$. Such systematic change in the properties of the paleosol must be known if the buried soil is to be used accurately as a stratigraphic marker, particularly if continuous tracing is not possible.

Paleosols, although called zones of weathering profiles in the older literature, have been the primary basis for separation of the Nebraskan, Kansan, Illinoian, and Wisconsin deposits of the Pleistocene from the Great Plains in Kansas and Nebraska, on the west, through the north central states to Ohio. (See Richmond and Frye, 1957, for references.) In the Rocky Mountain and Basin and Range Provinces, emphasis has been placed on use of soils for stratigraphic purposes (Hunt and Sokoloff, 1950; Hunt et al., 1953; Hunt, 1954; Malde, 1955; Richmond, 1962; Morri-

son, 1964). In fact, paleosols have been used to suggest a correlation of events from pluvial Lake Bonneville in Utah to pluvial Lake Lahontan in Nevada and the Sierra Nevada in California (Morrison, 1964).

Paleosols within the Pleistocene loesses have been identified and used for stratigraphic purposes over great distances. The Sangamon paleosol on Loveland loess has been traced from southwestern Iowa to the Great Plains in Nebraska (Condra and Reed, 1950; Schultz et al., 1951) and Kansas (Frye and Leonard, 1952). It also has been traced down the Missouri and Mississippi River Valleys into Louisiana (Wascher et al., 1948; Leighton and Willman, 1950). Even where not on Loveland loess, the Sangamon paleosol is so distinctive, according to Frye and Leonard (this volume), that it may be traced from Ohio through the type area in Illinois to southwestern Texas, a distance of approximately 2,000 miles.

Two paleosols are prominent in the widespread Wisconsin loess. A basal increment is separated from the overlying loess by an A-C buried soil that is radiocarbon-dated in the type area in Illinois at $22,900 \pm 900$ to $26,150 \pm 600$ years (Frye and Willman, 1960, p. 6). This paleosol has been identified at many places in Iowa where coniferous wood

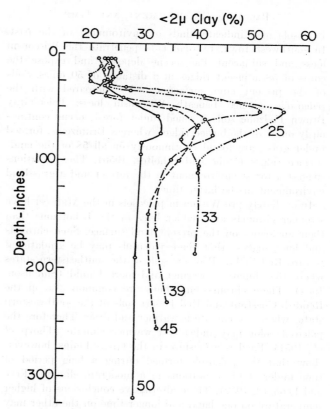

Figure 7. Systematic change in clay distribution in profiles of Sangamon paleosols across successive primary and secondary divide ridges in southwest Iowa. As loess thins from west to east, amount of clay in B-horizon in paleosols increases. Cuts 50 to 25 are along Rock Island Railroad in Pottawattamie County.

samples extracted from the buried A-horizon of the soil are 21,360 ± 850 (I-1023) and 24,500 ± 800 years (W-141) in the southwest part of the state. Organic carbon from the buried A-horizon is 20,290 ± 1,000 years (I-1022) in southeastern Iowa and 25,500 ± 2,500 (I-1267) and 29,000 ± 3,500 years (I-269) in northeastern Iowa.

Adjacent to the Missouri River in southwest Iowa the thin Farmdale A-C profile overlies the A2-B Sangamon profile in Loveland loess. Together they appear as a giant A1-A2-B paleosol. The Farmdale A1-horizon is the stratigraphic position of the *"Citellus zone"* of Nebraska and Kansas (Condra *et al.*, 1950, p. 31; Schultz *et al.*, 1951, p. 2-3; Frye and Leonard, 1952, p. 122), *i.e.* the ground surface and subjacent soil in which the ground squirrel, *Citellus*, made its burrows.

The Brady paleosol, an A-C-horizon soil, occurs within the Wisconsin loess above the Farmdale and has widespread distribution from the Missouri River westward to Kansas and Nebraska (Frye and Leonard, 1952, p. 132-135; Schultz *et al.*, 1951, p. 7). It has been used to separate two Wisconsin loesses on the Great Plains (Frye and Leonard, this volume). Little if any Brady soil can be identified in Wisconsin loesses east of the Missouri River.

PALEOSOLS, ENVIRONMENT, AND TIME

Paleosols may indicate kinds of environment of the past. In southwest Iowa, railroad cuts penetrate the Wisconsin loess and subjacent Pleistocene deposits and expose the cores of 58 adjacent ridges in a distance of 50 miles. Soils of the present land surface can be compared with the paleosolic surface beneath Wisconsin loess. Paleo-Gray Brown Podzolic soils, formed under forest, occur continuously on 57 of the buried ridges, whereas Brunizems, formed under grass, are found continuously on all 58 of the land-surface ridges (Ruhe and Scholtes, 1956). These relations suggest a forest environment in the former and a grassland environment in the latter time.

Immediately pre-Wisconsin paleosols in the Midwest have stronger chromas and redder hues in the B-horizons than their analogues on the present land surface. Such chromas and hues suggest that these paleosols may be gradational toward Red-Yellow Podzolic soils of the southeastern states where the climate is warmer and more humid (Simonson, 1954). These chromas and hues are common also in the Reddish Chestnut and Red Desert soils of the southwestern states where the climate is warmer and drier. Therefore the paleosol color may indicate a warmer climate (Thorp *et al.*, 1951). Field relationships in the Great Plains, however, show that the paleosols formed during a long period of time under stable conditions in a moderate climate (Frye and Leonard, 1952). These alternative conclusions of higher temperature on one hand and longer time on the other may both be correct, as the product of a long interval of time and low climatic intensity could be the same as the product of a short interval of time and a high climatic intensity (Simonson, 1954). Color alone, then, is not a valid indicator of climate or time alone.

In Kansas from the Missouri River westward to Colorado and southward to Oklahoma the Sangamon paleosol shows about the same degree of change geographically as the surface soils (Frye and Leonard, 1952, p. 122). Although the Sangamon paleosols are more strongly developed at the same locality, the analogy of buried and surface soils suggests that the climatic and vegetation zones in Sangamon time were similar to those of the present, although present boundary lines may be displaced somewhat to the east (p. 123).

Analysis of pollen from Sangamon Humic Gley paleosols in Indiana where overlain by Wisconsin deposits suggests a climatic sequence of a late-glacial boreal climate, climatic amelioration to a thermal maximum, and return to boreal climate (Kapp and Gooding, 1964, and references therein).

Properties of paleosols have been used to estimate time during the Pleistocene. Rate of formation of gumbotil was calculated from its relation to subjacent depths of carbonates below the gumbotil surface. Thus durations of the Aftonian, Yarmouth, and Sangamon interglacial ages were determined as 70, 200, and 150 thousand years, respectively (Kay, 1931). As pointed out previously, the gumbotil actually is different parts of different kinds of paleosol, and in some of these paleosols accretionary layers are involved. Hence the computations are invalid. One generalization, however, is valid—pre-Wisconsin paleosols are more strongly developed and more weathered than their intra-Wisconsin or postglacial land-surface analogues. Time may be one of the factors responsible for these basic differences.

Depth of leaching of carbonates has been used as a time determinant (Flint, 1949). Time is not the only factor controlling the depth of leaching, but texture, permeability, carbonate content, topography, rainfall, temperature, biotic environment, depth to ground water, among others, may also affect leaching. Of all factors, carbonate content seems to be the most important (Merritt and Muller, 1959), and mathematical manipulation of content and associated properties may permit time estimates. One method adjusts values of depth of leaching of highly calcareous materials to others with less carbonate. Adjusted values of the former and measured values of the latter are grouped and used for comparison of one set of data with another (Dreimanis, 1959).

Another method relates carbonate content to the rate of movement of soil moisture and the movement of carbonate by soil moisture. The first parameter is expressed in units of water-holding capacity per soil-horizon volume, and the second parameter is expressed as solubility of the carbonate. The total carbonate moved past any depth in a soil divided by the rate of water movement past that depth and by the solubility of the carbonates gives the minimum time required (Arkley, 1963).

Color of paleosols also has been related to time. One proposal is that paleosol colors become redder with time, ranging from hue of 2.5Y (Munsell soil colors) for Recent soils to hue 10R for early-Pleistocene and Pliocene soils (Carter, 1956). Some paleosols which formed between Kansan to Wisconsin time are gray, with hues of 5Y to 10YR. These paleosols formed on poorly drained topography (Ruhe, 1956). Paleosols of lesser age, an increment of Sangamon time, are dark brown to reddish brown, with hues of 7.5YR to 5YR, and formed on topographic positions with good soil aeration and internal drainage. Local soil environment may affect soil color, which usually is related to the nature of iron oxide in the soil. The color may not be related to time at all, but other factors may be involved.

Gradually paleopedology is assuming stature as a science. It is an important field of study in geology, pedology, ecology, and associated sciences. It has wide use in separating geologic and particularly Pleistocene deposits and permits a better evaluation of the nature and duration of the hiatuses between deposits. It permits better understanding of apparently anomalous associations of soils on a landscape. It may even permit better understanding of environmental changes within the physiographic history of an area.

REFERENCES

Allen, V. T., 1962, Gumbotil, gley, and accretion-gley: J. Geol., v. 70, p. 342-347

American Commission of Stratigraphic Nomenclature, 1961, Code of stratigraphic nomenclature: Amer. Assoc. Petroleum Geologists Bull., v. 45, p. 645-665

Arkley, R. J., 1963, Calculation of carbonate and water movement in soil from climatic data: Soil Sci., v. 96, p. 239-248

Bhattacharya, N., 1962, Weathering of glacial tills in Indiana, I. Clay minerals: Geol. Soc. Amer. Bull., v. 73, p. 1007-1020

—— 1963, Weathering of glacial tills in Indiana—heavy minerals: J. Sed. Petrology, v. 33, p. 789-794

Brophy, J. A., 1959, Heavy mineral ratios of Sangamon weathering profiles in Illinois: Illinois Geol. Surv. Circ. 273, 22 p.

Carter, G. F., 1956, On soil color and time: Southw. J. Anthrop., v. 12, p. 295-324

Condra, G. E., and Reed, E. C., 1950, Correlation of the Pleistocene deposits of Nebraska: Nebraska Geol. Surv. Bull. 15A, 74 p.

Dreimanis, Aleksis, 1959, Measurement of depth of carbonate leaching in service of Pleistocene stratigraphy: Geol. Fören. Stockholm Förhan., v. 81, p. 478-484

Droste, J. B., and Tharin, J. C., 1958, Alteration of clay minerals in Illinoian till by weathering: Geol. Soc. Amer. Bull., v. 69, p. 61-68

Ekblaw, G. E., and Willman, H. B., 1955, Farmdale drift near Danville, Illinois: Illinois Acad. Sci. Trans., v. 47, p. 129-138

Eveland, H. E., 1952, Pleistocene geology of the Danville region, Illinois: Illinois Geol. Surv. Rep. Inv. 159, 30 p.

Flint, R. F., 1949, Leaching of carbonates in glacial drift and loess as a basis for age correlation: J. Geol., v. 57, p. 297-303

Frye, J. C., and Leonard, A. B., 1952, Pleistocene geology of Kansas: Kansas Geol. Surv. Bull. 99, 230 p.

—— this volume, Quaternary of the southern Great Plains

Frye, J. C., Shaffer, P. R., Willman, H. B., and Ekblaw, G. E., 1960, Accretion-gley and the gumbotil dilemma: Amer. J. Sci., v. 258, p. 185-190

Frye, J. C., Willman, H. B., and Glass, H. D., 1960, Gumbotil, accretion-gley, and the weathering profile: Illinois Geol. Surv. Circ. 295, 39 p.

Frye, J. C., and Willman, H. B., 1960, Classification of the Wisconsinan stage in the Lake Michigan glacial lobe: Illinois Geol. Surv. Circ. 285, 16 p.

—— 1963, Loess stratigraphy, Wisconsinan classification, and accretion-gleys in central western Illinois: Illinois Geol. Surv. Guidebook, ser. 5, 37 p.

Hseung, Yi, Marshall, C. E., and Krusekopf, H. H., 1950, On the origin of gumbotil: Soil Sci. Soc. Amer. Proc., v. 14, p. 311-315

Hunt, C. B., 1954, Pleistocene and Recent deposits in the Denver area, Colorado: U.S. Geol. Surv. Bull. 996-C, p. 91-140

Hunt, C. B., and Sokoloff, V. P., 1950, Pre-Wisconsin soil in the Rocky Mountain region: U.S. Geol. Surv. Prof. Pap. 221-G, p. 109-123

Hunt, C. B., Varnes, Helen D., and Thomas, H. E., 1953, Lake Bonneville—geology of northern Utah Valley, Utah: U.S. Geol. Surv. Prof. Pap. 257-A, p. 1-99

Kapp, R. O., and Gooding, A. M., 1964, Pleistocene vegetational studies in the Whitewater Basin, southeastern Indiana: J. Geol., v. 72, p. 307-326

Kay, G. F., 1916a, Gumbotil, a new term in Pleistocene geology: Science, v. 44, p. 637-638

—— 1916b, Some features of the Kansan drift in southern Iowa (abst., with discussion by W. C. Alden, Frank Leverett, and C. E. Decker): Geol. Soc. Amer. Bull., v. 27, p. 115-119

—— 1931, Classification and duration of the Pleistocene period: Geol. Soc. Amer. Bull., v. 42, p. 425-466

Kay, G. F., and Apfel, E. T., 1929, The pre-Illinoian Pleistocene geology of Iowa: Iowa Geol. Surv. Ann. Rep., v. 34, p. 1-304

Leighton, M. M., 1958, Principles and viewpoints in formulating the stratigraphic classifications of the Pleistocene: J. Geol., v. 66, p. 700-709

—— 1959, Important elements in the classification of the Wisconsin glacial stage—a reply: J. Geol., v. 67, p. 594-598

Leighton, M. M., and MacClintock, Paul, 1930, Weathered zones of drift sheets of Illinois: J. Geol., v. 38, p. 28-53

—— 1962, The weathered mantle of glacial tills beneath original surfaces in north-central United States: J. Geol., v. 70, p. 267-293

Leighton, M. M., and Willman, H. B., 1950, Loess formations of the Mississippi Valley: J. Geol., v. 58, p. 599-623

Malde, H. E., 1955, Surficial geology of the Louisville Quadrangle, Colorado: U.S. Geol. Surv. Bull. 996-E, p. 217-259

Merritt, R. S., and Muller, E. H., 1959, Depths of leaching in relation to carbonate content of till in central New York State: Amer. J. Sci., v. 257, p. 465-480

Millet, J. L., and Drew, J. V., 1963, Characterization and genesis of Pawnee and Adair soils in southeastern Nebraska: Soil Sci. Soc. Amer. Proc., v. 27, p. 683-688

Morrison, R. B., 1964, Lake Lahontan—geology of southern Carson Desert, Nevada: U.S. Geol. Surv. Prof. Pap. 401, 156 p.

Perrin, R. M. S., Willis, E. H., and Hodge, C. A. H., 1964, Dating of humus podzols by residual radiocarbon activity: Nature, v. 202, p. 165-166

Richmond, G. M., 1962, Quaternary stratigraphy of the

LaSal Mountains, Utah: U.S. Geol. Surv. Prof. Pap. 324, 138 p.

Richmond, G. M., and Frye, J. C., 1957, Note 19—Status of soils in stratigraphic nomenclature: Amer. Assoc. Petroleum Geologists Bull., v. 41, p. 758-763

Ruhe, R. V., 1954, Relations of the properties of Wisconsin loess to topography in western Iowa: Amer. J. Sci., v. 252, p. 663-672

—— 1956, Geomorphic surfaces and the nature of soils: Soil Sci., v. 82, p. 441-455

—— 1960, Elements of the soil landscape: Madison, Wisconsin, 7th Intern. Congr. Soil Sci. Trans., v. 4, p. 165-170

Ruhe, R. V., and Scholtes, W. H., 1956, Ages and development of soil landscapes in relation to climatic and vegetational changes in Iowa: Soil Sci. Soc. Amer. Proc., v. 20, p. 264-273

Scholtes, W. H., Ruhe, R. V., and Riecken, F. F., 1951, Use of the morphology of buried soil profiles in the Pleistocene of Iowa: Iowa Acad. Sci. Proc., v. 58, p. 295-306

Schultz, C. B., Lueninghoener, G. C., and Frankforter, W. D., 1951, A graphic résumé of the Pleistocene of Nebraska: Univ. Nebraska State Mus. Bull., 41 p.

Simonson, R. W., 1941, Studies of buried soils formed from till in Iowa: Soil Sci. Soc. Amer. Proc., v. 6, p. 373-381

—— 1954, Identification and interpretation of buried soils. Amer. J. Sci., v. 252, p. 705-732

Soil Survey Staff, 1962, Soil survey manual—identification and nomenclature of soil horizons: p. 173-188, supplement to U.S. Dept. Agriculture Handbook 18, 1951, 503 p.

Stearns, H. T., 1935, Geology and ground-water resources of the island of Oahu, Hawaii: Hawaii Div. Hydrog. Bull. 1, p. 3-198

—— 1961, Eustatic shorelines on Pacific islands: Z. Geomorph. Suppl. v. 3, p. 1-16

Thorp, James, Johnson, W. M., and Reed, E. C., 1951, Some post-Pliocene buried soils of central United States: J. Soil Sci., v. 2, p. 1-19

Trowbridge, A. C., 1961, Accretion-gley and the gumbotil dilemma—discussion: Amer. J. Sci., v. 259, p. 154-157

Wallace, R. W., and Handy, R. L., 1961, Stone lines on Cary till: Iowa Acad. Sci. Proc., v. 68, p. 372-379

Wascher, H. L., Humbert, R. P., and Cady, J. G., 1948, Loess in the southern Mississippi Valley—identification and distribution of the loess sheets: Soil Sci. Soc. Amer. Proc., v. 12, p. 389-399

Summary

Relict, buried, and exhumed paleosols are soils that formed on landscapes of the past and are recognized by properties that are used to identify analogous soils on the present land surface. Paleosols are the upper part of the weathering profile and change laterally, whereas the rest of the weathering profile may not change. Hence, the simple weathering profile may not adequately explain paleo-landscapes.

Paleosols may be analyzed on the basis of their physical, mineralogical, and chemical properties, but in some cases certain of these properties cannot be used where secondary enrichment has occurred.

Paleosols are used principally for stratigraphic purposes, for regional correlation of Quaternary deposits and features, and for environmental interpretations of inter- or intraglacial or -pluvial regimens. The gumbotil of the Midwest includes paleosols that are analogues of Planosols, Humic-Gley soils, Gray-Brown Podzolic soils, and Grumusols and separates glacial stages. Geographic tracing of these paleosols is the main basis for regional correlation of Nebraskan, Kansan, and Illinoian drifts. Paleosols are the basis of correlation of events from pluvial Lake Bonneville in Utah to pluvial Lake Lahontan in Nevada and the Sierra Nevada in California. A prominent Sangamon paleosol has been used to separate the Loveland (Illinoian) loess from the overlying Wisconsin loess from the Great Plains to Ohio and down the Mississippi River Valley to near the Gulf of Mexico.

In southern Iowa the surface soils were dominantly formed under prairie, whereas more than 90% of the immediately pre-Wisconsin paleosols are paleo-Gray Brown Podzolic soils formed under forest. Redder colors of Sangamon paleosols, compared to surface soils in the Midwest, suggest warmer climate and/or longer weathering in Sangamon time. In addition to color, depth of leaching of carbonates and properties of the solum of paleosols have been used to estimate duration of weathering or time between Pleistocene events. Valid estimates require a complete understanding of soil properties and processes.

GEOCHEMISTRY OF SOME QUATERNARY LAKE SEDIMENTS
OF NORTH AMERICA*

F. M. SWAIN[1]

THE PRESENT discussion is by no means a thorough treatment of the subject; rather, it is intended to provide a brief survey of some recent advances in Quaternary lacustrine geochemistry of North America.

GENERAL CHARACTERISTICS OF LAKE SEDIMENTS
OF FORMER PERIGLACIAL OR GLACIAL REGIONS
IN NORTH AMERICA

The deposits of lowland lakes that formed in shallow depressions of glacial origin typically begin with a meter or two of sand and gravel followed by silt and clay (oligotrophic to mesotrophic stages), which are overlain in lime-rich areas by marl (alkalitrophic stages). The marl is gradational upward into pulpy copropel or gyttja (eutrophic stage). If the lake changes to a bog, lake peat or förna succeeds the gyttja, followed by sedge and forest peat. A typical sequence lacking marl is that of Linsley Pond, Connecticut (Fig. 1). A similar sequence of sediments but with abundant marl was found in Cedar Creek Bog, Minnesota, by Lindeman (1941, p. 107) (Fig. 2). Other sequences in Minnesota glaciated areas lack marl and resemble the physical stratigraphy of Linsley Pond, i.e. Kirchner Marsh (Wright et al., 1963) (Fig. 3) and Weber Lake (Fries, 1962).

In these areas of continental glaciation a succession of plant populations, inferred from their pollen record in the lake sediments, accompanied the stratigraphic changes (Fig. 3). In other localities, even nearby, the detailed succession may differ in both physical stratigraphy and in record of plant types, but the broader relationships, maintained over large area, are those of late-glacial, poorly organic sediments with tundra-plant remains (Watts and Winter, 1965), followed by more and more highly organic deposits with successively spruce, pine-birch, and perhaps predominant

* Gunta Venteris prepared amino acid analyses from Kirchner Marsh, and she and June M. Gilby assisted in compiling the illustrations. Ruta Millers prepared the amino acid analyses from Weber Lake and Deadman Lake. H. E. Wright contributed the discussion of amino acids from Kirchner Marsh. This paper represents Contribution No. 21, Limnological Research Center, University of Minnesota. Figure 1 reproduced with permission from Amer. J. Sci.; Figure 3 reproduced with permission from Geol. Soc. Amer. Bull.; Figures 4 and 5 and Tables 2 and 3 reproduced with the permission of the Minnesota Iron Range Resources and Rehabilitation Commission.

[1] Department of Geology and Geophysics, University of Minnesota, Minneapolis, Minnesota.

hardwoods, if the area is at low enough latitude (Wright et al., 1963).

Lake-sediment succession in Lake Washington near Seattle, Washington (Gould and Budinger, 1958), represents freshwater deposits of a fairly deep lake that overlie marine and estuarine clays, as follows:

Limnic clay, 10-20 ft
Varved limnic peat, 1 ft, ± 5,000 years B.P. (before the present)
Limnic clay, 5 ft
Volcanic ash, 2 in., 6,700 years B.P.
Limnic peat, 0-25 ft
Varved limnic peat and blue clay, 1 ft, 13,650 years B.P.
Pre-limnic blue clay 35 ft +, contains marine fossils

Thus, in the lake-sediment succession of a region of steep relief the eutrophic cycle that characterizes the shallow interior lake may be modified by rapid fluvial sedimentation.

Varved sediments of periglacial, glacial, or early postglacial lakes of either continental or mountain areas precede the eutrophication cycle discussed above. In mountain lakes, both deep and shallow, the oligotrophic part of the cycle is typically prolonged, and the sediment stratigraphy is predominantly inorganic. Flathead Lake, Montana, a deep oligotrophic lake (Swain, 1961a), occupies a fault-trough depression and is receiving sediments from streams originating in glaciated mountains. Its bottom sediments comprise offshore gray and reddish-gray silty, slightly diatomaceous clays, along with nearshore sands and gravels. The thickness of sediments is unknown. A thin black sapropelic layer occurs at the present mud-water interface, but oligotrophy will probably prevail in the lake for centuries owing to the steep relief and cool-temperate climate of the region.

Mountain lakes near the outer fringe of glaciated areas, as in Deadman Lake, Chuska Mountains, New Mexico (Fig. 9), also have principally inorganic sediments, although a succession of organic stages may be preserved in the record of pollen and invertebrates (Megard, 1964). Such records, at least at higher latitudes, probably result from a slower rate of inorganic sedimentation than in mountain glacier lakes.

GENERAL CHARACTERISTICS OF LAKE SEDIMENTS
OF UNGLACIATED REGIONS

The Quaternary lake sediments of unglaciated regions vary with the character of source material, relief surrounding the lake basin, and climatic conditions. Lake basins in those areas are of tectonic origin, are formed on river floodplains

765

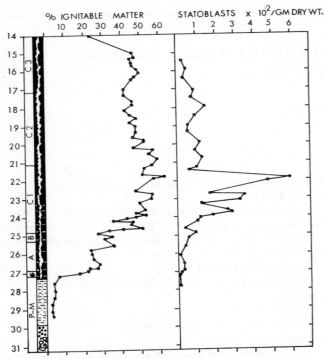

Figure 1. Sequence of lake and bog sediments at Linsley Pond, North Branford, Connecticut (Vallentyne and Swabey, 1955), showing percent ignitable matter and *Plumatella* (bryozoan) statoblasts ($\times 10^{-2}$) per gram dry weight. Broken black, copropel; broken black with horizontal white lines, banded copropel; dash and dot pattern, silt and clay; small circles, sand; large circles, gravel. Depth in meters given at left. Pollen zones at left as follows: P-M, ?Pre-Mankato; G, gray zone (= Two Creeks); A, Spruce; B, Pine; C1, oak, hemlock, C2, hickory, oak and hemlock, C3, chestnut, hemlock, oak.

or as marine basins separated from the sea by sand bars, or perhaps are eolian depressions. Lakes forming in such basins soon show in their sediments conditions of eutrophication that reflect prevailing climate and source of nutrients. Once the stage of nutritive development for the area has been established in the lake, sedimentary conditions are more stable than in lakes of recently glaciated regions. If the climate changes, or other factors intervene, corresponding changes in lake-sediment stratigraphy will result. Examples of American lake deposits of unglaciated regions are given below.

The "bay lakes" of the Bladen County, North Carolina, coastal plain (Frey, 1949), contain *dy* and *copropel* up to 12 ft thick overlying sand derived from the underlying Miocene Duplin Marl. Eutrophication started soon after formation of the lake basins and persisted more or less unchanged until the present time. The deposits of Dismal Swamp, Virginia, near Lake Drummond (Swain *et al.*, 1959), consist of about 3 ft of dark brown copropelic, fibrous, herbaceous lake peat overlying early- or pre-limnic(?) sand, in turn overlain by 4 ft of reddish-brown woody peat that represents forest encroachment over the lake peat.

Pleistocene-Recent lake sediments of the Mexico City Basin (Foreman, 1955) are up to 80 m or more thick and consist of diatomaceous volcanic ash, ashy clay, sand, and molluscan, ostracodal coquinas. Several zones have been recognized that are defined on mineralogic and paleontologic differences and represent intermittent intervals of volcanic activity and of drier or moister climate.

Catahoula Lake, central Louisiana, represents an overflow basin of Black River and is subject to striking seasonal variation in level. Its bottom sediments (Swain, 1961a) consist of light-gray and reddish-brown organic silty clay. The gray clay occupies the middle part of the lake basin, where reducing conditions prevail, while the red clay occurs in the marginal oxidized part of the basin. The lake clay rests in a basin of late-Tertiary sands. Except for thin sand intercalations the lake-sediment stratigraphy is relatively simple.

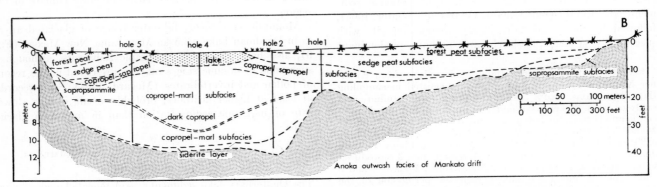

Figure 2. Northwest-southeast cross-section through part of Cedar Creek Forest, Anoka County, Minnesota (Swain and Prokopovich, 1954, after Lindeman, 1941). Shown are subfacies of peat and marl and locations of drill cores on which section is based.

The sequence of saline sediments of Searles Lake, California and their Quaternary history was discussed by Bradley (1963, p. 649-650).

Pyramid Lake, Nevada (Swain and Meader, 1958), is a remnant of Pleistocene Lake Lahonton, which was formed in part by glacial drainage. Today it is a nonglacial lake in a fault-block depression. The profundal bottom sediments are calcareous, diatomaceous gray and black sapropelic silty clay grading shoreward at the south end into deltaic silts and nearshore sands. The brackishness of the water, about 5,000 parts per million, restricts the level of organic productivity so that eutrophication is virtually inhibited. Furthermore, the bicarbonate content is very high, 830 ppm, as a result of its introduction by hot springs issuing from limestones along part of the lake bottom. Thus a particular limnetic regimen (apatotrophic) has been imposed on the lake, as a result of which a certain succession of sediments is forming and will continue to accumulate until the geologic setting changes. The thickness of the profundal sediments is unknown, but stiff, green pre-limnic clay was found beneath a few centimeters of lake sediment near Anaho Island, whereas nearby areas have more than one meter of uniform lake sediment, and in general the lake sediment must be many meters thick. Sublacustrine slumping probably accounts for thinness of sediment in some places.

Lake Nicaragua, Central America, is an example of a large subtropical lake characterized by uniform profundal volcanic, copropelic silts to depths of 3 m or more (Swain, 1961b; Swain and Gilby, 1965). The pattern of sedimentation has not changed for at least the length of time required to deposit 2 m of peat, which is equivalent to about 3 m of offshore sediment. The lake is richly productive of diatoms and *Elaeophyton* algae and receives sediments from surrounding Tertiary and Quaternary volcanic ash and lava flows as well as from Mesozoic shales.

The foregoing are examples of several stratigraphic sequences of lake sediment in North and Central America. For additional description of Quaternary lake deposits in North America see Bradley (1963). In the following discussion some geochemical features of lake sediments will be summarized.

INORGANIC GEOCHEMISTRY OF SELECTED NORTH AMERICAN LAKE DEPOSITS

A few examples of the stratigraphic sequence of inorganic constituents of lake samples have been chosen to show the general range in these substances as related to environment.

LINSLEY POND, CONNECTICUT

The postglacial stratigraphy of this small lake was given by Hutchinson and Wollack (1940). Table 1 shows the distribution of the inorganic constituents. The silica as quartz, the alumina as feldspar and clay, and the titania as zircon are mainly detrital from the surrounding source materials. A little of the silica may be authigenic diatom frustules, but the amount is not significant. The high silica values at the base of the sediment represent the oligotrophic to mesotrophic stages of the lake; the relatively low silica of unit 2 (34-40 ft) results from the abundant organic matter formed under the eutrophic stage. Organic matter is still

being formed today, but the silt content in the upper meter has risen as a result of cultivation of the surrounding land.

While a certain amount may be detrital, the iron in the lake sediments probably has been in part precipitated as ferrous sulphide hydrate ("melnikovite") from the lake water; a small amount may occur as siderite, but carbonate ion was not determined. Some of the iron may be associated

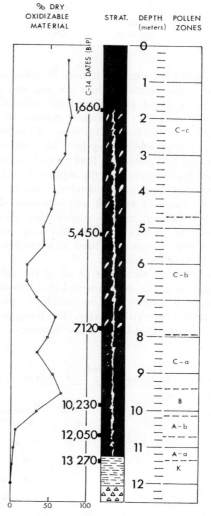

Figure 3. Sequence of lake and bog sediments for core K-1 at Kirchner Marsh, Dakota County, Minnesota, from Wright *et al.* (1963). Shown are sediment types, depths, C¹⁴ dates, percent dry oxidizable matter, and pollen zones. Solid black, peat; broken black with large diagonal white spots, peaty copropel; broken black with small diagonal spots, moss-rich copropel; dashes, clay; triangles, till. Pollen zones: K, spruce, sedge; A-a, spruce with larch and maxima of ash and *Ambrosia;* A-b, irregular spruce maximum, *Artemisia* maximum; B, birch, pine; C-a, oak, elm; C-b, herb maxima, with strong fluctuations; C-c, oak.

TABLE 1

Inorganic Constituents of Sediments of Linsley Pond, Connecticut
(After Hutchinson and Wollack, 1940)

Constituent	Silty clay 40-43 ft	Clay and gyttja 34-40 ft	Coarse-detritus gyttja 3-34 ft	Silty gyttja 0-3 ft
SiO₂	47.3	28.6-37.8	50.0-50.2	63.6-73.0
Fe₂O₃	12.1	3.1-7.8	9.3	4.3-9.2
Al₂O₃	5.5	3.3-5.0	6.2-8.4	10.3-15.0
TiO₂	0.08	0.05-0.18	0.25	0.63-0.71
P₂O₅	0.254	0.096-0.140	0.055-0.087	0.078-0.105
MnO	0.23	0.08-0.15	0.30-0.55	0.11-1.03
CaO	1.2	1.0-1.5	2.1-2.7	1.2-1.9
MgO	1.0	0.27-0.68	0.48-0.62	1.2-1.77
SO₃	1.0	1.0-2.1	1.9-3.2	0.44-2.1
Loss on ignition	2.8	46.0-59.0	23.8-28.7	2.9-7.4

with the diatoms, and some of it may be complexed with humic matter in the sediment. Both the iron and the manganese in Linsley Pond are believed by Hutchinson and Wollack (1940) to reflect biochemical changes in the lake rather than events outside the lake. Some of the iron in the anthropogenic zone, however, may have been introduced by erosion of cleared and cultivated land around the lake.

The low calcium content and the relatively high Mg/Ca ratios suggest that both are in detrital form to a certain extent. No discussion of mollusk and ostracode shells was given, but low calcium values suggest that these fossils must be scarce in the lake sediment. The small increase in CaO at 38 ft may represent a brief alkalitrophic stage in the early history of the lake.

The authors believe that most or all of the sulphite occurred as sulphide in the sediments and that, because of the excess of iron, it occurs as iron sulphide, precipitated through anaerobic bacterial activity. The manganese probably was also precipitated by the same process.

The phosphate content of the sediments at 40 ft is at a maximum for the deposit. Drake and Owen (1950) showed that, with high pH, phosphorous in the presence of calcium carbonate tends to be precipitated as calcium orthophosphate. In addition, photosynthesis may result in precipitation of phosphates together with calcium carbonate; with a return of excess CO_2, the precipitated phosphates go into solution again (Truog, 1916).

$$Ca_3(PO_4)_2 + 2H_2CO_3 \rightarrow Ca_2H_2(PO_4)_2 + Ca(HCO_3)_2$$

Studies by Moyle (1954) showed that in stratified lakes in Minnesota the concentration of phosphorus below the thermocline is much higher than above it.

According to Livingston and Boykin (1962) the concentrations of phosphorus in the lower third of Linsley Pond sediments are the result of sorption of phosphorus with

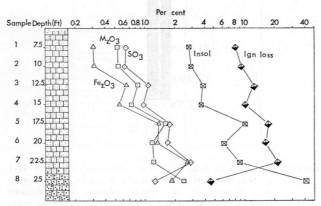

Figure 4. Sequence of lake sediments and changes in abundance of Fe₂O₃, M₂O₃, SO₃, insoluble material, and ignition loss at Station CN 12, Nisswa Lake, Crow Wing County, Minnesota, after Roepke (1959). Fine-dotted blocks, silty marl; coarse-dotted blocks, sandy marl.

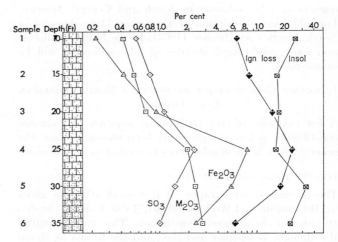

Figure 5. Sequence of lake sediments and changes in abundance of Fe₂O₃, M₂O₃, SO₃, insoluble material, and ignition loss at Station CN 29, Nisswa Lake, Crow Wing County, Minnesota, after Roepke (1959). Sediment pattern represents silty marl; see Fig. 4 for other symbols.

TABLE 2

Percentage Analyses of Marl Deposits near Southwestern Edge of Nisswa Lake, Crow Wing County, Minnesota
(Roepke, 1959)

	7.5 ft	10 ft	12.5 ft	15 ft	17.5 ft	20 ft	22.5 ft	25 ft
CO_2	38.12	37.24	34.77	36.04	27.93	30.85	25.48	20.49
CaO	47.21	46.67	43.65	45.01	35.58	38.95	32.94	24.05
MgO	1.05	1.04	1.09	1.38	0.96	1.00	0.85	2.04
MnO	0.08	0.09	0.11	0.10	0.10	0.09	0.23	0.06
Fe_2O_3	0.31	0.32	0.65	0.56	1.40	1.34	2.72	1.89
M_2O_3	0.53	0.54	0.85	0.74	1.58	1.18	1.22	2.45
Insol. mat.	2.75	2.89	3.79	3.66	10.00	6.22	8.84	41.45
SO_3	0.64	0.63	1.10	0.99	1.76	1.67	2.87	1.28
H_2O	1.26	1.35	1.70	1.37	3.08	2.40	2.91	1.51
Ignition loss	8.14	9.30	12.36	10.33	17.59	16.10	21.69	4.69
Total	100.09	100.07	100.07	100.18	99.78	99.80	99.75	99.81

mineral matter. They suggest that high ion-exchange capacity of the lake mud in early stages of lake development is responsible for the concentrations observed. Further, they believe productivity is inversely related to exchange capacity during lake history. In the surface sediments of Linsley Pond the slight rise in phosphorus probably results from detrital apatite from cultivated and deforested areas around the lake.

NISSWA LAKE MARL DEPOSIT, MINNESOTA

The lacustrine marl deposits of Nisswa Lake, Crow Wing County, Minnesota, were analyzed by Roepke (1959). Two analyses of core samples from marginal and medial parts of the deposit are shown in Figures 4 and 5. The greater content of insolubles and smaller ignition loss in the lowest sample of the marginal core probably represents an early oligotrophic stage of the lake. Roepke (Tables 2, 3) demonstrated correlation between M_2O_3 and insolubles, probably caused by the abundant clastic feldspars, clays, and other alumino-silicates in the marl samples. Quartz grains and diatoms, which make up most of the remaining insolubles, account for the observed deviation between M_2O_3 and insolubles. Roepke also showed a correlation among Fe_2O_3, SO_3, and ignition loss, perhaps reflecting iron-sulfide formation in the presence of abundant organic matter. He believes that ferric hydroxide undergoes reduction beneath the thermocline during summer stagnation and reacts with H_2S that is evolved from decaying organic matter to form pyrite. The increase in sulfite (probably represented by sulfide in the sediments) below 15 ft can be accounted for in this way.

Manganese shows slight concentrations below 15 ft in the medial core but there is no such effect in the marginal lake core. The precipitation of manganese has probably occurred most readily in the profundal part of the lake. The marginal area may have remained within the thermocline much of the time during which sedimentation occurred, thereby limiting the accumulation of manganese. Roepke notes a departure, in the upper sediments of the medial core, of the correlation between insolubles and M_2O_3.

No well-defined trends in lateral distribution of the inorganic constituents other than carbonate were noted in the

TABLE 3

Percentage Analyses of Marl Deposits in Northern Part of Nisswa Lake, Crow Wing County, Minnesota
(Roepke, 1959)

	10 ft	15 ft	20 ft	25 ft	30 ft	35 ft
CO_2	28.34	31.18	27.18	19.61	15.29	27.82
CaO	35.42	39.41	35.01	23.10	18.85	34.49
MgO	0.52	0.71	0.79	0.77	0.91	1.22
MnO	0.04	0.05	0.05	0.28	0.27	0.62
Fe_2O_3	0.22	0.43	0.92	8.05	5.54	2.38
M_2O_3	0.42	0.55	0.72	1.97	2.38	2.74
Insol. mat.	25.67	16.29	16.77	15.51	32.88	22.19
SO_3	0.58	0.80	1.12	2.30	1.45	0.99
H_2O	2.29	2.24	2.63	4.70	4.15	1.37
Ignition loss (%)	6.36	8.38	14.71	23.60	17.95	5.96

Nisswa Lake deposit. The carbonate concentration is highest in the shallow parts of the basin, which are largely marginal in distribution. Variability in the other inorganic constituents results from the influence of factors such as water depth, distance from shore, relationship to direction of prevailing winds, proximity to springs and surface streams, climate, and local physiography.

As no pollen or C^{14} studies have been made of the Nisswa deposit, it is not possible to tie it to the postglacial geochronology that has been worked out for Minnesota. The increase in marl formation above 15 ft at Nisswa Lake may represent the onset of the drier hypsithermal interval that characterized the period ∼8,000 to ∼4,000 years ago in Minnesota, but the explanation is at present uncertain.

LAKE PATZCUARO, MICHOACAN, MEXICO

The stratigraphy of Lake Patzcuaro, which occupies a basin of interior drainage, southwestern Mexico, has been described and interpreted by Hutchinson *et al.* (1956). The basin lies in a volcanic plateau in which late-Tertiary and Pleistocene lavas have covered Cretaceous and early-Tertiary rocks. The lake water is high in Na- and K-bicarbonate, low in Ca and Mg, moderate in Cl and SO_3. The lake is subject to seasonal range in level of about 60 cm and is up to about 15 m deep. The analysis of a core from the

TABLE 4

Analyses of Cores P-1 and P-3, Lake Patzcuaro, Mexico.
Percentage Composition of Samples Dried at 105°-110° C
(From Hutchinson *et al.*, 1956)

	Depth, m	Ignition loss	SiO_2	$(Al, Fe)_2O_3$	CaO
P-1	4.7	11.63	40.75	39.09	2.38
	5.6	16.84	40.71	12.51	18.37
	6.8	25.40	48.34	14.33	5.47
P-3	3.0	18.90	40.60	—	0.59
	3.1	16.90	43.00	—	0.92
	3.2	12.45	43.51	39.85	2.49
	3.4	20.00	42.07	—	0.33
	3.9	14.91	40.58	35.75	1.51
	4.0	28.70	36.66	—	1.50
	4.5	30.07	39.30	17.33	5.72
	4.9	23.90	54.96	—	0.93
	5.0	16.33	50.55	24.19	1.22
	5.4	27.40	52.03	—	2.64
	5.5	19.00	34.43	12.94	21.63
	5.9	28.40	44.59	—	8.70
	6.0	19.38	55.51	13.30	4.55
	6.4	22.90	57.64	—	2.76
	6.5	18.60	59.05	—	3.90
	6.9	21.50	52.42	—	3.04
	7.0	11.93	53.58	22.42	5.30
	7.9	26.20	50.15	—	2.15
	8.0	20.80	50.88	19.07	3.10
	9.0	25.60	54.67	—	2.97
	9.1	17.85	54.32	18.64	2.72

lake sediments from a depth of 3 m to 9.1 m is shown in Table 4. A study of the pollen and the sedimentation rates, together with indirect C^{14} dating, suggests that a moist period began at 7.9 m, about 3,300 years ago, and continued until 2,300 years ago, when a dry interval marked by a distinct rise in CaO content began. The lowest lake level would have been reached about 1,700 years ago, corresponding to a CaO maximum at 5.5 m depth. The period of low water and high dissolved calcium is indicated by the presence of diatoms *Navicula oblonga* (Kutzing), *Anomoeoneis sphaerophora* (Kutzing), *A. polygramma* (Ehrenberg), and *Amphora ovalis* var. *affinis* (Kutzing), which frequently occur in alkaline waters; it also marks the beginning of one of the driest intervals, as recorded by arboreal pollen. A small

increase in CaO at 4.5 m may represent another shorter period of low water level.

The increase in Al_2O_3 and Fe_2O_3 in the upper part of the sediment is thought by the authors to have been caused by changes in details of erosion in the drainage basin, perhaps in part of cultural origin.

EL BAJO DE SANTA FE, GUATEMALA

This area is formed of a large swamp forest in eastern Guatemala, east of Lake Peten near the southern edge of the Yucatan Peninsula. It lies near the ruins of the Mayan city Peten. The swamp deposits were studied by Cowgill and Hutchinson (1963).

The Bajo de Santa Fe sediments consist of an uppermost dark brown clay a few centimeters thick, underlain by gray clay with live roots to a depth of about 1 m; below this is 4 m of yellowish gray clay, underlain by black structureless carbonaceous material. The latter gives a radiocarbon age of $11,560 \pm 360$ years B.P. The upper and lower parts of the clay section contain large angular chert fragments, but these are rare in the middle. Abundant gypsum, filling root cavities, occurs in the middle. Hematite stain is irregularly distributed throughout the sediment. Aside from roots and near-surface *Pomacea flagellata* (a snail), no fossils were found; pollen is absent. The sediments are thought to have originated through slow deposition of mass-wasted material derived from the Tertiary limestone terrane. At no time was there open water in the swamp.

The following summarizes the geochemistry of the Bajo sediments. Little if any trend can be seen in SiO_2, TiO_2, and Fe_2O_3. In the lower 3.5 m, Al_2O_3 is somewhat more abundant. MgO and CaO also are higher below 3.5 m, but both are irregular. Na_2O is enriched appreciably in the uppermost sediment, and MnO and total Zr also show conspicuous near-surface enrichment.

Both zirconium and manganese are suggested to be first concentrated in the tree roots from which they are continually transferred to the leaves; the latter fall to the ground, thus always providing a greater concentration of these elements near the surface than in the root zone below. A similar process may affect the distribution in the Bajo of V, Cr, and Co, but not Ni, Cu, Be, Sc, Y, and La. Strontium

TABLE 5

Partial Inorganic Analyses of Some of the Cedar Creek Bog Samples[a]
(From Swain and Prokopovich, 1954)

Station	Depth, ft	$CaCO_3$, %	$MgCO_3$, %	SO_4, %	Total S,[b] %	Total Fe,[c] %	Total P,[d] %
1	4-5	7.99	0.96	nil	0.21	2.27	
1	7-8	6.88	0.90	nil	0.32	1.59	
1	9-10	7.11	0.88	nil	0.80	1.72	
1	11-12	74.80	2.37	nil	0.37	1.04	0.021
1	13-14	40.75	2.05	nil	1.46	2.01	0.036
2	35-36	38.60	1.13	nil	0.43	15.63	0.255

[a] Analyses by Mines Experiment Station, University of Minnesota; Vernon Bye, analyst.
[b] May be present as sulfide, native sulfur, or an organic compound.
[c] May occur as siderite, ankerite, marcasite, ferrous sulfide hydrate, or some other form.
[d] May occur as inorganic apatite, vivianite ($Fe_3P_2O_8 \cdot 8H_2O$), bobierrite ($Mg_3P_2O_8 \cdot 8H_2O$), or organic phosphate ("collophane").

and lanthanum concentrations at 330 cm are associated with the rare-earth-bearing Ca-Sr-Pb-Al phosphate mineral crandallite. Yttrium, also abundant in the 330-cm sample, occurs in some unknown form, not churchite. A barium maximum at 250 cm matches a chloride and sulphate maximum, but its mineralogy is unknown.

The irregular concentration of chloride is thought by the authors to have resulted from rainfall and subsequent evapotranspiration, which excludes most of the chlorides.

Sulphate, like chloride, is thought to have entered the Bajo in the rainfall. Its lower solubility resulted in crystallization as gypsum in root cavities. Concentration of gypsum at 250-300 cm probably resulted from percolation of sulphate solutions from higher levels through root cavities.

Acid-soluble phosphorus and probably total phosphorus also are more abundant in the 3.0-4.1 m interval than either above or below. Erosion of a more phosphatic limestone in the vicinity may account for the increase.

The exchangeable cations Ca, Mg, Na, K, Si, and Li (but not Sr) show an irregular increase with depth, at least below the live root zone. To some extent the calcium, potassium, and magnesium are associated with the clays of the deposit. The latter are mainly montmorillonite, with a little halloysite, and were derived from the weathering of limestone like that exposed in an escarpment near the Bajo.

UPPER PART OF SEDIMENTS OF SILVER BAY AREA, LAKE SUPERIOR

The sediments of Silver Bay, northwestern Lake Superior, an oligotrophic lake, were studied by Swain and Prokopovich (1957). In a few cores, about 1 m long, chemical analyses were obtained of the top and bottom of the cores. The upper part of the sediment in the cores is pale yellowish-brown silty clay, in part diatomaceous and sandy.

The silica and alumina content are fairly uniform from top to bottom of all cores except one, which shows a sharp decrease in SiO_2 at the bottom. Ferric iron decreases and ferrous iron increases downward in all the cores, as a result of decrease in Eh. CaO and MgO are fairly uniform, except for an increase at the bottom of one of the cores, probably caused by Ca- and Mg-bearing mineral fragments, although these were not seen in the sediment samples. TiO_2 and P_2O_5 are relatively constant within this sediment. MnO shows marked decrease from top to bottom of the core. The concentration of MnO in the upper sediments, although small, possibly results from precipitation by microorganisms, but the downward decrease in these deep-water sediments is at present not clearly understood.

CEDAR CREEK BOG, MINNESOTA

Incomplete chemical analyses were obtained on the peats and underlying marls of this late-senescent stage bog (Swain and Prokopovich, 1954). They are referred to here because a discussion of organic constituents will be presented later. Table 5 shows the abrupt change at 11 ft from calcareous copropel above to marl below. The Ca/Mg ratio also changes abruptly from about 8:1 to between 20:1 and 30:1; dolomitization may be taking place in the peat carbonates. The high sulfur value at 13-14 ft is matched by a slight increase in iron, and both probably occur as ferrous sulfide, both at that depth and at shallower levels in the bog. At 35-36 ft, however, the iron content is very high and sulfur very low; iron carbonate is present at that depth. The total phosphorus is low in the only two shallow samples analyzed, but it is higher by 10-fold at the 35-36-ft level. The phosphate probably occurs as vivianite or similar bog-phosphate, which has been seen in other bogs of the area. The phosphate may have been concentrated by sorption with associated mineral matter, as discussed by Livingstone and Boykin (1962) for Linsley Pond, Connecticut.

ORGANIC GEOCHEMISTRY OF SOME NORTH AMERICAN LAKE AND BOG DEPOSITS

LIPOID SUBSTANCES, AMINO ACIDS, AND POSSIBLE FLAVINOID AND RELATED PIGMENTS FROM CEDAR CREEK BOG, MINNESOTA

The distribution of lipoid substances as related to stratigraphy in Cedar Creek Bog was discussed by Swain and Prokopovich (1954) and Swain (1956). The lipoid extracts were separated by means of absorption chromatography into four fractions: paraffin-naphthenic hydrocarbons, aromatic hydrocarbons, asphaltenes, and polar organic substances remaining adsorbed on alumina (Table 6). Most of the saturated hydrocarbons are irregularly distributed and, except for an apparent concentration in sapropelic copropel just above the marl, do not show a relationship to stratigraphy. There is also great variability in aromatic hydrocarbon content that is not noticeably related to stratigraphy. The asphaltic content is lower, and the polar compounds somewhat higher, in the 8-10-ft level in the lower part of the sapropelic copropel.

The protein amino acids separated by paper chromatography from HCl hydrolyzates of Cedar Creek samples of peat, copropel, and marl are shown in Figure 6. A striking increase in total amino acids 3-5 ft below the surface of the peat is believed to result from vertical concentration of amino acids attached to water-soluble humic acid micelles (Swain et al., 1959). Total amino acids are very low in the 20-21-ft marl sample, perhaps as a result of more rapid inorganic sedimentation at that level. The slight increase of total amino acids at 26-27 ft corresponds to a dark copropel layer that marked a lessening of inorganic (marl) sedimentation. The pollen and spores from that level suggest a period of drying of the lake and encroachment of a *Dryopteris* vegetation over the marl (Cushing, 1963). The individual amino acids do not show much if any relationship to detailed stratigraphy. The apparent absence of basic amino acids from the Cedar Creek peat samples is thought to result from the alkaline condition in the bog, which encourages loss of basic amino acids through de-amination by anaerobic bacteria (Swain, 1961a). Acidic and neutral amino acids under these same alkaline conditions tend to form stable salts through hybrid-ion reactions and are to a greater extent protected from degradation.

Studies have recently been made of the natural stability of protein amino acids (Swain, Venteris, and Ting, 1964) and of thermal reaction kinetics of amino acids (Vallentyne, 1964). The more abundant and seasonally stable amino acids of aquatic plants are those most likely to occur in the associated accumulating sediments. According to Vallentyne's conclusions, glycine and alanine, together with smaller amounts of proline, aminobutyric acid, and other products, might form from some of the other amino acids, as follows (Vallentyne, 1964, p. 163):

aspartic acid → malic acid, ammonia

glutamic acid → aminobutyric acid

glycine → methylamine

valine → gly

leucine → unknown Rf 0:82 in butanol:acetic acid: water

isoleucine → unknown Rf 0:29 in BuOH:HAC:H$_2$O

serine → gly, ala, ethanolamine

threonine → gly

cystine-S → ?

methionine → gly, ala, unknown Rf 0:42 in BOH:HAC: H$_2$O (= α-aminobutyric acid?)

phenylalanine → phenethylamine, unknown Rf 0:55 in BOH:HAC:H$_2$O (= benzylamine?), unknown Rf 0:23, unknown Rf 0:11

tyrosine → gly

proline → none

OH-proline → none

histidine-HCL → ?

lysine → unknown Rf 0:35 in BuOH:HAC:H$_2$O, unknown Rf 0:45

arginine-HCL → pro, near ornithine

Comparison in Cedar Creek peats of the distribution of glycine and the other amino acids that might degrade to it shows little or no evidence of enrichment of glycine with increasing age, at the expense of the others.

Fluorescent substances related to flavo-proteins and indole acids were detected in many of the amino-acid extracts of Cedar Creek Bog sediments (Swain and Venteris, 1964).

They are generally more abundant in the upper peaty and copropelic sediments and scarce in the marl. The substances form through the biological activity of mudeaters. Substances having the absorption spectra, color of fluorescence, and Rf values on paper chromatograms for riboflavin and riboflavin phosphate are the commonest materials detected in Cedar Creek peat and marl; indole acid substances are more erratic in distribution and perhaps are less stable. Riboflavin is absent in the deeper part of Cedar Creek Bog except at the 26-27-ft level in the dark copropel layer mentioned above. The phosphate is also a little richer at that depth.

AMINO ACIDS IN SEDIMENTS OF KIRCHNER MARSH, DAKOTA COUNTY, MINNESOTA

Kirchner Marsh is an ice-block depression in the St. Croix Moraine of late-Wisconsin age in southeastern Minnesota (Wright et al., 1963). Protein amino acids have been analyzed from sections of the core that cross pollen-zone boundaries or distinctive sediment types (Fig. 7). In the late-glacial section (Zones A-a and A-b), with spruce pollen dominant, total amino acids increase upward, as reflected in all the individual curves. This trend results from the gradual change in sediment type from silty gyttja to gyttja (see also curves for C and N). Of the total amino acids, however, there is a decrease in the proportion of basic types (his, arg, lys), implying more acid conditions above about 1,120 cm.

A short section of the core across the Zone C-b/C-c boundary shows a clear double peak in total amino acids, as well as in most of the individual curves. The double peak matches a double peak in the curve that shows the ratio of seeds of aquatic and semi-aquatic plants to seeds of weedy annuals—a measure of the intermittent flooding and

TABLE 6

Chromatographic Analyses of Lipoid Extracts from Cedar Creek Bog Peat, Anoka County, Minnesota

Depth, ft	Predominant material	Paraff.-Naphth. fractions		Aromatic fractions		Asphaltic fractions	Remaining on alumina, % of lipoids	Combined hydrocarbons, % of sample
		% of hydrocarbons	% of lipoids	% of hydrocarbons	% of lipoids	% of lipoids		
Station 1								
1-2	peat	44.5	5.9	55.5	7.5	28.4	58.2	0.98
2-3	copropel	27.5	1.1	72.5	3.0	28.4	67.5	0.22
3-4	peat	34.0	5.6	66.0	10.9	35.2	48.3	0.85
4-5	peat	47.0	7.7	53.0	8.5	30.8	53.0	1.27
5-6	peat	92.0	2.5	8.0	0.2	24.3	73.0	0.17
6-7	peat	60.0	8.4	40.0	5.5	27.0	59.1	0.87
7-8	copropel	40.5	3.2	59.5	4.7	26.7	65.4	0.48
8-9	sapropel	0		100.0	4.8	11.7	83.5	0.48
9-10	sapropel	40.0	0.9	60.0	1.3	14.5	83.3	0.16
10-11	sapropel	93.0	29.8	7.0	2.2	28.0	40.0	1.38
11-12	marl	40.5	4.2	59.5	6.1	34.5	55.2	0.16
12-13	sandy marl	24.5	3.4	74.5	10.2	23.4	63.0	0.18
13-14	marl	66.0	5.1	34.0	2.6	29.3	63.0	0.17
14-15	sand	29.0	8.3	71.0	19.7	44.3	27.7	0.14
Station 2								
25-26	marl	65.0	8.6	35.0	4.6	26.0	60.8	0.17
35-36	sideritic marl	30.0	5.5	70.0	10.9	21.9	6.2	0.29

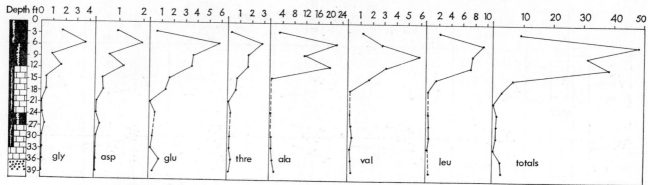

Figure 6. Vertical distribution of amino acids in hydrochloric-acid hydrolyzates of peat and marl from Cedar Creek Bog, Anoka County, Minnesota, after Swain *et al.* (1959). Values are in parts per 10,000 of wet sediments. Solid black, peat; broken black, copropel and sapropel; blocks, marl; circles, sand.

drying of the lake bottom (Watts and Winter, 1965). Pollen Zone C-b is characterized by several such sharp changes in the seed and pollen curves that imply many fluctuations in the water level during the warm and/or dry period 5,000-7,000 years ago when prairie invaded the deciduous forest of southern Minnesota (Wright *et al.*, 1963; Watts and Winter, 1965). Thus when the lake intermittently dried up during a few decades, the dominance of aquatic plants in the seed record was replaced by a dominance of weedy annuals (mostly *Cyperus* spp.), representing plants that spread intermittently over the lake bottom whenever it was dry. The lower content of amino acids in the sediments of these drying intervals does not necessarily result from reduced organic productivity or dilution by organic sediments, because the curve for ash content is steady. It is more likely that amino acids were leached from the surface during the drying intervals. The slightly higher proportion of basic amino acids during the drying intervals implies more acid conditions in the water during these times, favoring preservation of basic types.

Three analyses near the top of the core showed that peat contained only half as much amino acid as the underlying gyttja.

AMINO ACIDS AND FLAVINOID PIGMENTS IN PEAT FROM DISMAL SWAMP, VIRGINIA

Examination of protein amino acids of Dismal Swamp peats, Virginia, was made by Swain *et al.* (1959) (Fig. 8). As in Cedar Creek Bog there is a marked increase in total amino acid a few feet below the present bog surface. A decrease in total amino acids occurs in dark copropelic peat, below reddish-brown peat. These phenomena are believed to be due to natural degradation with depth plus downward concentration of amino acids attached to water-soluble humic complexes; migration farther downward in Dismal Swamp ceases or slows considerably in the relatively impervious copropel. Basic amino acids, for example histidine, are more plentiful in the acid Dismal Swamp peats owing to their formation as stable salts. Acidic amino acids may be degraded more readily in the acidic environment due to bacterial decarboxylation (Swain, 1961a).

Flavinoid substances were also detected in Dismal Swamp

peats. These likewise decrease from the red woody peat downward into the dark copropelic peat, largely as a result of natural degradation with increasing age, but also as a result of decrease in biological activity in the copropel.

No pronounced hiatus is suggested by the change in peat stratigraphy of Dismal Swamp, but a climatic change may have occurred following the copropel deposition. Pollen analysis and C^{14} studies of Dismal Swamp peats should be made.

AMINO ACIDS IN SEDIMENTS OF WEBER LAKE, LAKE COUNTY, MINNESOTA

The muskeg-bog sediments of this northeastern Minnesota lake (Fries, 1962) consist of brown and green gyttja. In contrast to the lakes in central Minnesota, the protein amino acid content does not change appreciably with increasing depth (Table 7). In the acid bog environment the basic amino acids form a relatively larger proportion of the total than in more alkaline bogs of central Minnesota. Distinct changes in the pollen spectrum are only vaguely reflected in the few samples examined for amino acids.

AMINO ACIDS IN SEDIMENTS OF DEADMAN LAKE, NORTHWESTERN NEW MEXICO

The vertical distribution of amino acids in the sediments of this mountain lake shows marked increase with depth despite a relatively uniform sedimentary sequence (Fig. 9) and lack of evidence from pollen of an earlier major change in vegetation in that area. It is possible that downward post-depositional concentration of amino acids occurred through ground-water activity, as discussed above for Cedar Creek Bog and Dismal Swamp.

CARBOHYDRATES, AMINO ACIDS, AND CHLORINOID PIGMENTS IN SEDIMENTS FROM BLUE LAKE, ISANTI COUNTY, MINNESOTA

This small lake represents an elongate ice-block depression in an old drainage course in red gravel and till of the Superior ice lobe, Isanti County, east-central Minnesota. The lake is eutrophic-alkalitrophic: 112 ppm total alkalinity, 4.5 ppm sulfate, 0.012 ppm total phosphorus, 0.36 ppm total nitrogen (Swain, Venteris, and Ting, 1964). Bottom sedi-

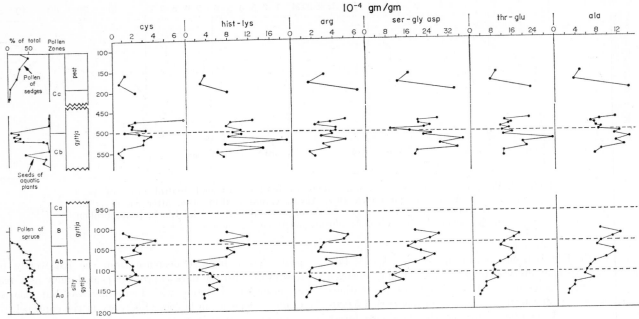

Figure 7.

ments are sapropelic marl. Amino-acid distribution (acid-extractable) in the lake is shown in Figure 10. A well-defined relationship exists between stratigraphy and total amino acids; the lower but not basal part of the sediment shows a relative increase in concentration of amino acids as a probable result of a period of high organic productivity in the early lake history (but see below); several of the individual amino acids also increase at that depth. A general stability series of amino acids under natural lacustrine conditions in Minnesota has been established (Swain, Venteris, and Ting, 1964) (Fig. 11). The absence of proline and methionine in the Blue Lake core is an indication that they are unstable under these conditions; decrease with depth of lysine and tyrosine also reflects their relative instability.

The change in sedimentary sugars separated by acid hydrolysis and paper chromatography from the Blue Lake core was studied by Rogers (1965) (Fig. 12). Increased concentration in the lower part of the core does not quite match the high concentration of the amino acids. Both are possibly the result, he believes, of periods of drought, low lake level, and concentration of shallow-water vegetation. Rogers did not find significant changes with increasing depth of any individual sugars.

The pheophytin residues of Blue Lake sediments (Swain, Paulsen, and Ting, 1964) show a similar increase at the same level as the amino acids; this results from the same phenomena of lower water and increased organic accumulation, relative to the rate of inorganic sedimentation.

CAROTENOID AND CHLORINOID PIGMENTS AND CARBOHY-
DRATES IN POSTGLACIAL LAKE SEDIMENTS
FROM CONNECTICUT

Carotenoid pigments from the petroleum ether epiphase of methanol extracts of lake sediments were found to include α- and β-Carotene, myxoxanthin(?), rhodoviolascin (?), and two unidentified carotenoids (Vallentyne, 1956).

Xanthophylls of the methanol hypophase after treatment with ether were not studied. The distribution of carotenoids and sedimentary chlorinoids varies with depth in Bethany Bog and Lower Linsley Pond, Connecticut. The greatest concentration of carotene occurs just prior to change of the lake from a mesotrophic to a dystrophic stage, according to diatom evidence (Patrick, 1954). Rhodoviolascin was concentrated in the upper peaty dystrophic sediment and may have originated in purple bacteria in the accumulating mud beneath the present surface. Myxoxanthin occurs in no freshwater organisms except blue-green algae. It occurs in detectable amounts in the mesotrophic but not in the dystrophic sediments of Bethany Bog, and it is proportional to the amounts originally deposited, a conclusion supported by graphs showing pigment units as per gram of ignitable matter (Fig. 1). Free glucose was found (Vallentyne and Bidwell, 1956) to occur in the Bethany Bog cores in amounts which, although small, reach their maximum at the same depth (9 m) that had maximum carotenes, representing the presumed time of maximum productivity.

DISTRIBUTION OF CHLORINOID PIGMENTS AND RELATED
PORPHYRINS IN SEDIMENTS OF NORTH
COOKING LAKE, ALBERTA

An example from the work of Hodgson *et al.* (1960) is cited to show biochemical changes in chlorinoid pigments in accumulating lake sediments. This lake lies 22 miles east-southeast of Edmonton, Alberta, and represents a shallow-water depression in ground moraine; it contains up to 3.7 m of gyttja overlying 0.6 m of blue-black clay, 3.6 m of water-laid silt and sand that rests on till. Late winter pH readings were 8.1 in the lake water, 7.4 in the gyttja, 7.6-8.6 in the sand, and 6.7 in the till.

The chlorinoid pigment content of North Cooking Lake sediments extracted with 90% acetone decreases downward from the gyttja to the blue clay and markedly in the silt

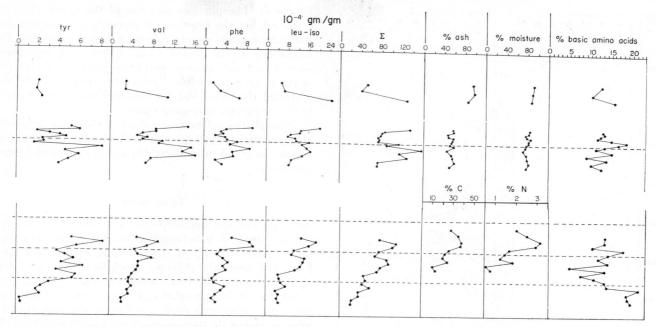

Figure 7. Vertical distribution of amino acids in sediments of core K-2, Kirchner Marsh, Dakota County, Minnesota. Shown are depths, sediment types, pollen zones, selected pollen and seed curves (after Wright *et al.*, 1963, and Watts and Winter, 1965), and amino acids (analyzed by G. Venteris).

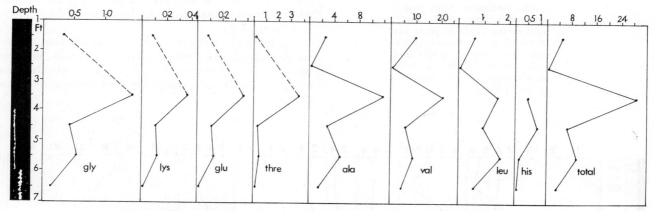

Figure 8. Vertical distribution of amino acids in peat from Dismal Swamp, Chesapeake County, Virginia, after Swain *et al.* (1959). Solid black, woody peat; broken black, to left, fibrous peat; broken black, center, sandy copropel. Values of amino acids are in parts per 10,000 of wet peat.

TABLE 7

Distribution of Amino Acids in Sediments from near Shore of Weber Lake, Lake County, Minnesota
(Values are in parts per 10,000 of wet sediment)

Core No.	Depth, cm	Lys	His, arg	Asp, ser, gly	Glu, thr	Ala	Val	Phe	Isoleuc, leuc	Sum
2	325-333	0.1	0.7	0.2	0.06	0.2	0.04	—	0.04	1.34
4	502-510	0.2	1.1	0.2	0.2	0.4	0.1	0.1	0.1	2.4
5	642-650	0.2	0.8	0.1	2.5	0.3	0.03	0.06	0.1	3.89
6	720-728	0.2	0.8	0.2	0.3	0.4	0.06	0.07	0.1	2.13

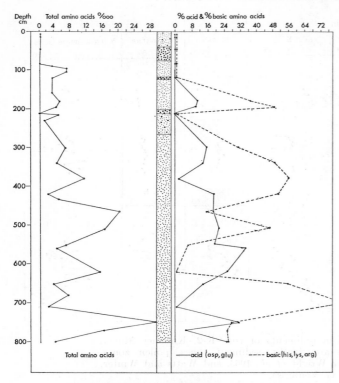

Figure 9. Vertical distribution of amino acids in sediments of Deadman Lake, Chuska Mountains, New Mexico. Shown are depths, sediment types (small dots, silt; large dots, sand), total amino acids in parts per 10,000 of wet sediment (left), and percentage of acidic and basic amino acids to total amino acids (right). Analyses by R. Millers.

(Table 8). Pheophytin-*a* was one of the major pigments extracted, but the aggregate of pigments was complex and contained a single metalporphyrin complex in the silt. The complexing metal proved to be nickel, and experiment showed that formation of porphyrin from the pheophytin of the gyttja was possible. Freshwater plants plausibly concentrated the nickel and through decomposition yielded it to the gyttja and interstitial water.

Although the sediments involved in the study are probably postglacial, application of similar studies to Pleistocene deposits may aid in stratigraphic and environmental interpretations.

Discussion

Although perhaps oversimplified with respect to detailed stratigraphy and paleolimnology in this report, the Quaternary lake deposits of glaciated and periglacial regions have had generally different geochemical histories from those of regions far from continental ice.

Sulfides, oxides, phosphates, and carbonates of iron and manganese along with calcium carbonate and perhaps dolomite are among the more common compounds authigenically enriched in the lake sediments of recently deglaciated regions. The abundance of a particular compound depends upon the source area around the lake, pH, Eh, microflora, depth of water, and other factors that characterized the lake at various stages in its late-glacial or postglacial development. Early oligotrophic, alkalitrophic, and dystrophic stages of a lake or swamp may be reflected in the inorganic mineral concentrations, as shown by studies of Linsley Pond and Nisswa Lake.

The inorganic authigenic mineral concentrations of present-day glacial and arctic regions are generally low compared to the detrital portion of the sediments. Iron and manganese oxides are perhaps the most common concentra-

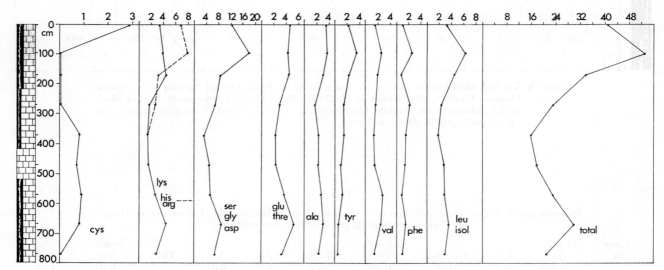

Figure 10. Vertical distribution of amino acids in sediments from Blue Lake, Isanti County, Minnesota, after Swain, Venteris, and Ting (1964). Broken black, copropel; blocks, marl; dots, silt. Values are in parts per 10,000 of wet sediment

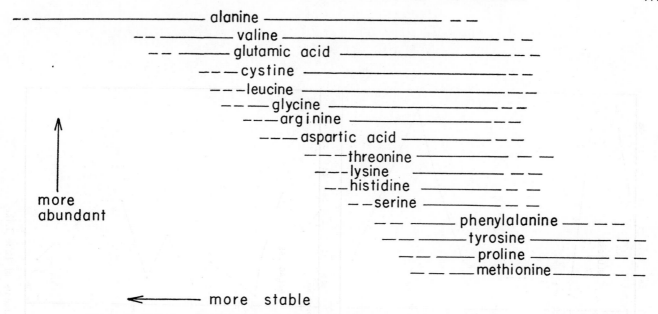

Figure 11. Relative abundance and stability of protein amino acids separated from aquatic plants of Blue Lake, Isanti County, and Clear Lake, Sherburne County, Minnesota (after Swain, Venteris, and Ting, 1964).

tions in such sediments, although they have not been studied sufficiently. It would not be anticipated that significant changes in the mineral concentrations would occur in glacial-lake sediments as long as a cold climate persists.

Mineral concentrations in shallow lakes and swamps of unglaciated regions are dependent on source materials and climate. Once the lake has formed its state of trophication is soon stabilized, and authigenic minerals to be precipitated will form more or less uninterruptedly in the sediments until a climatic change occurs or until the lake basin has filled. Thus, no marked differences in composition of the sediments of Lake Patzcuaro were noted except during a period of increasing aridity, lowering of lake level, and increasing alkalinity of the waters.

A swamp deposit such as El Bajo de Santa Fe, which accumulated more or less as a periodically aerated soil in a tropical climate, is characterized by many unusual mineral concentrations, in which evapotranspiration by trees played an important part. Trace metals in particular are concentrated to a much greater extent than in more completely aquatic environments.

The authigenic mineralogy of the sediment sequences of deep volcanic lakes and of artificial lakes in North America has been only slightly studied. Nelson (1961) found little or no evidence of authigenic mineral concentrations in the profundal sediments of Crater Lake, Oregon. On the other hand the sediments of artificial Kerr Lake, Virginia–North Carolina, seem, on the basis of a brief study by the writer, to be accumulating iron oxides.

The problem of post-depositional concentrations of minerals in bogs requires additional study. Livingston and Boykin (1962) believe phosphorus accumulations in the lower part of Linsley Pond mud are authigenic and presumably accumulated with the sediments. Wright *et al.* (1963, p. 1377) imply that white iron phosphate of Lake Carlson in

Dakota County, Minnesota, is primary. They suggest it is an indication of reducing conditions at time of deposition, as the white mineral, probably vivianite, oxidizes rapidly to the more familiar blue form on exposure to air. On the other hand, the downward concentration of mineral substances in bogs owing to fluctuating water levels and changes of oxidation-reduction conditions has long been suggested, *e.g.* siderite in English coal swamps (Deans, 1934; Spencer, 1925), and may in part account for the phosphate distributions of lake and bog muds.

As far as can be determined on the basis of rather limited studies, residual organic substances in lake and bog sediments show at least a generalized relationship to trophic and climatic history of the body of water. Total amino acids derived from proteins, total hydrolyzable sugars, and chlorinoid pigments show increases related to periods of high organic productivity in the lake water. A certain relationship between environment and major groups of amino acids may also be noted as a function of their hybrid ion properties.

With the possible exception of Kirchner Marsh, no specific variation in individual amino acids or carbohydrates with respect to environment has been noted. In the case of amino acids, however, the problem is complicated by their possible post-depositional migration within the lake or bog sediments.

Degradation of chlorinoid pigments to metal-complexed prophyrins in lake and bog sediments represents one of the more striking changes in sedimentary organic matter. Further study of changes in chlorinoid, carotenoid (Anderson and Gunderson, 1955), and flavinoid pigments will be helpful in paleolimnology. Several changes in carotenoid pigments were noted by Vallentyne to be related to progress of specific trophic stages in lake and bog deposits.

Most of the biogeochemical studies of lake sediments have

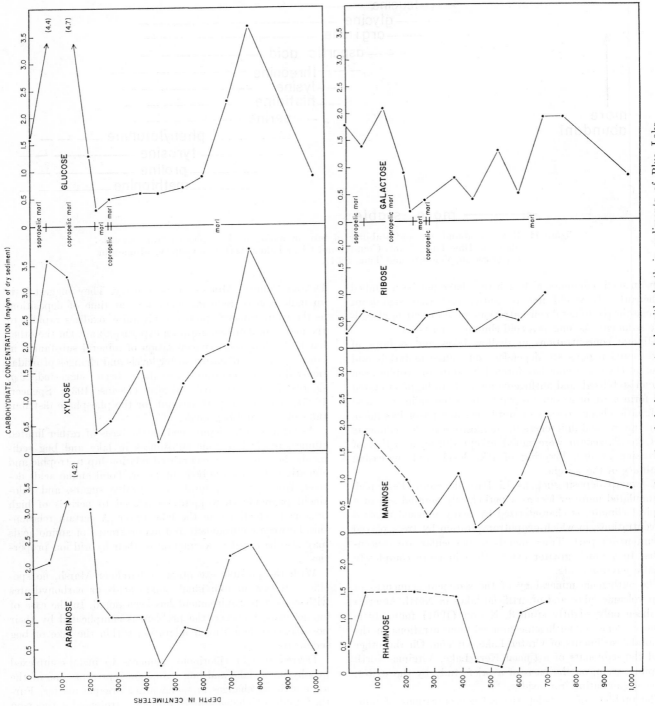

Figure 12. Fluctuations of carbohydrate materials with depth in sediments of Blue Lake, Isanti County, Minnesota, from Rogers (1965).

TABLE 8

Chlorinoid Pigment Content of North Cooking Lake Sediments
(From Hodgson *et al.*, 1960)

Sampling point	10	9	8
Distance from shore (m)	15	70	225
Thickness of sampled section (m)	1.4	1.3	2.6
Pigment concentration (ppm dry wt.)			
Sample 1 gyttja (copropel)	300	280	350
Sample 2 gyttja	250	140	310
Sample 3 gyttja		72	360
Sample 4 gyttja		78	280
Sample 5 blue clay			110
Sample 6 silt			2

been in deglaciated regions. Analyses of a few nonglacial lake sequences, however, suggest, as in Dismal Swamp, a relationship of amino acids and pigments to major changes in vegetation.

It would be most helpful to paleolimnologists if small-scale biochemical changes in lake sediments were found to correlate with fluctuations in pollen spectra or other paleontologic phenomena. With more detailed biogeochemical work such correlations may be found. At present, as noted above, only broader environmental changes appear to be recorded biogeochemically in the sediments.

Several problems in lacustrine biogeochemistry can be cited to illustrate the limited knowledge in this field and the need for further work. Increases in concentrations of sedimentary amino acids, carbohydrates, and pigments occur from a few centimeters to a meter or more below the surface of many lake and bog sediments (Swain *et al.*, 1959, 1964; Rogers, 1965). Such concentrations may be caused by microbial synthesis, downward concentration and sorption of the substances, changes in productivity of the lake, or other causes. Further study of such concentrations may yield useful paleolimnologic knowledge.

There is apparently a preferential preservation of the basic amino acids lysine, arginine, and histidine in sediments of acidic bogs, possibly the result of hybrid ion properties of amino acids (Swain, 1961a). The phenomenon should be investigated further to learn whether specific organic fractions and perhaps source organisms might be responsible for the observed occurrences of amino acids.

Saturated as well as aromatic hydrocarbons are known to occur in bog and lake sediments. The compounds have not been described, for the most part. Source organisms should be determined and diagenetic changes studied to ascertain possible paleoclimatologic implications of these hydrocarbons. Terpenoid pigments were found by Vallentyne (1956) to be preserved in lake sediments but not in overlying peats. He suggested a primary origin of the carotenoids, but the possibility of post-depositional biosynthesis has not been ruled out completely.

The widespread distribution of phenolic compounds in bog accumulations is significant in the biochemical history of the sediments, as these substances act as preservative media for other organic matter; they are stabilizing agents in the bog and are precursors for "coal tar" compounds of various kinds. Unpublished work by the writer shows that 2-naphthol is accumulating in a central Minnesota peat;

there is a possibility that auxins (growth accelerators) that have gone unused by rooted plants in the bog may yield the naphthol. Few studies of these compounds in lake sediments have been made.

Heterocyclic compounds such as pyridines, purines, and pyrimidines are obtained from the tars of many coals and are commonly found in terrestrial soils, but they are relatively scarce in lake sediments. Additional examination of the origin of these compounds, which is presumably mostly microbial, and of their source materials may give useful paleolimnologic information.

Complexing of organic sedimentary chlorinoid pigments with metals has been demonstrated (Hodgson *et al.*, 1960). Partial degradation of the pigments precedes the complexing. The common occurrence of such pigments in lake sediments makes them attractive for paleolimnologic study. Provenance of trace metals in lake pigments should be investigated further.

The foregoing are only a few of the many biogeochemical problems that face the paleolimnologist. It should be emphasized that a large amount of work has been done in lacustrine biogeochemistry outside North America that has not been discussed in this brief review.

REFERENCES

Anderson, S. T., and Gunderson, K., 1955, Ether soluble pigments in interglacial gyttja: Experientia, v. 11, p. 345-348

Bradley, W. H., 1963, Paleolimnology, *in* Frey, D. G. (ed.), Limnology in North America: Madison, Univ. Wisconsin Press, p. 621-652

Cowgill, Ursula M., and Hutchinson, G. E., 1963, El Bajo de Santa Fe: Amer. Philos. Soc. Trans., v. 53, pt. 7, p. 3-51

Cushing, E. J., 1963, Late-Wisconsin pollen stratigraphy in east-central Minnesota: Univ. Minnesota Ph.D. thesis, 165 p.

Deans, T., 1934, The spherulitic ironstones of West Yorkshire: Geol. Mag., v. 71, p. 49-65

Drake, J. A., and Owen, Richard, 1950, Report on the experimental removal of phosphorus from sewage effluents with lime: Minnesota Health Dept., 17 p., mimeo. (cited in Moyle, 1954)

Foreman, Fred, 1955, Palynology in southern North America. Part 2, Study of two cores from lake sediments of the Mexico City Basin: Geol. Soc. Amer. Bull., v. 66, p. 475-509

Frey, D. G., 1949, Morphometry and hydrography of some natural lakes of the North Carolina Coastal Plain; the Bay Lake as a morphometric type: J. Elisha Michell Sci. Soc., v. 65, p. 1-37

Fries, Magnus, 1962, Pollen profiles of late Pleistocene and Recent sediments from Weber Lake, Minnesota: Ecology, v. 43, p. 295-308

Gould, H. A., and Budinger, T. F., 1958, Control of sedimentation and bottom configuration by convection currents, Lake Washington, Washington: J. Mar. Res., v. 17, p. 183-198

Hodgson, G. W., Hitchon, B., Elofson, P. M., and Peake, E., 1960, Petroleum pigments from Recent freshwater sediments: Geochim. Cosmochim. Acta, v. 19, p. 272-288

Hutchinson, G. E., and Wollack, Anne, 1940, Studies on Connecticut lake sediments. ii, Chemical analyses of a core from Linsley Pond, North Branford: Amer. J. Sci., v. 238, p. 493-517

Hutchinson, G. E., Patrick, Ruth, and Deevey, E. S., Jr., 1956, Sediments of Lake Patzcuaro, Michoacan, Mexico: Geol. Soc. Amer. Bull., v. 67, p. 1491-1504

Jelgersma, Saskia, 1962, A late-glacial pollen diagram from Madelia, south-central Minnesota: Amer. J. Sci., v. 260, p. 522-529

Lindeman, J. L., 1941, The developmental history of Cedar Creek Bog, Minnesota: Amer. Midl. Nat., v. 25, p. 101-112

Livingstone, D. A., 1957, On the sigmoid growth phase in the history of Linsley Pond: Amer. J. Sci., v. 255, p. 364-373

Livingstone, D. A., and Boykin, J. C., 1962, Vertical distribution of phosphorus in Linsley Pond mud: Limnol. Oceanogr., v. 7, p. 57-62

Megard, R. O., 1964, Biostratigraphic history of Deadman Lake, Chuska Mountains, New Mexico: Ecology, v. 45, p. 529-546

Moyle, J. B., 1954, Some aspects of the chemistry of Minnesota surface waters as related to game and fish management: Minnesota Dept. Cons., Inv. Rep. 151, 36 p.

Nelson, C. H., 1961, Geological limnology of Crater Lake, Oregon: Univ. Minnesota M.S. thesis, 175 p.

Patrick, Ruth, 1954, The diatom flora of Bethany Bog: J. Protozool., v. 1, p. 34-47

Roepke, H. H., 1959, *in* Schwartz, G. M., *et al.*, Investigation of the commercial possibilities of marl in Minnesota: St. Paul, Iron Range Res. and Rehab. Comm., p. 50-105

Rogers, M. A., 1965, Carbohydrates of lake plants and associated sediments: Geochim. Cosmochim. Acta, v. 29, in press

Spencer, E., 1925, On some occurrences of spherulitic siderite and other carbonate in sediments: Geol. Soc. London Quart. J., v. 81, p. 667-705

Swain, F. M., 1956, Stratigraphy of lake deposits in central and northern Minnesota: Amer. Assoc. Petroleum Geologists Bull., v. 40, p. 600-653

—— 1961a, Limnology and amino-acid content of some lake deposits in Minnesota, Montana, Nevada and Louisiana: Geol. Soc. Amer. Bull., v. 72, p. 519-546

—— 1961b, Reporte preliminar de los sedimentos del fondo de los lagos Nicaragua y Managua, Nicaragua: Bol. Serv. Geol. Nac. Nicaragua, No. 5, p. 11-29

Swain, F. M., Blumentals, Ausma, and Millers, Ruta, 1959, Stratigraphic distribution of amino acids in peats from

Cedar Creek Bog, Minnesota, and Dismal Swamp, Virginia: Limnol. Oceonogr., v. 4, p. 119-127

Swain, F. M., and Gilby, J. M., 1965, Ecology and taxonomy of Ostracoda and an alga from Lake Nicaragua: Stazione Zool. Napoli Publ., v. 33 (suppl.), in press

Swain, F. M., and Meader, R. W., 1958, Bottom sediments of southern part of Pyramid Lake, Nevada: J. Sed. Petrology, v. 28, p. 286-297

Swain, F. M., and Prokopovich, N., 1954, Stratigraphic distribution of lipoid substances in Cedar Creek Bog, Minnesota: Geol. Soc. Amer. Bull., v. 65, p. 1183-1189

—— 1957, Stratigraphy of upper part of sediments of Silver Bay, Lake Superior: Geol. Soc. Amer. Bull., v. 68, p. 527-542

Swain, F. M., Paulsen, G. W., and Ting, F. T., 1964, Chlorinoid and flavinoid pigments from aquatic plants and associated lake and bay sediments: J. Sed. Petrology, v. 34, p. 25-45

Swain, F. M., Venteris, Gunta, and Ting, F. T., 1964, Relative abundance and order of stability of amino acids in some aquatic plants and associated freshwater sediments: J. Sed. Petrology, v. 34, 25-45

Swain, F. M., and Venteris, Gunta, 1964, Distribution of flavinoid and some other hetero-cyclic compounds in lake sediments, *in* Columbo, Umberto, and Hodson, G. D., Advances in organic geochemistry: Oxford, Pergamon Press, p. 199-214

Truog, E., 1916, The utilization of phosphate by agricultural crops, including a new theory regarding the feeding power of plants: Wisconsin Agric. Exp. Sta. Res. Bull. 41 (cited in Moyle, 1954)

Vallentyne, J. R., 1956, Epiphasic carotenoids in post-glacial lake sediments: Limnol. Oceanogr., v. 1, p. 252-262

—— 1964, Biogeochemistry of organic matter. ii, Thermal reaction kinetics and transformation products of amino acids: Geochim. Cosmochim. Acta, v. 28, p. 157-188

Vallentyne, J. R., and Bidwell, R. G. S., 1956, The relation between free sugars and sedimentary chlorophyll in lake mud: Ecology, v. 37, p. 495-500

Vallentyne, J. R., and Swabey, Y. S., 1955, A reinvestigation of the history of Lower Linsley Pond, Connecticut: Amer. J. Sci., v. 253, p. 313-340

Watts, W. A., and Winter, T. C., 1965, Plant microfossils from Kirchner Marsh, Minnesota—a paleoecological study: Geol. Soc. Amer. Bull., in press

Wright, H. E., Winter. T. C., and Patten, H. L., 1963, Two pollen diagrams from southeastern Minnesota; problems in the regional late-glacial and postglacial vegetational history: Geol. Soc. Amer. Bull., v. 74, p. 1371-1396

SUMMARY

The late-glacial and postglacial developmental history of lakes in glaciated regions is reflected to some extent in both the inorganic and organic chemical sedimentary residues. Detrital silica commonly decreases upward while authigenic silica from diatoms increases. Authigenic iron and manganese decrease upward. Carbonate increases, but still higher it decreases if eutrophication and dystrophication have become well developed. Sedimentary phosphorus decreases upward as eutrophication proceeds.

Total amino acid, carbohydrate, and chlorinoid and flavinoid pigment residues in lake and bog sediments typically increase upward. Carotenoid pigments increase upward in lake sediments but then decrease to mark the change from lake to bog. Maxima in many organic substances occur just beneath the surface of the sediment, perhaps owing both to microbial activity and to variable sorption with mineral matter or other organic substances. Conversion of pheophytin to metal-complexed porphyrin in postglacial lake sediments is a phenomenon of diagenesis that warrants similar study in other compounds. Postglacial climatic variation may modify these trends and be detectable in the sediments. With progress of time, the geochemistry of lake-sediments distant from former glacial borders is less well defined by changes listed above. Climatic variations, however, may be measured geochemically in lakes of such areas.

QUATERNARY PALEOHYDROLOGY *

S. A. SCHUMM[1]

"THE SCIENCE of hydrology encompasses the behavior of water as it occurs in the atmosphere, on the surface of the ground, and underground" (Amer. Soc. Civil Engineers, 1949, p. 1). Paleohydrology treats these phenomena, but it has reference to the past. In this paper the term paleohydrology will be restricted to that portion of the hydrologic cycle that involves the movement of water over the surface of the earth, because runoff and its sediment load are of major importance in determining the nonglacial erosional and depositional features of the Quaternary.

The study of Quaternary paleohydrology can be assisted if existing relations between climate and hydrology can be extrapolated into the past. It may be possible to do this, because the vegetation of the early Quaternary was very similar to that of the present (Kräusel, 1961, p. 230). If this were not so, then the relationships that now exist among runoff, sediment yield, temperature, and precipitation would not be directly applicable to past conditions.

In this attempt to apply modern hydrologic relations to the past, some estimates of past rates of runoff and sediment yield will be made on the basis of estimates of Quaternary variations of annual temperature and precipitation. The success of such an undertaking necessarily depends upon our knowledge of the relationships between modern climatic variables and hydrology. Although studies of these phenomena have been made, most of the relations developed are of a very generalized nature. Despite the recognized chain of uncertainties, estimates of the magnitude of Quaternary climatic changes will be used to estimate Quaternary runoff, sediment yields, and sediment concentrations. The estimates of Quaternary paleohydrology for the conterminous

* Publication authorized by the Director, U.S. Geological Survey. Robert W. Lichty, U.S. Geological Survey, read and criticized an early draft of the paper and his numerous suggestions are appreciated. W. B. Langbein and G. E. Harbeck, Jr., both of the Geological Survey, have made helpful comments concerning the sections of the paper dealing with hydrology. They were in agreement that the estimates of hydrologic changes probably are in the right direction and are of the correct order of magnitude, but both are of the opinion that the quantification of paleohydrology is more apparent than real. Professor H. E. Wright, Jr., University of Minnesota, and R. F. Flint, Yale University, reviewed the paper from the point of view of the Pleistocene stratigrapher and, although both were of the opinion that the approach was valid, their comments indicated a desire to reserve judgment until the results of additional field investigations are available. The writer concurs, for until additional hydrologic data have been collected, especially in arid regions, the estimates of hydrologic changes are crude estimates indeed. Furthermore, there is no questioning the fact that the proof or disproof of the hypotheses of river activity during a climate change lie in the field.
[1] U.S. Geological Survey, Federal Center, Denver, Colorado.

United States will then be used to discuss the probable effects of the climatic changes on nonglacial Quaternary landforms and sediment deposits.

RUNOFF

Runoff is that part of precipitation that appears in surface streams (Langbein and Iseri, 1960). It is, therefore, water that fashions and modifies the landscape. Runoff is usually expressed as either a volume (gallons, cubic feet, or acre-feet) or as a depth (inches) to which the drainage area would be covered if all the runoff for a given time period were uniformly distributed on it.

A map showing runoff depths for the conterminous United States has been prepared by Langbein et al. (1949) from runoff data collected at gauging stations maintained by the U.S. Geological Survey. In the preparation of this map, data were used only from those stations at which the discharge was not materially affected by diversion or regulations or at which adjustments for such influences could be made. To illustrate the general relation between climate and runoff, Langbein et al. (1949) developed a series of curves as shown on Figure 1. The position of each of the curves depends on weighted mean-annual temperature.

Weighting the annual temperature is a method of removing the effects of seasonal rainfall on runoff. For example, a given amount of precipitation will yield less runoff during the warmer months of summer than during the cool winter months. To adjust for this Langbein et al. (1949, p. 7) divided the sum of the products of monthly precipitation and temperature by annual precipitation. When the precipitation is evenly distributed throughout the year no change results, but if precipitation is greater during the summer the weighted mean temperature will be greater than mean annual temperature and vice versa (Langbein et al., 1949, Table 4).

Langbein (1962, Fig. 1) shows that for arid and semiarid regions runoff may be greatly changed depending on the seasonal distribution of precipitation. If it is assumed that precipitation during Pleistocene glaciation was concentrated during the summer months (Manley, 1955; Dillon, 1956), the increase in runoff would be somewhat less than that obtained from Figure 1. Nevertheless, this seasonal effect on runoff is minor compared with most of the changes that were induced by Quaternary changes of annual temperature and precipitation. Therefore, in all that follows it will be assumed that the distribution of precipitation was essentially uniform throughout the year.

Two curves of Figure 1, which were originally drawn to a minimum of 15 in. of precipitation, have been extended into still lower rainfall regimes on the basis of additional data

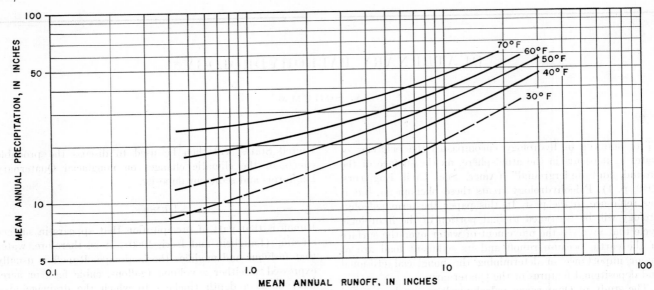

Figure 1. Curves illustrating the effect of temperature on the relation between mean annual
runoff and mean annual precipitation (after Langbein *et al.*, 1949).

(Langbein, 1962; C. H. Hardison, 1963, written communication). The family of curves shows that annual runoff increases as annual precipitation increases and that runoff decreases as temperature increases with constant precipitation. The curves allow an estimation of past runoff for nonglaciated areas when information on past temperature and precipitation is available. However, any such estimate is only a crude approximation at best, and it appears prudent to estimate only the direction and relative magnitude of such a change.

The density and type of vegetation found within a region exert an important effect on runoff. Numerous investigations have demonstrated that the removal of vegetation from a landscape causes not only a greater amount of runoff but also is responsible for higher flood peaks and a shorter duration of flood flow (Kittredge, 1948, p. 230-271; Colman, 1953, p. 280-354). Therefore a change in climate would not only affect runoff directly but would affect it indirectly through the subsequent response of vegetation to the climate change. It is difficult to evaluate changes in runoff for a combination of these factors. However, modern rates of runoff include the effects of vegetation type and density. Therefore runoff as measured from a given drainage basin under a given climate (Fig. 1) reflects not only the climate but vegetal influences as well.

SEDIMENT YIELD AND SEDIMENT CONCENTRATION

Sediment yield is the total amount of sediment removed from a drainage basin. It is usually calculated from measurements of the suspended-sediment concentration in a stream of water or from the total sediment load deposited in a reservoir. Sediment yield is usually expressed as a weight (tons) or as a volume (acre-feet) of sediment per unit area per year. Sediment concentration is expressed usually as a percent or as parts of sediment per million parts of water (ppm).

Langbein and Schumm (1958, Fig. 2) defined the rela-

tion between annual sediment yield and annual precipitation for drainage basins averaging about 1,500 sq. miles in the conterminous United States for an annual mean temperature of 50° F (Fig. 2). Although precipitation is the dominant climatic factor influencing sediment yields, the effect of temperature needs to be considered, because more precipitation is required to produce a given amount of runoff in a warm climate than in a cool climate. The 50° F curve of Figure 2, therefore, shows the relationship between sediment yield and precipitation adjusted to an annual mean temperature of 50° F (Langbein and Schumm, 1958, p. 1076). The definition of the 50° F curve of Figure 2 is based on known values of runoff for each drainage basin from which the sediment-yield data were obtained. These observed values of runoff were converted to an "effective precipitation," that is, the annual precipitation required to produce the known runoff at 50° F, by use of the 50° F rainfall–runoff curve of Figure 1. For example, if the mean annual runoff from a drainage basin is 8 in. at a mean annual temperature of 50° F, the effective precipitation required to produce this runoff is about 30 in. (Fig. 1). To produce the same runoff at 60° F about 35 in. of precipitation is required (Fig. 1).

The curve for 50° F, an estimate of the average annual temperature for the United States at the present, reveals that sediment yield is a maximum at about 12 in. of precipitation and then recedes to lower values with lesser and greater amounts of precipitation (Fig. 2). This variation in sediment yield with precipitation can be explained by the interaction of precipitation and vegetation on runoff and erosion. As precipitation increases above zero, sediment yields increase at a rapid rate, because more runoff becomes available to move sediment. Opposing this influence is that of the vegetation, which increases in density as precipitation increases. At about 12 in. of precipitation on the 50° F curve, the transition between desert shrubs and grass occurs. Above 12 in. of precipitation on the 50° F curve, sediment-yield rates decrease under the influence of the more effective grass and forest cover. Elsewhere in the world where monsoonal climates prevail, sediment-yield rates may increase again above 40 in. of precipitation under the influence of highly seasonal rainfall (Fournier, 1960).

In order to determine the effect of a climatic change on sediment yields it is necessary to consider the nature of the curves that might be derived for temperatures other than 50° F. The rainfall–runoff curves for temperatures of 40° F, 60° F, and 70° F (Fig. 1) were used to obtain the additional curves of Figure 2.

The new curves are displaced laterally with respect to the 50° F curve. Together they indicate that, as annual temperature increases, the peak of sediment yield should occur at higher amounts of annual precipitation. That is, because of higher rates of evaporation and transpiration, less of the precipitation at higher temperatures is available to support vegetation, runoff is less, and so the peak rate of sediment yield shifts to the right. The curves of Figure 2 may be used to estimate changes in sediment yield as temperature and precipitation or both changed during the past. Once again, however, only the direction and magnitude of the changes are meaningful.

In addition to the amount of sediment moved, its concentration in the water by which it is moved is important.

Curves were developed to show the relation between sediment concentration and precipitation at different weighted mean-annual temperatures (Fig. 3). To develop the curves, runoff for a given temperature was obtained from Figure 1, and sediment yields for a given temperature were obtained from Figure 2. Runoff was converted to tons, and sediment yield was divided by runoff to obtain a concentration. As might be expected, for a given annual precipitation sediment concentration increases with annual temperature, and for a given annual temperature sediment concentration decreases with an increase in annual precipitation.

An important portion of the total load of streams, the dissolved load, was ignored in the above computations. Although the concentration of dissolved solids is greater in streams draining arid and semiarid regions, the total yield of dissolved solids is less than from humid regions (Rainwater, 1962). As regards stream activity, changes in the amount of dissolved load would be much less important than changes in the amount of either suspended load or bedload.

Sediment yields and concentrations for a given climate will vary greatly if the vegetation is altered or destroyed (Baver, 1956, p. 440-446). A climatic change will act on both vegetation and runoff, which, in turn, will modify the sediment yields and concentrations. However, as in the case

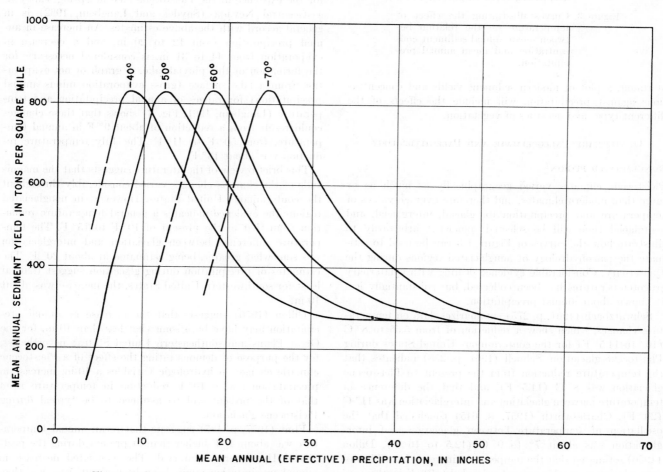

Figure 2. Curves illustrating the effect of temperature on the relation between mean annual sediment yield and mean annual precipitation.

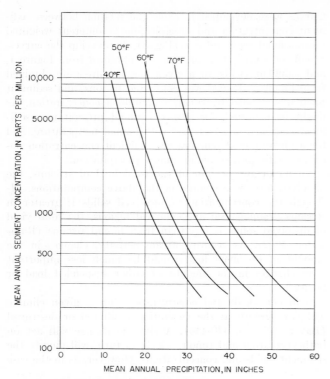

Figure 3. Curves illustrating the effect of temperature on the relation between mean annual sediment concentration and mean annual precipitation.

of runoff, a plot of modern sediment yields and concentrations against precipitation will include the effects of the different types and densities of vegetation.

QUATERNARY PALEOCLIMATE AND PALEOHYDROLOGY

NONGLACIATED REGIONS

Pleistocene climates varied geographically as much as or more than modern climates, and therefore average values of temperature and precipitation for glacial, interglacial, and postglacial time will be selected somewhat arbitrarily to illustrate how the curves of Figure 1–3 can be used to estimate the paleohydrology of nonglaciated regions during the Quaternary. Considerable evidence dealing with Quaternary paleotemperatures has been collected, but substantially less is known about annual precipitation.

Schwarzbach (1961, p. 275) summarizes data on temperature changes, which show a reduction of from 5.5° to 8° C (10° to 14.5° F) for the conterminous United States during Pleistocene glaciation. Schnell (1961, p. 258) indicates that the temperature reduction from the present to Pleistocene glaciation was 8° C (14.5° F), and that the difference in temperature between glaciation and interglaciation was 11° C (20° F). Charlesworth (1957, p. 645) concluded that the oscillation of temperature between glaciation and interglaciation was about 7° to 9° C (12.5 to 16° F). Dillon (1956) estimated that the temperature increase from Pleistocene glaciation to the present was about 10° F in the conterminous United States, and Manley (1955, p. 270) con-

cluded that the increase of mean annual temperature was about 13° F near the Gulf of Mexico, 20° F in the Ohio Valley, and 27° F at New York. Temperature gradients from south to north were steep, and probably no average temperature should be selected as representative of large areas during Pleistocene glaciation.

Estimates of the reduction of temperature and evaporation rates have been made for specific areas in southwestern United States in order to explain the existence of pluvial lakes. For example, Leopold (1951a) calculated that in order for Pleistocene Lake Estancia in north-central New Mexico to exist annual temperature should have been 12° F less and annual precipitation 10 in. greater than at present. Antevs (1954) agreed with Leopold that annual precipitation must have been about 10 in. greater than at present, but he believed that the reduction of the June–September temperature was at the most 10° F.

Antevs (1952) and Broecker and Orr (1958) agree that a doubling of annual precipitation from about 10 to 20 in. was necessary for the formation and maintenance of pluvial Lake Lahontan in northwestern Nevada, but Antevs' estimate of temperature reduction of 3° C (5.5° F) was less than the estimate of Broecker and Orr, which was 5° C (9° F).

The recent calculation of hydrologic conditions necessary for the existence of the Pleistocene lake in Spring Valley in east-central Nevada (Snyder and Langbein, 1962) is in general accord with the above estimates. An increase in annual precipitation from 12 to 20 in. and a decrease in evaporation from 44 to 31 in. is considered necessary for the formation of this pluvial lake. A graph of net evaporation from a lake surface (gross evaporation minus annual precipitation) for ranges of annual precipitation and temperature (Langbein, 1961, Fig. 3) shows that these changes could result from a reduction of about 9° F in annual temperature, from 50° F to 41° F. The July temperature reduction was about 13° F.

This brief review of the literature suggests that the magnitude of the climatic changes varied considerably throughout the conterminous United States. However, in nonglaciated regions the evidence indicates a general temperature reduction from that of the present of 10° F to 15° F. The temperature difference between glaciation and interglaciation was somewhat greater, being estimated at about 20° F. The estimates of precipitation during glaciation suggest that, at least for southwestern United States, the increase was about 10 in.

Dillon (1956) suggests that the increase in annual precipitation may have been somewhat less than 10 in. for the Great Plains and southeastern United States; nevertheless, for the purpose of demonstrating the effect of a Pleistocene climatic change on hydrologic variables a 10-in. increase in precipitation and a 10° F reduction in temperature from that of the present will be assumed to be typical during Pleistocene glaciation.

Flint (1957, p. 487) suggests that mean annual temperature was about 4° F higher than at present during the postglacial Hypsithermal interval. The associated decrease in annual precipitation might have been about 5 in. less than at present. Interglacial climates probably were similar to

TABLE 1

Estimated Effects of Climatic Change on Hydrologic Variables

Weighted mean annual temperature (degrees F)		Mean annual precipitation (in.)		Ratio of changed to present mean annual runoff	Ratio of changed to present mean annual sediment yield	Ratio of changed to present mean annual sediment concentration
Present	Changed	Present	Changed			
A. Change to climate during glaciation						
50	40	10	20	>20	0.6	<0.03
50	40	20	30	5	0.5	0.1
50	40	30	40	3	0.8	>0.2
50	40	40	50	2	0.9	—
60	50	10	20	>20	>2.0	—
60	50	20	30	8	0.4	0.05
60	50	30	40	3	0.7	0.2
60	50	40	50	2	0.9	>0.5
B. Change to climate during interglaciation or postglacial Hypsithermal interval						
50	55	10	5	—	—	—
50	55	20	15	0.2	1.2	>6
50	55	30	25	0.5	1.5	3
50	55	40	35	0.7	1.1	2
60	65	10	5	—	—	—
60	65	20	15	<0.1	0.7	—
60	65	30	25	0.3	1.7	7
60	65	40	35	0.5	1.4	3

that of the Hypsithermal interval. Therefore, an increase in temperature of 5° F and a decrease in precipitation of 5 in. from that of the present is assumed to be representative of both interglacial and Hypsithermal climates.

These estimates of Quaternary changes of climate are highly speculative, but they permit the use of Figures 1-3 to approximate corresponding changes in the hydrology of nonglaciated regions. In Table 1A, estimates obtained from Figures 1-3 are presented showing the effects of the above changes in temperature and precipitation on runoff, sediment yield, and sediment concentration from a present annual temperature of either 50° F or 60° F and a present annual precipitation of either 10, 20, 30, or 40 in.

In some cases the estimates were obtained by extrapolating the curves beyond the limits shown on Figures 1, 2, and 3. In these cases the magnitude of the changes are presented in Table 1 as greater or less than a number that is a conservative estimate of the probable change.

In all cases the change from the present to a glacial or pluvial climate causes an increase in runoff. This increase is greater for areas with drier climates. For example, a 20-fold increase in runoff would occur in a region with a present annual precipitation of 10 in. and a present annual temperature of 50° F; however, only a 2-fold increase in runoff would occur in a region of 40 in. of precipitation with an annual temperature of 50° F.

Attempts have been made recently to estimate past river discharge by the use of a relationship that has been found to exist between the meander characteristics of modern rivers and their discharge. Dury (1958, p. 113) estimated that the bankfull discharge of some English rivers was 150 times greater in the past, because the wavelength of valley meanders is about 9 times greater than the wavelengths of the meanders of the modern stream. Further study of rivers

in the conterminous United States has convinced him that the earlier estimate was too high, and that it is more likely that bankfull discharge was about 20 times greater than at present. None of the data in Table 1 refers to bankfull discharge; however, Dury (1965) has estimated that the increase in mean annual discharge along many rivers was from 5 to 10 times greater than at present. This is about the order of magnitude of some of the runoff changes obtained from Figure 1 (Table 1).

Sediment yields generally decrease with increased precipitation and decreased temperature because this type of climatic change improves the vegetal cover (Table 1A); the shift is down the right limb of the sediment-yield curves (Fig. 2). An exception occurs, however, when the change is from an arid (60° F and 10 in.) to a subhumid climate (50° F and 20 in.); the shift is up the left limb of the sediment-yield curves (Fig. 2). In this case the increase in sediment yield occurs because the increase in runoff is more effective in promoting erosion than the improved vegetal cover is in retarding erosion, and this results in increased sediment yields.

The decrease in sediment concentration is striking in each case for which data are available (Table 1).

The change from the present to an interglacial or Hypsithermal climate involves an increase in temperature and a decrease in precipitation. As shown in Table 1B such a change has an effect opposite to that of a change from the present to a glacial or pluvial climate. In all cases runoff decreases (Table 1B). In five of the six examples sediment yields increase, because the decrease in precipitation and increase in temperature weakens the protective vegetal cover; the shift is up the right limb of the sediment-yield curves (Fig. 2). In the remaining example sediment yield decreases, because the decrease in vegetal cover is more than compensated for by a major decrease in runoff; the shift is down the left limb of the sediment-yield curves (Fig. 2). In all cases sediment concentration increases.

In summary, the estimates of changed hydrologic conditions associated with the estimated Quaternary climatic changes of Table 1 are presented as examples of the use of Figures 1, 2, and 3. The temperature and precipitation changes used were arbitrarily selected and are not intended to be representative of Quaternary climate changes in all areas. For example, no consideration is given to hydrologic changes resulting when precipitation remains constant or decreases with a decrease in temperature during glaciation. Nevertheless, it appears that on the basis of Figures 1-3 estimates of runoff, sediment yields, and sediment concentrations for nonglaciated areas can be made for many combinations of temperature and precipitation changes.

PERIGLACIAL AND GLACIAL REGIONS

The previously estimated changes in runoff and sediment yields do not apply to those areas in close proximity to the ice sheet or to periglacial regions where, in general, temperatures were lower than in pluvial areas and precipitation was less (Büdel, 1959). In periglacial regions frost action and mass movement probably supply inordinately large amounts of debris to the rivers (Peltier, 1950). On frozen ground and during the melting of frozen ground in periglacial regions runoff rates would be very high (Tigerman and Rosa, 1949), but apparently so would the sediment yields and concentrations. Even in semiarid regions at the present time, minor frost action may play a major role in determining the geomorphology and the hydrology of a drainage basin (Schumm and Lusby, 1963).

Rivers that drain glaciers are highly charged with sediment as a result of glacial erosion. Comparison of sediment yields from two drainage basins in the Austrian Alps, one of which is glaciated, affords confirmation of the above statement (Lanser, 1958). The unglaciated basin, about 25 km² in area, had an annual sediment yield of 34.9 tons/km² (91 tons/mi²), whereas the other basin, 165 km² in area of which 45.7% was covered by a glacier, had an annual sediment yield of 1,512 tons/km² (3,900 tons/mi²). The sediment yield from the glaciated basin greatly exceeds even the maximum sediment-yield rates of Figure 1.

Borland (1961) obtained data on runoff and sediment yield from the presently glaciated Susitna River basin in south-central Alaska at two locations within the basin. From the upper 868 mi² of the drainage basin at a distance of 20.9 miles from the snout of the glacier, which occupies about 20% of the area of the basin, annual sediment yield was 14,000 tons/mi² (10.5 acre-ft/mi²). Farther downstream at a distance of 156.2 miles from the snout of the glacier, which at that point occupies 3.4% of the basin, the sediment yield had decreased to 1.02 acre-ft/mi². Borland found that mean annual sediment yield from this type of basin was an inverse function of the distance from the snout of the glacier and of the ratio of total drainage area to the area occupied by the glacier. Observations along the river reveal that it is aggrading as a result of the large amounts of sediment supplied by glacial erosion. Borland also presents data on the

flow characteristics of the river. In May 1957, the discharge increased from the winter low of about 2,000 ft³/sec to a maximum in June of about 40,000 ft³/sec. Summer discharge from mid-May to late October averages about 20,000 ft³/sec, whereas winter discharge is about 2,000 ft³/sec.

Sediment concentration in the flow during the winter is low, about 10 ppm, but it is much higher during the period of contribution of glacier melt water, up to 3,000 ppm. The discharge and sediment yields from glacial areas are highly seasonal, both discharge and sediment yield being low during the winter (Borland, 1961; Arnborg, 1955).

Corbel (1959, p. 18) states that the average sediment yield from a glacier basin is 4 times that from an unglaciated basin. His data also indicate that sediment yields from cold, snowy, and periglacial mountainous areas are about 1.5 times the sediment yields from the high mountains of Mediterranean climate.

The above information was obtained for drainage basins containing relatively small glaciers. The effect of continental glaciation on major rivers is undoubtedly in the same direction but perhaps of a different order of magnitude. Information on the volumes of sediment derived from a Pleistocene ice sheet must be indirect. For example, Broecker et al. (1958) present information on glacial and postglacial sedimentation rates from an analysis of an Atlantic deep-sea core. They concluded that an abrupt decrease in sedimentation rates occurred at the close of Wisconsin glaciation and that deposition during the Wisconsin glaciation was about 2.4 times greater than during post-Wisconsin time.

According to Table 1, sediment yields from humid, nonglaciated regions should be less during glaciation, which is exactly the reverse of the conclusion reached from the Atlantic cores. However, the higher rates of sedimentation in the ocean during glaciation can be explained by the high sediment loads of the rivers that drained from the ice sheets into the ocean and by the increased sediment yields caused by incision of the river channels near the coast, as a result of the lowered sea level.

SUMMARY

The curves of Figures 1, 2, and 3, which are based on modern runoff and sediment-yield data, suggest the changes in runoff, sediment yield, and sediment concentration that can be expected with a change in climate. In the same manner it is possible to estimate Quaternary changes of runoff, sediment yield, and sediment concentration from paleoclimatic information. One major limitation to the use of the curves is that they are not based on data from areas in which glaciation is important or where periglacial processes are a major factor influencing the variables. The information to be obtained on paleohydrology from these curves is applicable, therefore, only to nonglaciated or pluvial regions. For these regions a decrease in temperature and an increase in precipitation will cause an increase in runoff and a decrease in the sediment concentration (Table 1A). Sediment yield, however, can either increase or decrease depending on the temperature and precipitation before the change. On the other hand, an increase in temperature and a decrease in precipitation will cause a decrease in annual runoff and an increase in the sediment concentration (Table 1B). Sediment yield can either increase or decrease depending on the temperature and precipitation before the change.

SOME EFFECTS OF QUATERNARY HYDROLOGIC VARIATIONS

LANDFORMS

The changes in hydrologic variables that accompany a climatic change were estimated using Figures 1, 2, and 3 (Table 1). An attempt will be made, using these relationships, to suggest how the variations in the hydrology between glaciations and interglaciations could have influenced fluvial erosion and deposition and the resulting landforms and sedimentary deposits. For example, much has been written concerning Pleistocene and Recent river terraces and how they were influenced by Pleistocene changes of climate. The previously discussed hydrologic relations will be used to attempt to resolve some of the conflicting evidence regarding these features. However, before a discussion of Pleistocene river activity can be presented, the interfluve areas must be discussed because they are the source of much of the runoff and sediment that moves through a stream channel.

Interfluves. The density of vegetation, which is an indication of the effectiveness of vegetal cover as a protection against raindrop impact and runoff, increases with annual precipitation (Langbein and Schumm, 1958, Fig. 7). The rate of erosion of hillslopes should therefore decrease with increased precipitation. Exceptions occur, however, and in periglacial regions during a glacial advance intense frost action and solifluction increased slope erosion and even altered the form of the slope profile by the dominance of mass movement over runoff (Peltier, 1950; Cotton, 1958). In arid and semiarid regions the increase in precipitation also increased erosion by causing landslides and slumping along escarpments (Strahler, 1940; Watson and Wright, 1963).

The effects of Quaternary climatic changes on slopes were as variable as the processes operative and the materials involved. During pluvials, increased vegetal cover probably decreased slope erosion in semiarid and humid regions; however, in initially arid regions the increase in runoff probably more than compensated for the increase in vegetal cover, and initially arid slopes would have been subjected to more intense erosion. Although this last statement is conjectural, the peaks of the sediment–yield curves (Fig. 2) demonstrate that more sediment is exported from semiarid than from arid regions, and some of this increase must be derived from the slopes.

Moving down off the hillslopes to valley floors, particularly in arid and semiarid regions, one may encounter unchanneled extensions of the drainage networks or unchanneled alluvial deposits. In order to understand the effects of changed runoff on rivers, it appears necessary to understand what has happened in such areas; these are not truly interfluve areas, but they appear not to be part of the modern drainage system either.

Investigations into the relations among climate, runoff, and drainage density indicate that within a given climatic region drainage density (ratio of total channel length to drainage area) increases as annual runoff increases (Hadley and Schumm, 1961, p. 175-176) and as the mean annual flood volume increases (Carlston, 1963). These increases in runoff, however, are caused primarily by the effects of geology; for example, the highest runoff and drainage densities generally occur on shale, whereas less runoff and lower drainage densities occur on the more permeable soils of sandstones. Nevertheless, other studies suggest that in humid regions drainage density increases as the intensity of both precipitation and runoff increase (Chorley, 1957; Chorley and Morgan, 1962).

Melton (1958) demonstrated that drainage density is related closely to channel frequency (number of channels per unit area); that is, as the texture of topography becomes finer not only do the existing channels lengthen, but also new stream segments are added to the drainage network. On the basis of the above discussion alone one could conclude that increased runoff will cause extension of the drainage network and the addition of new tributaries, which will, in turn, cause dissection of the interfluves. An exception may occur, however, when the increase in runoff is accompanied by a major change in vegetational characteristics. The differences in drainage density as measured during the aforementioned studies were obtained for basins with comparable vegetation. However, if a major climatic change were to occur, causing a shift in vegetational type from shrubs to grasses and from grasses to forested conditions, it appears that the increased density of vegetation should prevent an increase of drainage density. Information is available to clarify this point. Peltier (1959) found, through worldwide measurements of terrain characteristics, that, for areas of comparable average slope, stream frequency is greatest in semiarid regions. Stream frequency is least in arid regions and intermediate in humid regions.

It appears, then, that a major increase in precipitation will either increase or decrease drainage density. The increase in precipitation and runoff accompanying a climatic change from arid to semiarid should increase drainage density. Similarly, in a humid region a further major increase in precipitation and runoff should increase the drainage density. However, in semiarid regions a major increase in precipitation could cause a change from shrubs to grass or from grass to trees, which would inhibit further channel development and might even cause obliteration of existing small channels, thereby decreasing drainage density. This suggests that if drainage density were to be substituted for sediment yield on the ordinate of Figure 2, the curves should indicate in a very general manner the variation of drainage density with climate.

In summary, Peltier's observations and the sediment-yield curves (Fig. 2) indicate that both drainage density and sediment yields are greatest in semiarid regions. The concurrence of maximum drainage densities and maximum sediment yields at the same climate suggests that the high sediment yields are a reflection of increased channel development and a more efficiently drained system. Hence, a shift to a semiarid climate from either an arid or a humid one should allow extension of the drainage network with increased channel and hillslope erosion.

Rivers. Before the preceding relationships can be brought to bear on the major problems of river terraces, the changed dimensions and patterns of rivers will be discussed briefly. If annual runoff is to increase significantly, a larger river channel must exist to carry it. The relations among mean annual discharge and channel width and depth of modern rivers have been studied by Leopold and Maddock (1953). They found that the width increased as the 0.5 power of mean annual discharge in a downstream direction, and the depth increased as the 0.4 power. The relations suggest that as discharge increases both channel width and depth will increase, although width will change more than depth, thereby increasing the width–depth ratio.

The previously noted relation between discharge and meander width and wavelength (Dury, 1958) suggests that not only the dimensions of the channel but also the dimensions of the meander pattern will change with discharge. However, the type of sediment transported by the river is another factor of major importance that can influence channel shape and pattern. If with an increase in discharge the river begins to transport a greater proportion of bedload, it appears that the width–depth ratio of the channel would increase (Schumm, 1963a) and the sinuosity of the river pattern would decrease (Schumm, 1963b). Conversely an increase in the proportion of suspended sediment load might have an opposite effect. Rivers draining from basins containing glaciers would be expected to be affected by an influx of coarser sediment and would behave accordingly. It is therefore very difficult to evaluate the effect of a climatic change on the width and depth of specific river channels.

The Cimarron River in Kansas (Schumm and Lichty, 1963) and the North Platte River in western Nebraska provide modern examples of major changes in river dimensions caused by changes in runoff. For example, the North Platte River in western Nebraska decreased in width from an average of 2,800 ft to 500 ft during the past 60 years. This change was caused by a decrease in the mean annual flood from 13,000 to 3,000 ft^3/sec and a decrease in mean annual

discharge from 2,300 to 560 ft^3/sec, as a result of river regulation and diversion of flow for irrigation (R. W. Lichty, 1964, oral communication).

Climatic river terraces. Undoubtedly the subject that has caused the most controversy and interest among students of fluvial deposits are climatic river terraces, that is, those terraces whose origin can be traced to a change in climate rather than to diastrophism. In every effort to summarize the cause of climatic river terraces it is generally agreed that the subject is very complex. Flint (1957, p. 218) explains as follows why such a variety of explanations for these terraces exist: "Climatic inferences from alluvial stratigraphy are difficult because of the number of variable factors involved. Any climate consists of a group of variables such as amount of precipitation, distribution of precipitation throughout the year, mean and seasonal temperature, and the like. The response of a stream, in terms of discharge and load, to a change in one or more of the climatic variables will be affected by local topographic texture, steepness of slopes, character of vegetation cover, and other circumstances. Hence a change in only one climatic factor might lead to very different responses in two different streams, and even in two different segments of a single long stream." All the information to be presented in the following discussion supports Flint's statement regarding the variability of response.

Frye (1961) has summarized five previously proposed theories of climatic terrace formation, which, although conflicting, may each be valid for the region to which it applies.

In Table 2 an effort has been made to summarize and in some cases to anticipate the results of field investigations in a range of climatic and topographic regions. Because discussion is restricted to the United States the complexities of tropical and monsoonal climates may be ignored. Even so, eight geographic and climatic regions must be listed on Table 2 and be discussed in some detail, for the rivers of each of these regions should react differently to the changing

TABLE 2

Summary of Possible Changes in Pleistocene Fluvial Processes
(D, deposition; E, erosion; S, stable)

Location or type of drainage basin	Climate change		River activity during designated phase					
	Interglacial →	Glacial	Late inter-glacial	Early glacial	Glacial	Late glacial	Early inter-glacial	Inter-glacial
1. Basin partly occupied by ice sheet	Warm, moist	Cooler, drier	S	D	D	E	E	S
2. Basin partly occupied by valley glaciers	Warm, moist	Cooler, wetter	S	D	D	E	E	S
3. Periglacial, no glaciers in basin	Warm, moist	Cooler, drier	S	D	D	E	E	S
4. Coastal	Warm, moist	Cooler, wetter	E	E	S	D	D	S
5. Closed interior basin	Hot, dry	Cooler, wetter	D	D	S	E	E	S
6. Unglaciated continental interior (humid, perennial streams)	Warm, moist	Cooler, wetter	S	E	E	D	D	S
7. Unglaciated continental interior (semiarid, ephemeral, and intermittent streams)	Warm, dry	Cooler, wetter	S	E	E	D	D	S
8. Unglaciated continental interior (arid, ephemeral streams)								
(a) Tributaries	Hot, dry	Cooler, wetter	S	E	E	D	D	S
(b) Main rivers	Hot, dry	Cooler, wetter	S	D	D	S	S	S

Quaternary climate and hydrology. Only one of the suggested schemes of river activity in Table 2 matches those previously discussed by Frye (1961), but in some cases the difference is merely a matter of including a period of stability in the scheme or starting an episode of erosion or deposition slightly sooner or later. Nevertheless, even these minor changes might significantly affect the stratigraphy and terrace sequence of a valley. For example, rivers that drained from areas of continental glaciation (Table 2, location 1) are indicated as behaving according to the schemes of river activity proposed by Penck and Brückner (Zeuner, 1959, p. 45-56) and Zeuner (1959, p. 49), except for the stipulation that the rivers should have been relatively stable during middle- and late-interglacial time. Stability here is used rather loosely. It means simply that the conditions prior to glaciation continue to prevail following glaciation. For example, a river may have been eroding a mountain valley prior to glaciation and following glaciation it may again be eroding the bedrock floor of its valley; it would be considered stable for the purposes of Table 2.

It appears certain that, for rivers draining continental and valley glaciers (Table 2, locations 1 and 2), fluvial deposition was associated with glaciation (Zeuner, 1959, p. 45-46). Melt-water from the glaciers transported huge loads of sediment and formed valley trains (Peltier, 1949; Krigstrom, 1962) and outwash plains. Following cessation of glacial erosion, the reduced sediment loads of the rivers would cause incision of deposits formed by deposition from the heavily loaded glacial rivers. Terraces would be formed as glacial activity waned.

In periglacial regions Zeuner (1959, p. 49) concluded that during late-interglacial and early-glacial time, as the climate became colder and as the forests disappeared, periglacial processes of erosion caused deposition of sediment in the upper valleys. As the ice sheets advanced, the climate became colder and drier, and steppe conditions prevailed. The resulting decrease in discharge of the rivers, coupled with increased sediment loads, caused aggradation in their middle courses. With the return of warmer, wetter conditions the forests returned, hindering mass movement of sediment to the rivers, and increase of discharge caused incision of the deposits. The periglacial scheme of river activity outlined in Table 2 (location 3) differs slightly from Zeuner's scheme in the assumption that during late-interglacial time the rivers were essentially stable. In the United States the drier steppe conditions may not have occurred; nevertheless, wherever severe periglacial erosion occurred, under either wetter or drier conditions, river aggradation would have accompanied it (Peltier, 1950, p. 231-232).

The coastal scheme of river activity (Table 2, location 4) is that as outlined by Fisk and McFarlan (1955) with no modification. Near the coasts late-interglacial and early-glacial lowering of sea level in response to growth of ice sheets caused river erosion. The rise of sea level accompanying melting of the ice sheets caused deposition. During the peak of glaciation and during interglaciation, sea-level stability should have promoted river stability.

The schemes of river activity outlined for the remaining locations of Table 2, with the exception of that for location 6, are for situations generally different from those proposed

previously. For example, the scheme of river activity for a closed interior basin (location 5) is the reverse of that for the coastal situation, because during late interglaciation and early glaciation the formation of a lake within the basin due to increased runoff would have raised the base level of the streams entering the lake and would have caused aggradation in the lower parts of the river courses.

The schemes of river activities for locations 1 through 5 are rather easily understood for changing base levels and the known effects of glacial and periglacial erosion on the sediment loads of rivers. The schemes outlined for locations 6, 7, and 8, which deal with river activity in nonglaciated regions above the effects of changing sea level, are based on the estimated hydrologic changes that one might expect to accompany the Pleistocene climatic changes as suggested in Table 1. Initial climate or the climate before the change is of critical importance here, for it determines the type of river to be considered. For example, in the humid region of location 6, the rivers were perennial, and they remained perennial following a shift to the cooler, wetter climate of the glacial period. The increased runoff, with a minor decrease in sediment yield (Table 1; 50°F, 40 in. to 40°F, 50 in.), should have permitted stream incision similar to that which occurred along the Red River during Pleistocene glaciation (Frye and Leonard, 1963).

Frye and Leonard (1963; Frye, 1961) studied climatic terraces in Texas far removed from the effects of glaciers. They concluded that from late-interglacial to mid-glacial time the Red River eroded because of the higher runoff from the nonglaciated basin. Sediment yields probably did not change greatly as precipitation and runoff increased, but the sediment concentration would have decreased. From the peak of glaciation to early-interglacial time, deposition occurred as discharge decreased. However, during interglaciation the river was probably stable. Because glaciers were not present within the drainage basin, deepening of the valley during erosion was greater than subsequent deposition, for the alluvial fills do not reach the height of the bedrock floor of the preceding cycle (Frye and Leonard, 1963, p. 31).

The situation differed somewhat for an initially semiarid region (Table 2, location 7), for the rivers were initially either intermittent or characterized by long periods of low flow. The smaller tributaries were ephemeral, as many are in humid regions, but according to Peltier (1959), many more drainage channels would have been present. With the shift to the wetter climate and greater runoff of glaciation, the major rivers and many of the tributaries became perennial. Vegetation became denser, and if a change from bunch grass to continuous grass cover or from grass to trees occurred, many small channels and the headward portions of larger channels would have been obliterated. As runoff increased, the sediment yield from the basin and the sediment concentration decreased (Table 1; 50° F, 10 in. to 40°F, 20 in.). The result was undoubtedly the enlargement and incision of the main channels. With a return to semiarid conditions, the sediment yield increased, as both hillslope and channel erosion increased and runoff decreased. Deposition in the main channels should have resulted, as the tributaries again reached their maximum extent and number.

It has not always been recognized that the changes in tributary channels might not conform to changes along the larger rivers. This may not be important in humid regions, but it becomes of major importance in arid regions, where unfortunately few hydrologic data are available from which one may estimate river response to climate change. Nevertheless, the increased precipitation during glaciation should have increased runoff in arid regions but probably not enough to convert the ephemeral rivers to perennial ones. The increased runoff should have eroded the tributaries (Table 2, location 8a) and extended the drainage network (Peltier, 1959). Sediment would have been flushed out of the tributary valleys into the main channels during local storms, and because the loss of water into the alluvium of the main channels would have been appreciable (Cornish, 1961), aggradation of the main channels could have resulted (Table 2, location 8b). The situation might have been similar to modern conditions along the Rio Grande, where trenching of the Rio Puerco and other tributaries during the past century has caused deposition in the Rio Grande itself (Rittenhouse, 1944). In effect, increased runoff in arid regions would shift stored sediment downstream, where it might be deposited before moving out of the system.

With a reversion to arid conditions during interglaciation, it is difficult to visualize how the lesser runoff could erode and clear the main channel, but the sediment contribution from the tributaries should have been substantially reduced, and some scour of the main channel could have resulted. Probably, in a truly arid climate the channel would simply continue to exist, although modified by aeolian activity, and it could be considered stable (Table 2, location 8a). However, without perennial flow the semiarid and arid rivers probably were always characterized by a normal instability (Schumm and Hadley, 1957), and arroyo cutting could have alternated with aggradation as a natural part of the cycle of erosion of these ephemeral stream channels. In these regions, a change from stability to erosion could occur in response to a change in the size and type of storm rather than to a change in the amount of annual precipitation (Leopold, 1951b).

Hunt (1953, p. 3) described the changes in alluvial deposits resulting from the change from a relatively moist Pleistocene climate to a more arid Recent climate in the Great Plains and Colorado Plateaus: ". . . late Pleistocene alluvium commonly is homogeneous in composition and texture longitudinally along the main streams, and the flood plain surface on this alluvium is nearly a plane. On the other hand, the Recent alluvium in the main valleys is composed of broad low coalescing fans that apex in the tributaries." The differences between the Pleistocene and Recent alluvium are consistent with the differences to be expected between the deposits of perennial and ephemeral streams.

As the schemes of river activity of Table 2 suggest, quite different changes could have occurred at different locations along the same river, as the climate and hydrology of the system altered. Consider the effect of a climatic change from that of the present to that of a glacial period on a river draining from mountains across an initially semiarid or humid region to the sea. The headwater section should behave according to schemes 1 and 2 (Peltier, 1949). The midsection should behave according to schemes 6 or 7 (Wenzel *et al.*, 1946, p. 48). The lowest section should behave according to scheme 4 (Fisk and McFarlan, 1955) unless the river were to enter a pluvial lake, in which case scheme 5 would pertain.

It appears that a terrace study along a portion of a river is probably applicable only to the area studied or to similar reaches along other rivers. An attempt to correlate river terraces by height or number of terraces over long distances appears unwise and likely to yield false correlations (Hadley, 1960).

SEDIMENTARY DEPOSITS

A brief statement concerning sedimentary deposits as related to paleohydrology will conclude this paper. Obviously the changed relations of runoff and sediment yield during and following a climatic change will influence both the type and amount of sediment deposited. Even yearly fluctuations of runoff cause significant variations in the amount of sediment deposited. For example, Granar (1956) has established a very good correlation between varve thickness and the annual maximum discharge of the Ångerman River for the years 1920–42. The relationship appears to be exponential, with varve thickness increasing greatly with an increase in the maximum discharge for any year.

With adequate sampling it should be possible to demonstrate that the curves for sediment yield and precipitation in Figure 2 portray reasonably well changes in sediment yields to be expected following a climatic change. Lakes not affected by glaciation should show rates of sedimentation consistent with the relations of Figure 2. For example, in arid regions an increase in precipitation associated with a glaciation should increase the sediment deposited during a unit of time. In semiarid regions an increase in precipitation should decrease the amount of sediment deposited in a unit of time. In humid regions the increase in precipitation should not greatly alter the rate of sediment yield.

The relationship between sediment yield and annual precipitation shown on Figure 2, although limited to conterminous United States, has been used to explain the sediment yields of Hawaiian rivers on the leeward and windward sides of Kauai (Inman *et al.*, 1963). In addition, Swann (1964) has used the relation between sediment yield and climate to explain some Late Mississippian rhythmic sedimentation. Clastic units were deposited as a delta prograded during periods of relatively dry climate; whereas limestones were deposited and the seas advanced over the delta during periods of relatively humid climate. These changes, according to Swann (1964), apparently reflect the effect of climate on vegetation and sediment yield.

CONCLUSIONS

Although interrelations among hydrologic phenomena as developed from modern observations are still incomplete, it may be possible to predict the direction and possibly the magnitude of a change in hydrologic variables resulting from a climatic change. These tentative relationships also suggest that the effect of the hydrologic changes on landforms and sedimentary deposits may be quite different depending on the original climate of a region prior to the change, the importance of glacial and periglacial erosion within the region, and baselevel changes. Each landform and deposit needs to be studied in relation to its own environment, and the conclusions resulting from a local or regional study should be extended beyond the limits of the investigation only with great care. As Hunt (1953, p. 20-21) indicated, "The field evidence indicates that the same kind of events occurred in the same sequence and in about the same degree throughout the Rocky Mountain region, but it does not necessarily follow that the events in different parts of the region were contemporaneous." The hydrologic relationships presented herein suggest strongly that such is indeed the case. The presence or absence of glaciers, the geographical location, and the climate preceding a climatic change all are important factors that may cause major geomorphic and depositional events to be out of phase regionally. Nevertheless, the hydrologic changes resulting from climatic changes, when better understood, will allow the development of explanations for variable rates of deposition and the alternation of erosion and deposition over large geographic areas.

REFERENCES

American Society of Civil Engineers, 1949, Hydrology handbook: Amer. Soc. Civ. Eng., Manuals Eng. Practice, No. 28, 184 p.

Antevs, Ernst, 1952, Cenozoic climates of the Great Basin: Geol. Rdsch., v. 40, p. 94-108

—— 1954, Climate of New Mexico during the last glaciopluvial: J. Geol., v. 62, p. 182-191

Arnborg, L., 1955, Hydrology of the glacial river Austurfljot: Geogr. Ann., v. 37, p. 185-201

Baver, L. D., 1956, Soil physics: New York, John Wiley & Sons, Inc., 489 p.

Borland, W. M., 1961, Sediment transport of glacier-fed streams in Alaska: J. Geophys. Res., v. 66, p. 3347-3350

Broecker, W. S., Turekian, K. K., and Heezen, B. C., 1958, The relation of deep sea sedimentation rates to variations in climate: Amer. J. Sci., v. 256, p. 503-517

Broecker, W. S., and Orr, P. C., 1958, Radiocarbon chronology of Lake Lahontan and Lake Bonneville: Geol. Soc. Amer. Bull., v. 69, p. 1009-1032

Büdel, Julius, 1959, The "periglacial"-morphologic effects of the Pleistocene climate over the entire world: Intern. Geol. Rev., v. 1, No. 3, p. 1-16 (translation by H. E. Wright and David Alt of paper originally published in Erdkunde, v. 7, p. 249-266, 1953)

Carlston, C. W., 1963, Drainage density and streamflow: U.S. Geol. Surv. Prof. Pap. 422-C, 8 p.

Charlesworth, J. K., 1957, The Quaternary Era with special reference to its glaciation: London, Edward Arnold Ltd., 2 vols., 1700 p.

Chorley, R. J., 1957, Climate and morphometry: J. Geol., v. 65, p. 628-638

Chorley, R. J., and Morgan, M. A., 1962, Comparison of morphometric features, Unaka Mountains, Tennessee and North Carolina, and Dartmoor, England: Geol. Soc. Amer. Bull., v. 73, p. 17-34

Colman, E. A., 1953, Vegetation and watershed management: New York, Ronald Press Co., 412 p.

Corbel, Jean, 1959, Vitesse de l'erosion: Z. Geomorph., v. 3, p. 1-28

Cornish, J. H., 1961, Flow losses in dry sandy channels: J. Geophys. Res., v. 66, p. 1845-1853

Cotton, C. A., 1958, Alternating Pleistocene morphogenetic systems: Geol. Mag., v. 95, p. 125-136

Dillon, L. S., 1956, Wisconsin climate and life zones in North America: Science, v. 123, p. 167-176

Dury, G. H., 1958, Tests of a general theory of misfit streams: Inst. Brit. Geogr. Trans. Publ. 25, p. 105-118

—— 1965, Theoretical implications of underfit streams: U.S. Geol. Surv. Prof. Pap. 452-C (in press)

Fisk, H. N., and McFarlan, E., Jr., 1955, Late Quaternary deltaic deposits of the Mississippi River: Geol. Soc. Amer. Spec. Pap. 62, p. 279-302

Flint, R. F., 1957, Glacial and Pleistocene geology: New York, John Wiley & Sons, Inc., 553 p.

Fournier, M. F., 1960, Climat et érosion: Paris, Presses Univ. France, 201 p.

Frye, J. C., 1961, Fluvial deposition and the glacial cycle: J. Geol., v. 69, p. 600-603

Frye, J. C., and Leonard, A. B., 1963, Pleistocene geology of Red River basin in Texas: Univ. Texas Bur. Econ. Geol. Rep. Invest. No. 49, 48 p.

Granar, Lars, 1956, Dating of recent fluvial sediments from the estuary of the Ångerman River: Geol. Fören. Stockholm Förh., v. 78, p. 654-658

Hadley, R. F., 1960, Recent sedimentation and erosional history of Fivemile Creek, Fremont County, Wyoming: U.S. Geol. Surv. Prof. Pap. 352-A, 16 p.

Hadley, R. F., and Schumm, S. A., 1961, Sediment sources and drainage basin characteristics in upper Cheyenne River basin: U.S. Geol. Surv. Water-Supply Pap. 1531-B, p. 137-196

Hunt, C. B., 1953, Pleistocene-Recent boundary in the Rocky Mountain region: U.S. Geol. Surv. Bull. 996-A, 25 p.

Inman, D. L., Gayman, W. R., and Cox, D. C., 1963, Littoral sedimentary processes on Kauai, a subtropical high island: Pac. Sci., v. 17, p. 106-130

Kittredge, Joseph, 1948, Forest influences: New York, McGraw-Hill Book Co., 394 p.

Kräusel, Richard, 1961, Paleobotanical evidence of climate, *in* Nairn, A. E. M., Descriptive paleoclimatology: New York, Interscience Publishers, Inc., p. 227-254

Krigström, Arne, 1962, Geomorphological studies of sandur plains and their braided rivers in Iceland: Geogr. Annaler, v. 44, p. 328-346

Langbein, W. B., 1961, Salinity and hydrology of closed lakes: U.S. Geol. Surv. Prof. Pap. 412, 20 p.

—— 1962, The water supply of arid valleys in intermountain regions in relation to climate: Intern. Assoc. Sci. Hydrol. Bull., v. 7, p. 34-39

Langbein, W. B., *et al.*, 1949, Annual runoff in the United States: U.S. Geol. Surv. Circ. 52, 14 p.

Langbein, W. B., and Schumm, S. A., 1958, Yield of sediment in relation to mean annual precipitation: Amer. Geophys. Union Trans., v. 39, p. 1076-1084

Langbein, W. B., and Iseri, K. T., 1960, General introduction and hydrologic definitions: U.S. Geol. Surv. Water-Supply Pap. 1541-A, 29 p.

Lanser, Otto, 1958, Reflexions sur les debits solides en suspension des cours d'eau glaciares: Intern. Assoc. Sci. Hydrol. Bull., v. 4, p. 37-43

Leopold, L. B., 1951a, Pleistocene climates in New Mexico: Amer. J. Sci., v. 249, p. 152-168

—— 1951b, Rainfall frequency—an aspect of climatic variation: Amer. Geophys. Union Trans., v. 32, p. 347-357

Leopold, L. B., and Maddock, Thomas, Jr., 1953, The hydraulic geometry of stream channels and some physiographic implications: U.S. Geol. Surv. Prof. Pap. 252, 57 p.

Manley, Gordon, 1955, A climatological survey of the retreat of the Laurentide ice sheet: Amer. J. Sci., v. 253, p. 256-273

Melton, M. A., 1958, Correlation structure of morphometric properties of drainage systems and their controlling agents: J. Geol., v. 66, p. 442-460

Peltier, L. C., 1949, Pleistocene terraces of the Susquehanna River, Pennsylvania: Pennsylvania Geol. Surv. Bull. G23, 158 p.

—— 1950, The geographic cycle in periglacial regions as it is related to climatic geomorphology: Assoc. Amer. Geogr. Ann., v. 40, p. 214-236

—— 1959, Area sampling for terrain analysis (abst.): Geol. Soc. Amer. Bull., v. 70, p. 1809

Rainwater, F. H., 1962, Stream composition of the conterminous United States: U.S. Geol. Surv. Hydrol. Invest. Atlas HA-61

Rittenhouse, Gordon, 1944, Sources of modern sands in the middle Rio Grande Valley, New Mexico: J. Geol., v. 52, p. 145-183

Schnell, I. I., 1961, Recent evidence about the nature of climate changes and its implications: New York Acad. Sci. Ann., v. 95, p. 251-270

Schumm, S. A., 1963a, A tentative classification of alluvial river channels: U.S. Geol. Surv. Circ. 477, 10 p.

—— 1963b, Sinuosity of alluvial rivers on the Great Plains: Geol. Soc. Amer. Bull., v. 74, p. 1089-1099

Schumm, S. A., and Hadley, R. F., 1957, Arroyos and the semiarid cycle of erosion: Amer. J. Sci., v. 255, p. 161-174

Schumm, S. A., and Lichty, R. W., 1963, Channel widening and flood-plain construction along Cimarron River in southwestern Kansas: U.S. Geol. Surv. Prof. Pap. 352-D, p. 71-87

Schumm, S. A., and Lusby, G. C., 1963, Seasonal variation of infiltration capacity and runoff on hillslopes in western Colorado: J. Geophys. Res., v. 68, p. 3655-3666

Schwarzbach, Martin, 1961, The climatic history of Europe and North America, *in* Nairn, A. E. M., Descriptive paleoclimatology: New York, Interscience Publishers Inc., p. 255-291

Snyder, C. T., and Langbein, W. B., 1962, The Pleistocene lake in Spring Valley, Nevada, and its climatic implications: J. Geophys. Res., v. 67, p. 2385-2394

Strahler, A. N., 1940, Landslides of the Vermilion and Echo Cliffs, northern Arizona: J. Geomorph., v. 3, p. 285-300

Swann, D. H., 1964, Late Mississippian rhythmic sediments of Mississippi Valley: Amer. Assoc. Petroleum Geologists Bull., v. 48, p. 637-658

Tigerman, M. H., and Rosa, J. M., 1949, Erosion from melting snow on frozen ground: J. For., v. 47, p. 807-809

Watson, R. A., and Wright, H. E., Jr., 1963, Landslides on the east flank of the Chuska Mountains, northwestern New Mexico: Amer. J. Sci., v. 261, p. 525-548

Wenzel, L. K., Cady, R. C., and Waite, H. A., 1946, Geology and ground-water resources of Scotts Bluff County, Nebraska: U.S. Geol. Surv. Water-Supply Pap. 943, 150 p.

Zeuner, F. E., 1959, The Pleistocene period: London, Hutchinson & Company, Ltd., 447 p.

SUMMARY

The modern relations that exist among the climatic and hydrologic variables of temperature, precipitation, runoff, sediment yield and sediment concentration are used to predict the hydrologic effects of Quaternary climatic changes. A decrease in temperature and an increase in precipitation of the magnitudes associated with Pleistocene glaciation will substantially increase runoff and decrease the sediment concentration of the runoff. Sediment yields, however, may either increase or decrease depending on the climate before the change. A change from an arid to a semiarid climate will increase the sediment yield, whereas a change from a semiarid to a humid climate will decrease the sediment yield.

The effect of a climatic change on river activity, through modification of hydrologic variables, is complicated by the variability of the hydrologic response and the effects of glacial activity or baselevel change. For example, river aggradation occurred during Pleistocene glaciation as the sediment load of a river was increased by glacial or periglacial erosion within the basin or by the extension of the drainage network by tributary incision in arid regions. The rise in baselevel caused by the formation of a pluvial lake in a closed basin caused aggradation in the rivers entering the lake. Elsewhere river erosion and terrace formation occurred during Pleistocene glaciation, for example as runoff was increased by higher precipitation along perennial rivers of humid regions and ephemeral rivers of semiarid regions. In addition, tributaries in arid regions incised, as the drainage network was extended by greater runoff, and the lower courses of rivers entering the sea incised, as sea level was lowered.

GLACIERS AND CLIMATE

MARK F. MEIER[1]

A MOST distinctive aspect of the Quaternary period was the recurrent expansion and contraction of the world's glacier cover. These glacier fluctuations indirectly influenced many other geological, biological, and climatological processes. In many areas the fluctuating glaciers left relatively indelible, datable marks on the landscape. The extent of these fluctuations suggests control by major, perhaps worldwide, changes in climate. Therefore it is only natural for these glaciations to be used as a primary basis for Pleistocene and Recent chronology.

The basic assumptions involved in using glacial advances to establish a usable chronology are: (1) the glacier advances were triggered by major climatic events; (2) the climatic events were felt on a worldwide basis, or at least over large geographic areas; and (3) the responses of the glaciers to these climatic events were essentially synchronous. In addition to these basic assumptions, some workers also appear to assume that (4) glacier responses were not only synchronous but essentially instantaneous, and (5) glacier advances indicate climatic change to a cooler and/or wetter regime. It is surprising that in spite of a huge amount of interest in the reconstruction of past glacier fluctuations (and through these, past climates), very little attention has been directed to the validity of these basic assumptions.

The problem can be put as follows: What sort of information about past climates can be obtained from the study of glacier variations, and how valid are these paleoclimatic reconstructions at our present state of knowledge? Answers to these questions are important to much of the past and present work on the Quaternary period. In this chapter are discussed the sequence of events leading from a climatic change to a glacier fluctuation, the present status of our ability to deduce climatic history from glacier variations, and how glacier variation and/or direct climatic information can be obtained from ice or ice-margin features or environments. Some of the more active current glaciological work in the United States that is pertinent to this broad problem is mentioned; glaciers and glacier variations in the United States are briefly described. The term glacier is taken to include ice caps and even ice sheets of continental dimensions.

Glaciology, the study of ice and snow in all of its aspects, is an interdisciplinary field almost as broad and diverse as is Quaternary research. Consequently it is impossible to do more than just introduce one rather narrow area of the field in this chapter. No attempt will be made to present a complete summary of current American glaciological work. Those interested in the scope of this effort are referred to

several recent summaries (Bender, 1963; Meier, 1963; Weeks, 1963; Crary, Field and Meier, 1962; Kingery, 1963).

THE RELATION OF GLACIER FLUCTUATIONS TO CLIMATIC CHANGES

The relation of a glacier's dimensions to its climatic environment can be pictured as a chain of distinct processes (Fig. 1). The general meteorologic environment determines

Figure 1. The chain of processes connecting the position of a glacier margin with a certain meteorologic environment.

the local mass- and energy-exchange processes at the glacier surface, producing varying rates of accumulation and ablation. The difference between the accumulation and ablation rates at a locality determines the net mass budget for that locality. If the net mass budget is positive for one or more years, then the glacier gains mass from its environment. This gain or loss of mass determines the dynamic response of the glacier: an increase of thickness generally causes a sensitive increase in flow rate, producing an extension of the glacier. Changes in glacier length cause changes in the surrounding landscape—modifications of the topography, the regimes of streams, and the plant or animal life—and some of these modifications in the environment may persist as evidence of the glacier's variation. These environmental modifications, however, cannot provide information on the causal fluctuations in the general meteorologic environment unless one has sufficient knowledge to trace back through *each* of the processes shown in Figure 1.

These processes are connected in series, and there are negative (degenerative) and positive (regenerative) feedback effects, so climatic reconstruction from knowledge of glacier variations is not a simple task. It is possible for a very slight fluctuation in climate to be greatly magnified, producing a drastic and spectacular change in the appearance and extent of a glacier; it is also possible for the effect of a major climatic change to be attenuated to such an extent that no change in the glacier's dimensions occurs. In some cases variations in glaciers can be caused by the triggering of instabilities in one or more of the processes in the chain, and be unrelated to climate.

[1] U.S. Geological Survey, Tacoma, Washington.

THE METEOROLOGIC PROBLEM

The effect of the general meteorologic environment on the mass and energy exchanges between a glacier and its immediate surroundings is considered first. This is perhaps the least understood and hardest to analyze of the several processes in the chain that links glaciers to climate.

In general, a glacier can exist in a steady-state condition only if the rate of snow and ice accumulation exceeds the rate of snow and ice ablation on some appreciable portion of its surface, when averaged over time intervals of a year or more. The rates of accumulation and ablation at each point, however, are determined by local processes that are not necessarily predictable from knowledge of the general environment.

Accumulation. Accumulation on glaciers is primarily caused by precipitation in the form of snow. The refreezing of rain and the accumulation of rime, hoar, etc. are not generally significant factors in a glacier regime. In many areas glaciers exist because of the orographic augmentation of precipitation; in other areas the accumulation distribution is greatly modified by katabatic winds. The topography that gives rise to orographic and katabatic effects may be the glacier profile itself; in the case of a large ice cap these effects are of predominant importance and illustrate the complex interrelation of glacier and climate. In steep mountains, accumulation patterns are very much determined by the complicated wind patterns during and after major storms. Studies on Dinwoody Glacier, Wyoming, and Grinnell Glacier, Montana, suggest that precipitation on these small cirque glaciers may be as much as twice the average precipitation at the same elevation elsewhere in these mountains. Avalanches also redistribute snow accumulation in the mountains, but the quantitative importance of this factor is not known.

Time-distributions of precipitation are also important in determining the accumulation on a glacier. Slight changes in the seasonal distribution of precipitation can cause marked changes in snow accumulation without affecting long-term averages of climatic parameters (Hubley, 1956, p. 672). Recent studies on the Blue and South Cascade Glaciers in Washington have shown the extreme sensitivity of these glaciers to temperatures or freezing-level elevations during times of precipitation in spring and fall.

Ablation. It is difficult to establish the relative importance of accumulation and ablation changes with relation to secular changes in climate. One reason for this is that increased precipitation and decreased temperatures often go hand-in-hand (*e.g.* Hubley, 1956, p. 673). However, many glaciologists consider variations in ablation of more direct importance in causing glacier fluctuations (Ahlmann, 1953, p. 7; Hoinkes, 1955, p. 497). Therefore it is important to consider how ablation is related to meteorologic factors. Ablation is caused by melting, wind, erosion, evaporation, calving, and other processes. In the case of all present-day American glaciers, melting is quantitatively of greatest importance. It is for this reason that much current glaciological interest attaches to the energy-exchange processes at the surface of melting snow or ice.

The energy required to melt snow or ice is supplied by short-wave radiation from the sun, long-wave radiation from the atmosphere and clouds, eddy conduction from the air, warm precipitation, and the heat released by the condensation of water vapor. Heat energy is removed from the surface by conduction into colder snow or ice below, long-wave rediation into space, evaporation, and melt. The major problem is the determination of energy transfer by eddy conductivity, because this term cannot be measured directly, and no reliable means has been found to calculate it from measurements of wind, temperature, and humidity (Hubley, 1957, p. 68).

Recent detailed studies of mass and energy exchange have been made on the Blue Glacier, Olympic Mountains,

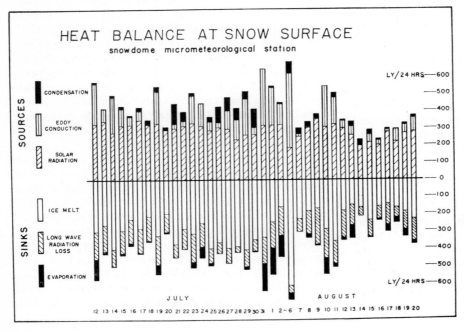

Figure 2. Heat balance at the snow surface, upper Blue Glacier, Washington, July 12 to August 20, 1958. From LaChapelle (1959, p. 448).

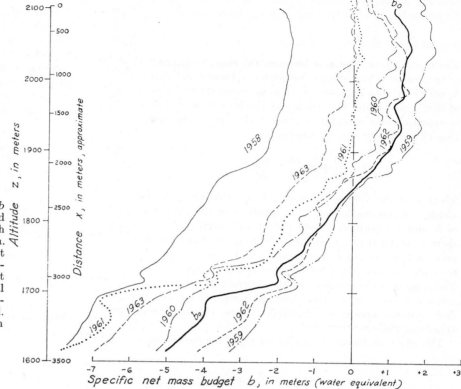

Figure 3. Specific net mass budget b as a function of altitude z and distance x, 1958-1963, South Cascade Glacier, Washington. The curve for steady-state net budget b_0 was obtained by subtracting the mean specific net budget from each individual curve and averaging the results at each altitude interval. From Meier and Tangborn (1965).

Washington. Typical results for a fair-weather summer period are shown in Figure 2. Although this glacier is in a highly maritime environment, 69% of the energy income was supplied by solar radiation during this period. Eddy conductivity contributed 25%, and condensation released 6%. Twenty-eight percent of the energy was lost as net long-wave radiation, 8% was absorbed as heat of vaporization, and 64% was available to melt ice. The snow was isothermal during this period, so heat was not conducted into underlying layers, and precipitation contributed a negligible amount of heat. High rates of ablation occurred during a few stormy days in fall; these days were characterized by higher energy incomes from eddy conductivity (resulting from increased air turbulence near the snow surface) and the heat of condensation and by decreased outgoing long-wave radiation balance. These results appear to be typical for many North American alpine glaciers. Other studies of the energy balance at a snow or ice surface have been conducted on the Lemon Creek (Hubley, 1957), McCall (Orvig, 1961), and Gulkana (Mayo and Péwé, 1963) Glaciers in Alaska.

THE NET MASS BUDGET

The difference between accumulation and ablation is termed the net mass budget. This quantity is the vital link between the climatic environment and the dynamic adjustment of a glacier to that environment; neither accumulation nor ablation matters individually.

The specific net mass flux $\dot{b}$ is defined by the expression

$$\dot{b} = \dot{c} - \dot{a} \qquad (1)$$

where $\dot{c}$ is the specific accumulation rate and $\dot{a}$ the specific ablation rate, measured in terms of mass per unit area per unit time, or simply as a length (depth of water-equivalent) per unit time (Meier, 1962, p. 254). The term "specific" refers to measurements made at a point. The specific net budget b is

$$b = \int_{t_1}^{t_2} \dot{b}\, dt \qquad (2)$$

where t_1 and t_2 are times of minima in the total mass of the glacier separated by about one year. The interval t_2-t_1 is termed a budget year. The integral of b over the whole glacier is the total net budget, and the total net budget divided by the area of the glacier is the mean specific net budget, $\bar{b}$.

If $\bar{b} = 0$, averaged over several years, the glacier is said to be in a steady-state condition and will have a characteristic distribution of specific net budget values over its surface. If these steady-state values of net budget (b_0) are known or can be computed, they can be compared with actual net budget values, b, for a given year, in order to determine the budget imbalance b_1. Thus,

$$b_1 = b - b_0 \qquad (3)$$

The budget imbalance b_1 (also referred to as a perturbation in net budget) is the critical quantity in any treatment of the response of a glacier to a climatic fluctuation. In many cases, the distribution of b with altitude or length along a glacier changes little from year to year, although the average value $\bar{b}$ may fluctuate widely (Fig. 3). This produces a simple situation in which b_1 is either constant along the length of the glacier or has a linear variation.

THE DYNAMIC-RESPONSE PROBLEM

Kinematic waves. The next stage in the chain of processes is to connect a climatically induced net budget imbalance b_1 with corresponding perturbations in glacier thickness, rate of flow, and length. The density of the ice within a glacier is approximately constant in space and time, so the equation of continuity can be written as

$$\frac{\partial q}{\partial x} + W \frac{\partial h}{\partial t} = \frac{bW}{\Delta t} \qquad (4)$$

where q is the volume discharge, h the thickness, W the width, Δt the number of years involved in the averaging of b, and x a position coordinate. At any given position x, there is assumed to be a relation between discharge, thickness, and surface slope. Variations in bed slope, bed roughness, etc. are accounted for by the dependence on position. The equation of continuity and the existence of a functional relation between q, h, and x leads to a class of motions in flow systems known as kinematic waves (Lighthill and Whitham, 1955).

The effect of kinematic waves on the dynamic response

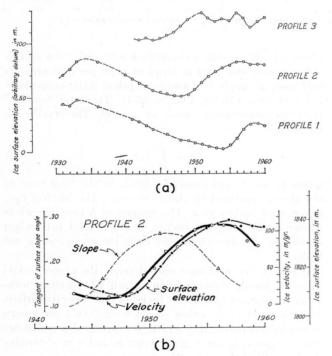

(a)

(b)

Figure 4. (a) Variations in ice-surface elevation at three profiles, 1931-1960, Nisqually Glacier, Washington. (b) Variations in ice surface elevation, velocity, and surface slope at Profile 2, 1943-1960, Nisqually Glacier, Washington. After Johnson (1960) and open-file reports of U.S. National Park Service and U.S. Geological Survey.

of a glacier to a climatic perturbation can be seen most easily by considering a linearized model of a glacier of constant width. The following treatment is taken directly from the work of Nye (1960, 1963a). The perturbations in discharge, thickness, slope, and net budget from an assumed datum state are considered small; the perturbations are designated by the subscript 1, and the datum-state values are designated by the subscript 0 as in Equation 3. Equation 4 is then rewritten in terms of these perturbations:

$$\frac{\partial q_1}{\partial x} + W_0 \frac{\partial h_1}{\partial t} = \frac{b_1 W_0}{\Delta t} \qquad (5)$$

It is assumed that the discharge at a given x is a function of h and the surface slope α. Therefore

$$q_1 = c_0 h_1 + D_0 \alpha_1 \qquad (6)$$

where $c_0 = (\partial q / \partial h)_0$ and $D_0 = (\partial q / \partial \alpha)_0$. Since $\alpha_1 = -\partial h_1 / \partial x$,

$$q_1 = c_0 h_1 - D_0 (\partial h_1 / \partial x) \qquad (7)$$

Assuming that c_0 and D_0 are known functions of x, then Equations 5 and 7 are two simultaneous equations for determining the change in discharge and thickness resulting from a change in net budget. In principle, then, the solution of these equations leads to the solution of the dynamic response of a known glacier to a given variation in net budget.

The meaning of $c_0 (x)$ and $D_0 (x)$, which are of great importance to this type of analysis, can be seen for the simple case where b_1 is independent of x. Differentiating Equation 5 with respect to x and Equation 7 with respect to t and combining,

$$\frac{\partial q_1}{\partial t} = \frac{c_0 b_1}{\Delta t} - \frac{c_0}{W_0} \frac{\partial q_1}{\partial x} + \frac{D_0}{W_0} \frac{\partial^2 q_1}{\partial x^2} \qquad (8)$$

If b_1 and D_0 are zero, Equation 8 reduces to the kinematic-wave equation of Lighthill and Whitham (1955), where c_0 / W_0 is the kinematic-wave velocity (the speed of propagation of perturbations in discharge). The last term represents the diffusion or broadening of the perturbation in discharge, analogous to diffusion in thermal-conductivity theory, with the diffusivity equal to D_0 / W_0. Thus the two essential parameters for describing the dynamic response of glaciers to given net-budget perturbations are the distribution of kinematic-wave velocity and diffusivity along the glacier.

If $\partial c_0 / \partial x$ is positive, which is generally the case in the accumulation zone of glaciers, then a net-budget perturbation b_1 produces a stable (damped) change in h. For instance, if the net budget suddenly changes to a new higher value, the thickness increases rapidly at first and then at a decreasing rate, finally approaching a new value just sufficient to compensate for the increased net budget. Thus changes in net budget produce only minor changes in glacier thickness in the accumulation zone.

If $\partial c_0 / \partial x$ is negative, which is generally the case in the lower or ablation zone of glaciers, the response is somewhat unstable. A small positive change in net budget triggers a thickening of the glacier which first accelerates in time, then decelerates. If the diffusivity is negligible, a new, higher profile is reached quickly. The effect of diffusion is to slow down the rate of thickening, prolong the time of adjustment, and cause a larger change in the final profile of the glacier (Nye, 1963b, p. 442-445). The change in profile is always greatest at the terminus, which explains why glacier termini are such sensitive indicators of changes in net budget.

A kinematic wave on Nisqually Glacier produced by a sudden net-budget increase in the mid-1940's is especially well documented (Hofmann, 1958; Johnson, 1960; Meier and Johnson, 1962). Variations in thickness at three different cross sections, together with velocity and surface-slope changes at the intermediate cross section, are shown in Figure 4. The changes in thickness (30 m) and surface velocity (20 times) at Profile 2 are striking; they are caused by the instability in this reach of the tongue where $\partial c/\partial x$ is strongly negative. The velocity of the kinematic wave varied between 2 and 6 times the mean ice velocity. The wave-form changed with time, because c increased with increasing h; therefore the linearized model described above is not strictly applicable.

The diffusion term in Equation 7 makes an exact mathematic solution for a real glacier very difficult, and diffusion cannot be ignored. Nye (1963a) has recently obtained solutions for the dynamic response of South Cascade Glacier, utilizing data obtained by Meier and Tangborn (1965). This represents a major advance in knowledge of the relation of glacier variations to climatic change, and Nye's results are briefly sketched here.

The Nye frequency-response solution. Nye solves Equations 5 and 7 by considering the response of the glacier thickness $h_1(x,t)$ to the various Fourier components with frequency ω of the variation in net budget $b_1(x,t)$. In the case of South Cascade Glacier, b_1 is independent of x. Thus

$$b_1(t) = B(\omega)e^{i\omega t} \qquad (9)$$

and the response is

$$h_1(x,t) = H(\omega)e^{i\omega t} \qquad (10)$$

H is the complex response of this linear system to the applied signal B. Equations 9 and 10 are then substituted in Equations 5 and 7, and these are solved by finding series approximations which are valid for high and low frequencies, respectively. The results are curves giving the thickness response H, the phase lag ϕ, and time delay ϕ/ω as functions of frequency ω (Fig. 5).

These solutions might be used directly to find the response to a known spectrum of net-budget variations. However, a more useful problem is to reconstruct net-budget variations from an observed history of advance or retreat. This is the approach needed to utilize information on Quaternary glacier variation. For small perturbations, thickness changes near the terminus are directly related to advance and retreat of the terminus. Thus one uses the advance or retreat variation to find the thickness variation $h_1(t)$ at a datum-terminus location; from this one deduces $H(\omega)$, thence $B(\omega)$, and finally $b_1(t)$. For instance, Nye finds that the net-budget variation b_1 for South Cas-

cade Glacier (written for $t = 1959$, and valid for low-frequency changes) is given by the series

$$b_1 = 0.00341\, h_1 + 0.149\, \dot{h}_1 + 1.55\, \ddot{h}_1 + 2\, \dddot{h}_1 + \dots \qquad (11)$$

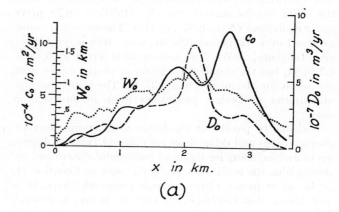

(a)

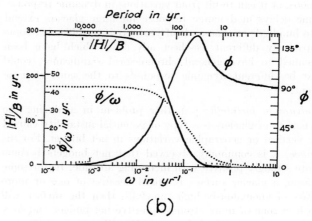

(b)

Figure 5. (a) W_0, c_0, and D_0 as functions of distance x, South Cascade Glacier, Washington, after Nye (1963a, p. 99, 104). W_0 is the width, c_0/W_0 is the kinematic-wave velocity, and D_0/W_0 is the kinematic wave diffusivity. These three parameters specify the dynamic-response characteristics of a glacier.

(b) Theoretical response H at the terminus of South Cascade Glacier to an oscillation in net budget of amplitude B and angular frequency ω, from Nye (1963a, p. 107). Shown are curves of $|H|/B$, the phase lag ϕ, and the time lag ϕ/ω between a maximum of b_1 and a maximum of h_1. Note that for high-frequency oscillations the time lag approaches zero and the phase lag approaches 90°, whereas for low-frequency variations (periods of several centuries) the time lag approaches 43.7 years and the phase lag approaches zero.

where the dots indicate successive time derivatives. The given data from South Cascade Glacier do not extend over a sufficiently long time interval to provide a rigorous test for the theoretical results. However, the results are consistent, and predictions based on simple assumptions produce approximate confirmations of the theory. For instance, the $h_1(t)$ results suggest that b_1 (1959) $= -0.79$ m/yr water equivalent (Nye, 1963a, p. 110). The measured value, averaged over the period 1957-61, was -0.88 m/yr (Meier and Tangborn, 1965). The measurement error in b_1 was 0.3 m/yr, but the standard deviation of yearly values from the mean for the period was 1.37 m. These are the first quantitative net-budget predictions from glacier-variation data.

It should be possible in the future to determine response characteristics and delay times for different types of glacier, up to and including ice sheets of continental dimensions, by determining the coefficients in a series such as Equation 11, or by other means (Nye, personal communication). It is well known that contemporary glaciers do not, in general, behave synchronously. This can result from variations in net budget resulting from different local meteorological conditions, or it can result from variations in dynamic response. Time delays in dynamic response for large glaciers extend into hundreds or thousands of years. It is possible that some apparently different ice-sheet advances, which have been assumed to have general chronological significance, could just be different dynamic responses to the same climatic event.

Bodvarsson instability. Another problem in analyzing the dynamics of glaciers is a type of potential instability caused by vertical or geographic variations in net budget. For instance, it is commonly observed that net budgets become more strongly positive with increasing altitude. If, for some reason, a glacier surface is raised because of one or more years of anomalously high snowfalls, then the surface will be in a zone of more strongly positive net budget and may continue to grow (Bodvarsson, 1955). Weertman (1961a) in an extension of this argument has shown that for some reasonable situations a stable steady-state condition is impossible. He suggests the possibility that this inherent instability of Quaternary ice sheets is in itself sufficient to explain both the formation and the disappearance of these ice sheets.

Weertman (1964) has also discussed the speed of growth or shrinkage of non-equilibrium glaciers. According to a simplified model, the time required to build up a major continental glacier is of the order of 15,000-30,000 years, if the positive net budget amounts to 0.2 to 0.6 m/yr. Shrinkage, however, can proceed at a faster rate, because in this case sliding on the bed ceases.

Unsolved problems involving dynamic response. Several large gaps remain in our knowledge of the response mechanism. One of these is a way to analyze variations in ice temperature. Temperature has a very sensitive effect on the flow law of ice. The thermodynamic considerations involved in glacier flow are poorly understood. Most of the present theory and experimental research has been done on temperate glaciers—glaciers in which the ice is at the melting

point throughout except for a thin surface layer which may be colder in the winter. Thermodynamic problems may be less important for these glaciers but cannot be ignored altogether.

One far-reaching difficulty is a lack of complete knowledge of the processes that control the slip of a glacier on its bed. Weertman (1957) has devised a theory that involves both regelation and creep-enhancement mechanisms to permit the flow of ice over and around protuberances. Recent observations by Kamb and LaChapelle (1964) confirm the qualitative, if not the quantitative, aspects of Weertman's theory. Apparently other effects should also be considered; variations in meltwater lubrication are certainly of some importance.

Another source of uncertainty is created by the fact that some glaciers seem to change their dimensions without any apparent relation to net-budget changes. Certain glaciers in Alaska (Post, 1960) and other parts of the world have suddenly advanced several kilometers in just a few months. No climatologic or earthquake trigger has yet been proved for this behavior. It appears that a drastic change of the coupling of the glacier to its bed must occur, perhaps caused by changes in thickness of the film of water between the ice and the rock (Weertman, 1962). The association of many of these glaciers with major fault zones (Post, 1960) or volcanoes suggests that abnormal geothermal heat flow may have an effect.

To summarize the chain of processes that begins with a variation in meteorological conditions and ends with an observable modification of the environment resulting from the advance or retreat of a glacier (Fig. 1), it should be emphasized that one cannot, at the present state of knowledge, extend results through this whole chain. Theory now exists that, in principle, can be used to predict net-budget variations from knowledge of terminus variations, if it is assumed that the distribution of kinematic-wave velocity and diffusivity can be determined. Complete solution of the dynamic problem, however, cannot yield information on the meteorologic or mass-exchange variations; one can only predict *net* mass budgets. To go from net mass budgets to climatic parameters requires more knowledge and understanding, and this extension of the analysis is not yet possible.

EVIDENCES OF GLACIER VARIATIONS

MORAINES AND OUTWASH FEATURES

An important but poorly understood glacial feature is the moraine, especially the so-called ground moraine. Almost nothing is known about why a glacier may erode at one spot and deposit debris subglacially at another place or at the same place at a different time. Much attention has been given to the shear moraines commonly found around the margin of polar and subpolar glaciers (Goldthwait, 1951; Bishop, 1957; Weertman, 1961b), but the mechanism for emplacing debris within a polar glacier that is frozen to its bed is still somewhat of an enigma.

Many existing Little Ice Age moraines are cored with ice. Recent work has shown that these ice cores may not be composed of glacier ice but of metamorphosed snowdrifts.

Some of these ice cores have proved to be very ancient; for instance, a moraine ridge in Norway, believed to date from the great advance of the 18th century, has been found to contain ice 2,600 years old (Østrem, 1961, p. 240). The implications of this for the interpretation of some Quaternary features are obvious.

Stream terraces and other valley-train or outwash features have been used to separate or correlate glacial stages, but the actual relation between glacier advance or retreat and stream erosion or deposition seems not to have been investigated extensively. A recent study of stream-channel characteristics below an active glacier in Washington (Fahnestock, 1963) shows that erosion or deposition of the valley train depends primarily on the stream discharge and the supply of debris. The streamflow depends mainly on the amount of precipitation and the water stored or released from the glacier (the net mass budget), and it varies with the growth or decline of the glacier. The debris load available to the stream comes largely from pre-existing moraine, outwash, or mudflow deposits; great changes in the availability of this material are caused by advance or retreat of the ice. Thus the relation between glacier variations and stream terraces may be complex.

BOTANICAL EVIDENCE OF GLACIER FLUCTUATIONS

Much recent work has been done on the locating and dating of previous glacier extents through botanical methods. This is a very useful tool, capable of producing many types of useful information. The immigration and growth of lower plants, especially lichens, is now beginning to yield some quantitative information on glacier retreat and advance. In those areas where glaciers penetrated into forested areas a larger amount of useful data can be obtained (*e.g.* Lawrence, 1950; Heusser, 1954; Sigafoos and Hendricks, 1961; Bray and Struik, 1963).

Glacier advances can be dated approximately by measuring the ages of trees on both sides of a trimline. Precise data require careful work, a large statistical sample, and some knowledge of the time it takes a persisting seedling to become established (ecesis time). Average ecesis periods have been estimated at from less than 2 to more than 30 years, depending on distance to seed source, type and stability of morainal material, climatic environment, and probably other factors. In many areas trees several decades old can be found growing on morainal debris overlying glacial ice. A glacier advance can be dated precisely by measuring the age at which a tree was partially knocked over, or partially buried, or accelerated in growth when the ice advance opened up a dense forest growth. A minimum age for a forest beyond a glacier advance can sometimes be extended through several generations of trees. On Mt. Rainier and in several other areas, the combination of botanical and pyroclastic evidence has proved more useful than either method used singly (Crandell *et al.*, 1962; Sigafoos and Hendricks, 1961).

DIRECT METHODS OF EXTRACTING CLIMATIC INFORMATION FROM GLACIERS

Several methods in glaciology partially circumvent the dynamic-response problem. One of the most exciting of these

comes from recent developments in core-drilling techniques. Cores have been obtained from depths of 300 to over 400 m in Greenland and Antarctica, and devices now under development may extend this range by an order of magnitude, bringing up direct samples of early-Pleistocene precipitation. In these cold glaciers it is possible to extract much direct information on past climate from shallow or deep cores. Mean annual or seasonal temperatures, precipitation and net-budget values, cosmic and terrestrial fallout, and the chemical composition of precipitation and atmospheric gases can be determined through glaciological, physical, isotope, radiation, and chemical analyses of samples (*e.g.* Diamond, 1956; Benson, 1961; Langway, 1962; Epstein *et al.*, 1963; Hattersley-Smith, 1963; Ragle *et al.*, 1964). However, proper analysis of deep-core data requires knowledge of flow paths and englacial strains (Crary *et al.*, 1962; Nye, 1963c).

Some of the dynamic-response problems can be circumvented by considering the varying altitude of the equilibrium line (the boundary separating the accumulation area from the ablation area, the line where the specific net budget is zero). Equilibrium-line elevations on present-day glaciers can be readily observed, and are a convenient

Figure 6. Part of Malaspina Glacier, Alaska. The piedmont lobe (ablation zone) alone covers about 2,200 km². This view, looking northeast, shows some of the prominent folded medial moraines along the eastern margin. In the middle distance the Lower Seward Glacier feeds ice into the Malaspina piedmont lobe. In the distance on the left is Mt. St. Elias (5,489 m), and on the right is Mt. Logan (6,050 m). Aerial photograph by Austin S. Post, August 24, 1963.

parameter for the statistical analysis of time and space variations of net budget (Meier and Post, 1962, p. 67-69). Equilibrium-line altitudes can be reconstructed from past glacier-extents if some knowledge of net budget–altitude distribution is available (Mercer, 1961), but this method must be used with caution. Cirque-floor altitudes provide at best a more tenuous and vague indication of glacier regime. Equilibrium-line altitudes do not, of course, coincide with isotherms of mean annual temperature.

GLACIERS IN THE UNITED STATES

DISTRIBUTION

The bulk of the glacier ice in the United States occurs in the State of Alaska, where glaciers cover about 50,000 km². Most of this is concentrated in the Coast, St. Elias, Chugach, and Kenai Mountains bordering the Pacific Ocean. Large glaciers also occur in the Wrangell, Alaska, and Aleutian Ranges; small glaciers occur in the Brooks Range and elsewhere. The largest glaciers are the Bering, which with its feeder tributaries covers about 5,700 km², and the Malaspina (Fig. 6). Equilibrium-line altitudes normally range from less than 500 m in the coastal Kenai and Chugach Mountains to over 2,000 m in the northeastern Brooks

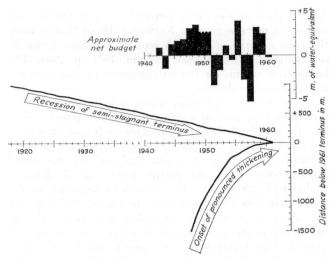

Figure 8. Recession of Nisqually Glacier, 1918-1961, together with the advance of a wave of pronounced thickening and the approximate net budget. Net-budget values taken from Meier and Post (1962, p. 65), other data from open-file reports of the U.S. National Park Service and the U.S. Geological Survey.

Range and the inland flank of the St. Elias Mountains (Meier and Post, 1962, p. 67).

More than 600 glaciers covering almost 400 km² occur in Washington State, mostly in the Northern Cascade Range. Many large glaciers occur on the volcanoes of the Middle Cascade Range (Mt. Adams, Mt. Saint Helens, and Mt. Rainier) in Washington. The state with the third largest glacierized area is Wyoming. Montana, Oregon, California, and Colorado contain small glaciers (Meier, 1961); Nevada and Idaho contain tiny patches of ice which might be called glaciers according to some definitions.

RECENT VARIATIONS

In general, glaciers in the United States (including Alaska) reached maximum recent extents in the middle 17th century, the early 18th century, or the first part of the 19th century. Many of the glaciers receded slowly in the last half of the 19th century and during the first two decades of the 20th century. From 1920 to 1950 recession was general and rapid; since 1950 the rate of recession has decreased, and many glaciers in the coastal mountains from Oregon to southeastern Alaska have advanced. However, exceptions to this general pattern can be found in every area. In some regions, such as around Glacier Bay in Alaska, the "exceptions" are so common that it is difficult to discern a consistent pattern. This is what one should expect from an area where large variations in meteorological conditions, net-budget distributions, and dynamic-response characteristics occur.

Recession of Nisqually Glacier. The record of terminus variations and thickness changes of Nisqually Glacier, Mt. Rainier, Washington (Fig. 7), is the longest and most com-

Figure 7. Nisqually Glacier, Washington. This glacier flows down the south side of Mt. Rainier (4,392 m), descending vertically 2,930 m in a horizontal distance of 6,300 m. Aerial photograph by Austin S. Post, September 7, 1962.

plete of any glacier in the United States. The recession record is essentially complete from 1918 to the present, and occasional observations were made before that time. The glacier stood at its maximum recent extent at about 1840 (Sigafoos and Hendricks, 1961). It retreated rather irregularly, perhaps with a few minor readvances (Harrison, 1954, p. 507-508), until the resent steady retreat rate began at about 1910. The record since the start of annual measurements is shown in Figure 8; this record is widely quoted in the literature. It can be seen that the rate of retreat has been essentially constant from 1918 to 1961. During this period the recession rate did not exceed 47 m/yr nor did it drop below 13 m/yr.

This recession pattern was not indicative of the state of health of the glacier. The approximate net-budget variation for 1943-61 (Fig. 8) was obtained by an indirect computation based on surface-elevation changes near the equilibrium line (Meier and Post, 1962, p. 65). From 1945 to 1952 the net budget was positive; from 1952 to 1961 it was approximately balanced. This produced a kinematic wave which traveled down the glacier, finally steepening into a "shock wave" (Meier and Johnson, 1962) which rode out over less active ice. The lower part of the glacier continued to retreat because it was virtually isolated from flow from above because of several constricted places. Finally in 1962 the face of the advancing active ice and that of the retreating, almost stagnant ice met. The behavior of the terminus from 1963 on may be more directly related to the general contemporaneous condition of the glacier. Examination of this detailed recession record points up the futility of basing assumptions about climatic change on a single glacier-recession record without consideration of the dynamic-response characteristics.

The positive net budgets and glacier thickening observed on Nisqually and other glaciers in western Washington in the late 1940's and early 1950's attracted considerable attention (Johnson, 1949; Hubley, 1956; Harrison, 1956; Long, 1956; Bengtson, 1956; Johnson, 1957; Hofmann, 1958; Meier, 1961; Johnson, 1960; LaChapelle, 1960; Meier and Post, 1962; Long, 1963). Similar advances or marked slowing of the recession rate have subsequently been observed in most of the areas of temperate alpine glacierization in the Northern Hemisphere, indicating that the cause was a major climatic event. It is interesting that in spite of the many difficulties in the interpretation of glacier variations as measures of climatic change, the important climatic event of the late 1940's was apparently first discovered, or at least first became widely known, through its effect on glaciers.

References

Ahlmann, H. W., 1953, Glacier variations and climatic fluctuations: Washington, Amer. Geogr. Soc., 51 p.

Bender, J. A., 1963, Snow and ice: Amer. Geophys. Union Trans., v. 4, p. 585-588.

Bengtson, K. B., 1956, Activity of the Coleman Glacier, Mt. Baker, Washington, USA, 1949-55: J. Glaciol. v. 2, p. 708-713

Benson, C. S., 1961, Stratigraphic studies in the snow and firn of the Greenland ice sheet: Symposium SD-2, Physi-

cal geography of Greenland: Geographica, v. 9, p. 13-37

Bishop, B. C., 1957, Shear moraines in the Thule area, northwest Greenland: U.S. Army Snow Ice and Permafrost Research Establishment, Res. Rep. 17, 46 p.

Bodvardsson, Gunnar, 1955, On the flow of ice-sheets and glaciers: Jökull, v. 5, p. 1-8

Bray, J. R., and Struik, G. J., 1963, Forest growth and glacial chronology in eastern British Columbia and their relation to climate trends: Can. J. Bot., v. 41, p. 1245-1271

Crandell, D. R., Mullineaux, D. R., Miller, R. D., and Rubin, Meyer, 1962, Pyroclastic deposits of Recent age at Mt. Rainier, Washington: U.S. Geol. Surv. Prof. Pap. 450-D, p. 64-67

Crary, A. P., Field, W. O., and Meier, M. F., 1962, The United States glaciological researches during the International Geophysical Year: J. Glaciol., v. 4, p. 5-24

Crary, A. P., Robinson, E. S., Bennet, M. F., and Boyd, W. W., Jr., 1962, Glaciological regime of the Ross Ice Shelf: J. Geophys. Res., v. 67, p. 2791-2807

Diamond, Marvin, 1956, Precipitation trends in Greenland during the past 30 years: U.S. Army Snow Ice and Permafrost Research Establishment, Res. Rep. 22, 4 p.

Epstein, Samuel, Sharp, R. P., and Goddard, Irene, 1963, Oxygen-isotope ratios in Antarctic snow, firn and ice: J. Geol., v. 71, p. 698-720

Fahnestock, R. K., 1963, Morphology and hydrology of a glacial stream—White River, Mount Rainier, Washington: U.S. Geol. Surv. Prof. Pap. 422-A, 70 p.

Goldthwait, R. P., 1951, Development of end moraines in east-central Baffin Island: J. Geol., v. 59, p. 567-577

Harrison, A. E., 1954, Fluctuations of the Nisqually Glacier, Mt. Rainier, Washington, during the last two centuries: Intern. Assoc. Sci. Hydrol., Rome, Publ. 39, p. 506-510

—— 1956, Glacial activity in the western United States: J. Glaciol., v. 2, p. 666-668

Hattersley-Smith, Geoffrey, 1963, Climatic inferences from firn studies in Northern Ellesmere Island: Geogr. Annaler, v. 45, p. 139-151

Heusser, C. J., 1954, Glacier fluctuation, forest succession, and climatic variation in the Canadian Rockies: Amer. Philos. Soc. 1954 Year Book, p. 155-162

Hofmann, Walther, 1958, Der Vorstoss des Nisqually-Gletschers am Mt. Rainier, USA, von 1952 bis 1956: Z. Gletschrk. u. Glazialgeol., v. 4, p. 47-60

Hoinkes, Herfried, 1955, Measurements of ablation and heat balance on Alpine glaciers: J. Glaciol., v. 2, p. 497-501

Hubley, R. C., 1956, Glaciers of the Washington Cascade and Olympic Mountains—their present activity and its relation to local climatic trends: J. Glaciol., v. 2, p. 669-674

—— 1957, An analysis of surface energy exchange during the ablation season on Lemon Creek Glacier, Alaska: Amer. Geophys. Union Trans., v. 38, p. 68-85

Johnson, Arthur, 1949, Nisqually Glacier, Washington: U.S. Geol. Surv., Tacoma, Washington, Progress Rep. 1946-48 on file, 3 p.

—— 1957, Comments on the paper of A. E. Harrison on

glacial activity in the western United States: J. Glaciol., v. 3, 50-52

—— 1960, Variations in surface elevation of the Nisqually Glacier, Mt. Rainier, Washington: Intern. Assoc. Sci. Hydrol. Bull. 19, p. 54-60

Kamb, Barclay, and LaChapelle, E. R., 1964, Direct observation of the mechanism of glacier sliding over bedrock: J. Glaciol., v. 5, p. 159-172

Kingery, W. D. (ed.), 1963, Ice and snow: Cambridge, Massachusetts Inst. Technol. Press. 684 p.

LaChapelle, E. R., 1959, Annual mass and energy exchange on the Blue Glacier: J. Geophys. Res., v. 64, p. 443-449

—— 1960, Recent glacier variations in western Washington (abst.): J. Geophys. Res., v. 65, p. 2505

Langway, C. C., Jr., 1962, Some physical and chemical investigations of a 411 m deep Greenland ice core for climatic changes: Intern. Assoc. Sci. Hydrol., Obergurgl Symposium, Publ. 58, p. 101-118

Lawrence, D. B., 1950, Estimating dates of recent glacier advances and recession rates by studying tree growth layers: Amer. Geophys. Union Trans., v. 31, p. 243-248

Lighthill, M. J., and Whitham, G. B., 1955, On kinematic waves, I. Flood movement in long rivers: Roy. Soc. Proc., ser. A, v. 229, p. 281-316

Long, W. A., 1956, Present growth and advance of Boulder Glacier: Sci. Monthly, v. 83, p. 37-39

—— 1963, Glaciers growing in North Cascades: Summit, v. 9, p. 16-17

Mayo, Lawrence, and Péwé, T. L., 1963, Ablation and net total radiation, Gulkana Glacier, Alaska, *in* Kingery, W. D. (ed.), Ice and snow: Cambridge, Massachusetts Inst. Technol. Press, p. 633-643

Meier, M. F., 1961, Distribution and variations of glaciers in the United States exclusive of Alaska: Intern. Assoc. Sci. Hydrol., Toronto, 1960, Publ. 54, p. 420-429

—— 1962, Proposed definitions for glacier mass budget terms: J. Glaciol., v. 4, p. 252-261

—— 1963, Glaciers: Amer. Geophys. Union Trans., v. 44, p. 581-585

Meier, M. F., and Johnson, J. N., 1962, The kinematic wave on Nisqually Glacier, Washington (abst.): J. Geophy. Res., v. 67, p. 886

Meier, M. F., and Post, A. S., 1962, Recent variations in mass net budgets of glaciers in Western North America:

Intern. Assoc. Sci. Hydrol., Obergurgl Symposium, Publ. 58, p. 63-77

Meier, M. F., and Tangborn, W. V., 1965, Net budget and flow of South Cascade Glacier, Washington: J. Glaciol. (in press)

Mercer, J. H., 1961, The estimation of the regimen and former firn limit of a glacier: J. Glaciol., v. 3, p. 1053-1062

Nye, J. F., 1960, The response of glaciers and ice sheets to seasonal and climatic changes: Roy. Soc. Proc., ser. A, v. 256, p. 559-584

—— 1963a, The response of a glacier to changes in the rate of nourishment and wastage: Roy. Soc. Proc., ser. A, v. 275, p. 87-112

—— 1963b, On the theory of the advance and retreat of glaciers: Roy. Astron. Soc. Geophys. J., v. 7, p. 431-456

—— 1963c, Correction factor for accumulation measured by the thickness of annual layers in an ice sheet: J. Glaciol., v. 4, p. 785-788

Orvig, Svenn, 1961, McCall Glacier, Alaska, meteorological observations 1957-58: Arctic Inst. North Amer. Res. Pap. 8, 196 p.

Østrem, Gunnar, 1961, Breer og morener i Jotunheimen: Norsk Geogr. Tidskr., v. 17, p. 210-243

Post, A. S., 1960, The exceptional advances of the Muldrow, Black Rapids, and Susitna Glaciers: J. Geophys. Res., v. 65, p. 3703-3712

Ragle, R. H., Blair, R. G., and Persson, L. E., 1964, Ice core studies of Ward Hunt Ice Shelf: J. Glaciol., v. 5, p. 39-59

Sigafoos, R. S., and Hendricks, E. L., 1961, Botanical evidence of the modern history of Nisqually Glacier, Washington: U. S. Geol. Surv. Prof. Pap. 387-A, 20 p.

Weeks, W. F., 1963, Sea and lake ice: Amer. Geophys. Union Trans., v. 44, p. 588-592

Weertman, Johannes, 1957, On the sliding of glaciers: J. Glaciol., v. 3, p. 33-38

—— 1961a, Stability of ice-age ice sheets: J. Geophys. Res., v. 66, p. 3783-3792

—— 1961b, Mechanism for the formation of inner moraines found near the edge of cold ice caps: U.S. Army Cold Reg. Res. Eng. Lab. Res. Rep. 94, 12 p.

—— 1962, Catastrophic glacier advances: Intern. Assoc. Sci. Hydrol., Obergurgl Symposium, Publ. 58, p. 31-39

—— 1964, Rate of growth or shrinkage of non-equilibrium ice sheets: J. Glaciol., v. 5, p. 145-158

Summary

Glacier variations may reflect or indicate variations in climate, but the connection is indirect and complex. The general meteorologic environment controls the precipitation of snow, but local influences, caused largely by topography, may greatly modify the resulting accumulation on a glacier. Slight changes in seasonal temperature or precipitation distribution may affect accumulation totals on a glacier. The energy for ablation on mountain glaciers in the United States is supplied chiefly from solar radiation; eddy conduction from the air is of secondary importance. Changes in the difference between accumulation and ablation (the net mass budget) cause changes in glacier thickness, speed of flow, and length (the dynamic response). The three parameters which control the dynamic-response characteristics of a glacier are width, kinematic-wave velocity, and kinematic-wave diffusivity. Nye has recently analyzed the response of South Cascade Glacier to harmonic variations of net budget. Glaciers can also grow or decline because of a form of instability caused by space variations in net budget (Bodvarsson instability).

Moraines and outwash features offer physical evidence of past glacier fluctuations, even though the exact meaning of some of these deposits is unclear. Botanical evidence of glacier variations can be especially useful. However, at the present stage of knowledge one cannot trace back from glacier variations to changes in climate, except in a gross, hypothetical way. The recent history of Nisqually Glacier illustrates some of the problems involved.

VOLCANIC-ASH CHRONOLOGY *

RAY E. WILCOX[1]

A Mantle of volcanic ash, deposited over a region during a moment of geologic time and thereupon buried, constitutes an ideal stratigraphic marker. This forms the basis of *volcanic-ash chronology*, or, more generally, *volcanic-ejecta chronology*. It has been used in stratigraphic problems in Argentina and Chile by Sahlstein (1932) and Auer (1950), in Central America by Meyer (1964), in Germany by Frechen (1952, 1959), Hofmann (1963), and others, in New Zealand by Ewart (1963, 1964), Healy (1964), and Vucetich and Pullar (1964). In Iceland Thorarinsson (1944, 1949) has given it the name *tephrochronology* in applying it to extremely detailed stratigraphic correlations of postglacial deposits (*cf.* also Thorarinsson *et al.*, 1959), and this terminology has been followed by Kaizuka (1961), Kobayashi and Shimizu (1962), and others in Japan.

In reviewing the status of ash chronology in the United States, one is impressed with the potential offered for solutions to problems in Quaternary geology, archaeology, paleopedology, and palynology. The presence of ash layers has been noted in many studies in these fields, but for only a few layers has the requisite work been done to enable their full use as stratigraphic tools. It is furthermore apparent that there were several large Quaternary eruptions whose corresponding ash layers, still to be identified in the Quaternary sediments in western United States, may become useful markers.

Besides being of value as a stratigraphic marker in layered sediments, an ash bed in an area where its stratigraphic age is established faunally, when traced to its source vent, establishes the stratigraphic age of that part of the chaotic volcanic pile. The radiocarbon age of an ash bed usually must be inferred from determinations on associated carbonaceous material. The potassium-argon (K-Ar) age, on the other hand, can be inferred from certain primary constituents of the ash itself, and the age is often more reliably determined on coarse near-source ejecta, in which the danger of contamination by detritus is minimal. Tracing of such a deposit outward from the source into bedded sediments then provides a marker bed carrying a radiometrically determined age.

The fact that an ancient ash fall may have covered a wide area and have spanned several climatic zones makes it a promising tool in paleoclimatic and paleoecological problems. More speculative is the use of the geographic distribution of remnants of an ash bed to infer the wind directions and atmospheric circulation at the time of eruption, for here many of the necessary data may be lacking.

In all these approaches to and applications of ash chronology it is of primary importance that the particular ash bed be identifiable in isolated occurrences and distinguishable from any ash beds associated with it. The present review therefore will give some attention to means of recognizing ash beds in the field and to means of distinguishing them from each other in the field and laboratory, as well as to some of the difficulties and limitations in the application of ash chronology.

QUATERNARY VOLCANISM IN THE UNITED STATES

Volcanic activity during the Quaternary was confined to the western part of the United States, including Alaska and Hawaii, and was probably not so intense on the whole as it had been in late Tertiary time. Many of the principal Quaternary vent areas in the western United States are shown on Figure 1, in which a distinction is attempted between vents furnishing mainly light-colored ash (rhyolitic, dacitic, etc.) and those furnishing darker ash (andesitic, basaltic, etc.). A few known vents in British Columbia and Baja California also are shown on Figure 1, as they may have contributed some ash deposits to areas within the United States. Tectonics is not considered in this chapter, although it obviously is related to some volcanic activity. The reader is referred to the chapter by King in this volume.

In the Cascade Range, the volcanoes Baker, Rainier, St. Helens, Adams, Hood, Jefferson, Three Sisters, Mazama, McLoughlin, Shasta, and Lassen attained their present height during the Quaternary (Williams, 1953); in fact much of the present cones of St. Helens and Lassen appear to have been built since the last retreat of glaciers. In northern Washington a major eruption of dacitic pumice and ash took place at Glacier Peak near the time of the last retreat of glacier ice in that area, and preliminary results of radiocarbon measurements indicate an age of about 12,000 years (Fryxell, 1965). In southern Oregon a cataclysmic eruption of Mount Mazama about 6,600 years ago resulted in formation of the caldera of Crater Lake through post-eruptive collapse (Williams, 1942). Besides great glowing avalanches of dacitic pumiceous material on the flanks of the volcano, quantities of finer ash were thrown into the air by this eruption, to be carried by winds across most of the Pacific Northwest (see description below).

*Publication authorized by the Director, U.S. Geological Survey. In writing the present review, I am indebted to many of my colleagues both in the Geological Survey and elsewhere who have made helpful suggestions and contributed material. I especially acknowledge the long-time help of Howard A. Powers in formulating many of the principles and criteria of correlation discussed here. Constructive criticism of the manuscript for the present paper was received from D. R. Mullineaux, D. L. Peck, and Gordon Eaton of the Geological Survey and from Roald Fryxell and Virginia Steen of Washington State University.
[1] U.S. Geological Survey, Federal Center, Denver, Colorado.

807

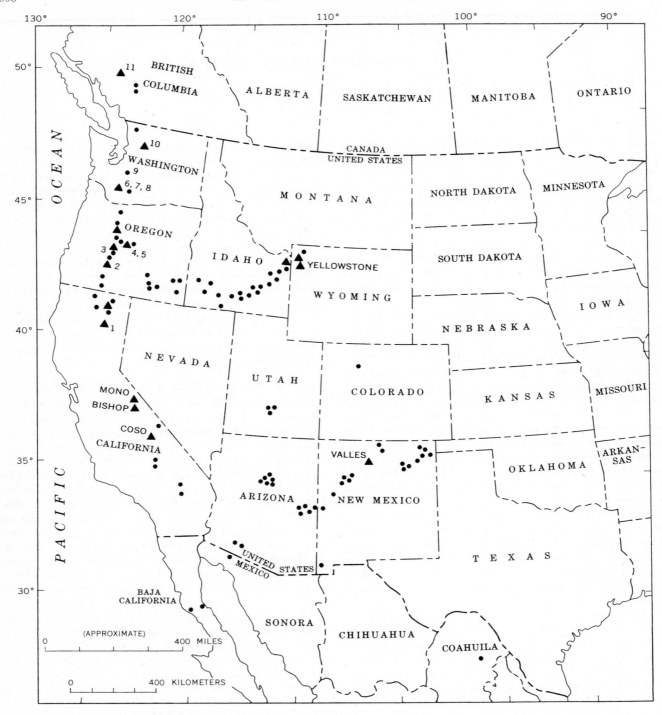

Figure 1. Locations of volcanic vents of Quaternary (some possibly late Pliocene) age, in western United States and adjacent regions. Triangle, vent area furnishing silica-rich ash and lava. Filled circle, vent area furnishing intermediate- and low-silica ash and lava. Vents numbered as in Figure 2.

In northern California, sites of strong volcanic activity during the Quaternary were in the Shasta (Williams, 1932a), Medicine Lake Highlands (Anderson, 1941; Powers, 1932), and Lassen areas (Williams, 1932b; Macdonald, 1963). From solid rocks now exposed in the Shasta cone one would infer that the younger erupted material was mainly andesitic. Some very young eruptions of the Medicine Lake Highlands furnished dacitic materials (Anderson, 1941), and a thick deposit of very young pumice extends northward from Glass Mountain (Chesterman, 1955). In the Lassen area, eruptions were copious and frequent during Quaternary time, and the details of this sequence have not yet been worked out. Much dacitic and andesitic material was apparently erupted, and remnants of the corresponding ash deposits must exist downwind.

The well-known Bishop Tuff of Gilbert (1938, 1941), mantling the slopes leading away from the northern and southeastern rims of Long Valley in eastern California, is made up of typical ash flows. Like those of the great Mazama eruption of Crater Lake, these ash flows overlie appreciable thicknesses of air-fall pumice and lapilli, the near-vent equivalent of what must have been an extensive ash-fall mantle downwind. Long Valley itself is regarded by Pakiser (1961) on geophysical evidence as possibly a volcanic-tectonic sink, and it seems quite likely that at least part of its collapse resulted from the eruption of the Bishop Tuff. The age of the Bishop Tuff is regarded by Putnam (1960; cf. also Rinehart and Ross, 1957) as post-Sherwin, thus considerably younger than the start of Quaternary glaciation. Although ages as great as 980,000 K-Ar years have been suggested for the Bishop Tuff (Evernden et al., 1964), more recent work would place the age near 700,000 K-Ar years (Dalrymple et al., in press).

In the Mono basin, a few kilometers north of Long Valley, a series of explosive rhyolitic eruptions during late glacial and postglacial time built up the arcuate line of pumice cones and domes of Mono Craters. The total volume of the ash from these eruptions was probably small compared to that of the Bishop eruption. In the Coso Hot Springs area, to the south near Owens Lake, another series of rhyolitic eruptions took place in Quaternary time (Ross and Yates, 1943) along a 15-km north-south zone to form pumice cones and domes and corresponding ash mantles.

For the Yellowstone Park region, Hague (1896) and some later workers list no major volcanic deposits younger than Pliocene; recent work, however, has shown that extensive obsidian flows on Pitchstone Plateau overlie glacial till of Bull Lake age and underlie till of Pinedale age (Richmond and Hamilton, 1960; Hamilton, 1960). It is furthermore possible that earlier Quaternary source vents are buried under these lavas. Just west of Yellowstone Park in Idaho is the large Island Park caldera (shown as a ring fault by Malde, this volume, Fig. 1), which according to Hamilton (in press) was also formed during a Quaternary eruption. Other Quaternary eruptive centers may be found with more detailed work in the region.

In northern New Mexico copious eruptions of rhyolitic material in early Pleistocene time led to the formation of the Valles caldera and a smaller, older caldera adjacent on the northeast (Ross et al., 1961; Smith et al., 1961). Both episodes produced extensive ash flows and significant amounts of air-fall pumice and lapilli. Here it may be noted that Swineford (1949) has suggested the Valles caldera as the source of the Pearlette ash fall of the central Great Plains, to be discussed at a later point in this paper. Rhyolitic explosive eruptions of lesser intensity from vents within the calderas subsequently produced ash mantles that may be recognized locally.

Finally, attention should be drawn to the many eruptions of basaltic and andesitic lavas during the Quaternary, the vents of which are marked by cinder cones surrounded by broad lava fields. Such vents are found in profusion in and adjacent to the Cascade Range, across southeastern Oregon and, as described by Malde (this volume), the Snake River Plains of Idaho. They also occur in a belt trending northeast across New Mexico. They occur sporadically in most other western states. Although few of the ash blankets from these eruptions were widespread, some, such as the distinctive phonolitic ash-fall deposits of the Capulin area, New Mexico, may be useful locally as stratigraphic markers after appropriate investigation.

REPRESENTATIVE ASH-FALL DEPOSITS

Only a few ash-fall deposits of the United States have been described in detail sufficient for purposes of correlation. Some Quaternary ash beds together with their sources, where known, are listed in Table 1. Also given are certain volcanic vent areas, the ash-fall deposits from which might become useful stratigraphic markers after adequate investigation. Although no specific localities are listed here for Alaska or Hawaii, the potential stratigraphic usefulness of ash beds in these areas of frequent Quaternary erup-

TABLE 1

Some Quaternary Ash-fall Deposits in the United States

Ash fall	Source	Age	Reference
"T" ("G")	Mt. St. Helens, Wash.	about 160 years	Mullineaux (1964)
"W"	Mt. St. Helens, Wash.	about 500 years	} Crandell et al. (1962)
"C"	Mt. Rainier, Wash.	2,000-2,300 C^{14} yrs	
"Y"	Mt. St. Helens, Wash.	about 3,000 C^{14} yrs	
Mazama (including "Galata" in part)	Crater Lake, Ore.	about 6,600 C^{14} yrs	{ Powers and Wilcox (1964), Rubin and Alexander { (1960), Fryxell (1965)
?	Chaos Crags, Lassen, Calif.	Recent	Macdonald (1963)
Glacier Peak	Glacier Peak, Wash.	about 12,000 C^{14} years	Powers and Wilcox (1964), Fryxell (1965)
?	Mono Craters, Calif.	Late Pleistocene	Putnam (1938)
?	Yellowstone Park, Wyo.	Pleistocene	Richmond and Hamilton (1960)
Pearlette	?	Late Kansan	Frye, Swineford and Leonard (1948)
?	Valles Caldera, N. Mex.	Pleistocene	Ross et al. (1961), Swineford (1949)
?	Island Park, Idaho	Pleistocene	Hamilton (1960)
?	Lassen, Calif.	Pleistocene	Macdonald (1963)
Bishop	Long Valley, Calif.	about 700,000 K-Ar years	{ Gilbert (1938, 1941), Putnam (1960), Dalrymple { et al. (in press)

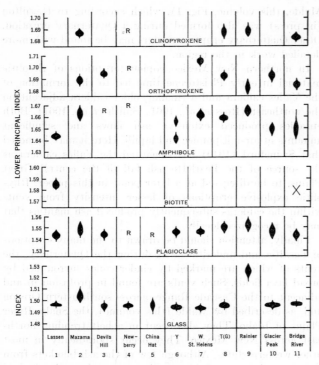

Figure 2. Refractive indices of constituents of pumices and ash of postglacial or very-late-glacial age from vents in the Cascade Range in order from south to north (numbered in Figure 1). Widest part of symbol indicates predominant index; vertical height indicates total range of index. R, rare phenocrysts; X, possibly xenocrystic; Blank, not found.

tions is indicated by studies such as those by Capps (1915; see also Fernald, 1963) and Wentworth (1938). The several deposits discussed below illustrate some of the variety of situations met in correlation of ash beds of Quaternary age in the United States.

MOUNT ST. HELENS AND MOUNT RAINIER ASH DEPOSITS

Although the present cone of Mount St. Helens, Washington, has been built mainly of andesitic lavas and fragmental material (Verhoogen, 1937), some of its explosive eruptions have furnished distinctive light-colored pumice and ash. These deposits, interlayered with similar explosive products of nearby Mount Rainier and other Cascade volcanoes and with other volcanic and glacial debris, typify the complex stratigraphic relations to be expected in areas near and within groups of concurrently active vents. A start towards unraveling the sequence in this area has been made in the studies of Crandell *et al.* (1962), Hopson *et al.* (1962), Fiske *et al.* (1963), and Mullineaux (1964). In Table 1 the letter designations of Crandell and Mullineaux have been followed for the different ash layers, and in Figure 2 optical characteristics of the Mount St. Helens and Mount Rainier layers are compared with those of some other young Cascade pumices.

The youngest layer "T" is attributed by Mullineaux

(1964) to an eruption of Mount St. Helens in 1802 and is regarded as equivalent to the grassroots layer "G" on the flanks of nearby Mount Rainier (Crandell *et al.*, 1962), where it contains various amounts of admixed local material. Layer "W" may be traced with generally decreasing grain size northeastward from Mount St. Helens across the flanks of Mount Rainier. Layer "C" was erupted from Mount Rainier, and according to recent C^{14} results its age is between about 2,000 and 2,300 years (Meyer Rubin, written communication 1964). Layer "Y", which is distinguished by cummingtonite and hornblende as the only ferromagnesian phenocrysts, extends as a north-northeast-trending lobe across Mount Rainier and has been found by Mullineaux (1964) as far as Lake Keechalus, about 150 km northnortheast of Mount St. Helens.

Further complicating the ash stratigraphy in the Mount St. Helens–Mount Rainier area, a still older layer of fine ash is widespread, designated locally as layer "O". Upon petrographic examination this ash has been found to match in all respects the characteristics of the extensive Mazama ash from Crater Lake, Oregon, which, as discussed below, has a radiocarbon age of about 6,600 years. Other still older layers have been noted in the area but will require more study to determine if they can be used reliably as markers.

THE MAZAMA ASH FALL

Ash from the great Mazama eruption at Crater Lake, Oregon, covered most of northwestern United States and southwestern Canada, as shown by the localities at which it has been identified (Fig. 3). This ash at many localities in northern Washington was once thought to have come from Glacier Peak volcano (Hansen, 1947; Rigg and Gould, 1957), the ash of which it closely resembles. The Mazama ash can be distinguished from Glacier Peak ash, however, by the presence of phenocrystic augite and by the higher refractive indices of the glass and hornblende (see Fig. 2), as well as by chemical characteristics (Powers and Wilcox, 1964). The age of the Mazama eruption should approximate the 6,600 radiocarbon years found for charred wood caught up in its ash flow near Crater Lake (Rubin and Alexander, 1960, p. 161), and radiocarbon measurements of material immediately over and under the ash-fall deposit at various sites in outlying regions are in general agreement with this age. This ash forms an important marker in archaeological sites in the Pacific Northwest, and its common occurrence interstratified with aeolian silts suggests that it was deposited in a drier climate than that of today (Fryxell, 1965), thus presumably during the Altithermal climatic interval.

Horberg and Robie (1955) described a series of ash samples from western Montana and Alberta, grouping them under the name "Galata" ash. Samples collected independently from occurrences at Galata, Montana, and Oldman River near Lethbridge, Alberta, however, have been assigned by Powers and Wilcox (1964) to the Mazama ash on the basis of chemical and petrographic characteristics, which are shown to be consistent in spite of extremely fine grain size, sparseness of phenocrysts, and presence of detrital contaminants. In view of the different refractive indices

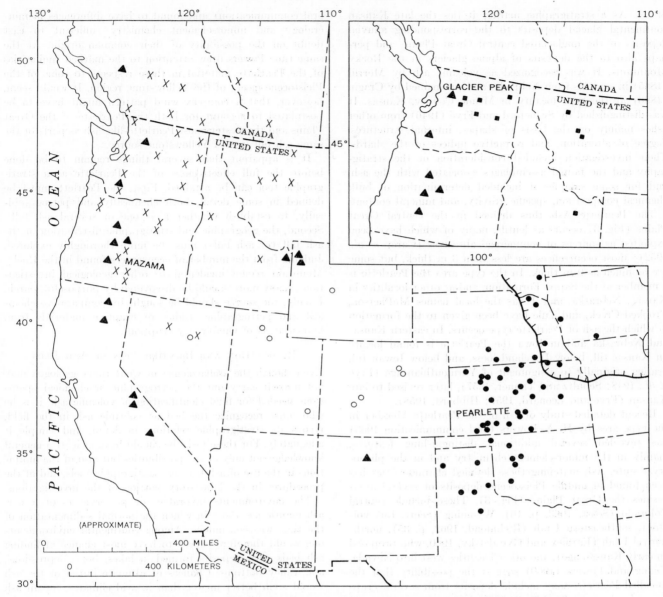

Figure 3. Locations of ash samples from several Quaternary vents of United States. Triangle, Quaternary volcanic vent. X, Mazama ash (Powers and Wilcox, 1964). Filled square, Glacier Peak ash (Fryxell, 1965). Filled circle, Pearlette ash sample (Frye *et al.*, 1948). Open circle, Pearlette-like ash. Hatchured line, approximate limit of Kansan glacial drift.

listed by Horberg and Robie for "Galata" ash at some other localities, additional study of the ash beds in this region seems advisable to ascertain if ash falls other than Mazama are involved.

THE GLACIER PEAK ASH

Although much of the ash in northern Washington that formerly was attributed to Glacier Peak has been found to belong to the ash-fall blanket of the Mazama eruption, a widespread ash fall that did originate at Glacier Peak Volcano, apparently in very-late-glacial time, has been recognized by Powers and Wilcox (1964) and independently by Fryxell (1965). Its distribution is shown in the inset of Figure 3, and some diagnostic petrographic characters are shown in Figure 2. Preliminary radiometric determinations (Fryxell, indicate the age of this ash to be near 12,000 years. The distribution of localities at which this ash has been found so far indicates that it spread over Washington, Idaho, and Montana. Thus it may be of wide use as a stratigraphic marker, and it may provide an important key in unraveling events of late-glacial time in the Northwest.

THE PEARLETTE ASH FALL

The Pearlette ash-fall deposit in the central Great Plains is probably the most widely known ash bed in the United

States. As a stratigraphic marker it ties the late Kansan continental glacial deposits to the corresponding alluvial deposits of the unglaciated central Great Plains, and perhaps also to the deposits of alpine glaciers in the Rocky Mountains. It was recognized as volcanic ash by Merrill (1885) in samples from Nebraska and was named by Cragin (1896) at the type locality in Meade County, Kansas. It was distinguished by Swineford and Frye (1946) from other ashes mainly on the basis of shapes, internal structures, degree of alteration, and refractive indices of the shards. Their investigation included consideration of the stratigraphy and the faunal assemblages associated with the ash, and for some samples it included determination of bulk chemical composition, specific gravity, and mineral content.

The Pearlette Ash thus defined in the central Great Plains (Fig. 3) occurs as lentils, many of which have been exploited as sources of commercial abrasives (Carey *et al.*, 1952); most occurrences are less than 3 m thick, but some are as much as 9 m thick. In the type area the Pearlette is a member of the Sappa Formation, and at other localities in Kansas, Nebraska, and Texas the local names McPherson, Crooked Creek, and Tule have been given to the formation in which the ash of Pearlette type occurs. In eastern Kansas and Nebraska and in Iowa the Pearlette is found locally on Kansas till, below Loveland loess, and below Iowan till, leading originally to assignment of Yarmouthian age (Frye *et al.*, 1948; Schultz and Tanner, 1957), later revised to late Kansan (Frye and Leonard, 1957; Hibbard, 1958).

Recent detailed study of ash of the Pearlette Member in the type area by H. A. Powers (oral communication 1963) has revealed several additional distinguishing features, mainly in the minor-element chemistry and in the phenocryst suite. Ash matching these detailed characteristics has been found in middle Pleistocene deposits of several areas besides the Great Plains (Fig. 3). These include central Colorado (Scott, 1963, p. 16), Wyoming (Scott, this volume), southeastern Utah (Richmond, 1962, p. 35), north-central Utah (Eardley and Gvosdetsky, 1960, who proposed an early Kansan age), and other localities west into Nevada. Young and Powers (1960) suggest the possibility that the so-called Pearlette may include deposits from several eruptions closely spaced in time.

The source of the Pearlette Ash has not been clearly established. If it be assumed that the Pearlette of the Great Plains and the Pearlette-like ash of localities farther west (Fig. 3) are one and the same ash fall, it would not seem out of line to look for the source in California or Oregon. So far, however, ejecta of the required chemical and mineralogical characteristics have not been found at vents of known large eruptions in this area. Swineford (1949) suggested that the Valles caldera of New Mexico might have been the source of the Pearlette Ash as then known in the central Great Plains. In regard to subsequently discovered Pearlette-like ash at localities farther west (Fig. 3), Swineford (1963) has pointed to the small likelihood that ash could have been carried in these directions by winds from Valles caldera and therefore to the possibility that these Pearlette-like ashes may have resulted from another ash fall. Ejecta of the Valles caldera eruption was compared in detail with the Pearlette ash of the central Great Plains by Powers (1963,

oral communication) and found to have differences in mineralogy and minor-element chemistry sufficient to cast doubt on the possibility of their common origin. At the same time Powers drew attention to the marked similarities of the Pearlette material in these respects to some of the Pleistocene ejecta of the Yellowstone region. It would seem, however, that a complex wind pattern might have to be postulated to account for both the Pearlette of the Great Plains and the westernmost Pearlette-like ash as parts of the same ash fall from a Yellowstone source.

It is apparent that several things remain to be done before the full effectiveness of the Pearlette as a stratigraphic tool can be attained. First, the Pearlette must be defined in some detail, both chemically and petrographically, to establish whether it is one or several ash falls. Second, the geographic and stratigraphic distribution of the ash fall (or ash falls) must be more thoroughly explored. Judging from the number of occurrences found in the Rocky Mountain region incidental to other geological investigations, many more should be discovered by purposeful search. Finally, the source should be sought by comparative chemical and petrographic studies of eruptive materials from known areas of Quaternary eruptions.

RECOGNITION AND IDENTIFICATION OF ASH BEDS

Even though the archaeologist or Quaternary geologist may not himself carry out the petrographic or chemical operations needed for final identification of volcanic ash, it is he who must recognize the bed as volcanic ash in the field, record its stratigraphic relations in detail, and sample it adequately. For these tasks he should have at least a general knowledge not only of the possibilities but also of the limitations in the use of ash beds as stratigraphic tools, and of the procedures in the laboratory portion of the investigations.

The environments favorable for preservation of a new ash mantle are those in which the normal sedimentation of the time was continuous. Among continental environments one would therefore expect to have most chance of finding ash beds with deposits formed in lakes, bogs, depressions, and valley bottoms. Chances of ultimate burial of the ash would seem better in wet than in arid climates, for an ash mantle on a dry unvegetated surface, such as a desert basin, may be quickly removed by deflation. A buried deposit locally may consist mainly of the ash that was stripped off slopes and redeposited by water. Since such reworking takes place pre-eminently during the first few seasons after the ash fall, the age of such a secondary ash deposit may for practical purposes be regarded as the same as the original ash mantle.

It must be expected therefore that, even before burial, large portions of the ash mantle will have been lost or modified. Furthermore, should a large expanse of the ash mantle be preserved by burial, for instance in a large lake bed or alluvial plain (*cf.* Powers and Malde, 1961), it is only rarely that subsequent dissection will expose it completely enough for the bed to be traced continuously for any great distance. In a few fortunate cases, such as that of the Summer Lake basin in Oregon described by Allison (1945), several varied ash layers are exposed in stratigraphic succession. Many basins of Quaternary sedimentation, however, remain virtually undissected, and samples of their ash beds may be obtainable only by coring. Such are the samples from shallow borings in postglacial peat bogs (Hansen, 1947; Rigg, 1958) and deep cores from major sedimentary basins (Eardley and Gvosdetsky, 1960).

In regard to their appearance in the field, siliceous ashes (rhyolitic, dacitic, quartz-latitic, etc.) are usually light-colored and often conspicuous in an otherwise drab-colored section of sedimentary layers. Less conspicuous but nevertheless apparent to the practiced eye may be the textural appearance, due to the manner of sorting and deposition of the ash by air fall. The predominant constituent is glass shards, which may be bubble wall fragments variously tri-pointed, curved, or flat, or pumiceous lumps (*cf.* Swineford and Frye, 1946, Figs. 2 and 3). The associated phenocrysts, seldom comprising more than 10% or 15% of the volume, may include feldspars, quartz, pyroxene, amphiboles, micas, and opaque oxides. Less siliceous ash (andesitic, basaltic, etc.) commonly is darker in color, usually shades of rusty brown caused by iron content. Although little use has been made of these less extensive deposits, they are perhaps more numerous than the spectacular light-colored ash beds, and they may be useful in many situations, at least locally. In them, crystalline constituents may be dominant over glass, and the glass present tends to alter rapidly to clay and iron oxides.

Any ash bed may be contaminated to varying degrees with extraneous material—sand grains, clay, and other detritus incorporated during deposition, including siliceous organic debris such as diatoms—or with chemical precipitates such as calcium carbonate. The extreme situation, wherein these foreign contaminants are dominant, provides an "ashy sand" or "ashy marl," which may not only be difficult to recognize in the field but also may be impractical to establish as a stratigraphic marker.

The thickness of an ash deposit decreases generally downwind, yet major irregularities may be caused by local rain-scavenging of the eruptive cloud and by water-reworking of the original mantle deposit into topographic lows. These processes may have contributed, for instance, to the formation of the lenticular ash deposits of the Pearlette in the central Great Plains, some of which have thicknesses as great as 9 m. Similarly the deposits of Mazama ash reaching thicknesses of more than 20 cm in Montana and Alberta, some 800 km from the source, are obviously pockets and lentils formed by reworking of a much thinner mantle.

Variations in the composition of erupted material can take place during the course of the eruption and have been demonstrated in some historic eruptions (Thorarinsson, 1954; Wilcox, 1954). But in many cases original variation appears to be averaged out in transit by turbulence and shearing in the ash cloud and locally by mild reworking immediately after initial deposition, so that the makeup of the resulting bed is remarkably uniform throughout its geographic extent. It is hardly to be expected that a particular ash-fall deposit would have one set of primary constituents at one locality and another set at another locality, and although variations occur from place to place in the size of particles and in the proportions of the constituents, rarely is any primary constituent totally lacking in a sample. Likewise there may be a range of composition of the glass, but most of this range is present in almost every sample of the ash. An exceptional occurrence of two lobes of contrasting ash type might result if major changes took place in both composition and wind direction at the same time during the eruption. Although the essential contemporaneity of the two might not be recognized without favorable exposure, each lobe nevertheless would retain its own time-stratigraphic value.

In the field, recognition of a bed as volcanic ash depends on the practiced use of the hand lens to determine the presence of glass shards and euhedral phenocrysts. The beginner will benefit by a few hours spent in hand-lens comparison of samples of known ash with those of ordinary sand and of mixed ash and sand. For especially dirty material it is sometimes possible in the field to confirm the presence of ash constituents by judicious washing and concentration in water or by treatment in dilute acid. Some ash beds have sufficiently unique macroscopic features to permit identification at the outcrop, but in most cases confirmatory microscopic examination, perhaps supplemented by chemical tests, are needed, and this requires collection of a representative sample or samples. In sampling, the lower part of the bed should not be neglected, for it often contains a greater proportion of the diagnostically important phenocrysts.

To identify a particular ash in the laboratory most effort is given to measurement of features expected to be consistent throughout the extent of the ash-fall deposit. In young ash falls, in the writer's experience, these include (1) refractive index of the glass, (2) minerals present as phenocrysts, (3) refractive indices of the phenocrysts, and (4) chemical composition of the glass. The refractive index of the glass of a particular ash may vary somewhat because of initial inhomogeneity or variation in degree of secondary hydration. The refractive index of the glass increases with hydration, and the general agreement in refractive index of ash shards of a particular ash fall over a wide range of climatic environments may therefore rest on a generally similar degree of hydration. Notable deviations may be expected in glass that has lain in a strongly alkaline environment, such as that of a playa lake. A convenient technique by which variation in refractive index can be recognized and quickly evaluated is that of "focal masking" (Cherkasov, 1957; Wilcox, 1962), which likewise finds application in measuring the refractive indices of the commonly zoned phenocrysts with the aid of the spindle stage (Wilcox, 1959).

Separation of crystals from shards by means of heavy liquid provides concentrates from which the phenocrysts may be taken for optical determination. In unaltered ash many of the phenocrysts carry partial or complete glass mantles, serving to distinguish them from the often-present detrital crystals, which of course have no bearing on the correlation of the ash and are therefore to be avoided. In highly altered ash the glass mantles may no longer be present, leaving only euhedral faces and sharp edges to indicate crystals that may be phenocrysts rather than detritus.

Chemical analyses of whole samples of ash deposits are generally not helpful for correlation purposes, because variations within the same ash deposit resulting from different amounts of primary phenocrysts and detrital contaminants may be greater than variations between separate ash deposits. If one constituent can be concentrated in sufficiently pure form, however, its chemical analysis is comparable from one sample to the next. Of the several constituents, the glass is usually the one most conveniently concentrated, and this may be done largely by specific-gravity and magnetic techniques after ultrasonic cleaning. To attain a sufficiently pure fraction of glass, much labor may be required, with repeated checking of the product under the microscope after each manipulation of the sample.

Features such as shard shapes and whole-sample size-frequency distributions are only of limited value in correlation of ash beds, for these as well as the phenocrysts-to-shards ratios may be expected to vary progressively downwind and also erratically because of flushing of the eruptive cloud by local rain and finally, after deposition, local reworking by surface water. Used with caution over a large area, however, these features may provide hints as to the general direction of the source of the ash. The intrinsic specific gravity of the glass of the shards would be a useful characteristic, but unfortunately no convenient method of measurement is available in the presence of the many inclusions of crystals and bubbles.

A graphical comparison of the petrographic and chemical data is helpful in making correlations. Figure 2 furnishes an instructive example, showing mineralogic characteristics of near-source pumice and ash from eleven separate postglacial or very-late-glacial eruptions in the Cascade Range (Wilcox and Powers, 1964). Most of the samples would be classed as dacitic, and petrographically and petrochemically they show a strong family resemblance to each other. Yet in detail nearly every one has some characteristic or combination of characteristics setting it apart from the rest.

Correlation of ash beds becomes difficult or impractical where too few remnants are available or, on the other hand, where too many layers of similar ash are present in a given stratigraphic range. It may be possible in the latter case, however, to use them as a group to indicate a broader interval of time (*cf.* Houston, 1963). With advanced age the refractive index of the glass becomes less useful for correlation because of progressive alteration. Furthermore, the glass of an ash fall in a strongly alkaline environment, such as a playa, may alter much more rapidly than that of the same ash fall in adjacent uplands. Glasses of some ashes of early Quaternary age have been completely altered to clay minerals and the phenocrysts partly destroyed, so that some of the most definitive primary characteristics are no longer available for purposes of identification.

In conclusion, it is apparent that many ash beds in the Quaternary deposits of the United States would be useful stratigraphic markers, if the necessary effort can be made to investigate their petrographic, chemical, and stratigraphic relations. Intensive study would seem justified alone for the possible time bases they might provide to link the stratigraphic successions of widely separated climatological and depositional environments, such as those of mountains and lowlands, glaciated and unglaciated areas, or continental and adjacent marine areas.

REFERENCES

Allison, I. S., 1945, Pumice beds at Summer Lake, Oregon: Geol. Soc. Amer. Bull., v. 56, p. 789-807

Anderson, C. A., 1941, Volcanoes of the Medicine Lake highland, California: Berkeley, Univ. Calif. Dept. Geol. Sci. Bull., v. 25, p. 347-422

Auer, Väinö, 1950, Las capas volcánicas como base de la cronología postglacial de Fuegopatagonia: Rev. Inv. Agríc. Argentina, v. 3, p. 49-208

Capps, S. R., 1915, An ancient volcanic eruption in the upper Yukon basin: U.S. Geol. Surv. Prof. Pap. 95-D, p. 59-64

Carey, J. S., Frye, J. C., Plummer, Norman, and Swineford, Ada, 1952, Kansas volcanic ash resources: Kansas State Geol. Surv. Bull. 96, pt. 1, p. 1-68

Cherkasov, Yu. A., 1957, Application of "focal screening" to measurement of indices of refraction by the immersion method: Sovremenye metody mineral. issledovaniia, Gos. Nauch.-Tekhn. Izdat., p. 184-207 (translation *in* Intern. Geol. Rev., 1960 v. 2, p. 218-235)

Chesterman, C. W., 1955, Age of the obsidian flow at Glass Mountain, Siskiyou County, California: Amer. J. Sci., v. 253, p. 418-424

Cragin, F. W., 1896, Preliminary notice of three late Neocene terranes of Kansas: Colorado Coll. Stud., v. 6, p. 53-54

Crandell, D. R., Mullineaux, D. R., Miller, R. D., and Rubin, Meyer, 1962, Pyroclastic deposits of Recent age at Mount Rainier, Washington: U.S. Geol. Surv. Prof. Pap. 450-D, p. 64-68

Dalrymple, G. B., Cox, Allan, and Doell, R. R., in press, Age of the Bishop Tuff: Geol. Soc. Amer. Bull.

Eardley, A. J., and Gvosdetsky, Vasyl, 1960, Analysis of Pleistocene core from Great Salt Lake, Utah: Geol. Soc. Amer. Bull., v. 71, p. 1323-1344

Evernden, J. F., Savage, D. E., Curtis, G. H., and James, G. T., 1964, Potassium-argon dates and the Cenozoic mammalian chronology of North America: Amer. J. Sci., v. 262, p. 145-198

Ewart, A., 1963, Petrology and petrogenesis of the Quaternary pumice ash in Taupo area, New Zealand: J. Petrology, v. 4, p. 392-430

——— 1964, The Taupo Quaternary pumice sequence and its bearing on the prediction of future ash eruptions: New Zealand J. Geol. Geophys., v. 7, p. 101-105

Fernald, A. T., 1963, Radiocarbon dates relating to a widespread volcanic ash deposit, eastern Alaska: U.S. Geol. Surv. Prof. Pap. 450-B, p. 29-30

Fiske, R. S., Hopson, C. A., and Waters, A. C., 1963, Geology of Mount Rainier National Park, Washington: U.S. Geol. Surv. Prof. Pap. 444, 93 p.

Frechen, Josef, 1952, Die Herkunft der spätglazialen Bimsstuffe in mittel- und süddeutschen Mooren: Geol. Jb., 67, p. 209-230

——— 1959, Die Tuffe des Laacher Vulkangebietes als quartär-geologische Leitgesteine und Zeitmarken: Fortschr. Geol. Rheinland u. Westf., v. 4, p. 363-370

Frye, J. C., and Leonard, A. B., 1957, Ecological interpretations of Pliocene and Pleistocene stratigraphy in the Great Plains region: Amer. J. Sci., v. 255, p. 1-11

Frye, J. C., Swineford, Ada, and Leonard, A. B., 1948, Correlation of Pleistocene deposits of the central Great Plains with the glacial section: J. Geol., v. 56, p. 501-525

Fryxell, Roald, 1965, Mazama and Glacier Peak volcanic ash layers; relative ages: Science, v. 147, p. 1288-1290

Gilbert, C. M., 1938, Welded tuff in eastern California: Geol. Soc. Amer. Bull., v. 49, p. 1829-1862

—— 1941, Late Tertiary geology southeast of Mono Lake, California: Geol. Soc. Amer. Bull., v. 52, p. 781-815

Hague, Arnold, 1896, The age of the igneous rocks of the Yellowstone National Park: Amer. J. Sci., 4th ser., v. 1, p. 445-457

Hamilton, Warren, 1960, Late Cenozoic tectonics and volcanism of the Yellowstone region, Wyoming, Montana and Idaho: Billings Geol. Soc. Guidebook 11th Ann. Field Conf., p. 92-105

—— in press, Geology and petrogenesis of the Island Park caldera of rhyolite and basalt, eastern Idaho: U.S. Geol. Surv. Prof. Pap. 504-C

Hansen, H. P., 1947, Postglacial forest succession, climate, and chronology in the Pacific Northwest: Amer. Philos. Soc. Trans., v. 37, pt. 1, 130 p.

Healy, James, 1964, Dating of the younger volcanic eruptions of the Taupo Region: New Zealand Geol. Surv., Bull. 73, pt. 1, p. 7-42

Hibbard, C. W., 1958, New stratigraphic names for early Pleistocene deposits in southwestern Kansas: Amer. J. Sci., v. 256, p. 54-59

Hofmann, Franz, 1963, Spätglaziale Bimstaublagen des Laachersee-Vulkanismus in schweizerischen Mooren: Eclog. Geol. Helvetiae, v. 56, p. 147-164

Hopson, C. A., Waters, A. C., Bender, V. R., and Rubin, Meyer, 1962, The latest eruptions from Mount Rainier volcano: J. Geol., v. 70, p. 635-647

Horberg, C. L., and Robie, R. A., 1955, Postglacial volcanic ash in the Rocky Mountain piedmont, Montana and Alberta: Geol. Soc. Amer. Bull., v. 66, p. 949-955

Houston, R. S., 1963, Non-paleontological methods of correlation of rocks of Tertiary age in Wyoming. Part III, The petrographic calender: Univ. Wyoming Geol. Contr. 2, p. 81-85

Kaizuka, Sōhei, 1961, Geochronology based on volcanic ejecta and its contributions to archeology in Japan: Asian Perspective (Far-Eastern Prehist. Assoc.), v. 5, p. 193-195

King, Philip B., this volume, Tectonics of Quaternary time in Middle North America

Kobayashi, Kunio, and Shimizu, Hideki, 1962, Pleistocene tephras in the northern part of Ina Valley, Central Japan: Shinshu Univ., J. Fac. Lib. Arts Sci., No. 12, v. 2, p. 20-45

Macdonald, G. A., 1963, Geology of the Manzanita Lake quadrangle, California: U.S. Geol. Surv. Geol. Quad. Map GQ-248

Malde, Harold E., this volume, Snake River Plain

Merrill, G. P., 1885, On deposits of volcanic dust and sand in southwestern Nebraska: U.S. Natl. Mus. Proc., v. 8, p. 99-100

Meyer, Joachim, 1964, Stratigraphie der Bimskiese und -aschen des Coatepeque-Vulkans im westlichen El Salva-

dor (Mittelamerika): Neues Jb. Geol. u. Paleont., v. 119, p. 215-246

Mullineaux, D. R., 1964, Extensive Recent pumice lapilli and ash layers from Mount St. Helens volcano, southern Washington (abst.): Geol. Soc. Amer. Spec. Pap. 76, p. 285

Pakiser, L. C., 1961, Gravity, volcanism, and crustal deformation in Long Valley, California: U.S. Geol. Surv. Prof. Pap. 424-B, p. 250-253

Powers, H. A., 1932, The lavas of the Modoc Lava Bed quadrangle, California: Amer. Mineralogist, v. 17, p. 253-294

Powers, H. A., and Malde, H. E., 1961, Volcanic ash beds as stratigraphic markers in basin deposits near Hagerman and Glenns Ferry, Idaho: U.S. Geol. Surv. Prof. Pap. 424-B, p. 167-170

Powers, H. A., and Wilcox, Ray E., 1964, Volcanic ash from Mount Mazama (Crater Lake) and from Glacier Peak: Science, v. 144, p. 1334-1336

Putnam, W. C., 1938, The Mono Craters, California: Geogr. Rev., v. 28, p. 68-82

—— 1960, Origin of Rock Creek and Owens River gorges, Mono County, California: Berkeley, Univ. Calif. Publ. Geol. Sci., v. 34, p. 221-280

Richmond, G. M., 1962, Quaternary stratigraphy of the La Sal Mountains, Utah: U.S. Geol. Surv. Prof. Pap. 324, 135 p.

Richmond, G. M., and Hamilton, Warren, 1960, The Late Quaternary age of obsidian—rhyolite flows in the western part of Yellowstone National Park, Wyoming: U.S. Geol. Surv. Prof. Pap. 400-B, p. 224-225

Rigg, G. B., 1958, Peat resources of Washington: Washington Dept. Conserv. Div. Mines Geol. Bull. 44, 272 p.

Rigg, G. B., and Gould, H. R., 1957, Age of Glacier Peak eruption and chronology of postglacial peat deposits in Washington and surrounding areas: Amer. J. Sci., v. 255, p. 341-363

Rinehart, C. D., and Ross, D. C., 1957, Geologic map of the Casa Diablo Mountain quadrangle, California: U.S. Geol. Surv. Map GQ-99

Ross, C. P., and Yates, R. G., 1943, The Coso quicksilver district, Inyo county, California: U.S. Geol. Surv. Bull. 936-Q, p. 395-416

Ross, C. S., Smith, R. L., and Bailey, R. A., 1961, Outline of the geology of the Jemez Mountains, New Mexico: New Mexico Geol. Soc., 12th Field Conf. Guidebook, p. 139-143

Rubin, Meyer, and Alexander, Corrine, 1960, U.S. Geological Survey radiocarbon dates v: Amer. J. Sci., Radiocarbon Suppl., v. 2, p. 129-185

Sahlstein, Th. G., 1932, Petrologie der postglazialen vulkanischen Aschen Feuerlands: Acta Geogr., v. 5, No. 1, p. 1-35

Schultz, C. B., and Tanner, L. G., 1957, Medial Pleistocene fossil vertebrate localities in Nebraska: Nebraska State Mus. Bull., v. 4, p. 59-81

Scott, G. R., 1963, Quaternary geology and geomorphic history of the Kassler quadrangle, Colorado: U.S. Geol. Surv. Prof. Pap. 421-A, 70 p.

—— this volume, Nonglacial Quaternary geology of the Southern and Middle Rocky Mountains

Smith, R. L., Bailey, R. A., and Ross, C. S., 1961, Structural evolution of the Valles Caldera, New Mexico, and its bearing on the emplacement of ring dikes: U.S. Geol. Surv. Prof. Pap. 424-D, p. 145-149

Swineford, Ada, 1949, Source area of Great Plains Pleistocene volcanic ash: J. Geol., v. 57, p. 307-311

—— 1963, The Pearlette ash as a stratigraphic marker: Kansas Acad. Sci. Trans., v. 66, p. 358-362

Swineford, Ada, and Frye, J. C., 1946, Petrographic comparison of Pliocene and Pleistocene volcanic ash from western Kansas: Kansas Geol. Surv. Bull. 64, pt. 1, 32 p.

Thorarinsson, Sigurdur, 1944, Tefrokronologiska studier på Island: Geogr. Annaler, p. 1-203 [English summary, p. 204-215]

—— 1949, Some tephrochronological contributions to the vulcanology and glaciology of Iceland: Geogr. Annaler, v. 31, p. 239-256

—— 1954, The tephra-fall from Hekla on March 29, 1947. Part II, The eruption of Hekla 1947-1948, Reykjavik, Visindafelag Islendinga (Soc. Sci. Islandica), No. 3, 68 p.

Thorarinsson, Sigurdur, Einarsson, Trausti, and Kjartansson, G., 1959, On the geology and geomorphology of Iceland: Geogr. Annaler, v. 41, p. 135-169

Verhoogen, Jean [John], 1937, Mount St. Helens, a recent Cascade volcano: Berkeley, Univ. Calif. Dept. Geol. Sci. Bull., v. 24, p. 263-302

Vucetich, C. G., and Pular, W. A., 1964, Stratigraphy of Holocene ash in the Rotorua and Gisborne Districts: New Zealand Geol. Surv., Bull. 73, Pt. 2, p. 43-88

Wentworth, C. K., 1938, Ash formations of the Island Hawaii: Hawaiian Volcano Observatory, 3rd Spec. Rep., 183 p.

Wilcox, Ray E., 1954, Petrology of Paricutin volcano, Mexico: U.S. Geol. Surv. Bull. 965-C, p. 281-353

—— 1959, Use of the spindle stage for determination of principal indices of refraction of crystal fragments: Amer. Mineralogist, v. 44, p. 1272-1293

—— 1962, Cherkasov's "focal screening" for determination of refractive index by the immersion method: Intern. Microscopy Symp., 1960 Proc., Chicago, McCrone Assoc., p. 160-165

Wilcox, R. E., and Powers, H. A., 1964, Petrographic characters of Recent pumice from volcanoes in the Cascade Range (abst.): Geol. Soc. Amer. Spec. Pap. 76, p. 232

Williams, Howel, 1932a, Mount Shasta, a Cascade volcano: J. Geol., v. 40, p. 417-429

—— 1932b, Geology of the Lassen Volcanic National Park, California: Berkeley, Univ. Calif. Dept. Geol. Sci. Bull., v. 21, p. 195-385

—— 1942, The geology of Crater Lake National Park, Oregon, with a reconnaissance of the Cascade Range southward to Mount Shasta: Carnegie Instn. Publ. 540, 162 p.

—— 1953, The ancient volcanoes of Oregon: Eugene, Oregon State System of Higher Education, 2nd ed., 68 p.

Young, E. J., and Powers, H. A., 1960, Chevkinite in volcanic ash: Amer. Mineralogist, v. 45, p. 875-881

SUMMARY

Several extensive ash-fall layers provide useful time-stratigraphic markers in the Quaternary deposits of western United States. The Mazama ash, erupted from Crater Lake, Oregon, about 6,600 years ago, mantled much of northwestern United States and adjacent parts of Canada. To it belongs most of the ash previously called "Glacier Peak" in Washington and "Galata" in Montana. The ash fall that actually had its source at Glacier Peak Volcano is about 12,000 years old, and it covered a broad zone to the east and southeast. The Pearlette ash fall (or ash falls) of late Kansan age spread over the Great Plains, and very similar ash has been found in middle Quaternary deposits in the Rocky Mountains and as far west as Nevada. Valles caldera in New Mexico and the Yellowstone Park region have been suggested as sources for the Pearlette ash fall, but further study appears necessary to establish which, if either, is the source and whether the Pearlette as now used is only one ash fall.

Many more Quaternary ash layers await investigation and application as time-stratigraphic markers. Some, such as the ash fall associated with the Bishop Tuff eruption in California, dated by potassium-argon methods, are probably extensive but are still to be traced outward from their sources. Satisfactory identification of individual ash beds requires detailed field investigation of the stratigraphic relations and thorough laboratory determinations of petrographic characteristics of the ash, supplemented in some cases by chemical analyses.

QUATERNARY PALEOMAGNETIC STRATIGRAPHY [*]

ALLAN COX,[1] RICHARD R. DOELL,[1] G. BRENT DALRYMPLE[1]

THREE NEW tools for physical dating and correlation have been placed in the hands of the Pleistocene stratigrapher during the past two decades: carbon-14 dating, potassium-argon dating, and paleomagnetic correlation. The accuracy of the results obtained from these techniques depends largely on how well conditions in nature are approximated by the simple physical models on which each technique is based. Consequently the application of these methods to geologic problems is best handled by the geologist who is familiar with both the geologic history of a suite of rocks and the physical basis and assumptions of the dating or correlation techniques.

In this chapter we shall focus first on what the Pleistocene stratigrapher needs to know about the physical basis of the paleomagnetic method, with emphasis on the development of a geochronometric time scale of geomagnetic polarity epochs. We shall then discuss paleomagnetic correlation of some Pleistocene rocks in the western United States, and shall finally attempt to correlate these results with similar studies in Iceland, southern Europe, Africa, and the U.S.S.R.

PHYSICAL BASIS OF THE PALEOMAGNETIC METHOD

The paleomagnetic correlation of rocks is based on two independent physical phenomena. The first is that the earth's magnetic field changes with time. The second is that certain rocks become permanently magnetized in the earth's field at the time they are formed. These rocks include most igneous and some sedimentary rocks. Because our own work has been almost entirely on rocks of volcanic origin, our discussion will center on problems connected with the paleomagnetism of volcanic rocks.

Before discussing the way in which volcanic rocks become magnetized, we shall briefly look at the changes that occur in the earth's magnetic field. The importance of these changes to paleomagnetic correlation is apparent when we realize that if the earth's magnetic field were as constant as the gravitational field there would be no basis whatsoever for paleomagnetic stratigraphy.

A first estimate of the changes undergone by the earth's magnetic field may be obtained from records of magnetic observatories (Table 1) that go back several centuries. Changes in direction of the field of 10° of arc per century are typical, although rates vary considerably from place to place and from time to time.

For information about the geomagnetic field prior to the beginning of observatory measurements, we must rely entirely on the results of paleomagnetic research. Figure 1 summarizes our paleomagnetic investigations on late Pliocene and Quaternary volcanic rocks in the western United States. Each datum represented is a declination, that is a magnetic azimuth, determined from a paleomagnetic study of 5 to 20 oriented samples from one outcrop. Each of these directions represents an ancient field direction with an accuracy of 3° to 5°.

The distribution is remarkably bimodal. One group of declinations centers about geographic north; this group is generally termed *normal*. The second group, centered about the geographic south direction, is termed *reversed*. Both groups include lava flows from Alaska, Idaho, California, Oregon, New Mexico, and Hawaii. The spread of several tens of degrees about the north and south directions is much larger than the experimental error, and is, in fact, sufficiently large to be useful for detailed correlation of individual flows.

However, it is the main bimodal distribution that is of greatest stratigraphic interest. Rocks of similar age from all over the world show a similar bimodal distribution, and it is now clear, at least among young volcanic rocks, that almost all of those in the reversed group formed at a time when the magnetic field was reversed all over the world. It is this that provides the basis for the worldwide stratigraphic correlation of rocks suitable for paleomagnetic analysis.

TABLE 1

Changes in the Direction of the Earth's Field
at Magnetic Observatories

Observatory	Duration of record	Change in direction[a]	Rate[b]
London	1580-1940	20°	8°
Boston	1780-1945	8°	5°
Rome	1640-1945	21°	7°
Azores	1780-1940	14°	8°
Shanghai	1840-1945	3°	3°
Hong Kong	1800-1940	7°	5°
Ascension Island	1750-1945	41°	21°
Callao, Peru	1790-1945	16°	10°
Rio de Janeiro	1750-1940	25°	13°
Capetown	1750-1940	22°	12°

[a] Maximum angle between any two recorded directions.
[b] Average rate of change of the direction of the geomagnetic field in degrees of arc per century. At some observatories the field has oscillated in direction or moved in a circular path, so the maximum change in direction may be less than the rate multiplied by the duration of the record.

[*] Publication authorized by the Director, U.S. Geological Survey.
[1] U.S. Geological Survey, Menlo Park, California.

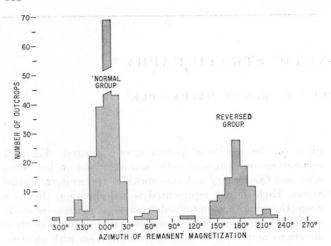

Figure 1. Histogram of the paleomagnetic declinations or azimuths of volcanic rocks from the western United States.

The usefulness of this method of correlation is enhanced by the ease and speed with which the geologist can determine whether an outcrop is normal or reversed. About half an hour's time is required with a portable magnetometer that weighs less than 1 kg (Doell and Cox, 1962).

INITIAL MAGNETIZATION

Magnetization during cooling. Almost all volcanic rocks, including rhyolites and most glasses, acquire a measureable remanent magnetization as they cool to a temperature 50-100° C below the Curie temperature, which is the temperature where cooling minerals first become ferromagnetic. Typical Curie temperatures for the minerals in volcanic rocks are 680° C for hematite, 582° C for magnetite, and 150° C to 582° C for titanomagnetite, depending on the titanium content.

The stratigrapher who wishes to use paleomagnetism to correlate volcanic deposits must first ask himself whether grains or blocks of the deposit have undergone rotation since cooling through the relevant Curie temperature. Airborne ash deposits and other tephra are unsuitable for paleomagnetic study unless they have remained above their Curie temperature during transport—an unusual circumstance. Conceivably, cooled ash grains might be aligned in the earth's magnetic field during descent despite the turbulence of the air, but no successful paleomagnetic study of such deposits has been reported.

In lahars, mudflows, and cold volcanic breccias, the direction of remanent magnetization is usually constant within an individual fragment but highly variable from one fragment to another. For this reason, paleomagnetism may yield useful information about the temperature of emplacement of this type of deposit (Aramaki and Akimoto, 1957) but generally is not useful for paleomagnetic stratigraphy.

Accuracy. To evaluate the accuracy of paleomagnetic methods applied to volcanic rocks, we have made a paleomagnetic study of lava flows on Hawaii extruded during historic times (Doell and Cox, 1963). Experimental results from

the three youngest flows are shown in Figure 2, together with the direction of the earth's field as measured by the nearby observatory at Honolulu. The directions of magnetization of individual oriented samples, as shown in Figure 2, differ by as much as 10° from the observatory measurements, but the average direction of five or more samples from one flow is within 3° to 5° of the observatory measurement. This appears to be the ultimate accuracy of the paleomagnetic method as applied to basaltic lava flows.

Our experience with other types of volcanic deposits indicates that accuracy at least this good can be obtained with most welded tuffs; somewhat greater scatter in direction of magnetization is commonly encountered in volcanic plugs and exogenous domes. Accuracies in the 3° to 5° range can also be attained in paleomagnetic studies of most older volcanic rocks, provided the effects of tectonic tilting or deformation can be recognized and corrections made.

Comparison of Figures 1 and 2 shows clearly that the accuracy of the paleomagnetic technique is adequate to detect magnetic differences between two volcanic bodies that cooled at different times, provided the direction of the earth's magnetic field changed 5° or more between the times of cooling. Conversely such differences may be used to show that two bodies in the same area cooled at different times. The use of this technique is illustrated in Figure 3, which shows the directions of magnetization of sets of oriented samples collected at three different outcrops of the Thousand Springs Basalt and at four outcrops of the Sand Springs Basalt, two Pleistocene formations within the Snake River Group of Pleistocene and Recent age (Malde and Powers, 1962). Maximum separation of outcrops of the Sand Springs Basalt is 37 km, that of the Thousand Springs several kilometers. It is clear that a few oriented samples from an outcrop would be sufficient to place it in one formation or the other.

If two nearby volcanic units have parallel magnetizations, it does not necessarily follow that they cooled at the same time. This is because each possible direction of the earth's field has recurred innumerable times in the past. Thus parallel directions of magnetization are a necessary but not a sufficient condition for establishing that two bodies of volcanic rock cooled simultaneously.

Stability. The remanent magnetization acquired by volcanic rocks as they cool is termed thermoremanent magnetization (TRM). The TRM acquired in the earth's field is characterized by its low intensity and its high stability. The low intensity is not surprising in view of the low intensity of the earth's magnetic field, which is less than 1/1000 as strong as the magnetic field required to completely magnetize (saturate) most volcanic rocks. However, in view of the weak field in which natural TRM is acquired, the extreme stability is both surprising and important for paleomagnetism. If it were not for this stability, thermal energies at low temperatures would destroy the TRM of most rocks in a geologically short time.

The physical basis for the stability of TRM ultimately involves the magnetic domain, which is of microscopic size and is the smallest unit of magnetization. Each domain is characterized by a coercive force, which is the magnetic field necessary to change the direction of remanent magnetization of the domain. The coercive force of a domain depends on composition, grain size, grain shape, strains and imperfections in the crystal lattice, and the presence of chemical impurities. In volcanic rocks these properties vary from grain to grain, so that a typical rock specimen is characterized by a spectrum of coercive forces rather than by one coercive force.

Fortunately, the different processes by which rocks may become magnetized are very selective with respect to coercive force, and TRM acquired in weak fields is extremely selective in the direction of high coercive forces. This results in a "hard" magnetization that resides in a relatively small number of domains with extremely high coercive forces—another way of saying that TRM is extremely stable. Experimental methods for measuring the stability of TRM with the use of alternating magnetic fields are discussed below.

MAGNETIC CHANGES AFTER COOLING

The time interval within which volcanic rocks become magnetized ranges from several hours to several tens of years, depending on the size of the body and the conditions of cooling. During all the rest of its geologic history, the rock is subjected to other magnetic fields which may change the

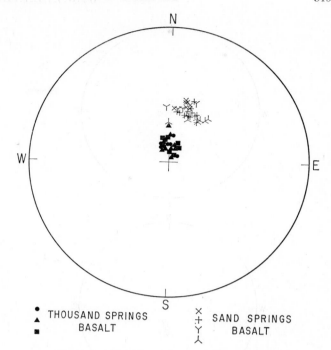

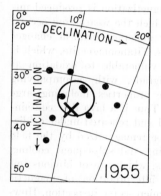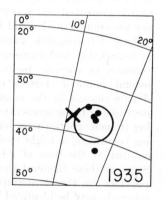

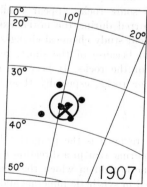

Figure 2. Directions of magnetization of individual oriented samples from three historic lava flows on Hawaii. Circles are 95% confidence limits around average direction of magnetization. ✕ is direction of earth's field at Honolulu Observatory at the time the flow cooled. Projections are portions of Lambert equal-area projection.

Figure 3. Direction of magnetization of two basalt flows from the Snake River area, Idaho. Different symbols represent samples from different outcrops. Magnetization vectors are plotted on the lower hemisphere of a Lambert equal-area projection, so that center of circle corresponds to a vector directed downward.

original TRM or add new components of magnetization. Because paleomagnetic correlation is meaningful only in terms of initial TRM, it is essential that initial TRM be distinguishable from magnetizations acquired subsequently. This section discusses some types of magnetization that can be acquired by a rock after cooling and how they can be distinguished from TRM.

Viscous magnetization. When rocks are exposed to weak magnetic fields like that of the earth for extremely long intervals of time, they acquire what is termed viscous magnetization. In Pleistocene rocks this magnetization is much less intense than the natural TRM and resides principally in domains with low coercive forces (Rimbert, 1956; Cox, 1961). Because it is relatively soft magnetically, viscous magnetization is easily removed by the partial demagnetization experiments described below.

Magnetization by lightning. A typical lightning bolt carries a current of 20,000 to 100,000 amperes. The intensity of the magnetic field accompanying this current ranges from several thousand oersteds near the path of the current to several hundred oersteds a meter away. Magnetic domains with coercive forces smaller than this are magnetized parallel to this field, with the result that magnetizations are produced which are fifty or more times larger than the natural TRM of the rocks (Cox, 1961; Graham, 1961).

In the collection of paleomagnetic samples, it is impor-

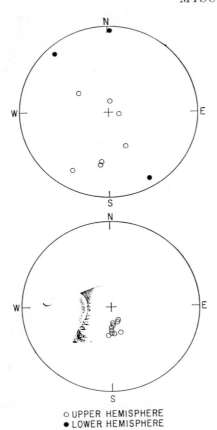

○ UPPER HEMISPHERE
● LOWER HEMISPHERE

Figure 4. Directions of magnetization before (upper diagram) and after
(lower diagram) partial demagnetization of 10 samples from a
member of the reversely magnetized Bruneau Formation of Idaho
(after Cox, 1961). Lambert equal-
area projection.

tant to avoid sites immediately adjacent to lightning strikes,
especially if measurements are to be made at the outcrop
without access to laboratory apparatus capable of removing
the effects of lightning. In our experience, fulgurites and
fused rock surfaces are so rare as to be of relatively little
use in detecting where lightning has struck. The most useful
indicator in volcanic rocks is the magnetic anomaly field
produced by the extremely strong magnetization of rocks
near the locus of current flow. In basalts, if this anomaly
causes a deflection of 5° or more of a compass needle, the
adjacent rock is probably too close to the lightning to be
useful for paleomagnetic study. Lightning strikes produce
smaller anomalies in less magnetic rocks such as rhyolite.

Magnetic cleaning. Except where specimens are collected immediately adjacent to lightning strikes, the magnetization
produced by lightning is much "softer" than TRM, and, like
viscous magnetization, it can be removed by the technique
of partial demagnetization. This is a process which selec-
tively destroys soft magnetization by randomizing it. Ran-
domization is achieved in an alternating magnetic field, the
peak intensity of which is smoothly reduced to zero. Peak
fields in the range 100 to 800 oersteds are usually sufficient

to remove the effects of lightning and viscous magnetization.
The TRM is so much more stable that, even after demagnetization at 800 oersteds, from 5% to 90% of the original TRM
remains, which is sufficient for accurate measurement.

For all the volcanic rocks included in our paleomagnetic
stratigraphic studies in the western United States, we have
submitted at least one specimen from each outcrop to alternating magnetic fields of 12.5, 25, 50, 100, 200, 400, and 800
oersteds, remeasuring the remanent magnetization at each
step. From changes in the direction and intensity of magnetization with this progressive partial demagnetization, it is
possible to determine at which peak field value all of the
soft magnetization has been removed. Our usual procedure
is then to demagnetize all the samples from that outcrop
in this same field. Where it is impossible to obtain samples
entirely free from the effects of lightning, as is commonly
true in the western United States, this technique permits
the recovery of useful paleomagnetic information from sets
of samples with widely scattered initial directions of magnetization, as may be seen in Figure 4.

Chemical changes. Whenever ferromagnetic minerals change
chemically, they also change magnetically. Thus when magnetite is altered to hematite during weathering, the initial
TRM is destroyed and a new magnetization is produced under the control of the field in which the weathering occurs.

Some ferromagnetic minerals undergo chemical changes
at remarkably low temperatures. Titanomagnetite, which is
common in volcanic rocks, is vulnerable to oxidation at
several hundred degrees centigrade, with accompanying
drastic changes in the magnetic properties, including large
increases in Curie temperature. Thus if a lava flow containing titanomagnetite were buried and reheated under oxidiz-
ing conditions, it might easily be remagnetized by the field
existing at the time of reheating and subsequent cooling.
Some of these chemical changes, which are of obvious importance to the stratigraphic interpretation of magnetic
reversals, may be identified by microscopic inspection. However a source of difficulty is that chemical changes due to
the reheating of some rocks appear similar to chemical
changes that occurred during the initial extrusion of other
rocks. In the present study chemical changes have not posed
a serious problem because of the short, relatively uncom-
plicated history of the rocks. It becomes increasingly important with older rocks, especially those that have been
deeply buried.

SELF REVERSAL

Description. Self reversal is the property that certain minerals have of acquiring TRM in a direction exactly 180° from
that of the magnetic field in which they cool. Self reversal
has been identified in synthetic minerals and in two minerals
that occur in rocks, ilmenohematite and pyrrhotite. These
are rarely found in volcanic rocks. Even when present,
ilmenohematite and pyrrhotite do not always produce self
reversal because the self reversal of these minerals is sensitive to changes in chemical composition and cooling rates.

Identification of self reversal. Interesting as self reversals
are to the physicist, to the stratigrapher they are mainly a
nuisance. His interest centers on the problem of identifying

those rocks which may be self reversed and hence unreliable for paleomagnetic correlation. We have found the following observations and experiments useful for this purpose. (1) The sample is heated and cooled in a known field; however, because of the dependence of self reversal on cooling rate, the fact that self reversal cannot be reproduced in the laboratory is not conclusive proof that the rock did not undergo self reversal when it originally cooled. (2) Samples are collected from parts of the flow that originally cooled at different rates; the presence of both normal and reversed samples in the same cooling unit would indicate self reversal. (3) Mineralogic examinations are made to determine whether ilmenohematite or pyrrhotite are present; if so, self reversal is a possibility even if it cannot be reproduced under the cooling rates available in the laboratory. (4) Samples are collected both from lava flows and from the underlying sediments baked by them; these originally cooled in the same magnetic field but generally contain different assemblages of ferromagnetic minerals, so that if one but not the other is reversely magnetized, self reversal is indicated. (5) Similar observations are made on xenoliths as well as on the host volcanic body, as shown in Figure 5, in order to get a variety of ferromagnetic minerals. (6) Various thermomagnetic experiments are conducted to detect any tendency toward self reversal; most significant is the mode of thermal decay of the TRM as a specimen is heated in the absence of a magnetic field. (For a more complete discussion of these techniques, see Cox et al., 1963a, b; for a more general discussion of the intricate problem of self reversal, see Uyeda, 1958; Cox and Doell, 1960; and Cox et al., 1964b.)

In applying these techniques to hundreds of samples of late Pliocene and Pleistocene age, we have never encountered both normal and reversed specimens in the same cooling unit, nor have we identified ilmenohematite or pyrrhotite in the range of composition that can be self reversing. For a small fraction of all samples investigated, the mode of thermal decay is sufficiently complex to suggest a possible self reversal at the time the rock originally cooled, but we have yet to encounter a sample that is self reversing in the laboratory. From these observations and experiments, we conclude that self reversals are rare among young volcanic rocks in the western United States, and presumably among similar rocks elsewhere in the world.

REVERSALS OF THE EARTH'S FIELD

We now turn to the phenomenon of changes in the geomagnetic field, which constitutes the second half of the physical basis for paleomagnetic correlation. Relatively rapid changes in the direction of the earth's field of 10° or so have previously been discussed (Table 1), as has the use of these changes for paleomagnetic correlation of nearby cooling units. Remaining to be discussed is the stratigraphic significance of the main bimodal distribution shown in Figure 1.

The importance of this bimodal distribution is that it has its origin in reversals of the earth's magnetic field. Because of this, normally and reversely magnetized rocks can be expected to occur in alternating sequences traceable as precise time-stratigraphic units all around the world.

Worldwide synchroneity of reversals. That reversals of the earth's field are necessarily synchronous and worldwide follows both from physical considerations concerning the source of the field and from paleomagnetic observations. There remains little doubt that almost all of the earth's field is generated by magnetohydrodynamic processes in the earth's fluid core. At the present time, these processes are producing a field which, to a first approximation, is that of a magnetic dipole at the earth's center. The persistence of the dipolar character of the field in the past is clearly established by paleomagnetic results from all over the world similar to those in Figure 1, which are closely grouped about two global dipole field configurations, one normal (Fig. 6a) and one reversed (Fig. 6b). Changes from one to the other of these configurations occur rapidly and are experienced on all parts of the earth's surface at exactly the same time.

Radiometric time scale. The final piece of information needed to provide a firm physical basis for the stratigraphic use of reversals is a time scale. We are currently in the process of developing such a time scale based on potassium-argon ages of Pliocene and Pleistocene volcanic rocks, and although some details remain to be filled in, the broad pattern of polarity epochs during the Pleistocene is fairly well established.

In the paleomagnetic part of this study, we have been especially concerned with the possibility of self reversals, because even a few that passed unrecognized would obscure the age relations of polarity epochs. We have concentrated

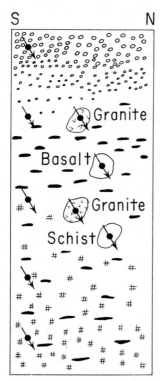

Figure 5. Stratigraphic section through the Bishop Tuff showing parallel directions of magnetization in xenoliths and throughout the entire flow from the welded base to the unwelded top.

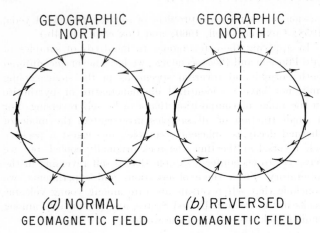

Figure 6. Directions at the earth's surface
of a normal (a) and a reserved
(b) axil dipole field. (After Cox
et al., 1964b.)

our efforts on those rocks for which radiometric ages were available, using the techniques previously described. No reproducible self reversals were found, but one sample (S12 of Cox *et al.*, 1963a) has been rejected because the mode of thermal decay was sufficiently complex to suggest a possible self reversal.

For our investigations, the potassium-argon ages were obtained on a variety of different minerals and glass, including sanidine, plagioclase, biotite, and several fresh obsidians; however, by far the largest number were from whole-rock samples of basalt, andesite, and latite. All whole-rock samples were examined with a petrographic microscope to be sure they contained no phase that might be an ineffective argon trap, *e.g.* glass, extremely fine-grained minerals, or alteration products. Any samples about which the slightest doubt existed, including those with a clouded or turbid mesostasis, were rejected as unsatisfactory for potassium-argon analysis. Potassium analyses were done by flame photometry; argon measurements were made with standard isotope-dilution techniques. We estimate the standard deviation of the precision of our data to average about ±5% in the age range of 0 to 4 milion years.

The magnetic polarities of volcanic rocks for which radiometric ages are known are shown in Figure 7, which includes the results of independent investigations by several laboratories. The normal and reversed rocks are distributed in time intervals during which the earth's field was predominantly normal or predominantly reversed. These time intervals we have called normal and reversed polarity epochs (Cox *et al.*, 1963a). To the two latest epochs we have assigned the names Brunhes and Matuyama, to honor two geophysicists who were among the first to recognize the significance of reversed magnetization in rocks (Cox *et al.*, 1964b). To the second youngest normal epoch we have previously assigned the name Gauss (Cox *et al.*, 1964b), and to the second youngest reversed polarity epoch we here assign the name Gilbert, in honor of the geophysicists K. F. Gauss (1777-1855) and W. Gilbert (1544-1603), who pioneered in the study of the earth's magnetic field.

We prefer names to a numerical system or other sequen-

tial designations for the following reasons. The numerical systems used previously count each change in polarity backward sequentially from the present (first normal, first reversed, second normal, etc.). With this system, the numbering system and hence the names of the polarity epochs must be changed whenever even a short new polarity interval is discovered. Stratigraphic correlations would become hopelessly confused after several reassignments of the same number to different polarity-epoch time intervals. On the other hand, a system of names may be easily modified in the light of new discoveries, as will be seen in the discussion of magnetic events.

Names for polarity epochs are preferable to numbers for yet another reason arising from their unequal lengths. The exact maximum length for a polarity epoch is not yet precisely known, but at least one epoch several tens of millions of years long occurred in the Permian. Such long epochs are separated by times when the earth's field switched polarity rapidly, but it is doubtful whether radiometric dating techniques will be able to resolve these shorter polarity intervals in rocks older than Pliocene. The long epochs, however, are stratigraphically useful, and it seems reasonable to identify them with names as Irving and Parry (1963) have already done for the long polarity epoch within the Permian.

Within the Matuyama reversed epoch there occurs a short interval of normal polarity with a duration of about 0.1 million years. This was first identified by Grommé and Hay (1963) in a basalt from Olduvai Gorge, Tanganyika, and was subsequently confirmed by our investigation of several basalt flows on the Pribilof Islands, Alaska. A similar short interval, but of reversed polarity, is thought to occur within the Gauss normal epoch on the basis of a basalt flow from Mammoth Lake, California (M9 of Fig. 8). A flow with about the same radiometric age from Oahu, Hawaii, is also reversely magnetized, but the calculated age is questionable on stratigraphic grounds (note M30, Fig. 8). We have termed these two short polarity intervals the Olduvai and Mammoth magnetic events. Events are distinguishable from epochs solely on the basis of their duration: the lengths of the last three epochs range from 0.9 to 1.4 million years, whereas events appear to be about one-tenth as long.

Transition time. The time required for a transition from normal to reversed polarity is of special stratigraphic interest because this determines the ultimate resolving power of the paleomagnetic method of correlation. From the strongly bimodal character of the distribution of directions of remanent magnetization (Fig. 1), it is clear that directions intermediate between normal and reversed are rare, so that the transition times are short relative to the length of polarity epochs. Several estimates of transition times of about 10,000 years have been made on the basis of the ratio of the number of lava flows or sedimentary strata with intermediate directions of magnetization relative to the number with normal or reversed directions (Hospers, 1954; Khramov, 1958; Doell and Cox, 1961a; Picard, 1964).

The set of 62 volcanic units for which we have both paleomagnetic measurements and radiometric dates provides an independent basis for estimating the length of the transition times. None of these 62 volcanic units has an inter-mediate direction of magnetization. There is a 96.5% probability against accidentally missing all of the seven transition zones shown in Figure 7 if the transitions are as long as 50,000 years, so that the time of transition is probably much shorter than this. Although radiometric dates from rocks within the transition zones will be required for precise determinations of the transition times, it already appears from the data at hand that the earlier estimates of 10,000 years are correct within a factor of two or three. The transitions are thus remarkably rapid and provide the stratigrapher with one of the sharpest marker horizons available for intercontinental correlation.

Stratigraphic sequences of volcanic and sedimentary rocks that formed during transitions of the magnetic field have been the subject of several paleomagnetic studies (Sigurgeirsson, 1957; Brynjolfsson, 1957; Khramov, 1958; Momose, 1963; van Zijl et al., 1962; Picard, 1964). Although these transitions occurred at different times and the results are not all entirely consistent, the following generalized picture of the geomagnetic field during transitions is emerging. The magnetic field vector generally moves the 180° from one polarity to another along a rather smooth path. Both declination and inclination typically change, so that during a transition the magnetic field vector is not confined to one plane but rather moves in a spiral having from half a loop to several loops. Minor irregular movements may or may not be superimposed on this smooth path. It is not yet known whether the field maintains its worldwide dipolar character during transitions, or whether it assumes a more complex configuration. If the former is true, pole positions calculated from paleomagnetic results from rocks all over the world that formed during the same transition will all

lie along the same path. Global studies of transitions are thus needed to determine whether the transitional field is dipolar. Conversely, if this can be established, it will be possible to correlate transitional strata with extremely fine precision.

The intensity of the magnetic field may decrease during transitions, perhaps by as much as a factor of five (Brynjolfsson, 1957; van Zijl et al., 1964), although the evidence for this is not conclusive. Such decreases would have the effect of decreasing the shielding of the earth from cosmic radiation (Uffen, 1963), but it is not yet known whether the effect is sufficiently large to be biologically significant.

STRATIGRAPHIC CORRELATIONS

WESTERN UNITED STATES

Paleomagnetic stratigraphic correlations between localities in the western United States as far apart as Alaska, New Mexico, and Hawaii are presented in Figure 8. Each datum point represents one or more cooling units, most of which are flows. Some of the data from Figure 7 are reproduced (large circles), and in addition many other paleomagnetic determinations are indicated for which we do not yet have radiometric dates (small circles). For the undated units, there has not been as exhaustive a search made for self-reversals as for the dated ones. However multiple samples were collected from all of the volcanic units investigated, and the effects of lightning and viscous magnetization were removed in alternating magnetic fields as previously described.

The stratigraphic positions of glacial deposits and fossils relative to the volcanic units are indicated by G and F, respectively, in Figure 8. Where such deposits are absent and

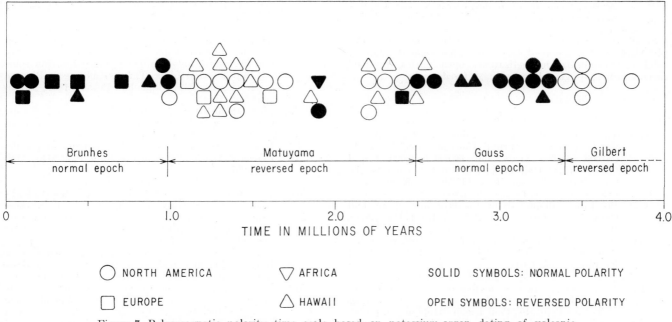

Figure 7. Paleomagnetic polarity time scale based on potassium-argon dating of volcanic rocks. The two normal polarities of 1.9 million years correspond to the Olduvai event and the reversed polarity at 3 million years to the Mammoth event. (Data are from Rutten, 1959; Cox *et al.*, 1963a, b, 1964a, b; Grommé and Hay, 1963; McDougall and Tarling, 1963; Evernden *et al.*, 1964.)

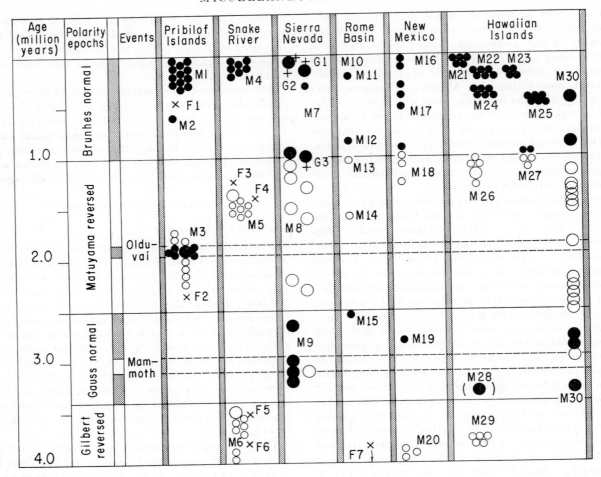

Figure 8. Paleomagnetic correlation of the Pribilof Islands, Alaska; Snake River, Idaho; Sierra Nevada, California; Rome Basin, Oregon; New Mexico; and Hawaiian Islands.

Small circles, no radiometric dates on paleomagnetic samples; large circles, radiometric dates on paleomagnetic samples; solid circles, normal magnetization; open circles, reversed magnetization; +, glacial deposits; ×, fossils.

References for Figure 8:

Glacial

G1: Tills correlated with the Tahoe Glaciation overlie the lava flow at Sawmill Canyon dated by K-Ar [90,000 ± 90,000 years and 60,000 ± 50,000 years] (Knopf, 1918; Dalrymple, 1964) and also overlie the lava flow at Sonora Pass [150,000 ± 30,000 years] (Slemmons, 1953; Dalrymple, 1964).

G2: Pre-Tahoe till underlying the lava flow at Sawmill Canyon (see G1 above) (Knopf, 1918; Dalrymple, 1964).

G3: [Glacial] Till underlying the Bishop Tuff, which has a K-Ar date of 0.98 million years (Putnam, 1960; Evernden et al., 1964).

Fossil

F1: Large nearly modern molluscan fauna in marine beds at Einahnuhto Bluff and in upper marine beds at Tolstoi Point, St. Paul Island (Hopkins, in press).

F2: Small number of mollusks of late-Pliocene or early-Pleistocene age from marine beds near Tolstoi Point, St. George Island (Hopkins, in press).

F3: Tooth of plesippine *Equus* (Malde and Powers, 1962).

F4: Mammals include *Mammuthus* sp. and a large

camel. Mollusks include the extinct *Promenetus kansasensis* (Baker) and also 24 living forms. Of 83 species of diatoms, 84% are found in living assemblages elsewhere (Malde and Powers, 1962).

F5: "Hagerman horse quarry" and related beds contain remains of shrew, gopher, vole, weasel, otter, rabbit, peccary, camel, antelope, horse, mastodon, and some fish, reptiles, and birds. This assemblage is Blancan in age (Gazin, 1936; Malde and Powers, 1962; Evernden et al., 1964).

F6: More than 100 species of fresh-water mollusks are reported. Most of these are lacustrine, and of these 94% are extinct (Malde and Powers, 1962).

F7: Beaver, horse, camel, and rodent remains of middle-Pliocene (Hemphillian) age underlie flow M15 (Wilson, 1937).

Magnetic

M1: Basaltic lava flows on St. Paul Island. Almost all the flows on the island were sampled and all of those sampled are normal. Preliminary K-Ar data (unpublished) indicate that all these flows are less than one-half million years old.

M2: Oldest lava flow on St. Paul Island at Einahnuhto Bluff. Preliminary K-Ar data (unpublished) indicate that this flow is between 1 and ½ million years old.

M3: Basaltic lava flows on St. George Island. Normally magnetized flows correlative with Olduvai event occur together with younger reversed flows near Sea Lion Point and near St. George village. Reversed flows underlie this section near Sea Lion Point (data unpublished).

M4: Late Pleistocene and Recent basaltic lava flows of the Snake River Group (Malde and Powers, 1962).

M5: Basaltic lava flows of the Bruneau Formation (Malde and Powers, 1962). K-Ar date by Evernden *et al.* (1964).

M6: Basaltic lava flows of the Glenns Ferry Formation (Malde and Powers, 1962). K-Ar date by Evernden *et al.* (1964).

M7: In order of increasing age the units of the Brunhes normal epoch are the basalt at Sawmill Canyon, the basalt at Sonora Pass, the basalt at Devils Post- pile, and the Bishop Tuff (Cox *et al.*, 1963a, 1963b). The undated point is the rhyolitic flow 1.2 miles south of Casa Diablo Hot Springs, U.S. Geological Survey Mt. Morrison topographic quadrangle (1:125,- 000).

M8: In order of increasing age the flows of the Matuyama reversed epoch are the rhyolitic obsidian flow near Big Pine, the olivine-latite flow near Bald Mountain, the olivine latite near Hirshdale, the andesite flow at Sutter Buttes, the dacite intrusive at Sutter Buttes, the andesite flow at Watson's Creek, and the andesite flow at Alder Hill (Cox *et al.*, 1963a, 1963b, 1964a, 1964b).

M9: The four normally magnetized units are the basaltic flows at McGee Mtn., at San Joaquin Mtn., and in Owens Gorge and the quartz latite at Two Teats Mtn. The reversed unit is the basalt flow at Mam- moth Lakes (Cox *et al.*, 1963a, 1963b, 1964a, 1964b).

M10: This and the succeeding units from the Rome Basin are located in Malheur County, Oregon; place names appear on the Army Map Service Jorden Valley quadrangle (1:250,000). Assignment of flows to polar- ity epochs is based in part on current investigations of vertebrate fossils by C. A. Repenning, U.S. Geologi- cal Survey, Menlo Park, California. Generalized geo- logic map of this region is given by Malde and Pow- ers (1962).

M11: Basaltic flows from Jackies Butte exposed at Rattle- snake Creek, Oregon.

M12: Basaltic lava flow at Burns Junction, Oregon.

M13: Basaltic flow on U.S. Highway 95, at Owyhee River, Oregon.

M14: Upper basaltic flow between Rattlesnake and Crooked Creeks, Oregon.

M15: Basaltic flow one-half mile northeast of crossing of Crooked Creek by U.S. Highway 95.

M16: This and succeeding units through M20 are in San- doval or Los Alamos Co., New Mexico. Most place names appear on the Army Map Service Albuquer- que quadrangle (1:250,000). Assignment of units to polarity epochs is based in part on the unpublished stratigraphy of R. L. Smith, R. A. Bailey, and C. S. Ross. A generalized geologic map of this region is given by Ross *et al.* (1961).

M17: Units in the Brunhes normal epoch include the rhyo- lite flow at Banco Bonito, the welded tuff at Battle- ship Rock, and the rhyolite domes of South Moun- tain, La Jara, San Antonio, and Abrigo III.

M18: Reversely magnetized units include the rhyolite domes of San Louis and Del Medio, and all welded units of the Tshirege Member of the Bandelier Tuff.

M19: Quartz-latite dome at Sawyer is probably in the Gauss normal epoch but may have formed prior to the Gilbert reversed epoch.

M20: Basaltic lava flows to the east and south of Los Alamos, and all welded units of the Otowi Member of the Bandelier Tuff.

M21: Historic flows and Puna Volcanic Series from Ki- lauea, Hawaii (Doell and Cox, 1961b).

M22: Kahuku Volcanic Series from Mauna Loa, Hawaii (Doell and Cox, 1961b).

M23: Hamakua Volcanic Series from Laupahoehoe Can- yon, Hawaii (Doell and Cox, 1961b).

M24: Pololu Volcanic Series from Waipio Valley, Hawaii (Doell and Cox, 1961b).

M25: Ninole Volcanic Series from Kaiholena Ridge, Ha- waii (Doell and Cox, 1961b).

M26: Koloa Volcanic Series from Lawai Gulch, Kauai. K-Ar date by Evernden *et al.* (1964).

M27: Koloa Volcanic Series from scattered localities on Kauai.

M28: Napali Formation of the Waimea Canyon Volcanic Series, Kauai. The indicated K-Ar age of 3.34 mil- lion years is that given by Evernden *et al.* (1964); in view of McDougall's (1964) dating of this formation at from 4.5 to 5.62 million years, the date of Evern- den *et al.* appears questionable and this unit, which is stratigraphically below the Makaweli Formation (M29), probably belongs to the normal epoch preced- ing the Gilbert.

M29: Makaweli Formation of the Waimea Canyon Vol- canic Series, Kauai. K-Ar ages from 3.5 to 4.0 mil- lion years were found by McDougall for samples collected independently from this formation, sup- porting the assignment to the Gilbert reversed epoch.

M30: Brunhes normal flows are from the Kula Volcanic Series, Maui. Matuyama reversed flows are from the Honolua and Wailuku Volcanic Series, Maui, from the East Molokai and West Molokai Volcanic Series, and from the Koolau Volcanic Series, Oahu. Gauss normal flows are from the Waianae Volcanic Series, Oahu. (All data from McDougall and Tarling, 1963.) Reversed point at 2.95 million years is from the lower member of the Waianae Volcanic Series, Oahu, but this age is questionable because ages of 3.27 and 3.65 have been found from the middle member of this formation (McDougall, 1964).

---

no radiometric dates are available, volcanic units are assigned to polarity epochs on the basis of superposition and other less direct evidence of relative age; for these points, the position in Figure 8 is with respect to the polarity epochs and not the time scale. Naturally, where radiometric and paleontological information is unknown, the assignments are less certain. Nonetheless, even in the absence of other data, much more can be said about stratigraphic correlation if paleomagnetic data are available than can be said without them.

In our experience, paleomagnetic reversals have proved most useful in correlating volcanic rocks that cooled during the youngest polarity epochs, the Brunhes normal and the Matuyama reversed. The situation is quite analogous to cor- relation based on glaciations and interglaciations. Although commonly the glacial and interglacial deposits can be clearly differentiated at a number of different localities, the dif- ficulty of correlating the glacial advances (or polarity epochs) from place to place increases with the age of the deposits because at any locality the record of one or more of the glaciations (or epochs) may be missing.

One of the more unexpected paleomagnetic results has been the discovery that the rocks exposed on the island of Hawaii are magnetized normally and therefore formed some- time after the early Pleistocene (Doell and Cox, 1961b). The northeastern part of the island is highly dissected, and a Pliocene age had previously been accepted as the most probable age of the oldest rocks. However this part of the island, like the rest, is magnetized normally, so that the rocks most probably formed during the Brunhes normal epoch. This was recently confirmed by radiometric dating (Evernden et al., 1964; McDougall, 1964).

On the older islands of the chain to the west of Hawaii, both normal and reversed flows have been found. The radiometric dates and magnetic polarities reported by McDougall and Tarling (1963) from these flows are in excellent agreement with results from elsewhere in the world (Figs. 7 and 8), as is our paleomagnetic study of the reversely magnetized flow from the Koloa Volcanic Series (M26) and the date of 1.2 million years obtained by Evernden et al. (1964) on a sample from the same flow.

A similar relationship exists on the Pribilof Islands in Alaska. St. Paul, the younger of the two islands of the group, has only normally magnetized rocks and hence formed during the Brunhes normal epoch. St. George—more highly eroded and faulted—contains both reversed and normal flows that, on the basis of paleontological control and radiometric dating, all belong to the Matuyama reversed epoch. The normal flows are of special interest because they, together with the normal flow in Olduvai Gorge with the same K-Ar age of 1.9 million years, serve as the basis for the recognition of the Olduvai event as a worldwide phenomenon.

CORRELATION WITH EUROPE

One of the most difficult problems facing the Pleistocene stratigrapher is that of intercontinental correlations, and perhaps the thorniest problem of all is that of the Pliocene-Pleistocene boundary. Enough paleomagnetic investigations have now been made in different parts of the world to contribute some information to this problem (Fig. 9).

Two definitions of the beginning of the Pleistocene are in current usage; one is in terms of the onset of glaciation and the other, that made by the 18th International Geological Congress, is in terms of the type section in Italy, beginning with basal Calabrian beds. The formal definition of the Pliocene-Pleistocene boundary is not central to the discussion which follows, but an attempt will be made to show the relation of paleomagnetic results to the boundary as defined both ways. In considering the boundary as defined by the type section in Italy, it is not presently possible to establish a direct stratigraphic correlation between Europe and North America, because rocks suitable for paleomagnetic study and radiometric dating have not been identified from the type Calabrian section. Thus for correlation it is necessary to turn to the type Villafranchian in northern Italy, which was named by the 18th International Geological Congress as equivalent to the Calabrian. This dual definition confuses the definition of the Pliocene-Pleistocene boundary in view of the possibility that this type Villafranchian may be younger than the basal Calabrian. However, in the absence of direct stratigraphic ties with the Calabrian, the most promising avenue of attack on the problem of the Pliocene-Pleistocene boundary in North America appears to be in establishing stratigraphic ties with the Villafranchian.

Durham et al. (1954) have pointed out that in a very general way, the Blancan mammal age in North America is equivalent, at least in part, to the Villafranchian. Limits to the time spanned by the Blancan have been determined by Evernden et al. (1964) from potassium-argon dates on volcanic rocks associated with deposits bearing mammal fossils.

From their work it appears that the Hemphillian-Blancan boundary is between 4.1 and 3.5 million years old. The lower limit of 4.1 million years is determined by a date on a basalt in the Bidahochi Formation that immediately underlies fossiliferous beds of Hemphillian Age. Another basalt of the same extrusive episode and having the same stratigraphic association with Hemphillian fossils is reversely magnetized (Doell, unpublished data; data point not shown). The age of 3.5 million years is that of a basalt interbedded with sedimentary deposits of the Glenns Ferry Formation containing Blancan fossils, and this is also reversely magnetized (Fig. 8, M6). Thus the Hemphillian-Blancan boundary is within the Gilbert reversed epoch.

The Blancan-Irvingtonian boundary is between 2.3 and 1.4 million years old. The lower limit of 2.3 million years is determined by a date on pumice interbedded with sedimentary deposits of the Coso Formation of California which contain a Blancan fauna (Evernden et al., 1964; no magnetic polarity reported). The upper limit of 1.4 million years is determined by the age of a reversely magnetized basalt of the Bruneau Formation (Fig. 8, M5), which contains mammals that are Irvingtonian or later. Two other reversely magnetized volcanic units with ages of 1.6 and 1.5 million years (Fig. 8, M8) and two other units of uncertain magnetic polarity with ages of 2.1 and 1.9 million years either overlie or intrude sediments of Blancan age (Evernden et al., 1964), but these units do little to define further the position of the boundary.

The Blancan Age thus began within the Gilbert reversed epoch, continued through the Gauss normal epoch, and terminated within the Matuyama reversed epoch. At least 0.4 million years elapsed between the end of the Blancan Age and the end of the Matuyama polarity epoch.

In Europe, the first problem is one of paleomagnetic terminology. In Europe, the symbols N1, R1, N2, etc. have been used to represent the ultimate normal epoch, the ultimate reversed, the penultimate normal epoch, etc. (Rutten and Wensink, 1960). With the discovery of the Olduvai event, the question arises whether R1 should be taken as the entire Matuyama reversed epoch or as the post-Olduvai portion of it. Equating R1 with the entire Matuyama reversed epoch appears to conform most closely with European stratigraphic interpretations, especially those from Iceland, as will be discussed. This interpretation carries the implication that paleomagnetic evidence for the Olduvai event has not as yet been identified in Europe, but such a possibility does not appear unreasonable in view of our experience in North America, where we have identified the Olduvai event in only one of six rather intensively studied localities.

A proposal that the Astian-Villafranchian boundary be taken as the beginning of the R1 or Metuyama(?) reversed epoch has been made by Rutten and Wensink (1960). This correlation was based principally on the paleomagnetic study by Roche (1951, 1956) of volcanic rocks in the Auvergne. However, there appears to be no evidence that these reversely magnetized volcanic rocks are at the base of the Villafranchian, so that the question of the correlation of the base of the Villafranchian with the paleomagnetic time scale appears to us to be open still. If the correlation suggested by Rutten and Wensink is correct, then, from the known position of the Blancan relative to the paleomagnetic time scale, it would follow that the Villafranchian began more than one million years after the beginning of the Blancan. On the other hand, if the Villafranchian is more nearly correlative with the Blancan (as seems likely on paleontological grounds), then the Villafranchian began during the Gauss normal epoch or possibly as early as the Gilbert reversed epoch.

Only two radiometric dates relevant to the age of the Villafranchian have been published. A basalt at Valros, France, dated at 1.6 million years by Evernden *et al.* (1964), is regarded by Kloosterman (1960) as at the Astian-Villafranchian boundary. From what we now know of the paleomagnetic time scale, this appears unlikely; it would make the base of the Villafranchian even younger than has been proposed by Rutten and Wensink. The Valros basalt lies conformably on upper Astian beds with no interposition of Villafranchian deposits, which are widespread elsewhere in that region. However, there are no Villafranchian deposits directly superimposed on the basalt, which therefore is certainly post-Astian but not necessarily close to the Astian-Villafranchian boundary. This basalt is reversed, in good agreement with the rest of the time scale.

A basalt in Olduvai Gorge dated by Evernden *et al.* (1964) at 1.9 million years underlies deposits bearing a fauna which, though different from that in Italy, has been described as Villafranchian. This basalt is normally magnetized (Grommé and Hay, 1963) and serves as part of the basis for recognizing the Olduvai event.

The paleomagnetic studies of Roche (1951, 1956) in France are especially important in setting limits to the age of the upper boundary of the Villafranchian. In the Auvergne, lava flows of late Villafranchian age are reversely magnetized, as are the younger flows of Saint Prestian age. Thus the upper boundary of the Villafranchian, like that of the Blancan, lies within the Matuyama reversed epoch and is greater than one million years old. The Saint Prestian (=Cromerian), in turn, is at least in part equivalent with the late Matuyama reversed epoch and hence may be correlative with the Bruneau Formation in Idaho, which is Irvingtonian or younger.

The classic paleomagnetic research in Iceland by Hospers (1954), Einarsson (1957), and Rutten and Wensink (1960) is shown schematically in Figure 9. The horizon marked F is a sedimentary sequence consisting of an upper unit containing plant remains indicating a warm climate, and a lower unit containing a cold-water fauna including *Portlandia arctica*, which has been regarded by Einarsson (1957) as being near the Pliocene-Pleistocene boundary. These rest locally on moraines. Below these deposits occurs a faulted sequence of flows that are normally and reversely magnetized, and moraines are probably intercalated in this sequence. Above the sedimentary deposits there is a sequence of reversely magnetized flows intercalated with at least one moraine, and above this a sequence of normally magnetized flows with intercalated glacial deposits.

Glaciation in Europe must have begun during the latter part of the Matuyama reversed epoch if the inferences of interglacial climatic conditions during deposition of certain of the mammalian fossil assemblages in the Auvergne of

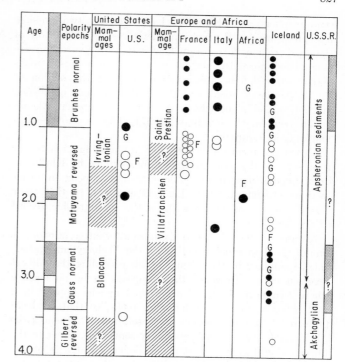

Figure 9. Paleomagnetic correlation between the western United States, southern Europe, Africa, Iceland, and the U.S.S.R. Closed circles, normal polarity; open circles, reversed polarity; large circles, radiometric dates; small circles, no radiometric dates; G, glacial deposits; F, fossils. Cross-hatched areas indicate range of uncertainty in mammal age boundaries.

France are correct (Movius, 1949). These deposits are intercalated between reversely magnetized lava flows and hence are clearly within the Matuyama. In North America a glacial till occurs beneath the Bishop Tuff in California, for which Evernden *et al.* (1964) give an age of 0.98 million years. In Iceland, on the other hand, glaciations began earlier; they clearly occurred throughout the Matuyama reversed epoch and probably began before it.

The final paleomagnetic results from Europe to be considered are those from Italy, shown in Figure 9 (Rutten, 1959; Evernden *et al.* 1964). In order of increasing age these include the volcanic rocks at Vico, Albano (younger), Bracciano, Albano (older), Cimini (two units), and Tolfa. It is of special interest that the paleomagnetic measurements were all made in the field with only a hand compass. With the exception of the Tolfa volcanics, the results are in good accord with the paleomagnetic time scale.

CORRELATION WITH TURKMENIA

In Russia, paleomagnetism has been used extensively for stratigraphic correlation. Probably the work that has attracted the greatest worldwide interest is that of Khramov (1957, 1958) on sediments of the Apsheronian and Akchagylian Stages in Turkmenia. The problem of the correlation of these two stages with western Europe has long perplexed stratigraphers, and Khramov has suggested two possible interpretations of the paleomagnetic results. "The top of the Apsheronian deposits on Chelekan and Kyurendag are magnetized normally; below is a zone of reversed magnetization, which occupies a large part of the section of the Apsheronian Stage, and then follows a zone of normal magnetizations, along which passes the Apsheronian-Akchagylian boundary" (Khramov, 1957). This is shown schematically in Figure 9.

Although a record of events such as the Olduvai is absent from some of the sedimentary sections studied by Khramov, brief fluctuations in magnetic direction appear in other sections (Khramov, 1958, Figs. 42 and 45), so that their absence may result from gaps in the stratigraphic record or the sampling.

Khramov (1958) has also given an alternative interpretation of the data which would place the Akchagylian-Apsheronian boundary in the normal epoch preceding the Gilbert reversed epoch. However there appears to be no locality where two normal and two reversed epochs appear in a continuous section of Apsheronian rocks, so that we have preferred Khramov's earlier interpretation. This places the Akchagylian-Apsheronian boundary somewhat, closer to the Pliocene-Pleistocene boundary as defined in terms of the base of the Villafranchian, although either interpretation falls within the range of uncertainty regarding the correlation of these two boundaries (Gromov *et al.*, 1960).

Conclusions

The paleomagnetic time scale now appears to be sufficiently well defined to be used stratigraphically. We estimate that the precision of the polarity epoch boundaries are as follows, where the ± figures are our estimates of the standard errors:

——————————— 0.0 million years ———————————
Brunhes normal polarity epoch
——————— 0.85 ± 0.15 million years ———————
Matuyama reversed polarity epoch
————————— 2.5 ± 0.2 million years —————————
Gauss normal polarity epoch
————————— 3.4 ± 0.1 million years —————————
Gilbert reversed polarity epoch

It has been possible to define these boundaries rather precisely from a relatively small number of radiometric dates, because both the dates and the remanent magnetizations correspond closely to the time of cooling of the same body of rock. In developing other time scales based on fossil deposits that cannot be dated directly, the problem has not been one of obtaining technically accurate dates so much as one of finding volcanic deposits that bear a significant stratigraphic relationship to fossil localities.

Similarly in paleomagnetic stratigraphy, the principal problem today is to find significant stratigraphic relations between rocks suitable for paleomagnetic study and rocks containing glacial deposits or stratigraphically useful fossils.

Note added in proof. We have redated the Bishop Tuff and find an age of about 0.7 million years. Contamination by xenolithic inclusions may be responsible for the 0.98-million-year date reported previously by Evernden *et al.* (1964). In the light of this new result, the age of the Brunhes-Matuyama boundary is uncertain within the interval 0.85 ± 0.15 million years, and the minimum age of the earliest glaciation in North America is reduced by more than one-quarter million years.

References

Aramaki, Shigeo, and Akimoto, Syun-iti, 1957, Temperature estimation of pyroclastic deposits by natural remanent magnetism: Amer. J. Sci., v. 255, p. 619-627

Brynjolfsson, Ari, 1957, Studies of remanent magnetism and viscous magnetism in the basalts of Iceland: Adv. Physics, v. 6, p. 247-254

Cox, Allan, 1961, Anomalous remanent magnetization of basalt: U.S. Geol. Surv. Bull. 1083-E, p. 131-160

Cox, Allan, and Doell, R. R., 1960, Review of paleomagnetism: Geol. Soc. Amer. Bull., v. 71, p. 645-768

Cox, Allan, Doell, R. R., and Dalrymple, G. B., 1963a, Geomagnetic polarity epochs and Pleistocene geochronometry: Nature, v. 198, p. 1049-1051

—— 1963b, Geomagnetic polarity epochs; Sierra Nevada II: Science, v. 142, p. 382-385

—— 1964a, Geomagnetic polarity epochs: Science, v. 143, p. 351-352

—— 1964b, Reversals of the earth's magnetic field: Science, v. 144, p. 1537-1543

Dalrymple, G. B., 1964, Potassium-argon dates of three Pleistocene interglacial basalt flows from the Sierra Nevada, California: Geol. Soc. Amer. Bull., v. 75, p. 753-758

Doell, R. R., and Cox, Allan, 1961a, Paleomagnetism: New York, Academic Press, Adv. Geophysics, v. 8, p. 221-313

—— 1961b, Palaeomagnetism of Hawaiian lava flows: Nature, v. 192, p. 645-646

—— 1962, Determination of the magnetic polarity of rock samples in the field: U.S. Geol. Surv. Prof. Pap. 450-D, p. 105-108

—— 1963, The accuracy of the paleomagnetic method as evaluated from historic Hawaiian lava flows: J. Geophys. Res., v. 68, p. 1997-2009

Durham, J. W., Jahns, R. H., and Savage, D. E., 1954, Marine-nonmarine relationships in the Cenozoic sections of California: California Div. Mines Bull. 170, pt. 7, p. 59-71

Einarsson, Trausti, 1957, Magneto-geological mapping in Iceland with the use of a compass: Philos. Mag. Supp., v. 6, p. 232-239

Evernden, J. F., Savage, D. E., Curtis, G. H., and James, G. T., 1964, Potassium-argon dates and the Cenozoic mammalian chronology of North America: Amer. J. Sci., v. 262, p. 145-198

Gazin, C. L., 1936, A study of the fossil horse remains from the upper Pliocene of Idaho: U.S. Natl. Mus. Proc., v. 83, p. 281-320

Graham, K. W. T., 1961, The re-magnetization of a surface outcrop by lightning currents: Roy. Astron. Soc. Geophys. J., v. 6, p. 85-102

Grommé, C. S., and Hay, R. L., 1963, Magnetization of basalt of Bed I, Olduvai Gorge, Tanganyika: Nature, v. 200, p. 560-561

Gromov, V. I., Krasnov, I. I., Nikitorova, K. V., and Schanzer, R. V., 1960, Principles of a stratigraphic subdivision of the Quaternary (Anthropogen) system and its lower boundary: 21st Intern. Geol. Congr., Copenhagen, Rep. Sec. 4, p. 7-26

Hopkins, D. M., Late Cenozoic marine transgression in Alaska, *in* Problems in the Pleistocene in the Arctic: U.S.S.R. Inst. for Geology of the Arctic (in Russian; translation to be available from Off. Tech. Serv., U.S. Dept. Comm.) (in press)

Hospers, Jan, 1954, Reversals of the main geomagnetic field III: Koninkl. Nederlandse Akad. Wetensch. Proc. Sec. Sci., pt. 3, ser. B, v. 57, p. 112-121

Irving, E., and Parry, L. G., 1963, The magnetism of some Permian rocks from New South Wales: Roy. Astron. Soc. Geophys. J., v. 7, p. 395-411

Khramov, A. N., 1957, Paleomagnetism the basis of a new method of correlation and subdivision of sedimentary strata: Proc. Acad. Sci. U.S.S.R., Geol. Sci. Sec., v. 112, issues 1-6 (English transl. Consultants Bureau Inc., 1958)

—— 1958, Palaeomagnetism and stratigraphic correlations: Gostoptechizdat, Leningrad, p. 204 (English transl. Canberra, Australian Natl. Univ., 1960)

Kloosterman, J. B., 1960, Le volcanisme de la region d'Agde, Heroult, France: Utrecht Rijksuniv., Mineralog.-Geolog. Inst. Geol. Ultraiectina, No. 6, 79 p.

Knopf, Adolph, 1918, A geologic reconnaissance of the Inyo Range and the eastern slope of the southern Sierra Nevada, California, with a section on the stratigraphy of the Inyo Range by Edwin Kirk: U.S. Geol. Surv. Prof. Pap. 110, 130 p.

Malde, H. E., and Powers, H. A., 1962, Upper Cenozoic stratigraphy of the western Snake River Plain, Idaho: Geol. Soc. Amer. Bull., v. 73, p. 1197-1219

McDougall, Ian, 1964, Potassium-argon ages from lavas of the Hawaiian Islands: Geol. Soc. Amer. Bull., v. 75, p. 107-127

McDougall, Ian, and Tarling, D. H., 1963, Dating of polarity zones in the Hawaiian Islands: Nature, v. 200, p. 54-56

Momose, Kan'ichi, 1963, Studies on the variations of the earth's magnetic field during Pliocene time: Tokyo Univ. Earthquake Res. Inst. Bull., v. 41, pt. 3, p. 487-534

Movius, H. L., Jr., 1949, Villafranchian stratigraphy in southern and southwestern Europe: J. Geol., v. 57, p. 380-412

Picard, M. D., 1964, Paleomagnetic correlation of units within Chugwater (Triassic) formation, west-central Wyoming: Amer. Assoc. Petroleum Geologists Bull., v. 48, No. 3, pt. 1, p. 269-291

Putnam, W. C., 1960, Origin of Rock Creek and Owens River gorges, Mono County, California: Berkeley, Univ. California Publ. Geol. Sci., v. 34, p. 221-279

Rimbert, Francine, 1956, Sur la désaimantation par action de champs magnétiques alternatifs de la magnétite et du sesquioxyde de fer$_\alpha$: Acad. Sci. [Paris] Compt. Rend., v. 242, p. 890-893

Roche, Alexandre, 1951, Sur les inversions de l'aimantation rémante des roches volcaniques dans les monts d'Auvergne: Acad. Sci. [Paris] Compt. Rend., v. 233, p. 1132-1134

—— 1956, Sur la date de la dernière inversion du champ magnétique terrestre: Acad. Sci. [Paris] Compt. Rend., v. 243, p. 812-814

Rutten, M. G., 1959, Paleomagnetic reconnaissance of mid-Italian volcanoes: Geol. Mijnbouw (Niew Ser.) 21e Jaargang, p. 373-374

Rutten, M. G., and Wensink, H., 1960, Paleomagnetic dating, glaciations and the chronology of the Plio-Pleistocene in Iceland: 21st Intern. Geol. Congr., Copenhagen, Rep. Sec. Pt. 4, p. 62-70

Sigurgeirsson, Thorbjörn, 1957, Direction of magnetization in Icelandic basalts: Philos. Mag. Supp., v. 6, p. 240-246

Slemmons, D. B., 1953, Geology of the Sonora Pass region: Berkeley, Univ. of California Ph.D. thesis, 201 p.

Smith, R. L., Bailey, R. A., and Ross, C. S., 1961, Structural evolution of the Valles Caldera, New Mexico, and its bearing on the emplacement of Ring Dikes: U.S. Geol. Surv. Prof. Pap. 424-D, p. 145-149

Uffen, R. J., 1963, Influence of the earth's core on the origin and evolution of life: Nature, v. 198, p. 143-144

Uyeda, Seiya, 1958, Thermo-remanent magnetism as a medium of palaeomagnetism, with special reference to reverse thermoremanent magnetism: Japan. J. Geophys., v. 2, p. 1-123

Van Zijl, J. S. V., Graham, K. W. T., and Hales, A. L., 1962, The palaeomagnetism of the Stormberg lavas, II. The behaviour of the magnetic field during a reversal: Roy. Astron. Soc. Geophys. J., v. 7, p. 169-182

Wilson, R. W., 1937, New middle Pliocene rodent and lagomorph faunas from Oregon and California: Carnegie Instn. Publ. 487, p. 1-19

SUMMARY

Paleomagnetic polarity epochs are defined as time intervals when the earth's magnetic field was entirely or predominantly of a uniform polarity. The following geochronometric-paleomagnetic time scale is presented:

———————————— 0.0 million years ————————————
Brunhes normal polarity epoch
———————— 0.85 ± 0.15 million years ————————
Matuyama reversed polarity epoch
———————— 2.5 ± 0.2 million years ————————
Gauss normal polarity epoch
———————— 3.4 ± 0.1 million years ————————
Gilbert reversed polarity epoch

In North America the Blancan mammal age began in the Gilbert reserved epoch, continued through the Gauss normal epoch, and terminated within the Matuyama reversed epoch. The Villafranchian age in Europe similarly terminated within the Matuyama reversed epoch, but its beginning has not yet been correlated with the polarity time scale. Both the Irvingtonian mammal age in North America and the Cromerian (= Saint Prestian) in Europe are correlative with the latter part of the Matuyama reversed epoch and hence are probably correlative, at least in part, with each other.

TECTONICS OF QUATERNARY TIME IN MIDDLE NORTH AMERICA*

PHILIP B. KING[1]

In this paper I shall explore the tectonics of the last two million years of earth history—the time of the Quaternary period. The paper deals with Quaternary features and events in Middle North America—that is, in the conterminous United States and adjacent parts of Canada and Mexico (Fig. 1). Earlier tectonic features and events, and contemporaneous features and events outside the region designated, are not of primary interest here, although they will be mentioned from time to time to provide the setting of the features and events that are principally treated.

This paper is a review, in which data on Quaternary tectonic features and events in different parts of Middle North America are summarized in geographic order. These data are voluminous and are derived from diverse disciplines, not only from Quaternary stratigraphy and geomorphology but from seismology, geophysics, volcanology, and many other sources. Because of the diversity of the data, my previous unfamiliarity with many of these data, and limitations of time for preparation, this paper is a reconnaissance, and it contains the errors and imperfections of all surveys of that kind. Many recent findings, published or unpublished, doubtless have escaped my notice; some of these are perhaps summarized in other articles in this volume, to which the reader should refer. The list of references to other publications is incomplete, but the many summary papers included in the list contain additional citations. Some areas are treated in more detail than others, partly to keep the account from becoming a mere catalogue of localities, but mainly in the hope that these areas will illustrate the general principles of Quaternary tectonics in the wider regions of which they are a part.

SEISMICITY

A useful clue to the present tectonic state of the crust in Middle North America is afforded by the seismicity of the region. Inferences derived therefrom can be extrapolated, with modifications, into a considerable part of Quaternary time. General features of the seismicity of Middle North America have been summarized by Gutenberg and Richter (1954). Woollard (1958) has provided additional useful data by plotting the epicenters of all recorded earthquakes in the region—that is, epicenters of all earthquakes within about the last 200 years, but with emphasis on the later part of the period when records are best.

Figure 2 summarizes Woollard's data (Woollard, 1958, Figs. 1-3, p. 1136, 1138). The map shows plainly the familiar crustal unrest of the Pacific coastal belt and of the interior as far east as the 110th meridian. Less expectable is the wide scatter of epicenters over the remaining and seemingly stable parts of Middle North America. Some of these, it is true, represent very minor shocks, but they include some of major intensity. Some concentrations of epicenters follow familiar tectonic lines, such as the axis of the Appalachians; others have little obvious relation to known geologic or tectonic features.

The significance of seismic activity in specific parts of Middle North America will be mentioned in the regional discussions that follow, where reference will be made to the various features on Figure 2.

NORTHEASTERN REGION

LATE QUATERNARY REGIONAL UPLIFT

The northeastern part of Middle North America (Fig. 1) tells the familiar story of very late regional uplift, produced by isostatic rebound during and following the waning of the last (Wisconsin) continental ice sheet. This uplift was preceded during the glacial maximum by a downwarping of the same region under the load of the ice sheet, in a manner corresponding to that which still depresses the bedrock surface below sea level near the centers of the Greenland and Antarctic ice caps.

Evidence for the story is found along the periphery of the former ice sheet where Quaternary shorelines are uplifted and tilted. In the southern segment these are the shorelines of the precursors of the present Great Lakes, in the southwestern segment they are the shorelines of precursors of the large lakes of west-central Canada (including

* Publication authorized by the Director, U.S. Geological Survey. In preparing this paper, which has involved a review of large amounts of data hitherto unfamiliar to me, I am deeply indebted to my colleagues of the U.S. Geological Survey who have read various parts of the manuscript that deal with areas for which they have special knowledge—especially Paul C. Bateman, Russell H. Campbell, Max D. Crittenden, Ward C. Smith, John G. Vedder, and Clyde Wahrhaftig. I am indebted most of all to David M. Hopkins, who has encouraged me to prepare the paper, and who has read the whole of several successive versions; he has shared with me his wide knowledge of Quaternary geology in Middle North America, and his knowledge of its voluminous literature, thus contributing in no small measure to the undertaking. I have profited by exchange of ideas and concepts with these geologists. Nevertheless, we have not always agreed on interpretations, and, for better or for worse, the judgments expressed herein are my own. Finally, I acknowledge the great help given to me by Helen Bailey of the Menlo Park branch of the U.S. Geological Survey Library, who freely gave her time to search out the many publications referred to herein.

[1] U.S. Geological Survey, Menlo Park, California.

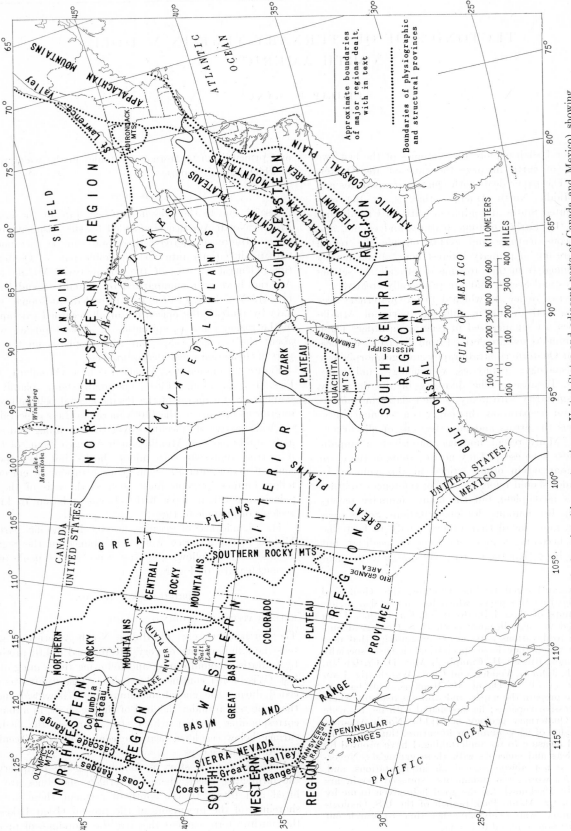

Figure 1. Map of Middle North America (the conterminous United States and adjacent parts of Canada and Mexico) showing the regions into which it has been arbitrarily subdivided for purpose of discussion and the principal physiographic and structural provinces mentioned in the text. Some areas not specifically mentioned are unlabeled.

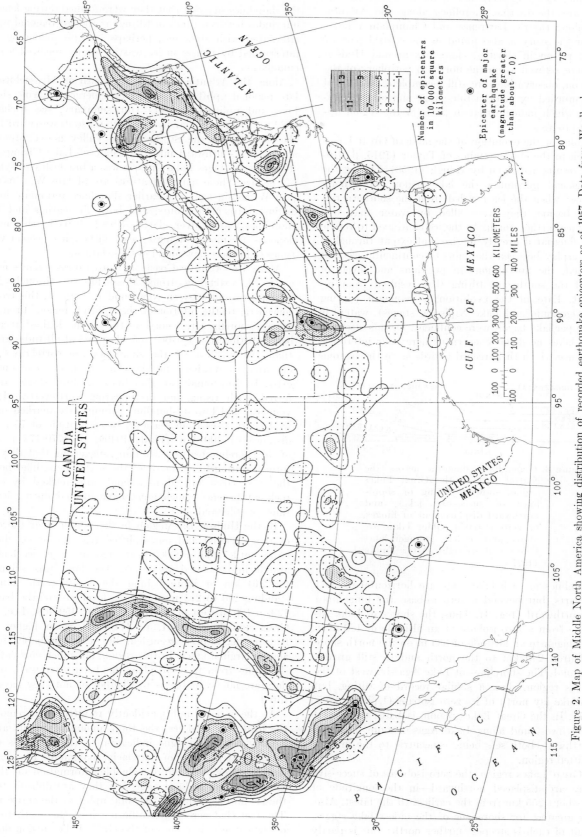

Figure 2. Map of Middle North America showing distribution of recorded earthquake epicenters as of 1957. Data from Woollard (1958, Fig. 1), contours prepared by P. B. King.

those of former Lake Agassiz) and in the southeastern segment they are the marine shorelines along the Atlantic Coast and along the St. Lawrence and Champlain valleys. Evidence for the story is also found in the central part of the uplifted region in elevated shorelines around Hudson Bay, but there, as well as on the northern periphery of the uplifted region, observations are still incomplete. Additional evidence is afforded by modern tide-gauge and other shoreline records, which indicate that in parts of the region uplift is still in progress.

For the story of the evolution of the modern Great Lakes we owe much to the classic studies of Taylor (1915, p. 316-518); later results are given by Hough (1958). During the Wisconsin glacial maximum the lake region was wholly buried by ice; when the ice receded from the southern rim of the lake basins, they were filled by water that was dammed by ice farther north. As the ice continued to recede these lakes fluctuated greatly in size and extent through a complex interplay between the dams of continental ice that still remained, the fluctuations in positions and levels of outlets, and the southward tilting that resulted from regional uplift. Late in the evolutionary sequence (during the Lake Algonquin and Lake Nipissing stages), waters in the three upper lake basins were confluent. Details of evolution of the lakes need not concern us here; our interest is in the evidence which their record affords as to the tectonic history.

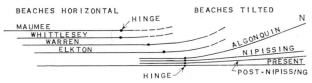

Figure 3. Generalized diagram across the central part of the Great Lakes region, showing tilting of shorelines of successive lakes, and northward displacement of hinges, or zero isobases. Older lakes are above and to left, younger lakes below and to right. After Taylor (1927).

The shorelines of each lake stage are horizontal in their southern parts, but beyond a zero isobase (or hinge-line) they rise northward (Fig. 3). Thus, the shores of Lake Algonquin rise from a zero isobase at an altitude of 180 m in central Michigan to an altitude of 335 m on the north shore of Lake Huron 240 km to the north and to still greater heights beyond. The shorelines of Lake Agassiz, west of the Great Lakes region, show a similar record of tilting, but all of this lake lay north of its zero isobase (Upham, 1895, p. 227-237). In the Great Lakes region, isobases trend west to west-northwest and along Lake Agassiz more decidedly to the northwest, both sets being concentric to the interior of the uplifted region.

In the Great Lakes region, the zero isobases of successive lake stages are displaced northward—in the longitude of Michigan about 255 km from the earliest to the latest. Also, the tilt is greatest for shorelines of the oldest lake stages, and the tilt of each is steepest farther north; this is partly because each successive shoreline participated only in the

subsequent tilting of the region. The perfection of some of the shorelines suggests that they were formed during lengthy interludes between times of tilting, as though regional uplift alternated with stillstand, perhaps because unloading was interrupted by pauses in ice wasting or by renewed ice accumulation.

Along the Atlantic Coast as far south as Massachusetts, late regional uplift is indicated by emergent marine shorelines and uplifted deposits (for summary, see Richards, 1962, p. 10-12). Similar features extend southwestward from the Atlantic up the St. Lawrence Valley above Montreal and thence southward into the valley of Lake Champlain; during some stages Lake Ontario was a brackish embayment of the sea. These marine features are of late Wisconsin or post-Wisconsin age. The earlier shorelines terminate inland against former ice fronts, and both the earlier and later shorelines extend over glacial drifts; shells in the marine deposits are mostly living species, although of cooler-water types than those now found in these latitudes.

Along the Atlantic Coast the zero isobase trends northeastward, extending from Massachusetts through Nova Scotia into southeastern Newfoundland. Again, this trend is concentric to the interior of the uplifted region. From this isobase shorelines rise northwestward, the highest recorded being northwest of Quebec and Montreal at altitudes greater than 185 m. Not all the shorelines are correlative from one area to another, and shorelines of more than one age exist. In Newfoundland, shorelines of three stages are inferred, each rising and disappearing northwestward; the youngest and lowest shoreline, prominently marked on the west coast, rises from sea level to an altitude of 75 m in a distance of 400 km (Flint, 1940a, p. 1770-1771). Some of the shoreline features are faint, suggesting that they were formed during brief stands of the sea; others, like those on the west coast of Newfoundland, are marked by strong rock-cut benches which must have formed during lengthy times of stillstand.

In the Hudson Bay region farther north, near the center of the glaciated and now-uplifted region, the sea did not enter until 7,000 or 8,000 years ago, after the ice had separated into isolated remnants. The land was submerged for 240 km or more behind the coasts, with shorelines standing 250 to 275 m above sea level east of the bay and 120 to 180 m west of it (Bird, 1954, p. 459-460; Lee, 1960; Craig and Fyles, 1961, p. 414-415). Some higher shore features have been recorded, but they probably formed along marginal lakes. In this region, not much correlation of shorelines from place to place has been attempted, so that data are not available as to whether or not they have been tilted.

As the regional uplift evidently resulted from removal of the load of glacial ice, the total amount of uplift at each locality must give some indication of the thickness of the ice there at the time of the glacial maximum. The shoreline data just reviewed afford valuable information on the uplift and tilting in local areas but they are difficult to synthesize into a picture of the total uplift of the entire region. The fact that zero isobases lie north of the southern edges of the earliest shorelines of the Great Lakes region does not mean that the area south of the isobases was never uplifted, but merely that no uplift occurred there after the formation of the shoreline; uplift may have occurred to the south before the lakes were formed. Also, the marine shorelines along the Atlantic Coast do not indicate the amount of total uplift, as sea level has risen eustatically in postglacial time. Total uplift may have been several hundred meters greater. In the Hudson Bay region, the last area deglaciated, the emerged shorelines formed only during the last part of the regional uplift; earlier uplift before the disappearance of the ice is unrecorded, but the uplift might have occurred later than elsewhere. Contours drawn on the highest marine shorelines (Fig. 4A) observed at the different localities (Farrand and Gadja, 1962, p. 12) indicate only the minimum possible total uplift. Nevertheless, these contours confirm Daly's early deductions (1934, p. 106) that the maximum uplift centered along the east side of Hudson Bay, where it was at least 300 m.

RATES OF UPLIFT

The general pattern of uplift and the rate of uplift in the glaciated region of northeastern North America can be inferred from radiocarbon dating of shoreline and other deposits (Farrand, 1962). These data suggest that uplift at each locality began before complete deglaciation of the vicinity, that it was most rapid at that time, and that it diminished thereafter. Rates of uplift are similar at all localities but the uplift was displaced inward with time toward the diminishing ice centers.

Tide-gauge records and other observations indicate that uplift is still in progress in parts of the glaciated region (Gutenberg, 1941, p. 739-750). Along Hudson Bay near the center of the region, Eskimo traditions and the distribution of archaeological sites suggest a rate of uplift of about 1 m per century, but quantitative data from gauge records are still inconclusive (Gutenberg, 1941, p. 747-750; Bird, 1954, p. 463). In the Great Lakes, water is receding from the northern shores and is rising on the southern shores. According to gauge records the northern shore of Lake Superior is thus rising at a rate of 50 cm per century with respect to southern Lake Michigan and Lake Erie—a rate of tilting of 1 mm per 100 km per year. When these data are adjusted to sea level the tilting appears to be mostly negative, or downward toward the south rather than upward toward the north (Moore, 1948, p. 704-705), but sea level itself is not an absolute datum and is probably rising eustatically.

Along the New England coast near the zero isobase, records of the fall and rise of sea level during the last 10,000 years have been worked out in many places, with the aid of radiocarbon dating. These records do not all harmonize, and both crustal warping and eustatic rise in sea level are involved, making the actual movement pattern difficult to analyze (Bloom and Stuiver, 1963; Bloom, 1963, p. 871; Kaye and Barghoorn, 1964, p. 78-79). North of the zero isobase an uplift of 25 to 100 m occurred between the end of glaciation and 5,000 to 8,000 years ago, so that the land stood higher above sea level than now. Both here and south of the zero isobase, however, there was a contemporaneous eustatic rise in sea level, which continued at a fairly rapid rate until about 3,000 years ago. Between 3,000 years ago

and the present, sea level was either nearly stable or rose about 3 m to its present level. How much of this last rise in sea level resulted from eustatic causes and how much from crustal downwarping has been debated, but the amount is small and the factors of error are large (Kaye and Barghoorn, 1964, p. 76). Farther northeast, along most of the east coast of Newfoundland, sea level seems to be falling at a rate of 30 to 60 cm per century, probably by crustal upwarping, but on the Avalon Peninsula southeast of the zero isobase, sea level is rising at a rate of about 70 cm per century; as this rate exceeds inferred eustatic rises elsewhere, crustal downwarping may be in progress here (Jenness, 1960, p. 177).

To what extent is the region once depressed by the ice caps still uncompensated? According to Flint (1957, p. 240): "In both regions [Fennoscandia and northeastern North America] even the incomplete data obtained thus far show that gravity anomalies are negative, and that they increase toward the central parts of the glaciated areas, indicating that crustal equilibrium in these regions has not been reached." Gravity observations in Fennoscandia are in agreement with this statement, but those in northeastern North America are as yet inconclusive (Innes, 1960, p. 327). The glaciated region of central Canada shows weakly negative Bouguer gravity anomalies, with a few larger maxima and minima that are related to local crustal variations in rocks and structures (Fig. 4B) (Dominion Observatories of Canada, 1956); this pattern does not differ significantly from the pattern in the nonglaciated lowlands farther south in the United States. Conversion of these data to Hayford isostatic anomalies does show a decrease of about 30 milligals northeastward across Manitoba and Ontario, from the edge of the Canadian Shield to Hudson Bay (Innes, 1960, p. 325-326), and later surveys in Hudson Bay itself suggest a marked negative gravity field (M. J. S. Innes, written communication, 1964); these anomalies may be partly residual from the glacial downwarp, although they are difficult to untangle from the effects of bedrock structure. More positive indications that the glaciated region is still uncompensated are afforded by configuration of the geoid (Fischer, 1959a, b). Geoidal contours indicate a depression of about 15 m in the center of the region (Fig. 4C); their pattern conforms remarkably to the outlines of the former continental ice caps and to the shapes of contours showing postglacial uplift (Fig. 4A).

SEISMIC DATA

Modern instability of parts of northeastern Middle North America is further attested by concentrations of recorded earthquake epicenters in New England, New York State, and southeastern Canada (Fig. 2). A relation has been suggested between the earthquakes and the late Quaternary postglacial uplift already discussed (Hodgson, 1945, p. 166; Woollard, 1958, p. 1144), but epicenters are concentrated along the southeastern margin of the uplifted region; the interior of the Canadian Shield (the area of maximum postglacial uplift and of present most rapid uplift) appears to be almost completely aseismic (Gutenberg and Richter, 1954, p. 91). The New England and New York earthquakes are significantly clustered along pre-existing tectonic features in

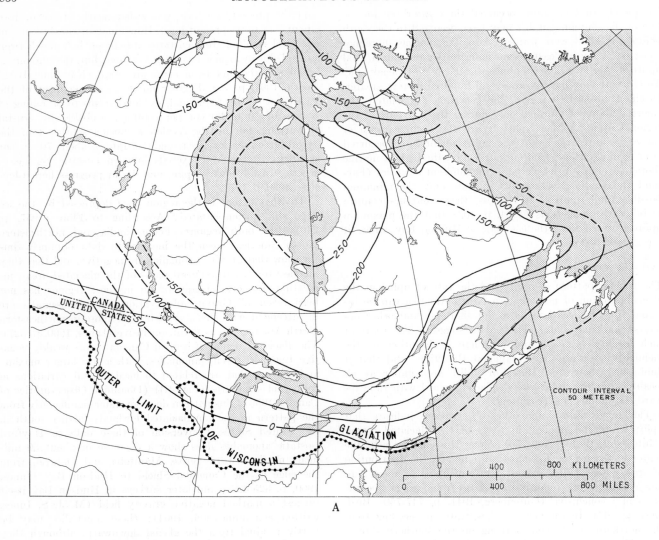

A

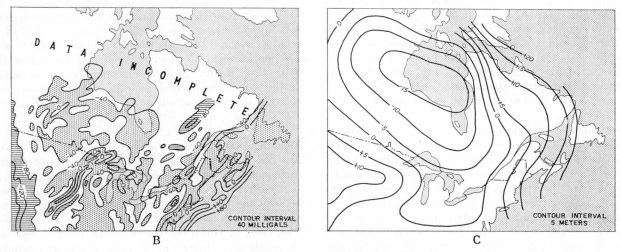

B   C

Figure 4. Maps of northeastern North America illustrating postglacial uplift. A: Contours on the highest observed marine shorelines indicating the minimum amount of postglacial uplift. Compiled from Farrand and Gadja (1962) and other sources.
B: Generalized Bouguer gravity anomalies, which seem to be little related to the postglacial uplift. Compiled from
gravity maps by Dominion Observatory of Canada and U.S. Geological Survey. C: Contours on the surface of the geoid,
which is significantly depressed in the area of maximum glaciation. After Fischer (1959a, Fig. 4).

the bedrock—the Appalachian belt and the Adirondack uplift. In Canada epicenters are especially clustered along the St. Lawrence Valley (Hodgson, 1945, p. 155-167; Smith, 1962). Some of the earthquakes in the St. Lawrence Valley, such as those of 1663 and 1925 near Trois Rivières, Quebec, were major shocks with magnitudes of 7 or 8 and were perceptible over large parts of eastern North America. Although none of the St. Lawrence Valley earthquakes produced faulting at the surface, they may be related to an otherwise obscure belt of crustal weakness, trending northeastward along the southeastern margin of the Canadian Shield. Record epicenters of weaker earthquakes prolong this trend southwestward (Fig. 2) through a region in the eastern interior of the United States that is otherwise lacking in surface deformation, seemingly to join the strongly seismic area at the upper end of the Mississippi Embayment (see below). This trend is also marked by better than normal transmission of earthquake effects, as shown by isoseismal lines compiled for specific earthquakes in the region (Woollard, 1958, Figs. 6-7).

FEATURES OLDER THAN LATE QUATERNARY

The regional uplift of the northeastern part of Middle North America described above involved only the latest part of Quaternary time, during and following the waning of the last (Wisconsin) glaciation. One may suppose that before Wisconsin time the region also underwent similar downwarping during the earlier glaciations, and that it underwent uplift during the integlaciations. Little indication of such movements remains in the fragments of pre-Wisconsin features and deposits that are preserved. Slight regional distortion of marine deposits probably equivalent to the Sangamon Interglaciation (between Wisconsin and Illinoian) is suggested in the coastal segment from New Jersey to New England and may have been inherited from pre-Wisconsin time. The deposits of New Jersey (Cape May Formation) stand at altitudes of about 10 m, and continue at this altitude southward. Those of Long Island and the offshore islands of Massachusetts (Gardiners Clay) are nearer sea level and pass below sea level under Long Island Sound and adjacent waters (MacClintock and Richards, 1936, p. 330-332; Richards, 1962, p. 39).

All the Quaternary isostatic movements were superposed on a much greater, long-term trend of epeirogenic movements in the Canadian Shield and its surroundings. Vast areas of the Labrador Peninsula are a subdued, high-level upland, evidently worn down during Tertiary and earlier times. In the eastern part of the peninsula the upland stands at altitudes of more than 1,000 m, and exceeds 1,500 m in the Torngat Mountains to the north; it breaks off steeply toward the Atlantic Ocean and Gulf of St. Lawrence on the east and southeast and slopes gently westward toward Hudson Bay. On the declivities bordering the Atlantic and the St. Lawrence, it is incised by canyons 300 m or more deep. These canyons are partly filled by glacial drift and are certainly of pre-Wisconsin age. They were interpreted by Cooke (1929, p. 117) as of late Tertiary age, but Ambrose (1964, p. 824) believes that they had been cut even before Paleozoic time. The high-level upland and the canyons that incise it suggest an uplift and westward tilting

of the Labrador Peninsula much earlier than late Quaternary time. In Newfoundland a similar high-level upland slopes southeastward (Twenhofel and MacClintock, 1940, p. 1718-1723) and seems to have been tilted away from the uplift in Labrador. Beneath Hudson Bay the Precambrian rocks of the Canadian Shield are extensively covered by Paleozoic strata, downwarped into a shallow basin whose edges emerge in the James Bay lowlands and on Southampton Island to the south and north. The bay owes its submergence largely to effects of the last glaciation, but it has been a long-persistent negative area as well.

SOUTHEASTERN REGION

APPALACHIAN MOUNTAINS

The rocks of the Appalachian orogenic belt were deformed during Paleozoic and early Mesozoic time, and those in the southeastern part were also metamorphosed and invaded by plutonic rocks. From late Mesozoic time onward, the belt was epeirogenically warped, the northwestern part being raised to form the present Appalachian Mountains (Fig. 1), the southeastern and southern parts being depressed and covered by deposits to form the Atlantic and Gulf Coastal Plains. According to classical concepts, remnants of former erosion surfaces, or peneplains, occur in the mountains at various altitudes—including an imperfectly preserved surface near the present summits and a more extensively preserved surface on the valley floors between the mountains—but the validity of part or all of these inferred surfaces has been questioned by some geomorphologist. If such surfaces were formed, it was during lengthy times of stillstand, and if so the epeirogenic uplift of the mountains was episodic. The epeirogenic subsidence of the contiguous coastal plains was certainly episodic, as their Cretaceous and Tertiary sediments record many times of transgression and regression.

Opinions differ both as to the existence and as to the ages of erosion surfaces in the Appalachian Mountains, but the extensively preserved valley-floor surface ("Harrisburg peneplain") is generally believed to have been leveled before the end of Tertiary time. Most of this surface stands at altitudes of less than 500 m, so that any uplift that occurred later, as during Quaternary time, could only have been moderate. The valley floor surface is now trenched by valleys to depths of 100 m or more, and minor benches and terraces occur below it. Valley trenching and the formation of benches and terraces were influenced by so many geomorphic and climatic factors that it is difficult to determine what tectonic influences may have aided in shaping them.

Clearer indications of late crustal instability in the southeastern region are afforded by the distribution of recorded earthquake epicenters along the axis of the Appalachian Mountains (Fig. 2) (Woollard, 1958, p. 1144, 1147), the earthquakes being related to epeirogenic uplift that is still in progress. Nevertheless, epicenters are concentrated along some parts of the axis (as in central Virginia and western North Carolina) in a manner little related to known Quaternary of older structures. Even more anomalous is the transverse belt of epicenters extending southeastward from the Appalachian Mountains across the coastal plain of

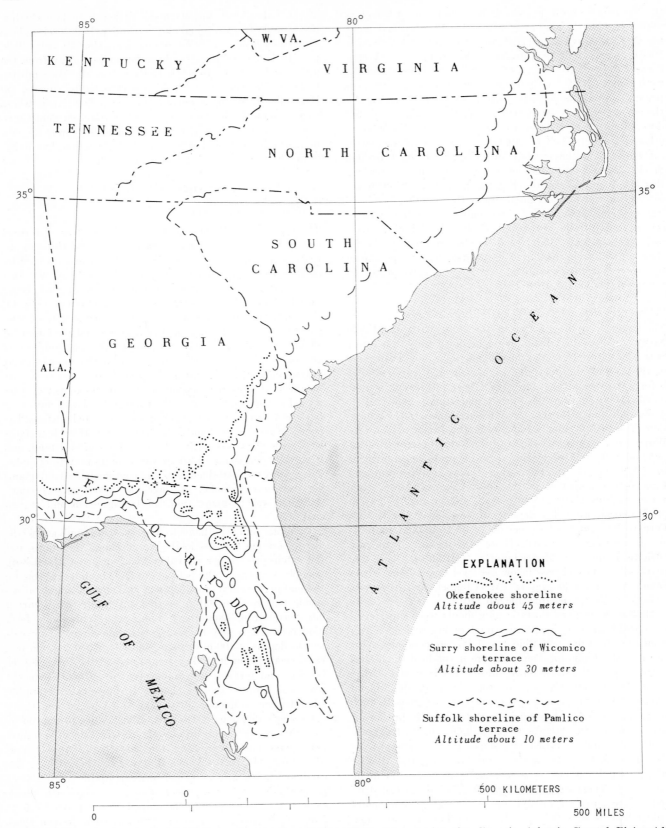

Figure 5. Map of southeastern Middle North America showing Quaternary marine shorelines in Atlantic Coastal Plain. After Flint (1940b) and MacNeil (1950).

South Carolina; this belt includes the epicenters of the Charleston earthquake of 1886, which had a magnitude of nearly 8 (Dutton, 1889; Wood, 1945). The only obvious tectonic feature near this transverse belt is the broad vague Cape Fear arch to the northeast, where the pre-Quaternary coastal plain formations have been so upwarped that Cretaceous strata lie at the surface nearly to the coast; however, epicenters are nearly lacking on this structure.

ATLANTIC COASTAL PLAIN

Characteristic morphological features of the seaward-sloping surfaces of the Atlantic and Gulf Coastal Plains are stepped plains or terraces, covered by Quaternary deposits that are at least partly of marine origin (Richards, 1962, p. 14-20; see also Richards and Judson, this volume).

The terraces and their deposits have been diversely interpreted. A traditional view, elaborated in many papers by Cooke (1931, 1935, 1936, and other publications), proposes the existence of seven terraces at altitudes of from 7 to 80 m, all supposed to be of marine origin. Other geologists have failed to find convincing evidence for the marine origin of the higher terraces; the existence of some is doubted and the remainder are believed to be of fluviatile origin (Flint, 1940b, p. 783-784; Hack, 1955, p. 34-37). From Virginia southward, however, two marine shorelines and accompanying offshore terraces are clearly marked—the Surry shoreline and Wicomico terrace at 30 m and the Suffolk shoreline and Pamlico terrace at 10 m (Fig. 5) (Flint, 1940b, p. 773-777). Only the lower of these marine features can be traced northward into New Jersey, where it is represented by the Cape May Formation that stands at the same height (MacClintock and Richards, 1936, p. 305-317), but in Florida and Georgia a higher Okefenokee shoreline and terrace has been recognized at 45 m and a lower Silver Bluff shoreline and terrace at 3 m (MacNeil, 1950, p. 99).

Possible submerged terraces offshore on the continental shelf have been reported from time to time but are difficult to verify without precise oceanographic work. The most convincing is one off the New Jersey coast, recently indicated by measurements with sub-bottom depth-recording equipment; it lies near the shelf edge at a depth of 146 m (Ewing *et al.*, 1960). Marine fossils collected from this submerged terrace indicate a cool-water environment; marine fossils preserved in the deposits of the lower of the emerged terraces on the coastal plain indicate waters slightly warmer than present (Richards, 1962, p. 15-17).

Most observers have stressed the nearly uniform altitudes of the terrace features in the Atlantic Coastal Plain south of the glaciated region, and they have accordingly ascribed them to eustatic rises of the sea during times of maximum interglaciation; presumably any submerged terraces off the coast represent time of maximum glaciation. In the traditional concept, the seven terraces were correlated with successive interglaciations or interstadial intervals beginning with the Aftonian (following the Nebraskan Glaciation). As we have seen, however, the higher terraces are questionable and may require other interpretations. Eustatic control seems more certainly to apply to the lower, better authenticated marine features, but correlation with specific interglaciations is uncertain; there is some evidence that the Pamlico terrace and Cape May Formation are equivalent to the Sangamon Interglaciation (between Illinoian and Wisconsin Glaciations). If the shorelines and terraces at the 30-m level and lower are the only valid marine features, they could have originated solely from eustatic rises in sea level; if higher levels are accepted as marine features, progressive emergence of the land would be required, either as a result of continental uplift or of lowering of the ocean bottoms.

A long-continued tectonic stability of the southeastern region is implied by the uniform altitudes of the marine features in the Atlantic Coastal Plain, but this stability is shared by neither the glaciated coast to the north (see above) or the Gulf Coast to the west (see below). However, Hack (1955, p. 39-40) points out the difficulties in detecting slight distortions in non-marine deposits and concludes that although crustal warping in southern Maryland is possible it cannot be proved. Doering (1960, p. 201), as a result of a regional study, proposes that non-marine surficial deposits of the inner part of the Atlantic Coastal Plain were downwarped toward the coast early in Pleistocene time, with lesser warping somewhat later, but like most other observers he believes that the younger marine shorelines and terraces nearer the coast were not perceptibly deformed.

SOUTH-CENTRAL REGION

The south-central region includes the Mississippi Embayment, the Mississippi delta, and the Gulf Coastal Plain to the east and west (Fig. 1); in this account chief attention will be given to the first two features. On geologic and tectonic maps the Mississippi Embayment is conspicuous as the deep indentation and downwarp of Cretaceous and Tertiary coastal plain deposits that extend across the Paleozoic rocks of the interior region as far as southern Illinois (Fig. 6A). The downwarp probably took form a little before the beginning of Tertiary time; earlier Cretaceous depositional patterns were different (Stearns and Marcher, 1962, p. 1392-1393). The upper half of the embayment was largely downwarped and filled with deposits by the end of the Eocene, after which depositional centers shifted southward, where the Gulf Coast geosyncline began to take form (Fisk, 1944, Figs. 61-70; Cushing *et al.*, 1964). During the Quaternary the surface of the embayment was dissected by the Mississippi River and its tributaries at times of lowered sea level and was covered by deposits of these streams at times of higher sea level. The younger part of these deposits forms the surfaces of the present alluvial valley of the Mississippi River and its delta.

The Mississippi River system assumed its present form as a result of drainage changes imposed by Pleistocene continental glaciation; large parts of the northern headwaters had previously flowed northward toward the Hudson Bay region. The extent to which preglacial rivers flowed southward into the embayment has been variously interpreted (Fisk, 1944, p. 68 and Fig. 76; Horberg and Anderson, 1956, p. 103-107). Nevertheless, the tectonically created Mississippi Embayment would seem to have been a natural funnel that would have entrapped drainage from extensive areas of the interior region during much of

Cenozoic time; certainly it has been such a funnel throughout Quaternary time.

NORTHERN PART OF MISSISSIPPI EMBAYMENT

Although most of the shaping of the northern part of the Mississippi Embayment occurred a little before the beginning of Cenozoic time, it still remains one of the most unstable parts of eastern Middle North America, as indicated by the dense clustering there of recorded earthquake epicenters (Fig. 2) (Woollard, 1958, p. 1144). These epicenters include those of the earthquakes between December 1811 and February 1812, known collectively as the New Madrid earthquake, several of which certainly exceeded a magnitude of 8; they rank among the greatest shocks in North America during historic time (Fuller, 1912). The earthquakes of 1811-1812 were not isolated phenomena;

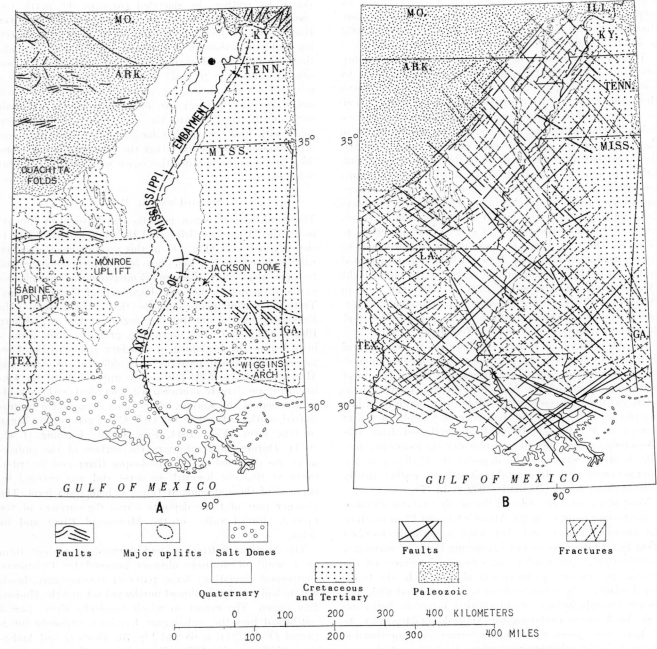

Figure 6. Maps of south-central part of Middle North America showing structures in Mississippi Embayment and Mississippi Delta. A: Structures in Tertiary and older rocks. B: Fault and fracture pattern in Quaternary and older rocks. After Fisk (1944, Figs. 5, 6, and 71).

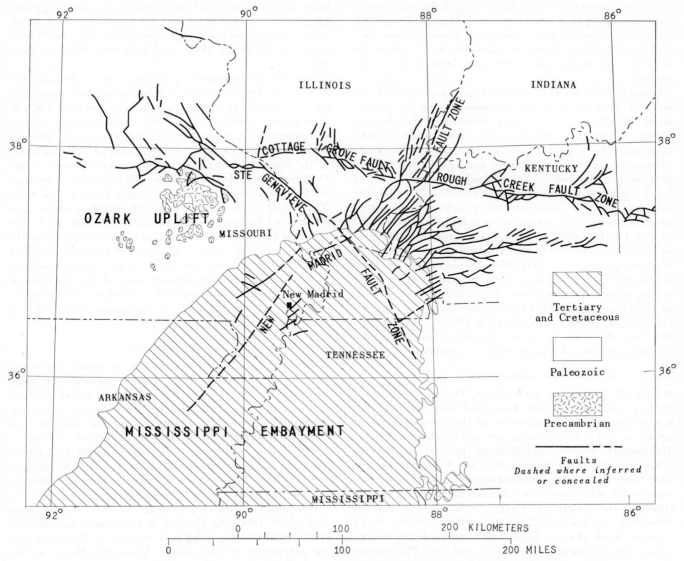

Figure 7. Map of northern part of Mississippi Embayment and adjacent parts of interior region showing faults in Paleozoic rocks and their inferred extensions into the younger rocks of the embayment. After Heyl and Brock (1961).

traditions prior to 1811 indicate an earlier instability, and many minor earthquakes occurred in the same region after 1812.

As the surface of much of the epicentral area is formed of poorly consolidated alluvial materials of the Mississippi River system, the New Madrid earthquake produced spectacular ground disturbances over most of the northern part of the embayment—within an area of 77,000 to 130,000 km². Ground fissuring, landslides, and sand boils were extensive. The ground surface was updomed near the epicenters and was depressed to the east and west, where extensive lakes and swamps were created by ponding of the waters (Fuller, 1912, Pl. 1, p. 47-95).

As in the area of the previously noted Charleston earthquake on the Atlantic Coast, the relation of earthquakes to geologic and tectonic features in the northern part of the Mississippi Embayment is obscure. The gross structures of this part of the embayment formed early in Cenozoic time, and afterward depositional and tectonic activity shifted farther south. The most significant structural feature of this part of the embayment seems to be the zone of bending along its axis (Stearns and Marcher, 1962, p. 1393). Also, the northern part of the embayment closely adjoins terranes of intensely faulted Paleozoic rocks—to the northeast in the Kentucky-Illinois fluorspar district and to the northwest in the southeastern part of the Ozark uplift (Fig. 7). The faults at the upper end of the embayment observably displace only the Paleozoic rocks and are truncated by Cretaceous deposits, but the faulted terrane undoubtedly extends beneath the younger deposits. Heyl and Brock (1961, p. D3-D4) suggest that two major lineaments of the faulted terrane, the Ste. Genevieve and New Madrid fault zones, extend across the upper part of the embayment. Shocks resulting from recent minor displacements on such faults would produce more prominent effects in areas covered by the alluvial deposits of the embayment than in the areas to the north, where Paleozoic bedrock is at the surface.

Other parts of the Gulf Coastal Plain have a much lower order of seismicity than the northern part of the embayment (Fig. 2). Many parts lack recorded earthquake epicenters, and the few that have been recorded are of small magnitude. The seismicity of the coastal plain seems to decrease coastward from its inner margin (Sheets, 1947, p. 204), despite the fact that the subsidence and warping of late Cenozoic time is greatest near the coast. Possibly the sediments near the coast are too poorly consolidated to produce shocks when subjected to deformation. According to Fisk (1944, p. 66-67, Figs. 6, 71) a conjugate pattern of faults and fractures extends over the whole Mississippi Embayment and delta (Fig. 6B). Displacements on these faults are slight, but they have markedly affected the stream courses, meander scars, and other ground patterns in the alluvial area. Minor faults of recent date are reported elsewhere in the coastal plain (Sheets, 1947, p. 209-214), but they seem to be less systematic, and many were probably produced by compaction of sediments.

TERRACES OF MISSISSIPPI EMBAYMENT

Within the Mississippi Embayment, Fisk (1939, p. 186; 1944, p. 63, Fig. 77) has recognized four terraces that border the modern alluvial valley of the Mississippi River, named in order of increasing age and height the Prairie, Montgomery, Bentley, and Williana. In addition, Doering (1956, p. 1832-1837) believes that the Citronelle Formation, which Fisk had correlated with the Williana, represents a still older terrace-like deposit. Each terrace surface truncates the underlying Tertiary strata and is covered by deposits as much as 25 to 90 m thick near the major streams. Each deposit begins with a basal gravel and passes upward through sand into silt and clay. The terraces differ in gradient; in central Louisiana the lowest slopes southward only a little more steeply than the modern alluvium, but successively higher terraces have gradients of 0.27, 0.95, and 1.5 m per km; the southward slopes of all the terraces apparently decrease farther upstream.

The terraces of the embayment area seem to be most satisfactorily explained within the context of the Pleistocene glaciations and interglaciations (Fisk and McFarlan, 1955, p. 290-297). During each glaciation, sea level was eustatically lowered many hundreds of meters and the Gulf shoreline retreated beyond the edge of the continental shelf; the floor of the Mississippi valley was then eroded, and deposition occurred only on the continental slope. With the waning of each glaciation sea level gradually rose, so that coarse and then fine deposits were laid on the valley floor, after which the cycle was interrupted by the next glaciation. The final cycle, after the last (Wisconsin) glaciation, produced the present alluvial deposits of the valley. Despite the general plausibility of this picture, attempts at correlation of the terraces of the embayment northward into the glaciated region of the upper Mississippi valley

have yielded conflicting and inconclusive results (Trowbridge, 1954, p. 798-801), and questions have been raised as to correlation of the terraces southward with the Pleistocene deposits of the delta area (Doering, 1956, p. 1832-1837).

As each successively older terrace, and its deposits, lies at a greater height, and as each has been tilted, more than eustatic changes in sea level were required to place them in their present positions; apparently the continental interior was being raised progressively during Quaternary time by regional epeirogenic uplift. Confirmation of such an uplift of the interior is suggested by the erosional record of the Driftless Area of Iowa and Wisconsin in the head drainage of the Mississippi River (Trowbridge, 1954, p. 801-804). The upland surface of this area is 90 to 180 m higher than the alluvial bottoms of the present valleys and 205 to 222 m higher than the bedrock bottoms of the valleys. In northeastern Iowa it is covered in places by remnants of till of Nebraskan age, whereas the valleys contain till and outwash of Kansan and later glaciations; most of the dissection of the Driftless Area occurred after the Nebraskan Glaciation, at least partly as a result of epeirogenic uplifts during Quaternary time.

MISSISSIPPI DELTA AND ITS PRECURSORS

A belt along the Gulf Coast in Louisiana and Texas was the site of extremely thick marine sedimentation from middle Cenozoic time onward; it has been called the Gulf Coast geosyncline. Total thickness of sediments above the Oligocene is as much as 19,000 m; Miocene sediments are as much as 15,000 m thick, Pliocene sediments as much as 1,800 m, and Quaternary sediments as much as 2,400 m (Crouch, 1959). Larger problems of the Gulf Coast geosyncline have been treated in many earlier publications; our interest is only in its later phases.

Quaternary sedimentation along the coast differed from that of the preceding Tertiary in being more localized, its depositional maxima being in a segment in Louisiana near the debouchure of the present Mississippi River and its antecedents, as though most of the sediments had been brought down to the coast by that river system. Moreover, Quaternary sedimentation appears to have been more nearly cyclical than the preceding sedimentation, the cycles being closely related to the terraces up the river valley, and both, ultimately, to the glacial, interglacial, and postglacial events of Quaternary time (Fisk and McFarlan, 1955, p. 290-297).

As each of the tilted terraces, and its accompanying deposits, in the Mississippi Embayment is traced downstream, its slope carries it beneath the younger alluvial deposits (Fig. 8). The Quaternary deposits of the coastal area to the south are divisible into formations that correspond in age to the several terrace deposits, but there these occur in reverse order, with the youngest at the top. The formations can be distinguished for some distance southward by their coarse basal deposits, which are equivalent to the coarse basal deposits of the terrace material to the north. Some geologists have applied the terrace names to the formations of the coastal area (Russell, 1940, p. 1214-1215; Akers and Holck, 1957, p. 984-986); others prefer to apply older

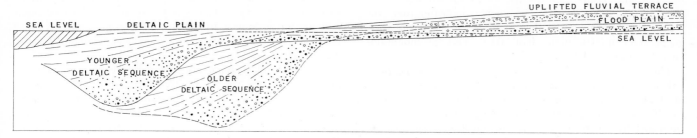

Figure 8. Diagrammatic section showing relation between Quaternary terrace and floodplain deposits of Mississippi Embayment and Quaternary deltaic sequences of Gulf Coast. Length of section about 300 km. Vertical scale much exaggerated. After Fisk (1944, Fig. 74).

names from the Texas coastal area, such as Willis, Lissie, Beaumont, and their subdivisions (Doering, 1956, p. 1822-1823). Presumably each deposit formed in an interglacial time; during glaciations the sea level was lower, and most of the sediments were carried beyond the edge of the continental shelf. Deposition of the final unit in the delta of the modern Mississippi River began after the time of the last glacial maximum.

Like the terrace deposits, the Quaternary deposits of the coastal area are tilted southward, but at much steeper gradients; the base of the next to the last formation (the Prairie Formation of some geologists) slopes southward at 19 to 24 m per km near its inner edge and steepens toward the coast; the bases of older and lower formations are even steeper (Fig. 8). Each formation is a wedge of deposits that thickens rapidly gulfward, changing from fluviatile and near-shore deposits to offshore marine deposits that are dominantly argillaceous. Successive formations are interpreted as having differently placed centers of maximum deposition, which are believed to be related to shifts in the point of debouchment of the Mississippi River system (Fig. 9) (Russell, 1940, Fig. 4, p. 1216). Offshore drilling a little west of the meridian of New Orleans has revealed the greatest known thickness of the Pleistocene deposits, nearly 2,400 m (Crouch, 1959, p. 1286).

The floor of the Quaternary deposits of the coastal area and the floors of the component formations each form a half-basin, open toward the Gulf (Fig. 8), and it is clear from the nature of the deposits that the floors of the half-basins subsided as sedimentation progressed. If the interpretations just reviewed are correct, areas of maximum subsidence and deposition of sediments correspond closely to areas of maximum delivery of sediments by the river system; this has been variously interpreted. Many geologists believe that the subsidence was caused by isostatic adjustment resulting from the loading with sediments (Fisk, 1939, p. 192-198; Russell, 1940, p. 1227; Lyons, 1957, p. 3-5). This would, however, require displacement of dense material at depth by light sediments above. A possible alternative is that the weight of sediments of each new cycle displaced the already existing mass of poorly consolidated sediments, rather than any more deeply lying material (Fisk and McFarlan, 1955, p. 301). Moreover, a possibility that the subsidence resulted from more fundamental

tectonic processes deserves further consideration (Lowman, 1949, p. 1989-1994); the river system itself owes its position ultimately to tectonic control, and this control may have been exerted on the structure of its offshore deposits as well. The data on conditions at depth are as yet insufficient to provide convincing evidence for or against any of these various possibilities.

GULF COASTAL PLAIN OF TEXAS

Quaternary formations fringe the coast westward from the Mississippi delta into Texas, and thence southward into Mexico. Equivalents of the units of the delta region can be recognized, although they are much thinner. Older units inland slope seaward at steeper gradients than the younger (Doering, 1956, p. 1837-1847). The units are largely nonmarine and of fluviatile origin, but marine fossils occur in the coastal part of the Beaumont Clay (Oberlin and Eunice Formations of Doering, 1956); these fossiliferous marine beds stand at altitudes of about 6 m in the north, but have been downwarped to sea level or lower near the mouth of the Rio Grande (Price, 1958, p. 42). Gradients of terraces along such Texas rivers as the Colorado and Nueces steepen progressively upstream and from youngest to oldest (Doering, 1956, p. 1840-1844, Fig. 6) like those in the Mississippi Embayment, and like them suggest a regional epeirogenic uplift of the continental interior during Quaternary time.

WESTERN INTERIOR REGION

CENTRAL AND SOUTHERN ROCKY MOUNTAINS
AND COLORADO PLATEAU

The Central and Southern Rocky Mountains of Wyoming and Colorado, and the Colorado Plateau southwest of them (Fig. 1), underwent a complex morphologic and tectonic evolution during Cenozoic time, only the later phases of which are of direct interest here.

The region was orogenically deformed during the late Mesozoic and the early Cenozoic (Paleocene and Eocene), producing a characteristic pattern of mountain uplifts with exposed cores of basement rocks in the Rocky Mountains, of wide basins between the uplifts, and of lesser upwarps and downwarps in the Colorado Plateau. During the deformation, the uplifted mountains were deeply eroded and the subsiding basins were thickly filled with sediments. The faunas and floras of the sediments indicate that the region stood much lower then than now—the basin areas at altitudes of little more than 300 m, and the mountains only 1,000 m or so higher.

This ancient geography contrasts with that of the present, when even the lowlands of the region stand at altitudes of about 2,000 m and many of the mountain ranges project to altitudes above 4,000 m. This geographical change was produced by the tectonic events of late Cenozoic time and by erosional and climatic regimes that resulted at least partly therefrom. While all observers agree on parts of the story of the tectonic events of late Cenozoic time, they

disagree significantly on other parts. The region has been so far from the sea and so near the headwaters of drainage systems for so long a time that the relative values of the tectonic, erosional, and climatic influences upon it are difficult to assess.

The essential tectonic event of late Cenozoic time was great regional epeirogenic uplift, which raised not only the Rocky Mountains, but also the Great Plains on the east and the Colorado Plateau on the west. According to traditional views, most of this uplift was accomplished near the end of the Tertiary, but with further episodes during the Pleistocene; in middle Tertiary time the region was lower and was subjected to widespread leveling, the moun-

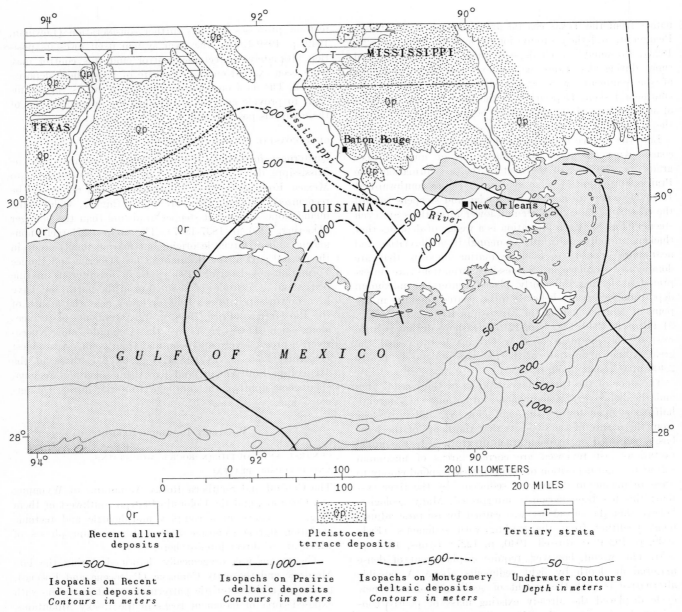

Figure 9. Map of southern Louisiana showing area of maximum deposition of Quaternary deltaic formations of Mississippi Delta area. Compiled from Russell (1940) and Fisk and McFarlan (1955).

tains being worn down to a "Rocky Mountain peneplain" and the surrounding lowlands being overspread by sheets of detritus (Atwood and Atwood, 1938, p. 964-978). The regional uplift of late Tertiary time was believed to have been accompanied in places (as in the San Juan Mountains of southwestern Colorado) by local uparching of the peneplained surface by as much as 1,200 m (Atwood and Mather, 1932, p. 21-26).

These views cannot be reconciled with the observation in the Uinta Mountains that the Gilbert Peak surface (or local representative of the "Rocky Mountain peneplain") is a pediment that was cut under arid conditions, whose steep gradients were initial and were not produced later by local arching of the mountains (Bradley, 1936, p. 174-179)—especially since similar observations have been made regarding the summit areas of the other mountains in the region. These observations harmonize, moreover, with indications that the late Tertiary sediments around the mountains and in the Great Plains were produced during conditions of increasing aridity and at progressively greater altitudes; the nature of deposits in the Great Plains indicates that they could only have been deposited by streams flowing on a surface whose gradient away from the mountains was not less than the present slope (Mackin, 1947, p. 106-107). Regional uplift was thus in progress during a longer span of late Tertiary time than was previously supposed, and the increasing aridity not only accompanied the uplift but was caused by it.

Quaternary time records the destruction of this relatively featureless erosional and depositional surface, formed at a high altitude in an arid climate; erosion was greatly invigorated, etching out the present mountains and basins. To what extent was this drastic change in erosional regime a result of tectonic forces? The traditional view has been that the great uplift of late Tertiary time quickened the work of the streams by increasing their gradients and by increasing their volume as a result of greater rainfall in the upraised mountain areas (Blackwelder, 1934, p. 561; Atwood and Atwood, 1938, p. 968). However, the later observations and interpretations just summarized prompt a heretical view that regional uplift during Quaternary time was no more than 300 to 600 m, and that much of the invigoration of erosion and increase in stream volume was produced by a worldwide secular change toward a humid climate that accompanied the Quaternary glaciations (Mackin, 1947, p. 113).

The alternative view just mentioned implies that the Central and Southern Rocky Mountains and Colorado Plateau have been relatively stable through much of Quaternary time. While it is true that faults, folds, and warps of probable Quaternary age have been reported in places (Hunt, 1956, p. 61-62), they appear to be minor and local. Present relative stability of the region is indicated by the wide scatter and random distribution of recorded earthquake epicenters (Fig. 2); the pattern does not differ significantly from that of the plains country east of the mountains but contrasts greatly with the seismically unstable belt immediately to the west and northwest, in the eastern part of the Great Basin and in the Northern Rocky Mountains.

BASIN AND RANGE PROVINCE

The Basin and Range province, characterized topographically by short sub-parallel ranges and intervening desert basins, extends across an enormous area near the central axis of the Cordillera of Middle North America, from Nevada and Utah on the northwest to New Mexico and west Texas on the southeast, with continuations into northern Mexico (Fig. 1). The origin of the Basin and Range topographic forms and their relations to tectonic and erosional processes have been dealt with in a voluminous literature (for summary see Nolan, 1943, p. 178-186). Suffice it to say that many of the ranges were raised by block-faulting at various times during the late Cenozoic, some so recently that their initial block forms are preserved, some so long ago that their initial forms are now destroyed by erosion. The block-faulting is a postorogenic process that was imposed on a varied bedrock; parts had earlier undergone much deformation, as in Utah and Nevada, but other parts had undergone little deformation, as in New Mexico. Most of the block faults are normal and hence are of tensional origin, although faults with strike-slip displacement occur and may be more prevalent than has been recognized. The tensional faulting did not produce a collapse of the crust; much evidence in the northwestern or Great Basin part of the province indicates that the surface has there risen many hundreds of meters since Eocene time.

Modern tectonic conditions in the Basin and Range province are indicated by the distribution of recorded earthquake epicenters (Fig. 2) (Woollard, 1958, p. 1141-1142). Epicenters are notably concentrated along the eastern and western borders of the Great Basin, the eastern belt continuing northward into the Northern Rocky Mountains (see below). Another concentration occurs in the block-faulted belt along the Rio Grande in New Mexico. Some other parts of the province lack epicenters entirely and are seemingly stable now—notably the central part of the Great Basin of Nevada and Utah and the Sonoran Desert region of southern Arizona. The pattern thus revealed corresponds remarkably to regions of late block-faulting marked by youthful, tectonically controlled topographic forms, and to regions of early block-faulting marked by mature or old, erosionally controlled topographic forms. Apparently, modern tectonic conditions in the Basin and Range province are representative of those that have prevailed during long periods of earlier Quaternary time.

Our interest here is in the extent to which block-faulting in the Basin and Range province occurred during Quaternary time. Ranges that preserve their initial block forms probably underwent their major uplift at some time during the Quaternary. The record in the block-faulted belt along the Rio Grande in New Mexico typifies that of many other parts of the province. Here, investigations by Kirk Bryan and his associates indicate that shaping of the modern ranges by block-faulting occurred early in Quaternary time (Bryan and McCann, 1938, p. 818-828; Wright, 1946, p. 428-431; and other publications); as a result of this shaping, the Pliocene and early Pleistocene deposits of the Santa Fe Group that occupy the intervening basins were greatly faulted and tilted near the mountain borders. The Santa Fe Group itself was deposited in pre-existing depressions, but

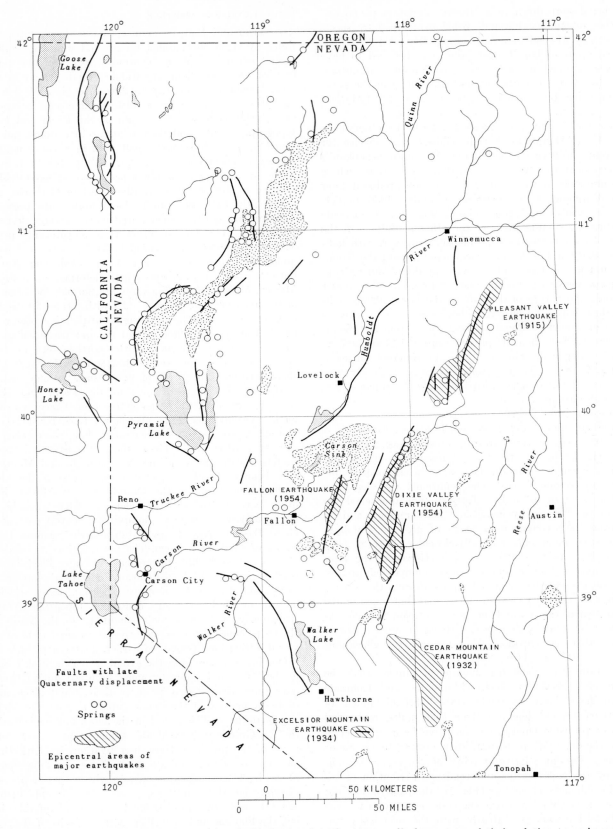

Figure 10. Map of northwestern Nevada showing faults having late Quaternary displacement and their relation to springs and to epicentral areas of major earthquakes. After Slemmons (1956).

whether these were produced primarily by faulting or primarily by downwarping is uncertain; faults border the depressions in at least some places (Kelley and Silver, 1952, p. 161-168). The earliest deposits in the depressions, and oldest components of the Santa Fe Group, are of Miocene age, but in other parts of the Basin and Range province Miocene volcanic rocks have been uplifted into mountain blocks, and the deposits of the intervening basins are younger.

Indications of faulting during late Quaternary time in the Basin and Range province are much plainer than those of earlier Quaternary time, but they are more localized. The escarpment faces of the block-faulted ranges originated as fault surfaces, but their upper parts, exposed to view before late Quaternary time, are now greatly battered and recessed by weathering and erosion. By contrast, the lower parts of many of these escarpments preserve the initial fault surfaces and end downward along even baselines. Here and there along the baselines the border faults themselves come to view, separating the bedrock of the mountains from the deposits of the intermontane depressions. Also, in parts of the province, thermal springs are common along the faulted mountain borders (Fig. 10). Where fresh escarpment bases occur, renewed upfaulting of the mountain blocks during late Quaternary time can be inferred, following a major mountain shaping during earlier Quaternary time, or even before.

In many places the surfaces of the deposits of the intermontane basins are offset by scarplets of late Quaternary age near the mountain borders. These were observed during the early geological investigations in the Great Basin (Gilbert, 1890, p. 340-362; Russell, 1885, p. 274-283), and were termed "piedmont scarps" by Gilbert (1928, p. 33). Scarplets more than 8 m high occur in places, but most are lower. Many of them indicate a downthrow away from the mountains, but some are paired to produce small grabens. The scarplets are approximately parallel to the fronts of the adjacent mountains but their traces are less regular, probably because of deflection of the displacements through the unconsolidated material; in places the scarplets join faults in the bedrock at the mountain bases. Those along the front of the Wasatch Mountains in Utah displace not only the intermontane deposits but glacial moraines and the shorelines of former Lake Bonneville (Fig. 11); those in northwestern Nevada displace the shorelines of former Lake Lahontan.

The scarplets show varying degrees of destruction by erosion, some being very fresh, others nearly obliterated or else perceptible only on air photographs. In some areas scarplets of more than one generation occur, indicating repetition of movements over a considerable period of time. Any individual generation of scarplets in a single area was probably produced simultaneously during ground movements accompanying one major earthquake, as has been confirmed by observations on the effects of earthquakes between 1915 and 1955 in the seismically active area of northwestern Nevada (Fig. 12) (Page, 1935; Gianella and Callahan, 1934; Slemmons, 1956, 1957).

The extent of late Quaternary faulting has not yet been plotted in detail so that only general relations in the entire

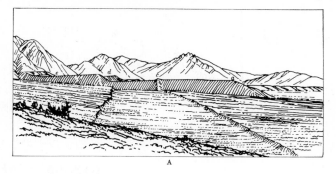

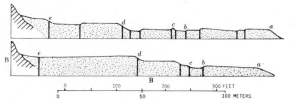

Figure 11. Scarplets produced by late Quaternary faulting in the Rock Canyon delta of former Lake Bonneville, on front of Wasatch Mountains near Provo, Utah. A: View from north. B: Two profiles on delta about 300 m apart, with correlative features indicated by letters. After Gilbert (1890).

Basin and Range province are known; the faulting in northwestern Nevada is shown in Figure 10. Faults of late Quaternary age are extensive along the western borders of the Great Basin in western Nevada and southeastern California, as well as along the eastern border of the Great Basin at the edges of the Wasatch Mountains and other ranges in Utah. Late Quaternary faults also occur throughout the length of the intermontane Salt Basin in western Texas (King, 1948, p. 113-114), and they have been recorded at many places in the Basin and Range province of New Mexico to the north. Late Quaternary faults seem to be missing in the more stabilized parts of the province, as in southern Arizona. So far as the extent of the late Quaternary faulting is known, it corresponds closely to areas where recorded earthquake epicenters are concentrated (Fig. 2).

The preceding account indicates that much of the present topography of the Basin and Range province was produced during the Quaternary by block-faulting and by associated erosion, sedimentation, and volcanism; it suggests that the faulting was concentrated in several episodes. As shown by Morrison (this volume), these episodes are well documented in the Great Basin part of the province, from their relations to dated Quaternary deposits. There, "essentially all" the existing topography was formed during Quaternary time, and very little now remains of the landforms of the early part of the period. A major episode of faulting occurred in very early Pleistocene time (Blancan), and a somewhat lesser episode in early middle Pleistocene time (post-Blancan, pre-Illinoian), after which faulting diminished and some areas became relatively stable. Topographic relief increased to a maximum at the close of the second episode,

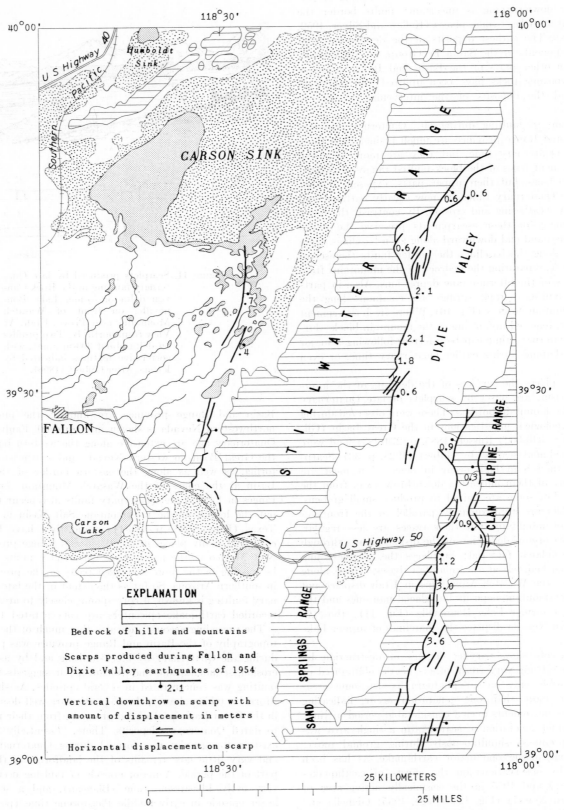

Figure 12. Map of area east of Fallon, Nevada, showing fault scarplets produced by ground movements accompanying the Fallon and Dixie Valley earthquakes of 1954. After Slemmons (1956, 1957).

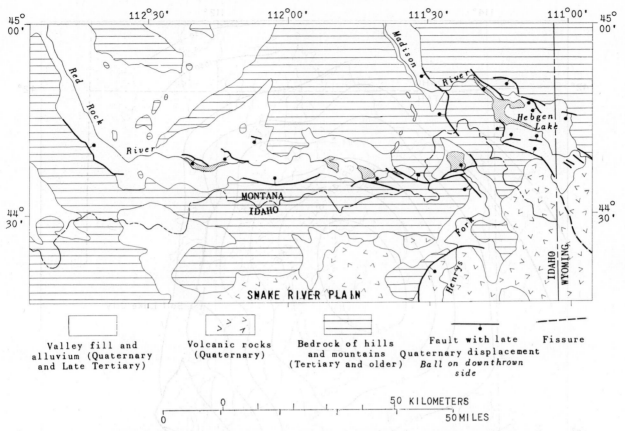

Figure 13. Map of parts of Montana and Idaho showing faults having late Quaternary displacement. After Myers and Hamilton (1964).

after which it decreased because of modifications by erosion and sedimentation.

NORTHERN ROCKY MOUNTAINS

Many data regarding Quaternary tectonics in the Northern Rocky Mountains were gathered during an investigation by the U.S. Geological Survey of the Hebgen Lake earthquake of August, 1959 (Witkind *et al.*, 1964). This earthquake occurred within the belt of recorded earthquake epicenters that extends northward from the eastern edge of the Great Basin (Fig. 2) (Woollard, 1958, p. 1141-1142; Ross and Nelson, 1964, p. 25-29) through a part of the Northern Rocky Mountains that was block-faulted during Cenozoic time in much the same manner as the Basin and Range province (Pardee, 1950).

The Hebgen Lake earthquake is the largest known in the region during historic time, with a magnitude of 7.1; its epicentral area was in the mountains of southwestern Montana, west of Yellowstone National Park. Ground movements that accompanied the earthquake produced a pair of basins trending northwest, each about 16 km long and 5 m or more deep, bordered by faults on their northeastern side (Fraser *et al.*, 1964, Fig. 50). Within the surrounding region, many older fault scarps are visible in the bedrock and Quaternary deposits, produced by movement during late Quaternary time. Their general trend and distribution is westward from the epicentral area, which sug-

gests that a transverse belt of structures has recently formed that crosses the prevailing northerly trend of this part of the Northern Rocky Mountains (Fig. 13) (Myers and Hamilton, 1964, p. 89-95)—a belt that parallels the Snake River Plain to the south, which was downwarped and deeply filled by lavas during Quaternary time (see below).

WARPING OF FORMER LAKE SHORES IN GREAT BASIN

Within the Basin and Range province are indications of many former lakes, large and small, that filled the depressions during a pluvial maximum that corresponds to the last (Wisconsin) glacial maximum. These lakes were most extensive in the northern Great Basin where the largest were Lake Bonneville and Lake Lahontan along the eastern and western sides (Gilbert, 1890; Russell, 1885; Morrison, this volume). At its greatest extent Lake Bonneville had an area of 52,000 km² and was as much as 335 m deep; it maintained a depth of 150 m over wide areas. At its greatest extent Lake Lahontan had an area of 22,000 km² and was as much as 270 m deep, but much of this former lake was only 100 m deep or less.

The classic studies of Gilbert (1890, p 362-386) revealed that the shorelines of Lake Bonneville have been upwarped in the central area with respect to the margins since the disappearance of the lake (Fig. 14). Gilbert correctly deduced that this upwarp resulted from isostatic adjustments following the removal of the load of lake waters, reproduc-

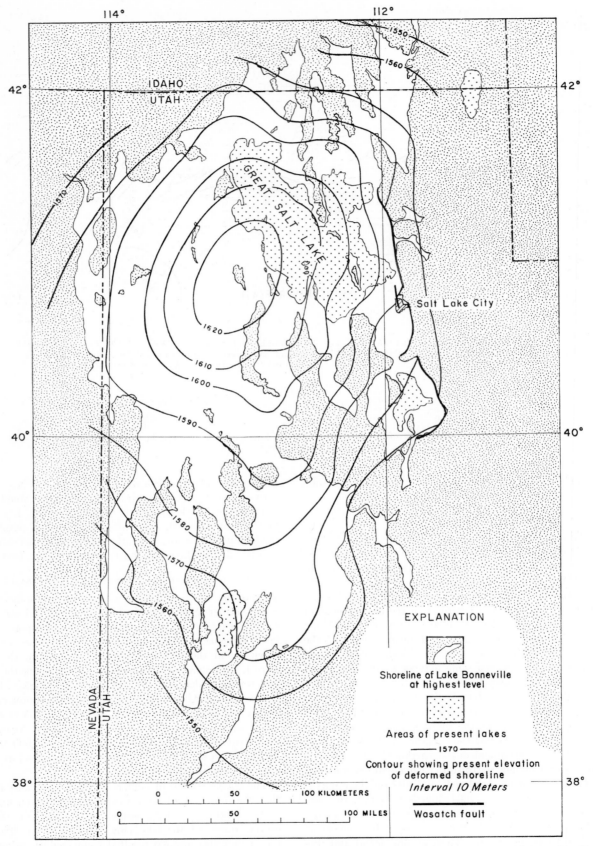

Figure 14. Map of northwestern Utah showing maximum area of Lake Bonneville and deformation of its highest shoreline. After Crittenden (1963).

ing on a small scale the uplift of the glaciated region of northeastern North America following removal of the continental ice caps. Observations on the shorelines of Lake Bonneville have recently been refined and amplified, and show that the upwarping amounted to as much as 64 m (Crittenden, 1963). Russell (1885, p. 101, 274-283) also recorded differences in altitudes of the shorelines of Lake Lahontan but ascribed them to faulting subsequent to the lacustrine period. Morrison (this volume) reports isostatic deformation of the highest Lahontan shoreline as 6 to 9 m. Probably Lake Lahontan was too small and too shallow to cause significant distortions in the crust; moreover, this lake lay in an area of active late Quaternary faulting; the resulting displacements would effectively mask any small isostatic adjustments that might have occurred.

NORTHWESTERN REGION

The northwestern region of Middle North America includes the states of Idaho, Oregon, and Washington and adjacent parts of the province of British Columbia (Fig. 1). The region differs much in geology and tectonic style from neighboring parts of the Cordillera, for here Cenozoic volcanic rocks and structures dominate the scene nearly to the exclusion of all others—lava plateaus, volcanic cones, eruptive ranges that were produced by upbuilding, and folded or block-faulted ranges that were produced by deformation of the volcanic materials. Cenozoic volcanic rocks, and the sedimentary rocks associated with them, extend along the coast for 480 km, and extend inland for as much as 680 km. Although pre-Cenozoic rocks form much of the periphery of the volcanic area, within it they emerge only as occasional inliers.

At the present time the northwestern region appears to be somewhat more stable than adjacent parts of the Cordillera. Most of its volcanoes are dormant, although a few have erupted within historic time. Epicenters of recorded earthquakes are fewer than to the east and south (Fig. 2).[2] On the east, this area of low seismicity is bordered by the belt of high seismicity that extends from the eastern side of the Great Basin into the Northern Rocky Mountains (see above). To the south, it passes abruptly into the area of high seismicity of the southwestern region along a boundary near the 41st parallel. This boundary seems to be the eastward extension of the Mendocino fracture zone of the Pacific Ocean floor, which is little expressed in the surface rocks of the continent. Within the northwestern region, the main seismic areas are in a belt that extends southward from Puget Sound through the Willamette Valley and a belt that extends northwestward from the western end of the Snake River Plain.

PRE-QUATERNARY FRAMEWORK

The pre-Cenozoic rocks of the inliers and at the periphery of the volcanic area are parts of eugeosynclinal sequences

of Mesozoic and Paleozoic age which were deformed, partly metamorphosed, and invaded by large plutons of granitic rocks during the last half of Mesozoic time. The eugeosynclinal and plutonic rocks form an arc, strongly convex toward the east, whose recess encloses the lower basin of the Columbia River. The arc, which may lie between parts of the crust of different character, much influenced the location and nature of the volcanic fields that were built over it during Cenozoic time. Volcanic rocks are not extensive north and east of the arc, but they do extend well to the southeast of it.

The volcanism during pre-Quaternary time has been treated at length in many other publications (for summary, see Waters, 1955, p. 704-713; Snavely and Wagner, 1963). The main Tertiary volcanic elements are: (a) submarine pillow basalts of lower Eocene age that are interbedded with graywackes of a eugeosyncline that existed on the site of the present Coast Ranges; (b) pyroclastics and lavas of andesitic and basaltic composition, largely of Miocene age, on the site of the present Cascade Range; (c) the Columbia River Basalt of Miocene age in the Columbia Plateau east of the Cascade Range in the recess of the arc of Mesozoic time; and (d) volcanic rocks of varied ages and compositions southeast of the arc in Idaho, Oregon, and California.

QUATERNARY VOLCANISM

During Quaternary time volcanism in the northwestern region was less extensive than during Tertiary time, but it produced notable features in the Snake River Plain and the Cascade Range.

The volcanic field of the Snake River Plain is southeast of the arc of Mesozoic time and extends transversely across the Cordillera through southern Idaho for a distance of 650 km, with a width of 65 to 160 km (for details, see Malde, this volume). The plain is broadly curved, its eastern two-thirds trending eastward and east-northeastward, its western third northwestward. It received accumulations of volcanics and associated sediments during late Tertiary time and through much of Quaternary time, the earlier volcanics including large silicic components, the later being dominantly basaltic (Stearns *et al.*, 1938, p. 25-32). The total accumulation of late Tertiary and Quaternary volcanic and sedimentary rocks near the axis of the plain is more than 3,000 m.

The volcanics of the Snake River Plain were probably erupted along a deep-seated line or lines of crustal weakness that broke transversely across the previous structures of the Cordillera late in geologic time, the pre-volcanic floor beneath the plain subsiding as the eruptions progressed. Deep-seated tectonic control of the volcanic field is indicated by its prevailingly positive Bouguer gravity anomaly (minus 100 milligals or less, compared with minus 200 milligals or greater in adjacent parts of the Cordillera). In the eastern two-thirds of the plain, subsidence was probably mainly by downwarping (Kirkham, 1931, p. 471-482; LaFehr and Pakiser, 1962, p. D77); older northerly trending Cordilleran structures plunge toward it from the north and south, and the lavas themselves are tilted toward the axis. In the western third of the plain subsidence was

---

[2] Figure 2 suggests a lack of seismicity off the coast to the west, but the data used were incomplete. Earthquakes have been recorded there, and Berg and Baker (1963, p. 106-107) suggest they may lie on an extension of the San Andreas fault zone of California.

accompanied by much faulting; on the northeastern side the downthrow of the faults exceeds 2,750 m in the older part of the volcanic sequence, but decreases in the higher parts (Malde, 1959). The western third of the plain has a larger gravity maximum than the eastern two-thirds, and is probably underlain by a greater thickness of volcanics (Hill et al., 1961). Continued instability of the western third is suggested by recorded earthquake epicenters (Fig. 2), which are part of a belt that extends much farther northwestward (Woollard, 1958, p. 1137) into an area where the belt appears to be little related to surface geology or structure.

The middle Tertiary andesitic and basaltic eruptions on the site of the Cascade Range were followed by a period of relative quiescence, during which the range was upheaved and maturely eroded (Lowry and Baldwin, 1952, p. 23). Upon this foundation was built a new andesitic and basaltic volcanic sequence, largely during Quaternary time but beginning a little earlier in places (Williams, 1942, 1953, p. 34-35; Waters, 1955, p. 711; Fiske et al., 1963, p. 65-91). Although the volcanic sequence includes moderately extensive flows, its most prominent manifestations are the chain of great volcanic cones, more than a dozen in number, that crown the Cascade Range between the 40th and 49th parallels, from California through Oregon and Washington. These include Mount Rainier (altitude 4,392 m), Mount Shasta (altitude 4,317 m), and other lofty summits. The volcanoes are aligned along a trend somewhat to the east of the vents that existed during Tertiary time (Peck, 1960, p. B310), both trends probably having formed over zones of deep-seated crustal weakness.

Records of eruption and cone building during glacial and postglacial time are plentiful (see Wilcox, this volume). One of the northerly volcanoes, Mount Garibaldi, 65 km north of Vancouver, British Columbia, was partly built over the Cordilleran ice cap of the Wisconsin glaciation, so that spectacular collapse and landslide features resulted when the ice disappeared (Mathews, 1952, p. 97-100). The collapse of former Mount Mazama to produce the caldera of Crater Lake, Oregon, has been dated at 6,600 years ago. Ash from this eruption has been spread over much of the northwestern conterminous United States and into southwestern Canada (Powers and Wilcox, 1964); part of that ash had been incorrectly ascribed to an eruption of Glacier Peak farther north (Rigg and Gould, 1957), but the last main eruption of the latter was about 12,000 years ago (R. E. Wilcox, written communication, 1964). Various minor eruptions of the volcanoes in Washington were reported during the first half of the 19th century, but some may not be authentic (Fiske et al., 1963, p. 82). The only eruption during the 20th century has been that of Mount Lassen, California, between 1914 and 1917 (Williams, 1932, p. 321-330).

QUATERNARY DEFORMATION

The coastal part of the northwestern region, a belt of 100 to 200 km wide, includes a set of Coast Ranges that culminate in the Olympic Mountains and a succession of lowlands between them and the Cascade Range that extend southward from Puget Sound in Washington and into the valley of the Willamette River in Oregon. The ranges and lowlands are formed of folded and faulted volcanic and sedimentary rocks of Tertiary age, broadly anticlinal in the ranges and broadly synclinal in the lowlands. In the lowlands the Tertiary rocks are covered in part by thin to thick Quaternary deposits, including much glacial drift and outwash in the north. The structural grain is reflected in the pattern of strong, localized Bouguer gravity anomalies, ranging from plus 40 milligals to minus 120 milligals (Stuart, 1961, p. 274), which are probably related, respectively, to large bodies of mafic volcanic rocks and to large bodies of sedimentary rocks.

Much of the deformation of the ranges and lowlands was completed before Quaternary time, although epeirogenic upwarping and downwarping has continued (Lowry and Baldwin, 1952, p. 22-23). Nevertheless, folds and faults in the Quaternary deposits have been observed in places (Crandell, this volume). Along the coast of the Strait of Juan de Fuca on the north flank of the Olympic Mountains, early Quaternary deposits in places are tilted as steeply as the adjacent Tertiary and are overlain unconformably by undisturbed outwash of the Vashon Glaciation (P. D. Snavely, oral communication, 1964). The Olympic Mountains themselves have a large negative gravity anomaly, unlike any other area close to the Pacific Coast, which indicates a deep-seated mass deficiency (Stuart, 1961, p. C275). As much as 100 m of downcutting has occurred on the north flank of these mountains since the Vashon Glaciation (P. D. Snavely, oral communication, 1964); evidently they are still in process of uplift and deformation.

Continued instability of the lowland belt between the Coast Ranges and Cascade Range is attested by the concentration there of recorded earthquake epicenters, especially in the north (Fig. 2); the greatest earthquake within historic time was in southern Puget Sound in 1946, with a magnitude greater than 6 (Barksdale and Coombs, 1946). Effects of the shocks were especially great in the Puget Sound area, where glacial drift is as much as 300 m thick in places. Some of the seismic activity there might be related to crustal warping associated with the last glaciation, but a relation to deformation of the rocks of the lowland seems more likely; one earthquake near Puget Sound has been ascribed to faulting along the western base of the Cascade Range (Bradford and Waters, 1934, p. 58-62).

TILTING AND CHANGES IN LEVEL RESULTING FROM GLACIATION

The northwestern region of Middle North America, as here delimited (Fig. 1), lies mainly south of the region of continental glaciation. The ice cap which covered most of the Cordillera farther north in Canada projected southward in lobes only into the lowland of Puget Sound on the west and the highlands north of the Columbia Plateau on the east; mountain glaciers were abundant farther south but are not of tectonic interest. In the Puget Sound area four glaciations have been recognized, of which the latest, or Vashon, is clearly equivalent to the Wisconsin Glaciation of the standard sequence of the continental interior (Crandell et al., 1958, p. 384-385; Crandell, this volume); as in the northeastern region of Middle North America, this latest glaciation was accompanied and followed by tilting and changes in level.

Changes in level are best documented in the northern part of the Puget Sound lowland near Bellingham, Washington, where a complex sequence has been unraveled (Easterbrook, 1963). Late in the Vashon Glaciation, about 12,000 years ago, the lobe of Cordilleran ice which covered the lowlands had thinned to about 100 m; as the crust had been depressed by the ice cap, sea water flooded the area and floated the thin lobe of ice both here and in the Fraser River valley to the north (Armstrong and Brown, 1954, p. 362). An emergence of a hundred meters or so followed, succeeded by a readvance of the ice several thousand years later, which was accompanied by a new submergence to a level of 150 m or more above present sea level; after this, the present emergence of the region began. These notable fluctuations in sea level in the space of a few thousand years resulted from combinations of isostatic uplift of the land during glacial unloading, eustatic rise in sea level, and local deformation (Easterbrook, 1963, p. 1480-1481).

Flint (1937, p. 230, and earlier publications) investigated the possibility of crustal warping near the former ice border in northeastern Washington. He observed that the upper surface of lake silts in Grand Coulee rises northward at a rate of 0.95 m per km, probably as a result of such warping, but concluded that other possible indications of warping are equivocal.

COASTAL TERRACES

The slopes along the Pacific Coast in the northwestern region are cut by a succession of emerged marine terraces, the highest terrace standing at an altitude of about 450 m, and each lower one being better preserved and more persistent than the ones above. Along the Oregon coast the lowest and most prominent terrace stands at an average altitude of about 30 m but has been somewhat warped, so that it descends to sea level in places and rises to an altitude of 70 m in others; its wave-cut surface is covered by the fossiliferous marine deposits of the Elk River Beds, probably of latest Pleistocene age (Baldwin, 1945, p. 35-36, 42-44). The deposits of this lowest terrace, and of several other well-marked terraces as high as 120 m, have been prospected in southwestern Oregon for their chromite-bearing sands (Griggs, 1945, p. 113-118). Terraces extend northward into Washington, but there the coast is more interrupted by inlets and the land between them is lower, so that the terraces are less clearly displayed; they resemble those in Oregon (Cooper, 1958, p. 10).

The lower valleys of the Columbia and Willamette Rivers are marked to altitudes as high as 120 m by terraces that are probably related to those along the coast, but the shaping of these valleys was influenced by changes in river volume, volcanism, and tectonic warping. The latest changes in level have drowned the lower courses of the rivers (Lowry and Baldwin, 1952, p. 22-23).

The coastal terraces were formed by progressive emergence of the land during Quaternary time, which was produced by a complex interplay among regional uplift, local uplift, and eustatic changes in sea level related to waxing and waning of the continental ice caps. The problem of the origin of the Pacific coastal terraces will be considered

further in the discussion of the southwestern region (see below).

SOUTHWESTERN REGION

The southwestern region of Middle North America includes the Sierra Nevada, Great Valley, Coast Ranges, and Transverse Ranges, all in California, and the Peninsular Ranges that extend southward from California into Baja California (Fig. 1). All parts of the southwestern region share a record of Quaternary tectonic activity greater than that of most other regions of Middle North America, even adjacent areas in the Cordillera. Modern crustal instability in the region is indicated by a dense concentration of recorded earthquake epicenters, as shown on Figure 2 (Woollard, 1958, p. 1141) —so much so, in fact, that little detail of pattern emerges within the scale of the figure. This concentration of epicenters extends eastward into the western part of the Great Basin, but it drops off abruptly northward along a boundary near the 41st parallel (see above). Similar crustal instability throughout Quaternary time is evident from the geologic record of the region, as set forth below.

Although the various parts of the southwestern region share a common Quaternary crustal instability, they differ much from one another in their geology and tectonics (for details, see Wahrhaftig, this volume). The Sierra Nevada and Peninsular Ranges are uplifted and tilted blocks, little disrupted internally, formed of rocks that were thoroughly consolidated by orogenies before Cenozoic time. The Great Valley is the depressed western part of the Sierra Nevada block that has been thickly covered by Cenozoic sediments. The Coast Ranges and Transverse Ranges have remained highly mobile to the present time, and throughout the Cenozoic were truly orogenic regions that underwent many pulses of folding and thrusting. Within these ranges there is, besides, a complex network of high-angle faults with dominant strike-slip displacement, on many of which movements are still in progress. The relation of these faults to the remainder of the tectonic fabric is not fully understood.

SIERRA NEVADA

The Sierra Nevada and large tracts adjacent to it were a eugeosynclinal area during Paleozoic and early Mesozoic time; later in the Mesozoic the deposits laid down there were deformed, steeply upended, partly metamorphosed, and invaded by large plutons of granitic rocks (Bateman et al., 1963, p. 5-9). By early Cenozoic time this deformed terrane had been deeply eroded; then it was more or less blanketed by sediments and volcanics. During these later times the tectonic style of the Sierra Nevada changed from one of deep-seated deformation and plutonism to one of tilting, block-faulting, and warping—a style it has retained to the present.

The Tertiary deposits that were laid over the surface of the Sierra Nevada were at first thought to be a rather simple "Superjacent Series" of auriferous gravels and associated volcanics, but they are now known to be much more complex and to include many rather thin formations of various ages, from Eocene to Pliocene. These accumulated on a deeply weathered surface of low to moderate relief, extensively preserved on the broad western slope of the

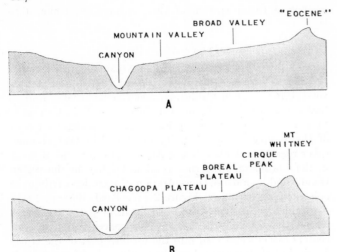

Figure 15. Diagrammatic profiles of summit areas and canyons on western slope of Sierra Nevada, as interpreted by Matthes, showing surfaces that were cut during erosional stages that occurred between uplifts of the range. A: Yosemite Valley segment. B: Mount Whitney–Kern River segment. After Dalrymple (1963).

range, where the surface and its cover of deposits have been tilted westward and greatly dissected. The range crest at the upper end of the tilted surface includes such eminences as Mount Whitney (altitude 4,418 m). The crest breaks off eastward in imposing escarpments, shaped by faulting and warping, whose bases are fringed by the westernmost intermontane depressions of the Great Basin. The faults on the east side of the range have dominant dip-slip displacements, although small right-lateral displacements occurred on some of them during the major Owens Valley earthquake of 1872 (Bateman, 1961).

As a result of the tilting, faulting, and warping, the crest of the Sierra Nevada block has risen progressively throughout Cenozoic time. Much of the block stood not far above sea level at the beginning; the crest now attains altitudes of 2,000 to 3,000 m in the northern half and altitudes of more than 4,000 m in the southern half. Details of the Cenozoic tilting and uplift, and especially the amount of such movements during Quaternary time have been variously interpreted (Wahrhaftig, 1962, p. 38-41). The record is plainest in the lower northern half, where remnants of the Tertiary "superjacent" deposits are extensive not only on the western slope but over the mountain crest. The record is weakest in the higher southern half where the cover of deposits, if it once existed, is now largely missing, and where the metamorphic and plutonic bedrock of the summits preserves erosion surfaces whose ages and structural history must be interpreted mainly by means of more tenuous geomorphic criteria.

Matthes, in his classic studies of the Cenozoic history of the high southern part of the Sierra Nevada, traced and correlated the erosion surfaces extensively, partly by iden-

tification of preserved remnants, partly by projection of gradients of the major streams and their tributaries. In the drainage areas of the Merced River (including Yosemite Valley) and the San Joaquin River to the south he recognized four stages of erosion (Matthes, 1930, p. 28-33; 1960, p. 40-41): a stage recorded only by remnants of a surface on the highest summits, possibly of Eocene age; a Broad Valley stage, supposed to have been completed near the end of the Miocene; a Mountain Valley stage, supposed to have been completed near the end of the Pliocene; and a Canyon stage when Yosemite and other valleys were incised during early Quaternary time. Glacial sculpture of the valleys occurred later (Fig. 15A). In the Mount Whitney and Kern River area farther south he recognized similar erosional stages (Mount Whitney, Cirque Peak, Boreal Plateau, Chagoopa Plateau, and Canyon stages; Fig. 15B), but he did not correlate them specifically with those in the Yosemite region (Matthes, 1937, see also Webb, 1946, p. 362-366). Matthes concluded that the site of the Sierra Nevada was stable and low-lying through much of the earlier part of Tertiary time, until the completion of the Broad Valley stage; after this it was uplifted to about half its present height before the completion of the Mountain Valley stage; and then the remaining half of the uplift occurred during the Canyon stage in early Quaternary time (Matthes, 1930, p. 28-29).

Subsequent investigators have sought to add more precision to the ages assigned to the erosional stages and times of uplift in this part of the Sierra Nevada, by use of a variety of techniques:

1. *Paleobotanical data.* According to Axelrod (1957, p. 34-38), the floras of late Miocene and early Pliocene age in the Sierra Nevada and Great Basin existed in similar climates, and those near the present crest of the Sierra Nevada could not have lived at altitudes greater than 750 m; it is inferred that the Sierra Nevada was then too low to cast an effective rain shadow over the Great Basin and that major uplift of the range sufficient to create the present rain shadow came later. More specifically, pollen in sediments that lie on correlatives of the supposed Eocene surface are believed to indicate a late Pliocene age, and pollen in sediments that lie on correlatives of the Broad Valley surface are believed to indicate an early Pleistocene (Kansan) age; it is inferred that the range was uplifted 900 to 1,800 m later in the Quaternary (Axelrod, 1962).

2. *Stream gradients.* Hudson (1955, 1960) has greatly expanded the earlier analyses of stream gradients by Matthes and others, in both the northern and southern Sierra Nevada. From these data he concludes that there has been much more internal deformation in the mountain block and substantially less uplift than was previously supposed—less than 600 m near Donner Pass and less than 1,200 m near Yosemite Valley. Downstream projection of former gradients of the Merced River is believed to indicate a correlation of the Broad Valley stage in the mountains with a pediment in the foothills that is assigned an early Pleistocene age; most of the uplift in this segment is therefore inferred to have occurred during the Quaternary (Hudson, 1960, p. 1552-1554).

3. *Radiometric dating.* Dalrymple (1963, p. 384-387) has obtained potassium-argon dates on basalt flows that are related to the erosion surfaces in the southern Sierra Nevada. These dates suggest that the Broad Valley surface was being dissected by canyons as much as 250 m deep before the end of the Pliocene and that the Mountain Valley stage of erosion had begun by early Pliocene time. These data lead to the inference that this part of the Sierra Nevada had a minimum relief of 1,200 m during the Pliocene.

4. *Sedimentary record in San Joaquin Valley.* Cenozoic sedimentation in the Great Valley, or depressed western part of the Sierra Nevada block, is closely related to Cenozoic erosion and uplift in the elevated eastern part of the block. The southern half, or San Joaquin Valley, opposite the high southern part of the Sierra Nevada, received a maximum of about 12,000 m of sediments during Cenozoic time, the thickness increasing toward the deep southern end, near Bakersfield, and also upward in the sequence (Hoots *et al.*, 1954, Figs. 4-10; Wahrhaftig, this volume). Upper Miocene sediments are notably thicker than those beneath, but are mostly fine grained. Pliocene and lower Pleistocene sediments that overlie the Miocene unconformably are equally thick but include notable quantities of coarse detritus derived from the Sierra Nevada. The remaining Pleistocene deposits are thinner and finer grained; they include the Corcoran Clay (a member of the Tulare Formation) near the top, a lacustrine deposit 60 to 240 m thick that covers an area of 13,000 km² (Frink and Kues, 1954, p. 2360-2363). Along the eastern edge of the valley, the youngest feature that has been significantly tilted away from the Sierra Nevada is the China Hat pediment, which is assigned a Pliocene age (Arkley, 1962, p. 29). The record of sedimentation in the San Joaquin Valley suggests that the major uplifts of the Sierra Nevada occurred from late Miocene to early Pleistocene time, and mainly in the Pliocene.

The four sets of data just enumerated do not harmonize either as to the times or the amounts of uplift in the Sierra Nevada, and some are as yet irreconcilable. It is worth noting, however, that the radiometric data and the record of sedimentation in the San Joaquin Valley agree broadly with Matthes' interpretation that most of the uplift occurred during the late Tertiary and early Quaternary. Interpretations that major uplifts have occurred during later Quaternary time seem to require further proof.

Data on the eastern escarpment, especially the segment between Mono Lake and Owens Valley, east of Yosemite Valley—the type area of the named glacial units of the Sierra Nevada (Blackwelder, 1931; see also Sharp and Birman, 1963; Birman, 1964, p. 11-12)—also have a bearing on the tectonic history of the Sierra Nevada during Quaternary time. Deposits of the earliest recorded glaciation, or McGee Till, form erosional remnants on ridge tops a little below the range summits and 900 m above the lowlands that fringe the base of the escarpment; clearly, they have been upfaulted high above their original positions (Putnam, 1962, p. 192-195); the till overlies basalt that has yielded a potassium-argon date of 2.6 million years

(Dalrymple, 1963, p. 387). Younger glacial deposits are more closely related to the present topography—the much weathered and eroded Sherwin Till fringes the mountain bases, and the fresher Tahoe, Tenaya, and Tioga Tills form looped terminal moraines at the canyon mouths; even these later tills are somewhat disturbed by faulting.

The lowlands east of the mountains had a complex late Cenozoic volcanic history (Gilbert, 1941; Wilcox, this volume). Two basins, at Mono Lake and Long Valley, seem to have originated as calderas, and geophysical surveys suggest that they are filled by poorly consolidated volcanic and sedimentary material to depths as great as 5,500 m (Pakiser, 1960, p. 155). The most extensive unit of the lowlands is the Bishop Tuff, which was spread widely as an ignimbrite; it overlies glacial till, and both tuff and till have been much warped and moderately faulted. The underlying till has been correlated with the Sherwin (Putnam, 1960, p. 233-237). Certainly it is of an early Pleistocene age, because the Bishop Tuff has yielded a potassium-argon date of 980,000 years,[3] and basalt beneath the till a date of 3.2 million years (Dalrymple, 1963, p. 387; Evernden *et al.*, 1964, p. 175).

The younger tills in this sequence seem obviously to correspond to subdivisions of the Wisconsin Glaciation of the standard sequence; correlations of the earlier ones are more speculative. It has been suggested that the McGee Till corresponds to the Kansan Glaciation, with the implication that this part of the Sierra Nevada had not been uplifted and upfaulted sufficiently before Kansan time to nourish earlier glaciations (Putnam, 1962, p. 204-205). However, the extreme age of the till beneath the radiometrically dated Bishop Tuff suggests that glaciation in the area had begun early in the Pleistocene; for this and other reasons the McGee has alternatively been correlated with the Nebraskan Glaciation (Sharp and Birman, 1963, p. 1084-1085; Morrison, this volume). Regardless of details of correlation it is clear that this part of the Sierra Nevada escarpment has undergone much faulting and major relative uplift during early Quaternary time and that lesser movements have continued since the last glacial maximum. It is tempting to relate this faulting and uplift to the tilting of the west slope of the Sierra Nevada block, but it is possible that they may relate more closely to a collapse and subsidence of the lowland block to the east (Wahrhaftig, 1962, p. 39).

COAST RANGES AND TRANSVERSE RANGES

The Coast Ranges of the southwestern region extend south-southeastward along the Pacific Coast for 925 km, from Cape Mendocino past San Francisco Bay to Point Concepion, and are separated from the Sierra Nevada farther inland by the Great Valley. South of Los Angeles the Peninsular Ranges similarly extend south-southeastward into Baja California. In the intervening area are the eastward-trending Transverse Ranges. Cenozoic strata, largely of marine origin, are thick and extensive in the Coast Ranges south of San Francisco Bay, as well as in parts of

---

[3] Revised date for the Bishop Tuff is **700,000** years (Cox *et al.*, this volume).

the Transverse Ranges and in adjacent basins. It is these parts of the coastal mountains that are chiefly discussed here.

In most of the Transverse Ranges and in parts of the Coast Ranges the Cenozoic strata are underlain by a metamorphic and plutonic basement, similar to that of the Sierra Nevada and Peninsular Ranges. In large parts of the Coast Ranges, however, the Cenozoic strata are underlain by a thick mass of late Mesozoic deposits, mainly the Franciscan Formation—a much disordered assemblage of graywackes, argillites, cherts, and pillow basalts. The original relations of this Franciscan basement to the metamorphic and plutonic basement are unknown, as the two are everywhere separated by faults. Differences between the two basements have much influenced the style of the Cenozoic deformation; blocks underlain by metamorphic and plutonic basement have been relatively rigid, whereas Cenozoic rocks overlying the blocks of Franciscan basement have been much folded.

The complex record of Cenozoic sedimentation in the Coast Ranges and Transverse Ranges need not be traced in detail (see Reed and Hollister, 1936, p. 1559-1597; Taliaferro, 1943, p. 135-149). Deposits of Miocene and earlier ages are extensive and mainly marine, but some of them grade eastward into continental equivalents. Pliocene marine deposits occur in more restricted areas, such as the Los Angeles, Ventura, and Santa Maria basins, the San Francisco Peninsula, and elsewhere along the coast, as well as in the Great Valley east of the Coast Ranges, especially in the San Joaquin or southern part (Woodford *et al.*, 1954, p. 73-74; Bailey and Jahns, 1954, p. 91-92; Hoots *et al.*, 1954, p. 123-124). Marine Pliocene strata attain a maximum thickness of 4,000 to 4,500 m in the Ventura basin (Pico Formation and lower part of Santa Barbara Formation) and are nearly as thick in the other basins mentioned; non-marine Pliocene strata in various basins within the ranges are even thicker (Wahrhaftig, this volume).

In most of the basins the marine Pliocene deposits are succeeded with little or no discordance by lower Pleistocene marine and brackish-water deposits. Although these are thinner than the Pliocene they still have impressive proportions; in the Ventura basin they attain a thickness of 1,200 to 1,500 m (upper part of Santa Barbara Formation and San Pedro Formation) (Bailey, 1943, p. 1556-1562; Bailey and Jahns, 1954, p. 92-93). The early Pleistocene age of these deposits has been established by correlation with standard marine sequences; their relation to the glacial sequences of the continental interior is undetermined, and they might even be preglacial (Eaton, 1928, p. 138-139); an alleged cool-water facies of the faunas, suggesting a glacial climate, cannot be justified (Woodring, 1952, p. 406-407). In all the exposed sequences a wide gap separates the lower Pleistocene basin deposits from the upper Pleistocene marine terrace deposits and alluvium; this gap may not have the same duration at all places, and it probably disappears in the centers of the basins where middle Pleistocene deposits are buried (Woodring, 1952, p. 402). Differences between the early and late Pleistocene marine faunas are not of zonal significance, the first being of a basinal facies whose marginal facies is no longer preserved, the second

being of shallow-water, near-shore facies (Valentine, 1961, p. 347-348).

The Cenozoic sequence of the Coast Ranges and Transverse Ranges records an eventful tectonic history, with times of deformation indicated at so many levels and with such varying magnitude from place to place that the deformations are difficult to generalize into sets of orogenic climaxes (Gilluly, 1949, p. 567-569). Perhaps this is not only because of the persistent mobility of the region but also because of the completeness of the record. Nevertheless, a group of deformations during middle and late Miocene time appears to have been important, to have deformed the earlier Cenozoic strata widely, and to have restricted the areas of subsequent sedimentation (Reed and Hollister, 1936, p. 1589-1592; Taliaferro, 1943, p. 141-142). Throughout most of the Coast Ranges from San Francisco to Santa Barbara the lower Pliocene and older strata were strongly deformed before the Plio-Pleistocene deposits were laid over them, but this deformation ends eastward at the edge of the San Joaquin Valley (Wahrhaftig, this volume). A final climax of deformations occurred during Quaternary time, mainly during the gap between the lower and upper Pleistocene deposits (Reed and Hollister, 1936, p. 1594-1596; Taliaferro, 1943, p. 147-149; Bailey, 1943, p. 1562-1564).

The effects of this mid-Pleistocene orogeny are well displayed in the Palos Verdes Hills at the southwestern edge of the Los Angeles basin, where lower Pleistocene strata are tilted nearly as steeply as the older formations, and are overlain unconformably by upper Pleistocene marine terrace deposits which are only moderately tilted (Woodring *et al.*, 1946, p. 109-110). It is even more pronounced in the Ventura basin, where the angular unconformity between lower and upper Pleistocene is nearly right-angled in places (Fig. 16B) (Putnam, 1942, p. 750-751; Bailey, 1943, p. 1555-1556). There, the lower Pleistocene and underlying Pliocene were steeply upended and strongly folded and were overridden by thrusts from both the north and south (Fig. 16A). Along the west side of the San Joaquin Valley the folded Pliocene and lower Pleistocene Tulare Formation forms the surface of most of the anticlines (Hoots *et al.*, 1954, p. 128). The Pliocene and lower Pleistocene Merced Formation of the San Francisco Peninsula is likewise folded and overlain unconformably by upper Pleistocene deposits (Glen, 1959, p. 150-151). Similar deformation reported in most of the other late Cenozoic basins has generally been ascribed to the mid-Pleistocene orogeny, although it cannot everywhere be dated so exactly by strata contiguous to the unconformity.

Deformation during mid-Pleistocene time in the Coast Ranges and Transverse Ranges is judged to have been greater than the mid-Miocene deformation, and it has been stated that its "magnitude and intensity . . . exceeded that of any disturbance since the Nevadan revolution of the late Jurassic" (Hoots *et al.*, 1954, p. 128). It was dignified as the "Pasadenan orogeny" by Stille (1936, p. 867-868), who considered it to be the latest of a sequence of major orogenies of worldwide extent.

However, the magnitude of this mid-Pleistocene orogeny seems to have been somewhat overrated. Most of the ex-

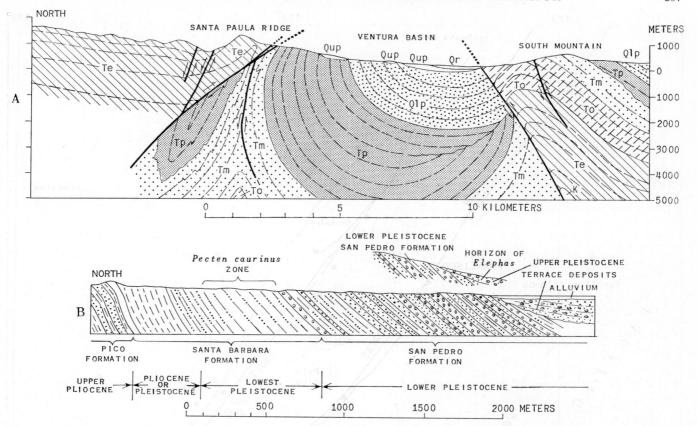

Figure 16. Sections illustrating mid-Pleistocene deformation in Ventura basin. A: General section across the basin, about 20 km east of Ventura, showing structure of Tertiary and Quaternary rocks. After Bailey and Jahns (1954). B: Detailed section of Pleistocene formations in north part of basin, in Hall Canyon near Ventura; the short section above shows additional features east of the canyon. After Bailey (1943). *Explanation of symbols:* K, Cretaceous; Te, Eocene; To, Oligocene; Tm, Miocene; Tp, Pliocene (Pico Formation and lower part of Santa Barbara Formation); Qlp, lower Pleistocene (upper part of Santa Barbara Formation and San Pedro Formation); Qup, upper Pleistocene (Terrace deposits); Qr, Recent (alluvium of Santa Clara River valley).

amples of extreme deformation occur along the edges of basinal areas that had been formed either upon a weak Franciscan basement or between blocks of metamorphic and plutonic basement; the deformation is therefore "frame-folding," as was recognized by Stille (1936, p. 868). Even within the basins, many of the localities of notable mid-Pleistocene deformation are adjoined by localities where the rocks are either little deformed or had been deformed at other times (Gilluly, 1963, p. 151); strata in the centers of the basins were probably little disturbed, and deposition during the Pleistocene was nearly continuous (Gilluly, 1950, p. 104-105). Moreover, a significant part of the deformation of the Pliocene and older rocks in the Coast Ranges west of the San Joaquin Valley that is usually ascribed to the mid-Pleistocene orogeny was probably produced by orogeny during the Pliocene (Wahrhaftig, this volume). It is unlikely that all the marked deformation that is evident in the different areas occurred simultaneously; in this respect the mid-Pleistocene orogeny probably does not differ from earlier orogenies for which the record is less

perfect. Major mid-Pleistocene deformation has also been proposed for the mountain areas outside the basins (*e.g.*, Taliaferro, 1943, p. 147-149). It is true that these mountain areas are in a very youthful state of development, with steep ridges and slopes on even the least resistant rocks; but it seems likely that these youthful mountain forms were produced quite as much by vertical uplift as by tangential compression.

HIGH-ANGLE FAULTS OF COAST RANGES
AND TRANSVERSE RANGES

The structure of the Coast Ranges and Transverse Ranges is greatly confused by a multitude of faults, including low-angle to high-angle thrusts that are mostly of short length, as well as other high-angle faults of much greater length that have dominant components of strike-slip displacement. The latter mostly cross the grain of the ranges at an acute angle in a northwestward direction, but a conspicuous set trends eastward in the Transverse Ranges (for general review, see Crowell, 1962). Strike-slip displacement on the

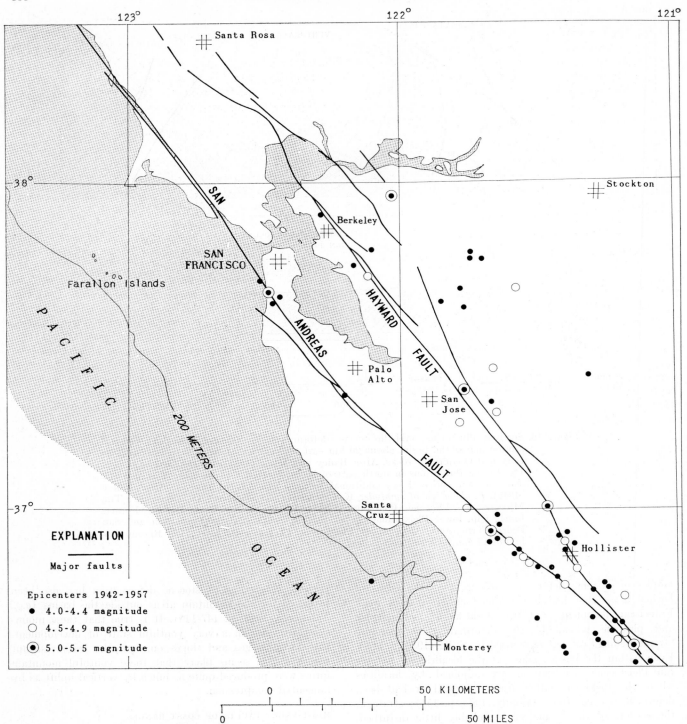

Figure 17. Map of San Francisco region showing traces of the San Andreas, Hayward, and other major faults and the location of earthquake epicenters recorded between 1942 and 1957. After Tocher (1959).

northwest-trending set is dominantly right lateral and on the eastward-trending set dominantly left lateral. The most lengthy of the high-angle faults is the San Andreas—the fault that crosses diagonally all the coastal ranges from northern California to the Mexican border with a nearly straight southeastward course, except for a mild eastward deflection where it passes through the Transverse Ranges.

Nearly every aspect of the high-angle faults of the Coast Ranges and Transverse Ranges has been diversely interpreted—the time of their inception, the magnitude of their movements, and their role in the geologic history of the region. The San Andreas fault has been variously estimated to have originated before Cretaceous time and to have been displaced as much as 560 km (Hill and Dibblee, 1953, p. 449); or to have originated during Quaternary time and to have been displaced less than 2 km (Taliaferro, 1943, p. 161). Some of these conflicting estimates arise from failure to recognize that the modern San Andreas fault is only one part of a broader and older fault zone (Wallace, 1949, p. 803). These problems regarding the high-angle faults do not greatly concern us here; our main interest is in their Quaternary history. Along the San Andreas fault and many others in the region there are overwhelming indications of marked displacement and deformation during Quaternary time and of continuing activity today (Fig. 17).

Modern activity along the high-angle faults of the Coast Ranges and Transverse Ranges is attested by the fact that many of the earthquake epicenters of the region (Fig. 17) are located on or near them (Gutenberg and Richter, 1954, p. 32-33), and by ground breakage along the faults at the times of such earthquakes; a right-lateral offset of as much as 6.4 m occurred along the San Andreas fault at the time of the San Francisco earthquake of April 1906 (Byerly, 1951, p. 153). Besides sudden ground breakage along the faults at the times of major earthquakes, slow persistent creep occurs along them, shown in places by distortion of buildings (Tocher, 1960). Other fault movements during the last few hundred or few thousand years are attested by characteristic landforms along the fault traces—fault trenches or rifts, and pressure ridges and sag ponds within the rifts (Sharp, 1954, p. 21-25). Even more striking is the distortion of the modern topography across the faults, shown by the offsets of ridges and stream channels that cross them. Stream channels crossing the San Andreas fault are offset right-laterally by 100 to 1,500 m, with abandoned valleys that are so placed as to suggest earlier and still greater offsets (Fig. 18).

Less is known about displacements earlier in Quaternary time along the high-angle faults. One of the few segments along the San Andreas fault where the Pleistocene formations have been studied in detail is between Soledad Pass and Cajon Pass north of Los Angeles in southern California, where the two principal units are the Harold Formation and Shoemaker Gravel (Noble, 1954, p. 41-42, 46). Both units are more deformed than the oldest parts of the overlying alluvium, being gently tilted at some distance from the fault and violently disturbed and faulted within the rift zone. Moreover, the Harold Formation north of the fault differs lithologically from the Harold Formation juxtaposed on the south side, but it is lithologically like the Harold Formation on the south side 3 to 8 km to the west, suggesting an offset of comparable distance since it was deposited. Indications of similar offsets during Quaternary time may be discovered elsewhere along the San Andreas and other faults when the Pleistocene deposits associated with them are given similar scrutiny.

The record of displacement along the San Andreas and other high-angle faults during Quaternary time suggests that movements were progressive. Thus, each of the features mentioned above is more offset and more deformed

the greater its age, mainly because each feature has participated in all the subsequent progressive movements on the faults. Whether there have been conspicuous climaxes or pauses in such movements is more difficult to ascertain, although climaxes are suggested in the Soledad Pass–Cajon Pass area by the unconformable relation between the early Pleistocene deposits and the later alluvium.

MARINE TERRACES

The coastal slopes of the southwestern region, like those of the northwestern region, are marked by emerged marine terraces (Fig. 19). Southward from Oregon (where we have already described them) they occur along the whole coast of California and Baja California, as well as on the offshore islands (for summaries, see Putnam, 1954; Emery, 1960, p. 5-8). They were observed long ago by Lawson (1893), who ascribed them to a marked epeirogenic uplift of the land during Quaternary time, accompanied by local deformation. Here, we shall discuss mainly the terraces of southern California for which many data are available; those elsewhere along the coast are similar (Wahrhaftig, this volume).

One of the best displays of terraces is in the Palos Verdes Hills on the coast southwest of the Los Angeles basin (Fig. 20) (Woodring, *et al.*, 1946, p. 113-116, Pl. 22). The hills are cut into a flight of terrace steps, 13 in number, the lowest at an altitude of 30 m and the highest at 395 m, or only a little below the highest summit; in most of the hills the terraces are nearly undeformed, but on their northeastern side the lowest has been tilted as steeply as 26° toward the Los Angeles basin (Woodring *et al.*, 1946, p. 109-110; Secs. II', JJ', and KK', Pl. 22). Many of the terraces (9 of the 13) are covered by marine gravels; the terraces and their deposits truncate the deformed underlying rocks, including the lower Pleistocene in places. Fossil shells in the marine deposits on the terraces are of species now living off the Pacific Coast, although some of the species are north or south of their present ranges.

Similar terraces occur farther northwest along the coast. In the Santa Monica Mountains and the Ventura basin the highest are at altitudes of 250 m and 400 m, but marine deposits are well preserved only on terraces lower down, and many terraces are masked by later hill wash and colluvium (Davis, 1933, p. 1063-1073; Putnam, 1942, p. 739-745; Putnam, 1954). Near Ventura, as in the Palos Verdes Hills, they truncate deformed Pliocene and lower Pleistocene deposits (Fig. 16B), and they are themselves warped and locally faulted. West of Santa Barbara terraces that bear marine fossiliferous deposits are prominent at 18 and 27 m, but as many as 15 less well preserved terraces extend up to heights of 500 m (Upson, 1951, p. 423-428).

Terraces are also preserved on the offshore islands. They are especially prominent on San Clemente and San Nicolas Islands—the islands farthest out to sea. On San Clemente Island the highest is at an altitude of 580 m; on San Nicolas Island 13 terraces occur up to an altitude of 275 m, and nearly all bear fossiliferous marine deposits (Vedder and Norris, 1963, p. 8-10). On Santa Rosa Island two terraces at altitudes of 30 and 75 m are prominent, but there are higher ones also (Orr, 1960, p. 1113). The prominent terraces on San Clemente Island are cut in resistant volcanic rocks, yet such terraces are lacking on nearby Santa Catalina Island, composed of equally resistant rocks. Lawson (1893, p. 138-139) supposed that Santa Catalina had a different Quaternary history from the neighboring islands, but traces of former stands of the sea seem to be expressed here by flattenings on the ridge profiles (Emery, 1960, p. 7-8).

The Quaternary of Baja California is known mainly from reconnaissance studies, and details have been worked out only in places (Beal, 1948, p. 28-33). The Peninsular Ranges and their metamorphic and plutonic rocks form the backbone of the peninsula down to the 28th parallel. On their western slope the Tertiary rocks and even the latest Cre-

taceous are much less deformed than in the Transverse Ranges and Coast Ranges of California; presumably the Quaternary is equally undisturbed. Along many parts of the west coast there is a prominent terrace at altitudes of 3 to 8 m, capped by fossiliferous marine Pleistocene deposits (Emerson, 1956, p. 321-324; Addicott and Emerson, 1959, p. 7-13, 24-29), but inland there are much higher terraces. Near the 29th parallel five terraces extend up to altitudes of 425 m (Arnold, 1957, p. 247-248). On the east coast and on the islands in the Gulf of California marine terraces have been observed as high as 90 m (Anderson, 1950, p. 46-47). Besides the terraces, banks of shells and scattered shells, all nearly identical to modern species, occur at greater altitudes; they are abundant up to 560 m, and some have been reported as high as 900 m (Beal, 1948, p.

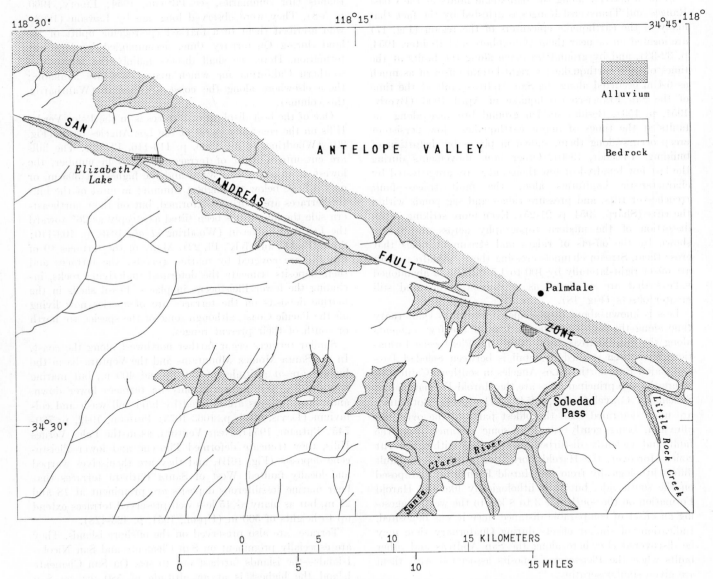

Figure 18. Map of a segment of the San Andreas fault zone near Soledad Pass, north of Los Angeles in southern California, showing deflection of drainage that crosses the zone. Much of the deflection results from right-lateral fault displacement. Note especially the course of Little Rock Creek at east edge of map. After Wallace (1949).

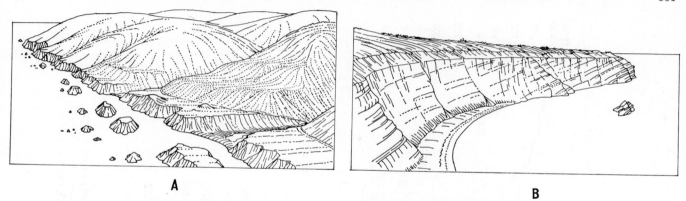

A   **B**

Figure 19. Views of late Pleistocene marine terraces along Pacific Coast of California. A:
Well-preserved lower terrace and fainter higher terraces on the coast near Cape
Viscaino north of San Francisco, at latitude 39°45′. B: Terrace about 30 m above
sea level truncating tilted Miocene strata, near Laguna south of Los Angeles, at
latitude 33°30′. From drawings by W. M. Davis (1933).

31-32). Some of these may be in kitchen middens of the aboriginal inhabitants, others may represent former stands of the sea.

Until recently all discussion of marine terraces dealt with those above sea level and on the land, but precise surveys at sea now show that submerged terraces also exist, not only along the mainland but also around the offshore islands and on the adjacent banks (Fig. 20) (Emery, 1958, 1960, p. 32-37). As many as five submerged terraces can be recognized, down to depths of 150 m; calcareous algae dredged from them at depths of 100 to 115 m lived in much shallower water, and support the interpretation that the terraces were formed during lower stands of the sea (Emery, 1958, p. 56). Lower stands of the sea are further suggested by the alluviated lower courses of coastal valleys, whose underlying rock-cut floors are as deep as 90 m below sea level (Upson, 1949, p. 95-108), and by gullied submarine slopes below depths of 90 m, which are thought to have been cut by subaerial erosion (Buffington and Moore, 1963, p. 365-369).

Submergence that began in late-Pliocene time drowned the lower end of the Sacramento–San Joaquin drainage to depths of 210 to 300 m. Part of the drowned area still remains as San Francisco Bay; the remainder was built into land by sedimentation during Quaternary time (Howard, 1951, p. 105; Wahrhaftig, this volume). Late-Pleistocene formations in the bay area record times of falling and rising sea level, probably related to glaciations and interglaciations. The fourth and last rise in sea level, during post-Wisconsin time, gave the bay its present outline.

The marine terrace deposits are believed to be of late Pleistocene age; if any of them are correlative with the early Pleistocene basin deposits it remains to be proved; Valentine (1961, p. 428) suggests that the gap between the basin deposits and terrace deposits "may thus include some of either Yarmouthian or Aftonian through much of Sangamonian time." Discrepancies between occurrence of species in the terrace faunas and the modern ranges of these species to the north or south suggest climatic controls that may be related to Pleistocene glaciations and interglaciations, but these discrepancies involve so many other ecological factors that climatic control is difficult to prove (Woodring *et al.,* p. 100-103; Valentine, 1961, p. 423-425). The low terrace deposits at altitudes of about 30 m at various places along the coast from Santa Cruz southward beyond San Diego have yielded radiocarbon dates that are greater than 30,000 or 40,000 years (Bradley, 1956, p. 676; Addicott and Emerson, 1959, p. 26-29; Orr, 1960, p. 1115; Vedder and Norris, 1963, p. 53), and these deposits may have formed during the Sangamon Interglaciation. Calcareous algae from submerged terraces at depths at 100 to 115 m have yielded radiocarbon dates of 17,000 to 24,500 years and may have formed during the succeeding Wisconsin Glaciation (Emery, 1958, p. 56).

The emerged and submerged marine terraces along the coast of the southwestern region have clearly been produced by combinations of eustatic falls and rises of sea level related to glaciations and interglaciations, regional uplift and depression, and local tectonic warping, but the relative value of these influences are difficult to appraise (Putnam, 1954, p. 48). In a region so unstable tectonically, correlations of terrace sequences from one area to another are hazardous—the hazards being greater the higher and older the terraces. Modern knowledge indicates that there were not only epochs of emergence, as previously believed, but also epochs of submergence, although the relations of the emergences to the submergences are not yet completely understood. The older terraces, some at altitudes as great as 400 to 500 m, seem to be much higher than could have been produced by eustatic rises in sea level, and they were very likely produced by regional or local uplifts, as originally proposed by Lawson (1893). An anomaly, as yet unexplained, is the fact that valleys behind the coast afford no evidence for such deep submergence, but instead they commonly contain Quaternary continental deposits at much lower altitudes (Wahrhaftig, this volume). The lowest emerged terraces and the submerged terraces seem to be related to interglaciations and glaciations, and their eustatic control is more plausible. After the cutting of the last submerged terrace, sea-level fluctuations have probably been mainly upward, as shown by the alluviated valleys along the southern coast.

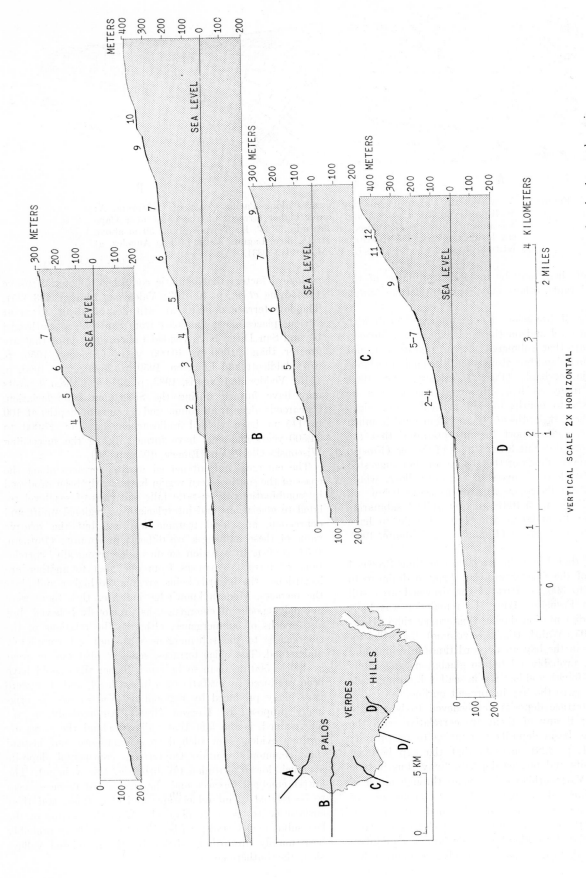

Figure 20. Profiles of Palos Verdes Hills and offshore area, southwest of Los Angeles, to show emerged and submerged marine terraces. Compiled from Woodring et al. (1946) and Emery (1958). Numbers on emerged terraces are those assigned by Woodring et al. and Kew. Profile A corresponds to profiles 14 and A-A' of the originals; B to 15 and C-C'; C to 16 and E-E'; D to 18 and F-F'.

SYNTHESIS

Knowledge of the Quaternary and its tectonics helps significantly in understanding the evolution of the earth's crust during a longer span of geologic time. Much more can be learned regarding tectonic events and processes of the Quaternary—the time now existing and the time recently past—than about those of earlier times, for which the records are more fragmentary.

Can the tectonic record of Quaternary time set forth in the first part of this paper be assembled into a synthesis with broad meaning? Would the synthesis, if made, indicate that the tectonic record of the present, and of Quaternary time in general, is like that of earlier times or that it is significantly different? To what extent is the uniformitarian principle of Hutton and Lyell applicable to the problem? Is the present the key to the past, and are existing processes, acting in the same manner as at present, sufficient to account for all geological changes (Neilson *et al.*, 1951, p. 2777; Gilluly *et al.*, 1951, p. 68)?

Several geologists have sought an underlying meaning for the tectonics of Quaternary time and have propounded various and differing philosophies, some of which will now be examined. Later, the tectonic record of Quaternary time in Middle North America will be summarized, and then I shall offer my own judgments and convictions.

PHILOSOPHIES OF QUATERNARY TECTONICS

Philosophy of Stille. By far the most completely integrated philosophy of the tectonics of Quaternary time is that which has been evolved by Stille, who has presented his ideas in successive publications of which two in English are representative (1936, 1955).

According to Stille, Quaternary time included a major, worldwide Pasadenan orogeny that began about 500,000 years ago[4] and quickly reached its culmination. Although this orogeny is still continuing now, the earth is probably on the threshold of an anorogenic phase. The observable duration of the Pasadenan orogeny demonstrates the shortness of orogenic phases in general, as well as the much greater length of the intervening anorogenic phases.

Although the Pasadenan orogeny was a worldwide event, it did not produce alpinotype deformation, characterized by paroxysms in the orthogeosynclines and formation of nappe structures. Instead, it produced germanotype deformation, which in California was a frame-folding of basin areas between more rigid blocks. Even the island arcs and trenches around the Pacific border, which some geologists have thought were alpinotype structures in state of growth, are merely an exaggerated form of germanotype tectonics.

Absence of alpinotype deformation during the Pasadenan orogeny reflects the present nearly complete consolidation of the earth's crust. This consolidation has been in progress since the "Algonkischer Umbruch" of Middle Precambrian time; the "Umbruch" destroyed the consolidated crust of late Archean time and created a new system of broad, worldwide orthogeosynclines. Consolidation has been accomplished by a closing up of the orthogeosynclines during successive orogenies, each of which added more and more of the former orthogeosynclines to the cratonic areas, until no orthogeosynclines now remain. With increasing consolidation of the crust, diastrophism has accelerated, and spacing between orogenic phases has become progressively shorter. Because consolidation of the crust is now nearly complete, Stille believes that another "Umbruch" is to be anticipated in the near geologic future.

Philosophy of Nikolaev and Schultz. Another view has been expressed by Nikolaev and Schultz (1960; see also King, 1962) and provides the theoretical basis for the Neotectonic Map of the U.S.S.R. These geologists, and their Russian colleagues, have used the term "neotectonics" for the tectonics of Quaternary and later Tertiary time. They believe that the early part of the Neogene (mid-Tertiary time) was a period of maximum stability and planation, marking the end of the tangential movements that had created the Alpine chains. The neotectonic phase followed thereafter, although its beginning was probably not everywhere contemporaneous.

Nikolaev and Schultz state that their compilation of the map of the U.S.S.R. has revealed the following characteristics of the neotectonic phase: (1) Movements were omnipresent. (2) They were of differing intensities from place to place. (3) Movements were predominantly vertical, either upward or downward, rather than tangential. (4) Upward and downward movements occurred in alternately placed areas. (5) Faulting occurred along both new and old lines of dislocation. (6) Neotectonic movements created the present configuration of the land surface and the ocean bottoms.

They explain further (as paraphrased from the original, 1960): The map establishes the leading importance of vertical tectonic movements during the neotectonic phase. Little indication of horizontal movements appears on the map, and such movements are rather insignificant, consisting only of gentle overthrusts in some areas of mountain building. These results are comparable to previous deductions of V. V. Beloussov and others as to the leading role of vertical movements during earlier stages of tectonic evolution of the crust.

Philosophy of Gilluly. The features of Quaternary tectonics were appraised by Gilluly (1949, p. 562-567) as part of his study of the distribution of mountain building in geologic time, and examples are cited of tectonic activity now in progress. Observations during the past half century indicate that some of the folds in California are being uplifted at rates of 1 to 6 m per century, and that France as a whole is being tilted northward at a rate of 3 m per century. If these movements should persist for 200,000 years, the folds in California would be raised to mountainous heights, and France would be flooded by the sea. Thus, the present is an orogenic rather than an anorogenic time. Moreover, deformational processes ordinarily considered to be distinct in origin and time are concurrently in progress at one place or another—orogenic and epeirogenic, compressional and tensional.

---

[4] This figure is given in the later publication (1955, p. 175); the earlier publication gives 250,000 to 300,000 years (1936, p. 870).

Deformational processes like those active at present have taken place through much of the near past, as shown by the 42 or more unconformities recorded in the Quaternary and Tertiary sedimentary sequence in California. In some places in California thick sequences of clastic sediments indicate nearly continuous uplift and deformation of the source areas for 10 to 15 million years, or far longer than has been assumed for the duration of an orogenic period. Events of earlier geologic time are blurred by the increasingly incomplete record in the older and older rocks, but there is no convincing evidence that these events differed from the better documented events of Quaternary and Tertiary time.

Gilluly believes it unlikely that diastrophism has been periodic, that it has been accelerating from the distant past to the present, or that the tectonic events of the present and of Quaternary time in general differ significantly from those of earlier times. "The uniformitarianism of Lyell seems not yet to require any of the amendments that have been suggested. . . . I believe we should, as geologists, . . . not assume changes in actualistic geology until they are compelled by observations. It is my belief that such changes are not required by the evidence in hand" (1949, p. 589).

Some extensions of the uniformitarian concept. In concluding the discussion of the philosophies of Quaternary tectonics, I should like to examine possible extensions of the uniformitarian concept, although such extensions are implied, rather than specifically stated in publications. If existing processes, acting in the same manner in the past as at present, are sufficient to account for all geological changes, did these processes operate at the same rate, or were they concentrated during significant episodes in the past? Are the tectonic and other geologic episodes suggested by the record merely an illusion—the cumulative effect of many small increments, imposed through long periods of time, in a non-episodic, steady-state regime?

Regarding the mountain belt of western North America, Gilluly (1963, p. 168) proposes that tectonic and volcanic activity have been essentially uniform in intensity from the beginning of Cambrian time, although they have been highly episodic locally. A steady-state regime is thus assumed for a large region, but not for its smaller parts.

On the other hand, Hack (1960, p. 95-96), in interpreting the erosional history of the Appalachian region in the eastern United States, rejects the episodic interpretation previously made for it, which required times of stillstand and planation, separated by times of uplift and dissection. He believes that the landforms of the region were eroded during a prolonged condition of dynamic equilibrium, probably during a single period of dying orogeny or of isostatic adjustment.

Along the San Andreas fault of southern California, Wallace (1949, p. 799-803) describes progressively greater displacements in successively older Quaternary and Tertiary formations, without indicating significant climaxes or pauses of movement. He suggests a possible average rate of displacement along the whole fault zone of 1 km per 250,000 years (1 mile per 400,000 years). With Wallace's data and an assumption of 2,000,000 years for the duration

of the Quaternary, total displacement during the period would be about 8 km. If such relatively steady displacement has occurred, Quaternary formations near the fault would become more and more disordered and deformed the greater their age, without any deformational climaxes.

Similar calculatons, which would produce similar results, might be made for other areas where deformation is now in progress, such as in the Coast Ranges of California and the Basin and Range province farther east. These calculations would suggest the possibility that, given the known rates of deformation today and the great lengths of time involved, even during the Quaternary, the structural features of these regions might have been created without the assistance of any deformational climaxes.

Summary. From this review, it is clear that notably divergent views have been expressed as to the nature of the tectonics of Quaternary time. It has been proposed that the tectonic regime of this time was very much like that of earlier times (Gilluly), or that it was materially different—either a new and distinct phase (Nikolaev and Schultz) or the culmination of successive changes over a very long period (Stille). It has been proposed that tectonic events occurred during periodic, worldwide episodes (Stille) or during episodic local events that blend into a worldwide steady state of tectonic activity (Gilluly), or that a steady state of tectonic activity existed not only throughout the world but in local areas (extended uniformitarian concept).

QUATERNARY TECTONICS IN MIDDLE NORTH AMERICA

The Quaternary tectonics in Middle North America, which has been reviewed at length in this paper, is an adequate sample of Quaternary tectonics in general and contributes significantly to any philosophical interpretation. The tectonic features and events in this sample include:

1. Depressions and uplifts of the crust caused by isostatic adjustments. In northeastern and northwestern North America these resulted from the emplacement and removal of masses of continental ice, and in the Great Basin from loading and unloading by the waters of large lakes.

2. Epeirogenic or vertical upwarping of broad parts of the crust. Upwarping has been in progress during the Quaternary in the Appalachian and Rocky Mountains, although perhaps at a slower rate than earlier; it also seems to have occurred in much of the continental lowlands. Epeirogeny has seemingly been accompanied by reactivation of older structural trends, as suggested by patterns of recorded earthquake epicenters.

3. Downwarping of coastal plains and continental shelves, accompanied by sedimentation, especially near the Gulf Coast. This downwarping was produced in part by isostatic adjustments resulting from sedimentary loading, and perhaps in part by independent tectonic processes.

4. Block-faulting, which has transformed an extensive terrane in the Basin and Range province into a succession of parallel mountain ranges and intervening troughs.

5. Volcanism, especially in the northwestern region, where lava floods covered the Snake River Plain. Volcanic cones were built up along the Cascade Range. This volcanism was less extensive than earlier volcanism in the same area, per-

haps because of the shorter time involved. It seems to have been localized along deep-seated lines of crustal weakness.

6. Orogenic deformation in the coastal mountains of California and adjacent areas, where tangential forces have created complex folds and thrust faults, and where blocks have been shifted by strike-slip displacements along high-angle faults.

7. Emergence and submergence on nearly all the coasts south of the glaciated region. Some emergence and submergence resulted from local or regional tectonic movements, but much of it was caused by eustatic rises and falls of sea level related to interglaciations and glaciations.

APPRAISAL

The tectonic record of Quaternary time in the sample from Middle North America seems on first view to be rather diverse and miscellaneous. Its most distinctive feature, and its most obvious difference from earlier times, is the kind of data available. Observable tectonic features of Quaternary time are surface or near-surface phenomena, produced by processes that are either still at work or that were at work in the recent past. Most of the observable tectonic features of pre-Quaternary time formed well below the surface and were produced by processes that are no longer operative. If the same kinds of data were available for both Quaternary and pre-Quaternary time, the tectonic features would appear to be much more alike. The only features that are unique to the Quaternary are those produced isostatically or eustatically as an effect of the unusual climates of the time—warping resulting from loading and unloading of the ice caps, and sea-level changes resulting from waxing and waning of the ice caps.

The nature of the remaining Quaternary tectonic features of Middle North America supports Gilluly's contention that they were produced by forces and under conditions that do not differ significantly from those of earlier geologic periods. Over large areas they are products of vertical rather than tangential forces, but this situation is not unique in the Quaternary and late Tertiary, as is implied by Nikolaev and Schultz. Similar vertical movements were probably in progress throughout geologic time in the cratonic areas, as well as in the dormant mountain chains; active tangential deformation was always confined to localized orogenic belts, as it now is. There is thus no clear separation between a "neotectonic" phase and earlier tectonic phases. Stille's concepts are supported to the extent that North America has become progressively more emergent and higher through Tertiary and Quaternary time, and to the extent that the part of North America subject to orogenic deformation has become more restricted. Whether this situation is a culmination of processes that originated as early as Precambrian time is beyond the scope of our inquiry; its more immediate cause is the great orogenies of late Mesozoic and early Cenozoic time and their aftermaths. The record of the Quaternary gives little support to Stille's contention that deformation during the orogenies has become more germanotype and less alpinotype during the later periods. It appears quite as likely that alpinotype deformation has shifted into new areas along or beyond the continental margins, and that structures as complex as those of earlier periods may be still forming there.

The tectonic record of Quaternary time in Middle North America thus generally supports the concept of uniformitarianism. Nevertheless, I cannot subscribe to the assumption that this concept requires a non-episodic, steady-stage regime of tectonic and other geologic processes in local areas, although some such activity was certainly taking place at all times. More likely these processes attained a succession of climaxes; these climaxes are not always easy to prove, but for Quaternary time, at least, an unusual array of techniques is available for testing their reality. This is not to say that the climaxes were necessarily synchronous over great areas; perhaps some were, many others were probably not. I therefore reaffirm my earlier conviction regarding the episodic nature of tectonic activity (King, 1955, p. 737-738)—that during later geologic time it resulted in major episodes of orogenic activity in the Coast Ranges, of block-faulting in the Basin and Range province, and of epeirogenic uplift in the Rocky Mountains and in the Appalachians.

REFERENCES

Addicott, W. O., and Emerson, W. K., 1959, Late Pleistocene invertebrates from Punta Cabras, Baja California, Mexico: Amer. Mus. Nat. Hist. Novitates, No. 1925, 33 p.

Akers, W. H., and Holck, A. J. J., 1957, Pleistocene beds near the edge of the continental shelf, southeastern Louisiana: Geol. Soc. Amer. Bull., v. 68, p. 983-991

Ambrose, J. W., 1964, Exhumed paleoplains of the Precambrian Shield of North America: Amer. J. Sci., v. 262, p. 817-857

Anderson, C. A., 1950, Geology of islands and neighboring land areas, *in* 1940 E. W. Scripps cruise to the Gulf of California: Geol. Soc. Amer. Mem. 43, pt. 1, 52 p.

Arkley, R. J., 1962, The geology, geomorphology, and soils of the San Joaquin Valley in the vicinity of the Merced River, California, *in* Geologic guide to the Merced Canyon and Yosemite Valley, California: California Div. Mines Geol. Bull. 182, p. 25-31

Armstrong, J. E., and Brown, W. L., 1954, Late Wisconsin marine drift and associated sediments of the Lower Fraser valley, British Columbia, Canada: Geol. Soc. Amer. Bull., v. 65, p. 349-363

Arnold, B. A., 1957, Late Pleistocene and Recent changes in land forms, climate, and archaeology in central Baja California: Berkeley, Univ. California Publ. Geog., v. 10, p. 201-318

Atwood, W. W., and Atwood, W. W., Jr., 1938, Working hypothesis for the physiographic history of the Rocky Mountain region: Geol. Soc. Amer. Bull., v. 49, p. 957-980

Atwood, W. W., and Mather, K. F., 1932, Physiography and Quaternary geology of the San Juan Mountains, Colorado: U.S. Geol. Surv. Prof. Pap. 166, 176 p.

Axelrod, D. I., 1957, Late Tertiary floras and the Sierra Nevada uplift [California-Nevada]: Geol. Soc. Amer. Bull., v. 68, p. 19-45

—— 1962, Post-Pliocene uplift of the Sierra Nevada, California: Geol. Soc. Amer. Bull., v. 73, p. 183-198

Bailey, T. L., 1943, Late Pleistocene Coast Range orogenesis in southern California: Geol. Soc. Amer. Bull., v. 54, p. 1549-1567

Bailey, T. L., and Jahns, R. H., 1954, Geology of the Transverse Range province, southern California, *in* Jahns, R. H. (ed.), Geology of southern California: California Div. Mines Bull. 170, p. 83-106

Baldwin, E. M., 1945, Some revisions of the late Cenozoic stratigraphy of the southern Oregon coast: J. Geol., v. 53, p. 35-46

Barksdale, J. D., and Coombs, H. A., 1946, The Puget Sound earthquake of February 14, 1946: Seismol. Soc. Amer. Bull., v. 36, p. 349-354

Bateman, P. C., 1961, Willard D. Johnson and the strike-slip component of fault movement in the Owens Valley, California, earthquake of 1872: Seismol. Soc. Amer. Bull., v. 51, p. 483-493

Bateman, P. C., Clark, L. D., Huber, N. K., Moore, J. G., and Rinehart, C. D., 1963, The Sierra Nevada batholith—a synthesis of recent work across the central part: U.S. Geol. Surv. Prof. Pap. 414-D, p. 1-46

Beal, C. H., 1948, Reconnaissance of the geology and oil possibilities of Baja California, Mexico: Geol. Soc. Amer. Mem. 31, 138 p.

Berg, J. W., Jr., Baker, C. D., 1963, Oregon earthquakes, 1841 through 1958: Seismol. Soc. Amer. Bull., v. 53, p. 95-108

Bird, J. B., 1954, Postglacial marine submergence in central Arctic Canada: Geol. Soc. Amer. Bull., v. 65, p. 457-464

Birman, J. H., 1964, Glacial geology across the crest of the Sierra Nevada, California: Geol. Soc. Amer. Spec. Pap. 75, 80 p.

Blackwelder, Eliot, 1931, Pleistocene glaciation in the Sierra Nevada and Basin Ranges: Geol. Soc. Amer. Bull., v. 42, p. 865-922

—— 1934, Origin of the Colorado River: Geol. Soc. Amer. Bull., v. 45, p. 551-566

Bloom, A. L., 1963, Late-Pleistocene fluctuations of sealevel and postglacial crustal rebound in coastal Maine: Amer. J. Sci., v. 261, p. 862-879

Bloom, A. L., and Stuiver, Minze, 1963, Submergence of the Connecticut coast: Science, v. 139, p. 332-334

Bradford, D. C., and Waters, A. C., 1934, The Tolt River earthquake and its bearing on the structure of the Cascade Range: Seismol. Soc. Amer. Bull., v. 24, p. 51-62

Bradley, W. C., 1956, Carbon-14 date for a marine terrace at Santa Cruz, California: Geol. Soc. Amer. Bull., v. 67, p. 675-678

Bradley, W. H., 1936, Geomorphology of the north flank of the Uinta Mountains [Utah]: U.S. Geol. Surv. Prof. Pap. 185-I, p. 163-199

Bryan, Kirk, and McCann, F. T., 1937, The Ceja del Rio Puerco, a border feature of the Basin and Range province in New Mexico. I, Stratigraphy and structure: J. Geol., v. 45, p. 801-8282

Buffington, E. C., and Moore, D. G., 1963, Geophysical evidence on the origin of gullied submarine slopes, San Clemente, California: J. Geol., v. 71, p. 356-370

Byerly, Perry, 1951, History of earthquakes in the San Francisco Bay area, *in* Jenkins, O. P. (ed.), Geologic guidebook of the San Francisco Bay counties: California Div. Mines Bull. 154, p. 151-160

Cooke, C. W., 1931, Seven coastal terraces in the southeastern States: Washington Acad. Sci. J., v. 21, p. 503-513

—— 1935, Tentative ages of Pleistocene shore lines: Washington Acad. Sci. J., v. 25, p. 331-333

—— 1936, Geology of the Coastal Plain of South Carolina: U.S. Geol. Surv. Bull. 867, 196 p.

Cooke, H. C., 1929, Studies of the physiography of the Canadian Shield. I, Mature valleys of the Labrador Peninsula: Roy. Soc. Can. Trans., ser. 3, v. 23, sec. 4, p. 91-120

Cooper, W. S., 1958, Coastal sand dunes of Oregon and Washington: Geol. Soc. Amer. Mem. 72, 169 p.

Craig, B. G., and Fyles, J. G., 1961, Pleistocene geology of Arctic Canada, *in* Raasch, G. O. (ed.), Geology of the Arctic: Toronto, Univ. Toronto Press, v. 1, p. 403-419

Crandell, D. R., this volume, The glacial history of western Washington and Oregon

Crandell, D. R., Mullineaux, D. R., and Waldron, H. H., 1958, Pleistocene sequence in southeastern part of the Puget Sound lowland, Washington: Amer. J. Sci., v. 256, p. 384-397

Crittenden, M. D., Jr., 1963, New data on the isostatic deformation of Lake Bonneville: U.S. Geol. Surv. Prof. Pap. 454-E, 31 p.

Crouch, R. W., 1959, Inspissation of post-Oligocene sediments in southern Louisiana: Geol. Soc. Amer. Bull., v. 70, p. 1283-1292

Crowell, J. C., 1962, Displacement along the San Andreas fault, California: Geol. Soc. Amer. Spec. Pap. 71, 61 p.

Cushing, E. M., Boswell, E. H., and Hosman, R. L., 1964, General geology of the Mississippi Embayment: U.S. Geol. Surv. Prof. Pap. 448-B, p. 1-28

Dalrymple, G. B., 1963, Potassium-argon dates of some Cenozoic volcanic rocks of the Sierra Nevada, California: Geol. Soc. Amer. Bull., v. 74, p. 379-390

Daly, R. A., 1934, The changing world of the ice age: New Haven, Yale Univ. Press, 271 p.

Davis, W. M., 1933, Glacial epochs of the Santa Monica Mountains, California: Geol. Soc. Amer. Bull., v. 44, p. 1041-1133

Doering, J. A., 1956, Review of Quaternary surface formations of Gulf Coast region: Amer. Assoc. Petroleum Geologists Bull., v. 40, p. 1816-1862

—— 1960, Quaternary surface formations of southern part of Atlantic Coastal Plain: J. Geol., v. 68, p. 182-202

Dominion Observatories of Canada, 1956, Gravity anomaly map of Canada [scale 1:6,336,000]: Canada Dept. Mines Tech. Surveys, Dominion Observatories

Dutton, C. E., 1889, The Charleston earthquake of August 31, 1886: U.S. Geol. Surv. Ann. Rep. 9, p. 203-528

Easterbrook, D. J., 1963, Late Pleistocene glacial events and relative sea-level changes in the northern Puget Lowland, Washington: Geol. Soc. Amer. Bull., v. 74, p. 1465-1484

Eaton, J. E., 1928, Divisions and duration of the Pleistocene in southern California: Amer. Assoc. Petroleum Geologists Bull., v. 12, p. 111-141

Emerson, W. K., 1956, Pleistocene invertebrates from Punta China, Baja California, Mexico, with remarks on the composition of the Pacific Coast Quaternary faunas: Amer. Mus. Nat. Hist. Bull., v. 111, p. 317-342

Emery, K. O., 1958, Shallow submerged marine terraces of southern California: Geol. Soc. Amer. Bull., v. 69, p. 39-59

—— 1960, The sea off southern California, a modern habitat of petroleum: New York, John Wiley & Sons, 366 p.

Evernden, J. F., Savage, D. E., Curtis, G. H., and James, G. T., 1964, Potassium-argon dates and the Cenozoic mammalian chronology of North America: Amer. J. Sci., v. 262, p. 145-198

Ewing, Maurice, Ewing, John, and Fray, Charles, 1960, Buried erosional terrace on the edge of the continental shelf east of New Jersey (abst.): Geol. Soc. Amer. Bull., v. 71, p. 1860

Farrand, W. R., 1962, Postglacial uplift in North America: Amer. J. Sci., v. 260, p. 181-199

Farrand, W. R., and Gajda, R. T., 1962, Isobases on the Wisconsin marine limit in Canada: Canada Dept. Mines Tech. Surv., Geogr. Branch, Geogr. Bull. 17, p. 5-22

Fischer, Irene, 1959a, A tentative world datum from geoidal heights based on the Hough ellipsoid and the Columbus geoid: J. Geophys. Res., v. 64, p. 73-84

—— 1959b, The impact of the ice age on the present form of the geoid: J. Geophys. Res., v. 64, p. 85-87

Fisk, H. N., 1939, Depositional terrace slopes in Louisiana: J. Geomorph., v. 2, p. 181-199

—— 1944, Geological investigation of the alluvial valley of the lower Mississippi River: Vicksburg, Miss., U.S. Army Corps of Engineers, Mississippi River Comm., 78 p.

Fisk, H. N., and McFarlan, Edward, Jr., 1955, Late Quaternary deltaic deposits of the Mississippi River, *in* Poldervaart, Arie (ed.), Crust of the earth—a symposium: Geol. Soc. Amer. Spec. Pap. 62, p. 279-302

Fiske, R. S., Hopson, C. A., and Waters, A. C., 1963, Geology of Mount Rainier National Park, Washington: U.S. Geol. Surv. Prof. Pap. 444, 93 p.

Flint, R. F., 1937, Pleistocene drift border in eastern Washington: Geol. Soc. Amer. Bull., v. 48, p. 203-232

—— 1940a, Late Quaternary changes of level in western and southern Newfoundland: Geol. Soc. Amer. Bull., v. 51, p. 1757-1780

—— 1940b, Pleistocene features of the Atlantic Coastal Plain: Amer. J. Sci., v. 238, p. 757-787

—— 1957, Glacial and Pleistocene geology: New York, John Wiley & Sons, 553 p.

Fraser, G. D., Witkind, I. J., and Nelson, W. H., 1964, A geological interpretation of the epicentral area; the dual-basin concept: U.S. Geol. Surv. Prof. Pap. 435-J, p. 99-106

Frink, J. W., and Kues, H. A., 1954, Corcoran clay; a Pleistocene lacustrine deposit in San Joaquin Valley, California: Amer. Assoc. Petroleum Geologists Bull., v. 38, p. 2357-2371

Fuller, M. L., 1912, The New Madrid earthquake: U.S. Geol. Surv. Bull. 494, 119 p.

Gianella, V. P., and Callahan, Eugene, 1934, The earthquake of December 20, 1932, at Cedar Mountain, Nevada, and its bearing on the genesis of Basin-Range structure: J. Geol., v. 42, p. 1-22

Gilbert, C. M., 1941, Late Tertiary geology southeast of Mono Lake, California: Geol. Soc. Amer. Bull., v. 52, p. 781-816

Gilbert, G. K., 1890, Lake Bonneville: U.S. Geol. Surv. Monogr. 1, 438 p.

—— 1928, Studies of Basin-Range structure: U. S. Geol. Surv. Prof. Pap. 153, 92 p.

Gilluly, James, 1949, Distribution of mountain building in geologic time: Geol. Soc. Amer. Bull., v. 60, p. 561-590

—— 1950, Reply to discussion by Hans Stille, *in* Stille, Hans, *et al.*, Struktur und Zeit: Geol. Rdsch., v. 38, p. 103-107

—— 1963, The tectonic evolution of the western United States: Geol. Soc. London Quart. J., v. 119, p. 133-174

Gilluly, James, Waters, A. C., and Woodford, A. O., 1951, Principles of geology: San Francisco, W. H. Freeman and Co., 631 p.

Glen, William, 1959, Pliocene and lower Pleistocene of the western part of the San Francisco Peninsula: Berkeley, Univ. California Publ. Geol. Sci., v. 36, p. 147-198

Griggs, A. B., 1945, Chromite-bearing sands of the southern part of the coast of Oregon: U.S. Geol. Surv. Bull. 945-E, p. 113-150

Gutenberg, Beno, 1941, Changes in sea level, postglacial uplift, and mobility of the earth's interior: Geol. Soc. Amer. Bull., v. 52, p. 721-772

Gutenberg, Beno, and Richter, C. F., 1954, Seismicity of the earth and associated phenomena: Princeton, N.J., Princeton Univ. Press, 2nd ed., 310 p.

Hack, J. T., 1955, Geology of the Brandywine area and the origin of the upland of southern Maryland: U.S. Geol. Surv. Prof. Pap. 267-A, p. 1-43

Hack, J. T., 1960, Interpretation of erosional topography in humid temperate regions: Amer. J. Sci., v. 258-A (Bradley vol.), p. 80-97

Heyl, A. V., Jr., and Brock, M. R., 1961, Structural framework of the Illinois-Kentucky mining district and its relation to mineral deposits: U.S. Geol. Surv. Prof. Pap. 424-D, p. 3-6

Hill, D. P., Baldwin, H. L., Jr., and Pakiser, L. C., 1961, Gravity volcanism, and crustal deformation in the Snake River Plain, Idaho: U.S. Geol. Surv. Prof. Pap. 424-B, p. 248-250

Hill, M. L., and Dibblee, T. W., Jr., 1953, San Andreas, Garlock, and Big Pine faults, California—a study of the character, history, and tectonic significance of their displacements: Geol. Soc. Amer. Bull., v. 64, p. 443-458

Hodgson, E. A., 1945, Industrial earthquake hazards in eastern Canada: Seismol. Soc. Amer. Bull., v. 35, p. 151-174

Hoots, H. W., Bear, T. L., and Kleinpell, W. D., 1954, Geological summary of the San Joaquin Valley, California, *in* Jahns, R. H. (ed.), Geology of southern California: California Div. Mines Bull. 170, p. 113-129

Horberg, Leland, and Anderson, R. C., 1956, Bedrock topography and Pleistocene glacial lobes in central United States: J. Geol., v. 64, p. 101-116

Hough, J. L., 1958, Geology of the Great Lakes: Urbana, Illinois, Univ. Illinois Press, 313 p.

Howard, A. D., 1951, Development of the landscape of the San Francisco Bay counties, *in* Jenkins, O. P. (ed.), Geologic guidebook of the San Francisco Bay counties: California Div. Mines Bull. 154, p. 95-106

Hudson, F. S., 1955, Measurements of the deformation of the Sierra Nevada, California, since middle Eocene: Geol. Soc. Amer. Bull., v. 66, p. 835-870

—— 1960, Post-Pliocene uplift of the Sierra Nevada, California: Geol. Soc. Amer. Bull., v. 71, p. 1547-1574

Hunt, C. B., 1956, Cenozoic geology of the Colorado Plateau: U.S. Geol. Surv. Prof. Pap. 279, 99 p.

Innes, M. J. S., 1960, Gravity and isostasy in northern Ontario and Manitoba: Dominion Observatory Canada Publ., v. 21, No. 6, 338 p.

Jenness, S. E., 1960, Late Pleistocene glaciation of eastern Newfoundland: Geol. Soc. Amer. Bull., v. 71, p. 161-180

Kaye, C. A., and Barghoorn, E. S., 1964, Late Quaternary sea level change and crustal rise at Boston, Massachusetts, with notes on the autocompaction of peat: Geol. Soc. Amer. Bull., v. 75, p. 63-80

Kelley, V. C., and Silver, Caswell, 1952, Geology of the Caballo Mountains: Univ. New Mexico Publ. Geology, No. 4, 286 p.

King, P. B., 1948, Geology of the southern Guadalupe Mountains, Texas: U.S. Geol. Surv. Prof. Pap. 215, 183 p.

—— 1955, Orogeny and epeirogeny through time, in Poldervaart, Arie (ed.), Crust of the earth—a symposium: Geol. Soc. Amer. Spec. Pap. 62, p. 723-740

—— 1962, Neotectonic map of U.S.S.R. (review): Amer. Assoc. Petroleum Geologists Bull., v. 46, p. 1947-1950

Kirkham, V. R. D., 1931, Snake River downwarp: J. Geol., v. 39, p. 456-482

LaFehr, T. R., and Pakiser, L. C., 1962, Gravity, volcanism, and crustal deformation in the eastern Snake River Plain, Idaho: U.S. Geol. Surv. Prof. Pap. 450-D, p. 76-78

Lawson, A. C., 1893, The post-Pliocene diastrophism of the coast of southern California: Berkeley, Univ. California, Dept. Geol. Bull., v. 1, p. 115-160

Lee, H. A., 1960, Late glacial and postglacial Hudson Bay sea episode: Science, v. 131, p. 1609-1611

Lowman, S. W., 1949, Sedimentary facies in Gulf coast: Amer. Assoc. Petroleum Geologists Bull., v. 33, p. 1939-1997

Lowry, W. D., and Baldwin, E. M., 1952, Late Cenozoic geology of the lower Columbia River Valley, Oregon and Washington: Geol. Soc. Amer. Bull., v. 63, p. 1-24

Lyons, P. L., 1957, Geology and geophysics of the Gulf of Mexico: Gulf Coast Assoc. Geol. Soc. Trans., v. 7, p. 1-10

MacClintock, Paul, and Richards, H. G., 1936, Correlation of Pleistocene marine and glacial deposits of New Jersey and New York: Geol. Soc. Amer. Bull., v. 47, p. 289-338

Mackin, J. H., 1947, Altitude and local relief of the Bighorn area during the Cenozoic: Wyoming Geol. Assoc., Field Conference, Bighorn Basin, Guidebook, p. 103-120

MacNeil, F. S., 1950, Pleistocene shore lines in Florida and Georgia: U.S. Geol. Surv. Prof. Pap. 221-F, p. 95-107

Malde, H. E., 1959, Fault zone along northern boundary of western Snake River Plain, Idaho: Science, v. 130, p. 272

—— this volume, Snake River Plain

Mathews, W. H., 1952, Mount Garibaldi, a supraglacial Pleistocene volcano in southwestern British Columbia: Amer. J. Sci., v. 250, p. 81-103

Matthes, F. E., 1930, Geologic history of the Yosemite Valley: U.S. Geol. Surv. Prof. Pap. 160, 137 p.

—— 1937, The geologic history of Mount Whitney: Sierra Club Bull., v. 22, p. 1-18

—— 1960, Reconnaissance of the geomorphology and glacial geology of the San Joaquin basin, Sierra Nevada, California: U.S. Geol. Surv. Prof. Pap. 329, 62 p.

Moore, Sherman, 1948, Crustal movement in the Great Lakes area: Geol. Soc. Amer. Bull., v. 59, p. 699-709

Morrison, R. B., this volume, Quaternary geology of the Great Basin

Myers, W. B., and Hamilton, Warren, 1964, Deformation accompanying the Hebgen Lake earthquake of August 17, 1959: U.S. Geol. Surv. Prof. Pap. 435-I, p. 55-98

Neilson, W. A., Knott, T. A., and Carhart, P. W. (eds.), 1951, Webster's new international dictionary of the English language: Springfield, Mass., G. and C. Merriam Co., 2nd ed., 3214 p.

Nikolaev, N. I., and Schultz, S. S., 1959, Neotectonic map of the U.S.S.R. [scale 1:5,000,000]: U.S.S.R., Acad. Sci., Div. Geol. Geogr. Sci.

Nikolaev, N. I., and Schultz, S. S., 1960, Map of neotectonics of the U.S.S.R., scale 1:5,000,000, Commission on Tectonic Maps of the U.S.S.R. Academy of Sciences: 21st Intern. Geol. Congr., Norden, Comm. Geol. Map of the World, Subcomm. Tectonic Map of the World, 12 p.

Noble, L. F., 1954, The San Andreas fault zone from Soledad Pass to Cajon Pass, California, in Jahns, R. H. (ed.), Geology of southern California: California Div. Mines Bull. 170, p. 37-48

Nolan, T. B., 1943, The Basin and Range province in Utah, Nevada, and California: U.S. Geol. Surv. Prof. Pap. 197-D, p. 141-196

Orr, P. C., 1960, Late Pleistocene marine terraces on Santa Rosa Island, California: Geol. Soc. Amer. Bull., v. 71, p. 1113-1120

Page, B. M., 1935, Basin-range faulting of 1915 in Pleasant Valley, Nevada: J. Geol., v. 43, p. 690-707

Pakiser, L. C., 1960, Transcurrent faulting and volcanism in Owens Valley, California: Geol. Soc. Amer. Bull., v. 71, p. 153-160

Pardee, J. T., 1950, Late Cenozoic block faulting in western Montana: Geol. Soc. Amer. Bull., v. 61, p. 359-406

Peck, D. L., 1960, Cenozoic volcanism in the Oregon Cascades: U.S. Geol. Surv. Prof. Pap. 400-B, p. 308-310

Powers, H. A., and Wilcox, R. E., 1964, Volcanic ash from Mount Mazama (Crater Lake) and from Glacier Peak: Science, v. 144, p. 1334-1336

Price, W. A., 1958, Sedimentology and Quaternary geomorphology of south Texas: Gulf Coast Assoc. Geol. Soc. Trans., v. 8, p. 41-75

Putnam, W. C., 1942, Geomorphology of the Ventura region, California: Geol. Soc. Amer. Bull., v. 53, p. 691-754

—— 1954, Marine terraces of the Ventura region and the Santa Monica Mountains, California, in Jahns, R. H. (ed.), Geology of Southern California: California Div. Mines Bull. 170, p. 45-48

—— 1960, Origin of Rock Creek and Owens River gorges, Mono County, California: Berkeley, Univ. California Publ. Geol. Sci., v. 34, p. 221-280

——— 1962, Late Cenozoic geology of McGee Mountain, Mono County, California: Berkeley, Univ. California Publ. Geol. Sci., v. 40, p. 181-217

Reed, R. D., and Hollister, J. S., 1936, Structural evolution of southern California: Amer. Assoc. Petroleum Geologists Bull., v. 20, p. 1529-1704

Richards, H. G., 1962, Studies on the marine Pleistocene. Part I. The marine Pleistocene of the Americas and Europe: Amer. Philos. Soc. Trans., v. 52, p. 5-41

Richards, H. G., and Judson, S., this volume, The Atlantic Coastal Plain and the Appalachian Highlands in the Quaternary

Rigg, G. B., and Gould, H. R., 1957, Age of Glacier Peak eruption and chronology of post-glacial peat deposits in Washington and surrounding areas: Amer. J. Sci., v. 255, p. 341-363

Ross, C. P., and Nelson, W. H., 1964, Regional seismicity and brief history of Montana earthquake: U.S. Geol. Surv. Prof. Pap. 435-E, p. 25-30

Russell, I. C., 1885, Geological history of Lake Lahontan, a Quaternary lake of northwestern Nevada: U.S. Geol. Surv. Monogr. 11, 288 p.

Russell, R. J., 1940, Quaternary history of Louisiana: Geol. Soc. Amer. Bull., v. 51, p. 1199-1233

Sharp, R. P., 1954, Physiographic features of faulting in southern California, *in* Jahns, R. H. (ed.), Geology of southern California: California Div. Mines Bull. 170, p. 21-28

Sharp, R. P., and Birman, J. H., 1963, Additions to classical sequence of Pleistocene glaciations, Sierra Nevada, California: Geol. Soc. Amer. Bull., v. 74, p. 1079-1086

Sheets, M. M., 1947, Diastrophism during historic time in Gulf Coastal Plain: Amer. Assoc. Petroleum Geologists Bull., v. 31, p. 201-226

Slemmons, D. B., 1956, Geologic setting for the Fallon-Stillwater earthquakes of 1954: Seismol. Soc. Amer. Bull., v. 46, p. 4-9

——— 1957, Geological effects of the Dixie Valley-Fairview Peak, Nevada, earthquakes of December 16, 1954: Seismol. Soc. Amer. Bull., v. 47, p. 353-375

Smith, W. E. T., 1962, Earthquakes of eastern Canada and adjacent areas, 1534-1927: Ottawa, Dominion Observatory, Publ., v. 26, p. 271-301

Snavely, P. D., Jr., and Wagner, H. C., 1963, Tertiary geologic history of western Oregon and Washington: Washington Div. Mines Geol., Rep. Inv. 22, 25 p.

Stearns, H. T., Crandall, Lynn, and Stewart, W. G., 1938, Geology and ground-water resources of the Snake River plain in southeastern Idaho: U.S. Geol. Surv. Water-Supply Pap. 774, 268 p.

Stearns, R. G., and Marcher, M. V., 1962, Late Cretaceous and subsequent structural development of the northern Mississippi Embayment area: Geol. Soc. Amer. Bull., v. 73, p. 1387-1394

Stille, Hans W., 1936, The present tectonic state of the earth: Amer. Assoc. Petroleum Geologists Bull., v. 20, p. 849-880

——— 1955, Recent deformations of the earth's crust in the light of those of earlier epochs, *in* Poldervaart, Arie (ed.), Crust of the earth—a symposium: Geol. Soc. Amer. Spec. Pap. 62, p. 171-191

Stuart, D. J., 1961, Gravity study of crustal structure in western Washington: U.S. Geol. Surv. Prof. Pap. 424-C, p. 273-276

Taliaferro, N. L., 1943, Geologic history and structure of the central Coast Ranges of California: California Div. Mines Bull. 118, p. 119-163

Taylor, F. B., *in* Leverett, Frank, and Taylor, F. B., 1915, The Pleistocene of Indiana and Michigan and the history of the Great Lakes: U.S. Geol. Surv. Monogr. 53, 529 p.

——— 1927, The present and recent rate of land tilting in the region of the Great Lakes: Michigan Acad. Sci. Pap., v. 7, p. 145-157

Tocher, Don, 1959, Seismic history of the San Francisco region, *in* San Francisco earthquake of March, 1957: California Div. Mines Spec. Rep. 57, p. 39-48

——— 1960, Creep on the San Andreas fault. II, Creep rate and related measurements at Vineyard, California: Seismol. Soc. Amer. Bull., v. 50, p. 396-404

Trowbridge, A. C., 1954, Mississippi River and Gulf Coast terraces and sediments as related to Pleistocene history—a problem: Geol. Soc. Amer. Bull., v. 65, p. 793-812

Twenhofel, W. H., and MacClintock, Paul, 1940, Surface of Newfoundland: Geol. Soc. Amer. Bull., v. 51, p. 1665-1728

Upham, Warren, 1895, The glacial Lake Agassiz: U.S. Geol. Surv. Monogr. 25, 658 p.

Upson, J. E., 1949, Late Pleistocene and Recent changes of sea level along the coast of Santa Barbara County, California: Amer. J. Sci., v. 247, p. 94-115

——— 1951, Former marine shorelines of the Gaviota quadrangle, Santa Barbara County, California: J. Geol., v. 59, p. 415-446

Valentine, J. W., 1961, Paleoecologic molluscan geography of the California Pleistocene: Berkeley, Univ. California Publ. Geol. Sci., v. 34, p. 309-442

Vedder, J. G., and Norris, R. M., 1963, Geology of San Nicolas Island, California: U.S. Geol. Surv. Prof. Pap. 369, 65 p.

Wahrhaftig, Clyde, 1962, Geomorphology of the Yosemite Valley region, California, *in* Geologic guide to the Merced Canyon and Yosemite Valley, California: California Div. Mines Geol. Bull. 182, p. 33-46

Wahrhaftig, Clyde, and Birman, J. H., this volume, The Quaternary of the Pacific mountain system in California

Wallace, R. E., 1949, Structure of a portion of the San Andreas rift in southern California: Geol. Soc. Amer. Bull., v. 60, p. 781-806

Waters, A. C., 1955, Volcanic rocks and the tectonic cycle, *in* Poldervaart, Arie (ed.), Crust of the earth—a symposium: Geol. Soc. Amer. Spec. Pap. 62, p. 703-722

Webb, R. W., 1946, Geomorphology of the middle Kern River Basin, southern Sierra Nevada, California: Geol. Soc. Amer. Bull., v. 57, p. 355-382

Wilcox, R. E., this volume, Volcanic-ash chronology

Williams, Howel, 1932, Geology of the Lassen Volcanic National Park, California: Berkeley, Univ. California Dept. Geol. Sci. Bull., v. 21, p. 195-385

——— 1942, The geology of Crater Lake National Park, Oregon, with a reconnaissance of the Cascade Range southward to Mount Shasta: Carnegie Instn. Publ. 540, 162 p.

—— 1953, The ancient volcanoes of Oregon: Eugene, Oregon, Oregon State System of Higher Education, Condon Lecturers, 2nd ed., 68 p.

Witkind, I. J., 1964, *in* The Hebgen Lake, Montana, earthquake of August 17, 1959: U.S. Geol. Surv. Prof. Pap. 435, 242 p.

Wood, H. O., 1945, A note on the Charleston earthquake: Seismol. Soc. Amer. Bull., v. 35, p. 49-56

Woodford, A. O., Schoellhamer, J. E., Vedder, J. G., and Yerkes, R. F., 1954, Geology of the Los Angeles basin, *in* Jahns, R. H. (ed.), Geology of southern California: California Div. Mines Bull. 170, p. 65-81

Woodring, W. P., 1952, Pliocene-Pleistocene boundary in California Coast Ranges: Amer. J. Sci., v. 250, p. 401-410

Woodring, W. P., Bramlette, M. N., and Kew, W. S. W., 1946, Geology and paleontology of Palos Verdes Hills, California: U.S. Geol. Surv. Prof. Pap. 207, 145 p.

Woollard, G. P., 1958, Areas of tectonic activity in the United States as indicated by earthquake epicenters: Amer. Geophys. Union Trans., v. 39, p. 1135-1150

Wright, H. E., Jr., 1946, Tertiary and Quaternary geology of the lower Rio Puerco area, New Mexico: Geol. Soc. Amer. Bull., v. 57, p. 383-456

Summary

This paper reviews the tectonic features and events of Quaternary time in the various regions of Middle North America—that is, in the conterminous United States, and in adjacent parts of Canada and Mexico. Over this broad region the features and events are varied and have different causes, which include: (1) Depressions and uplifts caused by isostatic adjustments following loading and unloading of masses of continental ice (in northeastern North America), and of the waters of large lakes (in the Great Basin). (2) Epeirogenic or vertical uplifts of broad parts of the continent, probably accompanied by reactivation of old structural trends as shown by the patterns of earthquake epicenters (in much of Middle North America, from the Rocky Mountains eastward). (3) Downwarping that accompanied sedimentation on the coastal plains and continental shelves, resulting either from isostatic or tectonic forces (especially in Gulf Coastal Plain). (4) Block-faulting, which has broken extensive terrains into a succession of mountains and troughs (in Basin and Range province). (5) Volcanism, probably related to deep-seated zones of crustal weakness (in northwestern Middle North America). (6) Orogenic deformation produced by tangential forces, which has resulted in complex folding and faulting (in California and adjacent parts of southwestern Middle North America). (7) Emergence and submergence along the coasts, an important part of which resulted from eustatic changes in sea level related to the glaciations and interglaciations of Quaternary time, but some of which resulted from local tectonic movement.

Some geologists have speculated that the tectonics of Quaternary time differs significantly from the tectonics of earlier times—that the spacing of tectonic events has accelerated, that the crust is more consolidated than formerly so that deformation has produced different tectonic results, that vertical movements dominate over tangential movements, and the like.

The tectonics of Quaternary time in Middle North America, summarized above, is presumably a representative sample of Quaternary tectonics in general, and it seems too diverse to be synthesized into the coherent themes implied by these speculations. It is true that most of the observable Quaternary features and events differ from those dealt with in conventional tectonics; instead of being phenomena of deep-seated origin produced by long-dead forces, they all formed at or near the present surface, by processes that are still at work, or that were at work in the very recent past. These differences, however, reflect merely the kinds of data available for observation and study. The only uniquely Quaternary features are those produced isostatically or eustatically, as indirect results of the unusual climatic conditions of the time. The remaining tectonic features seem to have been produced by forces and under conditions that did not differ significantly from those of earlier geological periods.

DENDROCHRONOLOGY

HAROLD C. FRITTS[1]

THE SCIENCE of dendrochonology is the systematic study of tree-rings applied to dating past events and evaluating climatic history. Dendrochronology has been most widely applied along the semiarid forest border, where low moisture usually limits growth (Bannister, 1963; McGinnies, 1963; Schulman, 1956), and at northern latitudes, where low temperature during the growing season frequently limits growth (Giddings, 1941; Siren, 1961). However, dendrochonological techniques have been used throughout temperate regions wherever well-defined rings are formed (Glock, 1955). Gymnosperms generally are considered more suitable for study, but many angiosperms have been used with considerable success (Ferguson, 1964; Fritts, 1961, 1962).

The tree-ring is typically an annual growth layer in the wood or xylem. In gymnosperms the ring includes an inner zone of large, thin-walled earlywood cells and an outer zone of smaller, thick-walled latewood cells (Larson, 1962). There is usually a gradual transition from the earlywood to the latewood cell type within a given ring, but a sharp boundary occurs between the latewood and the earlywood of adjacent rings.

A temporary early-season drought followed by more favorable growing conditions may produce within the annual ring a band of small latewood cells, followed by larger earlywood cells. Such a band is called a false ring; it can usually be distinguished from a true annual ring by the more gradual change in cell size along the outer margin of the band. During exceptionally unfavorable years cambial activity may not be initiated at all, especially in the older, slower-growing portions of some trees. When a ring is not formed on a certain radius but is found elsewhere on the same cross section, it is referred to as a locally absent or discontinuous ring. Extreme cases of multiple and discontinuous ring formation have been studied in detail (Glock *et al.*, 1960), and in such cases accurate tree-ring dating may not be possible.

TECHNIQUES

While the simple counting of rings from actively growing trees has been successfully employed to establish the age of forest stands and the minimum age of soil, as in dating of landslides, alluvial terraces, and glacial moraines (Bray and Struik, 1963; Sigafoos and Hendricks, 1961), age estimates by this procedure are accurate only if a single ring is formed each year. Therefore this straightforward application is most successful in areas where the environment causes the tree to form a single well-defined ring for each year. In such cases, ring width may show little relationship to climatic

[1] Laboratory of Tree-Ring Research, University of Arizona, Tucson, Arizona.

factors, although it may vary as a function of tree age and site.

More refined techniques have been developed for ring studies on trees from stress areas such as the semiarid forest border of western North America (Douglass, 1919, 1928, 1936, 1946; Schulman, 1956). Techniques involving site selection, cross-dating, and chronology-building are necessary to obtain a precise record of climatic fluctuations from tree-rings and to ensure accurate dating by correct identification of false or locally absent rings (Bannister, 1963; Douglass, 1946; Schulman, 1956).

SITE SELECTION

In sites where soil moisture is usually adequate, tree-rings may be wide and exhibit little variation from year to year except for a gradual decrease in width with increasing tree age. Such a tree-ring series is called "complacent." In extreme sites such as are found near the lower forest border in semiarid North America, tree-rings are narrow and exhibit marked variation from year to year. Trees from such sites are said to show "sensitive" ring series.

The changing characteristics of tree-ring relationships near the semiarid forest border as described by Douglass (1919) and Schulman (1956) have been analyzed by Fritts *et al.* (1965a). Figure 1 diagrammatically illustrates these relationships. The commercially productive portion of the forest (sometimes referred to as the interior portion—J, Fig. 1) is characterized by high precipitation, so that moisture is rarely the most limiting factor to ring growth. The rings are usually wide, and their variability may largely reflect difference in biotic and edaphic factors such as competition, age, disease, and soil type. At the semiarid forest border (M, Fig. 1), precipitation is lower and more variable from year to year, and, as a result, low soil moisture more frequently limits the growth-controlling processes in trees. Absent rings are more common in trees near these marginal habitats, average ring width is less, and the arboreal vegetative cover is less dominant. Because climate is the primary controlling factor of growth at the semiarid forest border, the correlation of ring patterns among and within trees is higher than in the forest interior, and variability in ring width from year to year increases, as shown by increases in the statistical parameters of mean sensitivity and standard deviation from J to M in Figure 1. Therefore, year-to-year climatic variability may be most accurately recorded in ring widths of those trees nearest the semiarid forest border (Fritts *et al.*, 1965a).

Location L in Figure 1 represents the type site near the forest border where climate is most highly related to ring-width patterns and where ring-width variation correlates

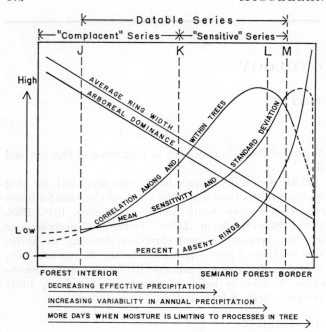

Figure 1. A graphical illustration of changes in some tree-ring and vegetation characteristics that can be observed along a gradient from the forest interior to the semiarid lower forest border. Climatic differences are indicated below the figure and dendrochronological categories above. Average ring width and dominance of arboreal species decrease with increased aridity from J through M, while correlation among and within trees, mean sensitivity, standard deviation, and percent absent rings generally increase from J to L. Cross-dating is not applicable in trees of the forest interior (to the left of J) because of ring-series "complacency" and low correlations among trees. Cross-dating is not practical at the extreme forest border (to the right of M) because of low correlations among trees, accompanied by high frequencies of absent rings (Fritts *et al.*, 1965a).

most highly among and within trees. At the extreme border to the right of M, climatic stress is so great that the high percent of absent rings and great divergence between tree-ring responses of individual trees make it difficult or impossible to achieve reliable cross-dating (Glock *et al.*, 1960). Toward the forest interior, area J–K, tree-ring series are less variable and referred to as somewhat more "complacent," but, in spite of lower correlation among trees, they can be readily dated because absent or confusing double rings rarely occur. In the most optimum growth sites to the left of J, where climatic factors have little control over growth, the ring patterns differ from tree to tree and the correlation among trees is too low to ensure cross-dating.

CROSS-DATING AND CHRONOLOGY-BUILDING

The cross-dating technique is an application of the principle that, when the growth of several trees is influenced by a common fluctuating environment, similar and synchronous ring patterns will be produced (Douglass, 1946). In dendrochronological studies using series from stress sites, it is absolutely essential that all anomalies of annual ring formation be resolved in order to ensure a precisely dated chronology. False and partial rings usually can be detected through careful visual inspection of pertinent anatomical characteristics. Absent rings in a given specimen may be identified by comparison of the relative ring pattern with ring patterns from other specimens in the same area. Final verification of the accuracy in identification of specific false and absent rings is made certain by continued, successful cross-dating with specimens that contain the same ring-width patterns.

It is necessary to base cross-dating controls for any given area on the painstaking analysis of a large number of trees representing available sites and species. Many ring series are studied and compared, and, where a lack of synchrony is noted in the ring patterns, re-examination of the samples will often show that a small ring was overlooked or, less frequently, that a false ring was confused with an annual ring. Young, fast-growing trees from favorable sites generally provide easily interpretable series containing few or no missing rings and few troublesome rings. More slowly growing trees from more extreme sites afford "sensitive" series with the most precise record of climatic fluctuations, but all locally absent rings must be identified. Cross-dating provides the means by which it is possible to combine the accuracy of dating in fast-growing trees, with the reliable climatic records found in more slowly growing trees on stress sites.

Once a reliable regional master chronology has been prepared, new samples may be accurately dated by careful comparison and correlation of the ring series with the established standard. Because climate probably limits tree growth most during drought years, particular attention is given to the matching of narrow rings rather than rings of average width, which have limited diagnostic value.

Older specimens can be added to a master chronology to extend the sequence into earlier periods (Stallings, 1949). In this manner, a chronology may be developed and extended into prehistoric time. In addition, a group of specimens with unknown cutting dates may be cross-dated among themselves, and a "floating" chronology developed that provides relative dating of the individual specimens but lacks absolute dating because it cannot be cross-dated with the modern chronology based on living trees (Bannister, 1963). But when the "floating" chronology is finally extended and sufficiently overlaps with a modern series to allow reliable cross-dating, all undated specimens of the "floating" chronology can immediately be assigned absolute dates. Numerous methods and techniques of specimen analysis have been described (Bannister, 1963; Douglass, 1946; McGinnies, 1963; Schulman, 1956).

STATISTICAL TECHNIQUES

The mathematical properties of tree-ring series were first given serious consideration by A. E. Douglass (1919). During the last decade there has been a wide variety of statistical treatments of ring-width measurements. It is generally recognized that tree-ring widths exhibit gradual changes associated with aging of trees (Duff and Nolan, 1953). These changes are sometimes referred to as the growth function and are customarily approximated by a curve, line, or series of running means (Fritts, 1963a, 1963b). In order to remove this growth function from a measured tree-ring series, ring widths are converted into ring indices by dividing each ring-width measurement by the estimated value of the growth function for that year, a procedure called standardization. Unlike the variance of ring widths, the variance of standardized indices has been shown to be relatively independent of tree age (Matalas, 1962). Therefore the tree-ring indices are more satisfactory for climatic interpretation (Fritts, 1963a).

Many standardized tree-ring series are not randomly distributed with respect to time but are significantly correlated serially (Fritts, 1963a; Matalas, 1962). First-order serial correlation coefficients may be as high as 0.78. Because of this interrelationship between adjacent rings, the degrees of freedom represented by a given series are not proportional to sample size. Also, the standard deviation may not provide a satisfactory measure of the year-to-year variation of ring indices. In such cases mean sensitivity, which is the absolute difference between adjacent indices or ring widths divided by the mean of the two adjacent values, provides a more suitable measure of the year-to-year variation (Fritts *et al.*, 1965a; Schulman, 1956).

Correlation studies and analyses of variance and covariance have been applied in a variety of investigations. Early workers devoted considerable time to the study of solar cycles and their relation to tree-ring series (Douglass, 1919, 1928, 1936), but modern variance-spectra analyses so far fail to demonstrate any major periodicities (Bryson and Dutton, 1961). Recent analyses (Fritts and Smith, 1963) show that some tree-ring series may exhibit significant correlations with other series at distances as great as 1,750 km if the two series lie in an area of similar atmospheric-circulation patterns. Correlations between well-documented series from western North America are generally significant if the paired chronologies are less than 500 km apart (Fritts, 1963b; Fritts and Smith, 1963).

DENDROCLIMATOLOGICAL TECHNIQUES

The late Edmund Schulman at the Laboratory of Tree-Ring Research, University of Arizona, was first to recognize the necessity in dendroclimatic analysis of studying old trees with long "sensitive" ring series. Investigations on bristlecone pine (*Pinus aristata* Engelm.), a species of the high elevations, show the presence of "sensitive" growth-ring series in trees which reach ages well in exess of 4,000 years. Limber pine (*P. flexilis* James) chronologies may reach 2,000 years in length, while chronologies from some individual trees of pinyon pine (*P. edulis* Engelm.), ponderosa

pine (*P. ponderosa* Laws.), and Douglas-fir (*Pseudotsuga menziesii* (Mirb.) Franco) may exceed 800 years in length. Trees of *Sequoia gigantea* (Lindl.) Decne. provide series as long as 3,200 years in length, but serial correlation is high, and the tree-ring patterns are less satisfactory for interpretations of yearly fluctuations in climate (Schulman, 1956).

Tree-ring analysis is the only method that can be used to evaluate paleoclimatic fluctuation on a yearly basis. Periods of favorable or unfavorable years can be precisely defined and dated. In order to ensure that a tree-ring sequence contains trends due only to climatic changes, a growth curve must be fitted to each series of ring measurements, and indices must be determined. Thus gradual changes in climate that may occur over the entire length of a tree-ring specimen may be lost from the final chronology because these changes cannot be distinguished from a growth curve in the standardization procedures. Because of this inherent difficulty, dendrochronology cannot provide a reliable measure of long-term changes in climate that equal or exceed the length of the shortest specimen used in the chronology.

TREE-RINGS AND ENVIRONMENT

Many early students of dendrochronology were interested in deducing climatic fluctuations from variation in ring widths (Douglass, 1919; Glock, 1955). Tree-ring series from northern latitudes have been shown to be related to temperatures during the growing season (Giddings, 1941; Siren, 1961; Fritts, 1963c), while ring series from semiarid regions exhibit good agreement with moisture regimes. Numerous studies have been made in intermediate areas, and, in many cases, both temperature and moisture may relate directly to ring-width patterns (Fritts, 1961, 1963a; Glock, 1955). Some workers have intensively studied conditions such as frost or extreme drought that produce anomalous patterns of continuous or false rings (Glock *et al.*, 1960).

Tree-ring growth may be successfully correlated with runoff data that coincide with the climatic interval controlling ring growth (Schulman, 1945, 1956). Correlations between ring indices and runoff have been as high as 0.81 for Conejos River at Mogote, Colorado (Gatewood *et al.*, 1964). Regional correlations between indices and runoff range from 0.35 to 0.88. Although summer rainfall in some areas of western North America may amount to about half the annual total, its conversion into measureable runoff is very inefficient as compared to winter rainfall. Thus the fluctuations in the annual stream-flow data are largely governed by winter storms and so may safely be compared with fluctuations in tree growth, which similarly are more related to winter than to summer precipitation (Schulman, 1945).

Until recently some of the very basic problems of tree growth were inadequately studied. Very little was known about the growth regimes of the drought-sensitive tree species used in dendrochronology, for much of the forest research has concerned itself mainly with the rapidly growing trees on relatively drought-free sites. Fritts *et al.* (1965b) report that Douglas-fir growing in southwestern Colorado at its lowest elevations initiates radial growth in late April and completes growth in June. Other species, including many of the pines, initiate growth in late May or June and continue until August. Some species, such as ponderosa pine, may show a response to winter moisture in the first-formed portion of the ring and a response to summer moisture in the latter portion of the ring. However, many of the species used in dendrochronology show little growth response to summer rains that occur in the latter part of the growing season.

It is now thought that growing-stem tips and leaves produce hormones that may have a pronounced effect upon latewood and false-ring formation (Larson, 1962). Climate, through its influence on leaf growth (Lotan and Zahner, 1963; Fritts *et al.*, 1965b), may alter hormone concentrations within trees and influence the formation of earlywood and latewood. Also, it can control the amount of photosynthetic area that is produced and hence affect the food-making capacity of the trees. Needle lengths in drought-sensitive trees vary markedly from year to year (Fritts *et al.*, 1965b), and in many cases the length correlates highly with ring width. Differences between species in the timing of terminal and radial growth may account for differences in the percent of latewood or frequency of false rings.

Recent developments in dendrochonology show that tree-ring indices from the semiarid forest border are highly related to climatic factors if (1) temperature as well as precipitation is included as a factor, (2) the climate during different seasons of the year can assume different degrees of importance, and (3) serial correlation within tree-ring series is taken into account (Fritts *et al.*, 1965b). Stepwise multiple-regression analyses (Fritts, 1962) have been obtained between climate and growth of Utah juniper [*Juniperus osteosperma* (Torr.) Little], pinyon pine, and Douglas-fir, which account for all but 9% to 13% of the explainable variance in tree-ring indices. This is thought to be well within expectations for biological relationships, and it is doubtful that significantly higher correlations can be obtained through further analysis.

The climatic conditions that were found to be related to narrow ring formation are listed and numbered in order of importance in Table 1. The influence of changes in monthly mean maximum temperature and total precipitation during different intervals of the year on the tree-ring index were calculated by substituting selected values for these variables in the regression equations. The results of these calculations are included in Table 2. The table shows that if total precipitation and maximum temperatures during June are respectively one inch above and two degrees below average, and if the climate for the rest of the year was average, the tree-rings formed during the following season in Douglas-fir may be expected to be 12% to 13% larger than average, while rings formed during the current season will be expected to be 11% to 12% larger. The rings of pinyon pine for the current season will be influenced only by temperature and in the above case will be expected to be 6% above average, while the rings of juniper will be expected to show no deviation from average. On the other hand, maximum temperatures two degrees above average during the same period may counter the direct effects of above-average precipitation on growth of Douglas-fir and cause a 4% to 5% reduction in the following year's growth and a 13% reduction in growth during the current season in old trees but 11% increase in young trees. However, larger and different growth variation due to precipitation and, to a lesser extent, to temperature during August through May is characteristic of many drought-sensitive conifers (Table 2). The predicted departure of the ring-index value for any climatic regime can be estimated from Table 2 by summing the individual effects of deviations from average climate during each period of the growing season.

These data show that the greater portion of the ring-width variation is related to the moisture regime from October through May. Precipitation of the previous June through September may relate only to growth of Douglas-fir. High temperatures during June may completely counter effects of high precipitation, but during March through May temperature may be directly related to ring growth. The only influence of summer climate on pinyon pine growth is an inverse effect of July maximum temperatures.

It may be inferred that late-summer, autumn, winter,

TABLE 1

Climatic Conditions that Produce Narrow Rings in Three Species at Mesa Verde National Park
(Numbers from 1 to 6 indicate the rank of importance from high to low for the climate interval. Results are based upon analyses of rings from 4 groups of trees, 5 trees per group, 4 radii per tree, for the years 1922 through 1963)

	Site:	Wetherill Mesa		Navajo Canyon	
	Age:	400-year	250-year	260-year	500- to 800-year
Interval	Species:	Utah juniper	Pinyon pine	Douglas-fir	Douglas-fir
Previous June		no effect	no effect	6 warm, dry*	6 warm, dry
Previous July		no effect	no effect	no effect	no effect
Previous Aug.-Sept.		no effect	no effect	3 dry**	3 dry**
Previous Oct.-Nov.		3 dry, warm**	1 dry**	1 dry**	2 dry**
Previous Dec.-Feb.		1 dry, cool**	2 dry**	2 dry**	5 dry*
Current Mar.-May		2 dry, warm**	4 dry, cool*	4 dry, cool**	1 dry, cool**
Current June		no effect	no effect	5 dry*	4 warm**
Current July		no effect	3 warm**	no effect	no effect

   * Significant $P < 0.05$
** Highly significant $P < 0.01$

TABLE 2

The Calculated Effect of One-Inch-per-Month Departures from Average Precipitation and Two-Degree Departures
in Mean Maximum Temperature on the Width of Tree-Rings at Mesa Verde National Park
(Ring width is expressed as percent departure from average. Results are based upon analyses of rings
from 4 groups of trees, 5 trees per group, 4 radii per tree, for the years 1922 through 1963)

Site:		Wetherill Mesa						Navajo Canyon					
Age:		400-year			250-year			260-year			500- to 800-year		
Species:		Utah Juniper			Pinyon Pine			Douglas-fir			Douglas-fir		
Interval	Departure of total precip. in inches	— Departure of maximum temperature in F°											
		−2	Av.	+2	−2	Av.	+2	−2	Av.	+2	−2	Av.	+2
Previous June	+1	no effect			no effect			+13	+4	−4	+12	+3	−5
	average							+4	Av.	−4	+3	Av.	−4
	no precip.ᵃ							−3	−3	−3	−2	−2	−2
Previous Aug.-Sept.	+2	no effect			no effect			+14	+14	+14	+15	+15	+15
	average							Av.	Av.	Av.	Av.	Av.	Av.
	−2							−14	−14	−14	−15	−15	−15
	no precip.							−28	−28	−28	−28	−28	−28
Previous Oct.-Nov.	+2	+51	+37	+23	+26	+26	+26	+24	+24	+24	+28	+28	+28
	average	+8	Av.	−8	Av.	Av.	Av.	Av.	Av.	Av.	Av.	Av.	Av.
	−2	−35	−37	−39	−26	−26	−26	−24	−24	−24	−28	−28	−28
	no precip.	−48	−48	−48	−35	−35	−35	−31	−31	−31	−37	−37	−37
Previous Dec.-Feb.	+3	+57	+66	+74	+26	+26	+26	+27	+27	+27	+17	+17	+17
	average	−5	Av.	+5	Av.	Av.	Av.	Av.	Av.	Av.	Av.	Av.	Av.
	−3	−68	−66	−63	−26	−26	−26	−27	−27	−27	−17	−17	−17
	no precip.	−114	−114	−114	−44	−44	−44	−46	−46	−46	−30	−30	−30
Current Mar.-May	+3	+35	+26	+17	+10	+11	+11	+17	+18	+20	+28	+30	+33
	average	+11	Av.	−11	Av.	Av.	Av.	−1	Av.	+1	−1	Av.	+1
	−3	−14	−26	−39	−11	−11	−10	−18	−18	−18	−31	−30	−30
	no precip.	−22	−34	−47	−14	−14	−14	−24	−24	−24	−39	−39	−39
Current June	+1	no effect			no effect			+11	+11	+11	+12	0	−13
	average							Av.	Av.	Av.	+5	Av.	−5
	no precip.ᵃ							−7	−7	−7	Av.	Av.	Av.
Current July	+1	no effect			+6	Av.	−6	no effect			no effect		
	average				+6	Av.	−6						
	−1				+6	Av.	−6						
	no precip.				+6	Av.	−6						

ᵃ Average monthly precipitation is less than 1 in. Thus zero precipitation is the only meaningful negative departure.

and spring precipitation is the major climatic control of tree-ring growth along the semiarid forest border in southwestern United States. The climate of the summer may influence the following year's growth in Douglas-fir and the current growth of ponderosa pine, but apparently it has little influence on the growth of Utah juniper and pinyon pine at Mesa Verde National Park.

In the same paper (Fritts *et al.*, 1965b) it is also shown that the ring widths of pinyon pine and Douglas-fir are directly related to the widths of the rings that were formed three years earlier. This phenomenon has been observed in several other studies. Its explanation will probably be found either in the statistical interrelationships involved or in details of the life history and physiology of trees in semiarid sites.

The results of these analyses were applied to an evaluation of the 13th-century climate at Mesa Verde National Park, Colorado, which is the time the prehistoric cliff dwellings were apparently abandoned. A severe drought was definitely evident in the Mesa Verde tree-ring materials, although the drought does not appear to have been so long and severe as in neighboring areas (see Fig. 3) and during a number of other periods. The differences in the response of the several species to summer precipitation were also used to evaluate the hypothesis of Martin (1963, p. 66) that an increase in the summer rainfall may have accompanied the dry winters of A.D. 1276-1299 and have caused the arroyo cutting that has been described for that period. It was argued by Fritts *et al.* (1965b) that moist summers would have contributed to more ring growth in Douglas-fir than in pinyon pine or Utah juniper (see Tables 1 and 2). A survey of the tree-ring records of the three species showed no such relationship. Douglas-fir growth was generally equal to or less than the growth of the other two species, so it was concluded that both the summers and winters must have been relatively dry.

The Dendroclimatic Model

Studies at the Laboratory of Tree-Ring Research show that drought-sensitive conifers can carry on significant amounts of photosynthesis during the winter and spring months; but during dry summer periods respiration frequently exceeds photosynthesis, and little sugar can be accumulated. These studies, as well as the statistical screening analyses (Fritts *et al.*, 1965b), indicate that ring-width growth is probably a direct function of the available food supplies that may be made by current photosynthesis or may have been accumulated throughout the previous year. Climate may influence growth indirectly through its control of photosynthesis and respiration and the accumulation of stored food supplies. These interrelationships between climate and tree-ring growth are diagrammed in Figure 2.

Precipitation is the primary climatic control, but temperature may modify its effects. These two factors influence the water relations of the tree, which in turn govern photosynthesis and the accumulation of food (Fig. 2). Cambial activity and growth in the spring and early summer prob-

ably continue until this stored food is expended or until climatic conditions become severe enough to directly induce the cessation of growth. Temperature influences food accumulation through its control of respiration and the consumption of foods in the plant. During a hot and dry summer, food consumption may exceed food production, but during cooler portions of the year respiration will be lower, water relations will be less critical, and the net accumulation of photosynthate may be greater. The availability of foods may influence root growth and water absorption, and this in turn may also affect the water stress in the tree.

Other interacting influences are illustrated in Figure 2. High water stress may reduce cell enlargement in the meristems of the growing buds. This may reduce hormone concentrations and perhaps shorten the current growing season or reduce cell enlargement of the new-formed xylem cells. High water stress may also decrease the number and size of new stems and leaves, limiting the yearly increment in the photosynthetic area of the tree. With fewer and shorter needles, the efficiency of photosynthesis in subsequent years is correspondingly reduced. This accumulative

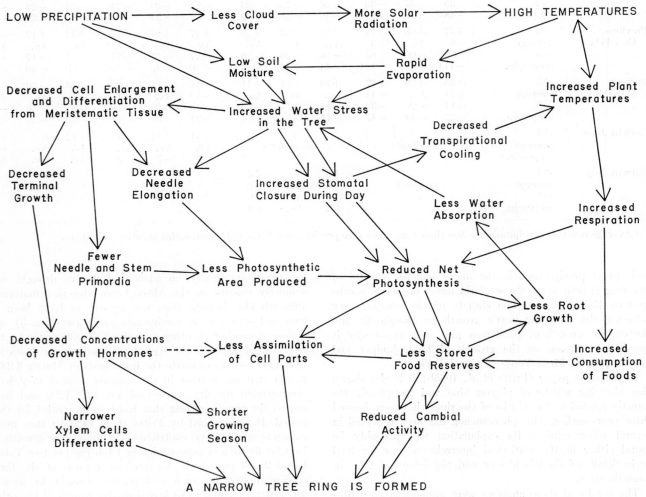

Figure 2. A schematic diagram of the model for the relationship between precipitation and temperature and the production of narrow rings in coniferous trees from semiarid sites.

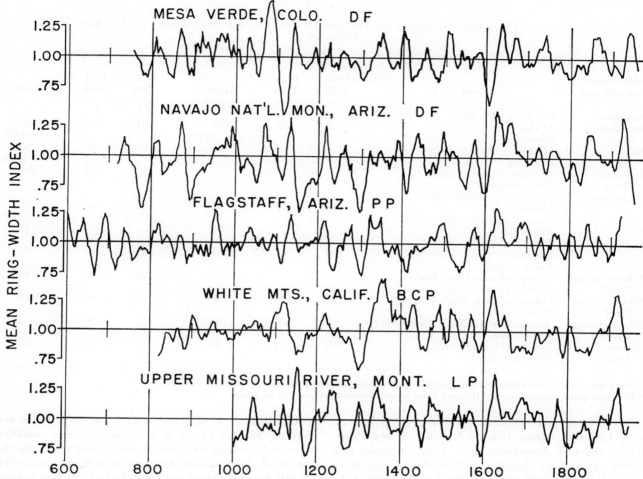

Figure 3. Twenty-year means of tree-ring indices from five chronologies in western United States. The mean values for the 20-year periods are plotted every five years on the last year of the period: DF, Douglas-fir; PP, ponderosa pine; BCP, bristlecone pine; LP, limber pine.

influence of climate probably creates the serial correlation of tree-ring widths.

DENDROCLIMATOLOGY IN NORTH AMERICA

The publication of the book, *Dendroclimatic Changes in Semiarid America,* by Edmund Schulman (1956) established the field of dendroclimatology. Schulman presents numerous tables, plots, and statistical data on tree-rings as they relate to climatic and hydrologic factors. His data show that droughts have been as frequent in the past as in the present throughout western North America. The most notable ones are the droughts of A.D. 1215 through 1299 and A.D. 1573 through 1593, which were severe over a considerable geographic area (see Fig. 3). He also reported that the long-term trends in tree-ring widths for the Colorado River Basin, especially in southern Arizona, has been downward since A.D. 1921, indicating a period of drought unequalled since the drought of the 13th century.

Schulman noted patterns in periods of high and low precipitation which he inferred from tree-ring evidence. He noted for southern California and the Colorado River Basin

that prior to A.D. 1650 intervals of high and low precipitation tended to exhibit longer periodicities than during more recent times. He also noted that the chronologies from the Missouri River basin showed an opposite trend, with short fluctuations in high and low precipitation occurring before A.D. 1650 and longer periods following that date.

Schulman analyzed his dendrochronological sequences in north-south transects along the Rocky Mountain and the Pacific slopes. He found no predictable systematic displacement in drought patterns, but he did note a tendency for ring series from southern United States to be inversely correlated with ring series along the northern United States and southern Canadian borders. He proposed that a more detailed examination of dendrochronologic data might provide a basis for evaluating long-term changes in the general circulation of the atmosphere. Schulman's book contains a wealth of data awaiting a rigorous climatic evaluation by modern statistical analyses. The report by Fritts and Smith (1963) represents a first step in this direction.

A significant stride in paleoclimatic interpretation from tree-ring data was made at the Conference on the Climate

TABLE 3

Summary of Tree-Ring Averages for the 11th and 16th Centuries as Percent of Mean for 1851-1950
(Fritts, 1963c)

Major climatic factor indicated	Area and species	11th Century			16th Century		
		1001-1050	1051-1100	Mean	1501-1550	1551-1600	Mean
Temperature	(*Northern timberline*)						
June-July Mean[a]	Alaska *Picea spp.*	132	109	123 ($\leqslant +2.3$°C)	111	105	1C8 ($\leqslant +0.8$°C)
July Mean[a]	Mackenzie Valley *Picea spp.*				93	88	90 ($\leqslant -1.0$°C)
June-July Mean[a]	Northern Fennoscandia *Pinus silvestris*				103	107	105
Precipitation	(*U.S.A. lower forest border*)						
	Montana *Pinus flexilis* var. *reflexa*	98	87	92	94	86	90
	California *Sequoia gigantea*			95			89
	California *Pinus aristata*	100	101	101	97	95	96
Winter-Spring Total[b]	Upper Colorado River Basin *Pseudotsuga menziesii*				88	86	87
Winter-Spring Total[b]	Colorado (Mesa Verde Park) *P. menziesii*	97	120	108	98	86	92
Winter-Spring Total[b]	Arizona (Navajo Nat'l. Monument) *P. menziesii*	90	108	99	92	93	92
Annual Total[b]	Arizona (Flagstaff area) *Pinus ponderosa*	100	94	97	83	97	90

[a] Temperature estimates inferred from correlations and regressions with climatic data.

[b] Effective precipitation interval inferred from recent screening regression analyses.

of the Eleventh and Sixteenth Centuries, which met at Aspen, Colorado, during June 16-24, 1962. Temperature-sensitive tree-ring chronologies from Alaska, Canada, and Finland, as well as drought-sensitive chronologies from western North America, were analyzed in an attempt to evaluate the climate during the two centuries. Table 3 summarizes some of the most pertinent data that were examined and published, and Figure 3 is a plot of 20-year running means for several tree-ring series from the United States.

The biology section of the conference concluded (Fritts, 1963c):

"The *summer temperature* series from northern Alaska indicate an average temperature for the eleventh century that was estimated to be higher than, but by no more than 2.3° C. above, the 1851-1950 average in Alaska; 1.0° C. below the average in the Mackenzie Valley of Canada, and 0.5° above the average for Fennoscandia.

"The *precipitation* series indicate that during the eleventh century, southwestern United States had essentially the same average precipitation as the 1851-1950 period. The single series from northwestern United States suggests a possible precipitation deficit during the eleventh century. In the sixteenth century, all series were below the 1851-1950 norm, especially during the latter half, indicating a greater number of drought years. Additional evidence substantiated that this very high frequency of drought years during the latter part of the century was present in most series from western United States, but not in those from the Canadian Rocky Mountains."

On the basis of all types of data presented at the conference, Shapiro (1963) hypothesized climatic conditions that could account for the anomalous winter conditions that produced the unusually low tree growth in southwestern North America during the latter half of the 16th century. He states:

"Precipitation in the southwest part of the United States in the winter is produced by cyclonic storms that move across the Pacific. Therefore, in order for dry conditions to have prevailed during this period in the southwest, cyclonic systems must have moved well to the north of their normal paths. This situation could be brought about by a large wedge of high pressure over the southwest."

CONCLUSIONS

It is quite apparent from the literature that tree growth, as reflected by width of tree-rings, can be used in numerous ways to interpret historical events and climatic conditions in the past. Relationships between ring width and factors of the environment that control growth are often complex, and the intricate procedures of sampling, dating, and processing tree-ring data are frequently time-consuming. However, great strides are being made in unraveling the complexities of the tree-growth models and in developing more rapid and precise techniques. There is little doubt that reliable climatic and hydrologic inferences can be drawn from tree-ring evidence, if exact sampling and cross-dating procedures are employed and appropriate models of climate and tree growth are applied.

REFERENCES

Bannister, Bryant, 1963, Dendrochronology, *in* Brothwell, D., and Higgs, E. (ed.), Science in archaeology: New York, Basic Books, Inc., p. 162-176

Bray, J. R., and Struik, G. J., 1963, Forest growth and glacial chronology in eastern British Columbia, and their relation to recent climatic trends: Can. J. Bot., v. 41, p. 1245-1271

Bryson, R. A., and Dutton, J. A., 1961, Some aspects of the variance spectra of tree-rings and varves: New York Acad. Sci. Ann., v. 95, p. 580-604

Douglass, A. E., 1919, 1928, 1936, Climatic cycles and tree growth: Carnegie Instn. Publ. 289, v. 1, 2, 3

—— 1946, Precision of ring dating in tree-ring chronologies: Univ. Arizona Bull., v. 17, p. 1-21

Duff, G. H., and Nolan, Norah J., 1953, Growth and morphogenesis in the Canadian forest species. I, The controls of cambial and apical activity in *Pinus resinosa* Ait.: Can. J. Bot., v. 31, p. 471-513

Ferguson, C. W., 1964, Annual rings in big sagebrush, *Artemisia tridentata:* Tucson, Univ. Arizona Press, 95 p.

Fritts, H. C., 1961, The relation of growth rings in American beech and white oak to variation in climate: Tree-Ring Bull., v. 25, Nos. 1-2, p. 2-10

—— 1962, An approach to dendroclimatology: screening by means of multiple regression techniques: J. Geophys. Res., v. 67, p. 1413-1420

—— 1963a, Recent advances in dendrochronology in America with reference to the significance of climatic change: Arid Zone Research xx, Changes of Climate, UNESCO, Paris, p. 255-263

—— 1963b, Computer programs for tree-ring research: Tree-Ring Bull., v. 25, Nos. 3-4, p. 2-7

—— 1963c, Summary report of the biology section, *in* Bryson, R. A. and Julian, P. R. (eds.), Proceedings of the conference on the climate of the eleventh and sixteenth centuries: Boulder, Colorado, Natl. Cent. Atmos. Res. Tech. Notes 63-1, p. 21-24

Fritts, H. C., and Smith, D. G., 1963, Report on dendroclimatological research for 1963 sponsored in part by the U.S. Weather Bureau, Laboratory of Tree-Ring Research: Tucson, Univ. Arizona, 32 p.

Fritts, H. C., Smith, D. G., Cardis, J. W., and Budelsky, C. A., 1964a, Tree-ring characteristics along a vegetation gradient in Northern Arizona: Ecology, v. 46, No. 4 (in press)

Fritts, H. C., Smith, D. G., and Stokes, M. A., 1964b, The biological model for paleoclimatic interpretation of Mesa Verde tree-ring series: Soc. Amer. Arch. Mem. (in press)

Gatewood, J. S., Wilson, Alfonso, Thomas, H. E., and Kister, L. R., 1964, General effects of drought on water resources of the Southwest: U.S. Geol. Surv. Prof. Pap. 372-B, 53 p.

Giddings, J. L., Jr., 1941, Dendrochronology in northern Alaska: Univ. Arizona Bull., v. 12, p. 1-107

Glock, W. S., 1955, Tree growth. II, Growth rings and climate: Bot. Rev., v. 21, p. 73-188

Glock, W. S., Studhalter, R. A., and Agerter, S. R., 1960, Classification and multiplicity of growth layers in branches of trees at the extreme lower forest border: Smithson. Instn. Misc. Coll., v. 140, 290 p.

Larson, P. R., 1962, Auxin gradients and the regulation of cambial activity, *in* Kozlowski, T. T. (ed.), Tree growth: New York, Ronald Press, p. 97-117

Lotan, J. E., and Zahner, Robert, 1963, Shoot and needle responses of 20-year-old red pine to current soil moisture regimes: For. Sci., v. 9, p. 497-506

Martin, P. S., 1963, The last 10,000 years: Tucson, Univ. Arizona Press, 87 p.

Matalas, N. C., 1962, Statistical properties of tree-ring data: Intern. Assoc. Sci. Hydrol. Publ., v. 7, p. 39-47

McGinnies, W. G., 1963, Dendrochronology: J. For., v. 61, p. 5-11

Schulman, Edmund, 1945, Tree-ring hydrology of the Colorado River basin, Univ. Arizona Bull. 16, p. 1-51

—— 1956, Dendroclimatic changes in semiarid America, Tucson, Univ. Arizona Press, 142 p.

Shapiro, Ralph, 1963, Transcript of discussions of the circulation pattern, winter 1550-1600., *in* Bryson, R. A. and Julian, P. R. (ed.), Proceedings of the conference on the climate of the eleventh and sixteenth centuries: Boulder, Colorado, Natl. Cent. Atmos. Res. Tech. Notes 63-1, p. 59-74

Sigafoos, R. S., and Hendricks, E. L., 1961, Botanical evidence of the modern history of Nisqually Glacier, Washington: U.S. Geol. Surv. Prof. Pap. 387-A, 20 p.

Siren, Gustaf, 1961, Skogsgranstallen som indikator for klimatfluktuationerna i norra Fennoskandien under historisk tid: Metsantutkimuslaitoksen Julkaisuja, v. 54, p. 1-66

Stallings, W. S., Jr., 1949, Dating prehistoric ruins by tree-rings: Santa Fe, New Mexico, Lab. of Anthro, Gen. Ser. Bull. No. 8, 18 p.

SUMMARY

The variation in widths of annual rings of woody species can be used to date and to evaluate past patterns of precipitation and/or temperature occurring during the life of the plant. The primary techniques of dendrochronology are site selection, cross-dating, and chronology building. However, new statistical and botanical approaches to tree-ring analyses are also being used. In semiarid regions tree-ring widths in coniferous species relate primarily to the precipitation during the late-summer, autumn, winter, and spring periods that precede the initiation of growth. Temperatures during the summer months may counter or augment the effects of precipitation through their influence on water relations. Climate is thought to influence growth largely through its control of net photosynthesis and the accumulation of food in the plant. Therefore the ring width that is produced is largely a function of the stored food and hence is related to the variations in climate. Dendrochronology provides the only method that can be used to evaluate yearly fluctuations in past climates.

THEORETICAL PALEOCLIMATOLOGY

J. MURRAY MITCHELL, JR.[1]

REMARKABLE VARIATIONS of climate have occurred during the Earth's history. The climatologist has long been fascinated by the implications of this and likes to watch over the paleoscientist's shoulder as he discovers, deciphers, and dates an ever increasing number and variety of the elaborate and subtle imprints in the Earth by which he is able to piece together this paleoclimatic drama. Although it is true that the climatologist has made some modest contributions of his own to this effort, in particular to deciphering some of the imprints, he has felt rather inadequate to do more. His larger ambition is of course to make meteorological sense of the paleoclimatic record as a whole, particularly as regards physical cause and effect. To date, his efforts in this direction have not been very illuminating, but his optimism has been buoyed in recent years by some important developments in meteorological theory.

In essence, the climatologist's problem can be visualized as twofold. First, if he is to comprehend climatic change as a *physical problem,* he must be able to specify the worldwide distribution of climate—as we know it today—as an explicit function of the Earth-environmental influences that shape it, and to ascertain the sensitivity of climate to variations in the magnitude of these influences. In many aspects of climate, if not all, he can now do this reasonably well although there remains much room for refinement. Second, if he is to comprehend (and not merely to describe) climatic change *as a chronology,* he must have some means of ascertaining not only the extent to which each of these environmental influences on climate may have varied in the past, but the chronology of all variations of these influences that have in fact occurred. Knowledge in these respects cannot be said to exist at present in anything approaching adequate detail, and for its ultimate acquisition the climatologist will have to look to his colleagues in such diverse fields as oceanography, tectonophysics, volcanology, solar physics, and terrestrial biochemistry. There can be no guarantee, of course, that all the genius of modern scientific inquiry will ever suffice to acquire this knowledge in full.

In consonance with this view of the problem of paleoclimatology, the present chapter will be devoted primarily to an *inductive* analysis of the phenomenon of climatic change and its causes. It will not therefore be concerned with deductive interpretations of the paleoclimatic chronology *per se,* along the lines that have more commonly been pursued in the past.

The task before us requires that we begin with a rather comprehensive review of the basic theory of planetary climate, and identify the specific environmental factors that are indicated by this theory to determine present-day con-

ditions of climate. We shall then be prepared to consider which of these environmental factors may be believed to have varied with time in the period leading into and during the Quaternary, and to surmise the potential importance of each in shaping the climatic history of the period.

The discussion in this chapter presupposes some knowledge on the part of the reader concerning descriptive climatology and the general relationship between climate and the atmospheric circulation pattern. For the reader who has never before ventured into the modern literature on these topics, I may particularly recommend as background reading the chapter, "Fundamentals of Climate," by H. H. Lamb *in* Nairn (1961, pp. 8-44). Moreover, citations of the literature on theoretical climatology will be limited mostly to those of recent survey articles and other particularly significant published papers that the interested reader may consult for additional references.

FACTORS THAT DETERMINE WORLD CLIMATE

THE ASTRONOMICAL SETTING

From the astronomical viewpoint, planet Earth can be described in part as a nearly spheroidal rotating mass exposed to a distant source of radiant energy (the Sun), whose axis of rotation is inclined about 23° from perpendicularity to the plane of its orbit around the Sun. Let us for the moment neglect all nonuniformities of the surface and suppose the atmosphere to be removed. From geometric considerations, it is obvious that not all points on the Earth can receive equal daily total amounts of solar radiation (per unit surface area). Milankovitch (1920, 1930) was the first to show how the total daily radiation I (per square centimeter of surface) can be expressed as a function of latitude φ, time of year (characterized by solar declination δ), the solar constant $S \simeq 2$ cal cm^{-2} min^{-1}, the length of the day T_d (in minutes), and the distance between the Earth and Sun r (in astronomical units). This relationship is

$$I = \frac{ST_d}{\pi r^2} (\sin \omega_0 \cos \delta \cos \varphi + \omega_0 \sin \delta \sin \varphi) \qquad (1)$$

Where $\omega_0 = \cos^{-1} (- \tan \delta \tan \varphi)$ is the sunrise hour angle. Solutions of this equation, which have been widely tabulated and graphed, indicate that the equatorial regions receive more radiation than the polar regions throughout the year, except in the summer hemisphere during a relatively brief interval around the time of the summer solstice, when the reverse is true. For any point on the Earth, this incident radiation will in part be reflected back to space, the fraction reflected being equal to the local reflectivity (or *albedo*) of the surface material. The remainder will be absorbed in the

[1] U.S. Weather Bureau, Washington, D.C.

881

surface and converted to heat. The temperature of the surface will thus increase until an equilibrium is reached in which processes able to remove this heat will do so at an average rate equal to that of the radiation absorbed. In the absence of an overlying atmosphere, the only process available to remove the heat (neglecting transient heat storage and conduction into deeper layers) is long-wave heat eradiation from the surface to space. This, in turn, varies as the fourth power of the surface temperature.

The climate that would result, in this case being limited to purely thermal conditions, would be readily determinable for all points on the Earth. (With regard to the effect of the Earth's topography, as well as other details of the problem of insolation climate, see Lee, 1963.)

In the main, the planetary distribution of temperature in the absence of an atmosphere would coincide closely with that of solar radiation given by Equation 1.

THE BASIC ROLE OF THE ATMOSPHERE

Let us continue to consider the Earth as a uniform, featureless planet, but add an overlying atmosphere. To start with, suppose that this atmosphere is completely transparent to solar radiation (*i.e.* it contains neither dust, clouds, nor gases such as water vapor that absorb solar radiation). Neglecting small effects due to atmospheric refraction and molecular scattering, the Earth's surface would then receive the same amount and distribution of solar radiation as it would in the absence of the atmosphere. However, part of the heat produced at the surface by radiative absorption would now be imparted to the atmosphere by conduction and convection, and this in turn would ultimately become lost to space by long-wave eradiation from the atmosphere. The atmosphere would then become *differentially* heated, the heating being greater in tropical latitudes than in polar ones except briefly around the time of the summer solstice, when the sense of the meridional heating gradient would be reversed.

The fact that the atmosphere is differentially heated (as a function of latitude) is of particular importance because this is sufficient to give rise to a planetary-scale atmospheric circulation. The circulation in turn will transport some of the excess heat supplied by solar radiation in the tropics to higher (cooler) latitudes before it is ultimately eradiated into space. That is to say, the atmosphere will operate as a heat engine, working across its own temperature gradient and striving to equalize the temperatures at different latitudes.

In this way, the atmosphere would greatly influence the planetary distribution of temperature, and it would of course introduce wind as an element of climate. The further characteristics of this circulation, and the extent of its influence on global climate, will be discussed in a later section.

Now let us permit the atmosphere to take on many of the complex properties of the real atmosphere. We shall continue to think of the Earth itself as a featureless ball, except that we shall be more realistic and allow its surface to consist in large part of water. To start with, the real atmosphere is not wholly transparent. It contains dust and other aerosols that scatter the incoming solar radiation to a much greater extent than air molecules alone, and that

may on occasion interfere with terrestrial eradiation as well. The real atmosphere also contains clouds (due to changes of state of one of its gaseous constituents, water vapor), which efficiently intercept a large portion of solar radiation and back-scatter it to space before it ever reaches the surface. Two minor gaseous constituents of the real atmosphere (ozone and water vapor) strongly absorb solar radiation at certain wavelengths, and two such constituents (carbon dioxide and water vapor) strongly absorb terrestrial eradiation as well. Moreover, very large quantities of heat are continually extracted from the Earth's surface (primarily the oceans) by evaporation of water, and they are transported considerable horizontal and vertical distances in the atmosphere in latent form; this latent heat can energize the circulation only at the eventual point of condensation as clouds and precipitation.

Inasmuch as all of the above-mentioned phenomena have a considerable effect on the distribution of heating and cooling in the real atmosphere, and therefore an effect on circulation and climate, they must be allowed for in the theory of terrestrial climate. This, however, is not as straightforward as it may seem because their effects continually vary in time, primarily in response to the transient state of the circulation itself (so as to give rise to "feedback" effects) and also in response to events at or beyond the boundaries of the atmosphere.

THE TERRESTRIAL HEAT BUDGET

General aspects. The heat balance of the atmosphere and of the underlying surface is of fundamental importance in the theory of climate, not merely because it affects local terrestrial temperature directly but also because its geographical inequalities (most of all its inequalities with latitude, as noted in the previous section) provide the source of energy that maintains the general atmospheric circulation and thereby influences climatic conditions at a distance.

The principal factors in the heat budget of the Earth in terms of average annual conditions over the whole Northern Hemisphere, are shown quantitatively in Figure 1. (Corresponding data for the Southern Hemisphere are comparable but not identical.) Here we can get an idea of the importance of the various atmospheric phenomena already listed. It should be kept in mind, however, that the total budget (when expressed in absolute units of heat flux) and the relative magnitudes of the various items in it each varies considerably with geographical location and time of year.

Certain implications of the numbers in Figure 1 are worth stressing. First, the solar radiation returned directly to space is about 35% of the total incoming value (this figure corresponds to the so-called *planetary albedo*); more than two-thirds of this in turn is attributable to back-scattering by clouds. This is a clear indication of the great importance of cloudiness to surface climate and of the *potentially* great importance of changes of cloudiness as a factor in climatic change.

Second, by far the largest fraction of total planetary long-wave eradiation to space (57 + 3 = 60 units) is from the atmosphere; only 5 units derive from the Earth's surface. That is to say, the atmosphere is nearly opaque to heat

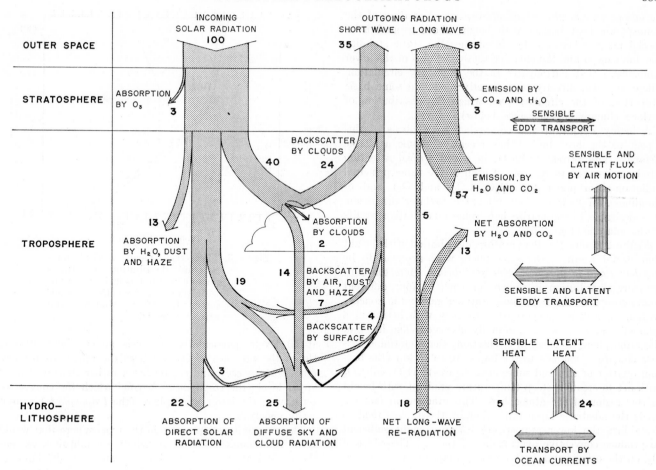

Figure 1. Mean annual heat budget of planet Earth, showing principal items affecting disposition of short-wave solar radiation (fine stippling) and long-wave terrestrial eradiation (coarse stippling), and heat transport by air motions. Units are percent of insolation arriving at top of atmosphere. Based mostly on estimates for Northern Hemisphere by Budyko and Kondratiev (1964). Units of sensible and latent heat flux through Earth's surface (lower right) are estimates for whole planet.

radiation from the ground, and it has the effect of maintaining a much warmer surface climate than could be maintained by a transparent atmosphere (or no atmosphere at all). This warming influence, commonly known as the *greenhouse effect* of the atmosphere, is almost entirely attributable to the presence of two relatively minor gaseous constituents (water vapor and carbon dioxide). Its magnitude depends on the concentrations of these gases in the atmosphere, both of which are capable of varying with time.

Third, the heating of the atmosphere—from which the energy of the general circulation is derived—is effected principally by the flux of *latent* heat of water vapor (24 units, nearly all from the oceans). Next in importance are direct absorption of solar radiation and absorption of long-wave eradiation from the surface (13 units each). All three of these heat sources enter the atmospheric dynamics at some distance above the base of the atmosphere. Only about 10% of the heat that is supplied to the atmosphere is supplied strictly at ground level (by sensible heat flux, 5 units).

Fourth, the influence of the oceans on planetary climate is not an altogether passive one. The oceans, like the atmosphere, have a general circulation of their own. Although this circulation is much more sluggish than that of the atmosphere, the much higher heat capacity of ocean water enables it to transport heat into higher latitudes at an average rate of up to one-third the atmospheric transport (Bryan, 1962). This is one indication of the fact that no theory of planetary climate can be fully satisfactory if it omits consideration of ocean currents. It happens that about half of the total heat transport is accomplished by a mode of ocean circulation that is strongly "coupled" with the atmospheric circulation. That is to say, it is partly wind-driven, to which extent it may be handled theoretically without our having to delve into intricate details of ocean behavior.

From this picture of the terrestrial heat budget, it is obvious that water in its various phases (including snow and ice, for that matter) emerges in several respects as a variable of cardinal importance in shaping climate.

Variation with height in the atmosphere. Variation of the atmospheric heat budget with height above ground is of special interest because this determines the static stability (*i.e.* buoyancy) and the effective total thickness of the lower atmosphere that participates in the planetary circulation. These, in turn, directly or indirectly modulate some basic properties of the circulation on which the distribution of surface climate depends (see below).

A highly significant and comprehensive analysis of this aspect of the heat budget has recently become available (Manabe and Strickler, 1964), in which special attention has been devoted to the role of each of the three principal radiation-absorbing gases (H_2O, CO_2, and O_3) and of cloudiness. In view of their relevance to later discussion, it is desirable to summarize here some quantitative results of this analysis (Figs. 2-5).

Figure 2 shows the temperature distribution with height that would result if the atmosphere were assumed to be *cloud-free and in pure radiative equilibrium.* Here the temperature distribution is shown for each of four different combinations of the radiation-absorbing gases; the concentration of each gas is permitted to vary with height in a manner typical of what is actually observed. The layer of the atmosphere involved in circulations that determine *surface* climate is confined to the lowest 10 to 15 km (the bottom quarter of this and subsequent figures); H_2O and CO_2 both act to create a steep temperature gradient with height in this region of the atmosphere. This gradient in fact exceeds the adiabatic lapse rate, whereby these gases tend to destabilize the lower atmosphere by an amount sufficient to produce convective overturning of the air. The effect of O_3, on the other hand, is to offset this lapse of temperature

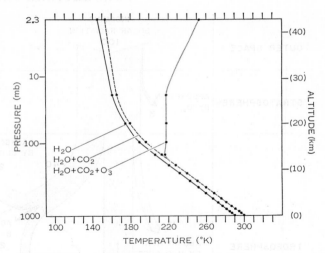

Figure 3. Theoretical mean vertical temperature distribution in atmosphere computed as in Figure 2 but with allowance for convective adjustment. After Manabe and Strickler (1964).

at all levels, particularly at levels above about 10 km. Hence the presence of O_3 stabilizes the upper atmosphere (the *stratosphere*), and establishes a rather sharply defined upper level (the *tropopause*) beyond which the convective activity of the lower atmosphere (the *troposphere*) cannot easily penetrate.

The temperature lapse rate in the troposphere that would arise from conditions of pure radiative equilibrium exceeds the critical average observed lapse rate of 6.5°C km⁻¹ to which the real atmosphere tends to adjust itself through vertical motion. For this reason, it would be appropriate to allow for convective adjustment in the computation of the vertical temperature distribution. The consequences of this, again for the case of a cloud-free atmosphere, are as shown in Figure 3. Here the effect of H_2O is seen to bring the troposphere to the critical lapse rate throughout its depth (below about 15 km); the effect of CO_2 added to the H_2O is to warm the atmosphere rather uniformly throughout its entire depth by several degrees, and the effect of O_3 added to the H_2O and the CO_2 is to produce a rather sharply defined tropopause without appreciably affecting the lapse rate within the troposphere below.

Figure 4 shows the influence of cloudiness on the vertical temperature distribution in the atmosphere. The solid curve represents the typical temperature distribution that is actually observed (the so-called U.S. Standard Atmosphere). The dot-dashed curve, identical to the right-hand curve in Figure 3, represents the computed temperature distribution for a cloud-free atmosphere with convective adjustment and for typical observed distributions of the three absorbing gases. The dashed curve, on the other hand, represents the computed temperature distribution under the same conditions as above except that the influence of cloudiness has been taken into account (the clouds being assumed to lie at three discrete levels each with its typical observed average decimal fraction of sky cover indicated in the figure). This comparison reveals that the net influence of

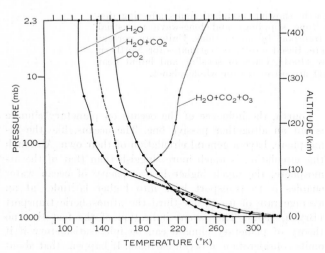

Figure 2. Theoretical mean vertical temperature distribution in atmosphere computed for various combinations of radiation-absorbing gases (water vapor, carbon dioxide, and ozone). Amounts and vertical distributions of gases assumed typical of those observed. Based on assumption of pure radiative equilibrium with no convection. After Manabe and Strickler (1964).

clouds is to cool the entire troposphere by about 10°, bringing the theoretical temperatures there into excellent agreement with the observed. On the other hand, it specifies a somewhat higher and cooler tropopause than is actually observed, the discrepancy most probably being attributable to the neglect in the theoretical model of large-scale meridional circulation.

The effect of cloudiness on the vertical temperature structure of the atmosphere can be seen from a somewhat different viewpoint in Figure 5. Here one can compare the effect of an overcast of cloud at each of five altitudes, where the radiative transmissivity and reflectivity of the clouds have been allowed to vary realistically with altitude of formation. As formerly, a convective adjustment of the temperature lapse rate in the troposphere has been included. Figure 5 clearly shows that only middle and lower cloud layers are capable of cooling the troposphere by appreciable amounts (the cooling effect is due primarily to the relatively high cloud albedo). In order for high (cirriform) clouds to have any very important influence on the temperature distribution, these clouds must evidently be located at altitudes higher than the prevailing height of the tropopause, where in fact they are very seldom observed.

In summary, one may arrive at the following conclusions. The mean temperature of the lower atmosphere varies

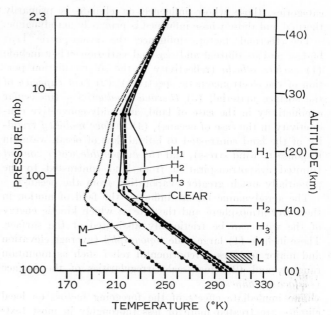

Figure 5. Theoretical mean vertical temperature distributions in atmosphere each computed for assumption of cloud overcast at one of five levels indicated. Distribution for cloudless atmosphere (labelled "clear") added for comparison. After Manabe and Strickler (1964).

directly with the atmospheric concentration of water vapor and carbon dioxide, and inversely with the amount of clouds (except cirriform clouds). The instability of the lower atmosphere (*i.e.* propensity for convective circulation) varies directly with the concentration of water vapor and carbon dioxide, and inversely with the amount of clouds and (to a slight degree) ozone. The thickness of the lower atmosphere that is involved in the planetary tropospheric circulation is controlled principally by ozone (as well as by the intensity of convection from the Earth's surface), but this thickness apparently does not vary to a marked extent as the result of variations in the amount (or distribution) of ozone, carbon dioxide, water vapor, or tropospheric cloudiness.

The effect of dust and haze in the atmosphere on the vertical temperature distribution has not been considered thus far in this discussion. To an approximation this effect may be compared to the effect of a relatively small amount of cloud at corresponding altitudes. As we shall note later, volcanic dust layers are sometimes found in the stratosphere at or above the 20-km level; the effect of these on temperature would be comparable to the effect of cirriform clouds at level H_1 shown in Figure 5, that is, to lower the height of the tropopause.

GEOGRAPHICAL FACTORS

The surface of the Earth is intricately partitioned between land masses and oceans, which have many contrasting physical properties capable of inducing geographical inequalities of climate. These properties may be divided into two broad

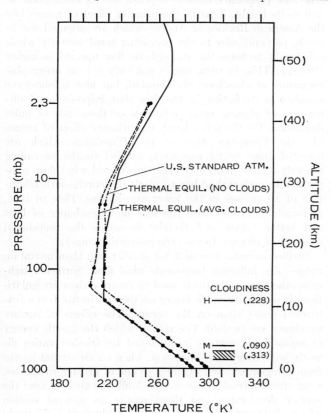

Figure 4. Observed and computed mean vertical temperature distributions in atmosphere. Computed distributions are with and without allowance for mean cloudiness. After Manabe and Strickler (1964).

categories, those whose influence on climate is primarily thermal and those whose influence is primarily aerodynamic.

The thermal factors influence the atmospheric heat budget and its diurnal and seasonal variation. They include (1) *surface albedo* (reflectivity in the solar-radiation portion of the electromagnetic spectrum), (2) *heat capacity* of the surface material, (3) *thermal conductivity* (molecular conductivity in the case of land, and eddy-convective conductivity in the case of oceans), (4) *surface mobility* (rigidity of the land contrasted to lateral flow of ocean water in response to wind stress), and (5) *evaporable water content* (limited evapotranspiration from land contrasted to the potentially much greater evaporation from the oceans).

The aerodynamic factors influence the field of motion in the lower atmosphere and the rate at which kinetic energy of the wind can be frictionally dissipated at the surface. These include (1) large-scale *topography* (average elevation and major features of continental relief such as mountain ranges), and (2) small-scale irregularities of the surface (*surface roughness*).

The immediate effects of the foregoing factors on local climate are treated more or less thoroughly in most textbooks on physical climatology and/or micrometeorology. In this discussion I shall summarize them only very briefly in the following terms.

Continental altitude. Owing in part to the normal decrease of temperature with height in the free atmosphere, and in part to the fact that a major fraction of the water vapor and carbon dioxide that contributes to the greenhouse warming of the surface is contained in the lowest layers of the atmosphere, average climatic temperature normally decreases markedly with increasing continental elevation. This relationship between surface temperature and surface elevation is such that, under conditions of pronounced continental uplift, not only is the mean temperature in the uplifted highlands locally much lower than it would otherwise be, but the *world* mean surface temperature is also likely to be somewhat lower.

Albedo. The most dramatic changes of surface albedo are those associated with the advance or retreat of a snow cover or an ice sheet. The albedo of a soil surface or vegetation being of the order of 10%, and that of a snow or ice surface being often as high as 80%, it is not difficult to appreciate the importance of variations of the extent of subpolar ice and snow to the planetary heat budget and to the geographical distribution of climate.

Heat capacity of the oceans. The relatively large specific heat capacity of water, together with the ability of the oceans to mix convectively through a depth of tens or hundreds of meters in response to thermally induced density changes at the surface, enables the oceans to store anomalous quantities of heat, far in excess of those able to be stored in the atmosphere or in the surface layers of the continents. As a result, the oceans are capable of exchanging climatologically important quantities of latent and sensible heat with the atmosphere.

The exchange of heat between the atmosphere and oceans is such as to moderate seasonal extremes of regional climate

and of the meridional atmospheric heating gradient by which the pattern of atmospheric circulation as a whole is largely governed. In other words, the oceans can be likened to a thermal flywheel by which seasonal (and to some extent interannual) changes of planetary climate and circulation are resisted.

Especially in the Northern Hemisphere, where vast continental and ocean surfaces coexist, the large difference in thermal storage capacity between the two kinds of surface produces a marked seasonal alternation in their relative temperature. In particular, ocean temperatures are unable to change much between winter and summer, whereas continental temperatures change a great deal under the influence of varying insolation, with the result that in winter the oceans are warmer than the continents and in summer they are cooler. These temperature differences, in turn, give rise to seasonably reversing patterns of differential atmospheric heating that are responsible for the well-known *monsoonal* component of the planetary circulation.

Topography. The continents, unlike the oceans, present formidable aerodynamic obstacles to the atmospheric wind field. The largest of these obstacles are of course the major mountain ranges of the world.

The effect of a mountain range on atmospheric circulation and (regional) climate depends on its orientation as well as its height. That is, the primary effect of ranges like the American Rockies or Andes—which are oriented north-south, perpendicular to the prevailing zonal westerly winds—is locally to force the atmospheric flow upward to higher altitudes. This, in turn, causes not only a local orographic maximum of cloudiness and rainfall, but also a long-wave *standing perturbation* in the flow that imposes zonal differences of climate many hundreds or thousands of miles downwind. On the other hand, the primary effect of ranges like the European Alps or the Himalayas—which are oriented more nearly east-west, parallel to the prevailing westerly winds—is to leave the upper-level wind flow comparatively undisturbed but to block the north-south migration of air masses in the lower atmosphere. This, in turn, regionally interferes with the meridional exchange of heat and water vapor and thereby increases the meridional gradient of climate (across the mountain range).

Surface irregularities of a far smaller size than mountain ranges also influence large-scale wind flow. Surface roughness—the term collectively used to describe these irregularities—is ordinarily much larger on the continents (even featureless ones) than on the oceans. The effects of surface roughness are twofold. The rate at which the kinetic energy of atmospheric motion is destroyed by friction varies directly with roughness. Moreover, when an air stream moves from a region of low roughness to one of greater roughness, as in crossing from an ocean onto land, the air flow near the surface decelerates, and there results an upward motion whose effects on climate are not unlike those of a relatively small mountain range. Conversely, when an air stream moves from land to water, the decrease of roughness locally results in a tendency for downward motion of the air rather like that found in the lee of a small mountain range.

In summary, the many contrasting physical properties of the continents and oceans are capable of influencing climate not only locally but also at a distance. At the end of the next section I shall return briefly to this matter in the context of the zonal inequalities of climate and circulation for the planet as a whole, as related to the Earth's topography and to zonal inequalities of atmospheric heating and surface roughness.

GENERAL ATMOSPHERIC CIRCULATION AND THE DYNAMICAL THEORY OF CLIMATE

It was remarked earlier that differential (solar) heating of the rotating Earth is sufficient to generate a planetary-scale circulation in its atmosphere. I propose now to define some basic properties of this circulation and to indicate their significance to world climate.

Circulation for the case of a uniform featureless Earth. Let us imagine for the present an atmosphere of uniform composition overlying a uniform, featureless Earth that is heated differentially as a function of latitude only by solar radiation. The essential form of the circulation that would arise under these simplified conditions, as well as under more realistically complex ones, can be inferred from the results of both hydrodynamic and mathematical modeling experiments. (For a lucid summary of planetary circulation theory derived from these experiments, see Mintz, 1961, 1962.)

To begin with, for the particular combination of physical circumstances applying to the Earth, among them its angular speed of axial rotation, the magnitude of the net meridional atmospheric-heating gradient, and the mean temperature and vertical temperature distribution of the atmosphere, one has to expect the planetary circulation to resemble the time-varying wavelike form that is in fact observed. For certain other combinations of these physical circumstances (as might apply to some other planets in the solar system), an altogether different mode of circulation— and a correspondingly different distribution of surface climate—would prevail. Basic features of the circulation that are both observed and predicted include a "direct" thermal convection cell in low latitudes of each hemisphere and an entirely different regime poleward of this that is characterized by "horizontal eddies." These eddies, in turn, are identifiable on daily weather maps as migratory high- and low-pressure systems at the surface and as associated wavelike undulations in the prevailing zonal westerlies found at temperate latitudes aloft.

Modern theory of atmospheric dynamics is adequate to establish many details of this circulation with a measure of quantitative precision (Smagorinsky, 1963). Some of these pertain to the structure, behavior, and life history of the individual eddies, and as such form the basis of present techniques of short-range numerical weather prediction. Others pertain rather to the *statistics* of these eddies, most particularly to statistics of the *planetary Rossby waves*, which are the principal manifestation of the eddies in the zonal westerlies at upper levels in the atmosphere. Indeed, present circulation theory is good enough in this respect to account for many facts of observation (Mintz, 1961, 1962), among them the mean equilibrium number of planetary waves around each hemisphere (about 6), their mean eastward displacement (several degrees of longitude per day,

depending on the actual wave number), the mean speed of the zonal westerlies (13 m sec^{-1} at the 500-millibar or 5-km level, and about 20 m sec^{-1} at the 200-mb or 10-km level), and the root mean square amplitude of the meridional component of wind speed aloft (about 10 m sec^{-1} at the 500-mb level). It will be necessary for later discussion to outline some functional relationships between these quantities and certain potentially variable properties of the atmosphere on which they depend. Although these relationships can be expressed in various ways, we shall adopt here a highly generalized version of them derived from linearized theory (see Mintz, 1961, 1962).

The mean equilibrium number of planetary Rossby waves is an inverse measure of the dominant scale size of the eddies in the planetary circulation at mid-latitudes. This number is given by the proportionality relation

$$N \sim (\overline{T}s)^{-1/2} \qquad (2)$$

where $\overline{T}$ is the mean temperature of the whole atmosphere at mid-levels, and s is the *effective static stability*, a quantity that is intimately related to the vertical temperature lapse rate in the troposphere and an inverse measure of the convective buoyancy of the air.

The planetary waves migrate around the Earth at an eastward rate given approximately by

$$c \simeq U - \frac{a\Omega}{\sqrt{2}\,N^2}, \quad N > 2 \text{ or } 3 \qquad (3)$$

where U is the mean speed of the zonal westerly current in which the waves are imbedded, and a and Ω are respectively the radius and rate of rotation of the Earth. For $N = 6$, this equation yields $c \simeq 4.4°$ longitude per day, an average that agrees well with observation.

The mean zonal wind speed U that appears in Equation 3 can in turn be written as

$$U \sim \overline{T}s \qquad (4)$$

where $\overline{T}$ and s are as defined under Equation 2.

Finally, the root mean square amplitude of the meridional component of the planetary wind aloft

$$\text{r.m.s. } (V) \sim (N \cdot \Delta Q)^{1/2} \qquad (5)$$

where ΔQ is the effective meridional heating gradient of the atmosphere, to be defined more fully below. The statistic r.m.s. (V) can be regarded as a crude measure of the meridional flux of heat, water vapor, and certain other properties of the atmosphere.

The above proportionality relationships indicate that any factor tending to stabilize the troposphere (*i.e.* to cool the surface layers or to warm the upper layers beneath the tropopause), and/or tending substantially to increase the mean temperature of the atmosphere, will serve to increase the strength of the zonal westerlies aloft, to increase the average wavelength of the planetary waves (*i.e.* to decrease N), and to decrease slightly the amplitude of the planetary waves. As may be seen by substitution of Equations 2 and 4 into Equation 3, this factor would also tend to increase the (eastward) phase speed of the planetary waves. The overall effect would thus be to increase the zonality of both world climate and circulation, *i.e.* to favor the so-called "high-index" type of circulation. Conversely, any factor tending to decrease atmospheric stability and/or mean temperature would tend to decrease zonality, *i.e.* to favor the so-called "low-index" type of circulation.

In view of the fact that the form of atmospheric circulation depends—as already noted—on the magnitude of the meridional atmospheric heating gradient ΔQ, it may seem surprising that among the various statistics noted above only the meridional wind speed given by Equation 5 depends explicitly on ΔQ. The reason for this is that the wave regime characterizing the circulation is so efficient in maintaining the required meridional heat flux that all of the above statistics except the meridional wind speed [measured here by r.m.s. (V)] are relatively unaffected by variations of ΔQ *so long as* ΔQ *exceeds a critical minimum value.* (Below this critical value the circulation would be changed to an altogether different mode.) For present conditions on the Earth, this critical value of ΔQ is always exceeded, even in summer despite a brief reversal of the meridional gradient of isolation at that time of year. It is likely, in fact, that the critical value of ΔQ has been exceeded throughout geological history, and therefore that in a *qualitative* sense the general circulation has probably resembled its present form at all times during the Quaternary.

At this point we should digress briefly to explain how the meridional atmospheric heating gradient ΔQ is determined. If we concern ourselves only with annual average conditions, so that effects of seasonal heat storage can be neglected, ΔQ can be equated to twice the integral of *net* radiation R_n between the equator and the latitude φ^* at which the meridional heat transport in the atmosphere is a maximum. (For convenience φ^* is frequently assumed equal to 45°, which however is between 5° and 10° too far poleward in the annual mean.) Now, R_n may in general be approximated as a function of latitude by the relation

$$R_n = I(1 - A) - W \qquad (6)$$

where I is the astronomically determined insolation from Equation 1, A is the planetary albedo for the latitude involved (including the contribution of cloudiness), and W is the net long-wave eradiation from the Earth and atmosphere to space. The eradiation W, in turn, derives mainly from atmospheric water vapor, which happens to be distributed in such a manner that W is nearly invariant with latitude. This means that we may obtain a rough estimate of ΔQ simply by forming the difference between the areally integrated values of effective insolation $I(1 - A)$ equatorward and poleward of latitude φ^*.

If we wish to examine *seasonal* differences of ΔQ, however, we have to take account also of the contribution of heat storage in the oceans in specifying ΔQ. Inasmuch as most of the differential heating of the atmosphere actually derives from latent heat flux and long-wave eradiation from the ocean surface (see section on Terrestrial Heat Budget), both of which are comparatively invariant over the course of the year owing to the modest extent of seasonal changes of sea surface temperature, it turns out that ΔQ is only about four times larger in winter than in summer despite the fact that the meridional gradient of $I(1 - A)$ actually reverses sign between these two seasons. Consequently, the statistics of the winter circulation normally differ very little

from those of the summer circulation, except that the root mean square meridional wind speed given by Equation 5 has a value in winter about twice as large as that in summer.

Thus far in this discussion of planetary circulation, I have made only oblique reference to its implications for surface climate. We shall now examine some of these implications a bit more explicitly.

Recalling that we are still concerned with an Earth for which ocean-continent contrasts and topography can be neglected, we should realize that in the long run the effect of the circulation on surface climate is a function of latitude only. Indeed, the principal effect of the circulation of the real atmosphere is to transport heat poleward and to tend to equalize temperatures at all latitudes. There now arises the important question of estimating the meridional surface-temperature distribution that is consistent with this poleward heat transport by the circulation.

An approximate answer to this question can be had by manipulating the same simplified circulation theory that led to Equations 2-5. Thus the meridional temperature *gradient,* expressed in terms of its mean value in mid-latitudes and at mid-levels of the atmosphere, is given roughly by the equation

$$-dT/d\varphi = b\overline{T}s \qquad (7)$$

(Mintz, 1961), where b is a constant that depends only on certain thermodynamic properties of air, and where $\overline{T}$ and s are the temperature and static stability defined under Equation 2. This can be taken as representative of the meridional gradient also at the surface. Numerically, Equation 7 yields about 0.5° C per degree of latitude in the annual mean, which compares closely with the observed annual mean gradients in mid-latitudes both at the surface and aloft. By reverting to more generalized forms of the equations governing atmospheric behavior, one can confidently expect ever more refined answers to this question to come from general-circulation research in the years ahead.

An interim method of dealing with this important problem is a disarmingly simple one in which the efficiency of the flux-inducing mechanisms of the circulation—the method does not require that these mechanisms be known in detail—is expressed by a single parameter known as an *austausch coefficient* (analogous to a diffusion coefficient). The appropriate numerical value of the coefficient can usually be estimated by empirical means.

By this simple device it is possible to specify the meridional distribution of surface temperature as a *general* (*i.e.* non-linear) function of latitude and for each season of the year individually, as a function of the principal meridionally varying terms of the terrestrial heat budget, including interseasonal heat-storage terms. Adem (1962, 1963) has used this method to achieve a remarkably accurate specification of the meridional temperature distribution in all seasons of the year. A few of Adem's results are illustrated in Figure 6.

Variations of this same method have been adapted by Öpik (1953a, b) and by Fritz (1960) to the related problem of estimating the meridional pattern of surface temperature *changes* that would follow from postulated changes of effective insolational heating of the atmosphere (*e.g.* changes of solar constant).

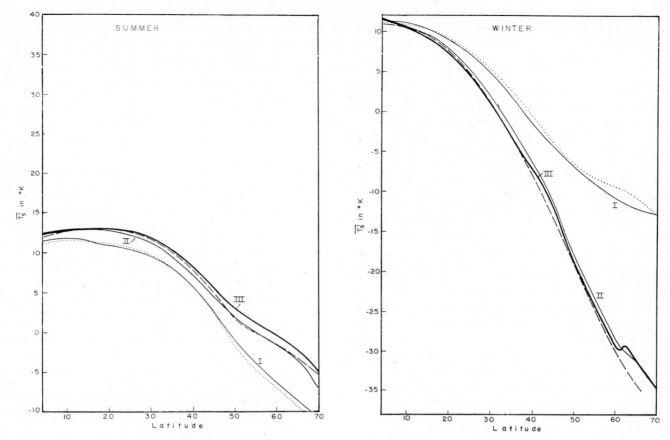

Figure 6. Meridional distribution of mean surface temperature in Northern Hemisphere, in summer and winter seasons, expressed as departure from planetary annual mean (287° K). Solid curves are computed from heat-budget data and austausch model of atmospheric-heat transport (see text). Curve I is distribution over oceans only; Curves II and III are mean distributions for entire hemisphere, assuming two different values for depth of oceans involved in seasonal heat storage. Dotted and dashed curves are observed distributions. After Adem (1963).

The results of most studies of this kind suggest that the austausch coefficient in mid-latitudes is roughly twice as large in winter as in summer; this is consistent with the relative seasonal variation of mean meridional wind speed aloft (as inferred, for example, by use of Equation 5) to which the austausch exchange is expected to be proportional. A consequence of this is the fact that the polar regions are kept much warmer (and the tropics, cooler) in winter than they are in summer, relative to conditions that would exist in the absence of the planetary circulation. Moreover, it can be affirmed that the absolute magnitude of the austausch coefficient is always sufficiently small that changes of effective insolation (*e.g.* of the solar constant) result in changes of mean terrestrial temperature that are fairly similar at all latitudes. As Fritz (1960) has pointed out, this constitutes a strong argument against the validity of Simpson's famous "warmer Sun–cooler Earth" theory of ice ages.

In view of the many possible ways to look at atmospheric behavior, it is not surprising that various investigators have found other useful means of describing it that differ considerably from the approach described above. Of special interest in the study of climatic change is a class of statistical measures of the total kinetic energy of the planetary circulation that can be derived from dynamical theory, in which no distinction is made between the many different modes and scale sizes of motion possible in the atmosphere. A measure of this sort, introduced by Kraus (1961), is one in which the total vigor of the circulation is expressed in terms of its rate of kinetic energy generation $\dot{E}$. According to Kraus, this can be given to a first approximation as a function of the appropriately weighted upward mean flux density of (sensible) heat $\overline{H}$, the mean atmospheric pressure at the Earth's surface $\overline{p}_0$, the mean pressure $\overline{p}_h$ at the highest atmospheric level to which convective elements of the circulation are able to transport latent and sensible heat, and the horizontal variance of p_h denoted by var(p_h). Specifically,

$$\dot{E} \simeq k\overline{H}\left[\log\left(\frac{\overline{p}_0}{\overline{p}_h}\right) + \frac{\mathrm{var}(p_h)}{2\overline{p}_h{}^2}\right] \qquad (8')$$

where k is a constant depending only on the Earth's surface area and on thermodynamic properties of air, and log represents the Naperian logarithm. Since p_h corresponds rather closely to the pressure of the tropopause, Equation 8′ can be expressed in approximate terms of the tropopause height h directly, namely,

$$\dot{E} \simeq k\overline{H}\left[c\overline{h} + \frac{c^2\,\mathrm{var}(h)}{2}\right] \qquad (8)$$

Here, $\overline{h}$ is the mean height of the tropopause over the Earth, $\mathrm{var}(h)$ the variance of tropopause height with latitude (and longitude), and c is a constant having the dimensions of inverse length. In words, Equation 8 states that the overall vigor of the planetary circulation is directly proportional to the average intensity of atmospheric heating from below and to the mean thickness of the troposphere participating in the circulation, and it depends as well on the spatial (geographical) variations of this thickness.

Although the total energy of the atmospheric circulation does not uniquely specify the distribution of world climate, certain properties of climate—for example, the world average rainfall rate—are likely to be correlated with it. As illustrated by Kraus (1961), when taken together with independent lines of reasoning, such measures of total energy can be a useful tool for evaluating possible causes of climatic change. I shall apply Equation 8 in this manner toward the end of the chapter.

Circulation of the case of a nonuniform Earth. Qualitatively the effect of nonuniformities of the Earth's surface is not so much to change the picture of the atmospheric circulation from that already described for a uniform Earth as it is to introduce zonal (east-west) biases in the statistics of the circulation. On daily weather maps, these biases are quite well hidden by the migratory planetary Rossby waves aloft and by their associated high- and low-pressure systems at the surface. When, however, the circulation pattern is examined in terms of its averages over periods of months or years, these migratory features are smoothed away to reveal the zonal biases quite clearly.

The geographical pattern of these biases, usually referred to as *standing*, or quasi-permanent, *perturbations* in the circulation, varies to some extent with the season of the year, but in general it is determined by the geographical pattern of various *forcing fields* associated with the distribution of the continents and the oceans. These forcing fields include continental-scale topography, zonal differences of both surface heating and aerodynamic roughness, and a type of interaction with the travelling Rossby waves that occurs mostly off the east coasts of the continents where abrupt land-ocean temperature contrasts are favorable to vigorous storm genesis. Aloft, the standing perturbation pattern in mid-latitudes is characterized mainly by a maximum poleward displacement of the zonal westerlies near the western edges of the major continents, especially in the case of the Americas, where the winds must cross high mountain ranges; it is also characterized by a maximum equatorward displacement of the zonal westerlies near the western edges of the major oceans.

In the Northern Hemisphere, the continents are so distributed that the standing perturbations somewhat resemble a system of uniformly spaced Rossby waves with a wave number (N) equal usually to 3 and sometimes to 4. In the Southern Hemisphere, the absence of large continents in

mid-latitudes results in a much less pronounced standing component of the circulation there. It should be remarked in passing that, despite the resemblance of these standing waves to the migratory Rossby waves that appear on daily weather maps, the two cannot be expected on theoretical grounds to exhibit altogether the same dynamical behavior. To be sure, application of equations such as (2) and (3) to the standing perturbations, as a means of interpreting the irregular phase and wavelength changes of these perturbations from month to month or over a period of years, is not strictly valid.

A general theory of the standing perturbations in the mid-latitude planetary circulation has recently been synthesized by Saltzman and Rao (1963). A numerical calculation of the vertical motion field associated with the perturbations, based on an idealized harmonic distribution of the continents, is shown together with the observed field of motion in Figure 7. The comparison is quite satisfactory, and Saltzman has listed a number of possible refinements of theory that, when incorporated into his model, can be expected to improve it further. It remains for future research to establish how the forcing field responsible for the standing perturbations has varied in the historical and geological past, and precisely what changes in the *zonal* distribution of world climate would have followed. By the same token, it is not too

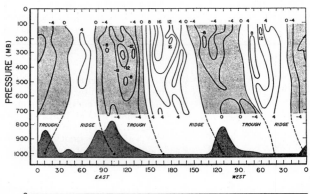

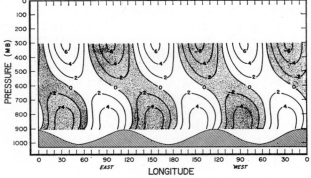

Figure 7. Longitude-altitude cross-section of standing perturbation field in zonal westerlies of Northern Hemisphere, represented by field of mean vertical wind speed (upward motion shown by positive numbers). Observed field (above) and field computed by Saltzman (1963) (below). Data refer to temperate latitudes in winter.

optimistic to suppose that independent historical evidence of ancient circulation patterns differing from the modern pattern may some day be interpreted by means of this theory to yield otherwise unavailable information about paleogeography, orogenic uplift, and anomalous ocean-temperature patterns in the past.

Blocking patterns of atmospheric circulation. A rather large fraction of the time—especially in the winter half of the year—the planetary circulation takes on a special form in which one or more well-developed, quasi-stationary, "warm" anticyclones appear in the higher latitudes. These anticyclones, which normally develop only at certain longitudes (the Gulf of Alaska and near the Greenwich meridian in the Northern Hemisphere), may persist a week or longer before the circulation returns to its predominant, zonally more uniform state (see Fig. 8). They are commonly called *blocking highs* because they tend locally to obstruct the normal eastward course of the zonal wind-flow aloft and of the surface weather systems around the hemisphere. The dynamical cause of blocking is not fully understood, but it seems likely that blocking is a form of safety valve in the atmosphere by which the speed of the zonal westerlies is prevented from exceeding a critical, dynamically unstable magnitude (Rex, 1950). Inasmuch as blocking patterns occur in hydrodynamic models of the atmosphere in which the underlying surface can be assumed to be uniform (Fultz, 1959), it would appear that whereas surface irregularities of the Earth must clearly account for the fact that blocks favor certain longitudes of formation, these irregularities are not necessary to the very existence of blocking patterns in the atmosphere.

In the regions where blocking occurs, marked influences of blocking on climate can be noted (Rex, 1950). Inasmuch as these regions include the western continental cordilleras, where portions of the Pleistocene ice sheets are thought to have originated, it is important to note that blocking climate is not considered to be favorable to the origin of continental ice sheets, although it may well encourage their maintenance once initiated under other circulation conditions.

THEORIES OF CLIMATIC VARIATION

POTENTIAL CAUSATIVE FACTORS IN CLIMATIC CHANGE

This section will be devoted to a discussion of various environmental factors that may have contributed to the climatic changes of the Quaternary, and to a brief account of the principal climatic effects of each of these factors to be expected from atmospheric theory as outlined in the preceding section. Although this survey will not lead us to a definite conclusion as to the causes of Pleistocene glaciation and the climatic chronology of the Quaternary, it endeavors at least to circumscribe all *potentially* significant factors that must be left to future research to validate beyond a reasonable doubt and to rank in order of their quantitative importance in producing climatic change.

Autovariation of atmospheric circulation. In view of the highly non-linear form of the equations governing atmospheric dynamics, it has to be expected on theoretical grounds that both planetary circulation and world climate exhibit statistically unstable behavior. That is to say, variations of climate—on the scale of months and years, at any rate—are to be anticipated even when the atmospheric boundary conditions remain absolutely constant in time. Moreover, it is conceivable that under some circumstances very slight (observationally imperceptible) changes of the boundary conditions may suffice to evoke large changes of circulation and climate, and under slightly different circumstances relatively large changes of the boundary conditions may evoke only a negligible climatic response (Lorenz, 1964). Considerations such as these caution us not to be too hasty to dismiss spontaneous autovariation of the atmosphere as the basic cause of paleoclimatic change. On the other hand, it is known from the theory of fluid dynamics that the atmosphere is a *dissipative* system. This means that after a certain length of time the state of the circulation—and thus climate—can no longer remember what its initial state had been, and its behavior is thereafter determined entirely by the history of atmospheric boundary conditions. When the atmosphere is viewed as an isolated system, unable to interact with its underlying surface (in particular with the oceans), its memory of its own past dynamical state is thought to be measured in months only. Hence, climatic fluctuations resulting from atmospheric autovariation alone are likely to be limited in characteristic wavelength to not more than a few years.

Air-sea interaction. The world oceans constitute a dissipative fluid-dynamical system quite like the atmosphere. Owing, however, to a very much greater longevity of the horizontal density gradients that give rise to their internal motions, oceanic memory of its own past dynamical state is believed to be from two to three orders of magnitude longer than atmospheric memory. Inasmuch as the oceans are in perpetually intimate contact with the atmosphere and are continually exchanging enormous quantities of (sensible and latent) heat with it, this long oceanic memory is likely to be shared to some extent by the atmosphere. Consequently the *ocean-atmosphere system* is probably capable of significant autovariation on the scale of centuries and millennia.

The mode of oceanic circulation that possesses this long memory is not the same wind-driven (*barotropic*) mode that is coupled to the atmospheric circulation. Rather, it is the internally driven (*thermohaline*) mode by which the abyssal water movements of all the world's oceans are interconnected presumably being "driven" by cold-water subsidence near the southern tip of Greenland and near the Weddell Sea in Antarctica (Stommel, 1958; Stommel and Arons, 1960). This circulation mode is characterized by overturning with time constants of many hundreds of years. Its consequences to climate might (but need not) extend to periodic variations with wavelengths of a similar order; more likely it gives rise to *aperiodic* climatic variations only.

The potentially vast importance of long-period air-sea interactions to climatic variation can be appreciated in another way by considering the oceans in terms merely of their passive roles as heat reservoirs. For certain assumptions about the manner in which the oceans exchange heat with the atmosphere (which appear to be consistent with actual observation), it can be shown that any factor imposing variations on the rate of heat gain or loss in the

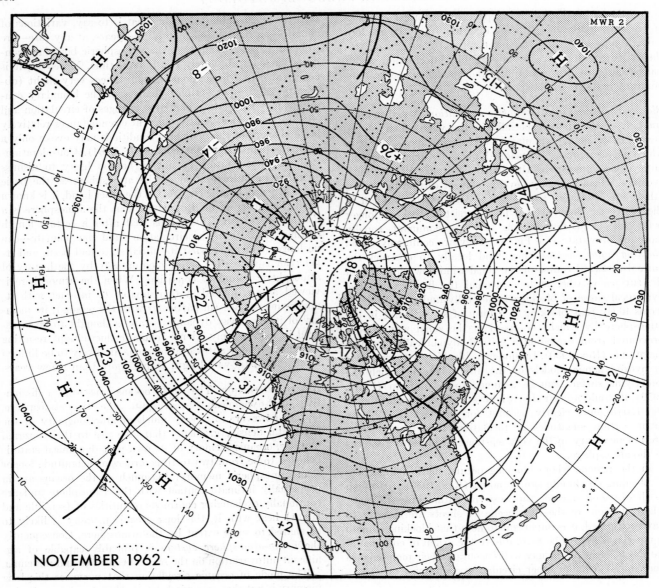

NOVEMBER 1962

oceans will tend to result in a *cumulative* temperature anomaly of the ocean-atmosphere system. Such a factor—which may be either random or systematic—might include, for example, short-term meteorological variability of the air temperature itself, variability of atmospheric transparency resulting, for instance, from dusty volcanic eruptions, or even changes of the solar constant. In any case, when viewed as a stochastic process, this cumulative heat-storage effect can be likened in statistical behavior to a simple "random walk" by which—given enough time—very persistent and wide swings of climate could result. It is possible that the ice ages themselves owe their existence to a "random" phenomenon like this; however, in view of certain oversimplifications in this picture of air-sea interaction, the model probably breaks down before conditions become as extreme as those of the ice ages.

The least one can say is that the ocean-atmosphere system is capable of autovariation far beyond the limits of magni-

tude and time scale possible in the atmosphere alone. In addition, it should be kept in mind that air-sea interactions are quite likely to alter the ultimate extent and pattern of atmospheric response to *other* geophysical factors potentially responsible for climatic change on the scale of decades, centuries, and millennia.

Polar wandering and continental drift. Passing down through the list of environmental phenomena that might potentially bear on paleoclimatic changes (see Table 1), we should pause at those characterized by minimum time scales of the order of 10^7 years. Although a factor with this time scale would not be expected to have had a critical bearing on the time of onset of the Pleistocene, it might nonetheless have set the stage for another, quicker-acting phenomena to become effective in precipitating an ice age for the first time during the Cenozoic. In this connection, we should mention polar wandering and continental drift. By and large, the

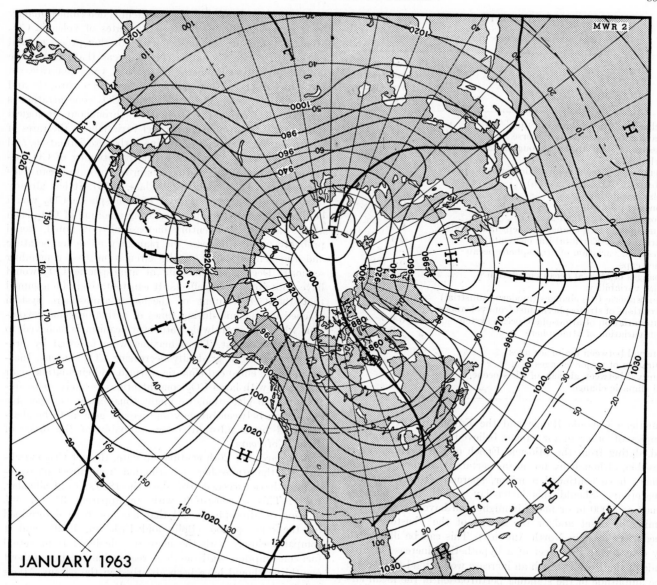

Figure 8. Examples of contrasting circulation patterns at mid-tropospheric levels of atmosphere, based on mean monthly data. Map for November 1962 illustrates zonal pattern; that for January 1963, an uncommonly well-developed blocking pattern (blocking highs are identified by "H" off west coast of U.S. and near British Isles). Fine solid lines are pressure-height contours paralleled by upper wind flow, generally from west to east. Other undulations in planetary flow consist partly of standing perturbations and partly of migratory Rossby waves. Both maps representative of winter conditions.

combined climatic effect of these factors during the late Tertiary would have been limited to the effect of a slight meridional displacement of the continents with respect to the pole by a few hundred kilometers toward eastern Asia (*e.g.* Runcorn, 1962, Chap. 1). This displacement might have incurred a regional temperature decline of a few degrees Celsius during the late Tertiary in the areas of Europe and North America where the Pleistocene ice sheets are believed to have originated. It is doubtful, however, whether the temperature change would have been large enough and rapid enough to have made any difference at all to the timing of the onset of glaciation.

Orogeny and continental uplift. It was remarked in an earlier section that the height and profile of major continental mountain ranges, and continental altitude as a whole, are capable of influencing circulation and climate over a large part of the hemisphere in which the continent lies. By the same token, changes in the large-scale topography of the Earth would be expected to result in changes of circulation and climate over equally extensive areas. The largest of the mountain ranges—the Himalayas, the North American Rockies, and the South American Andes—are believed to have been formed about 50 million years ago during the initial phases of the so-called Cenozoic revolution. The North

TABLE 1

Potential Causative Factors in Climatic Change

Factor	Probable range of time scales involved (years, power of ten)
Stellar evolution (aging of Sun)	9
Gravitational waves in universe	9 (?)
Passage of solar system through galactic dust clouds	9-8 (?)
Changes of gaseous composition of atmosphere (except CO_2, H_2O, and O_3)	9-8
Polar wandering	9-7
Continental drift	9-7
Orogeny and continental uplift	8-7
Atmospheric CO_2 changes (except industrial)	8-4
Variations of Earth-orbital elements	5-4
Feedback variation of atmosphere–ocean– ice caps	5-4 (?)
Changes of abyssal ocean circulation	6-3 (?)
Solar variability	8-1 (?)
Atmospheric CO_2 changes (modern industrial)	2-1
Variations of stratospheric dust from volcanoes	8-0 (?)
Autovariation of atmosphere-ocean system	3-0
Autovariation of atmosphere	1-0
Interval between major ice ages	8
Duration of major ice ages	7-6
Interval between glacials of Pleistocene	5-4
All climatic change	9-0

American Cascade Range and the European Alps are examples of other major ranges believed to be only half as old, dating from the Miocene Epoch of the Tertiary. It is possible, although by no means certain, that most of these ranges have continued a minor, sporadic growth into the Quaternary. Should this latter-day growth have been as much as 1,000 m or more, it might well have advanced the timing of onset and/or the extent of the Pleistocene ice sheets (at least in North America). This can be illustrated by considering the effect of a hypothetical increase of altitude of the Rockies. Such an increase would tend to increase the amplitude of the standing perturbation in the mean circulation over North America and the western Atlantic, but it would not greatly affect the phase and wavelength of the perturbation. The wind field over the interior of the continent would thus acquire a larger component from the north, and permit arctic and polar air masses to penetrate more frequently to low latitudes over the interior. This, in turn, would favor the maintenance (although not necessarily the genesis) of the continental ice sheets. The overall storminess of the western Atlantic would probably be increased as well, and some climatic repercussions might reach as far eastward as Europe.

The extent to which orogeny can influence circulation and climate depends, of course, on the extent of uplift involved. Until such time as the topographic changes of the late Tertiary and the Quaternary can be specified and dated in quantitative detail, it will be very difficult to gauge what specific role (if any) such changes have played in the climatic history of the period.

Variations of atmospheric carbon dioxide. The total amount of CO_2 in the ocean-atmosphere system is determined mainly by a quasi-equilibrium between the rates of volcanic CO_2 exhalation, organic and inorganic weathering processes, and marine carbonate formation. (It happens that, during the last century, because man has burned vast quantities of fossil fuel reserves, this equilibrium has been abruptly and significantly upset.) The atmospheric CO_2 concentration is believed to have varied somewhat throughout geological time, partly because of nonparallel variations in the rates of volcanism, weathering, and marine-carbonate formation, and partly because of deviations in the partitioning of CO_2 between the atmosphere and oceans in response to ocean temperature and volume changes (Plass, 1956). It has already been remarked that variations of atmospheric CO_2 would be likely to affect climate; increasing amounts of CO_2, such as the modern 20th-century increase already noted, would probably tend to increase the planetary mean temperature and the general vigor of the circulation (see concluding section). Decreasing amounts of atmospheric CO_2 would have opposite climatic effects. It can tentatively be assumed that the CO_2 content of the ocean-atmosphere system reached its maxima during times of active orogenic revolution when the worldwide rate of volcanism is believed to have been greatest. These maxima were followed by protracted periods of gradually decreasing CO_2 content. Inasmuch as the enhanced climatic warmth and circulation vigor associated with large CO_2 concentrations is likely to be unfavorable to glaciation, we might thus expect any possible connection between orogeny and ice-age genesis to be characterized by a substantial lag, probably of the order of millions of years.

As regards the 20th century, to date, the net CO_2 enrichment of the atmosphere is estimated from direct measurement to have exceeded 10% since the 1880's (*e.g.* Callendar, 1958). This is consistent with an apparent 3% or 4% dilution of atmospheric C^{14} that has also been determined for the same period (Bolin and Eriksson, 1959), and it compares closely with the increase calculated from actual fuel-consumption statistics if a reasonable fraction (about one-third) should have been absorbed in the oceans. Man's industrial activity may tend to result in a continuing net amelioration of climate in the future until fossil fuels are no longer consumed. Thereafter, the oceans can be expected gradually to absorb the excess atmospheric CO_2 and—other factors being equal—to restore world climate to cooler levels.

Explosive volcanic activity. In relatively modern times, volcanic eruptions comparable to the epochal eruption of Krakatoa in 1883 are believed to have occurred at the rate of a few per century. Such eruptions are significant to climate because their force is sufficient to inject large amounts of fine dust into the mid-stratosphere (altitudes near or above 20 km), where much of the dust can reside for years and be spread entirely around the world by the winds at that altitude. Backscattering of solar radiation by stratospheric dust layers may not only cool world climate (Mitchell, 1961) but may also weaken the planetary circulation (see Conclusions). In this respect, had unusually prolonged periods of *violent* volcanic activity occurred in the late

Tertiary or Quaternary, these would be expected to have encouraged the genesis and/or perpetuation of the Pleistocene glaciation. A definitive evaluation of this factor in accounting for the climatic history of the Quaternary is clearly handicapped by our lack of a quantitative chronology of volcanism in the period.

To the extent that "dusty" volcanic eruptions have coincided with periods of excessive volcanic CO_2 exhalation, it should be added that the two factors may have tended to compensate one another in terms of their climatic effects; any such coincidence would thus act to confuse the lag relation between periods of orogeny and ice-age genesis already hypothesized in connection with CO_2 variations.

Solar variability. Solar radiation may vary with time in several different ways. On the scale of the 11-year sunspot cycle, at least, it is presumed to vary as to the total solar constant, its ultraviolet component, and corpuscular emission. The ultraviolet component is known to fluctuate considerably with solar-flare activity. Variations of corpuscular emission are associated with the polar auroras and are presumed to be responsible for certain observed forms of geomagnetic activity. Both the ultraviolet and corpuscular changes are very important causes of variations in the state of very high atmospheric layers (the *ionosphere*). Their potential importance to tropospheric circulation and climate, on the other hand, is dubious. On the basis of statistical studies of atmospheric circulation (*e.g.* Willett, 1949), some Sun-climate relationships involving these factors have been claimed. However, a number of circumstances have militated against general acceptance of them: (1) The energies involved in these components of solar output are several orders of magnitude smaller than the energy of the total solar constant. (2) With the possible exception of ultraviolet-ozone relationships, physical mechanisms by which these small energies could suffice to make a significant impression on the circulation of the lower atmosphere are difficult to visualize. (3) The empirical evidence of these Sun-climate relationships has not thus far enjoyed a comfortably high level of statistical significance. At the risk of passing over a pearl in this particular bed of oysters, I therefore propose to limit further considerations of solar variability to the total solar constant (see, however, Conclusions).

The solar constant might conceivably have varied on any or all scales of time during the Earth's history. In modern times, the spectacular variations of sunspot numbers and of other surface features of the sun, especially those following the 11-yr activity cycle and longer-term sunspot trends, easily lure one to the supposition that the solar constant itself may change in parallel with them. Efforts to measure solar-constant changes in recent years have led to suggestive but inconclusive results. Direct measurements, based on extrapolation of surface pyrheliometric observations by C. G. Abbot and others of the Smithsonian Institution, have been regarded as suspect because of questionable assumptions about atmospheric transparency required by the method. Indirect measurements by spectrophotometric observations of the brightness of selected planets (Uranus and Neptune) in comparison with the brightness of background stars can be regarded as more reliable; these have hinted

at a real variation of solar constant since 1953 of the order of 1% (Serkowski, 1961). This apparent variation has more or less followed the 11-yr sunspot cycle, but further reductions of the data are considered necessary before the variation can be accepted at face value.

Variations of the solar constant following the double (22-yr) sunspot cycle or over longer periods—paralleling, for example, the roughly 90-yr variation in total solar spottedness and its asymmetry in the northern and southern solar hemispheres (Bell and Wolbach, 1962)—are conceivable but wholly unverifiable in available pyrheliometric data. The possibility of a 90-yr variation in recent centuries is suggested by some tendency for climate and dendrochronological indices to reflect periods of this particular length. Again, on the basis of a careful statistical analysis of aurora observations and astronomical sightings down through recorded history—which are presumed to indicate long-term variations of atmospheric seeing conditions—Link (1964) has claimed to have found indications of a solar period of about 400 years. Fragmentary records of unusual sunspot activity to compare with other historical variables are available as far back as the 6th century B.C. (Schove, 1955).

By way of evaluating Sun-climate relationships in historical times, it would of course be very fortunate if the solar constant turns out to be well correlated with total sunspot number. If such a correlation can be demonstrated in the modern 11-yr sunspot cycle, one might suppose it to apply to longer sunspot cycles as well. This raises an important question, the answer to which would have a crucial bearing on the way we should interpret our failure to demonstrate convincingly relationships between Sun and climate in the past century of modern meteorological observations. The question is, should we expect that the climatic response to a relatively rapid variation of solar energy, such as one following the 11-yr sunspot cycle, is the same as the response to an equal but slower variation over much longer intervals of time? The answer is, probably not. In the case of the more rapid variation, either the enormous thermal inertia of the oceans may smooth out the solar effect, or the solar effect may be submerged under the "noise" of air-sea *autovariation* to the point where a century or two of meteorological data are inadequate to sort it out statistically. In the case of the slower variation of solar constant, however, the oceans would have ample opportunity to share more fully in the atmospheric temperature reaction, and the air-sea autovariation to average itself out; the climatic response as a whole would then be more systematic and coherent. This suggests that solar influences on climate may be more important as regards long-period solar variability than one might suppose from modern studies based on the 11-yr cycle. On the other hand, the *reality* of long-term solar variability itself cannot be taken for granted until more is known about solar behavior in general.

The possibility that the solar constant varies on scales of time comparable to the duration of the entire Pleistocene, or to the interval between the glacials and interglacials in the Pleistocene, is another matter that deserves consideration. Many paleoclimatologists, who have been unable to account otherwise to their satisfaction for the origin of the ice ages, have turned to long-period variations of the solar

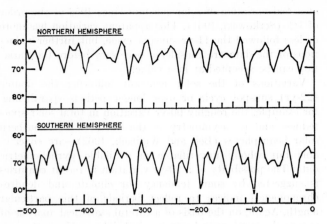

Figure 9. Chronology of variations of insolation during past 500,000 years for summer half year at 65° N and S latitude, converted to equivalent latitude. Abscissa units are time in thousands of years before present. Based on calculations of Earth's orbital elements, after van Woerkom (1953).

constant as the only likely explanation. To be sure, if the solar constant were in fact lowered by about 10% during the past million years, one would need look no further to account for the Pleistocene glaciation.

Unfortunately, present knowledge of solar physics is not adequate to establish the likelihood of variations of solar luminosity on extremely long time scales. Theoretical models of stellar interiors have nonetheless been proposed in which such variations are admissible. Öpik (1958), for example, has outlined a mechanism whereby solar upheavals at intervals of the order of 10^8 years might have led to the Eo-Cambrian, Permo-Carboniferous, and Quaternary sequence of major ice ages. In addition, Öpik (1953a) and Bhatnager (1953) had earlier suggested the existence of radiative disturbances in the Sun involving time scales of the order of 10^5 to 10^6 years, by which they supposed the glacial-interglacial sequence of the Pleistocene to be accounted for. Although the relevant theory of solar instability has been developed in detail, it has yet to gain general acceptance by astronomers.

In view of the many potential kinds of Earth-environmental change that may have accounted for paleoclimatic variation, coupled with our knowledge of modern historical climatic change suggesting a multiplicity of causes on this shorter time scale at least, it is almost certainly unnecessary to fall back on solar variability as the only plausible explanation of the ice ages. On the other hand, the possibility should not be dismissed too casually that the interior of the Sun is not the absolutely steady-state system that most astrophysicists consider it. In any case, the paleoclimatologist would do well to keep a watchful eye on future developments in stellar physics.

Changes of the Earth's orbital elements. According to the Croll-Milankovitch hypothesis (*e.g.* Milankovitch, 1930), the orbit and axial-rotation vector of the Earth have each varied during geologic time. Such variations would have produced quasi-periodic changes in the seasonal and latitudinal distributions of terrestrial insolation over time intervals of the order of tens of thousands of years.

Three principal factors are involved. (1) The *eccentricity of the Earth's orbit,* now about 0.016, may change between zero and about 0.053 over a period averaging about 96,000 years. The seasonal variation of average insolation over the whole Earth (now 7%) reaches a maximum of 20% when the eccentricity is largest. (2) The *precession of the equinoxes,* that is, the fluctuating distance between the points on the Earth's orbit corresponding to perihelion and to the occurrence of the solstices, is now such that the Earth-Sun distance is least in January. This minimum distance advances gradually through the year, completing a cycle in an average time of about 21,000 years. (3) The *obliquity of the ecliptic, i.e.* the angle between the plane of the Earth's orbit and the plane of its rotational equator, now about 23.5°, may vary by almost 2.5° over a period of about 41,000 years.

The orbital eccentricity and the precession of the equinoxes determine the *lengths* of the summer and winter half years, the lengths being defined in such a way that the total integrated radiation is identical in both halves. These factors affect the Northern and Southern Hemispheres oppositely. The obliquity, on the other hand, regulates the summer-to-winter contrast of climate, and the meridional gradient of insolation in winter. This factor affects the two hemispheres in parallel, season for season.

The joint effect of all three orbital factors on the terrestrial distribution of insolation can be represented in a variety of ways, just one of which is the chronology illustrated in Figure 9. Although the accuracy of such chronologies depends rather critically on the accuracy of determination of certain astronomical constants involved, these constants have been known well enough since Milankovitch's time that recent recalculation of the chronologies (van Woerkom, 1953) has necessitated only minor revisions. Indeed, the absolute radiation chronology resulting from orbital variations is now quite confidently known for the entire Quaternary.

The climatic effects of the orbital variations can scarcely avoid being significant, but the extent to which the glacial-interglacial sequence of the Pleistocene can be attributed to such variations is not yet clearly established. Emiliani and Geiss (1959) and Zeuner (1959), for example, have supposed the role of these variations to be decisive. Indeed, the Milankovitch chronology has sometimes been applied as a tool for absolute dating of the Pleistocene chronology itself. Others, for example Öpik (1953a, b), have calculated that the temperature effects of the variations must have been much smaller than the difference in global mean temperature (of about 6° to 10° C) between the glacials and interglacials, and on this basis have categorically rejected the Croll-Milankovitch hypothesis of glaciation. As far as it goes, the latter viewpoint is well taken; however, it is not a compelling argument because it fails to recognize that a global temperature fall substantially smaller than 6° to 10° may suffice to *initiate* glaciation and that subsequent developments—perhaps the existence of glaciation itself or cumulative heat storage in the oceans—would account for the remainder of the temperature difference.

FEEDBACK HYPOTHESES OF GLACIAL-INTERGLACIAL
ALTERNATION

Autovariation of the ocean-atmosphere system has already
been mentioned as a factor in climatic change. A number of
specific forms of autovariation, most of them involving the
ice caps as well as the ocean and atmosphere, have been
proposed to account for the glacial-interglacial alternation
of the Pleistocene. Three different hypotheses of this kind
deserve to be identified here, although the validity of each
remains very much open to debate.

The Ewing-Donn hypothesis. On the rather unorthodox
premise that an ice-free Arctic Ocean is favorable to glaciation of its surrounding continents, Ewing and Donn (1956,
1958) have described an interesting feedback mechanism by
which periodic melting and re-formation of the Pleistocene
ice caps could result. Briefly, the cycle of events begins with
an interglacial condition in which the Arctic Ocean is kept
ice free by a flow of warm water into it from the North
Atlantic. The accumulation of ice on the continents, which
this condition is thought to favor, then lowers the world sea
level to a point where a submarine ridge that exists between
Iceland and the Faroes Islands begins to block further flow
of warm water into the Arctic. This, in turn, causes the
Arctic Ocean to freeze over, and to prevent continued nourishment of the continental ice sheets. In time, these ice
sheets would thus waste away and restore world sea levels
to a point where the warm water flow into the Arctic is
restored; so the cycle begins anew. Ewing and Donn visualize
the period of this cycle as being of the required order of 10^5
years, and offer reasons why the mechanism cannot be expected to have operated as described prior to the Quaternary.

The Plass hypothesis. For certain general conditions believed
representative of the Quaternary, Plass (1956) visualizes an
air–sea–ice cap interaction involving the carbon dioxide factor in climatic change, by which the alternation of glacials
and interglacials in the Pleistocene can be accounted for.
Beginning with a period in which the planetary CO_2 supply had been reduced by several percent (reason unspeci-
fied), atmospheric temperatures would be lowered by some
$4°$ C. After a sufficient time, perhaps 50,000 years, the
oceans would cool by a corresponding amount and come to
a new CO_2 equilibrium with the atmosphere. The lowered
temperature would encourage glaciation on the continents
whereby the volume of the oceans would decrease by about
5%. The lowered ocean volume would in turn raise the
concentration of oceanic CO_2 and cause a new imbalance
of CO_2 equilibrium with the atmosphere, leading to a new
increase of atmospheric CO_2. Atmospheric temperatures
would be increased by the added CO_2, the glaciers would
melt, and the oceans would be restored to their original
volume. At this point, the oceans would be able to reabsorb
some atmospheric CO_2, and the cycle might repeat. According to Plass, an overall change of planetary CO_2 supply
would be required to interrupt the cycle.

The Wilson hypothesis. A third hypothesis that seeks to account for the glacial-interglacial sequence of the Pleistocene
is based on the idea of periodic collapses of the Antarctic

ice cap (Wilson, 1964). Beginning at a time when the total
thickness of the Antarctic ice is less than a critical value,
Wilson considers that the rate of thickening produced by
the accumulation of precipitation exceeds the rate of subsidence produced by plastic flow of the ice cap and the mass
loss through calving at its perimeter. When, however, the
thickness is ultimately built up by precipitation to a critical
value, the transverse shearing stress near the base of the
ice cap becomes so large that the ice flow abruptly accelerates. Friction produced by the quickened flow then
generates heat sufficient to produce melting, with the result
that the motion accelerates further and the entire ice cap
subsides at a more or less catastrophic rate. The subsidence
results in a considerable areal expansion of the ice cap out
over the Antarctic ocean. According to Wilson, this would
in turn have far-reaching climatic effects, partly because of
an increased total planetary albedo and partly because of
an enhanced cooling of the oceans by the floating ice. One
result is presumed to be a transient glaciation in the Northern Hemisphere. Meanwhile, the collapsed Antarctic ice cap
is free to begin a new period of thickening by precipitation,
culminating tens of thousands of years later in another
catastrophic subsidence. Wilson believes that this mechanism
could not have been so influential on world climate prior to
the Quaternary, because the Antarctic land mass was not
then situated close enough to the South Pole. The mechanism is, however, presumed to have operated to a lesser
extent in the Tertiary and to have been the cause of cy-
clothems at that time which Wilson views as "aborted" ice
ages.

The Chamberlin hypothesis. At present, the direction of the
abyssal circulation of the world oceans is determined by the
fact that the dense bottom water is formed by subsidence in
high latitudes. This water derives its high density from its
low temperature. According to an hypothesis first suggested
by T. R. Chamberlin in 1899 (see also Kraus, 1961), the
situation may have been otherwise during the Tertiary and
earlier nonglacial epochs. At times when atmospheric conditions favored much higher evaporation rates and lower
precipitation rates in the tropics than at present, the salinity
of the surface layers of the tropical oceans may have become so high that the water density in these layers exceeded
the density of the cold surface water in high latitudes. This,
in turn, could have resulted in a reversal of the deep ocean
circulation, and have replaced the cold bottom water that
exists today by considerably warmer, relatively saline water.
This interesting hypothesis provides a viable explanation of
the extraordinary warmth and meridionally uniform climate
believed typical of nonglacial periods.

Chamberlin supposed that the onset of climatic conditions
favorable to this reversed abyssal circulation was attributable to relatively high concentrations of atmospheric
CO_2. Any of a number of other possible factors might have
been just as effective, including an increase of the solar
constant. In any case, the hypothesis seems unlikely to have
any bearing on the glacial-interglacial succession of the
Pleistocene because each reversal of the abyssal circulation
would probably have required too long a period of time to
become organized.

CONCLUSIONS

Although the physical causes of the climatic events of the Quaternary may indeed be several, it is a bit farfetched to suppose that *all* the theories listed above—to the extent that they are individually valid in the first place—have played equally important roles in the Quaternary. It is equally farfetched, incidentally, to assume that the theories listed are exhaustive of all possibilities, or to deny that the ultimate answers might lie where no man has yet thought to look.

In the case of at least some of the theories of climatic change listed here, we may apply certain theoretical principles outlined earlier in this chapter to help evaluate their relative merits. In this category are the theories that involve changes of solar constant, the CO_2 content of the atmosphere, the O_3 content of the atmosphere, or volcanic dust in the stratosphere. Other theories, which depend on changes of the Earth's topography or geography and which essentially involve regional rather than global effects on climate, will not be considered further simply because the nature and extent of such changes that have occurred during the Quaternary are not well enough established for definite conclusions to be drawn about their climatic effects.

On the basis of various statistics of the general atmospheric circulation and climate, the estimated effects of four potential causative factors in climatic change are outlined in Table 2. The table indicates the sense of the correlation coefficient to be expected between changes of magnitude of each factor and the various climate-circulation statistics. A number of assumptions about atmospheric behavior have been incorporated into this table. For example, changes in the speed of the zonal westerlies (U) are assumed to be controlled primarily by changes of overall atmospheric stability (s) rather than by those of mean atmospheric temperature ($\overline{T}$). Again, "blocking" forms of the planetary circulation are assumed to be favored above all by increases of zonal wind (U). Other assumptions, which would require too much space to describe and justify in detail here, are of uncertain validity; another climatologist asked to verify this table would not necessarily agree with every detail of it. On the whole, however, the following conclusions based on this table can be accepted with a reasonable degree of confidence.

The effects of an *increase* of total solar constant, an *increase* of total atmospheric CO_2 (and/or water vapor), and a *decrease* of total stratospheric dust would appear to be very similar. In each case, a warming of world climate would result, the warming being greatest in higher latitudes (associated with a decreased meridional temperature gradient). The strength of the zonal westerlies would be *decreased,* but the total vigor of the atmospheric circulation—and thus the world mean precipitation rate—would be increased. Continentality would probably be increased, and a slight westward displacement in the phase of the standing perturbations in the circulation would be expected. A decreasing frequency of blocking activity in the circulation would also be expected. In the aggregate, these effects would almost certainly be *unfavorable* to general glaciation, although not necessarily to local alpine glaciation.

It should be realized that a likely concomitant to the effects listed above would be a world average increase of cloudiness. As may be seen in Table 2, the effects of a change of cloudiness on the circulation-climate statistics are

TABLE 2

Effect of Certain Hypothetical Factors in Climatic Change on Atmospheric Circulation and Climate
(Shown in terms of positive (+) or negative (−) sign of correlation coefficient between variations of each factor and each circulation-climate statistic. Derived from theory discussed in text[a])

	Factor					
	Solar constant	CO_2 and/or water vapor content of atmosphere	Ozone content of stratosphere	Volcanic dust content of stratosphere	Lower-tropospheric cloudiness	Extent of polar ice cap
Direct effects on atmosphere						
Tropospheric mean temperature ($\overline{T}$)	+	+	0	−	−	−
Static stability (s)	−	−	(+)	+	(+)	+
Tropopause height (h)	+	+	(−)	−	(−)	−
Meridional heating gradient (ΔQ)	+	0	0	−	−	+
Indirect effects on circulation and climate						
Zonal wind speed (U); Meridional temperature gradient ($-\partial T/\partial \varphi$)	−	−	(+)	+	(+)	+
Meridional heat and water vapor transport [r.m.s. (V)]	+	(+)	0	−	(−)	0
Total circulation vigor ($\dot{E}$)	+	+	(−)	−	−	(−)
Planetary wave number (N)	+	+	0	−	0	−
Planetary wave speed (c)	−	−	(+)	+	(+)	+
Continentality; Intensity of standing perturbations	+	(+)	(−)	−	(−)	−
Frequency of blocking-type circulation patterns	−	−	(+)	+	(+)	+
Global mean precipitation rate	+	+	(+)	−	−	(−)

[a] Parentheses denote that effect is relatively small or uncertain; zero (0) denotes that correlation is probably negligible.

such that this increase would tend to *oppose* the effects of the primary factor, and cause the ultimate climatic reaction to be less than one would otherwise expect. In this respect, cloudiness can be viewed as the source of an important negative feedback mechanism in the atmosphere by which climatic change caused by any of the class of causative factors we are discussing here would be moderated but hardly prevented.

Stratospheric ozone has been included as a factor in Table 2 because this is sometimes regarded as a fundamental atmospheric variable that responds to external influences, in particular to changes of solar ultraviolet emission. It would appear that changes in O_3—whatever their origin—are not likely to have major effects on (tropospheric) circulation and climate. At most, a substantial increase of total amount of O_3 would increase the zonal wind slightly but decrease the total vigor of the circulation. This, in turn, might result in a small reduction of continentality and a slight increase of blocking in the planetary circulation. To the extent that the amount of O_3 is in fact proportional to solar ultraviolet emission, and to the extent that solar ultraviolet emission might vary in parallel with the total solar constant (neither premise being verifiable as yet), then the climatic effects of the ozone factor would tend merely to supplement the effects of cloudiness in offsetting the primal reaction to changes of solar constant.

Digressing for a moment to the problem of climatic change in the 20th century, it may be remarked that the worldwide warming of the first few decades of this century has been variously attributed to an increase of solar constant accompanying a rise in mean sunspot number, to a secular increase of CO_2 content of the atmosphere, and to a secular decline in average atmospheric turbidity following a decline in volcanic activity during the period (see Mitchell, 1961; Wexler, 1956). From what has just been said, it would seem to be rather difficult to disentangle the effects of these factors on circulation and climate inasmuch as the atmospheric response to each factor would be similar. Through an analysis of the years since about 1950, however, when world mean temperatures have evidently been declining, some estimate of the relative importance of the three factors may be possible because the atmospheric CO_2 content has presumably continued to increase whereas the trend in either one or both of the other factors may have been reversed.

Turning finally to the general problem of the ice ages, we might ask whether enough is known about the climate and circulation during the Pleistocene to infer which of the many possible causes of glaciation are most likely to have been involved. In answering this, we must be careful because the state of the atmosphere that favored the *initiation* of Pleistocene glaciation was probably modified afterward by the presence of the ice sheets themselves, and most of what we know about Pleistocene climate pertains to conditions *during* glaciation. The right-hand column of Table 2 indicates what characteristics of climate we would expect during glaciation (represented by an expanded polar ice cap); this theoretical picture conforms reasonably well to conditions during the Pleistocene insofar as these have been reconstructed by "direct" means. The glacial pattern of

climate, typified by a strengthened meridional temperature gradient and zonal wind, by a somewhat lessened total vigor of the circulation and mean global precipitation rate, and by enhanced blocking activity, would appear to be favorable to perpetuation of the continental ice sheets. A lowered mean global precipitation rate, by the way, need not have been detrimental to maintaining the ice sheets, as some have supposed it to be. The lowered summer temperatures could probably have sufficed to reduce ablation below any rate of accumulation by snow in the colder months, just as is true today of the center of the Antarctic ice cap, where the ice budget is in near equilibrium although annual precipitation is perhaps as small as that to be found anywhere in the world (see Rubin, 1964).

The causes of Pleistocene glaciation, then, cannot now be specified with any certainty. On the face of it, any of a number of factors would probably have sufficed, the crucial requirement having been an ability in each case to reduce summer temperatures by several degrees Celsius in the higher latitudes over a period of many thousands of years. Whether a factor increased or decreased precipitation in the higher latitudes, whether it increased or decreased the vigor of the general circulation, and whatever other effects on the general circulation it may have imposed, would seem to have been of secondary significance. Once the ice sheets became established, the circulation is likely then to have been altered in a manner favorable to their perpetuation.

As regards the chronology of glacials and interglacials during the Pleistocene, it seems reasonable to suppose that the factors included in the Croll-Milankovitch hypothesis have played a significant causative role but not necessarily to the exclusion of other environmental variables or air-sea autovariation mechanisms that must be left to future research to identify.

In this discussion of the merits of various environmental factors in accounting for the climatic events of the Quaternary, if all the conclusions that I have ventured have one attribute in common it is that, to one degree or another, they are to be regarded as tentative. Speculation and hypothesis, over which this discussion has freely ranged in places, will—in due course—be upheld or be discarded according as it is revealed as substance or shadow by our ever-increasing depth of insight into atmospheric (and oceanic) behavior. Already, today, the atmospheric scientist is finding it possible to construct remarkably realistic mathematical models of the atmosphere (*e.g.* Smagorinsky, 1963), by which he can explore the nature and extent of various subtle forms of dynamical unrest that underlie the perpetual evolution of climate and circulation from one pattern to another. Indeed, he is now standing at the threshold of a new era in which, for the first time, he will be able to derive *quantitative* evaluations of a number of hypotheses of climatic change by means of suitable controlled experiments with these mathematical stand-ins for the real atmosphere. An illustration of what has already been achieved along these lines is the numerical investigation of the effect of variable static stability on the large-scale zonal and monsoonal components of the general atmospheric circulation (Kraus and Lorenz, 1963).

From all indications, the future of theoretical climatology

is a bright and promising one that will likely produce an impressive "spin-off" to the benefit of many paleosciences. Along the way, some long-cherished notions as to the origin of the ice ages will perhaps be numbered among the casualties of scientific progress, but at the same time some altogether new ideas will almost certainly rise to take their place.

REFERENCES

Adem, Julian, 1962, On the theory of the general circulation of the atmosphere: Tellus (Stockholm), v. 14, p. 102-115

—— 1963, Preliminary computations on the maintenance and prediction of seasonal temperatures in the troposphere: Monthly Weather Rev., v. 91, p. 375-386

Bell, Barbara, and Wolbach, J. G., 1962, North-south asymmetry in solar spottedness and in great-storm sources: Smithson. Instn. Contr. Astrophysics, v. 5, p. 187-208

Bhatnagar, P. L., 1953, Internal constitution of the Sun and climatic changes, *in* Shapley, Harlow (ed.), Climatic change: Cambridge, Harvard Univ. Press, p. 137-142

Bolin, Bert, and Eriksson, Erik, 1959, Changes in the carbon dioxide content of the atmosphere and sea due to fossil fuel combustion, *in* Bolin, Bert (ed.), The atmosphere and the sea in motion: New York, Rockefeller Inst./Oxford Univ. Press, p. 130-142

Bryan, Kirk, Jr., 1962, Measurements of meridional heat transport by ocean currents: J. Geophys. Res., v. 67, p. 3403-3414

Budyko, M. I., and Kondratiev, K. Y., 1964, The heat balance of the earth, *in* Odishaw, Hugh (ed.), Research in geophysics, v. 2: Cambridge, Massachusetts Inst. Technol. Press, p. 529-554

Callendar, G. S., 1958, On the amount of carbon dioxide in the atmosphere: Tellus (Stockholm), v. 10, p. 243-248

Emiliani, Cesare, and Geiss, Johannes, 1959, On glaciations and their causes: Geol. Rdsch., v. 46, p. 576-601

Ewing, Maurice, and Donn, W. L., 1956, A theory of ice ages: Science, v. 123, p. 1061-1066 (also 1958, v. 127, p. 1159-1162)

Fritz, Sigmund, 1960, The heating distribution in the atmosphere and climatic change, *in* Pfeffer, R. L. (ed.), Dynamics of climate: New York, Pergamon Press, p. 96-100

Fultz, Dave, *et al.*, 1959, Studies of thermal convection in a rotating cylinder with some implications for large-scale atmospheric motions: Meteorol. Monogr., v. 4, No. 21, 104 p.

Kraus, E. B., 1961, Physical aspects of deduced and actual climatic change: New York Acad. Sci. Ann., v. 95, p. 225-234

Kraus, E. B., and Lorenz, E. N., 1963, A numerical study of the effect of vertical stability on monsoonal and zonal circulations: Paris, UNESCO, Arid Zone Research No. 10, p. 361-372

Lee, Richard, 1963, Evaluation of solar beam irradiation as a climatic parameter of mountain watersheds: Fort Collins, Colorado State Univ., Hydrol. Pap. No. 2, 50 p.

Link, František, 1964, Manifestations de l'activité solaire dans le passé historique: Planetary and Space Sci., v. 12, p. 333-348

Lorenz, E. N., 1964, The problem of deducing the climate from the governing equations: Tellus (Stockholm), v. 16, p. 1-11

Manabe, Syukuro, and Strickler, R. F., 1964, Thermal equilibrium of the atmosphere with a convective adjustment: J. Atmosph. Sci., v. 21, p. 361-385

Milankovitch, M., 1920, Théorie mathématique des phénomènes thermiques produits par la radiation solaire: Paris, L'Ecole Polytechnique, 338 p.

—— 1930, Mathematische Klimalehre und astronomische Theorie der Klimaschwankungen: Handbuch der Klimatologie, Bd. I, Teil A, 176 p.

Mintz, Yale, 1961, The general circulation of planetary atmospheres, *in* The atmospheres of Mars and Venus: Washington, D.C., Natl. Acad. Sci.–Natl. Res. Council, Publ. 944, App. 8, p. 107-146

—— 1962, The general circulation of planetary atmospheres: Downey, California, North American Aviation, Lunar and Planetary Exploration Colloquium Proc., v. 3, No. 1, p. 1-21

Mitchell, J. M., Jr., 1961, Recent secular changes of global temperature: New York Acad. Sci. Ann., v. 95, p. 235-250

Nairn, A. E. M. (ed.), 1961, Descriptive palaeoclimatology: New York, Interscience Publishers, 380 p.

Öpik, E. J., 1953a, On the causes of paleoclimatic variations and of the Ice Ages in particular: J. Glaciol., v. 2, p. 213-218

—— 1953b, Convective transfer in the problem of climate: Dublin, Institute for Advanced Studies, School of Cosmic Physics, Geophys. Bull. 8, 70 p.

—— 1958, Solar variability and paleoclimatic changes: Irish Astron. J., v. 5, p. 97-109

Plass, G. N., 1956, The carbon dioxide theory of climatic change: Tellus (Stockholm), v. 8, p. 140-154

Rex, D. F., 1950, Blocking action in the middle troposphere and its effect upon regional climate: Tellus (Stockholm), v. 2, p. 196-211, p. 275-301

Rubin, M. J., 1964, Antarctic weather and climate, *in* Odishaw, Hugh (ed.), Research in Geophysics, v. 2: Cambridge, Mass., Massachusetts Inst. Technol. Press, p. 461-478

Runcorn, S. K. (ed.), 1962, Continental drift: New York, Academic Press, 338 p.

Saltzman, Barry, 1963, A generalized solution for the large-scale, time-average perturbations in the atmosphere: J. Atmosph. Sci., v. 20, p. 226-235

Saltzman, Barry, and Rao, M. S., 1963, A diagnostic study of the mean state of the atmosphere: J. Atmosph. Sci., v. 20, p. 328-447

Schove, D. J., 1955, The sunspot cycle 649 B.C. to A.D. 2000: J. Geophys. Res., v. 60, p. 127-146

Serkowski, K., 1961, The sun as a variable star, II: Flagstaff, Arizona, Lowell Observatory Bull., No. 116, 70 p.

Smagorinsky, Joseph, 1963, General circulation experiments with the primitive equations: Monthly Weather Rev., v. 91, p. 99-164

Stommel, H. M., 1958, The abyssal circulation: Deep-Sea Res., v. 5, p. 80-82

Stommel, H. M., and Arons, Arnold, 1960, On the abyssal

circulation of the World Ocean, II: Deep-Sea Res., v. 6, p. 217-223

Wexler, Harry, 1956, Variations in insolation, general circulation and climate: Tellus (Stockholm), v. 8, p. 480-494

Willett, H. C., 1949, Solar variability as a factor in the fluctuations of climate during geological time: Geogr. Annaler, v. 1-2, p. 295-315

Wilson, A. T., 1964, Origin of ice ages: an ice shelf theory for Pleistocene glaciation: Nature, v. 201, p. 147-149

Woerkom, A. J. J. van, 1953, The astronomical theory of climate changes, *in* Shapley, Harlow (ed.), Climate change: Cambridge, Harvard Univ. Press, p. 147-157

Zeuner, F. E., 1959, The Pleistocene period: London, Hutchinson and Co., 447 p.

SUMMARY

The central problem of climatic variation and its causes is examined in terms of the basic dynamical theory of world climate and the general atmospheric circulation. The specific atmospheric properties and Earth-environmental factors that are indicated by theory to specify present-day climate are identified, and the probable reaction of atmospheric circulation and climate to hypothetical changes in each of these factors is described. Various hypotheses that have been proposed to account for climatic change during the Quaternary are outlined and their potential climatological validity briefly considered. The fundamental pattern of planetary circulation and climate is suggested by theory to have remained qualitatively invariant throughout the Quaternary. Air-sea interactions are viewed as an important origin of climatic change on the scale of decades, centuries, and millennia. Reactions of planetary climate to any of such diverse influences as changes of solar constant, of atmospheric carbon dioxide content, and of volcanic dust content of the upper atmosphere, are believed to be almost identical. The ultimate cause of the Pleistocene ice age is not clear; a number of potential causes other than changes of solar constant deserve to be recognized. Any factor leading to a persistent lowering of subpolar summer temperatures—irrespective of its other consequences—may suffice to initiate glaciation. The effect of continental ice sheets on atmospheric circulation is such as to favor their self-maintenance. The cause of the glacial-interglacial succession of the Quaternary is not unlikely to have involved the Croll-Milankovitch chronology of insolation; however other environmental disturbances or a form of autovariability of the ocean–atmosphere–ice cap system may also have been involved.

INDEX OF AUTHORS CITED

FIRST AUTHORS ONLY

A

Aario, Leo, 647
Abramova, Anastasia, 488
Abrams, LeRoy, 462
Adam, William, 599
Adams, C. I., 203
Adams, C. T., 531
Adams, R. McC., 656
Addicott, W. O., 617, 860, 861
Adem, Julian, 888, 889
Agassiz, Louis, 3, 4, 405
Agogino, G. A., 688, 689
Ahlmann, H. W., 796
Akers, R. H., 45, 54, 148, 177-179
Akers, W. H., 842
Alden, W. C., 15, 25, 29, 31, 43, 50, 57, 115, 120, 217, 219, 225, 231, 234-236, 248
Aldrich, J. W., 531, 536
Alexander, C. S., 321
Allen, Don, 600
Allen, G. M., 511
Allen, V. T., 759
Alling, H. L., 108
Allison, I. S., 350, 351, 474, 812
Ambrose, J. W., 837
American Commission on Stratigraphic Nomenclature, 33, 43, 207, 387, 759, 761
American Ornithological Union Checklist, 528, 531, 532
American Society of Civil Engineers, 783
Andel, Tj. H. van, 724, 725
Anderson, A. L., 235, 237
Anderson, C. A., 309, 311, 313, 314, 316, 323, 324, 807, 860
Anderson, Edgar, 499, 501
Anderson, R. C., 45
Anderson, R. Y., 434
Anderson, Robert, 310, 315, 318
Anderson, S. T., 393, 410, 411, 426, 646, 657, 777
Ando, Hisatsugu, 491
Andrewartha, H. G., 644
Andrews, Edmund, 8
Andrews, G. W., 45
Antevs, Ernst, 57, 119, 122-124, 217, 228, 238, 240, 271, 272, 274, 276, 277, 279-281, 289, 291, 295, 442, 443, 697-699, 703, 715, 786
Applegate, S. P., 570
Aramaki, Shigeo, 818
Arata, A. A., 511, 560
Argus, G. W., 124, 393
Arkley, R. J., 313, 314, 762, 855
Armstrong, J. E., 346, 477, 479, 853
Arnborg, L., 788
Arnold, B. A., 860
Arnold, Ralph, 310, 314, 315, 329

Aronow, Saul, 18, 24
Aschmann, H. H., 697, 704
Ashley, G. H., 102, 317
Atwood, W. W., 217, 218, 220, 221, 223, 252, 266, 272, 292, 348, 845
Auer, Väinö, 807
Auffenberg, Walter, 447, 544, 546, 557-564
Austin, O. L., Jr., 533, 538
Averill, C. V., 306
Axelrod, D. I., 265, 267, 270, 305, 435, 436, 444-457, 854

B

Back, William, 323, 325
Bader, R. S., 511
Bailey, E. H., 299
Bailey, R. M., 570, 575, 577
Bailey, R. W., 295
Bailey, T. L., 327-329, 856, 857
Baily, T. L., Jr., 599
Bain, H. F., 29, 48
Baker, C. L., 203
Baker, F. C., 8, 599, 600, 625, 643
Baker, R. G., 36-38, 404-406, 412
Baldwin, E. M., 348, 351, 853
Baldwin, H. I., 384
Ball, C. R., 464
Ball, G. E., 593, 613, 619, 620, 622
Ball, J. R., 51
Ball, S. M., 217
Bank, T. P., 367
Banks, R. C., 533
Bannister, Bryant, 871, 872
Banta, B. H., 550
Barbat, W. F., 315
Barbour, E. H., 199, 511
Barclay, F. H., 418, 422, 427
Bardack, D., 528
Barendsen, G. W., 389, 390, 749
Barghoorn, E. S., Jr., 114
Barksdale, J. D., 852
Barnes, J. W., 737, 739
Bartholomew, G. A., 533
Barton, D. C., 146, 149
Bateman, P. C., 303, 304, 853, 854
Baumel, J. S., 531
Baumhoff, M. A., 714
Baver, L. D., 785
Baxter, G. W., 547
Bayer, F. M., 616
Bayne, C. K., 190
Beal, C. H., 618, 860
Beaman, J. H., 505
Bean, E. F., 45
Becker, H. F., 456
Becraft, G. E., 239
Beecher, W. J., 537, 538, 614
Beetham, Nellie, 389, 392
Behle, W. H., 533, 538

Bell, Barbara, 895
Bell, R. E., 693
Bell, Richard, 381
Bender, J. A., 795
Bender, V. R., 347
Bengtson, K. B., 803
Benninghoff, W. S., 394, 414, 471, 657
Benson, C. S., 801
Benson, Lyman, 433
Benson, R. H., 625
Benson, W. E., 21
Bent, Anne M., 435, 437, 438, 440
Benthem Jutting, Tera van, 599
Bentzen, Raymond, 692
Berg, J. W., Jr., 851
Berger, A. J., 535
Berger, Rainer, 710, 712
Bergquist, S. G., 68, 73
Berkey, C. P., 103
Bernard, H. A., 142, 145, 147-151, 153, 155-158, 161, 166, 170-174, 176-179
Berry, E. G., 599
Berry, E. W., 130, 177, 425
Bhatnagar, P. L., 896
Bhattacharya, Nityananda, 67, 578
Bird, J. B., 834
Birkeland, P. W., 265, 268, 272, 303, 304, 306, 307, 309
Birkenholz, D. E., 511, 516
Birman, J. H., 272, 280, 304, 306, 307, 310, 855
Bishop, B. C., 800
Bissell, H. J., 268, 275
Black, M. J., 662
Black, R. F., 48, 52, 54, 55, 57, 362, 365, 659, 711, 713
Blackwelder, Eliot, 217, 219, 220, 221, 224, 250, 266, 268, 270, 272, 278-280, 303, 306, 307, 310, 845, 855
Blair, A. P., 548, 550, 553
Blair, W. F., 511, 518, 531, 543, 544, 546-553, 561, 614, 645
Blake, E. R., 528
Blanchard, F. N., 561
Blanchard, R. L., 320, 321, 356, 364, 739
Bleakney, J. S., 547, 633, 634, 645
Bliss, W. L., 692
Bloom, A. L., 123, 125, 835
Bluhm, Elaine, 633
Bodvardsson, Gunnar, 800
Boettger, C. R., 599
Bogart, D. B., 125
Bogert, C. M., 546, 547, 553
Bolin, Bert, 894
Bond, J., 532
Booth, W. E., 455
Borchert, J. R., 408
Borden, C. E., 711, 713, 715
Borland, W. M., 788
Borns, H. W., Jr., 114, 123

Bousfield, E. L., 626
Bowen, O. E., Jr., 299
Bradford, D. C., 852
Bradley, W. C., 320, 845, 861
Bradley, W. H., 222, 250, 647, 767
Brainerd, G. W., 711
Brame, A. H., 545
Brandtner, Friedrich, 749
Branner, J. C., 319, 321
Brattstrom, B. H., 446, 557, 558, 560, 562-565
Braun, E. Lucy, 378, 380-382, 384, 396, 404, 405, 407, 417-419, 427, 543, 645, 678
Bray, J. R., 801, 871
Bray, W. L., 378, 383, 386
Bretz, J H., 56, 57, 64, 72, 76-78, 231, 235-237, 239, 346, 351
Brewer, M. C., 365
Brewer, R., 535, 536
Brice, J. C., 323, 324
Briggs, L. I., 315
Bright, R. C., 261, 276, 573, 578
Britton, M. E., 471
Brode, W. E., 574
Brodkorb, Pierce, 511, 527-532
Broecker, W. S., 57, 72, 73, 76, 79, 80, 122, 221, 223, 281, 393, 439, 440, 613, 622, 633, 659, 661, 698, 699, 724, 729, 733, 737, 739, 740, 742, 744-747, 749, 750, 786, 788
Bromley, S. W., 380, 383, 396
Brooks, A. H., 355
Brooks, J. L., 620
Brophy, J. A., 758, 759
Broughton, J. G., 99, 102
Brouwer, J., 750
Brown, Barnum, 511
Brown, C. A., 418, 419, 425
Brown, J. S., 547
Brown, R. D., Jr., 347, 351
Brown, R. E., 239
Brown, R. J. E., 365
Bryan, A. T., 697, 698, 702, 706
Bryan, Kirk, 101, 217, 218, 238, 245, 289, 292, 295, 310, 311, 316, 845, 883
Bryant, J. C., 104, 105
Brynjolfsson, Ari, 823
Bryson, R. A., 873
Büdel, Julius, 305, 788
Budyko, M. I., 883
Buell, M. F., 418-420, 425, 429, 585
Buffington, E. C., 861
Bull, W. B., 311, 315
Bullen, R. P., 511, 565, 672, 674, 680
Burmaster, E. R., 656
Burnett, E. K., 681
Burnford, S., 661
Burt, W. H., 511, 515-517
Bushnell, D. I., Jr., 673
Butler, B. R., 240, 702, 703
Butler, Patrick, 388, 394, 396
Butler, R. B., 713, 715
Butters, F. K., 405, 406
Butts, Charles, 101, 135
Byerly, Perry, 859
Byers, D. S., 125, 388, 658
Byers, Williams, 435
Byrne, J. V., 146

C

Cade, T. J., 533
Cahalane, V. H., 471

Cain, S. A., 385, 403-405, 418, 422, 425, 463, 469, 498, 662
Caldwell, D. W., 117, 123
Caldwell, J. R., 679, 680
California Department of Water Resources, 324, 325
California State Water Resources Board, 318, 319
Calkins, F. C., 238
Call, R. E., 598
Callendar, G. S., 894
Calvin, Samuel, 31
Cambron, J. W., 672
Cameron, A. W., 645
Camp, C. L., 511
Camp, W. H., 380
Campbell, C. D., 238
Campbell, E. W., 711, 714, 715
Campbell, J. M., 369
Campbell, M. R., 101, 102, 134
Capps, S. R., 8, 217, 810
Cardwell, G. T., 323
Carey, J. S., 812
Carll, J. F., 102
Carlston, C. W., 789
Carman, J. E., 29, 31, 32
Carozzi, A. V., 282
Carpenter, S. J., 591
Carr, A. F., Jr., 561, 563, 564
Carr, W. J., 511
Carroll, Gladys, 647
Carsey, J. B., 167
Carter, G. F., 710, 717, 762
Cary, A. S., 346
Cater, F. W., Jr., 321
Cavender, T. M., 570
Chamberlin, R. T., 48
Chamberlin, T. C., 3-6, 9, 10, 43, 49, 50, 52, 57, 102, 104, 108
Chaney, R. W., 239, 480, 501, 585
Chapman, C. A., 115, 123
Chapman, F. M., 537
Chapman, L. J., 80, 93
Charlesworth, J. K., 786
Cheatum, E. P., 600
Cherdyntsev, V. V., 739, 740
Cherkasov, Yu, 813
Cherry, John, 325
Chesterman, C. W., 808
Chisnell, T. C., 109
Chorley, R. J., 789
Christensen, M. N., 305, 315, 317
Church, H. V., Jr., 313
Church, R. E., 366
Chute, N. E., 121
Clafin, W. H., Jr., 680
Clark, A. L., 600
Clark, S. G., 321
Clark, W. B., 131
Clayton, Keith, 99
Clayton, Lee, 19, 22, 23
Clements, F. E., 384, 502
Clements, Thomas, 571, 573
Cline, A. C., 383
Clisby, Kathryn H., 434-436, 438, 440, 649
Coates, D. R., 103
Cocke, E. C., 418, 425, 426, 429
Cockerell, T. D. A., 454
Coe, J. L., 670, 672, 679
Coe, W. R., 616
Cohee, G. V., 313
Colbert, E. H., 511
Colby, W. E., 306

Cole, F. C., 657
Cole, G. A., 433
Cole, W. S., 101, 102
Coleman, A. P., 92, 573
Colinvaux, P. A., 365, 477, 480, 614, 619
Collins, F. R., 362, 368
Colman, E. A., 784
Colquhoun, D. J., 132
Colton, R. B., 15, 23, 122
Conant, Roger, 546, 547, 549, 558, 559, 562, 634
Condra, G. E., 194, 197-199, 511, 512, 761, 762
Connally, G. G., 106, 107
Conrad, T. A., 4
Cooch, F. G., 538
Coogan, A. N., 692
Cook, E. F., 258
Cook, S. F., 699, 710
Cooke, C. W., 129, 131-133, 561, 839
Cooke, H. C., 837
Cooley, M. E., 287
Coonrad, W. L., 362
Coope, G. R., 583, 624
Cooper, W. S., 37, 351, 409, 469, 633, 853
Cope, E. D., 570, 573, 576
Coppel, H. C., 593
Corbel, Jean, 788
Cornejo, John, 600
Cornish, J. H., 792
Cottam, W. P., 444, 633, 698
Cotter, R. D., 34
Coulter, H. W., 357-360
Cowgill, Ursula M., 770
Cowles, H. C., 382
Cox, Allan, 302, 303, 511, 512, 819-823, 825
Cox, D. D., 389, 394
Cragin, F. W., 207, 511, 512, 812
Craig, B. G., 834
Crandell, D. R., 231, 342, 345-347, 472, 477, 479, 648, 801, 809, 810, 852
Crane, H. R., 600, 689
Crary, A. P., 795, 801
Creager, J. S., 365
Cressey, G. B., 99
Cressman, L. S., 240, 711, 713
Crittenden, M. D., Jr., 266, 273, 275, 281, 318, 319, 850
Croizat, Leon, 443
Crook, W. W., Jr., 447, 689
Crouch, R. W., 842, 843
Crowell, J. C., 857
Crowl, G. H., 102
Cruxent, J. M., 710
Cuancara, A. M., 74
Culbertson, W. L., 486
Culver, H. E., 238
Cummings, J. C., 319
Cummins, W. F., 208
Curray, J. R., 148, 617, 723-725, 727, 729, 731
Currier, L. W., 120
Curtis, G. H., 299, 303, 304, 307
Curtis, J. T., 403-405, 408, 409, 414
Cushing, E. J., 34-37, 387, 409-412, 771
Cushing, E. M., 839
Cushman, R. V., 115

D

Dahl, Eilif, 501, 620
Dale, R. F., 305
Dall, W. H., 258

Dalquest, W. W., 511, 573, 600
Dalrymple, G. B., 270, 302, 303, 305, 307, 314, 436, 809, 824, 854, 855
Daly, R. A., 7, 167
Damon, P. E., 292, 437, 440
Dana, J. D., 5, 6, 10
Dansereau, Pierre, 380, 404, 414
Darlington, H. C., 418, 422, 427
Darlington, P. J., Jr., 532, 558
Darrow, R. A., 443, 444
Darton, N. H., 7, 203, 206, 251
Darwin, Charles, 453, 457
Daugherty, R. D., 240, 702, 705, 713, 715
Davidson, D. T., 362
Davidson, E. S., 289
Davis, E. M., 689
Davis, G. H., 311, 312, 314-316
Davis, J., 533, 537, 538
Davis, J. H., Jr., 418, 419, 560
Davis, J. T., 418, 425, 426
Davis, Margaret B., 120, 121, 124, 378-380, 386, 389-396, 412, 413, 645-647
Davis, P. H., 499
Davis, R. J., 455
Davis, S. N., 309, 310, 313, 314, 326, 327
Davis, W. M., 101, 134, 320, 329, 859, 861
Dawson, E. Y., 617, 618
Dawson, J. W., 573
Dawson, W. R., 532
Day, G. M., 383
Dayton, W. A., 446
Deam, C. C., 455
Dean, D. S., 499
Deans, T., 777
DeCosta, J. J., 625
Deevey, E. S., Jr., 121, 383, 384, 387-395, 397, 405, 408, 409, 417, 418, 439, 443, 543, 548, 613, 614, 616, 625, 633, 644-646, 658, 678, 749
DeJarnette, D. L., 672, 674, 679
Demaret, Fernand, 485
Dementiev, G. P., 531
Denning, D. G., 591
Dennis, W. A., 659
Denny, C. S., 102, 106, 107, 117, 120, 122, 125, 134, 292, 377
Detterman, R. L., 360, 361
Deussen, Alexander, 137, 176
DeVries, Hessel, 92, 737, 738, 746, 749, 750
Diamond, Marvin, 801
Dibblee, T. W., Jr., 287-300, 310, 320, 321
Dice, L. R., 561
Dickerman, R. W., 538
Dickinson, J. C., Jr., 536
Dietz, R. S., 726
Diller, J. S., 309, 316, 321, 323
Dillon, L. S., 73, 417, 418, 443, 536, 560, 613, 783, 786
Dixon, H. M., 433, 437
Dixon, K. L., 533, 536
Dobson, Peter, 3
Dobzhansky, Theodosius, 562
Doell, R. R., 818, 822, 825
Doering, J. A., 132, 150, 151, 176, 177, 584, 839, 842, 843
Dolan, E. M., 511
Dominion Observatories of Canada, 835
Donn, W. L., 614, 620, 733
Donner, J. J., 104, 118, 130, 391
Dorf, Erling, 585, 613
Dorofeev, P. I., 501

Dort, Wakefield, Jr., 222, 237
Douglass, A. E., 871-873
Dowling, H. G., 548, 557, 558
Downey, J. S., 511
Downs, Theodore, 529, 531, 571, 573
Drake, J. A., 768
Dreimanis, Aleksis, 69, 78, 79, 85, 92, 95, 105-107, 422, 658, 661, 665, 746, 762
Drewes, Harald, 300
Driver, H. L., 330
Droste, J. B., 108, 758
Drury, W. H., Jr., 382, 414, 471
Dryer, C. R., 63
DuBar, Jules, 132, 133
Duff, G. H., 873
Dumond, D. E., 369
Dunn, E. R., 545
Durham, D. L., 329
Durham, Forrest, 103
Durham, J. W., 316, 330, 826
Durrell, R. H., 85
Dury, G. H., 787, 790
Dutcher, L. C., 329
Dutton, C. E., 348, 839

E

Eardley, A. J., 271, 274, 276, 281, 282, 622, 812, 813
Easterbrook, D. J., 345, 346, 351, 853
Eaton, J. E., 327, 856
Edwards, A. M., 103
Einarsson, Trausti, 621, 827
Ekblaw, G. E., 48, 53, 54, 56, 66, 72, 585, 760
Ellis, A. J., 329
Ellis, R. W., 291
Ellison, Lincoln, 445
Ellsworth, E. W., 54, 57
Elson, J. A., 23, 24, 39, 40, 661
Emerson, W. K., 860
Emery, K. O., 299, 328, 329, 725, 726, 732, 859-862
Emiliani, Cesare, 329, 616, 617, 649, 741, 742, 744-746, 750, 896
Engeln, O. D. von, 99, 102, 103, 108
Englehardt, D. W., 67, 69, 73, 412, 648
Epling, Carl, 443
Epstein, Samuel, 801
Ericson, D. B., 649, 733, 741, 742, 744, 746, 750
Eschman, D. F., 218, 222, 249, 251
Estes, Richard, 544, 563
Etheridge, Richard, 511, 557, 562
Evans, G. L., 205, 208, 213, 511, 690
Eveland, H. E., 48, 66, 760
Evenson, R. E., 325
Evernden, J. F., 258, 259, 302, 313, 316, 317, 323, 509, 511, 512, 573, 649, 737, 740, 746, 809, 823-828, 855
Ewart, A., 807
Ewing, John, 131, 729, 730
Ewing, M. E., 137, 138, 145, 167, 355, 897

F

Faegri, Knut, 414, 466, 397
Fagerlind, Folke, 394, 395
Fahnestock, R. K., 801
Fairbanks, H. W., 319
Fairbridge, R. W., 663, 723-725
Fairchild, H. L., 78, 99, 102, 103, 108, 109
Fanale, F. P., 737, 740, 747

Farnham, R. S., 39
Farrand, W. R., 75-77, 79, 80, 661, 663, 835
Fassett, N. C., 405
Favarger, Claude, 498, 499, 501, 502
Fay, F. H., 533
Fejfar, Oldrich, 509, 511
Fenneman, N. M., 99, 113, 203, 287, 300, 417, 419, 584, 669, 671, 675
Ferguson, C. W., 871
Fernald, A. T., 360, 362, 363, 810
Fernald, M. L., 378-381, 384-386, 395, 403-405, 453
Ferrians, O. J., Jr., 363
Feth, J. H., 573
Fidlar, M. M., 68, 77
Fiedler, A. G., 290
Figgins, J. D., 688
Findley, J. S., 444
Fischer, Irene, 835, 836
Fisher, H. I., 531
Fisk, H. N., 48, 137, 145, 146, 148-151, 154, 157, 161-165, 167, 170, 171, 176, 177, 179, 585, 725, 731, 733, 791, 792, 839, 841-844
Fiske, R. S., 810, 825
Fitting, J. E., 660
Fitzpatrick, J. F., Jr., 623
Flaccus, Edward, 125
Fleming, W. L. S., 104
Flint, R. F., 15, 18-20, 22, 23, 48, 52-54, 63, 69-72, 75, 80, 86, 107, 108, 113-115, 117-123, 129, 131, 195, 198, 217, 223, 231, 235, 237, 238, 240, 280, 294, 305, 357, 388, 389, 397, 406, 418, 436, 437, 479, 509, 511, 573, 585, 621, 622, 646, 659, 698, 747, 762, 786, 790, 834, 835, 838, 853
Forcart, Lothar, 602, 608
Ford, E. B., 538
Ford, J. A., 672, 673, 680
Foreman, Fred, 291, 766
Forman, R. T. T., 406
Forsyth, Jane L., 85-89
Fournier, M. F., 785
Fowler, M. L., 660
Fox, W. S., 403, 404
Frankforter, W. D., 199
Franzen, Dorothea S., 599
Fraser, G. D., 849
Frechen, Josef, 807
Freeman, T. N., 593
Freeman, W. O., 255
Frey, D. G., 73, 412, 418-421, 425, 426, 429, 430, 560, 585, 613, 624, 625, 633, 766
Frick, Childs, 509, 511
Fridley, H. M., 101, 102
Fries, Magnus, 409-412, 765, 773
Frink, J. W., 179, 313, 315, 316, 855
Fritts, H. C., 871-876, 878
Fritz, Sigmund, 888, 889
Fromming, Ewald, 599
Frye, J. C., 20, 23, 31, 33, 39, 43, 45, 48-50, 52, 53, 55-58, 68, 86, 91, 115, 119, 120, 189, 195, 198, 203, 205-209, 211-214, 227, 268, 271, 274, 275, 291, 293, 405, 413, 511, 512, 585, 599, 600, 621, 732, 733, 755, 759, 760-762, 790, 791, 809, 811, 812
Fryxell, F. M., 217, 222
Fryxell, Roald, 226, 239, 241, 702, 807, 809-811
Fuller, G. D., 648

Fuller, M. L., 101, 103, 104, 115, 116, 118, 129, 840, 841
Fultz, Dave, 891

G

Gadd, N. R., 109
Gagliano, S. M., 670
Galbreath, E. C., 511, 529
Gale, H. S., 8, 9, 272, 278, 280
Galtsoff, P. S., 616
Gams, Helmut, 485, 486, 489
Garcia, Enriqueta, 445
Gard, L. M., Jr., 240
Gardner, R. A., 325
Garrison, L. E., 313
Garth, J. S., 617, 618
Gatewood, J. S., 873
Gazin, C. L., 258, 511, 560, 824
Gealey, W. K., 323
Gealy, B. L., 137, 167
Gehlbach, F. R., 445, 558, 635
Geikie, James, 4-6, 9
Geist, O. W., 368
Gerking, S. D., 645
Germain, Louis, 599
Gianella, V. P., 847
Giddings, J. L., Jr., 368, 369, 871, 873
Gidley, J. W., 511
Gilbert, C. M., 303, 809, 855
Gilbert, G. K., 4, 6, 7, 217, 245, 261, 273, 274, 276, 280, 282, 310, 847, 849
Gile, L. H., 293
Gilluly, James, 856, 857, 863, 864
Ginsburg, Isaac, 616
Ginsburg, R. N., 730
Gjullin, C. M., 593
Glass, H. D., 49, 56
Gleason, H. A., 403, 404, 406, 408, 413
Glen, William, 317, 856
Glenn, L. C., 101
Glenn, R. C., 57
Glock, W. S., 871-873
Glover, S. L., 351
Godwin, Harry, 485, 486, 723
Goel, P. S., 740
Goggin, J. M., 670, 676
Goin, C. J., 544
Goldberg, E. D., 737, 739, 743-745
Goldsmith, Richard, 120
Goldthwait, J. W., 57, 72, 114, 115, 120-123
Goldthwait, R. P., 85, 87-89, 123, 124, 360, 361, 657, 800
Goode, H. D., 273
Goodell, H. G., 730
Gooding, A. M., 63, 67-69, 71, 85, 87, 88, 92, 600
Goodlett, J. C., 378-383, 386, 396
Goodrich, Calvin, 600
Gorsline, D. S., 729
Gould, A. A., 599
Gould, H. A., 765
Gould, H. R., 146-148, 150, 151, 725, 730, 731
Goulden, C. E., 625
Grabau, A. W., 102
Graber, R. R., 638
Graham, Alan, 418-420, 430, 435, 437, 440
Graham, K. W. T., 819
Granar, Lars, 792
Grant, U. S., IV, 329
Gray, Asa, 7, 8

Gray, Jane, 435, 436
Green, F. E., 447
Green, Morton, 511
Greengo, R. E., 717
Greenman, N. H., 138, 144, 150, 167-169
Greenway, J. C., Jr., 532
Greenwood, Roberta S., 717
Gregg, W. O., 599
Gregory, R. A., 470
Gresitt, J. L., 619
Griffin, J. B., 656, 659, 661, 663, 664, 671, 679, 680, 690, 693
Griffin, J. W., 635
Griggs, A. B., 853
Grinnell, J., 533
Grinsfelder, S., 330
Grobman, A. B., 559
Grommé, C. S., 822, 823, 827
Gromov, V. I., 828
Grosscup, G. L., 699, 702
Grossu, A. V., 599
Guennel, G. K., 73
Guilday, J. E., 418, 422, 425, 511, 515, 528, 624, 626, 634, 635
Gurney, A. B., 590, 592
Gustafsson, Åke, 498, 499
Gut, H. J., 511, 560
Gutenberg, Beno, 75, 831, 835, 859
Gutentag, E. D., 621

H

Hack, J. T., 129, 131, 133-135, 226, 289, 294, 295, 382, 839, 864
Hadleigh-West, Frederick, 369
Hadley, R. F., 250, 789, 792
Hafsten, Ulf, 433, 435, 436, 438, 440
Hagerup, Olaf, 497, 498
Hague, Arnold, 809
Hairston, N. G., 552
Hall, C. A., Jr., 317, 318
Hall, E. R., 511, 516, 638
Halliday, W. E. D., 533
Hamilton, H. W., 681
Hamilton, T. H., 538
Hamilton, Warren, 255, 261, 809
Hammen, Thomas van der, 436
Hammon, J. H., 528, 529
Handley, C. O., Jr., 657
Hanefeld, Horst, 99, 100
Hanley, J. B., 117
Hansen, H. P., 58, 240, 345, 442, 469, 472-474, 477, 479, 480, 702, 706, 810, 813
Hansen, W. R., 114, 250
Harding, S. T., 281
Hardman, George, 281
Hargrave, L. L., 635
Harper, R. M., 561
Harrington, H. D., 455
Harrington, M. R., 511, 699
Harris, A. H., 444, 445
Harrison, A. E., 347, 803
Harrison, Wyman, 63, 68, 71, 129, 418, 419, 422, 427, 428
Hartman, Olga, 615
Hartshorn, J. H., 121, 124
Hartz, N., 412
Haskell, G., 499
Hastings, J. R., 433
Hattersley-Smith, Geoffrey, 801
Haury, E. W., 290, 438, 440, 445, 511, 689, 699
Hay, Dorothy, 462

Hay, O. P., 8, 509, 511, 562, 573, 643, 670, 677
Haynes, C. V., Jr., 440, 446, 614, 670, 689
Healy, James, 807
Hecht, M. K., 544, 559
Heckard, L. R., 500
Hecker, E. N., 179
Hedberg, Olov, 486, 500
Hedges, L. S., 15
Hedgpeth, J. W., 615, 616, 621
Heezen, B. C., 620
Heindl, L. A., 287
Heiser, C. B., 498, 500
Heizer, R. F., 367, 699, 703, 704, 709, 712, 713
Henderson, Junius, 598
Hermann, G., 501
Hershey, J. B., 74
Hershey, O. H., 237, 327
Herzog, Theodor, 492
Hesselbo, Augustus, 485, 488, 491
Hester, J. J., 446, 509, 511, 520, 674, 677
Heusser, C. J., 226, 344, 345, 347, 348, 361, 388, 396, 471, 474-477, 479, 501, 633, 648, 706, 801
Hevly, R. H., 433, 435, 437, 438, 440, 443
Heyl, A. V., Jr., 841
Hibbard, C. W., 208, 209, 213, 245, 258, 331, 446, 447, 509, 511, 512, 515, 518, 519, 528, 557-561, 564, 565, 572, 573, 575, 598-603, 605, 606, 621, 624, 648, 649, 657, 677, 812
Higgins, C. G., 317, 323, 325, 326
Highton, Richard, 561
Hill, D. P., 257, 852
Hill, M. L., 299, 859
Hinds, N. E. A., 300, 321
Hinton, M. A. C., 511
Hitchcock, C. H., 5, 7
Hitchcock, C. L., 455
Hitchcock, Edward, 4
Ho, Tong-yun, 207, 605
Hoare, J. M., 362
Hobbs, H. H., Jr., 623, 626
Hobbs, W. H., 238, 535
Hodgson, E. A., 835, 837
Hodgson, G. W., 774
Hofmann, Franz, 807
Hofmann, Walther, 799, 803
Hogan, J. D., 52, 55, 57
Hoinkes, Herfried, 796
Hole, F. D., 48, 49, 53
Holland, G. P., 593, 613
Holland, W. C., 146
Holm, Theodore, 454
Holman, J. A., 446, 511, 527-529, 531, 544, 557, 561, 562
Holman, Kjeld, 486, 488, 498, 501
Holmes, C. D., 106, 107
Holmes, F. S., 132
Holmes, G. W., 217, 249, 250, 358, 360, 361
Holmes, L. C., 310
Holmes, W. H., 673
Holmquist, Charlotte, 626
Holway, R. S., 327
Hooker, J. D., 453, 454, 457
Hoots, H. W., 310, 313-315, 855, 856
Hopkins, D. M., 356, 358, 360-368, 469, 471, 477, 480, 492, 511, 517, 518, 619, 824
Hopkins, M. L., 511
Hopson, C. A., 810
Horberg, C. L., 24

Horberg, Leland, 49, 54, 56, 71, 74, 217, 221, 222, 225, 585, 839
Horr, W. H., 413
Horsberg, C. L., 527
Horton, R. E., 289
Hospers, Jan, 822, 827
Hough, J. L., 56-58, 64, 72-80, 90, 109, 659, 661
Houston, R. S., 814
Howard, A. D., 21, 25, 320, 861
Howard, E. B., 688
Howard, Hildegarde, 511, 527-532, 573, 711
Howden, H. F., 443, 622, 626
Howe, H. V., 146, 178
Howell, T. R., 536
Hrdlicka, Ales, 688
Hseung, Yi, 760
Hubbard, Bela, 63
Hubbs, C. L., 266, 271, 278, 550, 573, 575, 577, 617, 618, 622, 623, 645, 703, 715
Hubendick, Bengt, 599
Hubley, R. C., 796, 797, 803
Hubricht, Leslie, 599
Hudson, F. S., 303, 305, 314, 854
Huey, A. S., 317, 318
Huffman, G. G., 152
Hull, Edward, 7
Hultén, Eric, 383, 385, 453, 455, 457, 460, 466, 469-471, 476, 501, 504, 620
Hummel, D., 4
Hunt, Alice P., 295
Hunt, C. B., 245, 247, 268-270, 273-275, 287, 293-296, 447, 761, 792, 793, 845
Huntington, C. E., 537
Hurt, W. R., Jr., 687, 689
Hussakof, Louis, 50, 573
Hutchins, L. W., 614, 618
Hutchinson, G. E., 767-770
Hutton, C. E., 32
Hyland, Fay, 390
Hyppä, Esa, 118, 121

I

Ingmanson, Earl, 670
Inman, D. L., 792
Innes, M. J. S., 835
Irving, E., 822
Irving, W. N., 369
Irwin, H. J., 692
Irwin, W. P., 300, 321
Ives, J. D., 385
Ives, P. C., 261, 274, 282
Ives, R. L., 222, 463
Iwatsuki, Zennoske, 490
Izett, G. A., 456

J

Jackiewicz, Maria, 599
Jaeger, E. C., 433
Jahns, R. H., 115, 120, 122, 125, 299, 328
Jakway, George, 200
Jamieson, T. F., 7
Jasnowski, Mieczyslaw, 485
Jelgersma, Saskia, 39, 411, 412, 723
Jelinek, A. J., 435, 437, 709, 710
Jenkins, O. P., 289, 299
Jenks, A. E., 661, 662
Jenness, S. E., 835
Jennings, C. W., 318, 321, 322

Jennings, J. D., 445, 691, 697, 698, 703-705, 713
Jepson, G. L., 688
Jewett, J. M., 189
Johnsgard, P. A., 538
Johnson, A. W., 471, 498, 499, 501, 503
Johnson, Arthur, 798, 799, 803
Johnson, B. L., 132
Johnson, D. W., 108, 125
Johnson, Elden, 662
Johnson, F. C., 550
Johnson, Frederick, 369, 663, 710
Johnson, H. R., 313, 323
Johnson, LeRoy, Jr., 435, 443
Johnson, Lionel, 626
Johnson, N. K., 536
Johnson, P. L., 455
Johnson, W. H., 50, 52
Johnston, C. S., 511, 599
Johnston, I. M., 455, 465
Johnston, R. F., 532, 538
Johnston, W. A., 8, 39
Jones, D. J., 271, 276, 281
Jones, G. N., 455, 469
Jones, Keith, 499
Jones, R. L., 86
Jones, W. D., 222
Jordan, D. S., 573
Jordan, R. R., 131
Jørgensen, C. A., 501
Judson, S. S., Jr., 117, 118, 121
Jury, W. W., 665

K

Kaiser, R. F., 106
Kaizuka, Sōhei, 807
Kamb, Barclay, 800
Kamimura, Minoru, 491
Kantrowitz, I. H., 103
Kapp, R. O., 63, 68, 69, 73, 412, 413, 486, 511, 621, 648, 664, 762
Karlstrom, E. L., 552
Karlstrom, T. N. V., 356, 357, 359-364, 603
Karrow, P. F., 78, 79, 85, 92, 93, 95, 102, 659
Kaufmann, Aaron, 737, 739, 740, 748, 750
Kay, G. F., 8, 29-32, 38, 511, 527, 759, 760, 762
Kaye, C. A., 115-117, 119-121, 124, 125, 511, 520, 659, 663, 835
Kearney, T. H., 455
Keith, M. L., 749
Kelley, V. C., 847
Kemp, J. F., 103, 108
Kempton, J. P., 52, 54, 86, 87
Kennard, A. S., 599
Kessel, Brina, 620
Kesseli, J. E., 272
Kew, W. S. W., 328, 329
Khramov, A. H., 822, 823, 827, 828
Kidd, K. E., 659
King, J. E., 433, 434, 437
King, P. B., 134, 291, 299, 329, 330, 351, 614, 847, 865
Kingery, W. D., 795
Kirkham, V. R. D., 238, 258, 851
Kirkland, D. W., 435, 436, 445, 646, 649
Kittredge, Joseph, 784
Kitts, D. B., 511, 600
Kivett, M. F., 693
Klingener, David, 509, 511, 519

Kloosterman, J. B., 827
Klots, A. B., 622
Klute, Fritz, 228
Knaben, Gunvar, 498, 502
Knapp, Rudiger, 501
Knechtal, M. M., 23
Knopf, Adolph, 303, 305, 306, 824
Knox, A. S., 394, 418, 423, 425, 426
Knuth, Eigil, 368
Kobayashi, Kunio, 807
Koenig, J. B., 322, 323
Kofoed, J. W., 730
Kohout, F. A., 249, 251
Konior, Konard, 485
Koteff, Carl, 121
Kottlowski, F. E., 292, 293
Kotzebue, Otto von, 355
Kramer, F. L., 280
Kraus, E. B., 889, 890, 897, 899
Kräusel, Richard, 783
Krauss, R. W., 394
Krekeler, C. H., 594, 644
Krieger, A. D., 669, 670, 679, 685, 687-690, 693, 694, 709, 710, 714, 715
Krigström, Arne, 791
Krystofovich, A. N., 501
Küchler, A. W., 407
Kukla, Jirí, 598, 602
Kundert, C. J., 318
Kunkel, Fred, 323
Kurtén, Björn, 511, 517, 519

L

LaChapelle, E. R., 796, 803
Lachenbruch, A. H., 365
Lachenbruch, M. C., 313
LaFehr, T. L., 257, 258, 851
Lagler, K. F., 569, 570
Laguna, Frederica de, 367, 369
Laidly, W. T., 74
Lambe, L. M., 573
Lance, J. F., 289, 573
Lane, C. W., 601
Lang, W. B., 445
Langbein, W. B., 783, 784, 786, 788
Langway, C. C., Jr., 801
Lanning, E. P., 699, 701, 704
Lanser, Otto, 788
Lanyon, W. E., 536
Large, Thomas, 237
Larimore, R. W., 636, 637
LaRivers, Ira, 571, 573
LaRocque, Aurèle, 87, 600, 605-607
Larsen, Helge, 367-369
Larsen, Kai, 498, 501
Larson, P. R., 871, 874
Laudermilk, J. D., 433, 435
Laughlin, W. S., 367
Lawrence, Barbara, 445, 560
Lawrence, D. B., 226, 281, 361, 801
Lawrence, W. E., 499
Lawson, A. C., 305, 306, 317, 319, 320, 323, 329, 859-861
Leavitt, H. W., 123
LeBlanc, R. J., 140, 147, 149, 153, 154, 157, 158, 161, 167, 168, 725
Lechner-Pock, Lore, 460, 461
LeConte, Joseph, 306
Lee, G. B., 57
Lee, H. A., 109, 834
Lee, Richard, 882
Lee, T. E., 660, 661

Lee, W. T., 287
Leffingwell, E. de K., 365
Legler, J. M., 563
Lehmer, D. J., 693
Leidy, Joseph, 573
Leighton, M. M., 20, 21, 23, 31, 43, 48, 50-56, 63, 64, 68, 69, 72, 240, 585, 759-761
Lemke, R. W., 20, 21, 221
Leonard, A. B., 52, 91, 198, 199, 207-209, 211, 213, 214, 290, 585, 586, 599, 600, 603, 605, 621
Leopold, Estella B., 345, 388, 389, 392, 418, 425, 426, 479, 646
Leopold, L. B., 228, 248, 249, 251, 295, 435, 443, 786, 790, 792
Lesquereux, L., 455
Leverett, Frank, 6, 9, 24, 30, 31, 33, 34, 37, 39, 43, 50, 52, 53, 57, 63, 64, 66-69, 71, 72, 74-79, 85, 102, 104, 109, 217, 268
Levings, W. S., 245
Lewis, Douglas, 106
Lewis, H. C., 104
Lewis, H. G., 237
Lewis, I. F., 418, 425, 429
Lewis, P. F., 238
Lewis, T. M. N., 672, 673, 679
Libby, W. F., 737
Lighthill, M. J., 798
Ligon, J. D., 511
Lincoln, D. F., 99
Lincoln, E. P., 445
Lindemann, J. L., 765, 766
Lindgren, Waldemar, 304-306, 309, 316
Lindholm, G. F., 362
Lindroth, C. H., 593, 613, 620, 621
Lindsay, H. L., 550
Lindsey, A. A., 433
Link, František, 895
Linsdale, J. M., 531
Little, E. L., Jr., 378-380, 470
Livingston, R. B., 464, 646
Livingstone, D. A., 387, 389-391, 396, 477, 768, 771, 777
Lobeck, A. K., 99
Logan, W. D., 691
Lohse, E. A., 170
Long, J. S., Jr., 315
Long, W. A., 346, 803
Longwell, C. R., 287
Lorenz, E. N., 891
Lotan, J. F., 874
Lotspeich, F. B., 238
Loud, L. L., 704
Louderback, G. D., 319, 321
Lougee, R. J., 120, 122, 390, 391
Louis, Herbert, 228
Löve, Áskell, 493, 497-502, 504, 614, 620
Löve, Doris, 385, 645
Lövkvist, Börje, 499, 500
Lowe, C. H., Jr., 433, 444, 546
Lowman, S. W., 843
Lowry, W. D., 351, 852, 853
Ložek, Vojen, 599, 602, 608
Lüdi, Werner, 455
Ludwick, J. C., 149, 731
Lugn, A. L., 194, 195, 197, 198, 248, 511, 512
Lundelius, E. L., Jr., 511
Lundqvist, Gosta, 485
Lutz, H. J., 380, 383, 471
Lyford, W. H., 125, 380, 381, 386
Lyons, P. L., 843

M

McAllister, J. F., 307
MacAlpin, Archie, 569
McAndrews, J. H., 408-411, 413
McCabe, T. T., 536
McCary, B. C., 673, 677
MacClintock, Paul, 49, 104-109, 114, 120, 122, 130, 646, 837, 839
McCallum, K. J., 633
McConnell, W. J., 577
McCoy, J. J., 511, 528
McCrady, Edward, 511
McCulloch, D. S., 356, 358, 364, 394
MacDonald, G. A., 309, 809
Macdonald, J. R., 511
McDougall, Ian, 823, 825
McFarlan, Edward, Jr., 148, 161, 179, 675, 723
McGee, W. J., 5-7, 9, 29, 31, 131
MacGinitie, H. D., 321, 323, 444, 455-457, 462, 543, 544
McGinnies, W. G., 871, 872
Macgowan, Kenneth, 687
McGrew, P. O., 511
McIntire, W. G., 658
McIntosh, R. P., 383
Mackay, J. R., 367, 369
Mackin, J. H., 103, 239, 248, 249, 346, 845
Maclaren, Charles, 7
McLaughlin, W. T., 404
Maclay, William, 8
MacLean, W. F., 75
MacNeish, R. S., 369, 661, 689
McVath, V. E., 306
McVaugh, Rogers, 443
Maher, L. J., Jr., 385, 422, 433-435, 437, 440, 442, 456, 457
Major, J., 455
Malde, H. E., 132, 245, 255, 257-261, 295, 433, 456, 511, 573, 576, 603, 645, 650, 697, 698, 706, 761, 809, 818, 824, 825, 851, 852
Malott, C. A., 63-65, 67
Manabe, Syukuro, 885
Mandahl-Barth, G., 599
Manley, Gorden, 783, 786
Manning, J. C., 320
Manton, Irene, 499
Mapel, P., 456
Marcus, L., 529
Marshall, J. T., 537
Martin, Bruce, 317
Martin, H. M., 63, 71
Martin, Lawrence, 54, 57, 74
Martin, P. S., 289, 295, 390, 414, 417-419, 422, 427, 433, 435-438, 440, 442-444, 446, 447, 511, 520, 543, 545, 561, 590, 613, 614, 622, 633, 634, 645, 646, 649, 674, 678, 697-700, 705, 706, 875
Maslin, T. P., 461, 547
Mason, L., 458, 465
Mason, R. J., 78, 446, 659-661, 669-671, 674, 675, 687
Masursky, Harold, 250
Matalas, N. C., 873
Mather, K. F., 78, 118-120, 124
Mathews, A. A. L., 282
Mathews, W. H., 226, 347, 852
Matson, G. C., 177
Matthes, F. E., 8, 217, 226, 228, 280, 304-307, 310, 854
Mattison, G. C., 167
Maxson, J. H., 321, 323, 325, 327

Maycock, P. F., 407
Mayer-Oakes, W. J., 690, 691
Mayfield, H. F., 533
Mayhew, W. W., 551
Mayo, Lawrence, 797
Mayr, E., 527, 528, 532, 533, 535, 538
Meacham, W. R., 553
Meade, G. E., 208, 511, 518
Mecham, J. S., 547, 549, 557, 561
Megard, R. O., 622, 624, 625, 765
Mehl, M. G., 511
Mehringer, P. J., Jr., 433-435, 437, 440, 442, 443, 446
Meier, M. F., 413, 795, 796, 799, 800, 802, 803
Meighan, C. W., 709
Meinzer, O. E., 6, 281, 289, 291
Meisler, Harold, 134
Melhorn, W. N., 64, 72
Melton, M. A., 789
Mendenhall, W. C., 310, 363
Mengel, R. M., 533-535
Mercer, J. H., 802
Merk, G. P., 252
Merkle, J., 469
Merklin, R. L., 364
Merriam, C. H., 433, 443
Merrill, G. P., 812
Merrill, J. R., 737, 740
Merritt, R. S., 106, 107, 762
Metzger, D. G., 289
Meyer, Joachim, 807
Meylan, Charles, 492
Michaud, T. C., 550
Milankovitch, M., 881, 896
Miller, A. H., 527-529, 532, 533, 536
Miller, B. B., 511, 599, 600, 605, 606
Miller, C. F., 674
Miller, D. H., 305
Miller, D. J., 356, 363, 365
Miller, H. A., 490
Miller, J. P., 217, 292
Miller, L., 527, 528, 531, 532
Miller, R. D., 357, 358, 359, 364, 600
Miller, R. R., 266, 278, 280, 433, 445, 550, 569, 570, 573, 575, 576, 636, 645, 648
Millet, J. L., 758
Mills, H. B., 593
Milstead, W. W., 551, 557, 558, 561-563
Minard, C. R., Jr., 325
Minard, J. P., 103
Mintz, Yale, 887, 888
Mitchell, G. F., 624
Mitchell, J. M., Jr., 894, 899
Momose, Kan'ichi, 823
Mönkemeyer, Wilhelm, 490
Montagne, J. M. de la, 251
Mooney, H. A., 499, 500
Moore, C. B., 681
Moore, D. G., 726-728, 730-732
Moore, D. M., 498
Moore, J. G., 303, 304
Moore, R. C., 205
Moore, Sherman, 75, 835
Moore, T. E., 593
Moore, W. E., 129
Moorehead, W. K., 681
Moreau, R. E., 527, 528, 531, 538
Morgan, A. M., 290
Morgan, J. P., 154
Moriarty, J. B., 711
Morris, D. A., 249, 250
Morrison, J. P. E., 599, 607

Morrison, M. E. S., 624
Morrison, R. B., 226, 266, 268, 269, 271-277, 279-281, 291, 299, 331, 622, 699, 702, 703, 748, 759, 761, 847, 849, 851
Mosquin, T. A., 444, 500, 505
Moss, E. H., 405
Moss, J. H., 105-107, 218, 226, 249, 250
Movius, H. L., Jr., 827
Mowery, D. H., 598, 600
Moyle, J. B., 768
Mozola, A. J., 65
Muehlberger, W. R., 292
Mueller, W. P., 625
Muir, John, 306, 443
Muller, C. H., 433
Muller, E. A., 129
Muller, E. H., 99, 102, 105-109, 360, 362
Müller, Karl, 491
Mulligan, G. A., 500
Mullineaux, D. R., 345, 809, 810
Mulloy, William, 690, 692, 693
Munns, E. N., 379-381, 423
Müntzing, Arne, 498
Munz, P. A., 433
Murray, G. E., 146, 179
Murray, K. F., 444, 622, 624
Murray, R. C., 57, 75
Myers, G. S., 550, 551
Myers, W. B., 849

N

Nairn, A. E. M., 881
Neill, W. T., 511, 518, 557, 558, 560, 561, 563, 590, 635, 674, 676
Neilson, W. A., 863
Nelson, C. H., 777
Nelson, J. W., 310
Nelson, R. L., 217, 220, 223
Nelson, R. N., 319
Neumann, R. W., 693
Newberry, J. S., 5, 74
Newcomb, R. C., 238
Newell, J. G., 100, 102
Newman, W. S., 429
Nichols, D. R., 363
Nichols, G. E., 407, 381, 382
Nichols, R. L., 125
Niering, W. A., 378, 379, 382, 383, 394, 396
Nikiforoff, C. C., 134
Nikolaev, N. I., 863
Noble, L. F., 859
Nobles, L. H., 235
Nobre, Augusto, 599
Nolan, T. B., 845
Norden, C. R., 571, 578
Norris, K. S., 443, 444
Nye, J. F., 798-801
Nyholm, Elsa, 490

O

Oakes, E. L., 54, 57
Oakeshott, G. B., 329
Oaks, R. Q., Jr., 131, 623
Odum, E. P., 532
Ogden, J. G., III, 377, 382, 383, 387-390, 393, 394, 396, 408, 413, 646
Ogilvie, Ida, 108
Ogle, Burdette A., 323, 325
Oldale, R. N., 121, 123
Olmsted, F. H., 289, 312-314, 316
Olson, Ada L., 590

Olson, E. A., 742
Olson, E. C., 511
Omodeo, P., 620
Oosting, H. T., 560
Öpik, E. J., 888, 896
Orians, G. H., 538
Orr, P. C., 329, 710, 712, 714, 860, 861
Ortalda, R. A., 318, 319
Ortmann, A. E., 625
Orvig, Svenn, 797
Osborn, H. F., 509, 511
Ostrem, Gunnar, 801
Otto, J. H., 73
Ownbey, Marion, 500

P

Packard, R. L., 664
Page, B. M., 346, 847
Page, R. W., 328
Pakiser, L. C., 809, 855
Palmer, R. H., 351
Pardee, J. T., 235, 236, 238, 239, 849
Parker, G. G., 133
Parker, R. H., 617, 619
Parkes, K. C., 532, 535
Parmalee, P. W., 57, 511, 634-636
Patrick, Ruth, 774
Patton, T. H., 511, 573
Paulson, G. R., 511, 512
Payne, T. G., 363
Peabody, F. E., 444
Pearson, R. G., 583, 624
Peattie, D. C., 404, 405
Peck, D. L., 852
Peck, J. H., Jr., 323
Peck, M. E., 469
Peltier, L. C., 133, 134, 788, 789, 791, 792
Pennak, R. W., 442, 456, 457, 460
Perkins, Beauregard, Jr., 261
Perrin, R. M. S., 757
Perring, F. H., 403
Persson, Herman, 465, 485, 491
Peterson, R. L., 533
Peterson, R. S., 463
Pettersson, H., 739
Péwé, T. L., 358, 360-362, 365, 366, 480
Phleger, F. B., 167, 616, 617
Picard, M. D., 822, 823
Piette, C. R., 57
Piggott, C. S., 737, 739
Pignatti, Sandro, 498, 499
Pilsbry, H. A., 598, 599, 603, 605
Piper, A. M., 310, 314, 316
Pipiringos, G. N., 250
Pitelka, F. A. 5 32, 538
Plafker, George, 360, 361
Plass, G. N., 894, 897
Poland, J. F., 319, 330
Polunin, Nicholas, 490
Porsild, A. E., 461
Porter, K. R., 552, 553
Porter, Steven, 360, 361
Post, A. S., 800
Post, Lennart von, 646
Potter, L. D., 433
Potter, P. E., 585
Potzger, J. E., 57, 73, 390, 392, 394, 396, 403, 408, 418-420, 425, 427, 430, 435, 437, 662
Powell, W. J., 252
Powers, H. A., 24, 220, 226, 241, 245, 255, 258, 474, 511, 512, 808-812, 852
Powers, W. E., 291

Prettyman, R. L., 73
Price, W. A., 133, 146, 843
Prouty, W. V., 133
Prufer, Olaf, 658, 672, 678
Pugh, G. T., 132
Pumpelly, Raphael, 6
Puri, G. S., 486
Puri, Harbans, 133
Putnam, W. C., 268, 270, 272, 278, 279, 303, 304, 306, 307, 310, 328, 329, 809, 824, 855, 856, 859, 861

Q

Quimby, G. I., 659, 661-663, 670, 677
Quinn, J. H., 177

R

Radbruch, Dorothy H., 319
Ragle, R. H., 801
Rainey, F. G., 368, 369
Rainwater, F. H., 785
Rand, A. L., 533, 536
Rasmussen, W. C., 134
Raup, H. M., 378-384, 386, 403
Rausch, R. L., 511, 516, 517, 520
Raven, P. H., 445
Ray, C. E., 511, 573
Ray, L. L., 66, 217, 222, 223, 291
Redfield, A. C., 125
Reed, E. C., 189, 190, 194, 195, 197-199
Reed, J. C., Jr., 360
Reed, R. D., 299, 856
Reese, Gerd, 497, 498, 500-502, 504
Reeves, C. C., Jr., 208, 209
Reger, R. D., 362, 370
Rehder, H. A., 616
Reiche, Parry, 315
Reid, G. K., Jr., 616
Rempel, J. G., 593
Rex, D. F., 891
Rhoades, Rendell, 623
Rhodehamel, E. C., 65
Rich, J. L., 120
Richards, H. G., 129-133, 426, 614, 834, 837
Richards, P. W., 490
Richmond, G. M., 20, 21, 23, 217-219, 221-227, 231, 250-252, 261, 268, 270-272, 276, 280, 291-296, 341, 351, 759, 761, 809, 812
Richmond, N. D., 511
Richthofen, Ferdinand von, 6
Ricker, K. E., 614, 626, 645
Ricker, W. E., 591
Ridley, F., 664
Rieger, Samuel, 238
Riemer, W. J., 552
Rigg, G. B., 474, 810, 813
Rimbert, Francine, 819
Rinehart, C. D., 303, 304, 809
Ritchie, J. C., 408-411
Ritchie, W. A., 659, 663, 664
Rittenhouse, Gordon, 792
Rivas, L. R., 616
Roberts, F. H. H., Jr., 687, 688
Robinson, G. D., 248
Roche, Alexandre, 826, 827
Rockie, W. A., 238
Roepke, H. H., 768, 769
Rogers, M. A., 774, 778, 779
Rogers, M. J., 711
Rohrer, W. L., 249, 434

Rolingson, M. A., 678, 679
Rollo, J. R., 148, 175, 179
Romer, A. S., 511
Rønning, O. I., 488
Roosa, W. B., 659
Roosma, Aino, 435, 437, 622
Rosen, D. E., 569, 570
Rosendahl, C. O., 405, 486
Rosholt, J. N., Jr., 594, 724, 737, 739, 742-744
Ross, C. A., 585
Ross, C. P., 809, 849, 852
Ross, C. S., 809
Ross, H. H., 588, 590-593, 644, 647
Rostlund, Erhard, 575
Rouse, Irving, 670, 674, 679
Rowe, J. S., 407, 662
Roy, C. J., 177
Rozaire, C. E., 703
Rubey, W. W., 48, 58, 600
Rubin, Meyer, 104, 225, 276, 389, 742, 748, 809, 810
Rubin, M. J., 899
Ruedemann, Rudolf, 103
Ruhe, R. V., 21, 23, 25, 29-32, 38, 86, 292, 293, 413, 757, 758, 760-762
Rumpp, L. N., 623
Runcorn, S. K., 893
Russell, I. C., 6, 238, 240, 255, 259, 272, 273, 276, 277, 280, 281, 306, 348, 847, 849, 851
Russell, R. D., 316
Russell, R. J., 146, 167, 511, 842-844
Ruthven, A. G., 559, 561
Rutten, M. G., 823, 826, 827
Rydberg, P. A., 454, 457
Rzedowski, Jerzy, 444

S

Sackett, W. M., 357, 737, 739, 740, 743-745
Safonov, Anatole, 311, 313
Sahlstein, Th. G., 807
Salisbury, R. D., 43, 130, 235, 237, 238
Saltzman, Barry, 890
Salwen, B., 663
Sanford, J. T., 656
Sarma, T. P., 737
Savage, D. E., 317, 509, 511, 512, 516, 517
Savich-Lyubitskaya, L. I., 485, 488
Say, Thomas, 599
Sayles, E. B., 699
Sayles, R. W., 8
Schaeffer, O. A., 737, 740
Schafer, J. P., 24, 116, 118-120
Scheid, V. E., 238
Schlocker, J., 319
Schlundt, Herman, 9
Schmidt, K. P., 559, 560, 634
Schneider, A. F., 34, 35, 71
Schnell, I. I., 786
Schoenwetter, James, 435, 443
Schoewe, W. H., 30, 51
Scholl, D. W., 365, 723, 725, 730
Scholtes, W. H., 31, 32, 759
Schott, W., 741
Schove, D. J., 895
Schrader, F. C., 363
Schrock, A. E., 418, 422
Schuierer, F. W., 550, 551
Schulman, Edmund, 871-873, 877

Schultz, C. B., 194, 195, 197, 198, 200, 246, 248, 511, 761, 762, 812
Schultz, J. R., 511
Schumm, S. A., 788, 790, 792
Schuster, R. M., 405, 490, 491
Schwartz, G. M., 74
Schwarzbach, Martin, 786
Schwennesen, A. T., 291
Scott, F. I., 498
Scott, G. H., 597
Scott, G. R., 219, 245, 247, 249, 511, 520, 599, 600, 812
Scott, I. D., 63
Scott, W. B., 637
Scruton, P. C., 167
Sears, P. B., 385, 388, 394, 396, 405, 408, 409, 413, 418, 422, 430, 434-436, 442, 700
Sears, W. H., 690
Segerstrale, S. G., 645
Selander, R. K., 533, 537
Selander, Sten, 502
Sellards, E. H., 205, 206, 511, 560, 669-671, 687-690
Semken, H. A., Jr., 511, 657
Serkowski, K., 895
Sethi, R. P., 569
Shaffer, P. R., 50, 51, 54
Shaler, N. S., 7, 115
Shanz, H. L., 438
Shapiro, Ralph, 878
Sharp, R. P., 56, 75, 266, 268, 270, 272, 280, 294, 307, 309, 326, 327, 330, 436, 855, 859
Shattuck, G. B., 7, 131
Shay, C. T., 39
Sheets, M. M., 842
Shelford, V. E., 418
Shepard, F. P., 74, 148, 157, 167, 614, 663, 716, 723-725, 728, 729, 731, 732
Shepps, V. C., 85, 90, 105, 107, 108
Sherrod, Neil, 573
Shetone, H. C., 655, 658
Shimeck, Bohumil, 6, 31, 48, 599, 602, 608
Short, L. L., Jr., 535, 536
Shotten, F. W., 620, 622
Shotwell, J. A., 572
Shreve, Forrest, 433
Shumaker, R. C., 105
Shuman, R. C., 291
Shumway, George, 711
Shutler, Richard, 698
Sibley, C. G., 532, 536, 537
Siebenthal, C. E., 252
Sigafoos, R. S., 226, 347, 470, 471, 801, 803, 871
Sigler, W. F., 578
Sigurgeirsson, Thorbjörn, 823
Silliman, Benjamin, 3
Simons, E. L., 445, 446
Simonson, R. W., 755, 757, 759, 760, 762
Simpson, G. G., 509, 511, 515-517, 531, 583
Simpson, H. E., 19, 198
Simpson, J. C., 676
Singewald, Q. D., 223, 249, 252
Siren, Gustaf, 871, 873
Sissons, J. B., 109
Skarland, Ivar, 369
Skeels, M. A., 657
Skinner, M. F., 509, 511
Slaughter, B. H., 437, 446, 447, 511, 573, 600

Slemmons, D. B., 824, 846-848
Sloan, R. S., 33
Smagorinsky, Joseph, 887, 899
Small, J. K., 561
Smiley, T. L., 635
Smirnova, Zoya N., 488
Smith, C. E., Jr., 445
Smith, C. L., 511, 570, 573, 575, 648
Smith, G. D., 53, 573, 575
Smith, G. I., 280, 281, 622
Smith, G. R., 511
Smith, H. E., 500
Smith, H. M., 547
Smith, H. T. U., 124, 133, 199, 215, 291
Smith, J. F., Jr., 294
Smith, P. S., 362
Smith, P. W., 408, 535, 547, 562, 626, 633-635, 637, 645, 646
Smith, R. L., 809
Smith, W. E. T., 837
Snavely, P. D., Jr., 342, 346, 851
Snyder, C. T., 266, 273, 278, 281, 786
Snyder, J. O., 577
Snyder, L. L., 637, 638
Soil Survey Staff, 758, 760
Sololavskaja, A. P., 498, 501, 502
Soós, Lajos, 599
Soper, J. H., 403, 405
Soule, J. D., 617, 619
Sparks, B. W., 624
Spaulding, A. C., 367, 368
Spencer, E., 777
Spencer, J. W., 74, 78, 102
Spiegal, Zane, 292
Spurr, S. H., 380, 382, 383, 385, 386, 396
Stahl, J. B., 625
Stalker, A. MacS., 21
Stallings, W. S., Jr., 872
Stanley, G. M., 74, 75, 79, 80
Stannard, L. J., 586
Staplin, F. L., 625, 648
Stark, J. T., 249, 252
Starrett, Andrew, 511
Stearns, C. E., 228, 292
Stearns, R. E. C., 599
Stebbins, G. L., 497-500
Stebbins, R. C., 433, 545, 550-552, 558, 562
Steece, F. V., 15, 19, 21, 23
Steere, W. C., 419, 485-491, 648
Stegmann, Boris, 619
Stein, R. C., 535
Stein, W. T., 445
Stephens, J. J., 511, 575, 649
Stephenson, L. W., 132
Sternberg, C. M., 657
Sterns, H. T., 261, 758, 759, 851
Sterns, R. G., 585, 839, 841
Stetson, H. C., 167, 729
Stettenheim, P., 529
Steven, T. A., 251
Stewart, B. K., 462
Stewart, D. P., 114, 122
Stewart, J. H., 703
Stille, H. W., 856, 857, 863, 865
Stimpson, William, 599
Stirton, R. A., 316, 323
Stock, Chester, 330, 509, 511, 515, 573
Stokes, W. L., 511, 517, 520, 571, 573, 575, 578
Stolz, H. P., 330
Stommel, H. M., 891
Storer, R. W., 538
Stout, B. B., 381, 386

Stout, M. L., 343
Stout, Wilbur, 65
Stovall, J. C., 349
Straaten, L. M. Van, 723
Strahler, A. N., 789
Strain, B. R., 499
Strain, W. S., 293
Strand, J. R., 239, 511
Strand, R. G., 321-323
Street, J. S., 105
Strelkova, O. S., 502
Stricklin, F. L., Jr., 176
Strong, W. D., 692
Stuart, D. J., 852
Stuckenrath, Robert, Jr., 672
Stuiver, Minze, 388, 389, 391, 747, 748
Stump, R. W., 362
Stutz, H. C., 444
Suess, H. E., 745
Suttner, L. J., 58
Svärdson, Gunnar, 645
Swain, F. M., 765-767, 770-772, 774-777, 779
Swann, D. H., 792
Swanson, E. H., 240, 713
Swickard, D. A., 73
Swineford, Ada, 197, 207, 214, 291, 292, 511, 512, 809, 812, 813
Swinnerton, A. C., 9
Szijj, L. J., 536

T

Taber, Stephen, 365
Taliaferro, N. L., 319, 856, 857, 859
Tamers, M. A., 698, 604
Tanner, J. T., 535, 536
Tanner, W. F., 730
Tarbet, L. A., 289
Tarr, R. S., 99, 101, 108
Tatsumoto, M., 739
Taverner, P. A., 536
Taylor, D. W., 207, 258, 511, 515, 520, 576, 597-599, 602, 603, 605, 606, 621, 625, 645, 648-650
Taylor, E. H., 562
Taylor, F. B., 78, 80, 109, 834
Taylor, R. F., 470
Taylor, W. R., 570, 577
Tedrow, J. C. F., 134
Terasmae, Jaan, 80, 85, 92, 646, 648, 659
Thayer, T. P., 348, 349
Theobald, W. L., 462
Thomas, E. A., 647
Thomas, E. S., 633, 634, 637, 638, 656
Thomas, H. E., 697
Thomas, J. A, 38
Thomas, R. G., 328
Thompson, G. A., 300, 303, 307
Thompson, Maurice, 63
Thompson, R. H., 673
Thompson, W. F., 123, 124
Thorarinsson, Sigurdur, 807, 813
Thornbury, W. D., 63, 65-69, 71
Thorp, James, 134, 198, 199, 224, 755, 760, 762
Thruston, G. P., 673
Thurber, D. L., 737, 739, 740, 747
Thurow, G. R., 552
Thwaites, F. T., 20, 45, 49, 53, 57, 58, 66, 72, 74
Tigermann, M. H., 788
Tight, W. G., 65
Tihen, J. A., 544, 545, 548, 562

Tipton, M. J., 19, 21, 23
Tischler, Georg, 497, 498
Titus, F. B., Jr., 292
Tocher, Don, 332, 858, 859
Toepfer, V., 511
Tolmachev, A. I., 453, 457, 502
Tordoff, H. B., 530
Totten, S. M., 90, 91
Townsend, R. C., 18
Trainer, F. W., 362
Transeau, E. N., 408, 559
Trask, P. D., 167 319-321, 560
Trautman, M. A., 388, 397
Trautman, M. B., 634, 635, 637
Travis, R. B., 323
Treasher, R. C., 238
Treganza, A. E., 714, 715
Trelease, S. F., 456
Trimble, D. E., 221, 240, 261, 273, 350, 351
Trowbridge, A. C., 45, 57, 759, 842
Troxell, E. L., 511
True, D. L., 712
Truog, E., 768
Tsukada, Matsuo, 647
Tuck, Ralph, 362
Tucker, J. M., 44, 445
Tullis, E. L., 238
Turner, H. W., 304, 306, 309
Tuthill, S. J., 21, 600
Tutin, T. G., 500
Tutin, Winifred, 647
Twenhofel, W. H., 837
Twente, J. W., Jr., 562
Twenter, F. R., 289

U

Uchupi, Elazar, 729
Udvardy, M. D. F., 532, 533, 538
Uffen, R. J., 823
Upham, Warren, 4, 7, 29, 39, 273, 834
Upson, J. E., 114, 125, 244, 252, 319-321, 324, 326, 328, 329, 388, 859, 861
Urquhart, F. A., 637
Uyeda, Seiya, 821
Uyeno, Teruya, 258, 569-573, 575-577
Uzzell, T. M., Jr., 552

V

Vaartaja, Olli, 386
Valentine, B. D., 547
Valentine, J. W., 329, 330, 856, 861
Vallentyne, J. R., 387, 766, 771, 772, 774, 779
Vanden Berghen, C., 485
VanderHoof, V. L., 314, 316, 332
Van Houten, F. B., 265, 267
Van Steeg, Karl, 101, 102
Van Winkle, Walton, 272
Van Zijl, J. S. V., 823
Varvaro, Gasper, 146
Veatch, A. C., 730
Veatch, Otto, 132
Vedder, J. G., 861
Verhoogen, Jean, 810
Vernon, R. O., 176
Vick, A. R., 418, 429
Vockeroth, J. R., 593
Volchok, H. L., 737
Voous, K. H., 538
Voss, John, 413, 648
Vucetich, C. G., 807

W

Wahrhaftig, Clyde, 268, 280, 305, 313, 356, 358, 360, 367, 853-857, 859, 861
Waldén, H. W., 598, 620
Walker, B. W., 617, 618
Walker, Bryant, 599
Walker, E. M., 626
Walker, G. E., 235
Walker, P. C., 388, 389, 394, 396
Wallace, A. R., 453
Wallace, R. E., 271, 859, 860
Wallace, R. W., 760
Wallace, W. J., 702, 712, 715
Wanek, A. A., 290
Wanless, H. R., 48, 53
Waring, A. J., 680
Warren, C. N., 699, 710-712, 715-717
Warren, C. R., 19
Wascher, H. L., 53, 55, 755, 761
Wasserman, A. O., 548, 549
Waters, A. C., 235, 238, 851, 852
Watson, R. A., 789
Watson, Sereno, 457, 462
Watt, A. K., 92, 600
Watts, W. A., 404, 405, 409, 418, 419, 427, 429, 765, 773, 775
Wayne, W. J., 63-69, 71-73, 600, 601
Weaver, C. E., 322, 323, 330
Weaver, D. K., 326
Weaver, J. E., 406
Webb, C. H., 673, 676
Webb, R. G., 562
Webb, R. W., 303, 854
Webb, W. M., 74
Webb, W. S., 679
Weber, Florence, 362, 363
Weber, R. H., 291
Weber, W. A., 454, 455, 463
Wedel, W. R., 685, 693
Weeks, W. F., 795
Weertman, Johannes, 800
Weidman, Samuel, 48, 57
Weigel, R. D., 511, 573
Weiss, Lawrence, 118
Welch, R. N., 146, 176
Weller, J. M., 45
Wells, B. W., 421
Wells, F. G., 248, 321
Wells, J. D., 245
Wells, P. V., 434, 437, 511, 520, 622, 624, 698
Wendorf, Fred, 291, 436, 446, 543, 546, 600, 622, 688, 689
Wentworth, C. K., 131, 810
Wenzel, L. K., 792
West, D. A., 536
West, R. G., 57, 58, 409-412
Westveld, Marinus, 379-382
Wetmore, A., 527-532
Wexler, Harry, 899
Weyer, E. M., 367
Wheeler, H. E., 259, 576, 577
White, E. M., 19
White, G. W., 85, 87, 90-92, 105, 107, 108
White, J. A., 511, 518
White, S. E., 120
Whitehead, D. R., 394, 396, 418-423, 425, 429, 614, 648
Whiteside, Melvin, 435, 437, 438, 440
Whitney, J. D., 6
Whittaker, R. H., 407, 414, 433
Whitten, C. A., 299
Whittlesey, Charles, 7

Wier, C. E., 66, 69

Wilcox, R. E., 24, 226, 241, 291, 292, 474, 813, 814, 852, 855

Wilimovsky, N. J., 570

Willett, H. C., 895

Willey, G. R., 669, 679, 680, 685, 687, 690

Williams, A. B., 623

Williams, H. S., 107

Williams, Howell, 309, 313, 348, 349, 807, 808, 852

Williams, J. R., 362

Williams, J. S., 275

Williams, P. A., 699

Williams, P. L., 217

Williams, Stephen, 511, 656, 670, 674, 677

Willman, H. B., 45, 48-50, 55, 56, 211, 213

Wilson, A. T., 897

Wilson, Druid, 570

Wilson, I. F., 319

Wilson, L. R., 57, 72, 394

Wilson, R. W., 258, 511, 824

Winchell, N. H., 4, 29

Wingard, N. E., 106

Winkler, E. M., 625

Winterer, E. L., 329

Winters, H. A., 21

Wirth, W. W., 592

Witkind, I. J., 21, 244, 849

Witthoft, J., 658, 672

Wittry, W. L., 659

Woerkom, A. J. J. van, 896

Wolfe, J. A., 456

Wolfe, P. E., 134

Wood, H. E., 258, 511, 512, 839

Wood, P. A., 446

Woodbury, R. B., 446

Woodford, A. O., 856

Woodring, W. P., 310, 314, 315, 319-321, 328-330, 856, 859, 861

Woodward, T. P., 146

Woodworth, J. B., 115-120

Woolard, G. P., 831, 833, 835, 837, 840, 845, 849, 852, 853

Woolfenden, G. E., 527, 528, 531

Wormington, H. Marie, 662, 669, 673, 687, 688, 699, 709

Worthen, A. H., 43, 52

Worzel, J. L., 103

Wright, C. W., 463

Wright, G. F., 8, 9, 77

Wright, H. E., Jr., 20, 23, 33-35, 38, 39, 69, 292, 295, 406, 408-413, 633, 765, 767, 772, 773, 775, 777, 845

Wright, H. P., 624

Wright, H. T., 664

Wright, L. A., 287

Wulff, E. V., 502

Wynne, F. E., 492

Wynne-Edwards, V. C., 383, 393, 405

Y

Yarnell, R. A., 680

Young, E. J., 812

Young, F. N., 625, 626

Youngquist, W. L., 258

Z

Zagwijn, W. H., 649, 749, 750

Zeigler, J. M., 113, 117, 119, 125

Zeuner, F. E., 511, 791, 896

Zhadin, V. I., 599

Zinderen Bakker, E. M. van, 486

Zoltai, S. C., 39, 40

Zumberge, J. H., 39, 48, 63, 64, 70-72, 74, 80, 661

Zwiefel, R. G., 444, 544, 552

SUBJECT INDEX

A

Ablation, 796, 797
Absaroka Mountains, Wyo., 244
Accretion gley, 50, 52. *See also* Gumbotil
Adirondack Mountains, N. Y., 101, 108
Advance, *see* Glacial stage
Agricultural plants, 395, 443, 500, 604, 680, 693
Albedo, 886
Alluvial terraces, *see* Terraces, river
Alluvium, *see* Formations
Alpine plants, 460, 461, 464, 466, 471, 504
Amphibians, 548-556, 634,-639
Ancestral Rivers, specific
  Allegheny River, N. Y., 102, 104
  Bad River, S. Dak., 15, 19
  Cannonball River, N. Dak., 19
  Cheyenne River, S. Dak., 15, 19
  Chicago River, Ill., 56
  Erigan River, N. Y., 102
  Genesee River, N. Y., 103
  Grand River, Mich., 56, 70, 77, 78
  Iowa River, Iowa, 53
  Knife River, N. Dak., 19
  Little Missouri River, N. Dak., 19
  Mississippi River, Ill., 49-51, 53
  Missouri River, Mont., 19
  Niobrara River, S. Dak., 19
  Ontarian River, N. Y., 102
  Red River, N. Dak., 19
  Souris River, N. Dak., 19
  "Susqueseneca" River, N. Y., 103
  Teays River, Indiana, 65, 66, 623, 624
  River Warren, Minn., 39
  White River, S. Dak., 15, 19
  Yellowstone River, Mont., 19
Antarctic ice cap, effect on climate, 897
Appalachian Highlands, Eastern U. S., 99, 101, 133-135
Aquarius Plateau, Utah, 221, 223
Archaeological cultures, *see* Cultures
Archaeological sites, specific
  Aden Crater, N. Mex., 446
  Agate Basin, Wyo., 687-689
  Allen, Neb., 687-689
  Aleuts, Alaska, 367
  Anangula, Alaska, 367, 711, 713
  Andrews, Mich., 656, 664
  Awatovi, Ariz., 445
  Barnes, Mich., 656, 659
  Bat Cave, N. Mex., 445
  Bering Strait, Alaska, 367
  Big Horn Canyon, Mont., 691
  Birdshead Cave, Wyo., 691, 692
  Blackwater Draw, N. Mex., 687, 688
  Boylston Street Fishweir, Mass., 656, 663
  Brohm, Ontario, 656, 661
  Browns Valley, Minn., 656, 662
  Bull Brook, Mass., 125, 656, 659, 671
  Burley, Ontario, 656, 664

Archaeological sites, specific (*cont.*)
  Burnett Cave, N. Mex., 687, 688
  Burnt Rock Middens, Tex., 691
  Catclaw Cave, Ariz., 445
  Chaluka, Alaska, 367
  Chapala Basin, Mexico, 715
  Clark Dry Lake, Calif., 718
  Danger Cave, Utah, 445, 697, 698, 703-705
  Dent, Colo., 687-689
  Durst Rock Shelter, Wis., 656, 659
  Engigstciak, Alaska, 369
  Etowah, Georgia, 681
  Farmington, Calif., 714, 715, 717
  Feheeley, Mich., 656, 664
  Finley, Wyo., 687, 688
  Fish Bone Cave, Nev., 699
  Flint Creek Rock Shelter, Tenn., 672
  Folsom, N. Mex., 687, 688
  Frank Bay, Ontario, 656, 664
  Frazer, Mich., 664
  Friesenhahn Cave, Tex., 687, 689
  Graham Cave, Missouri, 669, 686, 691
  George Lake, Ontario, 656, 660, 661
  Guano Cave, Nev., 699
  Gypsum Cave, Nev., 446, 699
  Hardaway, N. Car., 669
  Hell Gap, Wyo., 687-689
  Hidden Cave, Nev., 699
  Holcombe, Mich., 656, 660
  Horner, Wyo., 687, 688
  Humboldt Cave, Nev., 704
  Itchucknee Springs, Fla., 671
  Jimmy Allen, Wyo., 687, 688
  La Brea tar pits, Calif., 711, 717
  Lake La Jolla, Calif., 710, 712
  Lake LeConte, Calif., 710, 711, 717, 718
  Lake Manix, Calif., 710, 714
  Lake Mohave, Calif., 710, 711, 714, 715, 717
  Le Croy, Tenn., 669
  Lehner, Ariz., 440, 446, 686, 689, 698
  Leonard Rock Shelter, Nev., 698, 699, 703
  Lewisville, Tex., 447, 687-689
  Lime Creek, Neb., 687-689
  Lindenmeier, Colo., 687-690
  Lipscomb, Tex., 687, 688
  Lo Dais Ka, Colo., 691, 692
  Logan Creek, Neb., 691, 692
  Lovelock Cave, Nev., 702, 704
  Lubbock, Tex., 687-689
  Marmes Rock Shelter, Wash., 702
  McKean, Wyo., 691, 692
  Medicine Crow, S. Dak., 691, 692
  Miami, Tex., 687, 688
  Midland, Tex., 687
  Milnesand, N. Mex., 687, 688
  Modoc Rock Shelter, Ill., 656, 660, 669, 672
  Morrison's Island, Ontario, 656, 664
  Moundville, Ala., 681

Archaeological sites, specific (*cont.*)
  Naco, Ariz., 440, 446, 686, 689, 698
  Nebo Hill, Missouri, 687, 688
  Nuckolls, Tenn., 669, 672
  Oak Grove, Calif., 712
  Oconto, Wis., 656, 663, 664
  Parrish, Ky., 669
  Pictograph Cave, Mont., 691, 692
  Plainview, Tex., 687, 689
  Point Hope, Alaska, 367
  Point of Pines, Ariz., 445
  Pomranky, Mich., 664
  Powers-Yonkee, Mont., 691, 692
  Quadi, Ala., 669
  Ray Long, S. Dak., 687, 688
  Reagen, Vermont, 656, 659
  Red Lake, N. Y., 656, 664
  Red Smoke, Neb., 678, 688
  Renier, Wis., 656, 660, 661
  Rose Spring, Calif., 699
  Russell Cave, Ala., 673, 674
  San Dieguito, Calif., 711, 712, 715, 717
  San Jon, N. Mex., 687, 688
  Santa Rosa Island, Calif., 712, 717
  Scharbaur, Tex., 688, 689
  Schmidt, Mich., 656, 663
  Schultz, Mich., 656, 664
  Scottsbluff, Neb., 687, 688
  Scripps Campus, Calif., 714
  Sheguiandah, Ontario, 656, 660, 661
  Signal Butte, Neb., 691, 692
  Silver Spring, Fla., 699
  South Fork Rock Shelter, Nev., 704
  Spiro, Okla., 681
  Stallings Island, Georgia, 680
  Stanfield-Worley, Ala., 669, 672, 674, 678, 679
  Starved Rock, Ill., 686, 691
  Stroebel, Mich., 664
  Sub-mound, S. Dak., 691
  Texas Street, Calif., 714, 717
  Topanga, Calif., 712
  Tule Springs, Nev., 699, 714
  Union Lake, Mich., 662
  Ventana Cave, Ariz., 440, 445, 446
  Wapanucket, Mass., 659
  Weis Rock Shelter, Idaho, 702, 703
  Williamson, Virginia, 669, 673
  Willow Creek, Calif., 717
  Zuma Beach, Calif., 712
Arctic Ocean, effect on climate, 897
Arcto-Tertiary flora, 444, 501, 502
Arroyos, 289, 290, 294, 295, 792
Ash, *see* Volcanic ash
Atmospheric circulation, 882-891, 898

B

Basalt, *see* Formations
Bear Lake, Idaho, 577, 578, 645
Beds, *see* Formations
Bering land bridge, Alaska, 365

913

Beryllium dating, 740
Bighorn Basin, Wyo., 244, 248
Bighorn Mountains, Wyo., 244
Birds, 527-547, 620, 635-639
Black Hills, S. Dak., 25, 453, 457, 464, 590
Boreal forest, 380, 392, 425
Boreal plant species, 419-422, 425, 435, 453, 454, 460, 461

C

Cache la Poudre River, Colo., 222
Capulin Mountains, N. Mex., 809
Carbonate composition of till, Ill., 45
Carbon dioxide in atmosphere, 884, 885, 894, 897-899
Carolina Bays, Southeastern U. S., 134, 420, 421
Carson Desert, Nev., 277, 279
Cascade Range, Western U. S., 300, 301, 331, 341, 343, 345-348, 469, 472, 809, 810, 851, 852, 864
Channeled scablands, Wash., 239-240
Cheney-Palouse scabland, Wash., 240
Cheyenne River, S. Dak., 25
Chihuahuan Desert, Ariz., 561, 622
Chihuahuan floristic element, Southwestern U. S., 463
China Lake Valley, Calif., 279, 435
Chlorine dating, 740
Chuska Mountains, Ariz.–N. Mex., 293, 295, 437
Circumpolar plants, 454, 459, 460, 486
Clay, *see* Formations
Clay-minerals, in till, 45; soil, 758
Climatic changes, causes, 8, 891-900; effect on runoff, 784-793; effect on glaciers, 795-803; effect on tree growth, 872-878; effect on inland lakes, 267-281; effect on Early Man, 657, 704-706; effect on ocean temperatures, 741-745; effect on insects, 594; effect on mollusks, 603; effect on organisms, 633-639, 648
Climatic optimum, 633, 634
Climax vegetation, 381-384, 397, 406, 407, 470, 502, 633, 638
Coastal Plain, Atlantic, 7, 129-133, 417, 418
Coastal Plain, Gulf of Mexico, 137-179
Coast Range, Ore., 348, 349, 469, 472, 851-853
Coast Ranges, Calif., 300, 301, 311, 313, 317, 318, 321, 322, 331, 332, 855, 857-859
Colorado Desert, Calif., 288, 289, 301
Colorado Piedmont, Southern Great Plains, 203, 244, 245
Colorado Plateau, Colo., 288, 293-296, 437, 843
Colorado River, Ariz.–Calif., 287-289, 293, 294
Columbia Plateau, Wash., 231-242, 255, 702, 703
Columbia River, Idaho–Wash.–Ore., 232, 235, 237, 259, 341
Conglomerate, *see* Formations
Connecticut Valley, New England, 120, 121
Continental shelf, 723-733; of Atlantic coast, 730; Gulf of Mexico, 730, 731; Pacific Coast, 325, 731
Cook Inlet, Alaska, 363
Copper River basin, Alaska, 363
Coteau du Missouri, N. Dak., 15, 18, 23

Crater Lake, Ore., 348, 777, 807, 809, 810, 852
Craters of the Moon, Idaho, 261
Cultural foci, *see* Cultures
Cultural traditions, *see* Cultures
Cultures, specific
  Amargosa, Calif., 701
  Antelope Creek, Great Plains, 693
  Archaic, Eastern U. S., 655, 660-665, 670, 677, 679, 685, 690-692
  Candy Creek, Southeastern U. S., 674, 675
  Cazador, Southwestern U. S., 699, 700
  Chiricahua, Southwestern U. S., 699, 700
  Choris, Alaska, 369
  Clovis, Southwestern U. S., 655, 670-675, 678, 688-690
  Cochise, Ariz., 698, 699
  Coles Creek, Louisiana, 680
  Cottonwood, Calif., 701
  Craig Mountain, Columbia Plateau, 702
  Crane Flat, Calif., 701
  Cumberland, Southeastern U. S., 670-675, 678
  Dalton, Southeastern U. S., 670, 672, 673, 675, 678, 679
  Death Valley, Calif., 702
  Denbigh Flint, Alaska, 368-370
  "Desert Mohave," Calif., 701
  Eden-Scottsbluff, Great Plains, 661, 688, 689
  Fluted Point Hunters, Eastern U. S., 655, 656, 659-661, 673, 675-678
  Folsom, Great Plains and Northwestern U. S., 655, 671, 673, 688, 689
  Grave Creeks, Columbia Plateau, 702
  Holcombe, Mich.–Ohio, 659
  Hopewell, Eastern U. S., 622, 670, 680, 693
  Huff, Great Plains, 693
  Hunting, Southwestern U. S., 698, 699; Columbia Plateau, 702; Pacific Coast, 713, 715; Southeastern U. S., 688-692, 673, 679
  Ipiutak, Alaska, 368, 369
  Kings Beach, Calif., 701
  La Jolla, Calif., 710
  Lake Mohave, Calif., 701
  Lamoka, N. Y., 663
  Llano, Great Plains, 688-690
  Keith, Great Plains, 693
  Loeske Creek, Great Plains, 693
  Mariposa, Calif., 701
  Martis, Calif., 701
  Mattawan, Great Lakes region, 664
  Meso-Indian, Southeastern U. S., 670, 678, 679
  Mississippi, Southeastern U. S., 677, 680
  Monroe, Great Plains, 693
  Neo-Indian, Southeastern U. S., 670, 673, 678, 680
  Norton, Alaska, 369
  Nukleet, Alaska, 368
  Old Copper, Great Lakes region, 663, 664
  Old Whaling, Alaska, 369
  Optima, Great Plains, 693
  Over, Great Plains, 693
  Owens Lake, Calif., 701
  Paleo-Indian, 655-660, 685-690, 669, 670, 673, 675-678
  Palisades, Alaska, 370

Cultures, specific (*cont.*)
  Pinto, Calif., 701
  Plainview, Great Plains, 661, 689
  Plano, Great Plains, 661, 678, 689, 690
  Poverty Point, Louisiana, 680
  Punuk, Alaska, 368
  Quad, Southeastern U. S., 670-673, 679
  Redstone, Southeastern U. S., 671-675
  Rose Spring, Calif., 701
  San Patrice, Louisiana, 673-675
  San Pedro, Ariz., 700
  Santa Rosa, Fla., 680
  Shell-mound, Georgia, 679
  Sterns Creek, Great Plains, 693
  Sulphur Springs, Ariz., 698-700
  Suwannee, Fla., 670, 672-675
  Swift Creek, Georgia, 680
  Tamarack, Calif., 701
  Temple Mound, Southeastern U. S., 670
  Thomas Riggs, Great Plains, 693
  Thule, Alaska, 368, 378
  Valley, Great Plains, 693
  Village, 692-694
  Weeden Island, Fla., 670-680
  Woodland, Eastern U. S., 673, 680, 693
  Yuma, Great Plains, 688

D

Death Valley, Calif., 278, 279, 300
Deep-sea cores, 724, 742-745, 751
Delaware River, N. Y., 103
Dendrochronology, statistical techniques, 873; cross-dating, 872; site selection, 871; relation to climate, 873-878; relation to runoff, 873
Disjunctions, of plants, 384, 385, 405, 406, 460, 461, 464, 486, 489-493; birds, 537, 538, 547-552; reptiles, 559; insects, 583, 586, 587, 589, 590, 592; invertebrates, 614-618, 621; animals, in general, 634, 644, 645
Dispersal, insects, 583, 589, 592
Distribution, of vegetation, 428, 443, 455, 458, 476, 486, 497; birds, 532, 536, amphibians, 543-546, 549, 551; reptiles, 558, 562; fishes, 571, 575; invertebrates, 625
Drainage density, relation to climate, 789
Drainage pattern, Calif., 325
Drift, *see* Formations
Driftless Area, Wis.–Ill., 48, 49, 52, 54, 405, 406, 552, 842
Drumlins, in Montana, 23; Michigan, 72; Massachusetts, 117
Drumlins, specific
  Automba, Minn., 34, 36
  Brainard, Minn., 34, 35
  Fayette, Ind., 94
  Pierz, Minn., 34
  Southwold, Ontario, 94
  Split Rock, Minn., 34, 37
  Toimi, Minn., 34
  Wadena, Minn., 33, 34
Dunes, *see* Sand dunes

E

Earthquakes, 265, 831, 833, 835, 837, 840-842, 845, 847-849, 851-853, 858, 859
Edwards Plateau, Tex., 203
Endemic plants, 385, 406, 458, 460, 465, 466, 487; mammals, 516; insects, 589; mollusks, 606; invertebrates, 615, 619

Epeirogenic uplift, Rocky Mts., 844, 864, 865
Eskimos, Alaska, 368
Evolution, in mammals, 201, 518-520; birds, 527, 528, 533, 534, 536, 543, 544; amphibians, 548, 551, 553; reptiles, 557, 558, 562, 563; fishes, 575, 577; insects, 583, 587, 588, 590-593, 620, 622, 623; mollusks, 598, 601
Extinction, 636, 637; of mammals, 445-447, 520, 649, 656, 658, 670; birds, 527, 530-532; reptiles, 558, 563, 564; fishes 571, 574, 575; mollusks, 598, 602, 605

F

Faults, in California, 300-302, 318, 325, 328, 330, 332, 854, 855, 857-860, 865; Basin and Range area, 845-848, 864; Rocky Mountains, 849; Mississippi Embayment, 841, 842
Faunal age, *see* Land-mammal age
Fauna, local, specific
 Adams, Kan., 605, 606
 Bender, Kan., 514, 606
 Berends, Okla., 575, 605, 606
 Borchers, Kan., 514, 519
 Butler Spring, Kan., 514, 605, 606
 Clear Creek, Tex., 446
 Cragin Quarry, Kan., 512, 514, 605-607
 Cudahy, Kan., 514, 515, 519
 Deer Park, Kan., 514
 Dixon, Kan., 605
 Doby Springs, Kan., 519, 605, 606
 Jinglebob, Kan., 514, 519, 602, 605, 606
 Jones, Kan., 514, 605, 606
 Mt. Scott, Kan., 512, 514, 519, 575, 605-607
 Rexroad, Kan., 514, 519, 605, 606
 Sanders, Kan., 514, 519, 605, 606
 Saw Rock Canyon, Kan., 605
 Seger, Kan., 514
Faunal sites, mammals, 510, 511; fishes, 572, 573
Faunal sites, specific
 Arredondo, Fla., 528, 529
 Bahama Islands, 530
 Benson, Ariz., 528
 Bermuda, 530
 Burnet Cave, N. Mex., 622
 Carpinteria, Calif., 528
 Dead Man Lake, N. Mex., 622, 625
 Fossil Lake, Calif., 528
 Hagerman, Idaho, 528, 824
 Haile, Fla., 529
 Herrell Village, Missouri, 656
 Itchtucknee, Fla., 528
 Kings Ferry, N. Y., 658
 Linsley Pond, Conn., 625
 McKittrick, Calif., 528
 Melbourne, Fla., 674
 Natural Chimneys, Virginia, 528
 Orleton Farms, Ohio, 656
 Rampart Cave, Ariz., 445, 446
 Rancho La Brea, Calif., 528, 529, 530
 Reddick, Fla., 528, 529
 Richmond, Ind., 656, 657
 Rock Spring, Fla., 528
 San Josecito Cave, Mexico, 528
 Santa Rosa Island, Calif., 710
 Seminole, Fla., 528
 Smith Creek Cave, Nev., 528
 Tupperville, Ontario, 658
 Vallecito, Calif., 528, 529

Faunal sites, specific (*cont.*)
 Wapatki, Ariz., 445
 Williston, Fla., 528
Finger Lakes, N. Y., 99, 103
Fire, effect on vegetation, 383, 395, 398, 421, 537, 623
Firn line, *see* Snowline
Fish, 271, 616, 618, 622, 569-581, 635, 645
Fish, fossil faunas, 573
Flathead Lake, Mont., 765
Flaxville Plain, Mont., 16, 18, 23, 24
Floristic elements, 404, 444, 453-466, 501, 502, 537
Floristic provinces, 403, 404, 453
Formations and other lithologic units
 Aeolian Buttes Till, Calif., 270
 Alameda Formation, Calif., 319
 Alamosa Formation, Colo.-N. Mex., 252
 Alborn Till, Minn., 38
 Alpine Formation, Great Basin, 268, 273, 275, 276
 Anastasia Formation, Fla., 133
 Ancha Formation, N. Mex., 292
 Aquinnah Conglomerate, Mass., 115
 Aromas Red Sand, Calif., 319, 320
 Arroyo Seco Gravel, Calif., 314, 316
 Arvada Formation, Wyo., 251
 Ashtabula Till, Ohio, 90, 91, 93-94
 Atchison Formation, Kan.-Neb., 189, 190, 192, 193, 195-197, 206
 Atherton Formation, Ind., 66-68, 71, 73
 Banbury Basalt, Idaho, 456
 Bandelier Tuff, N. Mex., 292
 Battery Formation, Calif., 325
 Beacon Hill Formation, N. Jersey, 130
 Beaumont Formation, Gulf Coast, 139, 144, 145, 176, 177, 843
 Beaver Basin Formation, Utah, 223
 Beaver Creek Formation, Neb., 190, 192, 193, 196, 198
 Beaverdam Formation, Idaho, 456
 Becanour Till, Ontario, 92, 94
 Bentley Formation, Gulf Coast, 139, 144, 145, 147, 161, 171, 176, 177, 179
 Berlin Clay, New England, 118
 Bignell Formation, Kan., 189, 190, 192, 193, 196, 199
 Bishop Tuff, Calif., 265, 270, 303, 310, 332, 809, 820, 824, 825, 828, 855
 Black Mesa Gravel, Idaho, 259, 260
 Blanco Formation, Southern Great Plains, 204, 206, 208
 Blind Lake Drift, Utah, 223
 Bloomington Till, Ill., 55
 Bonneville Formation, Great Basin, 275, 276
 Bootlegger Cove Clay, Alaska, 357
 Borrego Formation, Calif., 289
 Boston Till, Mass., 118
 Bradtville Till, Ontario, 92, 94
 Brawley Formation, Calif., 289
 Bridgeton Formation, N. Jersey, 130
 "Broadwater" Formation, Neb.-Kan., 192, 195
 Bruneau Formation, Idaho, 259, 260, 650, 825, 826
 Buffalo Hart Till, Ill., 45, 46, 48, 49, 52
 Bull Lake Till, Wyo., 221
 Burlington Till, Vermont, 122
 Butlerville Till, Ind., 65, 67
 Cache Beds, Calif., 324, 326
 Cagle Loess, Ind., 67
 Caloosahatchee Formation, Fla., 133

Formations and other lithologic units (*cont.*)
 Canning Till, Ontario, 92
 Cape May Formation, N. Jersey, 130, 837, 839
 Carcass Creek Drift, Utah, 223
 Carlotta Formation, Calif., 325
 Cartersburg Till, Ind., 65, 67
 Casitas Formation, Calif., 328, 329
 Catfish Creek Drift, Ontario, 92, 94
 Cedar Bluffs Till, Neb., 190, 192, 193, 196, 197
 Center Grove Till, Ind., 65, 67, 69
 Cerro Till, Rocky Mts., 218, 223
 Champaign Till, Ill., 55
 Clarkson Till, Neb., 190, 192, 193, 196, 197
 Cloverdale Till, Ind., 65-67
 Colma Formation, Calif., 319
 Columbia Formation, Del., 131
 Corcoran Clay, Calif., 314-316, 855
 Crane Creek Gravel, Mont., 25
 Creede Formation, Colo., 456
 Crete Formation, Kan.-Neb., 189, 190, 192, 193, 198, 206
 Cropsey Till, Ill., 55
 Crowsnest Gravel, Idaho, 260, 261
 David City Formation, Kan., 189-196, 206, 208
 Don Beds, Ontario, 92, 94
 Donkey Creek Drift, Utah, 223
 Donner Lake Till, Calif., 270
 Draper Formation, Great Basin, 268, 275
 Dunwich Till, Ontario, 92, 94
 Durango Till, Colo., 220
 Ectza Formation, Great Basin, 268, 277, 279
 Elk Creek Till, Neb., 190, 192-194
 Etchegoin Formation, Calif., 314, 315
 Fallon Formation, Great Basin, 277, 281
 Farmdale Silt, Ill., 45, 51, 53, 55
 Farm Ridge Till, Ill., 55
 Flanner Beach Formation, N. Car., 132
 Florida Gravel, Colo.-N. Mex., 252
 Florissant Formation, Colo., 455, 462
 Fort Thompson Formation, Fla., 133
 Franciscan Formation, Calif., 299, 323, 330
 Frog Lake Till, Nev., 280
 Fullerton Formation, Kan.-Neb., 189, 190, 192, 193, 195, 196, 208
 Gahanna Drift, Ohio, 92, 94
 Gardiners Clay, N. Y., Mass., 104, 130
 Gentilly Till, Quebec, 94
 Gila Conglomerate, N. Mex., 291
 Gilman Canyon Formation, Neb., 190, 192, 193, 196, 198
 Glen Ellen Formation, Calif., 323, 324
 Glenns Ferry Formation, Idaho, 258, 260, 456, 576, 645, 650, 825, 826
 Gold Basin Formation, Utah, 223
 Grafton Formation, Neb., 198
 Grafton Loess, Neb., 190, 192, 193, 198
 Grand Island Formation, Great Plains, 189, 190, 192, 193, 196, 197, 204
 Grover Gravel, Ill., 48
 Gubik Formation, Alaska, 363
 Hamden Till, Mass., 117
 Harold Formation, Calif., 859
 Harpole Mesa Formation, Utah, 223
 Hartington Till, Neb., 190, 192, 193, 198

Formations and other lithologic units (*cont.*)

Hayesville Till, Ohio, 90, 91
Hempstead Gravel, N. Y., 104
Herod Gravel, N. Y., 104
Hiram Till, Ohio–N. Y., 90, 91, 94, 108
Hobart Till, Calif., 270
Holdredge Formation, Kan.–Neb., 189, 190, 192, 193, 195, 196, 208
Hookton Formation, Calif., 325
Horry Clay, S. Car., 129, 132, 425, 426
Huichica Formation, Calif., 323
Idaho Group, Idaho, 258
Illinoian Drift, Central U. S., 16, 30, 85-87, 89, 90, 92
Indian Lakes Formation, Great Basin, 277, 279
Iowan Drift, Iowa, 30
Iowa Point Till, Neb., 190, 192, 193, 195, 196
Irvington Gravels, Calif., 317
Jacksonville Till, Ill., 46, 48, 49
Jacob Sand, N. Y., 104, 118, 130
Jameco Gravel, N. Y., 104
Jeddito Formation, Ariz., 294
Jessup Formation, Ind., 65-67
Kates Peak Formation, Calif., 303
Kaycee Formation, Wyo., 251
Kennedy Drift, Mont., 222
Kent Till, Ohio, 90, 91, 94
Key Largo Limestone, Fla., 133
Kingsdown Formation, Kan., 512
Ladson Formation, S. Car., 132, 426
Lafayette Gravel, Ill.–Ind., 48, 64
Lagro Formation, Ind., 65, 67, 71
Laguna Formation, Calif., 314, 316, 317
LaHabra Formation, Calif., 329
Lahontan Valley Group, Great Basin, 277, 279
Lake Border Till, Ill., 55
Lake Chamberlain Till, Mass., 117
Lavery Till, Ohio, 90, 91, 94
Leaside Till, Ontario, 94
"Lisco" Formation, Great Plains, 192, 195
Lissie Formation, Gulf Coast, 177, 179, 843
Livermore Gravels, Calif., 317
Logan Hill Formation, Oregon, 342
Lomita Marl, Calif., 329
Lousetown Formation, Calif., 303
Loveland Loess (Formation), Central U. S., 19, 30, 31, 50, 67, 68, 189, 190, 192, 193, 196, 198, 204, 211, 512, 761
Madson Basalt, Idaho, 260
Manetto Gravel, N. Y., 103, 104
Manhasset Formation, N. Y., 104, 118
Marseilles Till, Ill., 55
Martinsville Formation, Ind., 67, 73
McGee Till, Calif., 303, 332, 855
Meade Formation, Great Plains, 204, 206
Mehrten Formation, Calif., 303, 314, 316
Melon Gravel, Idaho, 260, 261
Mendon Till, Ill., 46, 48-50
Merced Formation, Calif., 317, 323-325
Merritt Sand, Calif., 319
Miami Oolite, Fla., 133
Michaud Gravel, Idaho, 261
Millbrook Till, Ohio, 91
Minooka Till, Ill., 55
Modesto Formation, Calif., 313, 314, 316

Formations and other lithologic units (*cont.*)

Mogadore Till, Ohio, 91, 94
Montauk Till, N. Y., 104
Montgomery Formation, Gulf Coast, 139, 144, 145, 147, 161, 171, 176, 177, 179
Morton Loess, Ill., 45, 51, 55, 56
Naha Formation, Ariz., 295
Navarre Till, Ohio, 90, 91
Nebraska Till, Kan., 189, 208
New Holland Till, Ind., 72
Nickerson Till, Neb., 190, 192, 193, 196, 197
Nomlaki Tuff, Calif., 314, 316
Normal Till, Ill., 55
Ocotillo Conglomerate, Calif., 289
Ogallala Formation, Southern Great Plains, 204, 206, 247, 290
Ohlson Ranch Formation, Calif., 323-325
Olean Drift, N. Y., 105
Orcutt Sand, Calif., 320
Owl Mountain Till, Rocky Mts., 218
Packwood Gravels, Calif., 319
Pacoima Formation, Calif., 328
Paiute Formation, Great Basin, 268, 269
Palm Spring Formation, Calif., 289
Palos Verdes Sand, Calif., 325, 329, 330
Palouse Formation, Wash., 234, 238, 239
Pamlico Formation, N. Car., 132, 426
Paso Robles Formation, Calif., 319, 320
Pensauken Formation, N. Jersey, 130
Peoria Loess, Central U. S., 32, 45, 48, 49, 51, 56, 58, 67, 71, 190, 192, 193, 199, 206, 210, 213
Petaluma Formation, Calif., 323
Petersburg Silt, Ill., 49, 50
Pico Formation, Calif., 328, 856, 857
Placer Creek Formation, Utah, 223
Port Stanley Drift, Ontario, 94
Posey Formation, Calif., 319
Prairie Divide Till, Rocky Mts., 218
Prairie Formation, Gulf Coast, 139, 144, 145, 147, 161, 171, 176, 177, 179, 843
Presumpscot Formation, Maine, 123
Red Bluff Formation, Calif., 314, 316, 324
Red Cloud Formation, Neb., 190, 192, 193, 197
Rexroad Formation, Tex., 528
Richland Loess, Ill., 45, 56
Ringold Formation, Wash., 238
Riverbank Formation, Calif., 313, 314, 316
Roby Silt, Ill., 51
Rockian Drift, Wis., 46
Rohnerville Formation, Calif., 325
Roxana Silt, Ill., 45, 48, 49, 51, 53
St. George Formation, Calif., 323
Salt Lake Formation, Idaho, 456
San Antonio Formation, Calif., 319
San Benito Gravels, Calif., 319
San Joaquin Formation, Calif., 314, 316
Sankaty Sand, Mass., 116
San Pedro Formation, Calif., 328-329, 856-857
Santa Barbara Formation, Calif., 328-329, 856-857
Santa Clara Formation, Calif., 319
Santa Fe Group, N. Mex., 292
Santee Till, Neb., 190, 192-193, 196, 198

Formations and other lithologic units (*cont.*)

Sappa Formation, Kan.–Neb., 189-190, 192-193, 196-198, 204, 812
Saugus Formation, Calif., 328-329
Scarborough Beds, Ontario, 92, 94
Sehoo Formation, Great Basin, 268, 277, 279
Seward Formation, Neb., 190, 192-194, 196
Shelbyville Till, Ill.–Ind., 45, 55, 94
Sherwin Till, Calif., 303, 855
Shoemaker Gravel, Calif., 859
Slocum Alluvium, Colo., 245-246, 249
Snake River Group, Idaho, 259, 824
Sonoma Volcanics, Calif., 323
Southwold Till, Ontario, 92, 746
Sugar Bowl Gravel, 259-260
Sunderland Formation, Md., 131
Sunnybrook Till, Ontario, 92, 94
Tahoka Formation, Tex., 206, 213
Talbot Formation, Md., 131
Tehama Formation, Calif., 314, 316, 324
Tesuque Formation, N. Mex., 292
Thousand Springs Basalt, Idaho, 260
Timms Point Silt, Calif., 329
Tinley Till, Ill., 55
Todd Valley Sand, Neb., 190, 192-193, 196, 199
Touchet Beds, Wash., 240
Trafalgar Formation, Ind., 65, 67, 69
Troublesome Formation, Colo., 456
Tsegi Alluvium, Ariz., 295
Tuana Gravel, Idaho, 258, 260
Tulare Formation, Calif., 314-315, 317, 323, 855-856
Tule Formation, Southern Great Plains, 204, 206, 209-210
Turlock Lake Formation, Calif., 313-314, 316
Turupah Formation, Great Basin, 268, 277, 279
Tuscan Formation, Calif., 314
Ucross Formation, Wyo., 251
Valders Till, Wis., 45, 46, 51, 57
Valley Heads Drift, N. Y., 105
Valparaiso Till, Ill., 55
Vashon Drift, Wash., 346, 347, 351
Victor Formation, Calif., 314, 316-326
Walnut Creek Formation, Neb., 190, 192, 193, 197
Wentworth Till, Ohio, 93, 94
Whitewater Drift, Ind., 88
Wicomico Formation, Md., 131
Wildcat Group, Calif., 323
Williana Formation, Gulf Coast, 139, 144, 145, 147, 161, 171, 176, 177, 179
Willis Formation, Gulf Coast, 139, 144, 145, 176, 177, 179, 843
Winnebago Till, Minn., 46, 48, 49, 51, 53
Wyemaha Formation, Great Basin, 268, 277, 279
Yakataga Formation, Alaska, 355, 356
York Till, Ontario, 92, 94
Fossil sites, vertebrate, *see* Faunal sites
Fraser Lowland, Wash., 346
Front Range, Colo., 244

G

Genetics, 497-505, 614
Geochemical lake sites, specific
Bethany Bog., Conn., 774
Blue Lake, Minn., 773, 776-778

Geochemical lake sites, specific (*cont.*)
  Cedar Bog Lake, Minn., 770-773
  Clear Lake, Minn., 777
  Crater Lake, Ore., 777
  Dead Man Lake, N. Mex., 773, 776
  Dismal Swamp, Virginia, 773, 775
  El Bajo de Santa Fe, Guatemala, 770, 775
  Great Salt Lake, Utah, 282
  Kerr Lake, Virginia, 777
  Kirchner Marsh, Minn., 772, 775
  Lake Lahontan, Nev., 748
  Linsley Pond, Conn., 768, 774, 776, 777
  Nisswa Lake, Minn., 768, 769, 776
  North Cooking Lake, Alberta, 774, 779
  Searles Lake, Calif., 747, 748
  Silver Bay, Minn., 771
  Weber Lake, Minn., 773, 775
Gila River, Ariz., 287, 288, 290, 291
Glacial lakes, specific
  Agassiz, N. Dak.–Minn., 17, 19, 24, 29, 34, 38-40, 661, 662, 834
  Aitkin, Minn., 34, 36-38
  Algoma, Great Lakes area, 76, 80, 662, 664, 665
  Algonquin, Great Lakes area, 76, 78, 79, 658-661, 834
  Arkona, Great Lakes area, 76, 77, 79, 95
  Ashland, Mich., 75
  Bowmanville, Great Lakes area, 76
  Brule, Wis., 75
  Calumet, Great Lakes area, 76
  Calvin, Iowa, 30
  Cedar Point, Great Lakes area, 79
  Champlain (Sea), N. Y., 94, 109, 122, 123, 659, 660, 834
  Chicago, Great Lakes area, 51, 54, 56-58, 65, 70, 77
  Chippewa, Great Lakes area, 58, 76, 77, 80, 660-662
  Choteau, Mont., 16, 18
  Columbia, Wash., 232, 234, 237
  Coeur d'Alene, Idaho, 233, 234, 236, 237, 239
  Cutbank, Mont., 16, 18, 221, 225
  Dakota, N. Dak.–S. Dak., 17, 18
  Devils Lake, N. Dak., 17, 18, 24
  Elkton, Great Lakes area, 834
  Flatwoods, Ind., 68
  Frontenac, N. Y., 78, 79, 659
  Glendive, Mont., 16, 18
  Grantsburg, Minn., 34, 37
  Grassmere, Great Lakes area, 76, 78
  Great Falls, Mont., 16, 18, 25
  Great Lakes, 73-80, 660-661, 831, 834
  Herkimer, N. Y., 108
  Hitchcock, New England, 124
  Houghton, Mich., 76, 77
  Iroquois, Great Lakes area, 78, 95, 109, 659
  Jordan, Mont., 16, 18
  Keweenaw, Great Lakes area, 57, 76
  Kirkfield, Great Lakes area, 76, 79
  Korak, Great Lakes area, 79
  Lundy, Great Lakes area, 76, 78, 659
  Maumee, Great Lakes area, 65, 76, 77, 79, 90, 834
  Minong, Great Lakes area, 76, 77, 661
  Missoula, Mont., 233-237, 239
  Musselshell, Mont., 16, 18
  Nemadji, Minn., 34, 38, 75
  Newberry, N. Y., 109

Glacial lakes, specific (*cont.*)
  Nipissing, Great Lakes area, 76, 80, 662-665, 824
  Ontonagon, Mich., 40, 75
  Oshkosh, Wis., 57, 58
  Ottawa, Ill., 54, 56
  Patoka, Ind., 68
  Payette, Great Lakes area, 79, 661
  Pelican, Minn., 661
  Pend Oreille, Idaho, 233, 235, 236, 239
  Penetang, Great Lakes area, 79
  Pontiac, Ill., 54, 56
  Quincy, Ind., 68
  Saginaw, Great Lakes area, 70, 76, 77, 79
  Sault, Great Lakes area, 76
  Seguiandah, Mich., 77, 79
  Souris, N. Dak., 17, 18, 24
  Spokane, Wash., 232, 234, 235, 237
  Stanley, Great Lakes area, 76, 77, 79, 80, 660-662
  Tolleston, Great Lakes area, 76
  Upham, Minn., 34, 36-38
  Vermont, N. Y., 123, 659
  Warren, Great Lakes area, 76, 78, 90, 95, 109, 659, 834
  Watseka, Ill., 54, 56
  Wauponsee, Ill., 54, 56
  Wayne, Great Lakes area, 76, 78, 90
  Weyebridge, Great Lakes area, 79
  Whittlesey, Great Lakes area, 70, 76, 78, 79, 89, 90, 94, 95, 109, 834
  Wisconsin, Wis., 57, 58
Glacial rivers, *see* Ancestral rivers
Glacial (and interglacial) stages, substages, and related units
  Abington Interstage, Ind., 67
  Aftonian Interglacial Stage, Central U. S., 6, 46, 47, 49, 54, 66, 189, 195, 209, 649
  Agassiz Phase, Minn., 38
  Alapah Mountain Stage, Alaska, 360, 361
  Alaskan Stade, Alaska, 360, 361
  Alborn Phase, Minn., 34, 37, 39
  Alderton Interglacial Stage, Wash., 342, 477
  Alma Substage, Colo., 223
  Alpine Lake Substage, Calif., 327
  Alpine Stade, Ind., 67
  Altithermal Age, Western U. S., 225-227, 442-445, 691, 697, 716
  Altonian Substage, Ill., 46, 47, 51, 53, 54
  Ambler Stade, Alaska, 360
  American Lakes Substage, Colo., 222
  Anaktuvuk River Stade, Alaska, 360
  Anayaknaurak Stade, Alaska, 361
  Angel Lake Substage, Nev., 268, 271
  Anivik Lake Stade, Alaska, 360, 361
  Antler Valley Stade, Alaska, 360, 361
  Arapahoe Stage, Colo., 222
  Automba Phase, Minn., 34, 36
  Bemis Phase, Minn., 34, 38, 39
  Bigelow Substage, Colo., 223
  Binghamton Substage, N. Y., 107
  Black Forks Stage, Wyo., 222
  Boston Substage, Mass., 117, 121
  Brady Interstade, Great Plains, 199, 213, 214
  Branded Mountain Stade, Alaska, 360, 361
  Briscoe Substage, Colo., 223
  Brooks Lake Stade, Alaska, 360

Glacial (and interglacial) stages, substages, and related units (*cont.*)
  Browne Stade, Alaska, 360
  Buffalo Hart Substage, Ill., 46, 47, 52
  Buffalo Stage, Rocky Mts., 217, 222
  Bull Lake Glaciation, Rocky Mts., 220-223, 227, 272, 274-276
  Cambridge Readvance, Mass., 118, 120, 121
  Caribou Hills Stade, Alaska, 360
  Carlo Stade, Alaska, 360
  Cary Substage, Great Lakes region, 39, 53, 55, 70-72, 77
  Cedar Ridge Glaciation, Wyo., 219, 222, 227
  Centerville Stade, Ind., 67
  Chamberlin Stade, Alaska, 360
  Chapman Gulch Glaciation, Colo., 223
  Claremont Readvance, New England, 122
  Columbia Stade, Ind., 67
  Connersville Interstade, Ind., 67, 69, 94
  Corral Creek Stage, Colo., 222
  Darling Creek Stade, Alaska, 360
  Delta Glaciation, Alaska, 358, 360
  Denali Stade, Alaska, 360
  Donnelly Glaciation, Alaska, 358, 360
  Donner Lake Glaciation, Calif., 307
  Dry Creek Stade, Alaska, 360
  Durango Stage, Colo., 223
  Early Wisconsin(an) Substage, Central U. S., 46, 51-54, 69, 86, 88, 91, 92, 94, 105, 119-124
  Echooka River, Glaciation, Alaska, 361
  Eklutna Glaciation, Alaska, 357, 360
  El Portal Stage, Calif., 307, 308
  Evans Creek Stade, Wash., 344-346
  Everson Interstade, Wash., 344, 346
  Fairplay Substage, Colo., 223
  Fan Mountain Stade, Alaska, 360, 361
  Farewell Stade, Alaska, 360
  Farmdale (Farmdalian) Substage, Central U. S., 32, 46, 51, 55
  Fayette Stade, Ind., 67, 69
  Fraser Glaciation, Wash.–Ore., 340, 346-348
  Gannett Peak Stade, Wyo., 222, 226, 227
  Garrison Creek Interstade, Ind., 67
  Glacier Point Stage, Calif., 307
  Gould Substage, Colo., 222
  Healy Stade, Alaska, 360
  Hellgate Substage, Colo., 223
  Hewitt Phase, Minn., 33, 34, 39
  Hilgard Stade, Calif., 268, 280, 308, 310
  Hobart Glaciation, Calif., 307
  Home Substage, Colo., 222
  Iliuk Stade, Alaska, 360
  Illinoian Stage, Central U. S., 6, 19, 30, 46, 50, 54, 67, 68, 85-92, 189-193, 198, 211, 621
  Iowan Substage, Iowa, 31
  Iron Creek Stade, Alaska, 360
  Itasca Phase, Minn., 34
  Itkillik Glaciation, Alaska, 361
  Ivanhoe Substage, Colo., 223
  Jacksonville Substage, Ill., 46, 47, 51
  Johnston Hill Stade, Alaska, 360
  Kansan Stage, Central U. S., 6, 19, 29, 30, 45-47, 49, 66, 67, 85, 87, 189-195, 197, 198, 209, 621
  Kennebunk Advance, Maine, 123
  Kent Substage, N. Y., 107
  Killey Stade, Alaska, 360

Glacial (and interglacial) stages, substages, and related units (cont.)
Knik Glaciation, Alaska, 357, 359, 360
Kobuk Stade, Alaska, 360
Lake Erie Interstade, Ontario, 94
Lamoille Substage, Nev., 268, 272
Lexington Substage, Mass., 117, 121
Liman Substage, Ill., 46, 47, 50
Lime Creek Stage, Colo., 223
Little Dry Stage, Wyo., 222
Little Ice Age, Western U. S., 226, 310, 360
Long Draw Substage, Colo., 222
Mak Hill Stade, Alaska, 360
Mankato Substage, Great Lakes region, 34, 38, 39, 53, 70, 72
Marshall Pass Stade, Alaska, 360
Matthes Stade, Calif., 268, 280, 308, 310
McGee Glaciation, Calif., 268, 270, 307, 308, 310, 331
Middletown Readvance, Mass., 121, 122
Monarch Stage, Colo., 222
Mono Basin Glaciation, Great Basin, 268, 308-310, 331
Moosehorn Stade, Alaska, 360
Morris Meadow Substage, Calif., 327
Mount Osborn Stade, Alaska, 360
Mount Susitna Stade, Alaska, 360
Naptowne Glaciation, Alaska, 359-361
Nebraskan Stage, Central U. S., 6, 19, 29, 46-48, 66, 189-195, 208, 209
Neoglaciation, Western U. S., 222, 226, 227, 275, 280, 344, 347, 348
New Paris Interstade, Ind., 67, 69, 88, 94
Nickerson Phase, Minn., 34, 37, 39
Nome River Glaciation, Alaska, 356, 360
Olean Substage, N. Y., 106
Olympia Interglaciation, Wash., 344, 345, 348
Orting Glaciation, Ore., 342, 479
Owl Mountain Substage, Colo., 222
Peters Stade, Alaska, 360
Pine City Phase, Minn., 34, 36, 37, 39
Pinedale Glaciation, Rocky Mts., 222-224, 227, 272, 274-276
Plum Point Interstade, Ontario, 94
Port Huron Substage, Great Lakes region, 70, 72, 76, 78, 79
Port Talbot Interstade, Ontario, 92, 94, 746
Puyallup Interglaciation, Ore., 342, 479
Recess Peak Stade, Great Basin, 268, 280, 308
Richmond Stade, Ind., 67
Riley Creek Stade, Alaska, 360
Rockian Phase, Wis., 46, 51, 54
Rush Creek Substage, 327
Sacagawea Ridge Glaciation, Wyo., 219, 220, 222, 227
Sagavanirktok River Stade, Alaska, 360
St. Croix Phase, Minn., 34, 39
St. Johnsbury Readvance, New England, 122
St. Pierre Interstade, Ontario, 92, 94
Salmon Lake Stade, Alaska, 360
Salmon Springs Glaciation, Wash., 344-348, 479
Sangamon(ian) Interglacial Stage, Central U. S., 6, 31, 46, 47, 51, 52, 69, 92, 189, 198, 212, 648
Schrader Stade, Alaska, 360

Glacial (and interglacial) stages, substages, and related units (cont.)
Selatna Stade, Alaska, 360
Sherwin Glaciation, Calif., 268, 270, 307, 308, 310, 331
Sidney Interval, Ohio, 94
Silver Creek Substage, Colo., 222
Skilak Stade, Alaska, 360
Slow Fork Stade, Alaska, 360
Smith Fork Stage, Wyo., 222
Split Rock Phase, Minn., 34, 36-39
Sprague Stage, Colo., 222
Stillwater Stage, Colo., 222
Stuck Glaciation, Ore., 342, 479
Sumas Stade, Wash., 344, 346
Summit Lake Stade, Alaska, 360
Tahoe Glaciation, Calif., 268, 270, 272, 279, 303, 305, 307-310, 331, 332, 824, 855
Tanya Stade, Alaska, 360, 361
Tazewell Substage, Great Lakes region, 32, 39, 52, 55, 67, 71
Temple Lake Stade, Wyo., 222, 226, 227, 280
Tenaya Stade, Calif., 268, 272, 307-309, 331, 855
Thomasville Substage, Colo., 223
Tioga Glaciation, Calif., 268, 272, 279, 305, 307-309, 331, 332, 855
Tunnel Stade, Alaska, 360, 361
Tustumena Stade, Alaska, 360, 361
Two Creeks (Twocreekan) Interstadial, Great Lakes region, 39, 51, 53, 57, 72, 76, 78, 79, 659, 661
Unealeak Stade, Alaska, 360
Valders (Valderan) Substage, Great Lakes region, 23, 39, 46, 47, 51, 53, 57, 72, 73, 75-79
Valley Heads Substage, N. Y., 108
Vashon Stade, Wash., 344, 345, 347, 472, 477, 852
Vermilion Phase, Minn., 34, 36
Walker Lake Stade, Alaska, 360
Washakie Point Glaciation, Wyo., 219, 222, 227
Weller Stade, Alaska, 360
Whitewater Stade, Ind., 67, 69, 94
Wisconsin(an) Stage, Central U. S., 6, 21, 32-40, 46, 51, 52, 67, 69, 70, 87-92, 94, 103-109, 190-193, 198, 199
Wonder Lake Stade, Alaska, 360
Woodfordian Substage, Ill., 46, 47, 51-55
Worthington Stade, Alaska, 360
Xerothermic Interval, Eastern U. S., 409, 633, 634
Yarmouth(ian) Interglacial Stage, 6, 19, 21, 29, 46, 47, 50, 66, 198, 211, 648, 649
Glacial theory, 3, 99
Glacier flow, 795, 800
Glacier fluctuations, 795, 803
Glacier lobes, specific
Brainard, Minn., 34, 35
Bull River, Mont., 233, 235
Columbia River, Wash., 232, 235, 237
Colville, Wash., 232, 234, 235, 237
Des Moines, Minn., 33, 34, 37, 38, 54
Erie, Ohio–Ind.–Ill., 48-50, 55, 71, 85, 86
Flathead, Mont., 233, 234, 236
Grand River, Ohio, 86, 90
Grantsburg, Minn., 33, 34, 37
Green Bay, Wis., 45, 54

Glacier lobes, specific (cont.)
Huron, Mich.–Ind., 70
Killbuck, Ohio, 86, 90
Lake Michigan, Wis.–Mich.–Ind.–Ill., 43, 45, 50, 52, 54, 55, 70, 71
Lake Pend Oreille, Idaho, 233-237
Leeds, N. Dak., 24
Little Spokane River, Wash., 232, 235, 237
Miami, Ohio, 86, 87
Okanogan, Wash., 232, 234-237, 240
Oneida–Black River, N. Y., 108
Patrician, Minn., 34
Pierz, Minn., 34
Priest River, Idaho, 233, 235
Puget, Wash., 342, 345, 347, 351
Rainy, Minn., 33, 34, 36
Saginaw, Mich.–Ill., 48, 50, 70, 71
St. Louis, Minn., 33, 34, 37
San Poil, Wash., 232, 235
Scioto, Ohio, 86, 87, 89, 90
Souris River, N. Dak., 24
Superior, Minn.–Wis., 33-36, 54
Thompson River, Mont., 233, 235
Wadena, Minn., 33, 34
Glacier, mass budget of, 795, 797, 800, 801
Glacier National Park, Mont., 219, 220-222, 224-226
Glacier Peak, Wash., 343, 810, 811, 852
Glaciers, specific
Blue, Wash., 796
Dinwoody, Wyo., 796
Grinnell, Mont., 796
Malaspina, Alaska, 361, 801
Nisqually, Wash., 799, 802, 803
South Cascade, Wash., 796, 797, 799
Gould Lake, Colo., 251
Grand Canyon, Ariz., 294, 296
Grand Coulee, Wash., 232, 235, 237, 240
Grand River, N. Y., 102
Granite Mountains, Wyo., 244
Gravel, see Formations
Great Basin, 265-285, 577, 621, 622, 697-706, 845, 849
Great Divide Basin, Wyo., 244, 250
Great Plains, 15-25, 187-215, 512, 514-521, 560, 561, 599-608, 621, 648, 649, 697-707
Great Salt Lake, Utah, 282, 622
Great Valley, Calif., 300-302, 310-317, 332, 853, 855, 856
Green River Basin, Wyo., 244
Group, see Formations
Gulf Coast geosyncline, 842
Gulf of California, 617, 618
Gulf of California Embayment, 288-290
Gulf of Mexico, 138, 140-143, 145, 148, 150, 155, 161, 163, 167-169, 178, 179, 615
Gumbotil, 8, 29, 759-761. See also Accretion-gley

H

Hanna Basin, Wyo., 244, 250
Heat budget of the earth, 882, 883
Heavy-mineral analysis, loess, 238; till, 45, 48, 106
Henry Mountains, Utah, 293, 294
High Plateaus, Utah, 270
Highwood Mountains, Mont., 16, 18
Hudson River, N. Y., 101, 103, 123
Human disturbance of vegetation, 382, 395-398, 443, 537

Humptulips Lowland, Wash., 472, 478
Hybrids, frogs, 550; insects, 588

I

Idaho Lake, Idaho (Plio-Pleistocene), 573, 575-577
Imperial Depression, Calif., 288-290
Insects, 583-596, 613, 619-626
Interglacial stage, *see* Glacial stage
Interstade, *see* Glacial stage
Interval, *see* Glacial stage
Isostatic uplift, in Great Lakes region, 74, 75, 90, 95; Eastern U. S., 109, 121-123, 125, 831-837; Great Basin, 281, 849-851, 853
Isotope dating, 9, 735, 751

J

Jackson Hole, Wyo., 244
James River, N. Dak.–S. Dak., 17, 18, 23
Jemez Mountains, N. Mex., 291

K

Kankakee Flood, Ill.–Mich., 56, 72
Katabatic winds, 796
Kettle River, Minn., 38
Kinematic waves, 798, 799, 803
Klamath Mountains, Calif., 300, 301, 321-327, 332, 348, 349

L

La Brea tar pits, Calif., 330
Lake Champlain, N. Y., 101, 834
Lake Erie, Great Lakes region, 76, 77, 95, 100
Lake Hitchcock, Mass., 122
Lake Huron, Great Lakes region, 76, 77, 665
Lake Michigan, Great Lakes region, 76, 77
Lake Nicaragua, Central America, 767
Lake Ontario, Great Lakes region, 78, 95, 100
Lake Patzcuaro, Mexico, geochemistry of, 769, 770
Lake sediments, geochemistry of, 765-779
Lake Superior, Great Lakes region, 75, 76
Lake Washington, Wash., 765
Lakes, glacial, *see* Glacial lakes
Lakes, pluvial, *see* Pluvial lakes
Land bridges, 492, 614, 619, 620, 645
Land-mammal age, Blancan, 316, 331, 512, 514, 649, 826; Irvingtonian, 316, 317, 331, 332, 512, 514, 826; Rancholabrean, 316, 319, 330-332, 512, 514
Laramie Basin, Wyo., 244, 251
Laramie Range, Wyo., 244
La Sal Mountains, Utah, 219-221, 223, 226, 293, 294
Lemhi Range, Idaho, 222
Limestone, *see* Formations
Little Rocky Mountains, Mont., 18, 23
Lobes, *see* Glacial lobes
Local faunas, *see* Faunas, local
Loess, in Iowa, 30-32, 761; Illinois, 45, 46, 49-51, 53-57; Indiana, 68, 71; Ohio, 91; New England, 124; Eastern U. S., 134; Nebraska, 190, 193, 196-199; Kansas, 210-214; Colorado, 245, 246; Washington, 235, 238

Loess, distribution in U. S., 757; origen, 6. *See also* Formations
Long Island, N. Y., 101, 103
Los Angeles Basin, Calif., 302, 327, 329, 330, 856, 859

M

Madro-Tertiary floristic element, Colo., 444, 462, 463, 537
Magnetic field of the earth, 817
Magnetic self-reversal, 820, 821
Magnetization by lightning, 819
Mammal age, *see* Land-mammal age
Mammals, 57, 199-201, 215, 330, 345, 445-447, 509-525, 621, 626, 634-639, 645, 648, 649, 657, 658, 698-700, 703, 710, 711
Mammals, fossil faunas, 510, 511
Marine profile of equilibrium, 726, 727
Marine terraces, *see* Terraces, marine
Marine transgressions
  Anvilian, Alaska, 364, 365
  Beringian, Alaska, 364, 365
  Kotzebuan, Alaska, 364, 365
  Kruzensternian, Alaska, 364, 365, 369
  Pelukian, Alaska, 364, 365
  Woronzofian, Alaska, 364, 365
Medicine Bow Mountains, Wyo., 222
Middle Park, Colo., 244
Migrations, 613-626; of mammals, 200, 514-518, 530; plants, 386, 393, 404, 405, 412, 444, 453, 454, 458, 459, 493, 502; birds, 534-536; amphibians, 543; reptiles, 557, 559, 560; insects, 590, 602; mollusks, 606; Early Man, 689, 713
Mississippi Delta, 161-165, 839, 840, 842, 843
Mississippi Embayment, 839-843
Missouri River, 15, 19, 56, 248
Modoc Plateau, Calif., 300, 301, 331
Mogollon Highlands, Ariz., 288, 289
Mohawk River, N. Y., 78, 101
Mojave Desert, Calif., 300, 301, 699
Mollusks, 8, 57, 67-69, 73, 205, 209, 212, 258, 259, 363, 597-611, 615-622, 624, 625
Mollusks, fossil fauna, 599, 600
Mono Craters, Calif., 809
Moraines, formation of, 4, 800
Moraines, specific
  Alamo, N. Dak., 23
  Aland, N. Dak., 17
  Alden, N. Y., 109
  Alexandria, Minn., 33, 38
  Algona, Iowa, 34, 37, 38
  Almond, N. Y., 107
  Altamont, S. Dak.–Minn.–Iowa, 17, 18, 23, 30, 37, 38
  Arkport, N. Y., 107
  Arlington, Ill., 54
  Ashtabula, Ohio, 108
  Bemis, S. Dak.–Minn.–Iowa, 17, 23, 30, 34, 37, 38
  Big Stone, S. Dak.–Minn.–Iowa, 17, 23, 37, 38
  Blenheim, Ontario, 93
  Blodgett, Ill., 54
  Bloomington, Ill.–Ind., 51, 54, 65, 70
  Britton, S. Dak., 23
  Broadway, Ohio, 70, 87
  Buda, Ill., 54
  Buffalo Hart, Ill., 52
  Burnstad, N. Dak., 17

Moraines, specific (*cont.*)
  Buzzards Bay, Mass., 116, 118, 119
  Cable, Ohio, 87
  Camden, Ohio, 87
  Cape Cod, Mass., 120
  Cerro Gordo, Ill., 54
  Champaign, Ill., 54
  Charlestown, New England, 118-120
  Charlotte, Mich., 70
  Chatsworth, Ill.–Ind., 54, 65, 71
  Chicago, Ill., 54
  Clarendon, Ill., 54
  Clymer, N. Y., 107
  Cooperstown, N. Dak., 17, 24
  Coteau des Prairies, S. Dak., 17, 18
  Crawfordsville, Ind., 65, 71
  Cropsey, Ill., 54
  Cuba, Ohio, 87, 91, 94
  Darlingford, Manitoba, 24
  Dayton, N. Y., 108
  Deerfield, Ill., 54
  Defiance, Ohio–N. Y., 87, 94, 108
  Dog Lake, Ontario, 39
  Dorchester, Ontario, 93
  Edinburg, N. Dak., 17, 24
  Elburn, Ill., 54
  Ellisville, New England, 118
  Esboro, Ohio, 87
  Euclid, Ohio, 108
  Farmersville, Ohio, 87
  Findley, N. Y., 107
  Font Covington, N. Y., 109
  Fort Wayne, Ind.–Ohio, 65, 70, 87
  Fresh Pond, Mass., 121
  Galt, Ontario, 93
  Gary, S. Dak., 23
  Girard, Ohio, 108
  Glendon, Ohio, 87
  Gowanda, N. Y., 109
  Grace City, S. Dak., 17, 23
  Hamburg, N. Y., 109
  Harbor Hill, N. Y., 104, 118, 119
  Hartman, Ontario, 39
  Hartwell, Ohio, 87
  Heimdal, N. Dak., 17, 24
  Highland, Minn., 34, 36
  "Highland Front," Quebec, 109
  Holt, Minn., 24
  Ingersoll, Ontario, 93
  Iroquois, Ill.–Ind., 54, 65, 70, 71
  Itasca, Minn., 33, 34
  Johnston, Wis., 53
  Johnstown, Ohio, 87
  Kalamazoo, Mich., 70
  Kalispell, Mont., 234
  Kensal, S. Dak., 17, 23
  Kent, Ohio, 87
  Krem, N. Dak., 17, 23
  Lake Border, Ill., 51, 54, 56
  Lake Escarpment, N. Y., 108
  Lavery, N. Y., 108
  Ledyard, New England, 118
  London, Ohio, 87
  Long Lake, N. Dak., 17, 23
  Malone, N. Y., 109
  Marengo, Ill., 54
  Marilla, N. Y., 109
  Marks, Ontario, 39
  Martin, N. Dak., 17, 24
  Max, N. Dak., 18
  Maxinkukee, Ind., 65, 70, 71
  Metamora, Ill., 54
  Mille Lacs, Minn., 34, 36
  Minooka, Ill., 54, 71

Moraines, specific (cont.)
  Mission, Mont., 234
  Mississinewa, Ind.–Ohio, 65, 70, 72, 87
  Monee, Ill., 54
  Mono Basin, Calif., 270
  Nantucket, Mass., 118
  Newington, Maine, 123
  Niagara Falls, Ontario, 93
  Nickerson, Minn., 34, 38
  Normal, Ill., 54
  North Viking, N. Dak., 17, 24
  Oakes, S. Dak., 17, 23
  Oakridges, Ontario, 93
  Packerton, Ind., 65, 70, 71
  Painesville, Ohio, 108
  Palatine, Ill., 54
  Paris, Ontario, 93, 94
  Park Border, Colo., 222
  Park Ridge, Ill., 54
  Pine City, Minn., 34, 37
  Polson, Mont., 234
  Port Huron, Mich., 51, 72, 659
  Powell, Ohio, 70, 87, 93, 94
  Providence, Ill., 54
  Reesville, Ohio, 87, 91, 94
  Rice Lake, Ontario, 93
  Ridgetown, Ontario, 93
  Ronkonkoma, N. Y., 104, 118, 119
  St. Antonin, Quebec, 109
  St. Croix, Minn., 34
  St. John, Ohio, 70, 87
  St. Narcisse, Quebec, 94
  St. Thomas, Ontario, 93, 94
  Salamonie, Ind., 70
  Sandwich, Mass., 118, 119
  Seaforth, Ontario, 93
  Sheffield, Ill., 54
  Shelbyville, Ill.–Ind., 51, 54, 65
  Spencer, Ohio, 87
  Streeter, N. Dak., 17, 23
  Tekonsha, Mich., 70, 72
  Tillsonburg, Ontario, 93
  Tinley, Ill., 54, 56
  Union City, Ind.–Ohio, 70, 71, 87
  Urbana, Ill., 54
  Valparaiso, Ill.–Ind., 53, 54, 56, 65, 70,
    72
  Vermilion, Minn., 34
  Wabash, Ohio, 70, 87, 89
  Waterdown, Ontario, 93, 94
  West Chicago, Ill., 53, 56
  West Ridge, Ill., 54
  White Rock, Ill., 54
  Wyoming, Ontario, 93
  Zeeland, N. Dak., 17, 23
  Zurich, Ill., 54
Mosquito Range, Colo., 223, 224
Mount Garibaldi, British Columbia, 825
Mount Katahdin, Maine, 123, 124
Mount Lassen, Calif., 852
Mount Mazama, Ore., 348, 807, 810, 811,
  813, 852
Mount Rainier, Wash., 341–343, 346, 347,
  810, 852
Mount St. Helens, Wash., 810
Mount Shasta, Calif., 852
Mount Washington, New Hampshire, 123,
  124

N

Neotectonics, 863
Never Summer Range, Colo., 222
New England upland, 101

Niagara escarpment, N. Y., 102
Niagara River, N. Y., 8, 78, 90, 95, 109
North Park, Colo., 244, 251

O

Ocean circulation, effect on atmosphere,
  886, 891–893, 897, 899
Ocean temperature, 741
Ohio River, 56, 65, 624
Olympic Mountains, Wash., 341, 343, 345,
  347, 469, 472, 852
Oolite, see Formations
Osage Plains, Tex.–Okla.–Kan., 203
Outwash plains, specific
  Anoka, Minn., 34, 37
  Hinckley, Minn., 34
  Park Rapids, Minn., 35
Owens Valley, Calif., 278, 279
Owl Creek Mountains, Wyo., 244
Owl Mountains, Colo., 251
Oxygen-isotope ratio, 741, 742, 744, 751
Ozark faunal elements, insects, 589
Ozone in atmosphere, 884, 885, 898, 899

P

Paha, Iowa, 32
Paleohydrology, 576, 645, 783–793
Paleomagnetic correlation, in Western
  U. S., 823–826; Europe, 826, 827; Russia,
  827, 828
Paleomagnetic polarity epochs, 822, 823
Paleosols, 755–764; in Ohio, 85–87; New
  York, 103; Great Plains, 207; Rocky
  Mountains, 217, 219, 220, 224–226;
  Washington, 238; Great Basin, 269, 271;
  New Mexico, 292, 293; Utah, 295
Paleosols, specific
  Aftonian, Central U. S., 29, 49, 189,
    194, 206
  Brady, Great Plains, 189, 206, 210, 762
  Churchill, Great Basin, 271, 279
  Cocoon, Great Basin, 268, 270
  Dimple Dell, Great Basin, 268, 273, 275
  Fontanelle, Nev., 197
  Graniteville, Great Basin, 275, 276
  Harmon School, Great Basin, 268
  "L"-Drain Soil, Great Basin, 268, 281
  Midvale, Great Basin, 268, 270, 275,
    280
  Promontory, Great Basin, 268, 270, 273,
    275
  Sangamon, Central U. S., 31, 45, 52,
    53, 69, 90, 189, 198, 206, 210, 512,
    755, 761
  Toyeh, Great Basin, 268, 270–272, 277,
    280
  Two Creeks, Wis., 45
  Yarmouth, Central U. S., 30, 31, 45,
    50, 67, 189, 206, 210
Palos Verdes Hills, Calif., 856, 859, 862
Panamint Valley, Calif., 279
Pasadenan orogeny, 856, 863
Pasco Basin, Wash., 232, 238
Pecos Valley, N. Mex., 203, 290
Pediments, in Montana, 25; Iowa, 31;
  Rocky Mountains, 220, 249; Great
  Basin, 267; New Mexico, 293. See also
  Terraces, river
Peneplains, in New York, 101, 102;
  Appalachian Highlands, 134, 837; Cal-
  ifornia, 321; Rocky Mountains, 845

Peninsular Range, Calif., 300, 302, 330,
  853, 860
Periglacial features, 788, 791; in Montana,
  24; Wisconsin, 55; Illinois, 56; New
  England, 124; Appalachian Highlands,
  133; Alaska, 367
Permafrost, 365, 366, 471, 503
Phase, see Glacial stage
Phoenix Basin, Ariz., 288, 289
Playas, in Wyoming, 250, 251; Great
  Basin, 267
Pluvial lakes, 6, 7, 9; with archaeological
  sites, 703, 717; in Great Basin, 273, 281
Pluvial lakes, specific
  Animas, N. Mex., 291
  Bonneville, Utah, 221, 225, 226, 261,
    266, 268–270, 273, 276, 281, 282, 435,
    571, 578, 622, 697, 698, 703, 747, 748,
    761, 847, 849–851
  Clark Dry Lake, Calif., 718
  Cochise, Ariz., 289, 435
  Estancia, N. Mex., 291
  Harper, Calif., 278
  Humboldt, Nev., 702
  Lahontan, Nev., 266, 268–270, 272, 276,
    277, 279, 281, 282, 571, 698, 699, 703,
    747, 748, 761, 767, 847, 849, 851
  LeConte, Calif., 718
  Lomax, Tex., 206, 213, 215
  Long Valley, Calif., 278
  Manix, Calif., 278
  Manley, Calif., 278, 280
  Mohave, Calif., 278, 310
  Otero, N. Mex., 291
  Owens, Calif., 278
  Pahrump, Calif.–Nev., 278
  Panamint, Calif., 278, 280
  Russell, Calif., 278, 279
  San Augustin, N. Mex., 291, 295
  Searles, Calif., 278, 279, 698, 747, 748,
    751, 767
  Tahoka, Tex., 215
  Thatcher, Idaho, 276, 578
Pollen, sedimentation, 392, 393; size
  measurement, 423, 425, 646; rain, 457,
  647; redeposition, 410; sequences,
  dating of, 749
Pollen, in Indiana, 67, 69, 73; Alaska,
  365, 474–482; New England, 386–398,
  646, 647; Great Lakes region, 57, 408–
  414, 661, 662; Southeastern U. S., 418–
  431; Southwestern U. S., 433–447;
  Rocky Mountains, 455–457; Pacific
  Northwest, 472–474
Pollen sites, specific
  Afognak, Alaska, 475, 476
  Alabama Hills, Calif., 435
  Alaganik, Alaska, 475
  Alderton, Wash., 477
  Arch Lake, N. Mex., 435
  Bakeover Knob, Calif., 435
  Barnstable Marsh, Mass., 388, 396,
    397
  Bear Meadows, Penna., 418, 422
  Bladen County, N. Car., 421, 429
  Blaney Pond, Mass., 389
  Bog Pond, Minn., 408, 409
  Boggy Lake, N. Car., 418
  Brownington Pond, Vermont, 378, 392,
    394–397
  Burnett Pond, N. Car., 429
  Cambridge, Mass., 378, 392, 393
  Canton, Ill., 413
  Carolina Bays, N. Car., 418, 420–421

Pollen sites, specific (*cont.*)
Cedar Bog Lake, Minn., 409, 412, 765, 770
Chaco Canyon, N. Mex., 435
Chandler Lake, Alaska, 475, 477, 481
Channing, Tex., 436
Chesapeake Bay, 418, 422-423, 428, 430
China Lake, Calif., 435
Cienega Creek, Ariz., 435
Cranberry Glades, W. Virginia, 418, 422, 427
Crane Lake, Tex., 435, 439, 440
Crusoe Lake, N. Y., 388, 397
Crystal Lake, Penna., 389
Damp Cave, Tex., 435
Dead Man Lake, N. Mex., 435, 437-439, 773
Des Moines-Zenith, Wash., 479
Dismal Swamp, Virginia, 418, 422-424, 427, 429, 430, 773
Disterhaft Farm Bog, Wis., 409, 411, 412
Double Adobe, Ariz., 435
Duartes Bog, Mass., 389
Durham, Conn., 378, 388, 389, 392
Everett, Wash., 477
Flanner's Beach, N. Car., 418
Fort Sumner, N. Mex., 435
Franklin Bog, Tex., 435
Gause Bog, Tex., 419, 420, 430, 435
George Reserve, Mich., 409
Gillis Lake, Nova Scotia, 389
Glade Run Bog, Penna., 418, 422
Glen Canyon, Utah, 435
Gould's Bog, Mass., 378, 396
Granite Falls, Wash., 472-474, 481
Green River, Wash., 477
Guilford Marsh, Conn., 388
Gypsum Cave, Nev., 435
Harold Rud Salt Lake, N. Mex., 435
Hay Hollow Wash, Ariz., 435
Homer, Alaska, 475, 476, 481
Hooper Ranch, Ariz., 435
Humptulips, Alaska, 479
Imuruk Lake, Alaska, 475, 477, 480
Juan Cordova Lake, Tex., 435
Kennedy Meadows, Calif., 435
Kings Ferry, N. Y., 389
Kirchner Marsh, Minn., 409, 412, 765, 767, 772
Laguna Salada, Ariz., 435, 438, 439
Lehner Ranch, Ariz., 435, 442
Lewis Springs, Ariz., 435
Liberty Lake, Wash., 472-474, 481
Linsley Pond, Conn., 378, 388, 389, 765, 767, 769, 776
Little Lake, Calif., 435
Madelia, Minn., 411, 412
Malpais Spring, N. Mex., 435
Marsh, Penna., 418, 423, 425, 427
Martha's Vineyard, Mass., 378, 389, 392-393, 396
Martin Pond, Minn., 408
Mogollon Rim, Ariz., 437
Molas Lake, Colo., 435
Montana Creek, Alaska, 474-476, 481
Mud Lake, Fla., 418, 419, 427, 429
Munday Creek, Alaska, 475, 476, 481
Myrtle Beach, S. Car., 421
Navajo Dam, N. Mex., 435
Navajo National Monument, Ariz., 435
New Haven Harbor, Conn., 388
New Paris, Penna., 418, 425

Pollen sites, specific (*cont.*)
Newport, Ore., 480
Nome, Alaska, 475, 477, 481
Ogotoruk Creek, Alaska, 475, 477, 481
Onion Flats, Ore., 473, 474, 481
Owens Lake, Calif., 435
Patschke Bog, Tex., 419, 435, 437
Picuris Pueblo, N. Mex., 435
Pine Barrens, N. Jersey, 418, 427
Pleasant St. Bog, Mass., 389
Plissey Pond, Maine, 388
Pluvial Lake Cochise, Ariz., 437-439
Pluvial Searles Lake, Calif., 435, 437, 439
Point of Pines, Ariz., 435
Possession Point, Wash., 477
Potato Lake, Ariz., 435, 438-440
Rampart Cave, Ariz., 435
Red Maple Swamp, Conn., 378-389, 392
Reserve, N. Mex., 435
Rich Lake, Tex., 435-439
Riding Mountain, Manitoba, 408-409
Rita Blanca Lake, Tex., 435, 436
Rogers Lake, Conn., 378, 388, 389, 391-395
Safford, Ariz., 435, 436
St. Lawrence Island, Alaska, 475, 477, 481
Sandia Mountains, N. Mex., 437
San Augustin Plains, N. Mex., 435, 438, 440
San Jon Site, N. Mex., 435
San Simon Cienega, Ariz., 435
Secaucus Marsh, N. Jersey, 378, 388, 397
Seidel Lake, Wis., 409
Shady Valley Bog, Tenn., 418, 422, 427
Shepard Pond, N. Car., 418
Singletary Lake, N. Car., 420-421
Soefje Bog, Tex., 435
Spartanburg, S. C., 422
Spider Creek, Minn., 412
Sunbeam Prairie Bog, Ohio, 413
Tahoka Lake, Tex., 435
Terhell, Minn., 408
Tesuque, N. Mex., 435
Thompson, Minn., 408
Totoket Bog, Conn., 378, 389, 392
Tule Springs, Nev., 435, 437, 439-441
Umiat, Alaska, 475, 477, 481
Valle Grande, N. Mex., 435
Ventana Cave, Ariz., 437
Walker Cypress Swamp, Wash., 425
Ward Creek, Alaska, 474-476, 481
Washington, D. C., 418, 423
Weber Lake, Minn., 409, 411, 412, 765, 773
Wetherill Mesa, Colo., 435
Willcox Playa, Ariz., 435
Wolfe Ranch Canyon, N. Mex., 435
Polyploidy, 497-507
Potassium-argon dating, 740, 807, 822
Powder River Basin, Wyo., 251
Prairie floristic element, 464
Prairie peninsula, 407, 408
Preglacial drainage, Great Plains, 15, 19; New York, 102
Preglacial topography, in Minnesota, 33; Illinois, 45; Indiana-Michigan, 64; Great Lakes, 74; Ohio, 85; New York, 101-103; New England, 113
Preglacial weathering, New England, 114
Pribilof Islands, Alaska, 474, 477

Proglacial lakes, in Minnesota, 36; Ohio, 90; New York, 105; New England, 120-122; Washington, 345. *See also* Glacial lakes
Puget lowland, Wash., 472
Puget Sound, Wash., 341, 343, 346, 351, 852
Pyramid Lake, Great Basin, 276, 277, 281

Q

Quincy Basin, Wash., 232, 238, 240

R

Radiocarbon dating, 737, 742
Raton Section, Great Plains, 203
Readvance, *see* Glacial stage
Redeposited pollen, 394, 410, 421, 423
Red Rock Pass, Great Basin, 266, 273, 275, 578
Refuges for plants, New England, 383-385; Great Lakes area, 405; Alaska, 491
Relics, 645; among plants, 405, 406, 444, 453, 457, 462, 486, 487, 489; amphibians, 545-548, 550, 552, 553, 634; insects, 588, 614, 623, 626; marine invertebrates, 614, 616, 619
Reptiles, 444, 557-568, 634-639
Rio Grande, N. Mex., 290-293
River terraces, *see* Terraces, river
Rock glaciers, Alaska, 367
Rocky Mountain National Park, Colo., 222, 224, 226, 228
Ruby-East Humboldt Range, Nev., 272
Runoff, 783, 784, 792

S

St. Anthony Falls, Minn., 8, 29
St. Croix River, Minn.-Wis., 37, 38
St. Lawrence Valley, N. Y., 78, 79, 92, 95, 101, 834
St. Louis River, Minn., 36, 38
Salamanca re-entrant, N. Y., 100, 104
Salinity changes in ocean, 741
Salmon River Mountains, Utah, 221
San Bernardino Mountains, Calif., 302, 330
San Francisco Mountains, Ariz., 293, 294
San Gabriel Mountains, Calif., 300, 302
San Juan Mountains, Colo., 220, 221, 223, 224, 292, 293, 845
San Luis Valley, Colo., 248, 252
San Simon Valley, Ariz., 289
Sand, *see* Formations
Sand dunes, in South Dakota, 25; Massachusetts, 124; Atlantic coast, 134; Great Plains, 199, 215; Great Basin, 211; Rocky Mountains, 250, 251; Southwestern U. S., 252, 291, 295; Oregon, 351; Alaska, 361, 362
Sangre de Cristo Mountains, N. Mex., 220, 223, 228, 236, 291, 292
Santa Monica Mountains, Calif., 859
Saratoga Valley, Wyo., 244, 250
Sawatch Range, Colo., 220, 223
Scottsburg Lowland, Ind., 63
Sea level changes, effects on reptiles, 557, 561; marine organisms, 614, 617; Early Man, 711, 716, 663; land bridges, 619, 620, 597; continental shelf, 723-725, 732, 733

Sea level changes, in New England, 121, 123, 125; Atlantic coast, 129-133, 838, 839; Gulf coast, 137, 146, 149-151, 842; Pacific coast, 319-321, 324, 325, 329-331, 351, 853, 859-861; Alaska, 363

Sea level changes, glacial control, 7, 746

Searles Lake, Calif., 621

Sediment, relation to runoff, 784, 790, 792; climate, 785, 791, 792; glaciers, 788; drainage density, 789

Sedimentation rates, 744, 745

Seismicity, see Earthquakes

Shirley Basin, Wyo., 244, 251

Sierra Blanca, N. Mex., 223, 224, 291

Sierra Nevada, Calif., 265, 266, 272, 301, 302-310, 313, 330, 332, 436, 853, 854, 855

Silt, see Formations

Silver Lake, Colo., 251

Slope erosion, relation to climate, 789

Snake River, Idaho, 255, 260

Snake River Plain, Idaho, 255, 809, 849, 851, 864

Snowfall, 796

Snowline (firnline), in Rocky Mountains, 225, 228; California, 304, 305, 309, 327, 331; Washington, 346; Alaska, 358, 802, 855

Soil, buried, see Paleosol

Soil formation, rate of, 757, 762

Soil profile, 758

Soils, distribution of, 361, 757

Solar radiation, 881-886, 898; variations in distribution, 750, 751, 896, 899

Solar variability, effect on climate, 895, 896, 899

Sonoran Desert, Ariz., 561

South Park, Colo., 244, 252

Speciation, see Evolution

Stade, see Glacial stage

Stage, see Glacial stage

Stagnation deposits, in North Dakota, 23; Wisconsin, 57; Indiana, 71; New England, 120

"Stanford Man," 717

Stratigraphic correlation, 20; in Great Plains, 207; Rocky Mountains, 226; Great Basin, 269

Stratigraphic nomenclature, 5, 509, 732; in Great Plains, 21, 189, 207; Minnesota, 33; Illinois, 43, 52; Indiana, 63; New England, 387; Great Lakes region, 413

Stream terraces, see Terraces, river

Striations, 4, 5

Submarine canyons, 728

Subsidence, 864

Substage, see Glacial stage

Surfaces, see Terraces, river

Susquehanna River, N. Y., 103

Sutter Buttes, Calif., 313

Sweetgrass Hills, Mont., 16, 18, 23

T

Tanana Valley, Alaska, 363

Tectonic activity, rates of, 863-865

Tectonics, 831-865; effects on mollusks, 597; climate, 893, 894

Tectonics in Northeastern U. S., 831-837; Southeastern U. S., 837-839; South-central U. S., 839-842, 150, 733; Western interior, U. S., 843-851, 217, 243, 255, 265, 287, 291; Northwestern U. S., 851-853, 351; California, 853-861, 299, 300, 303, 305, 323, 326, 327, 329, 330, 332

Terraces, marine, on Atlantic coast, 129-133, 837-839; Gulf coast, 138-149, 171-178; Pacific coast, 320, 321, 324, 325, 327, 329, 331, 332, 717, 853, 859, 861, 862

Terraces, marine, specific
Chowan, Virginia, 131, 132
Coharie, Atlantic coast, 129, 133
Dismal Swamp, Virginia, 131
Okefenokee, Atlantic coast, 129, 132, 133, 839
Pamlico, Atlantic coast, 129, 131-133, 839
Penholloway, Atlantic coast, 129, 132
Princess Anne, Virginia, 131
Satilla, Georgia, 132
Silver Bluff, Georgia, 132, 133
Sunderland, Atlantic Coast, 129
Talbot, Atlantic Coast, 129
Wicomico, Atlantic Coast, 129, 132, 133, 839

Terraces, river, formation of, 801; bearing archaeological sites, 717; in relation to climate, 790-792

Terraces, river, in Montana, 25, 248; Nebraska, 194; Wyoming, 250-251; Colorado, 252; Great Basin, 271; Arizona, 289; New Mexico, 290, 292, 293, 295

Terraces, river and related surfaces specific
Almena, Kan., 213
Ambrose, Tex., 206, 213
Badger Creek Surface, Colo., 252
Broadway, Colo., 245-247, 249
Buffalo, Wyo., 249
China Hat Pediment, Calif., 314
Como Surface, Colo.-N. Mex., 252
Cooke, Tex., 206, 215
Eden, Wyo., 249
Faler, Wyo., 249
Farson, Wyo., 249
Greybull, Wyo., 249
Hardman, Tex., 206, 209, 210
Kaycee, Wyo., 251
Kirwin, Kan., 213
Lightning, Wyo., 251
Louviers, Colo., 245-247, 249
Lyman, Wyo., 250
Moorcroft, Wyo., 251
Newman, Kan., 213
Nussbaum, Colo., 245, 246, 249
Parker, Wyo., 249
Piney Creek, Colo., 246, 247, 249
Red Lodge-Cody, Wyo., 248, 249
Roberts-Emblem-Powell, Wyo., 248, 249
Rocky Flats, Colo., 245, 246, 249
Schoenchen, Kan., 213
Tatman-Pine Ridge, Wyo., 248, 249
Tipperary, Wyo., 250
Toboggan, Wyo., 249
Verdos, Colo., 245, 246, 248, 249
Teton Mountains, Wyo., 217, 222, 244
The Dalles, Ore., 711, 717
Thermoremanent magnetism, 818
Till, origin of, 4; composition of, 45, 48, 71, 85, 91, 105, 106, 113; fabric of, 106; depth of leaching in, 106. See also Formations
Trail Creek caves, Alaska, 369
Transverse Ranges, Calif., 300, 302, 331, 853, 855, 857-859
Travertine, 9
Triassic lowland, N. Y., 101

Trophication of lakes, 777

Tuff, see Formations

Tug Hill Plateau, N. Y., 100, 102

Tunnel valleys, Minn., 35

Turtle Mountains, N. Dak., 18, 24

U

Uinta Mountains, Utah, 222, 244, 250, 845

Uniformitarianism, 863-865

Uranium dating, 738-740, 744

V

Valles caldera, N. Mex., 809, 812

Vegetation types, in Northeastern U. S., 377-381; Great Lakes region, 406-408; Southeastern U. S., 417-419; Southwestern U. S., 433, 438, 439; Northwestern U. S., 469-472

Ventifacts, 124, 134

Ventura Basin, Calif., 327, 328, 856, 857

Volcanic ash, 807-816; in Idaho, 258

Volcanic ash, specific,
"Galata," 810
Glacier Peak, Wash., 24, 226, 234, 474
Mount Mazama, Ore., 24, 226, 234, 241, 474
Pearlette, in Great Plains, 189, 190, 192, 195, 197, 198, 204, 209, 210, 248, 512, 601, 649, 809, 811, 821; Rocky Mountains, 221, 250; Great Basin, 269, 271, 275; New Mexico, 291, 292

Volcanics, see Formations

Volcanism, effect on climate, 894, 898, 899; relation to paleomagnetism, 818

Volcanism, in Great Basin, 265; Southwestern U. S., 291, 294, 296; California, 301, 303, 313, 323, 332, 855; Northwestern U. S., 807-814, 851, 852, 864

W

Wabash Lowland, Ind., 63

Walker Lake, Nev., 276

Wallowa Mountains, Ore., 340, 349

Wasatch Mountains, Utah, 221, 223, 224, 270, 272, 275, 847

Washakie Basin, Wyo., 244, 250

Weathering, rates of, 8, 358

White Mountains, New Hampshire, 384

White River, S. Dak., 25

White River Plateau, Utah-Colo., 221, 223

Whitewater basin, Ind., 69

Willamette, Lowland, Ore., 340, 349

Wind River, Wyo., 217, 226

Wind River Basin, Wyo., 244, 250

Wind River Mountains, Wyo., 219-222, 224

Wisconsin River, Wis., 49

Y

Yellowstone National Park, Wyo., 221, 225

Yellowstone Plateau, Wyo., 222, 809, 849

Yellowstone River, Mont., 25

Yosemite Valley, Calif., 308, 854

Yukon Flats, Alaska, 363

DATE DUE

DEC 1 8 1976		
DEC 2 1977		
JAN 2 7 1981		
APR 1 4 1981		
MAY 2 0 1981		
DEC 1 5 1981		
MAY 2 2 1986		
GAYLORD		PRINTED IN U.S.A.